INTERNATIONAL LEGAL BOOKS IN PRINT 1990-1991

INTERNATIONAL LEGAL BOOKS IN PRINT

1990-1991

An annotated bibliography

VOLUME 1

AUTHOR/TITLE

1990
BOWKER-SAUR

London Melbourne Munich New York

Bowker-Saur is part of the Professional Publishing Division of Reed International Books

British Library Cataloguing in Publication Data
International legal books in print, 1990-1991 : an annotated bibliography.

1. Law - Bibliographies
I. Chapman, Michael D.
016.34
ISBN 0-86291-856-1
ISBN 0-86291-848-0 v. 1
ISBN 0-86291-849-9 v. 2

Library of Congress Cataloguing-in-Publication Data available on request

Cover design by Robin Caira, Typographics, Whitstable

Computer controlled typesetting by Computaprint Ltd., London
Printed and bound by Anthony Rowe Ltd., Chippenham

Printed on acid-free paper.

International Legal Books in Print,
1990-1991
is dedicated
to the memory of

Wallace Breem

Librarian and Keeper of Manuscripts
Honourable Society of the Inner Temple
who died on March 12th, 1990

CONTENTS

FOREWORD

In 1982, R R Bowker published Law Books 1876-1981 and decided that they would keep it up to date by producing monthly softcover and annual hardcover cumulations entitled Law Books and Serials in Print. The success of that venture into legal bibliography led to the establishment within Bowker of a Legal Reference Publishing Department, the first fruit of which, after extensive review of the volumes published between 1982 and 1987, was the Law Books and Serials in Print 1988: a Multimedia Sourcebook. The aim was to list all legal titles available in the United States and, to a lesser extent, internationally. That publication continues annually with quarterly cumulative supplements.

Bowker-Saur in London were sure that more than enough material had been excluded from the American publication to make a Commonwealth biased version a viable proposition. Consultation with myself and other law librarians confirmed them in this opinion. I was certainly convinced that a definite need existed within the United Kingdom and the Commonwealth for a bibliography of in-print legal materials. Within the Commonwealth, a reference work of this calibre that enables you to locate English-language law books from a single source is long overdue. The concept is a milestone in legal bibliography; it signals the end of what has always been a time consuming and difficult task. In the event, the brief was expanded still further to cover most non-U.S. titles published in the English language.

I was asked in early 1989 to form and to chair an Editorial Board which would advise the Bowker-Saur editors. The composition of the Board I intended to reflect the varied roles and views of legal information professionals. Its members therefore were drawn from law libraries catering for academic institution, law firm, professional society, public corporation and government department. We also received assistance in the form of advice from colleagues in other jurisdictions and, for the future, we have formed a network of contacts drawn from within the ranks of Commonwealth law librarians. It is intended that consultation should be a continuing process to ensure that this bibliography reflects and responds to the needs of its users. The title of the new publication was eventually settled as International Legal Books in Print.

International Legal Books in Print is not therefore a British bibliography with a mere smattering of titles from other jurisdictions. It is truly international in concept and in reality. Since, however, it does not seek to compete with, but rather to complement, its sister publication Law Books and Serials in Print, we have excluded for the most part United States' publications. The ultimate aim must be that, between the two, all English language legal titles are covered.

One of the first tasks to be set in motion by the Editorial Board was the compilation of a list of subject headings tailored exactly to the needs of this new publication and expressed in British and Commonwealth legal terminology. Sally Phillips was recruited to produce this vital component and she is to be commended for the thorough and energetic way in which she performed this task, shortly before moving from the Law Commission, where she had been librarian since 1983, to become Supreme Court Librarian in August 1989.

Michael Chapman, an experienced bibliographer, was the editor chosen by Bowker-Saur to be responsible for selecting and preparing the bibliographic entries for ILBIP, according to guidelines set out by the Editorial Board. Without his diligence and attention to detail, we would have been unable to progress as smoothly and efficiently as we have done and it is to his credit, more than to anyone else, that this publication has reached its successful conclusion.

That International Legal Books in Print is a significant contribution to legal bibliography is indisputable. That it can be improved by responding to user interest is also true and we hope that comments and suggestions will be forthcoming. We intend to ensure that the Bowker-Saur legal bibliographies are the standard by which others are judged and we pledge ourselves to this aim.

I end this foreword on a note of sadness. The most distinguished of our Editorial Board members, Wallace Breem, died suddenly on March 12th, 1990. He did not see ILBIP reach print and I hope that we have produced a publication with which he would have been proud to be associated. Wallace, friend and adviser to many of the current generation of law librarians in Britain and Ireland, had joined the staff of the Inner Temple Library in 1951, becoming its Librarian and Keeper of Manuscripts in 1965. He was a founder member of the British & Irish Association of Law Librarians, serving for many years as its Secretary/Treasurer and later as its Chairman. In 1988, in recognition of the very considerable contribution that Wallace had made, and was still making, to the field of law librarianship, the Association elected him as its President. As our tribute to a true professional, we dedicate this bibliography to his memory.

Donald Raistrick
Head of Library Services
Lord Chancellor's Department
March, 1990

INTRODUCTION

The first edition of International Legal Books in Print contains some 20,000 English language legal and law related titles. The geographical scope of ILBIP includes the United Kingdom, Western Europe and all the countries of the Commonwealth both past and present, thus providing unequalled access to legal sources in these areas.

Volume 1 is presented as a combined single alphabetical sequence of main author and title entries. Other persons involved in the authorship or editing of works have personal name cross references to the title concerned. Volume 2 presents title entries only within a subject heading scheme. Some 2,000 subject headings are available within the database from which ILBIP is produced and most of them may be sub-divided by country from another database file which covers over a hundred countries and regions. The final section of Volume 2 lists publishers' names and addresses together with telephone and fax numbers where possible.

The subject heading scheme itself was prepared by Sally Phillips who judiciously pruned and adapted over 50,000 subject headings for law books employed by the Library of Congress. The resulting list is by no means closed and will continue to be updated as the need arises in future editions. Approximately a third of the subject headings were provided on sight of the book concerned; the remainder were allocated by matching a "key word" from the title with a corresponding word in the subject heading list. This may be less than completely sound from an intellectual point of view and the editor craves the user's indulgence for any errors which may have arisen through this admittedly imperfect procedure.

Furthermore, several headings have been invented, such as dictionaries, indexes, digests, periodicals, which are normally descriptive only of form and these have not been sub-divided by country. None the less the scheme as it stands provides subject access to a body of material which is not likewise so accessible in any other publication, whether book or electronic.

The Publisher section of Volume 2 has been produced from two interconnected files; a publisher file containing address details and an imprint file. The intention is to show the relationship between owning publishing houses and their imprints. This has become necessary in the light of so many smaller publishers being overtaken and disappearing into very large corporations. It has also proved to be a useful way of providing cross references for variant occurences of a company name.

The main entry record in the database contains fields for the following items: author, title, statement of responsibility, edition, number of volumes, place of publication, size, series title, annotation, audience, ISBN, ISSN, binding and price. A typical entry is presented thus:

AUTHOR — **Matte, Nicholas M, et al**
TITLE — Aerospace law: telecommunications satellites/ Nicholas M. Matte, N. P. Munro, James Carter.- 2nd ed. 3 vols.- Toronto: Butterworths, 1982.- 1500p : illus; 23 cm.- (Communications Law Series).
Focuses on legal issues raised by the rapid development of satellite systems.
Barristers, solicitors.
ISBN 0409848654 Hbk $300

Labels: AUTHOR, TITLE, STATEMENT OF RESPONSIBILITY, EDITION, PLACE OF PUBLICATION, NO OF VOLUMES, PUBLISHER, DATE, PAGINATION, SERIES TITLE, ANNOTATION, SIZE, AUDIENCE, PRICE, ISBN/1SSN, BINDING

Many of the entries in this first edition of International Legal Books in Print have specially written descriptive annotations, drawn from publishers' promotional material, which provide information on chapter headings and specific topics or legislation covered by the book. These annotations occur with their entries, regardless of the entry point, throughout both volumes.

Apart from improvements in its coverage and currency, the next edition of ILBIP will address itself particularly to the creation of more annotations, further additions to the subject heading scheme and the most current price information.

ACKNOWLEDGEMENTS

I wish to pay particular thanks to the annotators: Michelle Aveline, Professional Books, Abingdon; John Sibbald, Professional Library Services, Edinburgh; Timothy Donkin, St. Edmunds Hall, Oxford. I am also indebted to Chloe Rigby, Barbara Lynch, Nigel Baxter and Alison Bennett for their editorial help; to Yolanda Dolling for her assistance with the allocation of subject headings and to my Managing Editors, Robert Balchin and Judi Vernau, for their guidance and support. Last, but not least, I extend my thanks to Martin Taylor of Computaprint for his ceaseless work on the construction of the Advanced Revelation database which holds International Legal Books in Print, 1990-1991.

Michael D. Chapman
Editor, Legal Reference
May, 1990

ABBREVIATIONS

c./ca.	circa
cm.	centimetres
ed.	edition
Hbk	hardback/cased
Llf	looseleaf/spiral bound/ringbound
no.	number
p./pp.	page(s)
Pbk	paperback/softcover
pt.	part(s)
T.p.	title-page
v./vol.	volume(s)

CURRENCY SYMBOLS

£	Pound sterling (UK)
A$	Australian dollar
B$	Bahamaian dollar
BDS$	Bermudan dollar
Bf	Belgian franc
C£	Cyprus pound
Can$	Canadian dollar
Dkr	Danish krona
DM	Deutsche Mark
F	French franc
Fmk	Markka (Finland)
G$	Guyana dollar
G£	Dalasi (Gambia)
Gld	Guilder (Netherlands)
HK$	Hong Kong dollar
Ir£	Irish pounds
J$	Jamaican dollar
K	Kina (Papua New Guinea)
Kr	Krona (Sweden)
KSh	Kenya shilling
L	Lira (Italy)
Le	Leone (Sierra Leone)
Lfr	Luxembourg franc
M$	Malaysian dollar
MK	Malawi kwacha
MR	Mauritius rupee
N	Naira (Nigeria)
NKr	Norwegian krone
NZ$	New Zealand dollar
P	Pula (Botswana)
PP	Philippine peso
Pta	Peseta (Spain)
Rp	Rupiah (Indonesia)
Rs	Indian rupee
S	Schilling (Austria)
Sfr	Swiss fr
S$	Singapore dollar
SL$	Solomon Islands dollar
SLR	Sri Lanka rupee
SR	Seychelles rupee
TSh	Tanzanian shilling
TT$	Trinidad & Tobago dollar
USh	Uganda shilling
WS$	Tala (Samoa)

101 Plus Uses Of A Police Helmet. – Police Review, 1985.
ISBN 0851640192 Pbk £1.95

1688-1988 : Time for a New Constitution / Elliot. – London : Macmillan.
ISBN 0333467019 Hbk £27.50
ISBN 0333467027 Pbk £8.85

1985/86 Income Tax Statutory Amendments and Recent Amendments to the Estate Duty Act Including Estate Planning Aspects. – Cape Town : Legal and Financial Publishing Co.
Hbk £8.50

1985 Australian master tax guide. – North Ryde, N.S.W. : CCH Australia, 1985.
1099p.
'This edition ... incorporates changes that have taken place up to 25 January 1985'. Includes index.
ISBN 0869036602

1986-87 Income Tax Legislation and Recent Estate Duty Amendments : Together with Income Tax and Estate Duty Tables. – Cape Town : Legal and Financial Publishing Co, 1987.
Hbk £8.50

1987 annual on terrorism / edited by Yonah Alexander, with contributing editors Abraham H. Foxman and Eugene Mastrangelo. – Dordrecht : Nijhoff (Martinus), 1989.
528. – (Annual on Terrorism).
Focuses on national, regional and global developments in the field of terrorism. This volume includes the analysis of domestic and international terrorism, selected papers written during 1987, a statistical synopsis and selected documents, reports and addresses.
ISBN 9024738016 Hbk Gld250.00

1987 Australian Income Tax Legislation, 3v. – North Ryde : C.C.H. Australia, 1987.
2,300p.
ISBN 0869038990 Hbk

1987 Municipal Law Amendments. – Vancouver : Continuing Legal Education Society of British Columbia, 1987.
34p.
ISBN 0865043361 Hbk £65.00

The 1988 Education Act : A Tactical Guide for Schools. – Oxford : Basil Blackwell.
ISBN 0631164553 Hbk £19.50
ISBN 0631164561 Pbk £6.95

200 mile exclusive economic zone in the new law of the sea. – Dordrecht : Nijhoff (Martinus), 1989.
408. – (Publications on ocean development 14).
Examines the rights and duties of states with regard to activities such as fisheries and navigation. Also evaluates the existing and potential impact of the EEZ upon the socioeconomic development of states and the reduction of disparities between the developing and industrialised countries.
ISBN 0792300742 Hbk £60

300 Years of Lloyds : Lloyd's List Special Supplement. – London : Lloyd's of London Press.
ISBN 185044188X Pbk £21.50

4 what it's worth / Harriet Wilson. – London : Thames, 1988.
192p; 20cm.
Includes index.
ISBN 0356148629 Pbk £5.95

75 years of law at Sheffield, 1909-1984 / edited by David C. Hoath. – Sheffield : University of Sheffield Faculty of Law, 1985.
viii,116p.
Includes bibliographical references.

A.A.A. Yearbook
Vol. 45/46: Computer and International Law /. – Dordrecht : Kluwer, 1981.
vi, 196p.
ISBN 902472323X Hbk £65.00
Vol. 47/48 (1977/78): Foreign Investments Today and Tomorrow. – 1986.
160p.
ISBN 9024725704 Pbk £75.00
Vol. 49/50 (1979-1980): Functions and Status of the Consul. – 1982.
200p.
ISBN 9024725712 Pbk £70.00
Vol. 51/52/53 (1981/82/83): International Scientific and Technical Co-operation. – 1985.
171p.
ISBN 9024731100 Pbk £75.00
Vol. 54/55/56: Natural Resources in International Law. – 1987.
320p.
ISBN 902473469X Pbk £150.00

'A' Level Law. – London : Butterworths, 1988.
ISBN 0406208506 Pbk £9.95

'A' Level Law / Pannett. – London : Financial Training, 1988.
– (SWOT).
ISBN 1851850651 Pbk £7.50

'A' level law : cases and materials / Brian Hogan, Peter Seago, Geoffrey Bennett. – London : Sweet & Maxwell, 1986.
xxvii,507p; 22cm.
Includes index.
ISBN 0421352906 Pbk £8.95
ISBN 042138820X Hbk £9.95

A.M.P.L.A. Yearbook. – Melbourne : Australian Mining and Petroleum Law Association.
600p.
Hbk £99.00

Aarnio, Aulis
On the Utility of Legal Theory / Mark van Hoecke. – Tampere : A-Tiete Oy.
ISBN 9519464352 Pbk £140.00
—Philosophical Perspectives in Jurisprudence. – Helsinki : Suomen filosofinen ydhistus ry, 1983.
288p.
ISBN 9519505490 Hbk £106.00

—Rational as reasonable : a treatise on legal justification / Aulis Aarnio. – Dordrecht : D. Reidel, 1986.
xix, 276p.
Includes index. Bibliography: p 261-271.
ISBN 9027722765 Hbk

Aaron, Benjamin → International labour law reports, Volume 7.

Aaron, H.
VAT : Experience of Some European Countries. – Dordrecht : Kluwer, 1982.
ISBN 9065440240 Hbk £155.00

Aaronson → Insanity Defense : A Critical Assessment of Law and Policy in Post-Hinckley Era.

AAT Study Text : Paper 12 Auditing and Taxation. – Revised ed. – London : BPP.
ISBN 0862771153 Pbk £14.95

Abac, S.
Turkey's banks and banking systems. – London : Euromoney, 1985.
ISBN 0903121859 Hbk £58.00

Abas
Law, Justice and the Judiciary : Transitional / Dato' Visu Sinnadurai. – Professional Law, 1988.
ISBN 09679958002 Hbk £95.00

Abbott
Business Law / N Pendlebury. – 3rd ed. – London : DP Publications, 1986.
ISBN 0905435672 Pbk £4.95

Abbott, Fiona → Valuation 85 : a Conceptual Outline.

Abbott, K. R.
Business Law : Instructional Manual / N. Pendlebury. – 3rd ed. – Winchester : DP Publications, 1982.
608p.
ISBN 0905435672 Pbk £5.25
—Company Law : Instructional Manual. – 2nd ed. – Winchester : DP Publications, 1983.
400p.
ISBN 0905435605 Pbk £4.95

ABC guide to the Federal Court of Australia. – North Ryde : Law Book Co, 1986.
xvii, 230p.
ISBN 0455206864 Pbk £29.50

ABC guide to the practice of matrimonial causes / by Roger Bird. – 2nd ed. – London : Sweet and Maxwell, 1987.
150p; 22cm.
Now covers the increasing role of conciliation, the principles applicable to ancillary relief applications and the 'clean break' under the Matrimonial and Family Proceedings Act 1984, ouster injunctions, foreign divorce, and the forthcoming changes following the Matrimonial Causes (Costs) Rules 1986.
ISBN 0421370904 Pbk

ABC guide to the practice of the county court / by Emlyn Williams. – 3rd ed. – London : Sweet & Maxwell, 1987.
200p; 22cm.
Includes amendments embodied in the County Courts Act 1984, and within other acts such as the Administration of Justice Act 1985, the Companies Act 1985 and the Insolvency Act 1986. Updated to cover amended Costs rules, the privatisation of registration of judgements, and the change of procedure in appeals to the Court of Appeal.
ISBN 0421346906 £14.50

ABC guide to the practice of the magistrates' courts / by Emlyn Williams. – London : Sweet & Maxwell, 1986.
viii,187p; 22cm.
ISBN 0421344903 Pbk £14.50

ABC Guide to the Practice of the Supreme Court, 1988-1989. – 45th ed. – Sweet & Maxwell.
ISBN 0421405902 Pbk £16.50

ABC of brain stem death / Christopher Pallis. – London : British Medical Journal, 1983.
33p; 29cm.
Articles published in the British Medical Journal.
ISBN 0727900994

ABC of copyright / Unesco. – Paris : Unesco, 1981.
88p.
Includes discussion of the moral and economic rights of authors, limits to copyright protection, copyright infringement and its remedies and international copyright.
ISBN 9231018892 Hbk

ABC of Evidence / C.R. Brahe. – 4th ed. – Mortdale : Petty Publishing Co, 1988.
ISBN 0908508026 Hbk £44.50

ABC of Liquor Law in New South Wales. – North Ryde : Law Book Co, 1983.
ix, 197p.
ISBN 0455204209 Pbk £23.50

Abdul Rahman, Leila
Singapore Property Tax Cases [1959-1986]. – Singapore : Malayan Law Journal, 1987.
xxii,413.
Collection of cases that was determined by the Judicial Committee of the Privy Council, the Court of Appeal, the High Court, and the Valuation Review Board of Singapore.
ISBN 9971700573 Hbk

Abdullahi, Zubair Alhaji
Guidance notes on Finance (Miscellaneous) Taxation Provisions Decree 1985 / by Zubair Alhaji Abdullahi. – Zaria, Nigeria? : the Author, 1986.
i,92p.
Includes index.

Abecassis, David W.
Oil pollution from ships : international, United Kingdom and United States law and practice / Richard L. Jarashow. – 2nd ed. – London : Stevens, 1985.
l,619p; 26cm.
Deals with the international law and practice relating to oil pollution from ships, and includes new chapters dealing with United States law and selected aspects of United Kingdom law. There are also chapters on salvage in oil pollution cases and rights and obligations in customary international law. The Civil Jurisdiction and Judgements Act 1982, and Law of the Sea Convention 1982 are included.
ISBN 042047000X £95.00

A'Beckett, G.
Comic Blackstone. – Southampton : Ashford Press, 1985.
ISBN 0907069398 Hbk £18.95
—Comic Blackstone. – 3rd ed. Repr. of 1887 ed. – Abingdon : Professional Books.
Hbk £75.00

Abeelen, Marc J. van den → African tax systems.

Abel
Lawyers in Society
Volume 1 The Common Law World / Lewis. – University of California Press.
ISBN 0520056035 Hbk

Abel, Richard L.
Lawyers in the United Kingdom / Richard Abel. – 1st draft. – S.l. : s.n., 1983.
xvi,209p.
'Prepared for the meeting of the Working Group for Comparative Study of Legal Professions of the ISA Research Committee on Sociology of Law, to be held at the Villa Serbelloni, Bellagio, Italy, July 16-21, 1984'. Bibliography: p.199-209.

—Legal profession in England and Wales / Richard L. Abel. – Oxford, Oxfordshire, UK : Blackwell, 1988.
xxiii, 548p.
Includes index. Bibliography: p.507-537.
ISBN 0631141111

→ Politics of informal justice.

Abella, Rosalie S
Alberta Family Law. – Student ed. – Toronto : Butterworths, 1983.
ISBN 0409996823 Hbk £26.95

→ Family law : dimensions of justice : selected papers presented at the Judicial Conference on Family Law, 1981.

→ Justice beyond Orwell.

Abichandani, R.K.
Indian Partnership Act. – 5th ed. – Bombay : Tripathi, 1987.
264p.
Hbk £80.00

Abolishing the Diplock courts : the case for restoring jury trial to scheduled offences in Northern Ireland / S.C. Greer, A. White. – London : Cobden Trust, 1986.
x,133p; 20cm.
Includes index.
ISBN 0900137274 Pbk £5.95

Abolitionism : towards a non-repressive approach to crime : proceedings of the Second International Conference on Prison Abolition, Amsterdam, 1985 / edited by Herman Bianchi, Rene van Swaaningen. – Amsterdam : Free University Press, 1986.
247p.
ISBN 9062561799

Aboriginal Australians / by Keith D. Suter, Kaye Stearman. – New ed. – London : Minority Rights Group, 1982.
20p. – (Report).
Previous ed. published 1978 as: Australia's policy towards Aborigines 1967-1977 / by H.C. Coombs. Bibliography: p.20.

Aboriginal Criminological Research. – Canberra : Australian Institute of Criminology.
Hbk £2.85

Aboriginal customary law : marriage, children and the distribution of property / Australian Law Reform Commission. – Sydney : Australian Law Reform Commission, 1982.
20p. – (Discussion paper).

Aboriginal customary law : the criminal law, evidence and procedure. – Sydney : Australian Law Reform Commission, 1984.
24p. – (Discussion paper).

Aboriginal land rights : a handbook / edited by Nicolas Peterson. – Canberra City : Australian Institute of Aboriginal Studies, 1981.
vi,297p.
The papers published here were originally prepared as background information for the Aboriginal Land Rights Symposium held as part of the Australian Institute of Aboriginal Studies Biennial Meeting 1981. Bibliography: p269-297.

Aboriginal land rights legislation : an examination of the publications associated with Commonwealth legislation / Gregory P. Jones. – Belconnen, A.C.T., Australia : Canberra College of Advanced Education, Library, 1983.
iii, 196 p.; 25 cm.
Includes bibliographical references.
ISBN 0858892391 Pbk £9.00

Aboriginal Landrights in New South Wales. – Chippendale : Alternative Publishing Cooperative, 1985.
ISBN 090918884X Hbk £22.50
ISBN 0909188858 Pbk £12.95

Aboriginal law bulletin. – Kensington : Aboriginal Law Research Unit, 1981.

Aboriginal Peoples and Section 25 of the Canadian Charter of Rights and Freedoms. – Saskatoon : University of Saskatchewan, Native Law Centre, 1988.
52p.
ISBN 0888801939 Hbk £15.00

Aboriginal peoples and the law : Indian, Metis and Inuit rights in Canada / edited by Bradford W. Morse. – Ottawa : Carleton University Press, 1985.
xlv,794p. – (Carleton Library Series).
ISBN 0886290198

Aboriginal reserves by-laws and human rights. – Canberra : Australian Government Publishing Service, 1983.
93p. – (Occasional paper).
ISBN 0644028939

Aboriginal Rights and Government Wrongs : Uranium Mining and Neocolonialism in Northern Saskatchewan. – Regina : Prairie Justice Research, 1988.
ISBN 0773101403 Hbk £12.00

Aboriginal Rights Provisions in the Constitution Act, 1982. – Saskatoon : University of Saskatchewan, Native Law Centre, 1987.
276p.
ISBN 0888801920 Hbk £50.00

Aboriginal Self-Government : Rights of Citizenship and Access to Governmental Services. – Kingston : Queen's University, Institute of Intergovernmental Relations, 70p.
ISBN 0889114226 Hbk £12.00

Aboriginal Self-Government and Constitutional Reform : Setbacks, Opportunities, and Arctic Experiences. – Ottawa : Canadian Arctic Resources Committee, 1988.
168p.
ISBN 0919996353 Pbk £20.00

Aboriginal Title and Mining Legislation in the Northwest Territories. – Saskatoon : University of Saskatchewan, Native Law Centre, 1982.
32p.
ISBN 0888801149 Hbk £8.00

Aboriginal Water Rights in Canada : a Study of Aboriginal Title to Water and Indian Water Rights. – Calgary : Canadian Institute of Resources Law.
231p.
ISBN 0919269230 Hbk £30.00

Aborigines and Mining Royalties in the Northern Territory. – Canberra City : Australian Institute of Aboriginal Studies, 1983.
182p.
ISBN 0855751495 Hbk £11.95

Aborigines and the law / Peter Hanks. – London : Allen & Unwin, 1984.
400p.
ISBN 0868615447 £20.00

Aborigines and the Law. – Canberra City : Australian Institute of Aboriginal Studies, 1987.
ISBN 0855751738 Pbk £44.95

Aborigines, Land and Land Rights / M. Langton. – Canberra City : Australian Institute of Aboriginal Studies, 1983.
476p.
ISBN 0855751436 Hbk £14.90

Aborigines Today : Land and Justice / Burger. – Third World Publications, 1988.
ISBN 0900918225 Pbk £4.95

Abortion and protection of the human fetus : legal problems in a cross-cultural perspective / edited by Stanislaw J. Frankowski, George F. Cole. – Dordrecht Netherlands : M. Nijhoff, 1988.
xv, 334 p.; 25 cm.
'Under the auspices of the Institute of International and Comparative Law, the University of Santa Clara.' Includes bibliographies.
ISBN 0898389224 Hbk £175.00

Abortion and the status of the fetus / edited by William B. Bondeson ... et al. – Dordrecht, Holland : D. Reidel, 1983.
xxxii, 349p.
'This volume grew out of a symposium, 'The Concept of person and its implications for the use of the fetus in biomedicine', held October 29, 30, and 31, 1980, at the Health Science Center of the University of Missouri-Columbia under the sponsorship of the Departments of Medicine and Philosophy, and the Program in Health Care and Human Values'–Editorial pref. Includes bibliographies and index.
ISBN 9027714932

Abortion, Doctors and the Law : Aspects of Legal Regulation of Abortion England 1802-1982. – Cambridge : Cambridge University Press.
ISBN 052134574X Hbk £22.50

Abortion Law and Public Policy. – Dordrecht : Kluwer, 1985.
104p.
ISBN 9024731070 Pbk £40.00

About You and Fostering / Goodman. – National Foster Care Association.
ISBN 0946015392 Hbk £5.90

Abraham, H.J.
Freedom and the Court Civil Rights and Liberties in the United States. – Oxford : Oxford University Press.
ISBN 0195055160 Pbk £12.95

Abrams, Charles- →Guide to the Financial Services Act 1986.

Abrams, Floyd
Right to know / Floyd Abrams, Michael Kirby, Lord Scarman. – London : Granada, 1985.
79p.
Includes bibliographical references.
ISBN 0586066810

Abramson →Tax and Financial Planning Through Pensions.

Abridgement of the Public Statutes in Force From Magna Carta : In Ninth Year of Henry III to Eleventh Year of George II Inclusive, Continued to First Year of George II inclusive, 2 Vols. – 2nd ed. Repr. of 1762 ed. – Abingdon : Professional Books.
567p.
Hbk £90.00

Abridgment of New Zealand Case Law : 1861-1967, 16 Vols. – Wellington : Butterworths.
ISBN 0409600008 Hbk
Supplement-1962-1973.
Supplement-1974-1978.
Supplement 1980-to date.

Abstracts of race relations research / edited by George Mair and Philip Stevens. – London : Home Office, 1982.
vii,86p.
Includes index.
ISBN 0862520436

Abuse of power : civil liberties in the United Kingdom / Patricia Hewitt. – Oxford : Robertson, 1982.
xiv,295p; 24cm.
Bibliography: p267-279. - Includes index.
ISBN 085520379X Hbk £15.00
ISBN 0855203803 Pbk £4.95

ACA Architect's Instruction. – London : Architectural Press.
– (ACA Contract Documents).
ISBN 0851397425 Pbk £6.32

ACA Contract Introductory Package. – London : Architectural Press, 1985.
– (ACA Contract Documents).
ISBN 0851397301 Hbk £20.00

ACA Final Certificate. – London : Architectural Press.
– (ACA Contract Documents).
ISBN 0851397433 Hbk

ACA Form of Building Agreement Nineteen Eighty-Two. – Association of Consultant Architects. – 1984 ed. – London : Architectural Press, 1984.
28p.
ISBN 0851397530 Pbk £7.50

ACA Form Of Sub-Contract Nineteen Eighty-Two. – Association of Consultant Architects. – London : Architectural Press, 1984.
12p. – (ACA Contract Documents).
ISBN 0851397557 Pbk £7.50

ACA Interim Certificate. – London : Architectural Press.
– (ACA Contract Documents).
ISBN 0851397417 Hbk £7.47

ACA Taking-Over Certificate. – London : Architectural Press.
– (ACA Contract Documents).
ISBN 0851397441 Hbk £6.32

Academic freedom under Israeli military occupation : report of WUS/ICJ mission of enquiry into higher education in the West Bank and Gaza / Adam Roberts, Boel Joergensen, Frank Newman. – London : World University Service (UK), 1984.
87p.
Bibliography: p.84-87.
ISBN 0906405203

Academie de Droit International de la Haye
Recueil des cours
Volume 208 (1988-1). – Academie de Droit International de la Haye. – Dordrecht : Nijhoff (Martinus), 1988.
406.
Includes chapters on the concept and claims of geographically disadvantaged states at the third UN Law of the Sea Conference, geographically disadvantaged states of the Exclusive Economic Zone, and these states and the exploitation of the mineral resources of the sea-bed and ocean floor.
ISBN 0792300580 Hbk £57.50

Academy of Criminal Justice Sciences →Juvenile justice policy : analyzing trends and outcomes.

ACCA Study and Revision Manual : 1.1 Accountancy. – London : BPP.
ISBN 1870941039 Pbk £9.95

ACCA Study and Revision Manual : 1.2 Cost and Management Accounting 1. – London : BPP.
ISBN 0905435745 Pbk £9.95

ACCA Study and Revision Manual : 2.3 Taxation. – London : BPP.
ISBN 1870941128 Pbk £9.95

ACCA Study and Revision Pack. – Pitman.
ISBN 0273028022 Pbk £10.95

Access : Links Between Children in Care and Their Parents. – Bristol : School of Applied Social Studies, University of Bristol.
ISBN 0862923018 Pbk £3.50

Access and privacy : the steps ahead. – Ottawa : Government of Canada, 1987.
x,57,63,xip.
French title on added t.p.: Acces et renseignements personnels. Pages numbered in opposite directions. Text in English and French.
ISBN 0662554728

Access Control and Personal Identification Systems. – London : Butterworths.
ISBN 0409900834 Hbk £24.95

Access to Cabinet Confidence. – Ottawa : Ken Rubin, 1986.
ISBN 092062112 Hbk £35.00

Access to information in local government / by Tim Harrison. – London : Sweet & Maxwell, 1988.
110p.
Covers the Local Government (Access to Information) Act 1985, including a chapter on access by elected members of councils. Also contains the Data Protection Act 1984 as it relates to councils, the Access to Personal Files Act 1987, and the common law.
ISBN 0421384107 £10.00

Access to justice and civil litigation in Northern Ireland : report of a conference organised by SLS Legal Publications (NI) and the Northern Ireland Consumer Council held in the Queen's University of Belfast on 29 March 1985. – Belfast : SLS Legal Publications, 1985.
ii,76p.

Access to justice and the welfare state / edited by Mauro Cappelletti : with the assistance of John Weisner and Monica Seccombe. – Alphen aan den Rijn : Sijthoff, 1981.
xiv,365p.
Revised reports considered at the Access to Justice conference, October 15-18, 1979.
ISBN 9028625410 Hbk £76.00

Access to personal social services records : Data Protection Act 1984, Section 29(2) Order : social work records, Northern Ireland. – Belfast : Department of Health and Social Services, 1985.
8 leaves.

Access to the law : a research and discussion peper. – Wellington : The Division, 1981.
214p. – (Study series).
Bibliography: p.203-204.

Accessions list : India : quinquennial serials cumulation : 1976 / Library of Congress. – 3 v. – New Delhi : Library of Congress Office, 1977.
ISBN 01457608

Accident compensation
Working paper 1 : A transport accidents scheme for New South Wales / New South Wales Law Reform Commission. – Sydney : The Commission, 1983.
xix,231p. – (Working paper 22).
Includes bibliographical references.
Interim report : Worker's Compensation (Amendment) Bill 1982 and cognate billsl / New South Wales Law Reform Commission. – 1983.
viii,62p. – (L.R.C. 41).
Final report 1 : Report on a transport accidents scheme for New South Wales / New South Wales Law Reform Commission. – 1984. – (L.R.C. 43).
Includes bibliographies and indexes. Accompanied by: Outline of report on a transport accidents scheme for New South Wales.

Accident Compensation Handbook (Vic.) / G. Hughes. – North Ryde : Law Book Co, 1986.
xix, 181p.
ISBN 0455206694 Pbk £25.00

Accident compensation in Australia : no-fault schemes / by Mark A. Robinson. – Sydney : Legal Books Pty., 1987.
xiv,94p.
Bibliography: pp.86-89. - Includes index.
ISBN 094955331X

Accident Compensation in New Zealand. – 2nd ed. – Butterworths, 1983.
Takes in new amendments (eg the reorganisation of the statutory body), and discusses the interpretations of the statutory provisions contained in many decisions reported since 1978.
ISBN 0409701602 Pbk £40.70

Accident compensation scheme : a discussion paper / Law Commission. – Wellington, N.Z. : The Commission, 1987.
v,58p. – (Preliminary paper).

Accident compensation scheme : interim report on aspects of funding / Law Commission. – Wellington, N.Z. : The Commission, 1987.
vii,39p. – (Report).

Accident compensation Victoria / by L.R. Boyes and M. O'Loghlen. – 1. – Sydney : Butterworths, 1987.
looseleaf.
Supersedes: Workers compensation, Victoria, by Anderson and Rendit. Includes: Accident and workers compensation reports.
ISBN 0409492795

Accidents, Compensation and The Law (LIC). – 4th ed. – Weidenfeld & Nicolson, 1987.
ISBN 0297790528 Hbk £30.00
ISBN 0297790536 Pbk £14.95

Accountabilities : five public services / Patricia Day, Rudolf Klein. – London : Tavistock, 1987.
259p; 22cm. – (Social science paperbacks).
Includes index.
ISBN 042279340X Hbk £18.00
ISBN 0422793507 Pbk £6.95

Accountability and prisons : opening up a closed world / edited by Mike Maguire, Jon Vagg, Rod Morgan. – London : Tavistock, 1985.
x,300p; 22cm.
Includes bibliography and index.
ISBN 042279600X Hbk £16.00 :
ISBN 0422796107 Pbk £7.95

Accountability in child care - which way forward?. – London : Family Rights Group, 1982.
49p; 21cm.
Subtitle: Background papers to a seminar organised on 19 February 1982 to discuss the issues raised by the House of Lords' judgement in A. v Liverpool City Council and to offer and invite suggestions for improving local authority practice and accountability in child care cases.

Accountability through self-evaluation : an introduction to self-evaluation for legal aid agencies. – Canberra : Commonwealth Legal Aid Commission, 1981.
20p.

Accountancy / Norkett. – Pitman, 1988.
ISBN 0273029657 Pbk £3.95

Accountancy : Study Text for Banking Students / Mellett. – Folkestone : Bankers Books.
ISBN 0852972091 Pbk £14.60

Accountancy In Banking. – Cambridge : Woodhead-Faulkner, 1983.
ISBN 0859411923 Hbk £19.95
ISBN 0859411931 Pbk £9.95

Accountants Guide to Practise Promotion, The. – London : Kogan Page.
ISBN 1850916292 Pbk £9.95

Accountant's professional negligence : developments in legal liability / Jonathan R.H.H. Pockson. – London : Macmillan, 1982.
xxi,212p; 23cm.
Bibliography: p192-208. - Includes index.
ISBN 0333278453 £25.00

Accountants' Reports for Prospectus Purposes. – Deloitte, Haskins and Sells. – London : Butterworths, 1985.
ISBN 0406500215 Pbk £20.00

Accountant's Reports on Takeovers, Mergers, Acquisitions and Realisations. – Deloitte, Haskins and Sells. – London : Butterworths, 1985.
ISBN 0406500207 Pbk £20.00

Accounting. – London : VanNostrand Reinhold, 1988.
ISBN 0278000096 Pbk £13.95

Accounting : Level 1.1. – Witney : A.T.C. Publications.
ISBN 0747700052 Pbk £13.95

Accounting : Questions and Answers. – London : Longman Professional.
ISBN 058202837X Pbk £3.50

Accounting and Audit Data. – 3rd ed. – Tolley Publishing, 1987.
ISBN 085459308X Pbk £6.95

Accounting and Financial Management For Charities / Blume. – Turnaround Press, 1985.
ISBN 0907164188 Pbk £5.95

Accounting For Banks. – Matthew Bender, 1982.
ISBN 0000999082 Hbk £55.00

Accounting for Damages : a Framework for Litigation Support. – Don Mills : CCH Canadian Ltd, 1987.
240p.
ISBN 0887963986 Hbk £40.00

Accounting for Data Processing Costs. – Quorum Press.
ISBN 0899302149 Hbk £32.95

Accounting for Foreign Exchange. – London : Butterworths, 1987.
ISBN 0406503206 Pbk £37.50

Accounting for goodwill : Accounting Standards Committee exposure draft no. 30 : memorandum / by the Society's Standing Committee on Company law. – London : Law Society, 1983.
4p.

Accounting for Non-Accountants. – Revised Edition. – Pan Books.
ISBN 0330302809 Pbk £7.50

Accounting For Pensions / Buchanan. – Cambridge : Woodhead-Faulkner, 1981.
ISBN 0859411249 Hbk £25.00

Accounting For Treasury Products / Conneely. – Cambridge : Woodhead-Faulkner, 1987.
ISBN 0859413896 Hbk £45.00

Accounting in a Law Office. – Toronto : Law Society of Upper Canada.
Hbk

Accounting in Business. – 5th ed. – London : Butterworths, 1984.
This book sets forth materials and problems in business accounting for accounting students in the United Kingdom. Cost accounting under SSAP 16 and limited company accounting under the 1981 Companies Act are both covered.
ISBN 0408014865 Pbk £13.50

Accounting Law and Practice for Limited Companies : Format and Disclosure Requirements Under the Irish Companies Acts, 1963 to 1986, and Accounting Standards. – Dublin : Gill and Macmillan, 1987.
ISBN 0717115186 Hbk £30.00

Accounting Research Database / Al-Najjar. – Routledge.
ISBN 0415000947 Hbk £35.00

Accounting Standards. – 2nd ed. – London : Pitman Publishing, 1988.
ISBN 0273027352 Pbk £10.95

Accounting Standards Committee → Accounting for goodwill : Accounting Standards Committee exposure draft no. 30 : memorandum.
→ Pension scheme accounts : a discussion paper by the Accounting Standards Committee : memorandum.

Accounts and Audits of Pension Schemes. – Spicer and Pegler. – London : Butterworths, 1987.
ISBN 040667910X Pbk £18.95

Accounts, Audit and Taxation of Clubs. – London : Butterworths, 1983.
Pbk

Accounts' Liability in the 1980's / Nobles. – Oxford : Croom Helm, 1985.
ISBN 0709918305 Hbk £25.00

Achar
Motor Transport Workers Act : with States Rules / Venkanna. – 3rd ed. – Allahabad : Law Book Company.
Hbk £200.00

Acheson, D. A., et al
Family Law Update. – Vancouver : British Columbia Continuing Legal Education Society, 1982.
226p.
ISBN 0865040869 Hbk £55.00

Achieving Quality in Financial Service Organizations How to Identify and Satisfy Customer Expectations / Hessick. – Quorum Press.
ISBN 0899302319 Hbk £32.95

Achike, Okay
Commercial law in Nigeria / by Okay Achike. – Enugu : Fourth Dimension, 1985.
xxii,496p.
Includes bibliographical references.
ISBN 9781561939

Acid rain and international law / by Irene H. van Lier. – Halifax : Dalhousie University, 1981.
xxii,278p.
Originally presented as the author's thesis (LL.M.) - Dalhousie University 1980. Bibliography: p.257-266.
ISBN 9028622314 Hbk
ISBN 0770301851 Hbk

Acid rain and the environment 1980-84 : a select bibliography / compiled and edited by Penny Farmer. – Letchworth : Technical Communications, 1984.
xx,108p; 30cm.
Includes index.
ISBN 0946655049 Pbk

A'court, P.
Estate Conveyancing. – London : Waterlow, 1984.
ISBN 0080391370 Hbk £19.50

ACP-EEC Council of Ministers → Second ACP-EEC Convention : signed at Lome on 31 October 1979 and related documents.

Acquired immune deficiency syndrome (A.I.D.S.) : guidelines for the testing of antibodies to the HTLV - III (A.I.D.S.) virus / Privacy Committee. – Sydney : The Committee, 1986.
5 leaves.

Acquisition of private companies. – 5th. – London : Longman Professional (UK), 1989.
New edition covers Financial Services Act 1986, the Finance Act 1986, the Income and Corporatin Taxes Act 1988, and the implications of the 1989 Budget. New section on merger control and competition, and includes precedents of agreements for sale both for individual and corporate vendors.
ISBN 085121438X Hbk £35.00

Acquisitions & Mergers : Accounting, Financial & Strategic Issues / Reynolds. – Routledge.
ISBN 0415004306 Hbk £27.50

Acquisitions in the United States of America. – Peat Marwick McLintock. – London : Butterworths.
ISBN 0406502552 Hbk £45.00

Acquittal rates / Sid Butler. – London : Home Office, 1983.
v,32p.
Bibliography: p.10.
ISBN 0862520967

Act of incorporation, articles of association, rules and regulations / International Air Transport Association. – 16th ed. 1. – Montreal : The Association, 1986.
looseleaf.
Previous ed.: 1981. Act of incorporation in English and French, articles of association and rules of procedure in English, French and Spanish.

Acta Juridica / W. H. B. Dean. – Kenwyn : Juta & Co, 1986.
Hbk £5400.00
Back issues avail. since 1958.

Acting for Banks and Their Customers. – Vancouver : Continuing Legal Education Society of British Columbia, 1984.
445p.
ISBN 0865041504 Hbk £75.00

Action for breach of confidence in Australia / by James Kearney. – Sydney : Legal Books, 1985.
xiv,97p.
Bibliography: p.91-93. - Includes index.
ISBN 0949553204

Action on Racial Harrassment : Legal Remedies and Local Authorities. – Sweet & Maxwell.
ISBN 0905099184 Pbk £10.00

Action-oriented research on youth crime : an international perspective / edited by Ugljesa Zvekic. – Rome : United Nations Social Defence Research Institute, 1986.
275p. – (Publication).
Bibliography: p235-270. Research workshop on perspectives in action-oriented research: youth, crime and juvenile justice held in the framework of the Seventh United Nations Congress on the Prevention of Crime and the Treatment of Offenders, Milan.
ISBN 9290780010

Acts. – Gaborone : Government Printer, 1966-.
Published as supplements to the Republic of Botswana government gazette.

Acts. – Zomba : Government Printer, 1964.
Supplement to: Malawi gazette.

Acts. – Lusaka : Government Printer, 1964.
Published as separate supplements to the Republic of Zambia government gazette.

Acts : Antigua and Barbuda. – Antigua and Barbuda : Government Printer, 1985.
Extracted from the Government gazette.

Acts : Lesotho. – Maseru : Government Printer, 1966-.
Supplements to the Government gazette.

Acts and orders relating to joint stock companies / by George R. Harding. – Brisbane : Watson, Ferguson, 1887.
xxviii,239p.
Includes index.

Acts and Ordinances Of the Interregnum 3 vols. – Professional Books.
ISBN 0862052637 Hbk £165.00

Acts and rules relating to insolvency / by George R. Harding and P. MacPherson. – Brisbane : Watson, Ferguson, 1887.
lviii,338p.
Includes index.

Acts and Statutes Made in a Parliament Began at Dublin 1769. – Repr. of 1770 ed. – Abingdon : Professional Books.
Hbk £125.00

Acts of David II 1329-71. – Edinburgh : Edinburgh University Press.
550p. – (Regesta Regum Scottorum Ser.: Vol. 6).
ISBN 0852243952 Hbk £35.00

Acts of Malcolm IV 1153-1165. – Edinburgh : Edinburgh University Press.
358p. – (Regesta Regum Scottorum Vol. 1).
ISBN 0852241410 Hbk £20.00

Acts of the Parliament. – Canberra : Australian Government Publishing Service, 1979-.
loose-leaf.
Reprints of Acts incorporating amendments, issued as pamphlets.

Acts of William I, 1165-1214. – Edinburgh : Edinburgh University Press.
570p. – (Regesta Regum Scottorum Vol. 2).
ISBN 0852241429 Hbk £20.00

Acts supplement to the Gazette of the United Republic of Tanzania. – Dar es Salaam : Government Printer, 1964.

Aculty jurisdiction of the Church of England. – Sweet & Maxwell, 1988.
xxix,262p.
Deals with the structure and workings of the court, and discusses reported case law since 1950. Analyses the problems faced by those who are entrusted with the care and development of historic buildings. Changes introduced by the Faculty Jurisdiction (Amendment) Rules 1987 are examined.
ISBN 0421387602 Pbk £12.20

Adams, Ernest Claude →New Zealand encyclopaedia of forms and precedents other than court forms.

Adams, George W.
Canadian labour law : a comprehensive text / George W. Adams. – Aurora, Ont. : Canada Law Book Inc., 1985.
cii,983p.
Includes index.
ISBN 088804030X

Adams, J. E.
Financial and Property Problems on Marriage Breakdown / Godfrey Gypps. – London : Law Society, 1982.
– (Oxford Weekend Courses).
Hbk £3.00
→ Rent reviews and variable rents.

Adams, J. G. →Family law 1981.
→ Family law 1984 style.
→ Family law 1986 style.

Adams, John N
Bibliography of eighteenth century legal literature : a subject and author catalogue of law treatises and all law related literature held in the main legal collections in England / by J.N. Adams and G. Averley : with historical and technical assistance from F.J.G. Robinson : for the BELL Project at the University of Kent in Canterbury. – Newcastle upon Tyne : Avero, 1982.
xvi,900p; 31cm.
Six microfiche in pocket.
ISBN 0907977014

—Cases and materials on sale of goods / John Adams. – London : Croom Helm, 1982.
174p; 21cm. – (Croom Helm study guides to commercial law).
Includes index.
ISBN 0709905092 Pbk £6.95

→ Essays for Clive Schmitthoff.

—Franchising : practice and precedents in business format franchising / John Adams, K.V. Prichard Jones. – 2nd ed. – London : Butterworths, 1987.
xxxvii,409p; 25cm.
Previous ed.: 1981. Includes index.
ISBN 0406101043 Hbk £50.00

—Hiring and Leasing : Practice and Precedents / K. V. Prichard Jones. – London : Butterworths, 1986.
A practical guide to the issues of leasing for the business attorney in the United Kingdom. An extensive appendix of caselaw and commentary is provided.
ISBN 0406101140 Pbk

—Law of Estate and Gift Duties in New Zealand / Richardson. – 5th ed. – London : Butterworths.
ISBN 0409606030 Hbk £30.80

—Merchandising intellectual property / John Adams : with an introduction by Iain C Baillie : and a chapter on taxation by K.V. Prichard Jones. – London : Butterworths, 1987.
xxxi,345p,2p of plates; 26cm.
Includes index.
ISBN 0406103402 £30.00

→ Schmitthoff's Export trade : the law and practice of international trade.

—Understanding contract law / John N. Adams and Roger Brownsword. – London : Fontana, 1987.
229p.
Bibliography: p213-216.
ISBN 0006860702

Adams, Neil
Law and teachers today / Neil Adams. – London : Hutchinson, 1983.
285p; 24cm.
Includes index.
ISBN 0091516102

Adams, Norma →Select cases from the ecclesiastical courts of the Province of Canterbury, c.1200-1301.

Adams, Stanley
Roche versus Adams / Stanley Adams. – London : Cape, 1984.
xii,236p,8p of plates; 23cm.
Includes index.
ISBN 022402180X £8.95

Adamson, A. J →Ghana, water supply and control : a record and analysis of legislation.

Adaptation and renegotiation of contracts in international trade and finance / edited by Norbert Horn. – Deventer, The Netherlands : Kluwer Law and Taxation Publishers, 1984.
452p.
Includes index.
ISBN 9065441824 Hbk £228.00

Adaptation of Contracts. – Paris : International Chamber of Commerce.
22p.
Hbk £4.50

Additional Protocol to the European Agreement on the Exchange of Therapeutic Substances of Human Origin. – Strasbourg : Council of Europe, 1983.
ISBN 9287101949 Hbk

Additional Protocol to the European Agreement on the Exchanges of Blood-Grouping Reagents. – Strasbourg : Council of Europe, 1983.
ISBN 9287101965

Adede, A.O.
IAEA Notification and Assistance Conventions in Case of a Nuclear Accident : Landmarks in the History of the Multilateral Treaty-Making Process. – Dordrecht : Kluwer, 1987.
226p.
ISBN 9024736161 Hbk £125.00

—System for Settlement of Disputes under the United Nations Convention on the Law of the Sea : a Drafting History and a Commentary. – Dordrecht : Kluwer, 1987.
302p.
ISBN 9024733243 Hbk £165.00

Ademuni-Odeke
Protectionism and the future of international shipping : the nature, development, and role of flag discriminations and preferences, cargo reservations and cabotage restrictions, state intervention and maritime subsidies / Dr. Ademuni-Odeke. – Dordrecht : M. Nijhoff, 1984.
xxviii,446p.
Includes bibliographies and index.
ISBN 9024729181 Hbk £235.00

Adeniji, Omolaja
Law and Practice of Banking in Nigeria. – Ile-Ife : Obafemi Awolowo Unviversity.
Hbk £15.00

Adeogun, A. A.
From contract to status in quest for security : an inaugural lecture delivered at the University of Lagos on Wednesday, 9th April, 1986 / by A.A. Adeogun. – Lagos : Lagos University Press, 1986.
60p. – (Inaugural lecture series).
Includes bibliographical references.
ISBN 9782264709
→ Law and development.

Adesola, S. M.
Income tax and administration in Nigeria / by S.M. Adesola. – Ife-Ife, Nigeria : University of Ife Press, 1986.
viii,264p.
Includes index.
ISBN 9781360585

—Income Tax Law and Administration in Nigeria. – Ile-Ife : Obafemi Awolowo University Press.
Hbk £10.00

Adhiya, S.N.
Guide to Sales Tax Laws in Maharashtra. – 4th ed. – Nagpur : Wadhura & Co, 1987.
Hbk £300.00

Adi, Isabella
Judicial attitudes to freedom of speech and the press with particular reference to contempt of court / by Isabella E. Adi. – Lagos : Nigerian Institute of Advanced Legal Studies, 1983.
23p.
Seminar paper presented at the Institute on Wednesday, April 20, 1983.
→ Marriage laws of Nigeria : papers presented at a national workshop held at the Nigerian Institute of Advanced Legal Studies.

Adiga →Negotiable Instruments Act.

Adjudication officers' guide / Chief Adjudication Officer. – London : HMSO, 1988.
looseleaf.
Index in each vol.. At head of t.p. : Department of Health and Social Security.

Adjudications for debt and related matters / Scottish Law Commission. – 2. – Edinburgh : The Commission, 1988.
– (Discussion paper).

Adjustment and financing in the developing world : the role of the International Monetary Fund / edited by Tony Killick. – London : Published by the International Monetary Fund in association with the Overseas Development Institute, 1982.
xviii,232p; 24cm.
Conference papers. Includes bibliographies.
ISBN 0939934183 Hbk £6.75
ISBN 0939934191 Pbk £4.50

Adjustments for tax purposes in highly inflationary economics : proceedings of a seminar held in Buenos Aires in 1984 during the 38th Congress of the International Fiscal Association. – Deventer, The Netherlands : Kluwer Law and Taxation Publishers, 1985.
ISBN 9065442162

Adkin, Benaiah W.
Adkin's landlord and tenant / Raymond Walton, Michael Essayan. – 18th ed. – London : Estates Gazette, 1982.
xxxiii,440p.
Includes index. .

Adkin's landlord and tenant / Raymond Walton, Michael Essayan. – 18th ed. – London : Estates Gazette, 1982.
xxxiii,440p.
Includes index. .

Adkins, R. T. →Guide to government department and other libraries 1988.

Adler, Elizabeth, et al
Justice for Aboriginal Australians : Report to the World Council of Churches Team Visit to the Aborigines, June 15 to July 3, 1981. – Sydney : Australian Council of Churches.
Hbk £3.50

Adler, Michael →Discretion and welfare.
—Origins and consequences of default : an examination of the impact of diligence (summary) / by Michael Adler and Edward Wozniak. – Edinburgh : Central Research Unit, 1981.
viii,71p; 30cm.
spiral

Adler, Ruth M.
Taking juvenile justice seriously / Ruth M. Adler. – Edinburgh : Scottish Academic Press, 1985.
viii,172p.
Bibliography: p157-167.
ISBN 0707304660

Adler, Zsuzsanna
Rape on trial / Zsuzsanna Adler. – London : Routledge & Kegan Paul, 1987.
viii,195p; 23cm.
Bibliography: p188-192. - Includes index.
ISBN 0710208049 £15.00

Administering Central/Local Relations 1871-1919. – Manchester : Manchester University Press.
ISBN 0719017572 Hbk £29.95

Administration of Corporate Security. – Cambridge : Woodhead-Faulkner, 1987.
ISBN 0902197258 Hbk £25.00

Administration of Deceased Estates Supplement-1984. – Kenwyn : Juta & Co.
31p.
ISBN 0702114898 Hbk £600.00

Administration of Family Law in Australia : Report to the Attorney-General. – Family Law Council. – Canberra : Australian Government Publishing Service, 1985.
185p : Illus.
ISBN 0644039892 Hbk £7.50

Administration of Foreign Estates. – Sweet & Maxwell, 1988.
ISBN 0421346507 Hbk £34.00

Administration of Insurance. – ICSA. – Cambridge : Woodhead-Faulkner, 1987.
ISBN 0902197428 Hbk £25.00

Administration of justice / Robin C.A. White. – Oxford : Blackwell, 1985.
400p.
Introduction to the English legal system of justice. Critique of how the system works in reality.
ISBN 0631143068 Hbk £27.50 :
ISBN 0631143076 Pbk £12.50

Administration of Justice Act 1982 / with annotations by Michael J. Goodman, J.W.R. Gray. – London : Sweet & Maxwell, 1983.
vii,83p; 24cm.
ISBN 0421312602 Pbk £6.50

Administration of Justice Act 1982 and the Assessment of Damages. – Belfast : Queen's University of Belfast, 1983.
28p.
Pbk £3.25

Administration of Justice Act 1982 and the assessment of damages for personal injuries in Northern Ireland : the text of a lecture delivered to the Belfast Solicitors' Association on 24 February 1983 / by D.S. Greer. – Belfast : SLS Legal Publications, 1983.
ii,28p.
Includes bibliographical references.

Administration of Justice in Ancient India. – New Delhi : Harnam Publications, 1988.
296p.
Hbk £240.00

Administration of Justice in Ireland / Lysaght. – repr. 1986. – Dublin : Institute of Public Administration.
105p.
Pbk £3.99

Administration of Justice in the Customary Courts of Yorubaland. – Ibadan : University Press, 1982.
128p.
Hbk £2.00

Administration of justice in the customary courts of Yorubaland / J.O. Ajibola. – Ibadan : University Press, 1982.
ix,89p.
ISBN 019575753X

Administration of Natural Justice in India. – New Delhi : Uppal Publishing House, 1986.
358p.
ISBN 818502409X Hbk £250.00

Administration of Property. – ICSA. – Cambridge : Woodhead-Faulkner, 1986.
ISBN 0902197371 updat £45.00

Administration of the courts : JUSTICE / a report by John Macdonald, Chairman of committee. – London : JUSTICE, 1986.
46p.
ISBN 0907247083

Administration of the Estates of Deceased Persons in Victoria. – 2nd ed. – Sydney : Butterworths, 1988.
288p.
Hbk £54.00

Administration of the Roman Empire 241 BC-AD 193. – Exeter : Exeter University.
ISBN 0859892042 Pbk £2.25

Administration procedure / Frank Wooldridge. – Bristol : Jordans, 1987.
xxii,113p; 21cm.
Includes index.
ISBN 0853081247 Pbk £8.50

Administrative College of Papua New Guinea
→Marriage in Papua New Guinea.

Administrative justice : some necessary reforms / (report of the Committee of the JUSTICE-ALL Souls Review of Administrative law in the United Kingdom). – Oxford : Clarendon, 1988.
xxxv,449p; 23cm.
Includes index.
ISBN 019825587X Hbk £25.00
ISBN 0198255861 Pbk £12.50

Administrative Law. – Vancouver : British Columbia Continuing Legal Education Society, 1985.
297p.
ISBN 0865042411 Hbk £65.00

Administrative law / Lawrence Baxter. – Cape Town : Juta, 1984.
lxi,796p.
Includes bibliographical references and index.
ISBN 0702115118

Administrative law / by P.P. Craig. – London : Sweet & Maxwell, 1983.
xxxiii,636p; 25cm.
Includes index.
ISBN 0421270500 Hbk £21.00
ISBN 0421270608 Pbk £15.50

Administrative law / David Foulkes. – 6th ed. – London : Butterworths, 1986.
xxxv,477p; 25cm.
This text is a thorough discussion of administrative law in the United Kingdom for students of the subject. Recent developments in caselaw and statutes are described.
ISBN 0406584095 Hbk £28.00
ISBN 0406584109 Pbk £17.95

Administrative Law. – 6th ed. – London : Butterworths, 1985.
ISBN 0406587981 Hbk £28.00
ISBN 040658799X Pbk £21.95

Administrative Law. – 2nd ed. – Lucknow : Eastern Book Company, 1985.
540p.
Hbk £60.00

Administrative Law / by David Gwynn Morgan and Gerard Hogan. – London : Sweet & Maxwell, 1986.
li,422p; 22cm.
Includes index.
ISBN 0421330600 Pbk £21.00

Administrative Law. – Allahabad : Orient Law House.
ISBN 0861310357 Pbk £35.00

Administrative Law. – Bombay : Tripathi, 1984.
Hbk £50.00

Administrative law / by H.W.R. Wade. – 6th ed. – Oxford : Clarendon Press, 1988.
lxxi,1028p.
Includes bibliographical references and index.
ISBN 0198762194 Pbk £30.00
ISBN 0198762208 Hbk £60.00

Administrative Law. – London : Butterworths.
ISBN 0409067040 Hbk £38.00
ISBN 0409067059 Pbk £25.00

Administrative Law : A Treatise
Vol. 1 / Louis Borgeat. – 2nd ed. – Agincourt : Carswell, 1986.
736p.
This work focuses on the structures, the arts, and the function of 'the Administration' through an examination of the definition of administrative law and its fundamental principles.
ISBN 045938080X Hbk £80.00

Administrative law : cases and materials / M H Matthews. – 2nd ed. – Oxford : Clarendon Press, 1988.
700.
A sourcebook for those studying administrative law. The new edition has been revised to include the New Procedural System, Discretionary Powers, and Remedies.
Students in their second or third years
ISBN 0198762062 Hbk £35.00
ISBN 0198762054 Pbk £18.50

Administrative law : cases, text, and materials / J.M. Evans ... et al. – 2nd ed. – Toronto : Emond Montgomery, 1984.
xlix,994p.
Previous ed.: 1980. Includes index.
ISBN 0920722156 Hbk £90.00

Administrative Law : Cases, Text and Materials / H. N. Janisch. – 2nd ed. – Aurora : Canada Law Book Co, 1984.
1100p. – (Case Books).
This text deals with the complex problems that arise in a wide range of governmental and regulatory contexts. Among other topics, the text discusses the impact of the Charter on administrative procedure, the emergence of the 'rational basis' test in jurisdiction cases and its relevance in other contexts, and the Constitutional right to judicial review.
Hbk £90.00

Administrative law : ladders and snakes : a public lecture / delivered by Sir Patrick Neill on ... 12th March 1985. – London : Inns of Court School of Law, 1985.
32p.

Administrative Law : Origin, Development Process, Power, Procedure, Justice and Tribunals. – 2nd ed. – Lucknow : Eastern Book Company, 1984.
1,100p.
Hbk £200.00

Administrative Law and Tribunal. – Calcutta : Eastern Law House, 1987.
Hbk £120.00

Administrative Law and Tribunals. – 2nd ed. – Allahabad : Law Book Company, 1988.
700p.
Hbk £200.00

Administrative Law First. – Butterworths, 1989.
ca 122p.
ISBN 0409494798 Pbk £10.95

Administrative law in Ireland / Ronald M. Stout. – Dublin : Institute of Public Administration, 1985.
514p.
Includes index.
ISBN 0906980402 £25.00

Administrative Law Reports. – Agincourt : Carswell.
Hbk £74.75
Vols. 1-30. – 1984-88.
This text contains the administrative law decisions from all the Canadian jurisdictions. Topics include the judicial review of decisions of administrative tribunals, both the availability of and grounds for, delegation of legislative powers, and remedies on judicial review.

Administrative Law, Second Edition. – New Delhi : Prentice-Hall, 1985.
624p.
ISBN 0876924402 Hbk £120.00

Administrative politics in British government / Andrew Gray and William I. Jenkins. – Brighton : Wheatsheaf, 1985.
x,259p; 23cm.
Bibliography: p235-250. - Includes index.
ISBN 0710801432 Hbk £18.95
ISBN 0312004613 £6.95

Administrative receivers and administrators / Gordon Stewart. – Bicester : CCH Editions, 1987.
xvii,359p; 23cm.
Traces receiverships and administrations from the events leading up to appointment through to termination and discharge of the office holder. Gives details of licensing requirements, and covers for both receivers and administrators, the appointment, nature and capacity, powers and duties. Also looks at payments and duties, termination, tax, and relevant forms.
ISBN 0863251404 Hbk
ISBN 0863250858 Pbk

Administrative Receivership Law & Practice England & Wales / Harting. – Sweet & Maxwell.
ISBN 0421409908 Hbk £20.00

Administrative Review Council
Administrative Review Council : Seventh Annual Report 1982-1983. – Administrative Review Council. – Canberra : Australian Government Publishing Service.
88p.
Hbk £4.90

—Review of Import Control and Customs Bylaw Decision. – Administrative Review Council. – Canberra : Australian Government Publishing Service, 1982.
22p.
ISBN 0642070679 Hbk £1.20

—Rights of review under the Migration Act 1958 and related legislation : interim report on the constitution for the Administrative Appeals Tribunal : report to the Attorney-General / Administrative Review Council. – Canberra : Australian Government Publishing Service, 1983.
v,6p. – (Report).
ISBN 0644028432

—Small Security Appeals. – Administrative Review Council. – Canberra : Australian Government Publishing Service, 1981.
144p.
ISBN 0642066663 Hbk £4.80

Administrative Review Council : Annual report 1983-84. – 8th ed. – Canberra : Australian Government Publishing Service, 1984.
101p.
Hbk £6.30

Administrative Review Council : Seventh Annual Report 1982-1983. – Administrative Review Council. – Canberra : Australian Government Publishing Service.
88p.
Hbk £4.90

Administrative Review Tribunal
Citizenship, Review and Appeals System : Report, 13 June 1980. – Administrative Review Tribunal. – Canberra : Australian Government Publishing Service, 1981.
8p.
ISBN 0642066981 Hbk £0.40

Administrative Tribunals Act, 1985. – Lucknow : Eastern Book Company, 1986.
932p.
Hbk £130.00

Administrative Tribunals Act, 1985, as Amended by the Adminstrative Tribunals (Amendment Act) 1986. – Bombay : Tripathi, 1987.
436p.
Hbk £120.00

Administrative Tribunals Handbook. – Wellington District Law Society. – Butterworths, 1989.
76p.
ISBN 0409702277 Pbk £27.00

Administrative Tribunals Litigation. – Vancouver : Continuing Legal Education Society of British Columbia, 1987.
354p.
ISBN 0865043566 Hbk £85.00

Administrator : the journal of the Institute of Chartered Secretaries and Administrators. – London : Institute of Chartered Secretaries and Administrators, 1982-.
Continues: Professional administration, new series vol. 1, no. 1(Jan. 1981)- 1, no. 11(Dec. 1981).

Administrators : part II of the Insolvency Act 1986 / Hamish Anderson. – London : Sweet & Maxwell, 1987.
250p; 26cm.
Guide to the insolvency procedure established by the Insolvency Act 1986, including a commentary on the relevant provisions, and statutory instruments. Examines the status and powers of an administrator, and the effects of an administration order on the members, creditors, and employees of a company.
ISBN 0421348208 £15.00

Adminstration of foreign estates / edited by John Pugh : contributors L. Ruiz Barrero ... et al. – London : Sweet & Maxwell, 1988.
300p; 25cm.
Guide to the probate procedures pertaining to eight countries, namely, Spain, Portugal, Italy, France, Guernsey, Jersey, the Isle of Man and also Florida. Covers areas such as registration of death, making a will, and the administration of realty and personalty, death duties, and the distribution of the estate. Each chapter has an appendix of forms.
ISBN 0421346507 £35.00

Adminstrative College of Papua New Guinea → Marriage and domestic violence in rural Papua New Guinea.

Admiralty jurisdiction. – Sydney : Law Reform Commission, 1984.
20p. – (Discussion paper).

Admiralty jurisdiction and practice in South Africa / by D. J. Shaw. – Cape Town : Juta, 1987.
xxvii,264p.
Bibliography: p. xi. - Includes index.
ISBN 0702118168

Admissibility of Statements. – 6th ed. – Toronto : Balmuir Book Publishing Ltd..
xx, 231p.
ISBN 0919511236 Pbk £12.95

Admission of Commonwealth lawyers : a technical survey for Commonwealth Law Ministers and the Commonwealth Lawyers' Association / Campbell Alan McLachlan. – London : Commonwealth Secretariat, 1985.
x, 168p.

Admission of securities to listing. – Stock Exchange. – New loose-leaf ed. Nov. 1984. – London : Council of the Stock Exchange, 1984.
1 v. (loose-leaf).
Includes index.
ISBN 0900872195

Adolescent subcultures and delinquency / Herman Schwendinger and Julia Siegel Schwendinger. – Research ed. – New York : Praeger, 1985.
xvi,524p; 25cm.
Bibliography: p497-511. - Includes index.
ISBN 0030009391 Hbk £76.95
ISBN 0030009421 Pbk

Adoption. – Tavistock, 1984.
ISBN 0422784109 Hbk £19.95

Adoption Act Manual. – London : Sweet & Maxwell, 1988.
ISBN 0421393505 Pbk £18.00

Adoption Of Children / Levy. – 10th ed. – London : Longman Professional, 1985.
ISBN 0851208665 Pbk £24.00

Adoption of children in Scotland. – 2nd. – Edinburgh : Green (W.) & Son, 1986.
Deals with adoptions in the sequence which occurs in practice and the relevant statute and case law. The appendices contain the Adoption (Scot.) Act 1978, the rules of court, and styles of writs, interlocutors and reports.
ISBN 0414007794 Pbk

Adoption practice and procedure / by Nasreen Pearce. – London : Fourmat, 1984.
xii,133p; 22cm.
Includes index.
ISBN 0906840791 Pbk

Adrian, C.R.
History of American City Government : The Emergence of the Metropolis 1920-45. – London : Eurospan.
ISBN 0819166499 Hbk £30.50

Adult prisons and prisoners in England and Wales 1970-1982 : a review of the findings of social research / Joy Mott. – London : H.M.S.O., 1985.
vi,68p.
Reviews social research results. Compares them with developments in the USA. Concludes that research in the UK has been inadequate, concentrating on prisoners and neglecting the prisons.
ISBN 0113408013

Advance rulings on tax liability / by John Prebble. – Wellington, N.Z. : Victoria University Press, 1986.
191p.
Bibliography: p.156-157. - Includes index. Published for the Institute of Policy Studies.
ISBN 0864730586

Advanced Accounting. – 4th ed. – Prentice-Hall, 1988.
ISBN 0130101826 Hbk £46.75

Advanced Accounting Practice : ACCA Study and Revision Manual 2.9. – London : BPP.
ISBN 1870941047 Pbk £19.90

Advanced Company Law and Corporate Income Tax. – Vancouver : Continuing Legal Education Society of British Columbia, 1985.
355p.
ISBN 0865042357 Hbk £70.00

Advanced Family Law Seminar. – Monash University, Faculty of Law. – Clayton : Monash University Press, 1984.
ISBN 086746318X Hbk £15.00

Advanced Financial Accounting. – Maidenhead : McGraw-Hill.
ISBN 0070033668 Hbk £32.95

Advanced Financial Accounting : Level 3.1. – Witney : A.T.C. Publications.
ISBN 074770001X Pbk £15.95

Advanced taxation / general editors Emile Woolf, Suresh Tanna, Karam Singh. – Plymouth : Macdonald & Evans, 1985.
xx,720p. – (M & E professional studies).
Includes index.
ISBN 0712104887 Pbk £18.50

Advanced topics of law and information technology / G P V Vandenberghe, Y Poullet. – Kluwer Law and Taxation, 1989.
210. – (Computer/Law Series).
Covers the law with regard to information technology, the challenge of computer law, privacy protection and transborder data flow, standards for computer crime, and expert systems and copyright.
ISBN 9065443916 Pbk £43.75/Dfl 135

Advertising and charging rules of the professions serving the construction industry : a report by the Director General of Fair Trading. – London : Office of Fair Trading, 1986.
84p.
Bibliography: p.60-63.

Advertising and marketing law and practice. – London : Frank Cass, 1984-.
Continues: Advertising law and practice.

Advertising and specialisation / New South Wales Law Reform Commission. – Sydney : The Commission, 1981.
xxxv,244p; 25cm. – (Discussion paper no 5).
Bibliography: p.228-244.

Advertising by solicitors : a guide / Eric Granados. – London : Stewart (Henry), 1984.
107p.
ISBN 0946700109 Pbk £12.50

Advertising by the professions : a review of the remaining significant restrictions / a report by the Director General of Fair Trading. – London : Office of Fair Trading, 1986.
56p.

Advertising Law. – Pitman, 1978.
ISBN 0712112391 Hbk £13.95

Advertising regulation / by Shenagh Barnes and Michael Blakeney. – Sydney : Law Book Co., 1982.
lii,612p.
Bibliography: p.xlv-lii. - Includes index.
ISBN 0455205450

Advertising Standards Authority →British code of advertising practice.
→ British code of sales promotion practice.

Adviser : a bi-monthly guide on social security, housing, money advice and employment. – London : National Association of Citizens Advice Bureaux and Shelter, 1986-.
Continues: Rights Workers Bulletin, Housing Aid and In the Black. Supplement: Computanews.

Advising a suspect in the police station : guidelines for solicitors. – Law Society's Criminal Law Committee. – London : Law Society.
Hbk £2.00

Advisory Committee on Animal Experiments
Report to the Secretary of State on the framework of legislation to replace the Cruelty to Animals Act 1876 / Advisory Committee on Animal Experiments. – London : Home Office, 1981.
40p.

Advisory Committee on Rent Rebates and Rent Allowances. – London : HMSO, 1983.
– (Report No. 3 (Final Report)).
ISBN 0117517119 Hbk £4.15

Advisory, Conciliation and Arbitration Service
Conciliation by ACAS in complaints by individuals to Industrial Tribunals / Advisory, Conciliation and Arbitration Service. – London : ACAS, 1982.
—Disciplinary and other procedures in employment : consultative document on a draft code of practice / Advisory, Conciliation and Arbitration Service. – London : The Service, 1985.
29p.
—Workplace communications / Advisory Conciliation and Arbitration Service. – rev. – London : ACAS, 1983.
– (Advisory booklet).
ISBN 0906073057 Hbk

Advocacy. – Law Society of Upper. – Toronto : DeBoo, 1982.
ISBN 0888201117 Hbk £100.00

Advocacy : views from the bench / Robert F. Reid and Richard E. Holland. – Aurora, Ont. : Canada Law Book, 1984.
xii,164p.
Includes index.
ISBN 0888040245

Advocacy and Mental Handicap / Raquel Schuster-Herr. – Brussels : International League of Societies for Persons with Mental Handicap, 1984.
Hbk £1.50

Advocacy at the Bar : a beginner's guide / written and illustrated by Keith Evans. – London : Financial Training, 1983.
ix,201p.
ISBN 0906322235

Advocacy in Child Welfare Cases. – Agincourt : Carswell, 1985.
258p.
This book discusses the representation of the parties to child welfare cases under the Child Welfare Act and the Child and Family Services Act of Canada.
Hbk £35.75

Advocacy in the Court of Appeal of British Columbia 1982. – Vancouver : Continuing Legal Education Society of British Columbia, 1982.
200p.
ISBN 0865040818 Hbk £55.00

Advocacy with Honour. – Allahabad : Law Book Company, 1985.
xi, 100p.
ISBN 0455206511 Pbk £14.00

Advocates Act and Legal Practitioners Act. – 5th ed. – Allahabad : Law Book Company, 1987.
600p.
Hbk £160.00

Advocates' Quarterly (1977-Present). – Aurora : Canada Law Book Co.
Hbk £75.00
Back Vols.. –
Hbk £36.00 ea.

Advocates' Quarterly (A.Q.) / Garry D. Watson. – Aurora : Canada Law Book Co.
Hbk £75.00

Advokatbyra, Carl S.
Swedish Companies Act 1975 : With Excerpts from the Accounting Act 1976. – Stockholm : Industriforbundet, 1986.
144p.
ISBN 9171761004 Hbk £180.00

Advokaterne Bredgade 3 →Merger control in the EEC : a survey of European competition laws.

Aerial piracy and international terrorism : the illegal diversion of aircraft and international law / Edward McWhinney. – 2nd rev. ed. – Dordrecht, the Netherlands : M. Nijhoff, 1987.
Re ed. of: Aerial piracy and international law / by Edward McWhinney and others. 1971. Includes index. Bibliography..
ISBN 0898389194

Aeronautical agreements and arrangements : tables of agreements and arrangements registered with the Organization, 1 January 1946 - 31 December 1985. – International Civil Aviation Organization. – 14th ed. – Montreal : International Civil Aviation Orgainization, 1986.
vi,373p. – (Doc 9460-LGB/382).
Kept up to date by supplements and lists. Supplements held: 1st, 1986; 2nd, 1987.

Aerospace Law : Telecommunications Satellites. – London : Butterworths, 1982.
ISBN 0409848654 Hbk £67.00

Affiliation Law and Practice. – 5th ed. – London : Longman Professional, 1985.
ISBN 0851209912 Pbk £15.95

Affirmative Action : the New Discrimination. – St. Leonards : Centre for Independent Studies.
116p.
ISBN 0949769274 Hbk £11.95

Affirmative action and preferential admissions in higher education : an annotated bibliography / by Kathryn Swanson. – Metuchen : Scarecrow, 1981.
viii,336p; 23cm.
Includes index.
ISBN 0810814110 £12.25

Affley, G.
Business Law. – 1st ed. Repr. of 1982 ed. – Plymouth : Macdonald & Evans, 1983.
288p. – (M and E Handbook Ser.).
ISBN 0712102612 Hbk £5.50
—Business Law. – 2nd ed. – London : Pitman Publishing, 1985.
ISBN 0712124055 Pbk £6.95

Afford, Jocelyn
Law and You : a Practical Guide for New Zealanders / J. Stephen Kos. – Birkenhead : Reed Methuen.
ISBN 0589013807 Hbk £9.95

Afghanistan : torture of political prisoners. – Amnesty International. – London : Amnesty International, 1986.
i,51p.
ISBN 0862101077

Africa and the Development of International Law. – 2nd ed. – Martinus Nijhoff, .
ISBN 9024737966 Hbk £59.50

Africa south of the Sahara. – London : Europa Publications, 1971-.

The African Slave Trade and the American Courts : the Pamphlet Literature. – London : Garland.
ISBN 0824067223 Hbk

African tax systems / Robert C. Hammond, Marc J. van den Abeelen. – 2. – Amsterdam : International Bureau of Fiscal Documentation, 1983.
loose-leaf.
Includes bibliography. 'Prepared at the request of the United Nations Economic Commission for Africa.' - Editors: Robert C. Hammond and Marc J. van den Abeelen.

Africa's Development Challenges and the World Bank : Hard Questions, Costly Choices. – London : Eurospan.
ISBN 155587116X Hbk £25.50

Africa's shared water resources : legal and institutional aspects of the Nile, Niger and Senegal river systems / by Bonaya Godana. – London : Pinter, 1985.
220p; 23cm.
Includes bibliography and index.
ISBN 086187563X £17.50

After legal instrumentalism? : strategic models of post- regulatory law / by Gunther Teubner. – Florence : European University Institute, 1984.
58p.
Bibliography: p.52-58. At head of title: European University Institute, Florence, Law Department.

...after sexual assault... : your guide to the criminal justice system / Department of Justice Canada. – Ottawa : The Department, 1986.
109p.
ISBN 0662147529

Afterman, A.B.
Cases and Materials on Corporations and Associations / R. Baxt. – 5th ed. – Butterworths, 1988.
823p.
Covers unincorporated associations, partnership, the company as a separate legal entity, the memorandum of association, powers of companies and ultra vires, articles of association and contacts within the company, relations between the company and outsiders, control and management of the company, oppression of minority shareholders, and takeovers and reconstructions.
ISBN 0409493058 Pbk £62.00 (incl. suppl.)

Aftermath of tribunal reinstatement and re-engagement / by Kevin Williams and David Lewis. – London : Department of Employment, 1981.
46p. – (Research paper).
Bibliography: p.45-46.

Afzal, M.
Commentaries on the U.P. Panchayat Raj Act, 1947, (U.P. Act no. 26 of 1947) as Amended Up-to-Date, with Rules, Orders, Notifications, and Other Allied Laws. – 4th ed. – Allahabad : Hind Publishing House, 1981.
x, 186, 292p.
Hbk £40.00

Against Criminology. – Oxford : Clio Distribution.
ISBN 0887381537 Hbk £24.30
ISBN 088738689X Pbk £11.80

Against oblivion : Amnesty International's fight for human rights / Jonathan Power. – London : Fontana, 1981.
254p; 18cm.
Includes index.
ISBN 0006364268 Pbk £1.95

Agarwal, H. O.
Implementation of human rights covenants : with special reference to India / H.O. Agarwal. – Allahabad : Kitab Mahal, 1983.
x,210p.
Includes index. Includes the text of the International Covenant on Economic, Social and Cultural Rights and the International Covenant on Civil and Political Rights.

Agarwal, Minu
Taxation of Income and Tax Laws. – New Delhi : Deep and Deep Publications.
240p.
Hbk £120.00

Agarwal, Om Prakash
Compulsory Acquisition of Land in India, 2 Vols. – Allahabad : Universal Book Agency, 1984.
Hbk £350.00

Agarwal, R.K.
Conservation of Foreign Exchange and Prevention of Smuggling Activities Act. – Allahabad : Law Book Company, 1987.
250p.
Hbk £85.00
—Law of Municipalities and Municipal Corporations. – 3rd ed. – Allahabad : Law Book Company, 1987.
1,800p.
Hbk £380.00

Agarwal, S.K.
All-India Criminal Digest, 1971-80, 3 Vols. – Allahabad : Law Book Company.
Hbk £450.00
—Law of Education and Educational Institutions in India, 3 Vols. – Allahabad : Law Book Company, 1982-83.
With 1988 supplement.
Hbk £600.00
—Law of Rent Control, Eviction and Leases in India, 3 Vols. – 2nd ed. 1980-1 repr. – Allahabad : Law Book Company, 1982.
Hbk £360.00
—New Horizons of International Law and Developing Countries. – Bombay : Tripathi, 1983.
Hbk £90.00
—Supreme Court Civil Digest 1950-80, 5 Vols. – 2nd ed. – Allahabad : Law Book Company, 1950-80.
Hbk £500.00
—Supreme Court Criminal Digest 1950-80, 2 Vols. – Allahabad : Law Book Company.
Hbk £180.00
—Supreme Court Services and Labour Digest 1950-1979. – Allahabad : Law Book Company, 1976-1979.
851p.
Hbk £250.00

Agarwal, V.K.
Government Contracts : Law and Procedure. – Delhi : Eastern Book Corporation, 1984.
xxxv, 532p.
ISBN 8185077010 Hbk £70.00

Agarwala, B.R.
Supreme Court Practice and Procedure. – 4th ed. – Lucknow : Eastern Book Company, 1985.
550p.
Hbk £135.00

Agarwala, D.D.
Guide to Revenue Law in U.P., 3 Vols. 1901-1976. – 4th ed. – Lucknow : Eastern Book Company, 1977.
986p.
Hbk £70.00

Agarwalla
Land Aquisition. – Allahabad : Universal Book Agency, 1985.
Hbk £350.00

Agbede, I. O.
Hon. Dr. T. Akinola Aguda : the man, his works and society / by I.O. Agbede. – Lagos : Nigerian Institute of Advanced Legal Studies, 1986.
v,30p. – (Occasional paper).
Bibliography: pp.21-30..

Agboola, A. T.
Nigerian elections : a bibliography / by A.T. Agboola. – Lagos : University of Lagos Library, 1983.
ix,45p.
Includes index.

Age and Crime. – Canberra : Australian Institute of Criminology.
Hbk £3.60

Age Concern in Scotland. – Edinburgh : Age Concern Scotland, 1988.
ISBN 0946505489 Pbk £1.00

Age Materials. – Canberra : Australian Government Publishing Service, 1984.
21p.
ISBN 0644035447 Pbk £2.60

Age Of Sex Crime. – Women's Press, 1988.
ISBN 0704341166 Pbk £5.95

Agell, Jonas
Tax Reforms and Asset Markets. – Stockholm : Industriens Utredningsinstitut, 1985.
181p.
Hbk £154.00

Agency. – Stockholm : Anderson Keenan, 1981. – (Law Unit).
ISBN 0906501237 Pbk £3.00

Agenda for Black Theology in South Africa. – Braamfontein : Skotaville Publishers, 1988.
Pbk £12.95

Agenda For Implementing New Law Product Liability. – Deddington : Pandora Press, 1987.
ISBN 1870317858 £84.00

Aggarwal
Sexual Harassment in the Workplace. – London : Butterworths.
ISBN 0409805351 Hbk £32.00

Aggarwal, Arjun P.
Sexual Harassment in the Workplace. – Butterworths, 1987.
256p.
Intends to clarify the meaning and concept of 'sexual harassment'. Identifies its social, economic and legal implications for victims, harassers and employers, and discusses its impact on the working environment. Refers to relevant Canadian case law, and highlights the procedure and criteria developed and adopted by human rights tribunals in Canada.
ISBN 0409805351 Hbk £39.95

Aggression and Crimes of Violence. – 2nd ed. – Oxford : Oxford University Press, 1986.
ISBN 0195039440 Pbk £9.00

Agich, George J. →Responsibility in health care.

Aging world : dilemmas and challenges for law and social policy / edited by John Eekelaar and D. Pearl. – Oxford : OUP, 1989.
900.
Critical examination on an international basis of the problems facing legal and social systems due to an increasing number of elderly within the world's population.
Lawyers, demographers, economists, sociologists and political scientists interested in problems of aging populations
ISBN 0198254091 Pbk £39.50

Agnew, J.
Competition Law. – London : Allen & Unwin, 1985.
ISBN 0043430023 Hbk £18.00
ISBN 0043430031 Pbk £7.95

Agnew, Sir Crispin, et al
Licensing (Scotland) Act 1976 / Heather Baillie. – 2nd. – Edinburgh : Green (W.) & Son, 1989.
Annotated text of the Act, originally produced by J. Allen and C.D. Chapman (1977), as subsequently amended and taking into account case law since the publication of the original edition. Also includes an expanded introduction and details of individual licensing boards.
ISBN 041400826X Pbk £16.00

Agostino, M. B →Nursing law and ethics.

Agrawal
Supreme Court Quinquennial Digest, 1981 to 1985. – Allahabad : Law Book Company.
1,000p.
Hbk £250.00

Agrawal, M.C.
Commentaries on State Financial Corporations Act, 1951 / Kumar Avadhesh Srivastava. – Allahabad : Law Book Company, 1988.
ca 300p.
Pbk £150.00

Agreement between the United Nations and the World Intellectual Property Organization. – Geneva : World Intellectual Property Organization.
55p.
Hbk £10.00

Agreements of the People's Republic of China. – 2nd rev. enl. ed. – Munich : Saur, 1988.
ca 660p.
ISBN 3598108400 Hbk £248.00

Agreements registered with the International Atomic Energy Agency : definitive entries up to 31 December 1980; provisional entries up to 31 December 1982. – International Atomic Energy Agency. – 9th ed. – Vienna : IAEA, 1985.
262p. – (Legal series).
ISBN 920176085X

Agreements registered with the International Atomic Energy Agency (up to 31 December 1978). – International Atomic Energy Agency. – 8th ed. – Vienna : International Atomic Energy Agency, 1981.
253p; 24cm. – (Legal series).
ISBN 9201760817

Agribusiness in Africa : a study of the impact of big business on Africa's food and agricultural production / Barbara Dinham & Colin Hines. – London : Earth Resources Research, 1983.
224p b ill; 21cm.
Includes index. Cover title.
ISBN 0946281009 Pbk £4.95

Agricultural census legislation / a joint publication by the Statistics Division and the Legislation Branch, Legal Office. – Rome : Food and Agriculture Organization of the United nations, 1984.
v,117p. – (Legislative study).
ISBN 9251013772

Agricultural Holdings. – Oxford : Blackwell Scientific, 1987.
ISBN 0003833364 Hbk £20.00

Agricultural Holdings. – 13th. 1 volume, supplement. – London : Sweet & Maxwell, 1987.
xxiv,200p.
States the law contained in the Agricultural Holdings Act 1986. Includes the nature and inception of the tenancy of an agricultural holding, termination by notice to quit and otherwise, and the procedure of agricultural land tribunals. Chapter on arbitration revised. Includes annotations, text of statutory instruments, and forms.
ISBN 0421318007 Hbk £95.00

Agricultural Holdings Act. – Sweet & Maxwell, 1986.
ISBN 0421318007 Hbk £95.00

Agricultural Holdings Bill : report on the consolidation of certain enactments relating to agricultural holdings / the Law Commission. – London : H.M.S.O., 1985.
7p.
ISBN 0101966504

Agricultural insurance legislation / by Beatriz Benilde Galan for Land and Water Legislation Section, Legislation Branch, Legal Office. – Rome : Food and Agriculture Organization of the United Nations, 1981.
vii, 149 p.; 27 cm. – (Legislative study).
ISBN 9251010358 £2.50

Agricultural law / McKay. – London : Longman Professional (UK), 1990.
Coverage includes agricultural holdings, milk quotas, product liability, finance and taxation, pollution, employment law, competition law, agrochemicals, recreation and diversification, contracts, housing and share farming.
Llf

Agricultural law / C Margrave-Jones. – London : Longman Professional (UK), 1989.
Covers the Agricultural Holdings Act of 1984 and 1986 tenancies, tied accomodation, security of tenure and its removal, and succession to holdings. Sets out cases for possession and compulsory purchase and the relevant compensatory proceedings. Also deals with taxation, public control of land use, resolving agricultural disputes, and European Agricultural law.
ISBN 0851214290 Hbk £27.50

Agricultural tenancies : law and practice / by C.P. Rodgers : consulting editor C.V. Margrave-Jones. – London : Butterworth, 1985.
xxxvii,447p; 25cm.
Includes index. Chapter 13 by C.V. Margrave-Jones.
ISBN 0406258406 Pbk £20.00

Agricultural Valuations. – London : Estates Gazette, 1985.
ISBN 0728200872 Pbk £11.00

Agriculture. – Agincourt : Carswell, 1983.
240p.
This textbook describes in detail all of the aspects of agricultural law as it is derived from the common law, statutes, and regulatory bodies of the Canadian federal and provincial governments. Extensive references are made to marketing boards, loan associations, and federal and provincial regulating authorities in the work.
Hbk £38.00

Agriculture : The Legal Framework. – Aurora : Canada Law Book Co, 1982.
300p. – (Text Books-Civil).
Hbk £45.00

Agriculture and pollution : the government response to the seventh report of the Royal Commission on Environmental Pollution. – London : H.M.S.O., 1983.
ISBN 0117500216

Agriculture, the countryside and land use : an economic critique / J.K. Bowers and Paul Cheshire. – London : Methuen, 1983.
x,170p; 20cm.
Includes index.
ISBN 0416318304 Pbk

Aguda, Timothy Akinola →Challenge of the Nigerian nation : an examination of its legal development, 1960-1985.

—Criminal law and procedure of the southern states of Nigeria / C. O. Madarikan. – 3rd ed. – London : Sweet & Maxwell, 1982.
lxxxiv,1061p; 23cm.
Previous ed.: published as Brett and McLean's The criminal law and procedure of the six southern states of Nigeria / by C.O. Madarikan and T. Akinola Aguda. 1974. Includes index.
ISBN 042124920X £58.00

—Crisis of justice / by T. Akinola Aguda. – Akure, Nigeria : Eresu Hills, 1986.
x,73p.

—Judiciary and the 1983 elections / by T. Akinola Aguda. – Lagos : Nigerian Institute of Advanced Legal Studies, 1983.
19p.
Notes of a seminar presented at the Institute on Wednesday, February 23, 1983.

—Judiciary in the government of Nigeria / by T. Akinola Aguda. – Ibadan : New Horn Press, 1983.
xii,183p.
Bibliography: p.183.
ISBN 9782266051

—Law of Evidence in Nigeria. – 3rd ed. – London : Sweet & Maxwell, 1987.
ISBN 0421378506 Pbk £20.00

—Legal implications of the creation of more states in Nigeria : being a paper presented at the National Conference on Creation of States in Nigeria / by T. Akinola Aguda. – Ile Ife : Nigerian Institute of Advanced Legal Studies, 1981.
20p; 25cm.

→ Marriage laws of Nigeria : papers presented at a national workshop held at the Nigerian Institute of Advanced Legal Studies.

—New perspective in law and justice in Nigeria : the distinguished annual lecture delivered at the National Institute on 25th October, 1985 / by Timothy Akinola Aguda. – Kuru, Nigeria : National Institute for Policy and Strategic Studies, 1985.
16p. – (Distinguished lecture series).
Includes bibliographical references.

Aguda, Tomothy Akinola
Quintessence of justice : University of Maiduguri, 6th convocation lecture delivered on Thursday, January 31st, 1985 / by Timothy Akinola Aguda. – Maiduguri, Nigeria : University of Maiduguri, 1985.
34p. – (Convocation lecture).
ISBN 9782323462

Aguolu, S. I. O.
Prerogative writs and orders under Nigerian law and constitution / by S.I.O. Aguolu. – Enugu : Star Printing and Publishing Company, 1981.
xxii,167p.
Includes index.

Agwarala
Pleading and Precedents in India. – 2nd ed. – Allahabad : Law Publishers, 1983.
Hbk £37.50

Ahern, J.
Victorian Conveyancing Costs Annotated. – 3rd ed. – Sydney : Butterworths, 1983.
80p.
ISBN 0409493112 Pbk

Ahern, John
Legal Costs, New South Wales / Kingsley Siebel. – Butterworths.
Llf

Ahmadu Bello University →Journal of Islamic and comparative law : journal of the Centre of Islamic Legal Studies, Faculty of Law, Ahmadu Bello University, Zaria, Nigeria.

Ahmadu Bello University law journal. – Zaria : Faculty of Law, Ahmadu Bello University, 1983-.

Ahmed, Ejaz
Commentaries on Uttar Pradesh Cooperative Societies Act, 1965 / Sushma Malik. – 4th ed. – Lucknow : Eastern Book Company, 1984.
756p.
Hbk £110.00

Ahuja, B.N.
World Constitution. – New Delhi : Varma Brothers.
Hbk £18.00

Aid : rhetoric and reality / Teresa Hayter, Catharine Watson. – London : Pluto, 1985.
xv,303p; 20cm.
Includes index.
ISBN 0861046269 Pbk £4.95

Aidoo, E. S.
Ghana : the people, the laws and the courts / by E.S. Aidoo. – Legon : Institute of Statistical, Social and Economic Research, University of Ghana, 1985.
37p.
'Paper first presented at the Seventh Annual Alumni Lecture of the University of Ghana'.

AIDS and Employment Law / Howard. – London : Financial Training, 1988.
ISBN 1851850937 Pbk £14.95

AIDS and the law : a guide for the public / edited by Harlon L. Dalton, Scott Burris and the Yale AIDS Law Project. – New Haven : Yale University Press, 1987.
384p; 24cm.
Includes bibliography and index.
ISBN 0300040776 Hbk £19.95 :
ISBN 0300040784 Pbk £6.95

Aihe, D. O.
Selected essays on Nigerian constitutional laws / D.O. Aihe. – Benin City : Idodo Umeh Publishers Ltd., 1985.
xxviii,264p.
Bibliography: p.255-257. - Includes index.
ISBN 9782340448

Ainger, P. L. →Gilgate Holdings Limited, Raybourne Group Limited, Calomefern Limited, Desadean Properties Limited : investigation under Section 165(b) of the Companies Act 1948.

Air and outer space law. – Thessaloniki : Institute of International Public Law and International Relations of Thessaloniki, 1981.
xvi,842p.
Includes bibliographies. Includes chapters in French and German.

Air cargo : regulation and claims / Jean-Louis Magdelenat. – Toronto : Butterworths, 1983.
xxvi,181p.
Bibliography: p.177-181. Summarizes the rules of liability. governing the carriage of goods by air. Surveys the economic and technical aspects of air cargo, systematically considering all their legal ratifications.
ISBN 0409847836 Hbk £55

Air law. – Deventer : Kluwer, 1975.
Index in each vol.
ISBN 01652079

Air Law / Beaumont. – 4th ed. – London : Butterworths, 1983.
Service to Date.
ISBN 0406373191 Hbk £280.00

Air Navigation : The Order and the Regulations, 2 ed. – Civil Aviation Authority. – 2nd. ed. Great Britain. – London : Civil Aviation Authority, 1981.
Illus.
ISBN 0860391248 Hbk £17.00

Air, noise, water and waste : a summary of the law in Scotland / by Francil Lyall. – Glasgow : Planning Exchange, 1982.
vii,195p; 21cm.
Includes index.
ISBN 0905011198 Pbk

Air pollution control : the government response to the Fifth Report of the Royal Commission on Environmental Pollution. – London : H.M.S.O., 1982.
At head of title: Department of the Environment, Central Directorate on Environmental Pollution.
ISBN 0117516546

Air transport and the consumer : a need for change? : a report on air transport regulation in Europe. – National Consumer Council. – London : H.M.S.O., 1986.
xiii,251p.
Includes bibliographical references.
ISBN 0117012688

Air Transport Users Committee
Annual report for the year ended 30 September ... / Air Transport Users Committee. – London : The Committee, 1978.
Continues: CIVIL AVIATION AUTHORITY. Airline Users Committee. Annual report.

Air worthy : liber amicorum, honouring Professor Dr. I.H.Ph. Diederiks-Verschoor / editors J.W.E. Storm van's Gravesande and A. van der Veen Vonk. – Deventer : Kluwer, 1985.
xv,301p.
Bibliography: p.293-301.
ISBN 9065442316

Aircraft Hijacking and the Developing Law. – New Delhi : Ashish Publishing House, 1985.
160p.
Hbk £100.00

Airey →Goods Operator Licensing.

Airline Marketing and Management. – 2nd ed. – Pitman, 1985.
ISBN 0273022407 Hbk £17.95

Airman and the carpenter : the Lindbergh kidnapping / Ludovic Kennedy. – London : Collins, 1985.
x,438p,32p ofplates; 24cm.
Bibliography: p425-428. - Includes index.
ISBN 0002170604 £12.95

Airport policy / presented to Parliament by the Secretary of State for Transport. – London : H.M.S.O., 1985.
65p.
ISBN 0101954204

Aitken, D. J. →International handbook of universities and other institutions of higher education.

Aitken, J. K. →Elements of drafting.

—Wills Precedents (Victoria) / N.B. Dowdle. – North Ryde : Law Book Co, 1986.
xvii, 144p.
ISBN 0455203067 Hbk £35.00

Aiyar
Law of Contempt of Courts, Legislatures and Public Servants. – 8th ed. – Allahabad : Law Book Company, 1989.
1,000p.
Hbk £300.00

Aiyar, A.N.
Law Provincial Insolvency Act. – 5th ed. – Allahabad : Universal Book Agency, 1988.
212p.
Hbk £150.00

Aiyar, P. Ramanatha
Law Lexicon. – rep. 1987. – Nagpur : Wadhura & Co.
£330.00

—Sale of Goods Act. – 3rd ed. – Allahabad : Universal Book Agency, 1987.
Hbk £160.00

Aiyar, S.K.
Law and Practice of Arms and Explosives : With Explosives Rules 1988. – 10th ed. – Allahabad : Law Book Company, 1988.
1,000p.
Hbk £275.00

AJ Contracts Guide to ACA Form of Building Agreement 1982. – 2nd ed. – London : Architectural Press, 1984.
– (ACA Contract Documents).
ISBN 0851397565 Hbk £4.95

AJ Index to 1985 Building Regulations. – London : Architectural Press, 1986.
ISBN 0851398383 Pbk £7.50

AJ Introduction and Complete Index to the 1985 Building Regulations. – London : Architectural Press.
60p : Illus.
ISBN 0851398383 Pbk £7.50

AJ Legal Handbook / Gregory Stone. – 4th ed. – London : Architectural Press, 1985.
ISBN 0851397514 Pbk £19.95

Ajayi, F. A. →Law Reports of Nigeria, 3 Vols.

Aje, Z. O.
Philosophy of law / by Z. O. Aje. – s.l. : s.n., 1986.
ix,160p.
Includes bibliographical references.

Ajibola, J. O.
Administration of justice in the customary courts of Yorubaland / J.O. Ajibola. – Ibadan : University Press, 1982.
ix,89p.
ISBN 019575753X

—Administration of Justice in the Customary Courts of Yorubaland. – Ibadan : University Press, 1982.
128p.
Hbk £2.00

Ajomo, M. A.
Of order and disorder : the relevance of international law : an inaugural lecture delivered at the University of Lagos on Wednesday, 15th February, 1984 / by M.A. Ajomo. – Lagos : Lagos University Press, 1984.
35p. – (Inaugural lecture series).
Includes bibliographical references.
ISBN 9782264490

—Proceedings of the 7th, 8th and 9th Annual Conferences of the Nigerian Society of International Law. – Lagos : Nigerian Institute of International Affairs, 1983.
227p.
Hbk £5.00

→ Proceedings of the seventh, eighth and ninth annual conferences of the Nigerian Society of International Law, 1975-1978.

→ T. O. Elias : citations, honours and awards.

Akademiia Nauk SSSR
Bibliography of the main publications on state and law of Great Britain issued in the USSR in 1946-1983. – Akademiia Nauk SSSR. – Moscow : The Institute, 1984.
14p.
'Prepared by the Group on Foreign Scientific Information of the Institute of State and Law of the Academy of Sciences of the USSR. Translated into English by Yu. D. Kouptsov'.

Akalin, Oguz →Law on the Federal Constitutional Court : documents on politics and society in the Federal Republic of Germany.

Akande, Jadesola O.
Constitution of the Federal Republic of Nigeria 1979 / with annotations by Jadesola O. Akande. – London : Sweet & Maxwell, 1982.
ca.300p.
Cover title: Introduction to the Nigerian constitution.
ISBN 0421289406

—Constitutional relevance of the provision for the seat of government / by Jadesola O. Akande. – Lagos : Nigerian Institute of Advanced Legal Studies, 1983.
15p.
Seminar paper presented at the Institute on Wednesday, March 23, 1983.

Akanle, Oluwole
Financing the states : the constitutionality of sales tax laws / by Oluwole Akanle. – Lagos : Nigerian Institute of Advanced Legal Studies, 1983.
21p.
Text of a paper presented at the Nigerian Institute of Advanced Legal Studies Staff Seminar Series on Wednesday, June 15, 1983. Includes bibliographical references.

Akhori, Brejendra K.
Labour Law : the Rights and Responsibilities of Employer-Employee. – Haryana : PB Publications, 1987.
515p.
Hbk £180.00

Akinjide, Richard O A
Africa and the Development of International Law. – 2nd ed. – Martinus Nijhoff, .
ISBN 9024737966 Hbk £59.50

—Law and democracy in Africa / by Richard Akinjide. – Lagos : Office of the President, Department of Information, 1981.
22p.

—Medicine and the law / convocation address at the Second Convocation of the National Post-graduate Medical College of Nigeria on March 10, 1983, in Lagos, Nigeria : by R.O.A. Akinjide. – Lagos : s.n., 1983.
16p.

—Mercenarism and international law / Chief R. O. A. Akinjide. – s.l. : s.n., 1986.
13p.
Lecture delivered at the International Law Seminar, Palais des nations, Geneva, on 27.5.1986.

Akpan, Moses E.
Constitution and constitutionalism : a analysis of the basic principles of the federal constitution of Nigeria (1979) / by Moses E. Akpan. – Lagos : Paico, 1984.
xiii,133p.
Bibliography: p.128-129. - Includes index.

Akroyd, R. I.
Guide to contracting, negotiation and the law / R.I. Akroyd. – London : Routledge & Kegan Paul, 1987.
256p; 22cm.
Includes bibliography and index.
ISBN 0710204868 £22.50

Akroyd, Robert
Guide to Contracting for the Sale of Goods. – London : Sweet & Maxwell, 1984.
Hbk £9.95

Akwa, Nana Mensa
Investment Laws and Opportunities in Africa. – Apapa : Heritage Books.
Hbk £8.50

Al-Azmeh
Islamic Law : Social and Historical Contexts. – Oxford : Croom Helm.
ISBN 0709905882 Hbk £22.50

Al Faruqi, Isma'il Ragi
Humanism and the law : the case of the shari'ah / by Isma'il R. Al Faruqi. – Lagos : Nigerian Institute of Advanced Legal Studies, 1983.
17p. – (Occasional paper).

Al-Najjar →Accounting Research Database.

Al-Otaiba, Mana Saeed
Petroleum concession agreements of the United Arab Emirates 1939-1981 (Abu Dhabi) Vol.2 : 1972-1981 / Mana Saeed Al-Otaiba. – London : Croom Helm, 1982.
385p.

Al-Qaradawi, Y.
Lawful and the Prohibited in Islam. – London : Shorouk International, 1985.
ISBN 1850240027 Pbk £6.50

Al-Qasem, Anis
Principles of petroleum legislation : the case of a developing country / by Anis Al-Qasem. – London : Graham & Trotman, 1985.
xiv,245p.
ISBN 0860105601

Al-Sowayegh, Abdulaziz H.
Arab petropolitics / Abdulaziz Al-Sowayegh. – London : Croom Helm, 1984.
207p; 23cm.
Includes index.
ISBN 0709905386 Hbk £15.95
ISBN 0709905408 Pbk £8.95

Alabi, Isa
Land Use Act revisited
Vol. 2 / by Alhaji Isa Alabi. – Kano, Nigeria : Alhaji Isa Alabi, 1984.
v,63p.

Alba, Enrique de
Panama / by Enrique de Alba. – London : Lloyds of London Press, 1987.
204p; 22cm.
ISBN 1850441413 £25.50

Albania : political imprisonment and the law. – Amnesty International. – London : Amnesty International Publications, 1984.
58p.
ISBN 086210078X

Albeda, W. →Collective bargaining in industrialised market economies : a reappraisal.

Albert, Michel →Investing in Europe's future.

Albert Venn Dicey : the man and his times / by Trowbridge H. Ford. – Chichester : Barry Rose, 1985.
354p.
Bibliography: p322-335.
ISBN 0859923568

Alberta
Revised statutes of Alberta 1980. – Alberta. – 8. – Edmonton : Queen's Printer, 1981.

Alberta Annual Bound Statutes : 1981-1987. – Agincourt : Carswell.
Hbk £405.00
Subject Index. –
Hbk £47.25

Alberta conveyancing law and practice / by John Sterk. – Toronto : Carswell, 1981.
xvi,279p.
ISBN 0459337106

Alberta Corporate Income Tax. – Toronto : Butterworths.
– (Alberta Annotated Legislation).
Hbk

Alberta Corporate Income Tax : Alberta Annotated Legislation Series, 1 Vol. – Butterworths.
Llf £125.00

Alberta Corporation Manual. – Toronto : DeBoo.
Looseleaf service.
ISBN 0888201303 Llf £295.00

Alberta Decisions : Civil and Criminal Cases (1980-Present). – Aurora : Canada Law Book Co.
– (Summary Services, Provincial Ser.).
Hbk £231.00

Alberta Decisions Citator (1981-Present). – Aurora : Canada Law Book Co.
– (Statute Services).
Pbk £87.00

Alberta Family Law. – Student ed. – Toronto : Butterworths, 1983.
ISBN 0409996823 Hbk £26.95

Alberta Law for the Nineteen Eighties
Vol. 3. – Legal Education Society of Alberta & Butterworth & Co. () Ltd. – Toronto : Butterworths, 1981.
250p.
ISBN 0409987034 Pbk £21.00

Alberta Law Reports. – 2nd ed. – Agincourt : Carswell.
Hbk £79.00

Alberta Law Reports : 1909-1932. – Carswell Legal Publications. – Agincourt : Carswell.

Alberta Legal Telephone Directory : 1986. – Aurora : Canada Law Book Co.
This telephone directory is arranged by name, listing every lawyer and law firm in Alberta. Each listing includes address, telephone number and firm association. Additional entries include, among others, listings for: Courts, Judges, and Court Officials; Land Registration Districts; Legal Services; Law Libraries and Universities; and Provincial Government Departments.
Pbk For 1-5 Copies 9.00 each

Alberta Limitations Manual. – Scarborough, Ontario : Butterworths (Canada).
ISBN 040999331X Hbk £32.00

Alberta Petroleum Incentives Program. – Toronto : Butterworths.
– (Alberta Annotated Legislation Ser.).
Hbk

Alberta Regulations Service. – 3 vols. – Toronto : Butterworths.
Hbk

Alberta Revised Statutes Sectional Tables of Concordance : 1970-1980. – Carswell Legal Publications. – Agincourt : Carswell, 1982.
207p.
This book contains the sources of the R.S.A. 1980 s and the disposition of the R.S.A. 1970 s. This book also affords you the opportunity to check and verify updated references with those which have been deleted or superseded from R.S.A. 1980 back to R.S.A. 1970 or from R.S.A. 1970 ahead to R.S.A. 1980.
Pbk £21.00

Alberta Rules of Court Judicially Considered : 1970-January 1987. – Agincourt : Carswell, 1987.
50p.
Pbk £17.00

Alberta Taxation Service. – Toronto : DeBoo.
Looseleaf service.
ISBN 0888201389 Llf £195.00

Alberta Weekly Law Digest. – Agincourt : Carswell, 1988.
Hbk £201.75

Alberta-Saskatchewan-Manitoba Criminal Conviction Cases. – Aurora : Canada Law Book Co.
– (Summary Services, Provincial Ser.).
Hbk £105.00

Albier, R.Z.
International money game. – 5th ed. – London : Macmillan, 1988.
ISBN 0333467817 Hbk £29.50
ISBN 0333467825 Pbk £9.95

Alboini, Victor P.
Securities Law and Practice, 4 Vols. – 2nd ed. – Agincourt : Carswell, 1984.
1570p.
This multi-volume work is a comprehensive guide to securities law in Canada. The Securities Act of Ontario, regulations, blanket rulings, policy statements, and practice notes of the Ontario Securities Commission are included in the work.
Llf £294.00

Albon, Robert
Rent Control : Cost and Consequences. – Turramura : Centre for Independent Studies.
256p.
ISBN 0959648577 Hbk £9.95

Albrecht, Hans Christian →Maritime Law Handbook.

Alcock, Pete
Welfare law and order : a critical introduction to law for social workers / Pete Alcock and Phil Harris. – London : Macmillan, 1982.
xvi,219p. – (Critical texts in social work and the welfare state).
Includes index. Bibliography: p207-213.
ISBN 0333294904

Alcohol and Crime. – Canberra : Australian Institute of Criminology.
Hbk £3.60

Alder, J.
Development Control. – 2nd ed. – Sweet & Maxwell.
ISBN 0421371706 Pbk £13.00

Alder, John → Applications for judicial review : law and practice.
—Housing association law / by John Alder and Christopher R. Handy. – London : Sweet & Maxwell, 1987.
xlii,330p; 21cm.
Text examines the partnership between public and private sector in providing low-cost housing, 'new' forms of tenure as a means of extending owner-occupation and tenant self-management, and tenants' rights and accountability to the Housing Corporation.
ISBN 042134430X Pbk £15.00

Alderman, Geoffrey
Pressure groups and government in Great Britain / Geoffrey Alderman. – Harlow : Longman, 1984.
vii,164p; 20cm.
Bibliography: p151-157. - Includes index.
ISBN 0582296269 Pbk £3.75

Alderson, John
Human rights and the police / by J. Alderson. – Strasbourg : Council of Europe, Directorate of Human Rights, 1984.
207p.
Illustrates how awareness of concepts of human rights defined by the European Convention should affect the way police carry out duties. Training guidelines and case law examples are considered.
ISBN 9287103666 Pbk £10.90
—Law and disorder / John Alderson. – London : Hamilton, 1984.
vii,247p; 23cm.
Includes index.
ISBN 0241112591 £8.95
—Police - where now? : a public lecture / delivered by John C. Alderson on ... 18th March 1982. – London : Inns of Court School of Law, 1982.
12p; 23cm.

Aldis, John → Tolley's Guide to Directors' Transactions.

Aldous, Graham
Housing Law for the Elderly. – London : Oyez Longman, 1982.
– (Oyez Longman Practice Note Ser.: No. 72).
ISBN 0851206875 Pbk £12.95

Aldous, Grahame
Applications for judicial review : law and practice / Grahame Aldous, John Alder. – London : Butterworths, 1985.
250p; 26cm.
Includes index.
ISBN 0406273200 Pbk

Aldous, William → Terrell on the law of patents.

Aldred, Jennifer → Fractured Federation?.

Aldred, P.
Convertibles and Warrants. – London : Euromoney, 1987.
ISBN 1870031202 Pbk £75.00

Aldridge, T. M. → Commonhold : freehold flats and freehold ownership of other interdependent buildings : report of a working group.

Aldridge, Trevor M.
Boundaries, walls and fences / Trevor M. Aldridge. – 6th ed. – London : Longman Professional, 1986.
66p; 22cm.
Previous ed.: London : Oyez Longman, 1982. Includes index.
ISBN 0851212344 Pbk £11.95
—Guide To Enquiries Before Contract. – London : Longman Professional, 1978.
ISBN 0851203876 Pbk £5.95
—Guide to Enquiries of Local Authorities. – 2nd ed. – London : Longman Professional, 1982.
ISBN 085120645X Pbk £5.95
—Guide to Law Society's Conditions of Sale. – London : Longman Professional, 1984.
ISBN 0851209521 Pbk £7.90
—Guide to National Conditions of Sale. – 20th ed. – London : Longman Professional, 1981.
ISBN 0851206204 Pbk £6.95
—Guide to the Law Society's Conditions of Sale. – London : Oyez Longman, 1981.
ISBN 0851205542 Hbk £2.95
—Housing Act 1980, as amended by the Housing and Building Control Act 1984 / Trevor M. Aldridge. – London : Longman Professional (UK), 1984.
xxxix,334p.
Previous ed.: 1980, titled The Housing Act 1980: a practical guide. Includes index.
ISBN 0851207650 Pbk £27.00
—Law of flats. – 2nd. – London : Longman Professional (UK), 1989.
– (Practitioner series).
New edition takes account of the Landlord and Tenant Acts of 1985 and 1987 and changes resulting from the Housing Act 1988, including assured tenancies. Includes new chapters on disposition, the landlord's identity and the right of first refusal.
ISBN 085121388X Hbk £27.50
—Leasehold Law (Service to Date). – London : Longman Professional.
ISBN 0851204716 Hbk £195.00
—Letting Business Premises. – 5th ed. – London : Longman Professional, 1985.
ISBN 0851209858 Hbk £28.00
—Letting business premises. – 6th. – London : Longman Professional (UK), 1989.
– (Practitioner series).
Coverage includes the statutory renewal procedure; compensation for tenants' improvements; and the law governing the major lease. Covenants relating to rent, user, alterations and improvements, and assignments and subletting, lettings to partnerships, and special types of business premises.
—Powers of Attorney. – 7th ed. – London : Longman Professional.
– (Practitioner Series).
ISBN 0851213901 Hbk £24.25
—Practical conveyancing precedents. – London : Longman Professional, 1985.
ISBN 0851207707 updat £95.00
—Practical lease precedents. – London : Longman Professional, 1988.
ISBN 0851211542 Llf £95.00
—Rent Act Nineteen Seventy-Seven Revised. – London : Oyez Longman, 1981.
ISBN 0851206131 Hbk £7.50
—Rent control and leasehold enfranchisement. – 9th. – London : Longman Professional (UK), 1989.
– (Practitioner series).
Guide to rent restriction rules governing the varius types of residential tenancies and the qualifications and procedure for enfranchisement. New edition revised to take account of the Landlord and Tenant Acts 1985, and 1987, and the Housing Act 1988, including details of assured tenancies.
ISBN 0851213871 Hbk £32.50

Alesander
Handbook of Financial Futures and Options / Krikic. – Cambridge : Woodhead-Faulkner, 1986.
ISBN 0859414116 Hbk £25.00

A-Level English Law / D M M Scott. – 6th ed. – London : Butterworths, 1984.
This work includes theoretical and empirical material designed to set legal principles in a sociological context for students requiring an introduction to the English legal system.
ISBN 0406657076 Hbk £14.00
ISBN 0406657084 Pbk £8.95

A-Level Law. – Plymouth : Macdonald & Evans, 1984.
240p. – (M and E Handbook Ser.).
ISBN 0712101608 Pbk £3.25
Supplement 1987. – 1984.
– (M and E Handbook Ser.).
ISBN 0712101926 Pbk £4.95

Alex Manoogian Cultural Centre Act, 1983, Bill Pr056 : An Act Respecting the Alex Manoogian Cultural Centre. – Ontario : Ontario Government Publications Service, 1983.
3p.
Hbk £0.30

Alexander → Principles of marine insurance.

Alexander, E., et al
Libel and Contempt : The Law and the Media. – Vancouver : British Columbia Continuing Legal Education Society, 1982.
414p.
ISBN 0865040834 Hbk £65.00

Alexander, G.J.
Writing a living will : using a durable power of attorney. – Praeger, 1988.
ISBN 0275928012 Hbk £24.95
ISBN 0275929396 Pbk £10.75

Alexander, Lionel → Law of clubs : with a note on unincorporated associations.

Alexander, R. S., et al
Solicitors' Considerations for Family Law Lawyers. – Vancouver : British Columbia Continuing Legal Education Society, 1983.
310p.
ISBN 0865040885 Hbk £60.00

Alexander, Yonah, et al
1987 annual on terrorism / edited by Yonah Alexander, with contributing editors Abraham H. Foxman and Eugene Mastrangelo. – Dordrecht : Nijhoff (Martinus), 1989.
528. – (Annual on Terrorism).
Focuses on national, regional and global developments in the field of terrorism. This volume includes the analysis of domestic and international terrorism, selected papers written during 1987, a statistical synopsis and selected documents, reports and addresses.
ISBN 9024738016 Hbk Gld250.00
→ Legislative responses to terrorism.

Alexandersson, Gunnar
Baltic Straits / by Gunnar Alexandersson. – The Hague : Nijhoff, 1982.
152p.
Includes index.
ISBN 902472595X Hbk £75.00

Alexis, Francis
Changing Caribbean constitutions / Francis Alexis. – St. Michael, Barbados : Antilles, 1983.
xxviii,281p.
Bibliography: p.270-274. - Includes index.
→ Commonwealth Caribbean legal essays.

Alexy, Robert W
Theory of local argumentation : the theory of rational discourse as a theory of legal justification. – Oxford : OUP, 1989.
320.
An attempt to define 'rational legal argument' and to justify the demand for rationality in legal affairs.
ISBN 0198255039 Hbk £30.00

Ali, Abdul Zahra Abdullah
Insurance development in the Arab world : retention relationship capacity and the demand for international reinsurance / by Abdul Zahra Abdullah Ali. – London : Graham & Trotman, 1985.
369p; 25cm.
Bibliography: p352-362. - Includes index.
ISBN 0860107078 £73.00

Ali, Firasat
Law Relating to C.I.F. Contracts. – New Delhi : Deep and Deep Publications, 1982.
142p.
Hbk £60.00

Alienation of land : being a supplement to The law of credit agreements and hire-purchase by Diemont and Aronstam / P.J. Aronstam. – Cape Town : Juta, 1985.
xxviii, 186 p.; 25 cm.
Includes indexes. Bibliography: p. 8.
ISBN 070211586X Pbk

All Africa Conference of Churches
Structures of Injustice : a Report of a Consultation on Violations of Human Rights, held in Khartoum, Sudan from 16-22 February, 1975. – All Africa Conference of Churches. – Nairobi Westlands : All Africa Conference of Churches.
47p.
Hbk £15.00

All Canada Weekly Summaries-National (A.C.W.S.) 1977-79, 9 Vols. – Law Book Publisher. – Aurora : Canada Law Book Co. – (First Ser.).
Hbk £261.00
Back Vols.. –
Hbk £31.00 each

All Canada Weekly Summaries-National (A.C.W.S.) 1980-1986, 39 Vols. – Law Book Publisher. – Aurora : Canada Law Book Co. – (Second Ser.).
Hbk £1365.00

All Canada Weekly Summaries-Ontario Edition (A.C.W.S. ONT) June 1981-1986, 30 Vols. – Law Book Publisher. – Aurora : Canada Law Book Co.
Hbk £780.00
Back Vols.. –
Hbk £26.00 each
Binder. –
Hbk £19.00

All England Law Reports. – Reprint. – London : Butterworths, 1558-1935.
ISBN 04060000X Hbk

All England Law Reports. – London : Butterworths, 1936-1988.
ISBN 0406685159X Hbk £2,991.50

All England Law Reports : 1936-1985, 143 Vols. / P. Hutchesson et al. – Wellington : Butterworths.
Weekly Parts-1986. –
Pbk
Bound Vols. Service-1986. –
Hbk
Noter-Up Service-1986. –
Pbk
Consolidated Index (1936-76) 3 Vols.. –
ISBN 0406862141 Hbk
Cumulative Table and Index (1977-80). –
ISBN 0406866759 Hbk
Back Vols. and Binding Services. –
Hbk
Reprint (1558-1935). –
Hbk £960.50

All England Law Reports Annual Review 1985. – London : Butterworths, 1986.
This work contains detailed analyses of decisions handed down in the Law Courts and the House of Lords during the previous year. The book is written for practitioners and students to provide synopses of current trends in English law.
ISBN 0406879621 Hbk £33.00

All jangle and riot: a legal history of the Bar. – Abingdon : Professional Books, 1986.
ISBN 0862050839 Hbk £14.95

All Nigeria Judges Conference papers : Ilorin, Kwana State, 8-16th March 1982. – London : Sweet & Maxwell, 1984.
xx,391p; 23cm.
Includes index.
ISBN 0421309008

All Nigeria Law Reports : 1961-1970, 10 Vols. – Repr. – London : Sweet & Maxwell, 1983.
Includes index 1961-1970. –
ISBN 0421300701 Hbk £460.00
Index 1983 alone. –
ISBN 0421313005 Hbk £39.00

All Nigeria Law Reports : Index 1983. – Sweet & Maxwell.
ISBN 0421313005 Hbk £45.00

All Souls College →Administrative justice : some necessary reforms.

Allan →Competition Law of the UK and the Republic of Ireland.

Allan, A. →Close Corporations Act 1984 : a basic introduction.

Allan, C.
Guide to VAT in Business. – London : CCH, 1988.
ISBN 0863251366 Pbk
—VAT and the New Business. – London : CCH, 1987.
ISBN 0863251056 Pbk £12.50

Allan, Colin
Constitution Making in New Island States. – Auckland : Legal Research Foundation, 1982.
Hbk £6.50

Allbeson, Janet
'We don't give clothing grants any more' : the 1980 supplementary benefit scheme / Janet Allbeson and Roger Smith. – London : Child Poverty Action Group, 1984.
113p.
Includes bibliographical references.
ISBN 0903963736

All-Canada Weekly Summaries First Ser. (1977-1979), 9 Vols. – Aurora : Canada Law Book Co.
– (Summary Services, National Series).
Hbk £297.00
Back Vols.. –
Hbk £31.00 ea.

All-Canada Weekly Summaries Ontario Edition Current Series (1981-Present). – Aurora : Canada Law Book Co.
– (Summary Services, Provincial Ser.).
Hbk £66.50
Parts only. –
Hbk £56.00
Back Vols.. –
Hbk £26.00 ea.

All-Canada Weekly Summaries Third Ser. (1986-Present). – Aurora : Canada Law Book Co.
– (Summary Services, National Series).
Hbk £118.00
Parts only. –
£108.00 per Vol.
Back Vols.. –
£100.00 ea.

All-Change in the City : The Revolution in Britain's Financial Sector. – London : Macmillan.
ISBN 0333362349 Hbk £17.95

Allegations Concerning a Judge : Report to the Senate. – Senate Select Committee. – Canberra : Australian Government Publishing Service, 1984.
Hbk £6.80

Allen, C.
Law In The Making. – 7th ed. – Oxford : Oxford University Press, 1964.
ISBN 0198810296 Pbk £8.50

Allen, Carleton Kemp
Bureaucracy Triumphant. – Repr. of 1931 ed. – Aalen Wuertt : Scientia.
451p.
ISBN 351109061X Hbk £33.00
—Legal Duties. – Repr. of 1931 ed. – Aalen Wuertt : Scientia.
xvi, 318p.
ISBN 3511090318 Hbk £80.00

Allen, Chris
Butterworth's Corporation Tax Program. – London : Butterworths.
Hbk

Allen, D.
Dynamic Management Accountancy. – London : Butterworths, 1983.
ISBN 0406258104 Pbk £8.00

Allen, David
Dynamic Management Accountancy. – London : Butterworths, 1983.
A theoretical management accounting text which presents new approaches to decision-making and performance measurement. Special attention is paid to questions of inflation accounting, currency realignment, and multinational corporation accounting.
ISBN 0406258104 Pbk

Allen, David K. →Civil liability for defective premises.
—Misrepresentation / by David K. Allen. – London : Sweet & Maxwell, 1988.
xxii,178p; 22cm.
Includes index.
ISBN 0421347201 Hbk £16.00
ISBN 0421347309 Pbk £10.00

Allen, Fola Mendy →Women and legal affairs.

Allen, Hilary
Norway and Europe in the 1970's. – Oslo : University of Forlag.
289p.
Hbk £31.00

Allen, J. C. →Marine claims handbook.
→ New Institute clauses : a commentary on the new standard policy forms for marine risks issued by the London insurance market.

Allen-Jones, Charles M. →Recent and Prospective Changes in Company Law.

Allen, Michael J.
Cost of Going to Law. – Belfast : Queen's University of Belfast, 1984.
70p.
ISBN 0853892148 Pbk £2.95
→ Sentencing law and practice.
→ Sentencing law and practice in Northern Ireland.

Allen, William P. G.
Estate Planning Handbook. – Agincourt : Carswell, 1985.
176p.
This practitioner's handbook of Canadian estate planning law presents numerous precedents and discussions of relevant law. Planning mechanisms to deal with incapacity, terminal illness, and the owner-managed business are addressed in depth.
Pbk £29.50

Alles, Anthony Christopher
Famous Criminal Cases of Sri Lanka, Vol. 4. – Colombo : Colombo Apothecaries Company, 1981.
Hbk £20.00

Alley, R.S.
Supreme Court on Church and State. – Oxford : Oxford University Press.
ISBN 0195050282 Hbk £35.00

Allianz Handbook of Loss Prevention. – Dusseldorf : VDI-Verlag, 1987.
xvi, 928p.
ISBN 3184191036 Hbk £198.00

Allied Dunbar
Business Tax And Law Guide. – London : Longman Professional.
ISBN 0851214622 Hbk £12.95
—Capital Taxes and Estate Planning Guide. – 3rd ed. – London : Longman Professional, 1986.
ISBN 0851212131 Hbk £12.50
—Expatriates Guide. – 2nd ed. – London : Longman Professional, 1986.
ISBN 0851212107 Hbk £13.50
—Investment Guide 1987-1988s (LIC). – London : Longman Professional.
ISBN 0851212905 Hbk £13.50
—Retirement planning guide. – Allied Dunbar. – 2nd ed. – London : Longman Professional (UK), 1988.
ISBN 0851212115 £13.50
—Tax Guide 1987-1988. – London : Longman Professional.
ISBN 0851212921 Hbk £12.95

Allied Dunbar Tax Guide 1988-89. – London : Longman Professional.
ISBN 0851214614 Hbk £13.50

Allied Hambro
Pensions guide. – Allied Hambro. – London : Longman Professional, 1984.
ISBN 0851209750 Hbk £11.95

Allied Hambro Expatriate Tax and Investment Guide. – London : Oyez Longman, 1984.
ISBN 0851208355 Hbk £9.95

Allied Hambro Investment Guide 1984. – London : Oyez Longman, 1984.
ISBN 085120838X Hbk £10.95

Allin →Torts In New Zealand : Cases and Materials.

All-India Central Bare Acts and Rules, 10 Vols. – Allahabad : Law Publishers, 1983.
Hbk £300.00

All-India Criminal Digest, 1971-80, 3 Vols. – Allahabad : Law Book Company.
Hbk £450.00

All-India Quinquennial Criminal Digest, 3 Vols. – Allahabad : Law Book Company.
Hbk £900.00 set
Vol. 1 : 1941-45.
Vol 2 : 1946-50.
Vol. 3 in preparation.

All-in-One Guide to European-Atlantic Organisations : Intergovernmental and Supporting Voluntary Bodies : What They Are, What They Do, and Where to Get Further Information. – European-Atlantic Movement. – 9th ed., revised ed. – Exeter : European Atlantic Movement, 1985.
ISBN 0854500057 Hbk £0.25

Allison, R.C.
Protection against the expropriation risk in investing abroad. – Matthew Bender, 1988.
ISBN 0000999071 Hbk £50.00

Allocation of council housing / Paul Spicker. – London : Shelter, 1983.
43p; 21cm.
ISBN 0901242683 Pbk £1.50

Allocation of taxing power under the Canadian constitution / G.V. La Forest. – 2nd ed. – Toronto : Canadian Tax Foundation, 1981.
viii,219p.

Allott, Antony →People's law and state law : the Bellagio papers.

Allsop, Kathlen
Local and Central Government. – 4th ed. – London : Hutchinson, 1984.
128p.
ISBN 0091588715 Pbk £3.95

Allsop, Peter
Criminal Law Review / Andrew Ashworth. – London : Sweet & Maxwell.
Hbk £46.00

Almanac of China's foreign economic relations and trade / the editorial board of the Almanac of China's foreign economic relations and trade. – Hong Kong : China Resources Trade Consultancy, 1986.
Title page also in Chinese.

Alper, Benedict S.
Beyond the courtroom : programs in community justice and conflict resolution / Benedict S. Alper, Lawrence T. Nichols. – Lexington, Mass. : Lexington Books, 1981.
xx,299p; 24cm.
Bibliography: p273-288. - Includes index.
ISBN 0669027243 £14.50

Alphabetical List of Titles of Federal Acts. – 4th ed. – Ottawa : Canadian Government Publishing Centre, 1986.
122p.
ISBN 0660531356 Pbk £7.50

Al-Shaybani Society of International Law
Palestine yearbook of international law. – Al-Shaybani Society of International Law. – Nicosia : Al Shaybani Society of International Law, 1984-.

Alston, A.
Law of Wills and Administration. – 5th ed. – Butterworths, 1984.
Takes into account the significant developments made by the Wills Amendment Act 1977, and amendments to the Administration Act 1969, and the Status of Children Act 1969.
ISBN 0409601306 Hbk £90.75

Alston, A.P.S.
Residential tenancies. – London : Butterworths, 1988.
ISBN 0409787507 Pbk £34.00
—Residential Tenancies Handbook. – Butterworths.
ISBN 0409787507 Hbk £47.30

Altaf, Javed →Workers' Children Ordinance 1972.

Alteration/Conversion Of Houses / Edmunds. – 6th ed. – London : Longman Professional, 1985.
ISBN 0851209971 Pbk £16.95

Alteration of ground levels / the Law Reform Commission of Western Australia. – Perth the Commission, 1984.
89p. – (Discussion paper).

Alterman, R.
Private Supply of Public Services : Evaluation Real Estate Exctions, Linkage, and Alternative Land Policies. – New York University Press.
ISBN 0814705898 Hbk £23.50

Alternative measures to imprisonment / by W. Rentzmann and J.P. Robert. – Strasbourg : Council of Europe, 1986.
35p. – (CDAP (85) 6).
A paper presented to the seventh Conference of Directors of Prison Administrations.

Alternatives to custody / edited by John Pointing. – 1. – Oxford : Blackwell, 1986.
22cm.
Discusses diversity of options available within the probation services including: autocrime and driver retraining, intermediate treatment for offenders threatened with incarceration, options for problem drinkers, daytime training centres and community work programs.
ISBN 0631147012 Pbk Hbk £17.50 :
ISBN 0631147020 Pbk £6.95

Alternatives to Imprisonment. – Canberra : Australian Institute of Criminology.
free

Alternatives to prison : an examination of non-custodial sentencing of offenders / Stephen Stanley and Mary Baginsky. – London : Peter Owen, 1984.
183p; 23cm.
Bibliography: p171-175. - Includes index.
ISBN 0720605229 Hbk £12.50
ISBN 0720606268 Pbk £6.95

Alternatives to unemployment : special employment measures in Britain / David Metcalf. – London : Policy Studies Institute, 1982.
66p. – (Policy Studies Institute).

Altman, J.C.
Aborigines and Mining Royalties in the Northern Territory. – Canberra City : Australian Institute of Aboriginal Studies, 1983.
182p.
ISBN 0855751495 Hbk £11.95

Aluminium industry and the Third World : multinational corporations and underdevelopment / Ronald Graham. – London : Zed, 1982.
xii,278p; 22cm.
Bibliography: p263-270. - Includes index.
ISBN 0862320577 Pbk

Amani, S.Z.
Justice Hidayatullah on Commercial Laws. – New Delhi : Deep and Deep Publications, 1982.
130p.
Hbk £60.00

Amao, T.
Nigerian Law of Contract (Nigerian Nutshells). – London : Sweet & Maxwell, 1987.
ISBN 0421361409 Pbk £3.95

Amarasinghe, C.F.
Defamation and Other Aspects of the Actio Inuriarum in Roman-Dutch Law. – Colombo : Lake House Investments.
Hbk £5.50
—Doctrines of Sovereignty and the Separation of Powers in the Laws of Ceylon. – Colombo : Lake House Investments.
Pbk £2.75
—Studies in International Law. – Colombo : Lake House Investments.
Hbk £1.40

Ambler, C.
Reports Court of Chancery : 1737-83. – Repr. of 1790 ed. – Abingdon : Professional Books.
344p.
Hbk £75.00

Amending the equality laws / Catherine Scorer and Ann Sedley. – London : NCCL Rights for Women Unit, 1983.
38p; 21cm.
ISBN 0946088047 Pbk £0.95

Amendment of the Companies Acts 1948-1983 : report under section 116 of the Companies Act 1981 / The Law Commission and the Scottish Law Commission. – London : H.M.S.O., 1983.
iv,42p; 25cm.
ISBN 0101911408

Amendment of the Equal Pay Act 1970 / Department of Employment. – London : The Department, 1983.
11p. – (Press notice).
Includes text of draft order, Sex discrimination: The Equal Pay (Amendment) Regulations 1983. - With Department of Employment press notice, Equal Pay Act - Amendment.

Amendments to the 1978 Edition of the 'Treaties Establishing the European Communities'. – Kirchberg : Commission of the European Communities, 1982.
32p.
Hbk

Amendments to the Combines Investigation Act : background information and explanatory notes. – Department of Consumer and Corporate Affairs. – Ottawa : The Department, 1984.
32p,37p.
With French t.p.: Modifications de la loi relative aux enquetes sur les coalitions. English and French text.

Amendments to the Convention on the International Regulations for Preventing Collisions at Sea: 1972
English. – International Maritime Organization. – London : International Maritime Organization, 1983.
Hbk £1.50
French. –
ISBN 9280121278 Hbk £1.50
Spanish. –
ISBN 9280130897 Hbk £1.50

Amendments to the International Convention for the Safety of Life at Sea : 1974
English Edition. – International Maritime Organization. – London : International Maritime Organization, 1982.
Hbk £3.50
French Edition. –
Hbk £4.50

Amerasinghe, C F
Documents on international administrative tribunals. – Oxford : Clarendon Press, 1989.
274.
A volume of documents, each of which sets out the interests, purposes, structureand powers of the tribunal to which it relates. Gives an account of the role and responsibility of each tribunal.
ISBN 0198256361 Hbk £27.50

Amerasinghe, G F
Law of the International Civil Service: as applied by internatinal administrative tribunals. – Oxford : Clarendon Press.
686.
ISBN 0198255608 Hbk £60
—Law of the International Civil Service: as applied by internatinal administrative tribunals. – Oxford : Clarendon Press.
1350.
On the law as applied by international administrative tribunals in the area of employment relations between international organisations and their staff. Analyses the way in which obligations and rights are enforced and recognised.
ISBN 0198256108 Hbk £60

Ameri, Houshang
Politics and process in the specialised agencies of the United Nations / Houshang Ameri. – Aldershot : Gower, 1982.
xiii,284p; 23cm.
Bibliography: p265-273. - Includes index.
ISBN 0566005387

American Association for the Advancement of Slavic Studies →Distinctiveness of Soviet law.

American Cultural Pluralism and Law / Nanda. – Praeger.
ISBN 0275926958 Hbk £40.50
ISBN 0275926966 Pbk £15.75

American Disease : Origins Of Narcotic Control. – 2nd ed. – Oxford : Oxford University Press, 1988.
ISBN 0195052110 Hbk £8.95

American Health Care : Realities, Rights and Reforms. – Oxford : Oxford University Press.
ISBN 0195052714 Hbk £22.50

American Indians, Time and the Law Native Societies in a Modern Constitutional Democracy. – Yale University Press.
ISBN 0300041365 Pbk £9.95

American Judicial Tradition : Profiles of Leading American Jud. – Oxford : Oxford University Press.
ISBN 019505685X Pbk £9.95

American Jury on Trial : Psychological Perspectives / Wrightsman. – Taylor & Francis.
ISBN 0891167374 Hbk £25.00

American Law Institute-American Bar Association Committee on Continuing Professional Education →Mining and environmental law : proceedings of the seminar held at Washington D.C., 4-8 April 1982, ... organised by the Committee on Environmental Law, Section on Business Law, of the International Bar Association, in conjunction with the American Law Institute-American Bar Association Committee on Continuing Professional Education.

American Society of Law and Medicine → Genetics and the law III.

American Studies Library Group
American studies library newsletter. – American Studies Library Group. – Manchester : American Studies Library Group, 1984-.
Continues: ASLG newsletter.

American studies library newsletter. – American Studies Library Group. – Manchester : American Studies Library Group, 1984-.
Continues: ASLG newsletter.

American tort process / John G. Fleming. – Oxford England : Clarendon Press, 1988.
viii, 271 p.; 23 cm.
Includes bibliographical references and index.
ISBN 0198255977

Amerindians of South America / by Andrew Gray. – London : Minority Rights Group, 1987.
26p. – (Report).
Includes bibliographical references.
ISBN 0946690529

Ames, James
Butterworth's British Columbia Family Law Quantum Service, 2 vol / Anisa Dhanji. – Toronto : Butterworths.
Hbk

Ames, Janet
Ontario Business Corporations Act annotated / Margot Lettner. – Scarborough, Ontario : Butterworths (Canada), 1990.
352.
ISBN 1234124312 Pbk £36

Ames, Janet M.
Butterworths British Columbia Family Law Quantum Service, 2 Vols. / Anisa Dhanji. – Butterworths.
Llf £135.00

Ames, S.M.
County Court Records of Accomack, Northampton, Virginia 1640-45. – London : Eurospan.
ISBN 0813903947 Hbk £17.50

Amighetti, L., et al
Current Wills and Estates Practice. – Vancouver : British Columbia Continuing Legal Education Society, 1982.
59p.
ISBN 086504046X Hbk £25.00

Amin
Law of Easements
Includes Supplement-1986 / Sastri. – 5th rev. ed. – Lucknow : Eastern Book Company, 1984.
846p.
Hbk £130.00

Amin, S.H.
Commercial Arbitration in Islamic and Iranian Law. – Royston.
ISBN 0946706468 Hbk £85.00
—International and legal problems of the gulf / S.H. Amin. – London : Middle East and North African Studies Press, 1981.
235p.
Bibls..
ISBN 0906559057
—Iran-Iraq war : legal implications / S.H. Amin. – Glasgow : Royston, 1982.
26p.
Reprinted from Marine Policy, vol. 6, no. 3 (July 1982).
—Islamic banking and finance : the experience of Iran / by Sayed Hassan Amin. – Glasgow : Royston, 1986.
128p; 22cm.
Includes bibliography and index.
ISBN 0946706301 £27.00
—Islamic Law and its Implications for the Modern World. – Royston.
ISBN 0946706492 Pbk £15.00
—Islamic law in the contemporary world : introduction, glossary and bibliography / by Sayed Hassan Amin. – Glasgow : Royston, 1985.
ix,190p; 22cm.
Bibliography: p153-172. - Includes index.
ISBN 0946706247 Pbk £15.00
—Law and justice in contemporary Yemen : the People's Democratic Republic of Yemen and the Yemen Arab Republic by S.H. Amin. – Glasgow : Royston, 1987.
v,159p; 23cm.
Bibliography: p129-140. - Includes index.
ISBN 0946706360 £18.75
—Law, Government and Business in Kuwait. – Royston.
ISBN 0946706522 Hbk £87.00
→ Legal and political structure of an Islamic state : implications for Iran and Pakistan.
—Marine pollution in international and Middle Eastern law / by Sayed Hassan Amin : foreword by John P. Grant. – Glasgow : Royston, 1986.
138p; 22cm.
Bibliography: p119-135. - Includes index.
ISBN 0946706263 £30.00
—Middle East legal systems / S.H. Amin. – Glasgow : Royston, 1985.
320p.
ISBN 0946706220 £29.95
—Remedies for breach of contract in Islamic and Iranian law. – Glasgow : Royston, 1984.
250p.
ISBN 0946706212 £45.95
—Usurpation and Tort Liability in Islamic and Iranian Law. – Royston.
ISBN 0946706514 Hbk £15.00

Amin, Sayed Hassan
Commercial law of Iran : by Sayed Hassan Amin. – Tehran : Vahid Publications, 1986.
vii,144p.
Bibliography: p137-140.
ISBN 0946706298

Amissah, A.
Contribution Of The Courts to Govt W African View '81. – Oxford : Oxford University Press.
ISBN 0198253567 Hbk £27.50

Amissah, A. N. E.
Contribution of the courts to government : a West African view / A.N.E. Amissah. – Oxford : Clarendon Press, 1981.
x,382p; 22cm.
Includes index.
ISBN 0198253567 £25.00

Amissah, Austin N E
Criminal Procedure in Ghana / A.N.E. Amissah. – London : Pitman Publishing, 1985.
ISBN 09964720092 Pbk £15.95

Amler : Precedents of Pleadings. – Durban : Professional Publishers, 1988.
ISBN 0409011002 Hbk

Amnesty International
Afghanistan : torture of political prisoners. – Amnesty International. – London : Amnesty International, 1986.
i,51p.
ISBN 0862101077
—Albania : political imprisonment and the law. – Amnesty International. – London : Amnesty International Publications, 1984.
58p.
ISBN 086210078X
→ ... and now for the next sketch ... cartoons for Amnesty.
—Bangladesh : unlawful killings and torture in the Chittagong hill tracts / Amnesty International. – London : Amnesty International, 1986.
38p.
ISBN 0862101107
—Bulgaria : imprisonment of ethnic Turks : human rights abuses during the forced assimilation of the ethnic Turkish minority / Amnesty International. – London : Amnesty International, 1986.
40p.
ISBN 0862100976
—Chile : Amnesty International briefing / Amnesty International. – London : Amnesty International, 1986.
22p.
—Chile : evidence of torture / Amnesty International. – London : Amnesty International Publications, 1983.
75p.
ISBN 0862100534
—China : violations of human rights : prisoners of conscience and the death penalty in the People's Republic of China. – Amnesty International. – London : Amnesty International Publications, 1984.
129p.
ISBN 0862100739
—Czechoslovakia . – Amnesty International. – 2nd ed. – London : Amnesty International, 1981.
17p. – (Amnesty International Briefing).
—Death penalty in Japan : report of an Amnesty International mission to Japan, 21 February - 3 March 1983. – Amnesty International. – s.l. : Amnesty International, 1983.
31p.
ISBN 0862100607
→ Diplock courts in Northern Ireland : a fair trial? : an analysis of the law, based on a study commissioned by Amnesty International.
—Disappearances in Sri Lanka / Amnesty International. – London : Amnesty International, 1986.
89p.
ISBN 0862101085
—East Timor : violations of human rights : extrajudicial executions, 'disappearances', torture and political imprisonment, 1975-1984. – Amnesty International. – London : Amnesty International Publications, 1985.
vii,92p.
ISBN 0862100852
—Egypt : violations of human rights / an Amnesty International report. – London : Amnesty International Publications, 1983.
38p.
ISBN 0862100526
—Extrajudicial executions in El Salvador : report of an Amnesty International mission to examine post-mortem and investigative procedures in political killings, 1-6 July 1983. – Amnesty International. – London : Amnesty International, 1984.
48p; 30cm.
ISBN 0862100704 Pbk
—Guatemala : a government program of political murder. – Amnesty International. – London : Amnesty International, 1981.
32p; 30cm.
Cover title.
ISBN 0862100267 Pbk
—Haiti : Amnesty International briefing. – Amnesty International. – London : Amnesty International, 1985.
14p; ill.
ISBN 086210081X
→ Iraq : evidence of torture : an Amnesty International report.
—Jamaica : the death penalty : report of an Amnesty International mission to Jamaica. – Amnesty International. – London : Amnesty International Publications, 1984.
63p.
ISBN 0862100763
—Nicaragua : the human rights record. – Amnesty International. – London : Amnesty International, 1986.
36p; 27cm.
ISBN 0862100941 Pbk
—Pakistan : human rights violations and the decline of the rule of law / an Amnesty International report. – London : Amnesty International, 1982.
57p; 30cm.
ISBN 0862100410
—Pakistan : the trial and treatment of political prisoners convicted by special military courts / Amnesty Internatiinal. – London : Amnesty International, 1985.
56p.
—Peru : Amnesty International briefing. – Amnesty International. – London : Amnesty International, 1985.
15p.
List of the 'disappeared' of Peru (November 1984) in pocket.
ISBN 0862100801
—Peru : disappearances, torture and summary executions by government forces after the prison revolts of June 1986 / Amnesty International. – London : Amnesty International, 1987.
ii,71p.
ISBN 0862101166
—Political killings by governments. – Amnesty International. – London : Amnesty International, 1983.
131p; 22cm.
Includes index.
ISBN 0862100518 Pbk
—Proposal for a commission of inquiry into the effect of domestic intelligence activities on criminal trials in the United States of America. – Amnesty International. – London : Amnesty International, 1981.
iii,141p; 30cm.
Cover title.
ISBN 0862100380 Pbk
—Report and recommendations of an Amnesty International mission to the government of the Republic of Iraq, 22-28 January 1983, including the government's response and Amnesty International comments. – Amnesty International. – s.l. : Amnesty International, 1983.
74p.
ISBN 0862100615
—Report from Amnesty International to the government of the Syrian Arab Republic. – Amnesty International. – s.l. : Amnesty International, 1983.
ii,65p.
ISBN 0862100585
—Report of an Amnesty International mission to Sri Lanka, 31 January-9 February 1982. – Amnesty International. – London : Amnesty International, 1983.
2,iii,72p; 30cm.
ISBN 0862100542 Pbk
—Report of an Amnesty International mission to the Republic of the Philippines 11-28 November 1981. – Amnesty International. – London : Amnesty International Publications, 1982.
ii,127p.
Includes bibliographical references.
ISBN 086210050X
—Report of an Amnesty International mission to the Socialist Republic of Viet Nam, 10-21 December 1979 : including memoranda exchanged between the government and Amnesty International. – Amnesty International. – London : Amnesty International, 1981.
ii,42p.
ISBN 086210033X
—Report on allegations of ill-treatment of prisoners at Archambault Institution, Quebec, Canada, including a memorandum to the Government of Canada following a mission from 10 to 15 April 1983 / Amnesty International. – London : Amnesty International, 1983.
ii,44p.
ISBN 0862100623
→ Republic of Korea : violations of human rights : an Amnesty International report.
—South Korea : violations of human rights. – Amnesty International. – London : Amnesty International Publications, 1986.
109p,18p. of plates.
ISBN 086210100X
—Spain : the question of torture : documents exchanged by Amnesty International & the Government of Spain. – Amnesty International. – London : Amnesty International Publications, 1985.
60p.
Translated from the Spanish.
ISBN 0862100860
—Summary : 1A : the Human Rights Committee. – Amnesty International. – 1. – London : Amnesty International, 1987.
various pagings.
'This is a summary of a paper with the same title'. - Cover. Includes the text of the International Covenant on Civil and Political Rights.
—Summary : 1B : the Human Rights Committee : examination of individual complaints under the optional protocol / Amnesty International. – London : Amnesty International, 1987.
71p in various pagings.
'This is a summary of a paper by the same title' - Cover. Includes the text of the International Covenant on Civil and Political Rights.
—Summary : 1C : general comments of the Human Rights Committee. – Amnesty International. – London : Amnesty International, 1987.
3,7,22,8p.
'This is a summary of a paper by the same title'. - Cover. Includes the text of the International Covenant on Civil and Political Rights.
—Summary : 2 : the Organization of African Unity and human rights. – Amnesty International. – London : Amnesty International, 1987.
21,10,1p.
'This is a summary of a paper by the same title'. - Cover. Bibliography: pp.17-21. Includes the text of the African Charter on Human and Peoples' Rights.
—Torture in the eighties. – Amnesty International. – Oxford : Robertson, 1984.
250p.
ISBN 0855207809 Hbk £15.00
ISBN 0855207817 Pbk £4.95
—Turkey : testimony on torture. – Amnesty International. – London : Amnesty International Publications, 1985.
76p.
ISBN 0862100887
—Uganda : six years after Amin : torture, killings, disappearances / Amnesty International. – London : Amnesty International, 1985.
40p.
—United States of America - the death penalty / Amnesty International. – London : Amnesty International, 1987.
vi,245p; 22cm.
ISBN 086210114X Pbk
—Voices for freedom. – Amnesty International. – London : Amnesty International, 1986.
208p; 27cm.
Includes index.
ISBN 086210095X Pbk
—Where is William Beausire? : disappearance in Chile. – Amnesty International. – London : Amnesty International, 1981.
57p.
—Yugoslavia : prisoners of conscience / Amnesty International. – New ed. – London : Amnesty International Publications, 1985.
95p.
ISBN 0862100844
—Yugoslavia : prisoners of conscience : an Amnesty International report. – Amnesty International. – London : Amnesty International, 1982.
50p.
ISBN 0862100437
—Zaire : reports of torture and killings committed by the armed forces in Shaba region / Amnesty International. – London : Amnesty International, 1986.
24p.
ISBN 0862100968

Amnesty International Report 1987. – Turnaround Press.
ISBN 0862101255 Pbk £6.95

Amos
Introduction To French Law / Walton. – 3rd ed. – Oxford : Oxford University Press, 1967.
ISBN 0198251785 Hbk £17.00

Analogical Reasoning in Islamic Jurisprudence. – Islamabad : Islamic Research Institute, 1986.
viii, 489p.
ISBN 9694080649 Hbk £20.00

Analysis Of Marine Insurance Clauses
Book 1. – Witherby, 1982.
ISBN 0900886765 Pbk £6.00
Book 2. – 1983.
ISBN 0900886897 Pbk £6.00

Analysis of the German tax system : general principles, taxation of income and capital, unilateral measures for the avoidance of double taxation / Helmut Debatin. – Updated ed. – Amsterdam, Netherlands : International Bureau of Fiscal Documentation, 1981.
1 v. (various pagings); 22 cm.
'Reprinted from Handbook on the United States-German tax convention.'.
ISBN 9070125218 Pbk

Analysis of the Laws of England : Introductory Discourse on the Study of the Law. – 3rd ed. Repr. of 1757 ed. – Abingdon : Professional Books.
Hbk £95.00

Anand
Constitution of India. – 3rd ed. – Dordrecht : Law Book Co., 1989.
850p.
Hbk £240.00

Anand, C.L.
Professional Ethics of the Bar. – 2nd ed. – Allahabad : Law Book Company, 1987.
370p.
Hbk £120.00

Anand, Iyer
Law of Specific Relief. – 8th ed. – Allahabad : Law Publishers, 1982.
£72.00

Anand, R.L.
Law of Compromises / S.K. Argawal. – 4th ed. – Allahabad : Law Book Company, 1986.
600p.
Hbk £140.00
—Law of Torts. – 5th ed. – Allahabad : Law Book Company, 1985.
lxxx, 103p.
Hbk £220.00

Anand, R. P
International law and the developing countries : confrontation or cooperation? / R.P. Anand. – Dordrecht : Martinus Nijhoff, 1987.
xii, 274p.
Includes index and bibliographies.
ISBN 902473438X Hbk £125.00
—Origin and development of the law of the sea : history of international law revisited / R.P. Anand. – The Hague : Nijhoff, 1983.
xvi,249p; 25cm.
Includes index.
ISBN 9024726174 Hbk £115.00

Anatomy of international law : a study of the role of international law in the contemporary world / by J.G. Merrills. – 2nd ed. – London : Sweet and Maxwell, 1981.
xv,146p; 19cm.
Previous ed.: 1976. Bibliography: p137-141. - Includes index.
ISBN 0421280107 Hbk £9.85
ISBN 0421280204 Pbk £6.00

Anatomy of Professional Practice. – London : Law Society.
ISBN 0948736003 Pbk £4.95

Ancestral Lands, Alien Laws : Judicial Perspectives on Aboriginal Title. – Saskatoon : University of Saskatchewan, Native Law Centre, 1983.
49p.
ISBN 0888801009 Hbk £9.00

Ancient constitution and the feudal law : a study of English historical thought in the seventeenth century / J.G.A. Pocock. – Reissue with a retrospect i.e. 2nd ed. – Cambridge : Cambridge University Press, 1987.
xv,402p; 24cm.
Second edition to a work examining seventeenth-century English ideas of constitutionalism as a set of beliefs based on the common law. The Retrospect considers how arguments in the original book may be improved in the light of recent work.
ISBN 0521303524 Hbk £27.50
ISBN 052131643X Pbk £8.95

And nothing but the truth / Alan King-Hamilton : foreword by Lord Diplock. – London : Weidenfeld and Nicolson, 1982.
xvi,237p,8p of plates; 24cm.
Includes index.
ISBN 0297780530 £12.50

... and now for the next sketch ... cartoons for Amnesty. – London : Amnesty International, 1986.
70p.
A collection of original cartoons exhibited at The Barbican Centre in May/June 1986 in commemoration of the 25th. anniversary of the foundation of Amnesty International..

Andah, P. O.
Ghana income tax law and practice
Vol. 1 / P.O. Andah. – Accra : Sedco, 1987.
xii,252p.
ISBN 9964720718

Anderman, Steven D
Labour Relations and the Law. – London : Butterworths, 1988.
ISBN 0406015503 Hbk
→ Law and the weaker party : an Anglo-Swedish comparative study, Vol. 2 : The English experience, edited by Steve Anderman.
—Law of Unfair Dismissal / John H. Angel. – 2nd ed. – Wellington : Butterworths, 1985.
xlv,444; 22cm.
This book provides a detailed discussion of the law of unfair dismissal in the United Kingdom. The work includes references to the changes brought about by recent legislation, such as, the Employment Protection (Consolidation) Act of 1978 and the Employment Acts of 1980 and 1982.
ISBN 0406107076 Pbk

Andersen, Arthur
Property companies : accounting, audit and tax. – London : Butterworths, 1988.
ISBN 0406005249 Pbk

Anderson → CIMA Stage 2 Financial Accounting.

Anderson, Hamish
Administrators : part II of the Insolvency Act 1986 / Hamish Anderson. – London : Sweet & Maxwell, 1987.
250p; 26cm.
Guide to the insolvency procedure established by the Insolvency Act 1986, including a commentary on the relevant provisions, and statutory instruments. Examines the status and powers of an administrator, and the effects of an administration order on the members, creditors, and employees of a company.
ISBN 0421348208 £15.00

Anderson, Kevin
Fossil in the Sandstone sound recording : the Recollecting Judge. – South Yarra : Louis Braille Productions Ltd..
ISBN 9ac £48.00

Anderson, Mary → Politics of clean air.

Anderson, N.
Law Reform in the Muslim World. – London : Athlone Press, 1976.
ISBN 048513411X Hbk £18.00

Anderson, Thomas G.
Family property / by Thomas G. Anderson and Michael Karton. – Victoria : Queen's Printer, 1986.
189p.
Date on front cover: 1985. 'A study paper prepared for the Law Reform Commission of British Columbia'. Includes bibliographical references.
ISBN 0771884931

Andersson, Jan
Drug criminality and drug abuse in Sweden, 1969-1981 / Jan Andersson, Artur Solarz. – Stockholm : Research Division, National Swedish Council for Crime Prevention, 1982.
53p. – (Report).
Includes bibliographies.
ISBN 9138072572

Anderton, B.
Law Relating to Banking (Q & A). – London : Financial Training, 1984.
ISBN 090632257X Pbk £6.50

Andreas Alciates, 2 Vols. – Toronto : University of Toronto Press, 1985.
ISBN 0802024254 Hbk £125.00

Andreewitch, Markus → Austrian Commercial Code : as of January 1, 1983.

Andreotti, Giulio
European union : one character in search of an author / by Giulio Andreotti. – Luxembourg : Office for Official Publications of the European Communities, 1985.
24p.

Andrew, Gillian
Wills and Estates. – 3rd ed. rev. ed. – Vancouver : Vancouver People's Law School.
39p : Illus.. – – (Public Legal Education Series).
ISBN 0888470304 Hbk £0.60

Andrew, K.
Bank Marketing Handbook, The. – Cambridge : Woodhead-Faulkner, 1986.
ISBN 0859413330 Hbk £35.00
ISBN 0859413349 Pbk £12.95

Andrew, Robert
Review of government legal services / report by Sir Robert Andrew. – London : HMSO, 1989.
102p.
At head of title: Cabinet Office.
ISBN 0114300348

Andrew, Warwick John → Criminal law and practice of Papua New Guinea.

Andrews, A.
Organisation of Solicitors Practice. – London : Longman Professional.
ISBN 0851204805 Pbk £85.00

Andrews, G.
Reports King's Bench : 1737-1738. – Repr. of 1754 ed. – Abingdon : Professional Books.
292p.
Hbk £55.00

Andrews, Geraldine Mary → Mareva injunctions : law and practice.

Andrews, John A
Criminal Evidence / J.M. Hirst. – Waterlow. – (Criminal Law Library Series No. 4).
ISBN 0080392377 Hbk £50.00
→ Human rights in criminal procedure : a comparative study.
—Keyguide to information sources on the international protection of human rights / J.A. Andrews and W.D. Hines. – London : Mansell, 1987.
xiii,169p; 24cm.
Includes index.
ISBN 0720118735 £25.00
—Legal Studies : The Journal of the Society of Public Teachers of Law. – London : Butterworths, 1986.
Pbk £76.00
—Welsh language in the courts / by J.A. Andrews and L.G. Henshaw. – Aberystwyth : University College of Wales, 1984.
ix,116p.
Includes index. With Welsh version of the oaths.

Andrews, John M
Coopers and Lybrand: tax and financial planning through pensions / Paul G Meins. – London : Butterworths, 1987.
ISBN 0406500800 Pbk £16.00

Aneke
Law for Everyman. – Onitsha : Africana-FEP.
Hbk £10.00

Angel, John H. → Law of Unfair Dismissal.

Angel, Shlomo → Land for housing the poor.

Angelo Branca. – Vancouver : Douglas and McIntyre, 1981.
ISBN 0888943237 Hbk £16.95

Anger and Honsberger: law of real property / Harry D. Anger, John David Honsberger, A. H. Oosterhoff, W. B. Rayner. – 2nd ed. 2 v. – Aurora, Ont. : Canada Law Book Inc., 1985.
cccvi,2099p.
First ed. had title: Canadian law of real property. Bibliography: p.xxvii-xxviii. - Includes index.
ISBN 0888040261 Hbk

Anger, Harry D. → Anger and Honsberger: law of real property.
—Anger and Honsberger: law of real property / Harry D. Anger, John David Honsberger, A. H. Oosterhoff, W. B. Rayner. – 2nd ed. 2 v. – Aurora, Ont. : Canada Law Book Inc., 1985.
cccvi,2099p.
First ed. had title: Canadian law of real property. Bibliography: p.xxvii-xxviii. - Includes index.
ISBN 0888040261 Hbk

Anger's Digest of Canadian Law. – 20th ed. – Aurora : Canada Law Book, 1987.
Hbk £50.00

Anglo-American privacy law : an economic analysis / Charles J. Hartmann and Stephen M. Renas. – s.l. : s.n., 1985.
36,12p.
Includes bibliographical references.

Anglo-Sakson gozuyle turk hukuku / An Anglo-Saxon view of Turkish law : Aubrey L. Diamond. – 1981.
2,10 leaves.
Paper presented at the 3rd Turkish Law Conference, Ankara, 1981. English text in typescript, bound with a Turkish translation published as a supplement to the Conference papers.

Anguilla → Laws of Anguilla : printed by authority.
—Laws of Anguilla : printed by authority. – Anguilla. – St. Michael, Barbados : Coles Printery, appointed as Government Printer for Anguilla, 1982.
Continues in part: Laws of Saint Christopher, Nevis and Anguilla, 1961-1970. Half title, 1972 onwards: Anguilla ordinances and statutory rules and orders.

Anguilla consolidated index of statutes and subsidiary legislation to 1st January 1983 / compiled at the Faculty of Law Library, University of the West Indies, Barbados. – Rev. ed. – Barbados : s.n., 1983.
v,73p.
Previous ed.: 1st January 1980. One of a series in the West Indian Legislation Indexing Project (WILIP) compiled in cooperation with the British Development Division.

Animal law / by Godfrey Sandys-Winsch. – 2nd ed. – London : Shaw & Sons, 1984.
xxxiv,260p.
Includes index.
ISBN 0721908012

Anisman, Philip → Media, the Courts and the Charter.

Annals of Air and Space Law
Vol. 6 /. – Montreal : Centre for Research of Air and Space Law, 1981.
Vol. 7. – 1982.
Vol. 8. – 1983.
570p.
Vol. 9. – 1984.
583p.
Vol. 10. – 1985.
609p.
Vol. 11. – 1986.
484p.
Vol. 12. – 1987.

Annals of Air and Space Law-Annales de Droit Aerien et Spatial
Vol. 4 /. – Agincourt : Carswell.
Hbk £23.75
Vol. 5. –
Hbk £19.75
Vol. 6. –
Hbk £23.75
Vol. 7. –
Hbk £31.75
Vol. 9. –
Hbk £39.50

Annand, Ruth
Contract / Ruth Annand, Richard Whish. – London : Sweet & Maxwell, 1987.
xxii,175p; 26cm.
Includes index.
ISBN 0421362405 £16.50
—Conveyancing Solution 3 : Remedies under Contract / Cain. – Sweet & Maxwell.
ISBN 0421381108 Hbk £19.50
—Conveyancing Solutions No. 2 : The Contract / Richard Whish. – London : Sweet & Maxwell, 1987.
Hbk £12.50
—Enquiries before contract / Ruth Annand, Brian Cain. – London : Sweet & Maxwell, 1986.
xvii,207p; 26cm.
Includes index.
ISBN 0421348100 £16.50

—Modern conveyancing / by Ruth Annand and Brian Cain. – London : Sweet & Maxwell, 1984.
xlii,514p; 24cm.
Includes index.
ISBN 0421320907 Hbk £
ISBN 0421321008 Pbk £15.95

—Remedies under the contract, CS No 3 / Cain. – London : Sweet & Maxwell, 1988.
ISBN 0421381108 Hbk £22.00

Annas, George J. →Genetics and the law III.

Annotated bibliography public opinion and social policy / by Donald J. Bourgeois. – Ottawa : Ministry of the Solicitor General, 1985.
56p. – (Usier report).

Annotated British Columbia Company Act. – Agincourt : Carswell, 1986.
268p.
This annotated edition of the British Columbia Company Act presents an analytical interweaving of case and statute law through the annotations in the work. The text of the Act, the regulations, and forms are included in the book.
Pbk £38.00

Annotated British Columbia Insurance (Motor Vehicle) Act / Cedric H.L. Hughes. – Agincourt : Carswell, 1987.
ca 220p.
This text contains the Insurance (Motor Vehicle) Act and the Revised Regulations with annotations. Topics include a description of the history of the legislation and the policy that governed its development. Current caselaw and pertinent older cases are discussed.
Hbk £46.00

Annotated Business Corporations Act of Alberta. – 3rd ed. – Agincourt : Carswell, 1988.
384p.
This volume includes a full annotated text of the Act, all regulations under the Act, and annotations on reported and unreported cases dealing with issues arising under the statute.
Pbk £57.25

Annotated Canada Shipping Act / Christopher Burke. – Butterworths, 1988.
464p.
Deals with Canadian judicial decisions and Canadian legal literature. Includes recent amendments to the legislation itself and to the regulations. Shows how Canada deals with this form of international commerce.
ISBN 0409811459 Hbk

Annotated Child Welfare Act. – Hartrick and Lazor. – Agincourt : Carswell, 1983.
460p.
Hbk £29.50

Annotated Competition Act / commentary prepared by Robert S. Nozick : annotations and index prepared by Charlotte Neff. – Toronto : Carswell, 1987.
xviii,290p.
ISBN 0459396609

Annotated Customs Act. – Carswell, 1988.
192p.
Hbk £50.50

Annotated Employment Law Statutes of Ontario / John H. McNair. – Agincourt : Carswell, 1987.
308p.
This text annotates the following: the Occupational Health and Safety Act, Employment Standards Act, Industrial Standards Act, Human Rights Code, Pension Benefits Act, of the Ontario employment legislation.
Hbk £41.75

Annotated guide to the 1986 insolvency legislation: Insolvency Act 1986, Company Directors Disqualification Act 1986 and Insolvency Rules 1986 (as amended) / David Milman. – 2nd. – Bicester : CCH Editions Ltd, 1988.
viii,994p; 23cm.
Reproduces the Act in full text, together with commentary and notes to each provision, explaining its meaning, effort and implications. Includes lists of statutory definitions, a table of destinations, reference to the rules and regulations, and a comprehensive index.
ISBN 0863251617 Hbk £26.00

Annotated Housing Benefit Legislation 1988-89. – Oxford : Bookspeed.
ISBN 0946744106 Pbk £12.95

Annotated Immigration Act of Canada 1988 / Henry M. Goslett. – Carswell, 1988.
482p.
Pbk £38.00

Annotated Insurance Act of Ontario, 2 Vols. – Agincourt : Carswell, 1986.
This two volume looseleaf work contains the Insurance Act of Ontario, with amendments, extensive case annotations, schedules, and regulations. Each section of the Act is cross-referenced to equivalent sections in the law of all Canadian common law provinces.
Llf £138.75

Annotated Insurance Act of Ontario / Harry B. Radomski. – Butterworths, 1987.
704p.
Contains summary and analysis of the law under each section of the Act, traces the legislative history of each section to the present, defines problem wording and terms, directing the reader to all possible interpretations, and covers several thousand relevant cases from all Canadian jurisdictions.
ISBN 0409811440 Hbk £120.00

Annotated legal chronology of the Malvinas (Falkland) Islands controversy / Cronologia legal anotada sobre la cuestion Malvinas (resumen) : Enrique Ferrer Vieyra. – Cordoba : Marcos Lerner, 1985.
173p.
Bibliography: p13-15. Inscribed by the author. Spanish summary.

Annotated Motor Vehicle Legislation in British Columbia. – Agincourt : Carswell, 1987.
200p.
This compact volume contains the complete text of the Motor Vehicle Act, Motor Dealer Act, and Motor Vehicle (All Terrain) Act of British Columbia, along with selected regulations under the Acts.
Hbk £48.75

Annotated Ontario Landlord and Tenant Statutes / John A. McNair. – Agincourt : Carswell, 1986.
300p.
This book fully annotates the Landlord and Tenant Act, the Residential Tenancies Act, and the Residential Complexes Financing Cost Restraint Act of Ontario, Canada. Digests of Residential Tenancy Commission decisions and relevant court decisions are included in the work.
Hbk £41.75

Annotated Takeovers Code. – North Ryde : Law Book Co, 1987.
ca 250p.
Pbk £49.50

Annotated Tax Cases : 1922-1975, 54 Vols. – Abingdon : Professional Books.
Hbk £950.00

Annotated Trade Practices Act / by Russell V. Miller. – 4th ed. – Sydney : Law Book Co., 1983.
339p.
Reproduced from: The Trade Practices Reporting Service. Includes index.

Annotated Trade Practices Act. – 8th ed. – North Ryde : Law Book Co, 1987.
xxxv, 413p.
ISBN 0455207399 Pbk £32.00

Annotated Unemployment Insurance Act. – 1st ed. – Agincourt : Carswell, 1988.
420p.
This book contains the full text of the Unemployment Insurance Act and Regulations. Also included are the annotated cases which are pertinent to particular sections. There is a complete table of cases and an index.
Hbk £54.75

Annotation of the Hong Kong Conveyancing and Property Ordinance. – Butterworths, 1987.
ca 300p.
Deals with the 1984 Conveyancing and Property Ordinance, and annotates the 1988 Conveyancing and Property (Amendment) Ordinance. Discusses the background and the intended effects of the Ordinance, and gives a detailed analysis of each section. Sets out case authorities for the common law position.
ISBN 0409995401 Hbk £50.00

Annotation of the Singapore Companies Act / Walter C M Woon. – Singapore : Butterworths (Asia).
700.
Covers the relevant case law with cross-references to rules and other relevant legislation, along with the cross-references to parliamentary reports.
ISBN 0409995681 Hbk

Annotation of the Singapore Companies (Amendment) Act 1987 / Dorothy Chan. – Singapore : Butterworths (Asia), 1987.
212.
Summarizes the changes effected by the Amendment Act and reproduces those provisions in the Companies Act which are affected by the Companies (Amendment) Act 1987. Covers shares, debentures and charges, judicial management, audit, winding-up, and various types of companies.
ISBN 0409995509 Pbk

Annual Catalogue of E.S.C. Opinions. Year 1984. – Luxembourg : Office for Official Publications of the European Communities, 1985.
38p.
ISBN 9283000757 Pbk

Annual Digest of Income Tax Reports, 1986. – Madras : Company Law Institute of India, 1986.
Hbk £80.00

Annual members' conference held in the Lord Chief Justice's Court on Saturday 22nd March 1986 : subject, public order / Chairman His Hon. Judge Hawser. – London : Justice, 1986.
38 leaves.

Annual members' conference held in the Lord Chief Justice's Court on Saturday, 30th March, 1985 : subject, the future of the legal profession / Chairman, Sir Nicholas Browne-Wilkinson. – London : Justice, 1985.
55 leaves.

Annual report
1979 / Nigeria Prisons Service. – Lagos : Federal Government Press, 1981.
50p.
19th, 1983-1984. – 1985.
v,67p; 25cm. – (HC).
ISBN 0102214859

Annual report / Department of Development Planning : Constitutional Development Services. – Pretoria : Government Printer, 1987.
Annual reports of two bodies published together. Text in Afikaans and English.

Annual report / Scottish Law Commission. – Edinburgh : H.M.S.O., 1966-.
Numbered in series Scot Law Com.

Annual report / the Law Commission. – London : HMSO, 1986.
v,71p.
ISBN 0102247862

Annual report / The Ombudsman, Ontario. – Toronto : The Ombudsman, 1977 -.
v.

Annual report / Law Reform Commission of Victoria. – Melbourne : The Commission, 1985.
v.
Published as part of the report series of the Commission.

Annual Report / Centre for Socio-Legal Studies. – Oxford : The Centre, 1984.
Continues: Report of the S.S.R.C. Centre for Socio-Legal Studies.

Annual report and financial statements / National Companies and Securities Commission. – Canberra : Australian Government Publishing Service, 1981.
Second and subsequent report years run 1st July to 30th June.

Annual report and review / Law Reform Commission of Saskatchewan. – Saskatoon : The Commission, 1988.
Supersedes: Yearly review.

Annual report / Canadian Law Information Council. – Canadian Law Information Council. – Ottawa : CLIC, 1982-.
Annual reports for 1978/1979 and 1979/1980 published as one volume entitled: Yesterday, today and tomorrow : 1978-1980 / Canadian Law Information Council. Annual report for 1980/1981 entitled: Progress through partnership : 1980/1981 / Canadian Law Information Council.

Annual report / Commonwealth Legal Aid Council. – 4 v. – Canberra : Australian Government Publishing Service, 1982-.
Continues: Annual report / Commonwealth Legal Aid Commission. Report year runs 1 July to 30 June.

Annual report/Commonwealth Ombudsman. – Canberra : Australian Government Publishing Service, 1977/78-.

Annual report for the period April ... to March ... from the Director of Public Prosecutions to the Attorney General / Crown Prosecution Service. – London : H.M.S.O., 1987-.
v.
Presented to Parliament in pursuance of Section 9 of the Prosecution of Offences Act 1985, Ch. 23.

Annual report for the year ended 30 September ... / Air Transport Users Committee. – London : The Committee, 1978.
Continues: CIVIL AVIATION AUTHORITY. Airline Users Committee. Annual report.

Annual report for the year ended 31 March ... / Restrictive Trade Practices Commission. – Ottawa : The Commission, 1981.
Text in English and French, 1982 onwards. Added t.p. in French, 1982 onwards: Rapport annuel pour l'exercise clos le 31 mars ... / Commission sur les pratiques restrictives du commerce.
ISBN 07115458

Annual report/Institute of Family Studies, Australia. – Institute of Family Studies. – Melbourne : Australian Institute of Family Studies, 1980-.

Annual report / Legal Aid Commission (A.C.T.). – Australian Capital Territory. – Canberra : Australian Government Publishing Service, 1978-.
Report year runs 1 July to 30 June.

Annual report of the Commissioner of South African Police. – Pretoria : Government Printer, 1945.

Annual report of the Council of the Law Society : intended to be presented to the general meeting of the members on ... – Law Society. – London : Spottiswoode, 1903.
Continues: Annual report of the Council of the Incorporated Law Society. 1975 onwards incorporates the interim report and accounts of the Solicitors Benevolent Association. Cover title, 1966/67 onwards: Annual report of the Council and accounts. Published by the Law Society, 1945 onwards.

Annual report of the Law Commission ... – Wellington, N.Z. : The Commission, 1987.
Published as part of the report series of the Commission. 1st report covers years ended 31 March 1986 and 31 March 1987.

Annual report of the Police Complaints Authority. – Police Complaints Authority. – London : H.M.S.O., 1986-.
Continues: Report of the Police Complaints Board.

Annual report of the Police Division, Republic of Seychelles. – Maye : Government Press, 1977.
Continues: Annual report of the Seychelles Police Force. Lacking 1978.

Annual report / Ontario Labour Relations Board. – Ontario Labour Relations Board. – Toronto : The Board, 1981.
Report year ends 31 Mar..
ISBN 071184 9X

Annual report / Servicing the Legal System, Queen's University of Belfast. – Servicing the Legal System. – Belfast : Servicing the Legal System, 1981-.
Servicing the Legal System was originally established as a committee of the Faculty of law, Queen's University of Belfast. Report year ends 31 July.

Annual report / Zimbabwe Advisory Committee on Law Reform. – Causeway : The Committee, 1982.

Annual Review of Criminal Law : 1987. – Agincourt : Carswell, Annual, 1986.
304p.
This text, the sixth volume in an annual series, provides a summary and a synopsis of the major issues in Canadian criminal law, practice and evidence. It contains an outline of the trends in judicial interpretations of the Charter. Also included is an index to pertinent periodical literature.
Hbk £40.50

Annual Review of Irish Law 1987 / Raymond Byrne. – Round Hall Press.
ISBN 0947686428 Hbk £35.00

Annual review of ocean affairs. – United Nations Office for Ocean Affairs and the Law of the Sea. – 2 vol. – London : Lloyds of London Press, 1989.
These two volumes contain protocols, conventions, treaties, decisions, and other matters enacted by governmental organisations concerned with ocean affairs. Includes illicit drug-trafficking, fisheries management, and the marine environment. This first edition contains documentation covering the years 1985-1987.

Annual Statutes (Chitty's) 1864-1948, 42 Vols. – Abingdon : Professional Books.
Hbk £95.00

Annual Statutes of Canada (1980-1983), 4 Vols. – Aurora : Canada Law Book Co, Official ed.. – (Statute Services).
Hbk £200.00

Annual Statutes of Canada : 1984, 2 Vols. – Law Book Publisher. – Aurora : Canada Law Book Co.
Hbk £185.00

Annual Survey of Australian Law
1979: 1980 /. – North Ryde : Law Book Co.
xxi, 467p.
ISBN 0455201226 £32.50
1980: 1981. –
576p.
£48.00
1985: 1986. –
xxii, 428p.
ISBN 0455206902 Hbk £65.00
1986: 1987. –
Hbk £65.00

Annual volume of the laws of Eastern Region of Nigeria ... : containing the ordinances of Eastern Region of Nigeria and subsidiary legislation made thereunder. – Eastern Region of Nigeria. – 19 v. – Enugu : Government Printer, 1952.
Originally published as individual supplements to Eastern Nigeria gazette. 1967 volume also contains legislation enacted by the Republic of Biafra. Entitled Laws Eastern Nigeria: 1959-1967.

Annual volume of the laws of Imo State of the Federal Republic of Nigeria containing edicts and subsidiary legislation. – Imo State of Nigeria. – Owerri : Government Printer, 1976.
Consolidated index 1976-1985 published separately, 1986.

Annual volume of the laws of Kaduna State of Nigeria ... – Kaduna, Nigeria : Government Printer, 1976.
Originally published as individual supplements to the Kaduna State of Nigeria gazette. Index in each vol.

Annual volume of the laws of Ogun State of Nigeria : containing the laws of Ogun state of Nigeria and subsidiary legislation made thereunder. – Abeokuta? : Government Printer?, 1976-.
Previously published as separate supplements to Ogun State of Nigeria Gazette.

Annual volume of the laws of the Cross River State of Nigeria containing edicts and subsidiary legislation made in the year ... – Kano : Government Printing Press, 1976-.
Originally published as individual supplements to Cross River State of Nigeria gazette.

Annual volume of the laws of the Western Region of Nigeria ... : containing the laws of the Western Region of Nigeria and subsidiary legislation made thereunder. – Western Region of Nigeria. – 15 v. – Ibadan : Government Printer, 1954-.
Previously published as separate supplements in the Western Regional Gazette, vol. 1 (1952)-9(1960) and the Western Nigeria Gazette, vol.10(1961)-15(1966).

Annual volumes of the laws of North-Eastern State of Nigeria ... – Kaduna, Nigeria : Government Printer, 1969-.
Originally published as individual supplements to the Norht-Eastern State of Nigeria gazette. Covers of vols. for 1971-1974 incorrectly headed: Gongola State of Nigeria. Annual except for 1967/1968 and 1969/1970.

Annual volumes of the laws of North-Eastern State of Nigeria ... i.e. Gongola State of Nigeria. – Jumeta, Nigeria? : Government Printer, 1977.
Originally published as individual supplements to the Gongola State of Nigeria gazette. Description based on: 1977 vol..

Annual volumes of the laws of the North-Central State of Nigeria ... – Kaduna, Nigeria : Government Printer, 1971-.
Originally published as individual supplements to the North-Central State of Nigeria gazette.

Annual volumes of the laws of Western State of Nigeria : containing the laws of Western State of Nigeria and subsidiary legislation made thereunder. – Ibadan : Government Printer, 1967-.
Previously published as separate supplements to the Western State of Nigeria Gazette, vol. 16(1967)-25 (1976).

Anonboke
Justyces of Peas. – 1st ed. 1986 Reprint. – London : Butterworths.
ISBN 0862053099 Hbk £17.15

Another Look at Statutory Interpretation. – Attorney-General's Department. – Canberra : Australian Government Publishing Service, 1982.
32p.
ISBN 0642068895 Hbk £2.00

Ansay, T. → Introduction to Swiss law.
→ Introduction to Turkish law.

Anson
Law of Contract / A G Guest. – 26th ed. – Oxford : Oxford University Press, 1984.
ISBN 0198761481 Hbk £32.50
ISBN 019876149X Pbk £16.95

Anson, William Reynell
Anson's Law of contract / A. G. Guest. – 26th ed. – Oxford : Clarendon, 1984.
lvi,641p; 24cm.
Previous ed.: 1979. Includes index.
ISBN 0198761481 Hbk £30.60
ISBN 019876149X Pbk £15.95

Anson's Law of contract / A. G. Guest. – 26th ed. – Oxford : Clarendon, 1984.
lvi,641p; 24cm.
Previous ed.: 1979. Includes index.
ISBN 0198761481 Hbk £30.60
ISBN 019876149X Pbk £15.95

Anstey, J.
Pleader's Guide. – 5th ed. Repr. of 1808 ed. – Abingdon : Professional Books.
262p.
Hbk £75.00

Answers to Bar Examination Questions
Civil Law (1975-1981). – Quezon City : University of the Philippines, Law Center, 1982.
148p.
Pbk £10.00
Taxation (1964-1981). – 1982.
312p.
Pbk £25.00

Answers to Dirleton's Doubts in the Laws of Scotland. – Repr. of 1715 ed. – Abingdon : Professional Books.
117p.
Hbk £220.00

Antarctic Law and Politics. – London : Dent (J M) & Sons, 1987.
ISBN 0905838394 Hbk £17.50

Antarctic resources policy : scientific, legal and political issues / edited by Francisco Orrego Vicuna. – Cambridge : Cambridge University Press, 1983.
viii,335p.
The contributions published in this book were prepared for the Conference on Antarctic Resources Policy organized by the Institute of International Studies of the University of Chile in the Antarctic Station Teniente Marsh, 6-9 October, 1982.

Antarctic Treaty regime : law, environment and resources / edited by Gillian D. Triggs under the general editorship of the British Institute of International and Comparative Law. – Cambridge : Cambridge University Press, 1987.
xxi,237p; 23cm.
Conference papers. Bibliography: p234-235.
ISBN 0521327660 £30.00

Antarctica and international law : a collection of inter-state and national documents / compiled by W.M. Bush. – 4. – London : Oceana Publications, 1982.
Vol. 4 is index.
ISBN 0379203200 V. 1 £45.00
ISBN 0379203219 V. 2 £45.00

Anten, Juhli
Small Claims Court Guide for British Columbia : How to Win Your Case!. – 18th ed. – North Vancouver : International Self-Counsel Press, 1986.
138p.
ISBN 0889081859 Hbk £7.95

Anthony & Berryman's Magistrates' court guide 1985 / by A.P. Carr. – London : Butterworths, 1985.
vii,457p.
Includes index.
ISBN 0406108382 Pbk £12.95

Anthony, E.
Anthony & Berryman's Magistrates' court guide 1985 / by A.P. Carr. – London : Butterworths, 1985.
vii,457p.
Includes index.
ISBN 0406108382 Pbk £12.95

Anthony, R.N.
Essentials of Accounting. – 4th ed. – London : Addison-Wesley.
ISBN 0201000172 Pbk £13.95

Anthony, Robert → Pease and Chitty's Law of Markets and Fairs.

Anthony, Russell J.
Handbook on the Conduct of Public Inquiries in Canada / Alastair R. Lucas. – Butterworths, 1985.
288p.
Brings together the considerations that participants should address in designing and operating an enquiry, and analyzes the legal and organizational options available for achieving the intended goals of the inquiry process.
ISBN 0409846732 Hbk £60.00

Anthropological jurisprudence? : Leopold Pospisil and the comparative study of legal cultures / by Csaba Varga. – Budapest : Hungarian Academy of Sciences, Institute of Sociology, 1986.
34p. – (Underdevelopment and modernization).
Bibliography: p.30-34.

Anthropology of law in the Netherlands : essays on legal pluralism / edited by Keebet von Benda-Beckmann and Fons Strijbosch. – Dordrecht : Foris Publications, 1986.
311p.
Includes bibliographical references.
ISBN 9067652032

Anti Discrimination Pay Act 1974 and the Employment Equality Act 1977. – Dublin : Round Hall Press, 1986.
ca 140p.
ISBN 0947686045 Hbk £13.50

Anti-avoidance legislation / R.K. Ashton. – London : Butterworths, 1981.
xvii,255p; 22cm.
Includes index.
ISBN 0406111405 Pbk

Anti-Avoidance Provisions. – Tolley Publishing.
ISBN 0854591516 Hbk £17.50

Anticombines and Antitrust : the Competition Law of Canada. – London : Butterworths.
ISBN 0409862800 Hbk £84.00

Anti-competitive practices : a guide to the provisions of the Competition Act 1980. – London : Office of Fair Trading, 1986.
39p.

Anti-discrimination staffing policies : implications of human rights legislation for employers and trade unions / by Harrish C. Jain. – Ottawa : Department of the Secretary of State of Canada, 1985.
iv,100p.
Includes bibliographical references.
ISBN 0662141474

Anti-dumping and anti-subsidy law : the European Communities / by J. i.e. H. F. Beseler and A.N. Williams. – London : Sweet & Maxwell, 1986.
xx,438p; 26cm.
Examines the interpretation and application of the anti-dumping and anti-subsidy laws in the EEC in the light of the relevant GATT codes. Compares practices with those of the USA and Canada. Deals with the current attempts within GATT to obtain an international consensus on the way anti-subsidy law should be applied in specific circumstances.
ISBN 0421358009 £58.00

Antidumping law and practice in the United States and the European Communities : a comparative analysis / Edwin A. Vermulst. – Amsterdam : North-Holland, 1987.
xx, 750 p.; 24 cm.
Includes bibliographical references and index.
ISBN 0444702229 Hbk

Antieau, Chester James
Constitutional construction / Chester James Antieau. – London : Oceana Publications, 1982.
xxiv, 255 p.; 25 cm.
Includes bibliographical references and index.
ISBN 037920682X

Antigua and Barbuda consolidated index of statutes and subsidiary legislation to !st January 1984 / compiled at the Faculty of Law Library, University of the West Indies, Barbados. – Barbados? : s.n., 1984.
iii,87p.
Previous ed.: 1st January 1981. One of a series in the West Indian Legislation Indexing Project (WILIP) compiled in cooperation with the British Development Division.

Antimonopoly legislation of Japan / edited by Masanao Nakagawa. – Tokyo : Kosei Torihiki Kyokai, 1984.
ix,361p.
Includes index. English-Japanese and Japanese-English indexes.
ISBN 4876220018

Anti-Poverty Policy in the European Community. – London : Policy Studies Institute, 1984.
271p. – (Conference Papers).
Hbk £5.00

Antitrust and direct regulation of international transfer of technology transactions : a comparison and evaluation / Guillermo Cabanellas. – Munich : Verlag Chemie for the Max Planck Institute for Foreign and International Patent Copyright and Competition Law, 1984.
175p.
ISBN 3527260013

Antitrust Cases from Common Market Law Reports : Cartels
Vol. 2. – London : European Law Centre.
Hbk £55.50

Antitrust Economics. – Oxford : Blackwell Scientific, 1987.
ISBN 0631153632 Hbk £32.50

Antl, B.
Swap Finance
Vol. 1. – London : Euromoney, 1987.
Service.
ISBN 0903121875 Pbk £75.00

Anton, A. E.
Civil jurisdiction in Scotland / by A.E. Anton. – Edinburgh : W. Green, 1984.
xxiii,306p; 24cm.
Kept up to date by supplements.
ISBN 0414007360

Anton Piller-type orders / South African Law Commission. – Pretoria : The Commission, 1986.
iii,23 leaves. – (Poject).

Anwar, Badar →Protection of Women under the Law : an Annotated Bibliography.

Anyebe, A. P.
Customary law : the war without arms / by A.P. Anyebe. – Enugu : Fourth Dimension, 1985.
159p.
Includes bibliographical references.
ISBN 978156184X

Apara, Akinola
Law is for all / by Hon. Justice Akin. Apara. – Enugu : Fourth Dimension Publishers, 1982.
x,118p.
Includes index.

Appeals / by David Price. – London : Fourmat, 1982.
xii,439p; 22cm.
Includes index.
ISBN 0906840422 Pbk £12.95

Appeals : Practice and Procedure. – London : Longman Professional, 1986.
ISBN 0851207626 Pbk £18.95

Appeals by the Prosecution Against Sentences and Acquittals : A Survey of the Situation in Some Commonwealth Countries / Jill Cottrell. – London : Commonwealth Secretariat, 1984.
ISBN 0850922259 Hbk £2.00

Appeals on questions of law from administrative tribunals : sixteenth report of the Public and Administrative Law Reform Committee : presented to the Minister of Justice, March 1982. – Wellington : the Committee?, 1982.
17,19p.

Appearing before a Value Added Tax Tribunal. – London : Deloitte Haskins & Sells.
ISBN 0863491227 Pbk £20.00

Appearing for the Crown : a Legal and Historical Review of Criminal Prosecutorial Authority in Canada. – Cowansville : Brown Legal Publications.
450p.
Pbk £39.95

Appellate decision making in the common law world / Alan Paterson : Aleksander Peczenik. – Arnhem : Gouda Quint, 1985.
52p.
Papers presented at the first Symposium on Legal Decision Making of the Institute of Legal Decision Making, Erasmus University.
ISBN 9060003772

Appellate Division Reports of the Union of South Africa : 1910-1946, 37 Vols. – Kenwyn : Juta & Co, 1985.
Microfiche only

Appellate mosaic : being the presidential address of the Rt. Hon. Lord Templeman, president of the Holdsworth Club of the Faculty of Law in the University of Birmingham 1938-84. – Birmingham : The Holdsworth Club of the University of Birmingham, 1984.
18p; 22cm. – (The Holdsworth Club).
ISBN 0704407132

Appendix 26 to the Radio Regulations : Geneva 1959. – Geneva : International Telecommunications Union.
Hbk £12.00

Appendix 27 Aer2 to the Radio Regulations French. – 1983 ed. – Geneva : International Telecommunications Union.
ISBN 9261015824 Hbk £18.00
English. –
ISBN 9261015816 Hbk £18.00
Spanish. –
ISBN 9261015832 Hbk £18.00

Applicable law in Singapore and Malaysia:a guide to reception, precedent and sources of law in the republic of Singapore and the federation of Malaysia. – Singapore : Malayan Law Journal, 1990.
600.
Account of the applicable law in Singapore and Malaysia, and a summary of legislation and case law. Appendices contain a digest of selected cases, politico-legal landmarks reception in other countries, comparative charts of the English and Singapore legal system, and a chart on precedent in Singapore.
Hbk

Application of customary law in southern Africa : the conflict of personal laws / T.W. Bennett. – Cape Town : Juta, 1985.
xxxvii,250p.
Bibliography: p.xv-xxi. - Includes index.
ISBN 0702116017

Application of Humanitarian Law. – Centre d'Etude et de Recherche de Droit International et de Relations Internationales. – Dordrecht : Kluwer, 1987.
106p.
ISBN 9024735084 Pbk £50.00

Application of humanitarian law : selective bibliography prepared by the Peace Palace Library / Center for Studies and Research of the Hague Academy of International Law : bibliographie selective preparee par la Bibliotheque du Palais de la Paix : Centre d'Etude et de Recherche de l'Academie du droit Internationale de la Haye. – The Hague : Center for Studies and Research of the Hague Academy of International Law, 1986.
80p.
Preliminary material in English and French.

Application of new legal techniques to mining agreements in developing countries / by Carl W. Dundas. – London : Commonwealth Secretariat, 1981.
46p.
Includes bibliographical references.

Application of the Competition Rules (Antitrust Law) of the European Economic Community to Enterprises and Arrangements External to the Common Market. – Dordrecht : Kluwer, 1981.
474p.
Hbk £104.00

Application of the European Convention on Human Rights / by J.E.S. Fawcett. – 2nd ed. – Oxford : Clarendon, 1987.
xiii,444p; 22cm.
Previous ed.: 1969. Includes index.
ISBN 0198255101 Hbk £25.00
ISBN 0198255098 Pbk £15.00

Application of the rule of exhaustion of local remedies in international law : its rationale in the international protection of individual rights / A.A. Cancado Trindade. – Cambridge Cambridgeshire : Cambridge University Press, 1983.
xiii,443p.
Includes index. Bibliography: p422-440.
ISBN 0521229472

Applications for judicial review : law and practice / Grahame Aldous, John Alder. – London : Butterworths, 1985.
250p; 26cm.
Includes index.
ISBN 0406273200 Pbk

Applications of computer technology to law (1979-1982) : a selected bibliography / compiled by Judith M. Cameron and edited by Lorna K. Rees-Potter and Allan Kling. – Ottawa : Canadian Law Information Council, 1983. – (Working paper).
Includes index. Cover title: Bibliography computers and law supplement (1979-1982).

Applications of computer technology to law : a selected bibliography (1969-1981) for British lawyers / Society for Computers and Law. – Didcot : Society for Computers and Law, 1982.
60p.
ISBN 0906122112

Apportionment of fault in tort / David Cheifetz. – Ontario : Canada Law Book, 1981.
xlii,355p.
ISBN 0888040091

Apportionment of liability in British Columbia. – Scarborough, Ontario : Butterworths (Canada).
Digest of the British Columbia Cases which address the question of liability in motor vehicle accidents. Each chapter begins with a topical index, and the text includes a table of cases.
Llf

Approach to International Law. – 2nd rev. ed. – New Dehli : Sterling Publishers, 1983.
384p.
ISBN 8120702395 Hbk £90.00
ISBN 8120704371 £22.50

Approach to Searching for Research and Evaluation Reports in the Field of Public Legal Education and Information (PLEI). – Ottawa : Canadian Law Information Council, 1984.
28p.
ISBN 0920358608 Pbk £7.50

Approach to the analysis of joint ventures / by Neil Kay, Jean-Philippe Robe and Patrizia Zagnoli. – Florence : European University Institute, 1987.
39p.

Apsion, G.
Keeping the Estate in the Family : Inheritance Tax. – Oxford : BSP Professional.
ISBN 063202505 Pbk £99.50
—Tax Shelters in the United Kingdom. – Oxford : BSP Professional.
ISBN 0632034895 Pbk £99.50

Apted →Building Subsidence.
→ Building Subsidence : Liability and Insurance.

AQUA Group
Pre-Contract Practice for Architects and Quantity Surveyors. – AQUA Group. – 7th ed. – London : Collins, 1986.
100p : Illus.
ISBN 0003832546 Hbk £8.95

Aquaculture. – Vancouver : Continuing Legal Education Society of British Columbia, 1988.
426p.
ISBN 0865049793 Hbk £85.00

Aquaculture : the Legal Framework. – Aurora : Canada Law Book, 1982.
Hbk £25.00

Aquaculture : the legal framework / Bruce H.Wildsmith. – Toronto : Emond-Montgomery, 1982.
xii,313p.
Bibliography: p.295-305. - Includes index.
ISBN 0920722083 Hbk £45.00

Arab comparative & commercial law : the international approach : proceedings : International Bar Association first Arab Regional Conference, Cairo 15-19 February 1987. – International Bar Association. – London : Graham & Trotman, 1987.
Contents: 1. The Sharia and its relevance to modern transnational transactions. The settlement of disputes through arbitration. Joint ventures. – 2. Energy law.
ISBN 086010978X v. 2

Arab law newsletter. – London : Lloyd's of London, 1985-.
Covers Arab Middle East, Gulf States and North Africa.

Arab law quarterly. – London : Lloyd's of London, 1985-.
Issued by: Society of Arab Comparative and International Law.

Arab petropolitics / Abdulaziz Al-Sowayegh. – London : Croom Helm, 1984.
207p; 23cm.
Includes index.
ISBN 0709905386 Hbk £15.95
ISBN 0709905408 Pbk £8.95

Arab women / edited by Ann Dearden. – 2nd rev. and updated ed. – London : Minority Rights Group, 1983.
16p. – (Report).
Bibliography: p.15.
ISBN 0903114887

Arabian Boundaries : Primary Documents 1853-1957, 25 Vols. / Blake. – London : Archive Editions.
On behalf International Boundaries Research.
ISBN 1852071303 Hbk £4,995.00

Arab-Israeli conflict : a politico-legal analysis / J.R. Gainsborough. – Aldershot : Gower, 1987.
xxxv,345p; 23cm.
Bibliography: p319-334. - Includes index.
ISBN 0566008181 £25.00

Araden
Landlord and Tenant Act 1985 / Siobhan McGrath. – London : Sweet & Maxwell, 1986.
ISBN 0421358904 Pbk £5.75

Arbetslivscentrum →Labour law research in twelve countries.

Arbitrage. – Cambridge : Woodhead-Faulkner, 1986.
ISBN 0859413535 Hbk £55.00

Arbitration. – Victoria : Government of British Columbia, 1982.
Hbk £6.35

Arbitration : an Element of International Law. – Stockholm : Almqvist & Wiksell, 1984.
166p.
ISBN 9122007342 Hbk £119.00

Arbitration : principles and practice / John Parris. – London : Granada, 1983.
xi,242p; 25cm.
Includes index.
ISBN 0246118997

Arbitration : Principles and Practice. – Oxford : Blackwell Scientific, 1983.
ISBN 000383171X Hbk £19.95

Arbitration : the IBA rules of evidence : supplementary rules governing the presentation and reception of evidence in international commercial arbitration / International Bar Association, Section on Business Law. – London : The Association, 1986.
8p.
ISBN 0948711043

Arbitration and conciliation under the UNCITRAL rules : a textual analysis / Issaak I. Dore. – Dordrecht : Nijhoff, 1986.
ISBN 0898389135

Arbitration and renegotiation of international investment agreements : a study with particular reference to means of conflict avoidance under natural resources investment agreements / Wolfgang Peter. – Dordrecht : M. Nijhoff, 1986.
xxiii, 297p.
Includes index. Bibliography: p.267-284.
ISBN 9024733146

Arbitration and state enterprises : a survey on the national and international state of law and practice / by Karl-Heinz Bockstiegel. – Deventer : Kluwer Law and Taxation, 1984.
vi,113p; 25cm.
'An international research study of the Institute of International Business Law and Practice of the International Chamber of Commerce'. Bibliography: p75-109.
ISBN 9065441840 Pbk

Arbitration for contractors / Douglas A. Stephenson. – London : Northwood Books, 1982.
ix,150p.
Bibliography: p.145. - Includes index.
ISBN 0719829003

Arbitration for the Practitioner. – Folkestone : Bailey Bros..
ISBN 0899502903 Hbk £18.50

Arbitration in Building Disputes. – London : Managment Update.
ISBN 0946679355 Hbk £14.95

Arbitration in France : the French law and national and international arbitration / Jean-Louis Delvolve. – Trilangual ed. – Antwerp : Kluwer Law and Taxation Publishers, 1982.
x, 165 p.; 19 cm.
English, French, and German. Bibliography: p. 165.
ISBN 9065440984

Arbitration in international trade / Rene David. – Antwerp : Kluwer Law and Taxation Publications, 1985.
xii,482p.
Includes legislation. Includes index. Bibliography: p459-465. Translation of: Arbitrage dans le commerce international.
ISBN 9065441646

Arbitration in settlement of international commercial disputes involving the Far East: arbitration in combined transportation / Pieter Sanders. – Kluwer Law and Taxation, 1989.
428. – (ICCA Congress Series).
Overview of the arbitration situation in the Far East concerning the settlement ofinternational commercial disputes. Also covers Latin America, the CMEA countries, the common law and civil law countries. Discusses ways to overcome regional differences. Examines arbitration in combined transportation.
ISBN 9065444068 Pbk £47/Dfl 150

Arbitration in Sweden. – Second (revised) edition. – Stockholm : The Stockholm Chamber of Commerce, 1984.
xvii,276p.
ISBN 9178100755

Arbitration in taxation / Gustaf Lindencrona, Nils Mattsson. – Deventer, The Netherlands : Kluwer, 1981.
92 p.; 22 cm.
Includes bibliographical references.
ISBN 9065440003 Pbk

Arbitration in the Yemen Arab Republic / Isam Ghanem. – Braunton : Merlin, 1988.
22p; 21cm.
ISBN 0863033784 Pbk £2.00

Arbitration in U.S.-German Business Relations : Schiedsgerichtsbarkeit im deutsch-amerikanischen / Karl-Heinz Bockstiegel. – Cologne : Carl Heymanns Verlag, 1985.
vi, 287p.
ISBN 3452202577 Pbk £230.00

Arbitration international. – London : Chartered Institute of Arbitrators, 1985.

Arbitration law and practice / Peter M.B. Rowland. – London : Institute of Chartered Accountants, 1988.
xxvii,185p.
ISBN 0852918887

Arbitration Law in Asia. – Paris : International Chamber of Commerce, 1986.
Hbk

Arbitration law in Europe. – Paris : International Chamber of Commerce, 1981.
368p.
Revision of: Commercial arbitration and the law throughout the world. Publication; no. 353.
ISBN 9284210143

Arboreal Emblem Act, 1983, Bill 143 : Arboreal Emblem Act, 1983. – Ontario : Ontario Government Publications Service, 1983.
1p.
Hbk £0.30

Arbuthnot
Common Man's Guide to the Common Market / Edwards. – 2nd ed. – London : Macmillan.
ISBN 0333409132 Hbk £27.50
ISBN 0333409140 Pbk £9.95

Archambault, J. R. Omer → Sentencing reform : a Canadian approach.

Archbold : Pleading, Evidence, and Practice in Criminal Cases. – 41st ed. – London : Sweet & Maxwell, 1983.
Fourth cumulative supplement. –
ISBN 0421273909 Pbk

Archbold, J.F.
Pleading, Evidence and Practice. – 43rd ed. – London : Sweet & Maxwell, 1988.
ISBN 0421363606 Hbk £49.00
ISBN 0421054808 Hbk £60.00
—Pleading, Evidence, and Practice in Criminal Cases 2 vols. – 43rd ed. – Sweet & Maxwell.
ISBN 0421375108 Hbk £110.00

Archdale, Richard → Chancery practice handbook.

Archer, Clive
International organizations / Clive Archer. – London : Allen & Unwin, 1983.
xii,193p; 23cm.
Bibliography: p180-188. - Includes index.
ISBN 0043201563 Hbk
ISBN 0043201571 Pbk

Archer, Peter → More law reform NOW : a collection of essays on law reform.

Archer, W.G.
Tribal Law and Justice : a Report on the Santal. – New Delhi : Concept Publishing Company, 1984.
xxxvi, 741p.
Hbk £200.00

Archipelagic Concept in the Law of the Sea : Problems and Perspectives. – Metro Manila : Development Academy of the Philippines, 1982.
vii, 26p.
ISBN 9711520028 Pbk £2.80

Architects Act, 1983, Bill 122 : An Act to Revise the Architects Act. – Ontario : Ontario Government Publications Service, 1983.
55p.
Hbk £0.70

Architects' and Builders' Price Book 1987 annual. – Spon (E & FN).
ISBN 0419144102 Hbk £32.00

Architects and Copyright. – Milsons Point : Australian Copyright Council.
Hbk £1.00

Architect's Guide to Fee Negotiations : An Architecture and Building Practice Guide Book. – London : Architectural Press, 1984.
160p.
ISBN 0946228051 Pbk £16.95

Ardagh, Anne
Administrative Law First. – Butterworths, 1989.
ca 122p.
ISBN 0409494798 Pbk £10.95

Arden, Andrew
Homeless persons : the Housing Act 1985 Part III / Andrew Arden. – 2nd ed. – London : Legal Action Group, 1986.
xxiii,200p.
Previous ed.: published as 'The Homeless Persons Act' 1982. Includes index. Includes text of act.
—Homeless person's handbook. – London : Allison & Busby, 1988.
ISBN 085031769 Pbk £4.95
—Housing Act 1985. – London : Sweet & Maxwell, 1986.
ISBN 0421353708 Pbk £17.50
→ Housing and Building Control Act 1984.
—Housing Associations Act 1985 / James Ramage. – London : Sweet & Maxwell, 1986.
ISBN 0421359005 Pbk £7.50
—Housing Consolidation 1985. – London : Sweet & Maxwell, 1986.
ISBN 0421360801 Pbk £25.00
—Housing law / Martin Partington. – London : Sweet & Maxwell, 1983.
ISBN 0421242108 Hbk £110.00
Supplement 2 (1986). –
Defines legal statues likely to affect all classes of occupiers of residential accomodation, deals with the law relating to housing finance, the private and public law relating to housing conditions, the rights of occupation in housing, and special categories of occupier such as agricultural workers and occupiers of mobile homes.
ISBN 0421362006 Pbk £22.00
—Housing Law Reports. – London : Sweet & Maxwell.
Hbk £89.00
→ Landlord and Tenant Act 1985.
—Manual of housing law. – 4th. – London : Sweet & Maxwell, 1989.
Taking into account changes due to the Housing Act 1988, covers occupation status, security of tenure by Rent and Housing Acts, restricted security, lack of security, harassment and illegal eviction, break-up of relationships, homelessness and disrepair, multiple occupation and common lodging houses, and overcrowding.
ISBN 042140650X Pbk £14.95
—Private tenants handbook. – London : Allison & Busby, 1985.
ISBN 0850316200 Pbk £3.95
—Quiet enjoyment : remedies for harassment and illegal eviction / by Andrew Arden and Martin Partington. Edited by S. Carrott and C. Hunter. – 3rd. – London : Legal Action Group, 1990.
127.
Includes index.
ISBN 0905099265 Pbk £11
→ Rent acts and regulations amended and annotated.

Arden, Mary
Tolley's Companies Act : 1980 / George Eccles. – Croydon : Tolley.
324p.
ISBN 0854590595 Hbk £11.95
ISBN 0510494153 Pbk £7.95

Ardis
Risk management / Comer. – Maidenhead : McGraw-Hill, 1986.
ISBN 0070849269 Hbk £19.95

Ardrey, R.
Eight Peak Index of Mass Spectra of Compounds of Forensic Interest / C. Brown. – Edinburgh : Scottish Academic Press Ltd, 1983.
296p.
ISBN 0707303419 Hbk £50.00

Are two legal professions necessary? / Peter Reeves. – London : Waterlow, 1986.
xiii,175p; 21cm.
Bibliography: p145-171. - Includes index.
ISBN 0080392180 Pbk £11.95

Arend, Anthony C. → Falklands war : lessons for strategy, diplomacy, and international law.

Arens
Auditing : An Integrated Approach / Loebecke. – 4th ed. – Prentice-Hall.
ISBN 0130509159 Hbk £45.30

Arestis, P.
Contemporary Issues in Money and Banking. – London : Macmillan.
ISBN 0333446879 Hbk £35.00

Argawal, Alka → Prevention of Blackmarketing and Maintenance of Supplies of Essential Commodities Act, 1980.

Argawal, R.K.
Prevention of Blackmarketing and Maintenance of Supplies of Essential Commodities Act, 1980 / Alka Argawal. – Allahabad : Law Book Company, 1987.
116p.
ISBN 8185029415 Hbk £40.00

Argawal, S.K. → Law of Compromises.

Argentine Supreme Court : the court of constitutional guarantees / German J. Bidart Campos : translated by William J. Brisk, based on the book by German J. Bidart Campos, 'La Corte Suprema, tribunal de las garantias constitucionales'. – Argentine ed. – Buenos Aires : Allende & Brea, 1982.
viii, 143 p.; 26 cm.
Includes bibliographical references.
ISBN 9500621142

Argument and Decisions in Remarkable Cases Before the High Court of Justiciary : 1670-1773. – Repr. of 1774 ed. – Abingdon : Professional Books.
76p.
Hbk £60.00

Arif, A. E. → Law and treatment of drug- and alcohol- dependent persons : a comparative study of existing legislation.

Aris, Stephen
Going bust : inside the bankruptcy business / Stephen Aris. – London : Deutsch, 1985.
194p; 23cm.
Includes index.
ISBN 0233976930 £8.95

Arizona : Its Constitution and Government. – 2nd ed. – University Press of America, 1988.
ISBN 0819161446 Pbk £9.25

Arkin
Prevention and prosecution of computer and high-tech crime / William E Kaplan. – Matthew Bender, 1988.
ISBN 0000999061 Hbk £50.00

Arlidge, Anthony
Fraud / Anthony J. Arlidge and Jacques Parry. – London : Waterlow, 1985.
xlii,368p; 24cm.
Includes index.
ISBN 008039163X £30.00
—Law of contempt / by Anthony Arlidge and David Eady : consulting editor - (Scotland) Herbert Kerrigan : with a foreword by Lord Justice Lawton. – London : Sweet & Maxwell, 1982.
xxxvi,479p; 26cm.
Intends to reduce the law to basic principles, consonant with the common law and modern statutes. Chapter on the impact of the 1981 Contempt of Court Act on the law of Scotland and Northern Ireland. Considers the effect of the European Convention on Human Rights on the development of the contempt jurisdiction.
ISBN 0421259205 £30.00

Armaments or disarmament? : SIPRI brochure / Stockholm International Peace Research Institute. – Bergshamra : The Institute, 1983.

Armed separatism in Southeast Asia / edited by Lim Joo-Jock and Vani S. – Singapore : Institute of Southeast Asian Studies, 1984.
270 p.; 23 cm.
ISBN 9971902869

Armenians / by David Marshall Lang and Christopher J. Walker. – New rev ed. – London : Minority Rights Group, 1987.
20p. – (Report).
Previous ed.: 1981. Bibliography: p.20.
ISBN 094669043X

Arming an Unarmed Police : Policy and Practice in the Metropolitan Police. – Police Foundation.
ISBN 0947692096 Pbk £8.95

Armitage, B.
Business Expansion Scheme. – VANN, 1984.
ISBN 0852913826 Pbk £8.95

Armour, Audrey
Issues in Environmental Impact Assessment. – Downsview : York University, Faculty of Environmental Studies, 1983.
128p.
ISBN 0919762220 pb

Armour, L.
Cases in Tort / G. H. Samuel. – Repr. of 1977 ed. – Plymouth : Macdonald & Evans, 1984.
352p. – (M and E Handbook Ser.).
ISBN 0712103562 Pbk £4.25

Arms Act, 1959 with Rules, 1962 (Annotated). – 4th ed. – Lucknow : Eastern Book Company, 1984.
Hbk £20.00

Arms Act, 1960 (Act 206) and Regulations 1961 and Firearms (Increased Penalties) Act 1971 (Act 37). – Kuala Lumpur : International Law Books Services.
Hbk £10.00

Arms and Explosives Manual. – Allahabad : Orient Law House, 1984.
Hbk £115.00

Arms Control Agreements : a Handbook. – Stockholm : Almqvist & Wiksell, 1983.
328p.
ISBN 0850662486 Hbk £139.00

Arms control and disarmament in outer space : lecture-seminars given at the Centre for Research of Air and Space Law / edited by Nicolas Mateesco Matte. – Montreal, Canada : Centre for Research of Air and Space Law, McGill University, 1985.
viii, 203 p.; 23 cm.
Includes bibliographical references.
ISBN 0771701233 Pbk
Vol 2. – 1987.
282p.
Pbk £25.00

Arms Control at Sea. – Routledge.
ISBN 0415012805 Hbk £30.00

Armstrong, Alice Kavanaugh
Law and the other sex : the legal position of women in Swaziland / by Alice Kavanagh Armstrong and Ronald Thandabantu Nhlapo. – Mbabane : Webster, 1985.
150p.
Bibliography: p148-150.

Armstrong, Anne E.
Estate Administration : A Solicitor's Reference Manual, 1 Vol. – Agincourt : Carswell, 1984.
700p.
This book is a guide for the solicitor dealing with all aspects of estate administration in Ontario, Canada. The text includes all relevant statutes and regulations. Numerous forms, letters, and checklists are provided.
Llf £109.25

Armstrong, David →Changing policing : a conference based on the Scarman Report, 1 May 1982 : proceedings.

Armstrong, George M
Soviet law of property : the right to control property and the construction of communism / by George M. Armstrong, Jr. – The Hague : M. Nijhoff Publishers, 1983.
vii,167p.
Includes index. Bibliography: p155-163. Based on the author's thesis (Ph. D.–Princeton).
ISBN 9024728649 Hbk £80.00

Armstrong, Mark
Broadcasting law and policy in Australia / Mark Armstrong. – Sydney : Butterworths, 1982.
xxviii,291p.
Includes index.
ISBN 0409309109
→ Communications law and policy in Australia : adapted from Mark Armstrong's Broadcasting law and policy in Australia.
—Media law in Australia / Mark Armstrong, Michael Blakeney, Ray Watterson. – Melbourne : Oxford University Press, 1983.
x,274p; 21cm.
Bibliography: p242-267. - Includes index.
ISBN 0195544447 Hbk
ISBN 0195544439 Pbk £13.00
→ New media : law & policy.

Armstrong, W. E. I.
Studies in Contractual Claims under the ICE Conditions of Contract. – 3rd rev. ed. – King's Ride : Institute of Building, 1987.
34p.
ISBN 0906600170 Hbk £7.75

Arnaud, A. A.
Investment trusts explained / A.A. Arnaud. – 2nd ed. – Cambridge : Woodhead-Faulkner in co-operation with the Association of Investment Trust Companies, 1983.
xiii,.145p; 24cm.
Previous ed.: 1977. Includes index.
ISBN 0859412431 Hbk
ISBN 0859412490 Pbk £6.95

Arnold-Baker, C.
Local Government, Planning and Land Act 1980. – London : Butterworths, 1981.
This book consists of an annotated guide to the complete Act. A table of cases and a guide to the definitions used in the Act is also included.
ISBN 0406584303 Hbk

Arnold, Brian J.
Income taxation of partnerships and their partners / by Brian J. Arnold, D. Keith McNair. – Toronto : Carswell, 1981.
v,212p.
Contents: Ch. 8 and part of ch. 19 of: Current tax planning / by Ward, Smith and Arnold.
ISBN 0459339109
—Taxation of controlled foreign corporations : an international comparison / Brian J. Arnold. – Toronto, Ont. : Canadian Tax Foundation, 1986.
xxiii, 816; 23 cm. – (Canadian tax paper).
Includes index. Bibliography: p. 797-811.
ISBN 0888080239 Pbk £75.00
—Taxation of Corporations and Shareholders : Cases and Materials
Includes 1987-88 Supplements / D. Keith McNair. – Agincourt : Carswell, 1986.
616p.
This text contains both cases and materials pertaining to corporate tax. The bulk of the text is explanatory in nature. These explanations are supplemented with short cases extracts to further illustrate a point.
Hbk £75.75
→ Taxation of domestic shareholders on undistributed income of foreign corporate affiliates : objectives, techniques, and consequences : proceedings of a seminar held in New York in 1986 during the 40th Congress of the International Fiscal Association.
—Timing and income taxation : the principles of income measurement for tax purposes / B. J. Arnold. – Toronto : Canadian Tax Foundation, 1983.
xiv,388p.
Includes index.
ISBN 088808014X

Arnold, Karl W →Switzerland's private international law statute.

Arnold, Morris S. →Select cases of trespass from the King's courts, 1307-1399, Vol. 2 : edited for the Selden Society by Morris S. Arnold.

Arnould, J.
Law of Marine Insurance and Average Supplement. – London : Sweet & Maxwell, 1988.
ISBN 0420445005 Hbk £150.00
—Law of Marine Insurance and Average (BSL). – 16th ed. 2 vols. – London : Sweet & Maxwell, 1981.
ISBN 0420445005 Hbk £170.00

Arnull, Anthony
General principles of EEC law and the individual. – Leicester : Leicester University Press, 1989.
320.
Examines the tendency for the European Court to go beyond the application of the written law to regulate the trading of corporations within member states and to apply general principles of law to individual's grievances.
ISBN 0718513193 Hbk £45

Arnup, John D.
Middleton : the Beloved Judge. – Toronto : McClelland & Stewart, 1988.
240p.
ISBN 0771007957 Hbk £37.50

Aron, N.
Liberty and Justice for All : Public Interest Law in the 1980's and Beyond. – Wildwood.
ISBN 0813306965 Hbk £23.50

Arons, Stephen →Legal rights and mental-health care.

Aronson, M.I., et al
Litigation : Evidence and Procedure. – 4th ed. – Butterworths, 1988.
1,108p.
ISBN 0409495077 Hbk £60.00

Aronson, Mark
Public torts and contracts / by Mark Aronson and Harry Whitmore. – Sydney : Law Book Co., 1982.
xviii, 296 p.; 25 cm.
Includes bibliographical references and indexes.
ISBN 0455204411 Pbk
—Review of administrative action / by Mark Aronson and Nicola Franklin : with a chapter on freedom of information legislation by Peter Bayne. – Sydney : Law Book Co., 1987.
lxvii,720p.
Includes bibliographical references and index.
ISBN 0455207216

Aronstam, P. J
Alienation of land : being a supplement to The law of credit agreements and hire-purchase by Diemont and Aronstam / P.J. Aronstam. – Cape Town : Juta, 1985.
xxviii, 186 p.; 25 cm.
Includes indexes. Bibliography: p. 8.
ISBN 070211586X Pbk
→ Law of credit agreements and hire-purchase in South Africa.

Arora, A. →Banking Law, Vol.1 : The law relating to domestic banking.
—Practical business law. – London : Pitman Publishing, 1983.
ISBN 0712104631 Pbk £8.50

Arora, Ann →Companies consolidation legislation 1985.

Arora, Anu →Bills of Exchange Act 1882.
—Electronic banking and the law / by Anu Arora. – London : IBC Financial, 1988.
188p.
Includes index.
ISBN 1852710403 £65.00

Arora, R.
Parliamentary Privileges in India. – New Delhi : Deep and Deep Publications, 1986.
268p.
Hbk £175.00

Arot, H.
Celebrated Criminal Trials in Scotland : 1536-1784. – Repr. of 1784 ed. – Abingdon : Professional Books.
Hbk £95.00

Arpin, Maurice J.
Law and You. – Toronto : Canadian Broadcasting Corporation Enterprises.
64p.
Pbk £1.50

Arrears Proceedings and Related Matters in the Magistrates' Court. – Lomax & Reynolds. – Chichester : Barry Rose, 1985.
250p.
ISBN 0859922340 Hbk £19.50

Arrest / Law Reform Commission of Canada. – Ottawa : The Commission, 1985.
143,161p. – (Working paper).
Includes bibliographical references. Added t.p. in French: L'arrestation. Cover title: Criminal law : arrest. Pages numbered in opposite directions. Text in English and French.
ISBN 0662538013

Arrest of ships 2 / Jan Th. F. Theunis ... et al. – 1. – London : Lloyd's, 1986.
22cm.
ISBN 1850440913 £25.00

Arrest of ships 3 : Malta, Panama, Sweden, United Arab Emirates / by Max Ganado ... et al. – London : Lloyd's of London, 1987.
xx,110p; 22cm.
ISBN 1850441006 £24.00

Arrest of ships 4 : People's Republic of China, Nigeria, Oman, Scotland / by Kaw Vun-Ping ... et al. – London : Lloyd's of London Press, 1987.
112p; 22cm.
ISBN 1850441014 £25.00

Arrest of ships 5 : Bangladesh, Finland, Saudi Arabia, South Africa / by M. Hafizullah ... et al. – London : Lloyd's of London, 1987.
xvi,95p.
ISBN 1850441022

Arrest of ships 6 : Denmark, Greece, Hong Kong, Kuwait, Qatar / by Allan Philip ... et al. – London : Lloyd's, 1987.
xviii,89p.
ISBN 1850441529

Arrowsmith, Sue
Government Procurement and Judicial Review. – Agincourt : Carswell, 1988.
375p.
Hbk £59.00

Arroyo, Ignacio
Yearbook Maritime Law. – Dordrecht : Kluwer, 1987.
528p.
ISBN 9065442545 Hbk Gld275.00

Arsanjani, M.H.
International Regulation of Internal Resources : a Study of Law and Policy. – London : Eurospan.
ISBN 0813908795 Hbk £32.95

Art of arbitration : essays on international arbitration : liber amicorum Pieter Sanders, 12 September 1912-1982 / editors, Jan C. Schultsz, Albert Jan van den Berg. – Deventer, Netherlands : Kluwer Law and Taxation Publishers, 1982.
xxi, 320 p.; 25 cm.
English or French. Includes bibliographical references and index.
ISBN 9065440542

Art of Attracting Clients. – Allahabad : Law Book Company, 1988.
64p.
Pbk £50.00

Art of Becoming a Successful Criminal Lawyer. – 3rd ed. – Allahabad : Law Book Company, 1988.
Hbk £40.00

Art of Conveyancing and Pleading. – 1974 2nd repr. – Lucknow : Eastern Book Company, 1983.
290p.
Pbk £15.00

Art of Cross Examination The. – 4th ed. – London : Macmillan, 1936.
ISBN 0020749600 Pbk £5.95

Art of Handling Hostile Courts. – Allahabad : Law Book Company, 1988.
70p.
Pbk £45.00

Art of Lawyer Advocacy : Cross Examination with Classes of Witnesses and Illustrative Cases. – Allahabad : Universal Book Agency, 1987.
Hbk £160.00

Arthur Andersen & Co. → Decade of change : banking in Europe : the next ten years.

Arthur Andersen: management buy-outs. – London : Butterworths, 1990.
ix,240; 248.
Sets out some of the main considerations investors and bankers take into account when deciding whether to back buy-outs. Contributions by legal, tax, and pension experts. Contains an executive guide, financing the deal, structuring the finance, buying the company, tax aspects of buy-outs, and legal aspects of buy-outs.
ISBN 0406518904 Hbk £65.00

Arthur Sanderson & Sons Limited : a report by the Director General of Fair Trading on an investigation under section 3 of the Competition Act 1980. – London : Office of Fair Trading, 1981.
53p.

Arthurs, Harry W.
Labour law and industrial relations in Canada / by H.W. Arthurs, D.D. Carter, H.J. Glasbeek. – 2nd ed. – Deventer : Kluwer Law and Taxation, 1984.
316p; 25cm.
Deals with Canadian labour movement, the individual employment relationship, legal status and democratic rule in trade unions, the collective bargaining process, industrial conflict and collective agreements. Presents policy themes and typical legal solutions as well as recording significant departures.
ISBN 9065441905
ISBN 0409811858 Hbk

—Without the law : administrative justice and legal pluralism in nineteenth-century England / H. W. Arthurs. – Toronto : University of Toronto Press, 1985.
xvi,312p; 24cm.
ISBN 0802056547

Article 177 EEC : Experiences and Problems. – Amsterdam : Elsevier Science Publishers, 1987.
xxxiv, 442p.
ISBN 0444700862 Hbk £200.00

Article 19
Freedom of information and expression in Poland. – Article 19. – London : Article 19, 1987.
28p.

—Freedom of information and expression in Senegal / a commentary by Article 19 on the report submitted to the United Nations Human Rights Committee by the government of the Republic of Senegal. – London : Article 19, 1987.
30p.
Bibliography: p.30.

—Freedom of information and expression in Tunisia. – Article 19. – London : Article 19, 1987.
29p.

→ Information, freedom and censorship : the Article 19 world report 1988.

Articling Handbook. – Butterworths, 1988.
ca 200p.
Guidance on how to deal with the everyday aspects of working in a law office. Advice on how to conduct interviews, handle incorporations, draft pleadings, conduct real estate searches and closings, prepare for examinations for discovery and for trial, and to attend on motions.
ISBN 0409804800 sb

Artificial conception : in vitro fertilization : discussion paper / New South Wales Law Reform Commission. – Sydney : Government Printer, 1987.
xxxiii,189p. – (D.P.).
Bibliography: p.165-183.
ISBN 0730544419

Artificial conception : report 1 : human artificial insemination / New South Wales Law Reform Commission. – Sydney : Government Printer, 1986.
xxxvii,177p. – (L.R.C.).
Bibliography: p.161-172.
ISBN 0730515907

Artificial conception : report 2 : in vitro fertilization / New South Wales Law Reform Commission. – Sydney : The Commission, 1988.
xxi,175p. – (L.R.C).
Bibliography: p.147-172.. Spine title: In vitro fertilization.
ISBN 0730555712

Artificial conception : surrogate motherhood : Australian public opinion / New South Wales Law Reform Commission. – Sydney : The Commission, 1987.
xxiii,85p. – (Research report).
Bibliography: p.85. Spine title: Surrogacy survey.
ISBN 0730537986

Artificial family : a consideration of artificial insemination by donor / R. Snowden and G.D. Mitchell. – London : Allen & Unwin, 1981.
138p; 23cm.
Bibliography: p128-136. - Includes index.
ISBN 0041760018

Artis
Land Law / Houghton. – London : Financial Training, 1987.
– (SWOT).
ISBN 1851850465 Pbk £7.50

Artis, Denise
Odour Nuisances and Their Control. – London : Shaw & Sons, 1984.
ISBN 0721910009 Pbk £9.00

As I was saying. – Police Review, 1985.
ISBN 0851640168 Pbk £6.95

Asante, Samuel K. B.
Transnational investment law and national development / by Samuel K.B. Asante. – Lagos : Published for the Faculty of Law, University of Lagos by the Lagos University Press, 1981.
111p.
ISBN 9782264148

Asbatankvoy charter : a special report / by D. Thomas McCune. – London : Lloyd's of London Press, 1984.
ii,95 leaves.
Includes indexes.
ISBN 1850440336

Asch → Financial Planning.

Asch, P.
Consumer Safety Regulation Good Intentions in Search of a Theory. – Oxford : Oxford University Press.
ISBN 0195049721 Hbk £18.00

Asche, Austin
Rights of the child / Austin Asche. – Melbourne : Institute of Family Studies, 1982.
18p. – (Discussion paper).
Includes bibliographical references. Paper delivered as the first Vernon Collins Memorial Lecture in Melbourne, 14 October, 1981.
ISBN 0642888000

Ashburner, Walter
Ashburner's Principles of Equity (1933). – 2nd ed. – Woolloomooloo : International Business Communications, 1983.
ISBN 0949553077 Hbk £60.00

Ashburner's Principles of Equity (1933). – 2nd ed. – Woolloomooloo : International Business Communications, 1983.
ISBN 0949553077 Hbk £60.00

Ashby, Eric → Eighth report : oil pollution of the sea.

—Politics of clean air / Eric Ashby and Mary Anderson. – Oxford : Clarendon, 1981.
viii,178p; 24cm.
Includes index.
ISBN 0198583303 £15.00

Ashcraft → Child Care and Adult Crime.

Ashdown, L. A. J.
Rating Relief for Charitable Organisations : Shaway Guide No. 8. – London : Shaw & Sons, 1982.
ISBN 0721908764 Pbk £2.50

Ashe, A. W. → Equity proceedings with precedents (New South Wales).

Ashman, Chuck
Outrage : the abuse of diplomatic immunity / Chuck Ashman and Pamela Trescott. – London : W.H. Allen, 1986.
224p; 24cm.
ISBN 0491037139 £10.95

Ashton, R.
UK financial accounting standards. – Cambridge : Woodhead-Faulkner, 1983.
ISBN 0859412016 Hbk £25.00
ISBN 0859412024 Pbk £10.95

Ashton, R. K.
Anti-avoidance legislation / R.K. Ashton. – London : Butterworths, 1981.
xvii,255p; 22cm.
Includes index.
ISBN 0406111405 Pbk

Ashworth, Andrew → Criminal Law Review.

—English criminal process : a review of empirical research / Andrew Ashworth. – Oxford : Centre for Criminological Research, University of Oxford, 1984.
135p. – (Occasional paper).
Bibliography: p131-135.
ISBN 094781101X

→ English sentencing system.

→ Prison system for the 80s and beyond.

—Sentencing and penal policy / Andrew Ashworth. – London : Weidenfeld and Nicolson, 1983.
xx,500p; 22cm.
Bibliography: p487-495. - Includes index.
ISBN 0297782363 Hbk

Ashworth, Georgina → Women, power and political systems.

Ashworth, J.
Product liability casebook. – London : Lloyd's of London Press, 1984.
ISBN 1850440158 Pbk £32.50

Ashworth, M. H.
British Airways : Civil Aviation Policy and the Privatisation of British Airways / P. J. Forsyth. – London : Institute for Fiscal Studies.
– (Report Ser.).
Hbk £6.00

Asian Capital and Money Markets / Message. – London : Butterworths, 1988.
ISBN 0406103607 Hbk

Asian Development Bank and Rural Development. – London : Macmillan.
ISBN 0333464362 Hbk £33.00

Asian income tax laws
Vol. 1 : Hong Kong, India & Malaysia / by D.S. Chopra. – Singapore : Malayan Law Journal Pte., 1986.
lx,992p.
Compendium of the substantive provisions of the tax laws of the three major Asian countries. Gives a brief introduction to the income-tax laws of each of the countries, covers all tax concessions, incentives, rebates and reliefs in the income-tax laws of each country, the current income-tax rates prevailing, and important judicial decisions in respect of the provisions of the income-tax laws of each country.
ISBN 9971700468

Asian Indigenous Law. – Routledge, 1987.
ISBN 0710301138 Hbk £40.00

Asian indigenous law in interaction with received law / edited by Masaji Chiba. – London : KPI, 1986.
xiii,416p.
ISBN 0710301138

Aspects of agricultural law. – Edinburgh : Law Society of Scotland, 1981.
93p.
Includes index.
ISBN 0902023055

Aspects of capital punishment / Advisory Committee on Law Reform. – Causeway : The Committee, 1982.
28p. – (Report).
Includes bibliographical references.

Aspects of insurance law (2) / a report by the Contracts and Commercial Law Reform Committee. – Wellington : Government Printer, 1983.
53p.
Contains text of a Draft Insurance Law Reform Bill.

Aspects of space law / E.R.C. van Bogaert. – Deventer : Kluwer, 1985.
ix, 307p.
Includes index. Bibliography: p.287-303.
ISBN 9065440488 Hbk £225.00

Aspects of the common-law powers and duties of company directors with special reference to (a) their authority to act on behalf of a company and (b) the scope and effect of certain legislative provisions / by John Stopford McLennan. – 1. – S.l. : s.n., 1984.
various pagings.
Offprints of 4 articles. Thesis (L.L.M.) - University of Witwatersrand 1984. Bibliography: p.i-ii. - Includes index.

Aspects of water law / by A.S. Wisdom. – Chichester : Rose (Barry), 1981.
xxi,102p; 21cm.
Includes index.
ISBN 0859921549 Pbk £12.50

Aspinalls Maritime Cases 1870-1940 20 vols. – Professional Books.
ISBN 0862052645 Hbk £1,075.00

Asquith, Stewart
Children and justice : decision-making in children's hearings and juvenile courts / by Stewart Asquith. – Edinburgh : Edinburgh University Press, 1983.
vii,258p; 22cm.
Bibliography: p238-250. - Includes index.
ISBN 0852244290 Hbk £8.50
ISBN 0852244665 Pbk

Assam
Contingency Manual / Meghalaya. – 2nd ed. – Allahabad : Orient Law House, 1984.
Hbk £60.00

Assault / Law Reform Commission of Canada. – Ottawa : the Commission, 1984.
59,68p. – (Working paper).
Includes bibliographical references. Added t.p. in French: Les voies de fait. Pages numbered in opposite directions. Text in English and French.
ISBN 0662534174

Assembly resolutions in force : (as of 10 May 1984) / International Civil Aviation Organization. – 1 v. – Montreal : I.C.A.O., 1984.
various pagings. – (Doc).
Includes index.

Assembly resolutions in force : (as of 10 October 1986). – International Civil Aviation Organization. – 1. – Montreal : International Civil Aviation Organization, 1986.
various pagings. – (Doc.).
Published by authority of the Secretary General.

Assembly resolutions in force : (as of 7 October 1980) / International Civil Aviation Organization. – 1. – Montreal : International Civil Aviation Organization, 1981.
various pagings. – (Doc).

Assessing Legal Aid Costs. – London : Longman Professional, 1984.
ISBN 0851209629 Pbk £8.95

Assessment of Damages for Personal Injury and Death. – 2nd ed. – London : Butterworths, 1983.
ISBN 0409491322 Hbk £48.00

Assessment of Medical Impairment and Disability. – Madhya Pradesh : Lawyers Home, 1987.
Hbk £100.00

Assessment of Personal Injury Damages. – Butterworths, 1985.
378p.
ISBN 0409814075 Hbk £75.00

Asset Valuation. – London : Macmillan, 1988.
ISBN 033336515 Pbk £5.95

Assheton, P. C.
Budget and Finance Bill 1985. – London : Law Society, 1985.
28p. – (Nineteen Eighty-Five Crash Course Transcripts).
Hbk £2.05

Assignments, Arrangements and Compositions by Debtors with Precedents. – 2nd ed. – Butterworths, 1986.
176p.
ISBN 0409490652 Hbk £45.00

Assignments of Choses in Action in Australia. – London : Butterworths, 1982.
ISBN 0409395900 Hbk £28.00

Assisting the victims of armed conflict and other disasters. – Dordrecht : Nijhoff (Martinus), 1989.
264.
Contains papers given at the conference, with brief summaries, and annexes giving the text of treaty provisions and other documents. Goes beyond armed conflict, and looks at other disasters as well, including problems of offering humanitarian assistance in such situations.
ISBN 0792301633 Hbk £47.50

Associated corporations / by Richard B. Miner. – Toronto : Carswell, 1983.
xvii,134p.
Includes index.
ISBN 0459354507

Association for Legal and Social Philosophy → Facts in law.
—Philosophy and the criminal law : Association for Legal and Social Philosophy Tenth Annual Conference at the University of Manchester, 8-10th April 1983 / edited by Antony Duff and Nigel Simmonds. – Wiesbaden West Germany : Franz Steiner, 1984.
120p.
Bibliography: p.117-120.
ISBN 3515041699

Association of Commonwealth Universities
Research opportunities in Commonwealth developing countries : universities, non-university research institutions : a register prepared by the Association of Commonwealth Universities in association with the Commonwealth Secretariat. – Association of Commonwealth Universities. – New ed. – London : The Association, 1984.
235p.
Previous ed. published as: Research strengths of universities in the developing countries of the Commonwealth. London, 1978. Includes index.

Association of Consultant Architects
ACA Form of Building Agreement Nineteen Eighty-Two. – Association of Consultant Architects. – 1984 ed. – London : Architectural Press, 1984.
28p.
ISBN 0851397530 Pbk £7.50
—ACA Form Of Sub-Contract Nineteen Eighty-Two. – Association of Consultant Architects. – London : Architectural Press, 1984.
12p. – (ACA Contract Documents).
ISBN 0851397557 Pbk £7.50

Association of County Councils
Children in care : memorandum of evidence / by the Association of County Councils. – London : The Association, 1983.
10p.
At head of title: House of Commons Social Services Committee.
—Who prosecutes? : the future of the prosecuting service / Association of County Councils. – London : The Association, 1983.
5p.

Association of Investment Trust Companies → Investment trusts explained.

Association of Law Societies of the Republic of South Africa → Ombudsman seminar, held at the Oude Libertas Centre, Stellenbosch, South Africa, on 30th and 31st March 1982.

Association of Law Teachers
Handbook / The Association of Law Teachers. – Sheffield? : Association of Law Teachers, 1986.
80p.

Association of Liberal Lawyers → Equal justice : report of a joint working party.

Association of Metropolitan Authorities
Policies for the Police Service / Association of Metropolitan Authorities. – London : The Association, 1982.
8p.

Asthana, K.B.
Donogh's Commentaries on the Indian Stamp Act. – 9th rev. ed. – Allahabad : Law Publishers, 1986.
Hbk £250.00

Astle, W. E.
Hague Rules law digest : a practical digest and comprehensive cross-referenced index to leading British cases governing the interpretation of the Hague Rules : by W.E. Astle. – London : Fairplay Publications, 1981.
ix,90p.
ISBN 0905045246
—Hamburg Rules : an appreciation of the cause and effect of the amendments to the Hague Rules and the Hague-Visby Rules / W.E. Astle. – London : Fairplay, 1981.
xii,163p; 25cm.
ISBN 0905045319 Pbk
—International cargo carriers' liabilities : the determination of some current contractual problems arising from the international carriage of goods / W.E. Astle. – London : Fairplay, 1983.
viii,140p; 25cm.
ISBN 0905045416 Pbk

→ International rules of law relating to bills of lading.

—Legal developments in maritime commerce : matters of general interest and importance arising out of selected legal issues / W.E. Astle. – London : Fairplay, 1983.
viii,125p; 25cm.
ISBN 0905045432 Pbk
—Limitation of Liability. – London : Fairplay Publication, 1984.
ISBN 0905045637 Pbk £12.00
—Right of appeal : a practical digest of charter-party disputes and the right of appeal under the Arbitration Act 1979 / W.E. Astle. – London : Fairplay, 1983.
153p; 24cm.
ISBN 0905045513 Pbk
—Safe port of berth reachable on arrival : charterers' and shipowners' responsibilities and liabilities / W.E. Astle. – London : Fairplay, 1986.
x,109p.
Cover title: The safe port.
ISBN 0905045912
—Time charter withdrawals : an examination of shipowners' rights to withdraw vessels from the service of time charterers / W.E. Astle. – London : Fairplay, 1984.
xxiii,136p; 25cm.
ISBN 0905045637 Pbk

Aston, Jennifer
Index to Irish Superior Court Written Judgments, 1976-1982 / Maeve Doyle. – Galway : Irish Association of Law Teachers.
ISBN 095093240X Hbk £0.00
→ Irish current law statutes annotated.

Atchuthen Pillai, P.S.
Law of Receivers / P.M.K. Nair. – 3rd ed. – Allahabad : Law Book Company, 1988.
1,000p.
Hbk £275.00

Atelan, J.
Reading Narrative : Form, Ethics, Ideology. – London : Eurospan.
ISBN 0814204589 Hbk £26.50

Athens, L.H.
Creation of Violent Criminals. – Routledge.
ISBN 041502837X Hbk £22.50

Atiyah, P. S.
Accidents, Compensation and The Law (LIC). – 4th ed. – Weidenfeld & Nicolson, 1987.
ISBN 0297790528 Hbk £30.00
ISBN 0297790536 Pbk £14.95
—Atiyah's accidents, compensation and the law / Peter Cane. – 4th ed. – London : Weidenfeld and Nicholson, 1987.
639p.
ISBN 0297790528
—Essays on contract. – Oxford : Clarendon Press, 1988.
364.
A collection of essays concerned with the theory and foundations of contractual liability, which have been published over the last twenty years. The author has tken the opportunity to revise, and rewrite some of them, and to answer previously made criticisms of his work.
ISBN 0198256418 Pbk £11.95
—Form and substance in Anglo-American law : a comparative study of legal reasoning, legal theory, and legal institutions / P.S. Atiyah and Robert S. Summers. – Oxford : Clarendon, 1987.
444p; 24cm.
Includes bibliography and index.
ISBN 0198255772 £35.00
—Introduction to the law of contract / by P.S. Atiyah. – 3rd ed. – Oxford : Clarendon, 1981.
x,335p; 23cm. – (Clarendon law series).
Previous ed.: 1971. Includes index.
ISBN 0198761406 Hbk £
ISBN 0198761414 Pbk £5.95
—Law and modern society / P.S. Atiyah. – Oxford : Oxford University Press, 1983.
viii,158p; 23cm.
Bibliography: p150-155. - Includes index.
ISBN 0192191667 £9.95
—Pragmatism and theory in English law / by P.S. Atiyah. – London : Stevens & Sons under the auspices of the Hamlyn Trust, 1987.
193p; 18cm.
Includes index.
ISBN 0420475907 Hbk £18.50
ISBN 0420476008 Pbk £10.50
—Promises, morals, and law / by P.S. Atiyah. – Oxford : Clarendon Press, 1981.
218p; 23cm.
Includes index.
ISBN 019825377X £14.00
—Sale of goods / P.S. Atiyah. – 7th ed. – London : Pitman, 1985.
xxxvi,448p; 22cm.
Previous ed.: 1980. Includes index.
ISBN 0273022067 Pbk £9.95

Atiyah's accidents, compensation and the law / Peter Cane. – 4th ed. – London : Weidenfeld and Nicholson, 1987.
639p.
ISBN 0297790528

Atkin, James Richard
Encyclopaedia of court forms in civil proceedings. – 2nd edition. – LLondon : Butterworths, 1961.

Atkin, James Richard Atkin → Atkin's encyclopaedia of court forms in civil proceedings : a user's guide.

Atkin's Encyclopaedia of Court Forms, 41 Vols. – 2nd. ed. – Abingdon : Professional Books, 1984.
Hbk £595.00

Atkin's Encyclopaedia of Court Forms in Civil Proceedings, 42 Vols. / J. M. Dyson. – 2nd ed. – Wellington : Butterworths.
Hbk

Atkin's encyclopaedia of court forms in civil proceedings : a user's guide / James Richard Atkin Atkin. – 2nd ed. – London : Butterworths, 1983.
24p; 25cm.

Atkins, Susan
Women and the law / Susan Atkins and Brenda Hoggett. – Oxford : Basil Blackwell, 1984.
234p; 24cm.
Includes index.
ISBN 0855201819 Hbk £17.50
ISBN 0855201800 Pbk

Atkinson, Max
Research paper on occupiers' liability law / Max Atkinson. – Hobart : Government Printer?, 1984.
iv,75p.

Atkyns, J. T.
Court of Chancery Reports. – Repr. of 1758 ed. – Abingdon : Professional Books.
344p.
Hbk £95.00

Atlantic Legal Directory : 1985-1986. – Aurora : Canada Law Book Co, 1985.
Hbk For 1-5 copies 8.50

Atlantic Legal Telephone Directory. – Aurora : Canada Law Book Co.
– (Directories).
The Atlantic Legal Telephone Directory unifies law-related offices of the four Atlantic Provinces into a single means of access. Included are listings for lawyers, law firms, law societies, courts, legal aid offices, provincial government departments and other key departments and offices.
Hbk £1-5 copies 8.50 ea.

Atlantic Provinces Taxation Service. – Toronto : DeBoo, 1984.
ISBN 0888201850 Hbk £1750.00

Atlantic Regional PLE Conference Papers and Resource Material. – Ottawa : Canadian Law Information Council, 1983.
53p.
ISBN 0920358462 Pbk £7.50

Atlantische Commissie
Future of European defence : proceedings of the Second International Round Table Conference of the Netherlands Atlantic Commission on May 24 and 25, 1985 / Frans Bletz and Rio Praaning editors. – Dordrecht : M. Nijhoff, 1986.
ISBN 9024732905 Pbk

Atlas of the Seabed Boundaries
Part 2 /. – Milan : Giuffre, 1987.
xv, 241p.
Hbk £35,000.00

Atlas of the Straigth Baselines. – Milan : Giuffre, 1986.
xii, 138p.
Hbk £18,000.00

Atrens, Jerome, et al
Criminal Procedure : Canadian Law and Practice, 3 vol. – Toronto : Butterworths.
Hbk £185.00

Attali, J.
Man of Influence : Sir Siegmund Warburg. – Weidenfeld & Nicolson, 1986.
ISBN 0297789783 Hbk £16.95

Attard, David Joseph
Exclusive economic zone in international law / David Joseph Attard. – Oxford : Clarendon, 1987.
256p; 24cm. – (Oxford monographs in international law).
Includes index.
ISBN 0198255411 £27.50

Attempted homicide / Scottish Law Commission. – Edinburgh : Scottish Law Commission, 1984.
52p. – (Consultative memorandum).

Attitudes of ethnic minorities / Simon Field. – London : HMSO, 1984.
49p; 25cm.
Review of currently available research literature on the subject. Indicates the need for caution about accepting commonly expressed judgements on black and Asian attitudes.
ISBN 0113407742

Attorney general, politics and the public interest / by John Ll. J. Edwards. – London : Sweet & Maxwell, 1984.
xxxi,533p; 26cm.
Bibliography: p491-498. - Includes index.
ISBN 0421301805 £30.00

Attorney General's Annual Report, 1983-84. – Canberra : Australian Government Publishing Service, 1984.
218p.
Hbk £13.00

Attorney General's Department; 1980-1981
Annual Report. – Canberra : Australian Government Publishing Service, 1981.
73p.
Hbk £4.40

Attorney General's Department; 1981-1982
Annual Report. – Canberra : Australian Government Publishing Service, 1982.
84p.
Hbk £4.00

Attorney General's Department; 1982-1983
Annual Report. – Canberra : Australian Government Publishing Service, 1983.
159p.
Hbk £9.70

Attorney-General's Department
Another Look at Statutory Interpretation. – Attorney-General's Department. – Canberra : Australian Government Publishing Service, 1982.
32p.
ISBN 0642068895 Hbk £2.00
—Deputy Crown Solicitors Office Perth : Report of Enquiry Concerning the Office. – Attorney-General's Department. – Canberra : Australian Government Publishing Service, 1983.
142p.
ISBN 0644024135 Hbk £5.00
—Guideline to Freedom of Information Act. – Attorney-General's Department. – Canberra : Australian Government Publishing Service, 1982.
398p.
ISBN 0644022752 Hbk £14.00
—Opinions of Attorneys General of the Commonwealth of Australia. – Attorney-General's Department. – Canberra : Australian Government Publishing Service, 1981.
723p.
ISBN 0642066043 Hbk £49.50

Attorney's Directory. Transvaal. – Durban : Professional Publishers, 1983.
ISBN 0409011541 Pbk

Aubert, Vilhelm
Continuity and development in law and society / Torstein Eckhoff. – Oxford : OUP.
Essays on general questions of law and legal reasoning. Presents the results of the author's research into the development of Norwegian constitutions in the nineteenth and twentieth centuries and the history of the legal profession to the first half of the eighteenth century. *Students of sociology of law, sociology and law*
ISBN 8200183661 Hbk £40.00
—In search of law : sociological approaches to law / Vilhelm Aubert. – Oxford : Martin Robertson, 1983.
180p; 22cm.
Bibliography: p174-175. - Includes index.
ISBN 0855204915

Aubrey, Crispin
Who's watching you? / Crispin Aubrey. – Harmondsworth : Penguin, 1981.
204p,8p of plates; 18cm. – (Pelican books).
Bibliography: p197-199. - Includes index.
ISBN 0140222839 Pbk £1.50

Auburn, F.
Antarctic Law and Politics. – London : Dent (J M) & Sons, 1987.
ISBN 0905838394 Hbk £17.50

Auburn, F. M.
Antarctic law and politics / F.M. Auburn. – London : Hurst, 1982.
xx,361p; 23cm.
Bibliography: p337-356. - Includes index.
ISBN 0905838394 £17.50

Auckland Law School centenary lectures / L.C.B. Gower ... et al. – Auckland : Legal Research Foundation, 1983.
103p.
ISBN 0908581297

Auctions : law and practice / Brian W. Harvey, Franklin Meisel. – London : Butterworths, 1985.
300p; 25cm.
Includes index.
ISBN 0406526605 Pbk £17.00

Auctions Law and Practice / Franklin Meisel. – London : Butterworths, 1985.
ISBN 0406526605 Pbk £29.00

Audas, J. M.
Builder's Guide to the Agreement for Minor Building Works. – King's Ride : Institute of Building, 1983.
ISBN 0906600324 Hbk £2.75
—Extensions of Time. – King's Ride : Institute of Building, 1983.
22p.
ISBN 0906600685 Hbk £6.60

Audit Commission for Local Authorities in England and Wales
Computer fraud survey. – Audit Commission for Local Authorities in England and Wales. – London : H.M.S.O., 1985.
55p.
ISBN 0117012815 Pbk £3.30
—Survey of computer fraud and abuse. – Audit Commission for Local Authorities in England and Wales. – London : H.M.S.O., 1987.
88p.
Report finds lack of basic control mechanisms. Suggests that the opportunity for fraud is widespread and a large numnber remain undiscovered.
ISBN 0117010650

Audit Guide. – Stoy Hayward & Co. – London : Butterworths, 1983.
ISBN 0406270600 Pbk £11.50

Audit Manual. – London : Butterworths, 1984.
ISBN 0406258120 Pbk

Audit Report. – London : Butterworths, 1984.
A review of the current state of audit reporting which outlines legal and other requirements of the audit. The book surveys a wide range of reporting styles and provides many examples, drawn from published reports, to illustrate problems in modern auditing.
ISBN 040601650X Pbk £15.00

Audit system for corporate enterprises in Japan : as compared with English company law / Yoshiki Nishiyama. – s.l. : s.n., 1987.
28p.
Offprint from: Kanazawa Law Review, vol. 30, no. 1 (1987).

Auditing. – Pitman, 8th ed.
– (M & E Handbook Series).
ISBN 0712107932 Pbk £6.95

Auditing. – Pitman.
– (ACCA Series).
ISBN 0273027972 Pbk £12.95

Auditing : An Integrated Approach / Loebecke. – 4th ed. – Prentice-Hall.
ISBN 0130509159 Hbk £45.30

Auditing : Level 2.1. – Witney : A.T.C. Publications.
ISBN 0747770060 Pbk £13.95

Auditing and Investigations : ACCA Study Text 3.4. – London : BPP.
ISBN 0862772540 Pbk £15.95

Auditing and Investigations : Level 3.4. – Witney : A.T.C. Publications.
ISBN 0747700044 Pbk £14.95

Auditing Development of Computer Systems. – London : Butterworths, 1987.
ISBN 0406500932 Pbk £26.50

Auditor's Manual / Keeton. – Cape Town : Legal & Financial Publishing, 1983.
ISBN 0869940198 Hbk £5.00

Audretsch, H. A. H.
Supervision in European Community law : observance by the member states of their treaty obligations : a treatise on international and supra-national supervision / H.A.H. Audretsch. – 2nd rev. ed. – Amsterdam : North-Holland, 1986.
xix,782p.
Previous ed.: 1978. Bibliography: p.591-613. - Includes index.
ISBN 0444700277

Auerbach →Blackstone's Guide to the Employment Act 1988.

Aughton, H.
Housing finance. – 2nd ed. – Turnaround Press, 1986.
ISBN 090120273X Pbk £3.95

Augustin, Venerando
Code of Agrarian Reform of the Philippines. – Quezon City : University of the Philippines, Law Center, 1981.
338p.
Hbk £70.00

Ault, Hugh J. →Introduction to United States international taxation.

Austin, Claire →Board of visitor adjudications. → Grievance procedures in prisons : a study of prisoners' applications and petitions.

Austin-Crowe →Property development.

Austin, John →Utilitarianism.

Austin, R.
Civil Liberties. – London : Butterworths, 1988.
ISBN 0406555109 Hbk
ISBN 0406555117 Pbk
—Law of Public Company Finance / R. Vann. – North Ryde : Law Book Co, 1986.
xxix, 593p.
ISBN 0455206856 Hbk £89.50

Austin, R. P. →Cases and materials on equity and trusts.

Australasian Computerised Legal Information Handbook. – Butterworths, 1988.
446p.
ISBN 0409494453 Pbk £39.00

Australasian Legal Information Retrieval Handbook / A. Mowbray. – Sydney : Butterworths, 1988.
208p.
This guide to legal databases includes descriptions of CLIRS, SCALE, LEXIS, MAYNELAW, AUSINET, ESTOPEL, and others. Also contained is an introduction of the principles of computerized legal information retrieval, a set of tutorials for the main retrieval systems, and a directory of all databases containing Australian, New Zealand, and common law.
Pbk £29.50

Australia →Accountability through self-evaluation : an introduction to self-evaluation for legal aid agencies.
—Australian employment legislation. – Australia. – 3. – Sydney : CCH Austalia, 1984.
loose-leaf.
Originally published: as part of Australian labour law reporter, 1977-. Includes index. Loose-leaf issues accompanied by a summary report.
ISBN 0869036513
—Australian national companies and securites legislation with state variations ... – Australia. – 5th ed. 2. – North Ryde, N.S.W. : CCH Australia, 1986.
ISBN 0869037013

—Australian national companies and securities legislation. – Australia. – 3rd ed. 1. – North Ryde, N.S.W. : CCH Australia, 1982.
various pagings.
Includes index.
ISBN 0869033700

—Australian national companies and securities legislation : up to date to 1 October 1987. – Australia. – 7th ed. 2. – North Ryde, N.S.W. : CCH Australia, 1987.
Index to legislation in vol. 1.
ISBN 1862640068

→ Australian trade practices reporter.

—CCH Australian companies and securities legislation / by the CCH company law editors. – 3. – North Ryde, N.S.W. : CCH Australia, 1987.
looseleaf.
'Publication originally issued in one volume in July 1982 (vol. 2 in November 1983) titled Australian companies legislation' - t.p. verso. Spine title: Australian companies and securities legislation.
ISBN 1862640270

—Circumstances surrounding the various court actions relating to the film 'The return of Captain Invincible' / Senate Standing Committee on Finance and Government Operations. – Canberra : Government Printer, 1987.
iv,66p. – (Parliamentary paper).
ISBN 064406546X

—Community law reform for the Australian Capital Territory
1st report : The community law reform program : Contributory negligence in fatal accident cases and breach of statutory duty cases : Funeral costs in fatal accident cases / Law Reform Commission. – Canberra : Australian Government Publishing Service, 1985.
ix,44p. – (Report).
Bibliography: p.41-42 - Includes index.
ISBN 0644013257

—Community law reform for the Australian Capital Territory : enduring powers of attorney / The Law Reform Commission. – Sydney : The Commission, 1987.
i,13p. – (Discussion paper).

—Contempt : disruption, disobedience and deliberate interference / The Law Reform Commission. – Sydney : The Commission, 1986.
130p. – (Discussion paper).
Includes bibliographical references.

—Contempt and family law / The Law Reform Commission. – Sydney : The Commission, 1985.
76p. – (Discussion paper).

—Contempt and the media / Australian Law Reform Commission. – Sydney : The Commission, 1986.
182p. – (Discussion paper).
Cover title. Bibliography: p.178-182.

—Criminal records / The Law Reform Commission. – Sydney : The Commission, 1985.
117p. – (Discussion paper).
Bibliography: p.114-117.

—Evidence
Research paper no. 1 : Comparison of evidence legislation applying in federal courts and courts of the territories / Australian Law Reform Commission. – Sydney : The Commission, 1981.
xiii,468p.

Research paper no. 2 : Common law evidence : areas of disagreement and uncertainty / Australian Law Reform Commission. – 1981.
viii,233p.
Bibliography: p.228-233.

—Evidence reference
Research paper no. 3 : Hearsay evidence proposal / Australian Law Reform Commission. – Sydney : The Commission, 1981.
v,174p.
Includes bibliographical references.

Research paper no. 4 : Secondary evidence of documents / Australian Law Reform Commission. – 1982.
v,87p.
Includes bibliographical references.

Research paper no. 5 : Competence and compellability of witnesses / Australian Law Reform Commission. – 1982.
vii,141p.
Includes bibliographical references.

Research paper no. 6 : Sworn and unsworn evidence / Australian Law Reform Commission. – 1982.
vii,133p.
Includes bibliographical references.

Research paper no. 7 : Relevance / Australian Law Reform Commission. – 1982.
iv,80p.
Includes bibliographical references.

Research paper no. 8 : Manner of giving evidence / Australian Law Reform Commission. – 1982.
x,255p.
Includes bibliographical references.

Research paper no. 9 : Hearsay evidence : which approach? / Australian Law Reform Commission. – 1982.
33p.
Includes bibliographical references.

Research paper no. 10 : The judge : adducing evidence and judicial notice / Australian Law Reform Commission. – 1982.
vii,154p.
Includes bibliographical references.

Research paper no. 11 : Character and conduct / Australian Law Reform Commission. – 1982.
xi,269p.
Bibliography: p.267-269.

Research paper no. 12 : Identification evidence / Australian Law Reform Commission. – 1982.
viii,96p.
Includes bibliographical references.

Research paper no. 13 : Opinion evidence / Australian Law Reform Commission. – 1983.
xiv,340p.
Bibliography: p.328-340.

Research paper no. 14 : Aspects of proof / Australian Law Reform Commission. – 1983.
xxi,119p.
Includes bibliographical references.

Research paper no. 15 : Admissions / Australian Law Reform Commission. – 1983.
xxxviii,340p.
Bibliography: p.334-340.

→ Federal deceptive practices and misleading advertising law : judgements, materials and policy.

—Final report of the Commonwealth Task Force on Occupational Superannuation. – Australia. – Canberra : Australian Government Publishing Service, 1983.
48p.
ISBN 0644026537

—Foreign state immunity / The Law Reform Commission. – Sydney : The Commission, 1983.
8p. – (Discussion paper).
Summary dicussion paper.

—General insolvency inquiry / The Law Reform Commission. – Sydney : The Commission, 1987.
xxv,252p. – (Discussion paper).
Accompanied by Appendix: Draft Legislation (99p.).

→ Guide to amendments to the Trade Practices Act.

→ Legal services for low income persons in the United States and Britain : trends for consideration in Australia.

—Occupiers' liability / The Law Reform Commission. – Sydney : The Commission, 1987.
13p. – (Discussion paper).
Bibliography: p.13.

→ Practice and procedure of the High Court and the Federal Court of Australia.

—Product liability / the Law Reform Commission. – Sydney : The Commission, 1988.
xii,86p. – (Discussion paper).
Bibliography: p.85-86.

—Reference on admiralty jurisdiction
Research paper no. 1 : Australian admiralty act : the ambit of admiralty jurisdiction / Australian Law Reform Commission. – Sydney : The Commission, 1984.
xvii,296p.
Bibliography: p.291-296.

Research paper no. 2 : Admiralty jurisdiction in Australia : the courts exercising original and appellate jurisdiction / Australian Law Reform Commission. – 1984.
v,77p.
Bibliography: p.75-77.

Research paper no.3 : Draft legislation : admiralty procedure and rules / Australian Law Reform Commission. – 1985.
iv,136p.
Includes bibliographical references.

Research paper no. 5 : Prize law, jurisdiction and procedure / Australian Law Reform Commission. – 1984.
iii,70 leaves.
Bibliography: p.68-70.

—Reference on contempt of courts, tribunals and commissions
Research paper no.1 : Contempt in relation to commissions and tribunals / Australian Law Reform Commission. – Sydney : The Commission, 1986.
vii,114p.
Bibliography: p.112-114.

Research paper no. 2 : Improper behaviour in court / Australian Law Reform Commission. – 1984.
viii,119p.
Includes bibliographical references.

Research paper 3 : Improper pressure on parties to court proceedings / Australian Law Reform Commission. – 1986.
iv,49p.
Includes bibliographical references.

Research paper no.4 : Prejudicial publicity and the courts / Australian Law Reform Commission. – 1986.
v,134p.
Bibliography: p.130-134.

Research paper no. 6A : Contempt and family law / Australian Law Reform Commission. – 1985.
various pagings.

—Reference on service and execution of process
Research paper no. 2 : Commencing process / Australian Law Reform Commission. – Sydney : The Commission, 1984.
v,175p.
Bibliography: p.175.

Research paper no. 3 : Tribunals / Australian Law Reform Commission. – 1984.
vii,87p.
Bibliography: p.86-87.

Research paper no. 4 : Enforcement of judgments / Australian Law Reform Commission. – 1984.
iv,89p.
Bibliography: p.89.

Research paper no. 5 : Service of other process / Australian Law Reform Commision. – 1984.
iv,64p.
Bibliography: p.64.

Reserach paper no. 7 : Discussion of reference : Draft Interstate Procedure Bill and regulations / Australian Law Reform Commission. – 1986.
iii,80p.
Includes text of draft bill.

—Reference on service and execution of warrants and writs of attachment
Research paper no. 6 : Interstate execution of warrants and writs of attachment / Australian Law Reform Commission. – Sydney : The Commission, 1984.
v,109,6p.
Bibliography: p.109.

→ Report of Providing and Funding Legal Aid Conference.

—Report relating to the use of or reference to the records of proceedings of the House in the courts : together with minutes of proceedings of the Committee / the Parliament of the Commonwealth of Australia, House of Representatives, Committee of Privileges. – Canberra : Commonwealth Government Printer, 1981.
vii,108p. – (Parliamentary paper).
ISBN 0642057206

—Royal Commission of Inquiry into Chamberlain Convictions / report of the Commissisoner T.R. Morling. – Canberra : Government Printer, 1987.
379p. – (Parliamentary paper).
At head of cover title: Parliament of the Commonwealth of Australia.
ISBN 0724512985

—Sentencing : penalties / the Law Reform Commission. – Sydney : The Commission, 1987.
234p. – (Discussion paper).
Bibliography: p.223-234..

—Sentencing : prisons / The Law Reform Commission. – Sydney : The Commission, 1987.
vii,64p. – (Discussion paper).
Bibliography: pp.63-64.

—Sentencing : procedure / The Law Reform Commission. – Sydney : The Commission, 1987.
xii,114p. – (Discussion paper).
Bibliography: pp.111-114.

—Statement of preliminary views / Constitutional Commission. Australian Judicial System Advisory Committee. – Canberra : The Commission, 1986.
40p.

Australian and New Zealand Citator to UK Reports 1588-1972
Cumulative supplement-1982. – Wellington : Butterworths.
ISBN 0409303100 Pbk

Australian and New Zealand commentary on Halsbury's Laws of England (Fourth Edition) / editor in chief, Garfield Barwick. – Sydney : Butterworths, 1974-.
loose-leaf.
In 2 series: Australian commentary (vols. A-), and New Zealand commentary (vols. A-). Spine title: Commentary on Halsbury's laws of England. - Vol. A of New Zealand commentary has spine sub-title: Australia and New Zealand.

Australian and New Zealand Income Tax Reports (AITR). – Wellington : Butterworths.
Hbk

Australian and New Zealand Journal of Criminology / John Willis. – Wellington : Butterworths.
Hbk
Back Vols. avail..

Australian Bankruptcy Act 1966 and Rules. – 4th ed. – North Ryde : C.C.H. Australia, 1986.
300p.
ISBN 0869036777 Hbk £24.00

Australian bankruptcy law / Lewis. – 8th ed. – North Ryde : Law Book Co., 1984.
xxiii,293p.
Includes bibliographical references and index.
ISBN 0455205205

Australian Bankruptcy Law / Dennis J Rose. – 8th ed. – London : Law Book Co, 1984.
ISBN 0455205213 Pbk £13.00

Australian Bar Association
Australian Bar review. – Australian Bar Association. – Sydney : Butterworths, 1985-.
'Published under the auspices of the Australian Bar Association'. - T.p..

Australian Bar review. – Australian Bar Association. – Sydney : Butterworths, 1985-.
'Published under the auspices of the Australian Bar Association'. - T.p..

Australian Capital Gains Tax / Michael W. Inglis. – Butterworths, 1986.
298p.
ISBN 0409491578 Pbk £42.00

Australian Capital Territory
Annual report / Legal Aid Commission (A.C.T.). – Australian Capital Territory. – Canberra : Australian Government Publishing Service, 1978-.
Report year runs 1 July to 30 June.
—Laws of the Australian Capital Territory made during the year ... – Australian Capital Territory. – Canberra : Commonwealth Government Printer, 1964.
Contains ordinances and regulations.
—Ordinances . – Australian Capital Territory. – Canberra : Commonwealth Government Printer, 1911.
Extracted from: Commonwealth of Australia Gazette. This library has 1939-1959 in this form. Ordinances 1960 onwards are included in the bound volumes of 'Laws of the Australian Capital Territory made during the year ...'.

Australian case citator. – 1. – North Ryde, N.S.W. : The Law Book Co., 1983.
loose-leaf.
Kept up to date by quarterly cumulative supplements.
ISBN 0455204349

Australian Citizenship Act, 1948. – Human Rights Commission. – Canberra : Australian Government Publishing Service, 1982.
27p.
ISBN 0644021373 Hbk £1.80

Australian citizenship law / by Michael Pryles. – Sydney : Law Book Co., 1981.
xxv,271p.
Includes index.
ISBN 0455203598

Australian civil procedure / Bernard C. Cairns. – 2nd ed. – Sydney : Law Book Company, 1985.
lxvi,584p.
ISBN 0455206260

Australian Commentary to Halsbury's Laws of England. – Wellington : Butterworths.
Hbk

Australian Commonwealth : a fundamental analysis of its constitution / M. J. Detmold. – Sydney : Law Book Company, 1985.
266p.
ISBN 0455205787

Australian Company Law, 4 Vols. / H. H. Ednie. – Wellington : Butterworths, 1982.
Pbk

Australian company law / John O'Hair, John (Sean) Kearns. – 4th ed. – Sydney : McGraw-Hill Book Co., 1985.
xvii, 469 p.; 25 cm.
Re ed. of: Australian company law / Harvey Mason. 3rd ed. 1981. Includes bibliographical references and indexes.
ISBN 0074520334 Pbk

Australian Company Law Casebook. – North Ryde : C.C.H. Australia, 1986.
486p.
ISBN 0869038265 Hbk

Australian Company Law Reports (ACLR) / H. H. Ednie. – Wellington : Butterworths.
Hbk

Australian Company Practice / J. C. Cooke. – 2nd ed. – Wellington : Butterworths, 1982.
Pbk

Australian Constitution : Australia's Most Important Document. – Kingston : Australian Government Publishing Service, 1988.
Pbk £19.95

Australian Constitutional Cases. – 4th ed. – North Ryde : Law Book Co, 1982.
xxxv, 774p.
ISBN 0455204608 Pbk £52.50
ISBN 0455204594 Hbk £73.00

Australian constitutional law / by P.J. Hanks. – 3rd ed. – Sydney : Butterworths, 1985.
xxix,792p.
Previous ed.: 1980, published as Fajgenbaum and Hanks' Australian constitutional law. Includes bibliographical references and index.
ISBN 0409494836 Hbk £53.00

Australian Constitutionalism. – London : Butterworths, 1983.
ISBN 0409493104 Pbk £20.00

Australian consumer sales and credit law reporter. – North Ryde, N.S.W. : CCH Australia, 1977.
looseleaf.
Looseleaf issues accompanied by a summary report. - Uniform credit law proposals 1978; Trade Practices Commission guidelines 1974-1982; and 1980- cases filed in transfer binders. 'Uniform credit law proposals 1978' filed in transfer binder.
ISBN 0869030760 v.3
ISBN 0869033077

Australian Corporate Law Reference / James G Jackson. – London : Legal Books, 1986.
ISBN 0949553263 Hbk £27.50

Australian courts of law / James Crawford. – Melbourne : Oxford University Press, 1982.
297 p.; 21 cm.
Includes bibliographical references and index.
ISBN 0195543076 Pbk

Australian Criminal Justice System : The Mid 1980's / Paul Wilson. – Butterworths, 1987.
348p.
The authors of this book, who include criminologists, sociologists, lawyers, and academics, cover such matters as sexual assault, corporate crime, terrorism, sentencing, organized crime, and juvenile offenses.
ISBN 0409491497 Hbk £46.00

Australian Current Law / Jean Malor. – Butterworths, 1987.
ISBN 0409410543 Llf £75.00

Australian Document Exchange Pty Limited
Australian Legal Directory. – Australian Document Exchange Pty Limited. – Sydney : Butterworths.

Australian employment legislation. – Australia. – 3. – Sydney : CCH Austalia, 1984.
loose-leaf.
Originally published: as part of Australian labour law reporter, 1977-. Includes index. Loose-leaf issues accompanied by a summary report.
ISBN 0869036513

Australian Encyclopaedia of Forms and Precedents : 1987 Cumulative Supplement. – Butterworths, 1987.
905p.
Pbk £67.50

Australian Environment Council-Environmental Noise Control Committee
Environmental Noise Control Legislation in Australia. – Australian Environment Council-Environmental Noise Control Committee. – Canberra : Australian Government Publishing Service, 1982.
27p.
ISBN 064401914X Hbk £2.50

Australian Evidence. – Butterworths, 1988.
443p.
ISBN 0409493562 Hbk £65.00
ISBN 0409493287 Pbk £42.50

Australian Evidence : Cases and Commentary. – Sydney : Butterworths, 1988.
608p.
This casebook contains materials on the burden of proof, circumstantial evidence, witnesses, judicial discretion, hearsay, res gestae, admissions, and other topics.
Pbk £55.00

Australian Family Formation Project →Living together : young couples in de facto relationships : a report using Australian Family Formation Project Data.

Australian family law / Richard Chisholm, Carol Foreman and Stephen O'Ryan. – Sydney : Butterworths, 1987.
Includes both Commonwealth and state legislation and practice and procedure of the Family Court.
ISBN 0409491950 Llf A$575

Australian Family Law Act 1975 Family Law Rules : Family Law Regulations. – Butterworths, 1988.
ISBN 0409493686 Hbk £29.00

Australian family law & practice reporter / by Malcolm D. Broun and Stuart G. Fowler with CCH editorial staff and contributions by Anthony F. Dickey. – North Ryde, N.S.W. : CCH Australia, 1975-.
loose-leaf; 26cm.
Includes current issues of: Australian family law cases. Loose-leaf issues accompanied by a summary report.

Australian family law cases. – North Ryde, N.S.W. : CCH Australia, 1975.
23cm.
Issued annually as bound volumes, with current issues forming part of the service to the loose-leaf publication: Australian family law & practice reporter.

Australian Family Law Forms and Precedents / Alexander Duff. – Woolloomooloo : International Business Communications, 1987.
ISBN 0949553247 Hbk £225.00

Australian family property law / by I. J. Hardingham and M. A. Neave. – Sydney : Law Book Company, 1984.
liii,647p.
ISBN 0455205132

Australian Federal Administrative Law Legislation : with Introductory Commentary. – North Ryde : C.C.H. Australia, 1985.
496p.
ISBN 0869037498 Hbk

Australian federal constitutional law / by Colin Howard. – 3rd ed. – Sydney : Law Book Company, 1985.
lxxviii,611p.
Bibliography: pxliii-li.
ISBN 0455205736

Australian Federal Government. – 3rd ed. – London : Butterworths.
ISBN 0409372056 Pbk £11.80

Australian Federal Taxation Penalties and Offences. – North Ryde : C.C.H. Australia, 1985.
395p.
ISBN 0869038427 Hbk

Australian Finance Conference →Credit revolution : papers from the seminar on the N.S.W. Credit Bill 1981, organised by the Faculty of Law, University of N.S.W., the N.S.W. Department of Consumer Affairs & the Australian Finance Conference, 13 July 1981.

Australian income tax guide 1988 / E.F. Mannix ... et al. – 33rd ed. – Sydney : Butterworths, 1988.
xxiv,1304p.
' ... the 33rd edition of Gunn's Guide to Commonwealth income tax'. - t.p.. Includes index.
ISBN 0409494267 Hbk

Australian income tax legislation. – 1985 ed. 3 v. – North Ryde, N.S.W. : CCH Australia, 1985.
'Incorporating all amendments to 31 December 1984'.
ISBN 086903684X

Australian industrial law review. – North Ryde, N.S.W. : CCH Australia, 1959-.
30cm.
'Digests of cases (in which reasons for decision have been published) from Federal and State Courts and Tribunals'.
Llf

Australian Institute of Family Studies
FAMILY thesaurus : Australian family studies indexing terms / prepared by the Australian Institute of Family Studies : edited by Deborah Whithear. – 2nd ed. – Melbourne : Australian Institute of Family Studies, 1987.
98p.
ISBN 0642118515

Australian Institute of Judicial Administration →Delays and efficiency in civil litigation.

Australian Insurance Law. – North Ryde : Law Book Co, 1987.
xlv, 368p.
ISBN 0455207232 Pbk £49.50

Australian journal of family law. – Sydney : Butterworths, 1986-.

Australian journal of law and society. – North Ryde : Macquarie University, School of Law, 1982.
ISBN 07293356

Australian Judicial System : Report of the Advisory Committee to the Constitutional Commission. – Kingston : Australian Government Publishing Service, 1987.
140p.
Hbk £9.95

Australian Labor Party
Law and justice / Australian Labor Party. – s.l. : The Party, 1983.
iii,24p.
'Policy launched by Senator Gareth Evans, ... Melbourne, 23 February, 1983'.

Australian labour law reporter. – 4. – North Ryde, N.S.W. : CCH Australia, 1977-.
loose-leaf.
Contents: 3 vols. of reports and index vol.. Loose-leaf issues accompanied by a summary report.
ISBN 0869031465 Hbk

Australian Law of Cheques and Payment Orders. – Butterworths, 1988.
199p.
ISBN 0409495417 Pbk £35.00

Australian Law Reform Agencies Conference : Hobart July 1981, Adelaide September 1982, Brisbane July 1983. – Australia : s.n., .
262p.
Includes index. Includes the records and minutes of the 6th, 7th and 8th Conferences.

Australian Law Reform Commission
Aboriginal customary law : marriage, children and the distribution of property / Australian Law Reform Commission. – Sydney : Australian Law Reform Commission, 1982.
20p. – (Discussion paper).
—Civil admiralty jurisdiction / the Law Reform Commission. – Canberra : Australian Government Publishing Service, 1986.
xxi,393p. – (Report).
Bibliography: p.381-387. - Includes index.
ISBN 0644013540
—Commonwealth Prisoners Act / Law Reform Commission. – Canberra : Australian Government Publishing Service, 1988.
xv,57p. – (Report (interim)).
Bibliography: p.57. Includes text of draft legislation.
ISBN 0644069007

—Community law reform for the Australian capital territory : second report : Loss of consortium : compensation for loss of capacity to do housework / the Law Reform Commission. – Canberra : Australian Government Publishing Service, 1986.
viii,28p. – (Report).
Bibliography: p.27. - Includes index.
ISBN 0644013516

—Contempt / Law Reform Commission. – Canberra : Australian Government Publishing Service, 1987.
xcii,643p. – (Report).
Includes index.
ISBN 0644013656

—Debt recovery and insolvency / Law Reform Commission. – Canberra : Australian Government Publishing Service, 1987.
xxxii,312p. – (Report).
ISBN 0644013648

—Domestic violence / Law Reform Commission. – Canberra : Australian Government Publishing Service, 1986.
xxvi,98p. – (Report).
Bibliography: p.94-96 - Includes index.
ISBN 0644013397

—Evidence / Law Reform Commission. – 2 v. – Canberra : Australian Government Publishing Service, 1985.
– (Report).
Interim report.
ISBN 0644013028

—Evidence / Law Reform Commission. – Canberra : Australian Government Publishing Service, 1987.
xliii,320p. – (Report).
Includes index.
ISBN 0644013710

—Matrimonial property law / Australian Law Reform Commission. – Sydney : Australian Law Reform Commission, 1985.
iv,105p. – (Discussion paper).

—Occupiers' liability / Law Reform Commission. – Canberra : Australian Government Publishing Service, 1988.
xi,54p. – (Report).
Bibliography: pp. 53-54. Includes draft legislation.
ISBN 0644068965

—Privacy / Law Reform Commission. – 3 v. – Canberra : Australian Government Publishing Service, 1983.
– (Report).

—Spent convictions / Law Reform Commission. – Canberra : Australian Government Publishing Service, 1987.
viii,126p. – (Report).
Bibliography: p.123-126.
ISBN 0644013702

—Standing in public interest litigation / Law Reform Commission. – Canberra : Australian Government Publishing Service, 1985.
xxx,273p. – (Report).
Bibliography: p.259-263 - Includes index.
ISBN 0644013109

Australian Law Reports (ALR) / J. D. Heydon. – Wellington : Butterworths.
Hbk

Australian legal dictionary / by S.E. Marantelli. – 6th reprint. – Caulfield East, Victoria : Edward Arnold Australia, 1985.
242p.
ISBN 0713181184

Australian Legal Director. – Butterworths, 1988.
968p.
ISBN 0000126527 Hbk £55.00

Australian Legal Directory. – Australian Document Exchange Pty Limited. – Sydney : Butterworths.

Australian legal directory / Law Council of Australia : in association with the Victoria Law Foundation. – Melbourne : Law Council of Australia, 1977-.
Hbk

Australian Legal History. – North Ryde : Law Book Co, 1982.
xx, 553p.
ISBN 04551956095 £63.00

Australian mercantile law / Yorston & Fortescue. – 16th ed. – Sydney : Law Book Co., 1981.
xxxi,784p.
Previous ed.: 1978. Includes index.
ISBN 0455203636

Australian Mining and Petroleum Law Association yearbook. – Melbourne : The Association, 1983.
Includes index.
ISBN 0812857X

Australian Mining and Petroleum Laws / Andrew G Lang. – 2nd ed. – Sydney : Butterworths, 1987.
360p.
This reference describes the Petroleum (Submerged Lands) Act 1982, the Mining Act 1983 (NT), the Petroleum Act 1984 (NT), the Mining Act 1978-81 (WA), the Mining Amendment Act 1985 (WA). Also included are materials on environmental law and joint ventures.
Hbk £55.00

Australian National Companies Act with Regulations. – 6th ed. – North Ryde : C.C.H. Australia, 1986.
2,000p.
ISBN 0869039792 Hbk

Australian national companies and securites legislation with state variations ... – Australia. – 5th ed. 2. – North Ryde, N.S.W. : CCH Australia, 1986.
ISBN 0869037013

Australian national companies and securities legislation. – Australia. – 3rd ed. 1. – North Ryde, N.S.W. : CCH Australia, 1982.
various pagings.
Includes index.
ISBN 0869033700

Australian national companies and securities legislation : up to date to 1 October 1987. – Australia. – 7th ed. 2. – North Ryde, N.S.W. : CCH Australia, 1987.
Index to legislation in vol. 1.
ISBN 1862640068

Australian National Railways Commission
General Bylaw : Boards of Appeal Bylaw. – Australian National Railways Commission. – Canberra : Australian Government Publishing Service, 1984.
11p.
ISBN 0644031697 Hbk £1.00

Australian Patent Law. – Butterworths, 1984.
349p.
ISBN 0409492035 Hbk £65.00

Australian Prisoners, 1982 / David Biles. – Canberra : Australian Institute of Criminology.
Hbk £3.00

Australian private international law / by Edward I. Sykes and Michael C. Pryles. – 2nd ed. – North Ryde, N.S.W. : Law Book Co, 1987.
lxxxix, 772 p.; 25 cm.
Includes bibliographical references and indexes.
ISBN 0455207038 Pbk

Australian Proprietary Company Articles : a Practical Guide with Precedents. – North Ryde : C.C.H. Australia, 1982.
320p.
Hbk £35.00

Australian Road Traffic Offences. – London : Butterworths, 1983.
ISBN 040949109X Hbk £28.80

Australian Sales Tax Legislation. – 5th ed. – North Ryde : C.C.H. Australia, 1987.
800p.
ISBN 0869039733 Hbk £24.00

Australian Science and Technology Council
Towards a cashless society? : a report to the Prime Minister / by the Australian Science and Technology Council (ASTEC) prepared by the Technological Change Committee. – Canberra : Australian Government Publishing Service, 1986.
xi,175p.
Includes bibliographies.
ISBN 0644049995

Australian securities law reporter. – 1. – North Ryde, N.S.W. : CCH Australia, 1972-.
looseleaf; 25cm.
Includes current issues of: Australian securities law cases. Loose-leaf issues accompanied by a summary report.
ISBN 0909720274 Hbk

Australian Sentencing Digest. – North Ryde : Law Book Co, 1985.
li, 929p.
Hbk £97.00
Supplement 1985. –
xvii, 194p.
ISBN 0455206112

Australian social security law, policy and administration / Terry Carney & Peter Hanks. – Melbourne : Oxford University Press, 1986.
xxv,334p.
Bibliography: p311-326.
ISBN 0195547543

Australian Social Security Legislation. – 2nd ed. – North Ryde : C.C.H. Australia, 1986.
250p.
ISBN 0869036300 Hbk £24.00

Australian Supplement to Borrie and Lowe's Law of Contempt / Athol Moffitt. – Butterworths, 1988.
ca 128p.
ISBN 0409494593 Pbk £29.00

Australian Takeovers Practice and Precedents Manual. – North Ryde : C.C.H. Australia, 1983.
200p.
ISBN 0869036807 Hbk £63.00

Australian Tax Office Practice. – Woolloomooloo : International Business Communications, 1986.
ISBN 0949072036 Llf £195.00

Australian Tax Reports Vols. 1-17 (1969-1986) and Australian and New Zealand Income Tax Reports Vols. 1-10 (1936-1968) Consolidated Index and Tables. – Butterworths. – Butterworths, 1989.
292p.
ISBN 0409300977 Hbk £110.00
ISBN £79.00 to subscribers

Australian Tenancy Practice and Precedents / Michael Redfern. – Butterworths, 1987.
ISBN 0409494909 Llf £235.00

Australian trade mark law and practice / by D.R. Shanahan. – Sydney : The Law Book Company Ltd, 1982.
lv,522p.
ISBN 0455201196 Hbk £35.00

Australian Trade Practices Legislation. – 8th ed. – North Ryde : C.C.H. Australia, 1986.
344p.
ISBN 0869035754 Hbk £24.00

Australian trade practices reporter / by CCH editorial staff : consultant editors R. Baxt, R.G. Blunt, A.I. Tonking. – 2. – North Ryde, N.S.W. : CCH Australia, 1972-.
loose-leaf; 26cm.
Includes current issues of: Australian trade practices reports. Loose-leaf issues accompanied by a summary report. Pre-current 'Commission decisions : authorizations and notifications' filed in transfer binders.
ISBN 0869030264 v.2
ISBN 0869030280 Hbk

Australian trade practices reports. – North Ryde, N.S.W. : CCH Australia, 1978-.
23cm.
Issued as bound volumes, with current issues forming part of the service to the loose-leaf publication: Australian trade practices reporter.

Australian Travel and Tourism Law Handbook. – Butterworths, 1988.
285p.
ISBN 0409493848 Pbk £22.50

Australian Wills Precedents (Italian Translation). – London : Butterworths.
ISBN 0409494410 Pbk £10.00

Australian workers compensation guide. – 3. – North Ryde, N.S.W. : CCH Australia, 1984.
looseleaf.
Originally published: as part of Australian labour law reporter, 1977-. Includes index. Loose-leaf issues accompanied by a summary report.
ISBN 0869034839

Australian-United States' relations : the extraterritorial application of United States laws / the Parliament of the Commonwealth of Australia Joint Committee on Foreign Affairs and Defence. – Canberra : Australian Government Publishing Service, 1983.
xiii,84p. – (Parliamentary paper).
Includes bibliographical references.

Australia's Constitution : Time for Change?. – North Sydney : Allen & Unwin, 1983.
432p.
ISBN 0868610399 Pbk £17.95

Australia's External Territory Police Forces. – Canberra : Australian Institute of Criminology.
Hbk £1.00

Australia's Government and Parliament. – 7th ed. – Melbourne : Nelson, 1987.
194p : Illus.
ISBN 0170071944 Hbk £16.95

Australia's Maritime Boundaries. – Deakin : Australian Institute of International Affairs, 1985.
Hbk £10.00

Austrian business law : legal, accounting and tax aspects of business in Austria / by Dr. Kurt Heller ... et al. – Deventer : Klumer Law and Taxation Publishing, 1984.
xxxviii,528p; 25cm.
Includes index.
ISBN 9065441883 Austria
ISBN 3214046012

Austrian Commercial Code : as of January 1, 1983 / translation into English by Markus Andreewitch. – Wien : Manz, 1987.
xii,180p.
Include indexes. German title on added t.p.: Das osterreichische Handelsgesetzbuch. Text in English and German.
ISBN 3214028987

Austrian Federal Constitution : as revised in 1929 together with subsequent additions and amendments and other important constitutional provisions including the Constitutional Law on the Neutrality of Austria / translated on behalf of the Austrian Federal Ministry for Foreign Affairs by Charles Kessler. – 2nd rev. and amplified ed. – Wien : Manzsche Verlags- und Universitatsbuchhandlung, 1983.
154 p.; 18 cm.
ISBN 3214060015 Pbk S190.00

Austrian law on companies with limited liability : as of January 1, 1984 with excerpted provisions of other relevant laws and annotations / editor Julie Goldberg. – Deventer : Kluwer Law and Taxation Publishers, 1985.
124p; 23 cm.
English and German. Includes index. Bibliography: p. 122.
ISBN 9065442294 Hbk £75.00

Authorised unit trust schemes : investment and borrowing powers : draft regulations under section 81(2)(d) of the Financial Services Act 1986 relating to properties unit trusts, futures and options funds and mixed funds / Department of Trade and Industry. – London : The Department, 1987.
3,6,5,4p.

Authority and participation in industry / Peter Brannen. – London : Batsford Academic and Educational, 1983.
173p; 22cm.
Bibliography: p157-168. - Includes index.
ISBN 0713443987 Pbk £6.95

Authority and politics in Australia : some key dynamics of Australian politics. – Victoria : Oxford University Press, 1988.
320.
Argues that a few basic principles underlie many features of Australian politics and government. It is maintained that in the Australian setting these processes have resulted in continuing restrictive features in Australian law and institutions.
ISBN 0195547446 Pbk £15.00

Authority of a guardian / Law Reform Commission of British Columbia. – Vancouver : Law Reform Commission of British Columbia, 1985.
13p.
ISBN 0771884664

Authority of the state / Leslie Green. – Oxford : Clarendon Press, 1988.
x,273p.
: Revision of thesis (D. Phil.)–University of Oxford, 1984. Includes bibliographic references and index.
ISBN 0198249268

Authorized unit trust schemes : investment and borrowing powers : draft regulations under section 81(2)(d) of the Financial Services Act 1986 relating to securities unit trusts and money market unit trusts / Department of Trade and Industry. – London : The Department, 1987.
20p.

Authors and Publishers : Agreements and Legal Aspects of Publishing. – 2nd ed. – Butterworths, 1987.
232p.
Examines the obligations of parties to publishing agreements. Covers all aspects of the law and business practice relating to author-publisher contracts and includes a clause-by-clause analysis of the fundamental provisions of agreements currently used. Revised to include the new copyright legislation and software agreements.
ISBN 0409806285 Hbk £50.00

Automated analysis of legal texts : logic, informatics, law : edited versions of selected papers from the Second International Conference on 'Logic, Informatics, Law,'Florence, Italy, September 1985 / edited by Antonio A. Martino, Fiorenza Socci Natali : editorial assistant, Simona Binazzi. – Amsterdam : North-Holland, 1986.
xxii, 938 p.; 25 cm.
Includes bibliographies and index.
ISBN 0444701117

Automated Office / Burgess. – Oxford : Blackwell Scientific, 1985.
ISBN 000383008X Pbk £7.95

Automation in the law school, including law libraries / by Betty W. Taylor and Dan F. Henke. – London : Glanville, 1986.
iv,124p.
Includes bibliographical references and appendices.
ISBN 0878020829

Autopoietic law : a new approach to law and society / edited by Gunther Teubner. – Berlin : W. de Gruyter, 1987.
Includes index and bibliography.

Auxier, Jane
Marriage and Family Law in British Columbia : the Rights of Husbands, Wives, Children, and Common-Law. – 6th ed. – North Vancouver : International Self-Counsel Press, 1985.
160p.
ISBN 0889081697 Hbk £7.95

Availability of Civil Remedies to Protect Persons and Property from Transfrontier Pollution Injury. – Hamburg : I.I.A., 1981.
ix, 163p.
Hbk £31.00

Averley, G. →Bibliography of eighteenth century legal literature : a subject and author catalogue of law treatises and all law related literature held in the main legal collections in England.

Avery Jones, J. F. →Simon's Taxes, 9 Vols.

Aviation Accident Law. – Matthew Bender, 1963.
ISBN 0000999056 Hbk £123.50

Aviation antitrust : the extraterritorial application of the United States antitrust laws and international air transportation / Patricia M. Barlow. – Deventer : Kluwer Law and Taxation, 1987.
xliv,210p.
Bibliography: pp.xxv-xxx - Includes index.
ISBN 9065442936

Aviation Claims. – London : Lloyd's of London Press, 1987.
ISBN 1850440948 Hbk

Aviation Insurance Abbreviations: Organs and instruments. – Witherby, 1983.
ISBN 0900886773 Pbk £4.50

Aviation Law for Applicants for the Private Pilot's Licence (CAP 85). – Civil Aviation Authority. – 7th ed. Ed. by Great Britain. – London : Civil Aviation Authority, 1985.
v, 62p : Illus.
ISBN 0860391833 Hbk £2.70

Aviation Law for Pilots / S.E.T. Taylor. – 6th ed. – Oxford : BSP Professional.
ISBN 0632023597 Pbk £9.95

Aviation Law for Pilots / H. A. Parmar. – 5th ed. – London : Collins, 1986.
172p.
ISBN 0003832732 Pbk £7.95

Aviation liabilities in the 1980s : a non-technical summary for insurers. – S.l. : Swiss Reinsurance Company, 1981.
36p.

Aviation Security. – London : Granada Publishing Ltd, 1983.
309p : Illus.
ISBN 0246117400 Hbk £30.00

Aviation security : digest of current ICAO policies and actions on the subject of unlawful interference with international civil aviation and its facilities. – International Civil Aviation Organization. – 4th ed. – Montreal : International Civil Aviation Organization, 1987.
iii,36p. – (Doc 8849-C/990/4).
Decisions taken and work done by ICAO on the subject of unlawful interference with international civil aviation and its facilities. Includes the texts of three international conventions.

Avins, Alfred
Employees' Misconduct : As Cause for Discipline and Dismissal in India and the Commonwealth. – Allahabad : Law Book Company, 1987.
900p.
Hbk £130.00

Avoidance of fraudulent transfers and related bankruptcy crimes : papers delivered at the meetings of Committee J - Creditor's Rights, Insolvency, Liquidation and Reorganizations, Vienna, 2-7 September 1984 / Barrett. – London : International Bar Association, 1984.
166p.
Chairman: John A. Barrett.

Avoiding Claims : a Practical Guide Construction Industry. – London : E & F N Spon.
ISBN 0419146202 Hbk £22.50

Avoiding liability for defective products : a guide to the law on disclaimer of liability clauses in contracts for the sale of goods / Derrick Owles. – London : Product Liability International, 1987.
ix,52p.
ISBN 1850441200 Pbk £14.50

Awasthi
Dowry Prohibition Act. – Allahabad : Orient Law House, 1984.
Hbk £50.00
—Railway Property (Unlawful Possession) Act. – Allahabad : Orient Law House, 1984.
Hbk £60.00

Awasthi, Rakesh
Supreme Court Industrial, Services and Labour Law Digest, 1977-87 : Central and States. – Allahabad : Law Book Company.
500p.
Hbk £150.00

Awogu, F. Olisa
Civil proceedings by and against the State in Nigeria / by F. Olisa Awogu. – Onitsha : Pacific College Press, 1981.
x,167p.
Includes index.
—Judiciary in the second republic of Nigeria, 1979-1983 / by F. Olisa Awogu. – Onitsha : Pacific Colege Press, 1984.
x,176p.
Bibliography: p.163-164. - Includes index.
ISBN 9782347108

Axelby
Cost Accounting Lecturer's Guide / Underdown. – Pitman.
ISBN 0273029207 Pbk £10.95

Ayadurai, Dunston
Employer, the employee and the law in Malaysia / Dunston Ayadurai. – Singapore : Butterworths, 1985.
xxiv,335p.
Discusses the Malaysian industrial relations system in the context of the laws in force. Deals with employer-employee relationships, covering both the collective and the individual relationship between employers and workers. Also covers trade unions, and other similar organisations.
ISBN 0409995045

Ayadurai, R.
Employer, the Employee and the Law in Malaysia. – London : Butterworths, 1985.
ISBN 0409995045 Hbk £32.00

Aykroyd, Peter W. →Lending and Recovery : Benefits and Pitfalls of Consulting Engagements.

Ayua, I. A. →Nigerian commercial laws : problems and perspectives.
—Nigerian Tax Law. – Abingdon : Professional Books, 1986.
350p.
ISBN 0862051169 Hbk

A-Z of Business Mathematics. – London : Kogan Page.
ISBN 185091673X Pbk £8.95

A-Z of Employment and Safety Law. – London : Kogan Page, 1981.
516p.
ISBN 085038446X Hbk £16.95

Baar, Carl →Judicial administration in Canada.

Baatz →Building Law Reports, Index to Volumes 1-38.
→ Building Law Reports Volume 42.

Babington
Juries and Prac. Co. Court Ireland. – London : Butterworths.
ISBN 0862053323 Hbk £36.50

BAC Business Law / Woods. – Agincourt : Carswell, 1986.
ISBN 045939520 Hbk £36.50

Bacchi, Carol Lee
Liberation Deferred? : the ideas of the English-Canadian Suffragists. – Toronto : University of Toronto Press, 1983.
ISBN 0802024556 Hbk £25.00
ISBN 0802064663 Pbk £9.95

Back, P.
Corporate Cash Management. – Cambridge : Woodhead-Faulkner, 1987.
ISBN 085941390X Hbk £40.00

Backett
Imprisonent Today : Current Issues in the Prison Debate / McNeill. – London : Macmillan.
ISBN 0333421957 Hbk £29.50

Background of current fiscal problems / J. Harvey Perry. – Toronto : Canadian Tax Foundation, 1982.
v,159p.
Includes index.
ISBN 0888080107

Background of the Common Law. – Oxford : Oxford University Press.
ISBN 0195849353 Pbk £4.95

Background of the common law : a historical sketch / Derek Roebuck. – Waigani : University of Papua New Guinea Press, 1983.
135p.
Includes index.

Background Reading Material on Intellectual Property. – Geneva : World Intellectual Property Organization, 1988.
400p.
Hbk £40.00

Backs Against the Tide : an Evaluation of the President's Council's Report on the Group Areas Act. – Johannesburg : South African Institute of Race Relations, 1987.
Hbk £4.00

Bacon, M.
New Abridgment of the Law : 1736-1766, 5 Vols. – Abingdon : Professional Books.
Hbk £650.00

Badger
Elements of Cargo Insurance / Geoffrey Whitehead. – Cambridge : Woodhead-Faulkner, 1983.
ISBN 085941227X Pbk £5.25

Badjatya, Mahendra
Company Law : an Immediate Approach. – Allahabad : Modern Law Publications, 1987.
Hbk £170.00

Badr, Gamal Moursi
State immunity : an analytical and prognostic view / Gamal Moursi Badr. – The Hague : M. Nijhoff, 1984.
248p.
Includes bibliographical references and index.
ISBN 9024728800 Hbk £120.00

Badshaw, F.M.
Law of Charitable Trusts. – Butterworths, 1983.
212p.
ISBN 0409490709 Hbk £52.00

Bael, Ivo van
Competition law of the EEC / Ivo van Bael, Jean-Francois Bellis. – Bicester : CCH Editions, 1987.
xii,690p; 23cm.
Analysis of EEC Competition Rules, with a critical commentary on the rules and practical guidance on their application. Covers basic provisions, including Articles 85 and 86, distribution, industrial and commercial property rights, co-operation agreements, mergers and acquisitions, trade associations and trade fairs, price fixing, market-sharing, boycotts and crisis cartels.
ISBN 0863250610 Pbk £30.00
—International trade law and practice of the European Community : EEC anti-dumping and other trade protection laws / Ivo van Bael, Jean-Francois Bellis. – Bicester : CCH, 1985.
viii,438p.
Discusses the Community's four main methods of trade protection; anti-dumping rules, anti-subsidy rules, safe-guard measures, and the 'New Commercial Policy Instrument', and comments on the EEC and ECSC Anti-dumping Regulations. Contains tables and annexes.
ISBN 0863250602
Baer, Marvin G.
Cases of the Canadian Law of Insurance / James A. Rendall. – 4th ed. – Agincourt : Carswell, 1988.
854p.
Hbk £82.50
→ Cases on the Canadian law of insurance.
Baer, W.E.
Arbitration for the Practitioner. – Folkestone : Bailey Bros..
ISBN 0899502903 Hbk £18.50
Bagehot, W.
English Constitution. – Reprint. – London : Fontana, 1983.
ISBN 0006327583 Pbk £2.50
Bagga, Rakesh →Central Criminal Minor Acts : With state Amendments.
Baggage Rules in India. – New Delhi : Nabhi Publications, 1984.
28p.
Hbk £30.00
Baginsky, Mary →Alternatives to prison : an examination of non-custodial sentencing of offenders.
Bagnall, K.
Judicial review. – Profex, 1985.
ISBN 095102860X Pbk £10.95
Bagnall, Roger S. →Studies in Roman law in memory of A. Arthur Schiller.
Bagri, P.R.
Law of Industrial Disputes : as Amended by Amendment Act No. 46 of 1982, 2 Vols. – 2nd ed. – New Delhi : Bharat Law House, 1986.
Hbk £135.00 ea.
Bahadur
Eve in the East. – Bombay : Jaico Publishing House.
Hbk £20.00
Baha'is of Iran / by Roger Cooper. – Rev. and updated ed. – London : Minority Rights Group, 1985.
16p. – (Report).
Bibliography: p.16.
ISBN 0946690316
Bahamas consolidated index of statutes and subsidiary legislation to 1st January 1982 / compiled at the Faculty of Law Library, University of the West Indies, Barbados. – Barbados : s.n., 1982.
iv,93p.
One of a series in the West Indian Legislation Indexing Project (WILIP) compiled in cooperation with the British Development Division.
Bahl, Roy W. →Urban government finance : emerging trends.
Baig, Nafees
Company Law and Secretarial Practice. – 2nd rev. ed. – New Delhi : Sterling Publishers, 1981.
352p.
ISBN 8120701852 Hbk £50.00
ISBN 8120704010 £17.50
Bail : County Court Practice Nineteen Eighty-Seven. – London : Butterworths, 1986.
ISBN 0406163235 Pbk
Bail : Issues and Prospects / Leslie T Wilkins. – Canberra : Australian Institute of Criminology.
Hbk £2.20
Bail : law and practice / Clifford Chatterton. – London : Butterworths, 1986.
xxiii,277p; 25cm.
Includes index.
ISBN 0406101809 Pbk £28.00
The bail lottery. – Prison Reform Trust. – London : Prison Reform Trust, 1986.
5 leaves.
Bailey
Cases and Materials In Administrative Law / Cross. – Sweet & Maxwell, 1977.
ISBN 042117370X Pbk £22.00
→ Cases and Materials On English Legal Systems.
—Family Assessment and Early Intervention / Simeonsson. – Merrill.
ISBN 067520996X Hbk £19.25
→ Longman Exam Guide : Business Law.
—Reform of Local Government Finafnce in Britain / Paddison. – Deddington : Routledge.
ISBN 0415005302 Pbk £27.50
—Remedies for victims of crime / Tucker. – London : Legal Action Group, 1984.
ISBN 0905099060 Pbk £5.00
→ Terminology of business and company law.
Bailey, Edward- →Bankruptcy : Law and practice.
Bailey-Harris, Rebecca →Family Law in Australia.
Bailey, Ian H.
Construction Law in Australia. – North Ryde : Law Book Co, 1981.
xviii, 318p.
ISBN 0455202605 Pbk £31.00
Bailey, Jeffrey →Land taxation.
Bailey, R. →Property and Finance in Family Law.
Bailey, R. C.
Nelson's Tables : Administration of Estates. – 7th ed. – London : Oyez Longman, 1983.
ISBN 0851207219 Hbk £2.95
Bailey, S.D.
The United States : A Short Political Guide. – 2nd ed. – London : Macmillan.
ISBN 0333461460 Hbk £25.00
ISBN 0333461452 Pbk £8.95
Bailey, S. H.
Civil liberties : cases and materials / S.H. Bailey, D.J. Harris, B.L. Jones. – 2nd ed. – London : Butterworths, 1985.
xxxvii, 612p.
ISBN 040655482X
→ Cross on local government law.
→ Modern English legal system.
Bailey, Sydney D.
How wars end : the United Nations and the termination of armed conflicts, 1946-1964 Vol.1. – Oxford : Clarendon Press, 1982.
400p.
ISBN 0198274246 £35.00
Vol.2. – 1982.
720p.
ISBN 0198274629 £45.00
—Making of Resolution 242. – Dordrecht : Kluwer, 1985.
230p.
ISBN 9024730732 Hbk £130.00
—Procedure of the UN Security Council / Sydney D. Bailey. – 2nd ed. – Oxford : Clarendon press, 1988.
xii,499p.
Bibliography: pp.449-452. - Includes index. A revised and updated edition, taking in new developments, including a new chapter on voting and veto. All aspects of the Security Council's prcedure are covered.
ISBN 0198275668 Hbk £45/$60
—War and conscience in the nuclear age / Sydney D. Bailey. – Basingstoke : Macmillan, 1987.
xviii,210p; 23cm.
Bibliography: p200-202. - Includes index.
ISBN 0333436857 Hbk £25.00
ISBN 0333443845 Pbk £12.95
Bailey, Victor
Delinquency and citizenship : reclaiming the young offender, 1914-1948 / Victor Bailey. – Oxford : Clarendon, 1987.
viii,352p; 22cm.
Bibliography: p331-341. - Includes index.
ISBN 0198226640 £30.00
Baillie, Heather →Licensing (Scotland) Act 1976.
Baillie, W. J., et al
Investing in the Oil and Gas Industry in Canada. – Vancouver : British Columbia Continuing Legal Education Society, 1981.
222p.
ISBN 0865040354 Hbk £40.00
Bain, George Sayers →Industrial relations in Britain.
Baines, Harold F. →Building Act 1984.
Bainham, Andrew
Children, parents and the state / by Andrew Bainham. – London : Sweet & Maxwell, 1988.
200p; 23cm.
Examines the relationship between children, their parents, and the state, and how their respective powers, duties, and responsibilities interact within the legal system. Also discusses the extent to which the state, through local authorities and the courts, can legitimately intervene in family life.
ISBN 042136310X Hbk £14.00 :
ISBN 0421363207 Pbk £11.95
Baird, David E. →Canadian Bankruptcy Reports.
Baker
Criminal Law P.P.H. 1 / Wilkie. – 7th ed. – London : Butterworths, 1981.
ISBN 0406841217 Pbk £5.95
→ Endorsement and Disqualification.
—General Police Duties / Wilkie. – 7th ed. – London : Butterworths, 1983.
– (Police Promotion Handbook Ser.: No. 3).
This work for United Kingdom police officers discusses the many changes in the law including: the Highways Act of 1980, the Child Care Act, and the Licensed Premises (Exclusion of Certain Persons) Act of 1980; and the effects on the duties of officers.
ISBN 040684142X Pbk £4.95
Baker, C. D.
Tort / by C.D. Baker. – 4th ed. – London : Sweet & Maxwell, 1986.
xxxii,398p; 23cm.
Previous ed.: 1981. Includes index.
ISBN 0421349409 Hbk £15.00
ISBN 0421349506 Pbk £8.95

Baker, Charles Arnold
Practical Law for Arts Administrators. – London : Offord Publications Ltd, 1983.
400p.
ISBN 0903931583 Hbk £8.95

Baker, David
Introduction to Torts. – North Ryde : Law Book Co, 1985.
xxxiv, 307p.
ISBN 0455205574 Hbk £41.50
ISBN 0455205582 Pbk £23.50

Baker, E. R.
Criminal Evidence and Procedure, No. 2 / Wilkie. – 7th ed. – London : Butterworths, 1981. – (Police Promotion Handbooks Ser.).
This work for United Kingdom police officers covers the basic rules of criminal evidence and procedure from the perspective of the officer working in the field.
Police officers
ISBN 0406841314 Pbk
—Police Promotion Handbooks. – London : Butterworths.
Pbk

Baker, F.E.
Advanced Financial Accounting. – Maidenhead : McGraw-Hill.
ISBN 0070033668 Hbk £32.95

Baker, George
Review of the operation of the Northern Ireland (Emergency Provisions) Act 1978 / by Sir George Baker : presented to Parliament by the Secretary of State for Northern Ireland. – London : H.M.S.O., 1984.
171p.
ISBN 0101922205

Baker, Howard A
Space debris: legal and policy implications. – Dordrecht : Nijhoff (Martinus), 1989.
192. – (Utrecht studies in air and space law 6).
Describes the legally relevant aspects of the space debris issue, and analyses the legal and policy implications derived from these facts. Includes discussion of the source of space debris, the risk posed by debris to space activities, and locations of space debris.
ISBN 0792301668 Hbk £43

Baker, J.
Solicitors' accounts : student guide. – 2nd ed. – London : Financial Training, 1985.
ISBN 0906322944 Pbk £8.95

Baker, J. H.
Classical English Law Texts Series, 136 Vols. – Abingdon : Professional Books.
Hbk
—English Legal Manuscripts
Vol. 1: Catalogue of the Manuscript Year Books, Readings and Law Reports in the Library of the Harvard Law School. – Zug : Inter Documentation Company.
ISBN 3857500093 Hbk £50.00

—Order of Serjeants at Law : a chronicle of creations, with related texts and a historical introduction / by J.H. Baker. – London : Selden Society, 1984.
xxvi,610p,xvip of plates.
Includes index.

→ Sources of English legal history : private law to 1750.

Baker, Nigel L.
Law and the Individual. – 1st ed. – Plymouth : Macdonald & Evans, 1982.
144p : Illus.. – – (M and E Handbook Ser.).
ISBN 071211260X Hbk £4.50

Baker, P. V.
Law Quarterly Review. – London : Sweet & Maxwell, 1982.
Hbk £37.00
→ Snell's Principles of equity.

Baker, Steven J. →Legislating Foreign Policy.

Baker, Stuart →Oke's Magisterial Formulist, 2 Vols.

Baker, Thornton
Audit Manual. – London : Butterworths, 1984.
ISBN 0406258120 Pbk

Bakshi, P.M.
Introduction to Legislative Drafting. – 2nd ed. in prep. – Bombay : Tripathi.
—Law of Defamation : Some Aspects. – Bombay : Tripathi, 1986.
151p.
Hbk £60.00

Bala, Nicholas
Canadian children's law : cases, notes and materials / by Nicholas Bala, Heino Lilles and George Thomson. – Toronto : Butterworths, 1982.
xxxi,754p.
Includes index.
ISBN 0409872237
—Young Offenders Act annotated / by Nicholas Bala and Heino Lilles. – Don Mills : R. De Boo, 1984.
xxxi,453p.
Includes index.
ISBN 0888201842

—Young Offenders Service, 2 vols / Heino Lilles. – Toronto : Butterworths.
Hbk £145.00

Balachandran, M.
Guide To Statistical Sources In Money Banking and Finance. – Oryx Press.
ISBN 0897742656 Hbk £30.00

Balance Development of Long-Term Benefits : Proceedings of the European Institute for Social Security. – European Institute for Social Security. – Dordrecht : Kluwer, 1987.
392p.
ISBN 9065442898 Hbk £85.00

Balance of criminal justice : summary of the report. – London : H.M.S.O., 1981.
17p.
Report itself published as Cmnd. 8092, Parliamentary Papers 1980-81.
ISBN 0117301310 Pbk £1.95

Balance Sheets and the Lending Banker / Dyer. – 6th ed. – London : Europa Publications, 1986.
ISBN 0946653291 Pbk £8.95

Balasubramanian, V.
Law and Practice of Estate Duty : with Rules and Forms. – 4th ed. 1982 repr. 1983. – New Delhi : Bharat Law House.
Hbk £150.00
—Law and Practice of Wealth Tax and Gift Tax : with Rules and Forms. – 4th ed. – New Delhi : Bharat Law House, 1983.
Hbk £120.00

Balchin, Paul N.
Housing Policy and Housing Needs. – London : Macmillan.
160p. – (Building and Survey Ser.).
ISBN 0333307011 Hbk £14.00
ISBN 0333236955 Pbk £6.95
—Urban land economics / Paul N. Balchin and Jeffrey L. Kieve. – 3rd ed. – London : Macmillan, 1985.
xvi,302p; 22cm. – (Macmillan building and surveying series).
Previous ed.: 1977. Bibliography: p282-283. - Includes index.
ISBN 0333397843 Pbk £7.95

Balck, G.
Financial Accounting. – Cambridge : Woodhead-Faulkner, 1986.
ISBN 0859413365 Pbk £12.00

Baldi, Roberto
Distributorship, Franchising, Agency : Community and National Laws and Practice in the EEC. – Dordrecht : Kluwer, 1987.
274p.
ISBN 9065443290 Hbk £120.00

Baldwin, Elizabeth G. →Cambridge lectures 1983 : selected papers based upon lectures at the Conference of the Canadian Institute for Advanced Legal Studies, 1983, held at Cambridge University, England.

Baldwin, Janet K. →Law in a Cynical Society? : Opinion and Law in the 1980's.

Baldwin, John →Courts, prosecution, and conviction.
—Pre-trial justice : a study of case settlement in magistrates' courts / John Baldwin. – Oxford : Blackwell, 1985.
vi,190p.
Observational research into case settlement in Magistrates' Courts.
ISBN 0631140646 £19.50

Baldwin, Richard
Tax and financial planning for sportsmen and entertainers / Richard Harvey. – London : Butterworths, 1987.
ISBN 040650220X Pbk £18.50

Baldwin, Richard C.
Divorce Guide for Oregon. – 4th ed. – North Vancouver : International Self-Counsel Press, 1988.
ISBN 088908825X Hbk

Baldwin, Robert
Police powers and politics / Richard Kinsey. – London : Quartet, 1982.
1v.
ISBN 0704323338 Hbk £9.95
ISBN 0704334127 Pbk £3.95
—Regulating the airlines : administrative justice and agency discretion / Robert Baldwin. – Oxford : Clarendon, 1985.
xvi,317p. – (Oxford socio-legal studies).
Includes index.
ISBN 0198275153 Hbk £22.50
ISBN 0198275161 Pbk £9.95
—Regulation and public law / Robert Baldwin, Christopher McCrudden with contributions by Paul Craig ... et al. – London : Weidenfeld and Nicolson, 1987.
xx,399p; 22cm.
Bibliography: p332-347. - Includes index.
ISBN 0297787802 Hbk
ISBN 0297787810 Pbk £14.95

Bale, Norman
Capital acquisitions tax / by Norman Bale & John Condon. – Dublin : Institute of Taxation in Ireland, 1982.
244p.
Includes index.

Balfour, Richard J. →Property Law : Cases, Text and Materials.

Ball
Law of Libel. – Sweet & Maxwell, 1912 Reprint.
ISBN 0421375604 Hbk £18.40
→ Planning for Stamp Duty Reserve Tax.
→ Social work and child abuse.

Ball, Alan R.
Pressure politics in industrial societies : a comparative introduction / Alan R. Ball and Frances Millard. – Basingstoke : Macmillan Education, 1986.
xi,308; 23cm.
Bibliography: p290-302. - Includes index.
ISBN 0333347579 Hbk £25.00
ISBN 0333347587 Pbk £6.95

Ball, C.
Law Report : Teaching Assessment of Law in Social Work Education. – London : Central Council for Education & Training in Social Work.
ISBN 0904488217 Pbk £7.00

Ball, John
Bibliography of material on Indonesian law in the English language / by John Ball. – 3rd ed. – Sydney : Faculty of Law, University of Sydney, 1981.
90p.
Includes index.
—Indonesian legal history 1602-1848. – Sydney : Oughtershaw Press, 1982.
viii,300p.
Bibliography: p.275-293. - Includes index.
ISBN 0959342001
—Indonesian legal history : British West Sumatra, 1685-1825 / John Ball. – Sydney : Oughtershaw Press, 1984.
viii, 307 p.; 21 cm.
Includes index. Bibliography: 296-299.
ISBN 095934201X Pbk

Ball, Minhael →Insurance Legislation Manual.

Ball, Susan →Tax on company reorganizations.

Balla, Audrey →Industrial Accidents : Employer Liability for Monetary Damages.

Ballantyne, W
Register of laws of the Arabian Gulf Supplements. – London : Graham & Trotman, 1989.
260.
A database of all laws and regulations originating in each country of the Arabian Gulf from the commencement of legislative promulgation to the present day. Drawn from original Arabic sources.
ISBN 1853331686 Llf £489

Ballantyne, W. M.
Index of Arab Laws. – London : LLoyd's of London Press, 1985.
Hbk
—Register of laws of the Arabian Gulf. – London : Graham & Trotman, 1989.
520.
ISBN 1853332534 Llf £545

Ballard, R. M. →Tolley's company law.

Ballots and trade union democracy / Roger Undy and Roderick Martin with the assistance of R. Blackwell and J. Hulton. – Oxford : Blackwell, 1984.
viii,240p; 24cm.
ISBN 0631135391 £19.50

Baltic Straits / by Gunnar Alexandersson. – The Hague : Nijhoff, 1982.
152p.
Includes index.
ISBN 902472595X Hbk £75.00

Baltus, Marc →Taxation and human rights : proceedings of a seminar held in Brussels in 1987 during the 41st Congress of the International Fiscal Association.

Baluchis and Pathans / by Robert G. Wirsing. – Rev & updated ed. – London : Minority Rights Group, 1987.
23p. – (Report).
Previous ed.: 1981. Bibliography: p.20.
ISBN 0946690510

Balvig, Flemming
Snow-white image : the hidden reality of crime in Switzerland / Flemming Balvig. – Oslo : Norwegian University Press, 1988.
123p.
Bibliography: p.119-123.. Translation of: Hvid som sne.
ISBN 8200074722 £17.50

Bamford, Brian
Bamford on the law of partnership and voluntary association in South Africa / by Brian Bamford. – 3rd ed. – Cape Town : Juta, 1982.
xlvii,274p.
Previous ed.: 1971. Includes index.
ISBN 0702112526
—Law of shipping and carriage in South Africa / by B.R. Bamford. – 3rd ed. – Cape Town : Juta, 1983.
xlvi,389p.
Previous ed.: 1973. Includes index.
ISBN 070211376X

Bamford on the law of partnership and voluntary association in South Africa / by Brian Bamford. – 3rd ed. – Cape Town : Juta, 1982.
xlvii,274p.
Previous ed.: 1971. Includes index.
ISBN 0702112526

Banerjee, Anil Chandra
Constitutional History of India, Vol. 1 : 1600-1858. – Calcutta : Mukherjee & Co, 1987.
586p.
Hbk £200.00
—English Law in India. – New Delhi : Abhinav Publications, 1984.
viii, 295p.
ISBN 8170171830 Hbk £120.00

Banerjee, B.N.
Criminal Pleadings. – 3rd ed. – Allahabad : Law Book Company, 1986.
1,000.
Hbk £220.00
—Law of Criminal Appeals and Revisions. – 4th ed. – Allahabad : Law Book Company, 1986.
ca 1000p.
Hbk £200.00

—Law of Execution. – 3rd ed. – Allahabad : Law Book Company, 1987.
1,600p.
ISBN 8185029431 Hbk £340.00

Banerjee, Gooroodas
Hindu Law of Marriage and Stridhana. – Delhi : Mittal Publications, 1984.
Hbk £300.00

Banerjee, S.C.
Specific Relief Act : Based on Tagore Law Lectures. – 8th ed. – Allahabad : Law Book Company, 1988.
1,100p.
Hbk £250.00

Bangladesh : unlawful killings and torture in the Chittagong hill tracts / Amnesty International. – London : Amnesty International, 1986.
38p.
ISBN 0862101107

Bank accounts : a world guide to confidentiality / Edouard Chambost : translated by Peter Walton and Margaret Thompson. – Chichester : Wiley, 1983.
xii,322p; 24cm.
Includes index. Translation from French.
ISBN 0471900761 Hbk

Bank Administration Manual. – 3rd ed. – Merehurst.
ISBN 01556231458 Hbk £53.95

Bank finance for companies / by R. Pennington. – London : Sweet & Maxwell, 1987.
150p; 22cm.
Discusses bank finance for specific purposes by way of letters of credit, bank guarantees and performance bonds, the issue of settling sterling commercial paper by companies, the legal implications of factoring, the provision of third party guarantees and securities for loans to companies within a group, and legal remedies available to banks to recover advances of all kinds made to them.
ISBN 0421384905 £15.00

Bank Manager's Handbook. – Cambridge : Woodhead-Faulkner, 1987.
ISBN 085941342X Hbk £25.00

Bank Marketing Handbook, The. – Cambridge : Woodhead-Faulkner, 1986.
ISBN 0859413330 Hbk £35.00
ISBN 0859413349 Pbk £12.95

Bank of England
Consolidated supervision of institutions authorised under the Banking Act 1979. – Bank of England. – London : Bank of England, 1985.
14,10,9 leaves.
Includes texts of European Communities Consolidated Supervision Directive and the revised Basle Concordat.
—Consultative paper by the Bank of England : the role of audit committees in banks. – Bank of England. – London : Bank of England, 1987.
12p.
—Relationships between the supervisors, auditors and managements of banks / consultative paper by the Bank of England. – London : The Bank, 1985.
13,5 leaves.
→ Syndicated credits market.

Bank Register. – London : Euromoney, 1988.
ISBN 187003161X Hbk £95.00

Bank security documents / J.R. Lingard. – 2nd ed. – London : Butterworths, 1988.
xxxiii,402p; 26cm.
Previous ed.: 1985. Includes index.
ISBN 0406106258 £45.00

Bank security documents / J.R. Lingard. – London : Butterworths, 1985.
xxvi,367p; 26cm.
Includes index.
ISBN 0406258198 £30.00

Banker's Almanac and Yearbook 1988 2 vols. – Skinner (Thomas).
ISBN 0611007231 Hbk £125.00

Banker's Almanac World Ranking 1989. – Skinner (Thomas).
ISBN 061100724X Hbk £75.00

Banker's documentary credits : issued in accordance with the Uniform customs and practice (1974 revision) of the International Chamber of Commerce / by F.M. Ventris. – 2nd ed. – London : Lloyd's of London Press, 1983.
xxi,350p.
Previous ed.: 1980. Includes index.
ISBN 0907432379

Banker's Handbook. – 3rd ed. – New York : Dow Jones-Irwin, 1988.
ISBN 1556230435 Hbk £69.50

Bankie, F.
Human Rights in Africa. – Apapa : Heritage Books.
Hbk £8.50

Banking : the Law in Canada. – Agincourt : Carswell, 1985.
This book describes the corporate structure of banks in Canada including the role of directors and officers and the rights of shareholders. The Bank Act and the Bills of Exchange Act are set out in the appendices to the work.
ISBN 045937290 Pbk £30.80

Banking and Business in South Africa. – London : Macmillan.
ISBN 0333444655 Hbk £29.50

Banking and Finance Law Review / Andrew Chant. – Agincourt : Carswell.
This book focuses on issues pertinent to the legal and financial communities. The text is divided into four parts: articles, commentaries on recent developents in banking in Canada and in the world, and casenotes and book reviews.
Hbk £75.75

Banking Dictionary. – Cambridge : Woodhead-Faulkner, 1984.
ISBN 3478512433 Hbk £25.00

Banking For Students. – Pitman, 1986.
ISBN 0273023209 Pbk £7.95

Banking in South African law / by Nigel Willis. – Cape Town : Juta, 1981.
xxxiii,388p.
Includes bibliographical notes and index.
ISBN 0702112593

Banking In The American South From The Age Of Jackson. – Louisiana : Louisiana State University Press, 1988.
ISBN 0807114030 Hbk £33.25

Banking Law
Vol.1 : The law relating to domestic banking / by G.A. Penn, A.M. Shea and A. Arora. – London : Sweet & Maxwell, 1987.
xlix,537p; 24cm.
In five sections covering bank regulation, the banker-customer relationship, negotiable instruments, guarantees and securities and insolvency. Covers the Insolvency Act 1986, the Financial Services Act 1986, and the Banking Act 1987.
ISBN 042139000X Hbk £
ISBN 0421360607 Pbk £18.95
Vol.2 : The law and practice of international banking / by G.A. Penn, A.M. Shea and A. Arora. – 1987.
500p.
Discusses the legal effect of specimen clauses, agreements and other documentation used in international banking transactions. Takes a practical approach to the principles and emerging issues in the area of international financial markets.
ISBN 0421390107 Hbk £
ISBN 0421390107 Pbk £25.00

Banking law / by Clive Hamblin. – London : Sweet & Maxwell, 1985.
xxvii,377p; 22cm. – (Concises College Texts).
Includes index.
ISBN 0421327502 Hbk £18.50
ISBN 042132760X Pbk £11.50

Banking Law / Howcroft. – Oxford : Blackwell, 1985.
ISBN 0631143025 Pbk £9.50

Banking Law / Saxena. – Delhi : SBD Enterprises.
Hbk £10.00

Banking Law : Leading Indian Cases. – 2nd ed. in prep. – Bombay : Tripathi.
Hbk

Banking Law and Practice, 1985 : Conference Papers. – Woolloomooloo : International Business Communications.
ISBN 0582939445 Hbk £49.95

Banking Law and Practice, 1986 : Conference Papers. – Woolloomooloo : International Business Communications.
ISBN 0949072087 Hbk £55.00

Banking Law and Practice, 1987 : Conference Papers. – Woolloomooloo : International Business Communications.
ISBN 0949072125 Hbk £55.00

Banking Law and Practice. – Delhi : Dhanpat Rai and Sons.
Hbk £30.00

Banking Law and Practice / S.P. Jain. – New Delhi : Kalyani Publishers.
Hbk £25.00

Banking Law and Practice. – New Delhi : Himalaya Publishing House, 1987.
200p.
Hbk £80.00

Banking Law and Practice. – 5th ed. – New Delhi : Kalyani Publishers, 1988.
ISBN 8170960916 Hbk £60.00

Banking Law and Practice in Australia / F.W. Coops. – 2nd ed. – Butterworths, 1988.
552p.
ISBN 0409494577 Pbk £45.00
ISBN 0409494569 Hbk £65.00

Banking Law in New Zealand. – North Ryde : 43.00, 1986.
xxxiii, 287p.
ISBN 0455206570 Hbk £27.50
ISBN 0455206589 Pbk

Banking Law in the USA. – London : Butterworths, 1987.
ISBN 040610350X Hbk £80.00

Banking Law Review 1987. – London : Butterworths, 1987.
ISBN 0406570582 Hbk £64.00

Banking Litigation 1986. – Vancouver : British Columbia Continuing Legal Education Society, 1986.
ISBN 0865042527 Hbk £55.00

Banking Operations. – London : DP Publications.
ISBN 0905435982 Pbk £7.95

Banking Points From Case and Statute Law / F. E. Perry. – London : Waterlow, 1982.
122p.
ISBN 0080390277 Pbk £4.95

Banking Policy in Japan American Efforts at Reform During the Occupation. – Routledge.
ISBN 0145000033 Hbk £30.00

Banking Regulation Act, 1949. – Allahabad : Law Publishers, 1983.
227p.
Hbk £18.00

Banking Regulation Act, 1949 : Together with the Banking Companies (Acquisition and Transfer of Undertakings) Act, 1980 and the Public Financial Institutions (Obligations as to Fidelity and Secrecy) Act, 1983. – Lucknow : Eastern Book Company, 1984.
163p.
Hbk £30.00

Banking Regulation Act along with Rules and Various Allied Laws. – 4th ed. – Allahabad : Law Publishers, 1983.
Hbk £18.00

Banking services and the consumer / a report by the National Consumer Council. – London : Methuen, 1983.
x,246p; 24cm.
ISBN 0416357601 Hbk £
ISBN 0416357709 Pbk

Banking supervision / presented to Parliament by the Chancellor of the Exchequer. – London : H.M.S.O., 1985.
36p.
ISBN 0101969503 Pbk £4.30

Banking Supervision. – London : Butterworths.
ISBN 0406136033 Hbk £30.00

Banking System of Hong Kong. – London : Butterworths, 1987.
ISBN 0409995320 Pbk £25.00

Banking Theory and Practice. – 4th ed. – London : Vikas.
ISBN 0706936841 Pbk £10.95

Bankowski, Zenon
Essays in Law and Society / Geoff Mungham. – London : Sweet & Maxwell, 1986.
Hbk £10.50
—Lay justice? / Z.K. Bankowski, N.R. Hutton and J.J. McManus. – Edinburgh : T. & T. Clark, 1987.
xi,187p; 22cm.
Includes index. An analysis of the work of lay justice and a comprehensive study of the structure, operation and criteria of the Scottish District Courts.
ISBN 0567291391 Pbk £9.95

Bankruptcy, 1984. – Vancouver : British Columbia Continuing Legal Education Society, 1984.
ISBN 0865041571 Hbk £65.00

Bankruptcy. – Edinburgh : Green (W.) & Son, 1989.
Commentary on the law and practice of bankruptcy since the Bankruptcy (Scotland) Act 1985. Includes the text of the Act with subsequent amendments.
ISBN 0414008944 Hbk

Bankruptcy : Law and practice / Christopher Berry, Edward Bailey : foreword by Sir Nicolas Browne-Wilkinson. – London : Butterworths, 1987.
lx,668p; 26cm.
Includes index.
ISBN 0406526109 £40.00

Bankruptcy : Law and Practice. – London : Fourmat, 1987.
ISBN 1851900322 Hbk £28.50

Bankruptcy Law. – 8th ed. – Plymouth : Macdonald & Evans, 1981.
ISBN 0712102647 Pbk £3.95

Bankruptcy law of Canada / by L.W. Houlden and C.H. Morawetz. – New ed. 2 v. – Toronto : Carswell, 1984.
looseleaf.
Previous ed.: 1960. Includes text of Bankruptcy Act.

Bankruptcy Manual. – Tolley Publishing, 1988.
ISBN 0854592199 Hbk

Bankruptcy of Individuals and Partnerships. – Bicester : CCH.
ISBN 0863251439 Hbk £48.00
ISBN 086325084X Pbk £36.00

Bankruptcy Procedure / Freize. – 9th ed. – London : Longman Professional, 1987.
ISBN 08512313073 Pbk £13.95

Bankruptcy (Scotland) Act 1985. – Tolley Publishing.
ISBN 854592814 Hbk £17.95

Bankruptcy, Winding-Up, Arrangements, Compositions and Similar Proceedings : Draft Convention and Report. – Kirchberg : Commission of the European Communities, 1982.
116p.
Hbk

Bankruptcy: the law and practice. – London : Fourmat, 1988.
534.
Discusses new insolvency legislation as it applies to bankruptcy.
ISBN 1851900322 Hbk £32.50

Banks abroad : establishment - operations - supervision / editors Friedrich Schwank & Frank R. Ryder. – London : Kluwer, 1986.
xi,423p.
Includes bibliographies and index.
ISBN 0903393964

Banks, B.
Questions and Answers for Professional Accountancy Students. – Bristol : SCCA Publishing.
ISBN 0950391352 Pbk

Banks, M.
Using a law library. – 4th ed. – Agincourt : Carswell, 1985.
ISBN 0459376101 Hbk £17.60

Banks, R. C. I'Anson
Encyclopedia of professional partnerships / by R.C. I'Anson Banks. – London : Sweet & Maxwell, 1987.
1000p; 25cm.
Includes index.
ISBN 0421332905 £165.00
→ Lindley on the law of partnership.

Bankson, Lloyd → Euronotes : RUFs, TRUFs, NIFs, SNIFs and BONUSes.

Bannon, C.J.
Australian Patent Law. – Butterworths, 1984.
349p.
ISBN 0409492035 Hbk £65.00

Bannon, Charles Joseph
Passing off trade deception trade marks / Charles Joseph Bannon. – Sydney : Butterworths, 1985.
xxv,172p.
ISBN 0409492442 A$59

Bansal, V.K.
Right to Life and Personal Liberty in India. – New Delhi : Deep and Deep Publications, 1987.
296p.
Hbk £175.00

Banton, Michael
Investigating robbery / Michael Banton. – Aldershot : Gower, 1985.
vii,126p; 22cm.
Bibliography: p109-110. - Includes index.
ISBN 0566051141 £16.50
—Teaching about prejudice / by Michael Banton ... et al. : edited by Ben Whitaker. – London : Minority Rights Group, 1983.
24p. – (Report).
Bibliography: p.23-24.
ISBN 0946690006

Bar Association of India →Judiuciary today : disturbing trends and suggestion for reforms.
→ State of emergency and permissible measures of derogation.

Bar finals guide / Catherine Newman. – 3rd ed. – London : Sweet & Maxwell, 1987.
300p; 23cm.
Previous ed.: 1984. Includes index.
ISBN 0421359102 Pbk £14.50

Bar List of the United Kingdom. – London : Sweet & Maxwell, 1982.
ISBN 0420465200 Pbk £48.25

Bar-Niv, Zvi H, et al
International labour law reports
Volume 7 / Benjamin Aaron, Thilo Ramm, Tore Sigeman, Jean-Maurice Verdier, Felice Morgenstern, Kenneth William Wedderburn of Charlton. – Dordrecht : Nijhoff (Martinus), 1989.
688. – (International labour law reports).
A volume in the series of annual publications of labour law judgements by the highest courts in a number of jurisdictions. Each judgement reprinted has Headnotes and usually an Annotation setting out the legal issues involved, and basic facts of the case if not included in the judgement. Judgements are normally printed in extenso.
ISBN 0792300998 Hbk £105

Bar Review Guide in Political Law. – 3rd ed. – Quezon City : University of the Philippines, Law Center, 1981.
190p.
Pbk £20.00

Barack, Boaz
Application of the Competition Rules (Antitrust Law) of the European Economic Community to Enterprises and Arrangements External to the Common Market. – Dordrecht : Kluwer, 1981.
474p.
Hbk £104.00

Baranek, Patricia M →Ordering of justice : a study of accused persons as dependants in the criminal process.

Baratta, Alessandro
Impact of sociology of law on government action: proceedings of a conference on sociology of law, Saarbrucken, Federal Republic of Germany, September 5th-8th, 1977. – Bern : Peter Lang, 1981.
448p.
ISBN 3820461736 Pbk £57.00

Barav, A →Yearbook of European law, Vol 8: 1988.

Barbados consolidated index of statutes and subsidiary legislation to 1st January 1986 / compiled at the Faculty of Law Library, University of the West Indies, Barbados. – Bridgetown : Faculty of Law Library, University of the West Indies, 1986.
xi,122p.
Previous ed.: 1st January 1985. 'One of a series in the West Indian Legislation Indexing Project (WILIP) compiled in co-operation with the British Development Division'.

Barbados law reports. – Barbados : Ministry of the Attorney General, 1981.
Being published retrospectively. First volume issued: Vol. 11(1976).

Barbados, Laws Of (Subsidiary Legis 78). – Sweet & Maxwell, 1983.
ISBN 0421317604 Hbk £260.00

Barberis, Julio A.
International groundwater resources law / by Julio A. Barberis for the Legislation Branch, FAO Legal Office. – Rome : Food and Agriculture Organization of the United Nations, 1986.
vii,67p. – (Legislative study).
ISBN 925102507X

Barc, Stephen →Tolley's company law.

Barclay et al, L.
Guide to South African Industrial Incentives. – Durban : 0409017000.
ISBN 0409016985 £295.00 (with binder)

Barcroft
Accounts, Audit and Taxation of Clubs. – London : Butterworths, 1983.
Pbk

Bardi, Luciano →Institutions and the decision-making process in the draft treaty.

Barefoot, J Kirk
Undercover investigation. – London : Butterworths, 1983.
ISBN 0409950769 Hbk £25.00

Barendt, E.
Freedom of Speech. – Oxford : Oxford University Press, 1985.
ISBN 0198253818 Hbk £35.00

Barendt, E. M.
Freedom of speech / Eric Barendt. – Oxford : Clarendon, 1985.
xxii,314p; 22cm.
Includes index.
ISBN 0198253818 £35.00
→ Law of social security.

Barker
Decision Making in Magistrates' Courts / Sturges. – London : Fourmat, 1986.
ISBN 1851900179 Pbk £4.95

Barker, Douglas
O'Brien's Encyclopedia of Forms : Division Four-Leases
Vol. 8. – Aurora : Canada Law Book Co. – (Abridgments and Encyclopedias).
Hbk £55.00

Barker, M.C. →Commentary on Standard Conditions of Contract : NZSS 623:1964.

Barlow →Solicitors and their business clients.

Barlow, John, et al
Wills administration and taxation: a practical guide / Lesley King, Anthony King. – 3rd. – London : Sweet & Maxwell, 1988.
Covers substantive law, tax considerations, will drafting. The chapter dealing with inheritance tax has been updated to include the new rules introduced in the Finance Act 1986. Also covers the new provisions of the Insolvency Act 1986. The text is illustrated with worked examples.
ISBN 0421382708 Pbk £17.50

Barlow, Patricia M
Aviation antitrust : the extraterritorial application of the United States antitrust laws and international air transportation / Patricia M. Barlow. – Deventer : Kluwer Law and Taxation, 1987.
xliv,210p.
Bibliography: pp.xxv-xxx - Includes index.
ISBN 9065442936

Barlow, R. F. D. →Williams' law relating to wills.
→ Williams on wills.

Barnard, A.H.
Bernard et al : The South African Law of Persons and Family Law / D.S.P. Cronje. – 3rd ed. – Durban : Professional Publishers, 1984.
ISBN 0409046205 Hbk £75.00
ISBN 0409046213 Pbk £65.00

Barnard, D.
Civil Court in Action. – 2nd ed. – London : Butterworths, 1985.
ISBN 0406556229 Hbk £21.00
ISBN 0406556237 Pbk £14.95

Barnard, David
Criminal court in action / David Barnard : assisted by Peter L. Gray, Paul S. Bogan. – 3rd ed. – London : Butterworth, 1988.
xviii,365p; 25cm.
Previous ed.: 1979. Includes index.
ISBN 0406556148 Hbk £16.50
ISBN 0406556156 Pbk £10.95
→ Evidence & advocacy.
—Family court in action / David Barnard. – London : Butterworths, 1983.
xiv,281p; 26cm.
Includes index.
ISBN 0406556504 Hbk £
ISBN 0406556512 Pbk

Barnard, Johan
European Parliament and Article 173 of the EEC Treaty / by John Barnard. – Florence : European University Institute, 1987.
59p.

Barnes
Pension Scheme Trustee / Spill. – 2nd ed. – Taxbriefs.
ISBN 00907342124 Hbk £17.00
—Sports and the Law in Canada. – Toronto : Butterworths, 1983.
400p.
ISBN 0409812919 Pbk £40.00

Barnes, John
Sports and the Law in Canada. – 2nd ed. – Butterworths, 1988.
416p.
Covers criminal prosecution for hockey violence, collective agreements and labour relations, agents and contract negotiations, government policies in support of sport, discrimination on the basis of sex and nationality, antitrust law aspects of professional league organisation, players' service contracts, public regulation of different sports, tort liability and compensation for sports injuries.
ISBN 0409811815 Pbk £30

Barnes, Michael →Hill and Redman's law of landlord and tenant.

Barnes, Paul
Building societies : the myth of mutuality / Paul Barnes : with a foreword by Ken Weetch. – London : Pluto, 1984.
xv,171p; 20cm.
ISBN 0861047591 Pbk £4.95

Barnes, Sheenagh →Consumer Credit Law in Australia : a Commentary on the New Credit Legislation.

Barnes, Shenagh
Advertising regulation / by Shenagh Barnes and Michael Blakeney. – Sydney : Law Book Co., 1982.
lii,612p.
Bibliography: p.xlv-lii. - Includes index.
ISBN 0455205450

Barnett, M →Eenvormige hofreels.
—South African Law Reports (1947 to Date) / J. L. Buchanan. – Durban : Butterworths.
Hbk

Barnett, Stephen R.
Law of international telecommunications in the United States / Stephen R. Barnett, Michael Botein, Eli M. Noam. – Baden-Baden : Nomos, 1988.
271p.
ISBN 3789013080

Barnsley, D
Land options. – 2nd. – London : Longman Professional (UK), 1990.
– (Practitioner series).
Covers the law relating to the creation, transfer and exercise of options to purchase, rights of pre-emption, options to renew and determine leases and rent review clauses. Comments on relevant precedents, and considers the tax implications.

Barnsley, D. G.
Barnsley's conveyancing law and practice. – 3rd ed. – London : Butterworth, 1988.
lxxviii,677p.
Previous ed.: 1982. Includes index.
ISBN 0406556342 Pbk £32.00
ISBN 0406556350 £19.95
—Barnsley's conveyancing law and practice / P. W. Smith. – 2nd ed. – London : Butterworths, 1982.
lvi,715p; 26cm.
Previous ed.: 1973. Includes index.
ISBN 0406556326 Hbk
ISBN 0406556334 Pbk
—Barnsley's Conveyancing Law and Practice. – 3rd ed. – London : Butterworths.
ISBN 0406556342 Hbk £40.00
ISBN 0406556350 Pbk £24.95

Barnsley's Conveyancing Law and Practice. – 3rd ed. – London : Butterworths.
ISBN 0406556342 Hbk £40.00
ISBN 0406556350 Pbk £24.95

Barnsley's conveyancing law and practice / P. W. Smith. – 2nd ed. – London : Butterworths, 1982.
lvi,715p; 26cm.
Previous ed.: 1973. Includes index.
ISBN 0406556326 Hbk
ISBN 0406556334 Pbk

Barnsley's conveyancing law and practice. – 3rd ed. – London : Butterworth, 1988.
lxxviii,677p.
Previous ed.: 1982. Includes index.
ISBN 0406556342 Pbk £32.00
ISBN 0406556350 £19.95

Barony of Strange / Committee for Privileges. – London : H.M.S.O., 1986.
1 leaf. – (1985-86 H.L. 175).
ISBN 0104175869

Barounos
Competition Law of the UK and the Republic of Ireland / Allan. – Matthew Bender, 1988.
ISBN 0000999068 Hbk £59.00

Barr, N. A. →Public finance in theory and practice.

Barratt, et al
Aviation Claims. – London : Lloyd's of London Press, 1987.
ISBN 1850440948 Hbk

Barrell, G.
Teachers and the Law / J. Partington. – 6th ed. – London : Sweet & Maxwell, 1985.
ISBN 0416421709 Hbk £22.50
ISBN 0416395309 Pbk £12.95

Barrett →Avoidance of fraudulent transfers and related bankruptcy crimes : papers delivered at the meetings of Committee J - Creditor's Rights, Insolvency, Liquidation and Reorganizations, Vienna, 2-7 September 1984.
—Principles of Income Taxation / Green. – Sydney : Butterworths, 1985.
256p.
ISBN 040949058X Hbk

Barrett, Brenda →Cases and statutes on tort.
—Employment and safety in the offshore oil industry / Brenda Barrett, Brian Hindley and Richard Howells. – London : Kogan Page, 1987.
200p; 24cm.
ISBN 1850910707 £45.00

Barrie-Vespra Annexation Act, 1983, Bill 142 : An Act Respecting the City of Barrie and the Township of Vespra. – Ontario : Ontario Government Publications Service, 1983.
6p.
Hbk £0.30

Barrister, A.
Every Man's Own Lawyer. – 71st ed. – London : Macmillan, 1981.
896p.
ISBN 0333218493 Hbk £15.00
ISBN 0333318358 Pbk £7.95

Barrister, M. A →Private company in Germany : a translation and commentary.

Barristers' clerks : the law's middlemen / John A. Flood. – Manchester : Manchester University Press, 1983.
vii,164p; 23cm.
Bibliography: p157-162. - Includes index.
ISBN 0719009286 £17.50

Barritt, Denis
Northern Ireland : A Problem to Every Solution. – London : Quaker Peace & Service, 1982.
147p.
ISBN 0901689173 Pbk £1.30

Barron, Jerome A.
Public Rights and the Private Press. – Toronto : Butterworths, 1981.
224p.
Examines the various points at which the law intersects with journalism, and looks into the complications arising from the increased tendency of the mass media to acquire a monopolistic status in society. Concludes with a speculative enquiry into what the future of media law will be like.
ISBN 0409812951 Hbk £19.95

Barrow
Court Divided : The Fifth Circuit Court of Appeals And the Policies of Judicial Reform / Walker. – Yale University Press.
ISBN 0300041659 Hbk £20.00

Barrow, Colin →Taking Up a Franchise.

Barrow, G. W. S.
Acts of Malcolm IV 1153-1165. – Edinburgh : Edinburgh University Press.
358p. – (Regesta Regum Scottorum Vol. 1).
ISBN 0852241410 Hbk £20.00
—Acts of William I, 1165-1214. – Edinburgh : Edinburgh University Press.
570p. – (Regesta Regum Scottorum Vol. 2).
ISBN 0852241429 Hbk £20.00

Barrow, Robin
Injustice, inequality and ethics : a philosophical introduction to moral problems / Robin Barrow. – Brighton, Sussex : Wheatsheaf, 1982.
xii,204p.
Includes index. Bibliography: p199-202.
ISBN 038920269X Barnes & Noble

Barry, Donald D →Law and the Gorbachev era : essays in honor of Dietrich Andre Loeber.

Barry, M.A.
Winding-up and bankruptcy procedures. – Shaws Linton Publications, 1988.
ISBN 0906653142 Hbk £12.95

Bartels, Martin →Bibliography on transnational law of natural resources.
—Contractual adaptation and conflict resolution, based on venture contracts for mining projects in developing countries / Martin Bartels : translation by James E. Silva. – Deventer, Netherlands : Kluwer Law and Taxation, 1985.
187 p.; 25 cm. – (Studies in transnational law of natural resources).
Includes bibliographical references. 'List of cited agreements': p. 177-187.
ISBN 3787540237

Barter, S.L.
Real Estate Finance. – London : Butterworths.
ISBN 0406115001 Hbk £50.00

Barthey, R.J.
ABC of Evidence / C.R. Brahe. – 4th ed. – Mortdale : Petty Publishing Co, 1988.
ISBN 0908508026 Hbk £44.50

Bartholomew, GW, et al
Sesquicentennial choronological tables of the written laws of the republic of Singapore 1834-1984 / Elizabeth Srinivasagam, Pascal Netto. – Singapore : Malayan Law Journal, 1987.
cxii,350.
Examines the legislative history of the Straits settlements and Singapore. Lists all the Indian acts from 22 November 1814 to 1 April 1867, and all other local legislation from 1867 to 1984. Each act is indicated as to its applicability to the present. Account of the various legislatures for Singapore over the last 150 years.
ISBN 9971700530 Hbk

Bartke, Wolfgang
Agreements of the People's Republic of China. – 2nd rev. enl. ed. – Munich : Saur, 1988.
ca 660p.
ISBN 3598108400 Hbk £248.00

Bartle, Ronald
Crime and the new magistrate / by Ronald Bartle. – Chichester : Rose, 1985.
vi,65p; 22cm.
Includes index.
ISBN 0859923312 Pbk £6.00
—Police Officer in Court : A Guide to Presenting Evidence. – London : Police Review Publishing, 1983.
ISBN 0851640060 Pbk

Bartlett, A.
Power, prejudice and pride. – Southampton : Ashford Press, 1987.
ISBN 0950764612 Hbk £8.95

Bartlett, A. V. B. →Butterworth's County Court Precedents and Pleadings.

Bartlett, Richard
Indian Reserves in Quebec. – Saskatoon : University of Saskatchewan, Native Law Centre, 1984.
44p.
ISBN 0888801408 Hbk £20.00
—Indian Reserves in the Atlantic Provinces of Canada. – Saskatoon : University of Saskatchewan, Native Law Centre, 1986.
92p.
ISBN 088880167X Hbk £25.00
—Indians and Taxation in Canada, Second Edition. – 2nd ed. – Saskatoon : University of Saskatchewan, Native Law Centre, 1987.
88p.
ISBN 0888801823 Hbk £25.00

Bartlett, Richard H.
Aboriginal Water Rights in Canada : a Study of Aboriginal Title to Water and Indian Water Rights. – Calgary : Canadian Institute of Resources Law.
231p.
ISBN 0919269230 Hbk £30.00
—Indian Act of Canada, Second Edition. – 2nd ed. – Saskatoon : University of Saskatchewan, Native Law Centre, 1988.
48p.
ISBN 0888802048 Hbk £10.00

Bartlett, Robert
Trial by fire and water : the medieval judicial ordeal / Robert Bartlett. – Oxford : Clarendon, 1986.
xiii,200p; 22cm.
Includes bibliography and index.
ISBN 0198219733 £19.50

Bartley, R.J.
Court is Open. – 3rd ed. 1987. – Mortdale : Petty Publishing Co, 1987.
208p.
ISBN 0908508042 Hbk £12.50

Bartley, Reg
ABC of Liquor Law in New South Wales. – North Ryde : Law Book Co, 1983.
ix, 197p.
ISBN 0455204209 Pbk £23.50
→ Crawford's Proof in criminal cases.
→ Criminal law in New South Wales, Vol. 2 : by Ray Watson and Reg Bartley.

Barton, Barry
Guide to Appearing Before the Surface Rights Board of Alberta / Barbara Roulston. – 2nd ed. – Calgary : Canadian Institute of Resources Law, 1986.
124p.
ISBN 0919269192 Hbk £17.00
—Reference Guide to Mining Legislation in Canada. – 2nd ed. – Calgary : Canadian Institute of Resources Law, 1988.
120p.
ISBN 0919269257 Hbk £30.00

Barton, Chris
Cohabitation contracts : extra-marital partnerships and law reform / Chris Barton. – Aldershot : Gower, 1985.
xxi,115p; 23cm.
Bibliography: p97-99. - Includes index.
ISBN 0566007118 £17.95

Barton, H.D.W.
Executorship Law and Accounts. – 8th ed. – London : Butterworths.
ISBN 0409600733 Pbk £18.80

Barton, P.G.
Criminal Procedure in Practice : a Manual for the Defence of Cases in Provincial Court / N.A. Peel. – 2nd ed. – Butterworths, 1983.
328p.
Outlines what a lawyer ought to do at each stage of the trial process. Covers preparation, tactics, 'case-flow management' and sound law-office administration, and speculation as to the effect of the Canadian Charter of Rights and Freedoms upon criminal procedure.
ISBN 0409812927 Hbk £60.00

Barton, S. J. →Butterworth's Company Law Service.

Bartrip, P. W. J.
Workmen's compensation in twentieth century Britain : law, history and social policy / P.W.J. Bartrip. – Aldershot : Gower, 1987.
262p; 22cm.
Includes index.
ISBN 056605485X £17.50
—Wounded soldiers of industry : industrial compensation policy 1833-1897 / P.W.J. Bartrip and S.B. Burman. – Oxford : Clarendon, 1983.
xi,253p; 23cm. – (Oxford socio-legal studies).
Includes index.
ISBN 0198275099 £15.00

Baruch →People and employment.

Barwick, Garfield →Australian and New Zealand commentary on Halsbury's Laws of England (Fourth Edition).
—Australian Commentary to Halsbury's Laws of England. – Wellington : Butterworths.
Hbk
—Sir John Did His Duty : Australian Constitutional Law. – Wamberal : Serendip Publications.
ISBN 094937900X Hbk £10.00

Basic Bookkeeping for Solicitors. – 2nd ed. – London : Sweet & Maxwell, 1982.
ISBN 0421297603 Pbk £5.95

Basic book-keeping for solicitors / Richard Halberstadt. – 3rd ed. – London : Sweet & Maxwell, 1985.
300p; 23cm.
Previous ed.: 1982. Includes index.
ISBN 042133830X £12.00

Basic Community Cases. – Oxford : Oxford University Press, 1987.
ISBN 0198762127 Hbk £30.00

Basic Community laws / edited by Bernard Rudden and Derrick Wyatt. – 2nd ed. – Oxford : Clarendon, 1986.
xvi,407p.
Previous ed.: 1980.
ISBN 0198761996 Pbk £25.00 :
ISBN 0198761988 £9.95

Basic Construction and Surveying Law. – Oxford : Blackwell Scientific, 1984.
ISBN 0246119632 Pbk £10.95

Basic crucial issues in major construction projects : papers presented at a seminar held jointly with the Institution of Civil Engineers, London, June 1985 / International Bar Association. Section on Business Law. International Construction Contracts Committee. – London : International Bar Association, 1986.
207p.
ISBN 0948711051

Basic documents
Vol. 1 / International Maritime Organization. – London : I.M.O., 1983.
107p.
ISBN 9280111531

Basic documents in international law / edited by Ian Brownlie. – 3rd ed. – Oxford : Clarendon, 1983.
xi,406p; 21cm.
Previous ed.: 1972. Includes index.
ISBN 0198761589 Hbk £15.00
ISBN 0198761597 Pbk £8.95

Basic documents on human rights / edited by Ian Brownlie. – 2nd ed. – Oxford : Clarendon Press, 1981.
x,505p; 24cm.
Previous ed.: 1971. Includes index.
ISBN 0198761244 Hbk £22.50
ISBN 0198761252 Pbk

Basic documents on international migration law / edited by Richard Plender. – Dordrecht : M. Nijhoff, 1988.
viii,411p.
Companion to: International migration law / Richard Plender. Re 2nd ed. 1988.
ISBN 9024736676 Pbk

Basic Documents on International Trade Law. – Dordrecht : Kluwer, 1986.
766p.
ISBN 9024731682 Hbk £350.00

Basic documents on United Nations and related peace-keeping forces / compiled by Robert C.R. Siekmann. – Dordrecht, Holland : M. Nijhoff, 1985.
At head of title: T.M.C. Asser Instituut.
ISBN 9024731631

Basic employment law / Julian Riekert. – Cape Town : Juta, 1987.
xvii,120p.
ISBN 0702118427

Basic Human Rights. – Dhaka : Islamic Foundation Bangladesh.
Hbk £0.50

BASIC Investment Appraisal. – London : Butterworths, 1985.
ISBN 0408015675 Pbk

Basic Law : An Introduction for Students. – 2nd ed. – Plymouth : Macdonald & Evans, 1985.
176p. – (M and E Handbook Ser.).

Students
ISBN 0712106553 Hbk £3.95

Basic Law and Hong Kong's Future / Albert H.Y. Chen. – Butterworths, 1988.
ca 400p.
Covers the present constitution of Hong Kong, the political values of the Hong Kong Chinese, the Hong Kong model of 'one country, two systems', the relationship between central government and the SAR, the protection of civil liberties, economic, cultural and social aspects, and foreign, external and defence affairs.
ISBN 0409995673 Pbk £145.00
ISBN 040999569X Hbk £230.00

Basic Law for Business. – Palmerston North : Dunmore Press Ltd., 1984.
117p.
ISBN 0864690258 Pbk £9.95

Basic resourses on Nigerian law / by M.O. Olaitan and Oluremi Jegede. – Lagos : Libriservice, 1983.
iii,64p.
ISBN 9782372048

Basic Rules of the Geneva Conventions and Their Additional Protocols. – Geneva : Comite International de la Croix-Rouge, 1983.
63p.
Hbk £4.00

Basis of judicial review in administrative law / by J.F. Northey. – Auckland : Legal Research Foundation, 1981.
31p.
Bibliography: p.30-31.
ISBN 0908581149

Basques and Catalans / by Professor Kenneth Medhurst. – Rev 3rd ed. – London : Minority Rights Group, 1987.
12p. – (Report).
Includes bibliographical references.
ISBN 0946690537

Bassett, John C. → Bean and Lockwood's Rating valuation practice.

Bassett, W. H.
Environmental health procedures / W.H. Bassett. – London : H.K. Lewis, 1983.
xiv,266p; 25cm.
ISBN 0718604709 £13.00

Bassiouni, M. Cherif → Draft international criminal code and draft statute for an international criminal tribunal.
—Draft international criminal code and draft statute for an international criminal tribunal / M. Cherif Bassiouni. – 2nd rev. & updated ed. – Dordrecht : M. Nijhoff, 1987.
xxii, 492p.
Re ed. of: International criminal law / M. Cherif Bassiouni, 1980. Bibliography: p.267-353.
ISBN 0898389186
→ European inter-state co-operation in criminal matters/la cooperation inter-etatique europeenne en matiere penale, The Council of Europe's legal instruments/les instruments juridiques du Conseil de l'Europe.
→ Islamic criminal justice system.

Bastard Feudalism and the Law. – Routledge.
ISBN 041502613X Hbk £25.00

Basu, Durga Das
Administrative Law, Second Edition. – New Delhi : Prentice-Hall, 1985.
624p.
ISBN 0876924402 Hbk £120.00
—Comparative Constitutional Law. – New Delhi : Prentice-Hall, 1984.
560p.
ISBN 0876922302 Hbk £150.00
—Comparative Federalism : General Principles. – New Delhi : Prentice-Hall, 1986.
560p.
ISBN 0876924429 Hbk £150.00
—Constitutional Aspects of Sikh Separatism. – New Delhi : Prentice-Hall, 1985.
24p.
ISBN 0876924151 Hbk £5.00
—Constitutional Law of India, Fourth Edition. – 6th repr 1985. – New Delhi : Prentice-Hall.
528p.
ISBN 0876923988 Hbk £65.00
—Equity, trusts, specific relief / Durga Das Basu. – 5th ed. – New Delhi : Prentice-Hall, 1983.
xxiv,336p.
Includes index.
ISBN 0876922329
—Introduction to the Constitution of India, Eleventh Edition. – 7th repr. 1985. – New Delhi : Prentice-Hall.
478p.
ISBN 0986924194 Hbk £35.00
—Law of the Press, Second Edition : Asutosh Lectures, Calcutta University. – 2nd ed. – New Delhi : Prentice-Hall, 1986.
606p.
ISBN 0876924186 Hbk £75.00
—Law of Torts, Tenth Edition. – 4th repr. 1984. – New Delhi : Prentice-Hall.
232p.
ISBN 0876920253 Hbk £25.00
—Shorter Constitution of India, Ninth Edition. – New Delhi : Prentice-Hall, 1984.
1,104p.
ISBN 0876923341 Hbk £150.00

Basu, H.G.
Partition Act. – 4th ed. – Allahabad : Law Publishers, 1983.
178p.
Hbk £15.00

Basu's Law of Receivers. – 3rd ed. – Calcutta : Eastern Law House, 1984.
Hbk £165.00

Basu's Motor Vehicles Act. – 6th ed. – Calcutta : Eastern Law House, 1984.
Hbk £110.00

Batchelor, Anthony C.
Taxation Aspects of Banking Operations / P. F. Swaine. – London : Butterworths, 1985.
This book describes the tax consequences of all significant banking operations and how the effect of various taxes on banks differs from other corporations. An in-depth look at the taxation of banks in the United Kingdom.
ISBN 0406010692 Hbk £35.00

Bate, Stephen de B. → Satellite and Cable : International Protection.
→ Satellite and cable television : international protection : a specially commissioned report.
→ Television by satellite : legal aspects.
—Video law : a specially commissioned report / by Stephen de B. Bate and Richard McD. Bridge. – London : Longman Professional, 1985.
x,119p.
Includes index.
ISBN 0851210287

Bates
Introduction To Family Law 1987. – London : Law Book Co.
ISBN 0455207607 Pbk £20.00
→ Legal Structures for Voluntary Organisations.

Bates, Chris
Hong Kong Banking Ordinance / Anthony Williams. – London : Butterworths, 1988.
350p.
Contains an annotation of the Banking Ordinance of 1986 and the Amendment Ordinance of 1988, annotations that consider the practical implications of the new provisions with reference to extensive legal authorities in Hong Kong and other countries.
ISBN 0409995398 Hbk

Bates, Christopher
Companies (Amendment) Ordinance 1984 in perspective / by Christopher Bates. – Hong Kong : Hong Kong Law Journal, 1985.
xv,116p.
Reprinted from the Hong Kong Law Journal vol. 15 (1985). Includes index.

Bates, David L.
Proof in Criminal Cases in New Zealand. – North Ryde : Law Book Co, 1984.
xxxii, 407p.
ISBN 0455205221 Hbk £49.00
ISBN 0455205930 Pbk £32.00

Bates, E., et al
Workers' Compensation Practice and Procedure. – Vancouver : British Columbia Continuing Legal Education Society, 1982.
265p.
ISBN 086504063X Hbk £50.00

Bates, F.
Principles of Evidence. – 3rd ed. – North Ryde : Law Book Co, 1985.
322p.
ISBN 0455206139 Pbk £27.50
ISBN 0455206147 Hbk £41.50

Bates, Frank
Family law casebook / by Frank Bates and J. Neville Turner. – North Ryde, N.S.W. : Law Book Co., 1985.
xxxvii,732p.
Includes bibliographical references and index.
ISBN 0455203946

Bates, G.M.
Environmental law in Australia / by G.M. Bates. – Sydney : Butterworths, 1983.
xxvi,236p.
Bibliography: p.224-231. - Includes index.
ISBN 0409495182

Bates, James
Financing of small business / Desmond L. Hally. – 3rd ed. – London : Sweet and Maxwell, 1982.
xviii,243p; 23cm.
Previous ed.: 1971. Bibliography: p235-238. - Includes index.
ISBN 0421292008 £17.75

Bates, John H. → Industry and the regulatory agencies : a collection of the papers given at the fourth seminar organised by Committee F of the International Bar Association's Section on Business Law in April 1985 at Stratford-upon-Avon.

Bates, John N
UK marine oil pollution legislation. – London : Lloyd's of London Press, 1987.
ISBN 185044028 Hbk £45.00
ISBN 185044109X Pbk £16.50

Bates, N.
Introduction to Legal Studies. – 4th ed. – Butterworths, 1984.
456p.
ISBN 0409494038 Pbk £22.50

Bates, St. John → In memoriam J.D.B. Mitchell.

Bates, T. St. J. N. → Legal system of Scotland : cases and materials.

Bateson, Phyllis
Equal Pay In Northern Ireland. – Belfast : Queen's University of Belfast, 1986.
60p.
Pbk
—Industrial Tribunals in Northern Ireland / John McKee. – 2nd ed. – Belfast : Queen's University of Belfast, 1986.
125p.
Pbk
—Industrial tribunals in Northern Ireland : a practical guide / by Phyllis Bateson and John McKee. – Belfast : SLS Publications, Faculty of Law, Queen's University, Belfast, 1981.
xi,146p; 21cm.
Includes index.
ISBN 0853891915 Pbk

Bather → British Constitution.

Batstone, Eric
Working order : workplace industrial relations over two decades / Eric Batstone. – Oxford : Basil Blackwell, 1984.
viii,363p; 24cm.
Bibliography: p344-357. - Includes index.
ISBN 0631137513 £19.50

Batten, Jack
Everyday Law : a Survival Guide for Canadians / Marjorie Harris. – Toronto : Key Key Porter Books, 1987.
224p.
ISBN 1550130412 Pbk £14.95
—Judges . – Toronto : Macmillan of Canada.
ISBN 0771597290 Hbk £24.95
—Judges . – Markham : Penguin Books Canada.
ISBN 0140100717 Pbk £6.95
—Lawyers . – Markham : Penguin Books Canada.
ISBN 0140073906 Pbk £9.95

Battle of Human Rights : Gross, Systematic Violations and the Inter-American System. – Dordrecht : Kluwer, 1988.
390p.
ISBN 9024736870 Hbk £170.00

Baty : Polarised Law. – Repr. of 1914 ed. – London : Sweet & Maxwell, 1986.
– (Sweet and Maxwell Library Reprints).
ISBN 0421355204 Hbk

Baty, T.
Polarised Law. – Sweet & Maxwell, 1914 Reprint.
ISBN 0421355204 Hbk £21.00

Baudin, Phil → Law Firm of the Future - Today : Materials Prepared for a Continuing Legal Education Seminar Held February 5, 1983.

Bauduin → Elsevier's Fiscal and Customs Dictionary.

Baugh, William E.
Introduction to the Social Services. – 4th ed. – London : Macmillan, 1983.
208p.
ISBN 0333335430 Pbk £4.95

Baughn, et al
Banker's Handbook. – 3rd ed. – New York : Dow Jones-Irwin, 1988.
ISBN 1556230435 Hbk £69.50

Baum, A.
Statutory variations. – Routledge, 1983.
ISBN 0710093489 Hbk £17.95

Baum, Daniel J.
Cases and Materials on Administrative Law. – Butterworths, 1987.
450p.
Focuses on judicial review of administrative action and includes a discussion of natural justice and fairness, rule-making, bias, standing, grounds for review, and discretionary powers and remedies. Contains excerpts from relevant Acts and materials, a table of cases, a chapter on freedom of information legislation and notes on delegation and privative clauses.
ISBN 0409806277 Pbk £68.00
→ Consumer Law.
→ Criminal Law.
→ Family Law.
—Law of Health Care Facility Administration. – Butterworths, 1988.
ca 224p.
Deals with issues such as quality assurance – payment for services, physicians privileges, liability issues and employment relations.
ISBN 0409801747 Hbk
→ Tort Law.

Bauw, F. de
China Trade Law / Bernard Dewit. – Dordrecht : Kluwer, 1983.
478p.
ISBN 9065441131 Hbk £175.00

Bawcutt, P.
Captive Insurance Companies. – 2nd ed. – Cambridge : Woodhead-Faulkner, 1987.
ISBN 0859413829 Hbk £45.00

Bax, K. C. → South African Attorneys handbook.

Baxi, Upendra
Crisis of the Indian legal system / Upendra Baxi. – New Delhi : Vikas, 1982.
xiii,405p.
Includes index. Bibliography: p393-400.
ISBN 0706913698
—Law of Intellectual Property. – Bombay : Tripathi.
Hbk
—Towards a Sociology of Law in India. – New Delhi : Satvahan Publications, 1986.
Hbk £96.00

Baxt, R. → Cases and Materials on Corporations and Associations.
—Cases and Materials on Taxation. – 2nd ed. – Butterworths, 1984.
790p.
ISBN 0409491624 Hbk £75.00 incl. suppl.
ISBN 0409491721 Pbk £62.50 incl. suppl.
→ Discretionary Trusts : with 1978 Supplement.
—Guidebook to Partnership Law in Australia. – 2nd ed. – North Ryde : C.C.H. Australia, 1984.
350p.
ISBN 086903457X Pbk £38.00
—Introduction to Company Law. – 3rd ed. – North Ryde : Law Book Co, 1985.
xx, 271p.
ISBN 0455204663 Pbk £25.00
ISBN 0455205655 Hbk £38.00
—Introduction to the Securities Industry Codes / C.M. Maxwell. – Sydney : Butterworths, 1988.
256p.
Pbk £37.50
—Stock Markets and the Securities Industry : Law and Practice. – 3rd ed. – Butterworths, 1988.
340p.
ISBN 0409494674 Pbk £45.00

Baxter, David → Foundations of Real Estate Financing : The Mathematical Basis.

Baxter, Ian F. G.
Law of banking / by Ian F.G. Baxter. – 3rd ed. – Toronto : Carswell, 1981.
xl,574p.
Previous eds. entitled: The law of banking and the Canadian Bank Act. Includes bibliographical notes and index. Includes text of Banks and Banking Law Revision Act, 1980.
ISBN 0459337408

Baxter, Lawrence
Administrative law / Lawrence Baxter. – Cape Town : Juta, 1984.
lxi,796p.
Includes bibliographical references and index.
ISBN 0702115118
→ Natal and KwaZulu : constitutional and political options; proceedings of the workshop.

Bayefsky, Anne F
Equality Rights and the Canadian Charter of Rights and Freedom : Carswell's Canadian Legal Classic Series / Mary Eberts. – Agincourt : Carswell, 1985.
600p.
This work is a collection of essays examining section 15 of the Canadian Charter of Rights concerning equality rights. Decisions under the Canadian Bill of Rights, federal and provincial human rights statutes are discussed in the book.
ISBN 045932210 Hbk £38.50
—Legal Theory Meets Legal Practice. – Montreal : Academic Printing and Publishing, 1988.
400p.
ISBN 0920980228 Hbk £69.95
ISBN 0920980236 Pbk £34.95

Bayfield
Tax Planning for Family Business. – London : Butterworths, 1984.
ISBN 0406556806 Pbk

Bayles, Michael → Justice, rights and tort law.

Bayles, Michael D
Principles of law : a normative analysis / Michael D. Bayles. – Dordrecht : D. Reidel, 1987.
xxi, 398p.
Includes index. Bibliography: p.372-380.
ISBN 902772413X Pbk

Baylies, Carolyn → Dynamics of the one-party state in Zambia.

Bayne, Peter → Constitutional Case Studies of Pacific Island States.
—Constitutional review jurisdiction in Papua New Guinea / researched and written by Peter Bayne. – Waigani : Law Reform Commission of Papua New Guinea, 1981.
iii,64p. – (Occasional paper).
—Freedom of Information. – North Ryde : Law Book Co, 1984.
xxix, 347p.
ISBN 0455203563 Hbk £36.00
→ Review of administrative action.

Bazen, Stephen
Low Wages, Family Circumstances and Minimum Wage Legislation. – London : Policy Studies Institute, 1985.
97p. – (Family Income Support Part 10).
Hbk £3.50

Bazeu
Endorsement and Disqualification / Baker. – London : Butterworths.
ISBN 040613801X Pbk £24.50

Beale, H. G.
Contract : cases and materials / H.G. Beale, W.D. Bishop, M.P. Furmston. – London : Butterworths, 1985.
xxxvi,737p; 26cm.
ISBN 0406005265 Hbk £
ISBN 0406005281 Pbk
→ Law and Social Change.

Beale, R.
Trading in gold futures. – Cambridge : Woodhead-Faulkner, 1985.
ISBN 0859412687 Hbk £25.00

Beaman, Roger T.
Ontario Municipal Board Reports (O.M.B.R.) 1972-Present. – Aurora : Canada Law Book Co.
1000p.
Hbk £80.00

Beams, F.A.
Advanced Accounting. – 4th ed. – Prentice-Hall, 1988.
ISBN 0130101826 Hbk £46.75

Bean and Lockwood's Rating valuation practice / Arthur Lockwood, John C. Bassett, David MacKmin, William Thomas. – 7th ed. – London : Sweet & Maxwell, 1987.
xxxiv,483p; 26cm.
New edition with an enlarged chapter dealing with appeals to the Local Valuation Court and Lands Tribunal, and the role of the valuer appearing before them. The valuation of properties, including retail, office and industrial property, and licensed premises is covered.
ISBN 042047420X £40.00

Bean, D.
Injunctions (LPPN66). – 4th ed. – London : Longman Professional, 1984.
ISBN 0851212980 Pbk £14.95

Bean, David
Injunctions / David Bean. – 3rd ed. – London : Oyez Longman, 1984.
xxvi,149p; 22cm. – (Oyez Longman practice notes).
Previous ed.: 1982. Includes index.
ISBN 0851208576 Pbk £9.95

Bean, P.
Adoption. – Tavistock, 1984.
ISBN 0422784109 Hbk £19.95

Bean, Philip
Mental disorder and legal control / Philip Bean. – Cambridge : Cambridge University Press, 1986.
304p.
Includes bibliographical references and index.
ISBN 0521302099 £27.50
—Punishment : a philosophical and criminological inquiry / Philip Bean. – Oxford : Robertson, 1981.
viii,215p; 23cm.
Bibliography: p202-210. - Includes index.
ISBN 0855203919 £12.50

Bean, Philip Rimmington
Bean and Lockwood's Rating valuation practice / Arthur Lockwood, John C. Bassett, David MacKmin, William Thomas. – 7th ed. – London : Sweet & Maxwell, 1987.
xxxiv,483p; 26cm.
New edition with an enlarged chapter dealing with appeals to the Local Valuation Court and Lands Tribunal, and the role of the valuer appearing before them. The valuation of properties, including retail, office and industrial property, and licensed premises is covered.
ISBN 042047420X £40.00

Bean, R.
Comparative industrial relations : an introduction to cross-national perspectives / R. Bean. – London : Croom Helm, 1985.
iv,288p.
Includes bibliography and index.
ISBN 0709932510 Hbk £19.95 :
ISBN 0709932812 Pbk £9.95

Beasley, M.
Family at Law. – Police Review, 1985.
ISBN 085164051X Pbk £2.50

Beat Officer's Companion. – 2nd ed. – Police Review, 1986.
ISBN 0851640249 Pbk £4.25

Beat Officer's Companion. – London : Police Review Publishing, 1983.
ISBN 0851640036 Pbk £3.25

Beaton, John Angus
Scots law terms and expressions / John Angus Beaton. – Edinburgh : Green, 1982.
116p.
ISBN 0414006917

Beatson, J
Administrative law : cases and materials / M H Matthews. – 2nd ed. – Oxford : Clarendon Press, 1988.
700.
A sourcebook for those studying administrative law. The new edition has been revised to include the New Procedural System, Discretionary Powers, and Remedies. *Students in their second or third years*
ISBN 0198762062 Hbk £35.00
ISBN 0198762054 Pbk £18.50

Beattie, J. M.
Crime and the courts in England, 1660-1800 / J.M. Beattie. – Oxford : Clarendon, 1986.
xxiv, 663p; 25cm.
Bibliography: p645-651. - Includes index.
ISBN 0198200587 Hbk £48.00
ISBN 0198200579 Pbk £15.00

Beatty, David M. → Canadian labour arbitration.
—Putting the Charter to Work : Designing a Constitutional Labour Code. – Montreal : McGill-Queen's University Press, 1987.
ca 240p.
ISBN 0773506004 Hbk £30.00
ISBN 0773506012 Pbk £14.95

Beauchamp, Kenneth P. → Maritime boundary delimitation : an annotated bibliography.

Beaudoin, Gerald A → Canadian charter of rights and freedoms : commentary.

Beaumont → Air Law.
→ Law of Evidence.

Beaumont, B.
Rent reviews. – Oxford : Blackwell Scientific, 1987.
ISBN 000383106X Hbk £19.50

Beaumont, John → Evidence : cases and argument.

Beaupre, Remi Michael
Interpreting bilingual legislation / Michael Beaupre. – 2nd ed. – Toronto : Carswell, 1986.
xvi, 236 p.; 24 cm.
Re ed. of: Construing bilingual legislation in Canada. Includes index. Bibliography: p. 223-227.
ISBN 0459390600

Bebr, Gerhard
Development of judicial control of the European Communities / Gerhard Bebr. – The Hague : Nijhoff, 1981.
xviii,882p; 25cm.
Bibliography: p719-808. - Includes index.
ISBN 9024725410 Hbk £360.00
—Rule of Law within the European Communities. – Brussels : Editions de l'Universite de Bruxelles.
34p.
ISBN 2800402644 Hbk £50.00

Becchio, Bruno → Swiss company law.

Beck
Summary Judgment Procedure. – Butterworths, 1988.
113p.
ISBN 0409788538 Hbk £40.00
→ Ward's Tax Law and Planning, 6 Vols.

Beck, Charles A.
Beck's theory and principles of pleading in civil actions / I. Isaacs. – 5th ed. – Pretoria : Butterworths, 1982.
lxxiii,358p.
Includes index.
ISBN 0409012351
ISBN 040901236X

Beck, Stanley M.
Canada and the New Constitution : the Unfinished Agenda, 2 Vols. / Ivan Bernier. – Ottawa : Institute for Research on Public Policy, 1983.
xii, 399p.
This work examines the principles of Canadian corporate and partnership law in depth. The book covers the fundamentals of corporate finance and distribution, duties of management, the rights and remedies of shareholders, and more.
ISBN 0920380735 Hbk £10.95

Beckett
Revenue investigations manual / B E V Sabine. – London : Butterworths, 1987.
ISBN 0406500703 Pbk £19.50

Beckett, Elizabeth
Vicarious liability of parents for actions of their children who are found to be delinquent / Elizabeth Beckett. – Ottawa : Ministry of the Solicitor General, 1985.
ii,79 leaves. – (User report).
Includes bibliographical references.

Beck's theory and principles of pleading in civil actions / I. Isaacs. – 5th ed. – Pretoria : Butterworths, 1982.
lxxiii,358p.
Includes index.
ISBN 0409012351
ISBN 040901236X

Beckton, Clare F. → Canadian Charter of Rights : law practice revolutionized.
→ Courts and the Charter.
—Law and the media in Canada / Clare F. Beckton. – Toronto, Canada : Carswell, 1982.
xvi, 161 p.; 24 cm.
Includes index. Bibliography: p. xi-xvi.
ISBN 0459344501 Pbk
—Recurring Issues in Canadian Federalism / A. Wayne Mackay. – Toronto : University of Toronto Press, 1986.
232p.
ISBN 0802073042 Hbk £14.95

Becton Dickinson UK Limited : the supply of hypodermic syringes and hypodermic needles / a report by the Director General of Fair Trading on an investigation under section 3 of the Competition Act 1980. – London : Office of Fair Trading, 1988.
39p.

Beddie, B. D.
Some aspects of aid to the civil power in Australia / B.D. Beddie and S. Moss. – Canberra : Department of Government, University of New South Wales, 1982.
92p. – (Occasional monograph).
ISBN 0959325409

Beecham, B.
Investment. – London : Pitman Publishing, 1988.
ISBN 0273028944 Pbk £9.95

Beek, Jan M. van der →Dutch business law : legal, accounting, and tax aspects of business in the Netherlands.
→ Tax aspects of acquisitions and mergers.

Beer, W.V. de
Newall : Law and Practice of Deeds Registration / R.F. Rorke. – 3rd ed. in prep. – Durban : Professional Publishers.
Hbk

Before You See A Solicitor (It's Your Law). – 2nd ed. – London : Longman Professional, 1983.
ISBN 0851207790 Pbk £6.95

Begbie, Matthew Baillie
Man for a New Country. – Victoria : Sono Nis Press.
334p.
ISBN 0888260687 Hbk £16.95

Begg, P. F. C.
Corporate acquisitions and mergers : a practical guide to the legal, financial and administrative implications / P.F.C. Begg : foreword by Lord Hanson. – 2nd ed. – London : Graham & Trotman, 1986.
320p; 22cm.
Previous ed.: 1985. Includes index.
ISBN 0860108139 Hbk £40.00 :
ISBN 0860108090 Pbk £20.00

Beggar your neighbours : apartheid power in Southern Africa / Joseph Hanlon. – London : Catholic Institute for International Relations in collaboration with Currey, 1986.
xi,352p; 24cm.
Includes index.
ISBN 0852553072 Hbk £25.00
ISBN 0946848270 CIIR (pbk) £8.95

Begho, Philip
Precedents on objects of incorporation / by Philip Begho. – s.l. : s.n., 1986.
92p.

Beginners' Guide To The Stock Market. – Penguin, 1986.
ISBN 0140093931 Pbk £3.95

Beginning Lives. – Oxford : Blackwell, 1987.
ISBN 0631153284 Pbk £8.95

Behan →Social work with young offenders.

Behan, David →Social work with young offenders.

Behaviour alteration and the criminal law / Law Reform Commission of Canada. – Ottawa : The Commission, 1985.
48,56p. – (Working paper).
Bibliography: p.44-48. Added t.p. in French: Les techniques de modification du comportement et de droit penal. Cover title: Protection of life : behaviour alteration and the criminal law. Pages numbered in opposite directions. Text in English and French.
ISBN 0662538579

Behind Closed Doors. – Thorsons, 1988.
ISBN 0722515677 Hbk £5.99

Beier, F. K.
Biotechnology and patent protection : an international review / by F.K. Beier, R.S. Crespi, J. Straus. – Paris : Organisation for Economic Co-operation and Development, 1985.
133p.
ISBN 9264127577
—German Industrial Property, Copyright and Antitrust Laws. – Veinheim : VCH.
ISBN 3527260048 Pbk £41.00

Bekker, J. C.
Marriage, money, property, and the law : a guide to the legal and financial consequences of a marriage between Africans / by J.C. Bekker. – Durban, South Africa : Butterworths, 1983.
53 p.; 24 cm.
Bibliography: p. 53.
ISBN 0409012106 Pbk
→ Seymour's Customary law in Southern Africa.

Belchambers
Law and Practice of Futures and Options / Cregan. – London : Sweet & Maxwell, 1988.
ISBN 04213914006 Hbk

Belgium and the draft treaty establishing the European Union / by Jan de Meyer. – Florence : European University Institute, 1985.
38p.

Beliveau, Andre →RCMP and the Management of National Security.

Belize
Statutory instruments. – Belize. – Belmopan : Government Printery, 1973.
Supplement to the Government gazette. Continues: Statutory instruments of British Honduras.

Belkaoui, A.
Inquiry and Accounting. – Quorum Press, 1988.
ISBN 089930222X Hbk £40.95
—New Environment In International Accounting : Issues and Practices. – Quorum Press.
ISBN 089930267X Hbk £40.95

Bell
House of Lords Appeals : 1821-1873, 28 Vols. 1842-1850, 7 Vols. /. – Abingdon : Professional Books.
Hbk

Bell, D.G. →Judges of New Brunswick and Their Times.

Bell, G. J.
Commentaries on the Law of Scotland in Relation to Mercantile and Maritime Laws, Movable and Heritable Rights and Bankruptcy, 2 Vols. – 3rd ed. Repr. of 1819 ed. – Abingdon : Professional Books.
Hbk £75.00
→ Year End and Accounting Period Tax Planning.

Bell, George J. →Tax and Financial Planning for Family Businesses.

Bell, George Joseph
Commentaries on some detached branches of the law of Scotland / By George Joseph Bell. – Edinburgh : Blackwood, 1828.
217p.
Originally published: in the 5th ed. of the author's Commentaries on the laws of Scotland, and on the principles of mercantile jurisprudence (1826).

Bell, John
Policy arguments in judicial decisions / by John Bell. – Oxford : Clarendon, 1983.
xiv,283p; 23cm.
Bibliography: p271-276. - Includes index.
ISBN 0198253974
→ Statutory interpretation.

Bell, Judith- →Border and territorial disputes.

Bell, Kathleen
Research Study on Supplementary Benefit Appeal Tribunals : Review of Main Findings; Conclusions; Recommendations. – London : HMSO.
55p.
ISBN 011760335X Hbk

Bell, S.
When salem came to the Boro. – Pan Books, 1988.
ISBN 0330305034 Pbk £3.99

Bell, T., et al
Drafting Commercial Documents. – Vancouver : British Columbia Continuing Legal Education Society, 1981.
278p.
ISBN 0865040206 Hbk £50.00

Bellamy, C.
Administering Central/Local Relations 1871-1919. – Manchester : Manchester University Press.
ISBN 0719017572 Hbk £29.95

Bellamy, C. W.
Common Market law of competition / Graham D. Child. – 3rd ed. – London : Sweet & Maxwell, 1987.
lviii,874p; 25cm.
Outlines the relevant provision of the EEC Treaty and of Community legislation. Examines collaboration in research, development, and production, industrial property rights, mergers and acquisitions, notification and its effects, civil remedies, enforcement and procedure, special sectors, and state aid. States the relationship between Community law and national law, especially British.
ISBN 0421282002

Bellamy, J.G.
Bastard Feudalism and the Law. – Routledge.
ISBN 041502613X Hbk £25.00

Bellis →EEC Anti-Dumping and other Trade Protection laws.

Bellis, Jean-Francois →Competition law of the EEC.
→ International trade law and practice of the European Community : EEC anti-dumping and other trade protection laws.

Belliveau, Jacques Bellemare
On Criminal Procedure / Jean-Pierre Lussier. – Agincourt : Carswell, 1982.
481p.
Hbk £42.00

Bellringer, David →Share Capital : Company Law and Taxation.

Belmont European Communitu Law Office → European company law : a guide to Community and member state legislation.

Belmont European Community Law Office → European banking law : a guide to Community and member state legislation.
—European insurance law : a guide to Community and member state legislation / Belmont European Community Law Office. – London : Financial Times Business Information, 1987.
ix,147p.
'The first edition of this report was published in 1982 and revised in 1983'. - T.p. verso.
ISBN 090210196X

Belobaba, E. P.
Consumer product warranty reform : regulation in search of rationality
Vol. 2 / E.P. Belobaba. – Ottawa : Policy research, Analysis and Liasion Directorate, Consumer and Corporate Affairs, 1983.
157p.
Vol. 1 published as: Products liability and personal injury compensation in Canada. Bibliography: p.151-157.
ISBN 0662124162
—Products liability and personal injury compensation in Canada : towards integration and rationalization
Vol. 1 / E.P. Belobaba. – Canada : Policy Research, Analysis and Liaison Directorate, Consumer and Corporate Affairs, 1983.
168p.
Bibliography: p.144-168.
ISBN 0662124154

Belobaba, Edward P.
New Constitution and the Charter of Rights : Fundamental Issues and Strategies / Eric Gertner. – Butterworths, 1983.
384p.
ISBN 0409832642 Hbk £55.00
—Supreme Court Law Review
Vol. 1: 1980 / Eric Gertner. – Butterworths.
544p.
ISBN 0409832618 Hbk £75.00

Belton, E.
Nanny for Your Child. – North Vancouver : International Self-Counsel Press, 1987.
Hbk £7.95

Belyavsky, D.
International Law of the Sea. – London : Central Books.
ISBN 0714727695 Hbk £6.95

Ben-Israel, Ruth
International labour standards : the case of freedom to strike / by Ruth Ben-Israel. – Deventer : Kluwer Law and Taxation Publishers, 1988.
vii,133p.
'A study prepared for the International Labour Office.' - T.p.. Includes index.
ISBN 9065443177

Benade, M.L. →Cilliers and Benade : Introduction to Company Law.

Bend and Bar in Nigeria. – Lagos : Nigerian Law Publications.
ISBN 9782325244 Hbk £100.00

Bender, D.
Computer Law. – Matthew Bender, 1977.
ISBN 0000999086 Hbk £112.00

Benedek, W. →New perspectives and conceptions of international law : an Afro-European dialogue.

Benedict On Admiralty / Norris. – 7th ed. – Matthew Bender, 1973.
ISBN 0000999052 Hbk £573.00

Benedictus, Roger
Labour law cases and materials / by Roger Benedictus & Brian Bercusson. – London : Sweet & Maxwell, 1987.
700p; 25cm.
Includes index.
ISBN 0421278609 Hbk £
ISBN 0421278706 Pbk

Benefits Conferred Under a Mistake of Law. – Victoria : Government of British Columbia, 1981.
Hbk £4.50

Benjamin, Michael →Family Mediation : Theory and Practice of Dispute Resolutions.

Benjamin's sale of goods / general editor, A.G. Guest. – 3rd ed. – London : Sweet & Maxwell, 1987.
xvi,1400p.
Contains chapters on the nature and formation of contracts, property and risk, performance, defective goods, consumer protection and remedies. Consideration of international sales, detailing the types of overseas sales, their financing and choice of rules. New edition includes over 100 new cases, and expanded discussion of bills of lading and their nature, c.i.f. contracts, f.o.b. contracts, and international carriage of goods by rail and container transport.
ISBN 0421346701 Hbk £110

Benn, Melissa
Rape controversy / Melissa Benn, Anna Coote, Tess Gill. – 3rd rev. and updated ed. – London : NCCL Rights for Women Unit, 1986.
32p; 20cm.
Re ed. - Previous ed. i.e. 2nd ed.: 1983. Bibliography: p32.
ISBN 0946088233 Pbk £1.50

Benn, S. I. →Public and private in social life.

Benn, Tony
Sizewell Syndrome : Nuclear Power, Nuclear Weapons and Public Policy. – London : Spokesman Books, 1984.
128p. – (Endpapers Ser. No. 7).
ISBN 0851244025 Hbk £3.95

Bennett and Cheesley : Let's Go Into Business / Roger G. Cheesley. – London : Butterworths, 1982.
ISBN 0372300235 Hbk £11.50

Bennett, C.
Barrie-Vespra Annexation Act, 1983, Bill 142 : An Act Respecting the City of Barrie and the Township of Vespra. – Ontario : Ontario Government Publications Service, 1983.
6p.
Hbk £0.30
—District Municipality of Muskoka Amendment Act, 1983, Bill 106 : An Act to Amend the District Municipality of Muskoka Act. – Ontario : Ontario Government Publications Service, 1983.
2p.
Hbk £0.30
—Municipal and School Tax Credit Assistance Lien Discharge Act, 1983, Bill 121 : An Act to Provide for the Discharge of Liens Registered Under the Municipal and School Tax Credit Assistance Act. – Ontario : Ontario Government Publications Service, 1983.
2p.
Hbk £0.30
—Municipal Private Acts Repeal Act, 1983, Bill 120 : An Act to Repeal Certain Private Acts Related to Municipalities. – Ontario : Ontario Government Publications Service, 1983.
9p.
Hbk £0.50
—Municipal Tax Sales Act, 1983, Bill 138 : An Act Respecting the Sale of Lands for Arrears of Municipal Taxes. – Ontario : Ontario Government Publications Service, 1983.
16p.
Hbk £0.50
—Residential leases : draftsman's handbook. – London : Longman Professional, 1985.
ISBN 085120774X Pbk £19.95

Bennett, C.S.C.
Insurances of Liability. – Witherby.
ISBN 0948691670 Pbk £4.95

Bennett, Charles
Drafting residential leases. – 2nd. – 1193, 1989.
Coverage includes the terms of the lease, premises, easements and ancillary rights, rents and rent increases, service charges anmd insurance. New edition covers changes resulting from the Housing Act 1988.
ISBN 0851214355 Hbk £35.00

Bennett, David
Subsistence vs. Commercial Use. – Ottawa : Canadian Arctic Resources Committee, 1982.
54p.
Pbk £6.00

Bennett, F.
Receiverships. – Agincourt : Carswell, 1985.
ISBN 0459374303 Hbk £38.75

Bennett, Fran → Opportunity lost : a response to the Green Paper on the Reform of Personal Taxation from the Child Poverty Action Group.

Bennett, Frank
Creditors' and Debtors' Rights 1987-1988. – Agincourt : Carswell, 1988.
563p. – (Bar Admission Course Material Ser.).
This is a guidebook to the rights of creditors and debtors. Topics include types of secured transactions, construction liens, personal property security, receivership and bankruptcy. Also included are sample forms and precedents used in different types of transactions and proceedings.
Hbk £75.75
—Receiverships : Carswell's Canadian Legal Classic Series. – Agincourt : Carswell, 1985.
588p.
This work explains all aspects of the receivership process in Canada from the use of consultants in the decision to appoint a receiver through to the discharge. A table of cases and extensive precedents are included in the book.
Hbk £80.00

Bennett, Graham → European Community environmental policy in practice, Vol. 2 : Netherlands : water and waste : a study of the implementation of the EEC directives : by Graham Bennett.

Bennett, J.M.
History of Solicitors in New South Wales. – Woolloomooloo : International Business Communications, 1984.
ISBN 094955314X Hbk £39.95

Bennett, John
Industrial relations : an international and comparative bibliography / compiled by John Bennett and Julian Fawcett for the British Universities Industrial Relations Association. – London : Mansell, 1985.
200p; 23cm.
Includes index.
ISBN 0720117879 £20.00

Bennett, R.
Chartered Assoc. Certified Accountants Organization & Management. – Pitman.
ISBN 027302941X Pbk £10.95

Bennett, Robert C.
Bennett and Cheesley : Let's Go Into Business / Roger G. Cheesley. – London : Butterworths, 1982.
ISBN 0372300235 Hbk £11.50

Bennett, S A
Short guide to divorce in the Sheriff Court. – 2nd. – Edinburgh : Green (W.) & Son, 1987.
A practical handbook detailing the more important rules and procedure with specimen craves, style divorce writs and the relevant Ordinary Cause forms.
ISBN 0414007816 Pbk
—Style writs for a Sheriff Court Ordinary Cause. – Edinburgh : Green (W.) & Son, 1989.
Provides styles of written pleading in a range of writs for a variety of ordinary action commonly encountered in a Sheriff Court practice.
ISBN 0414008456 Hbk

Bennett, T. W.
Acta Juridica / W. H. B. Dean. – Kenwyn : Juta & Co, 1986.
Hbk £5400.00
—Application of customary law in southern Africa : the conflict of personal laws / T.W. Bennett. – Cape Town : Juta, 1985.
xxxvii,250p.
Bibliography: p.xv-xxi. - Includes index.
ISBN 0702116017
→ Family law in the last two decades of the twentieth century : being a series of articles by a distinguished team of authors, first published in 'Acta juridica' 1983.
→ Private international law : the modern Roman-Dutch law including the jurisdiction of the Supreme Court.

Bennett, Trevor → Burglary in a dwelling : the offence, the offender and the victim.
→ Future of policing : papers presented to the 15th Cropwood Round-Table Conference, December 1982.

Bennett, W. Lance
Reconstructing reality in the courtroom / W. Lance Bennett and Martha S. Feldman. – London : Tavistock Publications, 1981.
x, 203p.

Bennion, F. A. R.
Consumer credit act manual / Francis Bennion. – 3rd ed. – London : Longman Professional (UK), 1986.
24cm.
ISBN 0851211003 Pbk £21
—Statute law. – 3rd. – London : Longman Professional (UK), 1990.
Investigation of the processes involved in creating statute law, with analysis of the problems resulting. New edition revised to take account of new European Community law, the Law Commission's report on the codification of criminal law, and amendments to the Interpretation Act 1978.

Benotto, Mary Lou → Income Tax and Family Law Handbook, 1 Vol.
→ Income tax and family law handbook.

Benson → Directing Corporate Growth.

Benson, Edward
Guide to Redundancy Law. – London : Macmillan, 1985.
256p.
ISBN 0333388526 Hbk £25.00
—Law of Industrial Conflict. – London : Macmillan, 1987.
ISBN 0333419138 Hbk £35.00

Benson, Henry
Reflections on the Royal Commission on Legal Services : a public lecture / delivered by Lord Benson. – London : Inns of Court School of Law, 1981.
10p; 23cm.

Bensouda, Amie → Women and legal affairs.

Bent, Stephen A. → Intellectual property rights in biotechnology worldwide.

Bentham and bureaucracy / L.J. Hume. – Cambridge : Cambridge University Press, 1981.
xii,320p; 23cm. – (Cambridge studies in the history and theory of politics).
Bibliography: p303-309. - Includes index.
ISBN 0521235421 £22.50

Bentham and the common law tradition. – Oxford : Clarendon Press, 1989.
506. – (Clarendon Law Series).
Offers a philosphical interpretation of the historical debate between Bentham and classical common law theory, which has shaped contemporary conceptions of the nature, tasks and limits of law and adjudication.
ISBN 0198256515 Pbk £15
ISBN 0198255055 Hbk £40

Bentham, J. → Rationale of Judicial Evidence Specially Applied to English Practice, 5 Vols.
→ Treatise on Judicial Evidence.

Bentham, Jeremy
Constitutional code
Vol.1 : edited by F. Rosen and J.H. Burns / Frederick Rosen, J. H. Burns. – Oxford : Clarendon Press, 1983.
xlv,612p,2folded leaves of plates; 24cm. – (The Collected works of Jeremy Bentham).
Includes index. Author: Jeremy Bentham.
ISBN 019822608X
—Correspondence of Jeremy Bentham
Vol. 6 : January 1798 to December 1801 : edited by J.R. Dinwiddy / J. R. Dinwiddy. – Oxford : Clarendon, 1984.
xxx,496p; 24cm.
Includes index.
ISBN 0198226136 £40.00
Vol.7 : January 1802 to December 1808 : edited by J.R. Dinwiddy. – 1988.
500p; 24cm.
Includes index.
ISBN 0198226144 £45.00
Vol. 8 : January 1809 to December 1816 : edited by Stephen Conway. – 1988.
480p; 24cm.
Includes index.
ISBN 0198226152
—Introduction to the Principles of Morals and Legislation. – Repr. of 1879 ed. – Abingdon : Professional Books.
Hbk £55.00
—Introduction to the Principles of Morals and Legislation. – London : Loughton.
ISBN 0879754346 Pbk £4.45
—Theory of Legislation / R. Hildreth. – Repr. of 1864 ed. – Abingdon : Professional Books.
Hbk £85.00
→ Utilitarianism.

Bentley, Christopher
Annotated Ontario Landlord and Tenant Statutes / John A. McNair. – Agincourt : Carswell, 1986.
300p.
This book fully annotates the Landlord and Tenant Act, the Residential Tenancies Act, and the Residential Complexes Financing Cost Restraint Act of Ontario, Canada. Digests of Residential Tenancy Commission decisions and relevant court decisions are included in the work.
Hbk £41.75

Bentley, Christopher A.
Annotated Employment Law Statutes of Ontario / John H. McNair. – Agincourt : Carswell, 1987.
308p.
This text annotates the following: the Occupational Health and Safety Act, Employment Standards Act, Industrial Standards Act, Human Rights Code, Pension Benefits Act, of the Ontario employment legislation.
Hbk £41.75

Bentley, Christopher A.W., et al
Williams and Rhodes on the Canadian Law of Landlord and Tenant. – 6th ed. – Agincourt : Carswell, 1988.
432p.
Llf £75.75

Bentley, Philip
State and community aids for European industry : their control and grant / Philip Bentley. – 1 v. – London : European Business Publications, 1983.
looseleaf.
ISBN 0946262012

Bentley, T.J.
Effective Communication for the Accountant. – London : Kogan Page.
ISBN 1850915202 Pbk £5.95

Benyon, John → Police : powers, procedures and proprieties.
→ Scarman and after : essays reflecting on Lord Scarman's report, the riots and their aftermath.

Benzie, Alasdair → Sweet & Maxwell's Statutes for the Law Society finals.

Beotra
Law of Forests : Central and States. – 5th ed. – Allahabad : Law Book Company.
Hbk £200.00
—Oaths Act / Shanglo. – 2nd ed. – Allahabad : Law Book Company, 1988.
60p.
Pbk £40.00

Beotra, B.R.
Customs Act : with Various Useful Appendices 1987. – 5th ed. – Allahabad : Law Book Company, 1988.
1,750p.
Hbk £375.00
—Immoral Traffic (Prevention) Act. – 4th ed. – Allahabad : Law Book Company, 1988.
600p.
Hbk £175.00
—Law of Cinematograph (Central and States), 1987. – 3rd ed. – Allahabad : Law Book Company, 1987.
Hbk £250.00

Bercusson, Brian → Employment Acts 1974-1980, with commentary.
→ Labour law cases and materials.

Bereskin →Research and development in Canada: a practical guide to financing, protecting and exploiting new technology.

Berg, Albert Jan van den →Art of arbitration : essays on international arbitration : liber amicorum Pieter Sanders, 12 September 1912-1982.

→ Netherlands Arbitration Act : Text and Annotations in English, French and German.

→ Yearbook Commercial Arbitration, 1989.

—Yearbook Commercial Arbitration, Volumes 1-12 (including Key). – Dordrecht : Kluwer.
ISBN 9065441352 Pbk Gld840.00

Berg, Gerard Pieter van den
Soviet system of Justice : figures and policy / by Ger P. van den Berg. – The Hague : M. Nijhoff Publishers, 1984.
Includes bibliographical references and index.
ISBN 9024730864

Berger, Raoul
Federalism : the founders' design / by Raoul Berger. – Norman : University of Oklahoma Press, 1987.
224p; 24cm.
Includes bibliography and index.
ISBN 0806120592 £16.50

Berger, Thomas R.
Fragile Freedoms : Human Rights and Dissent in Canada. – Richmond Hill : Irwin Publishing Inc..
298p.
ISBN 0772013586 Hbk £17.95
ISBN 0772013772 Pbk £9.95

→ Report of the Royal Commission on Family and Children's Law, 1st-13th, Summary of recommendations.

Berger, Vincent
Casebook on the European Court of Human Rights. – Dublin : Round Hall Press, 1988.
ca 350p.
ISBN 0947686371 Hbk £35.00

Bergman, David →Commentary on the JCT Intermediate Form of Building Contract.

Bergqvist, Sven-Runo →Decentralisation of local government at neighbourhood level.

Bergryd, Ulla →Political Value Patterns and Parties in Sweden.

Bergstrom, Villy
Studies in Swedish Post-War Industrial Investments. – Stockholm : Almqvist & Wiksell, 1982.
122p.
ISBN 9155413587 Hbk £62.00

Beri, B.P.
Law of Marriage and Divorce in India. – Lucknow : Eastern Book Company, 1982.
xxxii, 718p.
Hbk £100.00

Berkeley, F.
Butterworth's Costs Service, 2 Vols. – London : Butterworths, 1986.
Pbk

Berki, R. N.
Security and society : reflections on law, order and politics / R.N. Berki. – London : Dent, 1986.
256p.
Includes bibliography and index.
ISBN 0460046551 Hbk £15.00 :
ISBN 0460024698 Pbk £6.95

Berkin, Martyn
Matrimonial Suits and Property Proceedings : A Practitioner's Index of Practice and Procedure / Maurice Young. – 2nd ed. – Chichester : Barry Rose, 1986.
xliii, 222p.
ISBN 0859921328 Hbk £30.00

Berlin, Mark L.
Human Rights and Freedoms in Canada : Cases, Notes and Materials / William F Pentney. – Butterworths, 1987.
672p.
ISBN 0409813087 Pbk £80.00

Berlins, Marcel
Law machine / Marcel Berlins and Clare Dyer. – 2nd rev ed. – Harmondsworth : Penguin Books, 1986.
185p.
ISBN 0140226958

—Law machine / Marcel Berlins and Clare Dyer. – Harmondsworth : Penguin, 1982.
191p.
Includes index.
ISBN 0140224815

Bernard →Theoretical criminology.

Bernard et al : The South African Law of Persons and Family Law / D.S.P. Cronje. – 3rd ed. – Durban : Professional Publishers, 1984.
ISBN 0409046205 Hbk £75.00
ISBN 0409046213 Pbk £65.00

Berne Convention for the Protection of Literary and Artistic Works. – rep. 1987. – Geneva : World Intellectual Property Organization.
101p.
Hbk £20.00

Berne Convention for the Protection of Literary and Artistic Works : 1886-1986 / Sam Ricketson. – London : Centre for Commercial Law Studies, Queen Mary College, 1987.
lxii,1030p.
Bibliography: pp.981-1006. - Includes index. Includes the text of the Convention with revisions.

Berne Convention for the Protection of Literary and Artistic Works, Guide. – rep. 1987. – Geneva : World Intellectual Property Organization.
190p.
Hbk £55.00

Bernhardt, R. →Judical Settlement of International Disputes : International Court of Justice; Other Courts and Tribunals : Arbitration and Conciliation : an International Symposium.

Bernhardt, Rudolf →Encyclopedia of public international law.

→ International enforcement of human rights : reports submitted to the Colloquium of the International Association of Legal Science, Heidelberg, 28-30 August 1985.

Bernier, Ivan →Canada and the New Constitution : the Unfinished Agenda, 2 Vols.

→ Consumer protection, environmental law, and corporate power.

→ Family law and social welfare legislation in Canada.

—Labour Law and Urban Law in Canada / Andree Lajoie. – Toronto : University of Toronto Press, 1986.
232p.
ISBN 0802072976 Hbk £16.95

→ Law, society, and the economy.

—Regulations, Crown Corporations, and Adminstrative Tribunals / Andree Lajoie. – Toronto : University of Toronto Press, 1986.
224p.
ISBN 0802072933 Hbk £16.95

—Supreme Court of Canada as an Instrument of Political Change / Andree Lajoie. – Toronto : University of Toronto Press, 1986.
240p.
ISBN 0802072925 Hbk £16.95

Bernstein, Ronald
Handbook of arbitration practice / by Ronald Bernstein, contributors John Tackaberry ... et al. : foreword by Sir John Donaldson : introduction by Sir Michael Kerr. – London : Sweet & Maxwell in conjunction with the Chartered Institute of Arbitrators, 1987.
xxv,575p; 26cm.
Examines the constitution of the tribunal, the range of procedures available, conduct of the hearing, the role of advocates and expert witnesses, techniques of enforcement, and remuneration. Advises on arbitration in rent reviews, commodity contracts, maritime and construction disputes, and documents-only disputes.
ISBN 0421317906 £55.00

—Handbook of rent review / Ronald Bernstein and Kirk Reynolds : consultant editor on valuation and arbitration practice J.C. Hill. – 1. – London : Sweet & Maxwell in collaboration with the Royal Institution of Chartered Surveyors, 1981.
loose-leaf; 32cm.
Includes index.
ISBN 042127980X

Berry, Christopher
Bankruptcy : Law and practice / Christopher Berry, Edward Bailey : foreword by Sir Nicolas Browne-Wilkinson. – London : Butterworths, 1987.
lx,668p; 26cm.
Includes index.
ISBN 0406526109 £40.00

Berryessa
Global Investing / Kirzner. – New York : Dow Jones-Irwin, 1988.
ISBN 087094908X Hbk £26.50

Berryman, A.
Magistrates' Court Guide 1989. – London : Butterworths.
ISBN 0406108994 Pbk £16.95

Berryman, J. D. →Anthony & Berryman's Magistrates' court guide 1985.

Berryman, Jeffrey B., et al
Cases and Materials on Remedies. – Toronto : Edmond-Montgomery, 1988.
ca 1,000p.
Hbk £94.00

Berthoud →Costs of Care in Hostels.

—Credit Unions / Hinton. – Policy Studies Institute.
ISBN 085374405X Pbk £5.95

→ Money advice services.

Berthoud, R.
Credit Debt and Poverty. – London : Policy Studies Institute, 1988.
ISBN 0853743479 Pbk £8.95

Bertram, David
Cassell's UK Tax Guide 1988-89 : Comprehensive Aspects of Taxation / Edwards. – London : Cassell.
ISBN 0304315915 Pbk £19.95

—Tax consequences of receivership and liquidation / David Bertram. – London : Butterworths, 1982.
xxxii,423p; 22cm.
Includes index.
ISBN 0406220603 Pbk £20.00

Bertrand, Maurice
Third generation world organization. – Dordrecht : Nijhoff (Martinus), 1989.
232.
Describes why the search for peace through international organisations has always failed. Proposes a theory of peace and its relationship with the mode of production. Shows that the present United Nations System, including the Bretton Woods organizations, is not equipped for the needs of the modern world.
ISBN 0792303822 Hbk £40

Beseler, Dora von
Law dictionary : technical dictionary of the Anglo-Americal legal terminology including commercial and political terms : English-German / von Beseler/Jacobs-Wustefeld. – 4th rev. and enl. ed. – Berlin : W. de Gruyter, 1986.
ISBN 0899251773

Beseler, H. F.
Anti-dumping and anti-subsidy law : the European Communities / by J. i.e. H. F. Beseler and A.N. Williams. – London : Sweet & Maxwell, 1986.
xx,438p; 26cm.
Examines the interpretation and application of the anti-dumping and anti-subsidy laws in the EEC in the light of the relevant GATT codes. Compares practices with those of the USA and Canada. Deals with the current attempts within GATT to obtain an international consensus on the way anti-subsidy law should be applied in specific circumstances.
ISBN 0421358009 £58.00

Best
Right Way to Prove a Will. – Ibadan : African Universities Press.
Hbk £2.95

—Write Your Own Will. – Ibadan : African Universities Press.
Hbk £2.95

Best, G.
Humanity in warfare : International law conflicts. – Methuen, 1983.
ISBN 0416348106 Pbk £7.50

Best, Geoffrey
Nuremberg and after : the continuing history of war crimes and crimes against humanity / by Geoffrey Best. – Reading : University of Reading, 1984.
29p.
ISBN 0704902141

Bethell, Nicholas
Why do we sell butter to Russia? : and other common questions from the Common Market / by Nicholas Bethell. – London : European Democratic Group, 1987.
9 p.

Bettelheim →Investors' Guide to Commodities Futures Markets.

Betten, Lammy
Right to strike in Community law : the incorporation of fundamental rights in the legal order of the European Communities / by Lammy Betten. – Amsterdam : North-Holland, 1985.
xviii, 319p.
At head of title: T.M.C. Asser Instituut, The Hague. Includes index. Bibliography: p.291-306.
ISBN 0444878459

Better pensions for Canadians. – Ottawa, Ont. : Government of Canada, 1982.
vi, 61, 68, vi p.; 28 cm.
English and French. Title on added t.p.: De meilleures pensions pour les Canadiens.
ISBN 0662520513 Pbk

Better pensions for Canadians : focus on women. – Ottawa : Minister of Supply and Services, 1982.
18,19p.
With French t.p.: De meilleures pensions pour les Canadiens: la part des femmes. English and French text.
ISBN 066252053X

'Better way out' reviewed : memorandum / by the Society's Standing Committee on Family Law. – London : Law Society, 1982.
41p.

Between conviction and sentence : the process of mitigation / Joanna Shapland. – London : Routledge & Kegan Paul, 1981.
vi,167p.
Bibliography: p.165.
ISBN 0710009453

Beuthin : Basic Company Law. – 1984 rev. repr. – Durban. : Professional Publishers, 1987.
ISBN 0409012548 Pbk £48.00

Beuthin, R.C.
Beuthin : Basic Company Law. – 1984 rev. repr. – Durban. : Professional Publishers, 1987.
ISBN 0409012548 Pbk £48.00

Bevan, C. →Conveyancing Law.

Bevan, C. R.
Minimum Standard Guidelines for Australian Prisons. – Canberra : Australian Institute of Criminology.
Hbk £2.00

—Probation : Current Positions and New Directions. – Canberra : Australian Institute of Criminology.
Hbk £3.60

—Progress in Crime Prevention In Papua New Guinea. – Canberra : Australian Institute of Criminology.
free

Bevan, H. K. → Butterworth's Family Law Service.

—Child Law. – London : Butterworths.
ISBN 0406117039 Hbk £60.00

—Children act 1975 / by Hugh K. Bevan and Martin L. Parry. – London : Butterworths, 1978.
xviii, 307 p; 26 cm.
Includes index.
£13.50

—Law Relating to Children. – 2nd ed. – London : Butterworths.
ISBN 0406117004 Hbk £8.50
ISBN 0406117012 Pbk £7.50

Bevan, Vaughan
Development of British immigration law / Vaughan Bevan. – London : Croom Helm, 1986.
512p.
Includes bibliography and index.
ISBN 0709906633 £29.95
→ Practitioner's Guide to Child Care Law.

Bevan, Vaughan T.
Guide to the Police and Criminal Evidence Act 1984 / Vaughan T. Bevan and Ken W. Lidstone. – London : Butterworths, 1985.
xv,554.
This text gives a comprehensive dissertation on every aspect of the Act. The book includes a full text of the United Kingdom's Police and Criminal Evidence Act of 1984.
ISBN 0406014302 Pbk

Bexley → Child sexual abuse : joint investigative project : final report.

Beyleveld, Deryck
Law as a moral judgment / Deryck Beyleveld, Roger Brownsword. – London : Sweet & Maxwell, 1986.
xxix,483p; 24cm.
Bibliography: p457-462. - Includes index.
ISBN 0421329203 £30.00

Beyond Justice. – Oxford : Blackwell, 1987.
ISBN 0631152067 Hbk £25.00

Beyond Lex Loci Delicti : Conflicts Methodology and Multistate Torts in American Case Law. – Dordrecht : Kluwer, 1987.
550p.
ISBN 9065442766 Pbk £95.00

Beyond the courtroom : programs in community justice and conflict resolution / Benedict S. Alper, Lawrence T. Nichols. – Lexington, Mass. : Lexington Books, 1981.
xx,299p; 24cm.
Bibliography: p273-288. - Includes index.
ISBN 0669027243 £14.50

Beyond the ivory tower : social responsibilities of the modern university / Derek Bok. – Cambridge, Mass. : Harvard University Press, 1982.
318p; 25cm.
Includes index.
ISBN 0674068998 £11.20

Bhagwan, Vishnoo
Constitution of Great Britain / Vidya Bhushan. – New Delhi : Sterling Publishers, 1984.
166p.
ISBN 8120703421 £75.00

—Constitution of Switzerland, Canada, Japan and Australia / Vidya Bhushan. – New Delhi : Sterling Publishers, 1985.
136p.
ISBN 8120703448 Hbk £100.00

—Constitution of the United States of America / Vidya Bhushan. – New Delhi : Sterling Publishers, 1984.
172p.
ISBN 812070343X Hbk £75.00

—Constitution of U.S.S.R. and China / Vidya Bhushan. – New Delhi : Sterling Publishers, 1984.
228p.
ISBN 8120703413 Hbk £85.00

—World Constitutions / Bhushan Vidya. – New Delhi : Sterling Publishers, 1986.
752p.
ISBN 8120705459 Hbk £300.00
ISBN 8120704614 £45.00

Bhagwat, M.M.
Law of Surtax in India. – Bombay : Tripathi, 1983.
xx, 191p.
Pbk £60.00

Bhagwati, P.N.
Casebook on Income Tax Law. – Bombay : Tripathi, 1987.
832p.
Hbk £175.00

Bhalla, R. S.
Essays in constitutional law of Nigeria / by R.S. Bhalla. – s.l. : s.n., 1984.
v,112p.
Includes bibliographical references and index.
ISBN 9781660139

Bhandari, M.C.
Guide to Company Law Procedures, Vol. 1. – 11th ed. – Nagpur : Wadhura & Co, 1988.
Hbk £330.00

Bharati
Arms and Explosives Manual. – Allahabad : Orient Law House, 1984.
Hbk £115.00

—Explosives Manual. – Allahabad : Orient Law House, 1984.
Hbk £100.00

Bharatiya, V.P.
Religion-State Relationship and Constitutional Rights in India. – New Delhi : Deep and Deep Publications, 1987.
468p.
ISBN 8171000096 Hbk £325.00

Bhargava, Gopal
Socio-economic and legal implications of Urban Land (Ceiling and Regulation) Act, 1976 / Gopal Bhargava. – New Delhi : Adhinav, 1983.
xiv,172p.
Bibliography: p.167-170. - Includes index. Includes the text of the Urban Land Ceiling Bill.

Bhargava, Rajul → Language and Law.

Bharis in Bangladesh. – 4th rev. ed. – London : Minority Rights Group, 1982.
31p. – (Report).
Previous ed.: 1977.

Bhashyam
Negotiable Instruments Act / Adiga. – 14th ed. – New Delhi : Bharat Law House, 1983.
Hbk £160.00

Bhat, Shrikant
How Criminal Law Protects You. – Bombay : Jaico Publishing House.
Hbk £30.00

Bhatia, H.S.
Origin and Development of Legal and Political System in India, 3 Vols. – 2nd ed. – New Delhi : Deep and Deep Publications, 1982.
ca 700p.
Hbk £165.00

Bhatnagar
Companies Act. – Allahabad : Law Publishers, 1982.
Hbk £24.00
→ Law Relating to Notaries Act.

—Personal Laws in India. – Allahabad : Orient Law House, 1984.
Hbk £50.00

Bhatnagar, A.S.
Commentaries on Central Civil Services (Temporary Services) Rules. – Allahabad : Orient Law House, 1983.
Hbk £45.00

—Commentaries on Conduct Rules. – 2nd ed. – Allahabad : Orient Law House, 1983.
Hbk £60.00

—Guide to Departmental Promotions Enquiries, Punishments and Appeals. – 4th ed. 1983. – Allahabad : Orient Law House, 1983.
Hbk £90.00

Bhatnagar, Deepak
Labour Welfare and Social Security Legislation in India. – New Delhi : Deep and Deep Publications, 1984.
302p.
Hbk £150.00

Bhatnagar, J.P. → Commentaries on Notaries Act, 1985 : Act No. 53, 1952.

—Commentaries on the Societies Registration Act, 1860 / Vijay Malik. – 5th rev. ed. – Lucknow : Eastern Book Company, 1985.
314p.
Hbk £60.00

—Commentary on Sexual Offences. – Allahabad : Ashoka Law House, 1987.
1,000p.
Hbk £220.00

—Law of Arms and Explosives : Acts and Rules. – 3rd ed. – Allahabad : Ashoka Law House, 1987.
657p.
Hbk £160.00

Bhatnagar, R.P.
Language and Law / Rajul Bhargava. – New Delhi : Macmillan India.
224p.
Hbk £30.00

Bhatt, S.
Environmental Laws and Water Resources Management. – New Delhi : Radiant Pulbishers, 1986.
xii, 355p.
ISBN 8170270952 Hbk £20.00

Bhattacharjee, A.M.
Hindu Law and the Constitution. – Calcutta : Eastern Law House, 1983.
Pbk £20.00

—Muslim Law and the Constitution. – Calcutta : Eastern Law House, 1985.
Hbk £68.00

Bhattacharjee, Arun
Misconduct of students : a legal and disciplinary study / Arun Bhattacharjee. – New Delhi : Deep & Deep, 1981.
440p.
Bibliography: p.425-427. - Includes index.

Bhattacharya, Sukumar
Indian Direct Taxes Law and Practice. – Nagpur : Wadhura & Co, 1983.
Hbk £125.00

—Indian Income Tax Law and Practice. – 14th ed. – Nagpur : Wadhura & Co, 1982.
ca 1,050p.
Pbk £70.00

—Law and Practice of Wealth Tax, Gift Tax. – 9th ed. – Nagpur : Wadhura & Co, 1982.
ca 425p.
Pbk £35.00

Bhatter, Nandlal H.
Guide to company formation / by Nandlal H. Bhatter and Christopher N. Fernandes : foreword by V.B. Haribhakti. – Bombay : Tripathi, 1984.
viii,121p.

Bhaumik, K.N.
Public Demands Recovery Act. – 2nd ed. – Calcutta : Eastern Law House, 1959.
115p.
Hbk £5.50

Bhushan, Vidya → Constitution of Great Britain.
→ Constitution of Switzerland, Canada, Japan and Australia.
→ Constitution of the United States of America.
→ Constitution of U.S.S.R. and China.

Bianca, C. M.
Commentary on the international sales law : the 1980 Vienna Sales Convention / by C.M. Bianca, M.J. Bonell. – Milan : Giuffre, 1987.
xvii,886p.
Bibliography: pp.843-873. - Includes index. Includes texts of the Convention in English, Arabic, Chinese, French, Russian, Spanish, German and Italian.
ISBN 8814012768

Bianchi, Herman → Abolitionism : towards a non-repressive approach to crime : proceedings of the Second International Conference on Prison Abolition, Amsterdam, 1985.

Bias and impartiality in magistrates' courts / R.D.S. Stevens. – Chichester : Rose, 1982.
xvii,105p; 22cm.
Includes index.
ISBN 0859922316 Pbk £6.80

Bibliography of Abridgements, Digest, Dictionaries and Indexes of English Law to the Year 1800. – Abingdon : Professional Books, 1984.
ISBN 0862053714 Hbk £62.50

Bibliography of Air and Space Law Materials : Incorporating a Select Index to Australian Air Law Materials. – 2nd ed. – Clayton : Monash Law Book Co-operative, 1985.
ISBN 0959549749 Hbk

Bibliography of Canadian criminal justice history / Bibliographie sur l'histoire de la justice penale au Canada : Ministry of the Solicitor General, Research division. – Ottawa : Ministry of the Solicitor General, 1984.
426p. – (User report).

Bibliography of Canadian Law Supplement. – Ottawa : Canadian Law Information Council, 1982.
271p.
ISBN 0920358012 Hbk £25.00 set

Bibliography of computers and the law. – Melbourne : Victorian Society of Computers and Law, 1984.
22 leaves.

Bibliography of eighteenth century legal literature : a subject and author catalogue of law treatises and all law related literature held in the main legal collections in England / by J.N. Adams and G. Averley : with historical and technical assistance from F.J.G. Robinson : for the BELL Project at the University of Kent in Canterbury. – Newcastle upon Tyne : Avero, 1982.
xvi,900p; 31cm.
Six microfiche in pocket.
ISBN 0907977014

Bibliography of International Humanitarian Law. – Geneva : Comite International de la Croix-Rouge, 1987.
605p.
Hbk £30.00

Bibliography of Irish trials and other legal proceedings / Paul OHiggins. – Abingdon, Oxon. : Professional Books, 1986.
xxvii,504p.
Includes indexes.
ISBN 0862050804

Bibliography of Israeli law in European languages / Renee Sanilevici. – Jerusalem : Harry Sacher Institute for Legislative Research, 1985.
221p.
Supersedes: A bibliography of Israel law in English and other European languages / compiled by Judith Romney Wegner. 1972; and, A bibliography of Israel law ... 1972-1979 / compiled by Judith Deborah Wilkenfeld. 1979. Includes index.

Bibliography of material on Indonesian law in the English language / by John Ball. – 3rd ed. – Sydney : Faculty of Law, University of Sydney, 1981.
90p.
Includes index.

Bibliography of materials on legislative and other legal drafting and the interpretation of statutes. – 3rd rev. ed. – London : Commonwealth Secretariat (Legal Division), 1985.
62p.
Previous ed.: 1977.

Bibliography of South African criminal law : general principles / by Andre Rabie. – Cape Town : Juta, 1987.
viii,91p.
ISBN 0702118524

Bibliography of the Institute of State and Law Scholar's (sic) works (1978 - 1982). – Moscow : The Institute, 1983.
37p.
'Compiled by D. Vassilyev, translated by N. Gheraseva'. At head of title: Academy of Sciences of the USSR, Order of the Red Banner of Labour, Institute of State and Law.

Bibliography of the International Court. – International Court of Justice. – London : HMSO, 1984.
ISBN 0119836971 Hbk £1.90

Bibliography of the main publications on state and law of Great Britain issued in the USSR in 1946-1983. – Akademiia Nauk SSSR. – Moscow : The Institute, 1984.
14p.
'Prepared by the Group on Foreign Scientific Information of the Institute of State and Law of the Academy of Sciences of the USSR. Translated into English by Yu. D. Kouptsov'.

Bibliography on land-locked states / edited by M.I. Glassner. – 2nd rev. and enl. ed. – Dordrecht : M. Nijhoff, 1986.
xiii, 210p.
Includes indexes.
ISBN 9024732611

Bibliography on the constitutions of Nigeria / compiled by Oluremi Jegede. – London : Oceana, 1981.
vi,72p; 26cm.
Includes index.

Bibliography on the writings of the Hon. Judge T. O. Elias / by Oluremi Jegede. – 2nd ed. – Lagos : Nigerian Institute of Advanced Legal Studies, 1986.
viii, 51p. – (Occasional paper).
Includes index.
ISBN 9782353027

Bibliography on transnational law of natural resources / Martin Bartels...et al. – Deventer : Kluwer, 1981.
227p.
Published for the Institut fur Auslandisches und International Wirtschaftsrecht, Frankfurt am Main.
ISBN 9065440410

Bickenbach, Jerome E. → Fiercest Debate : Caesar Wright, the Benchers, and Legal Education in Ontario.

Bickley, Verner C.
Cultural Relations in the Global Community : Problems and Prospects / J. Philip Puthenparampil. – New Delhi : Abhinav Publications, 1981.
xii, 255p.
ISBN 8170171369 Hbk £75.00

Bicknell, Beroe Adrimar
Cases on the Law of the Constitution. – Repr. of 1926 ed. – Aalen Wuertt : Scientia.
xxxvi, 387p.
Hbk £65.00

Bidart Campos, German Jose
Argentine Supreme Court : the court of constitutional guarantees / German J. Bidart Campos : translated by William J. Brisk, based on the book by German J. Bidart Campos, 'La Corte Suprema, tribunal de las garantias constitucionales'. – Argentine ed. – Buenos Aires : Allende & Brea, 1982.
viii, 143 p.; 26 cm.
Includes bibliographical references.
ISBN 9500621142

Bieber, Roland → European Parliament : towards a uniform procedure for direct elections.
—Ever closer union : a critical analysis of the draft treaty establishing the European Union / Roland Bieber, Jean-Paul Jacque, Joseph H. H. Weiler. – Luxembourg : Office for Official Publications of the European Communities, 1985.
345p.
At head of title page: Commission of the European Communities.
ISBN 9282552209
—Institutions and the decision-making process in the Draft Treaty establishing the European Union / by Roland Bieber. – Badia Fiesolana : European University Institute, 1985.
26,3p.
Paper presented at a conference organised by the European Policy Unit of the European University Institute, in colloboration with the University of Strasbourg and TEPSA, October 1984. Includes bibliographical references.

Biederman, Karl
Trust in Liechtenstein law. – Watford : Alvescot Press, 1983.
512p.
Translation of: Die Treuhanderschaft des liechtensteinischen Rechts.
ISBN 0950583413 £45.00

Biennial report of the Mental Health Act Commission / laid before Parliament by the Secretary of State for Social Services pursuant to Section 121(10) of the Mental Health Act 1983. – London : H.M.S.O., 1985-.

Big Bang / N Ritchie. – Northcote House, 1988.
ISBN 0746305494 Pbk £4.95

Big Bang / by Ian M. Kerr. – London : Euromoney Publications, 1986.
180p.
ISBN 187003130X

Big Bank. – Weidenfeld & Nicolson, 1986.
ISBN 0297789848 Hbk £9.95

Big Brother or Democracy : The Case for the Abolition of the Australian Security Intelligence Organisation. – London : Spokesman Books, 1983.
161p.
ISBN 085124307X Pbk £2.95

Bigamy / Law Reform Commission of Canada. – Ottawa : The Commission, 1985.
32,34p. – (Working paper).
Includes bibliographical references. Added t.p. in French: La bigamie. Cover title: Criminal law : bigamy. Pages numbered in opposite directions. Text in English and French.
ISBN 0662538560

Bigelow, R.P.
Computer Contracts. – Matthew Bender, 1987.
ISBN 0000999060 Hbk £150.00

Bigger Bang. – Waterlow, 1987.
ISBN 0080331009 Pbk £5.50

Biggs, A.K.
County Court Costs and Fees. – 14th ed. – London : Fourmat.
ISBN 185190056X Pbk £4.95
—Matrimonial Proceedings. – 3rd ed. – London : Fourmat.
ISBN 1851900640 Hbk £12.95
—Matrimonial Proceedings. – 2nd ed. – London : Fourmat, 1984.
180p.
ISBN 0906840783 Pbk £9.95
—Probate practice and procedure / A P Rogers. – 3rd ed. – London : Fourmat, 1988.
ISBN 1851900403 Pbk £19.95
→ Rayden and Jackson's law and practice in divorce and family matters.

Biggs, J.E.
Lady in the Lords. – Weidenfeld & Nicolson.
ISBN 0297793217 Hbk £14.95

Bijnkershoek, Cornelius van
Quaestiones juris privati / by Cornelius van Bijnkershoek : translated by R.A. Whitaker. – 2. – Pretoria : Government Printer on behalf of the South African Law Commission, 1987. – (Research series).
Includes bibliographical references.

Bilateral Treaties for International Private Investment. – Paris : International Chamber of Commerce.
31p.
Hbk £4.50

Biles, David → Australian Prisoners, 1982.
—Car Stealing In Australia : Facts and Figures. – Canberra : Australian Institute of Criminology.
Hbk £1.40
—Crime In Papua New Guinea. – Canberra : Australian Institute of Criminology.
Hbk £2.25
—Crime Prevention in Developing Areas. – Canberra : Australian Institute of Criminology.
free
—Groote Eylandt Prisoners : A Research Report. – Canberra : Australian Institute of Criminology.
free
—Remand in Victoria : A Review of the Nature and Size of Facilities Needed. – Canberra : Australian Institute of Criminology.
Hbk £4.50
—Review of Australian Criminological Research, 1983. – Canberra : Australian Institute of Criminology.
Hbk £3.75
—Size of the Crime Problem in Australia. – 2nd ed. – Canberra : Australian Institute of Criminology.
free
—Women Prisoners In Victoria : A Review of the Nature and Size of Facilities Needed. – Canberra : Australian Institute of Criminology.
Hbk £4.50

Bilingual Editions of Cases
1961: Lawless. – European Court of Human Rights. – Cologne : Carl Heymanns Verlag.
1962: DeBecker.
1965-67: Case 'Relating to Certain Aspects of the Laws on the Use of Languages in Belgium' (Vol. 1).
1968: Case 'Relating to Certain Aspects of the Laws on the Use of Languages in Belgium' (Vol. 2).
1968: Wemhoff.
1969, 1975: Neumeister.
1970: Delcourt.
1970: Klass and others.
1970: Matznetter.
1970: Stogmuller.
1971, 1972, 1973: DeWilde, Ooms and Versyp.
1972, 1973, 1974: Ringeisen.
1975, 1976: 'National Union of Belgian Police' Case.
1975: Golder.
1976, 1977: Schmidt and Dahlstrom.
1976, 1977: 'Swedish Engine Drivers' Union' Case.
1976, 1979, 1981: Handyside.
1976, 1979: Kjeldsen, Busk, Madsen and Petersen.
1977, 1978: Engel and others.
1978, 1981: Ireland against United Kingdom.
1978: Tyrer.
1979, 1980, 1981: Luedicke, Belkacem and Koc.
1979: Konig.
1980, 1981: Airey.
1980: Deweer.
1980: Schiesser.
1980: Winterwerp.
1981: Artico.
1981: Buchholz.
1981: Guzzardi.
1981: Sunday Times.
1981: VanOosterwijck.

Bill Bresnan Speaks on Tax Planning under New Tax Law In Words of One Syllable. – Prentice-Hall.
ISBN 0130764728 Hbk £14.75

Bill of Rights? / Michael Zander. – 3rd ed. – London : Sweet & Maxwell, 1985.
viii,105p; 22cm.
Previous ed.: Chichester : Rose for the British Institute of Human Rights, 1979. Bibliography: p92-93.
ISBN 0421345101 Pbk £3.50

Bill of rights for Australia? : an exposure report for the consideration of senators / Senate Standing Committee on Constitutional and Legal Affairs. – Canberra : Australian Government Publishing Service, 1985.
xi,128p.
Includes the text of the International Covenant on Civil and Political Rights. Lists treaties relating to human rights to which Australia is a party.
ISBN 0644044748

Bill of Rights for New Zealand : a white paper / presented to the House of Representatives by leave by the Hon. Geoffrey Palmer, Minister of Justice. – Wellington : Goverment Printer, 1985.
157p.
Bibliography: p.119-123.

Bill of Rights for New Zealand : papers precsented by A. Sharp ... et al. / A. Sharp. – Auckland : Legal Research Foundation, 1985.
216p.
At head of title: Legal Research Foundation Inc. Seminar, 16 August, 1985.
ISBN 0908581386

Billington → Building Regulations Explained and Illustrated.

Bills of Exchange. – 26th ed. – Sweet & Maxwell, 1988.
ISBN 042138090X Hbk £72.00

Bills of Exchange Act 1882 / annotated by Anu Arora. – London : Lloyd's of London Press, 1987.
xvi, 100 p.; 22 cm.
Drafted by Sir Mackenzie Chalmers. Includes indexes.
ISBN 1850440956 Pbk

Bills of exchange and bankers' documentary credits / by William Hedley. – London : Lloyd's, 1986.
320p; 25cm.
Includes index.
ISBN 1850440840

Bills of Exchange and other Negotiable Instruments. – Cambridge : Woodhead-Faulkner.
ISBN 0859414523 Hbk £25.00

Bills of exchange, cheques and promissory notes in South African law / by F.R. Malan : assisted by C. R. de Beer. – Durban : Butterworths, 1983.
xii,441p.
Bibliography: p.377-391. - Includes index.
ISBN 0409040738 Hbk £47.00
ISBN 0409040746 Pbk £34.70

Bills of lading : law and practice / Alan Mitchelhill. – London : Chapman and Hall, 1982.
x,127p; 31cm.
Includes index.
ISBN 0412239604 Hbk £
ISBN 041223940X Pbk

Bills of Lading and Practice. – London : Sweet & Maxwell, 1982.
Hbk £16.00

Bills of Lading in International Law and Practice. – Lucknow : Eastern Book Company, 1985.
Hbk £80.00

BIM
Buying A Company : Checklist Guide. – BIM. – VANN, 1982.
ISBN 0859461211 Pbk £4.00

Bi-monthly bulletin : summary of cases decided by the Canada Labour Relations Board and court updates ... / Bulletin bimestriel. – Ottawa : The Board, 1987.
Continues: Summary of decisions of the Canada Labour Relations Board and court updates. Parallel text in English and French.

Binazzi, Simona → Automated analysis of legal texts : logic, informatics, law : edited versions of selected papers from the Second International Conference on 'Logic, Informatics, Law,'Florence, Italy, September 1985.

Binchy, William
Annual Review of Irish Law 1987 / Raymond Byrne. – Round Hall Press.
ISBN 0947686428 Hbk £35.00
—Casebook on Family Law in Ireland. – Abingdon : Professional Books, 1984.
Hbk
—Casebook on Irish Family Law. – London : Butterworths, 1984.
ISBN 0862050898 Pbk £22.50
→ Casebook on the Irish Law of Torts.
—Irish conflict of laws / by William Binchy. – Dublin? : Butterworths (Ireland), 1988.
lxxiv,691p.
Bibliography: p.lxxi-lxxi - Includes index.
ISBN 0862052203 Pbk £65.00
ISBN 0862052211 £25.00
→ Irish law of torts.
—Is divorce the answer? : an examination of no-fault divorce against the background of the Irish debate / William Binchy. – Blackrock, C. Dublin : Irish Academic, 1984.
115p; 22cm.
Bibliography: p111-115.
ISBN 071650314X Pbk £2.95

Binder
Investigations manual / Hamlyn. – London : Butterworths, 1985.
ISBN 0406142580 Pbk £13.50

Binder Hamlyn : Investigations Manual. – London : Butterworths.
ISBN 0406502145 Pbk £17.50

Binder Hamlyn Staff
Investigations Manual. – Binder Hamlyn Staff. – London : Butterworths, 1985.
Based on an in-house manual for investigation work, this book provides a reference for the preparation and conduct of an investigation. It is intended for use in the opening stages of an investigation to develop the quickest and most productive approach to the work.
ISBN 0406142580 Pbk

Bindra
Conveyancing, Draftsman and Legal Interpretation of Deeds, as Interpreted under Income-Tax Law, 5 Vols. – 6th ed. 5v. – Allahabad : Law Publishers, 1982.
Hbk £37.50 ea
—General Clauses Act. – 8th ed. – Allahabad : Law Book Company, 1985.
Hbk £160.00
—Intepretation of Statutes. – 7th ed. – Allahabad : Law Book Company, 1984.
400p.
Hbk £250.00
—Law Relating to Appointment : Enquiry and Disciplinary Action of Workmen, with Model Forms. – 2nd ed. – Allahabad : Law Publishers, 1982.
Hbk £18.00

Bindra, N.S.
Pleadings and Practice. 2 Vols. – 7th ed. – Allahabad : Law Book Company, 1984.
Hbk £300.00

Bing, Jon → Handbook of legal information retrieval.

Bingeman, J. B. → Principles of the law of workers' compensation, particularly in Victoria.

Bingham, Leonard
Bingham's motor claims cases / J. A. Taylor. – 9th ed. – London : Butterworths, 1986.
xlv,1003p; 26cm.
Previous ed.: 1980. Includes index.
ISBN 0406118132 £60.00

Bingham, R.
Modern Cases of Negligence
First supplement. – 3rd ed. – London : Sweet & Maxwell, 1985.
ISBN 042132810X Hbk £12.50

Bingham's motor claims cases / J. A. Taylor. – 9th ed. – London : Butterworths, 1986.
xlv,1003p; 26cm.
Previous ed.: 1980. Includes index.
ISBN 0406118132 £60.00

Biographical dictionary of the common law / edited by A.W.B. Simpson. – London : Butterworths, 1984.
xxv,559p,16p of plates; 23cm.
ISBN 040651657X

Biotechnology and patent protection : an international review / by F.K. Beier, R.S. Crespi, J. Straus. – Paris : Organisation for Economic Co-operation and Development, 1985.
133p.
ISBN 9264127577

Birchfield, Mary Eva
Complete reference guide to United Nations sales publications 1946-1978. – 2. – Berlin : de Gruyter, 1982.
Contents: 1. The catalogue / compiled and edited by Mary Eva Birchfield - 2. Indexes : sales number index, title index / compiled by Mary Eva Birchfield; KWIC index / compiled by Jacqueline Coolman.
ISBN 3110087197

Bird, Cathy
Register of policing research. No. 2. – London : Police Foundation, 1989.
220; 21.
Covers topics in a register of 200 police research projects - includes police management, organisation, policy making, operations, relations with voluntary and statutory agencies, and the history of policing and crime prevention.
ISBN 0947692126 Pbk £9.95

Bird, G.
Commercial Bank Lending and Third World Debt. – London : Macmillan.
ISBN 0333491416 Hbk £29.50
—Managing Global Money. – London : Macmillan.
ISBN 0333443772 Hbk £35.00

Bird, Graham
International financial policy and economic development : a disaggregated approach / Graham Bird. – Basingstoke : Macmillan, 1987.
xvi,348p; 23cm.
Bibliography: p338-343. - Includes index.
ISBN 033340890X £29.50
—International monetary system and the less developed countries / Graham Bird. – 2nd ed. – London : Macmillan, 1982.
xi,352p.
Bibliography: p331-350.
ISBN 0333330021
—World finance and adjustment : an agenda for reform / Graham Bird. – London : Macmillan, 1985.
288p.
Includes bibliography and index.
ISBN 0333314778 Hbk £25.00 :
ISBN 0333388771 Pbk £8.95

Bird, Greta
Process of Law in Australia : Intercultural Perspectives. – Butterworths, 1988.
454p.
ISBN 0409494488 Pbk £39.00

Bird, J. B.
Selections from the Laws of England, 2 Vols. – Repr. of 1806 ed. – Abingdon : Professional Books.
Hbk £35.00

Bird, P.
Understanding company accounts. – 2nd ed. – Pitman, 1983.
ISBN 0273019449 Pbk £4.95

Bird, R.
Starting in practice. – London : Sweet & Maxwell, 1984.
ISBN 0421320508 Pbk £6.95

Bird, Richard M.
Federal finance in comparative perspective / Richard M. Bird. – Toronto : Canadian Tax Foundation, 1986.
x,250p.
Includes bibliographical references.
ISBN 0888080247

Bird, Roger
ABC guide to the practice of matrimonial causes / by Roger Bird. – 2nd ed. – London : Sweet and Maxwell, 1987.
150p; 22cm.
Now covers the increasing role of conciliation, the principles applicable to ancillary relief applications and the 'clean break' under the Matrimonial and Family Proceedings Act 1984, ouster injunctions, foreign divorce, and the forthcoming changes following the Matrimonial Causes (Costs) Rules 1986.
ISBN 0421370904 Pbk
—Guide for Articled Clerks and Trainee Legal Executives. – London : Sweet & Maxwell, 1984.
ISBN 0421320508 Pbk £5.50
→ Osborn's Concise law dictionary.
—Precedents in matrimonial causes and ancillary matters / by Roger Bird and C.F. Turner. – 2nd ed. – London : Sweet & Maxwell, 1988.
looseleaf.
Previous ed.: 1985. Includes index.
ISBN 0421385200 £50.00

Birds, John → Boyle & Birds' Company law.
→ Encyclopedia of insurance law.
→ Handbook of company administration.
—Modern insurance law / by John Birds. – 2nd ed. – London : Sweet & Maxwell, 1988.
xxxviii,335p.
Explanation of the fundamental principles of insurance law, including the meaning of insurance, the basic elements of the contract – parties, the insurable interest, formation, void and voidable contracts and premiums, agency and asigment and mechanisms for claiming under the policy. Discusses the Insurance Companies Act 1982, and the Financial Services Act 1986.
ISBN 0421371404 Pbk
ISBN 0421371501

Birkinshaw, Patrick
Freedom of Information : the Law, the Practice, the Ideal. – Weidenfeld & Nicolson.
– (Law in Context Series).
ISBN 0297793446 Hbk £18.00
ISBN 00297793861 Pbk £11.95
—Grievances, remedies and the state / by Patrick Birkinshaw. – London : Sweet & Maxwell, 1985.
xix,192p; 23cm.
Includes index.
ISBN 042132600X Hbk £9.25
ISBN 0421326107 Pbk £8.95
—Open government : freedom of information and local government : a study conducted for the Local Government Legal Society Trust and the Society of Town Clerks' Education and Research Trust / Patrick Birkinshaw. – London : Local Government Legal Society Trust in association with the Society of Town Clerks' Education and Research Trust, 1985.
84p.
ISBN 0951110101

Birks → Legal Mind - Essays For Tony Honore.

Birks, Michael
Small claims in the county court : how to sue and defend actions without a solicitor / by Michael Birks. – Rev. ed. – London : Lord Chancellor's Department, 1984.
73p.

Birks, P.
Introduction to the Law of Restitution. – Oxford : Oxford University Press, 1985.
ISBN 0198760744 Hbk £45.00
ISBN 0198256450 Pbk £20.00
→ Restitution.

Birnie, D. A. G., et al
How to Survive Practicing Law in the 80's. – Vancouver : British Columbia Continuing Legal Education Society, 1982.
77p.
ISBN 0865040761 Hbk £7.50
—Solicitor's Guide to Corporate Tax Planning. – Vancouver : British Columbia Continuing Legal Education Society, 1983.
112p.
ISBN 0865040974 Hbk £45.00

Birth of the English Common Law. – 2nd ed. – Cambridge : Cambridge University Press.
ISBN 0521355958 Hbk £22.50
ISBN 0521356822 Pbk £7.95

Birts → Law of Trespass.

Birts, Peter
Law and Procedure / Alan Willis. – London : Butterworths, 1987.
ISBN 0406104816 Pbk

Bischoff, A. G.
From imported doctrine to municipal law : a sketch history of foreign influences on the growth of the English law of conflict / paper presented at the eigth British Legal History Conference, Cardiff, July 1987, by A. G. Bischoff. – London : Law Notes Lending Library, 1987.
52p.
Bibliography: pp.43-47..
ISBN 0900516100
—Towards a theory of contract / by A. G. Bischoff. – Reading : Bischoff (A. G.), 1984.
v,13p.
ISBN 0950971405

Bishop, John B
Criminal Procedure. – 2nd ed. – Sydney : Butterworths, 1988.
512p.
Hbk £59.00

—Prosecution without Trial. – Butterworths, 1989.
ca 336p.
ISBN 040949478X Hbk £55.00

Bishop, Olga B.
Canadian official publications / Olga B. Bishop. – Oxford : Pergamon, 1981.
ix,297p.
ISBN 0080246974

Bishop, W. D. →Choice by cable : the economics of a new era in television.
→ Contract : cases and materials.

Bishopp, C.
Limitation of Actions. – London : Butterworths.
ISBN 0406102309 Hbk £38.50

Bisset and Smith's Digest of South African Case Law
Annual Volumes, 1950-date, 31 Vols. /. – Abingdon : Professional Books.
Hbk
Incl. First Consolidated Edition, 1904-21, 6 Vols..
Second Consolidated Edition, 1922-33, 2 Vols..
Third Consolidated Edition, 1934-45, 2 Vols..
Fourth Consolidated Edition, 1946-49, 1 Vol..

Bissett-Johnson, Alastair
New divorce law : a commentary on the Divorce Act, 1985 / Alastair Bissett-Johnson and David C. Day. – Toronto : Carswell, 1986.
xxiii, 291 p.; 24 cm.
Includes legislation. Includes bibliographical references and index.
ISBN 0459387405 Pbk

Black, A.
Enforcement of a Judgement (LPPN4). – 7th ed. – London : Longman Professional, 1986.
ISBN 0851210236 Pbk £15.50

Black, Allan E. →Labour Law and Practice : Materials Prepared for a Continuing Legal Education Seminar Held in Vancouver, B. C., April 14-15, 1983.

Black Book of the Admiralty : with an appendix / edited by Sir Travers Twiss. – 4. – Abingdon, Oxon, : Professional Books, 1985.
A reprint of the original published in 1871?. Includes indexes.

Black communities and the legal profession / summary of Nottingham Regional Conference, October 1986. – s.l. : Standing Committee on the Black Communities and the Legal Profession, 1986.
11p.
Includes bibliographical references.

Black gold : the Mozambican miner, proletarian and peasant / Ruth First : pictures by Moira Forjaz : work-songs and interviews recorded by Alpheus Manghezi. – Brighton : Harvester, 1983.
xxxi,256p,xvip of plates; 23cm.
Bibliography: p207-211. - Includes index.
ISBN 0710803141 £30.00
ISBN 0312083181

Black, J.
Practical Approach to Family Law. – 2nd ed. – London : Blackstone Press, 1988.
ISBN 1851850097 Pbk £16.95

Black migration to South Africa : a selection of policy-oriented research / edited by W. R. Bohning. – Geneva : International Labour Office, 1981.
viii,184p.
Bibliography: p179-184.
ISBN 9221027589

Black people and the criminal justice system : report of the NACRO Race Issues Advisory Committee / Clement Richards. – London : NACRO, 1986.
48p.
Includes bibliographical references. Chairman: Clement Richards. Accompanied by 'Summary of the report of the NACRO Race Issues Advisory Committee'.
ISBN 0850690404

Black, Robert
Civil jurisdiction : the new rules : a guide for the perplexed / Robert Black. – Edinburgh : Law Society of Scotland, 1983.
vii,111p.
Includes index.
ISBN 0902023101

Black, T.
Practical guide to intellectual property. – London : Butterworths, 1988.
ISBN 040610140X Pbk

Blackford, R.
Specimen letters for solicitors. – London : Longman Professional, 1987.
ISBN 0851208630 Pbk £15.95

Blackford, Robert
Chancery practice handbook / Robert Blackford in collaboration with Colin Jaque : additional material by Richard Archdale. – London : Oyez Longman, 1983.
xx,252p; 24cm.
Includes bibliographies and index.
ISBN 0851207456 £16.50

—County court practice handbook / David Price, Robert Blackford. – 7th ed. – London : Oyez Longman, 1984.
xxii,242p; 22cm. – (Oyez Longman practitioner series).
Previous ed.: published as Notes on county court practice and procedure. 1983. Includes index.
ISBN 0851209513 Pbk £14.50

—Notes on County Court Practice and Procedure / David Price. – 6th ed. – London : Oyez Longman, 1982.
– (Oyez Longman Practitioner Ser.).
ISBN 0851206301 Hbk £9.95

Blackie, J →Medical responsibility in Western Europe : research study of the European Science Foundation.

Blackman, D. E. →Psychology and law : topics from an internatinal conference.

Blackman, Michael Sinclair
Mercantile Law and Mercantile Practice. – Rondebosch : University of Cape Town, 1985.
14p.
ISBN 0799210005 Pbk £0.30

Blackmore, S.
Reflections of a Country Magistrate. – Saracen.
ISBN 0951394606 Hbk £10.00

Blacksell, Mark
Legal services in rural Britain : access, accessibility and need / Mark Blacksell, Kim Economides and Charles Watkins. – Exeter : University of Exeter, 1984.
26p. – (Working paper).
Bibliography: p.22-26.
→ Spatial analysis of legal systems : towards a geography of law?.
→ Studying rural lawyers : research strategy and context.
→ Use of the law list to assess the distribution and characteristics of solicitors in England and Wales.

Blackshield, A.R., et al
Judgments of Justice Lionel Murphy. – Leichhardt : Primavera Press.
352p.
ISBN 0958949433 Hbk £19.95
→ Legal change : essays in honour of Julius Stone.

Blackstone
Commentaries on Laws of England. – Abingdon : Professional Books.
– (Classical English Law Texts Ser.).
Hbk £220.00

—Commentaries on the Laws England. 4 vols. – Reprint. – Abingdon : Professional Books, 1986.
ISBN 0862053102 Hbk £142.00

—Guide to perks from shares / John A Franks. – London : Kogan Page, 1988.
ISBN 185095237 Pbk

Blackstone, W.
Analysis of the Laws of England : Introductory Discourse on the Study of the Law. – 3rd ed. Repr. of 1757 ed. – Abingdon : Professional Books.
Hbk £95.00

Blackstone's Guide to the Employment Act 1988 / Auerbach. – London : Blackstone Press.
ISBN 1854310240 Pbk £12.95

Blackstones Statutes on Public Law / R G Lee. – London : Blackstone Press.
ISBN 1854310208 Pbk £10.95

Blackwell
Focus on Homelessness : a New Look at Housing Policy / Kennedy. – Oxford : Columbia Press.
ISBN 0948183543 Pbk £5.00

Blackwells Encyclopedia of Political Instructions. – Oxford : Blackwell Scientific, 1987.
ISBN 0631138412 Hbk £45.00

Blair, A.P.
Accident Compensation in New Zealand. – 2nd ed. – Butterworths, 1983.
Takes in new amendments (eg the reorganisation of the statutory body), and discusses the interpretations of the statutory provisions contained in many decisions reported since 1978.
ISBN 0409701602 Pbk £40.70

Blair, I.
Investigating Rape : New approaches for the Police. – Oxford : Croom Helm, 1985.
ISBN 0709920989 Hbk £14.95

Blair, Philip M.
Federalism and judicial review in West Germany / by Philip M. Blair. – Oxford : Clarendon Press, 1981.
xvii, 332p; 23cm.
Bibliography: p314-322. - Includes index.
ISBN 0198274270 £22.50

Blair, W. J. L. →Encyclopaedia of banking law.

BLAISE-LINE mini manual. – London : British Library, Automated Services Dept., 1984.
66p.
ISBN 0712310150 spiral £10.00 (1 copy free to subscribers)

BLAISE-LINE user manual. – 3. – London : The British Library, Bibliographic Services, 1988.
looseleaf.

Blake →Arabian Boundaries : Primary Documents 1853-1957, 25 Vols.

—Company Law / Bond. – 2nd ed. – London : Financial Training.
– (SWOT).
ISBN 1851850716 Pbk £7.95

Blake, Allan
Ombudsmen and the constitution / Allan Blake in association with Lancashire Polytechnic. – 2 videocassettes. – London : Sweet & Maxwell, 1985.
– (Sweet & Maxwell's lawfilms).
Contents: Ombudsmania - The Local Ombudsman investigates.

Blake, Charles →Huddy: Introduction to legal practice, Vol.1.
→ Introduction to legal practice, Vol.2 : edited by Charles Blake and Grenfell Huddy.

Blake, Gerald H. →Maritime boundaries and ocean resources.

Blake, J.
Accounting Standards. – 2nd ed. – London : Pitman Publishing, 1988.
ISBN 0273027352 Pbk £10.95

Blake, Nicholas →New nationality law.

Blake, Nick
Police, the law and the people / Nick Blake. – New ed. – London : Haldane Society of Socialist Lawyers, 1982.
55p.
Includes bibliographical references.
ISBN 0907412025

Blake, Sara →Handbook of administrative tribunals.

Blake, Susan M.
Law of marriage / Susan M. Blake. – Chichester : Rose, 1982.
liii,280p; 20cm.
Includes index.
ISBN 0859923142 Hbk £14.00
ISBN 0859923088 Pbk £10.50
→ Practical approach to revenue law.

Blakeney, M.
Intellectual Property : Commentary and Materials / J P McKeough. – North Ryde : Law Book Co, 1986.
xlviii, 741p.
ISBN 0455206945 Hbk A$80.00
ISBN 0455206953 Pbk A$59.50

Blakeney, Michael →Advertising regulation.
→ Media law in Australia.

Blakeway-Webb, Hugh
Stamp Duty Guide. – London : Butterworths, 1986.
This practical work for practitioners in the United Kingdom presents a transaction-based analysis of stamp duties. The book explains the administrative procedures involved and discusses how to avoid or minimize the duty wherever possible.
ISBN 0406260303 Pbk

Blanchard, Peter
Law of company receiverships in Australia and New Zealand / by Peter Blanchard. – Sydney : Butterworths, 1983.
xxvi,213p.
Includes index.
ISBN 0409491632

—Law of company receiverships in New Zealand and Australia / by Peter Blanchard. – Wellington : Butterworths, 1982.
xxvi,213p.
Covers the law governing receiverships initiated by the holders of charges over corporate assets in New Zealand and Australia.
ISBN 0409601330

Blanco White, T. A.
Patents for inventions : and the protection of industrial designs / by T.A. Blanco White. – 5th ed. – London : Stevens, 1983.
xxxv,304p; 26cm.
Previous ed.: 1974. Includes index.
ISBN 0420463100 Hbk £44.00

—Patents, trade marks, copyright and industrial designs / Robin Jacob. – 3rd ed. – London : Sweet & Maxwell, 1986.
xiv,182p; 22cm.
Previous ed.: 1978. Includes index.
ISBN 0421349603 Hbk £13.50
ISBN 0421349700 Pbk £8.95

Bland, J.
True Crime Diary. – London : Futura.
ISBN 0708842143 Pbk £3.50

Bland, Bland, David
UK oil taxation. – 2nd. – London : Longman Professional, 1988.
ISBN 0851214207 Pbk £50

Blanpain, R →Comparative labour law and industrial relations.
→ International encyclopaedia for labour law and industrial relations.
—International Encyclopaedia for Labour Law and Industrial Relations. Supplements 45. – Dordrecht : Kluwer.
Hbk £135.25
—OECD guidelines for multinational enterprises and labour relations, 1982-1984 : experience and review / by R. Blanpain : foreword by M. Eyskens. – Deventer : Kluwer Law and Taxation Publishers, 1985.
Includes index.
ISBN 9065442073
→ Restructuring labour in the enterprise : law and practice in France, F.R. of Germany, Italy, Sweden and the United Kingdom.
—Workers' participation in the European Community : the fifth directive / R. Blanpain, J. L. Janssen van Raay, A. Mouty. – Deventer : Kluwer, 1984.
ix,294p.
ISBN 9065441875

Blanpain, Roger →Equality and prohibition of discrimination in employment.

Blaser, Fred →Business and Tax Laws of the People's Republic of China.

Blasphemer and Reformer : Study of the works of James Leslie Mitchell. – Aberdeen : Aberdeen University Press.
224p.
ISBN 0080303730 Hbk £12.50

Blasphemy : an ancient wrong or a modern right? / by Louis Blom-Cooper. – London : Essex Hall, 1981.
14p. – (The 1981 Essex Hall lecture).

Blasphemy and the battle for faith. – London : Hodder & Stoughton, 1990.
208; 18.
ISBN 0340522798 Pbk £2.99

Bletz, Frans →Future of European defence : proceedings of the Second International Round Table Conference of the Netherlands Atlantic Commission on May 24 and 25, 1985.

Blind Justice / Peter Murtagh. – Dublin : Poolbag Press, 1984.
448p.
£6.50

Blinn, Keith W. →International petroleum exploration and exploitation agreements : legal, economic and policy aspects.

Bloch
Law of Breach of Confidence / Hoolahan. – London : Butterworths, 1984.
ISBN 0406120102 Hbk

Bloch, E.
Inside Investment Banking. – 2nd ed. – Merehurst.
ISBN 01556231288 Hbk £30.50

Block, Richard L →Juvenile delinquency in the Netherlands.

Block, Walter E.
On Discrimination. – Vancouver : Fraser Institute, 1985.
– (Focus Ser.).
ISBN 0889750807 Hbk £5.00
—Reaction : the New Combines Investigation Act. – Vancouver : Fraser Institute, 1986.
240p.
ISBN 0889750831 Pbk £14.95

Bloed, A →Essays on human rights in the Helsinki process.

Blom-Cooper, Louis
Blasphemy : an ancient wrong or a modern right? / by Louis Blom-Cooper. – London : Essex Hall, 1981.
14p. – (The 1981 Essex Hall lecture).
—Lawyers and public administrators : separate and unequal : a public lecture / delivered by Lousi Blom-Cooper on ... 1st March 1984. – London : Inns of Court School of Law, 1984.
20p; 23cm.

Blomqvist, Ake G.
Copyright, competition and Canadian culture : the impact of alternative Copyright Act import provisions on the book publishing and sound recording industries / Ake G. Blomqvist and Chin Lim. – 2 microfiches. – Ottawa : Minister of Supply and Services, 1981.
159 fr.; 10x15cm.
Bibliography: p.145-147.

Blondel
Discipline of Politics. – London : Butterworths, 1981.
ISBN 0408106855 Pbk £9.95

Blood, D.C.
Veterinary Law : Ethics, Etiquette and Convention. – North Hyde : Law Book Co, 1985.
xvi, 369p.
ISBN 0455205604 Hbk £32.50

Blood Justice : Lynching of Mack Charles Parker. – Oxford : Oxford University Press.
ISBN 00195054296 Pbk £5.95

Bloom →Decision Support Systems in Finance and Accounting.

Bloomfield, C.
Presenting financial proposals to banks. – London : Butterworths, 1986.
ISBN 0406100705 Pbk £15.00

Blount, T.
Law Dictionary : Interpreting Difficult and Obscure Words and Terms in Common or Statute, Ancient or Modern Laws. – 2nd ed. Repr. of 1691 ed. – Abingdon : Professional Books.
Hbk £175.00

Blown, N.
Step-Parent Adoptions. – North Vancouver : International Self-Counsel Press, 1987.
ISBN 0889086605 Hbk £12.95

Bloy, D.
Family Law (SWOT). – London : Blackstone Press, 1985.
ISBN 0906322901 Pbk £7.50
—SWOT Family Law. – London : Blackstone Press.
ISBN 1854310313 Pbk £8.50

Blueprint for Judicial Reform / Rader. – London : Eurospan.
ISBN 0942522087 Pbk £13.95

Bluglass →Psychiatry, Human Rights and the Law.

Blume →Accounting and Financial Management For Charities.

Blumenfeld, Jesmond →South Africa in crisis.

Blundell and Dobry's planning appeals and inquiries / George Dobry, Robert Carnwath. – 4th. – London : Sweet & Maxwell, 1988.
Reviews planning inquiry and appeals procedure at all levels. Deals with evidence, enforcement notices, refusals, determination of rights, and presentation of appeals before inspectors and the High Court. Includes referrals to the Secretary of State.
ISBN 0421390700 Pbk

Blundell, Lionel A.
Blundell and Dobry's planning appeals and inquiries / George Dobry, Robert Carnwath. – 4th. – London : Sweet & Maxwell, 1988.
Reviews planning inquiry and appeals procedure at all levels. Deals with evidence, enforcement notices, refusals, determination of rights, and presentation of appeals before inspectors and the High Court. Includes referrals to the Secretary of State.
ISBN 0421390700 Pbk

Boadway, Robin W.
Canadian tax policy / Robin W. Boadway, Harry M. Kitchen. – 2nd ed. – Toronto : Canadian Tax Foundation, 1984.
xvi,390p.
Includes bibliographical references and index.
ISBN 0888080212
—Taxes on capital income in Canada : analysis and policy / Robin W. Boadway, Neil Bruce, Jack M. Mintz. – Toronto : Canadian Tax Foundation, 1987.
xi,176p.
Includes index.
ISBN 088808028X Hbk

Boal, Arthur M →Court appointed experts in maritime cases : a comparative law study.

Boalt, Gunnar
Political Value Patterns and Parties in Sweden / Ulla Bergryd. – Stockholm : Almqvist & Wiksell.
ISBN 9122004130 Hbk £165.00

Board of Inland Revenue
Inland Revenue and the taxpayer : proposals in response to the recommendations of the Keith Committee on income tax, capital gains tax and corporation tax : a consultative document / Board of Inland Revenue. – London : H.M.S.O., 1986.
170p.
ISBN 0116413646

Board of visitor adjudications / David Smith, Claire Austin and John Ditchfield. – London : Home Office, 1981.
v,45p. – (Research Unit paper).
Bibliography: p40.
ISBN 0862520045

Boast, Carol →Subject compilations of state laws 1979-1983 : research guide and annotated bibliography.

Boberg, P. Q. R →Businessman's Law. Vol. 16.
—Law of delict / by P.Q.R. Boberg. – Cape Town : Juta, 1984.
v. 1; 26 cm.
Includes indexes. Bibliography: 1, p. xvii-xx. Contents: 1. Aquilian liability.
ISBN 070211426X

Bockstiegel, Karl-Heinz
Arbitration and state enterprises : a survey on the national and international state of law and practice / by Karl-Heinz Bockstiegel. – Deventer : Kluwer Law and Taxation, 1984.
vi,113p; 25cm.
'An international research study of the Institute of International Business Law and Practice of the International Chamber of Commerce'. Bibliography: p75-109.
ISBN 9065441840 Pbk
→ Arbitration in U.S.-German Business Relations : Schiedsgerichtsbarkeit im deutsch-amerikanischen.
—Space Law Changes and Expectations at the Turn to Commercial Space Law Activities. – Dordrecht : Kluwer, 1987.
32p.
ISBN 9065442561 Pbk £29.50

Boczek, Boleslaw Adam
Transfer of marine technology to developing nations in international law / Boleslaw A. Boczek. – Honolulu : Law of the Sea Institute, University of Hawaii, 1982.
vi,79p. – (Occasional paper).
Includes bibliographical references.

Body as property / Russell Scott. – London : Allen Lane, 1981.
x,274p; 24cm.
Includes index.
ISBN 0713913215 £7.95

Boer, B.W.
Law of Education / V.B. Gleeson. – Butterworths, 1982.
211p.
ISBN 0409309230 Pbk £39.00

Boer, Rolf →German Labour Management Relations Act.

Boer, T.M. de
Beyond Lex Loci Delicti : Conflicts Methodology and Multistate Torts in American Case Law. – Dordrecht : Kluwer, 1987.
550p.
ISBN 9065442766 Pbk £95.00

Boersma, Frederick Lister
Introduction to Fitzherbert's Abridgement / by Frederick Lister Boersma. – Abingdon : Professional Books, 1981.
6,117p; 23cm.
ISBN 0862050413
—Use of management techniques in regional and local government : report / prepared under the guidance of the Committee of Experts on Management in Local and Regional Government of the Steering Committee for Regional and Municipal Matters by F. Boersma. – Strasbourg : Council of Europe, 1985.
38p.
Bibliography: p.33.

Bogaert, E. R. C. van
Aspects of space law / E.R.C. van Bogaert. – Deventer : Kluwer, 1985.
ix, 307p.
Includes index. Bibliography: p.287-303.
ISBN 9065440488 Hbk £225.00

Bogan, Paul S. →Criminal court in action.

Bogdanor, V.
Blackwells Encyclopedia of Political Instructions. – Oxford : Blackwell Scientific, 1987.
ISBN 0631138412 Hbk £45.00

Bogsch, A.
Design Law and Treaties of the World : World Rights Outside the U.S.A. – Dordrecht : Kluwer.
Hbk

Boguslavskii, M. M
Private international law : the Soviet approach / by M.M. Boguslavskii : translated by David Winter and William B. Simons. – Dordrecht : Nijhoff, 1988.
272p.
Includes index and bibliography.
ISBN 9024736293 Hbk £165.00

Bohning, W. R. →Black migration to South Africa : a selection of policy-oriented research.
—Studies in international labour migration / W.R. Bohning. – London : Macmillan, 1984.
350p.
Bibliography: p293-308. - Includes index.
ISBN 0333369718 £30.00

Boidman, Nathan
Foreign affiliate system : Canadian taxation after 1982 : a structured overview / by Nathan Boidman. – Don Mills, Ont. : CCH Canadian Ltd., 1983.
ix,218p.
Includes index.
ISBN 0887962092
—New U.S. Residency Rules for Canadians : Tax Considerations. – North Ryde : C.C.H. Australia, 1986.
98p.
ISBN 0887963250 Pbk £12.00

Bois, F. de L.
Constitutional history of Jersey / F. de L. Bois. – Rev. repr. 1981. – Jersey : States' Greffe, Jersey, 1981.
311p.
Revision of: 1972 ed.. Includes index.

Bok, Derek
Beyond the ivory tower : social responsibilities of the modern university / Derek Bok. – Cambridge, Mass. : Harvard University Press, 1982.
318p; 25cm.
Includes index.
ISBN 0674068998 £11.20

Bok, Sissela
Secrets : on the ethics of concealment and revelation / Sissela Bok. – Oxford : Oxford University Press, 1984.
xviii,332p; 23cm.
Originally published: New York : Pantheon, 1983. Includes index.
ISBN 0192177338 Pbk £12.95

Boke of Justices of the Peas. – Abingdon : Professional Books.
– (Classical English Law Texts Ser.).
Hbk £24.00

Bokor, Hanna Szego → Hungarian perspectives on questions of international law.

Boland, B. J.
Struggle of Islam in modern Indonesia / B. J. Boland. – The Hague : Martinus Nijhoff, 1982.
viii,283p.
'Slightly revised reprint' of 1971 edition. Bibliography: p267-274.
ISBN 9024761816 Hbk

Boldt, Menno, et al
Quest for Justice : Aboriginal Peoples and Aboriginal Rights. – Toronto : University of Toronto Press, 1985.
ISBN 0802025722 Hbk £45.00
ISBN 0802065899 Pbk £17.50

Bollen, Jennifer → Let's Look at Law.

Bolton, P. Michael
Civil Rights : the Law, the Police, and You. – 8th ed. – North Vancouver : International Self-Counsel Press, 1985.
228p.
ISBN 0889086222 Hbk £8.95

—Criminal Procedure in Canada. – 7th ed. – North Vancouver : International Self-Counsel Press, 1986.
168p.
ISBN 0889086354 Hbk £16.95

Bomani, M.D.
Constitutional Options for Namibia : a Historical Perspective / C. Ushewkunze. – Lusaka : United Nations Institute for Namibia.
72p.
Hbk free

Bombay Civil Services Rules Explained. – 7th rev. ed. 1980 rep,. – Nagpur : Wadhura & Co, 1984.
Hbk £120.00

Bombin, Luis M.
Plant protection legislation / by Luis M. Bombin. – Rome : Food and Agriculture Organization of the United Nations, 1984.
165p. – (Legislative study).
ISBN 9251014604

Bonavia, David
Verdict in Peking : the trial of the Gang of Four / David Bonavia. – London : Burnett, 1984.
225p; 24cm.
Includes index.
ISBN 0091562007 £9.95

Bond → Company Law.

Bond, I. D.
Syndicated credits market / by I.D.Bond. – London : Economics Division, Bank of England, 1985.
67,28p. – (Bank of England discussion papers).
Bibliography: pi-iii.
ISBN 0903312735

Bond, J.
Complete Guide for Justices of the Peace : Containing the Common and Statute Laws and Most Authentic Precedents Which Concern the Same. – Repr. of 1687 ed. – Abingdon : Professional Books.
Hbk £110.00

Bond, Stephen
North Sea taxation for the 1990s / Stephen Bond, Michael Devereux and Michael Saunders. – London : Institute for Fiscal Studies, 1987.
113p; 22cm.
Bibliography: p112-113.
ISBN 0902992651 Pbk

Bondeson, William B. → Abortion and the status of the fetus.

Bonehill, R. C. → Law and practice of intestate succession.

Bonell, M. J. → Commentary on the international sales law : the 1980 Vienna Sales Convention.

Bonifacio, Manuel Flores
Survey of the Legal Profession in the Philippines : Focus on Region 4 / Merlin M. Magalona. – Quezon City : University of the Philippines, Law Center, 1982.
182p.
Pbk £20.00

Bonnell, B.
Commentary on International Sales Law. – Sweet & Maxwell.
ISBN 0421408405 Hbk £50.00

Bonnell, Susanne → Marriage and domestic violence in rural Papua New Guinea.

Bonner, David
Emergency powers in peacetime / by David Bonner. – London : Sweet & Maxwell, 1985.
220p; 22cm.
Includes index.
ISBN 0421310707 Hbk £14.00 :
ISBN 0421310804 Pbk £8.00
→ Non-means tested benefits : the legislation.

—Non-means tested benefits: the legislation / I Hooker, P Smith, R White. – 1989. – London : Sweet & Maxwell, 1989.
Guide to contributory benefits. Includes annotations of decisions of the Commissioners and the courts, definition of words and phrases, and text of statutes and regulations.
ISBN 0421415207 Pbk £21

Bonyhady, T.
Law and the countryside. – Abingdon : Professional Books, 1987.
ISBN 0862052564 Hbk £37.50

Book Called the Mirror of Justices : With the Book (By Sir Anthony Fitzherbert), Called the Divinity of Courts and Their Jurisdictions / William Hughes. – Repr. of 1646 ed. – Abingdon : Professional Books.
40p.
Hbk £125.00

Book Keeping and Accounting Examinations Explained / Rizvi. – Croydon : Telles Langdon, 1988.
ISBN 0904467147 Pbk £6.75

Book Keeping and Accounts Workbook. – Spicer and Pegler. – London : Butterworths.
ISBN 0406678138 Pbk £9.50

Book of Humorous Legal Anecdotes. – Springwood Books.
ISBN 0862541344 Hbk £7.95

Book of the Bench. – London : Wildy & Sons.
84p : Illus.
Hbk £35.00

Book trade year book / Publishers Association. – London : Publishhers Association, 1985.

Book-Keeping and Accounts. – Spicer and Pegler. – 19th ed. – London : Butterworths, 1985.
ISBN 0406678103 Pbk £13.50

Bookkeeping for Solicitors. – 4th ed. – Sweet & Maxwell.
ISBN 0421413700 Pbk £13.00

Books in Cambridge Inventories
Vol. 1. – Cambridge : Cambridge University Press.
ISBN 0521308739 Hbk £75.00

Boon, Dennis K.
Law Firm of the Future - Today : Materials Prepared for a Continuing Legal Education Seminar Held February 5, 1983 / Phil Baudin. – Vancouver : British Columbia Continuing Legal Education Society, 1983.
ISBN 0865041008 Llf £45.00

Booth, Harry → Practical Share Valuation.
→ Share Valuation Cases.

Booth, Heather → To ride the storm : the 1980 Bristol 'riot' and the state.

Booth, Ken
Law, force and diplomacy at sea / Ken Booth. – London : Allen & Unwin, 1985.
xiii,231p,1p folded leaf of plates; 24cm.
ISBN 0043410278 Hbk £18.00
ISBN 0043410286 Pbk £7.95

Booth, Margaret → Rayden and Jackson's law and practice in divorce and family matters.
→ Report of the Matrimonial Causes Procedure Committee : presented to the Lord Chancellor July 1985.

Booth, Neil D
DHSS Official Contributions Guides. – London : Oyez Longman, 1984.
ISBN 0851207391 Hbk £55.00

—National Insurance contributions. – London : Butterworths, 1988.
ISBN 0406504601 Pbk
→ Practical share valuation.

—Residence, domicile and UK taxation. – London : Butterworths, 1986.
ISBN 0406580103 Pbk £32.00

—Social security contributions / Neil D. Booth. – London : Butterworths, 1982.
xxviii,204p; 25cm.
Includes index.
ISBN 0406128995 Pbk £8.00

—Tolley's National Insurance Contributions 1988-89. – Tolley Publishing.
ISBN 0854593594 Hbk £18.95

Bootle, R.
Index-Linked Gilts. – Cambridge : Woodhead-Faulkner, 1985.
ISBN 085941289X Hbk £30.00

Bophuthatswana's Industrial Conciliation Act. – Johannesburg : South African Institute of Race Relations, 1984.
Hbk £2.00

Borchardt, D.H.
Checklist of Royal Commissions : Select Committees of Parliament and Boards of Inquiry, Commonwealth, New South Wales, Queensland, Tasmania and Victoria, 1960-1980 and South Australia 1970-1980. – Bundoora : La Trobe University, Borchardt Library, 1986.
ISBN 0858166429 Hbk £45.00

Border and territorial disputes / edited by Alan J. Day : contributors: Judith Bell ... et al. – Harlow : Longman, 1982.
x,406p; 26cm.
Bibliography: p389. - Includes index.
ISBN 0582902517 £
ISBN 0810320304

Borer, D. C. → Establishing a business in the United Kingdom.

Borgeat, Louis → Administrative Law : A Treatise, Vol. 1.

Borking, John J.
Third party protection of software and firmware : direct protection of zeros and ones / John J. Borking. – Amsterdam : North-Holland, 1985.
xx,521p; 24cm.
Bibliography: p491-510. - Includes index.
ISBN 0444876774 £48.78

Borkowski, Margaret
Marital violence : the community response / Margaret Borkowski, Mervyn Murch, Val Walker. – London : Tavistock, 1983.
x,230p; 23cm.
Bibliography: p216-222. - Includes index.
ISBN 0422781207 Hbk £
ISBN 0422781304 Pbk

Born, G. → Extraterritorial Application of National Laws.

Born, Gary B
International civil litigation in United States courts: commentary and materials / David Westin. – Kluwer Law and Taxation, 1989.
720.
A treatment of international civil litigation in US courts. Covers personal jurisdiction over foreign defendants, services outside the US, discovery of materials outside the US including the Hague Evidence Convention and the Aerospatiale decision.
ISBN 9065443800 Hbk £54/Dfl 168

Borno State of Nigeria
Government views on the report of the Advisory Committee on the Implementation of the Federal Government White Paper of Area Courts Reform / Borno State of Nigeria. – Maiduguri : Government Printer, 1987.
21p.

Borovoy, Alan
When Freedoms Collide : the Case for Our Civil Liberties. – Toronto : Lester & Orpen Dennys, 1988.
384p.
ISBN 0886191890 Hbk £27.95

Borrie and Lowe's Law of contempt / N. V. Lowe. – 2nd ed. – London : Butterworths, 1983.
xlv,479p; 26cm.
This book is a comprehensive statement of the law relating to civil and criminal contempt of court in the United Kingdom. The work deals in-depth with the changes brought about by the Contempt of Court Act of 1981.
ISBN 0406129517 Hbk

Borrie, Gordon
Borrie and Lowe's Law of contempt / N. V. Lowe. – 2nd ed. – London : Butterworths, 1983.
xlv,479p; 26cm.
This book is a comprehensive statement of the law relating to civil and criminal contempt of court in the United Kingdom. The work deals in-depth with the changes brought about by the Contempt of Court Act of 1981.
ISBN 0406129517 Hbk

—Commercial Law / Sir Gordon Borrie. – 6th ed. – London : Butterworths, 1988.
xxxi,354p; 22cm.
Previous ed.: 1980. Includes index.
ISBN 0406558450 Hbk £19.50
ISBN 0406558469 Pbk £13.95

—Consumer, society and the law / Gordon Borrie and Aubrey L. Diamond. – 4th ed. – Harmondsworth : Penguin, 1981.
360p; 20cm. – (Pelican books).
Previous ed.: 1973. Bibliography: p340-343. - Includes index. .
ISBN 0140206477 Pbk £2.95

—Development of consumer law and policy - bold spirits and timorous souls / by Sir Gordon Borrie. – London : Published under the auspices of the Hamlyn Trust by Stevens, 1984.
xii,138p; 18cm.
Includes index.
ISBN 0420467904 Hbk £14.50
ISBN 0420468005 Pbk £6.25

Borrow, G.
Celebrated Trials and Remarkable Cases of Criminal Jurisprudence : From the Earliest Records to the Year 1825, 6 Vols. – Repr. of 1825 ed. – Abingdon : Professional Books.
36p.
Hbk £450.00

Borrowdale, Andrew → Business transactions law.

Bory, Francoise
Origin and Development of International Humanitarian Law. – Geneva : Comite International de la Croix-Rouge, 1982.
40p.
Hbk £1.00

Bos, Adriaan
Realism in Law-Making : Essays on International Law in Honour of Willem Riphagen / Hugo Siblesz. – Dordrecht : Kluwer, 1986.
316p.
ISBN 9024733995 Hbk £165.00

Bos, Maarten →Liber amicorum for the Rt. Hon. Lord Wilberforce.
—Methodology of international law / by Maarten Bos. – Amsterdam : North-Holland, 1984.
xxi,357p; 23cm.
'Published in collaboration with Interuniversitair Instituut voor Internationaal Recht T.M.C. Asser Instituut' - T.p. verso. Includes index.
ISBN 044486847X

Bose, M.K.
Crash of 87. – Oxford : Bloomsbury, 1988.
ISBN 0747502137 Hbk £13.95

Bose, S.K.
Basu's Law of Receivers. – 3rd ed. – Calcutta : Eastern Law House, 1984.
Hbk £165.00
—Basu's Motor Vehicles Act. – 6th ed. – Calcutta : Eastern Law House, 1984.
Hbk £110.00

Boserup, Ester
Woman's role in economic development / Ester Boserup. – Aldershot : Gower, 1986.
283p.
Originally published: George Allen & Unwin, 1970. Bibliography: pp.263-275. - Includes index. Published in association with the London School of Economics and Political Science.
ISBN 0566051397

Bossons, John, et al
Regulation by Municipal Licensing. – Toronto : University of Toronto Press, 1984.
ISBN 0802033903 Pbk £6.50

Bossuyt, Marc J
Guide to the 'travaux preparatoires' of the International Covenant on Civil and Political Rights / Marc J. Bossuyt. – Dordrecht : M. Nijhoff, 1987.
Includes text of the covenant. Includes index. Bibliography.
ISBN 9024734673

Bossy, John →Disputes and settlements : law and human relations in the West.

Boston, Charles
Understanding residential leases / by Charles Boston. – 2nd ed. – London : Sweet & Maxwell, 1986.
22p; 21cm.
ISBN 0421366109 Pbk £1.75

Botein, Michael →Law of international telecommunications in the United States.

Bothe, Michael
International Law and Municipal Law : Deutsch-Argentinisches Verfassungsrechtskolloquium, Buenos Aires, April 1979. – Berlin : Duncker and Humblot.
322p.
ISBN 3428050738 Pbk £116.00
—New Rules for Victims of Armed Conflicts : Commentary on the Two 1977 Protocols Additional to the Geneva Convention of 1949 / Karl Josef Partsch. – Dordrecht : Kluwer, 1981.
1,100p.
ISBN 9024725372 Hbk Gld340.00

Botnick, David I.
Marriage and Family Law in Ontario : the Rights of Husbands, Wives, Children, and Common-Law Spouses. – 4th ed. – North Vancouver : International Self-Counsel Press, 1986.
203p.
ISBN 0889083606 Hbk £6.95
—Probate Guide for Ontario : a Step-by-Step Guide to Probating an Estate. – 4th ed. – North Vancouver : International Self-Counsel Press, 1986.
86p.
ISBN 088908355X Hbk £11.95

Botswana law reports. – Gaborone : Government Printer, 1966.
Continues: Bechuanaland law reports,.

Bottom Line. – Plymouth : Macdonald & Evans, 1988.
ISBN 0356155382 Hbk £7.95

Bottomley, A. Keith
Crime and punishment : interpreting the data / A. Keith Bottomley, Ken Pease. – Milton Keynes : Open University Press, 1986.
xviii,185p; 24cm.
Bibliography: p171-180. - Includes index.
ISBN 0335153909 Hbk £25.00
ISBN 0335153895 Pbk £8.95
—Understanding crime rates : police and public roles in the production of official statistics / Keith Bottomley, Clive Coleman. – Farnborough : Gower, 1981.
ix,170p; 23cm.
Bibliography: p155-160. - Includes index.
ISBN 0566003090 £11.50

Bottomley, Anne →Cohabitation handbook : a women's guide to the law.

Boudria
Used Car Buyers Protection Act, 1983, Bill 131 : An Act to Protect the Purchasers of Used Motor Vehicles. – Ontario : Ontario Government Publications Service, 1983.
4p.
Hbk £0.30

Bouey, Gerald K.
Monetary policy : finding a place to stand / Gerald K. Bouey. – Toronto : Per Jacobsson Foundation, 1983.
v,28p.
Lecture delivered at the University of Toronto, 5 September 1982.

Bough, Jenny
Company accounts / Jenny Bough. – London : Sweet & Maxwell, 1987.
xvii,227p; 26cm.
Includes index.
ISBN 0421360208 £16.50

Boulding, John →Tolley's capital gains tax 1986-87.
→ Tolley's capital gains tax 1987-88.
→ Tolley's captial gains tax 1988-89.
→ Tolley's corporation tax 1986-87.
→ Tolley's corporation tax 1987-88.
→ Tolley's corporation tax 1988-89.
—Tolley's taxation in the Channel Islands and Isle of Man 1987 / John Boulding. – Croydon : Tolley, 1987.
vi,207p.
ISBN 0854592954

Boulle, Laurence
South Africa and the consociational option : a constitutional analysis / by L.J. Boulle. – Cape Town : Juta, 1984.
xii, 270 p.; 25 cm.
Includes indexes. Bibliography: p. 227-229.
ISBN 0702114340 Pbk

Boulle, Laurence J. →Natal and KwaZulu : constitutional and political options; proceedings of the workshop.

Boult, Reynard
Bibliography of Canadian Law Supplement. – Ottawa : Canadian Law Information Council, 1982.
271p.
ISBN 0920358012 Hbk £25.00 set

Boulton, A. Harding →Handbook of company administration.

Boulton, Mark
Torts /. – North Ryde : Law Book Co, 1984.
xii, 108p. – (Nutshells).
ISBN 0455203474

Bound Australian and New Zealand Conveyancing Reports. – North Ryde : C.C.H. Australia, 1979/80.
Hbk £66.00 ea.

Bound Australian Company Law Cases 1971-1981, 3 Vols. – North Ryde : C.C.H. Australia.
Hbk

Bound Australian Tax Cases. – North Ryde : C.C.H. Australia.
Hbk

Bound Australian Tax Decisions, 6 Vols. – North Ryde : C.C.H. Australia.
Hbk £450.00

Bound Company Law, 3 Vols. – North Ryde : C.C.H. Australia.
Hbk £220.00

Bound Family Law Cases. – North Ryde : C.C.H. Australia, 1986.
770p.
Hbk

Boundaries and Surveys / Izaak de Rijcke. – Agincourt : Carswell, 1985.
235p.
This text covers the law of Ontario, Canada relating to boundaries and surveys. Relevant Ontario statutes and digests of cases from other provinces are provided in the appendices.
Hbk £38.00

Boundaries, walls and fences / Trevor M. Aldridge. – 6th ed. – London : Longman Professional, 1986.
66p; 22cm.
Previous ed.: London : Oyez Longman, 1982. Includes index.
ISBN 0851212344 Pbk £11.95

Bourdeaux, Michael
Religious minorities in the Soviet Union : a report / prepared for the Minority Rights Group by Michael Bourdeaux and two associates, Kathleen Matchett and Cornelia Gerstenmaier. – Rev. 4th ed. – London : Minority Rights Group, 1984.
24p. – (Report).
Bibliography: p.23.
ISBN 0946690154

Bourgeois, Donald J.
Annotated bibliography public opinion and social policy / by Donald J. Bourgeois. – Ottawa : Ministry of the Solicitor General, 1985.
56p. – (Usier report).

Bourgeois, J. H. J. →Protectionism and the European Community : import relief measures taken by the European Economic Community and the member states, and the legal remedies available to private parties.

Bourgoignie, Thierry →Consumer legislation in Belgium and Luxemburg : a study prepared for the EC Commission.
→ European consumer law : prospects for integration of consumer law and policy within the European Community : proceedings of the seminar held in Louvain-la-Neuve on May 14 and 15, 1981.
→ Integration through law : Europe and the American federal experience : a series, Vol.3 : Consumer law, common markets and federalism in Europe and the United States : by Thierry Bourgoignie and David Trubek : (with Louise Trubek and Denis Stingl).
—Unfair Terms in Consumer Contracts Legal Treatment, Effective Implementation and Final Impact on the Consumer : Proceedings of the Second European Workshop on Consumer Law. – Brussels : Emile Bruylant, 1983.
iv, 268p.
ISBN 2870771991 Hbk £860.00

Bourke, B.J., et al
Liquor Laws in Victoria. – Butterworths, 1982.
ISBN 0409351024 Llf £105.00

Bourn, Colin →Data protection : perspectives on information privacy : contributions made to a conference on 11 May 1983 at the University of Leicester.
—Discrimination equal pay / John Whitmore. – London : Sweet & Maxwell, 1989.
Presents the law of discrimination and institutions through which it functions. Looks at discrimination in employment, education, and the provision of goods and services. Also examines the practical aspects of the powers embodied in the Commission for Racial Equality, and the Equal Opportunities Commission, and tribunal procedures and remedies.
ISBN 0421389907 Hbk
—Redundancy law and practice / Colin Bourn. – London : Butterworths, 1983.
xxv,320p; 22cm.
Includes index.
ISBN 0406258147 Pbk

Bourne, C.B.
Canadian Yearbook of International Law. – Witney : Academic & University Publishing Group.
ISBN 0774803037 Hbk £48.00
—Canadian Yearbook of International Law - Annuaire Canadien de Droit International Vol. 1. – Vancouver : University of British Columbia Press.

Bourne, E. O.
Handbook of conveyancing searches / E.O. Bourne. – 2nd ed. – London : Sweet & Maxwell, 1986.
ix,87p.
ISBN 042136680X

Bourne, Felix
Enforcement and stop notices : a practical guide / Felix Bourne. – London : Sweet & Maxwell, 1986.
175p; 24cm.
Contains, in chronological order, the relevant information from a variety of statutes, statutory instruments and circulars. Follows procedure from the preliminary points of consideration to the questions arising on appeal, both from the perspective of the local authority, and that of the private developer.
ISBN 0421364106 Pbk £15.00

Bourne, Nicholas →Company directors : liabilities, rights and duties.

Bovey, Keith
Misuse of drugs. – London : Butterworths, 1986.
Summarises both English and Scots case law arranged in accordance with the sections of the 1971 Misuse of Drugs Act. With a glossary of controlled drugs and words and phrases likely to be encountered in practice. Published by Butterworths on behalf of the Law Society of Scotland.
ISBN 0406103909 Pbk

Bowden, G. T. W., et al
Estate Planning. – Vancouver : British Columbia Continuing Legal Education Society, 1983.
77p.
ISBN 0865040915 Hbk £45.00

Bowen
Guide to Export Finance / Mills. – London : Euromoney, 1987.
ISBN 1870031458 Pbk £75.00
—Know Your Rights When You Retire. – Kensington : Bay Books.
Pbk £3.95

Bowen, J. K. →Forensic science and the expert witness.

Bowen, Jan →Continuing legal education in the 1980's : papers and proceedings of the Conference on Continuing Legal Education in the 1980's, conducted by the Law Society of New South Wales and the Law Foundation of New South Wales at the College of Law, Sydney, 13-15 November 1980.

Bowen, Nicholas →Tolley's company law.
→ Tolley's value added tax 1988-89.

Bowers
Blackstone's Guide to the Employment Act 1988 / Auerbach. – London : Blackstone Press.
ISBN 1854310240 Pbk £12.95
—Modern law of strikes / Duggan. – London : Financial Training, 1987.
ISBN 185185066X Pbk £12.95

Bowers, D.M.
Access Control and Personal Identification Systems. – London : Butterworths.
ISBN 0409900834 Hbk £24.95

Bowers, J.
Termination of Employment. – London : Longman Professional.
ISBN 0851214444 Pbk £10.95

Bowers, J. K.
Agriculture, the countryside and land use : an economic critique / J.K. Bowers and Paul Cheshire. – London : Methuen, 1983.
x,170p; 20cm.
Includes index.
ISBN 0416318304 Pbk

Bowers, John
Industrial tribunal practice. – London : Longman Professional (UK), 1988.
– (Practitioner series).
Analysis of the expanding case law on procedure with practical hints. Takes account of the procedures ofr equal value claims, with worked examples, precedents and statutory materials.
ISBN 0851213766 Pbk £16.95
—Practical approach to employment law / John Bowers. – 2nd ed. – London : Financial Training, 1986.
liv,385p.
ISBN 1851850279
→ Transfer of undertakings : the legal pitfalls : a specially commissioned report.
→ Tribunals practice and procedure.

Bowett, D W →British Yearbook of International Law 1987.
—Law of international institutions / D.W. Bowett. – 4th ed. – London : Sweet & Maxwell, 1982.
xv,431p; 23cm.
Published under the auspices of the London Institute for World Affairs by Stevens & Sons Previous ed.: 1975. Includes index.
ISBN 0420460101 Hbk £30
ISBN 0420460209 Pbk £21

Bowey
Payment Systems and Productivity / Thorpe. – London : Macmillan, 1986.
ISBN 333394828 Hbk £29.50

Bowhill, Anthony
Planning Application Fees. – London : Oyez Longman, 1981.
ISBN 085120600X Hbk £2.95

Bowland, Adelyn
Handbook to the Ontario Human Rights Code / Connie Nakatsu. – Agincourt : Carswell, 1988.
250p.
This book focuses on issues pertinent to the Ontario Human Rights Code. Topics include policy of the code, prohibited grounds and areas of discrimination, processing a human rights complaint, jurisdiction of the commission, evidence required in human rights cases, findings and awards by Board of Inquiry, review and enforcement of board decisions and alternate remedies.
Pbk

Bowles, Roger A.
Law and the economy / Roger Bowles. – Oxford : Martin Robertson, 1982.
xvi,239p; 22cm.
Introduction to law and economics, relating the two subjects to each other.
ISBN 0855204656 Hbk £
ISBN 0855204745 Pbk £6.95

Bowman
Multilateral Treaties : Current Status and Index / Harris. – London : Butterworths, 1984.
ISBN 0406252785 Hbk £110.00

Bowman, M. J.
Multilateral treaties : index and current status / compiled and annotated within the University of Nottingham Treaty Centre by M.J. Bowman and D.J. Harris. – London : Butterworths, 1984.
xii,516p; 26cm.
Includes index. Kept up to date by supplements.
ISBN 0406252777 Hbk £85.00

Bownett, Derek →British year book of international law, Vol 59: 1988.

Bowstead on agency / F. M. B. Reynolds. – 15th ed. – London : Sweet & Maxwell, 1985.
cvi,559p; 26cm.
Previous ed.: 1976. Includes index.
ISBN 0421285508 £75

Bowstead, William
Bowstead on agency / F. M. B. Reynolds. – 15th ed. – London : Sweet & Maxwell, 1985.
cvi,559p; 26cm.
Previous ed.: 1976. Includes index.
ISBN 0421285508 £75

Bowstock →Practice of Law.

Bowyer, Jack
Small Works Contract Documentation : An Architectural Press Legal Guide. – 3rd ed. – London : Architectural Press, 1986.
176p : Illus.
ISBN 0851399762 Hbk £14.95

Box, Muriel
Rebel advocate : a biography of Gerald Gardiner / by Muriel Box. – London : Gollancz, 1983.
242p,8p of plates; 24cm.
Bibliography: p236. - Includes index.
ISBN 0575032693 £10.95

Box, Steven
Deviance, reality and society / Steven Box. – 2nd ed. – London : Holt, Rinehart and Winston, 1981.
vii,248p; 22cm.
Previous ed.: 1971. Includes bibliographies and index.
ISBN 0039102947 Pbk £4.95
—Power, crime, and mystification / Steven Box. – London : Tavistock, 1983.
xi,257p; 23cm. – (Tavistock studies in sociology).
Bibliography: p224-246. - Includes index.
ISBN 0422764000 Hbk £
ISBN 0422764108 Pbk
—Recession, crime and punishment / Steven Box. – London : Macmillan Education, 1987.
240p; 25cm.
Includes index.
ISBN 0333438523 Hbk £20.00 :
ISBN 0333438531 Pbk £6.95

Boyce, C. K.
Legal systems, North and South : a study prepared for the New Ireland Forum / by C. K. Boyce. – Dublin : Stationery Office, 1984.
60p.

Boyd, Dennis
Company law : recent legislative changes : the text of a lecture delivered to the Belfast Solicitors' Association on 10 November 1983 / by Dennis Boyd. – Belfast : SLS Legal Publications, 1983.
i,32p.
Includes bibliographical references.
Pbk £2.95

Boyd, Stewart C. →Law and practice of commercial arbitration in England.
→ Scrutton on charterparties and bills of lading.

Boydell, Craig L. →Canadian criminal justice system.

Boyden, Jo
Children : rights and responsibilities / Jo Boyden and Andy Hudson. – London : Minority Rights Group, 1985.
15p. – (Report).
Bibliography: p14-15.
ISBN 0946690340

Boyer, J. Patrick
Election Law in Canada : the Law and Procedure of Federal, Provincial and Territorial Elections, 2 Vols. – Butterworths, 1987.
1,632p.
Examines legal status and registration of political parties and candidates, electoral boundaries and representation, the calling of elections, election officials, compiling and revising the lists of voters, general conduct of elections, voting procedures, election results and recounts, election offences and corrupt practices, and controverted elections.
ISBN 0409816000 Hbk £170.00
—Lawmaking by the people : referendums and plebiscites in Canada / J. Patrick Boyer. – Toronto : Butterworths, 1982.
xxxii,304p.
Outlines the laws which make possible the existence of political rights in Canada by exploring constitutional conventions such as responsible government, parliamentary democracy, and the role of political parties. It examines municipal and provincial laws regarding signs, posters and parades, as well as federal broadcasting laws governing provincial elections.
ISBN 0409816019
—Local Elections in Canada : the Law Governing Elections of Municipal Councils, School Boards and Other Local Authorities. – Butterworths, 1988.
864p.
ISBN 0409816051 Hbk £100.00
—Money and Message : the Law Governing Election Financing, Advertising, Broadcasting and Election Campaigning in Canada. – Butterworths, 1983.
672p.
ISBN 0409816305 Hbk £95.00
—Political Rights : the Legal Framework of Elections in Canada. – London : Butterworths.
ISBN 0409816019 Hbk £64.00

Boyes, L. R.
Accident compensation Victoria / by L.R. Boyes and M. O'Loghlen. – 1. – Sydney : Butterworths, 1987.
looseleaf.
Supersedes: Workers compensation, Victoria, by Anderson and Rendit. Includes: Accident and workers compensation reports.
ISBN 0409492795

Boyle, A. J. →Boyle & Birds' Company law.
→ Gore-Browne on companies.

Boyle & Birds' Company law / editors, A.J. Boyle, John Birds, Graham Penn. – 2nd ed. – Bristol : Jordan, 1987.
lxxxviii,853p.
Previous ed.: 1983. Includes index.
ISBN 0853080909

Boyle, C. K.
Sentencing law and practice / by C.K. Boyle and M.J. Allen. – London : Sweet & Maxwell, 1985.
xxxvi,338p.
Includes index.
ISBN 0421344008 Pbk £15.00
—Sentencing law and practice in Northern Ireland / by C.K. Boyle and M.J. Allen. – Belfast : SLS Legal, 1983.
xxxix,256p; 23cm.
Includes index.
ISBN 0853892245

Boyle, Christine
Contracts : Cases and Commentaries / David Percy. – 3rd ed. – Agincourt : Carswell, 1985.
932p.
This third edition text updates the previous edition with comprehensive coverage of contracts induced by negligent misrepresentation, current key cases, and a review of statutory references.
ISBN 0459375105 Hbk £39.60
—Sexual Assault. – Agincourt : Carswell, 1984.
200p.
This book is a critical analysis of the Canadian Criminal Code provisions governing the offense of sexual assault. Statutory rape and incest, offenses against children, and many other issues are discussed in the work.
ISBN 045936720 Hbk £18.70

Boyle, Christine L.
Charterwatch : Reflections on Equality / A. Wayne MacKay. – Agincourt : Carswell, 1986.
320p.
This work presents eight essays on the political and legal implications of the guarantee of equality in the Canadian Charter of Rights and Freedom. The role of the judiciary in shaping the concept of equality in Canadian law is emphasized in the essays.
Hbk £40.50

Boyle, Joseph M. →Nuclear deterrence, morality and realism.

Boynton, John K.
Boynton's Guide to Compulsory Purchase and Compensation / David J. Hawkins. – 5th ed. – London : Oyez Longman, 1983.
– (Oyez Longman Practitioner Ser.).
ISBN 0851207138 Hbk £17.25

Boynton's Guide to Compulsory Purchase and Compensation / David J. Hawkins. – 5th ed. – London : Oyez Longman, 1983.
– (Oyez Longman Practitioner Ser.).
ISBN 0851207138 Hbk £17.25

BPF-ACA Form of Building Agreement 1984. – London : Architectural Press, 1984.
16p : Illus. – – (ACA Contract Documents).
ISBN 0851397565 Pbk £4.95

BR11 Manual of naval law / issued by command of the Defence Council. – 2 v. – London : H.M.S.O., 1981.
loose-leaf; 26cm.
Supersedes BR11 Naval Court Martial Manual dated 1969. Vol.2 contains Appendixes to BR11 Manual of Naval Law.
ISBN 0117723614

Bracken
Canadian Almanac and Directory. – Toronto : DeBoo, 1984.
ISBN 0773040536 Hbk £69.95

Bradbourne et al.
Butterworths International Taxation of Financial Instruments. – London : Butterworths.
ISBN 0406106614 Hbk £60.00

Bradbrook, Adrian J.
Easements and restrictive covenants in Australia / Adrian J. Bradbrook and Marcia A. Neave. – Sydney : Butterworths, 1981.
xlv,422p.
Includes index.
ISBN 0409300489 Hbk £65
—Manual of the Victorian Residential Tenancies Act. – North Ryde : Law Book Co, 1982.
xx, 299p.
ISBN 045520540X Pbk £37.00

—Residential tenancy law and practice / by Adrian J. Bradbrook, Susan V. MacCallum, Anthony P. Moore : with a foreword by the Honourable Mr. Justice King. – Sydney : Law Book Co., 1983.
lx,940p.
Bibliography: p.891-898. - Includes index. Includes texts of Residential Tenancies Act 1980 of Victorian jurisdiction and Residential Tenancies Act 1978-81 of South Australian jurisdiction.
ISBN 0455204977

—Solar Energy and the Law. – North Ryde : Law Book Co, 1984.
xxxiii, 324p.
ISBN 0455203407 Pbk £54.50

Bradbury, Paul L.
Cases and statutes on tort / by Paul L. Bradbury. – 3rd ed. – London : Sweet & Maxwell, 1984.
xviii,195p; 22cm.
Previous ed.: 1978. Includes index.
ISBN 0421322004 Pbk £7.85

Braddell, R.St.J.
Laws of the Straits Settlements : a Commentary. – Singapore : Oxford University Press, 1982.
308p.
ISBN 0195825594 Hbk £49.50

Braddick, W A G
Management for Bankers. – London : Butterworths, 1988.
ISBN 0406503400 Pbk £13.50

—Nature of Management. – London : Butterworths, 1987.
ISBN 0406503400 Pbk

Bradford disaster appeal : the administration of an appeal fund / by Roger W. Suddards : with contributions by Leolin Price and Hubert Picarda. – London : Sweet & Maxwell, 1986.
169p.
ISBN 0421379901

Bradgate →Business Law.

Bradley, A. →Public Law.

Bradley, A. W. →Constitutional and administrative law.

Bradlow →Judicial Enforcement of International Debt Obligations.

Bradney, Anthony, et al
How to study law. – London : Sweet & Maxwell, 1986.
ISBN 042134380X Hbk £9.50
ISBN 0421343907 Pbk £7.50

Bradshaw, J.
Guide to DIY House Buying : Supp. Leasehold Flats and Houses. – London : Castle Books, 1985.
ISBN 0950717096 Pbk £3.50

—Guide to DIY House Buying, Selling and Conveyancing. – 2nd ed. – London : Castle Books, 1983.
ISBN 0950717053 Pbk £4.95

—Guide to House Buying, Selling and Conveyancing for All. – London : Castle Books.
ISBN 0951043951 Pbk £6.95

Bradshaw, Kenneth →Parliamentary Assembly : procedure and practice.

Brady, D.
Yankee One and George. – Police Review, 1984.
ISBN 0851640133 Pbk £2.50

Brady, James P.
Justice and politics in People's China : legal order or continuing revolution? / James P. Brady. – London : Academic Press, 1982.
xiii,268p; 24cm.
Includes index.
ISBN 0121247503 £17.80

Brahams, Diana
Casebook on Rent Review and Lease Renewal / Mark Pawlowski. – Oxford : Blackwell Scientific, 1986.
600p.
ISBN 0003831957 Hbk £40

Brahams, Malcolm
Commercial leases / Malcolm Brahams with Norman Harker. – Oxford : Blackwell Scientific, 1985.
viii,198p.
Includes index.
ISBN 0003830446 Hbk £17.50

Brahe, C.R. →ABC of Evidence.

Brahm, L.J.
Intellectual Property Law in the PRC. – London : Longman Professional.
ISBN 0582999685 Hbk

Braithwaite, John
Corporate Crime in the Pharmaceutical Industry. – London : Sweet & Maxwell, 1984.
ISBN 0710200498 Hbk £30.00
→ Of manners gentle : enforcement strategies of Australian business regulatory agencies.

Braithwaite, Paul →Effective Insurance : A Guide For Buyer and Seller.

Braithwaite, Tunji
Jurisprudence of the living oracles / Tunji Braithwaite. – Benin City, Nigeria : Ethiope, 1987.
xviii,308p.
Bibliography: p.296-297 . - Includes index. Includes the texts of the Charter of the United Nations and Statute of the International Court of Justice, and the Universal Declaration of Human Rights.
ISBN 9781233176

Bramwell
Inheritance tax on lifetime gifts / T P G Ivory. – London : Sweet & Maxwell, 1987.
ISBN 04212379103 Hbk £24.50

Bramwell, Hartley
Conveyancing in Hong Kong / Hartley Bramwell. – London : Butterworths, 1981.
xxvii,403p; 23cm.
Includes index.
ISBN 040666210X

Bramwell, Richard
Taxation of Companies and Company Reconstructions. – 4th ed. – Sweet & Maxwell.
ISBN 0421404302 Hbk £75.00

Branch, Alan E
Dictionary of Commercial Terms and Abbreviations. – Witherby, 1984.
ISBN 0900886900 Pbk £9.50

—Dictionary of Shipping and International Trade Terms. – 2nd ed. – Witherby, 1983.
ISBN 0900886706 Pbk £7.50

—Elements of Export Marketing and Management. – London : Chapman & Hall, 1984.
ISBN 0412163500 Pbk £9.95

—Elements of Export Marketing and Management. – London : Sweet & Maxwell, 1984.
Hbk £17.50

—Elements of Export Practice. – 2nd ed. – London : Chapman & Hall, 1985.
ISBN 0412270005 Pbk £9.95

—Elements of Shipping. – 5th ed. – London : Chapman & Hall, 1981.
ISBN 0412237008 Hbk £20.00
ISBN 0412237105 Pbk £9.95

Brand, C. M. →Handbook of business tenancies.

Brand, Clive →Wills.

Brand, Clive M.
Enforcement of Planning Control. – London : Longman Professional, 1988.
ISBN 0851214096 Pbk £14.95

—Howell James' Notes on the Need for Planning Permission / D. W. Williams. – 3rd ed. – London : Oyez Longman, 1984.
ISBN 0851207146 Hbk

—Mobile homes and the law / by C.M. Brand. – London : Sweet & Maxwell, 1986.
xxiv,210p; 26cm.
Includes index.
ISBN 0421334703 £24.00

—Planning law. – London : Longman Professional (UK), 1988.
– (Longman practice notes).
Sets out procedure from initial stages to the final decision of the planning authority. Contains information on how to challenge a planning application, sample forms and precedents, and details time limits and fees.
ISBN 0851214452 Pbk £9.95

—Planning law for conveyancers / Clive Brand and D.W. Williams. – 3rd ed. – London : Longman Professional (UK), 1989.
– (Longman Practitioner Series).
Gives practical advice on how to solve such problems as planning authorities car parking standards, and conversion of roof space. Contains new chapters on planning policy guidance, housing action trust areas, and minerals policy, and covers the Town and Country Planning Regulations of 1988 and 1989, and the General Development Order 1988.
Conveyancing solicitors and licensed conveyancers, chartered surveyors, local authority planning departments, students
ISBN 0851216226 Pbk £22.50

Brandreth, Gyles
Law is an Ass. – London : Pan Books Ltd, 1984.
ISBN 0330282107 Hbk £1.95

Brannen, Peter
Authority and participation in industry / Peter Brannen. – London : Batsford Academic and Educational, 1983.
173p; 22cm.
Bibliography: p157-168. - Includes index.
ISBN 0713443987 Pbk £6.95

Brantingham, Patricia L. →Burnaby, British Columbia experimental public defender project : an evaluation.

Brassard, Jean E.
Agriculture. – Agincourt : Carswell, 1983.
240p.
This textbook describes in detail all of the aspects of agricultural law as it is derived from the common law, statutes, and regulatory bodies of the Canadian federal and provincial governments. Extensive references are made to marketing boards, loan associations, and federal and provincial regulating authorities in the work.
Hbk £38.00

Brassey, M.S.M. →New labour law : strikes, dismissals and the unfair labour practice in South African law.

Bratt, Christian
Labor relations in 17 countries / Christian Bratt : translated by David Jenkins. – Stockholm : Swedish Employers' Confederation, 1982.
134p.
Translated from 'Arbetsmarknaden i 16 lander' by David Jenkins.
ISBN 9171522514

Bratton, Ken
Work of the Commissioner for Local Administration in Scotland, 1975-1983 / by Ken Bratton. – Edmonton, Alta. : International Ombudsman Institute, 1984.
78p. – (Occasional paper).

Brau, Eduard H. →Recent multilateral debt restructurings with official and bank creditors.

Braund, D.
Administration of the Roman Empire 241 BC-AD 193. – Exeter : Exeter University.
ISBN 0859892042 Pbk £2.25

Brave, Jennifer
Law for retailers / Jennifer Brave. – London : Sweet & Maxwell, 1983.
xii,207p; 23cm.
Bibliography: p195-197. - Includes index.
ISBN 0421298103 Hbk £
ISBN 0421298200 Pbk £7.50

Bray, Edward
Law of Discovery 1885. – Woolloomooloo : International Business Communications, 1985.
872p.
ISBN 0949553212 Hbk £85.00

—Principles and practice of discovery : with an appendix of forms including suggested forms for stating objections to discovery / by Edward Bray. – London : Reeves and Turner, 1885.
xlix, 704 p.; 22 cm.
Slips inserted containing new material. Includes index.

Brazier, M.
Medicine, Patients and the Law. – Pelican, 1987.
ISBN 0140225579 Pbk £5.95

Brazier, Margaret
Law of torts / Margaret Brazier. – 8th ed. – London : Butterworths, 1988.
lix,562p.
Previous ed.: / by Harry Street. 1983. Includes index.
ISBN 0406662118 Hbk £34
ISBN 0406662126 Pbk £19.95

Brazier, Rodney →Constitutional and administrative law.

—Constitutional practice / Rodney Brazier. – Oxford : Clarendon Press, 1988.
xix,285p.
Includes index.
ISBN 0198255969

Breach of confidence / Francis Gurry. – Oxford : Clarendon, 1984.
xxvii,487p; 22cm.
Includes index.
ISBN 0198253788 Hbk £42.50

Breach of confidence : comments on Law Commission report on breach of confidence (Law Com. no. 110) : memorandum / by the Council's Law Reform Committee. – London : Law Society, 1982.
5p.

Breach of confidence : report on a reference under section 3 (1) (e) of the Law Commissions Act 1965 / the Law Commission. – London : H.M.S.O., 1981.
ix,239p; 25cm.
ISBN 0101838808

Breach of confidence : report on a reference under section 3(1)(e) of the Law Commissions Act 1965 / Scottish Law Commission. – Edinburgh : Scottish Law Commission, 1984.
vi,73p.
ISBN 0101938500

Breach of contract / by J. W. Carter. – Sydney : Law Book Company, 1984.
xlxi,551p.
ISBN 0455205051 Hbk £49

Breach of promise of marriage. – Law Reform Commission of British Columbia. – Vancouver : Law Reform Commission of British Columbia, 1983.
iii,67p. – (Working paper).

Breach of statutory duty in tort / by K.M. Stanton. – London : Sweet & Maxwell, 1986.
xvii,155p; 23cm.
Includes index.
ISBN 0421331402 Hbk £12.50
ISBN 042133150X Pbk £9.50

Breach of treaty / by Shabtai Rosenne. – Cambridge : Grotius Publications, 1981.
xii,142p; 24cm.
At head of title: University of Cambridge Research Centre for International Law.
ISBN 0906496365

Breaches of Trust in Singapore and Malaysia / Meng Heong Stanley Yeo. – Butterworths, 1984.
98p.
ISBN 0406181152 Pbk £13.00

Brealey
Principles of corporate finance / Myers. – 2nd ed. – Maidenhead : McGraw-Hill, 1986.
ISBN 007007383X Pbk £14.50

Brealey, M → Encyclopedia of road traffic law and practice.

Brean, Donald J. S.
International issues in taxation : the Canadian perspective / Donald J.S. Brean. – Toronto : Canadian Tax Foundation, 1984.
xiii,180p.
Bibliography: p.166-176. - Includes index.
ISBN 0888080190

Brearley, Nigel → Reparation and mediation : a bibliography.

Brech, Michael
Inward investment : policy options for the United Kingdom / Michael Brech and Margaret Sharp. – London : Routledge and Kegan Paul, 1983.

Brechbuhl, E.
Conversation Handbook for Policemen. – 2nd ed. – Plymouth : Macdonald & Evans, 1984.
128p.
ISBN 0712156259 Pbk £6.00

Brecknell, N. P. → Burdens on business : report of a scrutiny of administrative and legislative requirements.

Bredenkamp : The Small Claims Court. – Durban : Professional Publishers, 1986.
ISBN 0409013366 Pbk £29.00

Bredenkamp, I.M.
Bredenkamp : The Small Claims Court. – Durban : Professional Publishers, 1986.
ISBN 0409013366 Pbk £29.00

Brenchley, Frank
Living with terrorism : the problem of air piracy / Frank Brenchley. – London : Institute for the Study of Conflict, 1986.
iv,17p.

Brennan, D.
Provisional damages. – London : LEST, 1986.
ISBN 0907822835 Pbk £17.50

Brennan, G., et al
Taxation and Fiscal Federalism. – Pergamon.
ISBN 0080344011 Pbk £10.00

Bresler, Fenton
Second-best bed : a diversion on wills / Fenton Bresler : illustrations by Michael Heath. – London : Weidenfeld and Nicolson, 1983.
158p; 23cm.
ISBN 0297782134 £7.50
—Sex and the law / by Fenton Bresler. – London : Century, 1988.
192p; 22cm.
Includes bibliography and index.
ISBN 0091736838 £12.95

Bresnan, B.
Bill Bresnan Speaks on Tax Planning under New Tax Law In Words of One Syllable. – Prentice-Hall.
ISBN 0130764728 Hbk £14.75

Brett
Legal Protection of Computer Software / Lawrence Perry. – Oxford : ESC, 1981.
ISBN 0906214068 Pbk £16.25

Brett and Waller's Criminal Law : Text and Cases. – 5th ed. – Butterworths, 1984.
784p.
This introductory work, containing cases, statutory materials, and commentary, is intended to be equally useful in the common law states of New South Wales, South Australia, and Victoria. Variations in the law from one state to another are discussed.
ISBN 0409492116 Hbk £74.00

Brett, Lionel → Laws of Cross River State of Nigeria : containing the laws of the State in force on 30th September 1979 together with certain subsidiary legislation and Federal acts and decrees.

Brett, Waller and Williams Criminal Law Text and Cases / C.R. Williams. – Butterworths, 1989.
ca 960p.
ISBN 0409495336 Hbk £84.00
ISBN 0409495344 Pbk £66.00

Brewer-Carias, A.R.
Judicial Review in Corporate Law. – Cambridge : Cambridge University Press.
– (Cambridge Studies in International and Comparative Law).
ISBN 0521333873 Hbk £50.00

Brewer, John
Hong Kong private company : a manual of practice. – Singapore : Butterworths (Asia), 1989.
300.
A practical guide to Company Secetarial practice in Hong Kong. Includes forms and precedents, extensive cross-references, and coverage of topics such as future legal developments.
ISBN 0409995703 Hbk
→ Ungovernable people : the English and their law in the seventeenth and eighteenth centuries.

Breyer, Stephen
Regulation and its reform / Stephen Breyer. – Cambridge, Mass. : Harvard University Press, 1982.
xii,472p; 25cm.
Bibliography: p382-385. - Includes index.
ISBN 0674753755

Brice, Geoffrey
Maritime Law of Salvage. – London : Sweet & Maxwell, 1983.
ISBN 0420462406 Hbk £60.00

Bricks of shame : Britain's prisons / Vivien Stern. – Harmondsworth : Penguin, 1987.
309p; 20cm. – (Penguin special).
ISBN 0140523839

Briden → Introduction to English Canon Law.

Bridge, J. W. → Introduction to the law and institutions of the European Communities.
→ Law and institutions of the European Communities.

Bridge, Michael G.
Sale of Goods. – Butterworths, 1988.
1,024p.
Incorporates detailed references to modern Canadian consumer and personal property security legislation, and recent legislative and case law developments in the area, and includes material on equitable proprietary principles and on relief against forfeiture.
ISBN 0409816264 Hbk £125.00
—Sales and sales financing in Canada : cases and materials / by M.G. Bridge, F.H. Buckley, with the assistance of L.R. Ganong. – Toronto : Carswell, 1981.
xlix,694p.
Includes bibliographical references.
ISBN 0459337505

Bridge, Nigel Cyprian
Preserving freedom under the law : being the presidential address of the Rt. Hon. Lord Bridge of Harwich, President of the Holdsworth Club of the Faculty of Law in the University of Birmingham, 1981-82. – Birmingham : Holdsworth Club, 1982.
14p. – (Holdsworth Club Presidential Address 1982).
ISBN 0704406179

Bridge, Richard McD. → Video law : a specially commissioned report.

Bridge, S.
Housing Act 1988. – London : Blackstone Press.
ISBN 1854310453 Pbk £16.95

Brief Case : Collection of Papers on Tasmanian Legal Memorabilia and Tasmanian Places ... / P.B. Walker. – Sandy Bay : Melanie Publications, 1981.
xiv, 90p.
Hbk £20.00

Brief Outline of International Humanitarian Law. – Geneva : Comite International de la Croix-Rouge, 1984.
48p.
Hbk £3.00

Brief Outline of the Law Relating to Trusts, Wills, Executors, and Administrators. – 2nd ed. – Wellington : Butterworths, 1982.
ISBN 0409627127 Hbk

Brief to counsel / by Henry Cecil : illustrated by Edward Ardizzone. – 3rd ed. – Chichester : Rose, 1982.
204p; 21cm.
Previous ed.: i.e. New ed. London : Joseph, 1972.
Includes index.

Brief to the Legislative Committee considering Bill C-62 : an Act respecting employment equity / Canadian Human Rights Commission. – Ottawa : Minister of Supply and Services, 1986.
12,14p.
Added t.p. in French. Cover title: Employment equity. Text in English and French.
ISBN 0662541804

Briefing memorandum on the Police and Criminal Evidence Bill / the Law Society. – London : Law Society, 1982.
5 leaves.

Brierley, John E. C. → Major legal systems in the world today : an introduction to the comparative study of law.

Briffett, Richard → Sweet & Maxwell's tax computations and tables 1984/85.

Briggs → Credit Insurance.

Briggs, John Bonar → Muir Hunter on personal insolvency.

Briggs, Peter W.
Foreign Currency Exposure Management. – London : Butterworths, 1987.
ISBN 0406570906 Pbk £22

Brighouse, Henry
Brighouse's precedents of wills and life transfers / Edward F. George, Arthur George, Henry Brighouse. – 11th ed. – London : Sweet & Maxwell, 1986.
176p; 25cm.
Covers taxation, including the provisions of the Finance Act 1986, settled property, divorce, children and issues, agricultural and business property, unquoted shares, and transfers of value inter vivos and the exemptions. Contains 50 precedents, and 63 common form clauses.
ISBN 0421330708 £22.00

Brighouse's precedents of wills and life transfers / Edward F. George, Arthur George, Henry Brighouse. – 11th ed. – London : Sweet & Maxwell, 1986.
176p; 25cm.
Covers taxation, including the provisions of the Finance Act 1986, settled property, divorce, children and issues, agricultural and business property, unquoted shares, and transfers of value inter vivos and the exemptions. Contains 50 precedents, and 63 common form clauses.
ISBN 0421330708 £22.00

Bright → Practical Accounts, Book 1.

Brillenbourg, G.
Venezuela Law Governing Restrictive Business Practices. – London : Eurospan.
ISBN 0935328351 Hbk £66.50

Brindley, L. P. K.
Retirement Planning for Solicitors and Other Self-Employed Persons : 1984 Crash Course Lecture. – London : Law Society, 1984.
20p.
Hbk £1.95
—Revival of the Discretionary Trust : 1983 / Andrew R. Thornhill. – London : Law Society, 1983.
– (Oxford Weekend Courses).
Hbk £3.50

Brindman, Geoffrey → Human rights and the rule of law.

Bringing people together : mediation and reparation projects in Great Britain / Tony F. Marshall and Martin E. Walpole. – London : Home Office, 1985.
iv,89p.
ISBN 0862522196

Brink, A → Eenvormige hofreels.

Briscoe, W. G.
Research paper on computer misuse / by W.G. Briscoe. – Hobart? : Government Printer?, .
167p. – (Research paper).

Briskman, H.
English Business Law Q & A. – London : Financial Training, 1986.
ISBN 1851850104 Pbk £7.95

Bristow, David I. → Construction and Mechanics' Liens in Canada.

Bristow, Roger
Land-use planning in Hong Kong : history, policies and procedures / Roger Bristow. – Hong Kong : Oxford University Press, 1984.
xii, 328p, 8 leaves of plates.
Bibliography: p299-317.
ISBN 0195814967

Britain and the multinationals / John Stopford and Louis Turner. – Chichester : Wiley, 1985.
xiv,282p; 24cm. – (Wiley/IRM series on multinationals).
Includes index.
ISBN 0471908398 £12.75

Britain's inner cities / Paul Lawless. – London : Harper and Row, 1981.
224p.
ISBN 0063181843 Hbk £8.95
ISBN 0063181851 Pbk £4.95

Britain's shadow economy / Stephen Smith. – Oxford : Clarendon, 1986.
192p; 22cm.
Includes bibliography and index.
ISBN 0198285698 £16.95

British Airports Authority : arrangements for the provision of chauffer-driven hire car services at Gatwick Airport : a report / by the Director General of Fair Trading. – London : H.M.S.O., 1984.
50p; 30cm.

British Airways : Civil Aviation Policy and the Privatisation of British Airways / P. J. Forsyth. – London : Institute for Fiscal Studies.
– (Report Ser.).
Hbk £6.00

British and French statutory drafting : the proceedings of the Franco-British conference of 7 and 8 April 1986 / edited by Sir William Dale. – London : Institute of Advanced Legal Studies, 1986.
xix,176p; 21cm.
Conference organized by and held at the Institute of Advanced Legal Studies.

British and Irish Association of Law Librarians
→ Directory of law libraries in the British Isles.
→ Index to legal essays : English language legal essays in festschriften, memorial volumes, conference papers and other collections, 1975-1979.

→ Manual of law librarianship : the use and organization of legal literature.

—Newsletter / British and Irish Association of Law Librarians. – British and Irish Association of Law Librarians. – London : The Association, 1983.

British and Irish Legal Education Technology Association →Newsletter.

British Bankers Association →Regulation of banks in the member states of the EEC.

British Banking 1960-85 / Weale. – London : Macmillan, 1986.
ISBN 0333375084 Hbk £29.50

British Broadcasting Corporation →What's in a name.

British Broadcasting Corporation and Independent Television Publications Limited : the publication of programme information : a report by the Director General of Fair Trading on investigations under section 3 of the Competition Act 1980. – London : Office of Fair Trading, 1984.
72p; 30cm.

British code of advertising practice / Code of Advertising Prcatice Committee. – 7th ed. – London : Code of Advertising Practice Committee, 1985.
94p.
Includes index. ' ... under the general supervision of the Advertising Standards Authority'. - p.4.

British code of sales promotion practice / Code of Advertising Practice Committee. – 4th ed. – London : Code of Advertising Practice Committee, 1984.
28p.
Includes index. '... under the general supervision of the Advertising Standards Authority ...'. - p.2.

British Columbia →British Columbia statute citator : a complete annotating service for R.S.B.C.

—Ordinance of British Columbia. – British Columbia. – 63 leaflets. – Victoria? : s.n., 1864.
Continues British Columbia proclamations, 1858-1863. Continued by ordinances of the combined colonies of British Columbia and Vancouver Island, 1867-1870. This library has 1864 only. Bound with British Columbia proclamations, 1858-1863. Numbering begins anew each year.

—Proclamations / by James Douglas, governor and commander-in-chief of Her Majesty's colony of British Columbia and its dependencies. – 72 leaflets. – Victoria : s.n., 1858.
Continued by British Columbia ordinances, 1864-1866. Proclamations nos. 1-3, 1858 issued by James Douglas as governor of Vancouver Island and its dependencies. Bound together with British Columbia ordinances, 1864. Numbering begins anew each year.

—Report of the Royal Commission on Family and Children's Law
1st-13th, Summary of recommendations / Thomas R. Berger. – 20 v. – Vancouver : Queen's Printer, 1974.
Includes bibliographies. Chairman: Thomas R. Berger.

→ Report on co-ownership of land.

→ Report on the Land (Settled Estate) Act.

British Columbia Act and Regulations. – 3rd ed. – Toronto : DeBoo, 1982.
ISBN 0888201079 Hbk £19.95

British Columbia Annotated Industrial Relations Act, 2 Vols. / A B P DuMoulin. – Butterworths.
Llf £160.00

British Columbia annotated Industrial Relations Act / Russell, A B P DuMoulin. – 2 vols. – Scarborough, Ontario : Butterworths (Canada).
Provides a section by section annotation of the Act. Contains digests of key British Columbia Labour Relations Board and Curt decisions, with commentary, tables of concordance, and an index.
Llf

British Columbia Annual Bound Statutes, 1979-1985. – Agincourt : Carswell.
Hbk £336.00

British Columbia Company Act with Regulations. – Don Mills : CCH Canadian Ltd, 1986.
172p.
ISBN 0887963528 Pbk £8.95

British Columbia Continuing Legal Education Society
Western Labour Arbitration Cases
Vol. I (1979). – British Columbia Continuing Legal Education Society. – Vancouver : British Columbia Continuing Legal Education Society.
Llf £60.00

British Columbia Corporation Manual. – Toronto : DeBoo.
Looseleaf service.
ISBN 0888201311 Llf £295.00

British Columbia Court Forms, 3 vols / James Taylor. – Toronto : Butterworths.
Hbk

British Columbia Court Forms, 3 Vols. / James P. Taylor. – Butterworths.
Llf £450.00

British Columbia Court Forms / James Taylor. – London : Butterworths.
ISBN 0409994510 Hbk

British Columbia Decisions Civil Cases (1979-Present). – Aurora : Canada Law Book Co.
– (Summary Services, Provincial Ser.).
Hbk £299.50

British Columbia Decisions Civil Cases. – Aurora : Canada Law Book Co.
Llf £299.50

British Columbia Decisions Criminal Conviction and Sentence Cases (1979-Present). – Aurora : Canada Law Book Co.
– (Summary Services, Provincial Ser.).
Hbk £185.50

British Columbia Family Law, 2 Vols. – rev. ed. – Butterworths.
Llf £250.00

British Columbia Family Law. – Revised Edition. – London : Butterworths.
ISBN 0409994235 Hbk £200.00

British Columbia Labour Arbitration. – Aurora : Canada Law Book Co.
– (Summary Services, Provincial Ser.).
Hbk £215.00

British Columbia Labour Code, 2 vols. – Toronto : Butterworths.
– (British Columbia Annotated Legislation).
Hbk

British Columbia Labour Code : B.C. Annotated Legislation Series, 2 Vols. – Butterworths.
Llf £150.00

British Columbia Labour Relations Board Decisions (1979-Present). – Aurora : Canada Law Book Co.
– (Summary Services, Provincial Ser.).
Pbk £174.00

British Columbia Labour Relations Board Decisions. – Aurora : Canada Law Book Co.
Llf £174.00

British Columbia law reports. – Toronto : Carswell, 1977.
Consolidated indexes published for 1-10 and 31-70.

British Columbia Law Reports. – Agincourt : Carswell, 1988.
– (Second Ser., 1-18).
This text includes all the cases from the courts of British Columbia and appeals from that court to the Supreme Court of Canada. The cases are all headnoted, there is a topical index, and an index of cases reported.
Hbk £79.00

British Columbia Legal Services Society → Burnaby, British Columbia experimental public defender project : an evaluation.

British Columbia Legal Telephone Directory : 1985. – Aurora : Canada Law Book Co.
This volume, arranged by name, lists every lawyer and law firm in British Columbia. Each listing includes name, firm association, address and telephone. Listings are also provided for, among others: Courts, Judges and Court Officials; Land Registration Districts; Legal Services; and Law Libraries and Universities.
Hbk For 1-5 Copies 9.50 each

British Columbia Practice, 3 vols / James P Taylor. – 2nd ed. – Toronto : Butterworths.
Hbk

British Columbia Reports : 1867-1945, 63 Vols. – Carswell Legal Publications. – Agincourt : Carswell.

British Columbia Revised Statutes : 1979-Up-to-Date, 8 vols. – Agincourt : Carswell, 1985.
Hbk £336.00

British Columbia Rules Citator (1977-Present). – Aurora : Canada Law Book Co.
– (Statute Services).
Pbk £87.00

British Columbia Rules Citator. – Aurora : Canada Law Book Co.
Hbk £87.00

British Columbia Securities Act Forms. – Vancouver : Continuing Legal Education Society of British Columbia, 1987.
323p.
ISBN 0865043167 Hbk £60.00

British Columbia Securities Act, Regulations, and Policy Statements. – Vancouver : Continuing Legal Education Society of British Columbia, 1987.
563p.
ISBN 0865043183 Hbk £75.00

British Columbia Statues Judicially Considered : Case Annotates /. – Agincourt : Carswell.
Hbk £90.00

British Columbia Statute Citator (1979-Present). – Aurora : Canada Law Book Co.
– (Statute Services).
Hbk £147.00

British Columbia statute citator : a complete annotating service for R.S.B.C. – 1. – Agincourt, Ontario : Canada Law Book Co., 1960.
looseleaf.

British Columbia Supreme Court Rules. – Toronto : Butterworths.
Hbk

British Columbia Taxation Service. – Toronto : DeBoo.
Looseleaf service.
ISBN 0888201133 Llf £195.00

British Columbia Weekly Law Digest. – Agincourt : Carswell, 1987.
Hbk £300.75

British Companies Legislation, 2 Vols. – 4th ed. – London : CCH.
ISBN 0863251544 Pbk £19.00

British companies legislation. – 4th. 2 vols. – Bicester : CCH Editions Ltd.
Includes tables of derivations and destinations for both the 1985 companies consolidation and the 1986 insolvency consolidation, the Companies Securities (Insider Dealing) Act 1985, the Companies Consolidation (Consequential Provisions) Act 1985, the Insolvency Act 1986, the Company Directors Disqualification Act 1986 and the Financial Services Act 1986.
ISBN 0863251544 Hbk £19.00

British companies legislation. – Bicester : CCH Editions, 1985.
23cm.

British companies legislation. – Bicester, Oxon. : CCH Editions, 1983.
looseleaf.
Includes indexes. Accompanied by transfer binder: The Companies (Winding Up) Rules 1949.
ISBN 0863250106

British companies legislation : Companies Act 1985 and related legislation. – 1985 ed. 1 v. – Bicester : CCH Editions Ltd, 1985.
Includes index.
ISBN 0863250572

British company law & practice. – 2. – Bicester, Oxon. : CCH Editions, 1983.
looseleaf.
Includes index. Includes current year of British company law cases.
ISBN 0863250289

British company law cases. – Bicester, Oxon. : CCH Editions, 1986-.

British Computer Society
Computer generated output as admissible evidence in civil and criminal cases : a report / by the Professional Advisory Committee of the British Computer Society : edited by T.R.H. Sizer and A. Kelman. – London : Heyden on behalf of the British Computer Society, 1982.
x,41p.
ISBN 0855017414

British Constitution. – Rome : Bulzoni Editore.
Hbk £5.000

British Constitution / Bather. – 4th ed. – London : Macmillan, 1977.
ISBN 0333214706 Pbk £5.95

British Constitution. – 5th ed. – Cambridge : Cambridge University Press, 1966.
ISBN 0521091365 Pbk £7.95

British Constitution : Its Structure and Working. – New Delhi : S. Chand and Company, 1977.
386p.
Hbk £16.00

British Constitution and British Constitutional History. – Bombay : Universal Book Corporation.
Hbk £25.00

British Copyright Council
Reprographic copying of books and journals : a guide for librarians, teachers and all users of copyright works. – British Copyright Council. – London : British Copyright Council, 1985.
10p.
ISBN 0901737046

British crime survey : first report / by Mike Hough and Pat Mayhew. – London : H.M.S.O., 1983.
v,57p; 25cm.
'A Home Office Research and Planning Unit report'.
ISBN 0113407866 Pbk £4.35

British crime survey Scotland / edited by Gerry Chambers and Jacqueline Tombs. – Edinburgh : H.M.S.O., 1984.
vii,62p.
Survey on why crimes not reported to police; identifies groups with high risk of being victims, and describes public attitudes to the criminal justice system.
ISBN 0114923795

British Government and Politics. – 3rd ed. – Plymouth : Macdonald & Evans, 1984.
ISBN 0712124071 Pbk £3.95

British Government and Politics. – 3rd ed. – Plymouth : Macdonald & Evans, 1984.
xi, 288p. – (M and E Handbook Ser.).
ISBN 0712102922 Hbk £3.95

British government and the constitution : text, cases and materials / Colin Turpin. – London : Weidenfeld (George) & Nicolson, 1985.
xxviii,476p; 25cm.
Includes index.
ISBN 0297786512 Hbk £25.00
ISBN 0297786520 Pbk £15.00

British Institute of International and Comparative Law →Antarctic Treaty regime : law, environment and resources.

→ Survey of extradition and fugitive offenders legislation as between Commonwealth jurisdictions.

British Institute of International Comparative Law
Contemporary Problems in the Conflict of Laws : Essays in Honour of John Humphrey Carlile Morris. – British Institute of International Comparative Law. – Dordrecht : Kluwer.
ISBN 9028609687 Hbk Gld60.00

British Institute Studies in International and Comp Law, Vols 1-9. – Sweet & Maxwell.
ISBN 042038790 Hbk

British Intelligence Services in Action. – 2nd ed. – Newtownabbey : Dunrod Press, 1981.
312p.
ISBN 0862021111 Hbk £19.75

British international tax agreements. – 2. – Bicester : CCH Editions, 1984.
ISBN 0863250203 unbound

British Journal of Criminology. – London : Sweet & Maxwell.
Hbk £26.50
Bound volume. –
Hbk £15.95
Single copy. –
Hbk £9.90
Back vols. avail..

British Law and Arctic Men : the Celebrated Murder Trials of Sinnisiak and Uluksuk, First Inuit Tried Under White Man's law. – Saskatoon : Western Producer Prairie Books.
125p.
ISBN 0888330251 Pbk £8.95

British Legal Association
Independent solicitor : journal of the British Legal Association. – British Legal Association. – Tunbridge Wells : British Legal Association, .
From 1983 incorporates BLA solicitor.

British Library →BLAISE-LINE user manual.
—European Communities publications : a guide to British Library resources. – British Library. – London : British Library, 1983.
iii,46p.
ISBN 0712320156

British master tax guide 1987-88. – Bicester : CCH Editions, 1987.
vi,801p.
ISBN 0863251323

British Master Tax Guide 1988-89. – Bicester : CCH.
ISBN 0863251587 Pbk £17.00

British master tax guide : 1986-87. – 5th subscriber ed. – Bicester : CCH, 1986.
viii,744p.
Includes index.
ISBN 0863251137

British Medical Association
Medical evidence : the report of a Joint Committee of the British Medical Association, the Senate of the Inns of the Court and the Bar and the Law Society. – British Medical Association. – London : British Medical Association, 1981.
iiileaves,37p; 30cm.
spiral

British Nationality / Ian Martin. – 2nd ed. – London : CENT, 1984.
ISBN 0946088101 Pbk £2.95

British nationality : the new law / by Ivor Stanbrook. – London : Clement, 1982.
xxiii,213p; 23cm.
Includes text of the act.
ISBN 0907027024 £9.50

British Nationality Act 1981 / with annotations by M. D. A. Freeman. – London : Sweet and Maxwell, 1982.
various pagings; 25cm.
ISBN 0421300604

British nationality and the right of abode 1945-1983 / by K.J. Gray : by C.C. Turpin. – Deventer : Kluwer, 1986.
vii,269p.
Includes bibliographical references.
ISBN 9065442510

British Nationality Law. – 2nd ed. – London : Fourmat, 1986.
ISBN 1851900020 Pbk £12.95

British Nationality Law. – Repr. of 1956 ed. – Aalen Wuertt : Scientia.
xxviii, 306p.
Hbk £85.00

British perspectives on terrorism / edited by Paul Wilkinson. – London : Allen & Unwin, 1981.
193p; 23cm.
Originally published: in Terrorism, 5, no.1 and 2. Includes index.
ISBN 0043270646 Hbk £
ISBN 0043270654 Pbk

British prisons / Mike Fitzgerald and Joe Sim. – 2nd ed. – Oxford : Blackwell (Basil), 1982.
182p; 23cm.
Previous ed.: 1979. Bibliography: p167-170. - Includes index. Previous control number ISBN 0-631-12606-6.
ISBN 0631125299 Hbk £
ISBN 0631126066 Pbk

British Railways Board : admission of hackney carriages to Brighton Central Railway Station to ply for hire : a report by the Director General of Fair Trading on an investigation under Section 3 of the Competition Act 1980 / Office of Fair Trading. – London : Office of Fair Trading, 1982.
53p; 30cm.

British Railways Board : allocation of facilities on Motorail : a report by the Director General of Fair Trading on an investigation under Section 3 of the Competition Act,1980. – London : Office of Fair Trading, 1983.
33p; 30cm.

British Railways Board : Facilities for car hire and advertising of self-drive vehicle hire at railway stations / report by the Director General of Fair Trading on an investigation under section 3 of the Competition Act 1980. – London : Office of Fair Trading, 1983.
47p; 30cm.

British Red Cross Society →Conference on the application of international humanitarian law : March 12th, 1986, London SW1.

British Refugee Council
Selling for a future : proposals for a British policy on refugees / British Refugee Council. – London : The Council, 1987.
25p.

British tax cases. – Bicester, Oxon. : CCH Editions, 1986.
Kept up to date by looseleaf service.

British tax encyclopaedia / edited by G.S.A. Wheatcroft and T.M. Wedderburn. – London : Sweet & Maxwell, 1953-.
loose-leaf.
Supplementary pages issued at intervals.

British Tax Encylopaedia 6 vols.
Service 1988. – Belfast : Sweet & Maxwell.
ISBN 0421003103 updat £450.00

British tax legislation. – 3. – Bicester : CCH Editions, 1982.
Includes index.
ISBN 0863250017

British tax reporter : a set of volumes detailing British company tax, income tax, capital transfer tax, capital gains tax and development land tax. – 6. – Bicester : CCH, 1984.
loose-leaf.
ISBN 0863250270

British tax system / J.A. Kay, M.A. King. – 4th ed. – Oxford : Oxford University Press, 1986.
viii,261p; 23cm.
Previous ed.: 1983. Bibliography: p241-250. - Includes index.
ISBN 0198772637 Hbk £17.50
ISBN 0198772629 Pbk £6.95

British Telecom
Code of practice for consumers / British Telecom. – London : British Telecom, 1984.
24p.

British Telecommunications : (pricing policy for the placing of advertisements in yellow pages directories) : a report / by the Director General of Fair Trading .. – London : Office of Fair Trading, 1984.
54p; 30cm.

British Universities Industrial Relations Association →Industrial relations : an international and comparative bibliography.

British value added tax cases. – Bicester, Oxon. : CCH Editions, 1985-.
Includes index.

British Virgin Islands →British Virgin Islands consolidated index of statutes and subsidiary legislation to 1st January 1983.

British Virgin Islands consolidated index of statutes and subsidiary legislation to 1st January 1983 / compiled at the Faculty of Law Library, University of the West Indies, Barbados. – Rev. ed. – Barbados : s.n., 1983.
ii,56p.
Previous ed.: 1st January 1981. One of a series in the West Indian Legislation Indexing Project (WILIP) compiled in cooperation with the British Development Division.

British Virgin Islands consolidated index of statutes and subsidiary legislation to 1st January 1985 / compiled at the Faculty of Law Library, University of the West Indies, Barbados. – Barbados : s.n., 1985.
iv,67p.
Previous ed.: 1st January 1984. 'One of a series in the West Indian Legislation Indexing Project (WILIP) compiled in coorporation with the British Development Division'.

British workplace industrial relations 1980-1984 : the DE/PSI/ESRC/ACAS surveys / Neil Millward and Mark Stevens. – Aldershot : Gower, 1986.
xxi,341p; 22cm.
Includes index.
ISBN 0566053918 Hbk £22.50
ISBN 0566053969 Pbk £9.95

British year book of international law / Derek Bownett. – Oxford : Clarendon Press, 1989.
650; 23.5.
Contains major articles and reviews of books on international law, as well as surveys of decisions of British courts involving questions of international law. Also surveys decisions of the European Convention on Human Rights, and the Court of Justice of the European Communities.
ISBN 0198254083 Hbk £65.00

British Yearbook of International Law 1987 / D W Bowett. – Oxford : Oxford University Press.
ISBN 0198256191 Hbk £65.00

Britons in Brussels : Officials in the European Commission and Council Secretariat. – London : Policy Studies Institute, 1983.
ISBN 0853742170 Pbk £3.00

Brittan, Yvonne
Impact of residual disability from illness and injury on the distribution of household income : a lognormal approach / by Yvonne Brittan and Ioannis G. Vlachonikolis. – Oxford : SSRC-Social Science Research Council, 1981.
23p. – (Working paper).

Britton
Modern methods of valuation / Davies. – 2nd ed. – London : Estates Gazette, 1981.
ISBN 072820049X Hbk £10.00

Britton, Philip
Case through the courts : Ford v. Warwickshire / Philip Britton and Ian Thompson. – 1 videocassette. – London : Sweet & Maxwell in association with the University of Warwick, 1985.
– (Sweet & Maxwell's lawfilms).
Accompanied by Teaching materials. - 64p. (in folder).
—Land law & landscape / Philip Britton and Ian Thompson. – 1 videocassette. – London : Sweet & Maxwell in association with the University of Warwick, 1986.
– (Sweet & Maxwell's lawfilms).

Britts, M.G.
Pleading Precedents. – 3rd ed. – North Ryde : Law Book Co, 1984.
xvii, 285p.
ISBN 0455202923 Hbk £43.00

Brixton disorders 10-12 April 1981 : report of an enquiry / by Lord Scarman. – London : H.M.S.O., 1981.
viii,168p; 25cm.
Report of inquiry by Lord Scarman. Discusses causes of the riots and lessons for the future about riot control and prevention.
ISBN 0101842708 Pbk £8.00

Broad, Juliet →Study on the legislative framework, agreements and financial impositions affecting the mining industry in African Commonwealth countries.

Broadcasting in the '90s : competition, choice and quality : the government's plans for broadcasting legislation / presented to Parliament by the Secretary of State for the Home Department by Command of Her Majesty, November 1988. – London : HMSO, 1988.
iv,45p.
ISBN 0101051727

Broadcasting law and policy in Australia / Mark Armstrong. – Sydney : Butterworths, 1982.
xxviii,291p.
Includes index.
ISBN 0409309109

Broadcasting Law and Practice / D. Catterns. – North Ryde : Law Book Co, 1987.
ca 1,500p.
Llf £450.00

Broadcasting Law in Canada : Fairness in the Administrative Process. – Agincourt : Carswell, 1987.
120p.
This book provides a rigorous analysis of the legal problems inherent in the regulation of broadcasting in Canada. The work comprehensively reviews the application of the principles of procedural fairness to the administrative process of the C.T.R.C.
Hbk £33.00

Broadsheet on the law of contract / by Y.C. Onwuchekwa. – Lagos : s.n., 1984.
42p.

Broadwater Farm Inquiry. – London : CEMT, 1986.
ISBN 094691897 Pbk £4.95

Brock, R. R., et al
Medicine for Lawyers. – Vancouver : British Columbia Continuing Legal Education Society, 1982.
163p.
ISBN 0865040753 Hbk £50.00
—Products Liability : 1982. – Vancouver : British Columbia Continuing Legal Education Society, 1982.
114p.
ISBN 0865040494 Hbk £45.00

Brockington, R.
Concise Dictionary of Accounting and Finance. – Pitman, 1986.
ISBN 0712106847 Pbk £4.95

Brodie, David
Tolley's taxation of marriage and marriage breakdown / by David Brodie. – Croydon : Tolley, 1988.
xxiii,184p; 23cm.
Includes index.
ISBN 0854593233 Pbk £14.95

Brodie, Peter R.
Dictionary of shipping terms / by Peter R. Brodie. – London : Lloyd's of London, 1985.
155p; 22cm.
ISBN 1850440697 Pbk £15.00

Broekman, Jan M →Social justice and individual responsibility in the welfare state.

Brogden, Michael, et al
Introducing Police Work. – Unwin Hyman.
ISBN 004363012X Hbk £25.00
ISBN 0043630081 Pbk £9.95
—Police : autonomy and consent / Michael Brogden. – London : Academic Press, 1982.
xv,265p; 24cm.
Bibliography: p251-259. - Includes index.
ISBN 0121351807 £21.00

Bromley, P. M.
Family law / P.M. Bromley, N.V. Lowe. – 7th ed. – London : Butterworths, 1987.
lvi,793p; 25cm.
Previous ed. 1981. Includes index. Cover title: Bromley's family law.
ISBN 0406560145 Hbk £38.00
ISBN 0406560153 Pbk £23.95

Bronckers, M. C. E. J
Selective safeguard measures in multilateral trade relations : issues of protectionism in GATT, European Community, and United States law / M.C.E.J. Bronckers. – Deventer, Netherlands : Kluwer Law and Taxation Publishers, 1985.
306p.
Includes index and bibliography.
ISBN 9065442227 Hbk £150.00

Bronkhorst, H.J. →Leading Cases and Materials on the Agricultural Policy of the E.E.C.

Brookbank, C. Roy
Legislative Changes in the Construction Industry in Nova Scotia 1964 to 1975 : An Exercise in Industrial Democracy. – Halifax : Dalhousie University, Institute of Public Affairs.
v, 55p. – (Occasional Papers).
ISBN 088926810X Pbk £5.00

Brookbanks, W.
Defence of Compulsion : an Overview. – Auckland : Legal Research Foundation, 1982.
Hbk £6.50

Brooke, H.
Institute Cargo Clauses (Air). – Witherby, 1986.
ISBN 0900886277 Pbk £9.00

Brooke, R.
Brooke's Notary : Notarial Office & Practice in England & Overseas. – Belfast : Sweet & Maxwell.
ISBN 0420474307 Hbk £65.00

Brooke-Taylor
Guide to Stamp Duties. – London : CCH, 1987.
ISBN 0863251153 Pbk

Brooke's Notary : Notarial Office & Practice in England & Overseas. – Belfast : Sweet & Maxwell.
ISBN 0420474307 Hbk £65.00

Brooke's Treatise on the Office and Practice of a Notary of England. – Repr. of 1939 ed. – London : Sweet & Maxwell, 1985.
– (Sweet and Maxwell Library Reprints).
ISBN 0421351705 Hbk £50.00

Brookfield →Law and Practice of Conveyancing in New Zealand.

Brookfield, F.M.
Will-Draftsman's Handbook. – 4th ed. – Butterworths, 1987.
ISBN 0409652415 Hbk

Brooking
Tenancy Law and Practice Victoria / Chernov. – 2nd ed. – London : Butterworths.
ISBN 0409356115 Hbk £32.10

Brooking, Robert →Insurance law in Australia and New Zealand.

Brooks
Charity Accounting / Vincent. – London : Butterworths, 1987.
ISBN 0406261008 Pbk £19.95

Brooks, B.
Contract of Employment : Principles of Australian Employment Law. – 3rd ed. – North Ryde : C.C.H. Australia, 1986.
328p.
ISBN 0869036297 Hbk £38.00

Brooks, C. W.
Pettyfoggers and vipers of the Commonwealth : the 'lower branch' of the legal profession in early modern England / C.W. Brooks. – Cambridge : Cambridge University Press, 1986.
410p; 23cm. – (Cambridge studies in English legal history).
Researches professional and social history of attorneys, solicitors, clerical officials and court holders in early modern society. Examines the nature of legal services provided for the public, considers how the legal system responded to the increase in litigation of the late sixteenth century.
ISBN 0521305748 £30.00

Brooks, Jermyn →German Law Pertaining to Companies with Limited Liability : A Synoptic Translation Including Comprehensive Introductory Comments on the Laws Affecting the German GmbH.

Brooks, Jocelyn →Ill conceived : law and abortion practice in New Zealand.

Brooks, Neil
Police guidelines - pretrial eyewitness identification procedures : a study paper / prepared for the Law Reform Commission of Canada by Neil Brooks. – Ottawa : the Commission, 1983.
260p; 25cm. – (Criminal law series).
ISBN 0662127315
—Quest for Reform : The Royal Commission on Taxation Twenty Years Later. – Agincourt : Carswell, 1987.
475p.
This work analyzes the history of tax reform in Canada up to and including up-to-date proposals. The author outlines the process and substance of tax reform while comparing it to the Carter Report.
Hbk £58.50
—Quest for Tax Reform : Royal Commission on Taxation 20 Years Later. – Agincourt : Carswell, 1988.
475p.
Hbk £58.50

Brooks, P. E. J. →Modern Business Law.

Broom
Legal Maxims / Kersley. – Sweet & Maxwell, 1939 Reprint.
ISBN 0421160500 Hbk £28.00
—Practice of the Superior Courts of Common Law. – Repr. of 1850 ed. – Abingdon : Professional Books.
Hbk £20.00

Broomberg, E. B.
South African Tax Journal / H. R. Levin. – Durban : Butterworths, 1985.
Hbk
—Tax Strategy. – 2nd ed. – Durban : Butterworths, 1983.
ISBN 0409013595 Pbk

Brophy
Women in law / Carol Smart. – Routledge, 1985.
ISBN 0710202598 Pbk £7.50
ISBN 0710206070 Hbk £19.95

Brophy, Julia →Women-in-law : explorations in law, family and sexuality.

Brought to justice / Roy Lewis. – Durham : Casdec, 1983.
83p.
ISBN 0907595111

Broun, Malcolm D. →Australian family law & practice reporter.

Brown
Australian Road Traffic Offences. – London : Butterworths, 1983.
ISBN 040949109X Hbk £28.80
→ Committals for Trial to the Crown Court : the Law and Practice.
—Introduction to working in the Lloyds Market / Wormell. – Witherby, 1987.
ISBN 0948691387 Pbk £10.00
—Land acquisition. – 2nd ed. – London : Butterworths, 1983.
ISBN 0409490911 Hbk £31.30
—Law of Intellectual Property in New Zealand / Grant. – Butterworths, 1989.
715p.
ISBN 0409787981 Hbk £130.00
—Life Assurance : Its Tax Implications Etc / Trimm. – Witherby, 1977.
ISBN 090088620X Hbk £7.50
—Self-Help Groups for Drug Addicts' Families / Gay. – Policy Studies Institute.
ISBN 0853744076 Pbk £4.95
—Western Australian introduction to law. – 2nd ed. – London : Butterworths, 1986.
ISBN 0409490571 Pbk £18.00

Brown, A.
300 Years of Lloyds : Lloyd's List Special Supplement. – London : Lloyd's of London Press.
ISBN 185044188X Pbk £21.50
—Hazard unlimited. – 3rd ed. – London, 1987.
ISBN 1850441316 Pbk £5.95
ISBN 1850441375 Hbk £14.50

Brown, Bowman →International banking centres.

Brown, C. →Eight Peak Index of Mass Spectra of Compounds of Forensic Interest.

Brown, Carolyn S. →Information system dynamics : the impact of interactive information networks on the UK library and information system : final report for the period August 1979 - July 1982 : report to the British Library Research and Development Dept., on project SI/G/327.

Brown, Catherine A →Taxation and estate planning.

Brown, Craig
Insurance law in Canada : a treatise on the principles of indemnity insurance as applied in the common law provinces of Canada / by Craig Brown and Julio Menezes. – Toronto, Canada : Carswell, 1982.
lxxix, 518 p.; 26 cm.
Includes bibliographical references and indexes.
ISBN 0459339605
—No-Fault Automobile Insurance in Canada. – Agincourt : Carswell, 1988.
250p.
Hbk £46.25

Brown, D.
Land Acquisition. – 1983.
209p.
ISBN 0409490911 Hbk £59.00
—Traffic Offences. – London : Butterworths.
ISBN 0409495174 Hbk £35.00

Brown, David C.
Civilian review of complaints against the police : a survey of the United States literature / David C. Brown. – London : Home Office, 1983.
v,39p.
Bibliography: p.29-32.
ISBN 0862521041
—Community constables : a Study of a policing initiative / David Brown, Susan Iles. – London : Home Office, 1985.
v,51p.
Bibliography: p.42-43.
—Detention at the police station under the Police and Criminal Evidence Act 1984 / by David Brown. – London : HMSO, 1989.
v,88p.
Bibliography: pp.78-80. 'A Home Office Research and Planning Unit Report'. - T.p..
ISBN 0113409087
—Police complaints procedure : a survey of complainants' views / by David Brown. – London : H.M.S.O., 1987.
v,91p; 25cm.
Survey of complainants' views, carried out shortly before the Police and Criminal Evidence Act 1984. Explores tensions involved in the complaints procedure and assesses its effectiveness.
ISBN 0113408536
→ Prison struggle : changing Australia's penal system.

Brown, Donald J. M.
Canadian labour arbitration / David M. Beatty. – 2nd ed. – Aurora, Ont. : Canada Law Book Ltd., 1984.
clxxiv,723p.
Previous ed.: 1977. Includes index.
ISBN 0888040199

Brown, Douglas
Criminal Procedure in Uganda and Kenya. – Nairobi : East African Publishing House.
150p.
Hbk £5.50
—Motor Vehicle Reports. – Butterworths.
Hbk
—Traffic Offences. – 2nd ed. – Butterworths, 1988.
ca 304p.
ISBN 0409495174 Hbk £49.00
—Traffic offences : an examination of the principles of law governing offences committed by motorists on the roads in Australia / Douglas Brown. – Sydney : Butterworths, 1983.
lx,323p.
Includes index.
ISBN 040949190X

Brown, E. D.
Sea-bed energy and mineral resources and the law of the sea
Vol.1 : The areas within national jurisdiction : by E.D. Brown. – London : Graham & Trotman, 1984.
350p in various pagings; 25cm.
Includes index.
ISBN 0860104605 Hbk £39.00
ISBN 0860106152 unbound £35.00
Vol.2 : The areas beyond the limits of national jurisdiction / by E.D. Brown. – 1986.
400p; 24cm.
Includes index.
ISBN 0860106233 Hbk £45.00 :
ISBN 0860106217 Llf-leaf £45.00
Vol.3 : Selected documents, tables, bibliography / by E.D. Brown. – 1986.
520p; 24cm.
Includes bibliography.
ISBN 0860106241 Hbk £55.00 :
ISBN 0860106225 Llf-leaf £55.00

—UN Convention on the Law of the Sea 1982 : a guide for national policy making legislation and administration
Book 1 : General introduction / prepared by E.D. Brown in association with the Commonwealth Secretariat. – London : The Secretariat, 1987.
viii,132p.

—UN Draft Convention on the Law of the Sea : how it affects the United Kingdom's oil rights / E.D. Brown. – S.l. : s.n., 1981.
56p.
'Paper read at seminar on recent developments in U.K. petroleum law, London, June, 1981'. Includes bibliographical references.

Brown, Eddie →Contemporary problems of international law : essays in honour of Georg Schwarzenberger on his eightieth birthday.

Brown, Frank
Drinking and Driving : A Pocket Guide. – London : Police Review Publishing, 1984.
ISBN 0851640109 Pbk

Brown, G.D.
Brief Case : Collection of Papers on Tasmanian Legal Memorabilia and Tasmanian Places ... / P.B. Walker. – Sandy Bay : Melanie Publications, 1981.
xiv, 90p.
Hbk £20.00

Brown, G. G.
Brown on Divorce. – 2nd ed. – London : Shaw & Sons, 1986.
ISBN 0721910505 Llf £75.00

—Brown on Separation. – London : Shaw & Sons, 1981.
ISBN 0721908403 Pbk £16.00

Brown, Harold J. J.
Encyclopedia of the Law of Compulsory Purchase and Compensation, 2 Vols. – London : Sweet & Maxwell, 1985.
– (Local Government Library).
Includes tables of statutes and cases covered by the encyclopaedia, and a guide to the general principles of compulsory purchase law and practice. Covers rates of interest after entry regulations, and includes the Local Government Act 1988. Also contains a new section with details of major cases.
ISBN 0421007508 Hbk £125.00

—Journal of Planning and Environment Law. – London : Sweet & Maxwell.
Pbk £45.00

Brown, Henry Phelps
Origins of trade union power / by Henry Phelps Brown. – Oxford : Clarendon, 1983.
vi,320p; 25cm.
Includes index.
ISBN 0198771150 £15.00

Brown, J.C.
Child Benefit : Investing in the Future. – London : Central Books.
ISBN 0946744114 Pbk £3.95

Brown, J. W.
Practical Company Law. – London : Pan Books Ltd, 1984.
ISBN 0330282034 Hbk £2.95

Brown, Joan C.
Anti-Poverty Policy in the European Community. – London : Policy Studies Institute, 1984.
271p. – (Conference Papers).
Hbk £5.00

—Education and Poverty in the United Kingdom : A Background Paper. – London : Policy Studies Institute, 1981.
Hbk £3.60

—Low Pay and Poverty in the United Kingdom. – London : Policy Studies Institute, 1981.
Hbk £3.50

Brown, John
Canadian Regulatory Agencies. – Toronto : Butterworths, 1981.
288p.
ISBN 0409816302 Pbk £21.95

—Policing and Social Policy : Proceedings of the Cranfield-Wolfson Colloquium. – London : Police Review Publishing, 1984.
Hbk £8.75

—Policing by multi-racial consent : the Handsworth experience / John Brown. – London : Bedford Square Press, 1982.
xv,174p.
Bibligraphy: p173-174.

—Policing Minorities in Europe : Proceedings foom the Cranfield-Wolfson Colloquium. – London : Police Review Publishing, 1984.
ISBN 0851640087 Pbk

Brown, L.
Customs 88. – London : Kogan Page, 1988.
ISBN 1850915997 Pbk

—UK-France road freighting-legal guide. – London : Kogan Page, 1988.
ISBN 185091320X Pbk £28.00

Brown, L. Neville
Court of Justice of the European Communities / by L. Neville Brown and Francis G. Jacobs. – 2nd ed. – London : Sweet & Maxwell, 1983.
xxxi,305p; 19cm. – (Modern legal studies).
Previous ed.: 1977. Includes index.
ISBN 0421314001 Hbk £
ISBN 0421314109 Pbk £7.95

—French administrative law / J. F. Garner, Jean-Michel Galabert. – 3rd ed. – London : Butterworths, 1983.
xvii,218p.
Previous ed.: 1973. Bibliography: p.205-207.- Includes index.
ISBN 0406561524

Brown, Largent
Law for the Haulier. – London : Kogan Page, 1987.
250p.
ISBN 1850911479 Hbk £11.95

—Manager's Guide to International Road Freighting. – London : Kogan Page, 1986.
320p.
ISBN 1850911495 Hbk £12.95

Brown, Marcelle V.
Western Australian Industrial Relations Law. – Nedlands : University of Western Australia Press, 1987.
ca viii, 264p.
ISBN 0855642572 Pbk

—Western Australian Introduction to Law. – 2nd ed. – Butterworths, 1986.
255p.
ISBN 0409490571 Pbk £23.50

Brown, Marjorie J. →Online bibliographic databases : a directory and sourcebook.

Brown, Muriel
Introduction to Social Administration in Britain. – 6th ed. – London : Hutchinson, 1985.
– (Politics Ser.).
ISBN 0091599717 Hbk £7.95

Brown on Divorce. – 2nd ed. – London : Shaw & Sons, 1986.
ISBN 0721910505 Llf £75.00

Brown on Separation. – London : Shaw & Sons, 1981.
ISBN 0721908403 Pbk £16.00

Brown, P., et al
Costs and Fees in Family Law Cases. – Vancouver : British Columbia Continuing Legal Education Society, 1982.
118p.
ISBN 0865040842 Hbk £50.00

Brown, Paul →Halsbury's statutes of England and Wales.

Brown, R
Foreign Currency Options. – London : Butterworths.
ISBN 0406101604 Pbk £35.00

Brown, R. H. →Criminal Procedure According to the Law of Scotland.

Brown, Raymond
Law of Defamation. – Agincourt : Carswell, 1987.
1540p.
This treatise provides a thorough treatment of the Canadian law of defamation. All significant Canadian cases, as well as, major cases from the Commonwealth and U.S. on defamation are included in the work. The practice and procedure for defamation cases is discussed in the book.
ISBN 045939630 Hbk £55.00

—Law of Defamation in Canada, 2 Vols. – Agincourt : Carswell, 1987.
1,540p.
Hbk £122.50

Brown, Robert →Evaluation of fines enforcement.

—Nature of social laws. – Reprint. – Cambridge : Cambridge University Press, 1986.
ISBN 0521338298 Pbk £9.95

Brown, Robert H
Analysis Of Marine Insurance Clauses
Book 1. – Witherby, 1982.
ISBN 0900886765 Pbk £6.00

—Dictionary Of Marine Insurance Terms. – 4th ed. – Witherby, 1975.
ISBN 0900886110 Hbk £15.00

—Institute cargo clauses 1982 / by Robert H. Brown. – 2nd ed. – London : Witherby, 1983.
v,59p; 30cm.
Previous ed.: 1982. Includes index.
ISBN 0900886846 Pbk

—Institute time clauses - Hulls 1983 : full conditions / by Robert H. Brown. – London : Witherby, 1983.
vi,45p; 30cm.
ISBN 0900886897 Pbk

—Marine insurance
vol. 1 : Principles & basic practice / by Robert H. Brown. – 5th ed. – London : Witherby & Co. Ltd, 1986.
xix,343p; 22cm.
ISBN 0948691190

Vol.2 : Cargo practice : incorporating Marine cargo claims by John J. Novitt / by Robert H. Brown. – 1985.
xiii,442,xxxviip; 23cm.
Previous ed.: 1979. Includes index. Contains text of the clauses.
ISBN 0900886838

—Marine Insurance Abbreviations. – London : Witherby, 1968.
ISBN 0900886005 Pbk £2.00

—Marine reinsurance / by Robert H. Brown and Peter B. Reed. – London : Witherby, 1981.
xi,343p; 23cm.
Includes index.
ISBN 0900886617 £21.00

Brown, Robert M.C.
Superannuation and Retirement Benefits in Australia / John V. Edstein. – Butterworths, 1988.
ca 550p.
ISBN 0409494461 Llf £245.00

Brown, W.
Formulae Bene Placitandi : A Book of Entries Containing Precedents, 2 Vols. – Repr. of 1671 ed. – Abingdon : Professional Books.
264p.
Hbk £95.00

—Marriage, Divorce and Inheritance : Cambridge African Monographs No. 10. – London : African Studies Centre.
ISBN 0902993232 Pbk £5.50

Brown, W. J. →GCSE and 'O' level law.

—GCSE and O level law / by W.J. Brown. – 3rd ed. – London : Sweet & Maxwell, 1986.
280p; 22cm.
Previous ed.: published as O level law. 1982. Includes index.
ISBN 0421352507 Hbk £9.50
ISBN 0421352604 Pbk £6.95

Brown, William
Casebook on Theft Acts 1968-78. – 3rd ed. – London : Sweet & Maxwell, 1984.
ISBN 0851640117 Pbk £4.50
→ Changing contours of British industrial relations : a survey of manufacturing industry.

Browne, J. Patrick
Readings in Ohio Civil Procedure. – Agincourt : Carswell, 1987.
1216p.
This text analyzes and discusses common problems often not focused on in texts on this subject. The information is presented in a series of articles of varying length.
Hbk £85.00

Browne, Jeffrey F. →United States law of sovereign immunity relating to international financial transactions.

Brownie
British Yearbook of International Law 1987 / D W Bowett. – Oxford : Oxford University Press.
ISBN 0198256191 Hbk £65.00

Brownlee, D.
Law Courts. – London : MIT Press, 1984.
ISBN 0262021994 Hbk £37.50

Brownlie, Alistair
Crime Investigation : Art or Science?. – Edinburgh : Scottish Academic Press Ltd, 1984.
102p.
ISBN 0707304377 Hbk £10.00
ISBN 0707304385 Pbk

Brownlie, Alistair R. →Drink, drugs and driving.

Brownlie, Ian →Basic documents in international law.
→ Basic documents on human rights.

—British year book of international law / Derek Bownett. – Oxford : Clarendon Press, 1989.
650; 23.5.
Contains major articles and reviews of books on international law, as well as surveys of decisions of British courts involving questions of international law. Also surveys decisions of the European Convention on Human Rights, and the Court of Justice of the European Communities.
ISBN 0198254083 Hbk £65.00

—Brownlie's Law of public order and national security / edited by Michael Supperstone. – 2nd ed. – London : Butterworths, 1981.
lvii,415p.
Previous ed. entitled: The law relating to public order. Includes index.
ISBN 0406137013

—State responsibility
Pt.1 / by Ian Brownlie. – Oxford : Clarendon, 1983.
xvi,302p; 24cm.
Includes index.
ISBN 0198254520 £25.00

Brownlie's Law of public order and national security / edited by Michael Supperstone. – 2nd ed. – London : Butterworths, 1981.
lvii,415p.
Previous ed. entitled: The law relating to public order. Includes index.
ISBN 0406137013

Brownstone →Leaders and lawyers.

Brownsword, A.
Understanding contract law. – London : Fontana, 1987.
ISBN 0006860702 Pbk £4.95

Brownsword, Roger →Law as a moral judgment.
→ Understanding contract law.

Bruce
Criminal Evidence in Hong Kong / Gerard McCoy. – London : Butterworths, 1987.
ISBN 0409995479 Hbk £54.00

Bruce, Andrew
Law of Evidence in Criminal Trials in Hong Kong / Gerard McCoy. – Butterworths, 1987.
ca 350p.
Examines the principles which govern in Hong Kong the reception of evidence in criminal proceedings: trial, sentence, and appeal. Covers facts which need not be proved, burden and standard of proof, the rule against hearsay and its exceptions, similar fact evidence and other evidence of criminal conduct probative of the guilt of the accused.
ISBN 0409995479 Hbk £97.50

Bruce, Christopher J.
Assessment of Personal Injury Damages. – Butterworths, 1985.
378p.
ISBN 0409814075 Hbk £75.00

Bruce et al.
Handbook of Australian Corporate Finance. – London : Butterworths.
ISBN 0409302449 Pbk £27.00

Bruce, Neil →Taxes on capital income in Canada : analysis and policy.

Bruckner, Peter
Foreign affairs, powers and policy in the draft treaty establishing the European Union / by Peter Bruckner. – Florence : European University Institute, 1985.
30p.

Brugmans, Hendrik
Crisis in the Traditional Nation State. – Exeter : European Atlantic Movement, 1982.
Hbk £0.50

Brumter, Christian
North Atlantic Assembly / Christian Brumter. – Dordrecht : M. Nijhoff, 1986.
xi, 223p.
ISBN 9024733189

Brunel University →Guide to the records of the Lord Chancellor's Department.

Bruno, Francesco
Combatting drug abuse and related crime : comparative research on the effectiveness of socio-legal preventive and control measures in different countries on the interaction between criminal behaviour and drug abuse / by Francesco Bruno. – Rome : Fratelli Palombi, 1984.
251p. – (Publication).
Bibliography: p.212-244. 'Funded by the United Nations Fund for Drug Abuse'.
ISBN 8876218262

Bruun, Finn
Models of organisation for the government of conurbations : report / prepared under the guidance of the Committee of Experts on Local and Regional Structures of the Steering Committee for Regional and Municipal Matters by Finn Bruun. – Strasbourg : Council of Europe, 1986.
24p; 30cm.

Bryan, Greyson
Taxing unfair international trade practices : a study of U.S. antidumping and countervailing duty laws / Greyson Bryan. – Lexington : Lexington Books, 1981.
xxii,370p; 24cm.
Includes index.
ISBN 0669037524 £20.00

Bryant, R.
Sale of Real Property and Law of Agency in NSW. – 4th ed. – Sydney : Butterworths, 1983.
176p.
This book is a working guide for those involved in conveyancing transactions. The fourth edition has been revised and updated to include new materials on the contract of sale of land, strata titles, agents' commissions, registration of titles, valuation of land, and other topics.
ISBN 0409494119 Pbk £26.00

Bryant, Robin
Conveyancing Manual for New South Wales. – Woolloomooloo : International Business Communications, 1987.
ISBN 0949553328 Hbk £25.00

Bryson, W.H.
Dictionary of Sigla and Abbreviations Law Books Before 1607. – London : Eurospan.
ISBN 0813906156 Hbk £17.50
—Legal Education in Virginia 1779-1979 : a Bibliographical Approach. – London : Eurospan.
ISBN 0813909015 Hbk £41.25
—Virginia Law Reporters Before 1880. – London : Eurospan.
ISBN 0813907470 Hbk £9.95

Buchan, J.D.
Mortgages of Ships : Marine Security in Canada. – Butterworths, 1986.
264p.
ISBN 0409988316 Hbk £95.00

Buchanan →Accounting For Pensions.

Buchanan, Allen E.
Marx and justice : the radical critique of liberalism / Allen E. Buchanan. – London : Methuen, 1982.
xiv,206p; 25cm.
Bibliography: p197-199. - Includes index.
ISBN 0416334504 £12.95

Buchanan, J. L. →South African Law Reports (1947 to Date).

Buchanan, R. B.
Legal environment of the business world / R.B. Buchanan. – Cheltenham : Stanley Thornes, 1982.
xix,230p; 22cm.
Includes index.
ISBN 0859503054 Pbk £3.75

Buchanan's Appeal Cases, 1880-6 and 1904-11, 4 Vols. – Kenwyn : Juta & Co, 1985.
– (Cape Reports).

Buchanan's Reports, 1868-1879, 10 Vols. – Kenwyn : Juta & Co, 1985.
– (Cape Reports).

Buchholz, Hanns J.
Law of the Sea Zones in the Pacific Ocean. – Singapore : Institute of Southeast Asian Studies, 1987.
120p.
ISBN 9971988739 Hbk £26.00

Buckett, A.
VAT enforcement and appeals manual. – London : Butterworths, 1986.
ISBN 0406504202 Pbk £17.95

Buckland
Roman Law and Common Law / McNair. – 2nd ed. – Cambridge : Cambridge University Press, 1965.
ISBN 0521043611 Hbk £31.00

Buckley, F H
Companies Acts / Parker. – 14th ed. – London : Butterworths, 1981.
Service to Date.
ISBN 0406141037 Hbk £150.00
—Corporations : Cases, Text and Materials / Mark Q. Connelly. – 2nd ed. – Toronto : Edmond-Montgomery, 1988.
1,000p.
Hbk £90.00
—Corporations : Principles and Policies / Mark Q. Connelly. – 2nd ed. – Toronto : Edmond-Montgomery, 1988.
ca 1,050p.
ISBN 0920722253 Hbk £100.00
—Corporations : Principles and Policies. – 2nd ed. – Toronto : Edmond Montgomery.
ISBN 0020722253 Hbk £52.00
→ Sales and sales financing in Canada : cases and materials.

Buckley, Martin →Buckley on the Companies Acts.

Buckley on the Companies Acts / by the late Lord Wrenbury. – 14th ed. – London : Butterworths, 1981.
Previous ed.: 1957. Includes index. Post-consolidation materials are set out in a loose-leaf volume.
ISBN 0406141045 v.2
ISBN 0406141053

Buckley, R. A.
Law of nuisance / R. A. Buckley. – London : Butterworths, 1981.
xxxv,181p.
ISBN 040614110X Hbk £22.00
—Modern law of negligence / R.A. Buckley. – London : Butterworths, 1988.
lvii,402p.
Includes index.
ISBN 0406113009
→ Salmond and Heuston on the law of torts.

Bucknall, P.
Misuse of Drugs
2nd Supplement / Hamid Ghodse. – Waterlow. – (Criminal Law Library).
ISBN 0080331076 Pbk £10.00

Bucknell, Patrick
Misuse of drugs / Patrick Bucknell and Hamid Ghodse. – London : Waterlow, 1986.
512p; 23cm.
ISBN 0080392032 £30.00

Budapest Treaty on the International Recognition of the Deposit of Microorganisms for the Purposes of Patent Procedure : Original Text of the Treaty Adopted by the Budapest Conference (1977) and Regulations (as of Jan 31, 1981). – Geneva : World Intellectual Property Organization.
53p.
Hbk £10.00

Budget and Finance Bill 1985. – London : Law Society, 1985.
28p. – (Nineteen Eighty-Five Crash Course Transcripts).
Hbk £2.05

Budget and Policy Choices 1983 : Taxes, Defence, Entitlements. – London : Eurospan.
ISBN 0944237053 Pbk £8.50

Budget Tax Tables 1986. – Butterworths. – London : Butterworths, 1986.
ISBN 0406508410 Pbk £2.80

Budworth, G.
Knots and Crime. – London : Police Review, 1985.
ISBN 0851640176 Pbk £3.95

Budzender, Geoff
Incorporation and Exclusion : Recent Developments in Labour Law and Inflex Control. – Johannesburg : South African Institute of Race Relations, 1984.
Hbk

Bueno, Antonio →Paget's Law of banking.

Buergenthal, Thomas →Contemporary issues in international law : essays in honor of Louis B. Sohn.
—Protecting human rights in the Americas : selected problems / Thomas Buergenthal, Robert Norris, Dinah Shelton. – 2nd rev ed. – Kehl, W. Germany : Engel, 1986.
xviii,389p.
Previous ed.: 1982. Bibliography: pp.315-322. - Includes index. Includes the texts of the Charter of the Organization of American States, the American Convention on Human Rights and other basic documents.
ISBN 3883570559

Bugden, G.F.
Strata Title Management Practice in New South Wales. – 4th ed. – North Ryde : C.C.H. Australia, 1985.
480p.
ISBN 0869036378 Hbk £35.00

Buhr, Chris N. →Weekly Criminal Bulletin (W.C.B.) 1987-Present.

Bui, D.H.D.
Future of Health Care and Health Care Systems Industrial Soci. – Praeger.
ISBN 0275924912 Hbk £40.95

Build Homes, Build Hope : 1981 Campaign Report. – Shelter. – London : Shelter, 1981.
ISBN 0901242608 Pbk Individuals 2.25

Builder's Claims Under the JCT Form of Contract. – King's Ride : Institute of Building, 1983.
46p.
Hbk £4.00

Builder's Guide to the Agreement for Minor Building Works. – King's Ride : Institute of Building, 1983.
ISBN 0906600324 Hbk £2.75

Building a Successful Law Firm. – Vancouver : British Columbia Continuing Legal Education Society, 1985.
103p.
ISBN 0865042284 Hbk £50.00

Building Act 1984 / with annotations by Harold F. Baines. – London : Sweet & Maxwell, 1985.
164p.
Includes index.
ISBN 0421345500

Building and Civil Engineering Claims. – 3rd ed. – London : Estates Gazette, 1985.
ISBN 0728200775 Hbk £26.00

Building and Civil Engineering Claims In Perspective. – 2nd ed. – London : Longman Professional, 1986.
ISBN 0582494702 Hbk £29.00

Building and Civil Engineering Contracts in Ireland. – London : Butterworths.
ISBN 0406132011 Hbk

Building and Construction Contracts in Australia : Law and Practice / John J.A. Sharkey. – North Ryde : Law Book Co, 1981.
lv, 811p.
ISBN 0455200912 Hbk £90.50

Building and Engineering Claims / A. Ranson. – London : Oyez Longman, 1980 Incl. July 1980 supplement.
ISBN 0851204252 Hbk £9.95

Building and Engineering Contracts : Including the Duties and Liabilities of Architects, Engineers and Surveyors
Supplement only. – London : Sweet & Maxwell.
ISBN 042125730X Hbk £18.00

Building and Engineering Forms
Supplements 1 & 2. – Sweet & Maxwell, 1969.
ISBN 0421124504 Hbk £52.00

Building businesses - not barriers / presented to Parliament by the Secretary of State for Employment : supported by the Secretary of State for Foreign and Commonwealth Affairs ... et al. – London : H.M.S.O., 1986.
80p; 25cm.
ISBN 0101979401

Building contract casebook / Vincent Powell-Smith and Michael Furmston. – Rev ed. – Oxford : BSP Professional Books, 1987.
x,422p.
Previous ed.: 1984. Includes index.
ISBN 0632021098

Building contract claims / Vincent Powell-Smith and John Sims. – London : Granada, 1983.
319p; 25cm.
Includes index.
ISBN 0246119683

Building Contract Claims / John Sims. – 2nd ed. – Oxford : BSP Professional.
ISBN 0632020792 Hbk £25.00

Building Contract Claims / John Sims. – London : Collins, 1983.
320p.
ISBN 0003830942 Hbk £20.00

Building Contract Dictionary : An Architectural Press Legal Guide / David Chappell. – London : Architectural Press, 1985.
464p : Illus.
ISBN 0851397581 Hbk £35.00

Building Contract Disputes : Their Avoidance and Resolution. – London : Longman Scientific.
ISBN 0582037344 Hbk £25.00

Building contract litigation / Robert Fenwick Elliott. – 2nd ed. – London : Longman, 1985.
xx,206p.
Bibliography: p.200 - Includes index.
ISBN 0851208908

Building contract litigation. – 3rd. – London : Longman Professional (UK), 1989.
– (Prctitioner series).
Reviews the forms of contract and contractual proceedings, and assesses issues involved between litigation and arbitration.
ISBN 0851214274 Hbk £35.00

Building Contracts. – 4th ed. – Sweet & Maxwell, 1978.
ISBN 042119720X Hbk £70.00
Supplement 1 1982. –
ISBN 0421295600 Hbk £24.00
Supplement 2 1984. –
ISBN 0421326506 Pbk £11.00

Building Contracts Compared and Tabulated. – London : Architectural Press, 1987.
ISBN 0851397891 Pbk £39.50

Building Contracts - Practical Guide. – 4th ed. – London : Longman Professional, 1983.
ISBN 0711456569 Hbk £19.95

Building Contracts Tabulated and Compared : An Architectural Press Legal Guide / David Chappell. – London : Architectural Press, 1987.
320p : Illus.
ISBN 0851397891 Pbk £39.50

Building Control In Inner London : The London Building Acts and Bylaws and Their Interpretation / J. Dufton. – London : Architectural Press, 1983.
224p.
ISBN 0851397697 Pbk £16.50

Building Land and Estates. – 2nd ed. – London : Oyez Longman, 1983.
– (Oyez Longman Practice Note Ser.: No. 67).
ISBN 0851206964 Hbk £8.95

Building Law Reports
Index to Volumes 1-38 / Baatz. – London : Longman Professional.
ISBN 0582026229 Hbk £22.00
Volume 39. –
ISBN 0582019680 Hbk £22.00

Building Law Reports Vols 1-40 / Reese. – London : Longman Professional.
ISBN 0000999111 Hbk £880.00

Building Law Reports Volume 42 / Baatz. – London : Longman Professional.
ISBN 00582019656 Hbk £22.00

Building Legislation and Historic Buildings. – London : Architectural Press, 1987.
ISBN 0851397905 Pbk £14.95

Building Maintenance Management. – 3rd ed. – Oxford : Blackwell Scientific, 1987.
ISBN 0003833755 Pbk £14.95

Building Project Finance in Hong Kong : Law and Practice. – Butterworths, 1987.
265p.
Describes the law and practice of building project finance in Hong Kong. Examines the 'financing', 'project', and 'security' aspects of a project loan in a comprehensive manner. Explains the typical transactions involved, the roles of various documents, and the problems which have to be dealt with.
ISBN 0409995363 Hbk £110.00

Building Regulations 1976. – Northwood, 1978.
ISBN 0719836802 Hbk £13.50

Building Regulations 1981 : Second Amendment. – London : HMSO.
ISBN 0110173384 Hbk £4.50

Building Regulations 1983 : Third Amendment. – London : HMSO.
ISBN 0110361954 Hbk £1.30

Building Regulations 1985 Explained. – Northwood, 1986.
ISBN 1850320195 Hbk £24.95

Building Regulations : Explained and Illustrated / Vincent Powell Smith. – 7th ed. – London : Collins, 1986.
310p : Illus.
ISBN 0003832813 Hbk £18.50
ISBN 0003832260 Pbk £10.95

Building Regulations Explained and Illustrated / Billington. – 7th ed. – Oxford : Blackwell Scientific, 1986.
ISBN 0003832260 Pbk £14.00

Building societies : a new framework / Treasury : foreword by Nigel Lawson. – London : H.M.S.O., 1984.
iii,44p.
ISBN 0101931603

Building societies : the myth of mutuality / Paul Barnes : with a foreword by Ken Weetch. – London : Pluto, 1984.
xv,171p; 20cm.
ISBN 0861047591 Pbk £4.95

Building Societies Act 1986 / with annotations by Elizabeth Ovey and Malcolm Waters. – London : Sweet & Maxwell, 1987.
322,8p; 24cm.
Includes index.
ISBN 0421367008 Pbk

Building Societies and House Purchase in Scotland. – New York : Building Societies Association.
ISBN 1869839161 Pbk £00.50

Building Society Investors and Borrowers Tax Guide. – Tolley Publishing.
ISBN 085492377 Pbk £3.95

Building Society Law / Mills. – 15th ed. – Sweet & Maxwell, 1988.
ISBN 0420473009 Hbk

Building society law : cases and materials / C.E.I. Thornton and J.P. McBrien. – 3rd ed. – London : Sweet & Maxwell, 1988.
xxi,202p; 22cm.
Previous ed.: 1975. Includes index.
ISBN 0421383704 Pbk £9.95

Building Society Law and Practice. – Oxford : BPP, 1988.
ISBN 0862772249 Pbk £15.95

Building Standards (Scotland) Amendment Regulations 1982. – London : HMSO.
ISBN 011027878X Hbk £3.15

Building Standards (Scotland) Amendment Regulations 1984. – London : HMSO.
ISBN 0110476603 Hbk £1.30

Building Standards (Scotland) Regulations 1981. – London : HMSO.
ISBN 0110175964 Hbk £13.10

Building Sub-Contract Documentation / John Sims. – Oxford : Blackwell Scientific, 1988.
ISBN 0003831558 Hbk £17.00

Building Sub-contract Forms. – London : Collins, 1985.
314p.
ISBN 0003830152 Hbk £19.95

Building Subsidence / Apted. – Oxford : Blackwell Scientific, 1988.
ISBN 0003834190 Hbk £22.50

Building Subsidence : Liability and Insurance / Apted. – Oxford : BSP Professional.
ISBN 0632020776 Hbk £22.50

Building Your Business : Know Your Law. – London : Business Books, 1984.
ISBN 0091518113 Pbk £6.95

Bulajic, Milan
Principles of international development law : progressive development of the principles of international law relating to the new international economic order / Milan Bulajic. – Dordrecht, Netherlands : Martinus Nijhoff Publishers, 1986.
403p.
Bibliography: p.359-366.
ISBN 9024733049

Bulgaria : imprisonment of ethnic Turks : human rights abuses during the forced assimilation of the ethnic Turkish minority / Amnesty International. – London : Amnesty International, 1986.
40p.
ISBN 0862100976

Bulk sales legislation / Law Reform Commission of British Columbia. – Vancouver : The Commission, 1983.
v,115p. – (Working paper).
Includes bibliographical references.

Bulk Sales Legislation. – Victoria : Government of British Columbia, 1983.
Hbk £6.75

Bull, Hedley → Expansion of international society.
→ Intervention in world politics.

Bull, R. J.
Accounting in Business. – 5th ed. – London : Butterworths, 1984.
This book sets forth materials and problems in business accounting for accounting students in the United Kingdom. Cost accounting under SSAP 16 and limited company accounting under the 1981 Companies Act are both covered.
ISBN 0408014865 Pbk £13.50

Bulletin / LEXIS Educational User's Group. – 4. – London : The Group, 1984.

Bulletin / the Securities Association. – London : The Association, 1988.
Alternative title: TSA bulletin.

Bulletin : a report on developments ... relative to Third Basket issues of the Final Act of the Conference on Security and Cooperation in Europe / North Atlantic Assembly, Committtee on education, cultural affairs and information, Sub-committee on the free flow of information. – Brussels : International Secretariat of the North Atlantic Assembly, 1976.
English edition.

Bulletin : trade practices developments / Trade Practices Commission. – Belconnen, A.C.T. : Australian Trade Practices Commission, 1981.

Bulletin of Northern Ireland law. – Belfast : S.L.S., Faculty of Law, Queen's University, 1981-.

Bullion : Brinks-Mat Story Of Britain's Biggest Gold Robbery. – Penguin.
ISBN 014008567X Pbk £3.50

Bullivant, Brian M.
Getting a fair go : case studies of occupational socialization and perceptions of discrimination in a sample of seven Melbourne high schools / Brian M. Bullivant. – Canberra : Australian Government Publishing Service, 1986.
xi,296p. – (Occasional paper).
Bibliographical references: p259-296.
ISBN 0644055243

Bullock, Gareth
Euronotes and euro-commercial paper / Gareth Bullock. – London : Butterworths, 1987.
vii,136p; 23cm.
Includes index.
ISBN 0406104107 £32.00

Bullock, R. E. H. → Management by Objectives in Local Government.

Bullock, W. F.
Special requirements in probation or supervision orders : a local case study / W.F. Bullock, W.M.S. Tildesley. – Cambridge : Institute of Criminology, 1984.
iii,131p. – (Occasional paper).
Bibliography: p.129-131.

Bulwark of the law / the Right Honourable Lord Edmund-Davies. – Cardiff : Law Department, UWIST, 1984.
20p.

Bulygin, Eugenio → Man, law, and modern forms of life.
—Man, Law and Modern Forms of Life. – Dordrecht : Kluwer, 1985.
336p.
ISBN 9027718695 Hbk £125.00

Bunker, Anthony
Inland Revenue Clearances / Michael Wyatt. – London : Oyez Longman, 1984.
ISBN 0851207499 Hbk £50.00

Bunni, Nael G.
Construction insurance / Nael G. Bunni. – London : Elsevier Applied Science, 1986.
xviii,336p; 25cm.
Includes index.
ISBN 0853344388 £50.00

Bunt, Gail → Sentencing in environmental cases : a study paper.

Bunyard, R. S.
Police : Organisation and Command. – Plymouth : Macdonald & Evans, 1984.
400p : Illus.. – – (Police Studies Ser.).
ISBN 0712116710 Hbk £7.50

Buono, Vincent M. del
Law and Legality : Materials on Legal Decision Making. – Butterworths, 1982.
592p.
Describes the institutions of law and identifies the decision makers, and poses questions about the limits of decision making authority. Cases have been selected to increase awareness of the interactions amongst legal decision makers, giving an understanding of the attributes, limits and potential of the legal system.
ISBN 0409824003 Pbk £50.00

Burchell, E. M. → South African criminal law and procedure, Vol.1 : General principles of criminal law : by E.M. Burchell and P.M.A. Hunt.

Burchell, Jonathan M
Law of defamation in South Africa / Jonathan M. Burchell. – Cape Town : Juta, 1985.
xxxii, 359 p.; 26 cm.
Includes bibliographical references and index.
ISBN 0702115673
→ South African criminal law and procedure, Vol.1 : General principles of criminal law : by E.M. Burchell and P.M.A. Hunt.

Burchett, J.C.S.
Company Tax Recoupment Law / S.W. Gibb. – North Ryde : C.C.H. Australia, 1983.
215p.
ISBN 0869036327 Hbk £40.00

Burden of proof / general editor Albert Kiralfy. – Abingdon : Professional, 1987.
xxix,251p; 22cm.
Includes index.
ISBN 0862052157

Burden of proof in criminal proceedings : report / by the Senate Standing Committee on Constitutional and Legal Affairs. – Canberra : Australian Government Publishing Service, 1982.
xiii,93p. – (Parliamentary paper).
Includes text of the 11th report of the Criminal Law Revision Committee (Great Britain), 1972 (Cmnd. 4991), on evidence.
ISBN 0644022345

Burden of Tax in Punjab. – New Delhi : Concept Publishing Company, 1983.
xiv, 223p.
Hbk £90.00

Burden, Tom, et al
Business in Society Concensus and Conflict. – London : Butterworths.
ISBN 0408106948 Pbk

Burdens on business : report of a scrutiny of administrative and legislative requirements / for the Department of Trade and Industry. – London : H.M.S.O., 1985.
vi,71p.
Team leader: N. P. Brecknell.
ISBN 011513820X

Bureau of Transport Economics
Review of Road Freight Regulation in Britain. – Bureau of Transport Economics. – Canberra : Australian Government Publishing Service, 1981.
78p. – (BTE Occasional Paper: No. 43).
ISBN 0642067953 Hbk £3.80

Bureaucracy Triumphant. – Repr. of 1931 ed. – Aalen Wuertt : Scientia.
451p.
ISBN 351109061X Hbk £33.00

Burger →Aborigines Today : Land and Justice.

Burgers
United Nations Convention Against Torture International Studies in Human Rights / Danelius. – Martinus Nijhoff.
ISBN 9024736099 Hbk £44.95

Burgess →Automated Office.

Burgess, Andrew →West Indian cases on the law of contract.

Burgess, Ann Wolbert →Victim of rape : institutional reactions.

Burgess, Robert
Corporate Finance Law
Supplement. – London : Sweet & Maxwell, 1987.
ISBN 0421311207 Hbk £67.00
ISBN 0421374403 Pbk £12.50

—Law of borrowing. – London : Sweet & Maxwell, 1989.
Account of the institutional framework within which borrowing takes place, and consideration of the regulation and supervision of banks, building societies, the securities market, the wholesale money market, and consumer credit transactions. Chapter dealing with the characteristics of a loan, and types of loan.
ISBN 0421000000 Llf

Burglary : police actions and victims views / John Burrows. – London : Home Office, 1986.
v,97p.
Bibliography: p.95-97.
ISBN 0862522331

Burglary in a dwelling : the offence, the offender and the victim / Mike Maguire in collaboration with Trevor Bennett. – London : Heinemann, 1982.
ix,204p; 23cm. – (Heinemann library of criminology and penal reform).
Bibliography: p194-199. - Includes index.
ISBN 0435825674 £13.50

Burglary in schools : the prospects for prevention / Tim Hope. – London : Home Office, 1982.
iv,47p.
Bibliography: p.38-41.
ISBN 0862520703

Burgoyne, Jacqueline
Divorce matters / Jacqueline Burgoyne, Roger Ormrod and Martin Richards. – Harmondsworth : Penguin, 1987.
216p0; 20cm. – (A Pelican book).
ISBN 0140226133

Burhenne, W. E →Environmental law of the European communities : Droit de l'environnement des communautes Europeennes Umweltrecht der Europaischen Gemeinschaften.

→ International environment law : multilateral treaties Droit international de l'environnement : traites multilateraux Internationales Umweltrecht : multilaterale Vertrage.

—International Environmental Law Information System. – Berlin : Erich Schmidt.
354p. – (BZU Ser.: Vol. B3).
ISBN 3503010181 Pbk £39.00

Burholt, G. D
Regulatory framework for storage and disposal of radioactive waste in the member states of the European Community / G.D. Burholt and A. Martin. – London, UK : Published by Graham & Trotman for the Commission of the European Communities, 1988.
ix, 121 p.; 25 cm.
Includes bibliographies.
ISBN 1853331090

Burke →Dictionary of English Law.

Burke, Christopher →Annotated Canada Shipping Act.

Burke, Raymond L.
Lack of Discretion of Judgment because of Schizophrenia : Doctrine and Recent Rotal Jurisprudence. – Rome : Editrice Pontificia Universitana Gregoriana, 1986.
256p.
Hbk L35,000.00

Burke, Terence M. →Selected problems of construction law : international approach.

Burke, William T.
Impacts of the UN Convention on the Law of the Sea on tuna regulation / by W.T. Burke. – Rome : Food and Agriculture Organization of the United Nations, 1982.
v,19p. – (Norway funds-in-trust).
Discusses impact of the Third United Nations Convention on the Law of the Sea on tuna management, especially Article 64 concerning conservation.
ISBN 925101292X

→ Public Order of the Oceans : a Contemporary International Law of the Sea.

Burman, Sandra →Wounded soldiers of industry : industrial compensation policy 1833-1897.

Burn, E. H. →Cheshire and Burn's Modern law of real property.

→ Maudsley and Burn: trusts and trustees - cases and materials.

—Maudsley and Burn's land law : cases and materials / R. H. Maudsley. – 5th ed. – London : Butterworths, 1986.
850p; 26cm.
Previous ed.: published as Land law / by R.H. Maudsley and E.H. Burns. 1980. Includes index.
ISBN 0406623082 Hbk £33.00 :
ISBN 0406623090 Pbk £22.50

→ Maudsley and Burn's Trusts and trustees : cases and materials.

—Maudsley and Burn's Trusts and trustees - cases and materials. – London : Butterworths, 1990.
904; 24cm.
Part one deals with trusts - their nature, requirements and constitutions, trusts and creditors, resulting trusts, constructive trusts and non-charitable purpose trusts; part two covers charities - charitable trusts, Cy-pres, and the administration of charities; part three is trusts and taxes - income tax, capital gains tax and capital transfer tax; and part four deals with trustees - general principles, duties and powers of trustees, variations of trusts, and breach of trust.
ISBN 040659211X Pbk £25.95

→ Modern law of real property.

Burn, R.
Ecclesiastical Law, 4 Vols. – 8th ed. Repr. of 1824 ed. – Abingdon : Professional Books.
Hbk £75.00

Burnaby, British Columbia experimental public defender project : an evaluation / Patricia Brantingham et al. – 7 v. – Ottawa : Department of Justice, 1981.
Contents: Report 1. Summary - Report 2. Effectiveness analysis - Report 3. Cost analysis - Report 4. Client satisfaction analysis - Report 5. Tariff analysis - Report 6. Relationships analysis - Report 7. Distribution impact analysis. 'Undertaken under contract for the Department of Justice, Canada with the assistance of the British Columbia Legal Services Society'. Report 1 has added t.-p. in French. English and French text of report 1.

Burney, Elizabeth
Sentencing young people : what went wrong with the Criminal Justice Act 1982 / Elizabeth Burney. – Aldershot : Gower, 1985.
120p; 22cm.
ISBN 0566051273 £14.50

Burns
Criminal Injuries Compensation. – London : Butterworths.
ISBN 0409988286 Hbk £30.00

—Small business in Europe / Dewhurst. – London : Macmillan, 1986.
ISBN 0333384067 Pbk £12.95

Burns, A.F.
Ongoing Revolution in American Banking. – Stockholm : American Enterp Institute.
– (AEI Studies No. 472).
ISBN 0844736546 Hbk £14.75

Burns, Aubrey Loeb
Condominium : The Law and Administration in Ontario / Bradley N. McLellan. – Agincourt : Carswell, 1981.
606p.
This book gives a complete description of the law and administration of condominiums in Ontario, Canada. Registration of a condominium, declaration and description, the agreement of purchase and sale, HUDAC, meetings and records for the condominium, and other issues are discussed.
Hbk £71.50

Burns, Darrell E.
British Columbia Law Reports. – Agincourt : Carswell, 1988.
– (Second Ser., 1-18).
This text includes all the cases from the courts of British Columbia and appeals from that court to the Supreme Court of Canada. The cases are all headnoted, there is a topical index, and an index of cases reported.
Hbk £79.00

Burr, Martin
Law and Health Visitors. – London : B Edsall, 1982.
72p.
ISBN 0902623354 Pbk £3.00

Burrell : South African Patent Law and Practice. – 2nd ed. – Durban : Professional Publishers, 1985.
ISBN 0409013544 Hbk £139.00

Burrell, Timothy Donald
Burrell : South African Patent Law and Practice. – 2nd ed. – Durban : Professional Publishers, 1985.
ISBN 0409013544 Hbk £139.00

→ Burrell's patent law reports.

—South African patent law and practice / by Timothy Donald Burrell. – 2nd ed. – Durban : Butterworths, 1986.
xxxvii,699p.
ISBN 0409013552

Burrell's patent law reports / compiled and edited by Timothy D. Burrell. – 8. – Cape Town : Juta, 1981.

Burridge, Roger →Environmental health standards in housing.

Burris, Scott →AIDS and the law : a guide for the public.

Burrow, J.
Kings Bench Decision upon Settlement Cases : From 1732-76. – Repr. of 1776 ed. – Abingdon : Professional Books.
286p.
Hbk £95.00

Burrow, J. A. →That noble science of politics : a study in nineteenth-century intellectual history.

Burrows, et al
Cheshire and Fifoot's Law of Contract. – 7th ed. – Butterworths, 1988.
669p.
ISBN 0409788716 Hbk £120.00
ISBN 0409787973 Pbk £85.00

Burrows, A. S.
Remedies for torts and breach of contract / A.S. Burrows. – London : Butterworths, 1987.
lviii,435p; 22cm.
Includes index.
ISBN 0406501505 Hbk £18.00
ISBN 0406501513 Pbk £12.95

Burrows, F.
Free movement in European Community law / F. Burrows. – Oxford : Clarendon, 1987.
xxxvii,346p; 24cm.
Bibliography: xxxvii - Includes index.
ISBN 019825492X £35.00

Burrows, I.
Housing Act 1988 : A Shelter Guide. – Shelter.
ISBN 0901242853 Pbk £2.50

Burrows, John
Burglary : police actions and victims views / John Burrows. – London : Home Office, 1986.
v,97p.
Bibliography: p.95-97.
ISBN 0862522331

—Clearing up crime / by John Burrows and Roger Tarling. – London : H.M.S.O., 1982.
31p; 25cm.
Bibliography: p24-26. A Home Office Research and Planning Unit report.
ISBN 0113407688

—Investigating burglary : the measurement of police performance / by John Burrows. – London : H.M.S.O., 1986.
v,30p; 25cm.
Examines differences in clear-up rates in areas with similar problems. Finds that clear-up rates are not necessarily a reflection of success in arresting burglars, but involve questioning about previous offences.
ISBN 0113408242

→ Policing today.

Burrows, Les
Rent arrears and the courts : a report by the Lay Advocacy Service / by Les Burrows. – Bristol : Lay Advocacy Service, 1986.
63p.
ISBN 0951115006

Burrows, Noreen →Legal relevance of gender : some aspects of sex-based discrimination.

Burrows, Paul →Economic approach to law.

→ Policing pollution : a study of regulation and enforcement.

Burrows, Rita →Tolley's Tax Guide 1988-89.

Burstein, M.L.
Studies In Banking Theory, Financial History, Vertical Contr. – London : Macmillan.
ISBN 0333457390 Hbk £33.00

Burt
Endorsement of Driving Licence and Disqualification from Driving / Cooper. – 3rd ed. – Chichester : Barry Rose, 1984.
ISBN 0859923428 Pbk £7.50

Burton, Edward C.
Enforcement of Natural Resources Legislation : A Handbook. – Agincourt : Carswell, 1988.

Burton, Ivor
Legislation and public policy : public bills in the 1970-74 Parliament / by Ivor Burton and Gavin Drewry. – London : Macmillan, 1981.
xii,322p; 23cm.
Bibliography: p280-283. - Includes index.
ISBN 0333152042 £25.00

Burton, Tony, et al
Scottish Planning Law Practice. – Glasgow : Planning Exchange, 1983.
36p.
ISBN 01448196 Pbk £7.50

Burundi since the genocide / by Reginald Kay. – London : Minority Rights Group, 1987.
12p. – (Report).
'This report was first published under the title Selective genocide in Burundi by Professor Rene Lemarchand and David Martin in July 1974'. - Front cover verso.
ISBN 0946690472

Burwood, Stephen →Tax planning for medical practitioners.

Bush Capital : How Australia Chose Its Federal City. – Neutral Bay : Hale & Iremonger.
ISBN 0868060666 Hbk £24.95, 015

Bush, John
Guidebook to Taxation and Investment Law in Hong Kong. – 2nd ed. – North Ryde : C.C.H. Australia, 1985.
276p.
ISBN 0869037811

Bush, W. M →Antarctica and international law : a collection of inter-state and national documents.

Business Accounting
Vol 1. – 4th ed. – Pitman, 1984.
ISBN 0582412427 Pbk £7.50
Vol. 2. –
ISBN 0253025414 Pbk £4.95

Business and Investment Almanac 1988. – New York : Dow Jones-Irwin, 1988.
ISBN 1556230478 Hbk £31.95

Business and Tax Laws of the People's Republic of China / Fred Blaser. – North Ryde : C.C.H. Australia, 1986.
96p.
ISBN 0887963978 Pbk £14.95

Business and the Law. – Toronto : DeBoo, 1984.
ISBN 0888201699 Hbk £165.00

Business Associations. – Simmonds and Mercer. – Agincourt : Carswell, 1984.
806p.
Hbk £75.75

Business Expansion Scheme. – VANN, 1984.
ISBN 0852913826 Pbk £8.95

Business Expansion Scheme and Assured Tenancies : New Rules. – London : Longman Professional.
ISBN 0851214932 Pbk £12.50

Business Finance. – London : Butterworths, 1986.
ISBN 0406501408 Pbk £13.95

Business Firms and Companies. – Singapore : Times Books International.
128p.
ISBN 9971650916 Pbk £7.50

Business Guide to Privacy and Data 1970 : Protection Legislation. – Paris : International Chamber of Commerce.
310p.
Hbk £40.00

Business in Society Concensus and Conflict. – London : Butterworths.
ISBN 0408106948 Pbk

Business Interruption and Consequent Loss Insurance / Cloughton. – 6th ed. – London : Sweet & Maxwell, 1985.
ISBN 0421319208 Hbk £50.00

Business Law / N Pendlebury. – 3rd ed. – London : DP Publications, 1986.
ISBN 0905435672 Pbk £4.95

Business Law. – 2nd ed. – London : Pitman Publishing, 1985.
ISBN 0712124055 Pbk £6.95

Business Law. – 1st ed. Repr. of 1982 ed. – Plymouth : Macdonald & Evans, 1983.
288p. – (M and E Handbook Ser.).
ISBN 0712102612 Hbk £5.50

Business Law. – London : Pitman Publishing, 1982.
ISBN 0855050624 Pbk £3.95

Business Law / Riches. – Pitman, 1987.
ISBN 0273024159 Pbk £7.95

Business Law / Soulsby. – 3rd ed. – Maidenhead : McGraw-Hill, 1985.
ISBN 0070848769 Pbk £7.95

Business law / by Liam O'Malley. – London : Sweet & Maxwell, 1982.
xxxii,222p.
ISBN 0421285001

Business Law / Judith M. Woods. – Agincourt : Carswell, 1986.
616p. – (Bar Admission Course Materials Ser.).
Hbk £71.50

Business Law. – London : Butterworths, 1987.
ISBN 040601843X Pbk

Business Law : Including Banking Law; For B. Com Students / Saxena. – Delhi : SBD Enterprises.
Hbk £25.00

Business Law : Instructional Manual / N. Pendlebury. – 3rd ed. – Winchester : DP Publications, 1982.
608p.
ISBN 0905435672 Pbk £5.25

Business Law for Accountants / Ernest E Spicer. – 15th ed. – London : Butterworths.
ISBN 0406678308 Pbk £15.95

Business law guide to Germany / Strobl, Killius & Vorbrugg. – 2nd ed. – Bicester : CCH Editions, 1988.
450p; 23cm.
Updates the law concerning product liability, taxation, joint ventures, distribution, licensing, franchising and industrial property rights, and includes new material on anti-dumping, mergers and acquisitions, social insurances, leasing and hiring of personnel, real estate and construction and bankruptcy.
ISBN 0863251579 £35.00

Business Law (ILT). – London : Sweet & Maxwell, 1982.
ISBN 0421285001 Pbk £14.50

Business law in Egypt / by Michael H. Davies. – Deventer, Netherlands : Boston, 1984.
ISBN 9065440860

Business law in Europe : legal, tax and labour aspects of business operations in the ten European Community countries and Switzerland / edited by Maarten J. Ellis and Paul M. Storm : Prepared under the auspices of the Association europeenne d'etudes juridiques et fiscales. – Deventer : Kluwer, 1982.
xvi,606p.
Includes bibliographies.
ISBN 9065440402

Business Law in India. – New Delhi : Oxford University Press.
Hbk £65.00

Business law in Zimbabwe / R.H. Christie. – Cape Town : Juta, 1985.
lvii, 575 p.; 26 cm.
Includes index.
ISBN 0702115738

Business Law of Australia / K.E. Lindgren. – 5th ed. – Butterworths, 1987.
1,100p.
ISBN 0409492086 Hbk £39.50
Cumulative Supplement-1985. –
95p.
ISBN 0409491349

Business law reports. – Agincourt, Ont. : Carswell, 1977-.
24cm.
Cumulative indexes published at intervals.

Business Law Review. – London : Butterworths.
Pbk £185.00

Business Law Section of the Law Council of Australia →Corporate Securities and Creditors Rights on Insolvency 1984.

Business Law Today. – Palmerston North : Dunmore Press Ltd..
368p.
ISBN 0864690398 Pbk £38.45

Business laws in Korea : investment, taxation, and industrial property / Chan-jin Kim, editor. – Seoul, Korea : Panmun Book Co., 1982.
xii, 799 p.; 24 cm.
Includes bibliographical references.

Business laws of the United Arab Emirates Federal law No. 8 of 1984 Re: Commercial Companies / translated from Arabic into English by Marjorie J. Hall. – London : Graham & Trotman, 1984.
94p.
ISBN 0860105512

Business Maths and Information Technology : ACCA Study Text 1.5. – London : BPP.
ISBN 0862772397 Pbk £14.95

Business Names Act 1985. – London : HMSO.
12p.
ISBN 0105407852 Pbk £1.75

Business Names Guide. – 3rd ed. – North Ryde : C.C.H. Australia, 1985.
154p.
ISBN 0869034413 Hbk £28.00

Business of Banking / Valentine. – 2nd ed. – Northcote House.
ISBN 0746305354 Pbk £7.95

Business opportunites in United Arab Emirates : agency law : U.A.E. Federal Law no. 18 of 1981 Concerning the Organisation of Commercial Agencies / British Overseas Trade Board and the Department of Trade. – London : British Overseas Trade Board, 1986.
9 leaves.

Business records and computer output / Evidence Law Reform Committee. – s.l. : Evidence Law Reform Committee, 1985.
43 leaves, 2 leaves. – (Working paper).
Inlcudes bibliographical references.

Business Tax And Law Guide. – London : Longman Professional.
ISBN 0851214622 Hbk £12.95

Business tax handbook / editors Hugh Mainprice, Malcolm J. Finney, Colin P. Cretton. – 2. – London : Kluwer, 1983.
loose-leaf.
Includes index.
ISBN 0903393433

Business Tenancies. – 3rd ed. – London : Estates Gazette, 1978.
ISBN 0728200392 Hbk £10.00

Business tenancies. – London : Longman Professional (UK), 1989.
– (Longman practice notes).
Examines the law pertaining to assigning, subletting, parting with possession and repairs, with specimen letters. Contains details of time limits, costs and fees, and precedent forms for termination of a tenancy under s.25 and a request for a new tenancy under s.26 of the Landlord and Tenant Act 1954.
ISBN 0851215319 Pbk £9.95

Business transactions law / Robert Sharrock Andrew Borrowdale. – Cape Twon : Juta, 1986.
xiv,385p.
Includes index.
ISBN 070211684X

Business transfers and employee rights / John McMullen. – London : Butterworths, 1987.
xxix,253p; 22cm.
Bibliography: p239-241. - Includes index.
ISBN 0406658544 Pbk £15.00

Business transfers and employment law: a practical guide. – London : Sweet & Maxwell, 1989.
Outlines the development of the Transfer of Undertakings Regulations, including the loopholes and starting blocks facing the employer involved in a business transfer. Practical consideration of aspects of the law such as 'living down', the effect of regulations on both individual and collective employment law. Appendix of statutory instruments.
ISBN 0421405309 Hbk £27.50

Businessman's Guide to Microcomputers. – Deloitte, Haskins and Sells. – 2nd ed. – London : Butterworths, 1984.
ISBN 0406016003 Pbk £9.00

Businessman's Law. Vol. 16 / P. Q. R Boberg. – Kenwyn : Juta & Co, 1986.
Hbk £7900.00

But is it Legal? : Fundraising and the Law. – London : Bedford Square Press.
ISBN 0719912210 Pbk £4.95

But the People in Legal Said Yes ... Guide to Current Legal Issues in Advertising. – Merehurst.
ISBN 01556230915 Hbk £17.95

Butcher →Civil Service Today.

Butcher, David-
Official publications in Britain / David Butcher. – London : Bingley, 1983.
161p; 23cm.
Includes index.
ISBN 0851573517

Butler
Law Unit : Torts / Lucas. – Stockholm : Anderson Keenan, 1981.
ISBN 0906501245 Pbk £3.70

Butler, Alan
Housing alternatives for the elderly / Alan Butler and Anthea Tinker. – Leeds : Centre for Applied Social Studies, 1983.
28p. – (Occasional paper).
Includes bibliographical references.

Butler, D. W. →Sectional titles, share blocks and time-sharing.

Butler, J.
Guide to Importing. – Cambridge : Woodhead-Faulkner, 1987.
ISBN 0859413101 Pbk £14.95

Butler, John S.
Reinsurance law / John S. Butler and Robert M. Merkin. – 2. – London : Kluwer, 1986.
looseleaf.
ISBN 1870080076

Butler, M.
Business Law. – London : Pitman Publishing, 1982.
ISBN 0855050624 Pbk £3.95

Butler, Sid
Acquittal rates / Sid Butler. – London : Home Office, 1983.
v,32p.
Bibliography: p.10.
ISBN 0862520967

Butler, T.
Mental health, social policy and the law. – London : Macmillan, 1985.
ISBN 0333373014 Hbk £25.00

Butler, W E
Soviet law. – 2nd. – London : Butterworths, 1989.
– (Legal systems of the world).
ISBN 040656261X Hbk £21.95

Butler, William E. →Comparative labour law : Anglo-Soviet perspectives.
→ History of international law in Russia 1647-1917.

—International Law and the International System. – Dordrecht : Kluwer, 1987.
208p.
ISBN 9024735343 Hbk £125.00

→ Justice and comparative law : Anglo-Soviet perspectives on criminal law, evidence, procedure, and sentencing policy.

→ Mongolian legal system : contemporary legislation and documentation.

—Mongolian-English-Russian dictionary of legal terms and concepts / compiled and edited by W.E. Butler and A.J. Nathanson. – The Hague : M. Nijhoff, 1982.
ISBN 9024726778

—Non-use of force in international law. – Dordrecht : Nijhoff (Martinus), 1989.
256.
Collection of revised papers, dealing with force on a variety of levels; military, economic, law enforcement. Analyses the Nicaragua case.
ISBN 0792302931 Hbk £43.50

—Soviet law / W.E. Butler. – 2nd ed. – London : Butterworths, 1988.
xxiii,430p; 22cm. – (Butterworths' legal systems of the world).
Previous ed.: 1983. Bibliography: p403-414. - Includes index.
ISBN 040656261X Hbk £21.95
ISBN 0406562644 Pbk

—USSR, Eastern Europe and the development of the law of the sea / compiled, translated and edited by William E. Butler. – New ed. 2 v. – London : Oceana, 1983.
looseleaf.
Previously published as: The Eastern European states and the development of the law of the sea / by Viktor Sebek. 1979. Bibliography: Vol. 2.
ISBN 0379208512

Butt, P.J. →Perpetuities Act 1984.

Butt, Peter J.
Cumulative Supplement to the Standard Contract for Sale of Land in N.S.W. – North Ryde : Law Book Co, 1987.
146p.
Pbk £125.00

—Standard Contract for Sale of Land in New South Wales with Supplement. – North Ryde : Law Book Co, 1985.
lxxiv, 948p.
ISBN 045520697X Hbk £115.50

Butterfield, C. S. J. →Shipping practice : with consideration of the relevant law.

Butterworth, Douglas
Latin American urbanization / Douglas Butterworth, John K. Chance. – Cambridge : Cambridge University Press, 1981.
xi,243p; 24cm.
Bibliography: p216-237. - Includes index.
ISBN 0521237130 Hbk £15.00
ISBN 052128175X Pbk £5.50

Butterworth Staff
Butterworth's Costs, 2 Vols. – Butterworth Staff. – 5th ed. – London : Butterworths, 1984.
ISBN 0406142475 Llf

Butterworth United Kingdom Tax Guide. – London : Butterworths.
ISBN 0406504970 Pbk £13.00

Butterworths
Australian Tax Reports Vols. 1-17 (1969-1986) and Australian and New Zealand Income Tax Reports Vols. 1-10 (1936-1968) Consolidated Index and Tables. – Butterworths. – Butterworths, 1989.
292p.
ISBN 0409300977 Hbk £110.00
ISBN £79.00 to subscribers

—Budget Tax Tables 1986. – Butterworths. – London : Butterworths, 1986.
ISBN 0406508410 Pbk £2.80

—Capital Gains Tax Guide. – Butterworths. – London : Butterworths.
ISBN 0406513600 Pbk £17.95

—Commonwealth Taxation Board of Review Decisions : Consolidated Index and Tables 1925-1986. – Butterworths. – 1st ed. – Butterworths, 1988.
290p.
Hbk £110.00

—Cost Service. – Butterworths. – London : Butterworths, 1987.
Service to Date.
ISBN 0406107491 Llf £145.00

—County Court Practice. – Butterworths. – London : Butterworths, 1988.
ISBN 0406163243 Hbk £80.00

—Family Law Service. – Butterworths. – London : Butterworths.
Service to Date.
ISBN 040610719X Llf £120.00

—From Telecommunications to Electronic Services. – Butterworths. – London : Butterworths, 1986.
ISBN 0880631031 Hbk £27.00

—Handbook on CTT Act 1984. – Butterworths. – London : Butterworths, 1984.
ISBN 0406505349 Pbk £6.00

—Income Tax Service. – Butterworths. – London : Butterworths.
Service to Date.
ISBN 0406254753 Hbk £165.00

—Inheritance tax guide. – Butterworths. – London : Butterworths, 1986.
ISBN 0406500347 Pbk £16.50

—Landlord and Tenant Handbook. – Butterworths. – 2nd ed. – London : Butterworths, 1987.
ISBN 0406253714 Pbk £22.95

—Orange Tax Handbook 1986-1987. – Butterworths. – London : Butterworths.
ISBN 0406508321 Pbk £17.00

—Planning law handbook. – Butterworths. – London : Butterworths, 1987.
ISBN 0406505802 Pbk £22.50

—UK Tax Guide 1986-1987. – Butterworths. – London : Butterworths.
ISBN 0406504954 Pbk £12.00

—Yellow Tax Handbook 1986-1987. – Butterworths. – London : Butterworths.
ISBN 0406510032 Pbk £19.00

Butterworth's Annotated Legislation Service. – London : Butterworths.
This service for practitioners provides a working guide to the text of new statutes in the United Kingdom.
ISBN 040654834X Pbk

Butterworth's Annotated Legislation Service : 1939-1981, 280 Vols. – Abingdon : Professional Books.
Hbk £750.00

Butterworths annotations to the New Zealand statutes : 2nd ed. : 1908-1982 / by Martin Fine. – Wellington : Butterworths, 1982.
Previous ed.: Butterworths cases annotations of the New Zealand statutes reprint 1908-1957, published 1960-1961. Looseleaf issues accompanied by monthly Butterworths Automatic Annotations Bulletin.
ISBN 0409701262 Llf

Butterworths Australian Tax Handbook 1989. – Butterworths, 1989.
1,504p.
ISBN 0409302414 Pbk £39.00

Butterworths Australian Tax Legislation 1989. – Butterworths, 1989.
Pbk £54.00
Vol. 1A. –
ISBN 0409301523
Vol. 1B. –
ISBN 0409301531
Vol. 2. –
ISBN 040930154X

Butterworths banking and financial law review. – London : Butterworths, 1987.
Index in each vol..

Butterworth's British Columbia Family Law Quantum Service, 2 vol / Anisa Dhanji. – Toronto : Butterworths.
Hbk

Butterworths British Columbia Family Law Quantum Service, 2 Vols. / Anisa Dhanji. – Butterworths.
Llf £135.00

Butterworth's Budget Tax Tables, 1984. – London : Butterworths, 1984.
ISBN 0406508178 Pbk £6.00

Butterworth's Budget Tax Tables. – London : Butterworths, 1983.
ISBN 0406508186 Pbk £5.95

Butterworths Capital Gains Tax Guide : the New Regime. – London : Butterworths.
ISBN 0406513600 Pbk £16.95

Butterworth's Cases Annotations to the New Zealand Statutes Reprint : 1908-1964. – Abingdon : Professional Books, 1984.
Hbk

Butterworths CIMA Student Series : Management Accounting - Decision Making. – London : Butterworths, 1987.
ISBN 0406530041 Pbk £16.95
Stage 1-Business Law. – 1988.
ISBN 0406530033 Pbk £14.95
Stage 1-Economics. – 1987.
ISBN 0406530068 Pbk £13.95
Stage 1-Quantitative Methods. – 1987.
ISBN 040653005X Pbk £15.95
Stage 2-Financial Accounting. – 1988.
ISBN 0406530025 Pbk £15.95
Stage 4-Management Accounting-Control and Audit. – 1988.
ISBN 0406530009 Pbk £15.95

Butterworth's Commercial Brief. – Wellington : Butterworths.
Hbk

Butterworth's Commercial Law. – Wellington : Butterworths, 1985.
Hbk

Butterworths Commercial Law in New Zealand. – Butterworths, 1986.
Contains 48 chapters covering general principles of contract and quasi-contract, specific contracts, secured transactions and hire purchase, competition law, insolvency and dispute resolution. The law is as stated at January 1 1986. Appendices cover interests in land, New Zealand Courts, the present court structure in England and Wales, and a glossary of latin terms.
ISBN 0409702145 Pbk £86.90
ISBN 0409787574 Hbk £107.80

Butterworths Commercial Service. – Butterworths.
ISBN 0409681008 Llf

Butterworths' Companies Act 1981 : regulations and related legislation. – 1982 ed. 1. – Sydney : Butterworths, 1982.
various pagings.
Includes index.
ISBN 0409492302

Butterworths Companies and Securities Code, 2 Vols. – Butterworths, 1988.
ca 1090p 710p.
ISBN 0409493384 Pbk
Vol. 1. –
ISBN 0409493368 £29.00
Vol. 2. –
ISBN 0409493376 £9.50

Butterworth's Companies and Securities Codes Vols. 1 and 2. – 1987 ed. – Sydney : Butterworths.
ISBN 040949237X Pbk £32.00
Vol. I. –
ISBN 0409492353 Pbk £24.00
Vol. II. –
ISBN 0409492361 pap £16.50

Butterworths Company and Securities Codes, 1988 : And Related Legislation. – Combined ed. – Sydney : Butterworths, 1988.
1600p.
Codes vol.Pbk £29.00

Butterworth's Company Law Brief. – Wellington : Butterworths.
Hbk

Butterworths company law cases. – London : Butterworths, 1984.
Cumulative tables and index published annually.

Butterworths company law guide / general editor Michael Renshall : consultant editor Keith Walmsley. – London : Butterworths, 1985.
xxxix,452p.
ISBN 0406197008

Butterworths company law handbook / consultant editor Keith Walmsley. – 6th ed. – London : Butterworths, 1987.
1358,37p.
ISBN 0406143153

Butterworth's Company Law Service / S. J. Barton. – London : Butterworths.
Llf

Butterworth's Company Reports. – Wellington : Butterworths.
Hbk

Butterworths Company Reports. – Butterworths. – (Report Series).
Hbk £434.50

Butterworths competition law handbook / edited by Garth Lindrup. – London : Butterworths, 1987.
vii,419p.
Includes index.
ISBN 040610400X

Butterworths Consolidated Legislation Service. – Professional Publ.
ISBN 0409014478 Llf £15.00 (additional binder)
Credit Agreements Act 75 of 1980. –
32p.
ISBN 0409014141 £25.00
Criminal Procedure Act 51 of 1977. –
294p.
ISBN 0409014087 £45.00
Deeds Registries Act 47 of 1937. –
195p.
ISBN 0409014095 £40.00
Estate Duty Act 45 of 1955. –
85p.
ISBN 0409014117 £35.00
Insolvency Act 24 of 1936. –
146p.
ISBN 0409014176 £35.00
Insurance Act 27 of 1943. –
201p.
ISBN 0409014206 £55.00
Liquor Act 87 of 1977. –
249p.
ISBN 0409014230 £55.00
Magistrates Court Act 32 of 1944. –
264p.
ISBN 0409014265 £40.00
Motor Vehicle Accident Act 1984/86. –
50p.
ISBN 0409014338 £25.00
Road Transport Act 76 of 1977. –
85p.
ISBN 040901429X £30.00

Sectional Titles Act 94 of 1986. –
158p.
ISBN 0409014710 £40.00
Share Blocks Control Act 59 of 1980. –
40p.
ISBN 0409014680 £25.00
Stamp Duties Act 77 of 1968. –
116p.
ISBN 0409014354 £35.00
Supreme Court Act 59 of 1959. –
278p.
ISBN 0409014389 £45.00
Transfer Duty Act 40 of 1949. –
52p.
ISBN 0409014419 £25.00
Usury Act 73 of 1968. –
468p.
ISBN 0409014427 £65.00

Butterworth's Consolidated Legislation Service. – Durban : Butterworths, 1986.
ISBN 0409014001 Pbk

Butterworths Conveyancing Bulletin. – Butterworths.
ISBN 0409701815 Hbk

Butterworth's Corporation Tax Program. – London : Butterworths.
Hbk

Butterworth's Costs, 2 Vols. – Butterworth Staff. – 5th ed. – London : Butterworths, 1984.
ISBN 0406142475 Llf

Butterworth's Costs Service, 2 Vols. – London : Butterworths, 1986.
Pbk

Butterworth's County Court Precedents and Pleadings / A. V. B. Bartlett. – London : Butterworths.
Llf

Butterworths Current Law. – Butterworths.
Llf

Butterworth's Current Law / Phillippa Oldham. – Wellington : Butterworths.
Hbk

Butterworth's Dictionary of Company Law. – 2nd ed. – Wellington : Butterworths, 1985.
A practical guide to company law of the United Kingdom, this book gives brief details of the Companies Act provisions relating to the terms defined within. Technical phrases from business and finance are listed along with legal terms.
ISBN 0406681635 Hbk
ISBN 0406681643 Pbk

Butterworth's District Court Reports. – Wellington : Butterworths.
Hbk

Butterworths District Court Reports. – Butterworths.
Hbk

Butterworths Editorial Staff
Butterworths Handbook of Singapore Employment Law. – Butterworths Editorial Staff. – 2nd ed. – Butterworths, 1986.
787p.
Contains coverage of employment law, the central provident fund, skills development levy, payroll tax, redundancy payments fund, factories, workmen's compensations fund, industrial relations, trade disputes, and trade unions.
ISBN 0409995142 Pbk £99.00
—Butterworth's Income Tax Service. – Butterworths Editorial Staff. – London : Butterworths.
This looseleaf service for United Kingdom practitioners covers extra-statutory concessions, statements of practice, and tables of rates and relief. The work is updated with monthly bulletins and quarterly service issues.
Hbk
—Criminal Justice Act 1982 : A Guide to Fines. – Butterworths Editorial Staff. – London : Butterworths, 1983.
This text for magistrates in the United Kingdom provides a condensation of the changes in the fine schedules for Criminal Acts brought about by the Criminal Justice Act of 1982.
ISBN 0406008604 Pbk
—Is It In Force? 1987. – Butterworths Editorial Staff. – London : Butterworths, 1987.
ISBN 0406072825 Pbk £33.00
—Right to Buy' Handbook. – Butterworths Editorial Staff. – London : Butterworths, 1984.
This book sets out the text of the Housing and Building Control Act of 1984 concerning the 'right to buy' provisions of the United Kingdom Housing Act of 1980. Detailed annotations to the Act are provided.
ISBN 0406548250 Hbk

Butterworth's Emergency Legislation Service, 158 Vols. – Abingdon : Professional Books, 1984.
Hbk £300.00

Butterworths employment law handbook / edited by Peter Wallington. – 4th ed. – London : Butterworths, 1987.
xxx,892,14p.
ISBN 0406142637

Butterworth's Family Law Bulletin / Hellen Papadopoulos. – Wellington : Butterworths.
Hbk

Butterworths Family Law Bulletin. – Butterworths.
Hbk £44.00

Butterworths Family Law Guide. – 3rd ed. – Butterworths, 1989.
ISBN 0409788805 Pbk

Butterworth's Family Law Reports / Hellen Papadopoulos. – Wellington : Butterworths.
Hbk

Butterworths Family Law Reports. – Butterworths.
Llf

Butterworth's Family Law Service / H. K. Bevan. – Wellington : Butterworths, 1986.
ISBN 0406107203 Llf

Butterworths Financial Services Compliance Manual. – London : Butterworths.
ISBN 0406503745 Pbk £27.50

Butterworths guide to the community charge in Scotland. – London : Butterworths, 1989.
Full text of the Abolition of Domestic Rates, Etc (Scot.) Act 1987, with all subordinate legislation to 31 March 1989. With an introduction to the background to the legislation, and a comentary on the statutory provisions. Published by Butterworths on behalf of the Law Society of Scotland.
ISBN 0406147108 Pbk £15.00

Butterworths Handbook of Singapore Employment Law. – Butterworths Editorial Staff. – 2nd ed. – Butterworths, 1986.
787p.
Contains coverage of employment law, the central provident fund, skills development levy, payroll tax, redundancy payments fund, factories, workmen's compensations fund, industrial relations, trade disputes, and trade unions.
ISBN 0409995142 Pbk £99.00

Butterworths Handbook of Singapore Land Law. – Butterworths, 1986.
917p.
Examines the sale of property, statutes which affect the transfer of property, registration of property, planning and development control, maintenance and management of property, property tax and land revenue, land acquisition, and the control of rent.
ISBN 0409995169 Pbk £99.00

Butterworth's Handbook on the Value Added Tax Act 1983. – London : Butterworths, 1984.
This handbook contains the full text of the Capital Transfer Tax Act of 1984 for the United Kingdom practitioner. A table of cases, comprehensive index, and a destination table is included in the work.
ISBN 0406505349 Pbk

Butterworth's Income Tax Assessment Act 1987. – Sydney : Butterworths, 1987.
Pbk

Butterworths Income Tax Assessment Act and Related Legislation. – Butterworths, 1988.
1468p.
Pbk £78.00

Butterworth's Income Tax Computer Software. – London : Butterworths.
Hbk

Butterworth's Income Tax Service. – Butterworths Editorial Staff. – London : Butterworths.
This looseleaf service for United Kingdom practitioners covers extra-statutory concessions, statements of practice, and tables of rates and relief. The work is updated with monthly bulletins and quarterly service issues.
Hbk

Butterworths Income Tax Service. – Professional Publ.
ISBN 0409013706 Hbk £65.00 with binder
ISBN 0409013870 £25.00 binder only

Butterworth's Income Tax System. – London : Butterworths.
Hbk

Butterworth's Inheritance Tax Guide. – London : Butterworths, 1986.
ISBN 0406500347 Pbk £31.50

Butterworths insolvency law handbook / editor: Michael Crystal. – London : Butterworths, 1987.
vi,1005,29p.
ISBN 0406500061

Butterworths insurance law handbook / Richard-Hudson, E. R. Hardy Ivamy. – 2nd ed. – London : Butterworths, 1986.
591,10p; 25cm.
Previous ed.: 1983. Includes index.
ISBN 040617637X Pbk £22.00

Butterworths intellectual property law handbook. – London : Butterworths, 1989.
624; 248.
Includes patents, copyright, semiconductor typographies, registered designs, unregistered design right, trademarks, plant varieties protection, intellectual property and competition, professional status, and practice.
ISBN 0406504717 Pbk £19.95

Butterworths International Taxation of Financial Instruments. – London : Butterworths.
ISBN 0406106614 Hbk £60.00

Butterworths landlord and tenant handbook / edited by Lexis editorial staff : consulting editor David lloyd Evans. – London : Butterworths, 1982.
vii,597,9p.
Includes index. Contains statutes and statutory instruments up to date to 23 April 1982.
ISBN 0406253706

Butterworths Law Digest : Malaysia. – 2nd ed. – London : Butterworths, 1988.
ISBN 09515720 Hbk

Butterworths Law Directory 1988. – New York : British Media Publications, 1988.
ISBN 0611007169 Hbk £30.00

Butterworths Law Directory 1988. – Skinner (Thomas).
ISBN 0611007029 Hbk £30.00

Butterworth's Law Directory and Diary 1987. – 3rd ed. – London : Butterworths.
Pbk

Butterworths law of food and drugs / editor A.A. Painter : co-ordinating editor Brian Harvey. – 1. – London : Butterworths, 1981.
loose-leaf; 25cm.
Supersedes Bell and O'Keefe's Sale of food and drugs, 14th ed., 1968. 548 pages in various pagings on publication.
ISBN 0406116105

Butterworths Legal Services Directory 1988. – New York : British Media Publications, 1988.
ISBN 0611007215 Pbk £18.00

Butterworths Legal Services Directory 1989. – London : Butterworths.
ISBN 0611007355 Pbk £19.00

Butterworths Legislation Service for Black Local Government. – Professional Publ, 1984.
ISBN 0409069736 Llf £155.00

Butterworths of New Zealand
Family Law Statutes. – Butterworths of New Zealand. – 2nd ed. – Butterworths, 1988.
516p.
ISBN 0409788627 Pbk £54.00

Butterworth's Ontario Digest, 14 vols. – Toronto : Butterworths.
Hbk

Butterworths Ontario Digest. – London : Butterworths.
ISBN 0409993476 Hbk £300.00

Butterworth's Ontario Family Law Quantum Service, 2 vols / Ellen E. Mole. – Toronto : Butterworths.
Hbk

Butterworths Ontario Family Law Quantum Service, 2 Vols. / Ellen E. Mole. – Butterworths.
Llf £150.00

Butterworth's Orange Tax Handbook 1986-87. – London : Butterworths, 1986.
This annual handbook contains the up to date text of all United Kingdom enactments relating to capital transfer tax, national insurance contributions, stamp duty, and value added tax. The material is arranged chronologically.
ISBN 0406508321 Pbk £35.75

Butterworths Orange Tax Handbook 1988-89. – London : Butterworths.
ISBN 0406508356 Pbk £18.00

Butterworths planning law handbook / edited by Keith Davies. – London : Butterworths, 1987.
viii, 734, 11p.
ISBN 0406505802

Butterworths' Police Law. – 2nd ed. – London : Butterworths.
ISBN 0406840008 Pbk £14.95

Butterworths property law handbook / consulting editor Ernest H. Scamell. – London : Butterworths, 1984.
This work contains all the statutory law of the United Kingdom relevant to property law. The law of trusts, law of succession, law of family assets, and conveyancing are presented in their legislative form.
ISBN 0406258171 Pbk £14.95

Butterworth's Retirement Annuity Premiums Planner. – London : Butterworths.
Hbk

Butterworths Student Companions. – Butterworths.
Pbk £10.95
Contracts. – 1988.
144p.
ISBN 0409493252
Criminal Law. – 1984.
142p.
ISBN 0409491829
Family Law. – 1986.
ISBN 0409491365
Intellectual Property. – 1988.
111p.
ISBN 0409492892
Tax. – 1987.
117p.
ISBN 0409492469
Torts. – 1984.
128p.
ISBN 0409494127

Butterworth's Tax Brief. – Wellington : Butterworths.
Hbk

Butterworths Tax Guide, 3 Vols. – 1st ed. – Butterworths, 1989.
ca 1,650p.
Llf £340.00
Concise Tax subscribers. –
ISBN 0409303410 £260.00
With Legislation. –
£510.00

Butterworth's Tax Treaties. – London : Butterworths.
This looseleaf service contains the up to date texts of all the double tax agreements between the United Kingdom and other countries. Agreements relating to income tax, corporation tax, capital gains, and capital transfer tax are covered in this service.
Hbk

Butterworths Taxation Library, 3 Vols. – Butterworths.
ISBN 0409661287 Llf £770.00
Includes subscr. to New Zealand Current Taxation.

Butterworth's Trading Law Cases. – London : Butterworths.
This comprehensive looseleaf service covers cases dealing with such topics as trade descriptions, weights and measures, food and advertising, consumer credit, hallmarking, prices, and product safety in the United Kingdom.
Pbk

Butterworth's U.K. Tax Guide 1986-87. – London : Butterworths, 1986.
This work contains a detailed discussion of the workings and policy considerations underlying all the principal United Kingdom taxes, including stamp duty. The book includes numerous worked examples, tax tables, and a summary of the Finance Act of 1986.
ISBN 0406504954 Hbk £26.50

Butterworths UK tax guide. – London : Butterworths, 1982.

Butterworths Video videorecording : How Laws Are Made-VHS. – Butterworths.
video £59.00

Butterworth's Workmen's Compensation Cases : 1908-1950, 41 Vols. – Abingdon : Professional Books, 1984.
Hbk

Butterworths Wrongful Dismissal Practice Manual, 2 Vols. – Butterworths.
Llf £135.00

Butterworth's Wrongful Dismissal Practice Manual, 2 vols. – Toronto : Butterworths.
Hbk

Butterworth's Yellow Tax Handbook 1986-87. – London : Butterworths, 1986.
This work provides the text of all legislation in the United Kingdom relating to income tax, capital gains tax, and corporation tax for tax practitioners. The book is extensively cross-referenced and indexed.
ISBN 0406510032 Pbk £42.00

Butterworths Yellow Tax Handbook 1988-89. – London : Butterworths.
ISBN 0406510067 Pbk £20.00

Buttery
International audit in public sector / Simpson. – Cambridge : Woodhead-Faulkner, 1985.
ISBN 0859412725 Pbk £11.95

Buxbaum
Traditional and Modern Legal Institutions in Asia and Africa. – Leiden : E.J. Brill, 1967.
ISBN 9004010505 Hbk £48.00

Buxbaum, Richard M
Legal harmonization and the business enterprise : corporate and capital market law, harmonization policy in Europe and the U.S.A. / by Richard M. Buxbaum and Klaus J. Hopt. – Berlin : De Gruyter, 1988.
– (Series A–Law).
Includes index. Bibliography.
ISBN 0899251277 Hbk £96.00

Buyer's lien : a new consumer remedy / Law Reform Commission of British Columbia. – Vancouver : The Commission, 1986.
iii,52p. – (Working paper).
Includes bibliographical references.

Buying A Company : Checklist Guide. – BIM. – VANN, 1982.
ISBN 0859461211 Pbk £4.00

Buying and Selling a Business 1985. – Vancouver : Continuing Legal Education Society of British Columbia, 1985.
311p.
ISBN 0865041970 Hbk £65.00

Buying and Selling Commercial Property. – Vancouver : Continuing Legal Education Society of British Columbia, 1985.
433p.
ISBN 086504189X Hbk £70.00

Buying and selling private companies and businesses / Humphrey Wine. – 3rd ed. – London : Butterworths, 1986.
260p; 23cm.
Previous ed.: 1983. Includes index.
ISBN 0406424187 Pbk £22.50

Buying Your Home With Other People. – Shelter.
ISBN 090124799 Pbk £5.95

Buying Your Own House. – London : Longman Professional, 1988.
ISBN 0851213790 Pbk £4.95

Buzek, F.J. →Collision cases : judgments and diagrams.

Buzzard, A.J.
Medicine and Surgery for Lawyers. – North Ryde : Law Book Co, 1986.
xxi, 675p.
ISBN 0455206759 Hbk £89.50

Buzzard, John H, et al
Phipson on evidence / Richard May, M.N Howard. – 13th. – London : Sweet & Maxwell, 1982 & 1987.
– (Common Law Library).
Includes changes in the chapters which deal with problems that regularly arise in modern civil and criminal legislation, and new material in the chapters on confessions and the course of the trial. Extra sections have been added to the chapters on public policy and privilege.
ISBN 0421269901 Hbk £108
ISBN 042137070X SUPPLEMENT £9

By Reason of Doubt : the Belshaw Case. – Richmond Hill : Irwin Publishing Inc..
208p.
ISBN 0887801250 Pbk £4.95
ISBN 077201390X Pbk £9.95

Byers, R. B. →Deterrence in the 1980s : crisis and dilemma.

Byles, T.
Bills of Exchange. – 26th ed. – Sweet & Maxwell, 1988.
ISBN 042138090X Hbk £72.00

Byre, Angela D.
International human rights law in the Commonwealth Caribbean / edited for the International Center for the Legal Protection of Human Rights (Interights) by Angela D. Byre. – Dordrecht : Nijhoff (Martinus), 1989.
408. – (International Studies in Human Rights).
Collection of papers concerning the protection of human rights under Bills of Rights in Commonwealth Carribean countries and under regional and international human rights treaties. Demonstrates the relevance of international human rights law in domestic cases and considers practical ways of strengthening human rights protection.
ISBN 9024737850 Hbk Gld150.00

—Leading cases and materials on the social policy of the EEC. – Dordrecht : Kluwer, 1989.
556.
Guide to the scope of community law, using basic sources, such as treaty provisions and directives. Examines the problem of the direct effect on, and the relationship between, national and community law.
ISBN 9065443126 Pbk £39/Dfl 125

Byrne, D. →Cross on Evidence : with Supplement 1980.

Byrne, Dominic
Low pay check : reforming the Truck Acts / Dominic Byrne. – London : Low Pay Unit, 1983.
24p.

Byrne, Peter
Health Rights and Resources. – Oxford : Oxford University Press.
– (King Edwards Hospital Series).
ISBN 0197246451 Pbk £16.95

→ Medicine in contemporary society.

→ Rights and wrongs in medicine : King's College studies 1985-6.

Byrne, Raymond →Annual Review of Irish Law 1987.

—Irish Commercial Law. – 2nd ed. – Dublin : Round Hall Press, 1988.
200p.
ISBN 0947686398 Pbk £12.95
ISBN 0947686320 Hbk £20.00

—Irish Legal System : Cases and Materials / J P McCutcheon. – London : Butterworths, 1986.
ISBN 086205222X Hbk £22.50
ISBN 0862052238 Pbk £12.50

—Prisoners' rights : a study in Irish prison law / by Raymond Byrne, Gerard W. Hogan, Paul McDermott. – Dublin : Co-op Books, 1981.
xvi,145p.
ISBN 0905441400

Byrne, Roy
Jobs in Local Authorities. – London : Kogan Page, 1985.
95p. – (Jobs In...Ser.).
ISBN 085038978X Pbk £2.95

Byrt, W. J.
Framework of consensus : government, business and trade unions / W. J. Byrt. – Melbourne : Law Book Company Ltd., 1985.
ix,220p.
Bibliography: p211-218.
ISBN 0455205779

Bythewood, W. N. →Treatise of the Principle Grounds and Maximes of the Lawes of This Kingdome by W.N. A Dialogue and Treatise of the Laws of England and on Tenures, Estates, Heriditaments and Chattels.

C.A.L.T. Directory 1987-88. – Canadian Association of Law Teachers. – Agincourt : Carswell, 1987.
186p.
Pbk £17.50

C. E. R. : the business and law essentials : papers presented at seminar, University of Auckland, 22-23 July 1983. – 3. – Auckland : Legal Research Foundation Inc., 1983.
ISBN 0908581270

C.I.F. and F.O.B. contracts / H. Orren Merren. – 3rd ed. – London : Stevens, 1984.
xlv,528p; 26cm.
Previous ed.: 1975. Includes index.
ISBN 0420465308 £60.00

C.I.P.A. guide to The Patents Acts / The Chartered Institute of Patent Agents. – 3rd. – London : Sweet & Maxwell, 1989.
liii,772p; 26cm.
Includes tables of statutes, statutory instruments, EPO, PCT, and CPC references. Sections of the Act are printed in full and followed by the relevant rules, including the 1989 consolidation patent rules. Previous ed.: 1984. Kept up to date by supplements.
ISBN 0421397608 Hbk £95.00

C.P.A.G.'s income support, the social fund and family credit : the legislation / commentary John Mesher. – 1988 ed. – London : Sweet & Maxwell, 1988.
xxx,381p; 24cm.
Previous ed.: 1987. Includes index.
ISBN 0421402709 Pbk £19.50

C.P.A.G.'s supplementary benefit and family income supplement : the legislation / commentary by John Mesher. – 4th ed. – London : Sweet & Maxwell, 1987.
500p; 23cm.
Previous ed.: 1985. Kept up to date by supplements.
ISBN 0421382007 Pbk £17.50

C.P.A.G's supplementary benefit and family income supplement : the legislation / commentary by John Mesher. – 3rd ed. – London : Sweet & Maxwell, 1985.
xxviii,465p; 24cm.
Previous ed.: 1985. Includes index.
ISBN 0421353805 Pbk £15.00

C.P.A.G's supplementary benefit and family income supplement : the legislation / annotations by John Mesher. – 2nd ed. – London : Sweet & Maxwell, 1985.
400p.
Previous ed: published as CPAG's supplementary benefit legislation annotated. 1983. Includes index. Includes the text of the 1976 Supplementary Benefits Act, and the 1970 Family Income Supplements Act.
ISBN 0421342102 Pbk

Cabanellas, Guillermo
Antitrust and direct regulation of international transfer of technology transactions : a comparison and evaluation / Guillermo Cabanellas. – Munich : Verlag Chemie for the Max Planck Institute for Foreign and International Patent Copyright and Competition Law, 1984.
175p.
ISBN 3527260013

—Extraterritorial Effect of Antitrust Law on Transfer of Technology. – Veinheim : VCH.
– (IIC Studies in Industrial Property and Copyright Law).
ISBN 0895738279 Pbk £36.00

Cable television : agency franchising and economics / Cento Veljanovski. – London : Faculty of Laws, University College London, 1986.
25p; 30cm. – (Working papers).

Cable television : media and copyright law aspects : reports to an ALAI symposium / edited by Herman Cohen Jehoram. – Deventer : Kluwer Law and Taxation, 1983.
xix,236p; 25cm.
ISBN 9065441492 Pbk

Cable Television and Defamation. – Victoria : Government of British Columbia, 1981.
Hbk £1.05

Cadiz, Charles Fitzwilliam →Ordinances, laws and proclamations.

Cadman
Property development / Austin-Crowe. – 2nd ed. – Spon (E & FN), 1983.
ISBN 0419128204 Pbk £9.50

Caenegem, R.C. Van
Birth of the English Common Law. – 2nd ed. – Cambridge : Cambridge University Press.
ISBN 0521355958 Hbk £22.50
ISBN 0521356822 Pbk £7.95

—Judges, legislators and professors : chapters in European legal history / R.C. van Caenegem. – Cambridge : Cambridge University Press, 1987.
x,205p; 23cm.
Examines how continental and common law have come to differ substantially. Describes how European law developed through power struggles between various groups representing certain political and social ambitions.
ISBN 0521340772 £19.50

Caffrey, Bradford A.
Guidebook to Contract Law in Australia. – 3rd ed. – North Ryde : C.C.H. Australia, 1987.
350p.
ISBN 0869034715 Pbk £35.00

—International jurisdiction and the recognition and enforcement of foreign judgements in the LAWASIA region : a comparative study of the laws of eleven Asian countries inter-se and with the E.E.C. countries / Bradford A. Caffrey. – Sydney : CCH Australia, 1985.
xxxii,407p.
Cover title: Enforcement of foreign judgements.
ISBN 0869037897

Caflisch, Lucius →Legal Regime of International Rivers and Lakes.

Cage, R. A.
Scottish Poor Law 1745-1845. – Edinburgh : Scottish Academic Press Ltd, 1981.
186p.
ISBN 0707302897 Hbk £8.75

Cahu, L.L.A.
Professional Guide to Fund Raising, Corporate Giving People Giving to People. – London : Eurospan.
ISBN 0899302513 Hbk £29.95

Cain →Conveyancing Solution 3 : Remedies under Contract.
→ Remedies under the contract, CS No 3.

Cain, Brian →Enquiries before contract.
→ Modern conveyancing.

Cain, G.
Practice and Procedure of the High Court and Court of Appeal in New Zealand. – 12th ed. – Butterworths.
ISBN 0409667617 Llf £264.00
—Probate and Administration Practice in New Zealand / J.B.K. Curran. – 4th ed. – Butterworths, 1986.
Includes material from various statutes, regulations, the new High Court Rules, Court decisions, and textbooks. Covers the developments in probate and administration law in New Zealand. Cross-referenced to Garrow and Alston's Law of Wills and Administration 5th edition 1984.
ISBN 0409621412 Hbk £51.00

Cain, Maureen →Disputes and the law.

Cain, Thomas Ewan →Company law.

Cairncross, Frances →Capital city : London as a financial centre.

Cairns, Bernard C.
Australian civil procedure / Bernard C. Cairns. – 2nd ed. – Sydney : Law Book Company, 1985.
lxvi,584p.
ISBN 0455206260
—Law of discovery in Australia : documents, interrogatories and property / by Bernard C. Cairns. – Sydney : Law Book Co., 1984.
xxv,199p.
Bibliography: p.xx - Includes index.
ISBN 0455202842
—Sale of Real Property and Law of Agency in Queensland / W.B. Hutchinson. – Butterworths, 1986.
160p.
This is a working guide for students and those involved with conveyancing transactions. Included are materials on contracts for sale of land, strata titles, registration of titles, agents, commissions, unjust contracts, valuations of land, land subdivisions, and local authority requirements for land development.
ISBN 0409491179 Pbk £26.00

Cairns, David J.
Remedies for Trademark Infringement. – Agincourt : Carswell, 1988.
192p.
This book provides a comprehensive discussion of the remedies available for trademark infringement. Topics include the ramifications of injunctive relief, ancillary relief, and monetary remedies. The text also discusses how these various remedies interact with each other.
Hbk £43.75

Cairns, Elizabeth
Charities law and practice / Elizabeth Cairns. – London : Sweet & Maxwell, 1988.
xxi,258p; 26cm.
Includes the procedure for establishing a new charity and the relative advantages of trusts, companies, and unincorporated associations for different types of charity; how to draft the government instrument, and to what extent charities may engage in political activity. Taxation and administrative matters are also covered.
ISBN 0421358106 £19.50
—Handbook of Charity Law and Practice. – London : Sweet & Maxwell, 1988.
ISBN 0421358106 Pbk £27.50

Cairns, W. →Customs law of the European Economic Community.

Calabresi, Guido
Common law for the age of statutes / Guido Calabresi. – Cambridge, Mass. : Harvard University Press, 1982.
319p; 24cm.
Bibliography: p300-309. - Includes index.
ISBN 0674146042

Calderwood, S.C. →Commercial Securities in New Zealand : an introduction to the Law.

Caldicott →Workbook in accounting.

Caldwell →Criminal Law.

Caldwell, R. A. →Garrow and Caldwell's criminal law in New Zealand.

Calendar of Soviet treaties, 1958-1973 / by George Ginsburgs and Robert M. Slusser. – Alphen aan den Rijn : Sijthoff & Noordhoff, 1981.
xx,908p.

Calendar of Soviet treaties, 1974-1980 / George Ginsburgs. – Dordrecht : Martinus Nijhoff Publishers, 1987.
ISBN 9024736285 Hbk

Caley, Robert →Union list of law periodicals held in libraries within the City of Liverpool.
→ Union list of law reports and statutes held in libraries within the City of Liverpool.
→ Union list of legal bibliographies and digests and other law-related material held in libraries within the City of Liverpool.

Callaghan, R.W.
Safety and Industry Laws, New South Wales Vol. 1 / G.A. Miller. – Butterworths.
ISBN 0409412503 Hbk

Callahan, Marilyn
Welfare Rights and GAIN / Marjorie Martin. – 3rd ed. – Vancouver : Vancouver People's Law School.
Illus.. – – (Public Legal Education Series).
ISBN 0888470223 Hbk £0.60

Called to account : the case for police accountability in England and Wales / Sarah Spencer. – London : National Council for Civil Liberties, 1985.
146p; 20cm.
Includes bibliography.
ISBN 0946088128 Pbk £3.95

Callender Smith, R.
Press Law (CCT). – Sweet & Maxwell, 1978.
ISBN 0421234504 Pbk £7.75

Calligan, Stewart
Points to prove. – 2nd ed. – Police Review, 1987.
ISBN 085164032X Pbk £5.25
—Taking statements. – 2nd ed. – Police Review, 1987.
ISBN 0851640338 Pbk £3.75

Calnan, R. J.
Effect of disputed debts, set-offs and counterclaims on winding-up and bankruptcy petitions / by R. J. Calnan. – Auckland : Legal Research Foundation, 1981.
55p.
ISBN 0908581165
—Law of Set-Off. – London : Sweet & Maxwell, 1986.
ISBN 0421348607 Hbk

Calver
Calver's Powers of Arrest : Charges / Lewis Heavens. – 8th ed. – London : Butterworths, 1987.
ISBN 0406842051 Pbk £5.95

Calverley, John
Country risk analysis / John Calverley. – London : Butterworths, 1985.
ix,181p; 23cm.
Includes index.
ISBN 0406005508 Hbk £38.00

Calver's Powers of Arrest : Charges / Lewis Heavens. – 8th ed. – London : Butterworths, 1987.
ISBN 0406842051 Pbk £5.95

Calvert, Fred
Constable's Pocket Guide to Powers of Arrest and Charges / Lewis Heavens. – 7th ed. – London : Butterworths, 1982.
This work for practitioner and police officer gives a ready reference to the law on arrest and the formulation of charges. The work includes all new laws and the amendments of the old ones relevant to powers of arrest and charges.
Police officers
ISBN 0406842043 Pbk

Calvert, H.
Introduction to British constitutional law. – London : Blackstone Press, 1985.
ISBN 0906322685 Pbk £9.95

Calwell
Sea lawyer grade for yachtsmen. – 2nd ed. – Oxford : Collins, 1986.
ISBN 0229117627 Pbk £6.95

Cambridge
Demonstrating Successful Community Care / Knapp. – University of Kent.
ISBN 0904938018 Pbk £2.95

Cambridge Institute of Criminology : its background and scope : a report / by Sir Leon Radzinowicz : for the Home Office. – London : H.M.S.O., 1988.
viii,190p.
Describes the formation of the Institute, early problems, the scope and content of courses offered and how the work of the Institute has evolved over the years.
ISBN 0113408846

Cambridge Lectures 1979. – Butterworths, 1981.
304p.
ISBN 0409849073 Hbk £46.95

Cambridge lectures 1981 : selected papers based upon lectures delivered at the Conference of the Canadian Institute for Advanced Legal Studies, 1981, held at Cambridge University, England ... / edited by Nancy E. Eastham and Boris Krivy. – Toronto : Butterworths, 1982.
xix,433p.
Includes bibliographical references.
ISBN 040984392X Hbk £45.00

Cambridge lectures 1983 : selected papers based upon lectures at the Conference of the Canadian Institute for Advanced Legal Studies, 1983, held at Cambridge University, England / edited by Elizabeth G. Baldwin. – Toronto : Butterworths, 1985.
xvi,341p.
Includes bibliographical references.
ISBN 0409810320

Cambridge-Tilburg Law Lectures
Vol. 3 / J.R. Spencer. – Dordrecht : Kluwer, 1983.
68p.
ISBN 9065441077 Pbk £25.00
Vol. 5. – 1986.
270p.
ISBN 9065442510 Pbk £60.00

Cambridge-Tilbury Law Lectures
Vol. 4 /. – Dordrecht : Kluwer, 1983.
92p.
ISBN 9065441085 Pbk £30.00

Camejo, Pedro Miguel
Stop the Deportations!. – Sydney : Pathfinder Press.
16p.
Hbk £0.50

Cameron, Deborah
Lust to kill : a feminist investigation of sexual murder / Deborah Cameron and Elizabeth Frazer. – Cambridge : Polity in association with Basil Blackwell, 1987.
xv,207p; 22cm.
Bibliography: p195-203. - Includes index.
ISBN 0745603351 Hbk £25.00
ISBN 074560336X Pbk £7.95

Cameron, Joy
Prisons and punishment in Scotland : from the Middle Ages to the present / Joy Cameron. – Edinburgh : Canongate, 1983.
x,274p,16p of plates; 23cm.
Bibliography: p237-239. - Includes index.
ISBN 0862410312 £12.95

Cameron, Judith M. →Applications of computer technology to law (1979-1982) : a selected bibliography.

Cameron, Peter D
Oil supplies industry : a comparative study of legislative restrictions and their impact. – London : Financial Times Business Information, 1986.
ix,242p.
Bibliography: p.238-242..
ISBN 0903199920
—Petroleum licensing : a comparative study / Peter Cameron. – London : Financial Times Business Information, 1984.
x,195p.
Bibliography: pp.191-194.
ISBN 0903199785
—Property rights and sovereign rights : the case of North Sea oil / Peter D. Cameron. – London : Academic Press, 1983.
x,210p; 24cm.
Bibliography: p194-202. - Includes index.
ISBN 0121570606

Camilleri, B. J. →Practice and procedure of the High Court and the Federal Court of Australia.

Camp →Practical partnership, Supplement.

Camp, J. J., et al
Insurance Law : 1982. – Vancouver : British Columbia Continuing Legal Education Society, 1982.
115p.
ISBN 0865040745 Hbk £45.00

Camp, P. →Practical Partnership.
→ Practical partnership for solicitors.

Camp, Peter →Dismissal and taxation of employees.
→ Titman & Camp, individual employment law.

Campaign for Press Freedom →Changing contempt of court.

Campbell
Ending Lives / Collinson. – Oxford : Blackwell Scientific, 1988.
ISBN 0631153314 Pbk £6.95
→ Family at Law : In which the Hendersons find out what to do after an accident.

Campbell, A.
Waiting for a Move : Elderly People and Allocation Transfer Policies of Scottish Local Authorities. – London : Age Concern Scotland.
ISBN 0946505535 Pbk £1.50

Campbell, Alan
Common Market law / Alan Campbell. – 4 v. – London : Longmans, 1969.
25cm.
Supplement, published in 1975, assimilated the contents of previous loose-leaf binders. Earlier ed. by Campbell and D.C. Thompson.

Campbell, Anne
Girls in the gang : a report from New York City / Anne Campbell. – Oxford : Blackwell, 1984.
vii,277p; 24cm.
Study of girls in New York City gangs.
ISBN 0631133747 Hbk

Campbell, C. M. →Data processing and the law.

Campbell, D.
Comparative Law Yearbook
Vol. 1. – Dordrecht : Kluwer, 1978.
352p.
ISBN 9028606785 Hbk £105.00

Campbell, Dennis
Abortion Law and Public Policy. – Dordrecht : Kluwer, 1985.
104p.
ISBN 9024731070 Pbk £40.00
→ Effective dispute resolution for the international commercial lawyer.
→ From the Waidring Conferences, 4 Vols., Survey of the International Sale of Goods.
→ Legal aspects of business transactions and investment in the Far East.
→ Legal aspects of doing business in Africa.
→ Legal aspects of doing business in Asia and the Pacific.
→ Legal aspects of doing business in Eastern Europe and the Soviet Union.
→ Legal aspects of doing business in Latin America.
→ Legal aspects of doing business in the Middle East.
→ Legal aspects of doing business in Western Europe.
→ Legal aspects of international business transactions : the Edinburgh Institute on International Business Transactions 1983 : a project of University of the Pacific McGeorge School of Law international programs.
→ Legal aspects of joint ventures in Eastern Europe.
→ Transnational legal practice : a survey of selected countries.
→ U.S. legal system : a practice handbook.

Campbell, Don → International maritime fraud.

Campbell, Enid
Rules of Court : a Study of Rule-Making Powers and Procedures. – North Ryde : Law Book Co, 1985.
xxix, 271p.
ISBN 0455206309 Hbk £49.50
→ Well and truly tried : essays on evidence in honour of Sir Richard Eggleston.

Campbell, Ian
Canada Valuation Service. – Toronto : DeBoo.
ISBN 0888201370 Llf £275.00

Campbell, Ian G.
Mental Disorder and Criminal Law in Australia and New Zealand. – Butterworths, 1988.
ca 256p.
ISBN 0409494828 Hbk £55.00

Campbell, J.
Personal Equity Plans. – Cambridge : Woodhead-Faulkner, 1987.
ISBN 0859414191 Pbk £4.95

Campbell, Jean → South African criminal law and procedure, Vol.5 : Criminal procedure : by Alfred V. Lansdown : Evidence : Jean Campbell.

Campbell, Tom → Human rights : from rhetoric to reality.
—Left and rights : a conceptual analysis of the Socialist rights / Tom Campbell. – London : Routledge & Kegan Paul, 1982.
253p.
Includes bibliographical references and index. Bibliography: p216-249.
ISBN 0710090854 Pbk

Can knowledge survive? / Sir Harry Hookway. – London : British Library, 1986.
8p; 30cm. – (The Fourth British Library Annual Research Lecture).
ISBN 0712330747 Pbk ree

Canada
Report of the Commission of Inquiry Relating to the Security and Investigation Services Branch Within the Post Office Department / Rene J Marin. – Hull, Quebec : Canadian Government Publishing Centre, 1981.
iv,338p.
Commissioner: Rene J. Marin.
ISBN 0660108585

Canada : Income Tax. – Delhi : Rangnath Publications.
Hbk £200.00

Canada Act 1982 annotated / by Peter W. Hogg. – Toronto : Carswell, 1982.
155p.
Includes the Constitution Act, 1982 - the Canadian Bill of Rights - the American Bill of Rights - the International Covenant on Civil and Political Rights. Includes index.
ISBN 0459351303

Canada and the constitution, 1979-1982 : patriation and the charter of rights / Edward McWhinney. – Toronto : University of Toronto Press, 1982.
xii,227p.
Includes bibliographical references and index.
ISBN 0802065015 Pbk

Canada and the International Seabed Domestic Interests and External Constraints. – Montreal : McGill-Queen's University Press.
ISBN 0773506942 Hbk £34.95

Canada and the New Constitution : the Unfinished Agenda, 2 Vols. / Ivan Bernier. – Ottawa : Institute for Research on Public Policy, 1983.
xii, 399p.
This work examines the principles of Canadian corporate and partnership law in depth. The book covers the fundamentals of corporate finance and distribution, duties of management, the rights and remedies of shareholders, and more.
ISBN 0920380735 Hbk £10.95

Canada and the new international law of the sea / Douglas M. Johnston. – Toronto : University of Toronto Press in cooperation with the Royal Commission on the Economic Union and Development Prospects for Canada and the Canadian Government Publishing Centre, 1985.
xviii,124p. – (Collected research studies).
Includes bibliographical references.
ISBN 0802073018

Canada and the Reagan Challenge : Crisis in the Canadian-American Relationship. – Toronto : Lorimer & Co, 1985.
ISBN 0888627912 Hbk £26.95
ISBN 0888627904 Pbk £16.95

Canada Bankruptcy Legislation. – 2nd ed. – Don Mills : CCH Canadian Ltd, 1984.
360p.
ISBN 0887962505 Pbk £12.95

Canada Business Corporations Act : an Accountant's View of the Highlights. – 3rd ed. – Butterworths, 1987.
136p.
Includes a revised study of the law introduced (in 1975) by the new Act. Covers detailed disclosure requirements for financial statements, information not contained in the body of the Act, but substantially prescribed by regulations.
ISBN 0409806560 Pbk £18.95

Canada Business Corporations Act : with Regulations. – 6th ed. – Don Mills : CCH Canadian Ltd, 1985.
224p.
ISBN 0887962955 Pbk £8.95

Canada Corporation Manual, 3 Vols. – Toronto : DeBoo, 1984.
ISBN 0888201346 Hbk £325.00

Canada Energy Law Service, 3 Vols. – Canadian Institute of Resource Law. – Toronto : DeBoo, 1984.
This looseleaf service monitors the decisions of those tribunals which regulate Canada's energy resources. Included are commentaries, case digests, and legislation. Six updates per year are planned.
ISBN 0888201087 Hbk £650.00

Canada Estate Planning Service. – Toronto : DeBoo.
Looseleaf service.
ISBN 0888201125 Llf £260.00

Canada Federal Court Reports : 1971-1983. – Agincourt : Carswell, 1986.
Hbk £147.00

Canada From Abroad : Legal, Business and Tax Aspects. – North Ryde : C.C.H. Australia.
210p.
ISBN 0887963129 Pbk £16.95

Canada Gazette : Regulations, Pt. II. – Agincourt : Carswell, 1987.
Hbk £87.00

Canada Gazette : Statutes, Pt. III. – Agincourt : Carswell, 1987.
Hbk £22.75

Canada income tax guide. – 3. – Don Mills : CCH Canadian, 1982.
looseleaf.
Includes index.

Canada Income Tax Regulation Service. – Toronto : DeBoo.
This multi-volume looseleaf reference work includes Canadian Income Tax Regulations, Interpretation Bulletins, Information Circulars, tax rulings, current forms, and indices.
ISBN 0888201354 Llf £255.00

Canada Labour Relations Board : Federal Law and Practice. – Agincourt : Carswell, 1983.
450p.
This book provides a description and discussion of the character, activity, practice, and role of the Canadian Labour Relations Board in its historical, constitutional, and institutional setting.
Hbk £54.75

Canada Labour Relations Board Policies and Procedures. – Butterworths, 1986.
640p.
Describes the rules and practices of the Canada Labour Relations Board in the administration of Parts IV and V of the Canada Labour Code. Makes reference to all numbered decisions of the CLRB since 1973, decisions of the Federal Court and the Supreme Court of Canada, reviewing CLRB decisions. Also includes decisions of the Canadian common law courts which have interpreted the code.
ISBN 0409819751 Hbk £95.00

Canada Labour Service. – Toronto : DeBoo.
This looseleaf volume provides a Consolidation of all Federal and Provincial Canadian Labor Legislation.
ISBN 0888201435 Llf £285.00

Canada Law Reports : 1923-1970. – Agincourt : Carswell, 1984.

Canada Notwithstanding : The Making of a Constitution 1976-1982 / John D Whyte. – Agincourt : Carswell, 1984.
300p.
Hbk £40.50

Canada Regulations Index, 2 Vols. – Agincourt : Carswell, 1987.
Llf £309.25

Canada Revised Statutes : 1985, 11 Vols. – Agincourt : Carswell, 1988.

Canada Statute Annotations (1941-1971) R.S.C. – 1970 Ed. – Aurora : Canada Law Book Co.
523p. – (Statute Services).
Hbk £50.00

Canada Supreme Court Reports : 1876-1922, 64 Vols. – Agincourt : Carswell, 1984.

Canada Tax Cases. – Toronto : DeBoo.
This service, updated twice monthly, reports all judgments concerning federal taxation decided by the Supreme Court of Canada, the Federal Court, the Tax Court, and the upper courts of the provinces. Included are headnotes, editorial notes on important decisions, topical and statutory indices, and tables of appeals. Bound volumes of all reported cases are issued semi-annually.
ISBN 0888201672 Llf £325.00

Canada Tax Cases Index and Citator : Consolidated from 1972. – Toronto : DeBoo, 1983.
ISBN 0888201486 Hbk £95.00

Canada Tax Letter. – Toronto : DeBoo.
This series of studies, intended for the tax specialist, contains analyses and opinions of important legislation and jurisprudence. Approximately six issues per year are planned.
ISBN 0888201664 Hbk £140.00

Canada Tax Manual. – Toronto : DeBoo.
This two volume looseleaf sourcebook covers the Canadian Income Tax Act and includes discussion of individual taxation; corporate taxation; business, property, and employment income; taxation of non-residents; and tax appeals cases.
ISBN 0888201362 Llf £225.00

Canada Tax Service. – Toronto : DeBoo.
This multi-volume looseleaf service provides a seate taxation; business, property, and employment income; taxation of non-residents; and tax appeals cases.
ISBN 0888201656 Llf £725.00

Canada - U.S. Tax Treaty. – Vancouver : British Columbia Continuing Legal Education Society, 1985.
73p.
ISBN 0865041857 Hbk £55.00

Canada Valuation Service. – Toronto : DeBoo.
ISBN 0888201370 Llf £275.00

Canada's immigration law : an overview / Employment and Immigration Canada. – Hull, Quebec : Department of Supply and Services, 1983.
31,32p.
With French t.p.: Vue d'ensemble sur la legislation canadienne en matiere d'immigration. English and French texts.
ISBN 0662527798

Canada's Indians / by James Wilson. – Rev. ed. – London : Minority Rights Group, 1982.
20p. – (Report).
Previous ed.: 1977. Bibliography: p.20.

Canada's Lawyers Take Stand & Relate Their Funniest Stories. – London : Lavis Marketing.
ISBN 0458808903 Pbk £5.50

Canada's Tax Treaties, 2 Vols. – Butterworths.
Llf £145.00

Canada-U.S. Free Trade Agreement : Commentary and Related Documents / Richard G. Dearden. – North Ryde : C.C.H. Australia.
138p.
ISBN 0887964583 Pbk £14.95

Canada-U.S. Free Trade Agreement : Final Text and Analysis / Richard G. Dearden. – North Ryde : C.C.H. Australia.
420p.
ISBN 0887964621 Pbk £22.95

Canadian Abridgment, 110 Vols. – Carswell Legal Publications. – 2nd ed. – Agincourt : Carswell.
Hbk £2730.00

Canadian Abridgment, 41 Vols. – Abingdon : Professional Books, 1984.
Hbk

Canadian Advisory Council on the Status of Women → Women and the constitution in Canada.

Canadian Almanac and Directory. – Toronto : DeBoo, 1984.
ISBN 0773040536 Hbk £69.95

Canadian Arbitration, Conciliation and Amicable Composition Centre, Paul J. 710.21 → Proceedings of a seminar on commercial arbitration held in Ottawa, 19 June 1985.

Canadian Association of law Libraries
Directory / Canadian Association of Law Libraries : Association Canadienne des Bibliotheques de Droit. – Toronto : The Association, 1982.
Continues: List of members.
→ Introduction to Quebec legal bibliography : 1980 CALL pre- conference workshop, May 20, 1980 - Montreal, Quebec.

Canadian Association of Law Teachers
C.A.L.T. Directory 1987-88. – Canadian Association of Law Teachers. – Agincourt : Carswell, 1987.
186p.
Pbk £17.50

Canadian Bankruptcy Reports / David E. Baird. – Agincourt : Carswell.
Hbk £73.50

Canadian Bar Association : Proceedings of the First, Second and Third Meetings. – Agincourt : Carswell, 1984.
Hbk £14.00

Canadian Bar Review : 1923-Date. – Abingdon : Professional Books, 1984.
Hbk

Canadian bibliography of international law / Christian L. Wiktor. – Toronto : University of Toronto Press, 1984.
xxiii, 767 p.; 25 cm.
Includes indexes.
ISBN 0802056156

Canadian building contracts / Immanuel Goldsmith. – 3rd ed. – Toronto, Canada : Carswell, 1983.
lxi, 273 p.; 24 cm.
Includes bibliographical references.
ISBN 0459357905

Canadian Business Corporations / Pilkington. – Aurora : Canada Law Book, 1977.
Hbk £25.00

Canadian Business Law Journal (C.B.L.J.) 1976-Present. – Aurora : Canada Law Book Co.
Hbk £82.00
Current subscription-Outside Canada. –
Hbk £87.00
Back Vols.. –
£36.00 each

Canadian business organizations law / by Tom Hadden, Robert E. Forbes, Ralph L. Simmonds. – Toronto : Butterworths, 1984.
xlix,680p.
Relates common-law rules and statutory provisions to current commercial and industrial practice, distinguishing between the problems of small private businesses and larger public companies. Provides information on current corporate issues; practices and problems in designed instruments of corporate finance, securities law, corporate acquisitions, corporate groups, foreign acquisitions, and lease financing.
ISBN 0409834815 Hbk £95

Canadian Cases in Marketing Communications. – Butterworths, 1983.
480p.
ISBN 0409840645 Hbk £36.95

Canadian Cases on Employment Law
Vol. 14. – Agincourt : Carswell, 1987.
Hbk £75.00
Back Vols.. – 1984-1986.
This reference book contains key decisions in employment law outside the collective bargaining process. Cases on wrongful dismissal, dismissal for cause, constructive dismissal, demotion, employment contracts, employment standards, mandatory retirement policies, wage and remuneration, pensions and profit sharing are included.
Hbk £31.75 ea.

Canadian Cases on the Law of Torts
Vols. 1-31. – Agincourt : Carswell.
Hbk £734.75
Vol. 44. – 1987.
Hbk £67.25

Canadian Centre for Justice Statistics →Civil courts in Canada : Tribunaux civils au Canada.

Canadian Charter of Rights : law practice revolutionized / editor A. Wayne MacKay : associate editors Clare F. Beckton and Bruce H. Wildsmith. – Halifax, N.S. : Faculty of Law, Dalhousie University, 1982.
xv,391p. – (Dalhousie Continuing Legal Education Ser.: No. 22).
Jointly sponsored by Dalhousie Law School and University of Maine Law School.
ISBN 0770303226 Hbk £20.00

Canadian charter of rights : prosecution and defence of criminal and other statutory offences / by Roderick M. McLeod ... et al. – Toronto, Canada : Carswell, 1983.
1 v. (loose-leaf); 25 cm.
ISBN 0459357409

Canadian Charter of Rights and Freedoms. – Vancouver : University of British Columbia Law Review, 1982.
236p.
Special edition of: University of British Columbia Law Review (1982).

Canadian Charter of Rights and Freedoms. – Agincourt : Carswell, 1982.
ISBN 045934920 Hbk £33.00

Canadian charter of rights and freedoms : commentary / edited by Walter S. Tarnopolsky and Gerald-A. Beaudoin. – Toronto, Canada : Carswell, 1982.
liii, 590 p.; 26 cm.
Includes index. Bibliography: p. 563-579.
ISBN 045935230X Pbk

Canadian Charter of Rights Annotated / Edward L. Greenspan. – Aurora : Canada Law Book Co. – (Text Books-Civil).
Pbk £127.00

Canadian Children's Books - the Key to Legal Literacy. Books for Younger Children. – Ottawa : Canadian Law Information Council, 1983.
15p.
ISBN 0920358381 Hbk

Canadian Children's Books-the Key to Legal Literacy. Books for Older Children. – Ottawa : Canadian Law Information Council, 1983.
15p.
ISBN 092035839X Pbk

Canadian children's law : cases, notes and materials / by Nicholas Bala, Heino Lilles and George Thomson. – Toronto : Butterworths, 1982.
xxxi,754p.
Includes index.
ISBN 0409872237

Canadian Civil Procedure : Cases and Materials. – 3rd ed. – Toronto : Edmond-Montgomery, 1988.
925p.
ISBN 0920722245 Hbk £94.00

Canadian Company Law : Cases, Notes and Materials / Bruce Welling. – 3rd ed. – Butterworths, 1986.
640p.
Examines and discusses the main areas of company law in a sequential manner, making use of Canadian, American and Australian authorities. Covers new statutory developments, the corporate constitution, corporate entity, company liability, management, capital structure, and distributions.
ISBN 0409805106 Pbk £70.00

Canadian Competition Law. – Vancouver : British Columbia Continuing Legal Education Society, 1984.
341p.
ISBN 0865041555 Hbk £70.00

Canadian conflict of laws / J.-G. Castel. – 2nd ed. – Toronto : Butterworths, 1986.
clxvi,652p.
Includes bibliographical references and index.
ISBN 0409821284 Hbk £125

Canadian Constitution 1981 : a resolution adopted by the Parliament of Canada, December 1981. – Ottawa : Government of Canada, 1981.
vi,28,28,vip.
Accompanied by summary 'Highlights' pamphlet. Added t.p. in French: La constitution canadienne 1981: resolution adoptee par le Parlement du Canada en decembre 1981. Pages numbered in opposite directions. Text in English and French.
ISBN 0662516923

Canadian Constitution and the Courts : the Function and Scope of Judicial Review. – 3rd ed. – Butterworths, 1988.
400p.
New edition includes coverage of the major increase in the number of cases involving constitutional issues, the dominance of Charter questions in constitutional litigation, and the greatly heightened profile of the Supreme Court of Canada as innovating leader in the interpretation of the new constitutional provisions. Also notes early trends in judicial activism, or restraint, in Charter interpretation.
ISBN 0409806315 Hbk £80.00

Canadian Constitutional Law / W R Lederman. – 3rd ed. – Toronto : Butterworths, 1987.
ISBN 0409876046 Hbk
ISBN 0409876054 Pbk

Canadian Constitutional Law Handbook : Leading Statements, Principles and Precedents. – Aurora : Canada Law Book Co, 1985.
1182p. – (Text Books-Civil).
Hbk £195.00

Canadian Cooperative Credit Society Ltd.
Canadian Credit Union Law : a Detailed Survey. – Canadian Cooperative Credit Society Ltd. – Don Mills : CCH Canadian Ltd, 1987.
316p.
ISBN 0887964362 Pbk £29.95

Canadian coroner law : a legal study of coroner and medical examiner systems in Canada / by Christopher Granger. – Toronto, Canada : Carswell, 1984.
xxi, 418 p.; 24 cm.
Includes bibliographical references and indexes.
ISBN 045936460X

Canadian Corporation Precedents. – 3rd ed. – Agincourt : Carswell, 1987.
440p.
This third edition text provides corporation and securities law precedents. Sample forms utilized from incorporation to dissolution are included. Information pertaining to both private and public corporations are included. Additionally, selected forms and precedents have commentaries analyzing the legal history.
Hbk £75.75

Canadian Council on International Law : Conference Proceedings
10: International Law and the Practice of Law in Canada /. – Ottawa : Canadian Council on International Law, 1981.
£10.00
11: Communications and Information : International Legal Aspects. – 1982.
£12.00
13: Peaceful Settlement of Disputes. – 1984.
£15.00

Canadian Council on Social Development → Victims and witnesses of crime in Canada.

Canadian Credit Union Law : a Detailed Survey. – Canadian Cooperative Credit Society Ltd. – Don Mills : CCH Canadian Ltd, 1987.
316p.
ISBN 0887964362 Pbk £29.95

Canadian Criminal Cases : Index, Annotations, Table of Cases
Vols. 1-14 of Third Series. – Aurora : Canada Law Book Co, 1985.
– (Law Reports).
Pbk £25.50
Vols. 1-26. – 1985.
– (Third Ser.).
Vols. 1-20. –
Hbk £55.00
Vols. 1-70 of Second Series. – 1983.
1184p. – (Law Reports).
Hbk £98.50

Canadian Criminal Cases : New Series (1963-1970), 30 Vols. – North Ryde : Law Book Co.
Hbk £1,080.00

Canadian Criminal Cases : Second Series (1971-1983), 70 Vols. – North Ryde : Law Book Co.
Hbk £2,520.00 set
Vols. 1-70 Index, Annotations, Table of Cases. – 1983.
1,184p.
Hbk £98.50

Canadian Criminal Cases : Third Series (March, 1983-Present). – North Ryde : Law Book Co.
Hbk £85.00 full service
Vols. 1-27, index, Annotations, Table of Cases. – 1987.
Pbk £55.00
Vols. 1-34, Index, Annotations, Table of Cases. – 1988.
Hbk £55.00

Canadian Criminal Cases (C.C.C.) 1898-1962, 133 Vols. – Aurora : Canada Law Book Co.
– (Old Ser.).
Hbk £3857.00
Back Vols.. –
Hbk £29.00 each

Canadian Criminal Cases (C.C.C.) 1963-70, 30 Vols. – Aurora : Canada Law Book Co.
– (New Ser.).
Hbk £930.00
Back Vols.. –
Hbk £34.00 ea.

Canadian Criminal Cases (C.C.C.) 1971-83, 70 Vols. – Aurora : Canada Law Book Co.
– (Second Ser.).
Hbk £2380.00
Back Vols.. –
Hbk £34.00

Canadian Criminal Cases (C.C.C.) March 1983-Present. – Aurora : Canada Law Book Co.
– (Third Ser.).
Hbk £83.00
Current subscription-Outside Canada. –
Hbk £78.00
First 5 Back Vols.. –
Hbk £63.00 each
More Than 6 Back Vols.. –
£41.00

Canadian Criminal Cases New Series (1963-1970), 30 Vols. – Aurora : Canada Law Book Co.
– (Law Reports).
Hbk £102.00
Back Vols.. –
Hbk £34.00 ea.

Canadian Criminal Cases Old Series (1898-1962), 133 Vols. – Aurora : Canada Law Book Co.
– (Law Reports).
Hbk £4522.00
Back vols.. –
Hbk £34.00 ea.

Canadian Criminal Cases Second Series (1971-1983), 70 Vols. – Aurora : Canada Law Book Co.
– (Law Reports).
Hbk £2380.00
Back Vols.. –
Hbk £34.00 ea.

Canadian Criminal Cases Third Series (March 1983-Present). – Aurora : Canada Law Book Co.
– (Law Reports).
Hbk £78.00
Bound Vol.. –
Hbk £63.00

Canadian Criminal Code Offences, 1 vol. – Agincourt : Carswell, 1986.
ca 350p.
This handbook for the Canadian practitioner presents the fifty most commonly charged Criminal Code offenses in forty-seven chapters. A checklist of all facts that must be proved by the prosecution and a summary of the key features of the offense is included in each chapter.
Hbk £71.50

Canadian criminal evidence / by Peter K. McWilliams. – 2nd ed. – Aurora : Canada Law Book, 1984.
cxlii,1131p.
Previous ed.: 1974. Includes index.
ISBN 0888040180

Canadian Criminal Justice History. – University of Toronto, 1988.
ISBN 0802057209 Hbk £45.00

Canadian criminal justice system / Craig L. Boydell, Ingrid Arnet Connidis. – Canada : Holt, Rinehart and Winston, 1982.
311p.
Includes bibliographies.
ISBN 003920278X

Canadian criminal law : a treatise / by Don Stuart. – Toronto : Carswell, 1982.
liii,602p.
Bibliography: p.x - Includes index.
ISBN 0459348000

Canadian criminal law : cases and comments / by Douglas A. Schmeiser. – 5th ed. – Toronto : Butterworths, 1985.
848.
Previous ed.: published as 'Criminal law', 1977. Incorporates recent Supreme Court decisions on such topics as criminal and transferres intent, mistake of law, necessity, insanity, drunkeness, autrfois convict and autrefois acquit, issue estoppel, Crown liability, police powers, excessive force and attempt. Contains a detailed index.
ISBN 0409865389 Pbk

Canadian criminal law, international and transnational aspects / Sharon A. Williams, J.-G. Castel. – Toronto : Butterworths, 1981.
xxx, 513 p.; 24 cm.
Includes bibliographical references and indexes. Part one is devoted to jurisdiction and the criminal law under international law and Canadian law. Part two deals with Canadian law applicable to specific offences of an international and transnational nature. Part three covers international cooperation in the field of criminal law and criminal procedure.
ISBN 0409876348 £80.00

Canadian criminal procedure. – 4th ed. – Aurora, Ont. : Canada Law Book, 1984.
cv,610p.
Includes index. Latest supplement held: 2nd, 1986.
ISBN 0888040202

Canadian criminal procedure : cases, notes and materials / Vincent M. Del Buono. – Toronto : Butterworths, 1981.
xxx,929p.
Includes index.
ISBN 0409824801

Canadian Current Law. – Agincourt : Carswell, 1987.
Hbk £273.00
Issues and Index from 1985, 4 Vols.. –
Hbk £134.50
Issues and Index from 1984, 4 Vols.. –
Hbk £117.75
Issues and Index from 1983, 3 Vols.. –
Hbk £96.75

Canadian Current Tax, 1 Vol. – Butterworths.
Llf £175.00

Canadian Customs and Excise Reports Vols. 1-6. – Toronto : Butterworths.
ISBN 0409858129 £110.00
Looseleaf Vol.. –
ISBN 0409858110 Pbk £55.00
Back Vol. of Case Reports, Vol. 8. –
ISBN 0409857599 Hbk £40.00
Editorial Commentary Binder to Vols. 1-6. –
ISBN 0409811823 Hbk £15.00
Bound Vol. 1. –
ISBN 0409858137 Hbk £40.00
Bound Vol. 2. –
ISBN 0409858188 Hbk £40.00
Bound Vol. 3. –
ISBN 0409858234 Hbk £40.00
Bound Vol. 4. –
ISBN 0409858285 Hbk £40.00
Bound Vol. 5. –
ISBN 0409859079 Hbk £40.00
Bound Vol. 6. –
ISBN 0409859036 Hbk £40.00
Bound Vo7. 7. –
ISBN 0409857572 Hbk £40.00
Cumulative Index Vols. 1-7. –
ISBN 0409810444 Hbk £27.95

Canadian Customs and Excise Reports / Grant A. Jameson. – Butterworths.
Llf £150.00

Canadian Dental Law. – Butterworths, 1987.
152p.
ISBN 0409863351 Hbk £40.00

Canadian Directory of Public Legal Education and Information
British Columbia. – Ottawa : Canadian Law Information Council.
ISBN 0662104544 Hbk £5.00
National. –
ISBN 0662104536 Hbk £5.00
Ontario. –
ISBN 0662104587 Hbk £5.00
P.E.I.. –
ISBN 0662104609 Hbk £3.00
Quebec. –
ISBN 0662902726 Hbk £5.00

Canadian divorce law and practice / Lee K. Ferrier. – 2nd ed. – Toronto : Carswell, 1986.
Includes text of Divorce Act 1985.
ISBN 0459389505 Llf

Canadian Electricity Exports : Legal and Regulatory Issues / J. Owen Saunders. – Calgary : Canadian Institute of Resources Law.
40p.
Hbk £9.50

Canadian Encyclopedic Digest : Ontario, 38 Vols. – Carswell Legal Publications. – 3rd ed. – Agincourt : Carswell.
This set of volumes provides the provincial laws of Ontario and federal laws of Canada as derived from statutes and case law. The 150 subject titles contains an in-depth table of classifications and an index and tables of cases and statutes. A Research Guide and Key and The Legal Deskbook are also included.
Llf £2352.00

Canadian encyclopedic digest (Western) : being a complete digest on the encyclopedic plan of all reported decisions in Alberta, British Columbia, Manitoba, Saskatchewan and appealed therefrom. – 2nd ed. – Calgary : Burroughs, 1956-.
Gradually superseded by 3rd ed. - Those Titles not yet superseded kept up to date by supplements. Set includes: First permanent supplement 1969, Second permanent supplement 1976.

Canadian Environmental Law, 7 Vols. / Alastair R. Lucas. – Scarborough, Ontario : Butterworths (Canada).
Hbk £475.00 (partial)

Canadian Environmental Law Reports. – Agincourt : Carswell.
Hbk £74.00

Canadian Environmental Law Research Foundation →Environmental rights in Canada.

Canadian Family Law Cases 1983 Supplement. – Toronto : Butterworths, 1983.
ISBN 0409989967 Hbk £40.00

Canadian Family Law Cases : 1959-1977. – Toronto : Butterworths.
420p.
ISBN 0409989916 Pbk £60.00
Suppl. 1980. –
ISBN 0409989940 Pbk £40.00

Canadian Farm Law. – Saskatoon : Western Producer Prairie Books, 1982.
145p.
ISBN 0888330871 Pbk £8.95

Canadian Federal-Provincial Task Force on Justice for Victims of Crime report : highlights. – Ottawa : Solicitor General Canada, 1983.
35,29p.
With French t.p.: Rapport du Groupe d'Etude Federal-Provincial Canadien sur la Justice pour les Victimes d'Actes Criminels: points saillants. English and French text.
ISBN 0662526007

Canadian financial institutions : changing the regulatory environment / edited by Jacob Ziegel, Leonard Waverman, David W. Conklin. – Toronto : Ontario Economic Council, 1985.
viii,474p. – (Special research report).
Based on ' ... a conference entitled the Changing Regulatory Environment for Canadian Financial Institutions held 22-23 May 1985 at the Sutton Place Hotel, Toronto, Ontario'. - Foreword. Includes bibliographical references.
ISBN 0772909563

Canadian Firearms Law. – Butterworths, 1988.
152p.
Guidance on all aspects of the criminal and civil law relating to gun use and misuse in Canada. Provides an outline of history and purpose of current legislation, and analysis of current legislation and all relevant case law, a discussion of various types of certificates and permits required, contains a step by step procedure to be followed upon, and discussion of the law governing, refusal or revocation of certificates and permits.
ISBN 0409806455 Hbk £42.50

Canadian forms of wills / Rodney Hull, Michael M. K. Fitzpatrick. – 4th ed. – Toronto : Carswell, 1982.
lxix,333p.
Previous ed.: 1970. Bibliography: p.293. - Includes index.
ISBN 0459347004

Canadian Franchise Guide / Zaid. – Toronto : DeBoo.
Designed for franchisees, franchisors, and their professional advisors, this all-Canadian service discusses legal and tax considerations, current and future trends, marketing and financial planning strategies, and contains a selection of forms and agreements. Monthly updates are also provided.
ISBN 0888201397 Llf £275.00

Canadian Guide to Uniform Legal Citation. – McGill Law Journal. – 2nd ed. – Agincourt : Carswell, 1988.
288p.
Hbk £25.25

Canadian Human Rights Commission
Brief to the Legislative Committee considering Bill C-62 : an Act respecting employment equity / Canadian Human Rights Commission. – Ottawa : Minister of Supply and Services, 1986.
12,14p.
Added t.p. in French. Cover title: Employment equity. Text in English and French.
ISBN 0662541804
→ Unwanted sexual attention and sexual harassment : results of a survey of Canadians.

Canadian Human Rights Yearbook 1986. – Agincourt : Carswell, 1986.
308p.
Hbk £66.00

Canadian Human Rights Yearbook / Daniel Proulx. – Agincourt : Carswell, 1987.
308p.
Hbk £48.75

Canadian immigration law and procedure / Christopher J. Wydrzynski. – Aurora, Ont. : Canada Law Book, 1983.
xli,511p.
Includes index.
ISBN 0888040156

Canadian income taxation. – 4th ed. – Toronto : Butterworths, 1986.
xxv,776p.
Previous ed.: 1983. Includes index.
ISBN 0409805149

Canadian Industrial Incentives Legislation, 2 Vols. / Janice A. Lacke. – Scarborough, Ontario : Butterworths (Canada).
Llf £150.00

Canadian Institute for Advanced Legal Studies
Cambridge lectures 1981 : selected papers based upon lectures delivered at the Conference of the Canadian Institute for Advanced Legal Studies, 1981, held at Cambridge University, England ... / edited by Nancy E. Eastham and Boris Krivy. – Toronto : Butterworths, 1982.
xix,433p.
Includes bibliographical references.
ISBN 040984392X Hbk £45.00
—Cambridge lectures 1983 : selected papers based upon lectures at the Conference of the Canadian Institute for Advanced Legal Studies, 1983, held at Cambridge University, England / edited by Elizabeth G. Baldwin. – Toronto : Butterworths, 1985.
xvi,341p.
Includes bibliographical references.
ISBN 0409810320

Canadian Institute for Research →Matrimonial support failures : reasons, profiles and perceptions of individuals involved.

Canadian Institute of Resource Law
Canada Energy Law Service, 3 Vols. – Canadian Institute of Resource Law. – Toronto : DeBoo, 1984.
This looseleaf service monitors the decisions of those tribunals which regulate Canada's energy resources. Included are commentaries, case digests, and legislation. Six updates per year are planned.
ISBN 0888201087 Hbk £650.00

Canadian Institute of Resources Law →Canadian Regulation of Offshore Installations.

Canadian Insurance Law Review. – Agincourt : Carswell, 1988.
360p.
Hbk £69.50

Canadian Intellectual Property Reports. – Agincourt : Carswell, 1987.
This reference text contains the key decisions in the intellectual property law area. Topics include copyrights, industrial designs, patents of invention, and trademarks.
Hbk £102.50

Canadian journal of law and jurisprudence. – London, Ont. : Faculty of Law, University of Western Ontario, 1988-.
Continues: University of Western Ontario law review.

Canadian labour arbitration / David M. Beatty. – 2nd ed. – Aurora, Ont. : Canada Law Book Ltd., 1984.
clxxiv,723p.
Previous ed.: 1977. Includes index.
ISBN 0888040199

Canadian labour law : a comprehensive text / George W. Adams. – Aurora, Ont. : Canada Law Book Inc., 1985.
cii,983p.
Includes index.
ISBN 088804030X

Canadian Labour Relations Board Reports. – Labour Relations Board of British Columbia. – Butterworths.
Hbk £115.00

Canadian law faculties : a report to the Consultative Group on Research and Education in Law based on the 1981 survey of Canadian law faculties and statistics of the Canadian deans of law / John S. McKennirey. – Ottawa : Consultative Group on Research and Education in Law, 1982.
149p.

Canadian Law Information Council
Annual report / Canadian Law Information Council. – Canadian Law Information Council. – Ottawa : CLIC, 1982-.
Annual reports for 1978/1979 and 1979/1980 published as one volume entitled: Yesterday, today and tomorrow : 1978-1980 / Canadian Law Information Council. Annual report for 1980/1981 entitled: Progress through partnership : 1980/1981 / Canadian Law Information Council.

→ Chart of Privy Council decisions with reference to the British North America Act.

→ Comparison of automated and manual legal research : a computer study.

→ Guide to purchasing law reports.

—Progress through partnership : 1980/1981 / Canadian Law Information Council. – Ottawa : CLIC, 1981-.
36p.
Annual reports for 1978/1979 and 1979/1980 published as one volume entitled: Yesterday, today and tomorrow : 1978-1980 / Canadian Law Information Council. Continued by: Annual report / Canadian Law Information Council, 1981/1982 onwards. Includes annual report of CLIC for 1980/1981.

Canadian Law List. – Aurora : Canada Law Book Co.
1882p.
Hbk £63.50
For 1987 Edition Only. –
This volume lists all lawyers in Canada by province, municipality and firm. A special section listing lawyers alphabetically with firm association and location is also provided. Listings are also included for all Canadian Courts, judges, cabinets, departments, ministries, boards, crown corporations, legal aid offices and others, on a province by province basis.
Hbk £68.50

Canadian Law of Architecture and Engineering / Wilfred J. Wallace. – Butterworths, 1987.
544p.
Coverage includes contract and tort, claims avoidance, liability insurance, copyright and patents, and remuneration. Collection of form contracts, municipal forms, and explanatory notes. Canadian statutes and cases provide the focus of the study, but the laws of other jurisdictions, notably England are included. Analyses the civil law of Quebec.
ISBN 0409804819 Hbk £100.00

Canadian Law of Consent to Treatment / Fay A. Rozovsky. – Butterworths, 1988.
ca 288p.
Deals with specific medico-legal consent problems such as consent relating to the treatment of children, prisoners and the mentally handicapped. Details circumstances in which consent may be waived, examines the essential elements of consent litigation, discusses how to prevent consent litigation and includes a special section on documenting consent.
ISBN 0409806307 Hbk £70.00

Canadian Law of Patient Records / Rozovsky. – London : Butterworths.
ISBN 0409862886 Hbk £24.00

Canadian Law of Planning and Zoning, 1 Vol. – Agincourt : Carswell.
318p.
This looseleaf service covers every aspect of land use in Canada including: master plans, non-conforming uses, building construction permits, enforcement, appeals, and remedies. The work contains the text of planning legislation from all provinces.
Llf £113.50

Canadian law of wills / Thomas G. Feeney. – 3rd ed. – Toronto : Butterworths, 1987.
Volume 1 focuses on probate, containing new material on the support of dependants, the administration of settled estates, holograph wills and intestate succession. Volume 2 considers the rules affecting construction in relation to recent probate changes.
ISBN 0409810002 Hbk £140.00

Canadian law professors : a report to the Consultative Group on Research and Education in Law based on the 1981 survey of full-time law professors in Canada / John S. McKennirey. – Ottawa : Consultative Group on Research and Education in Law, 1982.
viii,133p.

Canadian law professors : a staff report on the survey of full-time law professors in Canada / submitted to the Consultative Group on Research and Education in Law by John S. McKennirey. – Ottawa : Social Sciences and Humanities Research Council of Canada, 1982.
vi,51,92 leaves.

Canadian law reports and statutes held by the Faculty of Law Library, University of the West Indies, Cave Hill, Barbados / S.G. Moss : with the assistance of Waveney Webster. – Cave Hill, Barbados : University of the West Indies, Faculty of Law Library, 1986.
42p.

Canadian Law Trade Marks and Unfair Competition. – 3rd ed. – Agincourt : Carswell, 1972.
ISBN 045931170 Hbk £59.40

Canadian legal materials in microform / compiled by Meena Nadkarni. – Downsview, Ont. : York University Law Library in co-operation with the Canadian Association of Law Libraries, 1981.
Llf

Canadian legal system / Gerald L. Gall. – 2nd ed. – Toronto : Carswell, 1983.
xxiv, 348 p.; 24 cm.
'With Chapter 8, The Quebec legal system, by Mr. Justice Paul Reeves of the Quebec Superior Court.'. Includes bibliographical references and index.
ISBN 0459358103 Pbk

Canadian Libel Practice / David Potts. – London : Butterworths.
ISBN 0409860891 Hbk £56.00

Canadian Maritime Law and the Offshore : a Primer. – Calgary : Canadian Institute of Resources Law.
65p.
Hbk £13.00

Canadian Market Place : a Consumer Rights Handbook / Patricia McNeill. – Toronto : Canadian Broadcasting Corporation Enterprises.
160p.
ISBN 0887941192 Pbk £5.95

Canadian Master Labour Guide. – 3rd ed. – Don Mills : CCH Canadian Ltd, 1988.
780p.
ISBN 088796429X Pbk £18.95
ISBN 0887964303 Hbk £21.50

Canadian Mining Law. – London : Butterworths.
ISBN 0409802794 Hbk £132.00

Canadian Mining Taxation. – London : Butterworths.
ISBN 0409859445 Hbk £24.00

Canadian mining taxation / Robert B. Parsons. – Toronto : Butterworths, 1982.
x,253p.
ISBN 0409859745

Canadian Mortgage Practice Reporter / Bernard Gershman. – Toronto : DeBoo.
ISBN 0888200870 Llf £375.00

Canadian Multinationals / Maule. – London : Butterworths.
ISBN 0409845256 Hbk £16.00

Canadian Municipal and Planning Law. – Agincourt : Carswell, 1983.
358p.
This work examines the structure, organization, and authority of local government in Canada. Municipal finance, zoning, land use control and development control, municipal planning process, and other related issues are discussed in the book.
Hbk £46.25

Canadian National Exhibition Association Act, 1983, Bill Pr017 : An Act Respecting the Canadian National Exhibition Association. – Ontario : Ontario Government Publications Service, 1983.
9p.
Hbk £0.50

Canadian Native Law Cases
Vol. 2 1870-1890 /. – Saskatoon : University of Saskatchewan, Native Law Centre, 1981.
634p.
ISBN 0888801068 Hbk £65.00
Vol. 3 1891-1910. – 1985.
663p.
ISBN 0888801467 Hbk £65.00
Vol. 4 1911-1930. – 1986.
491p.
ISBN 0888801734 Hbk £65.00
Vol. 5 1931-1959. – 1987.
691p.
ISBN 0888801750 Hbk £70.00
Vol. 6 1960-1970. – 1988.
781p.
ISBN 0888801947 Hbk £70.00
Vol. 7 1971-1973. – 1988.
550p.
ISBN 0888802110 Hbk £70.00

Canadian official publications / Olga B. Bishop. – Oxford : Pergamon, 1981.
ix,297p.
ISBN 0080246974

Canadian Oil and Gas, 9 Vols. / Andrew R. Thompson. – Butterworths.
Llf £265.00

Canadian Parliamentary Digest. – Agincourt : Carswell, 1987.
Hbk £357.00

Canadian Patent Reporter First Series (1942-1971) 65 Vols. – Aurora : Canada Law Book Co.
– (Law Reports).
Hbk £2925.00
Back Vols.. –
Hbk £45.00 ea.

Canadian Patent Reporter Second Series (1971-1984), 82 Vols. – Aurora : Canada Law Book Co.
– (Law Reports).
Hbk £3690.00
Back Vols.. –
Hbk £45.00 ea.

Canadian Patent Reporter Second Series : Table of Cases
Vols. 1-82. – Aurora : Canada Law Book Co.
– (Law Reports).
Hbk £50.00

Canadian Patent Reporter Third Series (1985-Present). – Aurora : Canada Law Book Co.
– (Law Reports).
Hbk £190.00
Back Vols.. –
Hbk £175.00 ea.

Canadian Patent Reporter: 1985. – Aurora : Canada Law Book Co, 1985.
– (Third Ser.).
Hbk £195.00
Back Vols.. –
Hbk £1st five copies 180.00

Canadian Police College → Community policing in the 1980's : recent advances in police programs.

Canadian Prison Law, 3 Vols. – Butterworths.
Llf £235.00

Canadian Private Security Manual / Robert J. Prouse. – Agincourt : Carswell, 1987.
352p.
This work for Canadian private security officers discusses the question of security for emergency situations, investigational procedures, and surveillance in depth.
Hbk £33.75

Canadian R & D incentives : their adequacy and impact / Donald G. McFetridge, Jacek P. Warda. – Toronto, Canada : Canadian Tax Foundation, 1983.
vii, 100 p.; 23 cm.
Includes index. Bibliography: p. 93-97.
ISBN 0888080131 Pbk £10.00

Canadian Regulation of International Trade and Investment. – Agincourt : Carswell, 1986.
470p.
This work describes and analyzes international conventions and domestic legislation that regulate Canadian world trade. International barriers to foreign investment and the new domestic laws that embody the flexible Canadian approach to the issues are discussed in the book.
Hbk £67.25

Canadian Regulation of Offshore Installations. – Calgary : Canadian Institute of Resources Law.
116p.
ISBN 0919269184 Hbk £17.00

Canadian Regulatory Agencies. – Toronto : Butterworths, 1981.
288p.
ISBN 0409816302 Pbk £21.95

Canadian Reports Appeal Cases : 1807-1913, 24 Vols. – Carswell Legal Publications. – Agincourt : Carswell, 1983.

Canadian Rights Reporter. – Butterworths.
Hbk £95.00

Canadian Securities Regulation. – Butterworths, 1977.
528p.
ISBN 0409841226 Hbk £95.00
Supplement-1983. –
80p.
ISBN 0409841218 £15.00

Canadian Sentencing Commission
Sentencing reform : a Canadian approach / report of the Canadian Sentencing Commission. – Ottawa : Minister of Supply and Services, 1986.
xl,592p.
Bibliography: pp.575-592. Chairman: J. R. Omer Archambault.
ISBN 0660122456

—Sentencing reform : a Canadian approach : summary / report of the Canadian Sentencing Commission. – Ottawa : Minister of Supply and Services, 1987.
34,37p.
French title on added t.p.: Reformer la sentence. Pages numbered in opposite directions. Text in English and French.
ISBN 0662550757

Canadian Sentencing Digest : Quantam Service, 2 Vols. / Clarey B. Sproule. – Agincourt : Carswell, 1981.
This looseleaf service digest all Canadian cases an quantum of sentence from 1970 to the present. The work is organized by statute and section.
Llf £214.25

Canadian Tax Foundation → Federal finance in comparative perspective.

→ Income tax considerations in corporate financing.

→ Selected income tax aspects of the purchase and sale of a business : Corporate Management Tax Confetence 1984.

→ Tax policy options in the 1980s.

Canadian Tax News. – Agincourt : Carswell, 1987.
Hbk £105.00

Canadian tax policy / Robin W. Boadway, Harry M. Kitchen. – 2nd ed. – Toronto : Canadian Tax Foundation, 1984.
xvi,390p.
Includes bibliographical references and index.
ISBN 0888080212

Canadian Tax Treaties, 2 vols. – Toronto : Butterworths.
Hbk

Canadian Taxation. – Toronto : DeBoo, 1981.
ISBN 0888201001 Hbk £39.95

Canadian Taxpayer. – Toronto : DeBoo, 1984.
ISBN 0888201680 Hbk 210.00

Canadian Telecommunications Regulation Bibliography. – Ottawa : Canadian Law Information Council.
ISBN 0921481063 £25.00

Canadian tort law / Allen M. Linden. – 4th. – Toronto : Butterworths, 1988.
840.
Includes bibliographical references and index. Earlier eds. published as Canadian negligence law. Examines the theoretical foundation of tort law, together with its practical application in the Canadian litigation arena. Contains a new chapter on statute and negligence, a discussion and new material on liability for economic losses, an analysis of the new judicial approach to limitations periods and torts, and a commentary on new privileges developing in the area of libel law.
ISBN 0409801917 Hbk

Canadian Tort Law. – 3rd ed. – London : Butterworths.
ISBN 0409845779 Hbk £68.00

Canadian Tort Law. – 4th ed. – London : Butterworths.
ISBN 0409801917 Hbk £100.00

Canadian Tort Law / Allen M. Linden. – 8th ed. – Butterworths, 1985.
1,072p.
Contains two new chapters on liability for negligent statements, and tort liability of public officials and bodies. The chapter on occupier's liability has been expanded, and the text also includes excerpts from law journals, treaties, and government documents, and review questions.
ISBN 0409845612 Pbk £75.00

Canadian Trademarks Act Annotated. – Toronto : DeBoo, 1984.
This volume covers the practice, procedure, and legislation of Canadian trade mark law. Practice notes from the Trade Marks Journal, references to the Trade Marks Examination Manual, and a list of 'confusing' and 'non-confusing' trademarks are included in the work.
ISBN 0888201583 Hbk £135.00

Canadian Transport Cases (1966-1977), 7 Vols. – Aurora : Canada Law Book Co. – (Law Reports).
Hbk £232.00

Canadian Transport Cases : 1966-77, 7 Vols. – Aurora : Canada Law Book Co. – (Earlier Series Entitled Canadian Railway and Transport Cases).
Hbk £232.00
Index (Vols. 50-85) of the Earlier Series. – Hbk £18.00

Canadian Weekly Law Sheet, 1 Vol. – Butterworths.
Llf £210.00

Canadian Weekly Law Sheet. – Toronto : Butterworths.
Hbk

Canadian Yearbook of International Law. – Witney : Academic & University Publishing Group.
ISBN 0774803037 Hbk £48.00

Canadian Yearbook of International Law : 1963-1973, 11 Vols. – Abingdon : Professional Books, 1984.
Hbk

Canadian Yearbook of International Law - Annuaire Canadien de Droit International Vol. 1. – Vancouver : University of British Columbia Press.
Vol. 24. – 1987.
488p.
ISBN 0774802812 Hbk £48.00

Vol. 25. – 1987.
580p.
ISBN 0774803037 Hbk £60.00

Canagarayar, J. K.
Diversion of traffic offenders / by J.K. Canagarayar : with a foreword by J.W. Mohr. – Singapore : Malayan Law Journal, 1981.
xi,229p; 22cm.
Analyses the role of diversion, the directions it should take, its limitations, and whether there is a need to develop identifiable uniform principles and guidelines during the different stages of diversion. Contains examples of various experiments and pilot projects.
ISBN 9971700158 £12.50

Canberra College of Advanced Education → Aboriginal land rights legislation : an examination of the publications associated with Commonwealth legislation.

Cancellation and nullity of trademarks in Colombia / German Cavelier. – Bogota, Colombia : Cavelier Abogados, 1986.
xii,235p.

Cane, Leon
Company flotations : tax and tax planning. – Butterworths, 1985.
An overall guide to the tax consdierations for UK companies both before and during a public sale. Tax planning for major shareholders and officers is treated in detail. A timetable for flotation is included in the appendix.
ISBN 0406259704 Pbk £20
—Guide to company law. – 2nd ed. – Bicester : CCH Editions, 1987.
307p; 23cm.
Explains the basic principles, alerts the leader to potential pitfalls, and provides solutions to frequently encountered problems. Case examples help to illustrate the commentary, appendices include the new Table A, and relevant schedules showing the prescribed format for company accounts, case table, legislation finding list, and comprehensive index.
ISBN 0863250955 Pbk

Cane, Peter → Atiyah's accidents, compensation and the law.
—Introduction to administrative law / Peter Cane. – Oxford : Clarendon, 1986.
xxii,325p; 23cm. – (Clarendon law series).
Includes index.
ISBN 0198254849 Hbk £22.50
ISBN 0198254857 Pbk £ 9.50
→ Law of torts in Australia.

Canenbley, Cornelis
Enforcing antitrust against foreign enterprises : procedural problems in the extraterritorial application of antitrust laws / general rapporteur, Cornelis Canenbley, with the assistance of Amanda Dalton. – Deventer, Netherlands : Kluwer, 1981.
xiii,125p.
'Report submitted to Committee C–Antitrust Law and Monopolies during the IBA Berlin Conference, August 1980.'.
ISBN 9065440143

Caney, L. R.
Caney's the law of suretyship in Africa / C. F. Forsyth. – 3rd ed. – Cape Town : Juta, 1982.
xxi,206p.
Previous ed.: 1970. Bibliography: p.xi-xii. - Includes index.
ISBN 0702113417

Caney's the law of suretyship in Africa / C. F. Forsyth. – 3rd ed. – Cape Town : Juta, 1982.
xxi,206p.
Previous ed.: 1970. Bibliography: p.xi-xii. - Includes index.
ISBN 0702113417

Cannar, Kenneth S
Essential cases in insurance law / Kenneth Cannar. – Cambridge : Woodhead-Faulkner, 1985.
240p.
ISBN 0859412849 £25.00
→ Insurance law reports.
—Liability Insurance Claims. – Witherby, 1983.
ISBN 0900886803 Hbk £28.00

Cannibalism and the common law. – University of Chicago Press, 1984.
ISBN 0226759423 Hbk £21.25

Cannon, P.
Tolley's Stamp Duties. – 3rd ed. – Tolly Publishing.
ISBN 0854593683 Hbk £9.95

Canon law and English common law / by R. H. Helmholz. – London : Selden Society, 1983.
24 p.
'Selden Society lecture delivered in the Old Hall of Lincoln's Inn, July 5th, 1982'.

Canon Law Society
Code of Canon Law. – Canon Law Society. – Oxford : Collins, 1983.
Pbk £4.95

Canons of the Church of England : Canons Ecclesiastical promulgated by the Convocations of Canterbury and York in 1964 and 1969 and by the General Synod of the Church of England from 1970. – Church of England. – 4th ed. 1 v. – London : Church House Publishing, 1986.
looseleaf.
ISBN 0715137115

Capewell, Stuart D.
Operation and management of protection and indemnity clubs / Stuart D. Capewell. – London : Insurance Institute of London, 1983.
81 leaves.
Bibliography: 1.61-64.

Capital acquisitions tax / by Norman Bale & John Condon. – Dublin : Institute of Taxation in Ireland, 1982.
244p.
Includes index.

Capital Allowances 1987-88. – Tolley Publishing.
ISBN 0854593055 Hbk £15.95

Capital allowances / by John W. Shock. – 2nd ed. – London : Sweet & Maxwell, 1984.
xxxiii,371p; 25cm.
Previous ed.: London : Oyez, 1981. Includes index.
ISBN 0421328207 Pbk £16.95

Capital Allowances. – London : Oyez Longman, 1980. Includes December 1982 supplement.
ISBN 0851204864 Hbk £25.00

Capital allowances in law and practice / R. J. Pickerill. – 2nd ed. – London : Institute of Chartered Accountants, 1981.
xix,307p. – (Chartac taxation guides).
ISBN 0852913079

Capital Changes Of Quoted Shares and Securities 1986-87. – Tolley Publishing.
ISBN 0854593039 Hbk £20.00

Capital city : London as a financial centre / Hamish McRae and Frances Cairncross. – New and fully rev. ed. – London : Methuen, 1984.
264p; 23cm.
Previous ed.: 1973. Includes index.
ISBN 0413511200 Hbk £8.95
ISBN 041357900X Pbk £3.95

Capital dividends / report of the Property Law and Equity Reform Committee. – Wellington? : the Committee?, 1984.
8,13p,1 leaf,2p.

Capital Gains Tax
1986 Supplement. – Pitman.
1988-89. –
ISBN 0854593489 Pbk £15.95

Supplement 1987. –
ISBN 042138980X Pbk £21.00

Capital Gains Tax. – 5th ed. – Plymouth : Macdonald & Evans, 1981.
ISBN 0712104607 Pbk £4.95

Capital Gains Tax. – London : Butterworths, 1981.
Service to Date.
ISBN 0406538824 Llf £80.00

Capital Gains Tax / Giles Clarke. – London : Butterworths, 1981.
Llf

Capital gains tax / by Anthony Sumption. – London : Butterworths, 1981.
ISBN 0406538824

Capital Gains Tax Guide. – Butterworths. – London : Butterworths.
ISBN 0406513600 Pbk £17.95

Capital Gains Tax on Business
Supplement only. – London : Sweet & Maxwell.
ISBN 0421310405 Hbk £3.50

Capital Gains Tax On Businesses / Harry J Ross. – 2nd ed. – Sweet & Maxwell, 1986.
ISBN 0421339608 Hbk £21.00

Capital gains tax on businesses / by Christopher Cox and Harry J. Ross. – London : Sweet & Maxwell, 1982.
xviii,221p,1folded leaf of plates; 23cm.
Includes index.
ISBN 0421282304 £18.00

Capital gains tax on businesses / by Christopher Cox and Harry J. Ross. – 2nd ed. – London : Sweet & Maxwell, 1986.
xix,231p; 22cm.
Previous ed.: 1982. Includes index.
ISBN 0421339608 Pbk £14.00

Capital Issues (Law and Procedure). – New Delhi : Bharat Law House, 1987.
Hbk £200.00

Capital punishment and the American agenda / Franklin E. Zimring, Gordon Hawkins. – Cambridge : Cambridge University Press, 1987.
xviii,192p; 24cm.
Includes index.
ISBN 0521330335 £20.00

Capital Punishment in India. – New Delhi : Deep and Deep Publications, 1986.
240p.
Hbk £175.00

Capital Taxes. – London : Longman Professional.
ISBN 0851208517 updat £180.00

Capital taxes : a quarterly commentary. – London : Sweet & Maxwell, 1984.
Index in each vol.
ISBN 02659514

Capital Taxes and Estate Planning Guide. – 3rd ed. – London : Longman Professional, 1986.
ISBN 0851212131 Hbk £12.50

Capital Taxes Encyclopaedia / Ian A. Marsh. – London : Butterworths.
This looseleaf service provides detailed coverage of capital transfer tax issues and legislation in the United Kingdom. Legislative developments, court decisions, and changes in practice are updated with six service issues per year.
ISBN 0406505101 Llf £150.00

Capital transfer tax / A.L. Chapman. – 6th ed. – London : Longman, 1985.
xlv,656p; 24cm.
ISBN 0851209335

Capital Transfer Tax. – 2nd ed. – Plymouth : Macdonald & Evans, 1981.
336p. – (M and E Handbook Ser.).
ISBN 0712103929 Hbk £4.95

Capital transfer tax / by Barry D. McCutcheon. – 2nd ed. 2. – London : Sweet & Maxwell, 1984.
26cm.
Previous ed.: published as Understanding and planning for capital transfer tax. Maidenhead : McGraw-Hill, 1980.
ISBN 042131950X £80.00

Capital transfer tax : discretionary trusts : memorandum by the Society's Standing Committee on Revenue Law commenting on draft clauses published by the Inland Revenue. – Law Society. – London : Law Society, 1982.
9p; 30cm.

Capital Transfer Tax Act 1984 / with annotations by Ian Ferrier. – London : Sweet & Maxwell, 1984.
237p.
ISBN 0421339500

Capitalist state : Marxist theories and methods / Bob Jessop. – Oxford : Robertson, 1982.
xvi,296p; 24cm.
Bibliography: p260-281. - Includes index.
ISBN 0855202696 Hbk £17.00
ISBN 0855202688 Pbk £5.95

Capitol Offences. – Toronto : Key Key Porter Books.
208p.
ISBN 1550130048 Hbk £19.95

Caplan, R.L.
Constitutional Brinkmanship Amending the Constitution by National Convention. – Oxford : Oxford University Press.
ISBN 019505573X Hbk £18.50

Caplan, Simon →Tolley's taxation in Gibraltar 1981-82.

Capoor
Commentaries on Prevention of Corruption Act. – Allahabad : Law Publishers, 1983.
Hbk £33.00
—Comments on Prevention of Food Adulteration Act with Central and All State Rules / Seth. – Allahabad : Law Publishers, 1982.
Hbk £40.50

Capotorti, Francesco →European Union treaty : commentary on the draft adopted by the European Parliament on 14 February 1984.

Cappalletti, Mauro
Judicial review in comparative perspective. – Oxford : Clarendon Press, 1989.
300.
Applies the comparative method to the analysis of basic features of the judicial process, and their evolution in modern societies, especially Europe and America.
ISBN 0198256345 Hbk £30.00

Cappelletti →Access to justice and the welfare state.

Cappelletti, Mauro →Access to justice and the welfare state.
—Integration through law : Europe and the American federal experience : a series
Vol. 4: Legal Harmonization and the Business Enterprise. – London : De Gruyter.
ISBN 3110107422 Hbk £20.00
—Judicial review, transnational and federal : its impact on integration / by Mauro Cappelletti and David Golay. – Florence : European University Institute, 1981.
143p.

Capper, David
Mareva injunctions / by David Capper. – London : Sweet & Maxwell, 1988.
xxii,135p; 22cm.
Contains the definition and nature of a Mareva injunction, including matters which must be proved, the procedure for application, orders for the discovery of assets, the writ ne exeat regno, Bayer orders, and Anton Piller orders, and Mareva injunctions and the criminal law. Includes an appendix of precedents.
ISBN 0421389605 Pbk

Capper, P.
Latent Damage Act 1986. – London : LEST, 1987.
ISBN 1852710080 Pbk £28.50

Capper, S.
But is it Legal? : Fundraising and the Law. – London : Bedford Square Press.
ISBN 0719912210 Pbk £4.95

Captive Insurance : A Tax and Financial Analysis. – 2nd ed. – London : Oyez Longman, 1984. – (Oyez Longman Intelligence Report Ser.).
ISBN 085120872X Hbk £65.00

Captive Insurance Companies. – 2nd ed. – Cambridge : Woodhead-Faulkner, 1987.
ISBN 0859413829 Hbk £45.00

Caputi, J.
Age Of Sex Crime. – Women's Press, 1988.
ISBN 0704341166 Pbk £5.95

Car Stealing In Australia : Facts and Figures. – Canberra : Australian Institute of Criminology.
Hbk £1.40

Caramazza, I. F.
Phenomenology of kidnappings in Sardinia : towards an international perspective of a local crime problem / by I.F. Caramazza, U. Leone. – Rome : Fratelli Palombi, 1984.
211p. – (Publication).
Bibliography: p.182-208.
ISBN 8876218270

Carasco, Emily F. →Legal framework for Canada-United States trade.

Carbonneau, T.E.
Resolving Transnational Disputes Through Intern. Arbitration. – London : Eurospan.
ISBN 0813910234 Hbk £26.50

Card →Police law.

Card, Richard →Introduction to criminal law.
—Law for Accountancy Students / Jennifer James. – 3rd ed. – London : Butterworths, 1986.
ISBN 0406708835 Pbk
—Law for Estate Management Students / John R Murdoch, Peter Schofield. – London : Butterworths, 1986.
A review of the basics of United Kingdom law for students of estate management. The English legal system, including elements of constitutional law, contracts, torts, and land law, are outlined in this book.
ISBN 0406562911 Pbk £18.95
—Public order - the new law / Richard Card. – London : Butterworths, 1987.
170p; 25cm.
Includes index.
ISBN 0406504407 Pbk £12.50

Cardinale, H.
Orders of Knighthood, Awards and the Holy See : The Authoritative, Juridical and Practical Compendium. – 3rd ed. – Gerrards Cross : Van Duren, 1985.
336p : Illus.
ISBN 0905715268 Hbk £29.50

Care and discretion : social workers' decisions with delinquents / Henri Giller, Allison Morris. – London : Burnett in association with Deutsch, 1981.
127p; 21cm.
Bibliography: p120-123. - Includes index.
ISBN 0233972943 Hbk £5.95
ISBN 0233973737 Pbk £3.50

Care cases : proposals for legal reform. – Family Rights Group. – London : Family Rights Group, 1985.
54p.
Includes bibliographical references.

Care Proceedings. – London : Longman Professional.
– (Longham Practitioner Series).
ISBN 085121309X Pbk £22.95

Care Proceedings. – 2nd ed. – London : Oyez Longman, 1983.
– (Oyez Longman Practitioner Ser.).
ISBN 0851207235 Hbk £22.95

Care proceedings : a practical guide for social workers, health visitors and others / Robert Dingwall and John Eekelaar. – Oxford : Basil Blackwell, 1982.
viii,140p; 23cm.
Bibliography: p135-136. - Includes index.
ISBN 0631127569 Hbk £
ISBN 0631127577 Pbk

Career and recruitment patterns of Italian legislators : a contribution to the understanding of a polarized political system / by Maurizio Cotta. – Florence : European University Institute, 1983.
49p.
At head of title page: European University Institute, Department of Political and Social Sciences.

Career in law / by Brian Hogan. – London : Sweet & Maxwell, 1981.
vii,98p; 18cm.
Bibliography: p92-95. - Includes index.
ISBN 0421280506 Pbk £1.95

Careers in Local Government. – London : Kogan Page, 1981.
96p.
ISBN 0850384370 Hbk £6.95
ISBN 0850384389 Pbk £2.95

Careers in Politics. – London : Kogan Page, 1984.
96p.
ISBN 0850388325 Hbk £6.95
ISBN 0850388333 Pbk £2.95

Careers in the law. – 2nd ed. – London : Kogan Page, 1986.
ISBN 1850911002 Pbk £3.25

Careers in the Police Force. – 2nd ed. – London : Kogan Page, 1986.
96p.
ISBN 18500911703 Hbk £2.95

Cargo key receipt and transport document replacement / Kurt Gronfors. – Goteburg : Akademiforlaget, 1982.
104p. – (Skrifter).
ISBN 9124160555

Caribbean law librarian : bulletin of the Caribbean Association of Law Libraries. – Jamaica : Caribbean Association of Law Librarians, 1984-.

Carl, Notger
Strategic Planning of U.S. Commercial Banks in a Changing Legal Environment. – Idstein : Schultz-Kirchner, 1985.
ISBN 3925196013

Carlen, Pat, et al
Criminal Women. – Oxford : Blackwell, 1985.
ISBN 0745600883 Pbk £5.95
—Gender Crime and Justice. – Open University Press, 1988.
ISBN 0335155057 Hbk £25.00
—Women's imprisonment : a study in social control / Pat Carlen. – London : Routledge & K. Paul, 1983.
viii,248p.
Includes index. Bibliography: p240-245.
ISBN 0710094418

Carlotto affair : a terrible injustice / International Committee 'Justice for Massimo Carlotto'. – London : the Committee, 1987.
40p.

Carmen, Elizabeth →Damages for Breach of Contract.

Carmi, Amnon
Medicolegal Library
Vol. 1 Child Abuse / H. Zimrin. – Berlin : Springer-Verlag.
ca 224p.
ISBN 3540124713 Pbk £128.00
Vol. 5 Psychiatry, Law and Ethics. – 1985.
ca 230p.
ISBN 3540157425 Pbk £178.00
Vol. 6 Drugs and Alcohol. – 1986.
ca 215p.
Pbk £152.00
Vol. 7 Hospital Law. – 1988.
ca 225p.
ISBN 3540186425 Pbk £148.00
→ Nursing law and ethics.
→ Psychiatry, law, and ethics.

Carmi et al., A.
Medicolegal Library
Vol. 3 Disability /. – Berlin : Springer-Verlag, 1984.
ca 225p.
Pbk £138.00

Carmichael, Ian
Sudden deaths and fatal accident inquiries. – Edinburgh : Green (W.) & Son, 1986.
Covers the duties of the procurator fiscal in investigating sudden and unexpected deaths. With a chapter on medical mattres, a summary of the duties of the coroner in England and guidance for the medical professions as to which deaths shuld be reported to the fiscal.
ISBN 0414007751 Pbk

Carmichael, K S
Corporation Tax Manual. – London : Butterworths, 1988.
ISBN 0406502167 Pbk
→ Irish income tax and corporation profits tax by F.N. Kelly and K.S. Carmichael.
—Taxation of Lloyd's Underwriters / Peter H Wolstenholme. – 3rd ed. – London : Butterworths, 1985.
ISBN 0406511012 Pbk £18.95

Carney
Drug Users & Law In Aus : From Crime Control To Welfare 1987. – London : Law Book Co.
ISBN 0455207143 Pbk £25.00

Carney, Terry
Australian social security law, policy and administration / Terry Carney & Peter Hanks. – Melbourne : Oxford University Press, 1986.
xxv,334p.
Bibliography: p311-326.
ISBN 0195547543
—Ethical and Legal Issues in Guardianship Options for Intellectually Disadvantaged People / Peter Singer. – Kingston : Australian Government Publishing Service, 1986.
124p.
ISBN 0644034335 Hbk £14.95

Carnwath, Robert →Blundell and Dobry's planning appeals and inquiries.

Caroe, Laurence C.
Wills for Ontario : How to Make Your Own Will. – 8th ed. – North Vancouver : International Self-Counsel Press, 1986.
112p.
ISBN 0889083584 Hbk £5.95

Carpenter : Introduction to South African Constitutional Law. – Durban : Professional Publishers, 1987.
ISBN 040901785X Hbk £78.00

Carpenter, G.
Carpenter : Introduction to South African Constitutional Law. – Durban : Professional Publishers, 1987.
ISBN 040901785X Hbk £78.00

Carpenter, M. C. L. →Copyright law in the United Kingdom and the rights of performers, authors and composers in Europe.

Carr
Law of Evidence / Beaumont. – London : Financial Training, 1985.
– (SWOT).
ISBN 090632274X Pbk £7.50

Carr, A →White, Carr and Lowe: a guide to the Children Act 1989.

Carr, A. P. →Anthony & Berryman's Magistrates' court guide 1985.
—Criminal Procedure in Magistrates' Courts. – London : Butterworths, 1984.
This work presents a narrative description of procedure in magistrates' courts when dealing with criminal cases in the United Kingdom. Extensive footnotes are included to provide authority for the material described in the text.
ISBN 0406010676 Pbk £21.95
—Magistrates' Court Guide 1988. – London : Butterworths, 1988.
ISBN 0406108412 Pbk £15.95

Carr, Brian R.
Taxation of Resource Industries. – Agincourt : Carswell, 1987.
392p.
This text discusses the relevant sections of the Income Tax Act. Also included are discussions on depletion, successor corporation rules and resource allowances. Special coverage includes sample calculations and tables listing the order of deductions for different types of enterprises.
Hbk £54.75

Carr, C. J. →Labour law.

Carr, Henry
Computer software : legal protection in the United Kingdom / by Henry Carr. – Oxford : ESC Publishing Ltd., 1987.
xxii, 228p.
ISBN 0906214327

Carriage of dangerous goods by sea : the role of the International Maritime Organisation in international legislation / by Cleopatra Henry. – London : Pinter, 1985.
iii,184; 23cm.
Includes index. Clarifies the work of the IMO revealing its methods and mandate for enacting maritime controls on the transportation of controversial toxins.
ISBN 0861875699 Hbk £25

Carriage of Goods. – Professional Books, 1987.
ISBN 0862052394 Pbk £24.50
ISBN 0862052599 Hbk £50.00

Carriage of goods by sea / edited by Peter Koh Soon Kwang. – Singapore : Butterworths, 1986.
xviii,198p.
Collection of papers which analyse the legal principles governing carriage of goods by sea, and the Hague/Visby rules. Includes coverage of maritime arbitration, shipowners' limitation of liability, unclean bill of lading, time charterparties, and proposed changes in Malaysian shipping law.
ISBN 0409995150

Carriage of Goods by Sea / E R Hardy Ivamy. – 12th ed. – London : Butterworths, 1985.
ISBN 0406640602 Hbk £18.00
ISBN 0406640610 Pbk £15.95

Carriage Of Goods By Sea / Katzman. – 7th ed. – Matthew Bender, 1973.
ISBN 0000999054 Hbk £112.00

Carriage of Goods by Sea. – Pitman.
ISBN 0273029878 Pbk £15.95

Carrier, Micheline →Women and the constitution in Canada.

Carroll, B.
Guide to Financial Futures. – London : Butterworths, 1988.
ISBN 0406200106 Hbk £35.00
—Practical Guide to Financial Futures Trading. – London : Butterworths.
ISBN 0406200106 Hbk £35.00

Carroll, Brian A. →Carroll's tax planning in Ireland.

Carroll, John
Termination of Employment. – 2nd ed. – North Ryde : C.C.H. Australia, 1984.
192p.
ISBN 0869037390 Hbk £23.00

Carroll's tax planning in Ireland / by Michael F. O'Reilly : consultant author Brian A. Carroll. – London : Sweet & Maxwell, 1986.
xxi,467p; 25cm.
Includes index.
ISBN 0421367504 £40.00

Carrothers, A.W.R., et al
Collective Bargaining Law in Canada. – 2nd ed. – Butterworths, 1986.
944p.
Updated and revised to include new material on discharge and discipline. Outlines the current law of collective bargaining in Canada as developed under statutory regulation along with its historic background. Expanded chapters on secondary picketing and consumer boycotting and the substantive law of strikes and lockouts.
ISBN 0409818798 Hbk £145.00

Carrott, S →Quiet enjoyment : remedies for harassment and illegal eviction.

Carruthers, David →Damages for personal injury and death in Canada.

Carson, Richard S.
Taxation of Partnerships in Canada / Carl F. Steiss. – Butterworths, 1983.
104p.
ISBN 0409859761 Hbk £29.95

Carson, T
Real Property Statutes. – Professional Books.
ISBN 0862053382 Hbk £37.75

Carson, W. G.
Other price of Britain's oil : safety and control in the North Sea / W.G. Carson. – Oxford : Robertson, 1981.
xi,320p; 24cm.
Includes index.
ISBN 0855203927 Hbk £15.00
ISBN 0855203935 Pbk £5.95

Carswell Legal Publications
Alberta Law Reports : 1909-1932. – Carswell Legal Publications. – Agincourt : Carswell.
—Alberta Revised Statutes Sectional Tables of Concordance : 1970-1980. – Carswell Legal Publications. – Agincourt : Carswell, 1982.
207p.
This book contains the sources of the R.S.A. 1980 s and the disposition of the R.S.A. 1970 s. This book also affords you the opportunity to check and verify updated references with those which have been deleted or superseded from R.S.A. 1980 back to R.S.A. 1970 or from R.S.A. 1970 ahead to R.S.A. 1980.
Pbk £21.00
—British Columbia Reports : 1867-1945, 63 Vols. – Carswell Legal Publications. – Agincourt : Carswell.
—Canadian Abridgment, 110 Vols. – Carswell Legal Publications. – 2nd ed. – Agincourt : Carswell.
Hbk £2730.00
—Canadian Encyclopedic Digest : Ontario, 38 Vols. – Carswell Legal Publications. – 3rd ed. – Agincourt : Carswell.
This set of volumes provides the provincial laws of Ontario and federal laws of Canada as derived from statutes and case law. The 150 subject titles contains an in-depth table of classifications and an index and tables of cases and statutes. A Research Guide and Key and The Legal Deskbook are also included.
Llf £2352.00
—Canadian Reports Appeal Cases : 1807-1913, 24 Vols. – Carswell Legal Publications. – Agincourt : Carswell, 1983.
—Criminal Justice : 1981 Conference of the Canadian Institute for the Administration of Justice. – Carswell Legal Publications. – Agincourt : Carswell, 1982.
300p.
Hbk £38.75
—Fox's Patent Cases : Canada, 22 Vols.
Vols. 1-44 bound in 11 Vols. with Index and Digest Vols. 1-30. – Carswell Legal Publications. – Agincourt : Carswell, 1983.
This multi-volume work covers the years 1940 to 1971 and contains all judgements of the Canadian courts on the patent law published in full. All relevant statutes, statutory amendments, Orders-in-Council, Rules of Practice, and other official acts impacting on patent law are included in the work.
Hbk £579.75
—Index to Canadian Legal Literature : Supplemental Volumes to the Canadian Abridgment, 3 Vols. – Carswell Legal Publications. – Agincourt : Carswell, 1985-1987.
This multi-volume series is a comprehensive index to legal materials published in Canada. The work contains full bibliographic references to Canadian legal monographs, articles, case comments, annotation, and audio-visual materials.
Hbk £185.00
—Manitoba Law Reports : 1884-1962, 67 Vols. – Carswell Legal Publications. – Agincourt : Carswell, 1983.
Hbk
—Maritime Provinces Reports : 1929-1968, 53 Vols. – Carswell Legal Publications. – Agincourt : Carswell, 1983.
Hbk
—Motor Vehicle Reports, 50 Vols. – Carswell Legal Publications. – Agincourt : Carswell, 1983.
Hbk £1260.00
—New Brunswick Reports : 1825-1930, 54 Vols. – Carswell Legal Publications. – Agincourt : Carswell, 1983.
Hbk
—Northwest Territories Supreme Court Reports : 1887-1898, 2 Vols. – Carswell Legal Publications. – Agincourt : Carswell, 1983.
Hbk
—Nova Scotia Reports : 1834-1930, 60 Vols. – Carswell Legal Publications. – Agincourt : Carswell, 1983.
Hbk £1008.00
—Ontario Weekly Notes, 13 Vols.
Series 1950-1962. – Carswell Legal Publications. – Agincourt : Carswell.
Hbk £302.50
—Reports of Family Law, 50
Vols. 1-50 incl. consolidated index, 4 Vols. – Carswell Legal Publications. – Agincourt : Carswell.
– (Second Ser.).
Hbk £1260.00
—Statutes of British Columbia Judicially Considered 1980 to date. – Carswell Legal Publications. – Agincourt : Carswell.
This text contains annotations of the decisions interpreting British Columbia statute law. Included are the Rules of Court, the Acts contained in the Revised Statutes of 1979 and the public statutes enacted since 1979 with cites to all amendments, repeals and new legislation.
Hbk £57.75
—Uniform Rules of Evidence : Report of the Federal-Provincial Task Force. – Carswell Legal Publications. – Agincourt : Carswell, 1982.
650p.
This report contains a complete statement of the current Canadian law of evidence, with proposals for reform.
Hbk £54.75
—Western Weekly Reports : 1911-1950, 108 Vols. – Carswell Legal Publications. – Agincourt : Carswell, 1983.
Hbk £2721.75
—Western Weekly Reports : 1951-1970, 75 Vols. – Carswell Legal Publications. – Agincourt : Carswell, 1983.
– (New Ser. 1951-1970).
Hbk £1890.00
—Western Weekly Reports : 1971-1980, 60 Vols. – Carswell Legal Publications. – Agincourt : Carswell, 1983.
Hbk £1512.00

Carswell's Family Law Digest : 3rd Permanent Supplement. – Agincourt : Carswell.
Hbk £269.50

Carswell's Family Law Digests, 9 Vols. – Agincourt : Carswell.
This text digests all the reported Canadian family law cases arranged according to the Canadian Abridgment classification system. This multi-volume set of books is supplemented by-annually. Special features include a Table of Cases, Index, and Cases and Statutes Judicially Considered.
Hbk £332.00

Carswell's Matrimonial Quantum and Custody Award Service. – Agincourt : Carswell.
Pbk £151.25

Carswell's practice cases. – Agincourt, Ont. : Carswell, 1977-.
24cm.
First series: vols. 1-50 (1977-85). - Second series: vol. 1, part 1 (Sept. 3, 1985)-. Cumulative index published at intervals.

Carter, B.E.
International Economic Sanctions : Improving the Haphazard US Legal Regime. – Cambridge : Cambridge University Press.
ISBN 0521342589 Hbk £25.00

Carter, Charles
Purposes of Government Expenditure. – London : Policy Studies Institute, 1984.
38p.
Hbk £1.30

Carter, D. D. →Labour law and industrial relations in Canada.

Carter, J. W.
Breach of contract / by J. W. Carter. – Sydney : Law Book Company, 1984.
xlxi,551p.
ISBN 0455205051 Hbk £49
—Cases and Materials on Contract Law in Australia. – Butterworths, 1988.
979p.
ISBN 040949366X Pbk £58.00
—Cases and Materials on Contract Law in Australia / D. J. Harland. – Sydney : Butterworths, 1988.
1000p.
Commentary on each of the decisions contained in this casebook includes its status, difficulties associated with it, and, when possible, an in-depth analysis. Among the topics covered are agreement, misrepresentation, duress, damages, and restitution.
Pbk £52.00

→ Contract law in Australia.

→ Helmore's personal property and mercantile law in New South Wales.

Carter, P. B.
Cases and statutes on evidence : being based upon Cockle's cases and statutes on evidence / by P.B. Carter. – London : Sweet & Maxwell, 1981.
lviii,864p; 26cm.
Includes index.
ISBN 042120320X Hbk £28.00
ISBN 0421203307 Pbk £15.00

Carter, Reginal Francis
Carter's Criminal Law of Queensland. – 7th ed. – Sydney : Butterworths, 1988.
1300p.
Hbk £98.00

Carter, Reginald Francis
Criminal Law of Queensland. – 7th ed. – Butterworths, 1988.
1,406p.
ISBN 0409493090 Hbk £98.00

Carter, Robert L.
Reinsurance / R.L. Carter. – 2nd ed. – Brentford : Kluwer in association with the Mercantile and General Reinsurance Company plc, 1983.
xv,630p; 24cm.
Previous ed.: 1979. Bibliography: p613-622. - Includes index.
ISBN 0903393654 £65.00

Carter, Ross W.
Australian Sentencing Digest. – North Ryde : Law Book Co, 1985.
li, 929p.
Hbk £97.00

Carter-Ruck, Peter F.
Carter-Ruck on libel and slander / Richard Walker. – 3rd ed. – London : Butterworths, 1985.
lvi,553p; 26cm.
Previous ed.: published as Libel & slander. London : Faber, 1972. Includes index.
ISBN 0406009708 Hbk £55

Carter, S.
Lex Custumaria. – 2nd ed. Repr. of 1701 ed. – Abingdon : Professional Books.
Hbk £75.00

Carter-Ruck on libel and slander / Richard Walker. – 3rd ed. – London : Butterworths, 1985.
lvi,553p; 26cm.
Previous ed.: published as Libel & slander. London : Faber, 1972. Includes index.
ISBN 0406009708 Hbk £55

Carter's Criminal Law of Queensland. – 7th ed. – Sydney : Butterworths, 1988.
1300p.
Hbk £98.00

Carthy, James J.
Ontario Annual Practice. – Aurora : Canada Law Book Co.
– (Text Books-Civil).
Hbk £1-10 copies 42.00 ea.
—Ontario Annual Practice (O.A.P) / W. A. Derry Miller. – Aurora : Canada Law Book Co.
This 1987-88 edition of Ontario Annual Practice provides a revised publication up-to-date on the Rules of Practice as well as all significant cases on the Rules of the past 30 years.
Hbk For 1-10 Copies 42.00 each

Carty, Anthony
Decay of international law? : a reappraisal of the limits of legal imagination in international affairs / Anthony Carty. – Manchester : Manchester University Press, 1986.
x,138p; 24cm. – (The Melland Schill monographs in international law).
Includes index.
ISBN 0719018501 £25.00

Carver, Thomas Gilbert
Carver's carriage by sea / Raoul Colinvaux. – 13th ed. – London : Stevens, 1982.
2v.
Previous ed.:1971.
ISBN 0420451102 Hbk £180.00

Carver's carriage by sea / Raoul Colinvaux. – 13th ed. – London : Stevens, 1982.
2v.
Previous ed.:1971.
ISBN 0420451102 Hbk £180.00

Carzo, Domenico →Semiotics, law and social science.

Casburn, Maggie →Receiving juvenile justice : adolescents and state care and control.

Case book on criminal law / by John Hatchard and Muna Ndulo. – Lusaka : Government Printer, 1983.
viii,425p.
Includes index.
ISBN 0903826585

Case for a national minimum wage / Chris Pond and Steve Winyard. – London : Low Pay Unit, 1983.
64p. – (Pamphlet).
Bibliography: p61-63.

Case for advice centres / N. Ralph. – Sheffield : Sheffield Advice Centres Group, 1985.
34p.

Case for divorce in the Irish Republic : a report commissioned by the Irish Council for Civil Liberties / William Duncan. – Rev. ed. with postscript. – Dublin : The Council, 1982.
107p.
Includes bibliographical references.

Case for summary trial : proposals for a redistribution of criminal business / the Justices' Clerks' Society. – Bristol : The Society, 1982.
26p.

Case for the conversational analysis of courtroom interaction : some interactional dimensions of legal procedures / by Philip Wilkinson. – Oxford : Centre for Socio-Legal Studies, 1981.
24p. – (Working paper).
Includes bibliographical references.

Case for the crown : the inside story of the Director of Public Prosecutions / Joshua Rozenberg : foreword by Sir Michael Havers. – Wellingborough : Equation, 1987.
206p,24p of plates; 24cm.
Bibliography: p201-202. - Includes index.
ISBN 0722515332 £12.95
ISBN 1853360112

Case Law on the Indian Constitution. – Allahabad : Orient Law House.
ISBN 0861250265 Pbk £45.00

Case of the Requisition / Alfred Hildesley. – Aalen Wuertt : Scientia.
xxiv, 307p.
Hbk £85.00

Case Studies in Industrial Relations. – London : Kogan Page, 1982.
226p.
ISBN 0850384184 Hbk £13.50

Case Studies In Management Accounting. – Deddington : Allan (Philip).
ISBN 0860035522 Hbk £45.00

Case studies on human rights and fundamental freedoms : a world survey / ed.-in-chief, Willem A. Veenhoven, assistant to the ed.-in-chief, Winifred Crum Ewing, associate editors, Clemens Amelunxen ... et al. – The Hague : Nijhoff, 1975.
5 v; 25 cm.
2 Includes bibliographical references.
fl. 75.00 per vol

Case study booklet / New South Wales. Law Reform Commission. – Sydney : Law Reform Commission of New South Wales, 1984.
x,66p.

Case through the courts : Ford v. Warwickshire / Philip Britton and Ian Thompson. – 1 videocassette. – London : Sweet & Maxwell in association with the University of Warwick, 1985.
– (Sweet & Maxwell's lawfilms).
Accompanied by Teaching materials. - 64p. (in folder).

Casebook on agency / E.R. Hardy Ivamy. – 3rd ed. – London : Lloyd's, 1987.
160p; 22cm.
Previous ed.: 1980. Includes index.
ISBN 185044112X Pbk £15.00

Casebook on Australian Company Law. – 4th ed. – Butterworths, 1983.
365p.
ISBN 0409491810 Pbk £31.50

Casebook on carriage by sea / by E.R. Hardy Ivamy. – 6th ed. – London : Lloyd's of London, 1985.
256p; 25cm.
Previous ed.: 1982. Includes index.
ISBN 1850440549 Pbk

Casebook on carriage by sea / by E.R. Hardy Ivamy. – 5th ed. – London : Lloyd's of London Press, 1982.
xxvii,203p.
Previous ed.: 1979. Includes index.
ISBN 0907432360

Casebook on Compulsory Purchase and Compensation. – Oxford : Blackwell Scientific, 1988.
ISBN 0003834085 Hbk £35.00

Casebook on Conflict of Laws. – London : Butterworths.
ISBN 0409435279 Pbk £28.80

Casebook on contract / by J.C. Smith and the late J.A.C. Thomas. – 7th ed. – London : Sweet & Maxwell, 1987.
xxxi,604p; 24cm.
Previous ed.: 1977. Includes index.
ISBN 0421283203 Hbk £
ISBN 0421283300 Pbk £12.95

Casebook on damages in Scotland / by Robin Gilmour McEwan and Ann Paton. – Edinburgh : Green, 1983.
xxiii,272p; 22cm.
Includes index.
ISBN 0414006984 Pbk

Casebook on Equity and Trusts in Ireland. – Abingdon : Professional Books, 1985.
700p.
ISBN 0862051126 Hbk £44.00
ISBN 0862051142 Pbk £34.00

Casebook on Family Law in Ireland. – Abingdon : Professional Books, 1984.
Hbk

Casebook on Income Tax Law. – Bombay : Tripathi, 1987.
832p.
Hbk £175.00

Casebook on Insurance Law. – 4th ed. – London : Butterworths, 1984.
ISBN 0406602638 Pbk £14.95

Casebook on Irish Company Law. – Dublin : Gill and Macmillan, 1987.
ISBN 0717114376 Pbk £19.95

Casebook on Irish Family Law. – London : Butterworths, 1984.
ISBN 0862050898 Pbk £22.50

Casebook on Irish land law / by J.C.W. Wylie. – Abingdon, Oxon. : Professional Books, 1984.
xxxxii,723p.
Includes index.
ISBN 0862050642

Casebook on Kenya Customary Law. – Abingdon : Professional Books, 1985.
350p.
ISBN 0862051118 Hbk £34.00

Casebook on Kenyan Customary Law. – Nairobi : Nairobi University Press.
348p.
Pbk £280.00

Casebook on Nigerian Family Law and Succession. – Abingdon : Professional Books, 1986.
800p.
ISBN 0862051150 Hbk £42.00

Casebook on Nigerian Law of Contract. – Professional Books, 1983.
ISBN 0862050472 Hbk £37.50
ISBN 0862050533 Pbk £22.00

Casebook on partnership / by E.R. Hardy Ivamy. – 2nd ed. – Abingdon, Oxfordshire : Professional Books, 1982.
xv,99p; 23cm.
ISBN 086205043X Hbk £13.20

Casebook on Profesional Negligence. – Oxford : Blackwell Scientific, 1988.
ISBN 0003834182 Hbk £30.00

Casebook on Rent Review and Lease Renewal / Mark Pawlowski. – Oxford : Blackwell Scientific, 1986.
600p.
ISBN 0003831957 Hbk £40

Casebook on repairs. – London : Estates Gazette, 1987.
ISBN 0728201038 Pbk £16.00

Casebook on sale of goods / E.R. Hardy Ivamy. – 5th ed. – London : Lloyd's of London, 1987.
ix,200p; 22cm.
Previous ed.: 1980. Includes index.
ISBN 1850441170 Pbk

Casebook on Scottish criminal law / by Christopher H.W. Gane, and Charles N. Stoddart. – 2nd ed. – Edinburgh : Green, 1988.
xxxiv,740p; 22cm.
Previous ed.: 1980. Includes index.
ISBN 041400843X Pbk £25.00

Casebook on shipping law / E.R. Hardy Ivamy. – 4th ed. – London : Lloyd's of London Press, 1987.
210p; 22cm.
Previous ed.: 1982. Includes index.
ISBN 1850441308 Pbk £14.50

Casebook on Taxation, Fourth Edition. – Quezon City : University of the Philippines, Law Center, 1981.
239p.
Pbk £20.00

Casebook on the European Court of Human Rights. – Dublin : Round Hall Press, 1988.
ca 350p.
ISBN 0947686371 Hbk £35.00

Casebook on the Irish Law of Torts / William Binchy. – London : Butterworths, 1983.
ISBN 0862050502 Hbk £35.00
ISBN 0862050561 Pbk £25.00

Casebook on the Nigerian law of contract / by I.E. Sagay. – Abingdon, Oxon. : Professional Books, 1983.
xxvi,518p.
Includes index.
ISBN 0862050472

Casebook on Theft Acts 1968-78. – 3rd ed. – London : Sweet & Maxwell, 1984.
ISBN 0851640117 Pbk £4.50

Casebook on Tort, A. – 6th ed. – Sweet & Maxwell.
ISBN 0421363908 Hbk £30.00
ISBN 0421364009 Pbk £21.00

Case-Law of the European Commission of Human Rights
Decisions and Reports (bilingual edition). – Strasbourg : Council of Europe.
Hbk £3.10
Summaries and Indexes Nos. 1-20. –
Hbk £5.00

Case-law on Article 5 of the Convention for the Protection of Human Rights and Fundamental Freedoms / by Marc-Andre Eissen. – Strasbourg : European Court of Human Rights, 1986.
40p.
ISBN 9287107769

Cases and Comment on Irish Commercial Law and Legal Technique. – 2nd ed. – Round Hall Press.
ISBN 0947686320 Hbk £22.50
ISBN 0947686398 Pbk £12.50

Cases and commentary on the law of trusts / Hayton and Marshall. – 8th ed. – London : Stevens, 1986.
796p; 25cm.
Previous ed.: / Nathan and Marshall. 1980. Includes index.
ISBN 042047370X Hbk £36.00
ISBN 0420473807 Pbk £27.00

Cases and material on contract / by S.S. Ujjannavar. – Hubli India : G. S. Ujjannavar, 1983.
xiv,543p.

Cases and Material on the Urban Land (Ceiling and Regulation) Act, 1976, Act No 33 of 1976 : Along with Rules and Notifications. – Madhya Pradesh : Lawyers Home, 1986.
152p.
Hbk £60.00

Cases and Materials In Administrative Law / Cross. – Sweet & Maxwell, 1977.
ISBN 042117370X Pbk £22.00

Cases and Materials in Company Law. – 3rd ed. – London : Butterworths, 1985.
ISBN 0406370125 Hbk £29.00
ISBN 0406370133 Pbk £18.95

Cases and Materials on Administrative Law. – Butterworths, 1987.
450p.
Focuses on judicial review of administrative action and includes a discussion of natural justice and fairness, rule-making, bias, standing, grounds for review, and discretionary powers and remedies. Contains excerpts from relevant Acts and materials, a table of cases, a chapter on freedom of information legislation and notes on delegation and privative clauses.
ISBN 0409806277 Pbk £68.00

Cases and materials on administrative law / Richard R. S. Tracey. – 4th ed. – Sydney : Butterworths, 1982.
lii,547p.
Previous ed.: 1975, by Peter Brett and Peter W. Hogg. First ed.: cases and materials in constitutional and administrative law. Includes index.
ISBN 0409309192 Hbk £54
ISBN 0409309206 Pbk £42.5

Cases and Materials on Bills of Lading. – Oxford : Blackwell Scientific, 1987.
ISBN 0003833844 Hbk £30.00

Cases and materials on civil procedure / by James A. Woods. – Toronto : Carswell, 1987.
xviii,838p.
ISBN 0459306618

Cases and Materials on Code of Civil Procedure / B. Nath. – 3rd rev. ed. – Lucknow : Eastern Book Company, 1981.
1,717p.
Hbk £165.00

Cases and materials on contract / by P.J. Hocker, Ann Dufty and Peter G. Heffey. – 5th ed. – Sydney : Law Book Co., 1985.
xli,983p.
4th ed., 1979 by C.L. Pannam and P.J. Hocker. Includes bibliographical references and index.
ISBN 0455204039

Cases and Materials on Contract Law in Australia. – Butterworths, 1988.
979p.
ISBN 040949366X Pbk £58.00

Cases and Materials on Contract Law in Australia / D. J. Harland. – Sydney : Butterworths, 1988.
1000p.
Commentary on each of the decisions contained in this casebook includes its status, difficulties associated with it, and, when possible, an in-depth analysis. Among the topics covered are agreement, misrepresentation, duress, damages, and restitution.
Pbk £52.00

Cases and Materials on Corporations and Associations / R. Baxt. – 5th ed. – Butterworths, 1988.
823p.
Covers unincorporated associations, partnership, the company as a separate legal entity, the memorandum of association, powers of companies and ultra vires, articles of association and contacts within the company, relations between the company and outsiders, control and management of the company, oppression of minority shareholders, and takeovers and reconstructions.
ISBN 0409493058 Pbk £62.00 (incl. suppl.)

Cases and Materials on Criminal Law / Brian Hogan. – 3rd ed. – London : Butterworths.
ISBN 0406658242 Hbk £29.00
ISBN 0406658250 Pbk £19.95

Cases and Materials on Criminal Procedure Code / P.L. Malik. – 2nd ed. – Lucknow : Eastern Book Company, 1984.
1,199p.
Hbk £130.00

Cases and Materials On English Legal Systems / Bailey. – Sweet & Maxwell, 1987.
ISBN 0421359404 Hbk
ISBN 0421359501 Pbk

Cases and Materials on Equity and Trusts / R.P. Austin. – 3rd ed. – Butterworths, 1989.
1024p.
ISBN 0409495239 Hbk £89.00
ISBN 0409495247 Pbk £69.00

Cases and materials on equity and trusts / by J.D. Heydon, W.M.C. Gummow, R.P. Austin. – 2nd ed. – Sydney : Butterworths, 1982.
xxxvi,934p.
This book introduces the main principles and remedies of Anglo-Australasian equity. A range of questions have been provided for undergraduate law students.
ISBN 0409309389

Cases and Materials on Evidence. – London : Butterworths, 1974.
ISBN 0409436410 Pbk £28.00

Cases and Materials on Evidence / C.R. Williams. – 2nd ed. – North Ryde : Law Book Co, 1985.
iii, 860p.
ISBN 0455205671 Hbk £37.50
ISBN 045520568X Pbk £27.50

Cases and materials on evidence in Malaysia and Singapore. – Singapore : Malayan Law Journal, 1990.
500.
Deals with the cases and statutory provisions on the law of evidence in Malaysia and Singapore, based on the Malaysian Evidence Act 1950 (revised 1971), and the Singapore Evidence Act 1976 (revised 1985). Examines the general position of the law, in each chapter, and then sets out the important judgements of cases in Singapore and Malaysia.
Hbk

Cases and materials on international business transactions / T.C. Hartley. – 9 v. – London : London School of Economics, 1984.

Cases and materials on international business transactions / T.C. Hartley. – London : London School of Economics, 1987.
8.
A collection of course material.

Cases and materials on international law / by D.J. Harris. – 3rd ed. – London : Sweet & Maxwell, 1983.
li,810p; 24cm.
Previous ed.: 1979. Includes index.
ISBN 0421292709 Hbk £26.00
ISBN 0421292806 Pbk £19.50

Cases and Materials On International Trade. – 2nd ed. – London : Laureate-Thomson Press, 1983.
ISBN 0907392105 Pbk £17.00

Cases and Materials on Law of Evidence Includes Supplement-1984. – Lucknow : Eastern Book Company, 1983.
578p.
Hbk £80.00

Cases and materials on private international law / J.H.C. Morris, P.M. North. – London : Butterworths, 1984.
xxviii,757p; 26cm.
Includes index.
ISBN 0406252645 Hbk £36.00
ISBN 0406252653 Pbk £25.95

Cases and Materials on Real Property. – 2nd ed. – North Ryde : Law Book Co, 1985.
xliii, 582p.
ISBN 0455203954 Hbk £63.00
ISBN 0455203962 Pbk £49.50

Cases and Materials on Remedies. – Toronto : Edmond-Montgomery, 1988.
ca 1,000p.
Hbk £94.00

Cases and Materials On Revenue Law. – Sweet & Maxwell, 1973.
ISBN 0421167807 Pbk £8.75

Cases and materials on review of administrative action / by S.D. Hotop. – 2nd ed. – Sydney : Law Book Co., 1983.
xxxiii,1219p.
Previous ed.: 1979. Includes bibliographical references and index.
ISBN 0455203776

Cases and materials on sale of goods / John Adams. – London : Croom Helm, 1982.
174p; 21cm. – (Croom Helm study guides to commercial law).
Includes index.
ISBN 0709905092 Pbk £6.95

Cases and Materials on Succession / R.A. Woodman. – 3rd ed. – North Ryde : Law Book Co, 1984.
xxxix, 794p.
ISBN 0455202826 Hbk £73.00
ISBN 0455202834 Pbk £60.00

Cases and Materials on Taxation. – 2nd ed. – Butterworths, 1984.
790p.
ISBN 0409491624 Hbk £75.00 incl. suppl.
ISBN 0409491721 Pbk £62.50 incl. suppl.
Cumulative Supplement-1986. –
ISBN 0409491152 £3.00

Cases and materials on the carriage of goods by sea / Martin Dockray. – Abingdon : Professional Books, 1987.
xxvi,804p.
ISBN 0862052599

Cases and Materials on the Constitution of India. – Bombay : Tripathi, 1987.
882p.
Hbk £160.00

Cases and materials on the criminal law of Liberia / by Johnnie N. Lewis. – 3. – S.l. : s.n., 1981.

Cases and materials on the English legal system / Michael Zander. – 4th ed. – London : Weidenfeld and Nicolson, 1984.
xxx,631p.
Previous ed.: 1980. Bibliography: p.xxviii-xxx. - Includes index. .
ISBN 0297784579 Hbk £19.50
ISBN 0297784587 Pbk £10.95

Cases and materials on the English legal system / Michael Zander. – 5th ed. – London : Weidenfeld and Nicolson, 1988.
xxix,641p; 23cm.
Previous ed.: 1984. Includes index.
ISBN 0297793535 Hbk
ISBN 0297793543 Pbk £14.95

Cases and materials on the law of international trade / edited by Mark S. W. Hoyle. – 2nd ed. – London : Laureate-Thomson, 1983.
xviii,342p; 25cm.
Previous ed.: 1980. Includes index.
ISBN 0907392105 Pbk £18.50

Cases and Materials on the Law of Torts / Bruce P. Feldthusen. – 2nd ed. – Agincourt : Carswell, 1986.
Hbk £75.75

Cases and materials on the principles of natural justice in Nigeria / by A. Toriola Oyewo. – Ibadan, Nigeria : Jator Publishing, 1987.
xi,153p.
Includes bibliographical references and index.
ISBN 9782660000

Cases and materials on the Thefts Acts / Janet M. Dine. – London : Financial Training, 1985.
xvii,223p.
Includes the text of the Theft Acts, 1968 and 1978.
ISBN 0906322804

Cases and statutes on criminal law / John C. N. Slater. – 2nd ed. – London : Sweet & Maxwell, 1981.
xix,146p; 22cm.
Previous ed.: / by John C.N. Slater. 1973. Includes index.
ISBN 0421248106 Pbk £8.25

Cases and statutes on evidence : being based upon Cockle's cases and statutes on evidence / by P.B. Carter. – London : Sweet & Maxwell, 1981.
lviii,864p; 26cm.
Includes index.
ISBN 042120320X Hbk £28.00
ISBN 0421203307 Pbk £15.00

Cases and statutes on land law / by E.L.G. Tyler. – 2nd ed. – London : Sweet & Maxwell, 1986.
334p; 22cm.
Previous ed.: 1974. Includes index.
ISBN 0421343508 Pbk £13

Cases and statutes on tort / by Paul L. Bradbury. – 3rd ed. – London : Sweet & Maxwell, 1984.
xviii,195p; 22cm.
Previous ed.: 1978. Includes index.
ISBN 0421322004 Pbk £7.85

Cases and text on insurance law: Australia and New Zealand. – North Ryde : Butterworths (Australia).
Explains the insurance law of Australia and New Zealand, and illustrates how the law is interpeted with a selection of modern cases as well as relevant statutory material.
ISBN 0409308706 Pbk

Cases Argued and Decreed in the High Court of Chancery : 1660-80. – 2nd ed. Repr. of 1707 ed. – Abingdon : Professional Books.
345p.
Hbk £25.00

Cases Determined at Nisi Prius in the Court of King's Bench from Easter Term : 30 Geo 3 to Michaelmas Term, 35 Geo 3. – Repr. of 1795 ed. – Abingdon : Professional Books.
335p.
Hbk £35.00

Cases for Students of Commercial Law. – North Ryde : C.C.H. Australia, 1987.
114p.
ISBN 0869039288 Hbk

Cases Illustrating the Principles of the Laws of Torts / John Charles Miles. – Repr. of 1904 ed. – Aalen Wuertt : Scientia.
xx, 628p.
Hbk £150.00

Cases Illustrative of Oriental Life and the Application of English Law to India-Decided in H.M. Supreme Court at Bombay. – 1853 repr. – New Delhi : Asian Educational Services, 1988.
620p.
Hbk £195.00

Cases In Banking Law. – 3rd ed. – Plymouth : Macdonald & Evans, 1983.
ISBN 0712104771 Pbk £4.95

Cases in Chancery During the Time of Lord Eldon. – Repr. of 1815 ed. – Abingdon : Professional Books.
77p.
Hbk £25.00

Cases In Company Financial Reporting / Wearing. – Paul Chapman, 1988.
ISBN 1853960047 Pbk £5.95

Cases in Company Law. – 4th ed. – Plymouth : Macdonald & Evans, 1984.
ISBN 0712104844 Pbk £7.50

Cases in Contract Law. – 3rd ed. Repr. of 1977 ed. – Plymouth : Macdonald & Evans, 1983.
256p. – (M and E Handbook Ser.).
ISBN 0712104801 Hbk £4.50

Cases in Criminal Law. – 2nd ed. Repr. of 1978 ed. – Plymouth : Macdonald & Evans, 1981.
400p. – (M and E Handbook Ser.).
ISBN 0712103767 Hbk £4.95

Cases in Equity : During the Time of Chancellor Talbot (1730-37) From Notes of Alexander Forrester. – Repr. of 1741 ed. – Abingdon : Professional Books.
345p.
Hbk £30.00

Cases in Income Tax Law. – 1st ed. – Plymouth : Macdonald & Evans, 1981.
276p. – (M and E Handbook Ser.).
ISBN 0712103783 Hbk £4.95

Cases in the Law of Banking 1983-1985. – 2nd ed. – London : Sweet & Maxwell, 1986.
ISBN 0421357606 Pbk £7.50

Cases in Tort / G. H. Samuel. – Repr. of 1977 ed. – Plymouth : Macdonald & Evans, 1984.
352p. – (M and E Handbook Ser.).
ISBN 0712103562 Pbk £4.25

Cases of the Canadian Law of Insurance / James A. Rendall. – 4th ed. – Agincourt : Carswell, 1988.
854p.
Hbk £82.50

Cases on Commercial Law. – 2nd ed. – North Ryde : Law Book Co, 1984.
ixi, 428p.
ISBN 0455204365 Pbk £29.50

Cases on evidence in Australia / by Eric J. Edwards. – 3rd ed. – Sydney : Law Book Co., 1981.
xxix,795p.
Includes index.
ISBN 0455202443 Pbk
ISBN 0455202435

Cases on Irish company law / Michael Forde. – Cork : Mercier, 1986.
461p; 23cm.
Includes index.
ISBN 0853427968 £40.00 (Irish)

Cases on Patents : A New Anthology. – Waterlow. – (Waterlow Practitioners Library).
ISBN 0080330878 Pbk £30.00

Cases on the Canadian law of insurance / edited by Marvin G. Baer, James A. Rendall. – 3rd ed. – Calgary, Alta. : Carswell, 1983.
xl,760p.

Cases on the Criminal Code / R.A. Hayes. – North Ryde : Law Book Co, 1984.
xxiii, 739p.
ISBN 0455204276 Hbk £70.50
ISBN 0455204284 Pbk £54.50

Cases on the Land Uses Act / J.A. Omotola. – Lagos : Lagos University Press, 1983.
170p.
ISBN 9782264407

Cases on the Law of the Constitution. – Repr. of 1926 ed. – Aalen Wuertt : Scientia.
xxxvi, 387p.
Hbk £65.00

Cases on torts / W.L. Morison ... et al. – 5th ed. – Sydney : Law Book Co., 1981.
xxxiv,1011p.
Includes bibliographical notes and index.
ISBN 0455202516 Pbk
ISBN 0455202524

Cases on Trusts. – 5th ed. – North Ryde : Law Book Co, 1984.
xxxiii, 925p.
ISBN 0455205116 Hbk £73.00
ISBN 0455205124 Pbk £58.50

Casey
Costs of Care in Hostels / Berthoud. – Policy Studies Institute.
ISBN 0853744246 Pbk £5.95
—Managing Institutional Change : Role of Staffing Commissions in the Public Sector / White. – Policy Studies Institute.
ISBN 0853744254 Pbk £7.95

Casey, James
Constitutional law in Ireland / by James Casey. – London : Sweet & Maxwell, 1987.
250p; 22cm.
Includes index.
ISBN 042131270X Pbk £19.00

Casey, M. E. →Report of the Penal Policy Review Committee, 1981.

Cash Flow and Credit Management / Slater. – Telegraph Publications, 1988.
ISBN 0863672264 Pbk £6.95

Cashmore, C →Introduction to the law of carriage of goods.

Cashmore, Ernest
Rastafarians / E. E. Cashmore. – London : Minority Rights Group, 1984.
11p. – (Report).
Bibliography: p11.

Caspari, M.
European Commission's Powers of Investigation in the Enforcement of Competition Law. – Luxembourg : Office for Official Publications of the European Communities, 1985.
81p.
ISBN 9282553612 Pbk

Cass, Steven →Trade Law Topics.

Cassell's UK Tax Guide 1988-89 : Comprehensive Aspects of Taxation / Edwards. – London : Cassell.
ISBN 0304315915 Pbk £19.95

Cassels, James →Tariff Board : a study prepared for the Law Reform Commission of Canada.

Cassese, Antonio →Change and stability in international law-making.
→ Current legal regulation of the use of force.
—International law in a divided world / Antonio Cassese. – Oxford : Clarendon, 1986.
xiii,420p; 24cm.
Includes bibliography and index.
ISBN 0198761945 £40.00
—Internationial law in a divided world. – Oxford : Oxford University Press, 1988.
ISBN 019876233X Pbk £16.95
—Legal Restraints on the Use of Force 40 Years after the UN Charter. – Dordrecht : Kluwer, 1986.
546p.
ISBN 9024732476 Hbk £215.00
—Violence and Law in the Modern Age. – Polity Press.
ISBN 0745604919 Hbk £19.50

Cassidy, Derek
Australian Tenancy Practice and Precedents / Michael Redfern. – Butterworths, 1987.
ISBN 0409494909 Llf £235.00

Casson, D. B.
Modern developments in the law of civic procedure / by D.B. Casson and I.H. Dennis. – London : Sweet & Maxwell, 1982.
xxv,112p; 22cm.
Includes index.
ISBN 0421290005 Pbk £4.95
→ Odgers' principles of pleading and practice in civil actions in the High Court of Justice.

Casson, Mark →Growth of international business.

Castel →International law : chiefly as interpreted and applied in Canada.

Castel, J.G.
Droit International Prive Quibecos. – London : Butterworths.
ISBN 0409821233 Hbk £76.00
→ International business transactions and economic relations : cases, notes and materials on the law as it applies to Canada.

Castel, Jean-Gabriel
Canadian conflict of laws / J.-G. Castel. – 2nd ed. – Toronto : Butterworths, 1986.
clxvi,652p.
Includes bibliographical references and index.
ISBN 0409821284 Hbk £125
→ Canadian criminal law, international and transnational aspects.
—Canadian Family Law Cases 1983 Supplement. – Toronto : Butterworths, 1983.
ISBN 0409989967 Hbk £40.00
—Conflict of Laws : Cases, Notes and Materials. – 6th ed. – Butterworths, 1988.
904p.
ISBN 0409805955 Pbk £75.00
—Extraterritoriality in International Trade : Canada and the United States of America Practices Compared. – Butterworths, 1988.
288p.
Study of conflicts of jurisdiction involving international busness transactions. Attempts to define the permissible limits to the assertion of jurisdiction to prescribe, to adjudicate and to enforce a rule of law under traditional principles of public international law and what these limits should be today in the economic field.
ISBN 0409805025 Hbk
—Introduction to Conflict of Laws. – 2nd ed. – Butterworths, 1986.
240p.
ISBN 0409805920 Pbk £38.95

Castles, A.C.
Australian Legal History. – North Ryde : Law Book Co, 1982.
xx, 553p.
ISBN 04551956095 £63.00

Castles, Alex
Compendium of human rights courses in Australian tertiary institutions / compiled by Alex Castles and Leonie Farrell. – Canberra : Australian Government Publishing Service, 1983.
xiv,39p. – (Occasional paper).
Includes index.
ISBN 0644027649
—Lawmakers and Wayward Whigs : Law and Justice in South Australia / Michael Harris. – Cowandilla : Wakefield Press, 1986.
256p.
ISBN 0949268607 Pbk £50.00
ISBN 0949268615 40.00 £75.00
ISBN 0949268623 Hbk

Castrilli, J. F.
Pesticides in Canada : an examination of federal law and policy / a study paper prepared for the Law Reform Commission of Canada by J.F. Castrilli, Toby Vigod. – Ottawa : The Commission, 1987.
131p. – (Study paper).
Added t.p. in French: Les pesticides au Canada. Pages numbered in opposite directions. Text in English and French.
ISBN 0662554132

Castro, E.H.
Understanding Income Tax Law the Flowchart Way. – 3rd ed. – Butterworths, 1985.
436p.
ISBN 0409491748 Pbk £39.00

Catalogue of British official publications not published by HMSO. – Cambridge : Chadwyck-Healey, 1981-.
30cm.

Catalogue of Community Legal Acts and Other Texts Relating to the Elimination of Technical Barriers to Trade for Industrial Products and Nomenclature for Iron and Steel Products : December 1983. – Kirchberg : Commission of the European Communities, 1984.
174p.
Hbk

Catalogue of the Law Library of Messrs. Hodding and Everett, Solicitors, Salisbury. – Repr. of 1834 ed. – Abingdon : Professional Books.
Hbk £20.00

Catalogue of the Van Zyl Collection of Antiquarian Legal Materials at the University of Cape Town. – Rondebosch : University of Cape Town, 1985.
ii, 164p.
ISBN 0799209856 Pbk £5.00

Catching Criminals : Some More Basic Skills. – London : Police Review Publishing, 1983.
ISBN 0851640044 Pbk £2.50

Catchpole, Louise →Local Government, Planning and Land Act 1980.

Catholic Institute for International Relations → Beggar your neighbours : apartheid power in Southern Africa.

Cathro, Susan →Mediation in New Zealand : the Attitudes of the Mediated.

Catinat, Michel →European challenge, 1992 : the benefits of a single market.

Cato, C. B.
Privilege against self-incrimination and reform of the practice of police interrogation / by C.B. Cato. – Auckland : Legal Research Foundation, 1985.
65,11p.
At head of title: Legal Research Foundation Inc. Seminar.
ISBN 0908581394

Catterall, D. M. →Termination of employment.

Catterns, D. →Broadcasting Law and Practice.

Cattle Trespass Act, 1871 / Vijay Malik. – 2nd ed. – Lucknow : Eastern Book Company, 1982.
138p.
Hbk £20.00

Cattle Trespass Act : as Amended Up-To-Date with Up-To-Date Case Law. – 3rd ed. – Allahabad : Law Book Company, 1988.
146p.
Hbk £65.00

Cattle Trespass Act along with Prevention of Cruelty of Animals Act. – 2nd ed. – Allahabad : Law Publishers, 1983.
Hbk £10.50

Caught in the Act : Critical Guide to the 1988 Housing Act. – SHAC.
ISBN 0948857315 Pbk £3.00

Caulfield, B. I.
Estate Tax Planning : Including Will Drafting. –. London : Law Society.
– (Nineteen Eighty-Five Crash Course Transcripts).
Hbk £2.05

Causation in the law / by H.L.A. Hart and Tony Honore. – 2nd ed. – Oxford : Clarendon, 1985.
lxxxi,516p; 23cm.
Previous ed.: 1959. Bibliography: p498-507. - Includes index.
ISBN 019825475X Hbk £25.00
ISBN 0198254741 Pbk £14.50

Causation, prediction and legal analysis / Stuart S. Nagel. – New York : Quarum, 1986.
xxii,276p; 25cm.
Bibliography: p261-268. - Includes index.
ISBN 0899301800

Causes of Crime. – Cambridge : Cambridge University Press, 1987.
ISBN 0521304024 Hbk £35.00

Causes of wars : and other essays / Michael Howard. – London : Temple Smith, 1983.
190p.
ISBN 0851172229 £10.00

Cautioning by the police : a consultative document / Home Office. – London : Home Office, 1984.
47p.
Bibliography: p.47.
ISBN 0862521513

Cavanagh, John → Immigration : Law and Practice.

Cavanagh, Stephen W.
Consumer Credit Law in Australia : a Commentary on the New Credit Legislation / Sheenagh Barnes. – Butterworths, 1988.
746p.
ISBN 0409494496 Hbk £89.00

—Product liability in Australia / S.W. Cavanagh and C.S. Phegan. – Sydney : Butterworths, 1983.
xxxvi, 267 p.; 25 cm.
Includes bibliographical references and index.
ISBN 0409491012 Hbk £30.00

Cave, D., et al
Legal Writing for Understanding, Clarity and Precision. – Vancouver : British Columbia Continuing Legal Education Society, 1982.
84p.
ISBN 0865040672 Hbk £35.00

Cavelier, German
Cancellation and nullity of trademarks in Colombia / German Cavelier. – Bogota, Colombia : Cavelier Abogados, 1986.
xii,235p.

—Importation of patented products in the Andean group / by German Cavelier. – Bogota, Columbia : Cavelier Abogados, 1985.
11 leaves.

—Importation of products with the same trademark / by German Cavelier. – Bogota, Colombia : Cavelier Abogados, 1985.
9 leaves.

→ Laws on the defense of the consumer.

Caves, Richard
Multinational enterprise and economic analysis / Richard E. Caves. – Cambridge : Cambridge University Press, 1982.
xi,346p; 22cm. – (Cambridge surveys of economic literature).
Bibliography: p306-335. - Includes index.
ISBN 0521249902 Hbk £20.00
ISBN 0521271150 Pbk £7.50

Cawthorn, John
Practical timesharing : UK and overseas. – London : Butterworths, 1988.
ISBN 0406100500 Pbk

—Residential estate conveyancing : practice and precedents / John Cawthorn. – London : Butterworths, 1983.
xviii,501p; 26cm.
Includes index.
ISBN 0406148201

—Sale and Management of Flats : Practice and Precedents. – London : Butterworths, 1985.
This book provides a practical guide to the subject of leasehold conveyancing in the United Kingdom. Particular attention is given to the establishment and maijntenance of subsequent management of the property from the tenant's and developer's point of view.
ISBN 0406526702 Hbk £38.00

Cawthra, B. I.
Patent licensing in Europe / by B.I. Cawthra. – 2nd ed. – London : Butterworths, 1986.
xxi,249p; 22cm.
Previous ed.: 1978. Bibliography: p236-240. - Includes index.
ISBN 0406148414 Hbk £47.00

Cay, J.
Abridgement of the Public Statutes in Force From Magna Carta : In Ninth Year of Henry III to Eleventh Year of George II Inclusive, Continued to First Year of George II inclusive, 2 Vols. – 2nd ed. Repr. of 1762 ed. – Abingdon : Professional Books.
567p.
Hbk £90.00

Cayman Islands law reports. – Oxford : Law Reports International, 1986-.

Caywood → Legal Environment for Foreign Direct Investment.

CCH Australia → Australian consumer sales and credit law reporter.
→ Australian labour law reporter.
→ Australian securities law reporter.
→ Australian trade practices reports.
→ Wage indexation and its aftermath.

CCH Australian companies and securities legislation / by the CCH company law editors. – 3. – North Ryde, N.S.W. : CCH Australia, 1987.
looseleaf.
'Publication originally issued in one volume in July 1982 (vol. 2 in November 1983) titled Australian companies legislation' - t.p. verso. Spine title: Australian companies and securities legislation.
ISBN 1862640270

CCH Guide to 1993 : Changes in European Economic Community Law. – London : CCH.
ISBN 0863252060 Pbk £15.00

Cecchim, P.
European Challenge : 1992. – Wildwood House, 1988.
ISBN 0704506130 Pbk £6.95

Cecchini, Paolo
European challenge, 1992 : the benefits of a single market / Paolo Cecchini : with Michel Catinat and Alexis Jacquemin. – English ed. – Aldershot : Gower, 1988.
xxi, 127 p.; 23 cm.
Spine title: 1992, the European challenge. Bibliography: p. 110-111.
ISBN 0704506130 Pbk

Cecil, Henry
Brief to counsel / by Henry Cecil : illustrated by Edward Ardizzone. – 3rd ed. – Chichester : Rose, 1982.
204p; 21cm.
Previous ed.: i.e. New ed. London : Joseph, 1972. Includes index.

Cecil, Ray
Professional Liability : An Architectural Press Legal Guide. – 2nd ed. – London : Architectural Press, 1986.
208p : Illus.
ISBN 0851399525 Hbk £19.95

Celebrated Criminal Trials in Scotland : 1536-1784. – Repr. of 1784 ed. – Abingdon : Professional Books.
Hbk £95.00

Celebrated Trials and Remarkable Cases of Criminal Jurisprudence : From the Earliest Records to the Year 1825, 6 Vols. – Repr. of 1825 ed. – Abingdon : Professional Books.
36p.
Hbk £450.00

Censorship and Political Communication Examples from Eastern Europe. – London : Pinter Publishers Ltd.
180p.
ISBN 0861872614 Hbk £19.00

Censorship and public morality / P. R. MacMillan. – Aldershot : Gower, 1983.
xxiii,547p; 24cm.
Bibliography: p521-530. - Includes index.
ISBN 0566003767 £22.95

Censorship in South Africa : being a commentary on the application of the Publications Act / J.C.W. van Rooyen. – Cape Town : Juta, 1987.
xxiv,152p.
Includes bibliograpical references and index.
ISBN 0702119059

Censorship, Legal Defence and Domestic Intelligence Service in W. Germany. – Russell Tribunal, III. – London : Spokesman Books, 1983.
50p.
Pbk individual 4.00

Centenary guide to the publications of the Selden Society. – Selden Society. – London : The Society, 1987.
242 p. – (Publications).
Supersedes: General guide to the Society's publications (1960).

Center for Studies and Research of the Hague Academy of International Law
Application of humanitarian law : selective bibliography prepared by the Peace Palace Library / Center for Studies and Research of the Hague Academy of International Law : bibliographie selective preparee par la Bibliotheque du Palais de la Paix : Centre d'Etude et de Recherche de l'Academie du droit Internationale de la Haye. – The Hague : Center for Studies and Research of the Hague Academy of International Law, 1986.
80p.
Preliminary material in English and French.

Central America's Indians / by David Stephen and Phillip Wearne : with a summary by Rodolfo Stavenhagen. – London : Minority Rights Group, 1984.
23p. – (Report).

Central Arbitration Committee Awards. – London : HMSO, 1984.
ISBN 0118885634 Hbk £7.85

Central Bank of Malaysia Ordinance 1958 (F.M. No. 61/1958). – Kuala Lumpur : International Law Books Services.
Hbk £6.00

Central Banking in Malaysia. – Singapore : Butterworths (Asia), 1987.
520.
Deals with powers over finance companies, merchant banks, Islamic banks and other deposit takers, issue of currency, monetary policy and regulation of the quantity and direction of credit, and the relationship with the government.
ISBN 0409995339 Hbk

Central Criminal Minor Acts : With state Amendments / Rakesh Bagga. – 3rd ed. – Allahabad : Law Book Company, 1988.
1,500p.
Hbk £350.00

Central Excise : Law, Practice and Procedure, 2 Vols. – Allahabad : Modern Law Publications, 1987.
Hbk £550.00

Central issues in jurisprudence : justice, law and rights / by N.E. Simmonds. – London : Sweet & Maxwell, 1986.
xi,155p; 22cm.
Includes bibliographies and index.
ISBN 0421351101 Hbk £18.00
ISBN 0421351209 Pbk £8.95

Central Legislature in India (1909-1935). – Calcutta, 1984.
282p.
ISBN 8185109389 Hbk £90.00

Central Sales Tax Act. – New Delhi : Bharat Law House, 1985.
Hbk £200.00

Central Sales Tax Laws / P. Kothary. – 6th ed. 2 vols. – Nagpur : Wadhura & Co, 1987.
Hbk £500.00

Central Trust Company Act, 1983, Bill 097 : An Act Respecting Central Trust Company and Crown Trust Company. – Ontario : Ontario Government Publications Service, 1983.
5p.
Hbk £0.30

Centre d'Etude et de Recherche de Droit International et de Relations Internationales
Application of Humanitarian Law. – Centre d'Etude et de Recherche de Droit International et de Relations Internationales. – Dordrecht : Kluwer, 1987.
106p.
ISBN 9024735084 Pbk £50.00

Centre for Advanced Land Use Studies
Commentary on a Commercial Lease. – Centre for Advanced Land Use Studies. – Reading : College of Estate Management, 1983.
ISBN 0902132725 Pbk £9.50

Centre for Environmental Management and Planning
Environmental assessment procedures : a study which focuses on certain oil and gas developments in Scotland in light of the proposed EEC directive : final report August 1984 / prepared by Centre for Environmental Management and Planning, University of Aberdeen. – Aberdeen : Centre for Environmental Management and Planning, 1984.
x, 68p, 6p.

Centre for Socio-Legal Studies → Case for the conversational analysis of courtroom interaction : some interactional dimensions of legal procedures.
→ New law-and-economics : a research review.

Centre for Socio-Legal Studies
Annual Report / Centre for Socio-Legal Studies. – Oxford : The Centre, 1984.
Continues: Report of the S.S.R.C. Centre for Socio-Legal Studies.

Centre for Studies and Research in International Law ad International Relations → Transfrontier Pollution and International Law : Pollution Transfrontiere et le Droit International.

Centre for Studies in Canadian Legal Education → Essays on legal education.

Centre of International and European Economic Law → Colloquy: Democracy and Human Rights.

Centre-State Relations in India : Constitutional Provisions, Judicial Review, Recent Trends. – New Delhi : Deep and Deep Publications, 1985.
826p.
Hbk £400.00

Centrum voor Grondslagenonderzoek van het Recht
Current legal theory : international journal for documentation on legal theory (bibliography - abstracts - reviews). – Centrum voor Grondslagenonderzoek van het Recht. – Leuven : Acco, 1983-.

Century of criminal justice : perspectives on the development of Canadian law / by Martin L. Friedland. – Toronto : Carswell Legal Publications, 1984.
xxii,245p.
ISBN 0459365800

Cerny, Philip G.
Socialism, The State, and Public Policy in France / Martin A. Schain. – London : Pinter Publishers Ltd, 1984.
220p.
ISBN 086187384X Hbk £21.00

Certain R.C.M.P. activities and the question of governmental knowledge : third report / Commission of Inquiry Concerning Certain Activities of the Royal Canadian Mounted Police. – Ottawa : Canadian Government Publishing Centre, 1981.
xv,527p; 25cm.
Chairman: D.C. McDonald.
ISBN 0660109530

Certoma, G.L., et al
Cases and Materials on Real Property. – 2nd ed. – North Ryde : Law Book Co, 1985.
xliii, 582p.
ISBN 0455203954 Hbk £63.00
ISBN 0455203962 Pbk £49.50
—Italian Legal System. – Sydney : Butterworths, 1985.
ISBN 0409490849 Hbk £37.00

Certoma, G. Leroy
Italian legal system / G. Leroy Certoma. – London : Butterworths, 1985.
xxiv,520p; 23cm. (Butterworths' legal systems of the world).
Bibliography: p493-500. - Includes index.
ISBN 040639993X Hbk £43.00

CGT Base Date Prices 31st March 1982. – Tolley Publishing, 1986.
ISBN 085459244X Pbk £15.00

Chadha, P.N.
Hindu Law (Students Ed.). – 6th ed. – Lucknow : Eastern Book Company, 1982.
354p.
Hbk £20.00
—Law of Partnership. – 3rd ed. – Lucknow : Eastern Book Company, 1982.
828p.
Hbk £110.00

Chai, Poh Chu
Law of insurance / by Poh Chu Chai. – Singapore : Malayan Law Journal Pte., 1986.
xxv,289p.
Covers the principles of insurance law with regard to insurable interest, duty of disclosure, formation of the contract of insurance, insurance agents, construction of policies, proximate cause of loss, subrogation and contribution, and assignment of policies. Three chapters cover motor insurance and the Motor Insurers' Bureau.
ISBN 9971700484

Chaikin, David A. →Guide to the Financial Services Act 1986.

Chairmanship in Magistrates' Courts / Keith Clarke. – Chichester : Barry Rose, 1981.
93p.
ISBN 0859921875 Hbk £4.00

Chakravarti, K.P.
Criminal Major Acts. – Calcutta : Eastern Law House, 1985.
Hbk £135.00

Chakraverti, S.
Cases and Materials on Code of Civil Procedure / B. Nath. – 3rd rev. ed. – Lucknow : Eastern Book Company, 1981.
1,717p.
Hbk £165.00

Chakraverti, Suranjan
Administrative Law and Tribunals. – 2nd ed. – Allahabad : Law Book Company, 1988.
700p.
Hbk £200.00
—Law of Dismissals. – 7th ed. – Allahabad : Law Book Company, 1985.
1,000p.
Hbk £250.00
—Law of Railway Servants. – 2nd ed. – Allahabad : Law Book Company, 1984.
With 1987 supplement.
Hbk £120.00
—Workmen's Compensation Act. – 3rd ed. – Allahabad : Law Book Company, 1986.
1,050p.
Hbk £220.00

Challenge of tax administration until the end of the 20th century : technical papers and reports of the 15th General Assembly of the Inter-American Center of Tax Administrators (CIAT), Mexico D.F., Mexico, 29 June - 3 July 1981. – Amsterdam : International Bureau of Fiscal Dopcumentation, 1984.
222p.
Bibliography: p.164-166.
ISBN 9070125242

Challenge of the Nigerian nation : an examination of its legal development, 1960-1985 / edited by T. Akinola Aguda. – Lagos : Nigerian Institute of Advanced Legal Studies, 1985.
xxxi,260p.
Includes bibliographical references and index.
ISBN 978129292X

Challenges to copyright and related rights in the European Community / Gillian Davies and Hans Hugo von Rauscher auf Weeg. – Oxford : ESC, 983.
xvii,271p.
Bibliography: p.253-258. - Includes index.
ISBN 0906214149

Challenges to the Legal Profession : Law and Investment in Developing Countries. – International Bar Association. – Lucknow : Eastern Book Company, 1985.
807p.
Hbk £200.00

Challenges to the legal profession : law and investment in developing countries : addresses, committee papers and reports of the 19th biennial conference of the International Bar Association at New Delhi. – International Bar Association. – Lucknow : Eastern Book Co. in co-ordination with the International Bar Association and the Bar Association of India, 1984.
xx,787p.

Challenging Capital Punishment : Legal and Social Science Approaches / Inciardi. – Sage Publications.
ISBN 0803929099 Hbk £32.00
ISBN 0803929102 Pbk £14.95

Challenging decision : papers from a conference held at Oxford, September 1985 / organised by the Bar Council, the Law Society and the Royal Institution of Chartered Surveyors. – London : Sweet & Maxwell, 1986.
vi,101p; 25cm.
Conference paper.
ISBN 0421361301 Pbk £22.00

Challenging Delegated Legislation. – Waterlow, 1988.
ISBN 0080330711 Hbk £19.95

Chalmers, D. R. C.
Criminal law and practice of Papua New Guinea / by Donald R. C. Chalmers, David Weisbrot, Warwick John Andrew. – 2nd ed. – Sydney : Law Book Co., 1985.
xxxiv,807p.
Previous ed.: 1979. Includes index.
ISBN 0455203989 Hbk £49.50
—Introduction to the law in Papua New Guinea / by D.R.C. Chalmers and A.H. Paliwala. – 2nd ed. – North Ryde, N.S.W. : Law Book Co, 1984.
xxiv,236p.
Includes bibliographies and index.
ISBN 0455203806
—Textbook for Legal Studies - Tasmania. – Butterworths, 1983.
322p.
ISBN 0409491209 Hbk £23.00
—Working paper on the law relating to contracts and the disposition of property by minors / by D.R.C. Chalmers. – Hobart? : Government Printer?, 1985.
49,iip.
Cover title.

Chalmers, M. D.
Chalmers' Marine Insurance Act 1906 / by the late Sir Mackenzie D. Chalmers. – 9th ed. – London : Butterworths, 1983.
xxxvi,288p; 23cm.
This book gives a detailed examination of the law of marine insurance in the United Kingdom. The new forms of policy used by Lloyd's and other insurance companies are reproduced in the appendices of this work.
ISBN 040656423X Hbk £20.50
—Chalmers' Sale of Goods Act 1979 : including the Factors Acts 1889 & 1890 / Michael Mark, Jonathan Mance. – 18th ed. – London : Butterworths, 1981.
xcv,405p; 23cm.
Sets out the Sale of Goods Act 1979 with annotations and commentaries. Other legislation covered includes: Unfair Contract Terms 1977, Consumer Safety Act 1978, Consumer Transaction (Restriction on Statements) 1976 to 1978, and the Price Markings (Bargain Offers) Order 1979.
ISBN 0406564485 Hbk £28.00
ISBN 0406564493 Pbk £18.00

Chalmers' Marine Insurance Act 1906 / by the late Sir Mackenzie D. Chalmers. – 9th ed. – London : Butterworths, 1983.
xxxvi,288p; 23cm.
This book gives a detailed examination of the law of marine insurance in the United Kingdom. The new forms of policy used by Lloyd's and other insurance companies are reproduced in the appendices of this work.
ISBN 040656423X Hbk £20.50

Chalmers' Sale of Goods Act 1979 : including the Factors Acts 1889 & 1890 / Michael Mark, Jonathan Mance. – 18th ed. – London : Butterworths, 1981.
xcv,405p; 23cm.
Sets out the Sale of Goods Act 1979 with annotations and commentaries. Other legislation covered includes: Unfair Contract Terms 1977, Consumer Safety Act 1978, Consumer Transaction (Restriction on Statements) 1976 to 1978, and the Price Markings (Bargain Offers) Order 1979.
ISBN 0406564485 Hbk £28.00
ISBN 0406564493 Pbk £18.00

Chalton, Simon →Data protection law.
→ Encyclopedia of data protection.

Chamber, Thomas J. →Practical Application of Evidence : Materials Prepared for a Continuing Legal Education Seminar Held in Vancouver, B.C., February 19, 1983.

Chamberlain, Edna R. →Implications of marital separation for young children.
—Legal services for low income persons in the United States and Britain : trends for consideration in Australia / Edna R. Chamberlain. – Canberra : Commonwealth Legal Aid Commission, 1981.
30p.
Includes bibliographical references.

Chamberlain, G.
Trading in options. – 2nd ed. – Cambridge : Woodhead-Faulkner, 1982.
ISBN 0859412180 Hbk £16.95

Chambers, G. A. →British crime survey Scotland.

Chambers, Gerry
Investigating sexual assault / Gerry Chambers, Ann Millar. – Edinburgh : H.M.S.O., 1983.
viii,142p. – (A Scottish Office social research study).
Bibliography: p.141-142.
ISBN 0114923272
—Prosecuting sexual assault / G. Chambers, A. Millar. – Edinburgh : H.M.S.O., 1986.
ix,144p.
Research by the Central Research Unit of the Scottish Office. Reports on police investigation of sexual assault cases and on prosecution and trial methods.
ISBN 0114933715

Chambers, M.
Managing Your Career in the Law. – London : Blackstone Press.
ISBN 1854310119 Hbk £8.00

Chambers Practice : 1988. – Vancouver : Continuing Legal Education Society of British Columbia, 1988.
89p.
ISBN 086504967X Hbk £65.00

Chambers, Robert
Course of lectures on the English law : delivered at the University of Oxford, 1767-1773 / by Sir Robert Chambers : and composed in association with Samuel Johnson : edited by Thomas M. Curley. – 2. – Oxford : Clarendon, 1986.
23cm.
Bibliography: p301-335. - Includes index.
ISBN 0198185448 £70.00

Chambost, Edouard
Bank accounts : a world guide to confidentiality / Edouard Chambost : translated by Peter Walton and Margaret Thompson. – Chichester : Wiley, 1983.
xii,322p; 24cm.
Includes index. Translation from French.
ISBN 0471900761 Hbk

Chan →Chinese Contract Cases.
—Governmental Accounting & Auditing : International Comparisons / Jones. – Routledge. – (International Accounting Series).
ISBN 0415012686 Hbk £30.00

Chan, Catherine
Divorce : an Australian Women's Guide. – Richmond : Heinemann.
144p.
ISBN 0858593114 Pbk £12.95

Chan, Dorothy →Annotation of the Singapore Companies (Amendment) Act 1987.

Chan, Helena H. M.
Introduction to the Singapore legal system / by Helena H.M. Chan. – Singapore : Malayan Law Journal Pte., 1986.
vi,140p.
Covers the legal history of Singapore, sources of law, structure of government, legal institutions, civil and criminal procedure, and a chapter devoted to legal culture and the future development of the law.
ISBN 9971700549

Chan, Janet B.L.
Law and the Chinese in Canada : a Case Study in Ethnic Perceptions of the Law / John Hagan. – Toronto : University of Toronto, Centre of Criminology, 1982.
viii, 103p.
ISBN 0919584551 Pbk £6.00

Chan, Johannes →Civil liberties in Hong Kong.

Chan, Julie S.
Practical Guide to Law Office Automation : 1988 / Kenneth A. Grant. – Agincourt : Carswell, 1988.
274p.
This 1988 edition provides information towards the selection and implementation of a law office automation system. Guidelines also include a comprehensive directory of software in Canada for lawyers and a glossary of common terms and definitions. The book also outlines the benefits of automation and the process of selecting and implementing a computer system.
Hbk £40.50

Chan, Laurence →Handbook of Singapore Tax Statutes, 1985-86 Edition.

Chan, P.
China Modernisation and Legal Development. – 2nd ed. – London : Longman Professional, 1987.
ISBN 0851208045 Hbk £27.50
ISBN 0851208043 Pbk £17.50

Chan, Peter P.
People's Republic of China : Modernisation and Legal Development. – London : Oyez Longman, 1983.
ISBN 0851208045 Hbk £22.50

Chance, John K. → Latin American urbanization.

Chancery practice / Edmund Heward. – London : Butterworths, 1983.
xx,198p.
Includes index.
ISBN 040622451X

Chancery practice handbook / Robert Blackford in collaboration with Colin Jaque : additional material by Richard Archdale. – London : Oyez Longman, 1983.
xx,252p; 24cm.
Includes bibliographies and index.
ISBN 0851207456 £16.50

Chand, Hari
Land Use Act : issues and controversies / by Hari C. Chand. – Jos, Nigeria : University of Jos, 1985.
22p. – (Postgraduate open lectures series).
Includes bibliographical references.
—Nigerian constitutional law / by Hari Chand. – 2nd ed. – Modinagar : Santosh Publishing House, 1982.
296p.
Includes index.

Chand, Tek
Law of Contempt of Court. – Allahabad : Universal Book Agency.
Hbk £225.00

Chandak
Law of Notices : Civil and Criminal, with Model Forms. – 4th ed. – Allahabad : Law Book Co, 1984.
Hbk £150.00

Chandler, Peter
A-Z of Employment and Safety Law. – London : Kogan Page, 1981.
516p.
ISBN 085038446X Hbk £16.95

Chandra, Mahesh
Gratuity Law in India. – Suppl. – Bombay : Tripathi, 1973.
Hbk £8.00

Chandra, Ramesh
Controls over public corporations in India / Ramesh Chandra : foreword by V. R. Krishna Iyer. – Delhi : Delhi University, 1981.
xx,487p.
Bibliography: p.447-482. - Includes index.

Chandra, Satish
Civil and Political Rights of the Aliens : a Study in National and International Laws. – New Delhi : Deep and Deep Publications, 1982.
224p.
Hbk £80.00
—Individual's Petition in International Law. – New Delhi : Deep and Deep Publications, 1985.
287p.
Hbk £150.00
—International Protection of Minorities. – Delhi : Mittal Publications, 1986.
Hbk £160.00
—Law of the Sea : Text of U.N. Conventions. – Delhi : Mittal Publications, 1985.
Hbk £190.00
—Minorities in National and International Laws. – New Delhi : Deep and Deep Publications, 1985.
376p.
Hbk £200.00

Chandra, Subhash
Commentary on the Working of the Customs Act 1962. – New Delhi : S. Chand and Company.
Hbk £10.00

Chandrasekhar, S.
Population and Law in India. – New Delhi : S. Chand and Company.
Hbk £30.00

Chang, Grace
Introduction to civil procedure in Malaysia and Singapore / by Grace Chang. – Singapore : Malayan Law Journal Pte., 1986.
iii,165p.
Includes index.
ISBN 997170045X

Chang, Min Tat → Mallal's Supreme Court Practice, Vol 1.

Change : a Time for Reflection : a National Invitational Symposium on Public Legal Education. – Ottawa : Canadian Law Information Council, 1983.
150p.
ISBN 0920358438 Pbk £15.00

Change and Adjustment : External Relations and Industrial Policy of the European Communities. – Dordrecht : Kluwer, 1983.
240p.
ISBN 9065440887 Pbk £120.00

Change and stability in international law-making / edited by Antonio Cassese and Joseph H.H. Weiler. – Berlin : De Gruyter, 1988.
x,214. – (Series A–Law).
Includes indexes. Based on the proceedings of two international colloquia held at the European University Institute, Florence.
ISBN 3110114941 Hbk £90

Change in Eastern Europe. – Exeter : European Atlantic Movement, 1982.
Hbk £0.50

Change in marriage : a collection of papers presented at the National Guidance Council study days. – Rugby : National Marriage Guidance Council, 1982.
139p; 21cm.
ISBN 0853510563 Pbk £3.50

Change of name. – 13th ed. – London : Longman Professional, 1985.
ISBN 0851209890 Pbk £11.95

Changing Caribbean constitutions / Francis Alexis. – St. Michael, Barbados : Antilles, 1983.
xxviii,281p.
Bibliography: p.270-274. - Includes index.

Changing constitution / edited by Jeffrey Jowell and Dawn Oliver. – Oxford : Clarendon, 1985.
xix,377p; 24cm.
Includes index.
ISBN 0198761767 Hbk £27.50
ISBN 0198761759 Pbk £13.95

Changing constitution / Jeffrey L Jowell, Dawn Oliver. – 2nd. – Oxford : Clarendon Press, 1989.
416; 23.5.
Collections of essays on the nature and evolutin of the British consitution. Essays on local government and on nationalised industries have been rewritten, and there is a new essay on Northern Ireland and the British Constitution.
Students and teachers of consitutional law and administrative law, and British government and politics
ISBN 0198252765 Hbk £40.00
ISBN 0198252773 Pbk £15.00

Changing contempt of court / by Andrew Nicol and Heather Rogers. – London : National Council for Civil Liberties, 1981.
40p.
ISBN 0901108928

Changing contours of British industrial relations : a survey of manufacturing industry / edited by William Brown : with contributions by Eric Batstone ... et al. – Oxford : Basil Blackwell, 1981.
xi,160p; 23cm.
Bibliography: p149-153. - Includes index.
ISBN 0631127755 Hbk £10.00
ISBN 0631128255 Pbk £4.50

Changing Image of the Magistracy. – 2nd ed. – London : Macmillan, 1984.
272p.
ISBN 0333362799 Hbk £33.00
ISBN 0333362802 Pbk £7.95

Changing law / Robin White, Patfield. – London : Pinter, 1990.
224.
A survey of the radical and rapid changes to English law in the last 25 years. Covers negligence, land, family, financial regulation, civil liberties, social security, EC law, reform of the legal profession and codification of common law principles.
ISBN 0718513312 Hbk £29.50

Changing Law, The. – Reprint. – Sweet & Maxwell, 1953.
ISBN 0421375809 Hbk £15.75

Changing laws for changing families / Patricia Harper. – Melbourne : Institute of Family Studies, 1982.
24p. – (Discussion paper).
Paper prepared for the 3rd Australian Conference on adoption, 'Changing Families', Adelaide, 14-19 May 1982.
ISBN 0642884552

Changing policing : a conference based on the Scarman Report, 1 May 1982 : proceedings / edited by David Armstrong. – London : University of London Department of Extra-Mural Studies, 1982.
70p.
'Proceedings of a conference held at the University of London, 1 May 1982'.

Changing structure of international economic law : a contribution of legal history, of comparative law and of general legal theory to the debate on a new international economic order / by Pieter VerLoren van Themaat. – The Hague : Martinus Nijhoff, 1981.
xxv,395p.
English edition of VerLoren van Themaat, P. : Rechtsgrondslagen van een nieuwe internationale economische orde.
ISBN 9024725402 Hbk £165.00

Changing structure of the world oil industry / edited by David Hawdon. – London : Croom Helm, 1985.
1v.
Conference papers.
ISBN 0709937172 £14.95

Changing the language of the law : the Sri Lanka experience / L. J. Mark Cooray. – Quebec : Presses de l'Universite Laval, 1985.
183p.
ISBN 2763770800

Changing the system : political and constitutional reform, some options and difficulties / by Donald Horne ... et al. – Bedford Park : Australasian Political Studies Association, 1981.
44 p.; 22 cm. – (Monograph / Australasian Political Studies Association).
ISBN 0909266190 Pbk

Channan, Omkar Nath
Role of the court interpreter / by Omkar Nath Channan : with a foreword by the Lord Hailsham of St Marylebone. – London : Shaw, 1982.
44p; 22cm.
ISBN 0721909205 Pbk

Channon, Gordon → Inheritance tax.

Chanock, Martin
Law, custom and social order : the colonial experience in Malawi and Zambia / Martin Chanock. – Cambridge : Cambridge University Press, 1985.
xi,286p; 24cm. – (African studies series).
Examines development of customary law in African law during the colonial period. Studies how customary law developed alongside criminal law in Malawi and Zambia.
ISBN 0521301378 £25.00

Chant, Andrew → Banking and Finance Law Review.

Chapell, Stuart
Tax and financial planning for Lloyd's members. – London : Longman Professional, 1988. – (A Longman Intelligence Report).
ISBN 0851213421 Hbk £85.00

Chaplais, Pierre
Essays in Medieval diplomacy and administration / Pierre Chaplais. – London : Hambledon, 1981.
496p in various pagings,16p of plates; 25cm.
Includes index. English and French text.
ISBN 0950688223

Chapman
Employment Claims in the County Court / Lloyd-Jones. – London : Low Pay Unit, 1988.
ISBN 0905211413 Pbk £1.00

Chapman, A. L.
Capital transfer tax / A.L. Chapman. – 6th ed. – London : Longman, 1985.
xlv,656p; 24cm.
ISBN 0851209335
—Inheritance tax. – 7th ed. – London : Longman Professional, 1987.
ISBN 085121326X Hbk £48.00
ISBN 0851214673 Pbk
→ Tolley's company law.
→ Tolley's tax planning 1982-83.
→ Tolleys tax planning supplement.

Chapman, Antony J. → Psychology and law : topics from an internatinal conference.

Chapman, Bruce → Justice, rights and tort law.

Chapman, Evadna
Conveyancing Made Easy : a Teaching Text for Lawyers and Their Secretaries. – Vancouver : Fountain Books, 1982.
254p.
ISBN 0969000901 Hbk £30.00

Chapman, Ivan
Leonski the Brown-out Strangler. – Neutral Bay : Hale & Iremonger.
ISBN 0908094981 Hbk £24.95, 015
ISBN 090809499X Pbk £11.95, 015

Chapman, Philippa
Youth and Social Control. – Canberra : Australian Institute of Criminology.
free

Chapman, R.
You and your home. – London : Shaw & Sons, 1984.
ISBN 0721909906 Pbk £4.50

Chapman, Tom
Has the Trade Union Movement a Place in Europe?. – Exeter : European Atlantic Movement, 1982.
Hbk £0.50

Chapman's Inheritance Tax Supplement. – London : Longman Professional.
ISBN 00851214673 Hbk £20.00

Chappell, David → Building Contract Dictionary : An Architectural Press Legal Guide.
→ Building Contracts Tabulated and Compared : An Architectural Press Legal Guide.
—JCT Intermediate Form of Contract : An Architectural Press Legal Guide / Vincent Powell-Smith. – London : Architectural Press, 1985.
232p : Illus.
ISBN 0851398855 Hbk £19.95
—JCT Minor Works Form of Contract : An Architectural Press Legal Guide / Vincent Powell-Smith. – London : Architectural Press, 1986.
176p : Illus.
ISBN 0851398863 Hbk £18.00

Chappell, Duncan
Australian Criminal Justice System : The Mid 1980's / Paul Wilson. – Butterworths, 1987.
348p.
The authors of this book, who include criminologists, sociologists, lawyers, and academics, cover such matters as sexual assault, corporate crime, terrorism, sentencing, organized crime, and juvenile offenses.
ISBN 0409491497 Hbk £46.00
—Criminal investigation : a selective literature review and bibliography / by Duncan Chappell, Robert Gordon, Rhonda Moore. – Ottawa : Ministry of the Solicitor General, Communication Division, 1982.
68p.
ISBN 0662120310

→ Rape law reform in South Australia : a study of the background to the reforms of 1975 and 1976 and of their subsequent impact.

Chappenden, W. J. →Helmore's personal property and mercantile law in New South Wales.
→ Joske's law and procedure at meetings in Australia.

Char
Income Support and Housing Benefit for Single People. – Turnaround Press.
ISBN 0906951399 Pbk £5.95
→ Poor law : the mass arrest of homeless claimants in Oxford.

Charendoff, Susan →Justice Delayed : Nazi War Criminals in Canada.

Charge document in criminal cases. – Law Reform Commission of. – Ottawa : The Commission, 1987.
57,63p. – (Working paper).
Includes bibliographical references. Added t.p. in French: Le document d'inculpation. Pages numbered in opposite directions. Text in English and French.
ISBN 0662549635

Charge-Sheet, Enquiry and Punishment. – Karachi : Bureau of Labour Publications, 1983.
36p.
Pbk £3.00

Chari, A.S.R.
Trials of Strength. – Allahabad : Orient Law House.
ISBN 0861253574 Hbk £13.00

Charitable status : a practical handbook / Andrew Phillips with Keith Smith. – 2nd ed. – London : Inter-Action, 1982.
83p; 22cm. – (Inter-action guides).
Previous ed.: 1980. Bibliography: p74-76. - Includes index.
ISBN 0904571394 Pbk £3.95

Charitable Status - A Practical Handbook / Kenneth Smith. – 2nd ed. – TUAR, 1982.
ISBN 0904571394 Pbk £4.50

Charities Administration. – ICSA. – Cambridge : Woodhead-Faulkner, 1986.
ISBN 0902197274 updat £55.00

Charities in Britain : conservatism or change? / David Gerard. – London : Bedford Square Press/NCVO, 1983.
187p; 22cm.
Bibliography: p171-179. - Includes index.
ISBN 0719910927 Pbk £5.95

Charities law and practice / Elizabeth Cairns. – London : Sweet & Maxwell, 1988.
xxi,258p; 26cm.
Includes the procedure for establishing a new charity and the relative advantages of trusts, companies, and unincorporated associations for different types of charity; how to draft the government instrument, and to what extent charities may engage in political activity. Taxation and administrative matters are also covered.
ISBN 0421358106 £19.50

Charities Manual. – 2nd ed. – Tolley Publishing, 1988.
ISBN 085459325X Hbk £25.00

Charities payroll giving schemes : proposals for tax relief / Inland Revenue. – London : Board of Inland Revenue, 1986.
12p.

Charity Accounting / Vincent. – London : Butterworths, 1987.
ISBN 0406261008 Pbk £19.95

Charity, law and social justice / Francis Gladstone. – London : Bedford Square Press, 1982.
v,211p.
ISBN 0719910846

Charles Dickens and The Poor Man's Tale of a Patent. – Oxford : ESC Publishing Ltd, 1984.
53p.
ISBN 0906214300 Hbk £5.50

Charles-Edward, T.M.
The Welsh Laws. – Cardiff : University of Wales Press.
ISBN 070831032X Pbk £3.50

Charles, W. H. R.
Supreme Court of Canada handbook on assessment of damages in personal injury cases / by W.H.R. Charles. – Ontario : Carswell Co., 1982.
129p.
'Reprint of an article in Volume 18 Part 1 of Canadian cases on the law of torts'.
ISBN 0459346709

Charlesworth & Percy on negligence / John Charlesworth, R. A. Percy. – 7th ed. – London : Sweet & Maxwell, 1983.
cxxxviii,1092p; 26cm.
Includes changes and developments in the law of negligence since the 1977 edition, and has been divided into six major sections. Updated to include the Unfair Contract Terms Act 1977, the Limitation Act 1980, the British Telecommunications Act 1981, the Civil Aviation Act 1982, and the Administration of Justice Act 1982.
ISBN 042129020X £70.00

Charlesworth, John
Charlesworth & Percy on negligence / John Charlesworth, R. A. Percy. – 7th ed. – London : Sweet & Maxwell, 1983.
cxxxviii,1092p; 26cm.
Includes changes and developments in the law of negligence since the 1977 edition, and has been divided into six major sections. Updated to include the Unfair Contract Terms Act 1977, the Limitation Act 1980, the British Telecommunications Act 1981, the Civil Aviation Act 1982, and the Administration of Justice Act 1982.
ISBN 042129020X £70.00
—Charlesworth's company law / Geoffrey Morse, Enid A. Marshall, Richard- Morris, John Charlesworth. – 13th ed. – London : Stevens & Sons, 1987.
xciv, 850p.
Previous ed.: published as Company law. 1983. Includes index.
ISBN 0420477209 Pbk £15.00
ISBN 0420477306 £9.50

—Charlesworth's Mercantile law / Clive M. Schmitthoff, David A. G. Sarre. – 14th ed. – London : Stevens, 1984.
ix,733p; 22cm.
Previous ed.: 1977. Includes index.
ISBN 0420465707 Pbk £
ISBN 0420465804 Pbk £6.50

—Company law / Thomas Ewan Cain, Geoffrey Morse, Enid A. Marshall. – 12th ed. – London : Stevens, 1983.
700p.
Previous ed.: 1977.
ISBN 0420460306 Hbk £12.00
ISBN 0420460403 Pbk £5.50

Charlesworth's company law / Geoffrey Morse, Enid A. Marshall, Richard- Morris, John Charlesworth. – 13th ed. – London : Stevens & Sons, 1987.
xciv, 850p.
Previous ed.: published as Company law. 1983. Includes index.
ISBN 0420477209 Pbk £15.00
ISBN 0420477306 £9.50

Charlesworth's Mercantile law / Clive M. Schmitthoff, David A. G. Sarre. – 14th ed. – London : Stevens, 1984.
ix,733p; 22cm.
Previous ed.: 1977. Includes index.
ISBN 0420465707 Pbk
ISBN 0420465804 Pbk £6.50

Charlterton, D A
Wills / Edited by Clive Brand. – London : Longman Professional, 1988.
– (Longman Practice Notes Series).
ISBN 085121410X Pbk

Charlton, Linda →Canadian Native Law Cases, Vol. 3 1891-1910.

Charlwood
Bank Register. – London : Euromoney, 1988.
ISBN 187003161X Hbk £95.00

Chart of Privy Council decisions with reference to the British North America Act. – 4 folded charts. – Ottawa : Canadian Law Information Council, .

Charter 77 and human rights in Czechoslovakia / H. Gordon Skilling. – London : Allen & Unwin, 1981.
xv,363p; 24cm.
Bibliography: p345-351. - Includes index.
ISBN 0043210260

Charter Issues in Civil Cases / Brian MacLeod Rogers. – Agincourt : Carswell, 1988.
327p.
Hbk £46.25

Charter Litigation. – Butterworths, 1987.
480p.
Examines the procedural, evidential and remedial issues arising in Charter litigation. Considers remedial issues and the use of social science data and other extrinsic evidence. Examines the relevance of American and European sources. Covers intervention and Amicus Curiae, the Charter and social change, proof of facts, legislative history, the relevance of American constitutional law, and damages as a Charter remedy.
ISBN 0409805270 Hbk £85.00

Charter of Rights, 1987. – Vancouver : Continuing Legal Education Society of British Columbia, 1987.
299p.
ISBN 0865043116 Hbk £70.00

Charter of Rights and administrative law, 1983-1984 / section head, Garry J. Smith. – Agincourt, Ont. : Carswell Legal Publications, 1983.
xxix, 184 p.; 29 cm. – (Bar admission course materials / Law Society of Upper Canada).
Includes index. Bibliography: p. 173-179.
ISBN 0459360906

Charter of Rights Decisions. – Aurora : Canada Law Book Co.
– (Summary Services, National Series).
Hbk £135.00
Back Vols.. –
Hbk £45.00 ea.

Charter of the Islamic Conference and legal framework of economic co-operation among its member states : a study of the charter, the General Agreement for Economic, Technical and Commercial Co-operation and the Agreement for Promotion, Protection and Guarantee of Investments among Member States of the OIC / Hasan Moinuddin. – Oxford : Clarendon, 1986.
xx,322p; 22cm.
Bibliography: p297-313. - Includes index.
ISBN 0198255241 £30.00

Charter Parties. – Oxford : Blackwell Scientific, 1988.
ISBN 063202061X Hbk

Charter principles and proof in criminal cases / David M. Paciocco. – Toronto : Carswell, 1987.
xlviii,616p.
Includes index.
ISBN 0459308114

Chartered Assoc. Certified Accountants Organization & Management. – Pitman.
ISBN 027302941X Pbk £10.95

Chartered Associaiton of Certified Accountants
→Role of an auditor in detecting fraud and other irregularities : a study.

Chartered Association of Certified Accountants Accounting. – Pitman.
ISBN 0273027956 Pbk £11.95

Chartered Association of Certified Accountants Economics. – Pitman.
ISBN 0273028057 Pbk £11.95

Chartered Institute of Building →Professional liability and construction.

Chartered Institute of Building, UK
Contracts and Building Law. Vol. 2. – Chartered Institute of Building, UK. – King's Ride : Institute of Building.
Hbk £6.60

Chartered Institute of Management Accountants
CIMA Study Text Stage 4 : Management Accounting. – Chartered Institute of Management Accountants. – London : BPP.
ISBN 0862771544 Pbk £15.95

Chartered Institute of Patent Agents →C.I.P.A. guide to The Patents Acts.
—European Patents Handbook, 3 Vols. – Chartered Institute of Patent Agents. – London : Oyez Longman, 1983.
ISBN 0851203299 Hbk £145.00
→ Patent co-operation treaty : a new era : papers prepared for presentation at a seminar held at the Brewery Conference Centre...November 11, 1985.

Charterers' liability insurance / by Dieter Schwampe : translated from the German by Burravoe Ltd. – London : Lloyd's of London Press, 1988.
xx,156p; 24cm.
Bibliography: pp.145-151. - Includes index. Translated from the German.
ISBN 1850441847 £45.00

Chartering documents / by Per Gram. – London : Lloyd's of London Press, 1981.
xiii,177p.
Includes index.
ISBN 0907432034

Charterparties : a comparative study of South African, English and American law / Anne Waring. – Cape Town : Juta, 1983.
lx,417p.
Based on a thesis submitted for PhD, University of the Witwatersrand, Johannesburg. Bibliography: p.xix-xxvi. - Includes index.
ISBN 0702113441

Charter-parties conference : a two-day conference / organised by Lloyd's of London Press. – 1. – London : Lloyd's of London Press, 1982.
various pagings.
ISBN 0907432476

Charterwatch : Reflections on Equality / A. Wayne MacKay. – Agincourt : Carswell, 1986.
320p.
This work presents eight essays on the political and legal implications of the guarantee of equality in the Canadian Charter of Rights and Freedom. The role of the judiciary in shaping the concept of equality in Canadian law is emphasized in the essays.
Hbk £40.50

Chatterjee, A.P.
Interpretation of Statutes. – 2nd ed. – Calcutta : Eastern Law House, 1983.
Hbk £108.00

Chatterjee, J.
Objective Type Questions and Answers in Mercantile Law. – New Delhi : Kalyani Publishers.
Hbk £12.00
—Problems in Mercantile Law. – New Delhi : Kalyani Publishers.
Hbk £12.00

Chatterjee, S. K
Legal aspects of international drug control / S.K. Chatterjee. – The Hague : Nijhoff, 1981.
xxiv,587p.
Includes index. Bibliography: p547-555. Based on the author's thesis (doctoral–University of London).
ISBN 9024725569 Hbk £285.00

Chatterjee, S.P.
West Bengal Premises Tenancy Act 1956. – Calcutta : B. Chand and Sons.
Hbk £8.00

Chatterton
Committals for Trial to the Crown Court : the Law and Practice / Brown. – London : Fourmat.
ISBN 1851900586 Pbk £18.95

Chatterton, Clifford E. M.
Bail : law and practice / Clifford Chatterton. – London : Butterworths, 1986.
xxiii,277p; 25cm.
Includes index.
ISBN 0406101809 Pbk £28.00
—Sentencing approach / Clifford E.M. Chatterton. – Chichester : Rose, 1984.
43p; 22cm.
ISBN 0859923576 Pbk £7.50
—Summary of the powers of the juvenile court / by Clifford E.M. Chatterton. – Plymouth : Basset Publications, 1985.
viii,33p.
ISBN 0946873089

Chatterton, D.A.
Wills Longman Practice Notes Series. – London : Longman Professional.
ISBN 095121410X Pbk £10.95

Chattopadhyaya, Digambar → Vivadaratnakara of Candesvara Thakkura : Law of Partition and Inheritance.

Chaturvedi
Elements of Income Tax Law. – Allahabad : Law Book Company.
Hbk £200.00
—Law of Fundamental Rights / Chaudhari. – 2nd ed. – Allahabad : Law Book Company, 1984.
Hbk £225.00

Chaturvedi, A.
District Administration : The Dynamics of Discord. – Sage Publications.
ISBN 0803995601 Hbk £17.25
ISBN 080399561X Pbk £10.50

Chaturvedi, A.N.
Rights of Accused under Indian Constitution. – New Delhi : Deep and Deep Publications, 1984.
380p.
Hbk £200.00

Chaturvedi, Arun
South Asian States and Sea Laws. – Bapu Nagar : Printwell, 1987.
218p.
ISBN 8170440467 Hbk £165.00

Chaturvedi, J.P.
Press Laws of the World. – New Delhi : Allied Publishers.
Hbk

Chaturvedi, K.
Central Sales Tax Laws / P. Kothary. – 6th ed. 2 vols. – Nagpur : Wadhura & Co, 1987.
Hbk £500.00
—Income Tax Law
Vol. 1: 1981 / S.M. Pithisaria. – 3rd ed. – Calcutta : Eastern Law House.
Hbk £180.00
—Principles of Sales Tax Laws, 2 Vols. / P. Kothary. – 5th ed. – Nagpur : Wadhura & Co, 1987.
£630.00

Chaturvedi, R.G.
Law and Procedure of Departmental Enquiries and Disciplinary Actions : Public and Private Servants. – Allahabad : Law Book Company, 1985.
Hbk £240.00
—Law of Claims. – Allahabad : Law Book Company, 1981.
Includes 1986 supplement.
Hbk £160.00
—Yearly All-India Criminal Digest, 1986. – Allahabad : Law Book Company, 1987.
400p.
Hbk £140.00

Chaudhari
Law of Confessions Approvers and Accomplices. – 7th ed. – Allahabad : Law Book Company, 1988.
ca 600p.
Hbk £200.00
→ Law of Fundamental Rights.

Chaudhary, Roop L.
Studies in Caribbean labour relations / Roop L. Chaudhary. – 2nd ed. – Barbados : Coles Printery, 1984.
xi,234p.
Includes index.
—West Indian cases on the law of contract / Roop L. Chaudhary and Andrew Burgess. – 2nd ed. – Barbados : Coles Printery, 1984.
xvii,316p.

Chaudhary, U.K.
Capital Issues (Law and Procedure). – New Delhi : Bharat Law House, 1987.
Hbk £200.00
—Idra and Industrial Licensing : With Rules Forms Notifications, Press Notes, Guidelines, Policies. – New Delhi : Bharat Law House, 1987.
Hbk £260.00

Chauhan, B. R.
Settlement of international water law disputes in international drainage basins / by B.R. Chauhan. – Berlin : Schmidt, 1981.
480p; 21cm.
ISBN 3503019294

Chavan, R.S.
Approach to International Law. – 2nd rev. ed. – New Dehli : Sterling Publishers, 1983.
384p.
ISBN 8120702395 Hbk £90.00
ISBN 8120704371 £22.50
—Indian Private International Law. – New Delhi : Sterling Publishers, 1982.
248p.
ISBN 8120702409 Hbk £75.00
ISBN 812070438X Pbk £25.00

Chawla, R.C.
Commercial Law / K.C. Garg. – rev. ed. – New Delhi : Kalyani Publishers, 1987.
Hbk £32.00
—Elements of Company Law / K.C. Garg. – New Delhi : Kalyani Publishers.
Hbk £18.00
—Indian Mercantile Law and Industrial Law / K.C. Garg. – New Delhi : Kalyani Publishers, 1984.
Hbk £25.00
—Industrial and Commercial Law / K.C. Garg. – 7th ed. 1986 repr. – New Delhi : Kalyani Publishers, 1987.
ISBN 8170960932 Hbk £60.00
—Mercantile Law / K.C. Garg. – 4th ed. 1987 repr. – New Delhi : Kalyani Publishers.
ISBN 8170960517 Hbk £60.00
—Textbook of Industrial Law / K.C. Garg. – 5th ed. – New Delhi : Kalyani Publishers, 1986.
Hbk £25.00

Chaytor → Forms of Action at Common Law.

Cheang, Molly → Index to Singapore/Malaysia legal periodicals 1932-1984.
—Law of negotiable instruments in Singapore and Malaysia. – Singapore : Malayan Law Journal, 1984.
xxviii,225.
Account of the basic law governing negotiable instruments, covering the curent practice where relevant. Includes status of parties to the bill upon its enforceability. Relevant Asian and English cases are discussed including some of the leading Commonwealth authorities from Australia and Canada.
ISBN 9971700409 Hbk £50.00
—New Tables of the Written Laws of the Republic of Singapore. – Kent Ridge : Malaya Law Review, 1982.
ISBN 9971620332 Hbk £99.00
→ Penal Codes of Singapore and Malaysia, Vol 2 : Cases, Materials and Comments.

Cheats at work : an anthropology of workplace crime / Gerald Mars. – London : Unwin Paperbacks, 1983.
xii,242p; 20cm.
Originally published: London : Allen and Unwin, 1982. Bibliography: p229-234. - Includes index.
ISBN 0043011667 Pbk £2.95

Checklist of law reports and statutes in Canadian law libraries
4 : Canadian statutes and regulations : Statuts et reglements du Canada / National Library of Canada Resources Survey Division, Collections Development Branch : Bibliotheque nationale du Canada, Division de l'inventaire des ressources, Direction du developpement des collections. – Ottawa : The Library, 1981.
xii,249p.
Includes index. Text in English and French.
ISBN 0660504529

Checklist of Royal Commissions : Select Committees of Parliament and Boards of Inquiry, Commonwealth, New South Wales, Queensland, Tasmania and Victoria, 1960-1980 and South Australia 1970-1980. – Bundoora : La Trobe University, Borchardt Library, 1986.
ISBN 0858166429 Hbk £45.00

Checklists For Solicitors. – 5th ed. – London : Longman Professional, 1987.
ISBN 0851211720 Pbk £15.95

Check-Lists for Solicitors. – 4th ed. – London : Oyez Longman, 1983.
Hbk £9.95

Cheeseright, Paul
Interference or Internationalism : The Extraterritorial Application of National Laws Regulating Business Activities
Vol. 4. – Enstone : Ditchley Foundation.
1982p.
Hbk
—Interference or Internationalism? Conference Report No. 3. – Entstone : Ditchley Foundation, 1982.
Hbk

Cheesley, Roger G. → Bennett and Cheesley : Let's Go Into Business.

Cheifetz, David
Apportionment of fault in tort / David Cheifetz. – Ontario : Canada Law Book, 1981.
xlii,355p.
ISBN 0888040091

Chell, Elizabeth → Worker-directors in private manufacturing industry in Great Britain.

Chemical industry and the projected chemical weapons convention : proceedings of a SIPRI/Pugwash conference. – 2. – Oxford : Published on behalf of Stockholm International Peace Research Institute by Oxford University Press, 1986.
30cm.
Includes bibliography.
ISBN 0198291094 Pbk £9.95

Chemicals Control Legislation : an International Glossary of Key Terms. – Paris : OECD, Organisation for Economic Co-operation and Development, 1982.
72p.
ISBN 9264123644 Hbk £13.50

Chen, Albert H.Y. → Basic Law and Hong Kong's Future.

Ch'en, Paul Heng-chao
Formation of the early Meiji legal order : the Japanese code of 1871 and its Chinese foundation / by Paul Heng-Chao Ch'en. – Oxford : Oxford University Press, 1981.
xxii,204p; 23cm.
Bibliography: p187-190. - Includes index.
ISBN 019713601X £12.00

Cheney, Christopher
English church and its laws 12th-14th centuries / C.R. Cheney. – London : Variorum Reprints, 1982.
348p in various pagings; 23cm. – (Collected studies series).
Includes index. Text in English and Latin.
ISBN 0860781089

Cheney, Christopher R.
Papacy and England : 12th-14th Centuries. – Northampton : Variorum, 1982.
346p : Illus.. – – (Collected Studies Ser.: CS 154).
ISBN 0860780996 Hbk £24.00

Cheng, B.
Law of International Air Transport. – Sweet & Maxwell, 1962.
ISBN 0420354808 Hbk £95.00

Cheng, Bin → Contemporary problems of international law : essays in honour of Georg Schwarzenberger on his eightieth birthday.
→ International law teaching and practice.
—Role of law in society : East and West, national and international / by Bin Cheng. – S.l. : s.n., 1981.
p.15-18.
Reprinted from: Chinese University bulletin, Winter 1978. Cover title with subtitle: 'Address on behalf of the honorary graduates at the twentieth Congregation of the Chinese University of Hong Kong on Thursday, 30th November 1978'.

Cheng, Chia-Jui
Basic Documents on International Trade Law. – Dordrecht : Kluwer, 1986.
766p.
ISBN 9024731682 Hbk £350.00

Chengsi, Zheng
Chinese intellectual property and technology transfer Law / by Zheng Chengsi with Michael D. Pendleton. – London : Sweet & Maxwell, 1987.
xli,331p; 26cm.
Presents a summary and analysis of Chinese intellectual property and technology transfer law covering the Chinese system, patents, trademarks, copyright, transfer of technology and software protection, taxation in the field of intellectual property, and containing appendices of original source material.
ISBN 0421383801 £50.00

Chernobyl : law and communication : transboundary nuclear air pollution : the legal materials / Philippe Sands. – Cambridge : Grotius, 1988.
xxxiii,312p.
Reproduces texts including multilateral and bilateral treaties, non-binding acts of international organisations and private associations of scholars, and national legislation. Covers the development of the law up to and including the 1986 IAEA Conventions on Early Notification and assistance, and the 1987 Resolution of the Institut de Droit International on Transboundary Air Pollution.
ISBN 0949009229 £38.00

Chernobyl : the real story / by Richard F. Mould. – Oxford : Pergamon, 1988.
90p; 25cm.
Includes index.
ISBN 0080357180 Hbk £12.90 :
ISBN 0080357199 Pbk £6.90

Chernobyl and the safety of nuclear reactors in OECD countries : report / by an NEA group of experts. – Paris : Nuclear Energy Agency, Organisation for Economic Co-operation and Development, 1987.
96 p.; 23 cm.
ISBN 9264129758 Pbk

Chernov → Tenancy Law and Practice Victoria.

Cheshire and Burn's Modern law of real property / E. H. Burn. – 14th ed. – London : Butterworths, 1988.
1012p; 25cm.
Previous ed.: 1982. Includes index.
ISBN 0406565473 Hbk £32.00 :
ISBN 0406565481 Pbk £21.95

Cheshire and Fifoot's Law of Contract. – 7th ed. – Butterworths, 1988.
669p.
ISBN 0409788716 Hbk £120.00
ISBN 0409787973 Pbk £85.00

Cheshire and Fifoot's Law of Contract : Fifth Australian Edition / N. C. Seddon. – Sydney : Butterworths, 1988.
880p.
This new edition has been revised to take into account the legislative and judicial developments in Australian contract law since 1981.
Hbk £85.00

Cheshire and North private international law / Peter M North, J. J. Fawcett. – 11th ed. – London : Butterworths, 1987.
xcviii,940p; 25cm.
Previous ed.: 1979. Bibliography: pxv-xvi. - Includes index.
ISBN 0406565708 Hbk £28.00
ISBN 0406565716 Pbk £19.00

Cheshire, Fifoot and Furmston's Law of contract / C. H. S. Fifoot, M. P. Furmston, G. C. Cheshire. – 11th ed. – London : Butterworth, 1986.
620p; 25cm.
Previous ed.: published as Cheshire and Fifoot's law of contract. 1981. Includes index.
ISBN 040656535X Hbk £33
ISBN 0406565368 Pbk £19.95

Cheshire, G. C.
Cheshire and Burn's Modern law of real property / E. H. Burn. – 14th ed. – London : Butterworths, 1988.
1012p; 25cm.
Previous ed.: 1982. Includes index.
ISBN 0406565473 Hbk £32.00 :
ISBN 0406565481 Pbk £21.95
—Cheshire and North private international law / Peter M North, J. J. Fawcett. – 11th ed. – London : Butterworths, 1987.
xcviii,940p; 25cm.
Previous ed.: 1979. Bibliography: pxv-xvi. - Includes index.
ISBN 0406565708 Hbk £28.00
ISBN 0406565716 Pbk £19.00

—Cheshire, Fifoot and Furmston's Law of contract / C. H. S. Fifoot, M. P. Furmston, G. C. Cheshire. – 11th ed. – London : Butterworth, 1986.
620p; 25cm.
Previous ed.: published as Cheshire and Fifoot's law of contract. 1981. Includes index.
ISBN 040656535X Hbk £33
ISBN 0406565368 Pbk £19.95

—Law of Contract : New Zealand Edition / C. H. S. Fifoot. – 6th ed. – Wellington : Butterworths, 1984.
ISBN 0409701645 Hbk
ISBN 0409701564 Pbk

—Modern law of real property / E H Burn. – 14th ed. – London : Butterworths, 1988.
ISBN 0406565481 Pbk
ISBN 0406565473 Hbk £38

—Private international law / North. – 11th ed. – London : Butterworths, 1987.
ISBN 0406565708 Hbk £38.00
ISBN 0406565716 Pbk £26.95

Cheshire, Paul C. → Agriculture, the countryside and land use : an economic critique.

Chester, Norman
English administrative system 1780-1870 / Sir Norman Chester. – Oxford : Clarendon Press, 1981.
398p; 23cm.
Bibliography: p385-389. - Includes index.
ISBN 0198226438 £22.50

Chesterman
Electronic Pirates : DIY Crime of the Century / Lipman. – Routledge.
ISBN 0415007399 Pbk £7.95
ISBN 0415007380 Hbk £25.00
→ Trusts Law : Texts and Materials.

Chesterman, Michael
Small businesses / by Michael Chesterman. – 2nd ed. – London : Sweet & Maxwell, 1982.
xxi,288p; 19cm.
Previous ed.: 1977. Includes index.
ISBN 0421286008 Hbk £13.00
ISBN 0421286105 Pbk £7.95

Chew → New Developments in International Finance.

Chhabra, T.N.
Banking Law and Practice. – Delhi : Dhanpat Rai and Sons.
Hbk £30.00
—Elements of Banking Law. – Delhi : Dhanpat Rai and Sons.
Hbk £10.00

Chhangani, R. C.
Illegal aliens under Nigerian law / R.C. Chhangani. – Jodhpur : Associated Law Publications, 1983.
91p.
Includes index.

Chi, K.L.
China's Policy Towards Territorial Disputes : The Case of the South China Sea Islands. – Routledge.
ISBN 0415009278 Hbk

Chiba, M.
Asian Indigenous Law. – Routledge, 1987.
ISBN 0710301138 Hbk £40.00

Chiba, Masaji → Asian indigenous law in interaction with received law.

Chief Justice Samuel Freedman : a great Canadian judge : a collection of the reasons for judgment of the Honourable Samuel Freedman, Justice of the Court of Queen's Bench of Manitobe (1952-60), Justice of the Court of Appeal of Manitoba (1960-83), and Chief Justice of Manitoba (1971-83) / selected and edited by Cameron Harvey : with a bibliographical note by Vivian Rachlis. – Winnipeg : Law Society of Manitoba, 1983.
xi,195p.
ISBN 0969130708

Chief Planning Inspector's report to the Secretary of State for the Environment, the Secretary of State for Transport and the Secretary of State for Wales / the Planning Inspectorate. – London : H.M.S.O., 1982.

Child abduction / Scottish Law Commission. – Edinburgh : The Commission, 1985.
116p. – (Consultative memorandum).

Child abduction : report on a reference under section 3(1)(e) of the Law Commissions Act 1965 ... / Scottish Law Commission. – Edinburgh : H.M.S.O., 1987.
vi,50p.
ISBN 010100642X

Child abuse : a community concern / edited by Kim Oates. – London : Butterworths, 1982.
xiv,321p.
Bibliographies.

Child abuse : a study of inquiry reports, 1973-1981 / Department of Health and Social Security. – London : H.M.S.O., 1982.
vi,93p; 21cm.
ISBN 0113207883

Child abuse : procedure and evidence in juvenile courts / by Jean Graham Hall and Douglas F. Martin. – 2nd ed. – London : Barry Rose, 1987.
xv,117p.
ISBN 187008070X

Child Abuse and the K C Factor. – Napier Press.
ISBN 1871479002 Pbk £12.00

Child abuse inquiries : a consultative paper from the Department of Health and Social Security. – London : The Department, 1985.
15p.

Child abuse: a community concern. – North Ryde : Butterworths (Australia).
Gives an overview of the problem of child abuse with particular emphasis on the needs and future development of the battered child. Discusses the various types of children and families who suffer from abuse, considers the emotional stresses that face the professional working with child abuse, and describes research studies which have practical implications for predicting and preventing child abuse.
ISBN 0409303305 Hbk

Child and Family Services Act : a Guide to Part 3 / Douglas J. Manning. – Butterworths, 1986.
208p.
Contains commentary following each section of the act, analysing both similarities and differences in the Child Welfare Act, major changes and modifications and intent in the new Act, selections of summaries of major cases decided under the old Act, and analyses key terms and categories, with reference to other relevant sections.
ISBN 0409805246 Hbk £55.00

Child and the state : the intervention of the state in family life / Philippe Meyer : translated by Judith Ennew and Janet Lloyd. – Cambridge : Cambridge University Press, 1983.
128p; 23cm.
Translation of: L'enfant et la raison d'etat.
ISBN 052124871X Hbk £18.50
ISBN 2735100626 France : Pbk £5.95

Child Benefit : Investing in the Future. – London : Central Books.
ISBN 0946744114 Pbk £3.95

Child Care and Adult Crime / Ashcraft. – Manchester : Manchester University Press, 1988.
ISBN 0719024692 Hbk £29.50

Child Care and the Courts / Lane. – London : Macmillan.
ISBN 0333420772 Pbk £6.95

Child care law : proposals for reform / the Law Society. – London : Law Society, 1983.
14 leaves.
'Prepared by the Law Society's Standing Committee on Criminal Law' - Introduction.

Child Care Manual. – 4th ed. – London : Butterworths.
ISBN 04062070031 Pbk £11.75
Supplement-1982.

Child custody : what chance for fathers? / Susan Maidment. – London : National Council for One Parent Families, 1981.
23p.
Bibliography: p.21-23.

Child Custody and Divorce. – Oxford : Croom Helm, 1984.
ISBN 0709917988 Pbk £8.95

Child custody and divorce : the law in social context / Susan Maidment. – London : Croom Helm, 1984.
324p; 23cm.
Bibliography: p293-306. - Includes index.
ISBN 0709917376 £16.95

Child, Graham D. → Common Market law of competition.

Child in mind : protection of children in a responsible society : the report of the Commission of Inquiry into the Circumstances Surrounding the Death of Kimberley Carlile / presented to the London Borough of Greenwich and the Greenwich Health Authority .. – London : The Borough, 1987.
xii,292p; 24cm.
Chairman: Louis Blom-Cooper.
ISBN 0904399060

Child in trust : the report of the Panel of Inquiry into the Circumstances Surrounding the Death of Jasmine Beckford / presented to Brent Borough Council and to Brent Health Authority by the Members of the Panel of Inquiry ... Louis Blom-Cooper (in the chair). – London : London Borough of Brent, 1985.
304,cxlp; 21cm.
Bibliography: pcxxxix-cxl.
ISBN 0951106805

Child Law. – London : Butterworths.
ISBN 0406117039 Hbk £60.00

Child Marriage Restraint Act. – 4th ed. – Allahabad : Law Book Company, 1988.
70p.
Pbk £40.00

Child Marriage Restraint (Amendment) Act, 1978. – Delhi : SBD Enterprises.
Hbk £5.00

Child Poverty Action Group → C.P.A.G.'s income support, the social fund and family credit : the legislation.
→ C.P.A.G.'s supplementary benefit and family income supplement : the legislation.
→ C.P.A.G's supplementary benefit and family income supplement : the legislation.
→ National welfare benefits handbook.
→ Opportunity lost : a response to the Green Paper on the Reform of Personal Taxation from the Child Poverty Action Group.
→ 'We don't give clothing grants any more' : the 1980 supplementary benefit scheme.

Child sexual abuse : joint investigative project : final report / Metropolitan Police and Bexley London Borough. – London : H.M.S.O., 1987.
93p.
Bibliographical references: p93.
ISBN 0113408862

Child Support. – Kingston : Australian Government Publishing Service.
Hbk £5.95

Child Support : From Debt Collection To Social Policy / Kamerman. – Sage Publications, 1988.
ISBN 080392979X Hbk £29.95

Child Support in America Practical Advice on Negotiating & Collecting Fair Settlement. – Yale University Press.
ISBN 0300042108 Pbk £5.95

Child Welfare Act annotated / by Michael D. Hartrick and Yan Arthur M. Lazor. – Toronto : Carswell, 1983.
xxix,431p.
Includes index. Includes text of the Ontario Child Welfare Act 1980 and related Regulations.
ISBN 0459357107

Child welfare and social defence / Tove Stang Dahl : translated by Gunvor Nyquist. – Oslo : Norwegian University Press, 1985.
185p; 23cm.
Bibliography: p175-185. Translation and revision of: Barneven og samfunnsvern.
ISBN 8200071146 £19.45

Child Witness : Do the Courts Abuse Children / David W Drinkwater. – New York : British Psychological Society, 1988.
ISBN 0901715891 Pbk £5.00

Child witnesses in sexual assault / Kate Warner. – Hobart : Law Reform Commission of Tasmania, 1987.
123p. – (Discussion paper).
Includes bibliographical references.

Children : rights and responsibilities / Jo Boyden and Andy Hudson. – London : Minority Rights Group, 1985.
15p. – (Report).
Bibliography: p14-15.
ISBN 0946690340

Children act 1975 / by Hugh K. Bevan and Martin L. Parry. – London : Butterworths, 1978.
xviii, 307 p; 26 cm.
Includes index.
£13.50

Children Act 1975 : custodianship orders / Department of Health and Social Security. – London : The Department, 1985.
15,xi,3,iip.

Children and divorce : economic factors / by Mavis Maclean and John Eekelaar. – Oxford : SSRC Centre for Socio-Legal Studies, 1983.
vii,39p; 22cm.
ISBN 0862260698

Children and justice : decision-making in children's hearings and juvenile courts / by Stewart Asquith. – Edinburgh : Edinburgh University Press, 1983.
vii,258p; 22cm.
Bibliography: p238-250. - Includes index.
ISBN 0852244290 Hbk £8.50
ISBN 0852244665 Pbk

Children in adult prisons : an international picture / Defence For Children International : compiled by Katarina Tomasevski. – London : Pinter, 1985.
280p; 33cm.
Includes index.
ISBN 0861876172 £18.50

Children in care : Government response to the second report from the Social Services Committee, session 1983-84 / presented to Parliament by the Secretary of State for Social Services. – London : H.M.S.O., 1984.
34p.
ISBN 0101929803

Children in care : memorandum of evidence / by the Association of County Councils. – London : The Association, 1983.
10p.
At head of title: House of Commons Social Services Committee.

Children in custody / Gill Stewart, Norman Tutt. – Aldershot : Avebury, 1987.
viii,237p; 23cm.
Bibliography: p223-230. - Includes index.
ISBN 0566050757 £17.50

Children in institutional and other forms of care : a national perspective : report of the Senate Standing Committee on Social Welfare. – Canberra : Australian Govt. Pub. Service, 1985.
xii, 121 p.; 25 cm.
At head of title: The Parliament of the Commonwealth of Australia. 'June 1985.'. Includes bibliographies.
ISBN 0644040955 Pbk

Children in stepfamilies : their legal and family status / Patricia Harper. – Melbourne : Institute of Family Studies, 1984.
– (Policy background paper).
Bibliography: p.28-29.
ISBN 0642876665

Children or Brethren : Aboriginal Rights in Colonial Iroquoia. – Saskatoon : University of Saskatchewan, Native Law Centre, 1985.
338p.
ISBN 0888801718 Hbk £75.00

Children out of court / F.M. Martin et al. – Edinburgh : Scottish Academic Press, 1981.
xi,331p.
Bibliography: p.322-324.
ISBN 0707302870

Children, parents and the state / by Andrew Bainham. – London : Sweet & Maxwell, 1988.
200p; 23cm.
Examines the relationship between children, their parents, and the state, and how their respective powers, duties, and responsibilities interact within the legal system. Also discusses the extent to which the state, through local authorities and the courts, can legitimately intervene in family life.
ISBN 042136310X Hbk £14.00 :
ISBN 0421363207 Pbk £11.95

Children's Hearings and the Sheriff Court. – London : Butterworths, 1987.
ISBN 0406105650 Hbk £41.00

Children's Legal Centre → Childright : a bulletin of law and policy affecting children and young people in England and Wales.
—Locked up in care : a report on the use of secure accommodation for young people in care. – Children's Legal Centre. – London : Children's Legal Centre, 1982.
36p; 30cm.
Bibliography: p36. 'Locked up in care - new legislation' (sheet (2p)) as insert.
ISBN 0946109001 Pbk £3.00

Children's rights in the practice of family law / edited by Barbara Landau. – Toronto : Carswell, 1986.
xxxviii,378p.
Includes bibliogrpahical references.
ISBN 0459390406

Childright : a bulletin of law and policy affecting children and young people in England and Wales. – London : The Children's Legal Centre, 1983.
ISBN 02651459

Childs, Brian A.
Northern Ireland Legal Quarterly. – Belfast : Queen's University of Belfast, 1986.
100p.
Hbk £28.00

Child's voice in the court of law : an account of the representation of minors in civil proceedings in Canada and some other (mostly common law) jurisdictions / Olive M. Stone. – Toronto : Butterworth & Co. (Canada), 1982.
x, 248p; 24cm.
Examination of the representation of minors in civil litigation, looking primarily at Canadian and English practices. Gives a historical discussion of women's legal position in the past and how the issue of guardianship was affected by it. Description of the relevant Canadian federal and provincial legislation in which each province is treated separately.
ISBN 0409870544 Hbk £30.00

Chile : Amnesty International briefing / Amnesty International. – London : Amnesty International, 1986.
22p.

Chile : evidence of torture / Amnesty International. – London : Amnesty International Publications, 1983.
75p.
ISBN 0862100534

Chilver, Henry
Exploitation of science and technology : a world force / by Sir Henry Chilver. – Southampton : University of Southampton, 1985.
At head of title page: The Fawley Foundation.

Chilvers
Litigation Support and Financial Assessment of Damages / Lemar. – London : Butterworths.
ISBN 0406504024 Hbk £55.00

Chin, N.Y.
Excluding Liability in Contracts. – Butterworths, 1985.
227p.
Examines the English and Australian models, and discusses the popular common law concepts of reasonableness and unconscionability. Includes a review of the major cases and legislation aimed at evolving acceptable solutions to the dilemma of exception clauses.
ISBN 0409995002 Hbk £48

Chin, T.Y.
Evidence in Singapore. – London : Butterworths, 1988.
– (Singapore Law Series).
ISBN 0409995355 Pbk
—Malaysian Taxation. – London : Butterworths, 1988.
ISBN 0409995622 Pbk

Chin, Yoong Kheong
Malaysian Taxation. – London : Butterworths.
ISBN 0409995622 Pbk £30.00

China : violations of human rights : prisoners of conscience and the death penalty in the People's Republic of China. – Amnesty International. – London : Amnesty International Publications, 1984.
129p.
ISBN 0862100739

China and the European Economic Community : the new connection / Harish Kapur. – Dordrecht : Nijhoff, 1986.
xv, 351p.
Includes index. Bibliography: p.99-110.
ISBN 9024732301

China Business Guide. – London : Longman Professional, 1986.
ISBN 0582998026 Pbk £14.95

China Investment Guide. – London : Longman Professional, 1987.
ISBN 0582997747 Hbk £75.00

China law and practice : documenting and analysing the development of the Chinese legal system. – Hong Kong : China Law and Practice, 1987.

China Law Yearbook 1987. – Butterworths, 1989.
645p.
ISBN 0409995630 Hbk £325.00

China Law Yearbook. – Munich : Saur, 1989.
xxii, 645p.
ISBN 3598075413 £398.00

China Modernisation and Legal Development. – 2nd ed. – London : Longman Professional, 1987.
ISBN 0851208045 Hbk £27.50
ISBN 0851208043 Pbk £17.50

China Tax Guide / Zee. – Oxford : Oxford University Press, 1988.
ISBN 0195840593 Hbk £25.00

China Trade Agreements. – 2nd ed. – Taylor & Francis.
ISBN 0800280008 Hbk £50.00

China Trade Documents. – 2nd ed. – Taylor & Francis.
ISBN 0800280016 Hbk £54.00

China Trade Law / Bernard Dewit. – Dordrecht : Kluwer, 1983.
478p.
ISBN 9065441131 Hbk £175.00

China trade law : code of the foreign trade law of the People's Republic of China / by Francois De Bauw and Bernard Dewit : preface by Michel Verwilghen. – Bruxelles : Bruylant (Emile), 1982.
572p.
Includes bibliographical references and index. At head of title: Universite Catholique de Louvain, Faculte de Droit, Centre de Droit des Obligations. Text in English. Preface, introduction, headings and index in French and English..
ISBN 2802702963

China's civil and commercial law / Henry R. Zheng. – Singapore : Butterworths, 1988.
lii,490p; 26cm.
Presents an overview of chinese laws and legislative structure, a review of the major principles of the Civil Code, and an examination of the different facets of Chinese business law. Covers principles of civil law, contract law, banking law, insurance law, and foreign investment law.
ISBN 040999555X Hbk £142.50

China's foreign economic legislation Chung-kuo tui wai ching chi fa kuei hui pien. – 1st ed. – Bejing, China : Foreign Languages Press, 1982.
v. 1; 19 cm.
ISBN 0835109836 Pbk

China's investment laws : new directions / Guiguo Wang. – Singapore : Butterworths, 1988.
ix,272p.
Covers China's investment environment, foreign investment, new revisions promulgated by the central government, the relaxed rules of the SEZ, the corporate law of the SEZ, SEZ regulations on foreign banks, comparative analysis of the new laws, and the practical significance of the new law. An appendix gives practical guidance to investing in China. With an index.
ISBN 0409995606 Hbk £119

China's Policy Towards Territorial Disputes : The Case of the South China Sea Islands. – Routledge.
ISBN 0415009278 Hbk

Chinese Contract Cases / Chan. – London : Longman Professional.
ISBN 0582049202 Hbk

Chinese in Indonesia, the Philippines and Malaysia / by Charles A. Coppel and Hugh and Ping-ching Mabbett. – Rev. ed. – London : Minority Rights Group, 1982.
16p. – (Report).
Previous ed. 1972. Bibliography: p.16.

Chinese intellectual property and technology transfer Law / by Zheng Chengsi with Michael D. Pendleton. – London : Sweet & Maxwell, 1987.
xli,331p; 26cm.
Presents a summary and analysis of Chinese intellectual property and technology transfer law covering the Chinese system, patents, trademarks, copyright, transfer of technology and software protection, taxation in the field of intellectual property, and containing appendices of original source material.
ISBN 0421383801 £50.00

Chinese Labour Under British Rule / Rear. – Oxford : Oxford University Press, 1981.
ISBN 0195802829 Hbk £12.50

Chinese Society of International Law → Chinese yearbook of international law and affairs.
→ Selected articles from Chinese yearbook of international law.

Chinese Treaties. – Dordrecht : Kluwer, 1975.
328p.
ISBN 9028602259 Hbk £78.00

Chinese yearbook of international law and affairs. – Baltimore : Occasional Papers/Reprints Series in Contemporary Asian Studies, Inc. for the Chinese Society of International Law - Chinese (Taiwan) Branch of International Law Association, 1983-.
Continues: The annals of the Chinese Society of International Law.

Chinkin, C. M. →Current problems of international trade financing.

Chisholm, Richard
Australian family law / Richard Chisholm, Carol Foreman and Stephen O'Ryan. – Sydney : Butterworths, 1987.
Includes both Commonwealth and state legislation and practice and procedure of the Family Court.
ISBN 0409491950 Llf A$575
—Understanding Law : Introduction to Australia's Legal System 1978 / Garth Nettheim. – 3rd ed. – Butterworths, 1988.
ca 152p.
This introductory text for first year law students provides an overview of the Australian legal system. Emphasized are the ways in which laws are made and the function of courts and lawyers. A list of suggested further reading is also included.
ISBN 0409495190 Pbk £14.00

Chisum, D.S.
Patents. – Matthew Bender, 1978.
ISBN 0000999073 Hbk £344.00

Chiswick, D. →Prosecution of the Mentally Disturbed.

Chitty and Jacob's Queen's Bench forms / Jack I. H. Jacob. – 21st ed. – London : Sweet & Maxwell, 1986.
xlv,1709p; 26cm.
Includes the appropriate forms other than pleadings, which may be used at any stage in the course of litigation undertaken in the Queen's Bench Division. Each chapter begins with a general note describing the relevant procedures in their operational context. Cross-referenced to 'The Supreme Court Practice'.
ISBN 0421206004 £98.00

Chitty, Joseph
Chitty on contracts / A. G. Guest. – 25th ed. 2. – London : Sweet & Maxwell, 1983.
various pagings; 26cm.
Previous ed.: 1977. Includes index.
ISBN 0421285605

Chitty, Jr., J.
Law of the Prerogatives of the Crown. – Repr. of 1820 ed. – Abingdon : Professional Books.
64p.
Hbk £40.00

Chitty on contracts / A. G. Guest. – 25th ed. 2. – London : Sweet & Maxwell, 1983.
various pagings; 26cm.
Previous ed.: 1977. Includes index.
ISBN 0421285605

Chitty, Thomas
Chitty and Jacob's Queen's Bench forms / Jack I. H. Jacob. – 21st ed. – London : Sweet & Maxwell, 1986.
xlv,1709p; 26cm.
Includes the appropriate forms other than pleadings, which may be used at any stage in the course of litigation undertaken in the Queen's Bench Division. Each chapter begins with a general note describing the relevant procedures in their operational context. Cross-referenced to 'The Supreme Court Practice'.
ISBN 0421206004 £98.00

Chitty's Abridgment of Canadian Cases (1892-1970), 5 Vols. – Aurora : Canada Law Book Co.
– (Abridgments and Encyclopedias).
Hbk £209.00

Chiu, T.C.E.
China Trade Agreements. – 2nd ed. – Taylor & Francis.
ISBN 0800280008 Hbk £50.00

Chiu, T.C.W.
China Trade Documents. – 2nd ed. – Taylor & Francis.
ISBN 0800280016 Hbk £54.00
—People's Republic of China Laws for Chinas Traders, Investors. – 2nd ed. – Taylor & Francis.
ISBN 0800280024 Hbk £64.00

Chiyod Seshagiri, Rao →Disputed Documents, Handwriting and Thumb-print Identification.

Choate, Clare E.
Annotated Unemployment Insurance Act. – 1st ed. – Agincourt : Carswell, 1988.
420p.
This book contains the full text of the Unemployment Insurance Act and Regulations. Also included are the annotated cases which are pertinent to particular sections. There is a complete table of cases and an index.
Hbk £54.75
—Unemployment Insurance. – 2nd ed. – Agincourt : Carswell, 1985.
418p.
Hbk £34.75
—Unemployment insurance / by Clare E. Choate. – Toronto : Carswell Co., 1982.
xii, 386 p.; 26 cm.
'Reprinted from the Canadian encyclopedic digest, third edition.'. Includes index.

Chodse →Understanding Criminal Law 1987.

Choice by cable : the economics of a new era in television / C.G.Veljanovski and W.D.Bishop. – London : Institute of Economic Affairs, 1983.
120p; 22cm.
ISBN 0255361599

Chopra, D. S.
Asian income tax laws
Vol. 1 : Hong Kong, India & Malaysia / by D.S. Chopra. – Singapore : Malayan Law Journal Pte., 1986.
lx,992p.
Compendium of the substantive provisions of the tax laws of the three major Asian countries. Gives a brief introduction to the income-tax laws of each of the countries, covers all tax concessions, incentives, rebates and reliefs in the income-tax laws of each country, the current income-tax rates prevailing, and important judicial decisions in respect of the provisions of the income-tax laws of each country.
ISBN 9971700468
—Industrial and Labour Law. – Calcutta : Eastern Law House.
1,298p.
Hbk £65.00
—Law Relating to Provident Funds. – Bombay : Tripathi, 1974.
Hbk £50.00
—Outlines of Labour Law. – Bombay : Tripathi, 1974.
Hbk £25.00
—Payment of Gratuity Act. – 3rd ed. – Calcutta : Eastern Law House, 1983.
Hbk £65.00

Chopra, Kamlesh →Labour Laws in Uttar Pradesh.

Chopra, Chopra, O.P., O.P.
Income Tax Law and Practice. – 2nd ed. – Allahabad : Orient Law House, 1980-1983.
Hbk £128.00 vol. 2 and 3

Chorafas, Dimitris N
Electronic funds transfer / Dimitris N. Chorafas. – London : Butterworths, 1988.
xi,361p; 24cm.
Includes index.
ISBN 0406101000 £38.00
—Implementing Networks In Banking and Financial Services. – London : Macmillan.
ISBN 0333440692 Hbk £35.00
—Strategic planning for electronic banking. – London : Butterworths, 1987.
ISBN 040610087X Pbk £45.00

Chorley and Giles' shipping law / O. C. Giles, N. J. J. Gaskell, C. Debattista, Richard J. Swatton. – 8th ed. – London : Pitman, 1987.
lxiii,704p; 23cm.
Previous ed.: 1980. Bibliography: plxii-lxiii. - Includes index.
ISBN 027302194X Pbk £19.95

Chorley and Smart leading cases in the law of banking / P. E. Smart, Robert Samuel Theodore Chorley Chorley. – 5th ed. – London : Sweet & Maxwell, 1983.
xlvi,397p; 23cm.
Previous ed.: 1977. Includes index.
ISBN 0421293403 Hbk £14.50
ISBN 0421293500 Pbk £10.00

Chorley, Robert Samuel Theodore Chorley
Chorley and Giles' shipping law / O. C. Giles, N. J. J. Gaskell, C. Debattista, Richard J. Swatton. – 8th ed. – London : Pitman, 1987.
lxiii,704p; 23cm.
Previous ed.: 1980. Bibliography: plxii-lxiii. - Includes index.
ISBN 027302194X Pbk £19.95
—Chorley and Smart leading cases in the law of banking / P. E. Smart, Robert Samuel Theodore Chorley Chorley. – 5th ed. – London : Sweet & Maxwell, 1983.
xlvi,397p; 23cm.
Previous ed.: 1977. Includes index.
ISBN 0421293403 Hbk £14.50
ISBN 0421293500 Pbk £10.00

Choudhury, T.G. →Law of Monopolies and Restructive Trade Practices in India.

Chow, Kog Fong
Construction Joint Ventures in Singapore. – Butterworths, 1985.
332p.
Covers legal form and operational structure, the sponsor, selection of the joint venture partners, constituting the joint venture, the management board, implications arising from the construction contract, legal implications of a joint venture partnership, legal issues affecting the corporate joint venture, governing law, and minority protection.
ISBN 0409995029 Hbk £75.00

Chowdhary, S.B.
Company Law and Auditing. – New Delhi : Kalyani Publishers.
Hbk £21.00

Chowdhury, S.K. Roy
Ghosh on Principles and Forms of Pleading / H.K. Saharay. – 4th ed. – Calcutta : Eastern Law House, 1984.
Hbk £175.00

Chowdhury, S R
Human rights in a state of emergency. – London : Pinter, 1989.
288.
Illustrates the International Law Association's attempt to develop minimum standards for a rule of law during a state of emergency.
ISBN 0861877373 Hbk £35

Chowdhury, Subrata Roy →Permanent sovereignty over natural resources in international law.

Chown, John F.
Foreign Exchange Risk : A Tax and Financial Analysis. – London : Oyez Longman, 1983.
– (Oyez Longman Intelligence Report Ser.).
ISBN 0851205313 Hbk £45.00

Chretien, Jean →Role of the United Kingdom in the amendment of the Canadian Constitution : background paper.

Christenson →International Claims : Their Preparation and Presentation.

Christian, C.
Computers for lawyers. – London : Longman Professional, 1985.
ISBN 0851210406 Pbk £10.50

Christian Jr, Ernest S →Value-added tax : orthodoxy and new thinking.

Christian, L.
Policing by coercion. – Pluto Press, 1983.
ISBN 071681336X Pbk £1.50

Christian, Louise
Policing by coercion / Louise Christian. – London : GLC Police Committee Support Unit, 1983.
vi,224p. – (Discussion paper).
At head of title page 'The Police and Criminal Evidence Bill'. Includes index.
ISBN 071681336X

Christian Magistrate and State Church. – Toronto : University of Toronto Press, 1982.
ISBN 0802055893 Hbk £30.00

Christian, Tim →Employee-Employer Rights in Alberta : a Guide to Alberta Labour Law.

Christiansen, Karl O. →Criminology.

Christiansen, W.K.
Fundamentals of Property Management. – London : Butterworths, 1988.
ISBN 0409787787 Pbk

Christie
Employment Law in Canada. – 2nd ed. – London : Butterworths.
ISBN 0409823988 Hbk

Christie, Erroll →Handbook of charities, 1987-1988.

Christie, George C.
Law, norms and authority / George C. Christie. – London : Duckworth, 1982.
x,181p; 23cm.
Includes index.
ISBN 0715615939 £18.00

Christie, I. M →Legal writing and research manual.

Christie, R. H
Business law in Zimbabwe / R.H. Christie. – Cape Town : Juta, 1985.
lvii, 575 p.; 26 cm.
Includes index.
ISBN 0702115738
—Law of contract in South Africa / by R.H. Christie. – Durban : Butterworths, 1981.
lxxiv,575p.
ISBN 0409018317

Christol, C.
Modern international law of outer space. – Pergamon, 1984.
ISBN 0080293670 Hbk £71.40

Christopher St. German on chancery and statute / by J.A. Guy. – London : Selden Society, 1985.
x,149p.

Chronicles of Newgate. – New Edition. – New York : Bracken Books.
ISBN 1851701427 Hbk £6.95

Chronological Account of Crime, Public Order and Police in Sydney 1788-1810. – Canberra : Australian Institute of Criminology.
free

Chronological and subject analysis of South Africa's multilateral and bilateral treaties, 1806-1979 / Jaqueline Audrey Kalley. – Johannesburg : s.n., 1985.
xvi,677 leaves.
Thesis (M.A.) - University of Witwatersrand 1985. Bibliography: p.659-677. - Includes index.

Chronological table of local legislation / the Law Commission and the Scottish Law Commission. – 2 v. – London : Law Commission, 1985.
Contents: Part 1. Local and personal acts 1797-1908 - Part 2. Local and personal acts 1909-1973, private acts 1539-1973.

Chronological Table of the Statutes, 2 Vols. – London : HMSO, 1983.
ISBN 0118402439 Hbk £84.00
ISBN 0118402552 Hbk £95.00

Chronological Table of the Statutes, 2 Vols. – London : HMSO, 1982.
ISBN 0118402323 Hbk £77.00

Chua →Managerial Accounting : Method and Meaning.

Chuang, Wei Ping
Forensic audiology / Chuang Wei Ping : foreword by Ronald Hinchcliffe. – Middlesbrough : Chuang Wei Ping, 1985.
108p in various pagings; 22cm.
ISBN 0951080008 Pbk £6.00

Chukkol, Kharisu Sufiyan
Defences to criminal liability in Nigerian law : a critical appraisal / by Kharisu Sufiyan Chukkol. – Zaria : Ahmadu Bello University Press, 1987.
xiii,135p.
Bibliography: pp.133-135.
ISBN 9781250429
—Law of Crimes / by Kharisu Sufiyan Chukkol. – Zaria : Ahmadu Bello University Press.
Hbk £15.00
—Law of crimes in Nigeria : skeletal notes and important references / Kharisu Sufiyan Chukkol. – Zaria : Ahmadu Bello University Press, 1981.
iv, 51 leaves.

Chukura, Olisa →Privy Council judgments : opinions of the Judicial Committee of the Privy Council in appeals from West Africa,1841 to 1973.

Chunder, Pratap C.
Socialist Legality and Indian Law. – Calcutta : Sujan Publications.
104p.
Hbk £35.00

Church courts, sex and marriage in England 1570-1640. – Cambridge : Cambridge University Press.
Examines the role of Elizabethan Church courts, their jurisdiction and the attitude of the people towards them. Based on records from courts in Wiltshire, Cambridgeshire, Leicestershire and West Sussex.
ISBN 0521232856

Church in the Sandalwood Islands 1960-1980. – Townsville : James Cook University Publications.
Hbk £3.00

Church of England
Canons of the Church of England : Canons Ecclesiastical promulgated by the Convocations of Canterbury and York in 1964 and 1969 and by the General Synod of the Church of England from 1970. – Church of England. – 4th ed. 1 v. – London : Church House Publishing, 1986.
looseleaf.
ISBN 0715137115
→ Clergyman's handbook, and churchwarden's guide : being a manual of the laws affecting the relative rights, position, and duties of the clergy and their parishioners ..., with appendices containing important statutes, including the Benefices Act, 1898.
→ Select cases from the ecclesiastical courts of the Province of Canterbury, c.1200-1301.

Church of England Faculty Jurisdiction. – Sweet & Maxwell, 1988.
ISBN 0421387602 Pbk £13.75

Churchill →Corporate Communications.

Churchill, R. R
EEC fisheries law / R.R. Churchill. – Dordrecht : M. Nijhoff, 1987.
xxviii, 299 p.; 25 cm.
Includes index. Bibliography: p. 285-289.
ISBN 9024735459 Hbk £165.00
—Law of the sea / R.R. Churchill and A.V. Lowe. – Manchester : Manchester University Press, 1983.
xxxiii,321p; 24cm.
Includes bibliographies and index.
ISBN 0719009367 £19.50

Ciampi, Constantino →Edited versions of selected papers from the international conference on 'Logic, Informatics, Law', Florence, Italy, April 1981, Vol.1 : Artificial intelligence and legal information systems : Constantino Ciampi, editor.

CIF and FOB Contracts (BSL) / H Orren Merren. – 3rd ed. – London : Sweet & Maxwell, 1984.
ISBN 0420465308 Hbk £80.00

Cilliers, A C
Law of costs / A.C. Cilliers. – 2nd ed. – Durban : Butterworths, 1984.
lvii, 330 p.; 25 cm.
Includes indexes. Bibliography: p. lvi-lvii.
ISBN 0409019097 R52.50

Cilliers and Benade : Company Law
1985 Noter-up Inclues: Commentary on the Close Corporation Act 1984. – Durban : Professional Publishers, 1985.
ISBN 0409018740 Pbk £26.00
1985 Supplement to 1985 Noter-up. – 1986.
ISBN 0409018767 Hbk £8.00

Cilliers and Benade : Introduction to Company Law
1986 Supplement. – Durban : Professional Publishers, 1986.
ISBN 0409018791

Cilliers, Benade et al : Corporate Law. – Durban : Professional Publishers, 1987.
ISBN 0409019631 Hbk £95.00
ISBN 0409019623 Pbk £65.00

Cilliers, Collin
Power of a Testator to Dispose of the Property of Another : a Study of the South African Law of Massing and Election, with a Comparative Look at English, Dutch and German Law. – Pijnacker : Dutch Efficiency Bureau.
ISBN 9062310273 Hbk £30.80

Cilliers, H.S.
Cilliers and Benade : Introduction to Company Law / M.L. Benade. – Durban : Professional Publishers, 1985.
ISBN 0409019542 Pbk £65.00

CIMA Stage 2 Financial Accounting / Anderson. – Pitman.
ISBN 0273028626 Pbk £11.95

CIMA Study Text Stage 4 : Management Accounting. – Chartered Institute of Management Accountants. – London : BPP.
ISBN 0862771544 Pbk £15.95

Cinderella Revisited : Rights and Responsibilities in Step-families. – Kingston : Australian Government Publishing Service, 1986.
40p.
ISBN 0644054360 Hbk £3.95

Cinemas Bill : report on the consolidation of the Cinematograph Acts 1909 to 1982 and related enactments... / the Law Commission. – London : H.M.S.O., 1985.
7p.
With errata.
ISBN 0101942508

CIPA
Guide to the Trademarks Act 1938. – CIPA. – London : Sweet & Maxwell, 1988.
ISBN 0421381205 Hbk

Circumstances surrounding the various court actions relating to the film 'The return of Captain Invincible' / Senate Standing Committee on Finance and Government Operations. – Canberra : Government Printer, 1987.
iv,66p. – (Parliamentary paper).
ISBN 064406546X

Circumstantial and Presumptive Evidence. – Nagpur : Wadhura & Co.
455p.
£25.00

Ciskei →Constitutions of Transkei, Bophuthatswana, Venda and Ciskei.

Cities in the developing world : policies for their equitable and efficient growth / Johannes F. Linn. – Oxford : Published for the World Bank by Oxford University Press, 1983.
xxi,230p; 24cm.
Bibliography: p213-223. - Includes index.
ISBN 0195203828 Hbk
ISBN 0195203836 Pbk

Citizen 16 : The Civil Law and You. – London : Macmillan, 1986.
ISBN 0333367944 Pbk £6.95

Citizenship law of the USSR / by George Ginsburgs. – The Hague : M. Nijhoff Publishers, 1984.
xii,394p.
Includes index. Bibliography: p379-390.
ISBN 9024728630 Hbk

Citizenship, Review and Appeals System : Report, 13 June 1980. – Administrative Review Tribunal. – Canberra : Australian Government Publishing Service, 1981.
8p.
ISBN 0642066981 Hbk £0.40

City code on take-overs and mergers. – Rev. – London : Issuing Houses Association, 1981.
81p; 22cm.
Previous ed.: / City Working Party. 1976. Pamphlets 'Practice note no.17', 'Principal amendments to the City code' in pocket.
Pbk £1.50

City code on take-overs and the rules governing substantial acquisitions of shares. – April 1985 ed. 1. – London : The Panel on Take-overs and Mergers, 1985.
loose-leaf.
Previous ed.: 1981.
ISBN 0950046663

City of North York Act, 1983, Bill Pr051 : An Act Respecting the City of North York. – Ontario : Ontario Government Publications Service, 1983.
6p.
Hbk £0.30

City of Owen Sound Act, 1983, Bill Pr053 : An Act Respecting the City of Owen Sound. – Ontario : Ontario Government Publications Service, 1983.
2p.
Hbk £0.30

City of Paris Mediateur : an ombudsman a la francaise / by David Clark. – Edmonton, Alta. : International Ombudsman Institute, 1983.
47p. – (Occasional paper).
Originally published: in Local government studies, vol. 8, no. 5 (Sept.-Oct. 1982).

City of Sault Ste. Marie Act, 1983, Bill Pr048 : An Act Respecting the City of Sault Ste. Marie. – Ontario : Ontario Government Publications Service, 1983.
2p.
Hbk £0.30

City of Toronto Act, 1983, Bill Pr036 : An Act Respecting the City of Toronto. – Ontario : Ontario Government Publications Service, 1983.
1p.
Hbk £0.30

City Working Party →City code on take-overs and mergers.

City-centre crime : the scope for situational prevention / Malcolm Ramsay. – London : Home Office, 1982.
v,50p.
Bibliography: p.42.
ISBN 0862520665

Civil actions against the police / by Richard Clayton and Hugh Tomlinson. – London : Sweet & Maxwell, 1987.
250p; 25cm.
Examines the rights and remedies of the individual against police misconduct. Covers traditional tort actions, assault, false imprisonment, trespass, interference with goods, and malicious prosecution. Emphasis on recent developments, and focuses on the circumstances that may lead to claims. Also contains discussion on civil liability under the Police and Criminal Evidence Act 1984.
ISBN 0421344202 £30.00

Civil admiralty jurisdiction / the Law Reform Commission. – Canberra : Australian Government Publishing Service, 1986.
xxi,393p. – (Report).
Bibliography: p.381-387. - Includes index.
ISBN 0644013540

Civil and criminal procedure in a nutshell / Elizabeth Stevens. – London : Sweet & Maxwell, 1981.
vii,86p; 18cm. – (New nutshells).
Includes index.
ISBN 0421280409 Pbk £1.75

Civil and Political Rights of the Aliens : a Study in National and International Laws. – New Delhi : Deep and Deep Publications, 1982.
224p.
Hbk £80.00

Civil Aviation Authority
Air Navigation : The Order and the Regulations, 2 ed. – Civil Aviation Authority. – 2nd. ed. Great Britain. – London : Civil Aviation Authority, 1981.
Illus.
ISBN 0860391248 Hbk £17.00
—Aviation Law for Applicants for the Private Pilot's Licence (CAP 85). – Civil Aviation Authority. – 7th ed. Ed. by Great Britain. – London : Civil Aviation Authority, 1985.
v, 62p : Illus.
ISBN 0860391833 Hbk £2.70
—Consultation paper : safeguards against monopolistic and anti-competitive behaviour / Civil Aviation Authority. – s.l. : s.n., 1987.
9p.
—Registration, Certification and Maintenance of Aircraft-A Guide : Notes on the Legislation Governing Airworthiness of Civil Aircraft Registered in the United Kingdom. – Civil Aviation Authority. – 5d ed. Ed. by Great Britain. – London : Civil Aviation Authority, 1981.
vi, 46p : Illus.
ISBN 0860391272 Hbk £1.00

Civil Code. – Seychelles Government. – Mahe : Seychelles National Printing Co.
Hbk £40.00

Civil Code of Japan / translated by Fukio Nakane. – Tokyo : Eibun Horei Sha, 1981.
iv,179,16p.
'Under authorization of the Ministry of Justice & the Codes Translation Committee'.

Civil Court in Action. – 2nd ed. – London : Butterworths, 1985.
ISBN 0406556229 Hbk £21.00
ISBN 0406556237 Pbk £14.95

Civil Court Practice. – 3rd ed. – Allahabad : Law Book Company, 1986.
1,100p.
Hbk £240.00

Civil courts in Canada : Tribunaux civils au Canada. – Ottawa : Statistics Canada, Canadian Centre for Justice Statistics, 1985.
183 p.; 29 cm.
English and French. 'July 1985.'.
ISBN 0660522497 Pbk £25.00 (£26.50 other countries)

Civil Courts Practice and Procedure. – Delhi : Vinod Prakashan, 1986.
Hbk £240,00

Civil disorder and civil liberties : evidence to the Scarman inquiry. – London : National Council for Civil Liberties, 1981.
46p; 21cm.
ISBN 0901108960

Civil Disputes Resolution : Avoiding a Trial. – Vancouver : Continuing Legal Education Society of British Columbia, 1986.
148p.
ISBN 0865043027 Hbk £65.00

Civil Engineering Claims / J Stephenson. – Oxford : Blackwell Scientific, 1987.
ISBN 0003830594 Hbk £25.00

Civil Engineering Contracts : Practice and Procedure / D. S. de Silva. – London : Butterworths, 1982.
ISBN 0408005262 Hbk

Civil Engineering Price Book 1988. – Spon (E & FN).
ISBN 0419136002 Hbk £30.00

Civil Evidence Handbook / Gordon D. Cudmore. – Agincourt : Carswell, 1987.
520p.
This text contains the Evidence Acts and the Canada Evidence Acts. Topics include admissibility, relevance, burden of proof, presumption, judicial notice, competence and compellability, pleadings, interpreters, examination in chief, impeaching your own witness, cross examination, re-examination, reply evidence, experts, parole evidence rule, hearsay, exceptions to the hearsay rule, and demonstrative evidence.
Hbk £71.50

Civil Evidence (Scotland) Act 1988. – Edinburgh : Green (W.) & Son, 1989.
Annotated text of the Act from Scottish Current Law Statutes, which introduced far-reaching changes to the law of evidence in civil proceedings, including the abolition of the requirement of cooroboration, the admission of hearsay, and authenticated business records.
ISBN 0414008650 Pbk

Civil imprisonment / Advisory Committee on Law Reform. – Causeway : The Committee, 1982.
13 leaves. – (Working paper).

Civil Judicial Statistics Scotland 1982. – London : HMSO, 1984.
ISBN 0101923503 Hbk £6.35

Civil jurisdiction : the new rules : a guide for the perplexed / Robert Black. – Edinburgh : Law Society of Scotland, 1983.
vii,111p.
Includes index.
ISBN 0902023101

Civil jurisdiction and enforcement of foreign judgments : the application in England and Wales of the Brussels Convention of 1968 on Jurisdiction and Enforcement of Judgments in Civil and Commercial Matters under the Civil Jurisdiction and Judgments Act 1982 / by Peter Kaye. – Abingdon : Professional Books, 1987.
cxvi, 1949p; 24cm.
Includes the text of the Civil Jurisdiction and Judgments Act 1982.
ISBN 0862050812

Civil jurisdiction and judgements : maritime claims / by D.C. Jackson. – London : Lloyds of London Press, 1987.
386p; 22cm.
Includes index.
ISBN 1850441448 £17.50

Civil jurisdiction and judgments : the application in England of the convention on jurisdiction and the enforcement of judgments in civil and commercial matters under the Civil Jurisdiction and Judgments Act 1982 / by T.C. Hartley. – London : Sweet & Maxwell, 1984.
xxi,233p; 25cm.
Includes index.
ISBN 0421311800 Pbk £18.00

Civil Jurisdiction and Judgments Act 1982. – London : Butterworths, 1983.
ISBN 0406005303 Hbk £32.50

Civil jurisdiction in Scotland / by A.E. Anton. – Edinburgh : W. Green, 1984.
xxiii,306p; 24cm.
Kept up to date by supplements.
ISBN 0414007360

Civil Jurisdictions and Judgment Acts 1982. – London : Butterworths, 1983.
This work provides a procedural guide to the Act. The 1982 Act incorporates into United Kingdom law the 1968 EEC Convention on jurisdiction and the enforcement of judgements in civil matters.
ISBN 0406005303 Hbk

Civil justice project : preliminary study / I. R. Scott, J. R. Pullen, A. J. Robbins. – Melbourne : Government Printer, 1984.
xviii,423p.
Cover title: Preliminary study concerning the administration of civil justice in Victoria.
ISBN 0908417179

Civil justice quarterly. – London : Sweet & Maxwell in association with the Institute of Judicial Administration at the University of Birmingham, 1982-.
25cm.
£35.00 per year

Civil justice review
Consultation paper no.1 : Personal injuries litigation / Lord Chancellors Department. – London : The Department, 1986.
50p.
Consultation paper no.2 : Small claims / Lord Chancellor's Department. – 1986.
50 leaves.
Cover title: Small claims in the County Court.
Consultation paper no. 3 : The Commercial Court / Lord Chancellor's Department. – 1986.
38 leaves.
Consultation paper no.4 : Enforcement of debt / Lord Chancellor's Department. – 1987.
76 leaves.
Consultation paper no.5 : Housing cases / Lord Chancellor's Department. – 1987.
52 leaves.
Consultation paper no.6 : General issues / Lord Chancellor's Department. – 1987.
109 leaves.
Study of the Commercial Court : final report : Coopers & Lybrand Associates Limited / Lord Chancellor's Department. – 1986.
98,25 leaves.

Civil justice review / report of the Review Body on Civil Justice. – London : H.M.S.O., 1988.
x,181p.
Presented to Parliament by the Lord High Chancellor by Command of Her Majesty, June 1988.
ISBN 0101039425

Civil justice review : consultation paper no. 6 : general issues / response by JUSTICE. – London : JUSTICE, 1987.
19p.

Civil justice review : study of debt enforcement procedures. – Touche Ross. – London : Touche Ross, 1986.
iii,90 leaves.
A study carried out as part of the Lord Chancellor's review of civil justice.

Civil justice review : study of housing cases b final report to Lord Chancellor's Department. – Bristol : University of Bristol, School for Advanced Urban Studies, 1987.
129p.

Civil Law Act, 1956 (Act 67). – Kuala Lumpur : International Law Books Services.
Hbk £7.00

Civil liability : contribution / Scottish Law Commission. – Edinburgh : Scottish Law Commission, 1986.
iv,230p. – (Consultative memorandum).

Civil Liability Act. – Dublin : Round Hall Press, 1985.
150p.
ISBN 0947686037 Hbk £13.50

Civil liability for defective premises / J. H. Holyoak, David K. Allen. – London : Butterworths, 1982.
xxvii,278p.
This book provides United Kingdom practitioners with a comprehensive guide to liabilities of occupier, owner, builder, and other parties in cases of defective premises. Measure of damages, claims for economic loss, limitation periods, and misrepresentation are also covered.
ISBN 0406233403 Hbk £34.00

Civil liability in relation to animals / Scottish Law Commission. – Edinburgh : Scottish Law Commission, 1982.
xiii,180p. – (Consultative memorandum).

Civil Liability Statutes. – London : Blackstone Press, 1987.
ISBN 1815850538 Pbk £8.95

Civil Liberties 1984. – Oxford : Blackwell, 1984.
ISBN 0855207027 Pbk £7.50

Civil Liberties. – London : Butterworths, 1988.
ISBN 0406555109 Hbk
ISBN 0406555117 Pbk

Civil liberties : cases and materials / S.H. Bailey, D.J. Harris, B.L. Jones. – 2nd ed. – London : Butterworths, 1985.
xxxvii, 612p.
ISBN 040655482X

Civil liberties cases in Zambia / compiled by Muna Ndulo and Kaye Turner. – Oxford : African Law Reports, 1984.
xxii,579p; 24cm.
Includes index.
ISBN 0903826704 Hbk
ISBN 0903826712 Pbk

Civil liberties in Australia / by Geoffrey A. Flick. – Sydney : Law Book Company Limited, 1981.
xxxviii,249p.
ISBN 045520084X

Civil liberties in Canada : entering the 1980s / edited by Gerald L. Gall. – Toronto : Butterworths, 1982.
xv,259p.
Examines the changing relationship between the individual and government bureaucracy, the law relating to women and children, international aspects of civil liberties, and the codification of rights in the Charter. Contains a historical perspective, a modern appraisal, current issues, and speculations for the future.
ISBN 0409832146 Hbk £36.00

Civil liberties in conflict / edited by Larry Gostin. – London : Routledge, 1988.
xix,215p.
Includes bibliographical references and index.
ISBN 0415006805 Pbk £8.95

Civil liberties in Hong Kong / editor, Raymond Wacks : contributors, Johannes Chan ... et al. – Hong Kong : Oxford University Press, 1988.
Includes index and bibliography.
ISBN 0195827244 £35.00

Civil liberties in Scotland : cases & materials / K.D. Ewing & W. Finnie. – Edinburgh : Green, 1982.
xiv,285p.
Includes index.
ISBN 0414007069

Civil liberties in Scotland: cases and materials / W Finnie. – 2nd. – Edinburgh : Green (W.) & Son, 1988.
Covers law on liberty and police powers, freedom from discrimination, freedom of religion, of expression and of assembly. There are special chapters on the European Convention on Human Rights and Privacy.
ISBN 0414008448 Pbk

Civil Litigation. – Calcutta : Eastern Law House.
Hbk

Civil litigation / John O'Hare, Robert N. Hill. – 4th ed. – London : Longman, 1986.
xxvi,507p; 24cm.
Previous ed.: Oyez Longman, 1985. Includes index.
ISBN 0851212220 Pbk £15.95

Civil Litigation : A Practical Handbook / David Stockwood. – 2nd ed. – Agincourt : Carswell, 1986.
286p.
This book presents a guide to modern civil litigation in Canada for the practitioner. Each step in the preparation of a case is accompanied by checklist and sample forms.
Hbk £44.00

Civil Litigation : a Practice Guide for Advocates. – Butterworths, 1985.
296p.
ISBN 0409492345 Hbk £49.00

Civil Litigation for Legal Assistants 1986. – Vancouver : Continuing Legal Education Society of British Columbia, 1986.
538p.
ISBN 0865042713 Hbk £65.00
Supplement-1987. –
162p.
ISBN 0865043272 ac £60.00

Civil practice of all courts for blacks in Southern Africa / J.A.M. Khumalo. – 3rd ed. – Cape Town : Juta, 1984.
xli,300p.
Previous ed. (1975) has title: Civil practice and procedure in all Bantu courts in Southern Africa. Bibliography: p.xix. - Includes index.
ISBN 0702114677

Civil procedure / L. D. J. Henderson. – 3rd ed. – London : Sweet & Maxwell, 1983.
xlvii,448p; 23cm.
Previous ed.: 1976. Includes index.
ISBN 0421289104 Hbk £
ISBN 0421289201 Pbk £9.45

Civil Procedure. – Lucknow : Eastern Book Company, 1983.
570p.
Hbk £40.00

Civil Procedure Code / Lal Jagadish. – 2nd ed. – Allahabad : Law Publishers, 1982.
Hbk £12.00

Civil Procedure Code / S. Venkataraman. – Allahabad : Orient Law House.
ISBN 0861256700 Hbk £25.00

Civil Procedure Code (Abridged). – Suppl. 1982 11th ed. – Bombay : Tripathi, 1982.
1070p.
Hbk £10.00

Civil Procedure Code, Vol 1. – 14th ed. – Bombay : Tripathi, 1981.
1040p.
Hbk £150.00

Civil procedure including courts and evidence / J. M. Jacob. – 1. – London : Butterworths, 1966.
various pagings.
Photocopies of articles from Annual survey of Commonwealth Law 1965-1977 bound together in one volume. Includes bibliographical references. 1972 article onwards by I.H. Jacob and J.M. Jacob. 1976 and 1977 articles entitled: Civil procedure including courts.

Civil Procedure Simplified / R.A. Meagher. – Butterworths, 1983.
336p.
Outline of civil procedure rules and practice. Covers originating and interlocutory applications in chambers, the conduct of actions during the retainer, pleading, discovery, application and trial stages, the subsequent appeal and enforcement of the judgement, and the drafting of court forms. Also looks at the status of more than 13 types of person subject to examination for discovery.
ISBN 0409848786 Hbk £50.00

Civil Procedure, South Australia. – Butterworths, 1987.
ISBN 0409492396 Llf £235.00

Civil Procedure, Victoria. – Butterworths.
Llf

Civil proceedings by and against the State in Nigeria / by F. Olisa Awogu. – Onitsha : Pacific College Press, 1981.
x,167p.
Includes index.

Civil proceedings in a beleaguered society : a public lecture / delivered by Lord Lowry on ... 17th March 1987. – London : Inns of Court School of Law, 1987.
23p.

Civil Remedies / M. Tilbury. – Sydney : Butterworths, 1988.
550p.
This work discusses the nature and interrelation of civil remedies. Included are materials on damages, restitution, statutory remedies, injuries to rights in tangible property, personal injuries, and other topics.
Hbk £69.00

Civil Rights : the Law, the Police, and You. – 8th ed. – North Vancouver : International Self-Counsel Press, 1985.
228p.
ISBN 0889086222 Hbk £8.95

Civil rights with special reference to the Commonwealth Caribbean : a select bibliography / Velma Newton. – Cave Hill, Barbados : Institute of Social and Economic Research (Eastern Caribbean), University of the West Indies, 1981.
110p. – (Occasional bibliography series).
Includes index.

Civil Service Rules : With Classified Extracts from Judgements and Decisions of the Supreme Court and High Courts in India, Govt of India's Orders, Instructions and Interpretations with Index. – Bombay : N.M. Khosla & Co., 1988.
Hbk £100.00

Civil Service Today / Butcher. – Oxford : Blackwell.
ISBN 0631154280 Hbk £29.95
ISBN 0631154299 Pbk £9.50

Civilian administration in the occupied West Bank : analysis of Israeli Military Government Order no. 947 / by Jonathan Kuttab and Raja Shehadeh. – Ramallah : Law in the Service of Man, 1982.
44p.
ISBN 9290370181

Civilian review of complaints against the police : a survey of the United States literature / David C. Brown. – London : Home Office, 1983.
v,39p.
Bibliography: p.29-32.
ISBN 0862521041

Civilian Writers of Doctors' Commons, London : Three Centuries of Juristic Innovation in Comparative, Commercial and International Law. – Berlin : Duncker and Humblot, 1988.
303p.
ISBN 3428061772 Hbk £148.00

Claims to the possession of land : the law and practice / by Philip Walter and James Harris. – London : Fourmat, 1987.
xlvii,616p; 26cm.
ISBN 1851900004 Hbk £37.50

Clamp, Hugh
Shorter forms of building contract. – 2nd ed. – Oxford : Blackwell Scientific, 1988.
ISBN 0003834123 Pbk £17.95
ISBN 0632018437 Hbk £19.95

Clanchy, M. T.
England and its rulers 1066-1272 : foreign lordship and national identity / M.T. Clanchy. – Oxford : Basil Blackwell in association with Fontana, 1983.
317p; 23cm.
First published by Fontana Paperbacks in the 'Fontana history of England', 1983. Bibliography: p299-308. - Includes index.
ISBN 0631133720 £15.00

Claringbould, M.H. → Transport : International Transport Treaties.

Clark
Law of Torts / Stephenson. – London : Financial Training, 1985.
– (SWOT).
ISBN 0906322731 Pbk £7.50
—SWOT Law of Torts / Stephenson. – London : Blackstone Press.
ISBN 1854310291 Pbk £7.95

Clark, Bruce A.
Indian Title in Canada. – Agincourt : Carswell, 1987.
154p.
This work focuses on the basis of Indian land claims in Canada and provides a thorough discussion of the court's responses to these claims. The author integrates history and law in explaining the issues.
Hbk £39.50

Clark, Charles → Publishing agreements : a book of precedents.

Clark, David
City of Paris Mediateur : an ombudsman a la francaise / by David Clark. – Edmonton, Alta. : International Ombudsman Institute, 1983.
47p. – (Occasional paper).
Originally published: in Local government studies, vol. 8, no. 5 (Sept.-Oct. 1982).

Clark, Hilary → Family home.

Clark, Ian
Waging war : a philosophical introduction / Ian Clark. – Oxford : Clarendon Press, 1988.
154 p.; 23 cm.
Bibliography: p. 143-147. Includes index.
ISBN 0198273258

Clark, J.B. → Law of wills, Supplement 1984.
—Parry and Clark: the law of succession. – 9th. – London : Sweet & Maxwell.
Includes the Family Law Reform Act 1987, and the Inheritance Tax Act of 1984. Also covers the Non-Contentious Probate Rules, and the Insolvency Act 1986. New cases are referred to throughout the text, in particular where they illustrate the exercise of the courts' power to order financial provision for the family of the deceased.
ISBN 0421359803 Hbk £34
ISBN 0421359900 Pbk £24.00
→ Theobald on wills.

Clark, John → Tax warranties and indemnities.

Clark, Philip
Organisation and Management of a Solicitor's Practice. – Woolloomooloo : International Business Communications, 1984.
ISBN 094907201X Llf £175.00

Clark, R. B.
Marine pollution / R.B. Clark. – Oxford : Clarendon, 1986.
xiii,215p; 24cm.
Bibliography: p208-209. - Includes index.
ISBN 019854183X Pbk £19.50
ISBN 0198541821 Pbk £9.50
—Waters around the British Isles : their conflicting uses : report of a study group of the David Davies Memorial Institute of International Studies / R.B. Clark. – Oxford : Clarendon, 1987.
xvi,386p; 24cm.
Includes index.
ISBN 0198284926 £32.50

Clark, Robert
Contract / by Robert Clark. – 2nd ed. 1. – London : Sweet & Maxwell, 1986.
22cm.
Previous ed.: 1982. Includes index.
ISBN 0421344806 Pbk £15.00

Clark, Robert W.
Inequality of bargaining power : judicial intervention in improvident and unconscionable bargains / Robert W. Clark. – Toronto : Carswell, 1987.
xxxvii,255p.
ISBN 0459388401

Clark, Roger
Micronesia : the problem of Palau / prepared by Roger Clark and Sue Rabitt Roff. – Rev ed. – London : Minority Rights Group, 1987.
22p. – (Report).
Includes bibliographical references.
ISBN 0946690146

Clark, T. M. → Leasing finance.

Clarke
Commercial and Consumer Law / Stephenson. – London : Financial Training, 1987.
– (SWOT).
ISBN 1851850430 Pbk £7.50
—Drainage Cases : Ontario 1898-1903, 2 Vols. / Scully. – Agincourt : Carswell, 1983.
Hbk £59.00
—International employment tax handbook / Reading. – Cambridge : Woodhead-Faulkner, 1982.
ISBN 0859411915 Hbk £115.00
→ Securities law in New Zealand.

Clarke, D N, et al
Rent reviews and variable rents / J E Adams. – 3rd. – London : Longman Professional (UK), 1989.
– (Practitioner series).
Examines rent review clauses and other methods. Analysis of some 100 cases decided since 1984, and model forms published by the Law Society, the Royal institute of Chartered Surveyors, and the ISVA.
ISBN 0851213863 Hbk £37.50

Clarke, Giles
Butterworths Capital Gains Tax Guide : the New Regime. – London : Butterworths.
ISBN 0406513600 Pbk £16.95
→ Capital Gains Tax.
→ Offshore tax planning.
→ Sumption and Clarke's tax and tax planning.

Clarke Hall
Law in Relation to Children / A C L Morrison. – 10th ed. – London : Butterworths, 1985.
Service to 31.3.89.
ISBN 0406158126 Llf £145.00

Clarke Hall and Morrison on Children, 2 Vols. / A.C.L. Morrison. – 10th ed. – London : Butterworths, 1986.
ISBN 040615807X Llf
Supplement. –
This looseleaf service in two volumes contains all the relevant statutory material on practice of law relating to children in the United Kingdom. Five main subjects make up the work.
ISBN 040615810X Pbk

Clarke, Keith → Chairmanship in Magistrates' Courts.

Clarke, Malcolm A.
International carriage of goods by road : CMR / by Malcolm A. Clarke. – London : Stevens, 1982.
xxvi,212p; 26cm.
Includes index. Appendix in French.
ISBN 0420464905 £19.50
—International carriage of goods by road - CMR / by Malcolm A. Clarke. – Sweet & Maxwell, 1982.
ISBN 0420464905 Hbk £38.00
—Regulating the city / by Malcolm A. Clarke. – Open University Press, 1986.
ISBN 0335153828 Pbk £7.95
→ Shipbuilding contracts.

Clarke, Michael
Corruption : Causes, Consequences and Control. – London : Pinter Publishers Ltd, 1983.
319p.
ISBN 0861873408 Hbk £29.50

Clarke, P.
Surveyor in Court. – London : Estates Gazette, 1985.
ISBN 0728200910 Pbk £25.00

Clarke, P. J.
Law relating to firearms / by P. J. Clarke and John W. Ellis. – London : Butterworths, 1981.
xxvi,272p.
ISBN 0406158207

Clarke, R. → Securities Law in New Zealand.

Clarke, R. V. G.
Crime and police effectiveness / by Ronald V. Clarke and Mike Hough. – London : H.M.S.O., 1984.
iv,28p; 28cm. – (A Home Office Research and Planning Unit report).
ISBN 0113407734

Clarke, W.M.
How the City of London Works : An Introduction to its Financial Markets. – 2nd ed. – Waterlow.
ISBN 008033105X Pbk £6.95

Clarke, William M.
Inside the city : a guide to London as a financial centre / William M. Clarke. – Rev. ed. – London : Allen & Unwin, 1983.
xii,283p; 22cm.
Previous ed.: 1979. Includes index.
ISBN 0043320910 Pbk £6.95

Clarkson
Understanding Criminal Law 1987 / Chodse. – London : Fontana.
ISBN 0006860745 Pbk £4.95

Clarkson, C. M. V.
Criminal law : text and materials / by C.M.V. Clarkson, H.M. Keating. – London : Sweet & Maxwell, 1984.
xxxiv,590p; 25cm.
Includes index.
ISBN 0421309202 Hbk £26.00
ISBN 042130930X Pbk £16.95

Clarkson, Stephen
Canada and the Reagan Challenge : Crisis in the Canadian-American Relationship. – Toronto : Lorimer & Co, 1985.
ISBN 0888627912 Hbk £26.95
ISBN 0888627904 Pbk £16.95

Class actions in the Scottish courts : a new way for consumers to obtain redress?. – Glasgow : Scottish Consumer Council, 1982.
v,53p; 30cm.
ISBN 0907067123 Pbk

Class and Subclass Titles of the International Patent Classification, 1984 (Fourth Edition) : Synopsis of Classes and Subclasses with Information on the Number of Subdivisions. – Geneva : World Intellectual Property Organization, 1984.
129p.
Hbk £30.00

Class Power and Urban Policy : Corporations and Labour Unions in City Politics. – London : Macmillan, 1982.
256p. – (Sociology, Politics and Cities, Ser.).
ISBN 0333260759 Hbk £12.50
ISBN 0333260767 Pbk £4.95

Classical English Law Texts Series, 136 Vols. – Abingdon : Professional Books.
Hbk

Classification of limitation in private international law : report on a reference under section 3(1)(e) of the Law Commissions Act 1965 / the Law Commission. – London : H.M.S.O., 1982.
v,60p.
ISBN 0101857004

Classification of offences / Law Reform Commission of Canada. – Ottawa : The Commission, 1986.
92,98p. – (Working paper).
Includes bibliographical references. Pages numbered in opposite directions. Text in English and French.
ISBN 0662545699

Classifying Non-Operating Interests in Oil and Gas. – Calgary : Canadian Institute of Resources Law.
Hbk £10.00

Clay
Modern Merchant Banking / Wheble. – 2nd ed. – Cambridge : Woodhead-Faulkner, 1983.
ISBN 0859412156 Pbk £9.95
ISBN 0859412164 Hbk £17.50

Clayden, Paul
Rights of way : a guide to law and practice / by Paul Clayden and John Trevelyan. – Henley-on-Thames : Open Spaces Society, 1983.
viii,359p; 21cm.
Includes index.
ISBN 0946574006 Pbk £4.00
ISBN 0900613491 Ramblers' Association
—Rights of way guide to law and practice / by Paul Clayden and John Trevelyan. – Open Spaces Society, 1983.
ISBN 0946574006 Hbk £4.00

Clayton, J.
Reports and Pleas of Assizes at York : 1631-50. – Repr. of 1651 ed. – Abingdon : Professional Books.
335p.
Hbk £120.00

Clayton, Patricia E
Consumer Law for the Small Business. – London : Kogan Page, 1983.
160p.
ISBN 0850386187 Hbk £11.95
ISBN 0850386489 Pbk £5.95
—Law for the Small Business. – 5th ed. – London : Kogan Page, 1987.
ISBN 0850912157 Pbk £7.50
—Law for the Small Business : The Daily Telegraph' Guide. – 4th ed. – London : Kogan Page, 1985.
264p.
ISBN 0850388937 Hbk £11.95
ISBN 0850388945 Pbk £6.95
—Law for the Small Business (Daily Telegraph Guide). – 6th ed. – London : Kogan Page.
ISBN 1850916438 Pbk £7.95

Clayton, R.
Practice and procedure in industrial tribunals. – London : Legal Action Group, 1986.
ISBN 0905099141 Pbk £7.50

Clayton, Richard
Civil actions against the police / by Richard Clayton and Hugh Tomlinson. – London : Sweet & Maxwell, 1987.
250p; 25cm.
Examines the rights and remedies of the individual against police misconduct. Covers traditional tort actions, assault, false imprisonment, trespass, interference with goods, and malicious prosecution. Emphasis on recent developments, and focuses on the circumstances that may lead to claims. Also contains discussion on civil liability under the Police and Criminal Evidence Act 1984.
ISBN 0421344202 £30.00
—Suing the police / Hugh Tomlinson. – London : Longman Professional (UK), 1989.
Identifies the clauses of the damages claim and explains the types of damages that can be included. Offers advice on every stage of the procedure from taking instructions and financing the case to the trial itself. Includes costs, fees, and precedents.
ISBN 0851215297 Pbk £14.95

Clayton, Richard J.
Parker's Conduct of Parliamentary Elections. – Tonbridge : Ernest Benn, 1983.
610p. – (Knight's Looseleaf Library).
ISBN 0853143137 Llf £47.50

Clean Air - Law and Practice. – 4th ed. – Shaw & Sons, 1976.
ISBN 072190680X Pbk £10.00

Clearing banks and the trade unions / by L. D. Cowan. – London : Institute of Bankers, 1984.
64p.
'Delivered under the auspices of King's College, London'.
ISBN 0852971168

Clearing up crime / by John Burrows and Roger Tarling. – London : H.M.S.O., 1982.
31p; 25cm.
Bibliography: p24-26. A Home Office Research and Planning Unit report.
ISBN 0113407688

Cledwyn
Referendum : The End of an Era. – Cardiff : University of Wales, 1981.
14p.
ISBN 0708308082 Pbk £0.95

Clegg → Evidence Law and Practice.

Clemens
Balance Sheets and the Lending Banker / Dyer. – 6th ed. – London : Europa Publications, 1986.
ISBN 0946653291 Pbk £8.95

Clement, Priscilla F. → History of Juvenile Delinquency, 2 Vols.

Clements, Kenneth W.
How Protection Taxes Exporters / Larry A. Sjaastad. – London : Trade Policy Research Centre, 1985.
87p.
Hbk £8.00

Clergyman's handbook, and churchwarden's guide : being a manual of the laws affecting the relative rights, position, and duties of the clergy and their parishioners ..., with appendices containing important statutes, including the Benefices Act, 1898 / by James Murray Dale. – 7th ed. – London : Seeley, 1898.
xx,507p.
Includes index. .

Clerk & Lindsell on torts / William Henry Barber Lindsell, R. W. M. Dias. – 15th ed. – London : Sweet & Maxwell, 1982.
cclxiv,1417p; 26cm.
Previous ed.: / general editors Sir Arthur L. Armitage and R.W.M. Dias. 1975. Includes index. Kept up to date by supplements.
ISBN 0421262508 £65.00

Clerk, John Frederic
Clerk & Lindsell on torts / William Henry Barber Lindsell, R. W. M. Dias. – 15th ed. – London : Sweet & Maxwell, 1982.
cclxiv,1417p; 26cm.
Previous ed.: / general editors Sir Arthur L. Armitage and R.W.M. Dias. 1975. Includes index. Kept up to date by supplements.
ISBN 0421262508 £65.00

Clews, R.
Textbook of insurance broking. – 2nd ed. – Cambridge : Woodhead-Faulkner, 1987.
ISBN 0859413861 Hbk £25.00

CLIC Abstracts on PLEI Research. – Ottawa : Canadian Law Information Council, 1983.
670p.
ISBN 0920358403 Llf £50.00
1985 Supplement. –
£15.00

CLIC Bibliography of Computers and Law 1983-1986. – Ottawa : Canadian Law Information Council.
106p.
ISBN 0921481128 Hbk £20.00

Client interviewing for lawyers : an analysis and guide / by Avrom Sherr. – London : Sweet & Maxwell, 1986.
190p; 22cm.
Includes bibliography and index.
ISBN 0421361603 Pbk £7.95

Clients' Rights : Report of a Working Party Established by the National Council for Voluntary Organisations. – London : Bedford Square Press, 1985.
Hbk £3.95

Clifford, Brian R. → Evaluating witness evidence : recent psychological research and new perspectives.

Clifford-Chance
Doing Business in the United Kingdom. – Matthew Bender, 1987.
ISBN 0000999036 Hbk £147.00

Clifford, W.
How to Combat Hijacking. – Canberra : Australian Institute of Criminology.
free

Clifford, William
Aboriginal Criminological Research. – Canberra : Australian Institute of Criminology.
Hbk £2.85
—Bail : Issues and Prospects / Leslie T Wilkins. – Canberra : Australian Institute of Criminology.
Hbk £2.20
—Cost of Criminal Justice : A Preliminary International Survey / J. Marjoram. – Canberra : Australian Institute of Criminology.
Hbk £2.00
—Cost of Imprisonment in Australia. – Canberra : Australian Institute of Criminology.
Hbk £3.00
—Crime Control in Japan. – Canberra : Australian Institute of Criminology.
Hbk £21.95
—Crime Prevention Planning : Proceedings of the United National Interregional Course. – Canberra : Australian Institute of Criminology.
Hbk £2.95
—Evaluation in the Criminal Justice Services. – Canberra : Australian Institute of Criminology.
free
—Human Rights Guarantees in the Administration of Criminal Justice / Leslie T Wilkins. – Canberra : Australian Institute of Criminology.
Hbk £2.00
—Human Rights in the Administration of Criminal Justice : Report on the United Nations Course. – Canberra : Australian Institute of Criminology.
Hbk £1.50
—Legal Control of Casinos. – Canberra : Australian Institute of Criminology.
free
—Planning Crime Prevention. – Canberra : Australian Institute of Criminology.
Hbk £18.95
—Plotting and Planning. – Canberra : Australian Institute of Criminology.
Hbk £5.00
—Policing a Democracy. – Canberra : Australian Institute of Criminology.
free
—Race Problems in ESCAP. – Canberra : Australian Institute of Criminology.
free
—Road Safety and Crime / J. Marjoram. – Canberra : Australian Institute of Criminology.
Hbk £2.00

Clinging to the wreckage. – Penguin, 1982.
ISBN 0297780107 Pbk £1.95

Clinical assessment before trial : legal issues and mental disorder / Christopher D. Webster, Robert J. Menzies, Margaret A. Jackson : with the collaboration of Brian T. Butler...et al. – Toronto : Butterworths, 1982.
xxvii,319p.
Discusses fitness to stand trial, psychiatric recommendations for treatment, evaluation of mental status and the clinical prediction of dangerous behaviour. Chapter deals with the effect of psychiatric opinion on judicial decision-making.
ISBN 0409875775

Clive
Directing Corporate Growth / Benson. – London : Fitzwilliam, 1988.
ISBN 1870555074 Hbk £25.00

Clive, Eric M.
Law of husband and wife in Scotland / by Eric M. Clive. – 2nd ed. – Edinburgh : Green (W.) & Son, 1982.
lxxiv,756p. – (Scottish Universities' Law Institute Ser.).
Chapters describe the general development of the law from before the Reformation to the present day, the formation and termination of marriage and the legal effects of marriage. Bibliography: plxxi-lxxi Published under the auspices of the Scottish Universities Law Institute.
ISBN 0414006682 Hbk £47
—Scots law for journalists / Bruce McKain. – 5th. – Edinburgh : Green (W.) & Son, 1988.
The standard text book on media law in Scotland, revised to include new judicial interpretation of the journalistic privilege in quoting from documents not read out in court, the publishing of leaked information, the effects of the Data Protection Act, public right of access to local authority meetings and the way divorces under the reformed procedures may be safely reported. With coverage of the European Courts of Justice and Human Rights, and the new procedure for judicial review.
ISBN 0414008146 Pbk

Close Corporations Act 1984 : a basic introduction / by A. Allan...et al. – Cape Town : Juta for the Bureau of Mercantile Law, University of Port Elizabeth, 1984.
xiv,70p.
ISBN 070211507X

Close Pursuit : Week In The Life Of A New York Homicide Cop. – Viking.
ISBN 0140083979 Pbk £3.50
ISBN 0670808377 Hbk £10.95

Closed shop agreements and arrangements : code of practice. – London : The Department, 1983.
24p.

Closing Chapter. – London : Butterworths, 1983.
ISBN 0406176116 Hbk £12.95
ISBN 0406176124 Pbk £8.95

Cloughton → Business Interruption and Consequent Loss Insurance.

Cloughton, David
Riley on business interruption and consequential loss insurances and claims / by David Cloughton. – 6th ed. – London : Sweet & Maxwell, 1985.
480p.
Examination of business interruption consequential loss insurances and claims with emphasis on practice and procedure. Covers loss of profits, wages, and book debts, and perils and contingencies such as labour disturbances, strikes, riots, and the special conditions applicable in Northern Ireland and South Africa.
ISBN 0421319208 £46.00

Clues to Murder. – Aurora : Cape, 1986.
ISBN 0370308522 Hbk £12.95

Clulow
In the child's best interest? / Vincent. – London : Sweet & Maxwell, 1987.
ISBN 042261260X Hbk £22.00
ISBN 0422612707 Pbk £10.95

CMEA uniform law for international sales / by Ivan Szasz. – 2nd rev. ed. – Dordrecht : Nijhoff, 1985.
viii,291p; 25cm.
Previous ed.: published as : A uniform law on international sales of goods, 1976. Includes index. Translation of: A KGST altalanos szalltasi feltelek.
ISBN 9024727855 Hbk £125.00

CMR : contracts for the international carriage of goods by road / by D.J. Hill and A.D. Messent. – London : Lloyd's of London Press, 1984.
xliii,288p; 26cm.
Contains the text of the Carriage of Goods by Road Act 1965 and the French (i.e., definitive) text of the CMR.
ISBN 0907432557

Cnossen, Sijbren →Comparative tax studies : essays in honor of Richard Goode.

Coal utilisation : technology, economics and policy / L. Grainger and J. Gibson. – London : Graham & Trotman, 1981.
xxii,503p; 25cm.
Bibliography: p489-496. - Includes index.
ISBN 0860102661 £18.00

Coastal area management and development / United Nations Department of International Economic and Social Affairs, Ocean Economics and Technology Branch. – Oxford : Pergamon, 1982.
xii,188p; 24cm.
ISBN 0080233937 Pbk £20.00

Coastal Law. – London : Lloyd's of London Press, 1988.
ISBN 1850441642 Hbk

Coastal state requirements for foreign fishing Vol.1 / by Gerald K. Moore. – Rev. ed. – Rome : Food and Agriculture Organization of the United Nations, 1983.
iv,242p. – (Legislative study).
Previous ed. published as: Legislation on coastal state requirements for foreign fishing.
ISBN 9251015031

Coastal State Requirements for Foreign Fishing. – Rome : FAO, Food and Agricultural Organization of the United Nations, 1985.
302p.
ISBN 925102359X Hbk £19.50

Coates, John
New Law of Expropriation / Stephen F. Waque. – Toronto : DeBoo, 1984.
This text provides analyses of reform legislation in Alberta, Manitoba, New Brunswick, Nova Scotia and Canada. Provincial statutes contain section-by-section commentaries. The main topics discussed are compensation where no land is taken, ways to prove expropriation claims, and types of claims successfully made.
ISBN 0888201532 Hbk £135.00

Coates, R.
Conveyancing. – London : Longman Professional. – (Longman Practice Notes Series).
ISBN 0851214460 Pbk £10.95

Cobbett, W.
Howell's State Trials : 1163-1820, 34 Vols. / T. J. Howell. – Repr. – Abingdon : Professional Books.
Hbk

Cobden Trust →Abolishing the Diplock courts : the case for restoring jury trial to scheduled offences in Northern Ireland.
→ Price of justice : costs and defendants.
→ Towards a just immigration policy.
→ Use and abuse of emergency legislation in Northern Ireland.

Cocaine Connection : Two Against the Drug Trade, A True Story / Milgate. – Sphere Books.
ISBN 0747402795 Pbk £3.50

Cockcroft, A. N.
Guide to the Collision Avoidance Rules / J. Lameijer. – London : Stanford Maritime Ltd.
224p.
Pbk £7.95

Cockerell, H.
Witherby dictionary of insurance. – 2nd ed. – London : Witherby & Co, 1987.
ISBN 0948691212 Hbk £14.50

Cockerell, Hugh →Liability for defective services.

Cockerell, M.
What goes on in insurance?. – Cambridge : Woodhead-Faulkner, 1982.
ISBN 0859411613 Pbk £3.95

Cockle, Ernest →Cases and statutes on evidence : being based upon Cockle's cases and statutes on evidence.

Cockram
Interpretation of statutes / Gail-Maryse Cockram. – 3rd ed. – Cape Town : Juta, 1987.
xvi,181p.
Previous ed.: 1983. Includes index.
ISBN 0702118346

Cocks, R.J.C.
Sir Henry Maine : a Study in Victorian Jurisprudence. – Cambridge : Cambridge University Press.
– (Cambridge Studies in English Law History).
ISBN 0521353432 Hbk £27.50

Cocks, Raymond
Foundations of the modern Bar / by Raymond Cocks. – London : Sweet & Maxwell, 1983.
vii,257p; 22cm.
Bibliography: p235-249. - Includes index.
ISBN 0421303603 Pbk £9.50

Code for the Construction and Equipment of Mobile Offshore Drilling Units : MODU Code French Edition /. – London : International Maritime Organization.
Hbk £3.00

Code of Advertising Practice Committee
British code of advertising practice / Code of Advertising Prcatice Committee. – 7th ed. – London : Code of Advertising Practice Committee, 1985.
94p.
Includes index. ' ... under the general supervision of the Advertising Standards Authority'. - p.4.
—British code of sales promotion practice / Code of Advertising Practice Committee. – 4th ed. – London : Code of Advertising Practice Committee, 1984.
28p.
Includes index. '... under the general supervision of the Advertising Standards Authority ...'. - p.2.

Code of Agrarian Reform of the Philippines. – Quezon City : University of the Philippines, Law Center, 1981.
338p.
Hbk £70.00

Code of Canon Law. – Canon Law Society. – Oxford : Collins, 1983.
Pbk £4.95

Code of Civil Procedure. – Seychelles Government. – Mahe : Seychelles National Printing Co.
Hbk £20.00

Code of Civil Procedure. – 3rd ed. – Calcutta : Eastern Law House, 1986.
Hbk £320.00

Code of Civil Procedure in 3 Vols. – 5th ed. – Allahabad : Law Book Company, 1982-84.
Hbk £450.00

Code of conduct for companies with interests in South Africa : government guidance to British companies on the code of conduct adopted by the governments of the member states of the European Community on 19 November 1985 / presented to Parliament by the Secretary of State for Trade and Industry. – London : H.M.S.O., 1986.
16p.
Supersedes code published in 1978 as Cmnd. 7233.
ISBN 0101986009

Code of conduct for the Bar of England and Wales : effective from 1st January 1981 / Senate of the Inns of Court and the Bar. – 2nd ed. Incorporating all amendments up to 31st December 1982. – London : The Senate, 1983.
76p.
Previous ed.: 1981. Includes index.

Code of conduct for the Bar of England and Wales : effective from 1st January 1981. – Senate of the Inns of Court and the Bar. – 3rd ed. (incorporating all amendments up to 31st December 1984). – London : The Senate, 1985.
74p.
Includes index.

Code of Criminal Procedure, 3 Vols. – Allahabad : Orient Law House, 1984.
Hbk £135.00

Code of Criminal Procedure. – 2nd ed. – Allahabad : Law Publishers, 1983.
Hbk £12.00

Code of Criminal Procedure / Dhirajlal. – 13th ed. – Nagpur : Wadhura & Co, 1987.
Hbk £220.00

Code of Criminal Procedure. – 3rd ed. – Allahabad : Law Book Company, 1988.
1,900p.
Hbk £350.00

Code of Criminal Procedure in 5 Vols. – 18th ed. – Allahabad : Law Book Company, 1984.
Hbk £700.00

Code of Muslim personal law / by Tanzil-ur-Rahman. – 2. – Karachi : Hamdard Academy, 1978.
Bibliography: vol.1, p.v-viii. - Includes index. Vol. 2 published: Karachi: Islamic Publishers.
ISBN 0195772857 v.2

Code of practice : race relations. – London : The Commission, 1983.
30p.
Cover title: Race relations code of practice for the elimination of racial discrimination and the promotion of equality of opportunity in employment.
ISBN 0907920292

Code of practice for consumers / British Telecom. – London : British Telecom, 1984.
24p.

Code of Safe Practice for Ships Carrying Timber Deck Cargoes
French Edition /. – London : International Maritime Organization.
Hbk £1.50
Supplement-1978 Amendments, French Edition. –
Hbk £1.25

Code of Safety for Nuclear Merchant Ships English Edition. – International Maritime Organization. – London : International Maritime Organization, 1982.
Hbk £3.00
French Edition. –
Hbk £4.00

Codes civils - The Civil Codes / by Lise Saintonge-Poitevin. – Reedition a jour au 1er dec. 1982. 1. – Montreal : Wilson & Lafleur, 1982-.
Previous ed.: 1978. Includes indexes.
ISBN 2891270177 Llf

Codex Ecclesiastici Anglicani : Statutes, Constitutions, Canons, Rubriks, and Articles of the Church of England Digested with a Commentary Historical and Judicial, and Introductory Discourse, and Appendix of Instruments, 2 Vols. – 2nd ed. Repr. of 1761 ed. – Abingdon : Professional Books.
168p.
Hbk £120.00

Codification of the criminal law : a public lecture / delivered by J.C. Smith on ... 17th March 1986. – London : Inns of Court School of Law, 1986.
16p.

Codification of the criminal law : memorandum on the Law Commission report / Justice. – London : Justice, 1986.
3 leaves.
A commentary on a Law Commission report entitled: Criminal law: codification of the criminal law: a report to the Law Commission.

Codification of the law of landlord and tenant : covenants regarding dispositions, alterations and change of user / The Law Commission. – London : H.M.S.O., 1985.
x,139p; 25cm. – (H.C. 1984-85).
ISBN 0102278857

Codification of the law of landlord and tenant : forfeiture of tenancies / The Law Commission. – London : H.M.S.O., 1985.
ix,195p; 25cm. – (H.C. 1984-85).
ISBN 0102279853

Coenenberg →International group accounting.

Coertze, J. J. J. →Seymour's Customary law in Southern Africa.

Co-existence in some plural European societies. – London : Minority Rights Group, 1986.
17p. – (Report).
ISBN 0946690448

Coffey, Peter
European monetary system–past, present, and future / by Peter Coffey. – 2nd rev. ed. – Dordrecht : Kluwer, 1987.
x,163p.
Includes bibliographical references and index.
ISBN 9024734460

Cognitive model of crime and delinquency prevention and rehabilitation, 2 Vols.
Vol. 1 : assessment procedures / Elizabeth A. Fabiano. – Ontario : Ontario Government Publications Service, 1983.
89p.
ISBN 0774386681 Hbk free

Cognitive Model of Crime and Delinquency Prevention and Rehabilitation : Intervention Techniques, 2 Vols.
Vol. 2 : intervention techniques / Elizabeth A. Fabiano. – Ontario : Ontario Government Publications Service, 1983.
89p.
ISBN 0774386673 Hbk free

Cohabitation / by Martin L. Parry : with a foreword by H.K. Bevan. – London : Sweet and Maxwell, 1981.
xxv,162p; 22cm.
Includes bibliographies and index.
ISBN 0421267305 Pbk £5.75

Cohabitation : the legal implications / Dawn Oliver. – Bicester : CCH Editions, 1987.
xvi,140p; 23cm.
Includes index.
ISBN 0863251080 Pbk

Cohabitation contracts : extra-marital partnerships and law reform / Chris Barton. – Aldershot : Gower, 1985.
xxi,115p; 23cm.
Bibliography: p97-99. - Includes index.
ISBN 0566007118 £17.95

Cohabitation handbook : a women's guide to the law / Anne Bottomley ... et al. – 2nd ed. – London : Pluto, 1984.
240p; 20cm.
Previous ed.: 1981. Includes index.
ISBN 0861047931 Pbk £5.50

Cohabitation without marriage : an essay in law and social policy / Michael D.A. Freeman and Christina M. Lyon. – Aldershot : Gower, 1983.
vii,228p; 23cm.
Includes index.
ISBN 0566004550

Cohabitees / Stephen Parker. – Chichester : Barry Rose, 1981.
xxii,230p.
Bibliography: p224-225.
ISBN 0859922103

Cohen
Benedict On Admiralty / Norris. – 7th ed. – Matthew Bender, 1973.
ISBN 0000999052 Hbk £573.00
—Chinese Contract Cases / Chan. – London : Longman Professional.
ISBN 0582049202 Hbk
—History of the English Bar 1929. – London : Wildy & Sons.
Hbk £13.75
—National welfare benefits handbook / Lakhani. – 16th ed. – London : CENT, 1986.
ISBN 0906963957 Pbk £4.00
—Single Payments : the Disappearing Safety Net 1988 / Tarpey. – London : Central Books.
ISBN 0946744076 Pbk £3.95
—Treaties and Related International Documents / Sann. – 7th ed. – Matthew Bender, 1973.
ISBN 0000999053 Hbk £112.00

Cohen, B. I., et al
Practice and Procedure in the Supreme Court of British Columbia. – Vancouver : British Columbia Continuing Legal Education Society, 1982.
167p.
ISBN 0865040559 Hbk £17.50

Cohen, B.J.
In Whose Interest? International Banking and American Foreign Policy. – Yale University Press.
ISBN 0300042051 Pbk £9.95

Cohen, Esther Rosalind
Human rights in the Israeli-occupied territories, 1967-1982 / Esther Rosalind Cohen. – Manchester : Manchester University Press, 1985.
xxii,500p.
Bibliography: p470-498. - Includes index.
ISBN 0719017262 £30.00

Cohen, Lenard, et al
Vision and the Game : the Canadian Constitution. – Calgary : Detselig Enterprises Ltd., 1987.
197p.
ISBN 0920490670 Pbk £14.95

Cohen, Marshall →Ronald Dworkin and contemporary jurisprudence.

Cohen, Maxwell
Lawyers and the Nuclear Debate / Margaret E. Gouin. – Ottawa : University of Ottawa Press, 1988.
xvi, 420p.
ISBN 0776602098 Hbk £65.00
ISBN 0776601997 Pbk £35.00

Cohen, S.
Against Criminology. – Oxford : Clio Distribution.
ISBN 0887381537 Hbk £24.30
ISBN 088738689X Pbk £11.80

Cohen, Stanley →Manufacture of news : social problems, deviance and the mass media.
—Psychological survival : the experience of long-term imprisonment / Stanley Cohen and Laurie Taylor. – 2nd ed. – Harmondsworth : Penguin, 1981.
239p; 19cm. – (Pelican books).
Previous ed.: 1972. Bibliography: p230-239.
ISBN 014021657X Pbk £2.25
→ Social control and the state : historical and comparative essays.
—Visions of social control : crime, punishment and classification / Stanley Cohen. – Cambridge : Polity, 1984.
300p.
ISBN 0745600204 Hbk £19.50
ISBN 0745600212 Pbk £7.95

Cohen, Stanley A.
Invasion of Privacy : Police and Electric Surveillance in Canada. – Agincourt : Carswell, 1983.
250p.
This book analyzes the legal and ethical dimensions of police surveillance in Canada and discusses the question of the extent of police surveillance powers.
Hbk £42.00

Cohl, Karen
Consumer Law / Daniel J. Baum. – Toronto : IPI Publishing, 1983.
84p. – (You and the Law Ser.).
ISBN 0458961302 Pbk £7.95
—Tort Law / Daniel J. Baum. – Toronto : IPI Publishing, 1982.
84p. – (You and the Law Ser.).
ISBN 0458957003 Pbk £7.95

Coke
Three law tracts. – Reprint. – Abingdon : Professional Books, 1986.
– (Classical English Law Texts Ser.).
ISBN 0862053129 Hbk £32.75

Coke, Edward
Compleate Copyholder : Wherein is Contained a Learned Discourse of the Antiquity and Nature of Manors and Copy-Holds, with the Forme of Keeping a Copy-Hold Court and Court Baron. – Repr. of 1673 ed. – Abingdon : Professional Books.
399p.
Hbk £225.00
—First Part of the Institutes of the Lawes of England : Commentary Upon Littleton. – Repr. of 1628 ed. – Abingdon : Professional Books.
449p.
Hbk £1450.00
—Second Part of the Institutes of the Lawes of England : Containing the Exposition of Many Ancient and Other Statutes. – Repr. of 1642 ed. – Abingdon : Professional Books.
546p.
Hbk £1600.00
—Third and Fourth Parts of the Institutes of the Lawes of England : Concerning High Treason and Other Pleas of the Crown and Criminal Causes. – Repr. of 1644 ed. – Abingdon : Professional Books.
360p.
Hbk £1900.00

Coker
Licensed to live / Martin. – Oxford : Blackwell, 1985.
ISBN 0631141650 Pbk £17.50

Cola, Graham
Deloitte, Haskins and Sells : Raising Finance in Capital Markets. – London : Butterworths, 1987.
Pbk

Colby, Richard
Resident landlords and owner-occupiers: law and practice. – London : Longman Professional (UK), 1987.
– (Practitioner series).
Details the issues raised by the relationship between resident landlords, owner-occupiers, and their tenants. Analyses the nature of tenancies, and gives advice on the correct formalities and procedures to be followed, including the right of the landlord to possession.
ISBN 085121293X Hbk £14.50
—Residential tenancies. – London : Longman Professional (UK), 1988.
– (Longman practice notes).
Contains information on the law and procedure of private residential tenancies. Covers precedents for use in court proceedings, and procedures such as obtaining possession of premises, applying for a fair rent, granting tenancies or bringing an action for arrears of rent.
ISBN 0851214479 Pbk £9.95

Cole
Law for Doctors and Nurses / Tingle. – London : Financial Training, 1988.
ISBN 1851851011 Pbk £15.00
—Medicine, Nursing, and the Law / Tingle et al. – London : Blackstone Press.
ISBN 1854310100 Hbk £15.00

Cole, George F. →Abortion and protection of the human fetus : legal problems in a cross-cultural perspective.

Cole, J. S. R
Irish cases on evidence / by J.S.R. Cole. – 2nd ed. – Dublin : Incorporated Law Society of Ireland, 1982.
xxi, 264 p.; 22 cm.
Includes index.
ISBN 0902027190

Coleman
Philosophy of Law / Paul. – Oxford : Blackwell Scientific, 1987.
ISBN 0631152571 Pbk £8.95

Coleman, Clive →Understanding crime rates : police and public roles in the production of official statistics.

Coleman, Cynthia →Taxation Law in Australia.

Coleman, J.
Markets, Morals and the Law. – Cambridge : Cambridge University Press.
ISBN 0521363055 Hbk £35.00
ISBN 0521368545 Pbk £12.95

Colinvaux, Raoul →Carver's carriage by sea.
—Law of insurance / by Raoul Colinvaux. – 5th ed. – London : Sweet & Maxwell, 1984.
xci,553p; 26cm.
Deals with policies of insurance, parties to insurance contracts, and special types of insurance. New chapter on marine insurance. Covers the Insurance Companies Act 1982, and the Insurance Companies Regulations. Implications of EEC membership, New York law, Lloyd's standard policy terms and the Marine Insurance Act are also included.
ISBN 042131110X £42.00
→ Ship Owners (BSL).

Coll, Alberto R. →Falklands war : lessons for strategy, diplomacy, and international law.

Collected Courses : Recueil des Cours. – Hague Academy of International Law. – Dordrecht : Kluwer.
Hbk

Collected Edition of the 'Travaux Preparatoires' of the European Convention on Human Rights Vol. 6 /. – Dordrecht : Kluwer, 1985.
318p.
ISBN 9024722306 Hbk Gld175.00
Vol. 7. – 1985.
347p.
ISBN 9024728924 Hbk Gld225.00
Vol. 8. – 1985.
221p.
ISBN 9024728932 Hbk Gld175.00

Collection of Acts and Records of Parliament : With Reports of Cases in Courts of Law and Equity (1224-1800) Respecting Tithes, 4 Vols. – Repr. of 1801 ed. – Abingdon : Professional Books.
192p.
Hbk £175.00

Collection of Agreements Concluded By the European Communities. – London : HMSO, 1984.
1557p.
ISBN 9282532321 Hbk £37.20

Collection of Decrees by the Court of Exchequer (1650-1798) in Tithe Causes, 4 Vols. – Repr. of 1799 ed. – Abingdon : Professional Books.
197p.
Hbk £30.00

Collection of international concessions and related instruments : contemporary series / edited and annotated by Peter Fischer : with the collaboration of Thomas W. Waelde. – London : Oceana, 1981.
Contains documents dated from 1975 onwards.

Collection of Modern Entries. – 4th ed. Repr. of 1771 ed. – Abingdon : Professional Books.
273p.
Hbk £45.00

Collection of resolutions adopted by the Committee of Ministers in application of Article 32 of the European Convention for the Protection of Human Rights and Fundamental Freedoms, 1959-1981. – Council of Europe. – Strasbourg : Council of Europe, 1981.
various pagings; 30cm.
At head of title: Human Rights.

Collection of resolutions adopted by the Committee of Ministers in application of article 54 of the European Convention for the Protection of Human Rights and Fundamental Freedoms / Recueil des resolutions du Comite des Ministres adoptees en application de l'article 54 de la Convention Europeenne de Sauvegarde des Droits de l'Homme et des Libertes Fondamentales. – Strasbourg : Council of Europe, 1981.
various pagings; 30cm.
Preface by Peter Leuprecht, Director of Human Rights. At head of title: Human Rights.

Collection of resolutions adopted by the Committee of Ministers in application of articles 32 and 54 of the European Convention for the Protection of Human Rights and Fundamental Freedoms, 1959-1983. – Council of Europe. – Strasbourg : Council of Europe, 1984.
148p; 30cm.
'Publication prepared by the Human Rights Documentation Centre...'. Kept up to date by supplements.

Collection of Statutes Connected With the General Administration of Law, 8 Vols. – Repr. of 1817 ed. – Abingdon : Professional Books.
116p.
Hbk £40.00

Collection of the Agreements Concluded by the European Communities
Vol. 11 (1981) Part 1. – Luxembourg : Office for Official Publications of the European Communities, 1985.
1,136p.
ISBN 9277002034 Hbk
Vol. 11 (1981) Part 2. – 1985.
xliv, 2,738p.
ISBN 9277002107 Hbk £3,700.00
Vol. 12 (1982). – 1986.
xxxvi, 1,482p.
ISBN 9277041137 Hbk £3,800.00

Collection of the Agreements Concluded by the European Communities : Index and Alphabetical List of Countries and International Organizations, Vol. 1-11. – Luxembourg : Office for Official Publications of the European Communities, 1986.
136p.
ISBN 9282403041 Pbk £200.00

Collection of Value Added Tax. – London : HMSO, 1984.
ISBN 011260501X Hbk £3.95

Collections. – Vancouver : Continuing Legal Education Society of British Columbia, 1988.
344p.
ISBN 0865049726 Hbk £80.00

Collective Agreement Arbitration in Canada. – Butterworths.
Hbk £130.00
Supplement-1986. –
144p.
Covers hearing and grievance procedures, evidentiary problems, the interpretation of collective agreements, discharge and discipline, insubordination, industrial offences, seniority, job benefits, the bargaining unit, and the protection of employment opportunities.
ISBN 0409806358 Pbk £27.95

Collective Bargaining. – Vancouver : British Columbia Continuing Legal Education Society, 1985.
134p.
ISBN 0865041997 Hbk £55.00

Collective bargaining in industrialised market economies : a reappraisal / J. P. Windmuller, W. Albeda. – Geneva : International Labour Office, 1987.
xii,333p; 24cm.
Contents: Part 1.: A comparative study, by John P. Windmuller - Part 2.: Country studies, by W. Albeda ... et al..
ISBN 9221056074

Collective Bargaining Law in Canada. – 2nd ed. – Butterworths, 1986.
944p.
Updated and revised to include new material on discharge and discipline. Outlines the current law of collective bargaining in Canada as developed under statutory regulation along with its historic background. Expanded chapters on secondary picketing and consumer boycotting and the substantive law of strikes and lockouts.
ISBN 0409818798 Hbk £145.00

Collective securities depositories and the transfer of securities / by F.R. Malan. – Johannesburg : Rand Afrikaans University, 1983.
iv,257p.
Bibliography: p.240-252. - Includes index.
ISBN 0869702491

College of Estate Management
Course in Arbitration, 3 Vols. – College of Estate Management. – Reading : College of Estate Management.
Hbk

Colliard, Claude Albert → Law and practice relating to pollution control in France.

Collier, John G.
Conflict of laws / J.G. Collier. – Cambridge : Cambridge University Press, 1987.
xlvi,377p; 23cm. – (Cambridge studies in international and comparative law).
Includes index.
ISBN 0521323959 Hbk £40.00
ISBN 052131187X Pbk £12.50

Collinge, J.
Law of Restrictive Trade Practices in New Zealand. – 2nd. ed. – Butterworths, 1982.
ISBN 040960125X Hbk £33.10
—Tutorials in Contract. – 4th ed. – North Ryde : Law Book Co, 1986.
xxii, 377p.
ISBN 0455206430 Hbk £35.00
ISBN 0455206449 Pbk £25.00

Collinge, N.E.
Laws of Indo-European. – Amsterdam : John Benjamins Publishing Co., 1985.
xviii, 273p.
ISBN 9027235309 Hbk £100.00
ISBN 0915027755 Pbk £16.00
ISBN 9027221022 Pbk £44.00

Collini, Stefan
That noble science of politics : a study in nineteenth-century intellectual history / Stefan Collini, Donald Winch, John Burrow. – Cambridge : Cambridge University Press, 1983.
x,385p; 24cm.
Includes index.
ISBN 052125762X Hbk £25.00
ISBN 0521277701 Pbk £9.95

Collins → Labor Law and Business Change : Theoretical and Transactional Perspectives.
→ Law for GCSE.
→ 'O' level law.
—Social work with young offenders / Behan. – London : Butterworths, 1981.
ISBN 0406556903 Pbk £7.50

Collins, Hugh
Law of contract / Hugh Collins. – London : Weidenfeld and Nicolson, 1986.
xi,236p; 23cm.
Bibliography: p210-224. - Includes index.
ISBN 0297787845 Hbk £14.95
ISBN 0297787853 Pbk £7.50
—Marxism and Law. – Oxford : Oxford University Press, 1982.
ISBN 0192851446 Pbk £4.50
—Marxism and law / Hugh Collins. – Oxford Oxfordshire : Clarendon Press, 1982.
viii,159p.
Bibliography: p150-155. .
ISBN 0198760930 Oxford University Press

Collins, Lawrence
Civil Jurisdiction and Judgments Act 1982. – London : Butterworths, 1983.
ISBN 0406005303 Hbk £32.50
—Civil Jurisdictions and Judgment Acts 1982. – London : Butterworths, 1983.
This work provides a procedural guide to the Act. The 1982 Act incorporates into United Kingdom law the 1968 EEC Convention on jurisdiction and the enforcement of judgements in civil matters.
ISBN 0406005303 Hbk
—European Community law in the United Kingdom / Lawrence Collins. – 3rd ed. – London : Butterworths, 1984.
xxxvi,233p; 22cm.
Previous ed.: 1980. Includes index.
ISBN 040626922X Hbk £17.50
ISBN 0406269238 Pbk £13.95

Collins, M.
Money and banking in the United Kingdom. – Routledge, 1988.
ISBN 0415004349 Hbk £45.00

Collins, Paulene → 'O' level law.

Collins, Stephen
Social work with young offenders / Stephen Collins, David Behan. – London : Butterworths, 1981.
xii,148p; 22cm.
The book emphasizes the practical aspects of working with young offenders within the court system of the United Kingdom. Assessment, the family, working with individual offenders, and working with groups are explored in depth in the text.
ISBN 0406556903 Pbk £4.95

Collins, V.
Recreation and the Law. – London : Sweet & Maxwell, 1984.
Hbk £15.50
—Recreation and the law. – Spon (E & FN), 1984.
ISBN 0419121900 Hbk £18.50
ISBN 0419122001 Pbk £8.95

Collinson → Ending Lives.

Collision cases : judgments and diagrams / by H.M.C. Holdert and F.J. Buzek. – London : Lloyd's, 1984.
xvii,190p.
ISBN 0907432964

Collision regulations : the application and enforcement of the Merchant Shipping (Distress Signals and Prevention of Collisions) Regulations 1983 / by R.H.B. Sturt : illustrations by Ann L. Sturt. – 2nd ed. – London : Lloyd's of London Press, 1984.
xlvi,177p, 5p of plates.
Previous ed.: 1977. Includes index.
ISBN 0907432670

Collisions at Sea / R.G. Marsden. – 12th ed. – Stevens & Sons.
– (British Shipping Law).
ISBN 0420448608 Hbk £100.00

Colloquium on choice of law in contract and the E.E.C. Contractual Obligations Convention / Peter M North. – 2. – s.l. : s.n., 1981.
Held from 15-16th Sept. 1981. Includes bibliographical references. Chairman: Peter North.

Colloquy: Democracy and Human Rights Report on human rights and foreign policy : presented by R. Higgins / organised by the Government of Greece and the Secretariat General of the Council of Europe in co-operation with the Centre of International and European Economic Law of Thessaloniki, Thessaloniki (Greece), 24-26 September 1987. – Strasbourg : Council of Europe, 1987.
17p. – (H/Coll (87) 6).
Includes bibliographical references.

Colman, Anthony D.
Practice and procedure of the Commercial Court / by Anthony D. Colman. – 2nd ed. – London : Lloyd's of London, 1986.
230p; 24cm.
Previous ed.: 1983. Includes index.
ISBN 1850440611

Colman, John
John Locke's moral philosophy / John Colman. – Edinburgh : Edinburgh University Press, 1983.
viii,282p; 22cm.
Bibliography: p270-276. - Includes index.
ISBN 0852244452 £20.00

Colombia
Laws on the defense of the consumer / German Cavelier. – Bogota : Cavelier Abogados, 1985.
41 leaves.
Contains the text of relevant laws, decrees and resolutions in English.

Colonial legal heritage in Nigeria / by Emmanuel Omoh Esiemokhai. – Akure, Nigeria : Fagbamigbe, 1986.
xii,82p.
Bibliography: p.79. - Includes index.
ISBN 9781642483

Colonization of Government Lands Act 1912 : Punjab. – Lahore : Pakistan Law Times.
Hbk £36.00

Colvin, Eric
Principles of Criminal Law. – Agincourt : Carswell, 1986.
380p.
This work for law students in Canada discusses the fundamental criminal law concepts of mens rea and acutus rea, strict and absolute liability, justification and excuse, diminished metal capacity, and secondary liability under Canadian law.
Hbk £48.75

Comaroff, John L.
Rules and processes : the cultural logic of dispute in an African context / John L. Comaroff, Simon Roberts. – Chicago : University of Chicago, 1981.
ix,293p; 23cm.
Bibliography: p277-288. - Includes index.
ISBN 0226114244 £19.25

Combating international commercial crime / by B. Rider. – Barking : International Maritime Bureau, 1984.
36p.

Combatting drug abuse and related crime : comparative research on the effectiveness of socio-legal preventive and control measures in different countries on the interaction between criminal behaviour and drug abuse / by Francesco Bruno. – Rome : Fratelli Palombi, 1984.
251p. – (Publication).
Bibliography: p.212-244. 'Funded by the United Nations Fund for Drug Abuse'.
ISBN 8876218262

Comer → Risk management.

Comer, Michael J.
Corporate fraud / Michael J. Comer. – 2nd ed. – London : McGraw-Hill, 1985.
xvi,453p; 23cm.
Previous ed.: 1977. Includes bibliography and index.
ISBN 0070847916 £16.50

Comic Blackstone. – 3rd ed. Repr. of 1887 ed. – Abingdon : Professional Books.
Hbk £75.00

Comic Blackstone. – Southampton : Ashford Press, 1985.
ISBN 0907069398 Hbk £18.95

Coming information society. – London : British Library, 1984.
1v.
ISBN 0712330364 Pbk

Coming to Terms with Policing : Perspectives on Policy / Smith. – Routledge.
ISBN 0415009421 Hbk £14.95

Comm, John Swan B.
Contracts : Cases, Text, and Materials / Barry J. Reiter. – 4th ed. – Toronto : Edmond-Montgomery, 1985.
732p.
ISBN 0920722164 Hbk £84.00

Command Papers. – London : HMSO, 1983.
– (Treaty Ser.).
ISBN 0101929404 Hbk £1.30

Command Papers. – London : HMSO, 1986.
– (Miscellaneous Ser.).
ISBN 0101981708 Hbk £0.80

Command Papers. – London : HMSO, 1984.
– (European Communities Ser.).
ISBN 0101927401 Hbk £0.75

Command Papers. – London : HMSO, 1985.
– (Treaty Ser.).
ISBN 0101982909 Hbk £2.90

Command Papers. – London : HMSO, 1985.
– (Country Ser.).
ISBN 0101974906 Hbk £1.35

Commencement of laytime / by Donald Davies. – London : Lloyd's of London Press, 1987.
164p; 22cm.
Includes index.
ISBN 1850441472 £30.00

Commentaries on Administrative Tribunals Act, 1986. – Lucknow : Eastern Book Company, 1987.
Hbk £165.00

Commentaries on Central Civil Services (Temporary Services) Rules. – Allahabad : Orient Law House, 1983.
Hbk £45.00

Commentaries on Central Excise Act. – 3rd ed. – Allahabad : Law Publishers, 1982.
Hbk £45.00

Commentaries on Conduct Rules. – 2nd ed. – Allahabad : Orient Law House, 1983.
Hbk £60.00

Commentaries on Contract Labour Act, 1970 : Regulation and Abolition / G. Saran. – 3rd rev. ed. – Lucknow : Eastern Book Company, 1982.
520p.
Hbk £70.00

Commentaries on Criminal Minor Acts, 6 Vols. – 2nd ed. – Allahabad : Law Publishers, 1982.
Hbk £37.50

Commentaries on Employees' Provident Funds and Miscellaneous Provisions Act, 1952 : Together with Schemes and Notifications. – 5th ed. – Lucknow : Eastern Book Company, 1985.
Hbk

Commentaries on Employees' State Insurance Act, 1948. – 3rd ed. – Lucknow : Eastern Book Company, 1986.
928p.
Hbk £150.00

Commentaries on Essential Commodities Act. – 4th ed. – Allahabad : Law Publishers, 1982.
Hbk £45.00

Commentaries on Foreign Exchange Regulations Act and Rules Notification with Model Forms and Allied Laws. – 2nd ed. – Allahabad : Law Publishers, 1982.
Hbk £27.00

Commentaries on General Clauses Act. – 2nd ed. – Allahabad, 1983.
Hbk £30.00

Commentaries on Hire-Purchase Act, 1972 with Model Forms. – 2nd ed. – Allahabad : Law Publishers, 1983.
Hbk £22.50

Commentaries on Indian Stamp Act as Applicable to Uttar Pradesh. – 7th ed. – Lucknow : Eastern Book Company, 1985.
Hbk

Commentaries on Industrial Disputes Act, 1947. – 6th ed. – Lucknow : Eastern Book Company, 1985.
1,590p.
Hbk £250.00

Commentaries on Industrial Employment Standing Orders Act, 1946 : Including Model Standing Orders, Recognition of Unions and Unfair Labour Practices. – 2nd ed. – Lucknow : Eastern Book Company, 1982.
844p.
Hbk £95.00

Commentaries on Laws of England. – Abingdon : Professional Books.
– (Classical English Law Texts Ser.).
Hbk £220.00

Commentaries on Motor Vehicles Act, 2 Vols. – 8th ed. – Lucknow : Eastern Book Company, 1982.
2,000p.
Hbk £240.00

Commentaries on Notaries Act, 1985 : Act No. 53, 1952 / J.P. Bhatnagar. – Allahabad : Ashoka Law House, 1987.
240p.
Hbk £90.00

Commentaries on Payment of Bonus Act with Rules. – 2nd ed. – Allahabad : Law Publishers, 1982.
Hbk £27.00

Commentaries on Payment of Gratuity Act, 1972. – 3rd ed. – Lucknow : Eastern Book Company, 1982.
593p.
Hbk £90.00

Commentaries on Payment of Wages Act, 1936. – 3rd ed. – Lucknow : Eastern Book Company, 1983.
814p.
Hbk £110.00

Commentaries on Prevention of Corruption Act, 1947. – 3rd ed. – Lucknow : Eastern Book Company, 1981.
699p.
Hbk £80.00

Commentaries on Prevention of Corruption Act. – Allahabad : Law Publishers, 1983.
Hbk £33.00

Commentaries on Probation of Offenders Act. – 4th ed. – Allahabad : Law Publishers, 1983.
Hbk £33.00

Commentaries on Registration Act. – 7th ed. – Allahabad : Law Publishers, 1982.
Hbk £45.00

Commentaries on some detached branches of the law of Scotland / By George Joseph Bell. – Edinburgh : Blackwood, 1828.
217p.
Originally published: in the 5th ed. of the author's Commentaries on the laws of Scotland, and on the principles of mercantile jurisprudence (1826).

Commentaries on State Financial Corporations Act, 1951 / Kumar Avadhesh Srivastava. – Allahabad : Law Book Company, 1988.
ca 300p.
Pbk £150.00

Commentaries on the Industrial Disputes Act 1947. – 3rd ed. – Allahabad : Law Publishing House, 1983.
ca 1,000p.
Hbk £150.00

Commentaries on the Law of Easements and Licences with Model Forms. – 2nd ed. – Allahabad : Law Publishers, 1982.
Hbk £27.00 ea

Commentaries on the Law of Scotland in Relation to Mercantile and Maritime Laws, Movable and Heritable Rights and Bankruptcy, 2 Vols. – 3rd ed. Repr. of 1819 ed. – Abingdon : Professional Books.
Hbk £75.00

Commentaries on the Law of Scotland Respecting Trial for Crimes. – Repr. of 1800 ed. – Abingdon : Professional Books.
52p.
Hbk £35.00

Commentaries on the Laws England. 4 vols. – Reprint. – Abingdon : Professional Books, 1986.
ISBN 0862053102 Hbk £142.00

Commentaries on the Limitation Act. – 4th ed. – Allahabad : Law Publishers, 1983.
Hbk £45.00

Commentaries on the Opium Act, 1878. – Lucknow : Eastern Book Company, 1984.
175p.
Hbk £30.00

Commentaries on the Societies Registration Act, 1860 / Vijay Malik. – 5th rev. ed. – Lucknow : Eastern Book Company, 1985.
314p.
Hbk £60.00

Commentaries on the U.P. Panchayat Raj Act, 1947, (U.P. Act no. 26 of 1947) as Amended Up-to-Date, with Rules, Orders, Notifications, and Other Allied Laws. – 4th ed. – Allahabad : Hind Publishing House, 1981.
x, 186, 292p.
Hbk £40.00

Commentaries on the Uttar Pradesh Industrial Disputes Act, 1947. – 4th ed. – Lucknow : Eastern Book Company.
Hbk

Commentaries on U.P. Government Servants' Conduct Rules, 1956. – 3rd ed. – Lucknow : Eastern Book Company, 1983.
163p.
Pbk £20.00

Commentaries on Urban Land (Ceiling and Regulation) Act, 1976. – 2nd ed. – Allahabad : Law Publishers, 1983.
Hbk £37.50

Commentaries on Uttar Pradesh Cooperative Societies Act, 1965 / Sushma Malik. – 4th ed. – Lucknow : Eastern Book Company, 1984.
756p.
Hbk £110.00

Commentaries on Uttar Pradesh Imposition of Ceiling on Land Holdings Act, 1960. – Lucknow : Eastern Book Company, 1977.
304p.
Hbk £35.00

Commentaries on Uttar Pradesh Kshettra Samitis and Zila Parishads Adhiniyam / P.L. Malik. – 2nd ed. – Lucknow : Eastern Book Company, 1978.
843p.
Hbk £75.00

Commentaries on Uttar Pradesh Municipalities Act, 1916. – Lucknow : Eastern Book Company, 1984.
366p.
Hbk £120.00

Commentaries on Uttar Pradesh Nagar Mahapalika Act, 1959. – Lucknow : Eastern Book Company, 1985.
818p.
Hbk £115.00

Commentaries on Uttar Pradesh Panchayat Raj Act, 1947. – Lucknow : Eastern Book Company, 1986.
346p.
Hbk £40.00

Commentaries on Uttar Pradesh Public Premises (Eviction of Unauthorised Occupants) Act, 1972. – 2nd ed. – Lucknow : Eastern Book Company, 1983.
154p.
Hbk £20.00

Commentaries on Uttar Pradesh Urban Buildings (Regulation of Letting, Rent and Eviction) Act, 1972. – 4th ed. – Lucknow : Eastern Book Company, 1981.
493p.
Hbk £40.00

Commentaries on Workmen's Compensation Act, 1923 / by K.D. Srivastava and G. Saran. – 4th rev. ed. – Lucknow : Eastern Book Company, 1984.
692p.
Hbk £100.00

Commentary on a Commercial Lease. – Centre for Advanced Land Use Studies. – Reading : College of Estate Management, 1983.
ISBN 0902132725 Pbk £9.50

Commentary on Bengal Public Demands Recovery Act, 1913. – Allahabad : Orient Law House, 1984.
Hbk £30.00

Commentary on International Sales Law. – Sweet & Maxwell.
ISBN 0421408405 Hbk £50.00

Commentary on Limitation Act. – Allahabad : Orient Law House, 1984.
Hbk £50.00

Commentary on Northern Ireland crime statistics ... – Belfast : HMSO, 1985.

Commentary on Sexual Offences. – Allahabad : Ashoka Law House, 1987.
1,000p.
Hbk £220.00

Commentary on Standard Conditions of Contract : NZSS 623:1964 / M.C. Barker. – Butterworths, 1983.
ISBN 0409600806 Pbk £52.80

Commentary on the additional protocols of 8 June 1977 to the Geneva Conventions of 12 August 1949 / Claude Pilloud ... et al : editors, Yves Sandoz, Christophe Swinarski, Bruno Zimmerman. – Geneva : International Committee of the Red Cross, 1987.
xxxv,1625p.
Bibliography: pp.1581-1596. - Includes index.
ISBN 9024734606 Hbk £250.00

Commentary on the Customs Act with Rule and Notifications. – 3rd ed. – Allahabad : Law Publishers, 1982.
Hbk £51.00

Commentary on the Czechoslovak civil code / by Th. J. Vondracek. – Dordrecht : Nijhoff, 1988.
504p.
Includes index.
ISBN 9024736692 Hbk £235.00

Commentary on the Industrial Court. – Durban : Professional Publishers, 1984.
Hbk £0409027189

Commentary on the Industrial Disputes Act, Vols 1 and 2. – 3rd ed. – Allahabad : Orient Law House, 1984.
Hbk £325.00

Commentary on the international sales law : the 1980 Vienna Sales Convention / by C.M. Bianca, M.J. Bonell. – Milan : Giuffre, 1987.
xvii,886p.
Bibliography: pp.843-873. - Includes index. Includes texts of the Convention in English, Arabic, Chinese, French, Russian, Spanish, German and Italian.
ISBN 8814012768

Commentary on the JCT Intermediate Form of Building Contract / Neil F. Jones and David Bergman. – London : Collins, 1985.
viii,351; 25cm.
Includes index.
ISBN 0003830241 Pbk

Commentary on the University Laws in India. – Madhya Pradesh, 1986.
220p.
Hbk £90.00

Commentary on the Working of the Customs Act 1962. – New Delhi : S. Chand and Company.
Hbk £10.00

Comments by JUSTICE on the white paper 'A revised framework for insolvency law' (Cmnd. 9175). – JUSTICE. – S.l. : JUSTICE, 1984.
7 leaves; 30cm.

Comments on civil justice review of housing cases / JUSTICE. – London : JUSTICE, 1987.
7 leaves.

Comments on Civil Procedure Code, 4 Vols. – 2nd ed. – Allahabad : Law Publishers, 1983.
Hbk £30.00

Comments on Company Law. – Karachi : Flecbon Corporation, 1987.
Hbk

Comments on consultation paper on personal injuries litigation : civil justice review / JUSTICE. – London : JUSTICE, 1986.
9p.

Comments on Finance Act, 1985 and Amendments in Mercantile Laws. – Karachi : Flecbon Corporation, 1987.
Hbk

Comments on Prevention of Food Adulteration Act with Central and All State Rules / Seth. – Allahabad : Law Publishers, 1982.
Hbk £40.50

Comments on the consultation paper no. 3 from the civil justice review relating to the commercial court / JUSTICE. – London : JUSTICE, 1987.
5p.

Comments on the Home Office discussion document : Review of appeals under the Immigration Act, 1971 / Justice. – London : Justice, 1981.
5p; 33cm.

Comments on the Justice-All Souls discussion paper on administrative law (April 1981) : memorandum / by the Council's Law Reform Committee. – London : Law Society, 1981.
13,2p.

Comments to Her Majesty's Government on the consultative document Cmnd. 8302 : reform of the law relating to copyright, designs and performers' protection / the Publishers Association. – London : The Association, 1982.
69p.

Commerce Clearing House → Australian employment legislation.
→ Australian workers compensation guide.
→ Canada income tax guide.

Commerce Clearing House (New Zealand) → New Zealand income tax law and practice.
→ New Zealand tax cases.

Commercial agreements and competition law : practice and procedure in the UK and EEC / Nicholas Green. – London : Graham & Trotman, 1986.
lxxviii,763p.
Bibliography: p.lxix-lxx - Includes index.
ISBN 0860107884

Commercial and consumer credit : an introduction / by Aubrey L. Diamond. – London : Butterworths, 1982.
xxvii,379p.
Includes index.
ISBN 0406574057

Commercial and Consumer Credit - An Introduction. – London : Butterworths, 1982.
ISBN 0406574057 Pbk £14.95

Commercial and Consumer Law / Stephenson. – London : Financial Training, 1987.
– (SWOT).
ISBN 1851850430 Pbk £7.50

Commercial and Consumer Transactions. – 2nd ed. – Toronto : Edmond-Montgomery, 1987.
ca 1,400p.
ISBN 0920722202 Hbk £96.00

Commercial and consumer transactions : cases, text and materials / by Jacob S. Ziegel, Benjamin Geva. – Toronto : Emond-Montgomery, 1981.
xlv,1230p.
Bibliography: p.xliii-xli - Includes index.
ISBN 0920722040

Commercial and Industrial Law. – New Delhi : Sterling Publishers, 1983.
1,078p.
ISBN 8120704398 Hbk £34.00

Commercial and Industrial Law. – 3rd ed. – Plymouth : Macdonald & Evans, 1984.
ISBN 0712101950 Pbk £6.50

Commercial Arbitration. – Vancouver : Continuing Legal Education Society of British Columbia, 1986.
240p.
ISBN 0865042977 Hbk £85.00

Commercial Arbitration / John B Dorter. – North Ryde : Law Book Co, 1986.
ISBN 0455205841 Hbk £29.75

Commercial arbitration and the law throughout the world : summary of the rules concerning arbitration agreements, procedure, arbitral awards, enforcement of awards, means of recourse / by International Headquarters of the International Chamber of Commerce. – 1. – Basel : Verlag fur Recht und Gesellschaft, 1949.
loose-leaf.
Superseded by the series: Arbitration throughout the world (1981-). Updated to supplement no. 3 (1964). Added t.p. in French. Parallel English and French texts.

Commercial Arbitration in Islamic and Iranian Law. – Royston.
ISBN 0946706468 Hbk £85.00

Commercial arbitration in the Arab Middle East : a study in Shara and statute law / Samir Saleh. – London : Published under the patronage of the International Chamber of Commerce by Graham & Trotman, 1984.
380p.
Bibliography: p445-455. - Includes index.
ISBN 0860104532 £55.00

Commercial arbitration in the Federal Republic of Germany / by Ottoarndt Glossner. – Deventer : Kluwer Law and Taxation, 1984.
xiv,137p; 25cm.
Bibliography: p113-134. - Includes index.
ISBN 9065441859 Hbk £90.00

Commercial arbitration institutions : an international directory and guide / Ludwik Kos-Rabcewicz-Zubkowski and Paul J. Davidson. – London : Oceana Publications, 1986.
ix, 186p.
Published under the auspices of the International Federation of Commercial Arbitration Institutions.
ISBN 0379207893

Commercial Arbitration Worldwide Guide. – London : LLoyd's of London Press, 1985.
ISBN 1850440530 Hbk

Commercial Bank Lending and Third World Debt. – London : Macmillan.
ISBN 0333491416 Hbk £29.50

Commercial, Business and Trade Laws : Hong Kong 2 volumes. – Dobbs Ferry : Oceana, 1982.
ISBN 0379231050 Llf £190.00

Commercial Case. – Vancouver : Continuing Legal Education Society of British Columbia, 1987.
198p.
ISBN 0865043345 Hbk £70.00

Commercial Cases 1-46 (1895-1941). – Professional Books.
ISBN 0862052661 Hbk £1,420.00

Commercial Cases : Reports of 1895-1941, 46 Vols. – Abingdon : Professional Books, 1895-1941.
Hbk £1950.00
Individual vols.. –
Hbk £53.00

Commercial Claimsmanship : With Special Reference to the FIDIC Form of Contract. – King's Ride : Institute of Building, 1983.
9p.
ISBN 0906600642 Hbk £2.00

Commercial Code & the Audit Special Exceptions Law of Japan. – Tokyo : Eibun Horei Sha, 1982.
iii,249,16p.
'Originally translated by the Codes Translation Committee & the Ministry of Justice, revised by Fukio Nakane & Ikue Nishimura'.

Commercial Contracts. – London : Collins, 1987.
208p.
ISBN 0003832341 Hbk £17.50

Commercial disputes settlement in China / Eric Lee. – London : Lloyds of London, 1985.
152p; 22cm.
Includes index.
ISBN 1850440638 Pbk

Commercial exploitation of personality. – London : Sweet & Maxwell, 1987.
ISBN 0455206929 Hbk £19.50

Commercial Insolvency Reporter. – London : Butterworths.
ISBN 0409492051 Hbk

Commercial Insolvency Reporter. – Toronto : Butterworths.
ISBN 0409806218 Hbk

Commercial Law / A. Freilich. – Butterworths, 1986.
94p. – (Butterworth's Student Companion Ser.).
ISBN 0409490873 Pbk £9.95

Commercial Law. – Hamilton : Society of Management Accountants of Canada.
Hbk £11.00

Commercial Law / Sir Gordon Borrie. – 6th ed. – London : Butterworths, 1988.
xxxi,354p; 22cm.
Previous ed.: 1980. Includes index.
ISBN 0406558450 Hbk £19.50
ISBN 0406558469 Pbk £13.95

Commercial Law / K.C. Garg. – rev. ed. – New Delhi : Kalyani Publishers, 1987.
Hbk £32.00

Commercial law / R.M. Goode. – Harmondsworth : Pelican, 1986.
1119p.
Includes bibliographical references and index.
ISBN 0140226346 Pbk £18.95

Commercial Law / N.A. Cunningham. – 3rd ed. – Butterworths, 1988.
582p.
ISBN 0409492485 Pbk £49.50
ISBN 0409492477 Hbk £65.00

Commercial law / by Robert Lowe. – 6th ed. – London : Sweet & Maxwell, 1983.
xlvi,578p; 23cm.
Previous ed.: 1976. Includes index.
ISBN 0421298707 Hbk £21.50
ISBN 0421298804 Pbk £14.50

Commercial Law. – Meerat : Pragati Prakashan, 1973.
380p.
Hbk £9.00

Commercial Law : Case Studies in a Business Context. – London : Macmillan.
ISBN 0333434668 Hbk £29.50

Commercial law : recent developments and emerging trends. – Don Mills : De Boo, 1985.
294p.
Includes bibliographical references and index.
ISBN 0888202164 Hbk £75.00

Commercial Law Digest. – Agincourt : Carswell.
Hbk £146.25

Commercial Law II /. – Butterworths, 1986.
90p. – (Butterworth's Student Companion Ser.).
ISBN 0409490954 Pbk £9.95

Commercial law in a changing economic climate / Clive M. Schmitthoff. – 2nd ed. – London : Sweet & Maxwell, 1981.
xii,78p; 22cm.
Previous ed.: 1977. Includes index. .
ISBN 0421268301 Pbk £5.25

Commercial law in New Zealand / Leys and Northey. – 7th ed. – Wellington : Butterworths, 1982.
xlviii,852p.
Previous ed.: 1978. Includes index.
ISBN 0409600881

Commercial law in Nigeria / by Okay Achike. – Enugu : Fourth Dimension, 1985.
xxii,496p.
Includes bibliographical references.
ISBN 9781561939

Commercial law of Iran : by Sayed Hassan Amin. – Tehran : Vahid Publications, 1986.
vii,144p.
Bibliography: p137-140.
ISBN 0946706298

Commercial law of New Zealand / by J.H. Luxford. – 2nd ed., rev. and enl. 6. – Wellington : Butterworths, 1961-.
loose-leaf.
Last supplement issued: Oct. 1974. - Kept up to date by Butterworths current law, No 1974-. Includes index.

Commercial law of Singapore : an introduction / Walter C.M. Woon. – Cambridge : Woodhead-Faulkner, 1986.
256p; 23cm.
Includes bibliography and index.
ISBN 0859412814 £45.00

Commercial laws & business regulations of the People's Republic of China 1949-1983 / Victor F.S. Sit, editor. – London : Macmillan, 1983.
xix,600p; 27cm.
ISBN 0333361172 £42.50

Commercial Laws of the Philippines with Introductory Features, Revised Edition. – Manila : National Book Store, 1981.
762p.
ISBN 9710816519 Pbk £5.00

Commercial leases / Malcolm Brahams with Norman Harker. – Oxford : Blackwell Scientific, 1985.
viii,198p.
Includes index.
ISBN 0003830446 Hbk £17.50

Commercial leases / Stephen Tromans. – London : Sweet & Maxwell, 1987.
250p; 23cm.
Examines the impact of recent case law, rating, and planning development. Covers licences, agreements for lease, rent reviews, 'clear leases', dilapidations, user and covenants, and the practicalities of leaseholding conveyancing in its own right.
ISBN 0421354607 £19.50

Commercial litigation : pre-emptive remedies / by Iain S. Goldrein and K.H. P. Wilkinson : with a foreword by Sir John Donaldson. – London : Sweet & Maxwell, 1987.
xlvii,793p; 26cm.
Covers topics in the commercial field where emergency relief may be necessary. Techniques are explained, and relevant reported cases are referred to, including the necessary statutes and court orders. Appendices include forms and precedents, and some Chancery and Queen's Bench Division Practice Directions.
ISBN 0421348003 Hbk £107

Commercial nuclear power / legal and constitutional issues : edited by Richard Macrory : with a foreword by the Lord Flowers. – London : Imperial College Centre for Environmental Technology, 1982.
69p; 22cm.
ISBN 0950774405 Pbk

Commercial paper / edited by Richard Felix. – London : Euromoney Publications, 1987.
ix,182p.
ISBN 1870031601

Commercial Real Estate Leasing. – Vancouver : Continuing Legal Education Society of British Columbia, 1986.
562p.
ISBN 0865042934 Hbk £85.00

Commercial Real Estate Transactions. – Vancouver : Continuing Legal Education Society of British Columbia, 1986.
250p.
ISBN 0865042608 Hbk £60.00

Commercial Rent Reviews : Law and Valuation Practice. – North Ryde : Law Book Co, 1986.
xxvii, 205p.
ISBN 0455206414 Pbk £27.50

Commercial Securities in New Zealand : an introduction to the Law / S.C. Calderwood. – 2nd ed. – North Ryde : Law Book Co, 1986.
xxxi, 214p.
ISBN 0455207070 Pbk £27.00

Commercial Tenancy Act. – Law Reform Commission of British Columbia. – Vancouver : Law Reform Commission of British Columbia, 1988.
v,185p. – (Working paper).
Includes extracts from legislation.
ISBN 0771886624

Commercial Transport for New Zealanders. – Wellington : Butterworths.
ISBN 0409627119 Pbk

Commins, S.J.
Africa's Development Challenges and the World Bank : Hard Questions, Costly Choices. – London : Eurospan.
ISBN 155587116X Hbk £25.50

Commission of Inquiry Concerning Certain Activities of the Royal Canadian Mounted Police
Certain R.C.M.P. activities and the question of governmental knowledge : third report / Commission of Inquiry Concerning Certain Activities of the Royal Canadian Mounted Police. – Ottawa : Canadian Government Publishing Centre, 1981.
xv,527p; 25cm.
Chairman: D.C. McDonald.
ISBN 0660109530

—Freedom and security under the law : second report / Commission of Inquiry Concerning Certain Activities of the Royal Canadian Mounted Police. – 2. – Ottawa : Canadian Government Publishing Centre, 1981.
xxii,1257p; 25cm.
Bibliography: p.1117-1144. Chairman: D.C. McDonald.
ISBN 0660109506 v.2
ISBN 0660109522

Commission of Inquiry into the Circumstances Surrounding the Death of Kimberley Carlile
Child in mind : protection of children in a responsible society : the report of the Commission of Inquiry into the Circumstances Surrounding the Death of Kimberley Carlile / presented to the London Borough of Greenwich and the Greenwich Health Authority .. – London : The Borough, 1987.
xii,292p; 24cm.
Chairman: Louis Blom-Cooper.
ISBN 0904399060

Commission of Inquiry into Township Establishment and Related Matters. – Pretoria : Government Printer, 1984.
2 v.; 30 cm.
Title on added t.p.: Kommissie van Ondersoek na Dorpstigting en Verwante Aangeleenthede. First and second reports of the commission.
ISBN 0621084395 Pbk : v. 2 R3.50 (R4.00 other countries)

Commission of Inquiry on War Criminals Report. – Ottawa : Canadian Government Publishing Centre, 1986.
966p.
ISBN 0660121727 Pbk £39.95

Commission of the European Communities → Common standards for legal retrieval systems : proposals for a model retrieval language for legal users.

→ Comparative tables of the social security schemes in the member states of the European Communities : General scheme (employees in industry and commerce).

—Completing the internal market : white paper from the Commission to the European Council. – Commission of the European Communities. – Luxembourg : Office for Official Publications of the European Communities, 1985.
55,35p. – (Document).
ISBN 9282554368

→ Consumer legislation in Belgium and Luxemburg : a study prepared for the EC Commission.

→ European Communities in the international order.

→ European Community and the Mediterranean Basin : study on the consequences of the process of enlargement both for the Mediterranean zone and for the Community itself and the conditions necessary for the definition of a global and forward-looking policy of the Community towards the Mediterranean basin.

→ Ever closer union : a critical analysis of the draft treaty establishing the European Union.

→ Finances of Europe.

—Green paper on copyright and the challenge of technology : copyright issues requiring immediate action / communication from the Commission. – Luxembourg : Office for Official Publication of the European Communities, 1988.
vi,237p. – (Document).
ISBN 9277367822

→ Law and practice concerning occupational health in the member states of the European Community.

→ Law and practice relating to pollution control in Denmark.

→ Law and practice relating to pollution control in France.

→ Law and practice relating to pollution control in Greece.

→ Law and practice relating to pollution control in Ireland.

→ Law and practice relating to pollution control in Italy.

→ Law and practice relating to pollution control in the Federal Republic of Germany.

→ Law and practice relating to pollution control in the member states of the European communities : a comparative survey.

→ Law and practice relating to pollution control in the member states of the European Communities : recent developments.

→ Law and practice relating to pollution control in the Netherlands.

→ Law and practice relating to pollution control in the United Kingdom.

→ Law of collective agreements in the countries of the European Community.

→ Lawyers in the European Community.

→ New impetus for consumer protection policy.

—Perspectives for the Common Agricultural Policy / communication of the Commission to the Council and the Parliament. – Luxembourg : Office for Official Publications of the European Communities, 1985.
viii,62p. – (Document).
Includes a statistical annex.
ISBN 9277070285

→ Piracy of phonograms : a study requested by the Commission of the European Communities.

→ Prevention and settlement of industrial conflict in the Community member states.

—Protective legislation for women in the member states of the European Community / communication by the Commission. – Luxembourg : Office for Official Publications of the European Communities, 1987.
29p. – (COM(87) 105 final).
Includes bibliographical references.
ISBN 9277228741

→ Public enterprise in Portugal and Spain : analysis from the point of view of competition policy.

→ Regulatory framework for storage and disposal of radioactive waste in the member states of the European Community.

—Relief from Taxes Granted to Imports Made by Private Persons. – Commission of the European Communities. – Kirchberg : Commission of the European Communities, 1984.
71p.
ISBN 9282512991

→ Rights of working women in the European Community.

—State of the environment in the European Community, 1986 / Commission of the European Communities, Directorate-General Environment, Consumer Protection and Nuclear Safety. – Luxembourg : Commission of the European Communities, 1987.
xvi,370p.
ISBN 928256973X

→ Supervision of securities markets in the member states of the European Economic Community.

—Television without frontiers : green paper on the establishment of the common market for broadcasting, especially by satellite and cable / communication from the Commission to the Council. – Luxembourg : Office for Official Publications of the European Communities, 1984.
xii,367p. – (Documents).
ISBN 9277010045

→ Thirty years of Community law.

—Towards a dynamic European economy : green paper on the development of the Common Market for telecommunications services and equipment / communication by the Commission. – Luxembourg : Commission of the European Communities, 987.
192p. – (Document).
ISBN 9277257415

—Working for Europe : January 1981 - January 1985 / The European Commission. – Luxembourg : Office for Official Publications of the European Communities, 1984.
79p; 25cm.
Preface by Gaston E. Thorn.
ISBN 928254740X

Commission on Folk Law and Legal Pluralism →People's law and state law : the Bellagio papers.

Commissioners' Decisions : Social Security and Child Benefit Acts
Vol. X, 1980-82. – London : HMSO, 1985.
ISBN 0117609218 Hbk
Vol. IX, 1983-84. –
ISBN 0117607851 Hbk £25.00

Committal to prison in respect of debt / South African Law Commission. – Pretoria : The Commission, 1986.
viii,37,9p. – (Report).
Includes the text of draft legislation.
ISBN 0621113468

Committals for Trial to the Crown Court : the Law and Practice / Brown. – London : Fourmat.
ISBN 1851900586 Pbk £18.95

Committee of Experts on Biotechnological Inventions and Industrial Property : third session, Geneva, June 29 to July 3, 1987 : report prepared by the International Bureau. – World Intellectual Property Organization. – Geneva : World Intellectual Property Organization, 1987.
32,11p. – (BioT/CE/III/3).
'Convened ... as part of the 1986/87 program of the International (Paris) Union for the Protection of Industrial Property ...'. - Introduction.

Committee of Experts on Biotechnological Inventions and Industrial Property : third session, Geneva, June 29 to July 3, 1987 : industrial property protection of biotechnological inventions / revised report prepared by the International Bureau. – Geneva : World Intellectual Property Organization, 1987.
73p. – (BioT/CE/III/2).
At head of cover: International Union for the Protection of Industrial Property (Paris Union).

Committee of Experts on Biotechological Inventions and Industrial property : first session, Geneva, November 5 to 9, 1984 / report adopted by the Committee of Experts. – Geneva : World Intellectual Property Organizatioan, 1984.
23,7p. – (BioT/CE/I/3).
'Convened ... as part of the 1984/85 program of the International (Paris) Union for the Protection of Industrial Property ... '. - Introduction.

Committee of Heads of University Law Schools
Law as an academic discipline : a response to the Leverhulme Report and the UGC letter on a strategy for Higher Education into the 1990's / the Committee of Heads of University Law Schools. – S.l. : The Committee, 1984.
iii,20 leaves.

Committee of Inquiry into Proposals to Amend the Shops Act
Report : The Shops Act : Late-night and Sunday Opening. – Committee of Inquiry into Proposals to Amend the Shops Act. – London : HMSO, 1984.
ISBN 0101937601 Hbk £9.15

Committee on Alternatives to Prosecution
Keeping Offenders Out of Court : Further Alternatives to Prosecution. – Committee on Alternatives to Prosecution. – London : HMSO, 1983.
ISBN 0101895801 Hbk £6.00

Committee on the Future of the Legal Profession
Time for change / report of the Committee. – London : General Council of the Bar, 1988.
221p.
At head of t.p.: The Committee on the Future of the Legal Profession (The Marre Committee). Chairman: Lady Marre.

Committee Reports Published by HMSO : Indexed By Chairman. – London : HMSO.
Hbk £11.00

Committees of the House of Commons and Northern Ireland Affairs. – Belfast : Queen's University of Belfast, 1984.
32p.
Pbk £2.00

Commmonwealth Secretariat →Hague Convention on the Civil Aspects of International Child Abduction : explanatory documentation.

Commodities futures trading. – London : Mansell, 1985.
ISBN 0720117038 Pbk £18.00

Commodities Trading Act, 1985 (Act 324) and Subsidiary Legislation Made Thereunder. – Kuala Lumpur : International Law Books Services.
Hbk £25.00

Common Agricultural Policy : past, present and future / Brian E. Hill. – London : Methuen, 1984.
xvi,168p; 23cm. – (The Methuen EEC series).
Bibliography: p160-163. - Includes index.
ISBN 0416321801 Hbk £
ISBN 0416321909 Pbk

Common agricultural policy of the EEC. – 2nd ed. – Oxford : Blackwell Scientific, 1987.
ISBN 0003833747 Pbk £15.00
ISBN 0632020571 Hbk £19.95

Common Agricultural Policy of the European Community : its institutional and administrative organisation / Rosemary Fennell. – 2nd ed. – Oxford : BSP Professional, 1987.
xii,227p; 24cm.
Previous ed.: London : Granada, 1979. Bibliography: p215-220. - Includes index.
ISBN 0632020571 £19.95

Common agricultural policy, prospects for change / Joan Pearce. – London : Published for Royal Institute of International Affairs by Routledge & K. Paul, 1981.
122p.
Includes bibliographical references.
ISBN 0710090692

Common crisis : North-South : cooperation for world recovery / the Brandt Commission. – London : Pan, 1983.
174p; 18cm. – (Pan world affairs).
Bibliography: p172-174.
ISBN 0330281305 Pbk £1.95

Common Gaming Houses Act, 1953 (Act 289). – Kuala Lumpur : International Law Books Services.
Hbk £5.00

Common ground : how changes in the Common Agricultural Policy affect the Third World / by Adrian Moyes. – Oxford : Oxfam, 1987.
98p; 21cm.
ISBN 0855980788 Pbk £1.50

Common heritage or common burden: the US position on the development of a regime for deep seabed mining in the law of the sea convention. – Oxford : Clarendon Press, 1989.
288; 23.5.
Assesses the US role in the negotiations on the UN Convention on the LAW of the Sea, particularly with regard to the ocean floor. Examines the US view of the lawfulness of deep seabed mining under international law. Suggests that despite significant compromises negotiated between the US and developing countries at the Conference up to 1980, the emerging seabed regime was not as widely endorsed by US officials as is assumed.
ISBN 0198252277 Hbk £30.00

Common law / by O.W. Holmes. – London : Macmillan, 1911.
xvi,422p.
Includes bibliographical references and index.

Common law aboriginal title. – Oxford : Clarendon Press.
360.
Addresses the land rights question applied throughout the British Empire. Assesses the impact of English law in a colony acquired by settlememt where no form of aboriginal land ownership had previously existed. Conclusions reached suggest a doctrinal approach which could be used to resolve outstanding aboriginal land claims.
Academics, lawyers representing aboriginal peoples, students of human rights
ISBN 0198252234 Hbk £35

Common law for the age of statutes / Guido Calabresi. – Cambridge, Mass. : Harvard University Press, 1982.
319p; 24cm.
Bibliography: p300-309. - Includes index.
ISBN 0674146042

Common Law in Singapore and Malaysia. – Butterworths, 1985.
401p.
Series of essays which, by presenting a number of case studies of different aspects of local law, explore the problems raised by the application of the common law in Singapore and Malaysia. Includes discussion of the Privy Council as court of last resort in Singapore and Malaysia 1957-1983, and the abuse of discretion. Also looks at Chinese marriage custom.
ISBN 0409995096 Hbk £110.00

Common Law Institute of Intellectual Property → Economic importance of copyright.
→ Piracy and counterfeiting of industrial property and copyright : papers given at the inaugural conference of the Common Law Institute of Intellectual Property Ltd in London on 28th and 29th January 1983.

Common Law of Kent. – 3rd ed. Repr. of 1822 ed. – Abingdon : Professional Books.
303p.
Hbk £30.00

Common law of restraint of trade : a legal and economic analysis / by Michael J. Trebilcock. – Toronto : Carswell, 1986.
xxvi,419p.
ISBN 0459396404 Hbk £35.00

Common law trust in the modern world / D.W.M. Waters. – Deventer : Kluwer, 1984.
24p; 25cm.
ISBN 9065442111

Common lawyers of pre-Reformation England : Thomas Kebell : a case study / by E.W. Ives. – Cambridge : Cambridge University Press, 1983.
xxx,536p; 23cm. – (Cambridge studies in English legal history).
Includes index.
ISBN 0521240115 £40.00

Common Man's Guide to the Common Market / Edwards. – 2nd ed. – London : Macmillan.
ISBN 0333409132 Hbk £27.50
ISBN 0333409140 Pbk £9.95

Common Market law / Alan Campbell. – 4 v. – London : Longmans, 1969.
25cm.
Supplement, published in 1975, assimilated the contents of previous loose-leaf binders. Earlier ed. by Campbell and D.C. Thompson.

Common Market law of competition / Graham D. Child. – 3rd ed. – London : Sweet & Maxwell, 1987.
lviii,874p; 25cm.
Outlines the relevant provision of the EEC Treaty and of Community legislation. Examines collaboration in research, development, and production, industrial property rights, mergers and acquisitions, notification and its effects, civil remedies, enforcement and procedure, special sectors, and state aid. States the relationship between Community law and national law, especially British.
ISBN 0421282002

Common Market law reports. – Edinburgh : Nelson, 1962-.
Decisions of the European Court of Justice.

Common Market law review. – London : Stevens, 1963.
Index in each vol.
ISBN 00103292

Common peace. – Cambridge : Cambridge University Press.
Examines attitudes behind the enforcement of criminal law in seventeenth-century England. Based on court records but concerned with popular rather than professional legal culture.
ISBN 052133313X Hbk £25.00

Common Recoveries : Their Nature and Use. – 2nd ed. Repr. of 1770 ed. – Abingdon : Professional Books.
490p.
Hbk £75.00

Common standards for legal retrieval systems : proposals for a model retrieval language for legal users / Important features of a common command language within a network of legal information systems : studies prepared for the Council of Europe and the Commission of the European Communities by Werner Robert Svoboda. – Strasbourg : Council of Europe, 1983.
104p; 21cm.
At head of title: Legal Affairs.
ISBN 9287102732

Commonhold : freehold flats and freehold ownership of other interdependent buildings : report of a working group / chairman: T.M. Aldridge. – London : H.M.S.O., 1987.
v,101p; 30cm.
ISBN 0101017928

Commons today / edited by S.A. Walkland and Michael Ryle for the Study of Parliament Group. – Rev. ed. – London : Fontana, 1981.
333p; 18cm.
Previous ed.: published as The Commons in the seventies. 1977. Includes index.
ISBN 0006361870 Pbk £2.95

Commonwealth administrative law / D.C. Pearce. – Sydney : Butterworths, 1986.
xxix,282p.
Includes index.
ISBN 0409490881 Hbk A$45.00
ISBN 0409490881 Pbk A$32.00

Commonwealth Caribbean legal essays / edited by Francis Alexis, P.K. Menon, Dorcas White. – Cave Hill, Barbados : Faculty of Law, University of the West Indies, 1982.
iv,303p.
UWI Law Faculty decennial (1970-80) lectures.

Commonwealth Caribbean legal literature : a bibliography of all primary sources to date and secondary sources for 1971-1985 / Velma Newton. – Cave Hill, Barbados : Faculty of Law Library, University of the West Indies, 1987.
492p.
Includes index.
ISBN 976800116X

Commonwealth Conference of Delegated Legislation Committees / Senate Standing Committee on Regulations and Ordinances. – 3 v. – Canberra : Australian Government Publishing Service, 1981.
– (Parliamentary Paper).
Includes bibliography: 2.p101-102. Contents: 1.Report of the Conference - 2.Documents of the Conference - 3.Transcripts of proceedings.
ISBN 0642057923

Commonwealth Developments in Health Law. – Legal Division, Commonwealth Secretariat. – London : Commonwealth Secretariat, 1984.
324p.
ISBN 0850922283 Hbk £6.00
ISBN 0850922070 Pbk £6.00

Commonwealth directory of post-graduate law programmes, 1986-87 : a guide to taught Masters programmes in law at Commonwealth universities, seminars and courses conducted by international organisations and sources of scholarship information. – London : Legal Division, Commonwealth Secretariat, 1987.
ix,112p.
ISBN 085092314X

Commonwealth government directory 1981 / compiled by the Information Services Division, Department of Administrative Services. – Canberra : Australian Government Publishing Service, 1981.
v,457p.
Includes index.

Commonwealth government directory Vol. 1 : Offices and personnel : March 1984. – Canberra : Australian Government Publishing, 1984.
v,403p.
Previous ed.: 1981. Includes indexes.

Commonwealth Group of Eminent Persons Mission to South Africa : the Commonwealth report / Malcolm Fraser, Olusegun Obasanjo. – Harmondsworth : Penguin Books for the Commonwealth Secretariat, 1986.
176p.
Co-chairmen: Malcolm Fraser and Olusegun Obasanjo.
ISBN 0140523847

Commonwealth Law Bulletin. – Legal Division, Commonwealth Secretariat. – London : Commonwealth Secretariat, 1983.
– (Quarterly).
Pbk £5.00

Commonwealth lawyer : the journal of the Commonwealth Lawyers' Association. – London : The Association, 1984.
ISBN 02658100

Commonwealth Lawyers' Association → Admission of Commonwealth lawyers : a technical survey for Commonwealth Law Ministers and the Commonwealth Lawyers' Association.

Commonwealth Legal Aid Council → Relationship between legal aid agencies and social agencies : research report for the Commonwealth Legal Aid Council.

Commonwealth Legal Education Association → Commonwealth directory of post-graduate law programmes, 1986-87 : a guide to taught Masters programmes in law at Commonwealth universities, seminars and courses conducted by international organisations and sources of scholarship information.
—Directory of schools of law in the Commonwealth / Commonwealth Legal Education Association. – 1985. – London : The Association, 1985.
60p.

→ Legal literature in small jurisdictions : a report of a conference held at Osgoode Hall Law School, York University, Downsview, Ontario on 3-5 November 1978.

—Newsletter / Commonwealth Legal Education Association. – Commonwealth Legal Education Association. – London : Commonwealth Legal Education Association, 1974.

Commonwealth Magistrates' Association → Report of the seventh Commonwealth Magistrates' Conference : Nicosia, Cyprus 8th to 14th September 1985.

Commonwealth Prisoners Act / Law Reform Commission. – Canberra : Australian Government Publishing Service, 1988.
xv,57p. – (Report (interim)).
Bibliography: p.57. Includes text of draft legislation.
ISBN 0644069007

Commonwealth Scholarship Commission in the United Kingdom
Twenty-eighth annual report of the Commonwealth Scholarship Commission in the United Kingdom : for the year ending 30 September 1987 to the Minister for Overseas Development. – Commonwealth Scholarship Commission in the United Kingdom. – London : The Commission, 1987.
110p.

Commonwealth Secretariat → Decade of women and the law in the Commonwealth.
→ Emerging issues in Commonwealth abortion laws, 1982.

→ Family law : the Commonwealth experience.

→ International conventions concerning applications for and awards of maintenance : explanatory documentation.

→ Law reform in the Commonwealth : law reform proposals and their implementation.

→ Layman as a magistrate.

→ Meeting of Commonwealth law ministers, Colombo,Sri Lanka, 14-18 February 1983 : memoranda.

→ Mission to South Africa : the Commonwealth report.

→ New York Convention on the Recognition and Enforcement of Foreign Arbitral Awards : explanatory documentation prepared for Commonwealth jurisdictions.

→ Ocean management : a regional perspective : the prospects for Commonwealth maritime co-operation in Asia and the Pacific.

→ Ombudsmen in the Commonwealth : a survey.

→ Practice relating to the appointment of Queen's Counsel and senior counsel in some Commonwealth jurisdictions.

→ Problems of jury trials in small jurisdictions.

→ Research opportunities in Commonwealth developing countries : universities, non-university research institutions : a register prepared by the Association of Commonwealth Universities in association with the Commonwealth Secretariat.

→ Survey of legal measures in the Commonwealth designed to assist the disabled.

—Three international conventions on hijacking and offences on board aircraft : (i) Convention on Offences and Certain Other Acts Committed on Board Aircraft ... 1963. (ii) Convention for Suppression of Unlawful Seizure of Aircraft ... 1970. (iii) Convention for the Suppression of Unlawful Acts Against the Safety of Civil Aviation ... 1971 : explanation documentation prepared for Commonwealth jurisdictions by David Lloyd Jones in association with the Commonwealth Secretariat / David Lloyd Jones. – London : Commonwealth Secretariat, 1982.
vi,146p; 30cm.
ISBN 0850922151

→ UN Convention on the Law of the Sea 1982 : a guide for national policy making legislation and administration.

→ Vulnerability : small states in the global society.

Commonwealth Tax Laws. – Delhi : Rangnath Publications.
Hbk £500.00

Commonwealth Taxation Board of Review Decisions : Consolidated Index and Tables 1925-1986. – Butterworths. – 1st ed. – Butterworths, 1988.
290p.
Hbk £110.00

Commonwealth Taxation Board of Review Decisions : Old and New Series. – Butterworths.
ISBN 0409426008 Hbk

Communicating Court Information : Towards a Canadian Records Handling System. – Ottawa : Canadian Law Information Council, 1984.
103p.
ISBN 0920358640 Pbk £15.00

Communications : a guide to the electronic office for practising lawyers / compiled by the Communications Committee of the Society for Computers and Law. – 2nd fully rev ed. – Didcot : The Society, 1985.
iii,67 leaves.
ISBN 0906122198

Communications : (includes telecommunications). – Thessaloniki, Greece : Institute of International Public Law and International Relations of Thessaloniki, 1987.
530p.
Includes bibliographical references. Text in English and French.

Communications deregulation : the unleashing of America's communications industry / Jeremy Tunstall. – Oxford : Blackwell, 1986.
425p; 23cm.
Includes bibliography and index.
ISBN 0631148191 £17.50

Communications in Prison (A Short Guide) 1981. – London : Home Office.
ISBN 0862520193 Hbk £5.00

Communications law and policy in Australia : adapted from Mark Armstrong's Broadcasting law and policy in Australia / Mark Armstrong. – Sydney : Butterworths, 1987.
ISBN 0409493759 Llf A$275

Communique of the national seminar on effective law library services in Nigeria, June 5-7, 1984, held under the sponsorship of the Nigerian Institute of Advanced Legal Studies. – Nigerian Institute of Advanced Legal Studies. – Lagos : The Institute, 1984.
8p.

Communist Ideology Law and Crime. – London : Macmillan, 1988.
ISBN 0333421078 Hbk £35.00

Community alternatives for juvenile offenders : development kit. – NACRO. – London : NACRO, 1983.
47p.
ISBN 0850690277

Community, anarchy and liberty / Michael Taylor. – Cambridge : Cambridge University Press, 1982.
184p; 23cm.
Bibliography: p172-180. - Includes index.
ISBN 0521246210 Hbk £14.00
ISBN 0521270146 Pbk £4.95

Community based preventive policing : a review 1984-90 / David K. Wasson, John D. Crawford & Company Ltd. – Ottawa : Ministry of the Solicitor General, 1984.
iii,198p. – (User report).
Bibliography: p.197-198.

Community constables : a Study of a policing initiative / David Brown, Susan Iles. – London : Home Office, 1985.
v,51p.
Bibliography: p.42-43.

Community Law. – Luxembourg : Office for Official Publications of the European Communities, 1987.
33p.
ISBN 9282569489 Pbk £150.00

Community Law. – Luxembourg : Office for Official Publications of the European Communities, 1986.
39p.
ISBN 9282562247 Pbk £150.00

Community Law : Offprint from the Sixteenth General Report on the Activities of the European Communities. – London : HMSO, 1983.
ISBN 9282534812 Hbk £1.40

Community Law and United Kingdom Value Added Tax. – London : Deloitte Haskins & Sells, 1988.
ISBN 0863491235 Hbk £45.00

Community Law Manual. – Montreal : McGill Campus Legal Aid Clinic, 1983.
300p.
Hbk £15.00

Community law reform for the Australian Capital Territory
1st report : The community law reform program : Contributory negligence in fatal accident cases and breach of statutory duty cases : Funeral costs in fatal accident cases / Law Reform Commission. – Canberra : Australian Government Publishing Service, 1985.
ix,44p. – (Report).
Bibliography: p.41-42 - Includes index.
ISBN 0644013257

Community law reform for the Australian Capital Territory : enduring powers of attorney / The Law Reform Commission. – Sydney : The Commission, 1987.
i,13p. – (Discussion paper).

Community law reform for the Australian capital territory : second report : Loss of consortium : compensation for loss of capacity to do housework / the Law Reform Commission. – Canberra : Australian Government Publishing Service, 1986.
viii,28p. – (Report).
Bibliography: p.27. - Includes index.
ISBN 0644013516

Community law reform program
11th report : Restitution of benefits conferred under mistake of law / New South Wales Law Reform Commission. – Sydney : Government Printer, 1987.
xiii,95p. – (L.R.C).
Bibliography: pp.79-81. Includes text of draft bill.
ISBN 073054429X

1st report : Insurance contracts : non-disclosure and misrepresentation / New South Wales Law Reform Commission. – 1983.
61p. – (L.R.C. 34).

9th report : Limitation of actions for personal injury claims / New South Wales Law Reform Commission. – 1986.
xv,89p. – (L.R.C.).
Includes bibliographical references.
ISBN 073052535X

2nd report : Interest on certain debts / New South Wales Law Reform Commission. – 1983.
46p. – (L.R.C. 35).

3rd report : Service of civil process on Sunday / New South Wales Law Reform Commission. – 1983.
61p. – (L.R.C. 37).

4th report : Sound recording of proceedings of courts and commissions : the media, authors and parties / New South Wales Law Reform Commission. – 1984.
115p. – (L.R.C. 39).
Bibliography: p.113-115.

5th report : Passing of risk between vendor and purchaser of land / New South Wales Law Reform Commission. – 1984.
84p. – (L.R.C. 40).
Bibliography: p.83-84.

6th report : Conscientious objection to jury service / New South Wales Law Reform Commission. – 1984.
53p. – (L.R.C. 42).

7th report : Attachment of moneys deposited with building societies and credit unions / New South Wales Law Reform Commission. – 1985.
xiii,123p. – (L.R.C. 46).
Includes bibliographical references.
ISBN 0730514714 Hbk

8th report : Wills - execution and revocation / New South Wales Law Reform Commission. – 1986.
175p. – (L.R.C. 47).
Includes bibliographical references.
ISBN 0730514943 Hbk

Community Legal Education Ontario
Criminal Law. – Community Legal Education Ontario. – Toronto : Community Legal Education Ontario, 1981.
49p.
ISBN 0889030553 Pbk £6.50

—Making a Will. – Community Legal Education Ontario. – 4th rev. ed. – Toronto : Community Legal Education Ontario, 1982.
30p.
ISBN 0889030561 Pbk £6.50

—Marriage and Divorce. – Community Legal Education Ontario. – 3rd rev. ed. – Toronto : Community Legal Education Ontario, 1982.
47p.
ISBN 088903057X Pbk £6.50

—Small Claims in Ontario. – Community Legal Education Ontario. – Toronto : Community Legal Education Ontario, 1982.
70p.
ISBN 0889030588 Pbk £6.50

Community of Property : Discussion Paper. – National Women's Advisory Council. – Canberra : Australian Government Publishing Service, 1982.
34p.
ISBN 0644021802 Hbk £2.00

Community Order and National Economic Policies : Disciplines Communautaires et Politiques Economiques Nationales. – Dordrecht : Kluwer.
538p.
ISBN 9065442014 Pbk £125.00

Community policing in the 1980's : recent advances in police programs / edited by Donald J. Loree and Chris Murphy. – Ottawa : Ministry of the Solicitor General, 1986.
v,154p.
'This conference was jointly sponsored by the Canadian Police College ... and by the Secretariat of the Ministry of the Solicitor General of Canada'. - T.p.. Held in Ottawa, March 17-19, 1986.
ISBN 0662158075

Community Secondary Legislation, 3 Vols. Vol. 3. – Edinburgh : W Green, 1985.
– (Encyclopedia of European Community Law Ser.).
ISBN 0421207604 Llf £480.00
Service for 1985 only (post-free). – Llf £205.00

Community service order : a first decade of promise / a review undertaken by Ken Pease on behalf of the Howard League for Penal Reform. – London : Howard League for Penal Reform, 1981.
ix,76p; 21cm.
Bibliography: p66-70.
Pbk £1.75

Companies Act 1948 : Investigations. – Department of Trade. – London : HMSO, 1983.
ISBN 0115136738 Hbk £20.00

Companies Act, 1965 (Act 125). – Kuala Lumpur : International Law Books Services.
Hbk £17.50

Companies act 1980 / by Clive M. Schmitthoff. – London : London Chamber of Commerce and Industry, 1981.
x,191p; 30cm.
Includes index.
ISBN 0901902535

Companies Act 1980. – Tolley Publishing.
ISBN 0854590390 Pbk £7.95
ISBN 0854590595 Hbk £11.95

Companies Act, 1980 : pre-emption rights of shareholders / Council for the Securities Industry. – London : The Council, 1981.
2p.

Companies Act 1980, sections 54 and 55 : transactions or arrangements in which a director has a material interest : memorandum / by the Society's Standing Committee on Company Law. – London : Law Society, 1981.
6p; 30cm.

Companies Act 1981 : text and commentary / L.H. Leigh, H.C. Edey. – London : Butterworths, 1981.
v,329p.
ISBN 0406845301

Companies Act 1985. – London : HMSO.
600p.
ISBN 0105406856 Hbk £21.00

Companies Act. – Allahabad : Law Publishers, 1982.
Hbk £24.00

Companies Act. – 2nd ed. – Allahabad : Law Book Company, 1986.
2,500p.
Hbk £425.00

Companies Act With Exhaustive Referencer. – Nagpur : Wadhura & Co, 1988.
Hbk £150.00

Companies Acts 1980 and 1981 : a practitioners' manual / by Robert R. Pennington. – London : Lloyds of London Press, 1983.
lxii,313p; 25cm.
Includes index.
ISBN 0907432573

Companies Acts / Parker. – 14th ed. – London : Butterworths, 1981.
Service to Date.
ISBN 0406141037 Hbk £150.00

Companies Acts : Table A 1856-1985. – 2nd ed. – London : Butterworths, 1985.
ISBN 0406351244 Hbk £25.00

Companies (Amendment) Ordinance 1984 in perspective / by Christopher Bates. – Hong Kong : Hong Kong Law Journal, 1985.
xv,116p.
Reprinted from the Hong Kong Law Journal vol. 15 (1985). Includes index.

Companies and Securities H/B Singapore and Malaysia. – London : Butterworths, 1984.
ISBN 040999507X Pbk £19.00

Companies and Securities Handbook Singapore and Malaysia
1984 with 1985 Supplement / by Philip N. Pillai. – Butterworths, 1984.
xxv,1401p.
Provides company and securities legislation in Singapore and Malaysia. Coverage includes the text of the Companies Acts and Companies Regulations for Singapore and Malaysia, as well as the Securities Industry legislation for the two legislations. Also contains the Practice Notes and Guidelines issues by the Registrars of Companies in both jurisdictions.
ISBN 0409181209 Pbk £195.00
1985 Supplement alone. –
ISBN 040999507X Pbk £35.00

Companies and securities law journal. – Sydney : Law Book Co., 1982-.

Companies and Taxes in Liechtenstein / Goup. – Vaduz, 1983.
99p.
Hbk £39.00

Companies Consolidation (Consequential Provisions) Act, 1985. – London : HMSO.
56p.
ISBN 0105409855 Hbk £4.50

Companies consolidation legislation 1985 / with annotations by Geoffrey Morse : in collaboration with Ann Arora ... et al. – 1. – London : Sweet & Maxwell, 1985.
various pagings.
Includes index. Contents: Companies Act 1985 - Business Names Act 1985 - Company Securities (Insider Dealing) Act 1985 - Companies Consolidation (Consequential Provisions) Act 1985.
ISBN 0421344407

Companies consolidation legislation 1987 / with annotations by Geoffrey Morse in collaboration with Anu Arora ... et al. – London : Sweet & Maxwell, 1987.
xiv,1015,11p; 24cm.
Includes index.
ISBN 0421383607 Pbk £27.00

Companies' Directors. – 2nd ed. – Allahabad : Law Book Company, 1988.
800p.
Hbk £200.00

Companies in 1983 Annual Report. – Insolvency Service of the Department of Trade and Industry. – London : HMSO, 1984.
ISBN 0115137025 Hbk £4.75

Companies in 1984 - Annual Report. – London : HMSO, 1985.
ISBN 0115138277 Hbk £4.95

Companies' marine policy : attached clauses. – Institute of London Underwriters. – London : The Institute, 1982.
26p.
Contents: Insurance cargo clauses (A), (B), and (C) - Institute war clauses (Cargo) - Institute strikes clauses (Cargo) - Institute war clauses (sendings by post) - Institute war clauses (Air cargo) (excluding sendings by post) - Institute cargo clauses (Air) (excluding sendings by post) - Institute strikes clauses (Air cargo) - Institute standard conditons for cargo contracts - Companies' marine policy form.

Companies operating overseas: UK tax, law and practice / John Dixon. – London : Longman Professional (UK), 1986.
– (Commercial series).
Examination of the UK tax implications for any company which trades abroad and is concerned with reducing the risks involved. Looks at problems such as the treatment of double taxation agreements, legislation on controlled foreign companies, and the international VAT implications.
ISBN 0851218770 Pbk £17.50

Companies purchasing their own shares : memorandum / by the Society's Standing Committee on Revenue Law. – London : Law Society, 1981.
9p; 30cm.
Submitted in reply to the Inland Revenue's consultative document: Companies purchasing their own shares.

Companies Regulations, Rules and Guide Lines on Mergers and Take-Overs. – Kuala Lumpur : International Law Books Services.
Hbk £12.50

Companies Winding-up. – 2nd ed. – Allahabad : Law Book Company, 1988.
700p.
Hbk £200.00

Companies (Winding-up) Rules, (P.U.(A) 289/1972). – Kuala Lumpur : International Law Books Services.
Hbk £10.00

Company Accounting Requirements / Wild. – 2nd ed. – London : Longman Professional, 1985.
ISBN 0851211461 Pbk £19.95

Company accounts / Jenny Bough. – London : Sweet & Maxwell, 1987.
xvii,227p; 26cm.
Includes index.
ISBN 0421360208 £16.50

Company Accounts. – 3rd ed. – Plymouth : Macdonald & Evans, 1982.
ISBN 0712104704 Pbk £6.95

Company acquisition of own shares / Michael Wyatt. – London : Longman, 1986.
180p; 22cm.
New ed.: Previous ed.: 1983. Includes index.
ISBN 0851212506 Pbk £19.95

Company administration orders and voluntary arrangements / Richard Floyd. – London : Longman Professional (UK), 1988.
– (Practitioner series).
Guide to the law and procedure relating to administration orders, and voluntary arrangements (resulting from the Insolvency Act 1986). Examines corporate administration orders from beginning to end, comparing them to other insolvency proceedings. Includes specimen proposals.
ISBN 0851214800 Hbk £18.95

Company Car Tax Guide 1988-89 / Lybrand. – London : CCH.
ISBN 086325165X Pbk £5.00

Company Cases 1987. – Stevens & Sons.
ISBN 0420480803 Hbk £28.00

Company Charges Plus Australian Supplement Australian supplement only. – Wellington : Butterworths.
ISBN 040949061X Pbk

Company director and the law. – 5th. – London : Longman Professional (UK), 1986.
Explains the legal responsibilities and obligations of the company director. Covers the changes made by the Companies Act 1985, and the Insolvency Act 1986.
ISBN 085121231X Pbk £17.95

Company Directors. – London : CCH, 1987.
ISBN 0863250947 Pbk £25.00

Company Directors : Law and Practice. – 2nd ed. – Durban : Professional Publisher, 1983.
ISBN 0409040711 Hbk

Company directors : liabilities, rights and duties / Christopher L. Ryan. – 2nd ed. – Bicester : CCH Editions, 1986.
xvi,407p; 23cm.
Covers the relevant provisions of the Business Names Act 1985, the Companies Act 1985, the Company Securities (Insider Dealing) Act 1985, the Insolvency Act 1986, the Company Directors Disqualification Act 1986, the Financial Services Act 1986, and other relevant statutes.
ISBN 0863250947 Pbk

Company donations to political parties : a suggested code of practice / Edmund Dell. – London : Constitutional Reform Centre, 1985.
34p.
'The report of the Working Party on Company Political Donations established jointly by the Constitutional Reform Centre and the Hansard Society for Parliamentary Government'. - Back Cover. Chairman: Edmund Dell.
ISBN 0948419008

Company flotations : tax and tax planning. – Butterworths, 1985.
An overall guide to the tax consdierations for UK companies both before and during a public sale. Tax planning for major shareholders and officers is treated in detail. A timetable for flotation is included in the appendix.
ISBN 0406259704 Pbk £20

Company Formations (Private and Public). – New Delhi : Bharat Law House, 1984.
Hbk £100.00

Company Forms Chart. – Cape Town : Legal & Financial Publishing, 1983.
– (Merlen P.A.Y.E. Registers Ser.).
Hbk £1.79

Company Forms Manual. – London : Butterworths, 1988.
ISBN 0406016305 Hbk £38.00

Company Insolvency and Liquidation / French. – London : Blackstone Press, 1988.
ISBN 1854310143 Hbk

Company Law 1988-89 / French. – 5th ed. – London : Blackstone Press.
ISBN 1854310186 Hbk £19.95

Company Law 2.2. – London : BPP.
– (ACCA Practice and Revision Kits Series).
ISBN 0862772680 Pbk £5.95

Company Law, 3 Vols.
Service only. – London : Sweet & Maxwell.
Hbk £90.00

Company Law. – Vancouver : Continuing Legal Education Society of British Columbia, 1987.
491p.
ISBN 0865043423 Hbk £90.00

Company Law. – 2nd ed. – Croydon : Tolley, 1987.
ISBN 0854592598 Pbk £33.95
ISBN 0854592687 Hbk £39.95

Company Law / Bond. – 2nd ed. – London : Financial Training.
– (SWOT).
ISBN 1851850716 Pbk £7.95

Company law / Thomas Ewan Cain, Geoffrey Morse, Enid A. Marshall. – 12th ed. – London : Stevens, 1983.
700p.
Previous ed.: 1977.
ISBN 0420460306 Hbk £12.00
ISBN 0420460403 Pbk £5.50

Company Law. – 4th ed. – Allahabad : Orient Law House, 1987.
Hbk £400.00

Company Law. – London : Castlevale Publishers, 1982.
ISBN 0907235018 Pbk £5.00

Company Law. – 2nd ed. – London : Butterworths, 1988.
ISBN 0406581622 Hbk £38.00
ISBN 0406581630 Pbk £22.50

Company law / John H. Farrar assisted by Nigel Furey, Brenda Hannigan with a chapter on company taxation by O.P. Wylie. – London : Butterworths, 1985.
xlvii,636p; 25cm.
Includes index.
ISBN 0406581606 Hbk £18.50
ISBN 0406581614 Pbk £12.50

Company Law. – 3rd ed. – New Delhi : Kalyani Publishers, 1987.
ISBN 817096010X Hbk £42.00

Company Law. – 10th ed. – Plymouth : Macdonald & Evans, 1987.
ISBN 0712106987 Hbk £6.50

Company Law. – Sydney : Butterworths, 1986.
117p. – (Butterworth's Student Companion Ser.).
ISBN 0409490962 Pbk £9.95

Company Law. – 5th ed. – London : Butterworths, 1985.
ISBN 0406336830 Hbk £39.00
ISBN 0406336857 Pbk £26.00

Company Law / Ernest E Spicer. – 13th ed. – London : Butterworths, 1987.
ISBN 0406678901 Pbk £14.95

Company Law / Saxena. – Delhi : SBD Enterprises.
Hbk £13.50

Company Law. – 7th ed. – Lucknow : Eastern Book Company, 1982.
493p.
Hbk £45.00

Company Law / Dennis Keenan. – 7th ed. – London : Pitman Publishing, 1987.
ISBN 0273027921 Pbk £12.95

Company Law. – North Ryde : Law Book Co, 1985.
xi, 116. – (Nutshells).
ISBN 0455205957

Company law : a discussion paper / Law Commission. – Wellington, N.Z. : The Commission, 1987.
xi,104p. – (Preliminary paper).

Company Law : ACCA Series Level 2.2. – Witney : A.T.C. Publications.
ISBN 0747700125 Pbk £11.95

Company Law : ACCA Study Text 2.2. – London : BPP.
ISBN 0862772419 Pbk £11.95

Company Law : an Immediate Approach. – Allahabad : Modern Law Publications, 1987.
Hbk £170.00

Company Law : Case Studies in a Business Context. – London : Macmillan.
ISBN 033343465X Pbk £29.95

Company Law : ICSA Study Text. – Revised edition. – London : BPP, 1988.
ISBN 0862772109 Pbk £13.95

Company Law : Instructional Manual. – 2nd ed. – Winchester : DP Publications, 1983.
400p.
ISBN 0905435605 Pbk £4.95

Company law : recent legislative changes : the text of a lecture delivered to the Belfast Solicitors' Association on 10 November 1983 / by Dennis Boyd. – Belfast : SLS Legal Publications, 1983.
i,32p.
Includes bibliographical references.
Pbk £2.95

Company Law and Auditing. – New Delhi : Kalyani Publishers.
Hbk £21.00

Company Law and Capitalism. – 3rd ed. – Weidenfeld & Nicolson.
ISBN 029778761 Hbk £25.00
ISBN 029778787X Pbk £15.95

Company law and commercial reality / by L.S. Sealy. – London : Sweet & Maxwell, 1984.
xii,91p; 22cm.
Includes index.
ISBN 0421333502 Pbk £12.00

Company Law and Company Taxation in South Africa / Keeton. – Cape Town : Legal & Financial Publishing, 1983.
ISBN 0869940171 Hbk £32.50

Company Law and Competition Policy. – S J Berwin.
ISBN 1852510277 Hbk £12.95

Company Law and Meetings. – Bombay : Tripathi.
Hbk

Company law and practice in Nigeria / by J. Olakunle Orojo. – 2nd ed. 2. – London : Sweet & Maxwell, 1984.
23cm.
Previous ed.: published in 1 1976. Includes index.
ISBN 0421312106 £85.00

Company Law and Secretarial Practice. – 2nd rev. ed. – New Delhi : Sterling Publishers, 1981.
352p.
ISBN 8120701852 Hbk £50.00
ISBN 8120704010 £17.50

Company Law and Securities Regulation in Malaysia. – London : Butterworths, 1987.
ISBN 0409995517 Pbk £28.00

Company Law and Securities Regulation in New Zealand / Mark W Russell. – London : Butterworths, 1984.
ISBN 0409701688 Pbk £38.00

Company Law and Securities Regulation in Singapore. – Butterworths, 1987.
ca 170p.
Examines corporate and securities regulation, with reference to Singapore legislation, regulations, non-statutory guidelines, case law and administrative practice.
ISBN 0409995495 Pbk £55.00

Company Law Cases
1983. – London : Butterworths.
ISBN 0406076510 Hbk £37.00
1984. –
ISBN 0406076545 Hbk £45.00
1985. –
ISBN 0406076596 Hbk £57.00
1986. –
ISBN 040607660X Hbk £61.00
1988. –
ISBN 00267145X Hbk £89.00

Company Law for Accountants. – London : Butterworths, 1985.
This text is a straightforward presentation of the company law of the United Kingdom for students of accounting.
ISBN 0406009600 Pbk £11.95

Company Law for Legal Assistants 1987. – Vancouver : Continuing Legal Education Society of British Columbia, 1987.
299p.
ISBN 0865043507 Hbk £80.00

Company Law Guide. – 2nd ed. – London : Butterworths, 1988.
ISBN 0406197024 Pbk

Company Law Handbook. – 6th ed. – London : Butterworths, 1987.
ISBN 0406143153 Pbk £16.95

Company law in a nutshell / Francis Roundell. – 3rd ed. – London : Sweet & Maxwell, 1985.
vii,88p. – (New nutshells).
Includes index.
ISBN 0421348402

Company Law in Australia / J. P. Hambrook. – Sydney : Butterworths, 1988.
544p.
Pbk £40.00

Company law in change / edited by B.G. Pettet. – London : Stevens, 1987.
144p; 22cm.
Includes index.
ISBN 0420477500 Pbk £15.00

Company law in Europe / P. Meinhardt. – 3rd ed. 1. – Farnborough, Hants. : Gower, 1981.
loose-leaf; 26cm.
Previous ed.: 1978. Includes bibliographies and index.
ISBN 0566022451 £40.00

Company law in Great Britain / Peter Meinhardt with the assistance of Nigel Davis. – Aldershot : Gower, 1982.
178p in various pagings; 24cm.
Bibliography: 2p. - Includes index.
ISBN 056602389X

Company Law in Hong Kong. – Butterworths, 1986.
393p.
Deals with Hong Kong company law, in light of the changes introduced by the Companies (Amendments) Ordinance 1984. Gives an account of Company law in Hong Kong, from the incorporation of a company, to its liquidation. Discussion of the registration requirements which companies incorporated overseas must comply if they wish to operate in Hong Kong.
ISBN 0409995223 Pbk £40.00

Company law in Ireland / Michael Forde. – Cork : Mercier, 1985.
xlix,552p; 23cm.
Includes index.
ISBN 0853427313 Hbk £45.00
ISBN 0853427666 Pbk £22.50

Company law in Ireland / by Patrick Ussher. – London : Sweet & Maxwell, 1986.
xlvii,577p; 22cm.
Includes index.
ISBN 0421297506 Pbk £18.95

Company Law in Pakistan : Companies Act 1913. – Lahore : Pakistan Law Times.
900p.
Hbk £120.00

Company law in the European Communities / Frank Wooldridge. – 3rd ed. – London : Oyez Longman, 1982.
viii,200p.
Previous ed., 1970, entitled: Companies in the Common Market.
ISBN 0851206387

Company Law in the Republic of Ireland. – London : Butterworths, 1985.
ISBN 0406272905 Hbk £22.00

Company Law Lunchtime Series. – Monash University, Faculty of Law. – Clayton : Monash University Press, 1984.
ISBN 086746318X Hbk £15.00

Company Law Materials. – 10th ed. – Bristol : Jordan & Sons Ltd, 1986.
ISBN 0853080879 Pbk £9.05

Company Law of Singapore and Malaysis. – Singapore : Quins.
Hbk
Vol. 1. –
xxviii, 462p.
Hbk £99.00
Vol. 1A. –
224p.
Llf £36.00
Vol. 2. –
xxxiv, 447p.
Hbk £99.00

Company Law Procedures. – 3rd ed. – New Delhi : Bharat Law House, 1984.
Hbk £200.00

Company Law (Q & A) / Gregory. – 2nd ed. – London : Financial Training.
ISBN 185185018X Pbk £7.50

Company Liquidations. – London : CCH.
ISBN 0863251447 Hbk £48.00
ISBN 0863250831 Pbk £36.00

Company liquidations : the substantive law / Robert Pennington. – Bristol : Jordans, 1987.
xxvi,150p; 21cm.
Includes index.
ISBN 0853081220 Pbk £8.50

Company Meetings, Accounts, Audit and Investigation. – 2nd ed. – Allahabad : Law Book Company, 1987.
Hbk £200.00

Company Precedents
Part 1 - General Forms. – Sweet & Maxwell, 1956.
ISBN 0420371907 Hbk £57.00
Part 2 - Winding-up Forms and Practice. – 1960.
ISBN 0420372008 Hbk £57.00

Company procedures manual. – London : Longman Professional (UK).
Selection of over 300 precedent documents, covering administration, shares and shareholders, officers and loan capital, and includes minutes, resolutions, notices, letters, agreements. Also available on disk.
ISBN 0851212263 Llf £85.00

Company receivers and managers / by James O'Donovan. – Sydney : Law Book Copany, 1981.
lxxxiii,545p.
Includes index.
ISBN 0455200823

Company Reorganisations : Tax and Tax Planning / Nicholas Noble. – London : Butterworths, 1986.
ISBN 0406501904 Hbk £35.00

Company Resolutions. – 3rd ed. repr. 1986. – New Delhi : Bharat Law House.
Hbk £150.00

Company Secretarial Handbook. – 9th ed. – London : Longman Professional, 1986.
ISBN 0851210686 Pbk £20.95

Company Secretarial Practice
1984 Supplement / Thom. – 6th ed. – Plymouth : Macdonald & Evans, 1984.
ISBN 071210478X Pbk £6.50

Company Securities (Insider Dealing) Act 1985. – London : HMSO.
16p.
ISBN 0105408859 Pbk £2.25

Company Share Register. – Cape Town : Legal & Financial Publishing, 1983.
– (Merlen Ser. of Registers).
Hbk £3.52

Company takeovers : a review of the law and practice in New Zealand
Volume 1 : Discussion and proposals for reform. – Wellington : the Commission, 1983.
119p.
Volume 2 : Reports of the Securities Commission on the takeovers of Bing Harris & Co. Limited by Brierley Investments Limited, Property Securities Limited by City Realities Limited, the Canterbury Frozen Meat Company Limited by Primary Producers Co-operative Society Limited. – 1983.
130p.
Volume 3 : Legislation in New Zealand and selected overseas jurisdictions. – 1983.
343p.

Company Tax Recoupment Law / S.W. Gibb. – North Ryde : C.C.H. Australia, 1983.
215p.
ISBN 0869036327 Hbk £40.00

Company's purchase of own shares : Section 53 and Schedule 9 Finance Act 1982 / Inland Revenue. – London : Inland Revenue, 1982.
2,vp. – (Statement of practice).

Comparative arbitration practice and public policy in arbitration / general editor, Pieter Sanders with the cooperation of the T.M.C. Asser Institute for International Law. – Deventer : Kluwer Law and Taxation Publishers, 1987.
x, 402 p.; 25 cm.
At head of title: International Council for Commercial Arbitration. 'VIIIth International Arbitration Congress, New York, 6-9 May 1986'–Series t.p. Includes bibliographical references.
ISBN 9065442960 Pbk £135.00

Comparative Constitutional Law. – New Delhi : Prentice-Hall, 1984.
560p.
ISBN 0876922302 Hbk £150.00

Comparative dismissal law / B.W. Napier, J.-C. Javillier and P. Verge. – London : Croom Helm, 1982.
175p; 23cm.
ISBN 0709918089 £12.50

Comparative Federalism : General Principles. – New Delhi : Prentice-Hall, 1986.
560p.
ISBN 0876924429 Hbk £150.00

Comparative industrial relations : an introduction to cross-national perspectives / R. Bean. – London : Croom Helm, 1985.
iv,288p.
Includes bibliography and index.
ISBN 0709932510 Hbk £19.95 :
ISBN 0709932812 Pbk £9.95

Comparative introduction to the German law of tort / B.S. Markesinis. – Oxford : Clarendon, 1986.
xxix,610p; 24cm.
Includes bibliographies and index. Spine title: The German law of torts.
ISBN 0198255314 £55.00

Comparative judicial systems : challenging frontiers in conceptual and empirical analysis / John R. Schmidhauser, editor. – London : Butterworths, 1987.
243p; 22cm.
Conference proceedings. Includes bibliographies.
ISBN 0408031654 £25.00

Comparative labour law : Anglo-Soviet perspectives / edited by W.E. Butler, B.A. Hepple, Alan C. Neal. – Aldershot : Gower in conjunction with the International journal of comparative labour law and industrial relations, 1987.
xii,219p; 23cm.
Conference proceedings. Bibliography: p217-219.
ISBN 056605387X £18.50

Comparative labour law and industrial relations / editor, Blanpain, R. : contributors Aaron, B. ... et al. – 3rd ed. – Deventer, The Netherlands : Kluwer Law and Taxation Publishers, 1987.
xiii, 527p.
Includes indexes.
ISBN 9065443169

Comparative law of monopolies. – London : Graham & Trotman, 1989.
590.
ISBN 1853332763 Llf £172
Supplement service. – 1989.
120.
Examines the laws on restrictive agreements, monopolies and mergers in the jurisdictions of the US, the UK, the Federal Republic of Germany and the European Community. Standards applied in each jurisdiction are analysed and the similarities and differences are explored in detail.
ISBN 1853332682 £54

Comparative Law of Trusts in the Commonwealth and the Irish Republic
Supplement 1981. – Chichester : Barry Rose.
ISBN 0859921751 Hbk £8.50

Comparative Law Yearbook
Vol. 1. – Dordrecht : Kluwer, 1978.
352p.
ISBN 9028606785 Hbk £105.00
Vol. 4. – 1981.
vi, 371p.
ISBN 9024725631 Hbk £150.00

Vol. 5. – 1982.
332p.
ISBN 9024726972 Hbk £180.00

Vol. 6. – 1983.
256p.
ISBN 9024728398 Hbk £145.00

Vol. 7. – 1984.
200p.
ISBN 9024729661 Hbk £145.00

Vol. 8. – 1985.
250p.
ISBN 902473178X Hbk £165.00

Vol. 9. – 1986.
232p.
ISBN 9024733502 Hbk £165.00

Comparative product liability / edited by C. J. Miller. – London : British Institute of International and Comparative Law, 1986.
xv,198p.
Based on revised papers and contributions originally submitted to a colloquium held by the United Kingdom National Committee for Comparative Law at the University of Edinburgh.
ISBN 0903067285

Comparative report on force majeure in Western Europe / edited by Matti Kurkela. – Jyvaskylassa : Union of the Finnish Lawyers Publishing Co., 1982.
134p.
ISBN 951640152X

Comparative survey of corporate investments
Vol. 1 : in the Far East and Middle East ... : edited by Gunther H. W. Stratmann : written by members of Committee G/Business Orgamisation of the Section on Business Law of the International Bar Association / Gunther H. W. Stratmann. – London : International Bar Association, 1983.
iv,198p.
Based on papers 'presented during the New Delhi Conference of the International Bar Assoiciation ...'. - Introduction.
Vol. 2 parts 1-2 : in Canada, Belgium, France, Federal Republic of Germany ... : written by members of Committee G/Business Organisations of the Section on Business Law of the International Bar Association. –
A 'set of papers ... presented during the Toronto Conference of the International Bar Association ...'. - Introduction.

Comparative Tables of Supreme Court Cases, 1950-85. – Lucknow : Eastern Book Company.
Hbk

Comparative tables of the social security schemes in the member states of the European Communities : General scheme (employees in industry and commerce). – 12th ed. – Luxembourg : Office for Official Publications of the European Communities, 1982.
119p.
ISBN 9282535207

Comparative tax studies : essays in honor of Richard Goode / edited by Sijbren Cnossen. – Amsterdam : North-Holland Pub. Co., 1983.
xiii, 444 p.; 23 cm.
'Bibliography: works of Richard Goode': p. 431-435. Includes bibliographies.
ISBN 0444864210

Comparing Legislations / Patterson. – London : Eurospan.
ISBN 081917050X Pbk £14.75

Comparison of automated and manual legal research : a computer study / by Michael Iosipescu and John Yogis. – Ottawa : Canadian Law Information Council, 1981.
ii, 86 p.; 28 cm. – (Canadian Law Information Council working paper).
Cover title: Legal research.
ISBN 092035808X Pbk £13.50

Compelling appearance, interim release and pre-trial detention / Law Reform Commission of Canada. – Ottawa : The Commission, 1988.
138,150p. – (Working paper).
Added t.p. in French: Les mesures assurant la comparution, la mise en liberte provisoire et la detention avant le proces. Pages numbered in opposite directions. Text in English and French.
ISBN 0662558960

Compendium of China's Laws and Regulations on External Economic Relations and Trade. – Hong Kong : Economic Information and Agency.
Hbk £40.00

Compendium of human rights courses in Australian tertiary institutions / compiled by Alex Castles and Leonie Farrell. – Canberra : Australian Government Publishing Service, 1983.
xiv,39p. – (Occasional paper).
Includes index.
ISBN 0644027649

Compendium of Legal Aid and Advice 1983 : Extracted from the Parliament House Book. – W. Green and Son Publishing. – Edinburgh : W Green, 1983.
ISBN 0414007220 Hbk £5.00

Compendium of the Northern Regulatory Regime. – Don Mills : CCH Canadian Ltd, 1986.
176p.
ISBN 0887963676 Pbk £39.95

Compensation and government torts / by Carol Harlow. – London : Sweet & Maxwell, 1982.
xvii,173p; 19cm.
Bibliography: p163-167. - Includes index.
ISBN 0421292504 Hbk £12.50
ISBN 0421292601 Pbk

Compensation and support for illness and injury / Donald Harris ... et al. – Oxford : Clarendon, 1984.
xix,412p; 22cm. – (Oxford socio-legal studies).
Includes bibliographies and index.
ISBN 0198275080 Hbk £20.00
ISBN 0198275137 Pbk £9.50

Compensation for criminal damage to property / by D.S. Greer and V.A. Mitchell. – Belfast : SLS Legal Publications (N.I.), 1982.
xxxviii,345p.
Includes index.

Compensation for criminal injuries / V A Mitchell. – Sweet & Maxwell, 1988.
ISBN 0421385804 Pbk

Compensation for dismissal. – Croydon : Tolley, 1987.
ISBN 0854592733 Pbk £13.95

Compensation for Industrial Disablement. – London : Butterworths, 1987.
ISBN 0862052149 Hbk £26.50

Compensation for industrial injury : a guide to the revised scheme of benefits for work accidents and diseases / by Richard Lewis. – Abingdon : Professional Books, 1987.
359p; 25cm.
ISBN 0862052149

Compensation for non-pecuniary loss / Law Reform Commission of British Columbia. – Vancouver : The Commission, 1983.
iii,53p. – (Working paper).
Includes bibliographical references.

Compensation for Non-Pecuniary Loss. – Victoria : Government of British Columbia, 1984.
Hbk £6.26

Compensation for pollution damage. – Paris : Organisation for Economic Co-operation and Development, 1981.
208 p.; 24 cm.
'Document'–Cover. Includes bibliographical references.
ISBN 9264122141 Pbk

Compensation for security interests in expropriated land / Institute of Law Research and Reform. – Edmonton : The Institute, 1984.
iii,30p. – (Report).

Compensation for security interests in expropriated land : memorandum for discussion. – Institute of Law Research and Reform. – Edmonton, Alta. : The Institute, 1982.
48p.

Compensation for victims of motor vehicle accidents / Law Reform Commission of Tasmania. – Hobart : Acting Government Printer, 1987.
76p. – (Report).

Compensation for wrongful imprisonment : a report / by JUSTICE : Chairman of Committee : Charles Wegg-Prosser. – London : JUSTICE, 1982.
35p; 22cm.
ISBN 0907247024

Competence of the European Parliament for Environmental Policy. – Berlin : Erich Schmidt.
101p. – (BZU Ser.: Vol. A63).
ISBN 3503015698 Pbk £22.50

Competency of Interdict in the Enforcement of Planning Control. – Glasgow : Planning Exchange, 1983.
41p. – (Scottish Planning Law and Practice Ser.).
Hbk £8.00

Competing Constitutional Visions : the Meech Lake Accord / Carol J. Rogerson. – Agincourt : Carswell, 1988.
338p.
Hbk £50.50

Competing equalities : law and the backward classes in India / Marc Galanter. – Berkeley : University of California Press, 1984.
xxii,625p; 24cm.
Bibliography: p575-611. - Includes index.
ISBN 0520042891 Pbk £38.25

Competing Rights to Mingled Property : in Clayton's Case. – Victoria : Government of British Columbia, 1983.
Hbk £8.75

Competing rights to mingled property tracing and the rule in Clayton's case / Law Reform Commission of British Columbia. – Vancouver : Law Reform Commission of British Columbia, 1982.
iv,122p. – (Working paper).
Includes bibliographical references and index.

Competition Act. – Vancouver : Continuing Legal Education Society of British Columbia, 1986.
461p.
ISBN 0865042802 Hbk £85.00

Competition among international airlines / by Richard Pryke. – Aldershot : Gower for the Trade Policy Research Centre, 1987.
100p; 22cm.
Includes bibliography.
ISBN 0566053330 Pbk £9.00

Competition and solvency : a framework for financial regulation / Economic Council of Canada. – Ottawa : Minister of Supply and Services, 1986.
x,46p.
ISBN 0660121921

Competition Law. – London : Allen & Unwin, 1985.
ISBN 0043430023 Hbk £18.00
ISBN 0043430031 Pbk £7.95

Competition law / Richard Whish. – London : Butterworths, 1985.
350p; 22cm.
Includes index.
ISBN 0406012784 Hbk £33.00
ISBN 0406012792 Pbk £21.95

Competition law : antitrust policy in the U.K. and the EEC / by Robert Merkin and Karen Williams. – London : Sweet & Maxwell, 1984.
xliii,492p; 22cm.
Bibliography: p485-486. - Includes index.
ISBN 0421307307 Hbk £30.00
ISBN 0421307404 Pbk £22.50

Competition law amendments : a schematic presentation of Bill C-91 and the present act. – Ottawa : Consumer and Corporate Affairs Canada, 1986.
98, 99 p.; 28 cm.
English and French. Title on added t.p.: Reforme de la legislation sur la concurrence. Includes complete text of the Competition Tribunal Act and the Competition Act, including the provisions of the current act that are replaced or changed by Bill C-91.
ISBN 0662542282 Pbk

Competition Law Handbook. – London : Butterworths, 1987.
ISBN 040610400X Pbk £25.00

Competition Law in the E.E.C. and in the E.C.S.C. – Luxembourg : Office for Official Publications of the European Communities, 1986.
220p.
ISBN 9282558320 Pbk

Competition Law in Western Europe and the USA. – Dordrecht : Kluwer, 1984.
Hbk Gld895.00
Supplement 59. – 1985.
Pbk Gld241.50
Supplement 60. – 1985.
192p.
Pbk Gld173.00
Supplement 61. – 1985.
192p.
Pbk Gld174.00
Supplement 62. – 1985.
144p.
Pbk Gld127.95

Competition law of Britain and the Common Market / by Valentine Korah. – 3rd ed. – The Hague : Martinus Nijhoff, 1982.
xxvii,352p.
Bibliography: p321-326. Includes index.
ISBN 9024726158 Hbk £140.00

Competition law of the EEC / Ivo van Bael, Jean-Francois Bellis. – Bicester : CCH Editions, 1987.
xii,690p; 23cm.
Analysis of EEC Competition Rules, with a critical commentary on the rules and practical guidance on their application. Covers basic provisions, including Articles 85 and 86, distribution, industrial and commercial property rights, co-operation agreements, mergers and acquisitions, trade associations and trade fairs, price fixing, market-sharing, boycotts and crisis cartels.
ISBN 0863250610 Pbk £30.00

Competition Law of the UK and the Republic of Ireland / Allan. – Matthew Bender, 1988.
ISBN 0000999068 Hbk £59.00

Competition policy and joint ventures / Organisation for Economic Co-operation and Development. – Paris : Organisation for Economic Co-operation and Development, 1986.
111p.
ISBN 9264128980

Competition policy in Britain : the silent revolution / D.P. O'Brien. – Durham : Department of Economics, University of Durham, 1981.
20 leaves. – (Working paper).
Includes bibliographical references.

Competitive Tendering For Engineering Contracts. – Spon (E & FN), 1983.
ISBN 0419116303 Hbk £19.95

Competitive Tendering for Engineering Contracts. – London : Sweet & Maxwell, 1983.
Hbk £18.95

Competitive Trading in New Zealand : the Commerce Act 1986 / Mark Jones. – Butterworths.
Format of annotated statute; each section of the Act is commented on, with commentary fully integrated with legislation. Appendices cover forms of application for authorisation of prices for controlled goods or services, for authorisation of a restrictive trade practice, form of notification for clearance or authorisation of a merger or takeover proposal, and the Commerce Act (Fees) Regulations 1986.
ISBN 0409787728 Pbk £71.50

Compilation of legal material dealing with transfer and development of technology / prepared by UNCTAD secretariat. – Geneva : UNCTAD, 1982.
245p. – (TD/B/C.6/81).

Complaints against the police : a sociological view / Ken Russell. – 3rd rev ed. – Glenfield, Leicester : Milltak, 1985.
iv,132p.
Bibliography: p.125-130. - Includes index.
ISBN 0950490660

Compleate Copyholder : Wherein is Contained a Learned Discourse of the Antiquity and Nature of Manors and Copy-Holds, with the Forme of Keeping a Copy-Hold Court and Court Baron. – Repr. of 1673 ed. – Abingdon : Professional Books.
399p.
Hbk £225.00

Complete Digest of Supreme Court Cases 1950 to Date, 16 Vols. – Lucknow : Eastern Book Company.
Hbk £85.00 ea.

Complete Guide for Justices of the Peace : Containing the Common and Statute Laws and Most Authentic Precedents Which Concern the Same. – Repr. of 1687 ed. – Abingdon : Professional Books.
Hbk £110.00

Complete Guide to Police Writing. – Agincourt : Carswell, 1984.
190p.
This work for law enforcement students offers an examination of the areas of written communication that are most problematic to police officers. On-the-job police writing and academic essay writing are discussed in the work.
Pbk £11.00

Complete Guide to Selling Your Home. – Merehurst.
ISBN 01556231237 Hbk £14.95

Complete reference guide to United Nations sales publications 1946-1978. – 2. – Berlin : de Gruyter, 1982.
Contents: 1. The catalogue / compiled and edited by Mary Eva Birchfield - 2. Indexes : sales number index, title index / compiled by Mary Eva Birchfield; KWIC index / compiled by Jacqueline Coolman.
ISBN 3110087197

Complete Set of Labour Laws. – 12th ed. – Karachi : Bureau of Labour Publications, 1986.
407p.
Pbk £30.00

Complete Supreme Court Criminal Digest 1950 to Date, 6 Vols. in 7. – Lucknow : Eastern Book Company, 1983.
Hbk £90.00 ea.

Complete Wiehahn report / with notes by N.E. Wiehahn. – Johannesburg : Lex Patria, 1982.
xxxvii,761p.
Contents: Report of the Commission of Inquiry into Labour Legislation, parts 1-6 and the White Paper on each part.
ISBN 0628021690

Completing the internal market : white paper from the Commission to the European Council. – Commission of the European Communities. – Luxembourg : Office for Official Publications of the European Communities, 1985.
55,35p. – (Document).
ISBN 9282554368

Comprehensive Aspects of Taxation. – London : Cassell, 1988.
ISBN 0304314250 Pbk £17.95

Compulsory acquisition of land in Australia / editor, Graham L. Fricke. – 2nd ed. – Sydney : Law Book Co., 1982.
xxxix,393p.
Previous ed.: 1975. Includes bibliographical references and index.
ISBN 0455204667

Compulsory Acquisition of Land in India, 2 Vols. – Allahabad : Universal Book Agency, 1984.
Hbk £350.00

Compulsory Acquisition of Land in New Zealand. – Butterworths, 1982.
An analysis of the Public Works Act 1981 concerning the taking of land for public purposes and the compensation provided for the acquisition. Includes citation of related cases.
ISBN 0409601225 Hbk £58.30

Compulsory arbitration in New Zealand : the first forty years / James Holt. – Auckland : Auckland University Press, 1986.
247p.
Bibliography: p236-242.
ISBN 1869400062

Compulsory Purchase and Compensation. – 2nd ed. – London : Estates Gazette, 1985.
ISBN 0728200899 Pbk £14.00

Compulsory winding up procedure. – 2nd ed. – London : Longman Professional, 1987.
ISBN 0851211798 Pbk £3.95

Compulsory winding-up procedure. – 2nd. – London : Longman Professional (UK), 1987.
Revised following the Insolvency Act 1986. Step by step guide through the process of compulsory winding-up for a limited liability company from the role of the liquidation committee to the proofs of debt and dividend. Appendix contains procedural forms.
ISBN 0851211798 Pbk £14.50

Computer Appreciation. – 3rd ed. – London : Butterworths, 1981.
ISBN 0408004924 Pbk £7.95

Computer Auditing. – London : Butterworths, 1984.
ISBN 0406252629 Pbk

Computer Board for Universities and Research Councils
Report of a working party on computer facilities for teaching in universities. – Computer Board for Universities and Research Councils. – London : The Board, 1983.
25,3,11p.
Includes bibliography.

Computer Contracts. – Dordrecht : Kluwer, 1984.
ISBN 9065441980 Pbk £125.00

Computer Contracts. – Matthew Bender, 1987.
ISBN 0000999060 Hbk £150.00

Computer contracts / Graham Stedman. – 3rd ed. – London : Longman, 1987.
x,434p; 24cm. – (Longman commercial series).
Previous ed.: 1984. Includes index.
ISBN 085121259X £40.00

Computer contracts : an international guide to agreements and software protection / Hilary E. Pearson. – London : Financial Training, 1984.
ISBN 0906322480

Computer Contracts : Principles and Practice 1987 / A. Sharpe. – London : Law Book Co.
ISBN 0455207364 Hbk £38.00

Computer contracts : the deeper issues : conference organised by the Society for Computers and Law on Monday 19th November 1984 at the Royal Garden Hotel, London, W.8 / speakers Martin Edwards ... et al. : conference organising committee Colin Ellis (Chairman) ... et al. – Didcot : Society for Computers and Law, 1984.
ii,72p.
ISBN 0906122163

Computer contracts handbook : precedents of contracts for the sale, purchase, support, distribution and licence of computers and computer software / by M.-T. Michele Rennie : consultant editor, Elizabeth Jarvie. – London : Sweet & Maxwell, 1985.
xi,136p; 30cm.
Includes precedents for software licence, software and support agreements, software distributions agreements, escrow agreements, sales agreements, and distribution agreement. Where appropriate, includes two agreements for each subject, one drafted when acting for the supplier, and one when acting for the purchaser.
ISBN 0421332301 Pbk £17.50

Computer crime / Scottish Law Commission. – Edinburgh : The Commission, 1986.
146p. – (Consultative memorandum).
Includes bibliographical references.

Computer fraud survey. – Audit Commission for Local Authorities in England and Wales. – London : H.M.S.O., 1985.
55p.
ISBN 0117012815 Pbk £3.30

Computer generated output as admissible evidence in civil and criminal cases : a report / by the Professional Advisory Committee of the British Computer Society : edited by T.R.H. Sizer and A. Kelman. – London : Heyden on behalf of the British Computer Society, 1982.
x,41p.
ISBN 0855017414

Computer in court : a guide to computer evidence for lawyers and computing professionals / Alistair Kelman, Richard Sizer. – Aldershot : Gower, 1982.
viii,104p; 22cm.
Bibliography: p99. - Includes index.
ISBN 0566034190

Computer insecurity / Adrian R.D. Norman. – London : Chapman and Hall, 1983.
xiv,351p; 24cm.
Bibliography: p337-342. - Includes index.
ISBN 0412223104

Computer Law. – Matthew Bender, 1977.
ISBN 0000999086 Hbk £112.00

Computer law / Colin Tapper. – 3rd ed. – London : Longman, 1983.
xxvii,242p. – (Business data processing).
Includes index. Bibliography: p231-234.
ISBN 0582497175

Computer law & practice : the journal of computer and communications law. – London : F. Cass, 1984-.

Computer law and security report. – Portsmouth : Solent Legal Exchange, 1985.

Computer law in Australia. – London : Legal Books, 1986.
ISBN 0949553271 Pbk £12.00

Computer law in Australia : a collection of essays / edited by W. John Taggart. – Sydney : Legal Books Pty., 1987.
xii,75p.
Bibliography: pp.61-64. - Includes index.
ISBN 0949553271

Computer misuse / the Law Commission. – London : HMSO, 1988.
viii,130p. – (Working paper).
Law Commission Working Paper, examines activities which might constitute computer misuse. Concludes present criminal law is sufficient to deal with computer misuse excepting unauthorised access which might require the creation of a new computer crime.
ISBN 0117301922

Computer Related Crime. – London : HMSO, 1986.
72p.
ISBN 9264128522 Pbk £4.00

Computer software : legal protection in the United Kingdom / by Henry Carr. – Oxford : ESC Publishing Ltd., 1987.
xxii, 228p.
ISBN 0906214327

Computer technology and the law in Canada / J. Frazer Mann. – Toronto : Carswell, 1987.
xxviii,455p.
ISBN 0459398504

Computer-Aided Management. – Cambridge : Woodhead-Faulkner, 1986.
ISBN 085941308X Hbk £19.95

Computer-Assisted Legal Research : a Guide for Canadian Law Students. – Ottawa : Canadian Law Information Council, 1984.
103p.
ISBN 0920358551 Pbk £15.00

Computerisation of county court procedures in debt cases : the claims registry / Lord Chancellor's Department. – London : The Department, 1987.
27 leaves.
Includes bibliographical references.

Computerized literature searching research stratagies and databases / Charles L. Gilreath. – Epping : Bowker, 1984.
xiv,177p; 24cm. – (Westview special studies in information science and management).
Includes index.
ISBN 0865315264

Computer-related crime : analysis of legal policy. – Paris : OECD, 1986.
71p.
' ... prepared for the Committee for Information, Computer and Communications Policy ...'. - p.3.

Computers and Legal Assistants. – Vancouver : Continuing Legal Education Society of British Columbia, 1988.
83p.
ISBN 0865049955 Hbk £65.00

Computers and Penal Legislation. – Oslo : Norwegian University Press, 1983.
166p.
ISBN 8200065707 Hbk £84.00

Computers and the Law. – Melbourne : Oxford University Press, 1986.
204p.
Considers many areas, including the liability arising from computer error, computer crime, computers and intellectual property, and difficulties in marketing, acquiring and applying computers.
ISBN 0195546571 Hbk £25.00

Computers and the Law / Salmon. – Oxford : Blackwell Scientific, 1987.
ISBN 0632018496 Hbk

Computers and the Law in South Africa. – Durban : Professional Publisher, 1983.
ISBN 0409049344 Pbk

Computers for lawyers. – London : Longman Professional, 1985.
ISBN 0851210406 Pbk £10.50

Computers in correctional administration and links with criminal justice : proceedings of the fourth Colloquy on the Use of Computers in the Administration of Justice, Stockholm, 3-5 September 1984 : reports presented at the colloquy. – Strasbourg : Council of Europe, 1985.
261p.
At head of cover title: Legal Affairs.
ISBN 9287103917

Comrie, R. G. →South African mercantile and company law.

Comyn, James
Irish at law : a selection of famous and unusual cases / James Comyn. – London : Sphere, 1983.
ix,261p; 18cm.
Originally published: London : Secker & Warburg, 1981.
ISBN 0722125615 Pbk £1.95
—Lost causes. – Secker & Warburg, 1982.
ISBN 0436105810 Hbk £8.50

Concept and present status of the international protection of human rights : forty years after the universal declaration. – Dordrecht : Nijhoff (Martinus), 1989.
624. – (International Studies in Human Rights 13).
In commemoration of the fortieth anniversary of the Universal Declaration of Human Rights. Explores how the United Nations has been able to establish and operate instruments and procedures of protection, to place a shield around groups in jeopardy. Deals with the concept of protection in existing law and practice, and practice notes from the author's files are appended to the chapters.
ISBN 9024737591 Hbk Gld295.00

Concept of international law / by Ingrid Detter De Lupis. – Stockholm : Norstedts Forlag, 1987.
145p.
Bibliography: p137-145.
ISBN 911867562X

Concept of international organization / edited by Georges Abi-Saab. – Paris : UNESCO, 1981.
245 p.; 25 cm.
Includes bibliographical references.
ISBN 923101742X

Concept Of Law. – Oxford : Oxford University Press, 1961.
ISBN 0198760728 Pbk £6.95

Concept of Socialist law. – Oxford : Clarendon Press.
21.5.
Intends to remedy the contempt for law prominent in Socialist writings. Argues that legal institutions would be necessary to adjudicate fairly conflict between private and public interest. Covers the rule of law, natural and legal rights, obligations, and the sources of law.
ISBN 0198252463 Hbk £25.00

Concepts and Problems in Mercantile Law. – New Delhi : Allied Publishers, 1984.
viii, 372p.
Hbk £30.00

Concepts for Financial Statements. – 2nd ed. – North Ryde : Law Book Co, 1984.
viii, 70p.
ISBN 0455202125 Pbk £8.50

Concepts of Justice and Equality in the Indian Tradition. – Allahabad : Orient Law House, 1985.
28p.
ISBN 0861316029 Hbk £15.00

Conceptual and policy basis of directors' fiduciary duties under English company law / by David Sugarman. – 2 v. – London : Middlesex Polytechnic Faculty of Business Studies and Management, 1982.
– (Working paper).
Includes bibliographies. Parts 1 and 2.
ISBN 0904804135 pt. 2

Conceptual thinking about the individual in international law / Rosalyn Higgins. – S.l. : s.n., 1981.
19p; 25cm.
Photocopy from: British Journal of International Studies 4 (1978).

Concerning crime / by John Croft. – London : H.M.S.O., 1982.
iv,16p; 25cm. – (A Home Office Research and Planning Unit report).
ISBN 011340770X Pbk £2.45

Conciliation and Arbitration Act 1904 : including Regulations and Sections 45D and 45E of the Trade Practice Act. – 9th ed. – North Ryde : C.C.H. Australia, 1984.
400p.
ISBN 0869038206 Hbk £24.00

Conciliation and Divorce. – Chichester : Barry Rose, 1981.
248p.
ISBN 0859923061 Hbk £3.85

Conciliation by ACAS in complaints by individuals to Industrial Tribunals / Advisory, Conciliation and Arbitration Service. – London : ACAS, 1982.

Conciliation in separation and divorce : finding common ground / Lisa Parkinson. – London : Croom-Helm, 1986.
192p; 23cm.
Includes bibliography and index.
ISBN 0709940475 Hbk £17.95
ISBN 070994053X Pbk £8.95

Conciliation under the Racial Discrimination Act 1975 : a study in theory and practice / by Patrick Pentony. – Canberra : Australian Government Publishing Service, 1986.
xi,206p. – (Occasional paper).
Bibliography: p203-205.
ISBN 064405672X

Concise Criminal Law / D. Pickover. – London : Police Review Publishing, 1984.
ISBN 0851640095 Pbk

Concise Dictionary of Accounting and Finance. – Pitman, 1986.
ISBN 0712106847 Pbk £4.95

Concise dictionary of law / editor Elizabeth A. Martin. – Oxford : Oxford University Press, 1983.
394p; 21cm.
ISBN 0198253990 Hbk £13.95
ISBN 0198251357 Pbk £4.95

Concise Guide to Accountancy. – London : VanNostrand Reinhold.
ISBN 0278000738 Pbk £5.95

Concise land registration practice / Christopher West. – 3rd ed. – London : Sweet & Maxwell, 1982.
xvii,313p; 23cm.
Previous ed.: / by Theodore B.F. Ruoff. 1967. Includes index.
ISBN 0421287705 £19.50

Concise Precedents in Modern Conveyancing, 2 Vols. – Repr. of 1853 ed. – Abingdon : Professional Books.
175p.
Hbk £45.00

Concise trade mark law and practice / Peter Meinhardt and Keith R. Havelock. – Aldershot : Gower, 1983.
xv,206p; 24cm.
Bibliography: p187-189. - Includes index.
ISBN 0566023695

Conditions of contract for minor works. – Institute of Civil Engineers. – Telford (Thomas), 1988.
ISBN 0727713299 Pbk £5.00

Conditions of detention and the European Convention on Human Rights and Fundamental Freedoms. – Strasbourg : Council of Europe, 1981.
37,ip.

Conditions of validity and cognition in modern legal thought / edited by Neil MacCormick, Stavros Panou, Luigi Lombardi Vallauri : preface by Ralf Dreier Geltungs- und Erkenntnisbedingungen im modernen Rechtsdenken / herausgegeben von Neil MacCormick, Stavros Panou, Luigi Lombardi Vallauri ; vorwort von Ralf Dreier. – Stuttgart : F. Steiner Verlag Wiesbaden, 1985.
214 p.; 24 cm. – (Archives for philosophy of law and social philosophy).
Papers presented at the IVR 11th World Congress, Helsinki, 1983. English, French, and German. Includes bibliographical references and index.
ISBN 3515044604 Pbk DM35.00

Condominium : The Law and Administration in Ontario / Bradley N. McLellan. – Agincourt : Carswell, 1981.
606p.
This book gives a complete description of the law and administration of condominiums in Ontario, Canada. Registration of a condominium, declaration and description, the agreement of purchase and sale, HUDAC, meetings and records for the condominium, and other issues are discussed.
Hbk £71.50

Condominium Law in Alberta. – Toronto : Butterworths, 1986.
ISBN 0409980293 Hbk

Condominium Law in British Columbia. – Butterworths, 1983.
434p.
Discusses the major participants in a condominium scheme, including the owner, the owner-developer, the lawyer, the Strata counsel, and the Strata corporation.
ISBN 0409988383 Hbk £75.00

Condominiums. – Vancouver : Continuing Legal Education Society of British Columbia, 1984.
403p.
ISBN 0865041539 Hbk £70.00

Condon, John →Capital acquisitions tax.

Conduct of an Action / R.J. Rolls. – Butterworths, 1982.
216p.
Examination of the legal and practical aspects of non-jury trials. Covers preparation, the brief, the course of the trial, nonsuit, examination in chief, cross-examination, re-examination, argument, and the rights and duties of judge and counsel at trial.
ISBN 0409877107 Hbk £50.00

Conduct of business rules : a new approach / Securities and Investments Board. – 1. – London : The Board, 1988.
various pagings.

Conduct of Canadian Meetings : Company Law and Common Law. – Toronto : Butterworths, 1983.
256p.
Explains the nature and purpose of meetings, the role of the players, and the proper procedures for the most successful progress of a meeting. Covers the chairman and secretary, notice, agenda, quorum, voting adjournment, motions and resolutions, minutes, the annual meeting, special share-holders meetings, directors and committee meetings.
ISBN 0409840653 Hbk £50.00

Conduct of Civil Litigation in British Columbia / John Horn. – London : Butterworths.
ISBN 0409993581 Hbk £292.00

Conduct of Meetings. – 22nd ed. – Bristol : Jordan & Sons Ltd, 1982.
ISBN 0907313019 Pbk £6.00

Conduct Unbecoming : The Social Construction of Police Deviance and Control. – London : Tavistock Publications, 1985.
300p.
ISBN 0422792101 Pbk £7.95

Conducting a Criminal Case. – Vancouver : British Columbia Continuing Legal Education Society, 1983.
331p.
ISBN 0865041369 Hbk £60.00

Conference of Local and Regional Authorities of Europe
Texts adopted / Conference of Local and Regional Authorities of Europe : Conference Permanente des Pouvoirs Locaux et Regionaux de l'Europe. – Strasbourg : Council of Europe, 1976-.
Continues: Texts adopted / European Conference of Local Authorities. - Continued by : Texts adopted / Standing Conference of Local and Regional Authorities of Europe. Parallel English and French texts.

Conference on prospects for the establishment of an inter-governmental human rights commission in the South Pacific / convened by the LAWASIA Human Rights Standing Committee in Fiji 12-14 April, 1985. – Sydney : Law Association for Asia and the Pacific, 1985.
iv,528p.

Conference on Security and Cooperation in Europe →Bulletin : a report on developments ... relative to Third Basket issues of the Final Act of the Conference on Security and Cooperation in Europe.

Conference on the application of international humanitarian law : March 12th, 1986, London SW1 / report on the proceedings by Michael A. Meyer. – s.l. : s.n., 1986.
23,vp.
'Organised by the British Red Cross Society'. - Front cover.

Conference on the Defence of Democracy against Terrorism in Europe - Tasks and Problems, Strasbourg, 12-14 November 1980 : compendium of documents. – 1. – Strasbourg : Council of Europe, 1981.
various pagings.
Includes bibliographies. Conferences organised by the Political Affairs Committee of the Parliamentary Assembly of the Council of Europe. Some documents in English and French.

Conference Reports. – Toronto : Canadian Tax Foundation, 1984.
Hbk £50.00

Confessions / Evidence Law Refrom Committee. – s.l. : Evidence Law Reform Committee, 1985.
18, 2 leaves. – (Working paper).
Includes bibliographical references.

Confessions / by Peter Mirfield. – London : Sweet & Maxwell, 1985.
165p; 22cm.
Includes index.
ISBN 0421303905 Hbk £12.25
ISBN 0421304006 Pbk £8.25

Confidentiality and the law / Brian C. Reid. – London : Waterlow, 1986.
xvi,208p; 24cm.
Includes index.
ISBN 0080392369 £20.00

Confidentiality of Data and Chemicals Control. – Paris : OECD, Organisation for Economic Co-operation and Development, 1982.
94p.
Hbk £13.00

Confiscation and Restoration : The Archbishopric Estates and the Civil War / W. J. Sheils. – York : St. Anthony's Press, 1981.
– (Borthwick Papers Ser.).
Pbk £3.00

Conflict and compromise : international law and world order in a revolutionary age / Edward McWhinney. – Alphen aan den Rijn : Sijthoff and Noordhoff, 1981.
160p.
Bibliography: p156-158.
ISBN 0887940900

Conflict and order : the police and labour disputes in England and Wales, 1900-1939 / Jane Morgan. – Oxford : Clarendon, 1987.
325p,4p of plates; 22cm.
Includes bibliography and index.
ISBN 0198201281 £30.00

Conflict of Law in the European Community / Stone. – London : Butterworths.
ISBN 0862050715 Hbk £25.95

Conflict of Laws, 2 Vols.
1984 supplement only. – London : Stevens & Sons.
ISBN 0420470204 Pbk

Conflict of laws / J.G. Collier. – Cambridge : Cambridge University Press, 1987.
xlvi,377p; 23cm. – (Cambridge studies in international and comparative law).
Includes index.
ISBN 0521323959 Hbk £40.00
ISBN 052131187X Pbk £12.50

Conflict of Laws. – Durban : Professional Publishers, 1984.
ISBN 0409026743 Pbk

Conflict of Laws. – Aurora : Canada Law Book, 1954.
Hbk £15.00

Conflict of Laws. – Agincourt : Carswell, 1983.
967p.
This textbook for Canadian law students tracts the historical development of the principles of conflict of laws and critically analyzes the policies underlying the rules. The book explores relevant English, American, and Commonwealth laws, in addition to Canadian law.
ISBN 045936860X Hbk £82.50

Conflict of Laws. – 3rd ed. – London : Sweet & Maxwell, 1984.
ISBN 0420468900 Hbk £30.00
ISBN 0420469001 Pbk £25.00

Conflict of Laws : Cases, Notes and Materials. – 6th ed. – Butterworths, 1988.
904p.
ISBN 0409805955 Pbk £75.00

Conflict of laws and contract / by P.R.H. Webb. – Auckland : Legal Research Foundation, 1985.
63p.
Includes bibliographical references.
ISBN 090858136X

Conflict of laws and European Community law : with special reference to the Community Conventions on private international law / Ian F. Fletcher. – Amsterdam : North-Holland, 1982.
xxix,395p.
Bibliography: p.xxvii-xxix. - Includes index.
ISBN 0444863761

Conflict of Laws in Australia. – 4th ed. – Butterworths, 1984.
608p.
ISBN 0409491926 Hbk £79.00
ISBN 0409492027 Pbk £59.00

Conflict of laws in the European Community / D. Lasok and P. A. Stone. – Abingdon : Professional Books, 1987.
xx,460p.
Bibliography: p xviii-xx.
ISBN 0862050715

Conflict or cooperation? : the growth of industrial democracy. – 2nd ed. – London : Kogan Page, 1983.
350p.
Previous ed.: 1978.
ISBN 0850387477 Hbk £12.00
ISBN 0850387582 Pbk £6.95

Conflicts and compromise : International law and world order in a revolutionary age. – Dordrecht : Kluwer, 1981.
160p.
ISBN 9028626719 Hbk Gld40 /$17.50

Conflicts and Tensions In Islamic Jurisprudence. – University of Chicago Press, 1969.
ISBN 0226116107 Hbk £10.25

Conflicts of interest in the changing financial world / edited by R.M. Goode. – 1. – London : Institute of Bankers, 1986.
22cm.
Conference proceedings. Includes index.
ISBN 0852971672 £22.75

Conflicts of national laws with international business activity : issues of extraterritoriality / by A.H. Hermann. – London : British North American Research Organisation, 1982.
xii,96p.
ISBN 0902594419

Confronting crime / edited by Roger Matthews and Jock Young. – London : Sage, 1986.
264p; 22cm.
Includes bibliography and index.
ISBN 0803997310 Hbk £27.50
ISBN 0803997329 Pbk £10.50

Coninx, R.
Foreign Exchange Dealer's Handbook. – 2nd ed. – Cambridge : Woodhead-Faulkner, 1986.
ISBN 0859413438 Hbk £35.00

Conklin, David W. → Canadian financial institutions : changing the regulatory environment.

Conklin, W.E. → Essays on Third World Perspectives in Jurisprudence.

Conn, R.
Current Practice Directions : Family and Probate. – London : Family Law, 1988.
ISBN 0853081085 Llf £35.00

Connecting law and society : an introduction to research and theory / Robert L. Kidder. – Englewood Cliffs, N.J. : Prentice-Hall, 1983.
xv,286p; 24cm.
Includes bibliographies and index.
ISBN 0131678094

Conneely → Accounting For Treasury Products.

Connell-Thouez, Katherine
Contemporary Trends in Family Law : A National Perspective / Bartha Maria Knoppers. – Agincourt : Carswell, 1984.
334p.
This work is a collection of papers on Canadian family law presented at the Family Law Section of the Canadian Association of Law Teachers.
Hbk £46.25

Connelly, Graeme → Teaching human rights.

Connelly, Mark Q. → Corporations : Cases, Text and Materials.
→ Corporations : Principles and Policies.

Connidis, Ingrid Arnet → Canadian criminal justice system.

Connor, Xavier
Media Law : Journalism v. the Law. – Melbourne : Law Institute of Victoria, 1986.
Hbk £25.00

Connors, Jane → Islamic family law.
→ Women in sub-Saharan Africa.

Connors, John A. → Protecting intellectual property in Asia - Pacific : a specially commissioned report.

Conquest of Grenada : sovereignty in the periphery / M. Shahabuddeen. – Georgetown : University of Guyana, 1986.
xiv,266p.
Includes bibliographical references. Includes the text of the Treaty Establishing the Orgainisation of Eastern Caribbean States.

Conrick, Brian
Law of Negotiable Instruments in Australia. – 2nd ed. – Butterworths, 1989.
256p.
ISBN 0409495271 Hbk £59.00
ISBN 040949528X Pbk £39.00

Conroy, J.S.
Canadian Prison Law, 3 Vols. – Butterworths.
Llf £235.00

Conscientious objection to compulsory military service : recommendation no. R(87)8 adopted by the Committee of Ministers on 9 April 1987 and explanatory report. – Council of Europe. – Strasbourg : Council of Europe, 1987.
10p. – (H (87) 3).

Consent to treatment / Mental Health Act Commission. – London : The Commission, 1985.
43p.

Conservation of Foreign Exchange and Prevention of Smuggling Activities Act. – Allahabad : Law Book Company, 1987.
250p.
Hbk £85.00

Conservatism in Modern Chinese Family Law. – Leiden : E.J. Brill, 1956.
ISBN 9004032630 Hbk £28.00

Conservative Party → Our unions, our democracy : LRD's response to the Tory green paper.

Consolidated Accounts. – 4th ed. – Witney : A.T.C. Publications.
ISBN 0747790019 Pbk £7.95

Consolidated Regulations of Canada, 1978, 18 Vols.
Canada Gazette /. – Aurora : Canada Law Book Co.
Pbk £69.00
Regulations and Index. –
Hbk £520.00
ISBN Pbk £320.00
Canada Gazette. –
Hbk £87.00
ISBN Pbk £69.00

Consolidated supervision of institutions authorised under the Banking Act 1979. – Bank of England. – London : Bank of England, 1985.
14,10,9 leaves.
Includes texts of European Communities Consolidated Supervision Directive and the revised Basle Concordat.

Consolidation of the Constitution Acts of 1867 to 1982. – Agincourt : Carswell, 1983.
86p.
This work is published by the Department of Justice of Canada and is bilingual. It features the British North America Act 1867 with amendments made to it since its enactment and the Constitution Act 1982. The Constitution Act 1982 contains the Canadian Charter of Rights and Freedoms and the procedure for amending the Constitution of Canada.
ISBN 0660421016 Pbk £4.25

Conspiracy : law, class and society / Robert Spicer. – London : Lawrence and Wishart, 1981.
190p; 23cm.
Bibliography: p178-184. - Includes index.
ISBN 0853155488 £7.50

Constable's Pocket Guide to Powers of Arrest and Charges / Lewis Heavens. – 7th ed. – London : Butterworths, 1982.
This work for practitioner and police officer gives a ready reference to the law on arrest and the formulation of charges. The work includes all new laws and the amendments of the old ones relevant to powers of arrest and charges.
Police officers
ISBN 0406842043 Pbk

Constituent Power of the Indian Parliament. – Delhi : Anmol Publications, 1987.
Hbk £125.00

Constitution 1982. – Ottawa : Canadian Government Publishing Centre, 1983.
120p.
ISBN 0660522934 Pbk £19.95
ISBN 0660522942 Hbk £29.95

Constitution : As Altered to 31 October 1986. – Kingston : Australian Government Publishing Service, 1986.
88p.
Hbk £4.95

Constitution : Getting Our Act Together. – Montreal : McGill Campus Legal Aid Clinic, 1982.
232p.
Hbk £3.00

Constitution Act, 1982 / La loi constitutionelle de 1982. – Ottawa : Canadian Government Publishing Centre, 1982.
23i.e.27p.
Parallel English and French text.
ISBN 0660516020

Constitution and constitutionalism : a analysis of the basic principles of the federal constitution of Nigeria (1979) / by Moses E. Akpan. – Lagos : Paico, 1984.
xiii,133p.
Bibliography: p.128-129. - Includes index.

Constitution and proof of voluntary obligations and the authentication of writings / Scottish Law Commission. – Edinburgh : The Commission, 1985.
v,203p. – (Consultative memorandum).

Constitution and the People of Canada. – Ottawa : Canadian Government Publishing Centre, 1982.
87p.
Pbk £3.00

Constitution and you. – Ottawa : Government of Canada, 1982.
32,35p.
Added t.p. in French: Notes sur la constitution. Pages numbered in opposite directions. Text in English and French.
ISBN 0662517547

Constitution, fifty years on. – Round Hall, 1988.
16p.
ISBN 094768641X Pbk

Constitution in flux / Philip Norton. – Oxford : Martin Robertson, 1982.
vii,312p; 22cm.
Bibliography: p295-300. - Includes index.
ISBN 0855205210 Hbk £
ISBN 0855205229 Pbk £8.50

Constitution Making in New Island States. – Auckland : Legal Research Foundation, 1982.
Hbk £6.50

Constitution of Canada. – Toronto : IPI Publishing, 1984.
120p. – (Orig.).
Pbk

Constitution of Canada : a suggested amendment relating to provincial administrative tribunals : a discussion paper / Department of Justice. – Ottawa : The Department, 1983.
13,14p.
With French t.p.: La Constitution du Canada. English and French texts.

Constitution of Great Britain / Vidya Bhushan. – New Delhi : Sterling Publishers, 1984.
166p.
ISBN 8120703421 £75.00

Constitution of India. – 3rd ed. – Dordrecht : Law Book Co., 1989.
850p.
Hbk £240.00

Constitution of India. – 7th ed. – New Delhi : Macmillan India.
422p.
ISBN 0333900588 Pbk £25.00

Constitution of India. – 3rd ed. – Delhi : Metropolitan Book Co.
850p.
bd £80.00

Constitution of India. – Allahabad : Law Publishers, 1982.
Hbk £10.50

Constitution of India. – New Delhi : S. Chand and Company, 1984.
Hbk £20.00

Constitution of India / D.K. Singh. – 7th ed. – Lucknow : Eastern Book Company, 1982.
871p.
Hbk £90.00

Constitution of India : as Amended Up to the Constitution 52nd Amendment Act, 1986 with Text of Recent Amending Acts, Subject-Index and Extensive Notes on Recent Supreme Court Case-Law. – 7th ed. – Lucknow : Eastern Book Company, 1986.
Hbk £28.00

Constitution of Malaysia / Harry Groves. – 4th. – Singapore : Malayan Law Journal, 1987.
649.
Discusses citizenship, relations between the federation and the states, financial provisions, elections, the judiciary, public services, special and emergency powers, additional protection for Sabah and Sarawak, and temporary and transitional provisions.
ISBN 9971700557 Hbk

Constitution of Malaysia : further perspectives and developments : essays in honour of Tun Mohamed Suffian / edited by F.A. Trindade and H.P. Lee. – Singapore : Oxford University Press, 1986.
xix,275p.
Includes bibliographical references and index.
ISBN 0195826442 Hbk £60.00

Constitution of Northern Ireland : problems and prospects / edited by David Watt. – London : Heinemann, 1981.
227p; 23cm.
Includes index.
ISBN 0435838075 Hbk £15.00
ISBN 0435838083 Pbk £7.50

Constitution Of Papua New Guinea : A Study In Legal Nationalism 1978. – London : Law Book Co.
ISBN 0455198403 Pbk £12.00

Constitution of Switzerland, Canada, Japan and Australia / Vidya Bhushan. – New Delhi : Sterling Publishers, 1985.
136p.
ISBN 8120703448 Hbk £100.00

Constitution of the Commonwealth of Australia / K.W. Ryan. – 4th ed. – Butterworths, 1986.
441p.
ISBN 0409491284 Hbk £59.00
ISBN 0409491292 Pbk £48.00

Constitution of the Commonwealth of Australia : Abridged Edition. – Kingston : Australian Government Publishing Service, 1987.
Hbk £8.95

Constitution of the Commonwealth of Australia annotated / by R.D. Lumb and K.W. Ryan. – 3rd ed. – Sydney : Butterworths, 1981.
xxiv, 426 p.; 25 cm.
Includes index. Bibliography: p. 405-410.
ISBN 0409300225 Pbk £42.00

Constitution of the Federal Republic of Nigeria 1979 / with annotations by Jadesola O. Akande. – London : Sweet & Maxwell, 1982.
ca.300p.
Cover title: Introduction to the Nigerian constitution.
ISBN 0421289406

Constitution of the Five Nations : or the Iroquois Book of the Great Law. – 1916 repr. – Oshweken : Iroqrafts.
158p.
ISBN 0919645003 Hbk £6.95

Constitution of the Kandyan Kingdom. – Dehiwala : Tisara Prakashakayo.
264p.
Hbk £250.00

Constitution of the People's Republic of China. – Oxford : Pergamon, 1983.
100p.
Translated from the Chinese.
ISBN 008030818X Hbk £9.95
ISBN 0080308171 Pbk £4.95

Constitution of the People's Republic of China : adopted on December 4, 1982 by the fifth National People's Congress of the People's Republic of China at its fifth session. – Beijing : Foreign Languages Press, 1983.
93p.
ISBN 0835110818

Constitution of the Portuguese Republic. – 1st revision, 1982. – Paris : Association of Secretaries General of Parliaments, 1983.
166p.
Published under the auspices of the Inter-Parliamentary Union.

Constitution of the United States of America / Vidya Bhushan. – New Delhi : Sterling Publishers, 1984.
172p.
ISBN 812070343X Hbk £75.00

Constitution of U.S.S.R. and China / Vidya Bhushan. – New Delhi : Sterling Publishers, 1984.
228p.
ISBN 8120703413 Hbk £85.00

Constitutional and Administrative Law Supplement 1987. – Plymouth : Macdonald & Evans, 1982.
ISBN 0712103988 Pbk £6.50
ELBS edition 1984. –
ISBN 0421333405 Hbk £3.50

Constitutional and administrative law / Harry Street and Rodney Brazier; editors. – 5th ed. – Harmondsworth : Penguin, 1985.
748p.
ISBN 0140226109 Pbk £11.95

Constitutional and administrative law / E.C.S. Wade and A.W. Bradley. – 10th ed. – London : Longman, 1985.
xlv,758p; 24cm.
Previous ed.: 1977. Bibliography: p741-748. - Includes index.
ISBN 058249124X Hbk £17.00
ISBN 0582491258 Pbk £14.95

Constitutional and administrative law in a nutshell / Greer Hogan. – London : Sweet & Maxwell, 1987.
122p; 22cm.
Includes index.
ISBN 0421368101 Pbk £3.95

Constitutional and Administrative Law (SWOT). – London : Blackstone Press, 1985.
ISBN 0906322723 Pbk £7.95

Constitutional and legislative provisions concerning the organisation of regional government
Addendum no.1 : Constitution of the Free State of Bavaria. – Council of Europe. – Strasbourg : Council of Europe, 1981.
31p; 30cm.
Document no.4 : Regional institutions in Belgium / Council of Europe. – 1982.
i,47p; 30cm.
Document no. 6 : The new regional structures in France. – 1982.
i,37p.
Part 2 : Statutes of three self-governing communities (1). – 1983.
72p.

Constitutional and National Development in India : Montagu-Chelmsford Report. – Great Britain, India Office. – New Delhi : Ess Ess Publications, 1981.
xix, viii, 243p.
Hbk £110.00

Constitutional Aspects of Sikh Separatism. – New Delhi : Prentice-Hall, 1985.
24p.
ISBN 0876924151 Hbk £5.00

Constitutional Brinkmanship Amending the Constitution by National Convention. – Oxford : Oxford University Press.
ISBN 019505573X Hbk £18.50

Constitutional Case Studies of Pacific Island States / Peter Bayne. – Suva : University of the South Pacific, Institute of Pacific Studies.
Hbk £7.00

Constitutional Challenge : Essays on the Australian Constitution, Constitutionalism and Parliamentary Practice / G. S. Reid. – Turramura : Centre for Independent Studies, 1982.
viii, 166p. – (CIS Readings Ser.).
ISBN 0949769010 Hbk £7.95

Constitutional Change in Canada : Lessons and Analogies From Across the Pacific. – North Ryde : Association for Canadian Studies in Australia and New Zealand, 1984.
Hbk £3.00

Constitutional change in South Africa : the next five years / (edited by) W. H. B. Dean and Dirk Van Zyl Smit. – Cape Town : Juta, 1983.
8,125p.
ISBN 0702113719

Constitutional code
Vol.1 : edited by F. Rosen and J.H. Burns / Frederick Rosen, J. H. Burns. – Oxford : Clarendon Press, 1983.
xlv,612p,2folded leaves of plates; 24cm. – (The Collected works of Jeremy Bentham).
Includes index. Author: Jeremy Bentham.
ISBN 019822608X

Constitutional Commission : First Report, Volumes 1 and 2, 2 Vols. – Kingston : Australian Government Publishing Service.
824p.
Hbk £29.95

Constitutional construction / Chester James Antieau. – London : Oceana Publications, 1982.
xxiv, 255 p.; 25 cm.
Includes bibliographical references and index.
ISBN 037920682X

Constitutional Convention. – Reprint. – Oxford : Oxford University Press, 1986.
ISBN 019876202X Pbk £8.95

Constitutional conventions : the rules and forms of political accountability / Geoffrey Marshall. – Oxford : Clarendon, 1984.
xvi,247p; 23cm.
Bibliography: p233-239. - Includes index.
ISBN 019876183X £16.50

Constitutional development in the USSR : a guide to the soviet constitutions / Aryeh L. Unger. – London : Methuen, 1981.
viii,310p; 22cm.
Bibliography: p297-298. - Includes index. Includes English text of the RSFSR constitution of 1918, and the USSR constitutions of 1924, 1936 and 1977.
ISBN 0416716806 Pbk £13.50
ISBN 0416716903 £7.50

Constitutional Government of India. – New Delhi : S. Chand and Company.
Hbk £120.00

Constitutional History of England / Fisher. – Cambridge : Cambridge University Press, 1908.
ISBN 0521091373 Pbk £22.50

Constitutional History of England : 1485-1760. – 7th ed. Repr. of 1850 ed. – Abingdon : Professional Books.
Hbk £145.00

Constitutional history of Germany : in the nineteenth and twentieth centuries / H.W. Koch. – London : Longman, 1984.
xiv,400p; 22cm.
Includes index.
ISBN 0582491827 Pbk £7.95

Constitutional History of India 1765-1984. – New Delhi : S. Chand and Company.
Hbk £65.00

Constitutional History of India. – New Delhi : S. Chand and Company.
Hbk £20.00

Constitutional History of India. – Allahabad : Orient Law House.
ISBN 0861250419 Hbk £35.00
ISBN 0861257227 Pbk £25.00

Constitutional History of India, Vol. 1 : 1600-1858. – Calcutta : Mukherjee & Co, 1987.
586p.
Hbk £200.00

Constitutional history of Jersey / F. de L. Bois. – Rev. repr. 1981. – Jersey : States' Greffe, Jersey, 1981.
311p.
Revision of: 1972 ed.. Includes index.

Constitutional History of Nigeria. – London : Dent (J M) & Sons, 1982.
ISBN 0905838793 Hbk £15.00

Constitutional instruments. – Accra : Ghana Publishing Corporation, .
Issued with: Ghana gazette.

Constitutional law. – 2nd. – Edinburgh : Green (W.) & Son, 1968.
Deals with the relationships of the contral institutions of government, politics, ideas, and their relationships. Copious references to a wide range of legal and non-legal material related to constitutional law. Published under the auspices of the Scottish Universities Law Institute.
ISBN 041400504X Pbk

Constitutional Law and Constitutional Rights in Ireland / Brian Doolan. – 2nd ed. – Dublin : Gill and Macmillan, 1987.
ISBN 0717115550 Pbk £17.95

Constitutional law and military rule in Nigeria / Abiola Ojo. – Ibadan, Nigeria : Evans Brothers, 1987.
vii,316p.
ISBN 9781675691

Constitutional law and practice in the International Labour Organisation / by E. Osieke. – The Hague : M. Hijhoff, 1984.
xxi, 266p.
Bibliography: p.243-258.
ISBN 9024729858 Hbk £160.00

Constitutional law in Ireland / by James Casey. – London : Sweet & Maxwell, 1987.
250p; 22cm.
Includes index.
ISBN 042131270X Pbk £19.00

Constitutional Law of Canada, 2 Vols. – 3rd ed. – Agincourt : Carswell, 1987.
ISBN 045930961 Hbk £61.60
ISBN 045930951X Pbk £36.00

Constitutional law of Canada : Cases, notes and materials / by Joseph Eliot Magnet. – Toronto : Carswell, 1983.
xxii,1229p.
ISBN 0459356704

Constitutional Law of India
Vol. 1. – 3rd ed. – London : Sweet & Maxwell, 1983.
ISBN 0421316608 Hbk £54.00
Vol. 2. –
ISBN 0421339705 Hbk £70.00

Constitutional Law of India. – 6th ed. – Lucknow : Eastern Book Company, 1984.
600p.
Pbk £50.00

Constitutional law of India : a critical commentary
Vol.1 / by H.M. Seervai. – 3rd ed. – Bombay : Tripathi, 1983.
xlvii,1071,262p; 26cm.
Previous ed.: 1975. Includes index. Includes text of the Constitution of India.
ISBN 0421316608 £45.00
Vol.2 / by H.M. Seervai. – 1984.
various pagings; 25cm.
Previous ed.: in 3 1975-1979. Includes index.
ISBN 0421339705 £70.00

Constitutional Law of India, Fourth Edition. – 6th repr 1985. – New Delhi : Prentice-Hall.
528p.
ISBN 0876923988 Hbk £65.00

Constitutional Law of India. Vol 1. – London : Lucas Publications, 1986.
ISBN 1851800123 Hbk £50.00

Constitutional Law of Ireland. – Cork : Mercier Press, 1987.
801p.
ISBN 0853428174 Hbk £60.00

Constitutional Law of Ireland : the law of the executive, legislature, and judicature / David Gwynn Morgan. – Blackrock, County Dublin, Ireland : Round Hall Press in association with Irish Academic Press, 1985.
271 p.; 22 cm.
Includes index. Bibliography: p. 215-253.
ISBN 0950872598 Pbk

Constitutional Miscellany. – Lucknow : Eastern Book Company, 1986.
256p.
Hbk £80.00

Constitutional Options for Namibia : a Historical Perspective / C. Ushewkunze. – Lusaka : United Nations Institute for Namibia.
72p.
Hbk free

Constitutional practice / Rodney Brazier. – Oxford : Clarendon Press, 1988.
xix,285p.
Includes index.
ISBN 0198255969

Constitutional reform : the quarterly review. – London : Constitutional Reform Centre, 1986-.
Annual index with Winter issue.

Constitutional relevance of the provision for the seat of government / by Jadesola O. Akande. – Lagos : Nigerian Institute of Advanced Legal Studies, 1983.
15p.
Seminar paper presented at the Institute on Wednesday, March 23, 1983.

Constitutional review jurisdiction in Papua New Guinea / researched and written by Peter Bayne. – Waigani : Law Reform Commission of Papua New Guinea, 1981.
iii,64p. – (Occasional paper).

Constitutional Rights of Prisoners. – Delhi : Mittal Publications, 1986.
Hbk £95.00

Constitutional Theory. – Oxford : Oxford University Press, 1971.
ISBN 019876121X Pbk £8.50

Constitutionalism in America
Vol. 1 /. – London : Eurospan.
ISBN 0819167770 Pbk £14.75
Vol. 1. –
ISBN 0819167762 Hbk £25.95
Vol. 2. –
ISBN 0819167789 Hbk £25.95
Vol. 2. –
ISBN 0819167797 Pbk £14.75

Constitutionalism in Emergent States. – London : Dent (J M) & Sons, 1973.
ISBN 0905838017 Pbk £7.50

Constitution-making : principles, process, practice / Edward McWhinney. – Toronto : University of Toronto Press, 1981.
xiii,231p; 24cm.
Bibliography: p219-225. - Includes index.
ISBN 0802055532 £12.00

Constitutions and Charitable Status Guide and Models for Voluntary Organisations in Scotland. – Scottish Council for Voluntary Organisations.
ISBN 1870904028 Hbk £10.00

Constitutions of Nations, 4 Vols. – Dordrecht : Kluwer.
Hbk £275.00 ea.

Constitutions of nations
Vol. 2 : Asia, Australia and Oceania / by Amos J. Peaslee. – Rev. 4th ed. – Dordecht : M. Nijhoff, 1985.
1824p.
ISBN 902472905X Hbk £60.00

Constitutions of the Independent States of Melanesia and Micronesia. – Suva : University of the South Pacific, Institute of Pacific Studies, 1986.
432p.
Hbk £12.00

Constitutions of the United States : A Primer for the People. – University of Chicago Press.
ISBN 0226131068 Hbk £16.75
ISBN 0226131076 Pbk £5.50

Constitutions of Transkei, Bophuthatswana, Venda and Ciskei / editors M.P. Vorster, M. Wiechers, D.J. van Vuuren. – Durban : Butterworths, 1985.
269p.
Includes the texts of the constitutions.
ISBN 040901964X

Constraints on the Waging of War. – Dordrecht : Kluwer, 1987.
175p.
ISBN 0898389240 Pbk Gld85.00

Construction and Mechanics' Liens in Canada / David I. Bristow. – 5th ed. – Agincourt : Carswell, 1985.
1,015p.
This work examines the Ontario Construction Lien Act of 1983 in detail and discusses the changes this new act makes to the law under the former Mechanics' Lien Act. The statute and case law of all Canadian provinces is presented in the text.
Hbk £77.50

Construction Contract Dictionary. – Reading : College of Estate Management, 1981.
120p.
ISBN 0902132652 Hbk £12.30
ISBN 0902132636 Pbk £7.50

Construction contracts : principles and policies in tort and contract / by I.N. Duncan Wallace. – London : Sweet & Maxwell, 1986.
xliii,696p; 26cm.
Contains articles on contractors' claims and owners' damages, certificates and their effect, guarantees and bonds in construction contracts, nominated sub-contractors, choice of contracting agreement, comparative law, the UK JCT standard forms, and the SIA Contract 1980.
ISBN 042134900X Hbk £74

Construction Disputes. – Vancouver : Continuing Legal Education Society of British Columbia, 1988.
177p.
ISBN 0865043728 Hbk £70.00

Construction insurance / Nael G. Bunni. – London : Elsevier Applied Science, 1986.
xviii,336p; 25cm.
Includes index.
ISBN 0853344388 £50.00

Construction Insurance Claims and Management. – Spon (E & FN), 1987.
ISBN 0419138404 Hbk £22.50

Construction Joint Ventures in Singapore. – Butterworths, 1985.
332p.
Covers legal form and operational structure, the sponsor, selection of the joint venture partners, constituting the joint venture, the management board, implications arising from the construction contract, legal implications of a joint venture partnership, legal issues affecting the corporate joint venture, governing law, and minority protection.
ISBN 0409995029 Hbk £75.00

Construction law : law and practice relating to the construction industry / by John Uff. – 4th ed. – London : Sweet & Maxwell, 1985.
xvii,350p; 22cm.
Deals with the principles of building and civil engineering contracts as well as the standard forms of contract issued by the JCT and the ICE. Enlarged section on the law and practice of arbitration, including an introduction to the ICE Arbitration Procedure 1983. Also covers the Building Act 1984, and the new Building Regulations.
ISBN 0421343605 Hbk £18
ISBN 0421343702 Pbk £16

Construction Law Digest, 3 Vols. – London : Collins.
Pbk £185.00
Vol. 3. – 1985.
490p.
Pbk £95.00

Construction law digest. – . – s.l. : Construction Law Digest, 1982-.
Parts issued in number order 10 to 1. Part 1 is annual index.
ISBN 02639351 Hbk

Construction Law Digest. – Oxford : Blackwell Scientific.
ISBN 0002639351 Hbk £225.00

Construction Law in Australia. – North Ryde : Law Book Co, 1981.
xviii, 318p.
ISBN 0455202605 Pbk £31.00

Construction Law in Singapore and Malaysia / Anthony P. Lavers. – Butterworths, 1988.
Explains the main principles governing the law of construction and refers to and treats in detail the local forms of building contracts amd statutory provisions in Singapore and Malaysia. The digest section contains summaries and extracts of cases referred to in the text.
ISBN 0409995614 Hbk £90.00

Construction law journal. – Andover : Sweet & Maxwell, 1984.
Index in each vol..
ISBN 02672359

Construction Law Reports 10 vols
Vol. 1 / Vincent Powell-Smith. – London : Architectural Press, 1985.
160p.
ISBN 0851397808 Hbk £18.50
Vol. 2. – 1985.
ISBN 0851397816 Hbk £18.50
Vol. 3. – 1985.
ISBN 0851397824 Hbk £18.50

Construction Law Reports
Vols. 1-19. – Agincourt : Carswell, 1985.
Vol. 31, 1988. –
This work contains the key construction law decisions from all Canadian jurisdictions. Topics include building contracts, remedies for their breach, construction liens and bonding issues. Cases on court actions by and against architects, engineers, contractors and subcontractors are also included.
Hbk £80.00

Construction Law Reports / Vincent Powell-Smith. – Vol. 11. – London : Architectural Press, 1988.
ISBN 0851392024 Hbk £25.00

Construction lien remedies in Ontario / by Kevin Patrick McGuinness. – Toronto, Canada : Carswell Legal Publications, 1983.
xxxiii, 423 p.; 24 cm.
Includes index. Bibliography: p. 415-418.
ISBN 0459359606

Construction of statutes / Elmer A. Driedger. – 2nd ed. – Toronto : Butterworths, 1983.
xvi,385p. – (Canadian legal manual series).
Contains a new chapter on bilingual statutes, and expanded discussion of departure from the ordinary meaning for the professed reason of 'absurdity', and a refinement of the author's commentary on the presumption against retrospective operation.
ISBN 0409828033

Construction refurbishment and design. – London : Estates Gazette, 1986.
ISBN 0728200996 Pbk £15.95

Constructive trusts / by A.J. Oakley. – 2nd ed. – London : Sweet & Maxwell, 1987.
200p; 22cm.
Previous ed.: 1978. Includes index.
ISBN 0421347406 Hbk £11.00 :
ISBN 0421347503 Pbk £7.85

Consuetodo Vel Lex Mercat. – 3rd ed. – Abingdon : Professional Books, 1986 Reprint.
ISBN 0862053250 Hbk £48.50

Consuetudo Vel Lex Mercatoria, 2 Vols. – Abingdon : Professional Books.
– (Classical English Law Texts Ser.).
Hbk £72.00

Consul
Law of Citizenship and Passports : with All Allied Laws. – 5th ed. – Allahabad : Law Book Company, 1987.
400p.
Hbk £120.00

—The Law of Foreigners and Registration of Foreigners, 1987 : Containing Commentaries on Foreigners Act, Registration of Foreigners Act and Orders, Rules, Notifications and Allied Laws. – 5th ed. – Allahabad : Law Book Company, 1987.
466p.
Hbk £140.00

—Probation of Offenders Act and Rules : Central and States. – 6th ed. – Allahabad : Law Book Company, 1988.
Hbk £200.00

Consulatative papers related to the revision of the Children and Young Persons Act (Northern Ireland) 1968 / Department of Helath and Social Services. – Belfast : The Department, 1987.
17,11 leaves.
Contents: Consultative paper on regulation of child minding, group day care and care and maintenance of children - Consultative paper on employment of children.

Consultation and government : report of the inquiry into processes of consultation in Victoria with special reference to the case of tenancy law reform / with papers by Ronald F. Henderson ... et al. – Melbourne : Victorian Council of Social Service, 1981.
xii,273p.
Includes bibliographical notes.
ISBN 0949748072

Consultation clauses as means of providing for treaty obedience : a study in the law of treaties / by Judo Umarto Kusumowidagdo. – Stockholm : Almqvist & Wiksell, 1981.
321p; 25cm.
Bibliography: p.311-321.
ISBN 9122004629 Pbk
ISBN 9122004602

Consultation document / Road Traffic Law Review. – London : The Review, 1985.
96,15p.
Chairman: P.M. North.

Consultation on valuation and pricing proposals / Inland Revenue. – London : Inland Revenue Press Office, 1987.
3,8p. – (Press release).

Consultation paper : removal, impounding and wheelclamping of vehicles / Road Traffic Law Review. – London : Road Traffic Law Review, 1986.
12,12p.
Chairman: P.M. North.

Consultation paper : safeguards against monopolistic and anti-competitive behaviour / Civil Aviation Authority. – s.l. : s.n., 1987.
9p.

Consultation paper on the Distress for Rent Rules 1983 / Lord Chancellor's Department. – London : The Department, 1987.
13,12 leaves. – (HH/290).
Includes the text of draft revised Distress for Rent Rules 1987.

Consultative paper by the Bank of England : the role of audit committees in banks. – Bank of England. – London : Bank of England, 1987.
12p.

Consultative paper on wages councils. – London : Department of Employment, 1985.
13p.

Consumer affairs : a select bibliography / Department of Trade Victoria Street Library : compiled by Linda Wishart. – London : The Library, 1982.
34p.
Includes index.

Consumer and commercial statutes. – London : Longman Professional (UK), 1989.
Covers the Bill of Lading 1855 through to the Consumer Protection Act of 1987, including the EEC Directive on Product Liability. Set out in chronological order including amendments to date.
ISBN 0851215173 Hbk £22.50

Consumer and trading law : cases and materials / C.J. Miller, Brian W. Harvey. – London : Butterworths, 1985.
xiv,550p.
Includes index.
ISBN 0406012601 Hbk
ISBN 040601261X Pbk

Consumer and Trading Law - Cases and Materials / Brian W Harvey. – London : Butterworths, 1985.
ISBN 0406012601 Hbk £36.00
ISBN 040601261X Pbk £23.95

Consumer Credit. – Plymouth : Macdonald & Evans, 1981.
ISBN 0712103996 Pbk £4.95

Consumer Credit. – London : Collins, 1987.
256p.
ISBN 0003833038 Hbk £20.00

Consumer credit : law and practice / by Alexander G.L. Hill-Smith. – London : Sweet & Maxwell, 1985.
xxxi,330p; 25cm.
Examines the terminology of the 1974 Consumer Credit Act, the agreements to which the regulations apply, withdrawal and cancellation, debtors' and creditors' rights, the provision of security, and the powers of the court as well as enforcement provisions. Appendix contains a model Cancellable Hire-Purchase Agreement.
ISBN 0421342900 Pbk £29

Consumer Credit : Points For the Practitioner. – London : Law Society, 1985.
19p. – (Nineteen Eighty-Five Crash Course Transcripts).
Hbk £2.05

Consumer credit act manual / Francis Bennion. – 3rd ed. – London : Longman Professional (UK), 1986.
24cm.
ISBN 0851211003 Pbk £21

Consumer Credit Agreements / Fielding. – London : Waterlow, 1985.
ISBN 0080392008 Pbk £18.50

Consumer Credit Agreements Act. – Nettlebed Publications, 1985.
ISBN 0946628025 updat £45.00

Consumer Credit Law in Australia : a Commentary on the New Credit Legislation / Sheenagh Barnes. – Butterworths, 1988.
746p.
ISBN 0409494496 Hbk £89.00

Consumer Credit Legislation / Yelland. – London : Butterworths, 1977.
Service to Date.
ISBN 0406211612 Llf £130.00

Consumer Debt Problems of Scottish Families. – Scottish Association of Citizens Advice Bureau, 1988.
ISBN 0905831063 Pbk £2.00

Consumer Law / Daniel J. Baum. – Toronto : IPI Publishing, 1983.
84p. – (You and the Law Ser.).
ISBN 0458961302 Pbk £7.95

Consumer law / M.J. Leder. – 2nd ed. – London : Pitman, 1986.
xxxiii,220p; 22cm. – (M & E handbook series).
Previous ed.: Plymouth : Macdonald & Evans, 1980. Includes index.
ISBN 0712106774 Pbk £4.95

Consumer law / Peter Walker. – 1st ed. – London : Longman Professional (UK), 1988.
– (Longman Practice Notes).
Covers consumer safety, unsolicited goods, resale prices, sale of goods and services, and consumer credit. Contains precedents and checklists.
ISBN 0851214495 Hbk £9.95

Consumer law and practice / by Robert Lowe and Geoffrey F. Woodroffe. – 2nd ed. – London : Sweet and Maxwell, 1985.
400p.
Includes the Supply of Goods and Services Act 1982, and explains the Consumer Credit Act 1974 regulations. Deals with the consumer and civil law, the consumer and the criminal law, fair trading, consumer credit, the EEC dimension, and selected codes of practice.
ISBN 0421334002 Hbk £17.75
ISBN 042133410X Pbk £14.00

Consumer Law for the Motor Trade. – 2nd ed. – London : Butterworths, 1987.
ISBN 0406425914 Pbk £13.95

Consumer Law for the Small Business. – London : Kogan Page, 1983.
160p.
ISBN 0850386187 Hbk £11.95
ISBN 0850386489 Pbk £5.95

Consumer law in New Zealand / R.D. Mulholland. – Palmerston North N.Z. : Dunmore Press, 1982.
163p.
Includes index.
ISBN 0908564821

Consumer Law in the EEC. – London : Sweet & Maxwell, 1984.
ISBN 0421326409 Pbk £10.00

Consumer Law Statutes. – 5th ed. – London : Monitor Press, 1986.
ISBN 0906533457 Pbk £14.95

Consumer legislation in Belgium and Luxemburg : a study prepared for the EC Commission / M. Fontaine, Th. Bourgoignie : translated from French by Michael Corkery. – Wokingham, Berkshire : Van Nostrand Reinhold (UK), 1982.
xvi, 229 p.; 24 cm.
Includes bibliographical references and indexes. Translation of: Droit de la consommation en Belgique et Luxembourg.
ISBN 0442304188

Consumer product warranty reform : regulation in search of rationality
Vol. 2 / E.P. Belobaba. – Ottawa : Policy research, Analysis and Liasion Directorate, Consumer and Corporate Affairs, 1983.
157p.
Vol. 1 published as: Products liability and personal injury compensation in Canada. Bibliography: p.151-157.
ISBN 0662124162

Consumer protection / Law Reform Commission of Papua New Guinea. – Waigani : The Commission, 1981.
18p. – (LRC working paper).
Includes summary in Papuan.

Consumer Protection. – London : Butterworths.
ISBN 0903486466 Hbk £28.00
ISBN 0903486490 Pbk £11.95

Consumer Protection : Text and Materials. – Weidenfeld & Nicolson.
ISBN 0297794981 Hbk £25.00
ISBN 029779499X Pbk £16.95

Consumer Protection Act 1987. – London : Longman Professional.
ISBN 0851213499 Hbk £13.95

Consumer Protection and Legal Control : Essays and Papers of the U.G.C. National Seminar at University of Cochin. – Lucknow : Eastern Book Company, 1984.
346p.
Hbk £60.00

Consumer protection by public control and legal regulation : report from a symposium in Bastad, Sweden, 21-24 September 1981. – Lund : Juridiska Foreningen i Lund, 1984.
46p.
ISBN 9154416310

Consumer protection, environmental law, and corporate power / Ivan Bernier and Andree Lajoie, research coordinators. – Toronto : University of Toronto Press, 1985.
xv, 220 p.; 23 cm.
'Published ... in cooperation with the Royal Commission on the Economic Union and Development Prospects for Canada and the Canadian Government Publishing Centre, Supply and Services Canada.'. Includes bibliographies.
ISBN 0802072968 Pbk

Consumer Protection Law in Australia / John Goldring, Laurence W. Maher. – 3rd ed. – London : Butterworths.
Includes index.
ISBN 0409491675 Hbk £56.00
ISBN 0409491683 Pbk £45.00

Consumer Redress : Supplement to the EC Bulletin. – Kirchberg : Commission of the European Communities.
43p.
Hbk

Consumer Rights Handbook. – Pluto Press.
ISBN 0745301622 Pbk £5.95

Consumer Safety Regulation Good Intentions in Search of a Theory. – Oxford : Oxford University Press.
ISBN 0195049721 Hbk £18.00

Consumer, society and the law / Gordon Borrie and Aubrey L. Diamond. – 4th ed. – Harmondsworth : Penguin, 1981.
360p; 20cm. – (Pelican books).
Previous ed.: 1973. Bibliography: p340-343. - Includes index. .
ISBN 0140206477 Pbk £2.95

Consumerist criminology / Leslie T. Wilkins. – London : Heinemann, 1984.
viii,184p; 23cm.
Includes index.
ISBN 0435825283 Pbk £16.00
ISBN 0389204102

Consumers : Know Your Rights. – 3rd ed. – London : Oyez Longman, 1983.
– (It's Your Law Ser.).
ISBN 0851207286 Hbk £8.50
ISBN 0851207278 Pbk £4.95

Consumers and the law / Ross Cranston. – 2nd ed. – London : Weidenfeld and Nicolson, 1984.
xli, 503p.
ISBN 029778272X

Consumers' Association
Memorandum and articles of association of Consumers' Association : incorporated 18 March 1957. – Consumers' Association. – London : Consumers' Association, 1981.
32p.
At foot of cover: The Companies Act 1948: company limited by guarantee and not having a share capital no. 580128.

Consumers' Association of Penang →Rural development and human rights in South East Asia : report of a seminar in Penang, December 1981.

Consumers, Crimes and the Law. – New Delhi : Ashish Publishing House, 1987.
370p.
ISBN 8170240794 Hbk £250.00

Consumers or Victims?. – North Sydney : Allen & Unwin, 1982.
172p.
ISBN 0868610208 Pbk £15.95

Consuming secrets : how official secrecy affects everyday life in Britain / edited by Rosemary Delbridge and Martin Smith : foreword by Harold Evans. – London : Burnett, 1982.
x,249p; 22cm.
Bibliography: p239-241. - Includes index. At head of title: The National Consumer Council.
ISBN 0091475902 Hbk £
ISBN 0091475910 Pbk £4.95

Contacts between police and public : findings from the British crime survey / by Peter Southgate and Paul Ekblom. – London : H.M.S.O., 1984.
v,37p; 25cm.
A Home Office Research and Planning Unit report.
ISBN 0113407718

Container lines : the strategy game / by R.F. Gibney. – Colchester : Lloyd's of London Press, 1984.
87p.
ISBN 0907432840

Contemporary issues in international law : essays in honor of Louis B. Sohn / edited by T. Buergenthal. – 1st ed. – Kehl : N.P. Engel, 1984.
viii, 571 p., 1 leaf of plates; 24 cm.
English, French, German, and Spanish. 'Louis B. Sohn bibliography': p. 561-570.
ISBN 3883570400

Contemporary Issues in Money and Banking. – London : Macmillan.
ISBN 0333446879 Hbk £35.00

Contemporary planning policies : papers from a conference entitled Making the Planning System Work held at Oxford, September 1983 / organised by the Bar Council, the Law Society, and the Royal Institution of Chartered Surveyors. – London : Sweet & Maxwell, 1984.
vi,72p; 25cm.
Conference papers.
ISBN 0421326603 Pbk £18.00

Contemporary problems in international arbitration / edited by Julian D. M. Lew. – London : Queen Mary College, Centre for Commercial Law Studies. School of International Arbitration, 1986.
xlv, 380p.
Based on papers presented at a conference organised by the School of International Arbitration, Queen Mary College. Includes bibliographical references and index.
ISBN 0951066412

Contemporary Problems in International Arbitration. – Dordrecht : Kluwer, 1987.
380p.
ISBN 0898389267 Pbk Gld125.00

Contemporary Problems in the Conflict of Laws : Essays in Honour of John Humphrey Carlile Morris. – British Institute of International Comparative Law. – Dordrecht : Kluwer.
ISBN 9028609687 Hbk Gld60.00

Contemporary problems of international law : essays in honour of Georg Schwarzenberger on his eightieth birthday / edited by Bin Cheng and Eddie Brown. – London : Stevens & Sons, 1988.
360p; 24cm.
Collection of essays written in honour of Professor Georg Schwarzenberger, in the field of international law and relations. Includes an appraisal of international arbitration and negotitation techniques, and the mechanism and functions of the United Nations. Also contains discussion of international terrorism, human rights, and the law of treaties.
ISBN 0420479201 Hbk £36.00

Contemporary Trends in Family Law : A National Perspective /. Bartha Maria Knoppers. – Agincourt : Carswell, 1984.
334p.
This work is a collection of papers on Canadian family law presented at the Family Law Section of the Canadian Association of Law Teachers.
Hbk £46.25

Contempt / Law Reform Commission. – Canberra : Australian Government Publishing Service, 1987.
xcii,643p. – (Report).
Includes index.
ISBN 0644013656

Contempt : disruption, disobedience and deliberate interference / The Law Reform Commission. – Sydney : The Commission, 1986.
130p. – (Discussion paper).
Includes bibliographical references.

Contempt and family law / The Law Reform Commission. – Sydney : The Commission, 1985.
76p. – (Discussion paper).

Contempt and the media / Australian Law Reform Commission. – Sydney : The Commission, 1986.
182p. – (Discussion paper).
Cover title. Bibliography: p.178-182.

Contempt of Court / Law Reform Commission of Canada. – Ontario : Law Reform Commission of Canada, 1982.
67,69p; 25cm. – (Report).
English and French texts bound in reverse.
ISBN 0662512995

Contempt of court / C.J. Miller. – 2nd ed. – Oxford : Clarendon Press, 1989.
lix,492p.
Previous ed.: 1976. Includes index. This new edition covers developments in the law of contempt and includes the Contempt of Court Act 1981.
ISBN 0198254784 Hbk £75

Contempt of Court / V.R. Gopalan. – 5th ed. – Lucknow : Eastern Book Company, 1983.
1,146p.
Hbk £140.00

Content and Historical Development of Forestry Legislation in Tasmania. – Hobart : University of Tasmania, Centre for Environmental Studies, 1981.
38p.
Hbk £5.00

Contentious Costs. – London : Longman Professional.
– (Longman Practice Notes).
ISBN 0851214509 Pbk £10.95

Contested trials in magistrates' courts / by Julie Vennard. – London : H.M.S.O., 1982.
v,32p; 25cm.
Bibliography: p.26-27. 'A Home Office Research and Planning Unit report.'.
ISBN 0113407661

Context of contract in Papua New Guinea / Derek Roebuck, Dhirendra K. Srivastava, John Nonggorr. – Waigani : University of Papua New Guinea Press, 1984.
268p.
Bibliography: p.256-262. - Includes index.
ISBN 9980840005

Continental systems of judicial review (I) / Hideo Wada. – Tokyo : Institute of Social Sciences, Meiji University, 1981.
30p.
Reprint from: Bulletin of the Institute of Social Sciences Meiji University, Vol. 5, no. 1 (1981).

Continental systems of judicial review (II) / Hideo Wada. – Tokyo : Institute of Social Sciences, Meiji University, 1981.
16p.
Reprint from: Bulletin of the Institute of Social Sciences Meiji University, Vol. 5, no. 2 (1981).

Contingency fees / presented to Parliament by the Lord High Chancellor by Command of Her Majesty, January 1989. – London : HMSO, 1989.
13p.
ISBN 0101057121

Contingency Manual / Meghalaya. – 2nd ed. – Allahabad : Orient Law House, 1984.
Hbk £60.00

Contingent Remainders. – Reprint 1986. – Professional Books, 1844.
ISBN 0862053161 Hbk £53.75

Continuing Canadian constitutional dilemmas : essays on the constitutional history, public law and federal system of Canada / W.R. Lederman. – Toronto : Butterworths, 1981.
xx,442p.
Includes bibliographical references.
ISBN 0409844616 Hbk 55.00
ISBN 0409844608 Pbk 35.00

Continuing legal education in the 1980's : papers and proceedings of the Conference on Continuing Legal Education in the 1980's, conducted by the Law Society of New South Wales and the Law Foundation of New South Wales at the College of Law, Sydney, 13-15 November 1980 / edited by Jan Bowen and Clem Mitchelmore. – Sydney : Law Foundation of New South Wales, 1981.
xii,214,vip.
ISBN 090913619X

Continuing Legal Education Society of British Columbia →Interest arbitration : measuring justice in employment.

Continuity and development in law and society / Torstein Eckhoff. – Oxford : OUP.
Essays on general questions of law and legal reasoning. Presents the results of the author's research into the development of Norwegian constitutions in the nineteenth and twentieth centuries and the history of the legal profession to the first half of the eighteenth century.
Students of sociology of law, sociology and law
ISBN 8200183661 Hbk £40.00

Contract / Ruth Annand, Richard Whish. – London : Sweet & Maxwell, 1987.
xxii,175p; 26cm.
Includes index.
ISBN 0421362405 £16.50

Contract / by Robert Clark. – 2nd ed. 1. – London : Sweet & Maxwell, 1986.
22cm.
Previous ed.: 1982. Includes index.
ISBN 0421344806 Pbk £15.00

Contract / by F.R. Davies. – 5th ed. – London : Sweet & Maxwell, 1986.
xxii,290p; 23cm.
Previous ed.: 1981. Includes index.
ISBN 0421350903 Hbk £9.50
ISBN 0421351004 Pbk £5.95

Contract /. – North Ryde : Law Book Co, 1984.
x, 133p. – (Nutshells).
ISBN 0455203466

Contract. – Sweet & Maxwell.
ISBN 0421364203 Hbk £14.00
ISBN 0421364303 Pbk £8.95

Contract : cases and materials / H.G. Beale, W.D. Bishop, M.P. Furmston. – London : Butterworths, 1985.
xxxvi,737p; 26cm.
ISBN 0406005265 Hbk
ISBN 0406005281 Pbk

Contract Act and Law Relating to Tenders etc., 3 Vols. – 9th ed. – Allahabad : Law Publishers, 1983.
Hbk £45.00

Contract and Conveyance. – 4th ed. – London : Oyez Longman, 1983.
ISBN 0851207715 Hbk £15.95

Contract and mercantile law : a source book Vol. 1 : General principles of contract, agency and representation : edited by Ellison Kahn, Carole Lewis and Coenraad Visser / by Ellison Kahn. – 2nd ed. – Cape Town : Juta, 1988.
lix,926p.
Includes index.
ISBN 0702119962

Contract and mercantile law through the cases Vol.2 : Specific contracts and mercantile law, security : by Ellison Kahn ... et al. / by Ellison Kahn. – 2nd ed. – Cape Town : Juta, 1985.
lix,970p.
Bibliography: p.xxv-xxxviii. - Includes index.
ISBN 0702116548

Contract and organization : legal analysis in the light of economic and social theory / edited by Terence Daintith and Gunther Teubner. – Berlin : W. de Gruyter, 1986.
– (Series A–Law).
Includes index. Bibliography.
ISBN 0899251722 Hbk £52.25

Contract as promise : a theory of contractual obligation / Charles Fried. – Cambridge, Mass. : Harvard University Press, 1981.
162p; 25cm.
Includes index.
ISBN 0674169255 £8.40

Contract conflicts : the EEC Convention on the Law Applicable to Contractual Obligations : a comparative study / edited by P.M. North. – Amsterdam : North-Holland, 1982.
xviii,401p; 23cm.
ISBN 0444864466 £24.26

Contract Documentation for Contractors / John Sims. – London : Collins, 1985.
320p.
ISBN 0003830187 Hbk £16.00

Contract for the Sale of Land in New South Wales / E.A. Francis. – 3rd ed. – Butterworths, 1986.
136p.
This book is a guide to land transactions in NSW. The third edition contains the standard form of the new 1986 contract in full and includes detailed commentary on each clause by relevant authorities.
ISBN 0409491659 Pbk £22.00

Contract in a nutshell / Robert Duxbury. – London : Sweet & Maxwell, 1987.
117p; 22cm.
Includes index.
ISBN 0421368004 Pbk £3.95

Contract in Roman law : from the Twelve Tables to the Glossators / Gy. Diosdi : translated by J. Szabo : translation edited by B. Nemenyi. – Budapest : Akademiai Kiado, 1981.
ISBN 9630524562

Contract Labour : Regulation and Abolition Act, 1970 / G. Saran. – 4th ed. – Lucknow : Eastern Book Company, 1987.
602p.
Hbk £125.00

Contract law / Inner London Education Authority, Learning Resources Branch. – 1 videocassette. – London : Sweet & Maxwell, 1986.
– (Sweet & Maxwell's lawfilms).

Contract Law / See Chim Tang. – Singapore : Times Booker International.
140p.
ISBN 9971653761 Pbk £9.50

Contract law : exchange of standard term forms in contract formation : law reform proposals / Scottish Law Commission. – 2 v. – Edinburgh : The Commission, 1982.
– (Consultation paper).

Contract law in Australia / K.E. Lindgren, J.W. Carter, D.J. Harland. – Sydney : Butterworths, 1986.
lxxvii,817p.
Bibliography: p.791-793. - Includes index.
ISBN 0409490970 Hbk A$76.00
ISBN 0409491268 Pbk A$59

Contract law in perspective / John Tillotson. – 2nd ed. – London : Butterworths, 1985.
ix,240p; 22cm.
Previous ed.: 1981. Includes bibliographies and index.
ISBN 0406666210 Pbk £9.95

Contract Law in the USSR and the United States : History and General Concept / Mozolin. – London : Eurospan.
ISBN 0935328475 Hbk £26.50

Contract law today: Anglo-French comparisons / Denis Tallon. – Oxford : Clarendon Press, 1989.
400.
The result of a joint research project by two research institutes, one in the UK and one in France. It examines the evolution of contract in England and France.
Contract lawyers, comparative lawyers
ISBN 0198355934 Hbk £40

Contract of Employment : Principles of Australian Employment Law. – 3rd ed. – North Ryde : C.C.H. Australia, 1986.
328p.
ISBN 0869036297 Hbk £38.00

Contract strategies for construction professionals. – Oxford : Blackwell Scientific, 1987.
ISBN 0003833259 Hbk £19.95

Contract Strategies for Construction Projects. – Oxford : Blackwell Scientific, 1988.
ISBN 0003832716 Hbk £19.95

Contract: death or change of life?. – 1 v. – London : Institute of Advanced Legal Studies, University of London, 1981.
various pagings. – (W.G. Hart Legal Workshop).
Includes bibliographical references.

Contractor, Farok J.
International technology licensing : compensation, costs, and negotiation / Farok J. Contractor. – Lexington : Lexington Books, 1981.
xiv,193p; 24cm.
Bibliography: p185-189. - Includes index.
ISBN 0669043591 £22.50

Contractor's Claims Under the GC-Works-1 : Edition 2 Form of Contract. – King's Ride : Institute of Building, 1986.
68p.
ISBN 0906600855 Hbk £7.75

Contractors' Liens and Charges. – 2nd ed. – London : Butterworths, 1981.
ISBN 0409676004 Hbk £15.80

Contracts : Cases and Commentaries / David Percy. – 3rd ed. – Agincourt : Carswell, 1985.
932p.
This third edition text updates the previous edition with comprehensive coverage of contracts induced by negligent misrepresentation, current key cases, and a review of statutory references.
ISBN 0459375105 Hbk £39.60

Contracts : Cases, Notes and Materials / Barry J. Reiter. – 3rd ed. – Aurora : Canada Law Book Co, 1985.
734p. – (Case Books).
This new edition provides a complete review of contract law including: Remedies for Breach of Contract, The Kinds of Promises that the Law Will Enforce, The Formation of Contracts, The Statute of Frauds, Contractual Undertakings – Their Determination and Range, and Remedies for Breach; Control of Contract Power, and Illegality.
Hbk £79.50

Contracts : Cases, Text, and Materials / Barry J. Reiter. – 4th ed. – Toronto : Edmond-Montgomery, 1985.
732p.
ISBN 0920722164 Hbk £84.00

Contracts Act, 1950 (Act 136) and Government Contracts Act, 1949 (Act 120). – Kuala Lumpur : International Law Books Services.
Hbk £12.50

Contracts and Building Law. Vol. 2. – Chartered Institute of Building, UK. – King's Ride : Institute of Building.
Hbk £6.60

Contracts and Commercial Law Reform Committee
Privity of contract / a report by the Contracts and Commercial Law Reform Committee. – New Zealand : The Committee, 1981.
iii,79p.

Contracts at work / Erich Suter. – London : Institute of Personnel Management, 1982.
x,276p; 22cm.
Includes index.
ISBN 0852922973 Pbk £13.95

Contracts Building and Engineering Their Planning and Administration. – Butterworths, 1983.
Covers elements of the law of contract, types of engineering and building contract, persons concerned with the contract and its administration, and contract document, calling for tenders, letting the contract, supervision and administration of the contract, trends, and references and a bibliography.
ISBN 0409701270 Pbk £25.85

Contracts for the Carriage of Goods by Sea. – Oxford : BSP Professional.
ISBN 063202061X Hbk £20.00

Contracts for Work in Industry (NSW) : Section 88F. – Butterworths, 1981.
ISBN 0409490474 Pbk £35.00

Contracts of Affreightments and Hybrid Conts / Ivre. – London : Lloyd's of London Press, 1985.
ISBN 1850440603 Hbk £25.85

Contracts of Employment
Nineteen Eighty-Three supplement only. – Wellington : Butterworths.
This work is a practical handbook for employment law in the United Kingdom. The book includes checklists and sample contracts of employment in its appendices.
ISBN 0406178224 Pbk

Contracts of Employment. – Oxford : BSP Professional.
ISBN 0632021454 Pbk £17.95

Contractual adaptation and conflict resolution, based on venture contracts for mining projects in developing countries / Martin Bartels : translation by James E. Silva. – Deventer, Netherlands : Kluwer Law and Taxation, 1985.
187 p.; 25 cm. – (Studies in transnational law of natural resources).
Includes bibliographical references. 'List of cited agreements': p. 177-187.
ISBN 3787540237

Contractual claims : an annotated bibliography / compiled by P.A. Harrow. – 4th ed. – Ascot : Chartered Institute of Building, 1986.
vi,25p; 25cm.
Previous ed.: 1979.
ISBN 0906600847 Pbk

Contractual Remedies Act 1979 / by Francis Dawson and David W. McLauchlan. – Auckland : Sweet & Maxwell, 1981.
xxii,217p.
Includes bibliographical references and index. Includes the text of the Act.
ISBN 0457017201 Pbk
ISBN 0457016906

Contrasts in tolerance : post-war penal policy in the Netherlands and England and Wales / David Downes. – Oxford : Clarendon Press, 1988.
226p.
Bibliography: pp.207-218. - Includes index.
ISBN 0198256086 Hbk £20.00

Contribution of the courts to government : a West African view / A.N.E. Amissah. – Oxford : Clarendon, 1981.
x,382p; 22cm.
Includes index.
ISBN 0198253567 £25.00

Contribution Of The Courts to Govt W African View '81. – Oxford : Oxford University Press.
ISBN 0198253567 Hbk £27.50

Control of commercial fraud / L.H. Leigh. – London : Heinemann, 1982.
xii,339p; 23cm. – (Cambridge studies in criminology).
Bibliography: p315-326p. - Includes index.
ISBN 0435825194 £16.50

Control of corporate groups / by Tom Hadden. – London : Institute of Advanced Legal Studies (University of London), 1983.
75p.,4 charts.
ISBN 0901190284

Control of Exclusion Clauses England and India. – Ravenswood, 1985.
ISBN 0901812595 Hbk £31.00

Control of marine pollution in international law / Ramanlal Soni. – Cape Town : Juta, 1985.
301p.
Bibliography: p277-293.
ISBN 0702116602

Control of pollution encyclopaedia / editor J.F. Garner : assistant editor D.J. Harris. – London : Butterworth, 1977-.
26cm.
Tab indexed. Includes index.
ISBN 0406205086

Control of power within the European Communities : being the presidential address of Lord Mackenzie Stuart, president of the Holdsworth Club of the Faculty of Law in the University of Birmingham, 1985-1986. – Birmingham : Holdsworth Club of the University of Birmingham, 1986.
18p. – (The Holdsworth Club).
ISBN 0704408953

Control of Private Rented Dwellings. – Dublin : Round Hall Press, 1984.
100p.
ISBN 0950872520 Hbk £15.00
ISBN 0950872512 Pbk £7.50

Control of Rent Act, 1966 (No. 56 of 1966). – Kuala Lumpur : International Law Books Services.
Hbk £7.00

Control of Rent and Tenancy Agreement. – Seychelles Government. – Mahe : Seychelles National Printing Co.
Hbk £4.00

Control of the acquisition of shares : the new national take-overs code / F.J.O. Ryan. – Sydney : Butterworths, 1981.
ix, 134 p.; 24 cm.
Includes indexes.
ISBN 040930025X Pbk

Control Without Custody / A. Swift. – Edinburgh : Scottish Academic Press Ltd, 1987.
256p : Illus.
ISBN 0707304571 Hbk £15.00

Controlled Drugs Law and Practice. – London : Butterworths, 1984.
ISBN 0406016100 Pbk £20.95

Controlling Corporate Sickness : Lessons from Experiences for Managers and Bankers / Sekhar. – Oxford : Oxford University Press.
ISBN 00195621042 Hbk £6.95

Controlling pollution : principles and prospects : the government's response to the tenth report of the Royal Commission on Environmental Pollution. – London : H.M.S.O., 1984.
vii,35p.
ISBN 0117517585

Controlling Subsidiary Companies. – Cambridge : Woodhead-Faulkner, 1986.
ISBN 0859413284 Hbk £40.00

Controlling the state : towards fairer administration / by an SDP working party on citizens' rights and the Social Democratic Lawyers' Association Working Party on Administrative Law : with a foreward by Robert MacLennan. – London : SDP Open Forum Committee, 1983.
26p.

Controls over public corporations in India / Ramesh Chandra : foreword by V. R. Krishna Iyer. – Delhi : Delhi University, 1981.
xx,487p.
Bibliography: p.447-482. - Includes index.

Convention establishing the European Free Trade Association. – New ed., incorporating all amendments up to 1st February 1982. 1. – Geneva : European Free Trade Association, 1982.
various pagings.
Previous ed.: 1979. Added t.-p. in French. Parallel English and French texts.

Convention for the Protection of Individuals with Regard to Automatic Processing of Personal Data. – Strasbourg : Council of Europe, 1981.
ISBN 9287100225 Hbk £1.00

Convention for the Protection of Individuals with regard to Automatic Processing of Personal Data (with explanatory report), Strasbourg, 28 January 1981. – London : H.M.S.O., 1981.
33p; 25cm. – (Miscellaneous).
ISBN 0101834101 Pbk £3.05

Convention on a Code of conduct for liner conferences → Shipping conferences.

Convention on Early Notification of a Nuclear Accident and Convention on Assistance in the Case of a Nuclear Accident or Radiological Emergency. – Vienna : International Atomic Energy Agency, 1987.
126p. – (Legal series).
ISBN 9201760876

Convention on International Trade in Endangered Species of Wild Fauna and Flora. E.C. Annual Report. – Luxembourg : Office for Official Publications of the European Communities, 1986.
426p.
ISBN 9282564983 Pbk £1,400.00

Convention on the Elimination of All Forms of Discrimination Against Women : explanatory documentation prepared for Commonwealth jurisdictions / Commonwealth Secretariat. – 4 pamphlets in folder. – London : Commonwealth Secretariat, .
Contents: The Convention on the Elimination of All Forms of Discrimination Against Women text. - Developments towards the elimination of discrimination against women in the Commonwealth. - The Convention on the Elimination of All Forms of Discrimination Against Women: a commentary on the Convention. - Directory of Commonwealth National Machinery.

Convention on the Law of the Sea. – Metro Manila : Development Academy of the Philippines, 1983.
xii, 263p.
ISBN 9711520788 Hbk £9.00

Convention on the law of the sea / Drafting Committee. – Geneva : The Conference, 1982.
xvii,221p. – (Working paper).
Text adopted on 30 April 1982 at the eleventh session of the Conference. - Supersedes: Draft convention on the law of the sea (August, 1981). 'This working paper has been prepared for the use of the Drafting Committee at the intersessional meeting to be held from 12 July to 13 or 20 August 1982'.

Convention on the physical protection of nuclear material. – Vienna : International Atomic Energy Agency, 1982.
– (Legal series).
ISBN 9201760825

Conversation Handbook for Policemen. – 2nd ed. – Plymouth : Macdonald & Evans, 1984.
128p.
ISBN 0712156259 Pbk £6.00

Conversations on Policy. – London : Policy Studies Institute, 1984.
88p. – (PSI's Discussion Papers).
Hbk £3.75

Conversion of building societies to company status : a consultative paper. – London : Treasury, 1985.
9p.
At head of title: Building Societies Bill.

Convertibles and Warrants. – London : Euromoney, 1987.
ISBN 1870031202 Pbk £75.00

Conveyancer and Property Lawyer. – London : Sweet & Maxwell.
Hbk £36.00
Bound volume. –
Hbk £18.50
Cordex binder. –
£8.75
Back vols. available.

Conveyancer's Guide To Local and Public Authorities. – London : Waterlow, 1988.
ISBN 0080331025 Hbk £12.95

Conveyancing 1985. – London : Law Society, 1985.
15p. – (Nineteen Eighty-Five Crash Course Transcripts).
Hbk £2.05

Conveyancing
Supplement 1981. – London : Law Notes Lending Library.
Vol. 1. –
ISBN 086205334X Hbk £64.50
Vol. 2. –
ISBN 0862053471 Hbk £64.00

Conveyancing. – London : Longman Professional. – (Longman Practice Notes Series).
ISBN 0851214460 Pbk £10.95

Conveyancing. – 2nd ed. – London : Butterworths, 1987.
This text for students of conveyancing is an introduction to the theory and practice of conveyancing of land in the United Kingdom. A comprehensive work including materials on landlord and tenant, housing, and land law.
ISBN 0406010641 Pbk £15.95

Conveyancing : Current Issues. – Vancouver : Continuing Legal Education Society of British Columbia, 1988.
162p.
ISBN 0865043809 Hbk £70.00

Conveyancing After the Act. – London : Butterworths, 1986.
ISBN 0406504105 Pbk £9.75

Conveyancing and miscellaneous matters. – Belfast : H.M.S.O., 1983.
vii,153p. – (Discussion document).
At head of title-page: Department of Finance and Personnel for Northern Ireland, Office of Law Reform.
ISBN 033723406X

Conveyancing and Residential Tenancies : Conditions of Sale and Other Recent Developments to March 1982. – London : Law Society, 1982.
Hbk £4.50

Conveyancing Committee
Second Report : Conveyancing Simplifications. – Conveyancing Committee. – London : HMSO, 1985.
ISBN 0113800029 Hbk £8.60

Conveyancing Costs Tables, NSW. – 2nd ed. – North Ryde : Law Book Co, 1986.
xxi, 112p.
ISBN 045520683X Pbk £12.50

Conveyancing, Draftsman and Legal Interpretation of Deeds, as Interpreted under Income-Tax Law, 5 Vols. – 6th ed. 5v. – Allahabad : Law Publishers, 1982.
Hbk £37.50 ea

Conveyancing Fees and Charges. – 12th ed. – London : Longman Professional.
ISBN 085121472X Pbk £6.95

Conveyancing Fees and Duties. – Fourmat Publishing. – 6th ed. – London : Fourmat, 1986. – (LCFS 5).
ISBN 1851900209 Pbk £4.50

Conveyancing for Legal Assistants 1986. – Vancouver : Continuing Legal Education Society of British Columbia, 1986.
292p.
ISBN 0865042640 Hbk £65.00
Supplement-1987. –
119p.
ISBN 0865043213 Hbk £55.00

Conveyancing in Hong Kong / Hartley Bramwell. – London : Butterworths, 1981.
xxvii,403p; 23cm.
Includes index.
ISBN 040666210X

Conveyancing in South Africa / R.J.M. Jones. – 3rd ed. – Cape Town : Juta, 1985.
xix, 540 p.; 26 cm.
Re ed. of: The law and practice of conveyancing in South Africa. 2nd ed. 1976. Includes indexes.
ISBN 0702115967

Conveyancing Law / C. Bevan. – 3rd. – Plymouth : Macdonald & Evans, 1986.
– (M and E Handbook Ser.).
ISBN 071210755X Pbk £6.50

Conveyancing Law and Practice. – 3rd ed. – London : Butterworths, 1982.
ISBN 040655553424 Hbk

Conveyancing law and practice in Scotland
Vol.1 / by John M. Halliday. – Edinburgh : W. Green under the auspices of the Scottish Universities Law Institute, 1985.
xxxviii,491p; 25cm.
Includes index.
ISBN 0414007603
Vol.2 : Feus and dispositions / by John M. Halliday. – 1986.
xxxvii,518p; 25cm.
Includes index.
ISBN 0414007891 Hbk £30.00
Vol.3 : Leases and heritable securities / by John M. Halliday. – 1987.
xxix,550p; 25cm.
Includes index.
ISBN 0414008154
Vol.4. Wills and succession. – 1990.
Deals with testate and intestate succession both before and after the Succession (Scotland) Act 1964, including statutory prior rights and legal rights, completion of title to both heritable and moveable estate, preparation of wills, administration of executries, destination, entails, judicial transmissons, compulsory acuisition, trusts, taxation, and pension schemes. Includes index for Vols. 1 to 4. Published under the auspices of the Scottish Universities law Institute.
ISBN 0414008936 Hbk

Conveyancing Made Easy : a Teaching Text for Lawyers and Their Secretaries. – Vancouver : Fountain Books, 1982.
254p.
ISBN 0969000901 Hbk £30.00

Conveyancing manual. – 4th. – Edinburgh : Clark (T. & T.) Ltd.
Primarily a student manual written by a former Professor of Conveyancing at Dundee University. Covers, in six parts, preliminary matters, feus, resulting rights of superior and vassal, subordinate rites in the feu - securities and leases, transmission of the feu, and reform.
ISBN 0567291715 Pbk

Conveyancing Manual for New South Wales. – Woolloomooloo : International Business Communications, 1987.
ISBN 0949553328 Hbk £25.00

Conveyancing Practice and Procedure / Vera Gittings. – 2nd ed. – London : Fourmat, 1985.
ISBN 0906840910 Pbk £9.95

Conveyancing, Precedents and Forms / G.C. Mathur. – 5th ed. – Lucknow : Eastern Book Company, 1983.
704p.
Hbk £70.00

Conveyancing requisitions. – Scarborough, Ontario : Butterworths (Canada).
232.
Aspects of a real estate transaction are covered, from drafting an agreement of purchase and sale to reviewing the abstract of title, to submission of and response to requisitions and all the requirements of closing.
ISBN 0409866270 Hbk

Conveyancing Searches and Enquiries. – London : Butterworths, 1985.
ISBN 040625513X Pbk £26.95

Conveyancing Solution 3 : Remedies under Contract / Cain. – Sweet & Maxwell.
ISBN 0421381108 Hbk £19.50

Conveyancing Solutions No. 2 : The Contract / Richard Whish. – London : Sweet & Maxwell, 1987.
Hbk £12.50

Conviction : law, the State and the construction of justice / by Doreen J. McBarnet. – London : Macmillan, 1981.
vii,182p.
ISBN 0333255364

Conway, Stephen →Correspondence of Jeremy Bentham, Vol. 8 : January 1809 to December 1816 : edited by Stephen Conway.

Cook, C. →Laying Down the Law : The Foundations of Legal Reasoning Research and Writing in Australia and New Zealand.

Cook, M.
Taxation of legal costs. – London : LEST, 1986.
ISBN 0907822657 Pbk £19.50

Cook, Pat
Ombudsman : an autobiography / by Pat Cook. – London : BKT, 1981.
155p; 22cm.
ISBN 0904677192 £6.95

Cook, Rebecca J.
Emerging issues in Commonwealth abortion laws, 1982 / by Rebecca J. Cook and Bernard M. Dickens. – London : Commonwealth Secretariat, 1983.
135p; 30cm.
ISBN 0850922305
—Issues in reproductice health law in the Commonwealth / by Rebecca J. Cook and Bernard M. Dickens. – London : Commonwealth Secretariat, 1986.
109p.
ISBN 085092295X

Cooke
International Mergers and Acquisitions. – Oxford : Blackwell Scientific.
ISBN 0631142489 Hbk

Cooke, J. C. →Australian Company Practice.

Cooke, Philip →Tax aspects of acquisitions and mergers.

Cooke, R. M.
Establishing a business in the United Kingdom / by R. M. Cooke and D. C. Borer. – 2nd ed. – London : Institute of Chartered Accountants, 1983.
viii,215p.
ISBN 0852913370

Cooke, T.
Mergers and acquisitions. – Oxford : Blackwell, 1986.
ISBN 0631147470 Hbk £35.00

Coomaraswamy, Radhika →Role of the judiciary in plural societies.

Coombes, David
Ireland and the European Communities : Ten Years of Membership. – Dublin : Gill & MacMillan, 1983.
ISBN 0717113264 Hbk £20.00

Coombes-Davies, M.
Avoiding Claims : a Practical Guide Construction Industry. – London : E & F N Spon.
ISBN 0419146202 Hbk £22.50

Coombes, John
Inheritance tax / by John Coombes and Gordon Channon. – London : Sweet & Maxwell, 1987.
xxxiv,305p; 22cm.
Includes index.
ISBN 0421370300 Pbk £18.00

Cooper
Company Car Tax Guide 1988-89 / Lybrand. – London : CCH.
ISBN 086325165X Pbk £5.00
—Critical Accounts / Hopper. – London : Macmillan.
ISBN 0333449703 Hbk £33.00
→ Endorsement of Driving Licence and Disqualification from Driving.
—Form and Content of Company Accounts / Lybrand. – 3rd ed. – Oxford : Croner Publications, 1986.
ISBN 1851850325 Pbk £9.95
—Social work and child abuse / Ball. – London : Macmillan, 1987.
ISBN 033363973 Hbk £15.00
ISBN 0333363981 Pbk £5.95

Cooper, Alan →Role of subscription agents.

Cooper, Beryl →Fraud trials : a report.

Cooper, Carole
Bophuthatswana's Industrial Conciliation Act. – Johannesburg : South African Institute of Race Relations, 1984.
Hbk £2.00
—Labour Relations Amendment Act. – Johannesburg : South African Institute of Race Relations, 1984.
Hbk £2.00
—PEBCO : a Black Mass Movement / K. Ensor. – Johannesburg : South African Institute of Race Relations, 1982.
58p.
Hbk £2.00

Cooper, E. J
Customs and excise law / by E.J. Cooper. – Sydney : Legal Books, 1984.
xli, 598 p.; 25 cm.
Includes bibliographies and index.
ISBN 0949553107

Cooper, F.L.
Law and the Software Marketeer. – Prentice-Hall.
ISBN 0135266335 Hbk £41.75

Cooper, G.
Cases in Chancery During the Time of Lord Eldon. – Repr. of 1815 ed. – Abingdon : Professional Books.
77p.
Hbk £25.00

Cooper, Gordon S.
Australian Capital Gains Tax / Michael W. Inglis. – Butterworths, 1986.
298p.
ISBN 0409491578 Pbk £42.00

Cooper, Helen
International Bar Association, Section on Energy & Natural Resources Law : seminar topics index 1975-84 : Stavanger, 1975; Cambridge 1, 1978; Cambridge II, 1979; Banff, 1981; Singapore, 1982; Houston, 1984; Oslo, 1984. – S.l. : International Bar Association, Section on Energy & Natural Resources Law, 1986.
24p.
ISBN 0948711027

Cooper, Ian →New financial instruments.

Cooper, Jeremy →Public interest law.
—Public legal services : a comparative study of policy, politics and practice / by Jeremy Cooper. – London : Sweet & Maxwell, 1983.
ix,320p; 22cm.
Bibliography: p305-313. - Includes index.
ISBN 0421303506 Pbk £9.50
—Public legal services in three countries : a study of the relationship between policy and practice / Jeremy Cooper. – Florence : European University Institute, Department of Law, 1981.
436p.
Thesis (Doctoral) - European University Institute,1981. Includes bibliographical references.

Cooper, John
Management and regulation of banks / John Cooper. – London : Macmillan, 1984.
xi,395p.
Bibliography: p383-386.
ISBN 0333342348

Cooper, M.
Introduction to animal law. – London : Academic Press, 1987.
ISBN 0121880303 Hbk

Cooper, Neil H. →Tolley's European insolvency guide.

Cooper, Roger
Baha'is of Iran / by Roger Cooper. – Rev. and updated ed. – London : Minority Rights Group, 1985.
16p. – (Report).
Bibliography: p.16.
ISBN 0946690316

Cooper-Stephenson, Kenneth D.
Personal injury damages in Canada / by Kenneth D. Cooper- Stephenson and Iwan B. Saunders. – Toronto : Carswell, 1981.
lii,762p; 26cm.
Includes index.
ISBN 0459333305

Cooper, Steven
Rural Poverty in the United Kingdom. – London : Policy Studies Institute, 1981.
Hbk £4.95

Cooper, W. E.
Motor law
Vol. 1 / by W.E. Cooper : specialist contributor T.G. Schwar. – Cape Town : Juta, 1982.
cxxvi,740p.
Replaces: South African motor law / by W.E. Cooper and B.R. Bamford. Bibliography: p.x - Includes index.
ISBN 0702112534
Vol. 2 : Principles of liability for patrimonial loss / by W.E. Cooper. – 1987.
li,507p.
Replaces: South African motor law / by W.E. Cooper and B.R. Bamford. Bibliography: p.xi-xiii. - Includes index.
ISBN 0702119067 Hbk

Cooperation and Conflict : Nordic Journal of International Politics. – Oslo : University of Forlag.
Hbk

Cooperation between management and labor : a survey of co-determination mechanisms in European corporations / Walter Kolvenbach. – Deventer, Netherlands : Kluwer Law and Taxation Publishers, 1982.
89 p.; 25 cm.
ISBN 9065440666 Pbk

Cooperation in the Nordic countries : achievements and obstacles / by Frantz Wendt. – Stockholm : Almqvist & Wiksell for the Nordic Council, 1981.
408p.
Bibliography: p.395-400. - Includes index. Translation by Geoffrey Dodd.
ISBN 9122004653

Co-operative companies and securities scheme / explanatory paper on exposure draft of Companies and Securities Legislation (Miscellaneous Amendments) Bill 1983 : prepared by the Business Affairs Division of the Commonwealth Attorney-General's Department for and on behalf of the Ministerial Council for Companies and Securities. – Parkes : The Department, 1982.
177p.

Cooperative Societies Act, 1948 and Rules and Regulations. – Allahabad : Law Book Company.
Hbk £9.00

Coopers & Lybrand Associates →Civil justice review.
—International Insurance, Industry Guide. – Coopers & Lybrand Associates. – 4th ed. – London : Lloyd's of London Press.
ISBN 1850441936 Hbk £19.50
→ Streamlining the cities : an analysis of the Government's case for reorganising local government in the six Metropolitan Counties : first report.
—Value Added Tax : A Practical Guide for Your Business. – Coopers & Lybrand Associates. – London : Kogan Page.
ISBN 1850917515 Hbk £12.95
ISBN 1850917493 Pbk £5.95

Coopers and Lybrand: tax and financial planning through pensions / Paul G Meins. – London : Butterworths, 1987.
ISBN 0406500800 Pbk £16.00

Coops, F.W. →Banking Law and Practice in Australia.

Cooray, L. J. M.
Changing the language of the law : the Sri Lanka experience / L. J. Mark Cooray. – Quebec : Presses de l'Universite Laval, 1985.
183p.
ISBN 2763770800

Cooray, M.J.A.
Judicial Role Under Constitutions of Ceylon (Sri Lanka). – Colombo
Pbk £13.00

Coote, Anna →Rape controversy.
—Women's rights : a practical guide / Anna Coote and Tess Gill : drawings by Posy Simmonds. – 3rd ed. – Harmondsworth : Penguin, 1981.
555p; 20cm.
Previous ed.: 1977. Includes index.
ISBN 0140465324 Pbk £3.95

Coote, H. C.
Practice of the Ecclesiastical Courts. – Repr. of 1847 ed. – Abingdon : Professional Books.
77p.
Hbk £20.00

Cootes →Probate Practice.

Co-ownership / M.P. Thompson. – London : Sweet & Maxwell, 1988.
xxv,151p.
Analyses forms of co-ownership of freehold and leasehold interests in real property, and such items of personal property as joint bank accounts. Explores the legal principles involved, and applies them to practical problems. Co-habitation, financial contribution, marriage, divorce, death and insolvency are also discussed.
ISBN 0421375000 £19.50

Co-ownership of land / Law Reform Commission of British Columbia. – Vancouver : The Commission, 1987.
ii,75p. – (Working paper).
Caatalogued from cover. Includes bibliographical references. Includes Draft Property Law Amendment Act.
ISBN 0771886071

Cop World. – London : Macmillan, 1984.
352p.
ISBN 0333306880 Hbk £12.95

Copeling, A J C
Copyright and the Act of 1978. – London : Butterworths.
ISBN 040902029 Pbk £17.00
—Copyright Law in South Africa. – 2nd ed. – Durban : Professional Publishers, 1983.
ISBN 0409020206 Hbk
—Students' Casebook on Mercantile Law. – Durban : Professional Publisher, 1975 repr. 1980.
ISBN 0409020303 Pbk £45.00

Coper, Michael
Encounters with the Australian Constitution sound recording. – South Yarra : Louis Braille Productions Ltd..
ISBN 14ac £68.00
—Franklin Dam Case. – Butterworths, 1983.
288p.
ISBN 0409494313 Pbk £175.00
—Freedom of interstate trade under the Australian constitution / by Michael Coper. – Sydney : Butterworths, 1983.
xiii,394p.
Bibliography: p.371-380. - Includes index.
ISBN 0409491802

Coppel, Charles A.
Chinese in Indonesia, the Philippines and Malaysia / by Charles A. Coppel and Hugh and Ping-ching Mabbett. – Rev. ed. – London : Minority Rights Group, 1982.
16p. – (Report).
Previous ed. 1972. Bibliography: p.16.

Copyright / edited by W.R. Cornish. – Oxford : ESC Publishing, 1985.
168p.
ISBN 0906214343

Copyright : Proceedings of the Workshop Held at the Annual Conference of the Canadian Library Association June 7, 1984, Toronto, Ontario. – Ottawa : Canadian Library Association, 1985.
72p.
ISBN 0888021925 Hbk £10.00

Copyright Act. – 5th ed. – Allahabad : Law Book Company, 1985.
435p.
Hbk £125.00

Copyright Amendment Act 1980. – Milsons Point : Australian Copyright Council.
Hbk £1.00

Copyright and Cable Television. – Milsons Point : Australian Copyright Council.
Hbk £1.00

Copyright and China. – Milsons Point : Australian Copyright Council.
Hbk £1.00

Copyright & computers / Cliff Dilloway. – London : Gower in association with Institute of Purchasing and Supply, 1985.
xii,126p; 23cm.
Bibliography: p123-126. Includes: Copyright & computers / R.J. Hart. Originally published: London : British Computer Society, 1983.
ISBN 0566025205 £21.45

Copyright and Film. – Milsons Point : Australian Copyright Council.
Hbk £6.50

Copyright and jurisprudence : selected papers / melanges : Stig Stromholm. – Stockholm : Norstedt, 1983.
291p.
Bibliography: p.271-291. 'Edited by the Faculty of Law, Uppsala University and P.A. Norstedt & Soners forlag, Stockholm' - Cover. Papers in English, French and German.
ISBN 9118276210

Copyright and Music. – Milsons Point : Australian Copyright Council.
Hbk £11.00

Copyright and neighboring rights laws and treaties / compiled and published by the World Intellectual Property Organization Geneva. – Geneva : World Intellectual Property Organization, 1987.
Llf

Copyright and the Act of 1978. – London : Butterworths.
ISBN 040902029 Pbk £17.00

Copyright and Trade Mark Litigation 1988. – Vancouver : Continuing Legal Education Society of British Columbia, 1988.
372p.
ISBN 0865049807 Hbk £85.00

Copyright and Treaties of the World, 3 Vols. and 23 supplements. – Paris : UNESCO.
ISBN 9231019465 Hbk £5,590.00
Supplement 22. – 1979-80.
ISBN 9231019457 Hbk £900.00

Copyright and Writers. – Milsons Point : Australian Copyright Council.
Hbk £8.00

Copyright Bulletin. – UNESCO. – London : HMSO.
Hbk £6.60
Single Issues. –
Hbk £2.10

Copyright Cases 1901-1949, 8 Vols. – London : Wildy & Sons.
Hbk £100.00

Copyright, competition and Canadian culture : the impact of alternative Copyright Act import provisions on the book publishing and sound recording industries / Ake G. Blomqvist and Chin Lim. – 2 microfiches. – Ottawa : Minister of Supply and Services, 1981.
159 fr.; 10x15cm.
Bibliography: p.145-147.

Copyright, Design and Patents Act 1988 / Taylor. – London : Blackstone Press.
ISBN 1854310232 Pbk £18.95

Copyright, Designs and Patents Bill H.L. – London : H.M.S.O., 1987.
xxviii,190p. – (H.L. Bill 1987 (12)).
ISBN 010870128X

Copyright, Designs and Patents Bill H.L. : as amended by Standing Committee E. – House of Lords. – London : HMSO, 1988.
xiii,217p. – (H.L. Bill 1987-88 (176)).
ISBN 0103176888

Copyright, Designs and Patents Bill H.L. : as amended in committee. – London : HMSO, 1988.
xii,191p. – (H.L. Bill 1987-1988 (37)).
ISBN 0108703789

Copyright for the Canadian Visual Artist. – repr. 1981. – Ottawa : CARFAC.
Hbk £6.00

Copyright in free and competitive markets / edited by W.R. Cornish. – Oxford : Published by ESC Publishing for l'Association Litteraire et Artistique Internationale and the British Literary and Artistic Copyright Association, 1986.
vii,138p.
Includes bibliographical references.
ISBN 0906214467

Copyright In Industrial Designs. – 5th ed. – Sweet & Maxwell, 1974.
ISBN 0421176008 Hbk £40.00

Copyright in the Performing Arts. – Wellington : Queen Elizabeth II Arts Council of New Zealand.
Hbk £3.00

Copyright law in Australia and the rights of performers, authors and composers in the Pacific region / by J.A.L. Sterling and Geoffrey E. Hart. – Sydney : Legal Books, 1981.
xli,278p; 23cm.
Bibliography: p.263-265. - Includes index.
ISBN 0959656871

Copyright Law in South Africa. – 2nd ed. – Durban : Professional Publishers, 1983.
ISBN 0409020206 Hbk

Copyright law in the United Kingdom and the rights of performers, authors and composers in Europe / by J.A.L. Sterling and M.C.L. Carpenter. – London : Legal Books, 1986.
cxi,749p; 26cm.
Kept up to date by supplements.
ISBN 0947926003
ISBN 0949553190

Copyright Laws and Treaties of the World. – Paris : UNESCO, 1979-1980.
ISBN 9231019457 Hbk

Copyright Laws and Treaties of the World : Supplement 1981-1983. – London : HMSO.
Review of the national and international laws of copyright and intellectual property protection.
ISBN 0119110636 Hbk £210.00

Copyright Licensing. – Bradford : MCB University Press.
– (Library Management Series).
ISBN 086176353X Hbk £27.95

Copyright Problems of Satellite and Cable Television in Europe. – Dordrecht : Kluwer, 1987.
208p.
ISBN 0860109526 Hbk Gld125.00

Copyright Protection : Conference Papers. – Woolloomooloo : International Business Communications, 1986.
ISBN 0949072060 Hbk £55.00

Copyright protection for artistic works industrially applied / Attorney-General's Department. – Canberra : Australian Government Publishing Service, 1987.
v,62p. – (Discussion paper).
Includes excerpts from the Copyright Act 1968.
ISBN 0644061391

Copyright system : practice and problems in developing countries / by Denis de Freitas. – London : Commonwealth Secretariat, 1983.
v,87p.
ISBN 085092233X

Copyright through the cases. – London : Waterlow, 1986.
ISBN 0080392083 Pbk £15.00

Coquillette, Daniel R.
Civilian Writers of Doctors' Commons, London : Three Centuries of Juristic Innovation in Comparative, Commercial and International Law. – Berlin : Duncker and Humblot, 1988.
303p.
ISBN 3428061772 Hbk £148.00

Corbeil, Laura
Farm Bankruptcies in Ontario. – Ontario : Ontario Government Publications Service, 1983.
5p. – (Research Review: No. 13).
Hbk £0.50

Corbett, Claire →Effects of crime and the work of victims support schemes.

Corcelle, Guy →Environmental policy of the European Communities.

Cordato, Anthony J.
Australian Travel and Tourism Law Handbook. – Butterworths, 1988.
285p.
ISBN 0409493848 Pbk £22.50

Corder, Hugh →Essays on law and social practice in South Africa.
—Judges at work : the role and attitudes of the South African appellate judiciary, 1910-50 / by Hugh Corder. – Cape Town : Juta, 1984.
xxxii,252p.
Bibliography: pxxi-xxvi.
ISBN 0702114359

Cordery, Arthur
Cordery's law relating to solicitors / Frederic T. Horne. – 8th ed. – London : Butterworths, 1988.
540p; 25cm.
Previous ed: 1981. Includes index.
ISBN 0406161712 £60.00
—On solicitors. – 8th ed. – London : Butterworths, 1988.
ISBN 04061617120 Hbk

Cordery on Solicitors
Nineteen Eighty-Four supplement only. – Wellington : Butterworths.
This book discusses the rights and liabilities of an English solicitor. Materials on a solicitors relationship with his client; his liability in negligence; his entitlement to remuneration; his relations with partners and employees; and The Law Society are included.
ISBN 0406161585 Pbk

Cordery's law relating to solicitors / Frederic T. Horne. – 8th ed. – London : Butterworths, 1988.
540p; 25cm.
Previous ed: 1981. Includes index.
ISBN 0406161712 £60.00

Cork, K.
Cork Report. – London : Macmillan.
ISBN 0333444795 Hbk £14.95

Cork, Kenneth →European insolvency practitioners' handbook : the AEPPC compendium of insolvency law and practice.
→ Insolvency law and practice : report of the Review Committee.

Cork Report. – London : Macmillan.
ISBN 0333444795 Hbk £14.95

Corke, Jim
Tourism law / Jim Corke. – Huntingdon, Cams. : Elm, 1988.
xxvi,288p.
Includes bibliography and index.
ISBN 0946139954 tutor's pack £10.95
ISBN 0946139962 £39.00

Corley
Legal Environment of Business / Reed. – 7th ed. – Maidenhead : McGraw-Hill, 1987.
ISBN 0070132569 Hbk £29.95

Cormack, Margaret
Paper Chasing : Resources for Legal Studies. – North Ryde : C.C.H. Australia, 1986.
308p.
ISBN 086903670X Hbk

Cornes, David L.
Design Liability in the Construction Industry / Davids L. Cornes. – 3rd ed. – Oxford : BSP Professional.
ISBN 0632022663 Hbk £22.50

Cornish, G. P.
Model handbook for interlending and copying / Graham P. Cornish. – Wetherby : Published jointly by IFLA Office for International Lending and Unesco, 1988.
79p; 30cm.
Bibliography: p72.
ISBN 0712320458 Pbk £5.00

Cornish, W R
Copyright. – Oxford : ESC, 1985. – (Casebook).
ISBN 0906214343 Pbk £9.00

—Copyright in Free and Competitive Markets. – Oxford : ESC.
ISBN 0906214467 Pbk £10.00

—Intellectual property : patents, copyright, trade marks and allied rights / by W.R. Cornish. – London : Sweet & Maxwell, 1981.
lxi,630p; 23cm.
Includes index.
ISBN 0421243104 Hbk £26.50
ISBN 0421243309 Pbk £16.50

→ Intellectual property case books, 1 : Patents and confidential information.

→ Piracy and counterfeiting of industrial property and copyright : papers given at the inaugural conference of the Common Law Institute of Intellectual Property Ltd in London on 28th and 29th January 1983.

—Trade marks and names. – Oxford : ESC, 1985. – (Casebook).
ISBN 0906214351 Pbk £9.00

Coroners bill : report on the consolidation of the Coroners Acts 1887 to 1980 and certain related enactments / the Law Commission. – London : H.M.S.O., 1987.
3p.
ISBN 0101017820

Coroners courts in England and Wales : a report / by JUSTICE : Chairman of Committee Evan Stone. – London : JUSTICE, 1986.
28p.
ISBN 0907247075

Coroners' rules and statutes / by Giles Kavanagh. – London : Sweet & Maxwell, 1985.
xviii,135p; 25cm.
Includes index.
ISBN 0421338806 Pbk £6.50

Coronial law and practice in New South Wales / by K.M. Waller. – 2nd ed. – Sydney : Law Book Co., 1982.
xvi,215p.
Previous ed.: 1973. Includes bibliographical references and index. Includes the text of the Coroners Act, 1980, No. 27.
ISBN 0455203652 Hbk £39.50

Corporate acquisitions and mergers : a practical guide to the legal, financial and administrative implications / P.F.C. Begg : foreword by Lord Hanson. – 2nd ed. – London : Graham & Trotman, 1986.
320p; 22cm.
Previous ed.: 1985. Includes index.
ISBN 0860108139 Hbk £40.00
ISBN 0860108090 Pbk £20.00

Corporate Cash Management. – Cambridge : Woodhead-Faulkner, 1987.
ISBN 085941390X Hbk £40.00

Corporate Communications / Churchill. – London : Fitzwilliam, 1988.
ISBN 1870555066 Hbk £25.00

Corporate control, corporate power / Edward S. Herman. – Cambridge : Cambridge University Press, 1981.
xv,432p; 24cm.
Includes index.
ISBN 0521239966 £25.00

Corporate Crime in the Pharmaceutical Industry. – London : Sweet & Maxwell, 1984.
ISBN 0710200498 Hbk £30.00

Corporate Debt Securities : Priority Rules. – Auckland : Legal Research Foundation, 1986.
Hbk £10.00

Corporate failure. – Maidenhead : McGraw-Hill, 1986.
ISBN 0070847940 Hbk £17.50

Corporate Finance. – Mosby, 1988.
ISBN 0801642116 Hbk £31.00

Corporate Finance. – London : Butterworths, 1987.
ISBN 0406259569 Hbk £42.00

Corporate Finance for Legal Assistants. – Vancouver : Continuing Legal Education Society of British Columbia, 1988.
299p.
ISBN 0865041644 Hbk £75.00

Corporate Finance in Multinational Companies. – London : Euromoney, 1986.
ISBN 1870031350 Pbk £75.00

Corporate Finance Law Supplement. – London : Sweet & Maxwell, 1987.
ISBN 0421311207 Hbk £67.00
ISBN 0421374403 Pbk £12.50

Corporate fraud / Michael J. Comer. – 2nd ed. – London : McGraw-Hill, 1985.
xvi,453p; 23cm.
Previous ed.: 1977. Includes bibliography and index.
ISBN 0070847916 £16.50

Corporate governance : practices, procedures and powers in British companies and their boards of directors / R.I. Tricker. – Aldershot : Gower, 1984.
vii,319p; 22cm.
Includes index.
ISBN 0566007495 £18.95

Corporate governance and directors' liabilities : legal, economic, and sociological analyses on corporate social responsibility / edited by Klaus J. Hopt, Gunther Teubner. – Berlin : W. de Gruyter, 1984.
462p. – (Series A, Law).
Includes index.
ISBN 3110100274 £75.00

Corporate Income Tax and Profit Rates. – New Delhi : Deep and Deep Publications, 1984.
268p.
Hbk £150.00

Corporate Insolvency / Durrant. – London : Sweet & Maxwell, 1987.
ISBN 0421365005 Hbk £24.00

Corporate insolvency / Peter Totty and Michael Crystal. – London : McGraw-Hill, 1982.
xv,155p; 26cm.
Includes index.
ISBN 0070845824 £12.95

Corporate Insolvency Practice Manual. – Touche Ross. – London : Butterworths, 1988.
ISBN 0406503508 Pbk

Corporate Law in Canada : the Governing Principles. – Butterworths, 1984.
784p.
Shows where old law may be safely discarded and demonstrates how current governing principles may be balanced in potential conflict situations. Also looks at the distinction between company statutes in each province, the role of the Charter of Rights in the regulation of corporate activity, corporate crime and tort capital structure, and the legal duties of corporate managers.
ISBN 0409857645 Hbk £100.00

Corporate law in the 80s. – Don Mills : Richard De Boo, 1982.
716 p.; 24 cm.
Includes index.
ISBN 0888201109

Corporate Law Locator 1988. – New York : Bowker, 1988.
ISBN 0835223523 Hbk £30.00

Corporate Procedures for Legal Assistants. – Agincourt : Carswell, 1985.
450p.
This book provides a step-by-step analysis of the incorporation procedure under Ontario and Canadian federal corporate law for legal assistants. Forms and precedents are provided in this 'how to' incorporation guide.
Hbk £40.00

Corporate receiverships : a practical approach / by Stanley Samwell. – London : Institute of Chartered Accountants in England and Wales, 1981.
xv,190p; 22cm.
Includes index.
ISBN 0852912870 Pbk £11.95

Corporate rescues and insolvencies / J.R. Lingard. – London : Butterworths, 1986.
xxvi,222p; 26cm.
Includes index.
ISBN 0406100403 Pbk £27

Corporate responsibility as a problem of company constitution / by Gunther Teubner. – Florence : European University Institute, 1983.
47p.
At head of title page: European University Institute, Florence, Law Department.

Corporate Securities and Creditors Rights on Insolvency 1984. – Monash University, Faculty of Law. – Clayton : Monash University Press, 1984.
ISBN 0867463414 Hbk £15.00

Corporate social responsibility in Papua New Guinea / Law Reform Commission of Papua New Guinea. – Waigani : The Commission, 1981.
ii,17p. – (Occasional paper).
'This paper was researched and written for the Commission by Edward F. Graziono'.

Corporate Taxation. – Aurora : Canada Law Book Co, 1984.
585p. – (Text Books-Civil).
Hbk £75.00

Corporate taxation / Kathleen A. Lahey. – Toronto : Emond Montgomery Publications, 1984.
lx,540p.
Includes bibliographical references and index.
ISBN 0920722113

Corporated donor's handbook. – Turnaround Press, 1987.
ISBN 0907164226 Pbk £12.50

Corporation Code of the Phillipines with the Omnibus Investment Code. – Quezon City : University of the Philippines, Law Center, 1981.
207p.
Pbk £20.00

Corporation Law for Canadian Business. – Butterworths, 1981.
448p.
ISBN 0409988340 Hbk £21.95

Corporation Tax 1988-89. – Tolley Publishing.
ISBN 0854593470 Pbk £14.95

Corporation tax. – London : H.M.S.O., 1982.
viii,153p; 25cm.
'Presented to Parliament by the Chancellor of the Exchequer'.
ISBN 010184560X Pbk £7.10

Corporation Tax. – Telegraph Publications, 1988.
ISBN 0863672280 Pbk £6.95

Corporation Tax. – 5th ed. – Plymouth : Macdonald & Evans, 1981.
ISBN 0712104674 Pbk £4.95

Corporation tax : the impact of the 1984 budget / M.P. Devereaux and C.P. Mayer. – London : Institute for Fiscal Studies, 1984.
47p.
Includes bibliographical references.
ISBN 0902992384

Corporation Tax Manual. – London : Butterworths, 1988.
ISBN 0406502167 Pbk

Corporations : Cases, Text and Materials / Mark Q. Connelly. – 2nd ed. – Toronto : Edmond-Montgomery, 1988.
1,000p.
Hbk £90.00

Corporations : Principles and Policies / Mark Q. Connelly. – 2nd ed. – Toronto : Edmond-Montgomery, 1988.
ca 1,050p.
ISBN 0920722253 Hbk £100.00

Corporations : Principles and Policies. – 2nd ed. – Toronto : Edmond Montgomery.
ISBN 0020722253 Hbk £52.00

Corporations in and under international law / by Ignaz Seidl-Hohenveldern. – Cambridge : Grotius, 1987.
xviii,138p.
Covers the nationality of corporations and the effect upon them of nationalisation measures, as well as the special responsibilities of state-owned corporations. The second part of the book examines problems connected with the legal personality of international organizations.
ISBN 0949009091

Corrado, Raymond R.
Current Issues in Juvenile Justice / Marc LeBlanc. – Butterworths, 1983.
400p.
ISBN 0409824135 Pbk £26.95

Correctional Officer. – Toronto : Butterworths, 1981.
342p.
ISBN 0409863203 Pbk £36.95

Corrections in Asia and the Pacific : Proceedings of the First Asian and Pacific Conference of Correctional Administrators. – Canberra : Australian Institute of Criminology.
Hbk £5.00

Corrections in Canada : Policy and Practice / Griffiths. – Toronto : Butterworths, 1984.
432p.
ISBN 0409834548 Pbk £23.95

Correspondence of Jeremy Bentham
Vol. 6 : January 1798 to December 1801 : edited by J.R. Dinwiddy / J. R. Dinwiddy. – Oxford : Clarendon, 1984.
xxx,496p; 24cm.
Includes index.
ISBN 0198226136 £40.00
Vol.7 : January 1802 to December 1808 : edited by J.R. Dinwiddy. – 1988.
500p; 24cm.
Includes index.
ISBN 0198226144 £45.00

Vol. 8 : January 1809 to December 1816 : edited by Stephen Conway. – 1988.
480p; 24cm.
Includes index.
ISBN 0198226152

Correspondent Banking. – London : Butterworths, 1987.
ISBN 0406007004 Pbk

Corrigan, Kieran
Tax Law. – London : Sweet & Maxwell. – (Irish Law Texts Ser.).
ISBN 0421299304 Hbk

Corruption : Causes, Consequences and Control. – London : Pinter Publishers Ltd, 1983.
319p.
ISBN 0861873408 Hbk £29.50

Corruption in British Politics 1895-1930. – Oxford : Oxford University Press, 1987.
ISBN 0198229151 Hbk £19.50

Corry, James Alexander
Power of the Law. – Toronto : Canadian Broadcasting Corporation Enterprises.
72p.
Pbk £2.50

Cortes and the King : Constitutional Monarchy in the Iberian World. – Glasgow : University of Glasgow, Institute of Latin American Studies, 1981.
– (Occasional Paper: No. 32).
Hbk £3.00

Cosell, D.
Horse and the law. – London : David & Charles, 1987.
ISBN 0715388134 Hbk £10.95

Cosgrove, Paul →Extension of customs jurisdiction over the Canadian Continental Shelf : a background paper.

Cost Accounting / Underdown. – London : Pitman Publishing, 1988.
ISBN 0273025007 Pbk £9.95

Cost Accounting Lecturer's Guide / Underdown. – Pitman.
ISBN 0273029207 Pbk £10.95

Cost and Management Accounting 1.2 Paper 1 : ACCA Series. – Witney : A.T.C. Publications.
ISBN 0747700133 Pbk £12.95

Cost and Management Accounting 1 : ACCA Study Text 1.2. – London : BPP.
ISBN 0862772362 Pbk £13.95

Cost and Management Accounting 1 ACCA Study and Revision Pack 1.2. – Pitman.
ISBN 0273027964 Pbk £11.95

Cost and Management Accounting 2 : ACCA Study and Revision Manual Level 2.4. – London : BPP.
ISBN 1870941071 Pbk £9.95

Cost and Management Accounting. – Cambridge : Woodhead-Faulkner, 1986.
ISBN 0859413713 Pbk £11.50

Cost management for library and information services / Stephen A. Roberts. – London : Butterworths, 1985.
181 p.
ISBN 0408013761

Cost of chaos : a survey of the housing benefits scheme / Peter Kemp. – London : SHAC, 1984.
85p; 22cm. – (SHAC research report).
ISBN 0903113759

Cost of Criminal Justice : A Preliminary International Survey / J. Marjoram. – Canberra : Australian Institute of Criminology.
Hbk £2.00

Cost of Criminal Justice : An Analysis. – Canberra : Australian Institute of Criminology.
Hbk £2.30

Cost of Going to Law. – Belfast : Queen's University of Belfast, 1984.
70p.
ISBN 0853892148 Pbk £2.95

Cost of Imprisonment in Australia. – Canberra : Australian Institute of Criminology.
Hbk £3.00

Cost of Management Accounting. – Pitman.
ISBN 0273029835 Pbk £6.95

COST Projects : Collected Agreements Concluded within the Framework of European Cooperation in the Field of Scientific and Technical Research Vol. 3. – Luxembourg : Office for Official Publications of the European Communities, 1986.
280p.
ISBN 9282402843 Pbk £1,000.00

Cost Service. – Butterworths. – London : Butterworths, 1987.
Service to Date.
ISBN 0406107491 Llf £145.00

Costs and Fees in Family Law Cases. – Vancouver : British Columbia Continuing Legal Education Society, 1982.
118p.
ISBN 0865040842 Hbk £50.00

Costs in Matrimonial Causes. – Format. – London : Fourmat, 1985.
– (LCFS 2).
ISBN 090684004X Pbk £2.45

Costs in Matrimonial Causes. – London : Butterworths, 1984.
This book gives practitioners a practical discussion of the control of costs in matrimonial causes in the United Kingdom. This work provides guidance to the lawyer seeking to avoid costs out of proportion to the settlement in the case.
ISBN 0406255202 Pbk

Costs of Care in Hostels / Berthoud. – Policy Studies Institute.
ISBN 0853744246 Pbk £5.95

Costs, Party and Party : Updated. – Law Society of Upper. – Toronto : Law Society of Upper Canada.
ISBN 0887590608 Hbk

Cotran, Eugene
Casebook on Kenya Customary Law. – Abingdon : Professional Books, 1985.
350p.
ISBN 0862051118 Hbk £34.00
—Casebook on Kenyan Customary Law. – Nairobi : Nairobi University Press.
348p.
Pbk £280.00

Cotta, Maurizio
Career and recruitment patterns of Italian legislators : a contribution to the understanding of a polarized political system / by Maurizio Cotta. – Florence : European University Institute, 1983.
49p.
At head of title page: European University Institute, Department of Political and Social Sciences.

Cotterell, Leslie
Performance. – 2nd ed. – London : Offord Publications Ltd, 1985.
600p.
ISBN 0903931362 Hbk £18.00
ISBN 0903931591 Pbk £14.95

Cotterrell, Roger
Sociology of law : an introduction / Roger Cotterrell. – London : Butterworths, 1984.
xiii,409p; 23cm.
Bibliography: p368-392. - Includes index.
ISBN 0406010684 Hbk £17.00
ISBN 0406010722 Pbk £16.95

Cottrell, Jill →Appeals by the Prosecution Against Sentences and Acquittals : A Survey of the Situation in Some Commonwealth Countries.

Coughlan, Anthony
Fooled again? : the Anglo-Irish Agreement and after / Anthony Coughlan. – Cork : Mercier, 1986.
88p; 21cm.
ISBN 0853427747 Pbk £4.95

Couldery, F.A.
Introduction to Accounting. – Pitman.
ISBN 0273028804 Pbk £6.95

Coulet, William →Law and practice relating to pollution control in France.

Coulson, N.
Conflicts and Tensions In Islamic Jurisprudence. – University of Chicago Press, 1969.
ISBN 0226116107 Hbk £10.25
—Succession in the Muslim Family. – Cambridge : Cambridge University Press, 1971.
ISBN 0521078520 Hbk £30.00

Council for the Securities Industry
Companies Act, 1980 : pre-emption rights of shareholders / Council for the Securities Industry. – London : The Council, 1981.
2p.
—Draft rules and regulations for licensed dealers in securities / Council for the Securities Industry. – London : The Council, 1982.
9p. – (Press statement).
—Guidelines for personal dealings by fund managers / Council for the Securities Industry. – Rev. ed. – London : The Council, 1982.
8p. – (CSI).
—Professor Gower's review of investor protection : views of the Council for the Securities Industry. – Council for the Securities Industry. – London : The Council, 1982.
9p.
—Revision of the licensed dealers' rules / Council for the Securities Industry. – London : The Council, 1982.
8p. – (Press statement).
Caption title.
—Rules governing substantial acquisition of shares : restrictions of market raids / Council for the Securities Industry. – Rev. ed. – London : The Council, 1982.
15p. – (CSI).
—Statement on insider dealing / Council for the Securities Industry. – London : The Council, 1981.
7p. – (CSI).

Council houses and the Housing Act 1980 / by Peter Liell. – London : Butterworths, 1981.
xxxi,457p.
Includes the text of the Act.
ISBN 0406270309

Council housing / by David C. Hoath. – 2nd ed. – London : Sweet & Maxwell, 1982.
xxvii,223p; 18cm.
Previous ed.: 1978. Includes index.
ISBN 042127610X Hbk £
ISBN 0421276207 Pbk £6.95

Council of Europe
Collection of resolutions adopted by the Committee of Ministers in application of Article 32 of the European Convention for the Protection of Human Rights and Fundamental Freedoms, 1959-1981. – Council of Europe. – Strasbourg : Council of Europe, 1981.
various pagings; 30cm.
At head of title: Human Rights.
—Collection of resolutions adopted by the Committee of Ministers in application of article 54 of the European Convention for the Protection of Human Rights and Fundamental Freedoms / Recueil des resolutions du Comite des Ministres adoptees en application de l'article 54 de la Convention Europeenne de Sauvegarde des Droits de l'Homme et des Libertes Fondamentales. – Strasbourg : Council of Europe, 1981.
various pagings; 30cm.
Preface by Peter Leuprecht, Director of Human Rights. At head of title: Human Rights.

→ Collection of resolutions adopted by the Committee of Ministers in application of articles 32 and 54 of the European Convention for the Protection of Human Rights and Fundamental Freedoms, 1959-1983.

—Collection of resolutions adopted by the Committee of Ministers in application of articles 32 and 54 of the European Convention for the Protection of Human Rights and Fundamental Freedoms, 1959-1983. – Council of Europe. – Strasbourg : Council of Europe, 1984.
148p; 30cm.
'Publication prepared by the Human Rights Documentation Centre...'. Kept up to date by supplements.

→ Computers in correctional administration and links with criminal justice : proceedings of the fourth Colloquy on the Use of Computers in the Administration of Justice, Stockholm, 3-5 September 1984 : reports presented at the colloquy.

→ Conference on the Defence of Democracy against Terrorism in Europe - Tasks and Problems, Strasbourg, 12-14 November 1980 : compendium of documents.

—Conscientious objection to compulsory military service : recommendation no. R(87)8 adopted by the Committee of Ministers on 9 April 1987 and explanatory report. – Council of Europe. – Strasbourg : Council of Europe, 1987.
10p. – (H (87) 3).

—Constitutional and legislative provisions concerning the organisation of regional government
Addendum no.1 : Constitution of the Free State of Bavaria. – Council of Europe. – Strasbourg : Council of Europe, 1981.
31p; 30cm.

Document no.4 : Regional institutions in Belgium / Council of Europe. – 1982.
i,47p; 30cm.

Document no. 6 : The new regional structures in France. – 1982.
i,37p.

Part 2 : Statutes of three self-governing communities (1). – 1983.
72p.

→ Decentralisation in France : the distribution of powers.

→ Decentralisation of local government at neighbourhood level.

—Development of maritime islands as extreme examples of peripheral regions / report prepared by the Committee of Experts on Social and Economic Activities of the Steering Committee for Regional and Municipal Matters, with the assistance of Italo Ferrari. – Strasbourg : Council of Europe, 1986.
26p.

→ Digest of Strasbourg case-law relating to the European Convention on Human Rights.

—Documentation sources in human rights / Council of Europe. Directorate of Human Rights. Human Rights Documentation Centre. – Strasbourg : The Council, 1987.
38p. – (H(87)2).

→ Economic crime.

—Economic crime / European Committee on Crime Problems. – Strasbourg : Council of Europe, 1981.
75p.
Recommendation No. R(81)12, adopted by the Committee of Ministers on 25 June 1981. At head of cover title: Council of Europe, Legal Affairs.

—Economic crisis and crime / European Committee on Crime Problems. – Strasbourg : Council of Europe, 1985.
157p; 21cm.
At head of cover-title: Council of Europe, Legal affairs.
ISBN 9287107807

→ EDP systems for court adminstration : proceedings of the 3rd Colloquy on the Use of Computers in the Administration of Justice, Strasbourg, 3-5 November.

→ EDP systems for the administration of courts and related systems : proceedings of the fifth Colloquy on the Use of Computers in the Administration of Justice, Madrid, 14-16 October 1986.

—Education and information in the field of human rights : activities of the Council of Europe / Secretariat memorandum prepared by the Directorate of Human Rights. – Strasbourg : Council of Europe, 1987.
11p. – (H (87) 5).
At head of cover title: Committee of Experts for the Promotion of Education and Information in the Field of Human Rights (DH-ED).

—Effects of the various international human rights instruments providing a mechanism for individual communications on the machinery of protection established under the European Convention on Human Rights : Secretariat memorandum / prepared by the Directorate of Human Rights of the Council of Europe. – Strasburg : Council of Europe, 1985.
25p. – (H(85)3).

→ European Convention for the Prevention of Torture and Inhuman or Degrading Treatment or Punishment : the text of the Convention and explanatory report.

→ European Convention on Human Rights : collected texts.

—European Convention on Human Rights International Conference Proceedings. – Council of Europe. – Martinus Nijhoff.
ISBN 9024735394 Hbk £167.50

→ European Court of Human Rights : its organisation and working.

→ European prison rules : recommendation no. R (87)3 adopted by the Committee of Ministers of the Council of Europe on 12 February 1987 and Explanatory memorandum.

—European prison rules : recommendation no. R (87)3 adopted by the Committee of Ministers of the Council of Europe on 12 February 1987 and Explanatory memorandum. – Council of Europe. – Strasbourg : Council of Europe, 1987.
92p.
At head of cover title : Council of Europe, Legal Affairs.
ISBN 9287110352

—European Social Charter. – Council of Europe. – Strasbourg : Directorate of Press and Information, 1981.
36p.

→ Explanatory report on the Convention for the Protection of Individuals with regard to Automatic Processing of Personal Data.

—Explanatory report on the European Convention for the Protection of Vertebrate Animals used for Experimental and other Scientific Purposes. – Council of Europe. – Strasbourg : Council of Europe, 1986.
75p.
Includes the text of the convention.
ISBN 9287108633

→ Explanatory report on the European Convention on Offences relating to Cultural Property.

→ Explanatory report on the European Convention on the Recognition of the Legal Personality of International Non-Governmental Organisations.

—Expression of consent by states to be bound by a treaty / Council of Europe Directorate of Legal Affairs. – Strasbourg : Council of Europe, 1987.
122p.
ISBN 9287110441

—Extortions under terrorist threats. – Council of Europe. – Strasbourg : Council of Europe, 1986.
14p; 21cm. – (Legal affairs).
'... prepared by a select committee of experts under the authority of the European Committee on Crime Problems ... The committee of Ministers of the Council of Europe authorised its publication' - p.3.
ISBN 9287108412

→ Financial apportionment and equalisation.

→ Financial resources for local and regional authorities : report.

—Foster families : recommendation no. R(87)6 adopted by the Committee of Ministers of the Council of Europe on 20 March 1987 and Explanatory memorandum. – Council of Europe. – Strasbourg : Council of Europe, 1987.
15p.
Prepared by the Committee of experts on family law set up under the authority of the European Committee on Legal Co-operation. At head of cover title : Council of Europe, Legal Affairs.
ISBN 9287110875

—Harmonisation of laws relating to the requirement of written proof and to the admissibility of reproductions of documents and recordings on computers : Recommendation No.R (81) 20 adopted by the Committee of Ministers of the Council of Europe on 11 December 1981 and Explanatory memorandum. – Council of Europe. – Straboug : Council of Europe, 1982.
21p; 21cm. – (Legal Affairs).
ISBN 9287100446

—Historical research on crime and criminal justice : sixth Criminological Colloquim (PC-CC), Strasbourg 21-23 November 1983. – Council of Europe. – Strasbourg : Council of Europe, 1984.
ii,153p.
Includes bibliographies. 'Secretariat memorandum prepared by the Directorate of Legal Affairs'.

→ Human rights : information sheet.

→ Human rights and the police.

→ Human Rights in Europe : Being an Account of the European Convention for the Protection of Human Rights and Fundamental Freedoms Signed in Rome on 4 November 1950 of the Protocol Thereto and of the Machinery Created Thereby : The European Commission of Human Rights and the European Court of Human Rights.

→ Human rights in international law : basic texts.

→ Human rights in prisons.

→ Human rights in Sweden : the annual reports 1982-1984 from the national correspondent for Sweden to the Documentation Center for Human Rights at the Directorate for Human Rights, Council of Europe.

→ Human rights of aliens in Europe : proceedings of the Colloquy on 'Human Rights of Aliens in Europe'.

→ Human rights or a way of life in a democracy.

→ Impact of European Community law on the implementation of the European Convention on Human Rights.

—Implementation of the European Convention on Human Rights in respect of young persons and children placed in care or in institutions following a decision of the administrative or judicial authorities : replies of Governments to the Secretary General's enquiry under Article 57 of the European Convention on Human Rights / Council of Europe. – Strasbourg : Council of Europe, 1986.
196p; 30cm. – (H (86) 1).
At head of cover title: Human rights.

→ International recognition of national identity cards : recommendation no.R(83)11 adopted by the Committee of Ministers of the Council of Europe on 23 September 1983 and Explanatory memorandum.

—International recognition of national identity cards : recommendation no.R(83)11 adopted by the Committee of Ministers of the Council of Europe on 23 September 1983 and Explanatory memorandum. – Council of Europe. – Strasbourg : Council of Europe, 1984.
10p; 21cm.
'... prepared by the ad hoc Committee of experts for identity documents and movement of persons (CAHID)'. At head of cover title: Legal Affairs.
ISBN 9287103186

→ Legal co-operation in Europe in the fields of civil, commercial, public and international law, 1957-1982.

—Legal protection against sex discrimination : recommendation No. R(85)2 adopted by the Committee of Ministers of the Council of Europe on 5 February 1985 and explanatory memorandum. – Council of Europe. – Strasbourg : Council of Europe, 1985.
33p.
'Prepared by a committee of experts set up under the authority of the European Committee on Legal Co-operation (CDCJ)'. At head of cover title: Legal Affairs.
ISBN 9287103895

—Legal protection of persons suffering from mental disorder placed as involuntary patients : Recommendation No.R(83)2 adopted by the Committee of Ministers of the Council of Europe on 22 February 1983, and Explanatory memorandum. – Council of Europe. – Strasbourg : Council of Europe, 1983.
22p; 21cm.
'... prepared by a committee of experts on Legal Problems in the Medical Field set up under the authority of the European Committee on Legal Co-operation'. At head of title: Legal Affairs.
ISBN 9287102996

—Legal protection of the collective interests of consumers by consumer agencies : Recommendation no. R(81)2 adopted by the Committee of Ministers of the Council of Europe on 23 January 1981 and explanatory memorandum. – Council of Europe. – Strasbourg : Council of Europe, 1981.
19p; 21cm.
'Prepared by a committee of experts set up under the authority of the European Committee on Legal Cooperation' - verso t.p.. At head of cover title: Council of Europe, Legal Affairs.

—Letters rogatory for the interception of telecommunications : Recommendation no.R (85) 10 adopted by the Committee of Ministers of the Council of Europe on 28 June 1985 and Explanatory memorandum. – Council of Europe. – Strasbourg : Council of Europe, 1986.
15p; 21cm. – (Legal affairs).
' ... prepared by a select committee of experts under the authority of the European Committee on Crime Problems' - p.3.
ISBN 9287108390

—Local authority accounting in Europe : report / prepared by the Committee of Experts on Local and Regional Finance of the Steering Committee for Regional and Municipal Matters. – Strasbourg : Council of Europe, 1985.
120p.

→ Management structures in local and regional government : report.

—Measures against the transfer and the safekeeping of funds of criminal origin : recommendation no. R(80)10 adopted by the Committee of Ministers of the Council of Europe on 27 June 1980 and explanatory memorandum. – Council of Europe. – Strasbourg : Council of Europe, 1981.
12p.
'Prepared by a select committee of experts under the authority of the European Committee on Crime Problems' - verso t.p.. At head of cover title: Council of Europe, Legal Affairs.

→ Measures facilitating access to justice : recommendation no. R(81)7 adopted by the Committee of Ministers of the Council of Europe on 14 May 1981 and explanatory memorandum.

—Measures facilitating access to justice : recommendation no. R(81)7 adopted by the Committee of Ministers of the Council of Europe on 14 May 1981 and explanatory memorandum. – Council of Europe. – Strasbourg : Council of Europe, 1981.
26p.
Prepared under the authority of the European Committee on Legal Co-operation. At head of cover title: Council of Europe, Legal Affairs.

→ Measures to be taken in cases of kidnapping followed by a ransom demand : Recommendation No.R(82)14 adopted by the Committee of Ministers of the Council of Europe on 24 September 1982 and Explanatory memorandum.

—Measures to be taken in cases of kidnapping followed by a ransom demand : Recommendation No.R(82)14 adopted by the Committee of Ministers of the Council of Europe on 24 September 1982 and Explanatory memorandum. – Council of Europe. – Strasbourg : Council of Europe, 1983.
13p; 21cm.
'... prepared by a select committee of experts under the authority of the European Committee on Crime Problems' - verso t.p.. At head of cover title: Legal Affairs.
ISBN 9287102309

—Measures to prevent and reduce the excessive workload in the courts : recommendation no. R (86)12 adopted by the Committee of Ministers of the Council of Europe on 16 September 1986 and Explanatory memorandum. – Council of Europe. – Strasbourg : Council of Europe, 1987.
17p.
Prepared by a committee of experts on the working of the judicial system set up under the authority of the European Committee on Legal Co-operation. At head of cover title : Council of Europe Legal Affairs.
ISBN 9287110778

—Model agreement to enable members of the family forming part of the household of a member of a diplomatic mission or consular post to engage in a gainful occupation : recommendation no. R(87)2 adopted by the Committee of Ministers of the Council of Europe on 12 February 1987 and Explanatory memorandum. – Council of Europe. – Strasbourg : Council of Europe, 1987.
13p.
Prepared by the Committee of experts on public international law (CJ-DI) set up under the authority of the European Committee on Legal Co-operation. At head of cover title : Council of Europe, Legal Affairs.
ISBN 9287110859

→ Models of organisation for the government of conurbations : report.

—Non-profit-making associations in some Council of Europe countries / Council of Europe Directorate of Legal Affairs. – Strasbourg : Council of Europe, 1981.
10p; 30cm. – (Legislative dossier).

—Parental responsibilities : recommendation no.R (84)4 adopted by the Committee of Ministers of the Council of Europe on 28 February 1984, and Explanatory memorandum. – Council of Europe. – Strasbourg : Council of Europe, 1984.
19p; 21cm.
'... prepared by the Committee of Experts on Family Law set up under the authority of the European Committee on Legal Co-operation' - preface..
ISBN 9287103291

—Parliamentary Assembly : procedure and practice / Kenneth Bradshaw, John Sweetman. – 8th ed. – Strasbourg : Council of Europe, 1983.
370p.
Includes index.
ISBN 9287102325

—Payment by the State of advances on child maintenance : Recommendation No.R (82) 2 adopted by the Committee of Ministers of the Council of Europe on 4 February 1982 and explanatory memorandum. – Council of Europe. – Strasbourg : Council of Europe, 1982.
15p; 21cm.
'Prepared by a committee of experts set up under the authority of the European Committee on Legal Co-operation'. At head of cover title : Council of Europe, Legal Affairs.
ISBN 9287101736

—Policies with regard to grants to local authorities / report prepared by the Committee of Experts on Local and Regional Finance of the Steering Committee for Regional and Municipal Matters and drafted by J. Lotz, Chairman. – Strasbourg : Council of Europe, 1986.
35p.

→ Prison information bulletin.

—Prison regimes / study prepared by the Select Committee of Experts on Prison Regimes and Prison Leave. – Strasbourg : Council of Europe, 1986.
33p. – (CDPC (84) 8 rev. addendum VI).

→ Problems encountered by local and regional authorites as a result of their new tasks in respect of environmental protection.

→ Problems of regional and local authorities involved in planning policies : report.

→ Problems raised by certain aspects of the present situation of refugees from the standpoint of the European Convention on Human Rights.

→ Proceedings of the Conference of Institutions Responsible for Teaching the Subject 'Computers and Law', Rome, 9-11 October 1985 : reports presented at the Conference.

→ Proceedings of the Round Table with European Ombudsmen : Madrid, 5-6 June 1985.

—Protection of human rights in Europe / Council of Europe. – New ed. – Strasbourg : Council of Europe, 1983.
16p.

→ Protection of personal data used for scientific research and statistics : recommendation no.R(83) 10 adopted by the Committee of Ministers of the Council of Europe on 23 September 1983, and Explanatory memorandum.

—Protection of personal data used for scientific research and statistics : recommendation no.R (83)10 adopted by the Committee of Ministers of the Council of Europe on 23 September 1983, and Explanatory memorandum. – Council of Europe. – Strasbourg : Council of Europe, 1984.
23p; 21cm.
'Prepared by the Committee of Experts on Data Protection set up under the authority of the European Committee on Legal Co-operation'. At head of cover title: Legal Affairs.
ISBN 9287103178

—Protection of personal data used for the purposes of direct marketing : recommendation no. R(85) 20 adopted by the Committee of Ministers of the Council of Europe on 25 October 1985 and Explanatory memorandum. – Council of Europe. – Strasbourg : Council of Europe, 1986.
19p.
Prepared by the committee of experts on data protection set up under the authority of the European Committee on Legal Co-operation. At head of cover title: Council of Europe, Legal Affairs.
ISBN 9287108765

—Protection of persons satisfying the criteria in the Geneva Convention who are not formally recognised as refugees : recommendation no.R (84)1 adopted by the Committee of Ministers of the Council of Europe on 25 January 1984, and Explanatory memorandum. – Council of Europe. – Strasbourg : Council of Europe, 1984.
10p; 21cm.
'... prepared by the ad hoc Committee of Experts on Legal Aspects of Territorial Asylum and Refugees' - preface.
ISBN 9287103275

→ Protection of users of computerised legal information services : Recommendation no.R (83) 3 adopted by the Committee of Ministers of the Council of Europe on 22 February 1983 and Explanatory memorandum.

—Protection of users of computerised legal information services : Recommendation no.R (83) 3 adopted by the Committee of Ministers of the Council of Europe on 22 February 1983 and Explanatory memorandum. – Council of Europe. – Strasbourg : Council of Europe, 1983.
23p; 21cm.
'... prepared by the Committee of Experts on Legal Data Processing un der the authority of the European Committee on Legal Co- operation'. At head of cover: Council of Europe, Legal Affairs.
ISBN 9287102791

—Public liability : Recommendation no.R(84) 15 adopted by the Committee of Ministers of the Council of Europe on 18 September 1984, and explanatory memorandum. – Council of Europe. – Strasbourg : Council of Europe, 1985.
19p; 21cm.
'... prepared by the committee of experts on administrative law set up under the authority of the European Committee on Legal Co-operation. On cover: Council of Europe, Legal Affairs.
ISBN 9287103798

—Recommendations of the Committee of Ministers being of particular interest to prison administrations. – Council of Europe. – Strasbourg : Council of Europe, 1981.
various pagings; 30cm.
Introduction by Directorate of Legal Affairs (Division of Crime Problems). At head of title: Legal Affairs.

→ Reforms of local and regional authorities in Europe : theory, practice and critical appraisal : colloquy organised by the Council of Europe, Linz, 5-6 November 1981.

→ Regional and local affairs : news.

→ Regional development agencies and peripheral regions : report.

→ Response of local authorities to central government incitement to reduce expenditure.

→ Right to liberty and the rights of persons deprived of their liberty as guaranteed by Article 5 of the European Convention on Human Rights.

→ Right to respect for private and family life, home and correspondence as guaranteed by Article 8 of the European Convention on Human Rights.

—Role of criminal law in consumer protection / European Committee on Crime Problems. – Strasbourg : Council of Europe, 1983.
24p; 21cm.
Report and recommendations of the European Committee on Crime Problems on the role of criminal law in protecting consumers from exploitation by suppliers.
ISBN 928710218X Pbk £1.25

→ Role of local authorities in promoting the creation or operation of small or medium-sized firms within a general policy of endogenous development.

—Sixth International Colloquy About the European Convention of Human Rights. – Council of Europe. – Dordrecht : Kluwer, 1987.
1,168p.
ISBN 9024735394 Hbk £550.00

—Studies on criminal responsibility and psychiatric treatment of mentally ill offenders : reports presented to the seventh Criminological Colloquium (1985). – Council of Europe. – Strasbourg : Council of Europe, 1986.
103p; 21cm. – (Legal affairs).
On cover: European Committee on Crime Problems.
ISBN 9287108994

→ Study on common standards for query languages in computerised legal retrieval systems.

→ Survey of computing in European local and regional authorities.

—Teaching, research and training in the field of computers and the law : recommendation no. R (80)3 adopted by the Committee of Ministers of the Council of Europe on 30 April 1980 and explanatory memorandum. – Council of Europe. – Strasbourg : Council of Europe, 1981.
12p.
'Prepared by the Committee of Experts on Legal Data Processing' - verso t.p.. At head of cover title: Council of Europe, Legal Affairs.

—Telephone tapping and the recording of telecommunications in some Council of Europe member states / Council of Europe Directorate of Legal Affairs. – Strasbourg : Council of Europe, 1982.
12p; 30cm. – (Legislative dossier).
ISBN 9287100551

→ Use of management techniques in regional and local government : report.

—Violence in the family : Recommendation no.R (85) 4 adopted by the Committee of Ministers of the Council of Europe on 26 March 1985 and Explanatory memorandum. – Council of Europe. – Strasbourg : Council of Europe, 1986.
15p; 21cm. – (Legal affairs).
' ... prepared by a select committee of experts under the authority of the European Committee on Crime Problems' - p.3.

Council of Europe : a concise guide. – Strasbourg : Directorate of Press and Information, Council of Europe, 1982.
85p.
Includes bibliographical refrences.

Council of Europe, Parliamentary Assembly
Opinions, Recommendations, Resolutions and Orders Adopted by the Assembly. – Council of Europe, Parliamentary Assembly. – Strasbourg : Council of Europe.
Hbk £1.90

Council of European Municipalities →Local taxes in Europe : an analysis of how they function.

Council of Law Reporting of Tasmania → Tasmanian reports.

Council of Polytechnic Librarians
Information technology and polytechnic libraries : discussion papers / Council of Polytechnic Librarians. – S.l. : COPOL, 1984.
28p.
ISBN 0907130062

Council of the European Communities
Draft protocol on the settlement of litigation concerning the infringement and validity of Community patents / as agreed by the Interim Committee at its 13th session of 11 and 12 July 1985. – Brussels : Community Patent Interim Committee, 1985.
54p. – (CIBC).
This draft is intended to serve as a basis for a possible Interngovernmental Conference. Includes the preliminary draft of a Protocol on Privileges and Immunities of the Community Patent Appeal Court.

→ Implementation of the sixth EC directive on company law : an explanatory and consultative note.

→ Implementation of the third EC directive on company law : an explanatory and consultative note.

—Proposal for an eleventh Council directive : based on article 54(3)(g) of the treaty concerning disclosure requirements in respect of branches opened in a member state by certain types of companies governed by the law of another state / Council of the European Communities. – London : Department of Trade and Industry, 1987.
17,7p.
Includes a 'Background note' from the Deparment of Trade and Industry.

→ Records of the Luxembourg Conference on the Community patent, 1975.

—Rules of procedure of the Council of 24 July 1979 as amended on 20 July 1987. – Council of the European Communities. – Luxembourg : Office for Official Publications of the European Communities, 1987.
9p.
ISBN 9282404803

→ Single European Act.

→ Texts established by the Luxembourg Conference on the Community Patent, 1985.

Council of the Stock Exchange in Great Britain and Ireland →Stock exchange listing : the new requirements.

Council on Tribunals
Social security - abolition of independent appeals under the social fund : special report / by the Council on Tribunals. – London : H.M.S.O., 1986.
6p; 25cm.
ISBN 0101972202

Councillor. – 10th ed. – London : Shaw & Sons, 1987.
ISBN 0721908519 Pbk £4.95

Councils, committees & boards : a handbook of advisory, consultative, executive & similar bodies in British public life / edited by Lindsay Sellar. – a 6th ed. – Beckenham, Kent : CBD Research, 1984.
xiv,430p; 30cm. – (A CBD research publication).
ISBN 090024643X

Counsel. – London : Sweet & Maxwell.
Hbk £5.00

Counsel : the journal of the Bar of England and Wales. – London : Senate of the Inns of Court and the Bar, 1985.
ISBN 02683784

Counsel's guide to computers for the Bar : an introduction for barristers, their clerks and instructing solictors. – London : Senate of Inns of Court and the Bar, 1986.
32p.
Published with Counsel: The Journal of the Bar of England and Wales, Easter term issue (1986)..

Counterfeiting and forgery : a practical guide to the law / Roland Rowell. – London : Butterworths, 1986.
220p; 22cm.
Includes index.
ISBN 0406101108 Pbk £32

Counterfeiting and national laws : counterfeiting and the Paris Convention / memorandum of the Director General. – Geneva : World Intellectual Property Organization, 1986.
46,4p. – (PAC/CE/I/2).
Prepared for an intergovernmental group of experts called Committee of Experts on the Protection Against Counterfeiting and scheduled to meet at W.I.P.O. Headquarters Geneva from May 5 to 7 1986'.

Countertrade / by Leo G.B. Welt. – London : Euromoney, 1985.
xv,185p.
Added cover title: Special Euromoney report.
ISBN 090312176X

Countertrade Handbook. – Cambridge : Woodhead-Faulkner, 1987.
ISBN 0859413519 Hbk £40.00

Countries and islands of the world : a guide to nomenclature / Julie Wilcocks. – London : Bingley, 1981.
133p; 23cm.
ISBN 085157338X

Country Justice. – 2nd ed. – Abingdon : Professional Books, 1986 Reprint.
– (Classical English Law Texts Ser.).
ISBN 0862053137 Hbk £30.00

Country risk analysis / John Calverley. – London : Butterworths, 1985.
ix,181p; 23cm.
Includes index.
ISBN 0406005508 Hbk £38.00

Countryside Planning in Practice. – Stirling University Press, 1988.
ISBN 0948812028 Hbk £22.50

County court : practice and procedure, general / by Nicholas Yell and W.T. West. – Chichester : Barry Rose, 1982.
184p; 22cm.
ISBN 0859923347 corrected £27.50

County Court Costs. – 7th ed. – London : Longman Professional, 1985.
– (LPPN24).
ISBN 0851209599 Pbk £11.95

County Court Costs and Fees. – 14th ed. – London : Fourmat.
ISBN 185190056X Pbk £4.95

County court litigation / by Eric Owen. – London : Sweet and Maxwell, 1988.
lv,405p; 26cm.
An exposition of practice and procedure in county courts, cross-referenced with the Green and White Books. Suggests ways of handling procedure, and includes a section on preparation for trial and giving evidence. Looks at circumstances such as the financial position of a client on legal aid, and at changes resulting from the Civil Jurisdiction and Judgements Acts.
ISBN 0421354704 £38.00

County Court Practice 1986 / D. E. Peck. – London : Butterworths, 1986.
ISBN 0406163227 Hbk

County Court Practice. – London : Butterworths, 1983.
ISBN 0406163162 Hbk £172.50

County Court Practice. – Butterworths. – London : Butterworths, 1988.
ISBN 0406163243 Hbk £80.00

County Court Practice and Procedure. – 3rd ed. – London : Fourmat, 1984.
160p.
ISBN 0906840805 Pbk £10.95

County court practice handbook / David Price, Robert Blackford. – 7th ed. – London : Oyez Longman, 1984.
xxii,242p; 22cm. – (Oyez Longman practitioner series).
Previous ed.: published as Notes on county court practice and procedure. 1983. Includes index.
ISBN 0851209513 Pbk £14.50

County Court Precedents. – London : Butterworths, 1985.
Service to Date.
ISBN 040629240X Hbk £110.00

County court procedure in Northern Ireland including a supplement for the Republic of Ireland / B. J. A. C. Valentine and T. F. Grass. – Belfast : SLS Publications, 1985.
lviii,350p.
Kept up to date by supplements.
ISBN 0853892342

County Court Records of Accomack, Northampton, Virginia 1640-45. – London : Eurospan.
ISBN 0813903947 Hbk £17.50

County Court Rules (Northern Ireland). – Consolidated ed. – Belfast : HMSO, 1987-.
looseleaf.
First published 1981.

County Courts Districts (England and Wales) Index of Place Names. – 12th ed. – London : HMSO, 1983.
ISBN 0113906315 Hbk £20.00

Couper, Alastair D. →Times atlas of the oceans.

Course in Arbitration, 3 Vols. – College of Estate Management. – Reading : College of Estate Management.
Hbk

Course, Keith
Probation : North American Literature Review (1971-1981) / Rae Matonovich. – Regina : Prairie Justice Research, 1982.
ISBN 0773100512 Hbk £22.00

Course of lectures on the English law : delivered at the University of Oxford, 1767-1773 / by Sir Robert Chambers : and composed in association with Samuel Johnson : edited by Thomas M. Curley. – 2. – Oxford : Clarendon, 1986.
23cm.
Bibliography: p301-335. - Includes index.
ISBN 0198185448 £70.00

Court appointed experts in maritime cases : a comparative law study / by Arthur M. Boal and David R. Owen. – Antwerp : International Maritime Committee, 1981.
ii,83p.
Contents: questionnaire answers, compiled by Arthur M. Boal and David R. Owen.

Court Divided : The Fifth Circuit Court of Appeals And the Policies of Judicial Reform / Walker. – Yale University Press.
ISBN 0300041659 Hbk £20.00

Court is Open. – 3rd ed. 1987. – Mortdale : Petty Publishing Co, 1987.
208p.
ISBN 0908508042 Hbk £12.50

Court Jesters. – Agincourt : Carswell.
This is a collection of stories written and contributed by people from across the country. It is entertaining and provides puns, practical jokes and sometimes brilliant ripostes of some of the sharpest minds in the land.
Hbk £16.00

Court of Appeal (Civil Division) judgments, 1951-1980 / Victor Tunkel. – Microfiche ed. 222 microfiches. – London : HMSO Books, 1986.
in 12 ring binders.
Includes indexes of judges, plaintiffs and defendants. Accompanied by looseleaf insert in binder 1: The Court of Appeal transcripts 1951-1980: the microfiche edition: an introduction / by Victor Tunkel. - 33p..

Court of Auditors : Annual Record Concerning the Financial Year 1983 Accompanied by the Replies of the Institutions-1983. – Kirchberg : Commission of the European Communities, 1984.
253p.
Hbk

Court of Auditors of the European Communities. – Kirchberg : Commission of the European Communities, 1984.
24p.
Hbk

Court of Chancery Reports. – Repr. of 1758 ed. – Abingdon : Professional Books.
344p.
Hbk £95.00

Court of Justice of the European Communities / by L. Neville Brown and Francis G. Jacobs. – 2nd ed. – London : Sweet & Maxwell, 1983.
xxxi,305p; 19cm. – (Modern legal studies).
Previous ed.: 1977. Includes index.
ISBN 0421314001 Hbk
ISBN 0421314109 Pbk £7.95

Court of Justice of the European Communities. – Luxembourg : Office for Official Publications of the European Communities, 1985.
Hbk

Court of Justice of the European Communities
Digest of case-law relating to the European Communities
Series A : Judgements of the Court of Justice of the European Communities excluding cases connected with the European civil service and cases on the Convention of 27 September 1968 on Jurisdiction and the enforcement of judgments in civil and commercial matters / Court of Justice of the European Communities. – 1. – Luxembourg : Office for Official Publications of the European Communities, 1984.
loose-leaf; 23cm.
Periodically updated by supplements.
ISBN 9282900614
D series : Judgements of the Court of Justice of the European Communities and selected discussions of courts of Member States on the Convention of 27 September 1969 on jurisdiction and the enforcement of judgements in civil and commercial matters. – 1981.
Judgements of the Court of Justice of the European Communities and selected decisions of courts of member states on the convention of jurisdiction and the enforcement of judgements in civil and commercial matters.
ISBN 9282900398 Pbk £25.60

Court of Justice of the European Communities : References for Preliminary Rulings Under Article 177 of the E.E.C. Treaty and Cooperation between the Court and National Courts. – Luxembourg : Office for Official Publications of the European Communities, 1986.
47p.
Pbk

Court of Justice of the European Community. – 4th ed. – Luxembourg : Office for Official Publications of the European Communities, 1987.
91p.
ISBN 9282566048 Hbk free

Court of protection : a legal and policy analysis of the guardianship of the estate / Larry Gostin : foreword by Peter Jefferys. – London : Mind, National Association for Mental Health, 1983.
60p.
Bibliography: p.48.
ISBN 0900557567

Court of Protection Handbook. – 7th ed. – London : Longman Professional, 1986.
– (LPPN 39).
ISBN 0851209920 Pbk £13.95

Court of Protection Practice
Supplement 1986 / Arnold Stewart Massey. – 11th ed. – London : Sweet & Maxwell, 1986.
ISBN 0420469206 Hbk £80.00

Court of Protection Procedure. – London : Oyez Longman, 1983.
– (Oyez Longman Practice Note Ser.: No. 39).
Hbk £7.95

Court of Session Bill : report on the consolidation of certain enactments, and the repeal of other enactments, relating to the Court of Session / presented to Parliament by the Lord Advocate by Command of Her Majesty : Scottish Law Commission. – Edinburgh : HMSO, 1988.
36p.
ISBN 0101031521

Court of Session Cases : Series 1-5, 1821-1906, 63 Vols.
Incl. 1st Series, 1821-1838, 16 Vols. – Abingdon : Professional Books.
Hbk

Court of Star Chamber and its records to the reign of Elizabeth I / by J. A. Guy. – London : H.M.S.O., 1985.
112 p.
ISBN 0114401918

Court of the official in pre-Reformation Scotland : based on the surviving records of the officials of St. Andrews and Edinburgh / by Simon Ollivant. – Edinburgh : The Stair Society, 1982.
x,224p. – (Publications).
Bibliography: p201-206.
ISBN 0902292099

Court Order Interest Act / Law Reform Commission of British Columbia. – Vancouver : The Commission, 1985.
xi,409p. – (Working paper).

Court surveys and studies 1978-1984, concerning the civil caseloads of the Supreme Court, the County Court and the Magistrates' Courts of Victoria / J.R. Pullen, N.F. Young, S.J. Geddes. – Melbourne : Civil Justice Committee, 1985.
xvi,403p.
At head of title: Civil Justice Committee.

Courtney, B.
Trust taxation manual. – London : Butterworths, 1986.
ISBN 0406503303 Pbk £18.50

Courtney, David
Investors' Guide to Commodities Futures Markets / Bettelheim. – London : Butterworths, 1986.
ISBN 0406101906 Hbk £17.95

Courtright, John T. D.
Securities regulation of take-over bids in Canada / by John T. D. Courtright. – Calgary, Alta. : Carswell Legal Publications, Western Division, 1985.
xxii, 122 p.; 24 cm.
Includes index.
ISBN 0459373404 Pbk

Courts and Administrators. – Weidenfeld & Nicolson.
ISBN 0297794973 Hbk £14.95

Courts and free markets : perspectives from the United States and Europe
Vol.1 / edited by Terrance Sandalow and Eric Stein. – Oxford : Clarendon, 1982.
xxxix,271p; 24cm.
ISBN 0198253664 Hbk £22.50
Vol.2 / edited by Terrance Sandalow and Eric Stein. – 1982.
vip,p273-600; 24cm.
ISBN 0198253923 Hbk £30

Courts and the Charter / Clare F. Beckton and A. Wayne MacKay, research coordinators. – Toronto : University of Toronto Press in cooperation with the Royal Commission on the Economic Union and Development Prospects for Canada and the Canadian Government Publishing Centre, 1985.
xv,279p. – (Collected research studies).
Includes bibliographies.
ISBN 0802073050

Courts and the Development of Commercial Law. – Berlin : Duncker and Humblot, 1987.
203p.
ISBN 3428061764 Pbk £78.00

Courts and the Media. – London : Butterworths.
ISBN 0409862851 Hbk £46.00

Courts, law libraries and legal information in a changing society : 25. IALL Anniversary, Freiburg i. Br., July 15-20, 1984. – S.l. : International Association of Law Libraries, 1984.
184p.
Conference proceedings. Includes bibliographical references.

Courts of appeals in the federal judicial systems : a study of the Second, Fifth, and District of Columbia Circuits / J. Woodford Howard, Jr. – Princeton : Princeton University Press, 1981.
xxvi,415p; 25cm.
Includes index.
ISBN 0691076235 Hbk £18.10
ISBN 0691101000 Pbk £7.00

Courts of Justice Act, Bill 100, 1983 : An Act to Revise and Consolidate the Law Respecting the Organization, Operation and Proceedings of Courts of Justice in Ontario. – Ministry of the Attorney-General. – Ontario : Ontario Government Publications Service, 1983.
91p.
Hbk £1.00

Courts of the County Palatine of Durham from earliest times to 1971 / by Kenneth Emsley and C.M. Fraser. – Durham City : Durham County Local History Society, 1984.
ix,112p; 21cm.
ISBN 0902958070

Courts, prosecution, and conviction / by Michael McConville and John Baldwin. – Oxford : Clarendon, 1981.
232p; 23cm.
Bibliography: p213-226. - Includes index.
ISBN 0198253559 £12.00

Cousens
New Horizons Day Centre Incorporated Act, 1983, Bill Pr038 : An Act Respecting New Horizons Day Centre Incorporated. – Ontario : Ontario Government Publications Service, 1983.
3p.
Hbk £0.30

Cousins, Edward F
Law of Mortgages. – Sweet & Maxwell. – (Property and Conveyancing Library).
ISBN 0421344105 Hbk £65.00
—Pease and Chitty's Law of Markets and Fairs / Robert Anthony. – 3rd ed. – Tonbridge : Ernest Benn, 1984.
414p. – (Knights Looseleaf Library).
ISBN 0853143188 Hbk £45.00

Coutts, G → Local government in Scotland.

Coval, S. C.
Law and its presuppositions : actions, agents and rules / S.C. Coval and J.C. Smith. – London : Routledge & Kegan Paul, 1986.
viii, 141p. – (International library of philosophy).
ISBN 0710204469

Covenants : A Practical Guide to the Tax Advantages of Giving. – 4th ed. – Turnaround Press.
ISBN 0907164390 Pbk

Covenants : Practical Guide To Tax Advantages. – TUAR, 1982.
ISBN 0907164080 Pbk £3.95

Covenants in restraint of trade / Law Reform Commission of British Columbia. – Vancouver : The Commission, 1983.
iii,69p. – (Working paper).
Includes bibliographical references.

Cowan, L. D.
Clearing banks and the trade unions / by L. D. Cowan. – London : Institute of Bankers, 1984.
64p.
'Delivered under the auspices of King's College, London'.
ISBN 0852971168

Cowell, P.M.
Arbitration in Building Disputes. – London : Managment Update.
ISBN 0946679355 Hbk £14.95

Cowen, Denis V.
Law of negotiable instruments in South Africa Vol.1 : General principles / Denis V. Cowen and Leonard Gering. – Cape Town : Juta, 1985.
xxiv,587.
ISBN 0702115703

Cowles, Ronald V. → World coal mining law : a comparative survey.

Cowley, John D.
Bibliography of Abridgements, Digest, Dictionaries and Indexes of English Law to the Year 1800. – Abingdon : Professional Books, 1984.
ISBN 0862053714 Hbk £62.50

Cowley, Simon
Practice development for accountants / Toby Mountford. – London : Butterworths, 1984.
ISBN 0406260400 Pbk £15.00

Cowper, F.
Prospect of Gray's Inn. – 2nd ed. – London : GRAY, 1985.
ISBN 0420473300 Hbk £10.00

Cowsill
Evidence Law and Practice / Clegg. – 2nd ed. – London : Longman Professional, 1985.
ISBN 0851213502 Pbk £15.95

Cox
Capital Gains Tax On Businesses / Harry J Ross. – 2nd ed. – Sweet & Maxwell, 1986.
ISBN 0421339608 Hbk £21.00
—Cox's Criminal Law Cases : 1843-1941, 31 Vols. – Cox. – Repr. of 1978 ed. – London : Butterworths.
This 31 volume work is a comprehensive record of English criminal law cases. The cases reported are those heard in the Courts of Criminal Appeal, the Superior Courts, the Central Criminal Court, the Assizes, and in Ireland.
ISBN 0406015007 Hbk

Cox and Crime. – Cambridge : Institute of Criminology, 1985.
Hbk £4.00

Cox, Anthony N.
International factoring / by Anthony N. Cox and John A. MacKenzie. – London : Euromoney Publications, 1986.
xv,112p.
ISBN 0903121913

Cox, B.
Law of Special Educational Needs. – Oxford : Croom Helm, 1985.
ISBN 070993498X Pbk £7.95

Cox, Christopher
Capital gains tax on businesses / by Christopher Cox and Harry J. Ross. – 2nd ed. – London : Sweet & Maxwell, 1986.
xix,231p; 22cm.
Previous ed.: 1982. Includes index.
ISBN 0421339608 Pbk £14.00
—Capital gains tax on businesses / by Christopher Cox and Harry J. Ross. – London : Sweet & Maxwell, 1982.
xviii,221p,1folded leaf of plates; 23cm.
Includes index.
ISBN 0421282304 £18.00

Cox, D.B.
Finance of International Trade. – 4th ed. – Northwick Publishers. – (Personal Course for Bankers Series).
ISBN 090713548X Hbk £12.00

Cox, Derek → Worker-directors in private manufacturing industry in Great Britain.

Cox, H.W.V.
Medical Jurisprudence and Toxicology. – 5th ed. – Allahabad : Law Book Company, 1987.
800p.
Hbk £275.00

Cox, Jenny → Tolley's Companies Act : 1981.

Cox's Criminal Law Cases : 1843-1941, 31 Vols. – Cox. – Repr. of 1978 ed. – London : Butterworths.
This 31 volume work is a comprehensive record of English criminal law cases. The cases reported are those heard in the Courts of Criminal Appeal, the Superior Courts, the Central Criminal Court, the Assizes, and in Ireland.
ISBN 0406015007 Hbk

Coyne → Spicer and Pegler's management buy-outs.

CPAG Incomeg Supp, The Social Fund & Family Cred : The Legis 88. – Sweet & Maxwell.
ISBN 0421402709 Pbk £19.50

Cracknell, D G
Cracknell's Law Students' Companion : Contract. – 6th ed. – London : Butterworths, 1982.
This book is an aid to study of English contract law. The work is especially suited to students who have limited access to law libraries. The full text of the Unfair Contract Terms Act is included.
ISBN 0406567034 Pbk £20.00
—Cracknell's Law Students' Companions : Torts. – 6th ed. – London : Butterworths, 1983.
This book for law students in the United Kingdom is intended to be used along with textbooks and lecture notes. The work includes case summaries arranged alphabetically by case and relevant statutory materials.
ISBN 040656714X Pbk £22.00
—Law relating to charities / D.G. Cracknell. – 3rd ed. – London : Longman Professional (UK), 1987.
ISBN 0851213006 Hbk £29.50

Cracknell's Law Students' Companion : Contract. – 6th ed. – London : Butterworths, 1982.
This book is an aid to study of English contract law. The work is especially suited to students who have limited access to law libraries. The full text of the Unfair Contract Terms Act is included.
ISBN 0406567034 Pbk £20.00

Cracknell's Law Students' Companions : Torts. – 6th ed. – London : Butterworths, 1983.
This book for law students in the United Kingdom is intended to be used along with textbooks and lecture notes. The work includes case summaries arranged alphabetically by case and relevant statutory materials.
ISBN 040656714X Pbk £22.00

Craddock, R. J. → Legal and practical effects of the Transport Licensing Act (No. 2) 1983 : papers presented by R.J. Craddock ... et al., University of Auckland, 23 February 1984.

Craies
Statutes Law / Edgar. – 7th ed. – Sweet & Maxwell, 1971.
ISBN 0421145102 Hbk £68.00

Craig, Christine → Labour market structure, industrial organisation and low pay.

Craig, M.
Successful investment strategy. – 2nd ed. – Cambridge : Woodhead-Faulkner, 1988.
ISBN 0859413837 Hbk £25.00

Craig, P. P.
Administrative law / by P.P. Craig. – London : Sweet & Maxwell, 1983.
xxxiii,636p; 25cm.
Includes index.
ISBN 0421270500 Hbk £21.00
ISBN 0421270608 Pbk £15.50

Craig, Russell
Keeping employees informed / Roger Hussey. – Sydney : Butterworths, 1982.
175p.
Discusses various forms of employee communication, including noticeboards, mass meetings and discussion groups. Aims at assisting the manager to assess and improve the standard of his own employee communications by presenting a detailed picture of the current practice in Australia.
ISBN 0409309435 Pbk

Craig, W. Laurence, et al
International Chamber of Commerce Arbitration. – Paris : International Chamber of Commerce.
704p.
Hbk £75.00

Crane, Paul
Gays and the law / Paul Crane. – London : Pluto, 1982.
x,244p; 20cm.
Includes index.
ISBN 0861043863 Pbk £4.95

Cranston, R.
Law, Government and Public Policy. – Oxford : Oxford University Press.
ISBN 0195548485 Hbk £25.00
ISBN 0195548507 Pbk £13.95
—Legal Foundations of the Welfare State (LIC). – Weidenfeld & Nicolson, 1985.
ISBN 0297784870 Hbk £18.95
ISBN 0297785346 Pbk £12.95

Cranston, Ross
Consumers and the law / Ross Cranston. – 2nd ed. – London : Weidenfeld and Nicolson, 1984.
xli, 503p.
ISBN 029778272X
→ Delays and efficiency in civil litigation.
→ Law and economics.
—Law, government and public policy. – Victoria : Oxford University Press, 1988.
308.
This book examines the relationship between law and public policy in Australia, including a study of legislation. The courts are covered; also how social issues have to be cast in legal terms to be litigated; the impact of decisions on society.
ISBN 0195548485 Hbk £22.50
ISBN 0195548507 Pbk £12.50
—Legal foundations of the Welfare State. – London : Weidenfeld & Nicolson, 1984.
400p.
ISBN 0297784870 Hbk £16.00
ISBN 0297785346 Pbk £9.00

Crash and The Coming Crisis. – Northcote House, 1988.
ISBN 0746305435 Pbk £4.95

Crash of 87. – Oxford : Bloomsbury, 1988.
ISBN 0747502137 Hbk £13.95

Crawford, Colin
'Free two pence' Section 137 of the Local Government Act 1972 and Section 83 of the Local Governement (Scotland) Act 1973 / by Colin Crawford and Victor Moore. – London : The Chartered Institute of Public Finance and Accountancy, 1983.
x,218p.
ISBN 0852992556
—Planning Office's Advice and Undertakings : Estoppel and Personal Bar in Public Law / Colin T. Reid. – Glasgow : Planning Exchange, 1982.
70p. – (Scottish Planning Law and Practice Occasional Paper Ser.: No. 3).
Pbk £6.00

Crawford, James
Australian courts of law / James Crawford. – Melbourne : Oxford University Press, 1982.
297 p.; 21 cm.
Includes bibliographical references and index.
ISBN 0195543076 Pbk
→ Rights of peoples.

Crawford, Michael G.
Journalist's Legal Guide. – Agincourt : Carswell, 1986.
266p.
This legal manual for working journalists in Canada addresses a variety of relevant legal subjects, including: access to information, contempt, defamation, police powers, court structure, and procedure. A glossary of legal terms is included in the text.
Hbk £33.75

Crawford, Peter → Witnesses in the criminal courts : a report.

Crawford, Roland → Report of the proceedings and papers of the second Magistrates' Workshop.

Crawford, Thomas Simpson
Crawford's Proof in criminal cases / Reg Bartley. – 4th ed. – Sydney : Law Book Co., 1982.
xxii, 279 p.; 23 cm.
'Table of cases': p. ix, xxii. Includes index.
ISBN 045520537X £22.50

Crawford's Proof in criminal cases / Reg Bartley. – 4th ed. – Sydney : Law Book Co., 1982.
xxii, 279 p.; 23 cm.
'Table of cases': p. ix, xxii. Includes index.
ISBN 045520537X £22.50

Crayencour, J.-P. de
Professions in the European Community : towards freedom of movement and mutual recognition of qualifications / J.-P. de Crayencour. – Luxembourg : Office for Official Publications of the European Communities, 1981.
137p.
ISBN 9282527913

Creamer, Harriet →Hybrid corporate securities : international legal aspects.

Creating an information service / Sylvia P. Webb : illustrated by Patricia Calderhead. – London : Aslib, 1983.
v,101p; 24cm.
ISBN 0851421865

Creation and Preservation : Law and the Cultural Heritage / Lyndel V Prott. – Abingdon : Professional Books, 1985.
– (Volume II).
ISBN 0862050774 Hbk £33.50
ISBN 0862050820 Pbk £22.00

Creation of the European Union and its relation to the EEC treaties / by Joseph Weiler and James Modrall. – Florence : European University Institute, 1985.
44p.

Creation of Violent Criminals. – Routledge.
ISBN 041502837X Hbk £22.50

Creation of world poverty / Teresa Hayter. – London : Pluto Press, 1981.
128p.
Bibliography: p.124-127.
ISBN 0861043391

Credit and Guarantee Financing, Transfer of Technology / edited by C.C.A. Voskuil, Z. Parac. J.A. Wade. – Dordrecht : M. Nijhoff, 1987.
xvii,372p.
Includes bibliographical references.
ISBN 9024735297 Hbk £165.00

Credit Cards / Charles W Ferrier. – London : Butterworths, 1984.
ISBN 0406259402 Pbk £10.95

Credit Cards and the Law. – London : Fourmat, 1988.
ISBN 1851900462 Hbk £14.95

Credit Contracts Act 1981 : an annotated edition of the Statute / by D. F. Dugdale. – Wellington : Butterworths, 1981.
vii,99p.
Includes index.
ISBN 0409601322

Credit Debt and Poverty. – London : Policy Studies Institute, 1988.
ISBN 0853743479 Pbk £8.95

Credit Insurance / Briggs. – Cambridge : Woodhead-Faulkner, 1987.
ISBN 0859411761 Hbk £40.00

Credit revolution : papers from the seminar on the N.S.W. Credit Bill 1981, organised by the Faculty of Law, University of N.S.W., the N.S.W. Department of Consumer Affairs & the Australian Finance Conference, 13 July 1981. – 1. – Kensington, N.S.W. : Faculty of Law, University of New South Wales, 1981.
various pagings.
At head of title: The University of New South Wales, Faculty of Law.

Credit scoring : A paper / by the Office of Fair Trading. – London : Office of Fair Trading, 1982.
11p.
Cover title: Credit scoring : a consultative document.

Credit Unions / Hinton. – Policy Studies Institute.
ISBN 085374405X Pbk £5.95

Creditor and Debtor Law in Australia and New Zealand. – 3rd ed. – North Ryde : C.C.H. Australia, 1986.
333p.
ISBN 0869035908 Hbk £35.00

Creditor-debtor law in Canada / by C.R.B. Dunlop : with chapter 14 / by P.J.M. Lown. – Toronto, Canada : Carswell, 1981.
cxxii, 563 p.; 26 cm.
'Table of cases': p. xiii-lxxxi 'Table of statutes, rules and regulations': p. lxxxv-cxvi. Includes index. Bibliography: p. cxvii-cxxii.
ISBN 0459340506 Pbk

Creditors' and Debtors' Rights 1987-1988. – Agincourt : Carswell, 1988.
563p. – (Bar Admission Course Material Ser.).
This is a guidebook to the rights of creditors and debtors. Topics include types of secured transactions, construction liens, personal property security, receivership and bankruptcy. Also included are sample forms and precedents used in different types of transactions and proceedings.
Hbk £75.75

Creditors' Remedies - 1985. – Vancouver : British Columbia Continuing Legal Education Society, 1985.
348p.
ISBN 0865042209 Hbk £65.00

Creditors' Remedies : 1985 Supplement. – Vancouver : Continuing Legal Education Society of British Columbia, 1986.
19p.
ISBN 0865043779 Hbk £15.00

Creditor's Remedies in Alberta / Peter Vaartnou. – Agincourt : Carswell, 1987.
ca 620p.
Hbk £76.75

Creditors' Remedies in Alberta / Peter Vaartnou. – Agincourt : Carswell, 1987.
620p.
This work focuses on collection practice in Alberta. Discussions are in-depth and include all the issues involved in the collection process, from making the decision to sue to drafting documents, realizing on security and enforcing judgments. Each chapter is arranged so that the procedures and possible problem areas are explained.
Hbk £81.50

Creery
Reducing Labor Turnover in Financial Institutions / Creery. – Quorum Press.
ISBN 0899302963 Hbk £32.95

Creery, Ian
Inuit (Eskimo) of Canada / by Ian Creery. – London : Minority Rights Group, 1983.
16p. – (Report).
Bibliography: p.16.

Cregan →Law and Practice of Futures and Options.

Creighton, Susan J.
Trends in child abuse, 1977-82 : the fourth report on the children placed on N.S.P.C.C. Special Unit registers / by Susan J. Creighton. – London : N.S.P.C.C., 1984.
57p.
Bibliography: p.35.
ISBN 0902498126

Creighton, W. B.
Labour law : materials and commentary / by W. B. Creighton, W. J. Ford, R. J. Mitchell. – North Ryde, N.S.W. : Law Book Co., 1983.
liii,944p; 25cm.
ISBN 0455204136
—Understanding Occupational Health and Safety Law in Victoria. – North Ryde : C.C.H. Australia, 1986.
236p.
ISBN 0869038389

Cremades, B M
Litigating in Spain: considerations for foreign practitioners including international judicial assistance, enforcement of foreign judgements, bankruptcy, arbitration and other civil proceedings in Spain. – Kluwer Law and Taxation, 1989.
579.
Informs investors, and potential investors how to protect their investments under Spanish law. Provides footnotes and other information relevant to precedents in Spanish courts. Contains a table of the Spanish Judicial Structure, and an appendix of all the International conventions ratified by Spain.
ISBN 9065443770 Hbk £52.75/Dfl 163

Cremades, Bernardo Maria →Spanish business law.

Crespi, R. S. →Biotechnology and patent protection : an international review.
—Patents : a Basic Guide to Patenting in Biotechnology. – Cambridge : Cambridge University Press.
– (Cambridge Studies in Biotechnology No. 6).
ISBN 052132954X Pbk £20.00

Cressey, Peter →Industrial democracy and participation : a Scottish survey.

Cresswell, Peter J. →Encyclopaedia of banking law.

Cretney, S M
Elements of Family Law. – London : Sweet & Maxwell, 1987.
ISBN 0421352302 Hbk £19.50
ISBN 042135240X Pbk £13.50
—Principles of family law / by S.M. Cretney. – 4th ed. – London : Sweet & Maxwell, 1984.
lxxx,1018p; 25cm.
Covers marriage, the termination of marriage, protection, children and family law, family financial obligations and property rights and the courts. Includes changes effected by the Matrimonial and Family Proceedings Act 1984, and the section on the law governing children in care has been expanded.
ISBN 042128840X Hbk
ISBN 0421288507 Pbk £19.50

Cretton, Colin P. →Business tax handbook.
—Investment in Shares and Securities. – London : Butterworths, 1988.
ISBN 0406504504 Pbk £40.00
—Taxation of Investment in Shares and Securities. – London : Butterworths.
ISBN 0406504504 Pbk £30.00

Crew, M. P. →Intellectual property in New Zealand and Australia.

Crichton
Understanding factoring and trade credit / Charles W Ferrier. – London : Waterlow, 1986.
ISBN 0080392040 Pbk £13.50

Crime
Vol.15 : Crime / by Monica A. Walker. – Oxford : Published for the Royal Statistical Society and the Social Science Research Council by Pergamon, 1981.
xii,406p; 26cm.
Bibliography: p281-284. - Includes index. Originally titled: Reviews of United Kingdom statistical sources.
ISBN 0080261043 £18.25

Crime and Criminal Justice System in India. – New Delhi : Deep and Deep Publications, 1984.
338p.
Hbk £200.00

Crime and criminology : a critical introduction / Nigel Walker. – Oxford : Oxford University Press, 1987.
xv,219p; 23cm.
Bibliography: p210-212. - Includes index.
ISBN 0192192124 Hbk £12.95
ISBN 0192891936 Pbk £4.95

Crime and Deviance : Issues in Sociology. – London : Macmillan.
ISBN 033344051X Pbk £4.25

Crime and justice statistics 1985 / Ministry of Finance and Economic Planning, Statistics Division. – Yola, Gongola State : The Ministry, 1986.
vii,85p.
'This issue of the Digest of crime and justice statistics is the first in this series'. - p.i.

Crime and penal policy / David Smith and A.J. Fowles. – York : Longman, 1986.
24p; 30cm.
Bibliography: p23-24.
ISBN 0582172551 Pbk

Crime and police effectiveness / by Ronald V. Clarke and Mike Hough. – London : H.M.S.O., 1984.
iv,28p; 28cm. – (A Home Office Research and Planning Unit report).
ISBN 0113407734

Crime and public housing : proceedings of a workshop held in September 1980 / edited by Mike Hough and Pat Mayhew. – London : Home Office, 1982.
v,77p. – (Research and Planning Unit paper).
Includes bibliographies.
ISBN 0862520347

Crime and punishment : interpreting the data / A. Keith Bottomley, Ken Pease. – Milton Keynes : Open University Press, 1986.
xviii,185p; 24cm.
Bibliography: p171-180. - Includes index.
ISBN 0335153909 Hbk £25.00
ISBN 0335153895 Pbk £8.95

Crime and Punishment in Britain : An Analysis of the Penal System in Theory, Law, and Practice. – Amsterdam : University Press.
Hbk

Crime and Punishment in Modern America / Pascale. – London : Eurospan.
ISBN 0942522001 Pbk £13.75

Crime and Social Justice / Paul Takagi. – London : Macmillan, 1981.
232p. – (Critical Criminology Ser.).
ISBN 0333282604 Hbk £18.00
ISBN 0333282612 Pbk £6.95

Crime and Social Reading In History and Theory. – Routledge.
ISBN 0710009445 Pbk £11.95

Crime and Society. – London : Macmillan.
ISBN 0333435273 Hbk £25.00
ISBN 0333435281 Pbk £7.95

Crime and society : readings in history and theory / compiled by Mike Fitzgerald, Gregor McLennan and Jennie Pawson. – London : Routledge & Kegan Paul in association with Open University Press, 1981.
vii,504p; 22cm. – (An Open University set book).
Includes bibliographies and index.
ISBN 0710009445 Pbk £8.95

Crime and the courts in England, 1660-1800 / J.M. Beattie. – Oxford : Clarendon, 1986.
xxiv, 663p; 25cm.
Bibliography: p645-651. - Includes index.
ISBN 0198200587 Hbk £48.00
ISBN 0198200579 Pbk £15.00

Crime and the criminal law : reflections of a magistrate and social scientist / by Barbara Wootton. – 2nd ed. – London : Stevens, 1981.
xii,119p; 19cm.
Previous ed.: 1963.
ISBN 0420461701 Hbk
ISBN 0420461809 Pbk £5.00

Crime and the new magistrate / by Ronald Bartle. – Chichester : Rose, 1985.
vi,65p; 22cm.
Includes index.
ISBN 0859923312 Pbk £6.00

Crime, Capitalism and Community. – Toronto : Butterworths, 1983.
168p.
ISBN 0409871923 Pbk £15.95

Crime control and the police : a review of research / by Pauline Morris and Kevin Heal. – London : H.M.S.O., 1981.
v,67p.
Bibliography: p56-67. A Home Office Research Unit report.
ISBN 0113407076

Crime Control in Japan. – Canberra : Australian Institute of Criminology.
Hbk £21.95

Crime Dictionary. – Revised Edition. – London : Facts On File.
ISBN 0816018723 Hbk £18.50

Crime, guilt, and punishment : a philosophical introduction / C.L. Ten. – Oxford : Clarendon, 1987.
176p; 22cm.
Includes bibliography and index.
ISBN 019875082X Hbk £19.50
ISBN 0198750811 Pbk £8.95

Crime in a New Community : The Case of Tuggeranong. – Canberra : Australian Institute of Criminology.
Hbk £1.50

Crime in Canadian society / James T Teevan. – 3rd. – Scarborough, Ontario : Butterworths (Canada).
440.
Opens with a discussion of the controversy surrounding the definition of crime, and then moves into a discussion and critique of the ways of measuring crime in Canada. Gives various explanations of crime from functional analysis to liberal criminology, labelling theory and critical theory. Concludes with a selection of contemporary Canadian criminological research.
ISBN 040986580X

Crime In Papua New Guinea. – Canberra : Australian Institute of Criminology.
Hbk £2.25

Crime in seventeenth century England. – Cambridge : Cambridge University Press.
Studes court records in Essex. Analyses social processes involved in prosecution.
ISBN 0521250749 Hbk £32.50

Crime Investigation : Art or Science?. – Edinburgh : Scottish Academic Press Ltd, 1984.
102p.
ISBN 0707304377 Hbk £10.00
ISBN 0707304385 Pbk

Crime, Justice, and Codification : Essays in Commemoration of Jacques Fortin. – Agincourt : Carswell, 1986.
196p.
This book contains eleven essays dealing with the theory, philosophy, reform and codification of criminal law. Rationality and legitimacy of criminal law the goals of reform are addressed in the essays.
Hbk £40.50

Crime, justice and the mass media : papers presented to the 14th Cropwood Round-Table Conference, December 1981 / edited by Colin Sumner. – Cambridge : University of Cambridge Institute of Criminology, 1982.
ii,123p.
Includes bibliographical references.

Crime, justice and underdevelopment / edited by Colin Sumner. – London : Heinemann, 1982.
xvi,345p; 23cm.
Bibliography: p312-331. - Includes index.
ISBN 0435828886 £19.50

Crime, Law and Business : The Sociological Sources of Australian Monopoly Law. – Canberra : Australian Institute of Criminology.
Hbk £3.00

Crime on the London Underground / report of a study by the Department of Transport in conjunction with London Underground ... et al. – London : H.M.S.O., 1986.
118p.
Describes a study by the Department of Transport – suggests crime on the Underground is relatively rare – 15300 offences (1600 violent) in 725 million journeys during 1985. Recognises that cost of crime to the system could be 10 million per year and shows that the public are afraid of violence and theft.
ISBN 0115508058

Crime Prevention : Planning and Participation in Geelong. – Canberra : Australian Institute of Criminology.
free

Crime Prevention in Developing Areas. – Canberra : Australian Institute of Criminology.
free

Crime Prevention Planning : Proceedings of the United National Interregional Course. – Canberra : Australian Institute of Criminology.
Hbk £2.95

Crime, proof and punishment : essays in memory of Sir Rupert Cross / Rupert Cross, Colin Tapper. – London : Butterworths, 1981.
xxvi,336p; 26cm.
Bibliography of works by Sir Rupert Cross: p.323-327. - Includes index. Edited by Colin Tapper.
ISBN 0406569991

Crime, protest, community and police in nineteenth-century Britain / David Jones. – London : Routledge & Kegan Paul, 1982.
xi, 247p.
Includes index. Includes bibliography.
ISBN 0710090080

Crime, race and culture : a study in a developing country / Howard Jones. – Chichester : Wiley, 1981.
xv,184p; 24cm.
Bibliography: p175-179. - Index.
ISBN 047127996X £12.75

Crime trends in twentieth-century Australia / Satyanshu Kumar Mukherjee, assisted by Evelyn N. Jacobsen, John R. Walker, R. W. Fitzgerald. – Wooden : Australian Institute of Criminology, 1981.
xviii,199p.
Includes bibliographical references and index.
ISBN 086861386X

Crime UK 1988 / Harrison. – Policy Journals.
ISBN 0946967245 Hbk £24.50

Crime victims : needs, services and the voluntary sector / R.I. Mawby, M.L. Gill. – London : Tavistock, 1987.
ix,261p; 22cm.
Bibliography: p241-254. - Includes index.
ISBN 0422614505 Pbk

Crimes : Commentary on the Narcotic Drugs and Psychotrophic Substances Act, 1985, and the Narcotic Drugs and Psychotrophic Substances Rules, 1985 with State Rules and Notifications. – Delhi : Vinod Prakashan, 1987.
615p.
Hbk £150.00

Crimes against the environment / Law Reform Commission of Canada. – Ottawa : The Commission, 1985.
75,85p. – (Working paper).
Bibliography: p.71-72. Cover title: Protection of life: crimes against the environment. Added t.p. in French: Les crimes contre l'environnement. Pages numbered in opposite directions. Text in English and French.
ISBN 0662539907

Crimes against the state / Law Reform Commission of Canada. – Ottawa : The Commission, 1986.
72,76p. – (Working paper).
Includes bibliographies. Added t.p. in French: Les crimes contre l'etat. Pages numbered in opposite directions. Text in English and French.

Criminal and victim : crime and society in early nineteenth-century England / George Rude. – Oxford : Clarendon, 1985.
ix,160p; 22cm.
Includes bibliography and index.
ISBN 0198226462 £17.50

Criminal Appeal Reports. – London : Sweet & Maxwell.
Hbk £90.00
Bound Vol.. –
Hbk £34.00
Back Vols..

Criminal Appeal Reports (Sentencing). – London : Sweet & Maxwell.
Hbk £52.00
Bound Vol.. –
Hbk £19.75
Indiv. parts. –
Hbk £28.00

Criminal appeals : a practical guide to appeals to and from the Crown Court / by Ian McLean. – 2nd ed. – London : Barry Rose, 1986.
xxxv,249p.
Previous ed.: 1980. Includes bibliographical references and index. Includes examples of court forms.
ISBN 085992372X

Criminal behaviour : an introduction to criminology and the penal system / Herschel Prins. – 2nd ed. – London : Tavistock, 1982.
x,309p; 21cm.
Previous ed.: London : Pitman, 1973. Includes bibliographies and index.
ISBN 0422776807 Hbk
ISBN 0422776904 Pbk

Criminal Code : 1893. – Repr. of 1980 ed. – Agincourt : Carswell.
1200p. – (Carswell's Classic Reprints).
This book is a reproduction of the 1893 treatise on the first Criminal Code of Canada.
Hbk £109.25

Criminal Code : 1988. – Agincourt : Carswell, 1987.
780p.
Pbk £62.25

Criminal Code Annotations : 1964-1970. – Agincourt : Carswell, 1981.
388p.
Hbk £50.50

Criminal Code Annotations : 1971-1986 Vol. 2. – Agincourt : Carswell.
Hbk £63.00

Criminal Code Driving Offences : Breathalyzer Law in Canada, 3 Vols. – Agincourt : Carswell, 1988.
This three volume set of looseleaf books provides a comprehensive treatment of the Criminal Code offenses. Offenses include criminal negligence, dangerous driving, failing to remain and driving while disqualified. The elements of each offense and caselaw analyzing such is discussed. Orders of prohibition and the Charter of Rights and Bill of Rights are discussed.
Hbk £189.00

Criminal Confiscation Orders : the New Law. – London : Butterworths.
ISBN 0406105294 Pbk £16.95

Criminal Court Handbook, Criminal Manual Major Acts. – Allahabad : Law Publisher, 1983.
Hbk £18.00

Criminal Court Handbook (Minor Acts), 4 Vols. – Lucknow : Eastern Book Company, 1985.
Hbk

Criminal Court Handbook (Three Major Acts). – 17th ed. 1982 repr. – Lucknow : Eastern Book Company, 1985.
808p.
Hbk £90.00

Criminal court in action / David Barnard : assisted by Peter L. Gray, Paul S. Bogan. – 3rd ed. – London : Butterworth, 1988.
xviii,365p; 25cm.
Previous ed.: 1979. Includes index.
ISBN 0406556148 Hbk £16.50
ISBN 0406556156 Pbk £10.95

Criminal Court Practice : with Model Forms. – 2nd ed. – North Ryde : Law Book Co, 1987.
Hbk £250.00

Criminal Defences / P.A. Fairall. – 2nd ed. – Butterworths, 1988.
288p.
ISBN 0409492760 Hbk £49.00

Criminal Evidence / J.M. Hirst. – Waterlow. – (Criminal Law Library Series No. 4).
ISBN 0080392377 Hbk £50.00

Criminal Evidence. – Vancouver : Continuing Legal Education Society of British Columbia, 1985.
81p.
ISBN 0865042381 Hbk £55.00

Criminal evidence / by Richard May. – London : Sweet & Maxwell, 1986.
xlii,368p.
Covers aspects of the law of criminal evidence with emphasis on their practical application. Includes sections on burden and standard of proof, exclusionary rules and exceptions, and rules of evidence connected with the trial. Includes the Police and Criminal Evidence Act 1984.
ISBN 0421302909 Pbk £24

Criminal evidence : affidavit evidence, hearsay and related matters in criminal proceedings / Scottish Law Commission. – Edinburgh : The Commission, 1988.
iv,145p. – (Discussion paper).
Includes excerpts from the Criminal Justice Act 1967 and the Police and Criminal Evidence Act 1984.

Criminal Evidence and Procedure, No. 2 / Wilkie. – 7th ed. – London : Butterworths, 1981. – (Police Promotion Handbooks Ser.).
This work for United Kingdom police officers covers the basic rules of criminal evidence and procedure from the perspective of the officer working in the field.
Police officers
ISBN 0406841314 Pbk

Criminal Evidence in Hong Kong / Gerard McCoy. – London : Butterworths, 1987.
ISBN 0409995479 Hbk £54.00

Criminal Fraud 1987 / Weinberg. – London : Law Book Co.
ISBN 0455207453 Hbk £37.50

Criminal fraud / J. Douglas Ewart. – Toronto : Carswell, 1986.
xv, 182 p.; 24 cm.
Includes bibliographical references and index.
ISBN 045938550X

Criminal Injuries Compensation. – London : Butterworths.
ISBN 0409988286 Hbk £30.00

Criminal Injuries Compensation. – 2nd ed. – London : Waterlow, 1986.
ISBN 008039244X Pbk £9.95

Criminal injuries compensation : a statutory scheme / report of an interdepartmental working party. – London : H.M.S.O., 1986.
90p.
Review of Criminal Injuries Compensation Scheme from 1979 to 1984. 68 recommendations for change, including legal right to compensation, allowing compensation in cases of family violence to cover all persons living together and fixed awards for victims of rape who bear children as a result.
ISBN 0113406258

Criminal Injuries Compensation Board
Twentieth Report. – Criminal Injuries Compensation Board. – London : HMSO, 1984.
ISBN 0101939906 Hbk £4.50

Criminal intrusion / Law Reform Commission of Canada. – Ottawa : The Commission, 1986.
25,30p. – (Working paper).
Includes bibliographical references. Added t.p. in French: L'intrusion criminelle. Pages numbered in opposite directions. Text in English and French.
ISBN 0662542061

Criminal investigation : a selective literature review and bibliography / by Duncan Chappell, Robert Gordon, Rhonda Moore. – Ottawa : Ministry of the Solicitor General, Communication Division, 1982.
68p.
ISBN 0662120310

Criminal Investigation : Interim Report. – Land Reform Commission. – Repr. of 1977 ed. – Canberra : Australian Government Publishing Service, 1983.
224p. – (ALRC Report: No. 2).
ISBN 0642017921 Hbk £13.00

Criminal jurisdiction of magistrates / by Brian Harris. – 11th ed. – Chichester? : Barry Rose, 1988.
lxxxi,848p.
Previous ed.: 1986. Includes index.
ISBN 1870080513

Criminal jurisdiction of magistrates in Papua New Guinea / by N.K.F. O'Neill and R.N. Desailly : with a foreword by Buri Kidu. – 1. – Sydney : New South Wales Institute of Technology, 1982.
loose-leaf.
Includes index.
ISBN 0909684375

Criminal Jurisprudence and Law of Insanity. – New Delhi : Deep and Deep Publications, 1988.
172p.
Hbk £125.00

Criminal Jury Trials. – Vancouver : Continuing Legal Education Society of British Columbia, 1988.
165p.
ISBN 0865049742 Hbk £70.00

Criminal Justice : 1981 Conference of the Canadian Institute for the Administration of Justice. – Carswell Legal Publications. – Agincourt : Carswell, 1982.
300p.
Hbk £38.75

Criminal justice : a working paper. – Rev. ed. – London : H.M.S.O., 1986.
51p.
'Designed and produced for the Home Office by the Central Office of Information'.
ISBN 086252265X

Criminal justice : a working paper. – London : Home Office, 1984.
36p.
'Prepared for the Home Office by the Central Office of Information'.
ISBN 0862521483

Criminal justice : plans for legislation : presented to Parliament by the Secretary of State for the Home Department ... / Home Office. – London : HMSO, 1986.
23p; 25cm.
ISBN 010196580X Hbk £2.80

Criminal justice : the story of Edith Thompson / by Rene Weis. – London : Hamish Hamilton, 1988.
xviii,327p,8p of plates; 24cm.
Includes index.
ISBN 0241122635 £14.95

Criminal Justice Act 1982 : A Guide to Fines. – Butterworths Editorial Staff. – London : Butterworths, 1983.
This text for magistrates in the United Kingdom provides a condensation of the changes in the fine schedules for Criminal Acts brought about by the Criminal Justice Act of 1982.
ISBN 0406008604 Pbk

Criminal Justice Acts 1987 and 1988 : A Commentary. – Waterlow.
– (Criminal Law Guides).
ISBN 0080330886 Pbk £14.95

Criminal justice comparisons : the case of Scotland and England and Wales / Lorna J.F. Smith. – London : Home Office, 1983.
v,57p.
Bibliography: p.50.
ISBN 0862521009

Criminal Justice History : An International Annual Volume 8. – London : Meckler, 1987.
ISBN 0887361714 Hbk £37.50

Criminal justice in Australia / Peter Sallmann and John Willis. – Melbourne : Oxford University Press, 1984.
240p.
Bibliography: p227-235.
ISBN 0195544595

Criminal justice in Canada: an introductory text / John F Klein, Simon B Verdun-Jones. – Scarborough, Ontario : Butterworths (Canada).
359.
Overview of the Canadian criminal justice system. Coverage includes corectional institutions, policing in Canada, police powers and discretion, the criminal court system, sentencing, the public and criminal justice system, community-based corrections, juvenile justice system, special categories of offenders, and trends in Canadian criminal justice.
ISBN 0409998022 Pbk

Criminal justice in South Africa : selected aspects of discretion / M.C.J. Olmesdahl, N.C. Steytler. – Cape Town : Juta, 1983.
viii,303p.
Includes bibliographical references.
ISBN 0702113379

Criminal Justice Policy : From Research to Reform. – Butterworths, 1983.
152p.
Asks whether a particular problem is actually as serious as it is assumed to be, and whether it deserves a prominent place in the agenda of the policy makers. Concludes that neither ple-bargaining nor court delay is as threatening as commonly supposed, and that the processing of minor crimes in court imposes unjustifiably heavy costs.
ISBN 0409868426 Hbk £40.00

Criminal Justice Research Methodology. – Canberra : Australian Institute of Criminology.
free

Criminal justice revolution : the third Sir Gwilym Morris memorial lecture delivered on 24th October 1986 / by Graham Zellick. – Cardiff? : University of Wales Institute of Science and Technology, 1986.
24p.
Includes bibliographical references.

Criminal justice (Scotland) Act 1980. – Edinburgh : Green (W.) & Son, 1981.
Annotated copy of this Act which introduced important changes relating to Scotttish criminal law and procedure. With the text of the Act of Adjournal providing for some of the procedures under the Act.
ISBN 0414006747 Pbk

Criminal justice system model : magistrates' courts sub-model / Susan Rice. – London : Home Office, 1984.
vi,66p.
Bibliography: p.59.
ISBN 0862521254

Criminal justice system model : the flow model / Hugh Pullinger. – London : Home Office, 1985.
vi,56p.
Bibliography: p.56.
ISBN 0862522234

Criminal Law. – Community Legal Education Ontario. – Toronto : Community Legal Education Ontario, 1981.
49p.
ISBN 0889030553 Pbk £6.50

Criminal Law / Daniel J. Baum. – Toronto : IPI Publishing, 1983.
84p. – (You and the Law Ser.).
ISBN 045896140X Pbk £7.95

Criminal Law / Caldwell. – 6th ed. – London : Butterworths, 1981.
ISBN 040960058X Hbk £46.70

Criminal law / by Peter Gillies. – Sydney : Law Book Co., 1985.
lvii,668p.
Includes bibliographical references and index.
ISBN 0455205981

Criminal Law / Manning. – 2nd ed. – London : Butterworths.
ISBN 0409849227 Hbk £72.00

Criminal Law. – 6th ed. – Bombay : Tripathi, 1982.
xxxii, 892p.
Pbk £60.00

Criminal Law / Ryan. – London : Financial Training, 1986.
– (SWOT).
ISBN 0906322987 Pbk £6.95

Criminal law / by Peter Seago. – 2nd ed. – London : Sweet & Maxwell, 1985.
xx,326p; 22cm.
Previous ed.: 1981. Bibliography: p317-318. - Includes index.
ISBN 0421338903 Pbk £9.50

Criminal law / by J.C. Smith and Brian Hogan. – 6th ed. – London : Butterworths, 1988.
900p; 25cm.
Previous ed.: 1983. Includes index.
ISBN 0406658110 Hbk £35.00 :
ISBN 0406658129 Pbk £19.00

Criminal law / by C.R. Snyman : translation by the author, assisted by Lesbury van Zyl. – Durban : Butterworths, 1984.
545; 25 cm.
Includes indexes. Bibliography: p. 486-492. Translation of: Strafreg.
ISBN 0409056189 Pbk R64.00

Criminal Law. – London : Butterworths, 1983.
ISBN 0409056170 Hbk £46.20
ISBN 0409056189 Pbk £34.70

Criminal law / Brian Harrie KevinB.H.K. Donovan. – North Ryde : Law Book Co, 1984.
xiv, 98p. – (Nutshells).
ISBN 0455203458 Hbk

Criminal law : art and part guilt of statutory offences / Scottish Law Commission. – Edinburgh : H.M.S.O., 1985.
v,21p.
ISBN 0101955103

Criminal law : binding over - the issues / The Law Commission. – London : H.M.S.O., 1987.
vi,113p; 21cm. – (Working paper).
ISBN 011730185X

Criminal law : cases and materials / J.C. Smith, Brian Hogan. – 3rd ed. – London : Butterworths, 1986.
700p; 25cm.
Previous ed.: 1980. Includes index.
ISBN 0406658242 Pbk £ :
ISBN 0406658250

Criminal law : codification of the criminal law : a report to the Law Commission. – London : H.M.S.O., 1985.
vi,245p.
ISBN 0102270856

Criminal law : conspiracy to defraud : an invitation for views / Law Commission. – London : The Commission, 1987.
14 leaves.

Criminal Law : Current Issues. – Vancouver : Continuing Legal Education Society of British Columbia, 1986.
91p.
ISBN 0865042535 Hbk £55.00

Criminal law : essays in honour of J.C. Smith / edited by Peter Smith : with a foreword by the Rt. Hon. Lord Edmund-Davies. – London : Butterworths, 1987.
xxvii,234p; 26cm.
A text for the student of criminal law in the United Kingdom, this work provides detailed explanations of the provisions of all current criminal legislation.
ISBN 0406501106 £19.00

Criminal law : offences against religion and public worship. – London : H.M.S.O., 1985.
iv,51p.
ISBN 0102442851

Criminal law : offences relating to public order / the Law Commission. – London : H.M.S.O., 1983.
vii,135p.
ISBN 0102085846

Criminal law : report on criminal libel / by the Law Commission. – London : HMSO, 1985.
iv,80p.
ISBN 0101961804

Criminal law : report on poison-pen letters / the Law Commission. – London : H.M.S.O., 1985.
v,39p.
ISBN 0102519854

Criminal Law : Text and Cases With Supplement 1980
Supplement-1980 only. – Wellington : Butterworths.
ISBN 0409433632

Criminal law : text and materials / by C.M.V. Clarkson, H.M. Keating. – London : Sweet & Maxwell, 1984.
xxxiv,590p; 25cm.
Includes index.
ISBN 0421309202 Hbk £26.00
ISBN 042130930X Pbk £16.95

Criminal law : the general part : liability and defences / Law Reform Commission of Canada. – Ottawa : Law Reform Commission of Canada, 1982.
12,204,239,10p; 25cm. – (Working paper).
Parallel text in French and English bound in reverse.
ISBN 0662514297

Criminal Law : The Protection of Property / A. J. Smith. – London : Sweet & Maxwell, 1986.
ISBN 0420470409 Hbk

Criminal Law Advocacy / Nicholas Pengelley. – Cowandilla : Wakefield Press, 1986.
192p.
ISBN 0949268445 Pbk £17.50

Criminal law and consumer protection / by Graham Stephenson. – Chichester : Rose, 1983.
xxxv,151p; 22cm.
Includes index.
ISBN 0859923096 corrected : Pbk £12.00

Criminal law and criminal justice / David Nelken (ed.). – London : University College London, Faculty of Laws, 1986.
70p; 30cm. – (Working papers).

Criminal Law and Evidence Statutes : State Books for Students. – London : Blackstone Press.
ISBN 1854310194 Hbk £10.00

Criminal law and justice : essays from the W.G. Hart workshop 1986 / edited by Ian H. Dennis. – London : Sweet & Maxwell, 1987.
215p; 22cm.
Includes index.
ISBN 0421377704 Hbk £28

Criminal law and practice of Papua New Guinea / by Donald R. C. Chalmers, David Weisbrot, Warwick John Andrew. – 2nd ed. – Sydney : Law Book Co., 1985.
xxxiv,807p.
Previous ed.: 1979. Includes index.
ISBN 0455203989 Hbk £49.50

Criminal law and procedure of the southern states of Nigeria / C. O. Madarikan. – 3rd ed. – London : Sweet & Maxwell, 1982.
lxxxiv,1061p; 23cm.
Previous ed.: published as Brett and McLean's The criminal law and procedure of the six southern states of Nigeria / by C.O. Madarikan and T. Akinola Aguda. 1974. Includes index.
ISBN 042124920X £58.00

Criminal law and psychiatry / by D.J. Power : co-author D.H.D. Selwood. – S.l. : Barry Rose, 1987.
xviii,265p.
ISBN 1870080254

Criminal Law and the Charter. – Vancouver : Continuing Legal Education Society of British Columbia, 1988.
224p.
ISBN 0865049785 Hbk £70.00

Criminal Law Defences. – Agincourt : Carswell.
200p.
This text contains a comprehensive summary of the 40 defenses used in Canadian criminal law. Principles for application of the defenses and more in-depth information is also included. The main topic headings include exemptions, justifications, excuses, procedural and other defenses.
Hbk £35.75

Criminal Law Digest, 9 Vols. – Rev. ed. – Agincourt : Carswell.
This work contains digests of all the reported Canadian criminal cases from 1800. It is a nine volume set that is supplemented every six months.
Hbk £416.00

Criminal Law Evidence : Practice and Procedure. – Agincourt : Carswell, 1988.
606p.
This looseleaf volume is a practical guide for researching evidentiary, procedural and practice questions arising in criminal law practice. Topics are varied and contain the relevant sections of the Criminal Code, Canada Evidence Act and the Charter of Rights and Freedoms.
Llf £80.00

Criminal Law Evidence, Practice and Procedure. – Agincourt : Carswell, 1988.
606p.
Llf £80.00

Criminal law in a nutshell / Marianne Giles. – London : Sweet & Maxwell, 1987.
121p; 23cm.
Includes index.
ISBN 0421368209 Pbk £4.95

Criminal Law in Action. – Dordrecht : Kluwer, 1986.
440p.
ISBN 9065442782 Hbk Gld100.00

Criminal law in Canadian society. – Ottawa : Govt. of Canada, 1982.
123 p.; 23 cm.
'Sets out the policy of the Government of Canada with respect to the purpose and principles of the criminal law'–Pref.
ISBN 0662120833 Pbk

Criminal law in Ghana / P.K. Twumasi. – Tema : Ghana Pub. Corp., 1985.
xlviii, 634 p.; 24 cm.
Includes bibliographical references and index.
ISBN 9964102933

Criminal law in Ireland / Sean E. Quinn. – Bray, Co. Wicklow : Magh Itha, 1988.
xxvii,227p.
Includes index.
ISBN 1871509009 Pbk £20.00
ISBN 1871509017 £10.00

Criminal law in New South Wales
Vol. 1 : by Ray Watson and Howard Purnell / Howard Purnell. – 2nd ed. – Sydney : Law Book Co., 1981-.
Loose-leaf.
Includes index. Contents: Indictable offences.
Vol. 2 : by Ray Watson and Reg Bartley. – 1978.
Loose-leaf.
Supersedes: Hamilton and Addison's Criminal law and procedure. Includes index. Contents: Summary offences.

Criminal law in the northern states of Nigeria / by E.H. Ofori-Amankwah. – Zaria, Nigeria : Gaskiya Coroporation, 1986.
xix,505p.
Includes bibliographical references.
ISBN 9781940808

Criminal Law of Queensland. – 7th ed. – Butterworths, 1988.
1,406p.
ISBN 0409493090 Hbk £98.00

Criminal Law P.P.H. 1 / Wilkie. – 7th ed. – London : Butterworths, 1981.
ISBN 0406841217 Pbk £5.95

Criminal Law Quarterly (C.L.Q.) 1958-Present. – Aurora : Canada Law Book Co.
Hbk £74.00
Current subscription-Outside Canada. – Hbk £79.00
Back Vols.. – Hbk £35.00 ea.
C.L.Q. Index (Vols. 1-26). – Hbk £12.00

Criminal Law Review / Andrew Ashworth. – London : Sweet & Maxwell.
Hbk £46.00
Bound Vol.. – Hbk £19.75
Single copy. – Hbk £5.75
Vol. 1-32. – Hbk £33.00 each

Criminal Law Revision Committee Reports 2 vols. – Professional Books.
ISBN 086205267X Hbk £54.50

Criminal Law Update. – Vancouver : Continuing Legal Education Society of British Columbia, 1987.
149p.
ISBN 0865043612 Hbk £60.00

Criminal Law, Victoria. – Butterworths, 1981.
ISBN 0409352039 Llf £220.00

Criminal law: conspiracy to defraud. – London : H.M.S.O., 1987.
x,238p. – (Working paper).
ISBN 0117301868

Criminal Law-Offences Against Person / D Pickover. – London : Police Review, 1987.
ISBN 085164029X Pbk £5.60

Criminal lawyers commonplace book. – 1 vol. – Scarborough, Ontario : Butterworths (Canada).
Deals with aspects of a criminal trial, such as cross-examination on criminal records, witnesses using notes, objectionable cross-examination techniques and evidence. Consists of legislation covering a range of issues and a series of digests of leading cases. Makes use of Western Canadian precedents, and those of the Supreme Court.
ISBN 0409994170 Llf

Criminal Legal Aid 1984. – London : Law Society.
Hbk £1.50

Criminal libel / the Law Commission. – London : H.M.S.O., 1982.
viii,207p; 21cm. – (Working paper).
ISBN 0117301647

Criminal Litigation / M. S. Iller. – London : Butterworths, 1985.
This work is a factual account of all stages in the practice and procedure of criminal litigation in the United Kingdom from investigation to conclusion of the criminal process. The book is directed at students of criminal evidence and procedure.
Students
ISBN 0406258139 Pbk

Criminal Major Acts. – Calcutta : Eastern Law House, 1985.
Hbk £135.00

Criminal Major Acts : Containing I.P.C., Cr.P.C. and Evidence Act. – 2nd ed. – Allahabad : Law Publishers, 1983.
Hbk £7.50

Criminal Major Acts (Pocket Ed.) / Surya Rao,. – Allahabad : Law Book Company, 1987.
Hbk £45.00

Criminal Manual. – Lucknow : Eastern Book Company, 1983.
550p.
Hbk £40.00

Criminal Pleadings. – 3rd ed. – Allahabad : Law Book Company, 1986.
1,000.
Hbk £220.00

Criminal Pleadings and Practice in Canada. – 2nd ed. – Aurora : Canada Law Book, 1987.
Llf £82.50

Criminal Policy, Traditional and Modern Trends. – Lagos : Nigerian Law Publications.
ISBN 9782325332 Hbk £10.00

Criminal Practice (1864-1986). – 16 vols. – Allahabad : Ashoka Law House, 1987.
Hbk £150.00 ea.

Criminal Practice, 6 Vols. – 7th ed. – Allahabad : Orient Law House.
Hbk £130.00 ea

Criminal Procedure. – 2nd ed. – Sydney : Butterworths, 1988.
512p.
Hbk £59.00

Criminal procedure / Celia Hampton. – 3rd ed. – London : Sweet & Maxwell, 1982.
lxi,472p; 22cm.
Previous ed.: 1977. Includes index.
ISBN 0421286601 Hbk
ISBN 0421286709 Pbk £8.95

Criminal Procedure / Marc Rosenberg. – 2nd ed. – Agincourt : Carswell, 1986.
403p. – (Bar Admission Course Materials Ser.).
This book for law students provides an overview of basic Canadian criminal procedure from police investigation and searches, through arrest, preliminary inquiry, interim release, trial, sentencing, and appeal. Proceedings under the Young Offenders Act is covered in the work.
Hbk £63.00

Criminal Procedure : Canadian Law and Practice, 3 vol. – Toronto : Butterworths.
Hbk £185.00

Criminal procedure : police powers of arrest and detention : discussion paper. – Sydney : Law Reform Commission of New South Wales, 1987.
xx,148p. – (D.P.).
Bibliography: p141-144.
ISBN 0730544567

Criminal procedure : procedure from charge to trial : a general proposal for reform : discussion paper / New South Wales Reform Commission. – Sydney : Government Printer, 1986.
iii,44p,20 leaves. – (D.P.).
ISBN 0730530868

Criminal procedure : procedure from charge to trial : specific problems and proposals : discussion paper / New South Wales Law Reform Commission. – Sydney : Government Printer, 1987.
xxii,644p. – (D.P.).
Bibliography: p.621-635.
ISBN 0730531333

Criminal procedure : the jury in a criminal trial : discussion paper / New South Wales Law Reform Commission. – Sydney : Government Printer, 1985.
xxx,285p. – (D.P.).
ISBN 0730514323

Criminal procedure : unsworn statements of accused persons : report / New South Wales Law Reform Commission. – Sydney : The Commission, 1985.
70p. – (L.R.C. 45).
Bibliography: p.65-66.
ISBN 0730514269 Hbk

Criminal Procedure According to the Law of Scotland / R. H. Brown. – 5th ed. – Edinburgh : W Green, 1983.
ISBN 0414007158 Hbk £110.00

Criminal Procedure Code / S. Venkataraman. – Allahabad : Orient Law House.
ISBN 086131154X Hbk £35.00

Criminal Procedure Code (F.M.S. Cap. 6). – Kuala Lumpur : International Law Books Services.
Hbk £16.50

Criminal Procedure Code of the People's Republic of China. – London : Sweet & Maxwell, 1982. – (American Series of Foreign Penal Codes: No. 25).
ISBN 0421300108 Hbk £33.00

Criminal Procedure in Canada. – 7th ed. – North Vancouver : International Self-Counsel Press, 1986.
168p.
ISBN 0889086354 Hbk £16.95

Criminal procedure in Canada : studies / edited by Vincent M. Del Buono. – Toronto : Butterworths, 1982.
xc,497p.
ISBN 0409824828

Criminal Procedure in Ghana / A.N.E. Amissah. – London : Pitman Publishing, 1985.
ISBN 09964720092 Pbk £15.95

Criminal Procedure in Magistrates' Courts. – London : Butterworths, 1984.
This work presents a narrative description of procedure in magistrates' courts when dealing with criminal cases in the United Kingdom. Extensive footnotes are included to provide authority for the material described in the text.
ISBN 0406010676 Pbk £21.95

Criminal Procedure in New Zealand. – 2nd ed. – North Ryde : Law Book Co, 1984.
xxi, 198p.
ISBN 0455203547 Pbk £21.00

Criminal Procedure in Practice : a Manual for the Defence of Cases in Provincial Court / N.A. Peel. – 2nd ed. – Butterworths, 1983.
328p.
Outlines what a lawyer ought to do at each stage of the trial process. Covers preparation, tactics, 'case-flow management' and sound law-office administration, and speculation as to the effect of the Canadian Charter of Rights and Freedoms upon criminal procedure.
ISBN 0409812927 Hbk £60.00

Criminal procedure in Scotland : cases & materials / C.H.W. Gane & C.N. Stoddart. – Edinburgh : W. Green, 1983.
xxviii,612p.
Includes index.
ISBN 0414007115

Criminal procedure in the Northern states of Nigeria / by B.M. Shani. – 2nd ed. – s.l. : s.n., 1985.
xxviii,536p.
Includes bibliographical references.

Criminal Procedure in Uganda and Kenya. – Nairobi : East African Publishing House.
150p.
Hbk £5.50

Criminal procedure report : the jury in a criminal trial / New South Wales Law Reform Commission. – Sydney : The Commission, 1986.
xxxi,203p. – (L.R.C. 48).
Includes bibliographical references.
ISBN 073051546X Hbk

Criminal procedure research report : the jury in a criminal trial : empirical studies. – Sydney : Law Reform Commission of New South Wales, 1986.
xii,ii,164p. – (RR).
ISBN 0730524477

Criminal Procedure (Scotland) Act 1975, 2 Vols. – London : HMSO.
ISBN 0114920044 Llf £47.00

Criminal Proceedings Against Juveniles. – London : Longman Professional, 1984.
ISBN 0851208460 Pbk £21.00

Criminal process and persons suffering from mental disorder / Law Reform Commission of Western Australia. – Perth : Law Reform Commission of Western Australia, 1987.
i,146p. – (Discussion paper).

Criminal prosecution and capital punishment of animals / E.P. Evans. – London : Faber, 1987.
xxxi,336p; 20cm.
Facsimile of: ed. published London : Heinemann, 1906.
Bibliography: p314-323. - Includes index.
ISBN 057114893X Pbk £4.95

Criminal records / The Law Reform Commission. – Sydney : The Commission, 1985.
117p. – (Discussion paper).
Bibliography: p.114-117.

Criminal Reference. – 3rd ed. – Calcutta : Eastern Law House, 1986.
£160.00

Criminal responsibility : intention and gross intoxication / Law Reform Commission of Victoria. – Melbourne : The Commission, 1986.
v,31p. – (Report no 6).
Includes bibliographical references.

Criminal Statistics England and Wales 1984. – London : HMSO, 1985.
ISBN 010196210X Hbk £12.70

Criminal Statistics, England and Wales : Supplementary Tables 1980, 4 Vols.
Vol. 1-Proceedings in Magistrates Courts. – London : Home Office.
ISBN 0862520134 Hbk £18.75
Vol. 2-Proceedings in the Crown Court. –
ISBN 0862520142 Hbk £12.75
Vol. 4-Convictions Cautions, D.P.P. Prosecutions, Mentally Disordered Offenders, Appeals Preogative of Mercy, Legal Aid. –
ISBN 0862520169 Hbk £9.75

Criminal Trial and Judgement / D.P. Varshni. – 3rd rev. ed. 1981 repr. – Lucknow : Eastern Book Company, 1985.
477p.
Hbk £70.00

Criminal trials : the search for truth / Tom Sargant, Peter Hill. – London : Fabian Society, 1986.
33p.
ISBN 0716313480

Criminal Women. – Oxford : Blackwell, 1985.
ISBN 0745600883 Pbk £5.95

Criminological diagnosis : an international perspective
Vol.1 / edited by Franco Ferracuti, Marvin E. Wolfgang. – Lexington, Mass. : Lexington Books, 1983.
xi,297p; 24cm.
ISBN 0669016241
Vol.2 / edited by Franco Ferracuti, Marvin E. Wolfgang. – 1983.
299-619; 24cm.
Bibliography: p543-613.
ISBN 0669059714 set
ISBN 0669064343 Hbk

Criminological Theory / Mcshane. – Prentice-Hall.
ISBN 0131936409 Pbk £10.35

Criminology / Karl O. Christiansen. – 2nd ed. – London : Allen & Unwin, 1983.
xvi,454p; 24cm.
Previous ed.: 1952. Bibliography: p417-443. - Includes index.
ISBN 0043640125

Criminology : Problems and Perspectives. – 2nd ed. – Lucknow : Eastern Book Company, 1983.
483p.
Hbk £50.00

Criminology and criminal justice / by J.E. Hall Williams. – London : Butterworths, 1982.
xvii,266p.
Bibliography: p243-254.
ISBN 0406593205

Criminology of Edwin Sutherland / Gaylord. – Oxford : Clio Distribution.
ISBN 0887381812 Hbk £18.50

CRIMJI : Canadian Criminal Jury Instructions. – Vancouver : Continuing Legal Education Society of British Columbia, 1987.
1,500p.
ISBN 0865043337 Hbk £300.00 (publication and disks)

Crimshaw, Patricia
Half Open Door / Lynne Strahan. – Neutral Bay : Hale & Iremonger.
ISBN 0868060488 Hbk £24.95, 015
ISBN 0868060496 Pbk £11.95, 015

Cripps, Yvonne
Legal implications of disclosure in the public interest : an analysis of prohibitions and protections with particular reference to employers and employees / Yvonne Cripps. – Oxford : ESC, 1986.
xx,299p; 24cm.
Bibliography: p289-296. - Includes index.
ISBN 0906214408 Pbk £32.50

Crisis in the Traditional Nation State. – Exeter : European Atlantic Movement, 1982.
Hbk £0.50

Crisis intervention training for police / Don Dutton and Bruce Levens under the auspices of United Way of the Lower Mainland. – Ottawa : Ministry of the Solicitor General, 1985.
66p. – (User report).
Bibliography: p.51.

Crisis of justice / by T. Akinola Aguda. – Akure, Nigeria : Eresu Hills, 1986.
x,73p.

Crisis of the Constitution : Essay in Constitutional & Political Thought England 1603-45. – Rutgers University Press.
ISBN 0813513162 Hbk £34.98
ISBN 0813513073 Pbk £12.95

Crisis of the Indian legal system / Upendra Baxi. – New Delhi : Vikas, 1982.
xiii,405p.
Includes index. Bibliography: p393-400.
ISBN 0706913698

Crisp, Jeff →Refugee dilemma.

Criteria for energy pricing policy : a collection of papers commissioned for the Energy Pricing Policy Workshop organized under the Regional Energy Development Programme (RAS/84/001), Bangkok, 8-11 May 1984 / edited by Corazon Morales Siddayao. – London : Graham & Trotman, 1985.
247p; 24cm.

Critical Accounts / Hopper. – London : Macmillan.
ISBN 0333449703 Hbk £33.00

Critical evaluation of the Chicago School of Antitrust Analysis / Jan B Rittaler. – Dordrecht : Kluwer, 1989.
145. – (Studies in industrial organization).
Examines the implications of the Chicago approach to antitrust theory with its implicit and explicit premises and discusses its policy recommendations. Includes chapters on antitrust theory and public policy, and the evaluation of anticompetition behaviour.
ISBN 9024737923 Hbk £36

Critical legal studies / edited by Peter Fitzpatrick and Alan Hunt. – Oxford : Basil Blackwell, 1987.
197p.
Originally issued as Journal of Law a philosophy, 14,no.1.
ISBN 0631157182

Critical legal studies movement / Roberto Mangabeira Unger. – Cambridge, Mass. : Harvard University Press, 1986.
128p; 24cm.
Bibliography: p121-122. - Includes index.
ISBN 0674177355 Hbk £15.25
ISBN 0674177363 Pbk

Critique of the Japanese study group's report on the ombudsman / by Donald C. Rowat. – Edmonton : International Ombudsman Institute, 1983.
16 leaves. – (Occasional paper).

Crockford, N.
Introduction to risk management. – 2nd ed. – Cambridge : Woodhead-Faulkner, 1986.
ISBN 0859413322 Hbk £19.95

Croft, et al
Questions in Commercial Law. – 2nd ed. – North Ryde : C.C.H. Australia, 1986.
147p.
ISBN 0869037587 Hbk

Croft, John
Concerning crime / by John Croft. – London : H.M.S.O., 1982.
iv,16p; 25cm. – (A Home Office Research and Planning Unit report).
ISBN 011340770X Pbk £2.45
—Managing criminological research / by John Croft. – London : H.M.S.O., 1981.
iv,13p.
A Home Office Research Unit report.
ISBN 0113407092

Cromie, Stephen
International commercial litigation / Stephen Cromie; consulting editor: William Park. – London : Butterworths, 1990.
600; 24cm.
Focuses on national commercial litigation in its international context. Covers procedural and substantive law of England and Wales, USA, Canada, Frane, Germany, Switzerland, Japan and Australia. The conduct of simultaneous proceedings in the various countries and how decisions may be enforced are also treated.
ISBN 0406290024 Hbk £120

Crommelin, Michael →Essays in legal theory : a collaborated work.

Crompton, I. W. →Family Law Reports. Vol. 6.

Cromwell, Thomas A.
Locus standi : a commentary on the law of standing in Canada. – Toronto : Carswell, 1986.
xxiv,221p.
Includes index.
ISBN 0459388207

Crone, Patricia
Roman, provincial and Islamic law : the origins of the Islamic patronate / Patricia Crone. – Cambridge : Cambridge University Press, 1987.
178p; 23cm. – (Cambridge studies in Islamic civilization).
Examines cultural origins of Islamic Law. Studies hypothesis that a substantial source was Roman law with reference to patronate. Concludes Roman law contributed only through being part of the law of Near Eastern provinces.
ISBN 0521322537 £25.00

Croner, Stan
Introduction to the World conservation strategy / prepared for the International Union for Conservation of Nature and Natural Resources by its Commission on Education : text and selection of photographs, Stan Croner. – Gland, Switzerland : IUCN, 1984.
28 p.; 30 cm.
ISBN 2880327024 Pbk £7.95

Croner's Buying and Selling Law. – New Malden : Croner Publications, 1986.
Llf £42.00
Annual renewal updates. –
Llf £22.00

Croner's Coach and Bus Operations. – New Malden : Croner Publications.
Pbk £35.90

Croner's Employment Law. – New Malden : Croner Publications, 1986.
Llf £50.50
Annual renewal updates. –
Llf £25.00

Croner's Guide to Corporation Tax. – New Malden : Croner Publications.
Llf £40.30

Croner's Guide to Fair Dismissal. – New Malden : Croner Publications.
Hbk £5.00

Croner's Hazardous Waste Disposal Guide. – Oxford : Croner Publications.
ISBN 0900319623 Pbk £25.00

Croner's Health and Safety at Work. – New Malden : Croner Publications, 1986.
Llf £51.00
Annual renewal updates. –
Llf £25.80

Croner's Reference Book for Employers. – New Malden : Croner Publications, 1986.
Llf £47.80
Annual renewal updates. –
Llf £26.80

Croner's Reference Book for Exporters. – New Malden : Croner Publications.
Pbk £44.90

Croner's Reference Book for Importers. – New Malden : Croner Publications, 1986.
Llf £35.10
Annual renewal updates. –
Llf £18.50

Croner's Reference Book for the Self-Employed and Smaller Business. – New Malden : Croner Publications.
Llf £39.90
Annual renewal updates. –
Llf £23.60

Croner's Reference Book for V.A.T. (Value Added Tax). – New Malden : Croner Publications, 1986.
Llf £42.30

Croner's Road Transport Operation. – New Malden : Croner Publications, 1986.
Llf £44.20
Annual renewal updates. –
Llf £26.70

Cronje, D.S.P. →Bernard et al : The South African Law of Persons and Family Law.

Crook, David
Records of the general eyre / David Crook. – London : H.M.S.O., 1982.
x, 271p.
ISBN 0114401233

Cropwood Round Table Conference
Women and crime : papers presented to the 13th Cropwood Round Table Conference, December 1980 / edited by Allison Morris with the assistance of Loraine Gelsthorpe. – Cambridge : University of Cambridge Institute of Criminology, 1981.
iii,141p.
Includes bibliographical references.

Cross →Cases and Materials In Administrative Law.
—Introduction to criminal law / Jones. – 10th ed. – London : Butterworths, 1984.
ISBN 0406570507 Hbk £20.00
ISBN 0406570515 Pbk £15.95
—Outline of the law of evidence / Wilkins. – 6th ed. – London : Butterworths, 1986.
ISBN 0406570809 Hbk £19.00
ISBN 0406570817 Pbk £12.95

Cross, C. A. →Highways Act 1980.

Cross, Charles Albert
Cross on local government law / S. H. Bailey, Charles Albert Cross. – 7th ed. – London : Sweet & Maxwell, 1986.
xiii,666p; 24cm.
Previous ed.: published as Principles of local government law. London : Sweet & Maxwell, 1981. Includes index.
ISBN 0421341904 Hbk £32.00
ISBN 0421342005 Pbk £22.00
—Law and Government under the Tudors : Essays Presented to Sir Geoffrey Elton on his Retirement. – Cambridge : Cambridge University Press.
ISBN 0521335108 Hbk £25.00
—Local Government Act 1985. – London : Sweet & Maxwell, 1985.
ISBN 0421353503 Pbk £9.75
—Principles of local government law / by C.A. Cross. – 6th ed. – London : Sweet & Maxwell, 1981.
ISBN 0421248602 Hbk
ISBN 042124870X Pbk

Cross examination in criminal trials / Marcus Stone. – London : Butterworths, 1988.
xix,224p.
Includes index.
ISBN 0406105057 Pbk £14.95

Cross Examination Practice and Procedure. – London : Legal Books, 1985.
ISBN 0949553166 Hbk £20.00

Cross on evidence / Colin Tapper, Rupert Cross. – 6th ed. – London : Butterworth, 1985.
xcvii,663p; 25cm.
Previous ed.: published as Evidence. 1979. Includes index.
ISBN 040657006X Hbk £27.00
ISBN 0406570078 Pbk £17.95

Cross on Evidence : 4th New Zealand Edition 1989. – Butterworths.
700p.
ISBN 0409616540 Hbk £92.95

Cross on Evidence : with Supplement 1980 / D. Byrne. – 3rd ed. – Butterworths, 1986.
734p.
ISBN 040949139X Hbk £89.00
ISBN 0409491489 Pbk £65.00

Cross on local government law / S. H. Bailey, Charles Albert Cross. – 7th ed. – London : Sweet & Maxwell, 1986.
xiii,666p; 24cm.
Previous ed.: published as Principles of local government law. London : Sweet & Maxwell, 1981. Includes index.
ISBN 0421341904 Hbk £32.00
ISBN 0421342005 Pbk £22.00

Cross, Rupert →Crime, proof and punishment : essays in memory of Sir Rupert Cross.
—Cross on evidence / Colin Tapper, Rupert Cross. – 6th ed. – London : Butterworth, 1985.
xcvii,663p; 25cm.
Previous ed.: published as Evidence. 1979. Includes index.
ISBN 040657006X Hbk £27.00
ISBN 0406570078 Pbk £17.95
—English sentencing system / Andrew Ashworth. – 3rd ed. – London : Butterworths, 1981.
xvii,244p; 23cm.
Previous ed.: 1975. Bibliography: p235-236. - Includes index.
ISBN 0406570140 Hbk
ISBN 0406570159 Pbk
—Evidence . – 6th ed. – London : Butterworths, 1985.
ISBN 0406570078 Pbk £21.95
—Introduction to criminal law / Philip Asterley Jones, Richard Card. – 11th ed. 1 (various pagings). – London : Butterworths, 1988.
22cm.
Previous ed.: 1984. Includes index.
ISBN 0406570523 Hbk £20.00
ISBN 0406570531 Pbk £13.95
—Outline of the law of evidence / Cross and Wilkins. – 6th ed. – London : Butterworths, 1986.
xxix,307p; 22cm.
Previous ed.: 1980. Includes index.
ISBN 0406570809 Hbk £14.00
ISBN 0406570817 Pbk £10.95
—Precedent In English Law. – 3rd ed. – Oxford : Oxford University Press, 1977.
ISBN 0198760736 Pbk £7.95
—Statutory interpretation / by the late Sir Rupert Cross. – 2nd ed. – London : Butterworths, 1987.
xviii,206p; 22cm.
Previous ed.: 1976. Includes index.
ISBN 0406570175 Pbk £12.95

Cross-Border Litigation : Environmental Rights in the Great Lakes Ecosystem. – Agincourt : Carswell, 1986.
445p.
Hbk £56.25

Cross-Border Litigation : Environmental Rights in the Great Lakes Ecosystem. – Agincourt : Carswell, 1986.
445p.
This book analyzes the pollution control legislation of the American states and Canadian provinces bordering the Great Lakes and discusses the procedural difficulties confronting potential individual litigants.
Hbk £65.75

Cross-border transactions between related companies : a summary of tax rules / edited by William R. Lawlor. – Deventer, The Netherlands : Kluwer Law and Taxation Publishers, 1985.
Derived from an international tax planning symposium in New York sponsored by Ernst & Whinney. 'Current to January 1985'–Foreword.
ISBN 9065442324 Pbk

Cross-Examination : the Art of the Advocate. – Butterworths, 1988.
152p.
Shows how to conduct an effective cross-examination of a witness in criminal and civil trials. Sets out how to properly examine various types of witness, attacking the method used by the expert witness, contradicting the witness by prior testimony, attacking identification evidence, and how to cross-examine on criminal record.
ISBN 0409809691 Hbk £39.95

Cross-Examination Arguments and Instructive Trials. – 5th ed. 1984. – Allahabad : Orient Law House, 1984.
Hbk £135.00

Cross-examination of law and literature. – Cambridge : Cambridge University Press, 1987.
312.
Studies the effect of the American legal system on the formation of American consciousess. Describes the relationship between law and literature in the nineteenth century.
ISBN 0521330815 Hbk £27.50

Crossick, Stanley
European Banking Law : An Analysis of Community and Member State Legislation / Margie Lindsay. – London : Financial Times Ltd, 1983.
Hbk £85.00
—European Insurance Law : An Analysis of Community and Member State Legislation / Margie Lindsay. – Rev. ed. – London : Financial Times Ltd, 1983.
Hbk £80.00

Crouch, Colin
Politics of industrial relations / Colin Crouch. – 2nd ed. – London : Fontana, 1982.
255p.
Bibliography: p223-239.

Crough, G.J. →Indigenous Resource Rights and Mining Companies in North America and Australia, February 1986.

Crow et al, I.
Unemployment, Crime and Offenders. – Routledge.
ISBN 041501834X Hbk £27.50

Crow, Iain
Unemployment and magistrates' courts / Iain Crow and Frances Simon. – London : NACRO, 1987.
52p.
ISBN 0850690579

Crowder, M.
Flogging of Phinehas McIntosh : A Tale of Colonial Folly and Injustice, Bechuanaland 1933. – Yale University Press.
ISBN 0300040989 Hbk £20.00

Crown as creditor : priorities and privileges. – Law Reform Commission of British Columbia. – Vancouver : Law Reform Commission of British Columbia, 1981.
v,179p. – (Working paper).

Crown Cases Reserved for Consideration and Decided by the Twelve Judges of England : 1824-1844, 2 Vols. – Repr. of 1844 ed. – Abingdon : Professional Books.
247p.
Hbk £40.00

Crown copyright in Canada : a legacy of confusion / Barry Torno. – 1 microfiche. – Ottawa : Minister of Supply and Services, 1981.
78 fr.; 10x15cm.
Bibliography: p.65-67.
ISBN 0662113942

Crown Corporations in Canada : The Calculus of Instrument Choice. – Toronto : Butterworths, 1983.
496p.
Considers the nature of the Crown corporation and how it becomes 'the instrument of choice' over other forms of government intervention. Covers the politics of public enterprise, the uncharted universe of federal public corporations, an overview of the origins, growth, size and functions of provincial crown corporations, and World War II crown corporations.
ISBN 0409859540 Hbk £60.00

Crown Court pattern of sentencing : offenders aged 14 and over : being extracts from the Criminal statisties for England and Wales 1971-1978 / by Ian McLean. – Chichester : Barry Rose, 1981.
254p.
ISBN 085992209X

Crown Law. – Reprint. – Abingdon : Professional Books, 1986.
– (Classical English Law Texts Ser.).
ISBN 0862053196 Hbk £33.50

Crown Office Proceedings. – London : Sweet & Maxwell, 1988.
ISBN 042137960X Hbk

Crown Pleas of the Devon Eyre of 1238. – Exeter : Devon & Cornwall Record Society, 1985.
ISBN 0901853283 Hbk £8.00

Crown priority in insolvency / Anne E. Hardy. – Toronto : Carswell, 1986.
xxxii, 195 p.; 24 cm.
Includes index. Bibliography: p. 179-181.
ISBN 0459391402

Crown Prosecution Service
Annual report for the period April ... to March ... from the Director of Public Prosecutions to the Attorney General / Crown Prosecution Service. – London : H.M.S.O., 1987-.
v.
Presented to Parliament in pursuance of Section 9 of the Prosecution of Offences Act 1985, Ch. 23.

Cruden, Gordon N.
Land compensation and valuation law in Hong Kong / Gordon N. Cruden. – Singapore : Butterworths, 1986.
xxxii,476p.
Collation and analysis of relevant statutory and case law. References are made to Hong Kong cases, as well as English, Scottish, Australian, Canadian, and New Zealand cases.
ISBN 0409995258 Hbk £78.00

Crutchley, J. S. →District Court Practice.

Crydenman, Brian
Police, Race and Ethnicity : A Guide For Law Enforcement Officers / Chris Toole. – Toronto : Butterworths, 1986.
256p.
Guidelines for 'on the street' level of policing and providing police officers with administrative considerations. Also considers the structure and practice of relevant criminal law and the function of the Ontario Human Rights Commission in enforcing the Ontario Human Rights Code. The mechanism of the Ontario Human Rights Commission.
ISBN 0409805017 Pbk £18.25

Crystal, Mark Melvin
Constitution of Canada. – Toronto : IPI Publishing, 1984.
120p. – (Orig.).
Pbk
—Criminal Law / Daniel J. Baum. – Toronto : IPI Publishing, 1983.
84p. – (You and the Law Ser.).
ISBN 045896140X Pbk £7.95
—Family Law / Daniel J. Baum. – Toronto : IPI Publishing, 1982.
84p. – (You and the Law Ser.).
Pbk £7.95

Crystal, Michael →Butterworths insolvency law handbook.
→ Corporate insolvency.
→ Loose on liquidators : the role of a liquidator in a voluntary winding-up.

CTISS file. – Bath : Computers in Teaching Initiative Support Service, 1986-.

Cudmore, Gordon D.
Civil Evidence Handbook / Gordon D. Cudmore. – Agincourt : Carswell, 1987.
520p.
This text contains the Evidence Acts and the Canada Evidence Acts. Topics include admissibility, relevance, burden of proof, presumption, judicial notice, competence and compellability, pleadings, interpreters, examination in chief, impeaching your own witness, cross examination, re-examination, reply evidence, experts, parole evidence rule, hearsay, exceptions to the hearsay rule, and demonstrative evidence.
Hbk £71.50

Cuisine, D. J.
Scottish Cases and Materials in Commercial Law / A. Forte. – London : Butterworths, 1987.
ISBN 0406108706 Pbk

Cullingworth, J. B.
Town and country planning in Britain / J.B. Cullingworth. – 9th ed. – London : Allen & Unwin, 1985.
430p; 22cm.
Previous ed.: 1982. Includes bibliography and index.
ISBN 0047110139 Pbk £8.95
—Town and country planning in Britain / J.B. Cullingworth. – 8th ed. – London : Allen & Unwin, 1982.
369p; 23cm.
Previous ed.: 1979. Bibliography: p349-360. - Includes index.
ISBN 0047110104 Hbk £
ISBN 0047110112 Pbk

Cullity, Maurice C → Probate Practice : MacDonell, Sheard and Hull.
—Taxation and estate planning / by Maurice C. Cullity and Catherine A. Brown. – 2nd ed. – Toronto, Canada : Carswell Co., 1984.
xxvi, 764 p.; 24 cm.
At head of title: Cullity, Forbes, Brown. Includes bibliographical references and index.
ISBN 0459362305 Pbk

Cultural and Educational Rights of the Minorities under Indian Constitution. – New Delhi : Deep and Deep Publications, 1985.
286p.
Hbk £150.00

Cultural norms, war and the environment / edited by Arthur H. Westing. – Oxford : Oxford University Press, 1988.
xiv,177p.
On t.p.: Sipri, Stockholm International Peace Research Institute; UNEP, United Nations Environment Programme. Includes bibliographical references and index.
ISBN 0198291256 Hbk £42.00

Cultural Relations in the Global Community : Problems and Prospects / J. Philip Puthenparampil. – New Delhi : Abhinav Publications, 1981.
xii, 255p.
ISBN 8170171369 Hbk £75.00

Culture and Censorship in Late Renaissance Italy and France. – Northampton : Variorum, 1981.
318p : Illus.. – – (Collected Studies Ser.: No. 138).
ISBN 0860780848 Hbk £24.00

Cuming, Ronald C. C.
Handbook on the Saskatchewan Personal Property Security Act / by Ronald C.C. Cuming and Roderick J. Wood. – Saskatoon? : Law Reform Commission of Saskatchewan, 1987.
xxx,386p.
'Funded by the Law Foundation of Saskatchewan.' - T.p..
ISBN 0921923007
→ Harmonization of business law in Canada.
→ Perspectives on the harmonization of law in Canada.

Cumper, Gloria
Family law : the Commonwealth experience / by Gloria Cumper. – London : Commonwealth Secretariat, 1984.
v,109p.
Includes bibliographies.
ISBN 0850922569
—Planning and implementing the Family Court project, Jamaica / Gloria Cumper. – Kingston, Jamaica : Institute of Social and Economic Research, University of the West Indies, 1981.
i,75p. – (Working paper).

Cumulative and Comprehensive Index to (1985) NWLR. – Lagos : Nigerian Law Publications.
ISBN 9782325335 Hbk £25.00

Cumulative Index to the Decisions of the Immigration Appeal Board. – Agincourt : Carswell, 1987.
180p.
Pbk £31.25

Cumulative index to the statute law of Lesotho 5 March 1960 to 31 December 1982 : including tables of repealed/amended statutes between 5 March 1960 and December 1982, statutes of Lesotho (including Cape statutes) in force on the 31 December 1982 / by Robert J.W. Kukubo. – Roma, Lesotho : University Press of Lesotho, 1983.
xiv,351p.
Includes an appendix for 1983.

Cumulative Supplement to the Standard Contract for Sale of Land in N.S.W. – North Ryde : Law Book Co, 1987.
146p.
Pbk £125.00

Cunnane, Joseph
Dumping and subsidies : the law and procedures governing the imposition of anti-dumping and countervailing duties in the European Community / Joseph Cunnane and Clive Stanbrook. – London : European Business Publications, 1983.
xvi,227p.
Includes index.
ISBN 0907027040

Cunningham, George
Careers in Politics. – London : Kogan Page, 1984.
96p.
ISBN 0850388325 Hbk £6.95
ISBN 0850388333 Pbk £2.95

Cunningham, N.A. → Commercial Law.

Cunningham, T.
Reports of Cases in King's Bench. – Repr. of 1766 ed. – Abingdon : Professional Books.
298p.
Hbk £55.00

Cureatz
Teco Mines and Oils Limited Act, 1983, Bill Pr052 : An Act to Revive Teco Mines and Oils Limited. – Ontario : Ontario Government Publications Service, 1983.
2p.
Hbk £0.30

Curnow, G. R.
Quangos : The Australian Experience / C. A. Saunders. – Neutral Bay : Hale & Iremonger, 1984.
ISBN 0868060860 Hbk £24.95
ISBN 0868060879 Pbk £11.95

Curran, J.B.K. → Probate and Administration Practice in New Zealand.

Curran, W. J. → Law and treatment of drug- and alcohol- dependent persons : a comparative study of existing legislation.

Currency and Interest Rate Swaps / Schuyler K Henderson. – 2nd ed. – London : Butterworths, 1988.
ISBN 0406073619 Hbk £40.00

Currency Fluctuation. – 2nd ed. – Cambridge : Woodhead-Faulkner, 1984.
ISBN 0859412652 Hbk £30.00

Currency Problems in Maritime Disputes / Howard. – London : Lloyd's of London Press.
ISBN 1850441677 Hbk

Current Accounting Law and Practice 1986. – Quinta.
ISBN 0906157099 Pbk £26.50

Current Bibliography of International Law. – London : Butterworths, 1978.
ISBN 0406623767 Hbk £33.00

Current developments in international securities commodities and financial futures markets / edited by Koh Kheng Lian ... et al. – Singapore : Butterworths on behalf of the Faculty of Law, National University of Singapore, 1987.
xxxvi,380p.
ISBN 0409995452

Current developments in measuring business income for tax purposes / Corporate Management Tax Conference, 1987. – 1. – Toronto : Canadian Tax Foundation, 1987.
various pagings.
ISBN 088808031X

Current International Treaties. – Oxford : Croom Helm, 1984.
ISBN 0709917589 Hbk £30.00

Current Issues in Canadian Business Law. – Agincourt : Carswell, 1985.
600p.
This work is a collection of essays on a variety of business law topics written by Canadian practitioners. The essays cover topics ranging from corporate and commercial law to secured transactions and instruments of payment.
Hbk £75.75

Current issues in international business law / edited by David L. Perrott, Istvan Pogany. – Aldershot : Avebury, 1988.
xxvii,239p.
Includes bibliographical references and index.
ISBN 0566054736

Current Issues in International Financial Law. – Kent Ridge : Malaya Law Review.

Current Issues in Juvenile Justice / Marc LeBlanc. – Butterworths, 1983.
400p.
ISBN 0409824135 Pbk £26.95

Current Issues in Medical Law. – Montreal : McGill Campus Legal Aid Clinic, 1982.
173p.
Hbk £2.50

Current Issues in Security Management. – London : Butterworths.
ISBN 0409901121 Pbk £19.95

Current issues of international financial law / edited by David G. Pierce ... et al. – Singapore : Malaya Law Review, 1985.
xv,507p.
A collection of papers from the Singapore Conference of International Financial Law. The material covers primarily international banking, bond issues, syndicated loans, South East Asian perspectives on international financial law, and the role of international development banks.
ISBN 0409995088

Current law. – London : Sweet & Maxwell, 1947.

Current Law / Erna Jansen. – Durban : Butterworths.

Current Law Back Volumes : Current Law Statutes Annotated 1981, 2 Vols. – London : Sweet & Maxwell, 1982.
ISBN 0421301406 Hbk £36.00

Current Law Back Volumes : Year Book 1981. – London : Sweet & Maxwell, 1982.
ISBN 0421301309 Hbk £14.00

Current Law Back Volumes : Year Book 1982. – London : Sweet & Maxwell.
ISBN 0421320605 Hbk £14.00

Current law case citator. – London : Sweet & Maxwell, 1977-.
Kept up to date by annual Current law citator.

Current Law Case Citator. – Sweet & Maxwell, 1947-1976.
ISBN 0421233109 Hbk £22.00

Current Law Statute Citator (1947-1971). – Sweet & Maxwell.
ISBN 0421197307 Hbk £25.00

Current Law Statutes. – 2 vols. – London : Sweet & Maxwell, 1987.
Hbk

Current Law Statutes Annotated 1983. – London : Sweet & Maxwell, 1984.
ISBN 0421325402 Hbk £30.00

Current Law Statutes Annotated 1984, 4 Vols. – London : Sweet & Maxwell, 1985.
ISBN 0421337907 Hbk £42.00

Current Law Statutes Annotated, 1988. – 2 vols. – London : Sweet & Maxwell, 1981-.
ISBN 042128420X Hbk £36.00

Current Law Statutes Annotated : 1982. – London : Sweet & Maxwell, 1983.
ISBN 0421314702 Hbk £30.00

Current law year book : being a complete statement of all the law... from every source. – London : Sweet & Maxwell, 1948.
Cumulation of monthly Current law. 1947-1951 superseded by Current law consolidation. Master volumes for 1956, 1961, 1966 and 1971.

Current Legal Problems : Lectures Delivered in the Faculty of Laws of University College London
Vol. 35 / Roger W Rideout. – London : Sweet & Maxwell, 1982.
ISBN 0420465405 Hbk £22.00
Vol. 36. – 1983.
ISBN 042046770X Hbk £22.00

Current legal regulation of the use of force / edited by A. Cassese. – Dordrecht : Martinus Nijhoff, 1986.
xiv,536p.
Includes bibliographical references.

Current legal theory : international journal for documentation on legal theory (bibliography - abstracts - reviews). – Centrum voor Grondslagenonderzoek van het Recht. – Leuven : Acco, 1983-.

Current Practice Directions : Family and Probate. – London : Family Law, 1988.
ISBN 0853081085 Llf £35.00

Current problems in property law / under the auspices of the Senate of the Inns of Court and the Bat and the Royal Institution of Chartered Surveyors. – London : Senate of the Inns of Court and the Bar, 1986.
217p.
A collection of five papers.

Current problems of international trade financing / edited by C.M. Chinkin, P.J. Davidson, W.J.M. Ricquier. – Singapore : Malaya Law Review, 1983.
xxiii,507p.
Includes index. At head of title: Singapore Conferences on International Business Law.
ISBN 0406181144

Current problems of letters of credit and bankers' quarantees / William C. Hillman. – London : International Bar Association, 1985.
iii,404p.
Papers presented at the seminar in Amsterdam, 8-9 May 1984. Seminar Chairman: Judge William C. Hillman.

Current Sentencing Practice. – London : Sweet & Maxwell, 1988.
ISBN 0421257407 Hbk £120.00

Current Wills and Estates Practice. – Vancouver : British Columbia Continuing Legal Education Society, 1982.
59p.
ISBN 086504046X Hbk £25.00

Currie, B. J.
Annotated Business Corporations Act of Alberta. – 3rd ed. – Agincourt : Carswell, 1988.
384p.
This volume includes a full annotated text of the Act, all regulations under the Act, and annotations on reported and unreported cases dealing with issues arising under the statute.
Pbk £57.25

Currie, D.P.
Constitutions of the United States : A Primer for the People. – University of Chicago Press.
ISBN 0226131068 Hbk £16.75
ISBN 0226131076 Pbk £5.50

Curtin, Deidre
Anti Discrimination Pay Act 1974 and the Employment Equality Act 1977. – Dublin : Round Hall Press, 1986.
ca 140p.
ISBN 0947686045 Hbk £13.50

—Employment Equality Law. – Dublin : Round Hall Press, 1988.
ca 140p.
ISBN 0947686045 Hbk £25.00

—Irish Employment Equality Law. – Round Hall Press.
ISBN 0947686045 Hbk £55.00

Curtis, H.
Accident Compensation Handbook (Vic.) / G. Hughes. – North Ryde : Law Book Co, 1986.
xix, 181p.
ISBN 0455206694 Pbk £25.00

Curzon, L. B.
Cases in Criminal Law. – 2nd ed. Repr. of 1978 ed. – Plymouth : Macdonald & Evans, 1981.
400p. – (M and E Handbook Ser.).
ISBN 0712103767 Hbk £4.95

—Dictionary of Law. – 2nd ed. Repr. of 1979 ed. – Plymouth : Macdonald & Evans, 1983.
viii, 416p. – (M and E Professional Dictionaries Series).
ISBN 0712104402 Hbk £10.95
ISBN 0712104399 Pbk £4.95

—Dictionary of Law. – 3rd ed. – London : Pitman Publishing, 1988.
ISBN 0712107916 Pbk £9.95

—Equity and Trusts. – Plymouth : Macdonald & Evans, 1985.
ISBN 0712106685 Pbk £7.95

—Land Law. – 4th ed. – Plymouth : Macdonald & Evans, 1982.
ISBN 0712112596 Pbk £6.50

—Law of Evidence. – 2nd ed. – Plymouth : Macdonald & Evans, 1986.
ISBN 0712106758 Pbk £6.50

—Law of Succession. – 2nd ed. – Plymouth : Macdonald & Evans, 1981.
272p. – (M and E Handbook Ser.).
ISBN 0712112561 Hbk £4.95

—Law of Trusts. – 2nd ed. Repr. of 1980 ed. – Plymouth : Macdonald & Evans, 1982.
352p. – (M and E Handbook Ser.).
ISBN 0712112553 Hbk £4.95

—Roman Law. – Repr. of 1966 ed. – Plymouth : Macdonald & Evans, 1984.
240p. – (M and E Handbook Ser.).
ISBN 0712118535 Pbk £4.95

Cushing, Luther Stearns
Elements of the Law and Practice of Legislative Assemblies in the U.S.A. – Dublin : Irish Academic Press.
560p.
ISBN 0716520206 Hbk £55.00

Cusine, Douglas J
New reproductive techniques : a legal perspective / Douglas J. Cusine. – Aldershot, Hants. : Gower, 1988.
x,261p.
Bibliography: pp238-254. - Includes index.
ISBN 0566054108

—Scottish cases and materials in commercial law / A Forte. – London : Butterworths, 1987.
ISBN 0406108706 Pbk £25.00

Custodial sentences for young offenders : a discussion paper / Home Office. – London : Home Office, 1986.
12p.

Custodianship : the law and practice / by Nasreen Pearce. – London : Fourmat, 1986.
xi,77p.
ISBN 1851900152 Pbk £7.95

Custody and Access. – 2nd ed. – London : Longman Professional.
ISBN 0851213162 Hbk £17.50

Custody jurisdiction in Papua New Guinea / by Owen Jessep. – Waigani : Law Reform Commission of Papua New Guinea, 1987.
37p. – (LRC working paper).
Includes text of the Infants Act.

Custody law in practice in the divorce and domestic courts / by J.A. Priest and J.C. Whybrow. – London : H.M.S.O., 1986.
vii,113p; 21.
Supplement to: Working paper no. 96, entitled Family law: review of child law: custody.
ISBN 0117301817

Custody of children on breakdown of marriage in Northern Ireland : report of the proceedings of a seminar held in the Queen's University, Belfst, on 12 June 1981 / chairman, the Hon. Mr. Justice MacDermott : editor, Gillian kerr. – Belfast : SLS Publications, 1982.
37,viiip.
Bibliography: p.36. Includes the text of the Matrimonial Causes (N.I.) Order 1978.

Customary international law and treaties : a study of their interactions and interrelations, with special consideration of the 1969 Vienna Convention on the Law of Treaties / Mark E. Villiger. – Dordrecht : Nijhoff, 1985.
xxxiii, 432p. – (Developments in international law).
Originally presented as the author's Habilitationsschrift (University of Zurich). Includes index. Bibliography: p.409-420.
ISBN 9024729807 Hbk £225.00

Customary Land Law in Africa : With Reference to Legislation Aimed at Adjusting Customary Tenures to the Needs of Development. – 2nd print 1985. – Rome : FAO, Food and Agricultural Organization of the United Nations, 1967.
96p.
ISBN 9251022267 Hbk £7.50

Customary Law. – 2nd ed. – Patiala : Punjab University, Publication Bureau.
Hbk £50.00

Customary law : the war without arms / by A.P. Anyebe. – Enugu : Fourth Dimension, 1985.
159p.
Includes bibliographical references.
ISBN 978156184X

Customary Law and Indian Constitution : With Sant Ram Dogra's Code of Tribal Custom. – New Delhi : Rima Publishing House, 1987.
250p.
Hbk £175.00

Customary law in Papua New Guinea : a Melanesian view / edited by Richard Scaglion. – Port Moresby : Law Reform Commission of Papua New Guinea, 1983.
x,198p. – (Monograph).
Bibliographies.
ISBN 0724707468

Customary law of the Dinka people of Sudan : in comparison with aspects of western and Islamic laws / by John Wuol Makec. – London : Afroworld, 1988.
287p.
Includes bibliographical references and index.
ISBN 0948583037

Customers and thieves : an ethnography of shoplifting / Daniel J.I. Murphy. – Aldershot : Gower, 1986.
xi,266; 23cm.
Bibliography: p246-256. - Includes index.
ISBN 0566008823 £15.00

Customs 88. – London : Kogan Page, 1988.
ISBN 1850915997 Pbk

Customs Act, 1962 / Subodh Markandeya. – Bombay : Jaico Publishing House.
Hbk £69.00

Customs Act, 1962. – 3rd ed. – Lucknow : Eastern Book Company, 1982.
649p.
Hbk £85.00

Customs Act, 1967 (Act 235) and Regulations 1977. – Kuala Lumpur : International Law Books Services.
Hbk £10.00

Customs Act : with Various Useful Appendices 1987. – 5th ed. – Allahabad : Law Book Company, 1988.
1,750p.
Hbk £375.00

Customs and Customary Law in British India. – Delhi : Mittal Publications, 1986.
Hbk £395.00

Customs and Excise. – Agincourt : Carswell, 1983.
182p.
This textbook provides a thorough examination of the law with respect to Canadian customs and excise. The work covers the Customs Act, the Anti-Dumping Act, Customs Tariff, the Excise Tax Act, and the Excise Act.
Hbk £33.75

Customs & Excise Casebook. – London : Waterlow, 1987.
ISBN 0080392458 Hbk £50.00

Customs and excise law / by E.J. Cooper. – Sydney : Legal Books, 1984.
xli, 598 p.; 25 cm.
Includes bibliographies and index.
ISBN 0949553107

Customs Duties. – London : Deloitte Haskins & Sells.
ISBN 0863491332 Pbk £20.00

Customs law of the European Economic Community / by D. Lasok and W. Cairns. – Deventer : Kluwer, 1983.
xxiii,292p.
Includes bibliography: p.287-289. - Includes index.
ISBN 9065440771

Customs union of the European Economic Community / by Nikolaus Vaulont : translated from the French. – Luxembourg : Office for Official Publications of the European Community, 1981.
87 p.; 25 cm.
Includes bibliographical references.
ISBN 9282519112 Pbk £5.00 (U.S.)

Customs Valuation : a Commentary on GATT Customs Valuation Code / H. Glashoff. – Dordrecht : Kluwer, 1988.
400p.
ISBN 9065443215 Hbk £153.00

Customs Valuation in Canada. – Don Mills : CCH Canadian Ltd, 1985.
292p.
ISBN 088796284X Hbk £45.00

Cuthbertson, Brian
Old Attorney General. – Halifax : Nimbus.
ISBN 0920852076 Hbk £3.95

Cutler, Antony
Justice and predictability / Antony Cutler and David Nye. – London : Macmillan, 1983.
xi,169p.
Includes index. Bibliography.
ISBN 0333315154

Cutter et al.
Budget and Policy Choices 1983 : Taxes, Defence, Entitlements. – London : Eurospan.
ISBN 0944237053 Pbk £8.50

Cutts, Martin
Small print : the language and layout of consumer contracts : Report to the National Consumer Council / Martin Cutts and Chrissie Maher : Plain English Campaign. – London : National Consumer Council, 1983.
39p.
ISBN 0905653661

Cuyvers, Luc
Strait of Dover / by Luc Cuyvers. – Dordrecht : Martinus Nijhoff, 1986.
xvi, 150p. – (International straits of the world).
ISBN 9024732522 Hbk £115.00

Cyprus / by Keith Kyle. – New 1984 ed. – London : Minority Rights Group, 1984.
23p. – (Report).
Bibliography: p.23.
ISBN 0946690103

Cyprus conflict : a lawyer's view / by Zaim M. Nedjatigil. – 2nd ed. – Nicosia : A-Z Publications, 1982.
xii,248p.
Previous ed.: 1981. Includes bibliographical references and index.

Cyprus question and the Turkish position in international law. – Oxford : OUP, 1989.
275.
Recounts the recent history o Cyprus and deals with the international law aspects of the developments since 1963. The 'doctrine of necessity', the Treaty of Guarantee and Turkish intervention of 1974, human rights and the constitutional proposals of the respective sides of future federation for Cyprus are discussed.
ISBN 0198252250 Hbk £27.50

Czechoslovakia. – Amnesty International. – 2nd ed. – London : Amnesty International, 1981.
17p. – (Amnesty International Briefing).

Dada, T. O.
Standard Holdings for Law Office Libraries in Nigeria. – Abingdon : Professional Books, 1986.
ISBN 0862050782 Hbk £14.00

DAE Labour Studies Group →Labour market structure, industrial organisation and low pay.

Daedalus in the Supreme Court : the common law today / D. P. Visser. – S.l. : University of Cape Town, 1985.
12 p. – (Inaugural lecture).
ISBN 0799209996

Daff, T A
Cost and Management Accounting. – Cambridge : Woodhead-Faulkner, 1986.
ISBN 0859413713 Pbk £11.50

—Cost of Management Accounting. – Pitman.
ISBN 0273029835 Pbk £6.95

Daga, Luigi
Opportunities for progress in systems, organisation and technology in prison administrations, especially with regard to automation and computer technology / by Luigi Daga. – Stasbourg : Council of Europe, 1986.
29p. – (CDAP (85) 5 rev).
A paper presented to the seventh conference of Directors of Prison Administrations. Bibliography: p.27-28.

Dagtoglou, P D →Toward a Community air transport policy: the legal dimension.

Dahl, Tove Stang
Child welfare and social defence / Tove Stang Dahl : translated by Gunvor Nyquist. – Oslo : Norwegian University Press, 1985.
185p; 23cm.
Bibliography: p175-185. Translation and revision of: Barneven og samfunnsvern.
ISBN 8200071146 £19.45

—Women's Law : an introduction to feminist jurisprudence / Tove Stang Dahl : translated by Ronald L. Craig. – Oslo : Norwegian University Press, 1987.
195p; 23cm.
A theoretical introduction, and a discussion of three areas within women's law; the legal situation affecting housewives, paid workers, and women as recipients of social security benefits.
ISBN 8200184900 £20.00

Dahlitz, Julie
Nuclear arms control : with effective international agreements / Julie Dahlitz : foreword by Rikhi Jaipal. – London : Allen & Unwin, 1983.
238p; 24cm.
Bibliography: p217-232. - Includes index.
ISBN 0043410235 Hbk £15.00
ISBN 0043410243 Pbk £4.95

Dahmani, M.
Fisheries Regime of the Exclusive Economic Zone. – Dordrecht : Kluwer, 1987.
200p.
ISBN 902473374X Hbk £145.00

Dahrendorf, Ralf
Law and order / by Ralf Dahrendorf. – London : Stevens, 1985.
160p. – (Hamlyn lectures).
Includes index.
ISBN 0420472401 Hbk £14.00
ISBN 0420472509 Pbk £8.25

Daily law reports index. – Hebden Bridge, W. Yorks. : Legal Information Resources, 1988.
v.
ISBN 09550798

Daily Mail
How to live with VAT. – Daily Mail. – Maidenhead : McGraw-Hill, 1987.
ISBN 0670849439 Pbk £6.75

Daily Mail Guide to Employment Law. – Southampton : Associated Magazines, 1988.
ISBN 0851444261 Pbk £5.95

Daily Telegraph Guide to Income Tax 1988-89. – Oxford : Collins.
Pbk £2.95

Daily Telegraph law reports. – London : The Daily Telegraph, 1987-.

Daintith, Terence → Contract and organization : legal analysis in the light of economic and social theory.

—Energy strategy in Europe : the legal framework / by Terence Daintith and Leigh Hancher. – Berlin : W. de Gruyter, 1986.
ix,190p. – (Series A, Law).
Includes bibliographical references and index.
ISBN 0899251730

→ Integration through law : Europe and the American Federal experience : a series, Vol. 5 : The legal integration of energy markets : by Terence Daintith and Stephen F. Williams.

→ Law as an instrument of economic policy : comparative and critical approaches.

—Legal analysis of economic policy / by Terence C. Daintith. – Florence : European University Institute, 1982.
13p.

→ Legal character of petroleum licences : a comparative study.

→ United Kingdom oil and gas law.

Dalal, J.H.
Law Relating to Protected Lincensees. – Bombay : Tripathi, 1975.
416p.
bd £30.00

Dale
Financial Deregulation. – Cambridge : Woodhead-Faulkner, 1986.
ISBN 0859413667 Hbk £30.00

Dale, James Murray
Clergyman's handbook, and churchwarden's guide : being a manual of the laws affecting the relative rights, position, and duties of the clergy and their parishioners ..., with appendices containing important statutes, including the Benefices Act, 1898 / by James Murray Dale. – 7th ed. – London : Seeley, 1898.
xx,507p.
Includes index. .

Dale, Richard
Regulation of international banking / Richard Dale. – Cambridge : Woodhead-Faulkner, 1984.
vii,208p.
ISBN 085941261X

Dale, W.
Law of the Parish Church. – 5th ed. – London : Butterworths, 1975.
ISBN 0406174016 Pbk £10.95

Dale, William → British and French statutory drafting : the proceedings of the Franco-British conference of 7 and 8 April 1986.

—Modern Commonwealth / Sir William Dale. – London : Butterworths, 1983.
xxxi,345p; 26cm.
Bibliography: pxxvii-xxx. - Includes index. Second copy inscribed by the author.
ISBN 0406174040

Dalgleish, L. I. → Implications of marital separation for young children.

Dallmeyer, Dorinda G, et al
Rights to oceanic resources / Louis DeVorsey, Jr. – Dordrecht : Nijhoff (Martinus), 1989.
224. – (Publications on ocean development 13).
Collection of presentations from a multi-disciplinary group of experts involved in the resolution of maritime jurisdictional disputes, at state, national, and international levels. Papers discuss equitable resource management, develop an international analytical methodology, and identify the possible impact of dispute resolution on the principles used as state level.
ISBN 079230019X Hbk £39

Dalton
Country Justice. – 2nd ed. – Abingdon : Professional Books, 1986 Reprint.
– (Classical English Law Texts Ser.).
ISBN 0862053137 Hbk £30.00

—Officium Vicecomitum (1623). – Reprint. – Abingdon : Professional Books, 1986.
ISBN 0862053455 Hbk £35.00

Dalton, Amanda → Enforcing antitrust against foreign enterprises : procedural problems in the extraterritorial application of antitrust laws.

Dalton, Harlon L. → AIDS and the law : a guide for the public.

Dalton, Patrick J.
Land law / Patrick J. Dalton. – 3rd ed. – London : Pitman, 1983.
xliii,377p; 22cm.
Previous ed.: London : Oyez, 1975. Includes index.
ISBN 0273018582 Pbk £9.95

Daly, B.D.
Handbook of Irish Case Law 1989. – Round Hall Press.
ISBN 0947686541 Pbk £11.95

Daly, Peter, et al
Andreas Alciates, 2 Vols. – Toronto : University of Toronto Press, 1985.
ISBN 0802024254 Hbk £125.00

Daly, Stephanie
Developing legal status of women in Trinidad and Tobago / by Stephanie Daly. – Port-of-Spain : National Commission on the Status of Women, 1982.
136p.
Includes bibliographical references and index.

Damage to property : arson / Law Reform Commission of Canada. – Ottawa : The Commission, 1984.
44,52p. – (Working paper).
Includes bibliographical references. Added t.p. in French: Les dommages aux biens : le crime d'incendie. Added t.p. in French: Les dommages aux biens : le crime d'incendie. Pages numbered in opposite directions. Text in English and French.
ISBN 0662532457

Damage to property - vandalism / Law Reform Commission of Canada. – Ottawa : the Commission, 1984.
65,77p; 25cm. – (Working paper).
Cover title: Criminal law - damage to property - vandalism. Added t.p. in French: Les dommages aux biens - le vandalisme. Pages numbered in opposite directions. In English and French.
ISBN 0662528956

Damages 1986. – Vancouver : Continuing Legal Education Society of British Columbia, 1986.
179p.
ISBN 0865042551 Hbk £55.00

Damages for Breach of Contract / Elizabeth Carmen. – Agincourt : Carswell, 1985.
260p.
This book reviews the principles underlying the law of contracts relating to damages for the Canadian Practitioner. The trends of Canadian cases and how the courts are treating breach of contract issues are discussed in depth.
ISBN 0459373307 Hbk £24.20

Damages for lost income / Robert J. Koch. – Cape Town : Juta, 1984.
xxxii,367p.
Bibliography: pxvii-xix.
ISBN 0702115126

Damages for personal injuries and death / John Munkman. – 7th ed. – London : Butterworths, 1985.
xxxiii,250p; 23cm.
Previous ed: 1980. Includes index.
ISBN 0406311137 Hbk £27.50

Damages for Personal Injuries and Death in Singapore and Malaysia. – Singapore : Malayan Law Journal, 1988.
ca 1,000p.
Presents the main principles governing the assessment of damages for personal injury and death in Singapore and Malaysia, with reference to pertinent cases and statutory provisions.
ISBN 9971700603 Hbk £265.00

Damages for personal injuries and fatal accidents in Hong Kong : a review of the law and a digest of the cases / Robyn Martin, Peter Rhodes. – London : Butterworths, 1982.
xxv,563p; 23cm.
Gives general principles of the assessment of damages in personal injuries, and in fatal accident cases, and how these have been applied in Hong Kong. Included in the appendices are multiplier tables, actuarial tables, a glossary of medical terms, and illustrations.
ISBN 0406357102 £45.00

Damages For Personal Injury and Death. – 3rd ed. – London : Longman Professional, 1986.
ISBN 0851211178 Pbk £18.95

Damages for personal injury and death in Canada / edited and with introductory notes by Immanuel Goldsmith : case abridgements prepared by Alan Burnside Harvey and by David Carruthers. – Toronto : Carswell, 1959.
xxiii,374p.
Includes index.

Damages-Loss of Expectation of Life : Survival and Deductibility. – Singapore : Malayan Law Journal, 1984.
xiii, 82p.
Explores the survival of the claim for loss of expectation of life and the methods employed by courts for its quantification. Intends to determine the justification, if any, for deducting the compensation awarded to the estate under the Fatal Accidents Act 1846-1908. Comparison of the law in England, Canada (Manitoba), Australia and Malaysia.
ISBN 9971700379 Hbk £25.00

Damaska, Mirjan R.
Faces of justice and state authority : a comparative approach to the legal process / Mirjan R. Damaska. – New Haven : Yale University Press, 1986.
288p; 24cm.
Includes index.
ISBN 0300035675 £26.00

D'Amato, Anthony A
Jurisprudence : a descriptive and normative analysis of law / Anthony D'Amato. – Dordrecht, The Netherlands : Nijhoff, 1984.
xiv, 334 p.; 25 cm.
Includes bibliographical references and index.
ISBN 902472919X Hbk £140.00

Damrosch, Lori Fisler → United States law of sovereign immunity relating to international financial transactions.

Dane, Jean
How to use a law library / by Jean Dane and Philip A. Thomas. – 2nd ed. 1. – London : Sweet & Maxwell, 1987.
23cm.
Previous ed.: 1979. Includes bibliography and index.
ISBN 0421360305 Hbk £12.50
ISBN 0421360402 Pbk £8.50

Danelius → United Nations Convention Against Torture International Studies in Human Rights.

Dangerous behaviour, the law, and mental disorder / Herschel Prins. – London : Tavistock, 1986.
xiii,258p; 20cm. – (Social science paperback).
Includes bibliographies and index.
ISBN 0422792209 Pbk £6.95

Dangerous Drugs Act 1952 (Act 234) and Drug Dependants (Treatment and Rehabilitation) Act, 1983 (Act 283) and Regulations and Rules. – Kuala Lumpur : International Law Books Services.
Hbk £12.50

Dangerous Substances. – New Malden : Croner Publications.
Pbk £64.50

Dangerousness : problems of assessment and prediction / edited by John W. Hinton. – London : Allen & Unwin, 1983.
x,177p; 25cm.
Bibliography: p158-171. - Includes index.
ISBN 0043640214

Dangerousness and criminal justice / Jean Floud and Warren Young. – London : Heinemann, 1981.
xvii,228p; 23cm.
Bibliography: p203-221. - Includes index. At head of title : Howard League for Penal Reform.
ISBN 0435823078 £14.50

Dangers and Pitfalls in Advising on Commercial Transactions. – Vancouver : British Columbia Continuing Legal Education Society, 1983.
283p.
ISBN 086504130X Hbk £55.00

Daniel
History of the Law Reports 1884. – London : Wildy & Sons.
Hbk £11.75

Daniel, E. R.
Practice in the High Court of Chancery, 2 Vols. – 8th ed. Repr. of 1914 ed. – Abingdon : Professional Books.
Hbk £95.00

Daniel, W. W.
Maternity Rights : The Experience of Employers. – London : Policy Studies Institute, 1981.
89p.
Hbk £5.00

—Workplace industrial relations and technical change / W.W. Daniel. – London : F. Pinter in association with Policy Studies Institute, 1987.
312 p.; 23 cm.
Includes bibliographical references and index.
ISBN 0861879171

—Workplace industrial relations in Britain : the DE/PSI/SSRC survey / W.W. Daniel and Neil Millward. – London : Heinemann Educational, 1983.
xiii,338p; 23cm.
Includes index.
ISBN 0435831909

Daniell, T.
Inns of Court. – Wildy & Sons, 1971.
ISBN 0854900012 Pbk £1.95

Daniells Practice in the High Court of Chancery. – 2 vols. – London : Sweet & Maxwell, 1985. – (Sweet and Maxwell Library Reprints).
ISBN 0421351802 Hbk £140.00

Danilov, Dan P.
Immigrating to the U.S.A. – 4th ed. – North Vancouver : International Self-Counsel Press, 1983.
208p.
ISBN 0889089124 Hbk £14.95

Danish Committee on Comparative Law → Danish law : a general survey.

Danish law : a general survey / edited by Hans Gammeltoft- Hansen, Bernhard Gomard, Allan Philip. – Copenhagen : G.E.C. Gad, 1982.
395p.
Previous ed.: published as 'Danish and Norwegian law', 1963. Copyright by the Danish Committee on Comparative Law.
ISBN 8712235253

Danks, Alan → Towards open government, 1 : General report.

Darlow, C.
Valuation and development appraisal. – London : Estates Gazette, 1982.
ISBN 0728201097 Pbk £16.50
—Valuation and investment appraisal. – London : Estates Gazette, 1983.
ISBN 0728200686 Pbk £18.00

Dartmouth College → Papers of Daniel Webster.

Darvell, P
Securities law in New Zealand / Clarke. – London : Butterworths, 1983.
ISBN 0409600490 Pbk £23.50

Darville, Richard
Preparing Information on the Law : Guidelines for Writing, Editing and Design / Gayla Reid. – Ottawa : Canadian Law Information Council, 1985.
84p.
ISBN 0920358810 Pbk £10.00
—Small Claims Court Materials : Can They Be Read? Can They Be Understood? / Marilyn Hiebert. – Ottawa : Canadian Law Information Council, 1985.
184p.
ISBN 0920358837 Pbk
—Trouble with Legal Language. – Ottawa : Canadian Law Information Council, 1985.
33p.
ISBN 0920358845 Pbk

Darwin
Law of the Sea Convention 1982 : Text and Commentary. – London : Butterworths, 1985.
ISBN 0406252610 Hbk

Das, M.N.
Ganguly's Criminal Court Practice and Procedure. – 8th ed. – Calcutta : Eastern Law House, 1984.
Hbk £120.00
→ On the law of ultra vires.

Das, Sarat Chandra
Indian Arbitration Act. – 5th ed. – Allahabad : Law Book Company, 1984.
xxxiv, 864p.
Hbk £220.00

Das, Satya Ranjan
On the law of ultra vires / Satya Ranjan Das. – 2nd ed. – Calcutta : Cambray, 1981.
xvi,340p.
Previous ed.: published as 'The law of ultra vires in British India', 1923. Includes index.

Dasgupta, S.K.
Commercial and Industrial Law. – New Delhi : Sterling Publishers, 1983.
1,078p.
ISBN 8120704398 Hbk £34.00
—Company Formations (Private and Public). – New Delhi : Bharat Law House, 1984.
Hbk £100.00
—Guide to Company Law. – New Delhi : Bharat Law House, 1986.
Hbk £250.00
—Guide to Company Management. – New Delhi : Bharat Law House, 1985.
Hbk £240.00

Dashwood, Alan
Guide to the civil jurisdiction and judgments convention / by Alan Dashwood, Richard Hacon & Robin White. – Deventer : Kluwer Law and Taxation, 1986.
648p.
Includes index and bibliography.
ISBN 9065442693 Hbk £265.00
→ Substantive law of the EEC.

Dass, K. S.
Subordinate courts practice 1981 / by K.S. Dass and Abdul Hamid Bin Haji Mohamed : with a foreword by Tun Mohamed Suffian Bin Hashim : and an introduction by Raja Tan Sri Dr. Azlan Shah. – Johor : Asian Book, 1981.
lix,945p.
Includes index.

Dassesse, Marc
EEC banking law / by Marc Dassesse and Stuart Isaacs. – London : Lloyd's of London, 1985.
xix,184p; 23cm.
ISBN 0907432808

Data base management packages / by Kathy Lang. – Southampton : Ashford Press, 1987.
350p.
ISBN 1852530235 unbound £80.00

Data Processing. – London : Butterworths, 1984.
ISBN 0408011718 Pbk £8.50

Data processing and the law / edited by Colin Campbell. – London : Sweet & Maxwell, 1984.
viii,264p; 22cm.
Includes index.
ISBN 0421320001 Pbk £20.00

Data protection : a guide for library and information management / J. Eric Davies. – Oxford : Elsevier International Bulletins, 1985.
220p. – (EIB report series).
Includes bibliography.
ISBN 0946395179 Pbk £20.00

Data protection : perspectives on information privacy : contributions made to a conference on 11 May 1983 at the University of Leicester / edited by Colin Bourn and John Benyon. – Leicester : University of Leicester, Continuing Education Unit, 1983.
101p; 21cm.
ISBN 090150727X Pbk £5.00

Data protection : the Government's proposals for legislation. – London : H.M.S.O., 1982.
23p; 25cm.
At head of title: Home Office.
ISBN 0101853904 unbound £2.30

Data Protection Act, 1984
Enforcement and appeals / The Data Protection Registrar. – Wilmslow : The Registrar, 1987.
24 p.
ISBN 1870466063
Individual rights / The Data Protection Registrar. – 1987.
28 p.
ISBN 1870466047
Introduction to the Act / The Data Protection Registrar. – 1987.
20 p.
ISBN 1870466004
Summary for computer bureaux / The Data Protection Registrar. – 1987.
8 p.
ISBN 1870466071
The data protection principles / The Data Protection Registrar. – 1987.
28 p.
ISBN 1870466039
The definitions / The Data Protection Registrar. – 1987.
40 p.
ISBN 1870466012
The exemptions / The Data Protection Registrar. – 1987.
36 p.
ISBN 1870466055
The register and registration / The Data Protection Registrar. – 1987.
32 p.
ISBN 1870466020

Data Protection Act 1984 / with commentary and annotations by Bryan Niblett. – London : Oyez Longman, 1984.
x,155p; 24cm.
ISBN 0851207766 Pbk £16.50

Data Protection Act 1984 : a guide to the new legislation / J.A.L. Sterling. – 2nd ed. – Bicester : CCH, 1985.
v,330p; 23cm.
Previous ed.: 1984?. Bibliography: p313-314. - Includes index.
ISBN 0863250769 Pbk

Data Protection Act 1984 : an introduction to the Act and guide for data users and computer bureaux. – Wilmslow, Cheshire : Data Protection Registrar, 1985.
36p.

Data Protection Act 1984 : New Problems For Solicitors and Their Clients. – London : Law Society, 1985.
27p. – (Nineteen Eighty-Five Crash Course Transcripts).
Hbk £2.05

Data Protection Act : subject access to personal health data : a consultation paper. – s.l. : s.n., . 9,3,2p.

Data Protection Bill : notes on the passage of the Bill from the House of Lords to the House of Commons / by the Council's Law Reform Committee. – London : The Committee, 1983.
8p.

Data protection in practice / Kenneth Gulleford. – London : Butterworths, 1986.
xi,306p; 25cm.
Includes index.
ISBN 0406177007 Pbk £20.00

Data Protection Kit. – Croydon : Tolley, 1985.
ISBN 085459146X Hbk £16.50

Data protection law / commentary by Simon Chalton, Shelagh Gaskill. – London : Sweet & Maxwell, 1988.
268p in various paging; 24cm.
Includes index.
ISBN 0421398205 Pbk £10.00

Data Protection Registrar → Data Protection Act, 1984.

Datta, C.R.
Company Law. – 4th ed. – Allahabad : Orient Law House, 1987.
Hbk £400.00
—On the Income Tax Law. – Allahabad : Orient Law House, 1983-1984.
Hbk £300.00

Datuk, Tan Sri
Mallal's Supreme Court Practice, Vol 1 / Min Tat Chang. – 2nd ed. – Singapore : Malayan Law Journal, 1983.
1,368p.
ISBN 9971700344 Hbk £500.00

Daunton-Fear, Mary W. → Probation and Parole : Interstate Supervision and Enforcement.
—Women as Participants In the Criminal Justice System. – Canberra : Australian Institute of Criminology.
free

Davey, Nigel T. → Partnership taxation.
→ Spicer and Pegler's the business of partnerships.

David Davies Memorial Institute of International Studies → Small is dangerous : micro states in a macro world: report of a Study Group of the David Davies Memorial Institute of International Studies.
→ Specialized agencies and the United Nations : the system in crisis.
→ Waters around the British Isles : their conflicting uses : report of a study group of the David Davies Memorial Institute of International Studies.

David, Heinz → Pinner's World unfair competition law : an encyclopedia.

David Marshall Trials. – Singapore : 10.50.
272p.
ISBN 9971651114 Pbk £9.50
ISBN 9971651106 Hbk

David, Rene
Arbitration in international trade / Rene David. – Antwerp : Kluwer Law and Taxation Publications, 1985.
xii,482p.
Includes legislation. Includes index. Bibliography: p459-465. Translation of: Arbitrage dans le commerce international.
ISBN 9065441646
—Major legal systems in the world today : an introduction to the comparative study of law / Rene David : translated and adapted by John E.C. Brierley. – 3rd ed. – London : Stevens, 1985.
xvi,624p; 22cm.
Previous ed.: 1978. Bibliography: p577-613. - Includes index. Translation of: Les grands systemes de droit contemporains.
ISBN 0420473408 Hbk £28
ISBN 0420473505 Pbk £23

David, Robin
Magistrate in the Crown Court / Robin David. – Chichester : Rose, 1982.
viii,48p; 21cm.
ISBN 0859922294 Pbk £4.25

David, S R
United States and the Law of the Sea Treaty / Peter Digester. – John Hopkins University, Foreign Policy Institute, 1990.
52; 23.
ISBN 0941700542 Pbk £12

Davidow, Robert P. → Natural rights and natural law : the legacy of George Mason.

Davidson
Family Separation. – Butterworths, 1988.
192p.
ISBN 0409788708 Pbk £40.00

Davidson, A. B., et al
Tax Aspects of Litigation. – Vancouver : British Columbia Continuing Legal Education Society, 1982.
138p.
ISBN 086504077X Hbk £40.00

Davidson et al., S.
Managerial Accounting. – 3rd ed. – New York : Dryden Press.
ISBN 0030119642 Hbk £23.95

Davidson, Fraser
Guide to the Wages Act 1986 / Fraser P. Davidson. – London : Financial Training, 1986.
136p; 22cm.
Includes index. Includes the text of the Wages Act 1986.
ISBN 1851850473 Pbk £8.50

Davidson, J. S. →Institutional framework of the European Communities.

Davidson, Laurie A. →Inventory of current legal research in Canada.

Davidson, Neil F. →Judicial review in Scotland.

Davidson, Paul J. →Commercial arbitration institutions : an international directory and guide.
→ Current problems of international trade financing.

—International money and the real world / Paul Davidson. – London : Macmillan, 1982.
XI,312p.

Davidson, R →Residential possession proceedings.

Davidson, Scott
Grenada : a study in politics and the limits of international law / Scott Davidson. – Aldershot : Avebury, 1987.
xii,196p; 22cm.
Bibliography: p184-190. - Includes index.
ISBN 0566050528 £18.50

Davies
Child Witness : Do the Courts Abuse Children / David W Drinkwater. – New York : British Psychological Society, 1988.
ISBN 0901715891 Pbk £5.00
→ Modern methods of valuation.

—Ward's Tax Law and Planning, 6 Vols. / Beck. – Agincourt : Carswell, 1983.
This multi-volume looseleaf service is a comprehensive treatise on Canadian tax law. Analysis of the statutory language of the Canadian Income Tax Act is the main focus of the work.
Llf £332.00

→ Your new pensions choice.

Davies, A.
Justice at Home. – 3rd ed. – Chichester : Barry Rose, 1983.
21p.
ISBN 0859923592 Hbk £3.50

Davies, Anne
Government Grants : An NCVO Practical Guide. – 4th ed. – London : Bedford Square Press, 1987.
ISBN 0719912008 Hbk £3.50

Davies, B. P. A. →Houseman and Davies law of life assurance.
—Pension Schemes. – London : Butterworths, 1982.
ISBN 0406406502 Hbk

Davies, Christine
Family law in Canada / by Christine Davies. – 4th ed. – Toronto : Carswell Legal Publications, 1984.
cl, 681 p.; 26 cm.
Re ed. of: Power on divorce and other matrimonial causes / W. Kent Power. 'Table of cases': p. xvii-cxx 'Table of statutes': p. cxxviii-cl. Includes bibliographical references, legislation, and index.
ISBN 045936300X Pbk

Davies, D.
How to turn round a company. – London : Fitzwilliam, 1988.
ISBN 1870555023 Hbk £35.00
—Justice at home. – 3rd ed. – Chichester : Barry Rose, 1983.
ISBN 0859923592 Pbk £5.00

Davies, D. T. →Will precedents and inheritance tax.
—Will precedents and inheritance tax / D.T. Davies. – 3rd ed. – London : Butterworth, 1988.
xxiii,283p.
Previous ed.: published as Will precedents and capital transfer tax. 1983. Includes index.
ISBN 0406175128 £25.00

Davies, D. T. A. →Jackson's matrimonial finance and taxation.

Davies, David R.
Principles of international double taxation relief / by David R. Davies. – London : Sweet & Maxwell, 1985.
xix,321p; 26cm.
Includes index.
ISBN 0421317507 Hbk £45.00

Davies, Donald
Commencement of laytime / by Donald Davies. – London : Lloyd's of London Press, 1987.
164p; 22cm.
Includes index.
ISBN 1850441472 £30.00

Davies, F. R.
Contract / by F.R. Davies. – 5th ed. – London : Sweet & Maxwell, 1986.
xxii,290p; 23cm.
Previous ed.: 1981. Includes index.
ISBN 0421350903 Hbk £9.50
ISBN 0421351004 Pbk £5.95
—Introduction to revenue law / F.R. Davies. – 2nd ed. – London : Sweet & Maxwell, 1985.
xxii,416p; 22cm.
Previous ed. by F.R. Davies. 1980. Includes index.
ISBN 0421334304 Hbk £18.00
ISBN 0421334401 Pbk £13.95

Davies, Gillian
Challenges to copyright and related rights in the European Community / Gillian Davies and Hans Hugo von Rauscher auf Weeg. – Oxford : ESC, 983.
xvii,271p.
Bibliography: p.253-258. - Includes index.
ISBN 0906214149
—Piracy of phonograms : a study requested by the Commission of the European Communities / Gillian Davies. – 2nd ed. – Oxford : ESC Publishing for the Commission of the European Communities Cultural Sector, 1986.
ix,151p.
ISBN 0906214424
—Private copying of sound and audio-visual recordings. – Oxford : ESC, 1984.
180p.
ISBN 0906214262 £22.00

Davies, Graham →Identification evidence : a psychological evaluation.

Davies, J. Eric
Data protection : a guide for library and information management / J. Eric Davies. – Oxford : Elsevier International Bulletins, 1985.
220p. – (EIB report series).
Includes bibliography.
ISBN 0946395179 Pbk £20.00

Davies, John
Norwest Holst Limited : investigation under section 165(b) of the Companies Act 1948 / report by John Davies and Thomas Garrard Harding. – London : H.M.S.O., 1981.
185p; 30cm.
At head of title: Department of Trade.
ISBN 0115134891 Pbk £12.50
—Political policing in Wales / John Davies, Lord Gifford, Tony Richards. – Cardiff : Welsh Campaign for Civil & Political Liberties, 1984.
111p; 19cm.
ISBN 0947740007 Pbk £1.50

Davies, Keith →Butterworths planning law handbook.
—Law of compulsory purchase and compensation / Keith Davies. – 4th ed. – London : Butterworths, 1984.
xxxv,364p; 23cm.
Previous ed.: 1978. Includes index.
ISBN 0406571872 Hbk £21.00
ISBN 0406571880 Pbk £17.95
—Local government law / Keith Davies. – London : Butterworths, 1983.
xxxvi,352p; 23cm.
Includes index.
ISBN 0406252661 Hbk £
ISBN 040625267X Pbk £17.95

Davies, M
Documentary Credits Handbook. – Cambridge : Woodhead-Faulkner, 1988.
ISBN 0859413721 Hbk £45.00

Davies, M R Russell
Law of Burial, Cremation and Exhumation. – 6th ed. – London : Shaw & Sons, 1988.
ISBN 072190064X Pbk

Davies, Michael H
Business law in Egypt / by Michael H. Davies. – Deventer, Netherlands : Boston, 1984.
ISBN 9065440860

Davies, P. L. →Kahn-Freund's Labour and the law.
—Labour law : text and materials / Paul Davies, Mark Freedland. – 2nd ed. – London : Weidenfeld and Nicolson, 1984.
xlii,964p; 24cm.
Previous ed.: 1979. Includes index.
ISBN 0297780891 Hbk £30.00
ISBN 0297780905 Pbk £17.95

Davies, Wendy →Settlement of disputes in early medieval Europe.

D'Avino, Carey
Investment in US Real Estate. – London : Oyez Longman, 1984.
– (Oyez Longman Intelligence Report Ser.).
ISBN 0851208495 Hbk
—Tax Planning Uses of the Caribbean. – London : Oyez Longman, 1984.
– (Oyez Longman Intelligence Report Ser.).
ISBN 0851208533 Hbk

Davis
Casebook on Conflict of Laws. – London : Butterworths.
ISBN 0409435279 Pbk £28.80
→ Law and Finance for the Farmer.
→ Law of Contract.

Davis, D. M. →Gordon and Getz on the South African law of insurance.

Davis, Gwynn
Grounds for divorce / Gwynn Davis and Mervyn Murch. – Oxford : Clarendon Press, 1988.
x,177p.
Bibliography: pp.169-171. - Includes index. Examines, through social research, the legal ending of marriage. Reviews the present law and suggests future reforms. The focus is on the relationship between the personal experience of parties and legal foms of divorce. The 'process over time' reform proposal has been adopted by the Law Commission.
ISBN 019825220X Hbk £20
—Matrimonial Proceedings / Marilyn Mornington. – London : Longman Professional.
– (Longman Practice Notes Series).
ISBN 0851214126 Pbk £10.95
—Partisans and mediators : the resolution of divorce disputes / Gwynn Davis. – Oxford : Clarendon Press, 1988.
x,219p.
Bibliography: pp.211-215. - Includes index. Concerns divorcing couples who seek help in negotiating over money or children, and the partisans or mediators who assist. Concludes that the prospect of a genuine non-coercive agreement is being undermined by such considerations as cost, and the limitations of the 'due process'.
ISBN 0198256124 Hbk £25

Davis, Louis B. Z.
Canadian Constitutional Law Handbook : Leading Statements, Principles and Precedents. – Aurora : Canada Law Book Co, 1985.
1182p. – (Text Books-Civil).
Hbk £195.00

Davis, Nigel →Company law in Great Britain.

Davis, Noel
Law of Superannuation in Australia. – Woolloomooloo : International Business Communications.
476p.
ISBN 0959029001 Hbk £60.00

Davis, Stanley Clinton
European Community : law in action / Stanley Clinton Davis. – Exeter : University of Exeter, 1986.
11p.

Davison, Frann
Grants From Europe. – 4th ed. – London : Bedford Square Press, 1987.
ISBN 0719912075 Hbk £5.25

Davison, Mark R. →Protection of trade secrets : a general guide.

Dawisha, Karen
Soviet Union : The Internal Situation and its Implications for the West. – Enstone : Ditchley Foundation, 1982.
– (The Ditchley Conference Reports).
Hbk

Dawson →Introduction to Business Law.

Dawson et al., S.
Safety at Work : the Limits of Self-Regulation. – Cambridge : Cambridge University Press.
ISBN 0521354978 Hbk £35.00

Dawson, Francis
Contractual Remedies Act 1979 / by Francis Dawson and David W. McLauchlan. – Auckland : Sweet & Maxwell, 1981.
xxii,217p.
Includes bibliographical references and index. Includes the text of the Act.
ISBN 0457017201 Pbk
ISBN 0457016906

Dawson, John →Mental health : a case for reform.

Dawson, Norma
Women and children first : the legal obligation to make provision on death for family and dependants / lecture delivered to the Belfast Solicitors' Association by Norma Dawson. – Belfast : SLS Legal Publications, 1984.
45p.
Bibliography: p.46.

Day, Alan J. →Border and territorial disputes.
→ Maritime affairs : a world handbook : a reference guide to maritime organizations, conventions and disputes and to the international politics of the sea.

Day centres and probation / S. Fairhead with the the assistance of J. Wilkinson-Grey. – London : Home Office, 1981.
v,39p. – (Research Unit paper).
Bibliography: p.34.
ISBN 0862520185

Day, D.M.
Law of international trade / by D.M. Day. – London : Butterworths, 1981.
xxii,254p,2p of plates; 22cm.
This book is an introduction to the law of international trade. Carriage of goods, insurance of goods in transit, government controls, EEC law, and statutory material are discussed in the work.
ISBN 040657202X Hbk
ISBN 0406572011 Pbk

Day, David C →New divorce law : a commentary on the Divorce Act, 1985.

Day, J.
Liberty and Justice. – Oxford : Croom Helm, 1986.
ISBN 070994523X Hbk £25.00

Day, Midge
Corporate Procedures for Legal Assistants. – Agincourt : Carswell, 1985.
450p.
This book provides a step-by-step analysis of the incorporation procedure under Ontario and Canadian federal corporate law for legal assistants. Forms and precedents are provided in this 'how to' incorporation guide.
Hbk £40.00

Day, Patricia-
Accountabilities : five public services / Patricia Day, Rudolf Klein. – London : Tavistock, 1987.
259p; 22cm. – (Social science paperbacks).
Includes index.
ISBN 042279340X Hbk £18.00
ISBN 0422793507 Pbk £6.95

Dayal, S.
Indian Company Law. – 9th ed. – Delhi : SBD Enterprises.
Hbk £21.00

De Aiba, E.
Skip Registries - Panama. – London : Lloyd's of London Press.
ISBN 1850441421 Hbk £25.00

de Alba, Enrique → Panama.

De Bauw, Francois
China trade law : code of the foreign trade law of the People's Republic of China / by Francois De Bauw and Bernard Dewit : preface by Michel Verwilghen. – Bruxelles : Bruylant (Emile), 1982.
572p.
Includes bibliographical references and index. At head of title: Universite Catholique de Louvain, Faculte de Droit, Centre de Droit des Obligations. Text in English. Preface, introduction, headings and index in French and English..
ISBN 2802702963

de Blacam, Marc
Drunken driving and the law / Marc de Blacam. – Dublin : Round Hall, 1986.
111p; 22cm.
Includes index.
ISBN 0947686134 Hbk £15.00
ISBN 0947686126 Pbk £8.95

de Caires, B.
GT Guide to World Equity Markets 1987. – 2nd ed. – London : Euromoney.
ISBN 1870031903 Hbk £85.00
—International Guide to Capital Markets 1988. – Cambridge : Woodhead-Faulkner.
ISBN 1870031172 Hbk £75.00

De Cesari, P → Index of multilateral treaties on the law of the sea.

De facto relationships / New South Wales Law Reform Commission. – Sydney : The Commission, 1981.
x,120p. – (Issues paper).
Bibliography: p.115-120. Accompanied by: Summary of issues paper (14p).

De Franchis, F.
English-Italian Law Dictionary. – London : Sweet & Maxwell, 1985.
ISBN 0421357401 Hbk £50.00

De Freitas, et al
Company Law. – London : Castlevale Publishers, 1982.
ISBN 0907235018 Pbk £5.00
→ General Principles of Business Law (Q & A).

de Graaff, W. → Pollution of outer space, in particular of the geostationary orbit, Scientific, policy and legal aspects.

De Haas, Margaret R.
Domestic injunctions / Margaret R. de Haas : with a foreword by H.H. Judge Nance. – London : Sweet & Maxwell, 1987.
xxviii,187p; 26cm.
Explains the steps involved in proceeding with an action, from originating application to enforcement, including procedures under the Child Abduction and Custody Act 1985. Includes selected rules of the Supreme and County Courts, precedents and forms, and a precis of decisions.
ISBN 0421365102 £19.50
→ Key to Personal Injury Practice and Compensation.
→ Personal Injury Litigation : Practice and Precedents.
→ Property distribution on divorce.

de L'Hoste Ranking, Devey F., et al
Spicer's and Pegler's Executorship Law and Accounts. – 21st ed. – London : HFL, 1983.
Llf £55.00

De Mara, Marilyn
Pension Plan Financial Statements. – Toronto : Butterworths, 1986.
96p.
ISBN 0409801798 Pbk

de Munter
Elsevier's Fiscal and Customs Dictionary / Baudüin. – Amsterdam : Elsevier, 1988.
ISBN 0444428917 Hbk

De Pace Regis Et Regni. – Abingdon : Professional Books.
– (Classical English Law Texts Ser.).
Hbk £37.50

De Pencier Wright, John
Division of Matrimonial Assets in Ontario. – Aurora : Canada Law Book Co, 1982.
438p. – (Text Books-Civil).
Hbk £45.00

De, R.R.
Disciplinary Proceedings in Industries and Adjudication. – 2nd ed. – Calcutta : Eastern Law House, 1984.
Hbk £102.00

de Rijcke, Izaak → Boundaries and Surveys.

de Silva, D. S. → Civil Engineering Contracts : Practice and Procedure.

De Silva, S. B. D.
Political economy of underdevelopment / S.B.D. de Silva. – London : Routledge & Kegan Paul in association with the Institute of Southeast Asian Studies, Singapore, 1983.
viii,645p; 22cm.
Includes index.
ISBN 0710202733 Pbk £12.50

De Smith, S. A.
Constitutional and administrative law / Harry Street and Rodney Brazier; editors. – 5th ed. – Harmondsworth : Penguin, 1985.
748p.
ISBN 0140226109 Pbk £11.95

De Villiers, J. E.
Law of agency in South Africa / De Villiers and Macintosh. – 3rd ed. – Cape Town : Juta, 1981.
lxviii,684p.
Previous ed.: 1956. Includes index.
ISBN 0702112542

De Voil
Value Added Tax. – London : Butterworths.
Service to Date.
ISBN 0406514593 Llf £160.00

De Vos, P. A. F. → Guide to Bankruptcy.

De Vries, Margaret Garritsen
International Monetary Fund 1972-1978 : Cooperation on trial / edited by Margaret Garritsen de Vries. – 3 v. – Washington, D.C. : International Monetary Fund, 1985.
Vols.I and II: Narrative and analysis. Vol.III: Documents.
ISBN 0939934434

de Waart et al, P.
International Law and Development. – Martinus Nijhoff.
ISBN 9024737184 Hbk £58.00

The Dealing Room : Getting Value for Money. – Online.
ISBN 0863531490 Pbk £75.00

Dealing with domestic violence / M.D.A. Freeman. – Bicester : CCH Editions, 1987.
xii,150p; 23cm.
Examines the problem, legal resources, divorce and judicial separation, the criminal law, injunctive relief, Matrimonial Homes Act 1983, Domestic Violence Act 1976, Supreme Court Act 1981/County Court Act 1984, Injunctions ancillary to other proceedings, protection in the Magistrates Court, criminal injuries compensation scheme, and the housing law implications of domestic violence.
ISBN 0863251102 Pbk

Dean, P.N.
Government Budgeting in Developing Countries. – Routledge.
– (International Accounting Series).
ISBN 0415004314 Hbk £30.00

Dean, W. H. B. → Acta Juridica.
→ Constitutional change in South Africa : the next five years.

Deane, K.D.
ACCA Study and Revision Manual : 2.3 Taxation. – London : BPP.
ISBN 1870941128 Pbk £9.95

Dearden, Ann → Arab women.

Dearden, Richard G. → Canada-U.S. Free Trade Agreement : Commentary and Related Documents.
→ Canada-U.S. Free Trade Agreement : Final Text and Analysis.

Death and Taxes / Patrick C Soares. – London : Longman Professional, 1986.
ISBN 0851209309 Pbk £19.95

De'ath, Erica
Services for Conciliation in Divorce / Lisa Parkinson. – Aberdeen : Aberdeen University Press, 1984.
ISBN 008030379X Hbk

Death penalty in Japan : report of an Amnesty International mission to Japan, 21 February - 3 March 1983. – Amnesty International. – s.l. : Amnesty International, 1983.
31p.
ISBN 0862100607

Death penalty: a worldwide perspective. – Oxford : Clarendon Press, 1989.
200; 21.5.
Survey of practice literature covering the death penalty, by analysis of the law and practice of all states where the death penalty is, or has been, used in recent years. Discusses whether or not the claimed deterrent effect of the death penalty has any basis in known fact.
ISBN 0198252722 Hbk £20.00

Debatin, Helmut
Analysis of the German tax system : general principles, taxation of income and capital, unilateral measures for the avoidance of double taxation / Helmut Debatin. – Updated ed. – Amsterdam, Netherlands : International Bureau of Fiscal Documentation, 1981.
1 v. (various pagings); 22 cm.
'Reprinted from Handbook on the United States-German tax convention.'.
ISBN 9070125218 Pbk
—Handbook on the United States-German Tax Convention / authors Helmut Debatin, Otto L. Walter : in cooperation with Ernst Weber and Eric Osterweil : general editors Piroska Soos and Eugen Jehle. – 4. – Amsterdam : International Bureau of Fiscal Documentation, 1966.
loose-leaf.
Includes texts of Convention and Protocol. With added title-page in German. Final loose-leaf supplement no. 50 (Dec. 1983). Parallel German and English texts.

DeBlacam, Mark
Control of Private Rented Dwellings. – Dublin : Round Hall Press, 1984.
100p.
ISBN 0950872520 Hbk £15.00
ISBN 0950872512 Pbk £7.50

Debt collection practices / Institute of Law Research and Reform. – Edmonton : The Institute.
vi,161p. – (Report no 42).

Debt Management and Collection. – London : Butterworths, 1988.
ISBN 040635880X Pbk

Debt Problems of Eastern Europe. – Cambridge : Cambridge University Press, 1988.
ISBN 0521335426 Hbk £25.00

Debt recovery : a review of creditors' practices and policies / by Barbara Doig and Ann R. Millar. – Edinburgh : Central Research Unit, Scottish Office, 1981.
vii,72p.

Debt recovery and insolvency / Law Reform Commission. – Canberra : Australian Government Publishing Service, 1987.
xxxii,312p. – (Report).
ISBN 0644013648

The Debt Rescheduling Process / Marko Milivojevic. – London : Pinter, 1985.
200p.
Includes bibliography and index.
ISBN 0861875753 £18.50

Debt Security Instruments : Creation and Perfection 1988. – Vancouver : Continuing Legal Education Society of British Columbia, 1988.
406p.
ISBN 0865049777 Hbk £85.00

Debt Security Instruments : Creation and Perfection, Pt. 1. – Vancouver : British Columbia Continuing Legal Education Society, 1981.
430p.
ISBN 0865040168 Hbk £22.00

Debt Survival Guide. – Redfern : Redfern Legal Centre Publishing, 1987.
328p.
Hbk £14.95

Debtor and Creditor : Cases and Commentary. – 3rd ed. – Agincourt : Carswell, 1987.
1,150p.
ISBN 0459304712 Hbk £45.00
ISBN 045930481X Pbk £23.00

Debtor and Creditor : Cases, Notes and Materials / Eric Gertner. – 2nd ed. – Aurora : Canada Law Book Co, 1982.
1200p. – (Case Books).
Hbk £89.50

Debtor-Creditor Law : Practice and Doctrine / Eric Gertner. – Butterworths, 1985.
768p.
Addresses the practical issues which dominate debtor-creditor law in Canada. Covers execution against negotiable instruments, third party demands, fraudulent conveyances and unjust preferences, PPSA, repossession, corporate receivership, construction liens, the enforcement of foreign judgements, executions against shares in BC and enforcement against life insurance, pensions, and RRSP's.
ISBN 0409868833 Hbk £95.00

Debtors Act, 1957 (Act 256). – Kuala Lumpur : International Law Books Services.
Hbk £6.00

Debtors and Creditors. – London : Butterworths, 1986.
ISBN 0862051010 Hbk £26.95

Debtors (Scotland) Act 1987. – Edinburgh : Green (W.) & Son, 1987.
Annotated text of the Act from Scottish Current Law Statutes with two introductory chapters, including a diagram showing the principal effects of the Act on the debt recovery process.
ISBN 0414008227 Pbk

Deburger →Serial murder.

Decade of change : banking in Europe : the next ten years. – London : Lafferty, 1986.
221p.
A study by Arthur Andersen & Co..
ISBN 094839403X

Decade of women and the law in the Commonwealth / prepared by Margaret Rogers for the Hubert Humphrey Institute of Public Affairs in association with the Commonwealth Secretariat. – London : Legal Division, Commonwealth Secretariat, 1985.
xvii,342p.
ISBN 0850922720

Decarceration : community treatment and the deviant : a radical view / Andrew Scull. – 2nd ed. – Cambridge : Polity Press, 1984.
202p.
1st ed.: Englewood Cliffs, N.J.: Prentice-Hall, 1977.
Bibliography: p191-198.

Decay of international law? : a reappraisal of the limits of legal imagination in international affairs / Anthony Carty. – Manchester : Manchester University Press, 1986.
x,138p; 24cm. – (The Melland Schill monographs in international law).
Includes index.
ISBN 0719018501 £25.00

Decedents' estates, wills, and trusts in the U.S.A. / by Frank G. Opton. – Deventer, The Netherlands : Kluwer Law and Taxation Publishers, 1986.
Includes index.
ISBN 9065442715 Hbk

Decentralisation in France : the distribution of powers. – Strasbourg : Council of Europe, 1984.
i,54p; 30cm.
Contents: Act no.83-8 of 7 January 1983 concerning the distribution of powers among the municipalities, departements, regions and central government (1); Act no.83-663 of 22 July 1983 supplementing Act no.83-8; Act no.82-659 of 30 July 1982 conferring special status on the region of Corsica (powers).

Decentralisation of local government at neighbourhood level / ... prepared by the Secretariat of the Steering Committee for Regional and Municipal Matters with the assistance of Sven-Runo Bergqvist. – Strasbourg : Council of Europe, 1981.
30p.

Decision Making in Magistrates' Courts / Sturges. – London : Fourmat, 1986.
ISBN 1851900179 Pbk £4.95

Decision making in statutory reviews on children in care / Ruth Sinclair. – Aldershot : Gower, 1984.
vi,171p; 23cm.
Bibliography: p165-171.
ISBN 0566007576 £16.45

Decision Support Systems in Finance and Accounting / Bloom. – Quorum Press.
ISBN 0899302696 Hbk £32.95

Decisions of international institutions before domestic courts / Christoph Schreuer. – London : Oceana, 1981.
xiii,407p; 25cm.
Revised and updated version of 1977 German original.
ISBN 0379207095

Decisions of the Boards of Appeal of the European Patent Office : Entscheidungen der Beschwerdekammern des Europaischen Patentamts
Vol. 1. – Cologne : Carl Heymanns Verlag, 1983.
xii, 432p.
ISBN 3452194817 Hbk £128.00
Vol. 2. – 1983.
xvi, 392p.
ISBN 3452194825 Hbk £128.00
Vol. 3. – 1984.
xvi, 352p.
ISBN 3452199592 Hbk £128.00
Vol. 4. – 1985.
xv, 323p.
ISBN 3452201511 Hbk £128.00

Decisions of the Commissioner : National Insurance Acts 1965-1974 and Social Security Act 1975 Invalidity Benefit. – London : HMSO.
Pbk £1.90

Decisions of the Court of Session : 1781-1822. – Repr. of 1839 ed. – Abingdon : Professional Books.
52p.
Hbk £70.00

Decisions of the Court of Session : Abridged in Form of a Dictionary / Woodhouselee. – Repr. of 1741 ed. – Abingdon : Professional Books.
57p.
Hbk £60.00

Decisions of the Court of Session from 1681-91. – Repr. of 1757 ed. – Abingdon : Professional Books.
51p.
Hbk £90.00

Decisions of the Courts Relating to Supplementary Benefits and Family Income Supplements Legislation 1980. – London : HMSO.
ISBN 0117606758 Llf £12.50
Supplement No. 1. –
Hbk £3.40
Supplement No. 2. –
Hbk £12.50

Decker, Scott H. →Juvenile justice policy : analyzing trends and outcomes.

Declaratory Judgments. – Sweet & Maxwell, 1962 Reprint.
ISBN 0421355700 Hbk £30.00

Declaratory Orders. – 2nd ed. – Butterworths, 1984.
276p.
ISBN 0409493538 Hbk £62.00

Decline of juridical reason : doctrine and theory in the legal order / N.E. Simmonds. – Manchester : Manchester University Press, 1984.
137p; 23cm.
Includes index.
ISBN 0719010896 £19.50

Decline, revival and future of the Roman-Dutch law of insurance in South Africa / by J.P. van Niekerk. – s.l. : Department of Mercantile Law, University of South Africa, 1986.
78p. – (Monograph series).
Includes bibliographical references.
ISBN 0869814001

Dedicated Clean Ballast Tanks. – International Maritime Organization. – London : International Maritime Organization, 1982.
Hbk £2.50

Dedijer, Vladimir →War Crimes in Vietnam.

Dee, Garth, et al
Workers' Compensation in Ontario. – Butterworths, 1987.
256p.
Guide to matters falling within the jurisdiction of the Ontario Workers' Compensation Board. Deals with practice and procedure of the Board as they currently exist, and makes reference to various published documents of the WCB on issues of policy and procedure. Section examines the availability of civil actions.
ISBN 0409804908 Hbk £80.00
—Workers' Compensation Practice Guide / Newhouse. – London : Butterworths.
ISBN 0409804908 Hbk £64.00

Deeds and escrows / the Law Commission. – London : H.M.S.O., 1987.
29p. – (1987/88 HC1).
ISBN 010200188X

Deeds and seals / Law Reform Commission of British Columbia. – Victoria : Government of British Columbia, 1987.
ii,39p. – (Working paper).
Includes bibliographical references.
ISBN 0771886020

Deeds of Covenant. – 3rd ed. – London : Longman Professional, 1987.
ISBN 0851212182 Pbk £9.50

Deepak, Lal
Resurrection of the Pauper-Labour Argument. – London : Trade Policy Research Centre, 1981.
82p.
Hbk £2.00

Deepsea mining and the law of the sea / Alexandra Merle Post. – The Hague : M. Nijhoff Publishers, 1983.
xxiii,358p.
Bibliography: p329-358.
ISBN 902473049X

Defamation / Brian Neill. – 2nd ed. – London : Butterworths, 1984.
ISBN 0406178305 Hbk £34.00

Defamation Act, 1957 (Act 286). – Kuala Lumpur : International Law Books Services.
Hbk £3.00

Defamation and Other Aspects of the Actio Inuriarum in Roman-Dutch Law. – Colombo : Lake House Investments.
Hbk £5.50

Default and rescheduling : corporate and sovereign borrowers / edited by David Suratgar. – London : Euromoney, in association with International Law Institute, Washington D.C., 1984.
viii,163p.
'Two international conferences, one in London in late 1981 and the other in New York in 1982, provided the basis for this book' - Editor's preface.
ISBN 0903121530

Default by sub-contractors and suppliers / John Parris. – London : Collins, 1985.
320p.
Includes index.
ISBN 0003830470 £17.50

Defects in Components and Ingredients. – Product Liability Briefing, 1988.
ISBN 1870317602 Pbk £4.95

Defects in Natural Commodities and Raw Materials. – Product Liability Briefing, 1988.
ISBN 1870317556 Pbk £4.95

Defects In Standards Of Product Marketing and Presentation. – Product Liability Briefing.
ISBN 1870317459 Pbk £6.50

Defects through Storage and Transport. – Product Liability Briefing, 1988.
ISBN 187031770X Pbk £4.95

Defence For Children International →Children in adult prisons : an international picture.

Defence of Compulsion : an Overview. – Auckland : Legal Research Foundation, 1982.
Hbk £6.50

Defence - the legal implications. – Pergamon, 1987.
ISBN 0080335969 Hbk £29.95

Defences to criminal liability in Nigerian law : a critical appraisal / by Kharisu Sufiyan Chukkol. – Zaria : Ahmadu Bello University Press, 1987.
xiii,135p.
Bibliography: pp.133-135.
ISBN 9781250429

Defences to provincial charges / Institute of Law Research and Reform. – Edmonton : The Institute, 1984.
ii,123p. – (Report).

Defending Lawyer's Practical Guide. – 2nd ed. – London : Beattie (Derek), 1984.
ISBN 0907591035 Pbk £8.50

Defending possession proceedings / Jan Luba, Nic Madge, and Derek McConnell. – London : Legal Action Group, 1987.
xlvi,229p.
ISBN 090509915X Pbk £14

Defending White-Collar Crime : A Portrait of Attorneys at Work. – Yale University Press.
ISBN 0300043686 Pbk £8.95

Defensive Practice of Real Estate. – Vancouver : British Columbia Continuing Legal Education Society, 1982.
124p.
ISBN 0865040486 Hbk £12.50

Defining status: a comprehensive analysis of United States/territorial relations. – Dordrecht : Nijhoff (Martinus), 1989.
752.
Analyses the possibility of Statehood for Guam and the Virgin Islands, and explores the bounds of the Commonwealth and Freely Associated States. These status alternatives are discussed against a backdrop of the political, economic, geographic, and cultural uniqueness of each territory.
ISBN 0792300696 Hbk £115

Definition and rule in legal theory : a reassessment of H.L.A. Hart and the positivist tradition / Robert N. Moles. – Oxford : Basil Blackwell, 1987.
xii,285p; 24cm.
Bibliography: p275-278. - Includes index.
ISBN 063115342X £25.00

Degenhardt, Henry W.
Maritime affairs : a world handbook : a reference guide to maritime organizations, conventions and disputes and to the international politics of the sea / compiled and written by Henry W. Degenhard : editorial consultant, Brian Meredith : general editor, Alan J. Day. – Harlow : Longman, 1985.
viii,412p; 26cm. – (A Keesing's reference publication).
Bibliography: p385-390. - Includes index.
ISBN 0582902630 £50.00
ISBN 0810320517
—Treaties and alliances of the world / compiled and written by Henry W. Degenhardt. – 3rd ed. – Harlow : Longman, 1981.
ix,409p; 26cm. – (A Keesing's reference publication).
Previous ed.: 1974. Includes index.
ISBN 0582902509 £27.00

Deighan, Maurice
County Court Practice and Procedure. – 3rd ed. – London : Fourmat, 1984.
160p.
ISBN 0906840805 Pbk £10.95

DeJong →Personal Property Security : An Introductory Analysis.

DeKoker et al, A.P.
Income Tax in South Africa. – Durban : Professional Publisher.
ISBN 0409104914 Hbk £85.00

Del Buono, Vincent M.
Canadian criminal procedure : cases, notes and materials / Vincent M. Del Buono. – Toronto : Butterworths, 1981.
xxx,929p.
Includes index.
ISBN 0409824801
—Reform of the Criminal Law. – Agincourt : Carswell.
130p.
This work contains papers that had been delivered at the July 1987 conference on criminal law reform held in London, England. Discussions include white collar crime, sentencing reform and the defenses.
Hbk

Delany
Administration of Justice in Ireland / Lysaght. – repr. 1986. – Dublin : Institute of Public Administration.
105p.
Pbk £3.99

Delays and Disruptions in Construction : Ascertaining the Cost-A Case Study in Assessing a Contractor's Claim. – King's Ride : Institute of Building, 1987.
68p.
ISBN 0906600928 Hbk £7.75

Delays and efficiency in civil litigation / Ross Cranston ... et al. – Melbourne : The Institute of Judicial Administration, 1984.
xviii,230p.
At head of title page: The Australian Institute of Judicial Administration Incorporated.
ISBN 0959002901

Delbridge, Rosemary →Consuming secrets : how official secrecy affects everyday life in Britain.

Delegalisation and normalisation / by Alain Supiot. – Florence : European University Institute, 1986.
34,xiiip.

Delegation of Powers Ordinance 1956 (F.M. Ord. 56/1956) and Oaths and Affirmation Act, 1949 (Act 194). – Kuala Lumpur : International Law Books Services.
Hbk £4.00

Delhi and Central Sales Tax / H.P.S. Kohli. – New Delhi : S. Chand and Company.
Hbk £5.50

Delhi Police Law : Containing Commentaries on Delhi Police Act, 1978 with Up-to-date Rules and Regulations. – Delhi : Allied Book Co., 1987.
303p.
Hbk £120.00

Delhi Sales Tax and Central Sales Tax Act / D.B. Narang. – New Delhi : Kalyani Publishers.
Hbk £7.50

Delineation of Universal Law. – Fettiplace Bellers. – 2nd ed. Repr. of 1750 ed. – Abingdon : Professional Books.
592p.
Hbk £15.00

Delinquency : its roots, careers and prospects / D.J. West. – London : Heinemann Educational, 1982.
186p; 23cm. – (The Heinemann library of criminology and penal reform).
Bibliography: p172-181. - Includes index.
ISBN 0435829327 Hbk £13.50
ISBN 0435829335 Pbk

Delinquency and citizenship : reclaiming the young offender, 1914-1948 / Victor Bailey. – Oxford : Clarendon, 1987.
viii,352p; 22cm.
Bibliography: p331-341. - Includes index.
ISBN 0198226640 £30.00

Delinquent : directions for social control / Masud Hoghughi. – London : Burnett, 1983.
317p; 24cm.
Bibliography: p295-310. - Includes index.
ISBN 0091506808 Hbk £15.00
ISBN 0091506816 Pbk £6.95

Delisle, Ronald Joseph
Evidence : Principles and Problems. – Agincourt : Carswell, 1984.
416p.
This textbook explores the historical background of existing Canadian Rules of Evidence and analyzes the rules in terms of underlying policy considerations. Numerous concrete examples drawn from hypothetical fact situations illustrate the general principles of the rules of evidence.
ISBN 0459364200 Hbk £34.50
→ Learning Canadian criminal law.
→ Learning Canadian Criminal Procedure.

Delivery of annual accounts and returns to the Registrar of Companies : a consultative document / Department of Trade and Industry. – London : Department of Trade and Industry, 1986.
35,7p,9 leaves.

Dell, Edmund →Company donations to political parties : a suggested code of practice.
→ Report of the Working Party on Company Residence, Tax Havens, and Upstream Loans.

Dell, Susanne
Murder into manslaughter. – Oxford : Oxford University Press, 1984.
ISBN 0197121519 Hbk £10.00
—Sentenced to hospital : offenders in Broadmoor / by Susanne Dell, Graham Robertson. – Oxford : Oxford University Press, 1988.
x, 170 p.; 25 cm.
Based on interviews with staff and patients at Broadmoor, it describes how men come to be sent to Broadmoor, and their subsequent treatment, including procedures and decision-making related to discharge. Recommends controversial changes in the law and in detention policy.
ISBN 019712156X Hbk £22.50

Dell'Arino, P. →Law and practice relating to pollution control in Italy.

Deloitte, Haskins and Sells
Accountants' Reports for Prospectus Purposes. – Deloitte, Haskins and Sells. – London : Butterworths, 1985.
ISBN 0406500215 Pbk £20.00
—Accountant's Reports on Takeovers, Mergers, Acquisitions and Realisations. – Deloitte, Haskins and Sells. – London : Butterworths, 1985.
ISBN 0406500207 Pbk £20.00
—Businessman's Guide to Microcomputers. – Deloitte, Haskins and Sells. – 2nd ed. – London : Butterworths, 1984.
ISBN 0406016003 Pbk £9.00
—Purchase by a Company of its Own Shares. – Deloitte, Haskins and Sells. – London : Butterworths, 1983.
ISBN 0406252688 Pbk £16.25
—Taxation in Europe : 1983. – Deloitte, Haskins and Sells. – London : Oyez Longman, 1983.
ISBN 0906052068 Hbk £10.95
—Trust Practice Manual. – Deloitte, Haskins and Sells. – London : Butterworths, 1985.
This book provides the basis for setting up standard procedures for the organization and operation of a trust department in a law office in the United Kingdom. Practical issues of management and procedures are addressed in the work.
ISBN 040650010X Pbk

Deloitte, Haskins and Sells : Raising Finance in Capital Markets. – London : Butterworths, 1987.
Pbk

Deloitte Staff
Businessman's Guide to Microcomputers. – Deloitte Staff. – London : Butterworths, 1984.
This book is designed to give business and legal practitioners a thorough introduction to microcomputers. The book provides in depth information on software packages with business applications.
ISBN 0406016003 Pbk

DeLong, Linwood
Guide to Canadian Diplomatic Relations 1925-1983. – Ottawa : Canadian Library Association, 1985.
Hbk £12.00

Delors, Jacques
Single act and Europe : a moment of truth / by Jacques Delors. – Luxembourg : Office for Official Publications of the European Communities, 1986.
37p.

Delport, H.J. →Partnership.

Delport, J.T.
Law of Partnership. – Durban : Professional Publishers, 1984.
ISBN 0409023620 Pbk
—Two lectures on law reform : delivered at the workshop on Marriage and Family Life by the Human Sciences Research Council on 26 September 1985 / by J.T. Delport and C.R.M. Dlamini. – Pretoria : Government Printer on behalf of the South African Law Comission, 1987.
iv,38p. – (Research series).
Bibliography: pp.19-21.
ISBN 0621106704

Delupis, Ingrid
Concept of international law / by Ingrid Detter De Lupis. – Stockholm : Norstedts Forlag, 1987.
145p.
Bibliography: p137-145.
ISBN 911867562X
—Finance and protection of investments in developing countries / Ingrid Detter De Lupis. – 2nd ed. – Aldershot : Gower, 1987.
xvii,183p; 23cm.
Previous ed.: 1973. Includes index.
ISBN 0566054655 £25.00
—Law of war / Ingrid Detter de Lupis. – Cambridge : Cambridge University Press, 1987.
xx,411p; 23cm.
Bibliography: p367-406. - Includes index.
ISBN 0521343372 Hbk £40.00
ISBN 0521348382 Pbk £15.00

Delvolve, Jean-Louis
Arbitration in France : the French law and national and international arbitration / Jean-Louis Delvolve. – Trilangual ed. – Antwerp : Kluwer Law and Taxation Publishers, 1982.
x, 165 p.; 19 cm.
English, French, and German. Bibliography: p. 165.
ISBN 9065440984

Demas, J.G. →Fourth Company Law Directive : Implementation by Member States.

Dembinski, Ludwik
Modern Law of Diplomacy : External Missions of States and International Organizations. – Dordrecht : Kluwer, 1988.
300p.
Hbk Gld135.00

deMestral, Armand L. C. →International business transactions and economic relations : cases, notes and materials on the law as it applies to Canada.

Democracy and Direct Action in Contemporary Europe. – Exeter : European Atlantic Movement, 1982.
Hbk £0.50

Democracy and the rule of law : liberal ideas and marxist critiques / Bob Fine. – London : Pluto, 1984.
viii,231p; 20cm.
Bibliography: p221-228. - Includes index.
ISBN 0861047842 Pbk £7.95

Democracy in peril : Sri Lanka : a country in crisis : report to the LAWASIA Human Rights Standing Committee / by Patricia Hyndman. – Sydney : LAWASIA, 1985.
xi,483p.

Democracy in trade unions / presented to Parliament by the Secretary of State for Employment. – London : H.M.S.O., 1983.
ii,37p.
ISBN 0101877803

Democracy Rediscovered : Study in Police Accountability. – Pluto Press.
ISBN 0745302629 Hbk £14.95

Democratic Constitution of India. – New Delhi : S. Chand and Company, 1983.
Hbk £14.00

Demonstrating Successful Community Care / Knapp. – University of Kent.
ISBN 0904938018 Pbk £2.95

Dempsters. – Nedlands : University of Western Australia Press, 1978.
xiv, 297p.
ISBN 0855641266 Hbk £18.95

DeMulder, R.V., et al
Sentencing by Computer : an Experiment. – Norwegian University Press, 1982.
246p.
ISBN 8200064360 Hbk £133.00

DeMulinen, Frederic
Handbook on the Law of War for Armed Forces. – Geneva : Comite International de la Croix-Rouge, 1987.
254p.
Hbk £20.00
—Law of War and the Armed Forces. – 2nd ed. – Geneva : Comite International de la Croix-Rouge, 1981.
44p.
Hbk £3.00

Demystification of Law for Women. – New Delhi : Lancer International, 1986.
112p.
Pbk £95.00

Denbow, Claude
Life Insurance Law in the Commonwealth Caribbean. – London : Butterworths, 1984.
xxiii,226; 23cm.
This book provides a comprehensive study of the English law of life insurance as it applies in Trinidad and Tobago.
ISBN 0406076308 Pbk £17.00

Dencher, J. S.
Personal Tax Losses. – London : Butterworths, 1984.
This practical book shows tax advisers how to maximize tax relief for clients through use of tax losses under the tax laws of the United Kingdom. The work presents a variety of realistic tax planning options in tax loss situations.
ISBN 0406263604 Pbk £16.50

Denham, Paul
Modern Introduction to Law. – London : Edward Arnold, 1984.
544p.
ISBN 0713109041 Pbk £8.95

Denning, Alfred
Changing Law, The. – Reprint. – Sweet & Maxwell, 1953.
ISBN 0421375809 Hbk £15.75
—Closing Chapter. – London : Butterworths, 1983.
ISBN 0406176116 Hbk £12.95
ISBN 0406176124 Pbk £8.95
—Family story / by Lord Denning. – London : Butterworths, 1981.
xi,270p,16p of plates; 24cm.
Includes index.
ISBN 0406176094 £8.50
—Freedom Under The Law (Hamlyn No 1). – Sweet & Maxwell, 1949.
ISBN 0420421408 Pbk £7.50
→ Jubilee lectures celebrating the foundation of the Faculty of Law, University of Birmingham.
—Landmarks in the Law. – London : Butterworths, 1984.
ISBN 0406176035 Hbk £14.95
ISBN 0406176140 Pbk £9.95
—Leaves from My Library / by Lord Denning. – London : Butterworths, 1986.
ISBN 0406176159 Hbk £13.95
—What Next in the Law. – Wellington : Butterworths, 1982.
This work deals with proposals for reform in various areas of the law of the United Kingdom, including: trial by jury, legal aid, personal injuries, libel, privacy, and confidence.
ISBN 0406176019 Hbk
ISBN 0406176027 Pbk

Denning, Alfred
Landmarks in the law / by Lord Denning. – London : Butterworths, 1984.
xvii,394p; 23cm.
Includes index.
ISBN 0406176035 Hbk £12.50
ISBN 0406176140 Pbk
—What next in the law / by Lord Denning. – London : Butterworths, 1982.
xxiii,352p.
Amended version of original ed. which was withdrawn from sale on legal advice shortly after publication. Includes index.
ISBN 0406176019 Hbk £13.95
ISBN 0406176027 Pbk £9.50

Denning law journal. – Buckingham : University of Buckingham, 1986.
ISBN 02691922

Dennis, I. H. → Criminal law and justice : essays from the W.G. Hart workshop 1986.
→ Modern developments in the law of civic procedure.
→ Sweet & Maxwell's criminal law statutes.

Dennison, S. R. → Low Pay or No Pay? A Review of the Theory and Practice of Minimum-Wage Laws.

Denny, M.
Introduction to General Average. – Witherby, 1986.
ISBN 0948691107 Pbk £6.00

Densham, H. A. C. → Law of Agricultural Holdings.

Dentists Bill : report on the consolidation of the Dentists Acts 1957 to 1983 / The Law Commission and The Scottish Law Commission. – London : H.M.S.O., 1984.
5p; 25cm.
ISBN 0101911904

Denton, Mariam
Women and legal affairs / a paper jointly prepared by Mariam Denton, Amie Bensouda, Fola Mendy Allen. – Banjul, the Gambia? : s.n., 1985.
10p.
At head of cover title: The Gambia National Women's Council and Bureau. Cover title: End of Women's Decade Conference on Women in Development, 24th-26th April 1985.

Denyer-Green, Barry P.D.
Compulsory Purchase and Compensation. – 2nd ed. – London : Estates Gazette, 1985.
ISBN 0728200899 Pbk £14.00
—Development and Planning Law. – 2nd ed. – London : Estates Gazette, 1987.
ISBN 0728201135 Pbk £6.00
—Land compensation : a study of compensation determination / Barry P.D. Denyer-Green. – Cambridge : Granta Editions, 1986.
xi,124p. – (Occasional paper).
Includes bibliographical references.
ISBN 0906782228

Deosaran, Ramesh
Trial by jury : social and psychological dynamics / Ramesh Deosaran. – St. Augustine, Trinidad, West Indies : Institute of Social and Economic Research, University of the West Indies, 1985.
324 p.; 23 cm.
Includes indexes. Bibliography: p. 283-297.
ISBN 9766180008 Pbk

Department of Consumer and Corporate Affairs
Amendments to the Combines Investigation Act : background information and explanatory notes. – Department of Consumer and Corporate Affairs. – Ottawa : The Department, 1984.
32p,37p.
With French t.p.: Modifications de la loi relative aux enquetes sur les coalitions. English and French text.

Department of Health
Operation of the Drug Treaties : Australia 1978-1980. – Department of Health. – Canberra : Australian Government Publishing Service, 1981.
19p.
ISBN 0642068070 Hbk £1.60

Department of Health and Social Security
Adjudication officers' guide / Chief Adjudication Officer. – London : HMSO, 1988.
looseleaf.
Index in each vol.. At head of t.p. : Department of Health and Social Security.
—Children Act 1975 : custodianship orders / Department of Health and Social Security. – London : The Department, 1985.
15,xi,3,iip.
—Draft guidelines for approval of social workers under the proposed Mental Health (Amendment) Act : Working Party draft for consultation. – Department of Health and Social Security. – London : The Department, 1981.
11p.
—Report of the inquiry into child abuse in Cleveland 1987 / presented to Parliament by the Secretary of State for Social Services by Command of Her Majesty, July 1988. – London : HMSO, 1988.
320p.
'Presented to the Secretary of State for Social Services by the Right Honourable Lord Justice Butler-Sloss DBE'. - p.i.
ISBN 0101041225
—Report of the inquiry into child abuse in Cleveland 1987 : short version extracted from the complete text / presented to Parliament by the Secretary of State for Social Services by Command of Her Majesty, July 1988. – London : HMSO, 1988.
21p.
Chairman: ELizabeth Butler-Sloss.
ISBN 0101041322

Department of Industrial Relations
Review of Australian Law and Practice Relating to the Conventions Adopted by the International Labour Conference. – Department of Industrial Relations. – Canberra : Australian Government Publishing Service, 1981.
ISBN 0642052166 Llf £14.20

Department of Industry → Development of cable systems and services.

Department of Industry & Commerce
Small Business and the Law. – Department of Industry & Commerce. – Repr. of 1981 ed. – Canberra : Australian Government Publishing Service, 1983.
40p. – (Managing the Small Business Ser.).
ISBN 0642069085 Hbk £2.30

Department of National Health and Welfare
Health protection and drug laws / Educational Services, Health Protection Branch, Department of National Health and Welfare. – Ottawa : The Department, 1982.
45p.
Includes bibliographies.
ISBN 0660112329

Department of Science and Technology
Legislation at Work : Safety and Health. – Department of Science and Technology. – 2nd ed. – Canberra : Australian Government Publishing Service, 1981.
41p. – (Occupational Safety & Health Working Environment: No. 4).
ISBN 0642052212 Hbk £1.90

Department of the Environment
Telecommunications development : draft development control policy note / Department of the Environment. – London : Department of the Environment, 1986.
24p.
—Water and the environment : the implementation of Part II of the Control of Pollution Act 1974 : joint circular / from the Department of the Environment and Welsh Office. – London : H.M.S.O., 1984.
– (Circular).
ISBN 0117517437
—Water environment : the next steps : the Government's proposals for environmental protection under a privatised water industry / Department of the Environment, Welsh Office. – London? : The Department, 1986.
44p.

Department of Trade
Companies Act 1948 : Investigations. – Department of Trade. – London : HMSO, 1983.
ISBN 0115136738 Hbk £20.00

Department of Trade and Industry
DTI : the department for enterprise / presented to Parliament by the Secretary of State for Trade and Industry and the Chancellor of the Duchy of Lancaster by command of Her Majesty, January 1988. – London : HMSO, 1988.
vii,41p.
ISBN 0101027826
—Harmonisation of company and related law in the European Community : progress on draft directives and other proposals / Department of Trade and Industry, Companies Division. – London : The Division, 1987.
13p.
—Implementation of EC directive on product liability : an explanatory and consultative note / Department of Trade and Industry. – London : The Department, 1985.
18,xivp.
—Regulation of authorised unit trust schemes : a consultative document on the proposed regulations for unit trust schemes authorised under the Financial Services Bill / Department of Trade and Industry. – London : HMSO, 1986.
viii.74p.
ISBN 0115138498
—Review of legislation on false and misleading price information : report of the inter-departmental working party / Department of Trade and Industry. – London : The Department, 1984.
67p.

Dependent accumulation and underdevelopment / Andre Gunder Frank. – 1st ed. reprinted. – London : Macmillan, 1982.
xx,226p.
Bibliography: p.202-219. - Includes index.
ISBN 0333239512

Dept. of Continuing Education → Costs, Party and Party : Updated.

Deputy Crown Solicitors Office Perth : Report of Enquiry Concerning the Office. – Attorney-General's Department. – Canberra : Australian Government Publishing Service, 1983.
142p.
ISBN 0644024135 Hbk £5.00

Deregulation for small private companies / Institute of Directors. – London : Institute of Directors, 1986.
13 leaves.

Deregulation of hire-purchase / Law Reform Commission of Victoria. – Melbourne : The Commission, 1986.
x,22p. – (Report no 4).
Bibliography: p.21-22. Includes text of Hire-purchase (Deregulation) Bill 1986.

Deregulation of the radio spectrum in the UK / by CSP International. – London : H.M.S.O., 1987.
192p; 30cm.
Bibliography: p185-192. At head of title: Department of Trade and Industry. Text on inside covers.
ISBN 0115139796 Pbk £9.50

Derham, David → Legal process : commentary and materials.

Derham, S. Rory
Set-off / S. Rory Derham. – Oxford : Clarendon, 1987.
320p; 22cm.
Includes bibliography and index.
ISBN 019825556X £40
—Subrogation in insurance law / by S.R. Derham. – North Ryde, N.S.W. : Law Book Co. Ltd., 1985.
xxxiii,164p.
Bibliography: p.xxix-xxxiii. - Includes index.
ISBN 0455205922

Derrett
Essays in Classical and Modern Hindu
Vol. 1: Dharmasastra and Related Ideas. – Leiden : E.J. Brill, 1976.
ISBN 9004044752 Hbk £96.00

Derry Miller, W. A. → Ontario Annual Practice (O.A.P).

Desai, Kumud
Indian Law of Marriage and Divorce. – 4th ed. – Bombay : Tripathi, 1981.
660p.
bd £125.00
→ Law of Torts.

Desai, S.K.
Law of Torts / Kumud Desai. – 8th ed. – Bombay : Tripathi, 1987.
744p.
bd £220.00

Desai, Sunderlal Trikamlal → Principles of Hindu law, with a general introduction to Hindu law and with commentaries on the Hindu Marriage Act, 1955, the Hindu Succession Act, 1956, the Hindu Minority & Guardianship Act, 1956, the Hindu Adoptions & Maintenance Act, 1956.

Desailly, R. N. → Criminal jurisdiction of magistrates in Papua New Guinea.

DeSchaepdrijver, P.
Guidelines to Buying and Contract Specifications for Sorghum Malt. – Pretoria : Council for Scientific and Industrial Research.
15p.
ISBN 0798803193
—Guidelines to Specifications for Bantu Beer Packaging Contracts. – Pretoria : Council for Scientific and Industrial Research.
19p.
ISBN 0798803207

Deschampneufs, M.
Export For The Small Business. – London : Kogan Page, 1984.
ISBN 085038771X Pbk £5.95

Desch$enes, Bernard M.
Study on marine casualty investigations in Canada (for the Minister of Transport) / Bernard M. Desch$enes. – Ottawa : Minister of Supply and Services, 1984.
x,273p.
ISBN 0662134036

Desch$enes, Jules → Judicial independence : the contemporary debate.

Descriptive study of incarerated dangerous offenders / J. Jakimiec ... et al. – Ottawa : Ministry of the Solicitor General, 1986.
23p. – (User report).
Bibliography: p.24.

Desgagne, Jean-Guy → Victims and witnesses of crime in Canada.

Deshpande, V.S.
Women and the New Law. – Patiala : Punjab University, Publication Bureau.
Hbk £50.00

Design : the modern law and practice / by A.I. Morris and Barry Quest. – London : Butterworth, 1987.
xxvii,377p,12p of plates; 25cm.
Bibliography: p369-370. - Includes index.
ISBN 0406103216 Hbk £52
ISBN 0406103208

Design and Build Contracts / Stephen J Pymont. – Oxford : Blackwell Scientific, 1987.
ISBN 0003830500 Hbk £19.95

Design and Building Contract Practice. – London : Longman Professional, 1986.
ISBN 0582494842 Pbk £19.50

Design Defects. – Product Liability Briefing, 1988.
ISBN 1870317505 Pbk £6.50

Design Law and Treaties of the World : World Rights Outside the U.S.A. – Dordrecht : Kluwer.
Hbk

Design Liability in the Construction Industry / Davids L. Cornes. – 3rd ed. – Oxford : BSP Professional.
ISBN 0632022663 Hbk £22.50

Design Protection. – 2nd ed. – London : Design Council Books, 1986.
ISBN 0850721652 Hbk £8.95
Guide to Law on Plagiarism for Manufacturers and Designers. –
ISBN 0850722489 Hbk £15.00

Despax, Michel
Labour law and industrial relations in France / by Michel Despax and Jacques Rojot. – Deventer : Kluwer Law and Taxation, 1987.
314p.
Includes index.
ISBN 9065443436
—Law and practice relating to pollution control in France / William Coulet, Claude Albert Colliard. – 2nd ed. – London : Graham & Trotman for the Commission of the European Communities, 1982.
xxvii,150p; 23cm.
Previous ed.: / by Claude-Albert Colliard. 1976.
Bibliography: p141-144. - Includes index.
ISBN 0860103072 £21.00

Dessemontet, F. → Introduction to Swiss law.

Detention and Torture in South Africa. – DENT, 1987.
ISBN 0852553188 Pbk £7.95

Detention at the police station under the Police and Criminal Evidence Act 1984 / by David Brown. – London : HMSO, 1989.
v,88p.
Bibliography: pp.78-80. 'A Home Office Research and Planning Unit Report'. – T.p..
ISBN 0113409087

Detention Without Trial in South Africa 1976-1977. – South Africa Institute of Race Relations. – Johannesburg : South African Institute of Race Relations.
Hbk

Determination and Suspension of Construction Contracts / John Sims. – London : Collins, 1985.
208p.
ISBN 0003831566 Hbk £17.50

Deterrence and compensation : legal liability in occupational safety and health / Felice Morgenstern. – Geneva : International Labour Office, 1982.
iii,76p.
Bibliography: p73-74.
ISBN 9221030105

Deterrence in the 1980s : crisis and dilemma / edited by R.B. Byers. – London : Croom Helm, 1985.
235p; 22cm.
Includes index.
ISBN 070993288X £18.95

Detmold, M. J.
Australian Commonwealth : a fundamental analysis of its constitution / M. J. Detmold. – Sydney : Law Book Company, 1985.
266p.
ISBN 0455205787
—Courts and Administrators. – Weidenfeld & Nicolson.
ISBN 0297794973 Hbk £14.95
—Unity of law and morality : a refutation of legal postivisim / M.J. Detmold. – London : Routledge & Kegan Paul, 1984.
xix,271p; 23cm.
Bibliography: p265-268. - Includes index.
ISBN 0710200307 £15.00

Deutsch, E → Medical responsibility in Western Europe : research study of the European Science Foundation.

Deutsch, R.L., et al
Butterworths Australian Tax Handbook 1989. – Butterworths, 1989.
1,504p.
ISBN 0409302414 Pbk £39.00
—Butterworths Tax Guide, 3 Vols. – 1st ed. – Butterworths, 1989.
ca 1,650p.
Llf £340.00

DeValera's Constitution and Ours. – Dublin : Gill and Macmillan, 1988.
ISBN 0717116123 Pbk £9.95

Developing countries in the GATT legal system / by Robert E. Hudec. – Aldershot : Gower for the Trade Policy Research Centre, 1987.
xix,259p.
Bibliography: p.236-250..
ISBN 0566056976

Developing Countries Western Interests and Actions. – Exeter : European Atlantic Movement, 1982.
Hbk £0.50

Developing legal status of women in Trinidad and Tobago / by Stephanie Daly. – Port-of-Spain : National Commission on the Status of Women, 1982.
136p.
Includes bibliographical references and index.

Development aid. – London : Butterworths, 1988.
ISBN 0408009918 Hbk £55.00

Development and Judicial Trial in Nigeria. – Onitsha : Africana-FEP.
Hbk

Development and Planning Law. – 2nd ed. – London : Estates Gazette, 1987.
ISBN 0728201135 Pbk £6.00

Development and Principles of International Humanitarian Law. – Geneva : Comite International de la Croix-Rouge, 1983.
99p.
Hbk £20.00

Development and principles of international humanitarian law : course given in July 1982 at the University of Strasbourg as part of the courses organized by the International Institute of Human Rights / by Jean Pictet. – Dordrecht Netherlands : M. Nijhoff, 1985.
108p.
Bibliography. Translation of: Developpement et principes du droit international humanitaire.
ISBN 9024731992 Pbk £49.50

Development and the environmental crisis : red or green alternatives? / Michael Redclift. – London : Methuen, 1984.
149p; 23cm.
Bibliography: p131-146. - Includes index.
ISBN 0416321305 Hbk
ISBN 0416321402 Pbk

Development and the Rule of Law, Prevention Versus Cure as a Human Rights Strategy. – Geneva : International Commission of Jurists, 1981.
125p.
Hbk £10.00

Development Control. – 2nd ed. – Sweet & Maxwell.
ISBN 0421371706 Pbk £13.00

Development Control / Susan Nott. – London : Butterworths, 1988.
ISBN 0406502501 Hbk £24.00
ISBN 040650551X Pbk

Development, human rights and the rule of law : report of a conference held in The Hague on 27 April-1 May 1981 / convened by the International Commission of Jurists. – Oxford : Pergamon, 1981.
vi,237p; 23cm.
ISBN 0080289215 Hbk
ISBN 0080289517 Pbk £3.75

Development Land and Development Charge in Singapore. – London : Butterworths, 1987.
ISBN 0409995371 Hbk £36.00

Development Land Tax 1976-1980 Supplement 1982. – London : HMSO.
ISBN 0116413670 Hbk £0.95
Supplement 1983. –
ISBN 0116413697 Hbk £0.40

Development land tax / by Robert W. Maas. – 4th ed. – Croydon : Tolley, 1982.
xiii,244p; 23cm.
Previous ed.: 1981. Includes index.
ISBN 0854590560 Pbk £10.50

Development Land Tax Guide / Tony Johnson. – London : Butterworths, 1984.
ISBN 040626287X Pbk

Development of British immigration law / Vaughan Bevan. – London : Croom Helm, 1986.
512p.
Includes bibliography and index.
ISBN 0709906633 £29.95

Development of cable systems and services / Home Office, Department of Industry. – London : H.M.S.O., 1983.
90p; 25cm.
ISBN 0101886608 Pbk £6.00

Development of consumer law and policy - bold spirits and timorous souls / by Sir Gordon Borrie. – London : Published under the auspices of the Hamlyn Trust by Stevens, 1984.
xii,138p; 18cm.
Includes index.
ISBN 0420467904 Hbk £14.50
ISBN 0420468005 Pbk £6.25

Development of Indian Legal System. – New Delhi : Deep and Deep Publications, 1987.
428p.
Hbk £275.00

Development of Intern. Law by European Court Human Rights. – Manchester : Manchester University Press.
ISBN 0719026652 Hbk £29.95

Development of international humanitarian law / by Geza Herczegh. – Budapest : Akademiai Kiado, 1984.
239p.
Bibliography: p231-235.
ISBN 9630534487

Development of International Law by the International Court. – Cambridge : Grotius.
408p.
ISBN 0906496306 Hbk £30.00

Development of judicial control of the European Communities / Gerhard Bebr. – The Hague : Nijhoff, 1981.
xviii,882p; 25cm.
Bibliography: p719-808. - Includes index.
ISBN 9024725410 Hbk £360.00

Development of maritime islands as extreme examples of peripheral regions / report prepared by the Committee of Experts on Social and Economic Activities of the Steering Committee for Regional and Municipal Matters, with the assistance of Italo Ferrari. – Strasbourg : Council of Europe, 1986.
26p.

Development of the law of the sea with special reference to the exclusive economic zone. – S.l. : s.n., 1982.
p.297-307.

Development of UK communications systems : discussion document / Department of Trade and Industry. – London : The Department, 1987.
14 leaves.

Development of UK Product Safety Law. – Product Liability Briefing, 1988.
ISBN 1870317807 Hbk £24.00

Development technology / H.J. Duller. – London : Routledge & K. Paul, 1982.
192p.
Includes index. Bibliography: p173-190.
ISBN 0710009909

Developments in homelessness and the law 1983-1985 / by Paul Q. Watchman and Peter Robson. – Glasgow : Planning Exchange, 1986.
ii, 118p.
Supplements the authors' Homelessness and the law (1983). Bilbiography: p.98-103 - Includes index.
ISBN 090501121X

Developments in Section 52 of the Trade Practices Act 1984-1985 : Centre for Commercial Law and Applied Legal Research. – Monash University, Faculty of Law. – Clayton : Monash University Press.
ISBN 086746397X Hbk £15.00

Developments in the law of product liability : being the presidential address of Lord Griffiths, president of the Holdsworth Club of the Faculty of Laws in the Univeristy of Birmingham, 1986-1987. – birmingham : The Holdsworth Club of the University of Birmingham, 1987.
17p. – (The Holdsworth Club).
ISBN 0704409259

Developments in the study of criminal behaviour Vol.1 : The prevention and control of offending / edited by Philip Feldman. – Chichester : Wiley, 1982.
x,238p; 24cm.
Includes bibliographies and index.
ISBN 0471101761 Hbk
Vol.2 : Violence / edited by Philip Feldman. – 1982.
x,254p; 24cm.
Includes bibliographies and index.
ISBN 047110373X Hbk £22.00

DeVere, Ross → What should be done about corruption and bribery?.

Devereux, M. P.
Corporation tax : the impact of the 1984 budget / M.P. Devereaux and C.P. Mayer. – London : Institute for Fiscal Studies, 1984.
47p.
Includes bibliographical references.
ISBN 0902992384
—North sea oil taxation : the development of the North Sea tax system / M. P. Devereux and C. N. Morris. – London : Institute for Fiscal Studies, 1983.
93p.
Bibliography: p90-91.
→ North Sea taxation for the 1990s.

Deviance, reality and society / Steven Box. – 2nd ed. – London : Holt, Rinehart and Winston, 1981.
vii,248p; 22cm.
Previous ed.: 1971. Includes bibliographies and index.
ISBN 0039102947 Pbk £4.95

Deviant Designations : Crime Law and Deviance in Canada / Visano. – Toronto : Butterworths, 1983.
512p.
Examines the reaction of communities to crime; issues involved in creating deviant designations and controlling the careers of those deemed deviant or criminal; the response of formal agents and agencies of social control (courts, police, and prisons) to be discredited, and emerging theoretical concerns.
ISBN 0409829846 Pbk £25.95

Devine, John Dermott
Southern Africa and the Law of the Sea : Problems Common, Uncommon and Unique. – Rondebosch : University of Cape Town, 1986.
17p.
ISBN 0799210242 Pbk £0.30

Devlin, Keith →Sentencing.

Devlin, Patrick
Easing the Passing. – London : CAPE, 1985.
ISBN 0370306279 Hbk £12.50
ISBN 0571139930 Pbk £4.95
—Easing the passing : the trial of Dr John Bodkin Adams / Patrick Devlin. – London : Bodley Head, 1985.
256p; 23cm.
ISBN 0370306279 £9.95
—Trial By Jury (Hamlyn No. 8). – Sweet & Maxwell, 1966.
ISBN 0420434909 Pbk £6.50

DeVoil
VAT. – London : Butterworths, 1984.
ISBN 0406514747 Llf £210.00

DeVorsey, Jr, Louis →Rights to oceanic resources, Deciding and drawing maritime boundaries. A Dean Rusk Center monograph.

Dewan, Vijay Kumar
Law of Citizenship, Foreigners and Passports. – Allahabad : Orient Law House, 1984.
Hbk £150.00
—North Eastern Region Local Acts, Vol. 9 : General Clauses to Home-Guards. – 2nd ed. – Allahabad : Orient Law House, 1986.
800p.
Hbk £150.00

Dewar, John- →Nuclear weapons, the peace movement and the law.

Dewees, Donald
Regulation of quality. – Scarborough, Ontario : Butterworths (Canada), 1983.
368.
Considers the subjects' ethical, political and legal framework, looking at the rationale for government regulation of quality, regulating quality in product markets, regulating enviromental quality, the administration of the Hazardous Products Acts, regulating occupational health and safety, markets for insurance, regulating the quality of psychotherapeutic services and the control of diesel exhaust pollution.
ISBN 040982495X Hbk

Dewhurst →Small business in Europe.

Dewis, M →Health and safety practice.
—Tolley's Health and Safety at Work Handbook. – 2nd ed. – Tolley Publishing.
ISBN 0854593829 Hbk £39.95

Dewit, Bernard →China Trade Law.
→ China trade law : code of the foreign trade law of the People's Republic of China.

Dewitt, David B. →Nuclear non-proliferation and global security.

Dhamija
Registration Act : with State Amendments, Rules and Table of Fees. – 3rd ed. – Allahabad : Law Book Company, 1988.
ca 900p.
Hbk £250.00

Dhanji, Anisa →Butterworth's British Columbia Family Law Quantum Service, 2 vol.
→ Butterworths British Columbia Family Law Quantum Service, 2 Vols.

Dhar, Pannalal
National Integration and Indian Constitution. – New Delhi : Deep and Deep Publications, 1986.
198p.
Hbk £150.00
—Preventive Detention under Indian Constitution. – New Delhi : Deep and Deep Publications, 1986.
324p.
Hbk £250.00

Dhavan, Rajeev →Judges and the judicial power : essays in honour of Justice V.R. Krishna Iyer.
—Litigating Exploitation in India. – Bombay : Tripathi, 1986.
189p.
Hbk £75.00
—Only the Good News : on the Law of the Press in India. – New Delhi, 1987.
514p.
Hbk Manohar Publications

Dhirajlal →Code of Criminal Procedure.
→ Indian Penal Code.
→ Law of Crimes, 2 Vols.
→ Law of Evidence.
→ Law of Torts.

Dholakia, S.K.
Rights of Minority Shareholders. – Bombay : Tripathi, 1983
£85.00

DHSS Official Contributions Guides. – London : Oyez Longman, 1984.
ISBN 0851207391 Hbk £55.00

Di Palma, Vera
Capital Gains Tax. – 5th ed. – Plymouth : Macdonald & Evans, 1981.
224p. – (M and E Handbook Ser.).
This looseleaf service for United Kingdom practitioners includes all the relevant Acts and regulations, extra-statutory concessions, statements of practice, case digests, and many worked examples. Specific provisions of capital gains tax relating to corporate bodies, trustees, and others are covered.
ISBN 0712104607 Hbk £4.95

Dialectic of nihilism : post-structuralism and law / Gillian Rose. – Oxford : Blackwell, 1984.
232p; 24cm.
Critique of post-structuralist theory related to law.
ISBN 0631131914 Hbk £22.00
ISBN 0631137084 Pbk

Diamond →Tax Havens Of The World.

Diamond, Aubrey L.
Anglo-Sakson gozuyle turk hukuku / An Anglo-Saxon view of Turkish law : Aubrey L. Diamond. – 1981.
2,10 leaves.
Paper presented at the 3rd Turkish Law Conference, Ankara, 1981. English text in typescript, bound with a Turkish translation published as a supplement to the Conference papers.
—Commercial and consumer credit : an introduction / by Aubrey L. Diamond. – London : Butterworths, 1982.
xxvii,379p.
Includes index.
ISBN 0406574057
—Commercial and Consumer Credit - An Introduction. – London : Butterworths, 1982.
ISBN 0406574057 Pbk £14.95
→ Consumer, society and the law.
—Security over property other than land : consultation document / by A.L. Diamond. – London : Department of Trade and Industry, 1986.
67p.
—Tax Havens Of The World / Diamond. – Matthew Bender, 1974.
ISBN 0000999084 Hbk £132.00

Diary of Hugh Gaitskell, 1945-1956 / Philip M. Williams. – London : Jonathan Cape, 1983.
ISBN 0224019112 Hbk £25.00

Diary of social legislation and policy. – Parkville, Vic. : Institute of Applied Economic and Social Research, University of Melbourne, 1981.
ISBN 07252455

Dias, C. J. →Lawyers in the Third World : comparative and developmental perspectives.

Dias, R. W. M. →Clerk & Lindsell on torts.
—Jurisprudence / R.W.M. Dias. – 5th ed. – London : Butterworths, 1985.
505p; cased.
Previous ed.: 1976. Includes index.
ISBN 0406574324 Pbk £24.50
ISBN 0406574316 £16.95
—Tort law / by R.W.M. Dias and B.S. Markesinis. – Oxford : Clarendon, 1984.
xxxiv,526p; 23cm.
Includes bibliographies and index.
ISBN 0198761503 Hbk £22.50
ISBN 0198761511 Pbk £15.00

DiCastri, Victor
Occupiers' Liability in Canada. – Agincourt : Carswell, 1981.
328p.
The book analyzes the common law rules of occupiers liability and comments on legislation in Ontario, Alberta and British Columbia.
Hbk £54.75

Dicey, A. V.
Dicey and Morris on the conflict of laws / Under the general editorship of L.A. Collins : with specialist editors. – 11th ed. 2. – London : Stevens, 1987.
Previous ed.: 1980. Includes index. Kept up to date by supplements.
ISBN 0420471308 Hbk £140
—Introduction To The Study Of The Constitution / Wade. – London : Macmillan, 1959.
ISBN 0333052552 Pbk £9.95

Dicey and Morris' Conflict of Laws, 2 Vols. Supplement-1983 /. – London : Sweet & Maxwell.

Dicey and Morris on the conflict of laws / Under the general editorship of L.A. Collins : with specialist editors. – 11th ed. 2. – London : Stevens, 1987.
Previous ed.: 1980. Includes index. Kept up to date by supplements.
ISBN 0420471308 Hbk £140

Dick H., Anthony
Family Law. – North Ryde : Law Book Co, 1985.
lxxxvi, 685p.
ISBN 0455203075 Hbk £66.00
ISBN 0455203083 Pbk £49.50

Dick, Robert C., et al
Estates and Trusts Quarterly (E. & T.Q.) 1974-Present. – Aurora : Canada Law Book Co.
Hbk £65.00
—Legal drafting / by Robert C. Dick. – 2nd ed. – Toronto : Carswell, 1985.
xiii,234p.
Includes bibliographical references and index.
ISBN 045937740X

Dickason, I. J.
JCT 80 and the Builder : An Introduction. – King's Ride : Institute of Building, 1985.
211p.
ISBN 0906600774 Hbk £12.75

Dickens, Bernard M. →Emerging issues in Commonwealth abortion laws, 1982.
→ Issues in reproductice health law in the Commonwealth.

Dickens, Linda →Dismissed : a study of unfair dismissal and the industrial tribunal system.

Dickey, Anthony
Family Law. – North Ryde : Law Book Co, 1985.
ISBN 0455203075 Hbk £31.00
ISBN 0455203083 Pbk £22.75
—Select Cases on the Family Law Act 1976-1985. – North Ryde : C.C.H. Australia, 1986.
1,006p.
Hbk £32.00

Dickinson, Gregory M.
Rights, Freedoms and the Education System in Canada : Cases and Materials / A. Wayne McKay. – Toronto : Edmond-Montgomery, 1988.
ca 750p.
ISBN 0920722237 Hbk £68.00

Dickinson, J.P.
A-Z of Business Mathematics. – London : Kogan Page.
ISBN 185091673X Pbk £8.95

Dicks, Anthony
Treaty, grant, usage or sufferance? : some legal aspects of the status of Hong Kong / by Anthony Dicks. – London : Contemporary China Institute, School of Oriental and African Studies, 1983.
p.427-455.
Offprint from: The China quarterly (September 1983).

Dickson, Brice
Legal system of Northern Ireland / by Brice Dickson. – Belfast : SLS Legal Publications (NI), 1984.
x,225p.
ISBN 0853892369
—Reservation of title clauses / Brice Dickson. – Belfast : SLS Legal Publications, 1987.
ii,96p.
Bibliography: pp.93-94..

Dickson, G. C. A.
Introduction to insurance / G.C.A. Dickson, J.T. Steele. – 2nd ed. – London : Pitman, 1984.
xii,212p.
Includes index.
ISBN 0273027905

Dickson, M.L.
Ontario Estate Practice / J.R. Wilson. – 2nd ed. – Don Mills : CCH Canadian Ltd, 1986.
604p.
ISBN 0887962998 Pbk £39.95

Dickson, Michael G. →Security on movable property and receivables in Europe : the principal forms of security in the European Community (except Greece) and Switzerland.

Dickson, Murray →French Canada in crisis : a new society in the making?.

Dickson, Robert Gary
Divorce Guide for Alberta : Step-by-Step Guide to Obtaining Your Own Divorce. – 5th ed. – North Vancouver : International Self-Counsel Press, 1986.
87p.
ISBN 088908243X Hbk £9.95

Dictionary Legal/Commercial Terms : German/English, 2 Vols. / Rutter. – London : Butterworths, 1984.
ISBN 0406038104 Hbk £98.00

Dictionary of Accounting Terms. – London : Financial Training, 1985.
ISBN 0906322677 Pbk £8.95

Dictionary of arbitration law & practice / Eric Lee. – London : Mansfield Law Publishers, 1986.
185p.

Dictionary of banking / F.E. Perry. – 2nd ed. – Plymouth : Macdonald and Evans, 1983.
385p; 23cm. – (M & E professional dictionaries).
Previous ed: 1979.
ISBN 0712104321 Hbk £12.50
ISBN 0712104372 Pbk

Dictionary of banking / F.E. Perry. – 3rd ed. – London : Pitman, 1988.
356p; 19cm.
Previous ed.: Plymouth : Macdonald and Evans, 1983.
ISBN 0712107657 Pbk £9.95
ISBN 0273029614 correct

Dictionary of Banking. – 3rd ed. – Pitman.
ISBN 0273029614 Pbk £9.95

Dictionary of Banking and Finance. – London : Pitman Publishing, 1985.
ISBN 0273018590 Hbk £35.00

Dictionary of Business Biography
Vol. 1 A-C. – London : Butterworths, 1984.
ISBN 0406273413 Hbk £72.00
Vol. 2 D-G. – 1984.
ISBN 0406273421 Hbk £72.00
Vol. 3 H-L. – 1985.
ISBN 040627343X Hbk £72.00
Vol. 4 M-R. – 1985.
ISBN 0406273448 Hbk £72.00
Vol. 5 S-Z. – 1986.
ISBN 0406273456 Hbk £72.00

Dictionary of Business Biography. – London : Butterworths.
This work contains over 1000 biographies of British businessmen from 1860 to 1980. Each subject is treated in terms of his major successes and failures, innovations, and management style and policies.
Pbk

Dictionary of Commercial Law. – London : Butterworths, 1983.
ISBN 0406681597 Hbk £15.00
ISBN 0406681600 Pbk £10.95

Dictionary of Commercial Terms and Abbreviations. – Witherby, 1984.
ISBN 0900886900 Pbk £9.50

Dictionary of company law / by E.R. Hardy Ivamy. – London : Butterworths, 1983.
265p; 23cm. – (Butterworths professional dictionary series).
ISBN 0406681619 Hbk
ISBN 0406681627 Pbk

Dictionary of criminology / edited by Dermot Walsh and Adrian Poole. – London : Routledge & Kegan Paul, 1983.
xi,242p.
ISBN 0710095562 Pbk

Dictionary of Economics and Financial Markets. – 5th ed. – London : Butterworths, 1986.
This work contains definitions of economic terminology and concepts and topics related to contemporary applied economics and financial institutions. A bibliography is included in the text.
ISBN 0408015705 £19.95

Dictionary of Employment Law. – London : Butterworths, 1985.
ISBN 0406207909 Hbk £17.00
ISBN 0406207917 Pbk £10.95

Dictionary of English Law / Burke. – 2nd ed. – Sweet & Maxwell, 1977.
ISBN 0421230908 Hbk £160.00
Supplement 1985. –
ISBN 0421293705 Hbk £25.00

Dictionary of Insurance Law. – London : Butterworths, 1981.
ISBN 0406603014 Pbk £10.95

Dictionary of Insurance Terms English-Arabic. – Witherby, 1985.
ISBN 090088696X Hbk £34.00

Dictionary of International Commerce. – London : Chapman & Hall, 1985.
ISBN 0412280108 Hbk £37.50

Dictionary of Irish Law. – Topaz.
ISBN 0951403206 Hbk £29.50
ISBN 0951403214 Pbk £19.50

Dictionary of Law. – 3rd ed. – London : Pitman Publishing, 1988.
ISBN 0712107916 Pbk £9.95

Dictionary of Law. – 2nd ed. Repr. of 1979 ed. – Plymouth : Macdonald & Evans, 1983.
viii, 416p. – (M and E Professional Dictionaries Series).
ISBN 0712104402 Hbk £10.95
ISBN 0712104399 Pbk £4.95

Dictionary of legal quotations / compiled and edited by Simon James and Chantal Stebbings. – London : Croom Helm, 1987.
250p; 24cm.
Includes indexes.
ISBN 0709914032 £15.00

Dictionary of Legal Words and Phrases, 4 vols. Vol. III /. – Durban : Butterworths.
ISBN 0409018929
Biennial cumulative suppls. avail. Third Cumulative Suppl.. – 1983.
ISBN 040901897X

Dictionary Of Marine Insurance Terms. – 4th ed. – Witherby, 1975.
ISBN 0900886110 Hbk £15.00

Dictionary of medical ethics / edited by A.S. Duncan, G.R. Dunstan and R.B. Welbourn. – Rev. and enl. ed. – London : Darton, Longman & Todd, 1981.
xxxi,459p; 23cm.
Previous ed.: 1977. Includes bibliographies.
ISBN 0232514925 £12.50

Dictionary of Modern Legal Usage. – Oxford : Oxford University Press, 1988.
ISBN 0195043774 Hbk £25.00

Dictionary of Political Thought. – London : Macmillan, 1982.
512p.
ISBN 0333334396 Hbk £12.00

Dictionary of Shipping and International Trade Terms. – 2nd ed. – Witherby, 1983.
ISBN 0900886706 Pbk £7.50

Dictionary of Shipping Law. – London : Butterworths, 1984.
ISBN 0406623996 Hbk £15.00
ISBN 0406624003 Pbk £10.95

Dictionary of Shipping Spanish/English. – London : Lloyd's of London Press, 1988.
ISBN 1850444537 Pbk

Dictionary of shipping terms / by Peter R. Brodie. – London : Lloyd's of London, 1985.
155p; 22cm.
ISBN 1850440697 Pbk £15.00

Dictionary of Sigla and Abbreviations Law Books Before 1607. – London : Eurospan.
ISBN 0813906156 Hbk £17.50

Dictionary of taxation / by Gerry Hart : consultant B.E.V. Sabine. – London : Butterworths, 1981.
v,236p; 23cm. – (Butterworths professional dictionaries series).
ISBN 040652159X Hbk £14.00
ISBN 0406521603 Pbk

Dictionary of the European Communities / John Paxton. – 2nd ed. – London : Macmillan, 1984.
282p; 23cm.
Previous ed.: published as A dictionary of the European Economic Community. 1977. Bibliography: p279-282.
ISBN 0333334388 Hbk £25.00
ISBN 0333370376 Pbk

Dictionnaire Juridique Fr/Eng Eng/Fr. – 2nd ed. – London : Edition de Navarre, 1984.
ISBN 2713300045 Pbk £31.00

Diederich, Rene →Migrant workers and civil liberties.

Diederiks-Verschoor, I. H. Ph.
Introduction to air law / by I.H. Ph. Diederiks-Verschoor. – Deventer, Netherlands : Kluwer Law and Taxation Publishers, 1983.
Includes index and bibliography. Translation of: Inleiding tot het luchtrecht.
ISBN 9065440976 : est.
—Introduction to air law / by I.H.Ph. Diederiks-Verschoor. – 3rd rev. & enl. ed. – Deventer : Kluwer Law and Taxation, 1988.
xxiv, 197p.
Bibliography: pp.177-189. - Includes index. Translation of: Inleiding tot het luchtrecht.
ISBN 9065443754

Diefenbaker for the Defence / Wilson. – Toronto : James Lorimer & Co, 1988.
250p.
ISBN 1550281046 Hbk £24.95

Diemont, M. A →Alienation of land : being a supplement to The law of credit agreements and hire-purchase by Diemont and Aronstam.
—Law of credit agreements and hire-purchase in South Africa / P. J. Aronstam. – 5th ed. – Cape Town : Juta, 1982.
lii,505p.
Previous ed., 1978, entitled: The law of hire-purchase in South Africa. Bibliography: p.xxi-xxiii. - Includes index.
ISBN 070211250X

Dierciex →Legal Aspects of the ECU.

Digest : annotated British, Commonwealth and European cases : formerly the English and Empire Digest : a user's guide. – London : Butterworths, 1983.
26p; 25cm.

Digest English Law Trust / L A Sheridan. – London : Butterworths.
ISBN 0862056504 Hbk £22.00

Digest of All India Control of Rent and Eviction Cases, 1970-1976. – Lucknow : Eastern Book Company, 1977.
136p.
Pbk £10.00

Digest of appeal cases ... : Supreme Court and Federal Court of Appeal. – Lagos, Nigeria : Olba Publishers, 1985-.

Digest of Australian Constitutional Cases. – 2nd ed. – North Ryde : Law Book Co, 1982.
xvi, 359p.
ISBN 0455204748 Hbk £49.00
ISBN 0455204756 Pbk £37.50

Digest of case-law relating to the European Communities
Series A : Judgements of the Court of Justice of the European Communities excluding cases connected with the European civil service and cases on the Convention of 27 September 1968 on Jurisdiction and the enforcement of judgments in civil and commercial matters / Court of Justice of the European Communities. – 1. – Luxembourg : Office for Official Publications of the European Communities, 1984.
loose-leaf; 23cm.
Periodically updated by supplements.
ISBN 9282900614
D series : Judgements of the Court of Justice of the European Communities and selected discussions of courts of Member States on the Convention of 27 September 1969 on jurisdiction and the enforcement of judgements in civil and commercial matters. – 1981.
Judgements of the Court of Justice of the European Communities and selected decisions of courts of member states on the convention of jurisdiction and the enforcement of judgements in civil and commercial matters.
ISBN 9282900398 Pbk £25.60

Digest of Cases Decided in the Supreme Courts of Scotland From 1800-1852. – Repr. of 1867 ed. – Abingdon : Professional Books.
104p.
Hbk £95.00

Digest of Central Excise and Customs Cases. – Nagpur : Wadhura & Co, 1987.
1,425p.
Hbk £350.00

Digest of Industrial and Labour Law Cases. – Woolloomooloo : International Business Communications, 1983.
430p.
Hbk £34.00

Digest of Industrial Labour Law Cases. – 1st ed. – London : Legal Books, 1983.
ISBN 0949553013 Hbk £20.00
ISBN 0949553018 Pbk £15.00

Digest of Northern Ireland law. – Belfast : SLS Legal Publications, 1988.
looseleaf.
Includes indexes.

Digest of Strasbourg case-law relating to the European Convention on Human Rights
v.1 : (Articles 1-5) / Council of Europe. – Koln : Heymanns-Verlag, 1984.
xvii,669p.
ISBN 3452194035 Hbk
v.2 : (Article 6) / Council of Europe. – 1984.
xviii,922p.
ISBN 3452194043 Hbk
v.3 : (Articles 7-12) / Council of Europe. – 1984.
xvii,601p.
ISBN 3452194051 Hbk
v.4 : (Articles 13-25) / Council of Europe. – 1985.
xviii,453p.
ISBN 345219406X Hbk
v.5 : (Articles 26-66, protocols to the Convention). – 1985.
xxvi,899p.
At head of title: Council of Europe.
ISBN 3452195260 Hbk
v.6 : General index to volumes 1-5. – 1985.
xxxix,662p.
ISBN 3452194116

Digest of Supreme Court Sales Tax Cases 1950-1987. – Allahabad : Modern Law Publications, 1987.
Hbk £140.00

Digest of the Law of Evidence on the Trial of Civil Actions (Nisi Prius) 5th ed. – Repr. of 1839 ed. – Abingdon : Professional Books.
306p.
Hbk £35.00

Digest of the Supreme Court Cases 10 volumes. – Lagos : Nigerian Law Publications, 1956-1984.
ISBN 09782325023 Hbk £1,500.00

Digest of Wealth Tax Cases 1957 to 1986. – Allahabad : Modern Law Publications, 1986.
Hbk £125.00

Digest Report Patent Cases 1884-1955 3 vols. – Professional Books.
ISBN 0862053757 Hbk £97.50

Digester, Peter →United States and the Law of the Sea Treaty.

Digests of Irish Reports and Irish Law Times Reports
Incl. 1867-93. – Abingdon : Professional Books.
Hbk

Dignity and honour of women as basic and fundamental human rights / by Yougindra Khushalani. – The Hague : Martinus Nijhoff Publishers, 1982.
153p.
Includes index.
ISBN 9024725852 Hbk £105.00

Dijk, J. van
Criminal Law in Action. – Dordrecht : Kluwer, 1986.
440p.
ISBN 9065442782 Hbk Gld100.00

Dijk, Pieter van → Essays on human rights in the Helsinki process.

—Restructuring the International Economic Order : the Role of Law and Lawyers. – Dordrecht : Kluwer, 1987.
280p.
ISBN 9065442758 Hbk £125.00

—Theory and practice of the European convention on human rights / P. van Dijk, G.J.H. van Hoof. – Deventer : Kluwer Law and Taxation, 1984.
xiii,512p; 25cm.
Bibliography: p489-493. - Includes index. Translated from Dutch.
ISBN 9065440798 Pbk

Dilemma of Toxic Substance Regulation. – London : MIT Press, 1988.
ISBN 0262132303 Hbk £31.50

Dilemmas of law in the welfare state / edited by Gunther Teubner. – Berlin : W. de Gruyter, 1986.
viii,341p. – (Series A, Law).
Includes bibliographies and index.
ISBN 0899251080

Diligence and debtor protection : consultation paper. – Scottish Courts Administration. – Edinburgh : Scottish Courts Administration on behalf of the Lord Advocate, 1985.
15 leaves.
Consultation paper on Scottish Law Commission's report on diligence and debtor protection (Scot. Law Com. no. 95.

Dillavou
Principles of Business Law / Howard. – Prentice-Hall.
ISBN 0137052790 Hbk £47.10

Dillon, C.
South African Maritime Law and Marine Insurance : Selected Topics. – Durban : Professional Publishers, 1983.
ISBN 0409023779 Pbk £55.00

Dilnot, A. W.
Reform of social security / A.W.Dilnot, J.A.Kay and C.N. Morris. – Oxford : Clarendon, 1984.
viii,166; 23cm.
Bibliography: p158-160. - Includes index.
ISBN 0198772262 Pbk £10.00
ISBN 0198772254 £3.95

Diminshed responsibility as a defence to murder / Law Reform Commissioner, Victoria. – Melbourne : The Commission, 1981.
40p. – (Working paper no 7).
Includes bibliographical references.

Dine, Janet M.
Cases and materials on the Thefts Acts / Janet M. Dine. – London : Financial Training, 1985.
xvii,223p.
Includes the text of the Theft Acts, 1968 and 1978.
ISBN 0906322804

—Theft Act 1978 / Janet M. Dine. – London : Financial Training, 1985.
xvii,223p.
Includes the text of the Theft Acts, 1968 and 1978.
ISBN 0906322804

Dineen, M.
Property Guide. – Unwin Hyman. – (Saga Guides).
ISBN 0044401728 Pbk £3.50

Dingwall, Robert
Care proceedings : a practical guide for social workers, health visitors and others / Robert Dingwall and John Eekelaar. – Oxford : Basil Blackwell, 1982.
viii,140p; 23cm.
Bibliography: p135-136. - Includes index.
ISBN 0631127569 Hbk £
ISBN 0631127577 Pbk

→ Divorce mediation and the legal process.

—Protection of children : state intervention and family life / Robert Dingwall, John Eekelaar, Topsy Murray. – Oxford : Basil Blackwell, 1983.
x,286p; 24cm.
Bibliography: p267-282. - Includes index.
ISBN 0631131051 £22.50

→ Sociology of the professions : lawyers, doctors and others.

Dinham, Barbara
Agribusiness in Africa : a study of the impact of big business on Africa's food and agricultural production / Barbara Dinham & Colin Hines. – London : Earth Resources Research, 1983.
224p b ill; 21cm.
Includes index. Cover title.
ISBN 0946281009 Pbk £4.95

Dinnage, James → EEC Law.

Dinsmore, Margaret-Ann
Separation and Divorce in Northern Ireland. – Belfast : Queen's University of Belfast, 1986.
125p.
Pbk

Dinstein, Yoram, et al
International law at a time of perplexity / Mala Tabory. – Dordrecht : Nijhoff (Martinus), 1989.
1040.
A collection of essays in honour of the seventieth birthday of Professor Rosenne. The contributions from friends and colleagues deal with humanitarian law, human rights, the law of treaties, and dispute settlement.
ISBN 9024736544 Hbk £142.50

—Israel Yearbook on Human Rights 1987. – Martinus Nijhoff.
ISBN 9024736463 Hbk £39.00

—Israel yearbook on human rights / Mala Tabory. – Dordrecht : Nijhoff (Martinus), 1989.
312. – (Israel yearbook on human rights 18).
Published under the auspices of the Faculty of Law of Tel Aviv University. Contains studies on human rights in peace and war, . with particular emphasis on problems relevant to the State of Israel, and the Jewish people. Summaries of judicial decisions, and military proclamations are included.
ISBN 0792300173 Hbk £42

—War, aggression and self-defence / Yoram Dinstein. – Cambridge : Grotius, 1988.
xxx,292p.
Re-examines the topics of war, aggression and self-defence, as well as related issues such as collective security, and the use of force short of war. The first part deals with such questions as what war is, whilst the second looks at the contemporary prohibition of the use of force and its standing as jus cogens. The third section deals with the concept of self-defence.
ISBN 0949009156 £46.00

Dinwiddy, J. R. → Correspondence of Jeremy Bentham, Vol. 6 : January 1798 to December 1801 : edited by J.R. Dinwiddy.

Diosdi, Gy.
Contract in Roman law : from the Twelve Tables to the Glossators / Gy. Diosdi : translated by J. Szabo : translation edited by B. Nemenyi. – Budapest : Akademiai Kiado, 1981.
ISBN 9630524562

Diplock courts in Northern Ireland : a fair trial? : an analysis of the law, based on a study commissioned by Amnesty International / by Douwe Korff. – Utrecht : Studie-en Informatiecentrum Mensenrechten, 1984.
115p.

Diplock, William John Kenneth Diplock
Interception of communications in Great Britain : report / by Lord Diplock. – London : H.M.S.O., 1981.
7p; 25cm.
ISBN 0101819102 unbound £1.10

Diplomacy : the dialogue between states / Adam Watson. – London : Eyre Methuen, 1982.
239p; 24cm.
Bibliography: p227-228. - Includes index.
ISBN 0413481905 £10.50

Diplomatic and consular yearbook 1988. – London : Diplomatic and Consular Yearbook, 1988.
344p.

Diplomatic Handbook. – London : Longman Professional.
ISBN 0582494613 Pbk £5.95

Diplomatic immunities and privileges : government report on review of the Vienna Convention on Diplomatic Relations and reply to 'The abuse of diplomatic immunities and privileges' : the first report from the Foreign Affairs Committee in the Session 1984-85. – London : H.M.S.O., 1985.
29p. – (Miscellaneous).
ISBN 0101949707

Diplomat's Handbook of International Law and Practice. – 3rd ed. – Martinus Nijhoff.
ISBN 9024736471 Hbk £65.00

Directing Corporate Growth / Benson. – London : Fitzwilliam, 1988.
ISBN 1870555074 Hbk £25.00

Directive on doorstep selling. – London : Department of Trade and Industry, 1986.
18 leaves.
Proposals for legislation implementing the European Community Council of Ministers Directive of 20 December 1985 (85/577/EEC).

Directive Principles of State Policy in Indian Constitution. – New Delhi : Deep and Deep Publications, 1988.
200p.
Hbk £150.00

Director of Public Prosecutions : principles and practices for the Crown Prosecutor : an inquiry carried out at the Centre for Criminological Research, University of Oxford / Graham Mansfield and Jill Peay : foreword by Sir Thomas Hetherington. – London : Tavistock, 1986.
viii,246p; 23cm.
Bibliography: p237-241. - Includes index.
ISBN 0422600008 £16.00

Directorate of Legal Affairs
Exchange of Information on Research in European Law. – Directorate of Legal Affairs. – London : HMSO, 1983.
112p.
Provides information on research projects in law currently underway in various European and non-European states. Gives publication dates and information on how to obtain copies of final reports.
ISBN 0119836300 Pbk £1.25

Director's duties and insider dealing / Philip L.R. Mitchell. – London : Butterworths, 1982.
xxiv,268p; 22cm.
Includes index.
ISBN 0406295808 Pbk £14.50

Directors' Duties and Liabilities / See Chim Tang. – Singapore : Times Booker International.
160p.
ISBN 9971651688 Pbk £9.90

Directors Handbook : Singapore and Malaysia. – Singapore : Quins, 1983.
Hbk £54.00

Directors' personal liability / Robert R. Pennington. – London : Collins Professional and Technical, 1987.
256p; 24cm.
Includes index.
ISBN 0003832945 £20.00

Directors' personal liability. – 1st. – Oxford : Blackwell Scientific.
270. – (Blackwell Law Library).
Examines the erosion by recent legislation of the principle that neither directors nor shareholders of limited companies are personally liable for their company debts and torts. Advice on potential liabilities is offered in the light of the Companies Act 1985 and the Insolvency Act 1986.
Company directors, Accountants, Solicitors
ISBN 0632026197 Pbk £19.50

Directory / Canadian Association of Law Libraries : Association Canadienne des Bibliotheques de Droit. – Toronto : The Association, 1982.
Continues: List of members.

Directory of American studies librarians in the UK. – Wetherby : British Library Lending Division, 1984.
100p.
ISBN 0712320237 Pbk

Directory of British associations & associations in Ireland / editors: G.P.Henderson & S.P.A.Henderson. – Edition 8. – Beckenham : CBD Research, 1985.
ISBN 0900246456

Directory of Community Legislation in Force / 1985. – Luxembourg : Office for Official Publications of the European Communities, 1985.
758p.
ISBN 9282548171 Pbk £2,500.00 (Vols. 1 and 2 together)
Vol. 1: Analytical Register. – 1985.
ISBN 9282548031
Vol. 2: Chronological and Alphabetical Indexes. – 1985.
ISBN 9282548104
Vol. 3: Addendum. – 1985.
ISBN 9282549313 free to purchasers of Vols. 1 and 2

Directory of Community Legislation in Force / 1986 /. – Luxembourg : Office for Official Publications of the European Communities, 1986.
859p.
ISBN 9282552136 Pbk £2,700.00 (Vols. 1 and 2 together)
Vol. 1: Analytical Register. – 1986.
ISBN 9282551997
Vol. 2: Chronological and Alphabetical Indexes. – 1986.
ISBN 9282552063

Directory of Community Legislation in Force / 1987 /. – Luxembourg : Office for Official Publications of the European Communities, 1987.
746p.
ISBN 9282570967 Pbk £2,800.00 (Vols. 1 and 2 together)
Vol. 1: Analytical Register. – 1987.
ISBN 9282570789
Vol. 2: Chronological and Alphabetical Indexes. – 1987.
ISBN 9282570878

Directory of Courts in the UK. – London : Shaw & Sons, 1987-1988.
ISBN 0721909841 Pbk £10.95

Directory of Courts in the United Kingdom : 1988/1989. – London : Shaw & Sons, 1988.
320p.
ISBN 072190985X Pbk £14.95

Directory of human rights information and documentation facilities in the field of human rights in western Europe. – 1. – London : Human Rights International Documentation System, 1982.
various pagings.
Includes index.

Directory of Islamic Banking and Financial Institutions. – Oxford : Croom Helm, 1988.
ISBN 0709913478 Hbk £50.00

Directory of law libraries in the British Isles / edited by Christine Miskin. – 3rd ed. – Hebden Bridge, W. Yorks. : Published for the British & Irish Association of Law Librarians by Legal Information Resources Limited, 1988.
ix,120p.
Previous ed.: 1984. Includes indexes.
ISBN 1870369025

Directory of Law Teachers. – Agincourt : Carswell, 1987-1988.
180p.
Pbk £17.00

Directory Of Local Authorities 1988/89. – London : Longman Professional.
ISBN 0851214320 Pbk £16.50

Directory of ombudsmen and other complaint-handlers. – Edmonton : International Ombudsman Institute, 1983.
29p.

Directory of Personal Financial Services. – London : Macmillan.
ISBN 0333459946 Hbk £95.00

Directory of Schools of Law in the Commonwealth 1985. – London : Commonwealth Secretariat.
Hbk £5.00

Directory of schools of law in the Commonwealth / Commonwealth Legal Education Association. – 1985. – London : The Association, 1985.
60p.

Directory of Specialists in Official Publications. – 2nd ed. – Scoop Publications, 1988.
ISBN 0951201115 Pbk £6.00

Disability : Legislation and Practice. – London : Macmillan, 1981.
264p.
ISBN 0333315758 Pbk £8.95

Disability and compensation claims / Philip Noble, Bart Hellyer, Elizabeth Fanshawe. – London : Sweet & Maxwell, 1986.
68p; 22cm.
ISBN 042136890X Pbk £6.50

'Disappearances' in Sri Lanka / Amnesty International. – London : Amnesty International, 1986.
89p.
ISBN 0862101085

Disarmament : the human factor : proceedings of a colloquium on the societal context for disarmament / sponsored by UNITAR and the Planetary Citizens and held at the United Nations, New York : edited by Ervin Laszlo and Donald Keys. – Oxford : Pergamon, 1981.
x,164p; 24cm.
Includes index.
ISBN 0080247032 Hbk £10.50
ISBN 008028129X Pbk

Disaster and resolution : two discussion papers dealing with distinct aspects of the aftermath of man-made disasters, the process of litigation, settlement and compensation and the factors affecting the provision of speedy relief and effective rehabiliation / David Wade, Carmel Goldwater : commissioned and published by Centre for Public Affairs Studies. – London : Centre for Public Affairs Studies, 1985.
viii,162p.

Disciplinary Action Against Government Servants and its Remedies. – 5th ed. – Lucknow : Eastern Book Company, 1985.
1,239p.
Hbk £225.00

Disciplinary and other procedures in employment : consultative document on a draft code of practice / Advisory, Conciliation and Arbitration Service. – London : The Service, 1985.
29p.

Disciplinary Proceedings in Industries and Adjudication. – 2nd ed. – Calcutta : Eastern Law House, 1984.
Hbk £102.00

Discipline of Politics. – London : Butterworths, 1981.
ISBN 0408106855 Pbk £9.95

Discourse of law / edited by Sally Humphreys. – London : Harwood Academic Publishers, 1985.
p.241-465.
Includes bibliographies.

Discover Book-Keeping and Accounts. – Pitman.
ISBN 0273028707 Pbk £5.95

Discovery : a comparison between English and American civil discovery law with reform proposals / Julius Byron Levine. – Oxford : Clarendon, 1982.
xl,208p; 23cm.
Bibliography: p154-160. - Includes index.
ISBN 0198253680 £20.00

Discovery and Interrogatories. – Butterworths, 1984.
325p.
ISBN 0409492728 Hbk £33.50

Discovery of documents and disclosure : Order 24. – London : Lord Chancellor's Department, 1987.
4 leaves.
Memorandum outlining amendments to Order 24 of the Rules of the Supreme Court.

Discretion and welfare / edited by Michael Adler and Stewart Asquith. – London : Heinemann Educational, 1981.
vii,296p; 23cm. – (Studies in social policy and welfare).
Conference papers. Bibliography: p273-287. - Index.
ISBN 0435820095 £15.00

Discretion in Criminal Justice. – 2nd Revised Edition. – London : Gabbay (E & J).
ISBN 095014486X Pbk £15.00

Discretionary powers : a legal study of official discretion / D.J. Galligan. – Oxford : Clarendon, 1986.
xxi,401p; 22cm.
Bibliography: p383-396. - Includes index.
ISBN 0198254989 £30.00

Discretionary Trusts : with 1978 Supplement / R. Baxt. – 2nd ed. – Butterworths, 1984.
235p.
ISBN 040949383X Hbk £55.00
Supplement. –
ISBN 0409312118 Pbk £10.00

Discrimination and the law in Canada / by Walter Surma Tarnopolsky. – Toronto : De Boo, 1982.
vii,595p.
Bibliography: p. 493-510. - Includes index.
ISBN 0888201052 Hbk

Discrimination equal pay / John Whitmore. – London : Sweet & Maxwell, 1989.
Presents the law of discrimination and institutions through which it functions. Looks at discrimination in employment, education, and the provision of goods and services. Also examines the practical aspects of the powers embodied in the Commission for Racial Equality, and the Equal Opportunities Commission, and tribunal procedures and remedies.
ISBN 0421389907 Hbk

Discriminatory Refusal of Carriage in North America. – Dordrecht : Kluwer, 1982.
310p.
ISBN 9065440496 Hbk £165.00

Discussion paper / J-AS Review of Administrative Law in the United Kingdom. – London : The Review, 1981.
97p.
ISBN 0907247016

Discussion paper on the laws in Chinese. – Hong Kong : Attorney General's Chambers, 1986.
99p.

Disease and the compensation debate / Jane Stapleton. – Oxford : Clarendon, 1986.
224p; 22cm.
Includes index.
ISBN 0198255527 £22.50

Dismissal and Redundancy Procedures / Margaret A. Mulgan. – Butterworths, 1985.
Outline of the different procedures which may be taken by the dismissed employee after the termination of the employment contract. Unjustified and 'victimisation' dismissals are examined in detail with the appropriate remedial procedures. Analyses judicial decisions, and deals with the problems of redundancy dismissals and payment of compensation.
ISBN 040970136X Hbk £57.20

Dismissal and taxation of employees / Barry Titman, Peter Camp. – London : Butterworths, 1982.
xxvi,233p.
ISBN 0406129010

Dismissal law in the Republic of Ireland / by Mary Redmond. – Dublin : Incorporated Law Society of Ireland, 1982.
xliii, 296 p.; 22 cm.
Includes indexes. Bibliography: p. 274-284.
ISBN 0902027220 Pbk

Dismissed : a study of unfair dismissal and the industrial tribunal system / Linda Dickens ... et al. – Oxford : Blackwell, 1985.
xvi,379p; 23cm.
A Study of Unfair Dismissal and the Industrial Tribunal System.
ISBN 0631139257 £25.00

Disney, J, et al
Lawyers. – North Ryde : Law Book Co, 1986.
xli, 944p.
ISBN 0455206538 Hbk £37.50
ISBN 0455206546 Pbk £29.50

Disorderly Conduct : Real Life Comedy from the Courtrooms / Victor J Sevilla. – London : Angus & Robertson.
ISBN 0207160007 Hbk £4.95

Disposal of Abandoned Vehicles and Other Refuse. – London : Shaw & Sons, 1981. – (Shaway Guide: No. 4).
ISBN 0721908756 Pbk £2.50

Dispute Resolution in Commercial Matters : Papers-Colloquium, Australian Academy of Science, Canberra, 6 June 1986. – Kingston : Australian Government Publishing Service, 1986.
175p.
ISBN 0644054344 Hbk £9.95

Dispute Resolutions in Australia-Japan Transactions / K. Iwasaki. – North Ryde : Law Book Co, 1983.
xxix, 185p.
ISBN 0455202648 Hbk £91.00

Dispute settlement in public international law : texts and materials / compiled by Karin Oellers-Frahm und Norbert Wuhler. – Berlin : Springer Verlag, 1984.
At head of title: Max-Planck-Institut fur Auslandisches Offentliches Recht und Volkerrecht. English and German text. Includes index. Bibliography:
ISBN 0387131906

Disputed Documents, Handwriting and Thumb-print Identification / Rao Chiyod Seshagiri. – 4th ed. – Allahabad : Law Book Company, 1988.
400p.
Pbk £125.00

Disputes and settlements : law and human relations in the West / edited by John Bossy. – Cambridge : Cambridge University Press, 1983.
ix,296p; 23cm.
Essays by British, American and French scholars to outline a social history of the West using records of the law in Western Europe from the fall of Rome to the Nineteenth Century.
ISBN 0521252830 £25.00

Disputes and the law / edited by Maureen Cain and Kalman Kulcsar for the European Coordination Centre for Research and Documentation in Social Sciences. – Budapest : Akademiai Kiado, 1983.
Contains a collection of papers given at a seminar held in Dubrovnik at the Inter-University Centre of Postgraduate Studies in September 1979.
ISBN 9630533790

Disqualification and personal liability of directors : a guide to the changes made by the insolvency legislation of 1985 and 1986 / by L.S. Sealy. – 2nd ed. – Bicester : CCH, 1987.
iv,53p.
Explains the rules regarding directors' disqualification, the imposition of personal liability on company directors and others (including wrongful trading), and the rules on the restriction of use of certain company names by directors and shadow directors.
ISBN 0863251307

Disregard of a legal entity fortax purposes. – Kluwer Law and Taxation, 1989.
560. – (Cahiers de droit fiscal internatinal LXXIVa).
Collections of writings by twenty tax experts in the systems in their own countries, presenting a comparison of the subject.
ISBN 9065444130 Pbk £48/Dfl 150

Dissenting and separate opinions at the World Court / Ijaz Hussain. – The Hague : M. Nijhoff Publishers, 1984.
xv,335p.
Revision of thesis (doctorate)–University of Nice, 1974 under title: Le role dialectique des opinions dissidentes et individuelles dans le developpement du droit international a la CIJ. Bibliography: p309-321. Includes index.
ISBN 9024729203 Hbk £145.00

Dissertation handbook : a guide to research and writing / by Peter Willis. – London : RIBA, 1983.
55p; 30cm.
ISBN 0900630868

Distinctiveness of Soviet law / edited by F.J.M. Feldbrugge. – Dordrecht : Martinus Nijhoff, 1988.
292p.
'Selected papers from The Third World Congress for Soviet and East European Studies, Washington, D.C., 30 October-4 November 1985, sponsored by the International Committee for Soviet and East European Studies and the American Association for the Advancement of Slavic Studies.'. Includes index.
ISBN 9024735769 Hbk £185.00

Distress for rent / the Law Commission. – London : H.M.S.O., 1986.
vi,146p. – (Working paper).
Includes bibliographical references.
ISBN 0117301787

Distress for Rent. – Victoria : Government of British Columbia, 1981.
Hbk £3.20

Distribution of business between the Crown Court and magistrates' courts. – London : Home Office, 1986.
17p.

Distribution of estates according to Shafii law. – Singapore : Malayan Law Journal, 1976.
vi,72.
Guide to the Islamic law of inheritance as it is practised in Malaysia and Singapore. Gives a summary of the law, and includes distribution of estates according to Shafii law, the Quranic heirs, the Agnatic heirs, the Bair-ul-mal, MINHAJ ET TALIBIN, a table of Quranic heirs, Quranic verses, and Hadith on the law of inheritance.
Hbk

Distribution of Matrimonial Assets on Divorce Supplement-1986. – London : Butterworths.

Distribution of matrimonial assets on divorce / Michael L. Rakusen, D. Peter Hunt. – 2nd ed. – London : Butterworths, 1982.
xxii,375p.

ISBN 0406351015 Hbk £46.00
ISBN 0406351023 Pbk £12.00

Distribution of Powers : Report of the Advisory Committee to the Constitutional Commission. – Kingston : Australian Government Publishing Service, 1987.
Hbk £9.95

Distribution on intestacy / the Law Commission. – London : HMSO, 1988.
vii,54p. – (Working paper).
ISBN 0117301906

Distribution on Intestacy. – London : Longman Professional, 1988.
ISBN 0851214010 Pbk £2.95

Distributions from share premium accounts : report of the Property Law and Equity Reform Committee. – Wellington? : Government Printer?, 1982.
8,2p.
Cover title.

Distributorship, Franchising, Agency : Community and National Laws and Practice in the EEC. – Dordrecht : Kluwer, 1987.
274p.
ISBN 9065443290 Hbk £120.00

District Administration : The Dynamics of Discord. – Sage Publications.
ISBN 0803995601 Hbk £17.25
ISBN 080399561X Pbk £10.50

District Court Practice / J. S. Crutchley. – 8th ed. – Wellington : Butterworths, 1981.
ISBN 0409600466 Hbk

District Municipality of Muskoka Amendment Act, 1983, Bill 106 : An Act to Amend the District Municipality of Muskoka Act. – Ontario : Ontario Government Publications Service, 1983.
2p.
Hbk £0.30

Ditchfield, John
Grievance procedures in prisons : a study of prisoners' applications and petitions / by John Ditchfield and Claire Austin. – London : H.M.S.O., 1986.
vi,71p; 25cm.
Study of prisoners' applications and petitions. Examines the operation of grievance procedures in six prisons for adult male offenders to identify differences in practice between prisons and assess the confidence which inmates and staff have in them.
ISBN 0113408390

Divaris, Costa →Silke on South African income tax : being an exposition of the law, practice and incidence of income tax in South Africa.

Diversion of traffic offenders / by J.K. Canagarayar : with a foreword by J.W. Mohr. – Singapore : Malayan Law Journal, 1981.
xi,229p; 22cm.
Analyses the role of diversion, the directions it should take, its limitations, and whether there is a need to develop identifiable uniform principles and guidelines during the different stages of diversion. Contains examples of various experiments and pilot projects.
ISBN 9971700158 £12.50

Divided Families. – Turnaround Press, 1987.
ISBN 0902397575 Pbk £2.95

Divided we stand : a report on the legal profession / Social Democratic Lawyers' Association : chairman William Goodhart. – London : The Association, 1986.
53p.

Division of labour in society / Emile Durkheim : translated by W.D. Halls : with an introduction by Lewis Coser. – 2nd ed. – Basingstoke : Macmillan, 1984.
lix,352p; 22cm.
Includes index.
ISBN 0333339800 Pbk £18.00
ISBN 0333339819

Division of Matrimonial Assets in Ontario. – Aurora : Canada Law Book Co, 1982.
438p. – (Text Books-Civil).
Hbk £45.00
Supplement-1985. –
Hbk £12.00

Divorce : an Australian Women's Guide. – Richmond : Heinemann.
144p.
ISBN 0858593114 Pbk £12.95

Divorce : The Financial Consequences. – Belfast : Queen's University of Belfast, 1986.
30p.
Pbk

Divorce Act Update. – Vancouver : Continuing Legal Education Society of British Columbia, 1987.
669p.
ISBN 0865043043 Hbk £75.00

Divorce conciliation : a study of services in England and abroad, with implications for Scotland. – Edinburgh : Scottish Council for Single Parents, 1982.
v,99p.
Includes bibliographies.

Divorce Guide for Alberta : Step-by-Step Guide to Obtaining Your Own Divorce. – 5th ed. – North Vancouver : International Self-Counsel Press, 1986.
87p.
ISBN 088908243X Hbk £9.95

Divorce Guide for British Columbia : Step-by-Step Guide to Obtaining Your Own Divorce. – 10th ed. – North Vancouver : International Self-Counsel Press, 1986.
88p.
ISBN 0889081816 Hbk £10.95

Divorce Guide for Manitoba. – North Vancouver : International Self-Counsel Press, 1987.
ISBN 0889085110 Hbk £11.95

Divorce Guide for Ontario : Step-By-Step Guide to Obtaining Your Own Divorce. – 7th ed. – North Vancouver : International Self-Counsel Press, 1988.
Hbk

Divorce Guide for Oregon. – 4th ed. – North Vancouver : International Self-Counsel Press, 1988.
ISBN 088908825X Hbk

Divorce Guide for Saskatchewan. – North Vancouver : International Self-Counsel Press, 1987.
ISBN 0889085129 Hbk £12.95

Divorce Guide for Washington : Step-By-Step Guide for Obtaining Your Own Divorce. – 5th ed. – North Vancouver : International Self-Counsel Press, 1988.
ISBN 0889087385 Hbk

Divorce Handbook. – London : Allison & Busby, 1986.
ISBN 185031724X Pbk £4.95

Divorce in Australia / by Donald E. Stewart and Margaret Harrison. – Melbourne, Vic. : Institute of Family Studies, 1982.
9 p.; 23 cm. – (Working paper).
Cover title. 'October 1982.'. Bibliography: p. 9.
ISBN 0642886504 Pbk

Divorce in New Zealand : a social history / Roderick Phillips. – Auckland : Oxford University Press, 1981.
154p.
Bibliography: p.149-152. - Includes index.
ISBN 019558077X

Divorce law in Canada : proposals for change. – Ottawa : Department of Justice, 1984.
32,32p.
French title: Propositions de reforme du droit du divorce au Canada. Pages numbered in opposite directions. English and French text.
ISBN 0662523504

Divorce matters / Jacqueline Burgoyne, Roger Ormrod and Martin Richards. – Harmondsworth : Penguin, 1987.
216p0; 20cm. – (A Pelican book).
ISBN 0140226133

Divorce mediation and the legal process / edited by Robert Dingwall and John Eekelaar. – Oxford : Clarendon Press, 1988.
197p.
Includes index. Bibliography: p.183-193.
ISBN 0198255756 Pbk £9.95
ISBN 0198255764 Hbk £20.00

Diwan, Paras
Customary Law. – 2nd ed. – Patiala : Punjab University, Publication Bureau.
Hbk £50.00
—Environment Protection : Problems, Policy Administration Law. – New Delhi : Deep and Deep Publications, 1987.
568p.
ISBN 8171000037 Hbk £350.00
—Family law : law of marriage and divorce in India / by Paras Diwan. – New Delhi : Sterling Publishers, 1983.
xxviii,470p.
Authors name on spine: Paras Diwan.
ISBN 8120702417 Hbk £150.00
—Private International Law : Indian and English. – New Delhi : Deep and Deep Publications, 1988.
700p.
Hbk £475.00

Dix, Andrew
Law for the Medical Profession. – Butterworths, 1988.
356p.
ISBN 040949318X Hbk £39.00

Dixon →Digests of Irish Reports and Irish Law Times Reports, 1867-93.
—Road traffic law / McVeagh. – London : Butterworths, 1981.
ISBN 0409798185 Llf £127.00

Dixon, Eileen
Theatre nurse and the law / Eileen Dixon. – London : Croom Helm, 1984.
141p; 22cm.
Includes index.
ISBN 0709908180 Pbk £8.95

Dixon, John →Companies operating overseas: UK tax, law and practice.

Dixon, R.
Investment Appraisals Guide for Managers. – London : Kogan Page.
ISBN 1850914680 Pbk £8.95

Dixon, Priddle, J.
New Cases Companion to Ryans Income Tax Manual. – 2nd ed. – North Ryde : Law Book Co, 1983.
xiii, 314p.
ISBN 0455204098 29.00

Djwa, Sandra
On F.R. Scott : Essays on His Contributions to Law, Literature, and Politics / Ronald St. J. MacDonald. – Montreal : McGill-Queen's University Press.
226p.
ISBN 0773503978 Hbk £25.00
ISBN 0773503986 Pbk £8.95
—Politics of the Imagination : a Life of F.R. Scott. – Toronto : McClelland & Stewart.
ISBN 0771028253 Hbk £39.95

Dlamini, C. R. M. →Two lectures on law reform : delivered at the workshop on Marriage and Family Life by the Human Sciences Research Council on 26 September 1985.

Dlamini, C R Moses
Hell-Hole, Robben Island : Reminiscences of a Political Prisoner. – London : Spokesman Books, 1984.
192p.
ISBN 0851244076 Hbk £13.50
ISBN 0851244017 Pbk £4.95

Dmitriev, A. G. →Handbook on foreign trade arbitration in the CMEA countries.

Do we know where we're going? / Sir Jeremy Morse. – s.l. : Per Jacobsson Foundation, 1985.
v,31p.
Given at the Sejong Cultural Center, Seoul, Korea, Sunday, October 6, 1985.

Do You Know Your Rights?. – Luxembourg : Office for Official Publications of the European Communities, 1985.
Hbk

Do Your Own Book-Keeping. – London : Kogan Page.
ISBN 1850917116 Hbk £12.95
ISBN 1850917108 Pbk £5.95

Dobash, et al
Imprisonment of women. – Oxford : Blackwell, 1986.
ISBN 063114319X Pbk £7.95

Dobkin, James A.
International Technology Joint Ventures in the Countries of the Pacific Rim. – Butterworths, 1988.
xvii, 211p.
Discusses the legal forms best suited for a joint venture in particular countries, how the operation is affected by the country's tax laws, and the available protection for intellectual property. Studies Australia, Canada, China, Taiwan, Hong Kong, Japan, Korea, New Zealand, Singapore, Thailand and the United States of America.
ISBN 0880632364 Hbk £125.00

Dobry, George →Blundell and Dobry's planning appeals and inquiries.

Dobson, A. P.
Cases and statutes on criminal law / John C. N. Slater. – 2nd ed. – London : Sweet & Maxwell, 1981.
xix,146p; 22cm.
Previous ed.: / by John C.N. Slater. 1973. Includes index.
ISBN 0421248106 Pbk £8.25
—Sale of goods and consumer credit / A.P. Dobson. – 3rd ed. – London : Sweet & Maxwell, 1984.
xxvii,369p; 22cm.
Previous ed.: 1979. Includes index.
ISBN 0421292105 Hbk £14.50
ISBN 0421292202 Pbk £9.50

Dobson, Paul
Consumer and commercial statutes. – London : Longman Professional (UK), 1989.
Covers the Bill of Lading 1855 through to the Consumer Protection Act of 1987, including the EEC Directive on Product Liability. Set out in chronological order including amendments to date.
ISBN 0851215173 Hbk £22.50

Dockray, M.
Carriage of Goods. – Professional Books, 1987.
ISBN 0862052394 Pbk £24.50
ISBN 0862052599 Hbk £50.00

Dockray, Martin
Cases and materials on the carriage of goods by sea / Martin Dockray. – Abingdon : Professional Books, 1987.
xxvi,804p.
ISBN 0862052599

Doctors and Rules : A Sociology of Professional Values. – Routledge.
ISBN 0415006880 Hbk £35.00

Doctrine and discretion in the law of contract : an inaugural lecture delivered before the University of Oxford on 7 March 1980 / by G.H. Treitel. – Oxford : Clarenden, 1981.
31p; 22cm.
ISBN 0199515271 Pbk £1.95

Doctrines of Sovereignty and the Separation of Powers in the Laws of Ceylon. – Colombo : Lake House Investments.
Pbk £2.75

Document User Guide : Ontario Land Registration Reform Act. – North Ryde : C.C.H. Australia, 1986.
148p.
ISBN 0887963404 Pbk £8.00

Documentary Credits. – Dordrecht : Kluwer, 1984.
ISBN 9065440755 Pbk £125.00

Documentary Credits Handbook. – Cambridge : Woodhead-Faulkner, 1988.
ISBN 0859413721 Hbk £45.00

Documentary evidence / Christopher Style, Charles Hollander : consulting editor: W.D. Park : with a foreword by Robert Alexander. – London : Oyez Longman, 1984.
xxi, 280p.
ISBN 085120970X

Documentary evidence in Canada / by J. Douglas Ewart in association with Michael Lomer and Jeff Casey. – Canada : Carswell Legal Publications, 1984.
xxxvii, 389 p.; 24 cm.
Includes bibliographical references and indexes.
ISBN 0459359509

Documentary history of the 1980 uniform law for international sales. – Kluwer Law and Taxation, 1989.
896.
Covers the United Nations Commission on International Trade Law (1969-1977) and the Vienna Diplomatic Conference (1980). Compiled from documents in the nine volumes of the UNCITRAL yaerbook and the Official Records on the 1980 Conference.
ISBN 9065443738 Hbk £105/Dfl 350

Documentation sources in human rights / Council of Europe. Directorate of Human Rights. Human Rights Documentation Centre. – Strasbourg : The Council, 1987.
38p. – (H(87)2).

Documents concerning the accessions to the European Communities : of the Kingdom of Denmark, Ireland and the United Kingdom of Great Britain and Northern Ireland, the Hellenic Republic, the Kingdom of Spain and the Portuguese Republic
Vol. 2. – Luxembourg : Office for Official Publications of the European Communites, 1987.
693p.
Vol. 1 entitled: Treaties establishing the European Communities. Also published in the other official languages of the Communities.
ISBN 9277193042

Documents on international administrative tribunals. – Oxford : Clarendon Press, 1989.
274.
A volume of documents, each of which sets out the interests, purposes, structureand powers of the tribunal to which it relates. Gives an account of the role and responsibility of each tribunal.
ISBN 0198256361 Hbk £27.50

Documents on the laws of war / edited by Adam Roberts and Richard Guelff. – Oxford : Clarendon Press, 1982.
xiii,498p.
Bibliography: p483-488.
ISBN 0198761171 Hbk £20.00
ISBN 019876118X Pbk £12.95

Documents on the Laws of War / Richard Guelff. – Geneva : Comite International de la Croix-Rouge, 1982.
498p.
Pbk £25.00

Dodd
Good Wigging / Hamilton. – London : Butterworths.
ISBN 0406509905 Hbk £20.00

Dodderidge
English Lawyer. – Reprint. – Abingdon : Professional Books, 1986.
– (Classical English Law Texts Ser.).
ISBN 0862053145 Hbk £27.00

Dodge, R.
Concise Guide to Accountancy. – London : VanNostrand Reinhold.
ISBN 0278000738 Pbk £5.95

Doern, G. Bruce
How Ottawa Spends Your Tax Dollars : The Liberals, The Opposition and Federal Priorities 1983. – Toronto : Lorimer & Co, 1983.
264p.
ISBN 0888626428 Pbk £12.95

Doernberg, R L →Structuring foreign investment in US real estate.

Doerr, Audrey →Women and the constitution in Canada.

Dog Problem : A Lawyer's View. – Potters Bar : Universities Federation for Animal Welfare.
ISBN 0900767553 Pbk £1.50

Doganis, Rigas
Flying off course : the economics of international airlines / Rigas Doganis. – London : Allen & Unwin, 1985.
ix,271p; 23cm.
Bibliography: p260-264. - Includes index.
ISBN 004387004X £18.00

Doggart, Caroline
Tax Havens and Their Uses. – new ed. – London : Economist Intelligence Unit, 1981.
Illus, updated to March 1983. – – (QER Special: No. 105).
ISBN 0900351403 Hbk £60.00

Doi, Abdur Rahman I.
Non-Muslims under Shari'ah : (Islamic Law). – Lahore : Kazi Publications.
Hbk £25.00
—Shariahi : Islamic Law. – Ta-Ha Publishers, 1984.
ISBN 0907461387 Pbk £6.50
—Woman in Shari'ah (Islamic law) / Abdur Rahman I. Doi. – s.l. : s.n., 1983.
286p.
Bibliography: pp.267-281. - Includes index.

Doig, Barbara
Debt recovery : a review of creditors' practices and policies / by Barbara Doig and Ann R. Millar. – Edinburgh : Central Research Unit, Scottish Office, 1981.
vii,72p.

Doing Business In Australia. – Matthew Bender, 1988.
ISBN 0000999043 Hbk £50.00

Doing Business in Canada, 3 Vols. / Elliott. – Agincourt : Carswell.
Service.
Llf £178.00

Doing Business in Canada and B.C. – Vancouver : British Columbia Continuing Legal Education Society, 1986.
234p.
ISBN 0865042195 Hbk £60.00

Doing Business in France. – Simeon Moquet Borde & Associates. – Matthew Bender, 1983.
ISBN 0000999039 Hbk £105.00

Doing Business in Ireland. – Matthew Bender, 1987.
ISBN 0000999034 Hbk £50.00

Doing business in Korea / edited by Arthur M. Whitehill. – London : Croom Helm, 1987.
xvi,121p; 23cm. – (The Croom Helm series in international business).
Conference papers.
ISBN 0709952260 £25.00

Doing Business in Spain. – Matthew Bender, 1987.
ISBN 0000999037 Hbk £50.00

Doing business in the European Community / John Drew. – 2nd ed. – London : Butterworths, 1983.
vii,293p; 25cm.
Previous ed.: 1979. Includes bibliographies and index.
ISBN 0408108363

Doing Business in the United Kingdom. – Matthew Bender, 1987.
ISBN 0000999036 Hbk £147.00

Doing business in the United States / Frank G. Opton, Herbert Feiler. – Deventer, Netherlands : Kluwer Law and Taxation Publishers, 1984.
Includes index and bibliography.
ISBN 9065441700

Doing the Business. – Oxford : Clarendon Press. – (Oxford Socio-Legal Studies).
ISBN 0198255985 Hbk £25.00

Do-It-Yourself Conveyancing. – 3rd ed. – London : David & Charles, 1984.
ISBN 0715386697 Hbk £6.95

Dokania, S.N.
Central Sales Tax Act. – New Delhi : Bharat Law House, 1985.
Hbk £200.00

Dollinger, Leslie G.
Income Tax Appeals : Law and Practice. – Toronto : Butterworths, 1981.
136p. – (Butterworths Tax Practice Ser.).
ISBN 0409827614 Hbk £31.95

Dolton →Tolley's Tax Data 1988-89.

Domesday book and beyond. – Cambridge : Cambridge University Press.
Uses information in the Domesday book to analyse the society, law, government, economy and culture of early medieval England.
ISBN 0521341124

Domestic Airline Regulation : Australian Debate. – Turramura : Centre for Independent Studies.
120p.
ISBN 0959648593 Hbk £5.50

Domestic Assault of Women. – London : Allyn & Bacon, 1988.
ISBN 0205113230 Hbk £28.90

Domestic Contracts. – Agincourt : Carswell, 1987.
450p.
This looseleaf work is a practitioners guide to the drafting of cohabitation, marriage and separation agreements under the law of Ontario and British Columbia. Checklist, sample agreements, income tax considerations and related materials are included in the volume.
Hbk £71.50

Domestic Contracts / Kirstie MacLise. – Agincourt : Carswell, 1987.
ca 420p.
Llf £56.25

Domestic Enquiry. – 3rd ed. in prep. – Bombay : Tripathi.
Hbk

Domestic injunctions / Margaret R. de Haas : with a foreword by H.H. Judge Nance. – London : Sweet & Maxwell, 1987.
xxviii,187p; 26cm.
Explains the steps involved in proceeding with an action, from originating application to enforcement, including procedures under the Child Abduction and Custody Act 1985. Includes selected rules of the Supreme and County Courts, precedents and forms, and a precis of decisions.
ISBN 0421365102 £19.50

Domestic Proceedings in Magistrates' Courts. – Belfast : Queen's University of Belfast, 1984.
26p.
Pbk £1.95

Domestic Proceedings in the Magistrates' Court. – 6th ed. – London : Oyez Longman, 1982.
– (Oyez Longman Practice Note Ser.: No. 30).
ISBN 0851206514 Hbk £12.50

Domestic violence / Law Reform Commission. – Canberra : Australian Government Publishing Service, 1986.
xxvi,98p. – (Report).
Bibliography: p.94-96 - Includes index.
ISBN 0644013397

Domestic violence : the Domestic Protection Bill 1982 : paper presented at Auckland law Faculty Seminar Series 1982 at University of Auckland / by Pauline Tapp. – Auckland : Legal Research Foundation Inc., 1982.
14,14p.
Includes the text of the Bill.
ISBN 090858122X

Domestic violence and the law : a study of S.99 of the Justices Act (S.A.) / by Ngaire Naffin. – 1. – Adelaide : Women's Adviser's Office, Department of the Premier and Cabinet, 1985.
various pagings.

Domestic violence in Papua New Guinea / edited by Susan Toft. – Port Moresby : Law Reform Commission, 1985.
160p. – (Monograph).
ISBN 9980550015

Domestic violence in urban Papua New Guinea / edited by Susan Toft. – Waigani : Law Reform Commission of Papua New Guinea, 1986.
vi,155p. – (Occasional paper).
Includes bibliographical references.
ISBN 9980550023

Domicile / South African Law Commission. – Pretoria : The Commission, 1987.
xiii,109p. – (Project).
Bibliography: pp.vi-x.. Includes the text of draft legislation.
ISBN 0797014365

Dominic, Josephine
General principles of law in a nutshell / Josephine Dominic. – London : Sweet & Maxwell, 1981.
vii,82p; 18cm. – (New nutshells).
Includes index.
ISBN 0421278307 Pbk £1.75

Dominica consolidated index of statutes and subsidiary legislation to 1st January 1984 / compiled at the Faculty of Law Library, University of the West Indies, Barbados. – Bridgetown? : Faculty of Law Library, University of the West Indies, 1984.
iv,97p.
One of a series in the West Indian Legislation Indexing Project (WILIP) compiled in cooperation with the British Development Division.

Dominican Republic : divorce law / Armando E. Gonzales. – Washington, D.C. : Law Library, Library of Congress, 1986.
v,43p.

Dominion Law Reports : 1969-1984, 150 Vols. – Aurora : Canada Law Book Co, 1984.
– (Third Ser.).
Hbk £5100.00
Back Vols.. –
Hbk £34.00 ea.

Dominion Law Reports (D.L.R.) 1912-22, 70 vols. – Aurora : Canada Law Book Co.
– (Old Ser.).
Hbk £2100.00
Back Vols.. –
Hbk £30.00 each

Dominion Law Reports (D.L.R.) 1923-55, 133 vols.
Back Vols. – Aurora : Canada Law Book Co.
Hbk £34.00 each

Dominion Law Reports (D.L.R.) 1956-68, 70 vols. – Aurora : Canada Law Book Co.
– (Second Ser.).
Hbk £2380.00
Back Vols.. –
Hbk £34.00 ea.
Table of Cases Vol.. –
Hbk £13.50

Dominion Law Reports (D.L.R.) 1984-present. – Aurora : Canada Law Book Co.
– (Fourth Ser.).
Hbk £78.50
Current subscription outside Canada. –
Hbk £83.00
Back Vols. 1-5 copies. –
Hbk £63.00 each
More than 6 Back Vols.. –
Hbk £41.00 each
Bound Vol. Only in Canada. –
Hbk £63.00

Dominion Law Reports Fourth Series (1984-Present). – Aurora : Canada Law Book Co.
– (Law Reports).
Hbk £78.00
Bound Vol. only. –
Hbk £63.00

Dominion Law Reports Fourth Series Index and Annotation Service. – Aurora : Canada Law Book Co, 1987.
– (Law Reports).
Hbk £78.00

Dominion Law Reports New Series, 133 Vols. – Aurora : Canada Law Book Co.
– (Law Reports).
Hbk £4522.00
Back Vols.. –
Hbk £34.00 ea.

Dominion Law Reports Old Series (1912-1922), 70 Vols. – Aurora : Canada Law Book Co.
– (Law Reports).
Hbk £2380.00
Back Vols.. –
Hbk £34.00 ea.

Dominion Law Reports Second and Third Series Annotation Service. – Aurora : Canada Law Book Co, 1984.
1084p. – (Law Reports).
Hbk £65.00

Dominion Law Reports (Second & Third Series) Annotation Service : 1984, 1 Vol. – Aurora : Canada Law Book Co.
1084p.
Hbk £65.00

Dominion Law Reports Second Series (1956-1968), 70 Vols. – Aurora : Canada Law Book Co.
– (Law Reports).
Hbk £2240.00
Back Vols.. –
Hbk £32.00 ea.
Table of Cases. –
Hbk £13.50

Dominion Law Reports Third Series (1969-1984), 150 Vols. – Aurora : Canada Law Book Co.
– (Law Reports).
Hbk £5100.00
Back Vols.. –
Hbk £34.00 ea.

Dominion Law Reports Third Series Index, 2 Vols. – Aurora : Canada Law Book Co, 1986.
– (Law Reports).
Hbk £275.00

Donahue, Charles → Select cases from the ecclesiastical courts of the Province of Canterbury, c.1200-1301.
—Why the history of canon law is not written / Selden Society lecture delivered in the Old Hall of Lincoln's Inn, July 3rd 1984 by Charles Donahue. – London : Selden Society, 1986.
31p. – (Selden Society lecture).
Includes bibliographical references.

Donahue, D.
British Constitution. – Rome : Bulzoni Editore.
Hbk £5.000

Donahue, Donald J.
Real Estate Practice in Ontario / Peter D. Quinn. – 3rd ed. – Toronto : Butterworths, 1982.
304p.
Explains judicial decisions and statutory changes since the second edition. Covers the Foreign Investment Review Act, Ontario New Home Warranties Act, Road Access Act, and the Family Law Reform Act, along with a reorganised chapter on the Planning Act. New chapters on real estate agents, and mortgage default proceeding.
ISBN 0409830046 Hbk £55.00

Donaldson, A.
Statute Law Review. – London : Sweet & Maxwell.
Hbk £40.00

Donaldson, Gordon → Formulary of old Scots legal documents.

Donaldson, J.A.
Medium-term loan market / J.A. Donaldson and T.H. Donaldson. – London : Macmillan, 1982.
viii,229p.
Includes index.
ISBN 0333326067

Donaldson, John Francis
Problems of a Master of the Rolls : being the presidential address of Sir John Donaldson, president of the Holdsworth Club of a the Faculty of Law in the University of Birmingham, 1985-1986. – Birmingham : University of Birmingham. Holdsworth Club, 1985.
14p. – (The Holdsworth Club).
ISBN 0704407744

Donaldson, T. H. → Medium-term loan market.

Donde, D.
Newcomer's Guide to the U.S.A. – North Vancouver : International Self-Counsel Press, 1987.
ISBN 0889089205 Hbk £12.95

Donelan, Edward J.
Energy and mineral resources law in Ireland / Edward J. Donelan : with a foreword by A.J.F. O'Reilly. – Blackrock : Round Hall in association with Irish Academic, 1985.
214p; 25cm.
Includes index.
ISBN 0950872547
→ Sale of goods and supply of services : a guide to the legislation.

Donell, R. A.
Landlord and Tenant Up-to-Date. – London : Law Society, 1985.
23p. – (Nineteen Eighty-Five Crash Course Transcripts).
Hbk £2.05

Donnelly, K.
Probate Procedure Notes. – Waterlow.
– (Procedure Notes Series).
ISBN 0080368980 Pbk £9.95

Donner, Andre M.
Role of the Lawyer in the European Communities. – Edinburgh : Edinburgh University Press.
106p.
Hbk £4.00

Donner, Ruth
Regulation of nationality in international law / Ruth Donner. – Helsinki : The Finnish Society of Sciences and Letters, 1983.
287p.
Bibliography: p273-284.
ISBN 9516531172

Donnison, et al
Neighbourhood watch : policing the people. – London : CENT, 1986.
ISBN 0951119508 Pbk £1.50

Donogh's Commentaries on the Indian Stamp Act. – 9th rev. ed. – Allahabad : Law Publishers, 1986.
Hbk £250.00

Donohue, Terence J. → Privacy and data protection : an international bibliography.

Donovan, Brian Harrie Kevin
Law of bail : practice, procedure and principles / by Brian Harrie Kevin Donovan : foreword by Mr Justice Roden : introduction by Roger Court. – Sydney : Legal Books, 1981.
xxi,186p.
Includes index.
ISBN 0959656855

Donovan, Brian Harrie Kevin → Criminal law.

Doob, Anthony
Perspectives in Criminal Law : Essays in Honour of John LL.J. Edwards / Edward L. Greenspan. – Aurora : Canada Law Book Co, 1984.
384p. – (Text Books-Criminal).
This collection of fifteen essays brings together some of the best legal minds in Canada and elsewhere to explore the key and perplexing issues in the fields of criminal law and criminology. This book also commemorates the founding of the University of Toronto's Centre of Criminology 21 years ago.
Hbk £53.00

Doolan, Brian
Casebook on Irish Company Law. – Dublin : Gill and Macmillan, 1987.
ISBN 0717114376 Pbk £19.95
—Constitutional Law and Constitutional Rights in Ireland / Brian Doolan. – 2nd ed. – Dublin : Gill and Macmillan, 1987.
ISBN 0717115550 Pbk £17.95
—Principles of Irish law / Brian Doolan. – 2nd ed. – Dublin : Gill and Macmillan, 1986.
xix,395p.
Previous ed.: 1981. Includes index.
ISBN 0717114384 Pbk £12.50

Dore, Isaak I.
Arbitration and conciliation under the UNCITRAL rules : a textual analysis / Issaak I. Dore. – Dordrecht : Nijhoff, 1986.
ISBN 0898389135

Dorey, Frederick C.
Aviation Security. – London : Granada Publishing Ltd, 1983.
309p : Illus.
ISBN 0246117400 Hbk £30.00

Dorsey, James E.
Canada Labour Relations Board : Federal Law and Practice. – Agincourt : Carswell, 1983.
450p.
This book provides a description and discussion of the character, activity, practice, and role of the Canadian Labour Relations Board in its historical, constitutional, and institutional setting.
Hbk £54.75
—Employee-Employer Rights : a Guide for the British Columbia Work Force. – 7th ed. – North Vancouver : International Self-Counsel Press, 1984.
137p.
ISBN 0889081522 Hbk £7.95

Dorter, John B.
Building and Construction Contracts in Australia : Law and Practice / John J.A. Sharkey. – North Ryde : Law Book Co, 1981.
lv, 811p.
ISBN 0455200912 Hbk £90.50
→ Commercial Arbitration.

Dossier : an inventory of Current Legal Research in Canada. – Ottawa : Canadian Law Information Council.
169p.
Pbk £20.00

Douch
Economics of Foreign Exchange / Sanderson. – Cambridge : Woodhead-Faulkner, 1988.
ISBN 0859413640 Hbk £40.00

Dougherty, C.J.
American Health Care : Realities, Rights and Reforms. – Oxford : Oxford University Press.
ISBN 0195052714 Hbk £22.50

Douglas, R.
Pilotage Act 1987. – London : Lloyd's of London Press, 1987.
ISBN 1850441391 Pbk £18.75

Douglas, R. P. A. → Law of pilotage.
—Nevill's Will Drafting Handbook. – 4th ed. – Butterworths, 1988.
149p.
ISBN 0409702226 Hbk £54.00

Dover, V.
Handbook To Marine Insurance. – 8th ed. – Witherby, 1975.
ISBN 0854930736 Hbk £18.00

Dowdle, N.B. → Wills Precedents (Victoria).

Dowell, et al
Emergency Procedures Handbook. – London : Legal Action Group, 1986.
ISBN 0905099109 Pbk

Dowling, J.A.
Ejectment for non-payment of rent / by J. A. Dowling : with a supplement for the Republic of Ireland by G. McCormack. – Belfast : Faculty of Law, the Queen's University of Belfast, 1986.
xvii,84p.
ISBN 0853892695

Dowling, M.J. → Employee participation : practice and attitudes in north-west manufacturing industry.

Downes
Textbook on Contract. – London : Financial Training.
ISBN 1851850767 Hbk £14.95

Downes, David
Contrasts in tolerance : post-war penal policy in the Netherlands and England and Wales / David Downes. – Oxford : Clarendon Press, 1988.
226p.
Bibliography: pp.207-218. - Includes index.
ISBN 0198256086 Hbk £20.00
—Law and order : theft of an issue / David Downes. – London : Fabian Society in association with Labour Campaign for Criminal Justice, 1983.
33p.
Bibliography: p32-33.
ISBN 0716304902
—Understanding deviance : a guide to the sociology of crime and rule-breaking / David Downes and Paul Rock. – 2nd ed. – Oxford : Clarendon Press, 1988.
viii,369p.
Bibliography: pp.335-360. - Includes index.
ISBN 0198762143 Hbk £30.00
ISBN 0198762135 Pbk £10.95

Downey, M.
Banking For Students. – Pitman, 1986.
ISBN 0273023209 Pbk £7.95

Downey, P. J.
New Zealand Law Journal. – Wellington : Butterworths.
Hbk

Downing, Paul B.
International Comparisons in Implementing Pollution Laws / Kenneth Hanf. – Dordrecht : Kluwer, 1983.
352p.
ISBN 089838110X Hbk £78.00

Dowrie, Norman →Petition procedure in the Court of Session.

Dowry Prohibition Act. – Allahabad : Orient Law House, 1984.
Hbk £50.00

Doxey, Margaret P.
International sanctions in contemporary perspective / Margaret P. Doxey. – Basingstoke : Macmillan, 1987.
xi,175p; 23cm.
Includes index.
ISBN 033338945X Hbk £27.50
ISBN 0333389468 Pbk £9.50

Doyle, E P
Practice of banking / Kelly. – 3rd ed. – Plymouth : Macdonald & Evans, 1981.
ISBN 0712117555 Pbk £5.95

Doyle, Maeve →Index to Irish Superior Court Written Judgments, 1976-1982.

D'Oyly, John
Constitution of the Kandyan Kingdom. – Dehiwala : Tisara Prakashakayo.
264p.
Hbk £250.00

Doz, Yves
Strategic management in multinational companies / by Yves Doz. – Oxford : Pergamon, 1985.
250p; 25cm.
ISBN 0080318088 Hbk £19.25
ISBN 008031807X Pbk £10.75

Dr. Bhimrao Ramji Ambedkar : a Study in Social Democracy. – Kuala Lumpur : Intellectual Book Corner, 1982.
vii, 270p.
Hbk £80.00

Drache, Arthur B
Canada Estate Planning Service. – Toronto : DeBoo.
Looseleaf service.
ISBN 0888201125 Llf £260.00
—Canadian Taxpayer. – Toronto : DeBoo, 1984.
ISBN 0888201680 Hbk 210.00

Draft agreement between the Government of the United Kingdom of Great Britain and Northern Ireland and the Government of the People's Republic of China on the future of Hong Kong / presented to Parliament by the Secretary of State for Foreign and Commonwealth Affairs. – London : H.M.S.O., 1984.
39p. – (Miscellaneous).
ISBN 010193520X

Draft agreement between the government of the United Kingdom of Great Britain and Northern Ireland and the government of the People's Republic of China on the future of Hong Kong. – Hong Kong : Government Printer, 1984.
46p.
'This White Paper reproduces the text of the White Paper published by Her Majesty's Government in London on 26 September 1984.'.

Draft clauses of a bill to reform the law of copyright and other intellectual property / Department of Trade and Industry. – London : The Department, 1987.
viii,74p.

Draft codes of practice for the detention, treatment, questioning and identification of persons by the police; for the searching of premises and seizure of property; and for the exercise of powers of stop and search. – London : Home Office, 1985.
iii,80p.
Previous ed.: 1984.

Draft codes of practice for the detention, treatment, questioning and identification of persons by the police and for the searching of premises and seizure of property. – Rev. ed. – London : Home Office, 1984.
iii,66p.
Previous ed.: 1983.
ISBN 0862521424

Draft codes of practice for the treatment, questioning and identification of persons suspected of crime / Home Office. – Revised draft. – London : Home Office, 1983.
51p.
ISBN 0862520975

Draft convention on the law of the sea / United Nations Third Conference on the Law of the Sea, resumed tenth session, Geneva, 3-28 August 1981. – Geneva : United Nations, 1981.
xix,175p; 28cm. – (Document).
Supersedes: Draft convention on the law of the sea: informal text.

Draft E.C. regulation on the European economic interest grouping (EEIG) : a consultative document. – London : Department of Trade and Industry, 1983.
15,109p.

Draft European Communities directive on procedures for informing and consulting employees / Draft European Communities fifth directive on the harmonisation of comapny law : Department of Employment, Department of Trade and Industry. – London : The Departments, 1983.
90p.

Draft guidelines for approval of social workers under the proposed Mental Health (Amendment) Act : Working Party draft for consultation. – Department of Health and Social Security. – London : The Department, 1981.
11p.

Draft international criminal code and draft statute for an international criminal tribunal / M. Cherif Bassiouni. – 2nd rev. & updated ed. – Dordrecht : M. Nijhoff, 1987.
xxii, 492p.
Re ed. of: International criminal law / M. Cherif Bassiouni, 1980. Bibliography: p.267-353.
ISBN 0898389186

Draft protocol on the settlement of litigation concerning the infringement and validity of Community patents / as agreed by the Interim Committee at its 13th session of 11 and 12 July 1985. – Brussels : Community Patent Interim Committee, 1985.
54p. – (CIBC).
This draft is intended to serve as a basis for a possible Interngovernmental Conference. Includes the preliminary draft of a Protocol on Privileges and Immunities of the Community Patent Appeal Court.

Draft rules and regulations for licensed dealers in securities / Council for the Securities Industry. – London : The Council, 1982.
9p. – (Press statement).

Draft Treaty : Memorandum of the Director General. – World Intellectual Property Organization. – Geneva : World Intellectual Property Organization, 1985.
29p. – (IPIC/CE/I/2).
The Committee met in Geneva from November 26 to 29, 1985. 'Draft treaty on the protection of intellectual property in respect of integrated circuits'.

Draft Treaty establishing the European Union : constitutional and political implications in Denmark / by Per Lachmann. – Badia Fiesolana : European University Institute, 1985.
39p.
Paper presented at a conference organised by the European Policy Unit of the European University Institute, in collaboration with the University of Strasbourg and TEPSA, October 1984.

Draft Treaty establishing the European Union : report on the Federal Republic of Germany / by Carl Otto Lenz. – Florence : European University Institute, 1985.
21p.

Draft Treaty establishing the European Union : report on the United Kingdom / by David Edward, Richard McAllister, Robert Lane. – Florence : European University Institute, 1985.
40p.

Draft Treaty establishing the European Union and the member states : Ireland / by John Temple-Lang. – Florence : European University Institute, 1985.
38,5p.

Draft treaty with explanatory notes / memorandum of the Director General. – Geneva : World Intellectual Property Organization, 1986.
45,3p. – (IPIC/CE/II/2).
'Submitted by the Director General of W.I.P.O. for what will be the second session of the W.I.P.O. Committee of Experts on Intellectual Property in Respect of Integrated Circuits ... to take place from June 23 to 27, 1986, at Geneva' - Background. Draft treaty entitled: Draft Treaty on the Protection of Intellectual Property in Respect of Semiconductor Integrated Circuits.

Drafting and Interpreting Legislation. – 3rd ed. – Agincourt : Carswell, 1988.
110p.
Hbk £33.25

Drafting and Negotiating Commercial Leases. – 2nd ed. – London : Butterworths, 1984.
ISBN 0406359075 Hbk £29.00

Drafting and Negotiating Commercial Leases in Scotland / A. H. Primrose. – London : Butterworths, 1985.
This work deals with the drafting, negotiating, and settling of commercial leases in Scotland. The book provides extensive references to English cases that may have a persuasive influence on judgements made in Scottish courts.
ISBN 0406359067 Hbk £27.00

Drafting and Negotiating Common Leases Scotland / D J McKichan. – London : Butterworths, 1985.
ISBN 0406359067 Hbk £41.50

Drafting Business Leases. – 2nd ed. – London : Longman Professional, 1986.
ISBN 0851210244 Hbk £28.95

Drafting Commercial Documents. – Vancouver : Continuing Legal Education Society of British Columbia, 1981.
278p.
ISBN 0865040206 Hbk £65.00

Drafting, Conveyancing and Pleadings. – 2nd ed. – Bombay : Tripathi, 1982.
460p.
bd £80.00

Drafting residential leases. – 2nd. – 1193, 1989.
Coverage includes the terms of the lease, premises, easements and ancillary rights, rents and rent increases, service charges anmd insurance. New edition covers changes resulting from the Housing Act 1988.
ISBN 0851214355 Hbk £35.00

Drafting Your Own Will. – Cape Town : Tafelberg Publishers, 1988.
80p.
Pbk £14.95

Drafting: its applications to conveyancing and commercial documents. – North Ryde : Butterworths (Australia), 1973.
Guide to the drafting of legal and commercial documents. Explains the underlying princples of drafting and demonstrates the link between those principles and the rule of law. Discusses the language of law, and generality of expression, and sets out the most salient features of parliamentary drafting practice relevant to document drafting.
ISBN 0409438251 Hbk

Draftsman's Handbook. – London : Longman Professional, 1985.
ISBN 0851209505 Pbk £19.50

Drainage Cases : Ontario 1898-1903, 2 Vols. / Scully. – Agincourt : Carswell, 1983.
Hbk £59.00

Drakakis-Smith, D. W.
Third World city / David Drakakis-Smith. – London : Methuen, 1987.
vi,116p; 21cm. – (Methuen introductions to development).
Includes bibliography and index.
ISBN 041691960X Pbk £
ISBN 0416919707 correct

Drake, Charles D.
Employment Acts 1974-1980, with commentary / by Charles D. Drake and Brian Bercusson. – London : Sweet & Maxwell, 1981.
ca.500p.
ISBN 0421282509
—Labour law / by Charles D. Drake. – 3rd ed. – London : Sweet & Maxwell, 1981.
278p; 23cm. – (Concise college texts).
Previous ed.: 1973. Includes index.
ISBN 0421281006 Hbk £
ISBN 0421281103 Pbk £7.50
—Law of health and safety at work : the new approach / by Charles D. Drake and Frank B. Wright : with a foreword by John H. Locke. – London : Sweet & Maxwell, 1983.
xii; 25cm.
Includes index.
ISBN 0421286202 Hbk £22.00
ISBN 042128630X Pbk £13.85
—Law of partnership / by Charles D. Drake. – 3rd ed. – London : Sweet & Maxwell, 1983.
xxx,391p; 22cm.
Previous ed.: 1977. Includes index.
ISBN 0421298405 Pbk £10.50
—Trade union acts. – London : Sweet & Maxwell, 1985.
ISBN 0421338008 Pbk £17.50

Drake, E. A.
Local Government Superannuation Scheme : An Explanation. – London : Shaw & Sons, 1982.
ISBN 0721903568 Pbk £0.48

Drake, M.
Affiliation Law and Practice. – 5th ed. – London : Longman Professional, 1985.
ISBN 0851209912 Pbk £15.95

Drakon and early Athenian homicide law / Michael Gagarin. – New Haven : Yale University Press, 1981.
xvii,175p; 22cm. – (Yale classical monographs).
Includes index. Includes the Greek text and English translation of Drakon's law.
ISBN 0300026277 Hbk

Dranoff, Linda Silver
Every Woman's Guide to the Law. – Markham : Fitzhenry and Whiteside.
256p.
ISBN 0889026459 Pbk £9.95
—Women in Canadian Law. – Markham : Fitzhenry and Whiteside.
96p.
ISBN 0889023778 Pbk £4.95

Draycott, A T →Stone's Justices' Manual.

Dreiss, Uwe
Decisions of the Boards of Appeal of the European Patent Office : Entscheidungen der Beschwerdekammern des Europaischen Patentamts
Vol. 1. – Cologne : Carl Heymanns Verlag, 1983.
xii, 432p.
ISBN 3452194817 Hbk £128.00

Drew, John
Doing Business in the European Community. – 2nd ed. – London : Butterworths, 1982.
ISBN 0408108363 Hbk £20.00

Drew, K.F.
Law and Society in Medieval Europe. – London : Variorum, 1988.
ISBN 0860782190 Hbk £32.00

Drewry, Gavin
Civil Service Today / Butcher. – Oxford : Blackwell.
ISBN 0631154280 Hbk £29.95
ISBN 0631154299 Pbk £9.50
→ Legislation and public policy : public bills in the 1970-74 Parliament.
→ New select committees : a study of the 1979 reforms.

Driedger, Elmer A.
Construction of statutes / Elmer A. Driedger. – 2nd ed. – Toronto : Butterworths, 1983.
xvi,385p. – (Canadian legal manual series).
Contains a new chapter on bilingual statutes, and expanded discussion of departure from the ordinary meaning for the professed reason of 'absurdity', and a refinement of the author's commentary on the presumption against retrospective operation.
ISBN 0409828033
—Manual of instructions for legislative and legal writing / Elmer A. Driedger. – Ottawa : Canadian Government Publishing Centre, 1982.
6 v, vi, 568.; 25 cm.
Includes bibliographical references.
ISBN 0660111187 Pbk : set £25.00 (£30.00 other countries)

Drink, drugs and driving / by H.J. Walls and Alistair R. Brownlie. – 2nd ed. – London : Sweet & Maxwell, 1985.
xxix,281p; 22cm.
Previous ed.: 1970. Bibliography: p247-268. - Includes index.
ISBN 0421296003 Pbk £19.50

Drinking and Driving : A Pocket Guide. – London : Police Review Publishing, 1984.
ISBN 0851640109 Pbk

Drinking and Driving - The Decided Cases. – Police Review, 1987.
ISBN 0851640281 Pbk £5.25

Drinking Driver and the Law. – 3rd ed. – London : Shaw & Sons, 1983.
ISBN 0721905226 Pbk £16.00

Drinkwater, David W →Child Witness : Do the Courts Abuse Children.
—Private Placements in Canada / William K. Orr. – Agincourt : Carswell, 1985.
224p.
This book discusses essential statutory concepts, private placement exemptions, offering memoranda, rules governing secondary trading, stock exchange requirements, and other issues pertaining to private placements under Canadian securities law.
Hbk £49.00

Droit International Prive Quibecos. – London : Butterworths.
ISBN 0409821233 Hbk £76.00

Drug Abuse Briefing. – New York : Drugs Dependence, 1988.
ISBN 0948830352 Pbk £1.50

Drug addiction research programme 1983 / Correctional Services Department, Hong Kong. – Hong Kong : The Department, 1983.
40p.

Drug criminality and drug abuse in Sweden, 1969-1981 / Jan Andersson, Artur Solarz. – Stockholm : Research Division, National Swedish Council for Crime Prevention, 1982.
53p. – (Report).
Includes bibliographies.
ISBN 9138072572

Drug Industry : A Case Study in Foreign Control / David John Fowler. – Toronto : Lorimer & Co, 1981.
ISBN 0888625367 Hbk £16.95
ISBN 0888625359 Pbk £8.95

Drug offences in Australia
Vol. 1 : Sentencing / by Fiori Rinaldi. – Sydney : Law Book Co., 1986.
xxv,247p.
Includes index.
ISBN 045520649X

Drug Offences in Canada. – 2nd ed. – Aurora : Canada Law Book Co, 1986.
800p. – (Text Books-Criminal).
This monograph is an important research tool for counsel involved in the prosecution or defense of substantive drug charges or drug conspiracies in Canada. The second edition is revised and reorganized to reflect the many judicial decisions delivered since the publication of the first edition, including a full review of the impact of the Canadian Charter of Rights and Freedoms.
Hbk £75.00

Drug Users & Law In Aus : From Crime Control To Welfare 1987. – London : Law Book Co.
ISBN 0455207143 Pbk £25.00

Drugs and Cosmetics Act, 1940 : Together with Drugs and Cosmetics Rules, 1945 and Drugs (Price control) Order, 1979. – 2nd ed. – Lucknow : Eastern Book Company, 1984.
447p.
Hbk £65.00

Drugs Law. – Chichester : Barry Rose, 1982.
ISBN 0859922286 Pbk £12.00

Drummond, Christina, et al
Guide to Accounting Pronouncements and Sources. – Toronto : Butterworths.
152p.
ISBN 0409805130 Pbk £21.95

Drunk-Driving : The New Law. – London : Oyez Longman, 1984.
– (Oyez Longman Practice Note Ser.: No. 65).
ISBN 0851208657

Drunken driving and the law / Marc de Blacam. – Dublin : Round Hall, 1986.
111p; 22cm.
Includes index.
ISBN 0947686134 Hbk £15.00
ISBN 0947686126 Pbk £8.95

Drury, A C
Credit Cards / Charles W Ferrier. – London : Butterworths, 1984.
ISBN 0406259402 Pbk £10.95

Drury, Tony
Credit cards / Tony Drury, Charles W. Ferrier. – London : Butterworths, 1984.
xiv,177p; 22cm.
Includes index.
ISBN 0406259402 Pbk £6.95

Drysdale, John →Law and Practice of Franchising.
—Passing off : law and practice / John Drysdale, Michael Silverleaf. – London : Butterworths, 1986.
xxxiv,224p; 26cm.
Includes index.
ISBN 0406253404 £25.00

Drysdall, A.R.
Mines and Minerals Act, 1969, and the Mineral Tax Act, 1970 / E.J. Langevad. – Lusaka : Geological Survey of Zambia.
Hbk £1.25

Drzemczewski, Andrew Z.
European human rights convention in domestic law : a comparative study / Andrew Z. Drzemczewski. – Oxford : Clarendon, 1983.
xiv,372p; 23cm.
Bibliography: p348-360. - Includes index.
ISBN 0198253966
—European Human Rights Convention on Domestic Law. – Oxford : Oxford University Press, 1983.
ISBN 019825525X Pbk £12.50
—Right to respect for private and family life, home and correspondence as guaranteed by Article 8 of the European Convention on Human Rights / by Andrew Drzemczewski. – Strasbourg : Council of Europe, Directorate of Human Rights, 1984.
29p.
ISBN 9287103526

D'Sa, Leo Barros
Professional liability and construction / Leo Barros D'Sa. – 1. – Ascot : Chartered Institute of Building, 1987.
30cm. – (Occasional paper).
ISBN 090660088X Pbk

D'Souza, Frances
Refugee dilemma / by Frances D'Souza and Jeff Crisp : additional research by Stevanne Hill : with a foreword by Prince Sadruddin Aga Khan. – New ed. – London : Minority Rights Group, 1985.
20p. – (Report).
Previous ed.: 1981. Bibliography: p.19.
ISBN 0946690235

DTI : the department for enterprise / presented to Parliament by the Secretary of State for Trade and Industry and the Chancellor of the Duchy of Lancaster by command of Her Majesty, January 1988. – London : HMSO, 1988.
vii,41p.
ISBN 0101027826

Du Plessis
Interpretation of Statutes. – Durban : Butterworths.
Hbk

Du Saussay, Christian
Legislation on wildlife and protected areas in Africa / by Christian du Saussay for Legislation Branch, Legal Office, FAO. – Rome : Food and Agriculture Organization of the United Nations, 1984.
vii,158p. – (Legislative study).
Includes bibliographical references.
ISBN 9251011710

Dube, M.P.
Role of Supreme Court in Indian Constitution. – New Delhi : Deep and Deep Publications, 1987.
208p.
Hbk £150.00

Dublin University law journal. – Dublin : Law School, Trinity College, Dublin, 1976-.

Duchene, Francois →European Community and the Mediterranean Basin : study on the consequences of the process of enlargement both for the Mediterranean zone and for the Community itself and the conditions necessary for the definition of a global and forward-looking policy of the Community towards the Mediterranean basin.

Duchy of Lancaster →DTI : the department for enterprise.

Duckworth, James →Kitchin's road transport law : a summary of the legislation affecting the construction, equipment and use of motor vehicles.

Duckworth, Peter
Matrimonial Property and Finance. – 3rd ed. – London : Longman Professional, 1987.
ISBN 0851212816 Hbk £47.50

Dudeja, V.J.
Judicial Review in India. – Sangam Books.
ISBN 0861321766 Hbk £12.95

Duff : a Life in the Law. – Vancouver : University of British Columbia Press, 1984.
344p.
ISBN 0774802030 Hbk £34.95

Duff, Alexander →Australian Family Law Forms and Precedents.

Duff, Antony →Philosophy and the criminal law : Association for Legal and Social Philosophy Tenth Annual Conference at the University of Manchester, 8-10th April 1983.

Duff, Peter →Jury under attack.

Duff, R. A.
Trials and punishments / R.A. Duff. – Cambridge : Cambridge University Press, 1986.
336p; 22cm. – (Cambridge studies in philosophy).
Includes bibliography and index.
ISBN 0521308186 £22.50

Dufton, J. →Building Control In Inner London : The London Building Acts and Bylaws and Their Interpretation.

Dufty, Ann →Cases and materials on contract.

Dugard, John
Recognition and the United Nationsby John Dugard. – Cambridge : Grotius, 1987.
xiv,192p.
An analysis of the impact on the law of recognition of recent developments in the practice of the United Nations on the admission of new members, and of the practical relevance of the modern concepts of peremptory norms of international law and jus cogens.
ISBN 0949009008

Dugdale
Professional negligence / K M Stanton. – 2nd ed. – London : Butterworths, 1988.
ISBN 0406179115 Hbk

Dugdale, Anthony M. →Introduction to legal method.
—Professional Negligence / K. M. Stanton. – 2nd ed. – Wellington : Butterworths, 1986.
This book presents a comprehensive review of the law of professional negligence in the United Kingdom. Breach of trust, conversion and fraud, and vicarious liability for conduct of a professional's employees are covered in the work, in addition to professional liability in contract or tort.
ISBN 0406179115 Hbk £35.00

Dugdale, D. F. →Credit Contracts Act 1981 : an annotated edition of the Statute.
—New Zealand Hire Purchase Law. – 3rd ed. – Butterworths, 1977.
ISBN 0409621811 Hbk £64.35

Duggan →Modern law of strikes.

Duggan, A. J.
Economics of consumer protection : a critique of the Chicago School case against intervention / A.J. Duggan. – Adelaide : Adelaide Law Review Association, 1982.
xii,151p.
Includes index.
ISBN 0908448015 Hbk

Duller, H. J
Development technology / H.J. Duller. – London : Routledge & K. Paul, 1982.
192p.
Includes index. Bibliography: p173-190.
ISBN 0710009909

Duman, Daniel
English and Colonial bars in the nineteenth century / Daniel Duman. – London : Croom Helm, 1983.
228p; 23cm.
Bibliography: p212-221. - Includes index.
ISBN 0856644684 £13.95
—Judicial Bench in England, 1727-1875 : The Reshaping of a Professional Elite. – London : Royal Historical Society, 1982.
– (Studies in History (London) Ser.: Vol. 29).
ISBN 0901050806 Hbk £19.60

Dummett, A. M. A. →Minorities : community and identity : report of the Dahlem Workshop on Minorities - Community and Identity, Berlin 1982, Nov. 28 - Dec. 3.

Dummett, Ann M A
British Nationality / Ian Martin. – 2nd ed. – London : CENT, 1984.
ISBN 0946088101 Pbk £2.95
—Towards a just immigration policy. – London : CENT, 1986.
ISBN 0900137266 Pbk £7.95

Dumont, M.
Treatise on Judicial Evidence / J. Bentham. – Repr. of 1825 ed. – Abingdon : Professional Books.
Hbk £60.00

DuMoulin, A B P → British Columbia Annotated Industrial Relations Act, 2 Vols.
→ British Columbia annotated Industrial Relations Act.
—Defensive Practice of Real Estate. – Vancouver : British Columbia Continuing Legal Education Society, 1982.
124p.
ISBN 0865040486 Hbk £12.50

Dumping and subsidies : the law and procedures governing the imposition of anti-dumping and countervailing duties in the European Community / Joseph Cunnane and Clive Stanbrook. – London : European Business Publications, 1983.
xvi,227p.
Includes index.
ISBN 0907027040

Dunbar, Liz → Plain words for consumers : the language and layout of consumer contracts : the case for a plain language law.

Duncan, A G M, et al
Rent (Scotland) Act 1984 / J Hope. – Edinburgh : Green (W.) & Son, 1986.
Annotated text of the Act reprinted from Scottish Current Law Statutes, along with the rent regulations passed under the earlier legislation, supplemented with a table of cases and index.
ISBN 0414007522 Pbk
—Research paper on actions of ejection and removing / by A.G.M. Duncan. – Edinburgh : Law Commission, 1984.
xv,204p.
'Published by the Scottish Law Commission in connection with Consultative Memorandum No. 59'. Includes bibliographical references.
→ Student's glossary of Scottish legal terms.

Duncan, A. S. → Dictionary of medical ethics.

Duncan and Neill on defamation / foreword to the first edition, Lord Salmon. – 2nd ed. – London : Butterworths, 1983.
xxii,205p; 26cm.
This work incorporates all the statutory material along with a full discussion of relevant United Kingdom cases on defamation. Where the common law is uncertain, the book suggests solutions which accord with the principles presented.
ISBN 0406178305

Duncan, Colin
Defamation / Brian Neill. – 2nd ed. – London : Butterworths, 1984.
ISBN 0406178305 Hbk £34.00
—Duncan and Neill on defamation / foreword to the first edition, Lord Salmon. – 2nd ed. – London : Butterworths, 1983.
xxii,205p; 26cm.
This work incorporates all the statutory material along with a full discussion of relevant United Kingdom cases on defamation. Where the common law is uncertain, the book suggests solutions which accord with the principles presented.
ISBN 0406178305

Duncan, Robyn M.
Legal Studies for New South Wales Years 11 and 12. – Butterworths, 1989.
ca 432p.
ISBN 0409494682 Pbk £22.50

Duncan, Sue
Preventing rent arrears / Sue Duncan, Keith Kirby. – London : H.M.S.O., 1983.
144p; 21cm.
At head of title: Department of the Environment.
ISBN 0117517100 Pbk £4.00

Duncan, W.D.
Real Estate Agency Law in Queensland. – North Ryde : Law Book Co, 1985.
xxiv, 273p.
ISBN 0455202915 Pbk £32.50

Duncan, William
Case for divorce in the Irish Republic : a report commissioned by the Irish Council for Civil Liberties / William Duncan. – Rev. ed. with postscript. – Dublin : The Council, 1982.
107p.
Includes bibliographical references.
→ Law and social policy : some current problems in Irish law.

Dundas, Carl W.
Application of new legal techniques to mining agreements in developing countries / by Carl W. Dundas. – London : Commonwealth Secretariat, 1981.
46p.
Includes bibliographical references.

Dunkerley, Harold B. → Urban land policy : issues and opportunities.

Dunlop
Court of Session Cases : Series 1-5, 1821-1906, 63 Vols.
2nd Series, 1838-1862, 24 Vols. /. – Abingdon : Professional Books.
Hbk
—Scots Revised Reports : 1707-1873, 45 Vols.
Court of Session Cases : 1838-1862, 13 Vols. /. – Abingdon : Professional Books.
Hbk

Dunlop, C. R. B
Creditor-debtor law in Canada / by C.R.B. Dunlop : with chapter 14 / by P.J.M. Lown. – Toronto, Canada : Carswell, 1981.
cxxii, 563 p.; 26 cm.
'Table of cases': p. xiii-lxxxi 'Table of statutes, rules and regulations': p. lxxxv-cxvi. Includes index. Bibliography: p. cxvii-cxxii.
ISBN 0459340506 Pbk

Dunlop Holdings Limited : investigation under Section 172 of the Companies Act 1948 : interim report / by Collingwood William Malcolm Ingram and Francis Herbert Pulling for the Department of Trade. – London : H.M.S.O., 1981.
50p; 30cm.
ISBN 0115131817 Pbk £6.00

Dunlop, J. Bruce, et al
Dominion Law Reports : 1969-1984, 150 Vols. – Aurora : Canada Law Book Co, 1984.
– (Third Ser.).
Hbk £5100.00
—Dominion Law Reports (D.L.R.) 1912-22, 70 vols. – Aurora : Canada Law Book Co.
– (Old Ser.).
Hbk £2100.00
—Dominion Law Reports (D.L.R.) 1923-55, 133 vols. – Aurora : Canada Law Book Co.
– (New Ser.).
Hbk £4522.00
—Dominion Law Reports (D.L.R.) 1956-68, 70 vols. – Aurora : Canada Law Book Co.
– (Second Ser.).
Hbk £2380.00
—Dominion Law Reports (D.L.R.) 1984-present. – Aurora : Canada Law Book Co.
– (Fourth Ser.).
Hbk £78.50
—Dominion Law Reports (Second & Third Series) Annotation Service : 1984, 1 Vol. – Aurora : Canada Law Book Co.
1084p.
Hbk £65.00
—Ontario Reports (O.R.) 1931-62, 32 Vols. – Aurora : Canada Law Book Co.
– (Old Ser.).
Hbk £1152.00
—Ontario Reports (O.R.) 1963-73, 26 Vols. – Aurora : Canada Law Book Co.
– (New Ser.).
Hbk £936.00
—Ontario Reports (O.R.) 1974-Present. – Aurora : Canada Law Book Co.
– (Second Ser.).
Hbk Back Vols. 36.00 each
—Ontario Reports Second Series (1974-Present). – Aurora : Canada Law Book Co.
– (Law Reports).
Hbk £68.00

Dunn, Angus
Export finance / by Angus Dunn and Martin Knight. – London : Euromoney Publications, 1982.
vi,154p.
ISBN 0903121328

Dunn, G. W. → Practice in mortgage actions in Ontario : the practice in mortgage actions and in exercising power of sale.

Dunne, M.
United States and the World Court 1920-1935. – Pinter.
ISBN 0861879716 Hbk £25.00

Dunning, Eric → Hooligans abroad : the behaviour and control of English fans in Continental Europe.

Dunning, John H.
International production and the multinational enterprise / John H. Dunning. – London : Allen & Unwin, 1981.
viii,439p; 23cm.
Includes bibliographies and index.
ISBN 0043303196 Hbk
ISBN 004330320X Pbk
→ Multinationals : company performance and global trends.

Dunstan, G. R. → Dictionary of medical ethics.

DuPlessis : The Interpretation of Statutes. – Durban : Professional Publishers, 1986.
ISBN 0409025089 Pbk £57.00

DuPlessis, Lourens M.
DuPlessis : The Interpretation of Statutes. – Durban : Professional Publishers, 1986.
ISBN 0409025089 Pbk £57.00
—Professional Conduct of the Jurist. – Durban : Professional Publishers, 1983.
ISBN 0409025054 Pbk

Dupuy, R.J.
Handbook on International Organisations. – Martinus Nijhoff.
ISBN 9024736587 Hbk £86.50

Dupuy, Rene-Jean
Future of International Law in a Multicultural World : Workshop 1983. – Dordrecht : Kluwer, 1984.
510p.
ISBN 9024730708 Hbk £135.00
—Future of the International Law of the Environment : Workshop 1984. – Dordrecht : Kluwer, 1985.
536p.
ISBN 9024732395 Hbk £155.00
—Management of Humanity's Resources : the Law of the Sea. Workshop 1981. – Dordrecht : Kluwer, 1982.
xvi, 434p.
ISBN 9024727626 Hbk £120.00
—Settlement of Disputes on the New Natural Resources : Workshop 1982. – Dordrecht : Kluwer, 1983.
502p.
ISBN 9024729017 Hbk £120.00

Durand, Andrew
European Court of Justice Reporter. – Oxford : ESC Publishing Ltd, 1982.
Pbk £140.00

Durie, R.
Broadcasting Law and Practice / D. Catterns. – North Ryde : Law Book Co, 1987.
ca 1,500p.
Llf £450.00

Durkheim and modern sociology / Steve Fenton with Robert Reiner and Ian Hamnet. – Cambridge : Cambridge University Press, 1984.
vi,276p; 24cm.
Bibliography: p260-273. - Includes index.
ISBN 0521259231 Hbk £20.00
ISBN 0521277639 Pbk

Durkheim, Emile
Division of labour in society / Emile Durkheim : translated by W.D. Halls : with an introduction by Lewis Coser. – 2nd ed. – Basingstoke : Macmillan, 1984.
lix,352p; 22cm.
Includes index.
ISBN 0333339800 Pbk £18.00
ISBN 0333339819
—Rules of sociological method and selected texts on sociology and its method / Emile Durkheim : edited with an introduction by Steven Lukes : translated by W. D. Halls. – London : Macmillan, 1982.
vi,264p.
ISBN 0333280717

Durrant → Corporate Insolvency.

Dussault, Rene
Administrative Law : A Treatise
Vol. 1 / Louis Borgeat. – 2nd ed. – Agincourt : Carswell, 1986.
736p.
This work focuses on the structures, the arts, and the function of 'the Administration' through an examination of the definition of administrative law and its fundamental principles.
ISBN 045938080X Hbk £80.00

Dutch business law : legal, accounting, and tax aspects of business in the Netherlands / by Steven R. Schuit and Jan M. van der Beek and Bonne K. Raap, and Michael W. den Boogert ... et al. – 2nd ed. – Deventer, Netherlands : Kluwer Law and Taxation Publishers, 1983.
xl, 552 p.; 25 cm.
Includes index.
ISBN 9065441220

Duties and Responsibilities of Company Secretaries and Directors in Australia. – North Ryde : C.C.H. Australia, 1987.
240p.
ISBN 0869030353 Hbk £27.00

Duties and Responsibilities of Pension Plan Trustees / Williams. – London : CCH, 1984.
ISBN 0863250300 Pbk £11.50

Duties of national courts under the constitutional law of the European Community / John Temple Lang. – Exeter : University of Exeter, 1987.
40p; 21cm.
The Dominik Lasok lecture in European Community law delivered in the University on 23rd January 1987.

Dutile, Fernand N. → Legal education and lawyer competency : curricula for change.

Dutta, K.K.
Treatise on Criminal Law. – Lucknow : Eastern Book Company, 1984.
Hbk £80.00

Dutton, Don
Crisis intervention training for police / Don Dutton and Bruce Levens under the auspices of United Way of the Lower Mainland. – Ottawa : Ministry of the Solicitor General, 1985.
66p. – (User report).
Bibliography: p.51.

Dutton, H.
Patent system and inventive activity. – Manchester : Manchester University Press, 1984.
ISBN 0719009979 Hbk £21.00

Duty solicitor scheme, HMP Strangeways / North Western Legal Services Committee. – S.l. : The Committee, 1985.
30p.

Duxbury, R. M. C. → Planning law and procedure.

Duxbury, Robert
Contract in a nutshell / Robert Duxbury. – London : Sweet & Maxwell, 1987.
117p; 22cm.
Includes index.
ISBN 0421368004 Pbk £3.95

Dvystattva of Raghunandana Bhattacharya : Ordeals in Classical Hindu Law. – New Delhi : Manohar Publications, 1981.
280p.
Hbk £110.00

Dwelling on the threshold. – London : Sweet & Maxwell, 1988.
ISBN 0459305611 Hbk £32.00

Dwelling on the threshold : critical essays on modern legal thought / Allan C. Hutchinson. – Toronto : Carswell, 1988.
ix,326p.
Bibliography: pp.324-325..
ISBN 0421400501

Dwivedi → Law of Employees State Insurance.

Dwivedi's Fatal Accidents Act : and Legal Representatives Suits Act. – 4th ed. – Allahabad : Law Book Company, 1988.
200p.
With 1986 supplement.
Hbk £80.00

Dworkin, Gerald
Copyright, Design and Patents Act 1988 / Taylor. – London : Blackstone Press.
ISBN 1854310232 Pbk £18.95
→ Information technology : the challenge to copyright.

Dworkin, R.
Philosophy Of Law, The. – Oxford : Oxford University Press, 1977.
ISBN 0198750226 Pbk £3.50

Dwyer, B. M. → Introduction to Property Law.

Dwyer, James W. → Intellectual Property in Australia : Patents, Designs, Trade Marks, Confidential Information and Unfair Competition.

Dyer → Balance Sheets and the Lending Banker.

Dyer, Adair
Report on trusts and analogous institutions Part 1 : 1ere partie / Rapport sur les trusts et institutions analogues : Adair Dyer, Hans van Loon. – Provisional ed. – La Haye : Bureau Permanent de la Conference de la Haye de droit international prive, 1982.
127p.
At head of title: Conference de La Haye de droit international prive Hague Conference on Private International Law. English and French tables of contents as inserts. Parallel English and French text.

Dyer, Clare
Fair to the family : a conciliation approach to divorce and separation / by Clare Dyer : illustrated by Claudia Aaron. – East Twickenham : Mediation in Divorce, 1988.
40p.
ISBN 0951313606
→ Law machine.

Dyer, L. S.
Lending in booms and slumps / by L.S. Dyer : delivered under the auspices of King's College London. – London : King's College London, 1981.
35p; 25cm.
Pbk £2.00

Dykstra, Gail, et al
CLIC Abstracts on PLEI Research. – Ottawa : Canadian Law Information Council, 1983.
670p.
ISBN 0920358403 Llf £50.00

Dymond, A. Christopher
Capital Taxes. – London : Longman Professional.
ISBN 0851208517 updat £180.00
—Income Tax Administration, Avoidance and Evasion / Robert J. Reid. – Butterworths, 1981.
192p.
ISBN 0409917028 Hbk £28.95

Dymond, Robert
Dymond's capital transfer tax
Vol.1 : Text / Roy R. Greenfield, Reginald K. Johns. – 2nd ed. – London : Oyez Longman, 1983.
cii,1328p; 24cm.
Previous ed.: 1977. Includes index.
ISBN 0851206425 set
Vol.2 : Statutes, etc.. – 1983.
vii,535p; 24cm.
Previous ed.: London : Oyez, 1977.
ISBN 0851206425 Hbk

Dymond's capital transfer tax
Vol.1 : Text / Roy R. Greenfield, Reginald K. Johns. – 2nd ed. – London : Oyez Longman, 1983.
cii,1328p; 24cm.
Previous ed.: 1977. Includes index.
ISBN 0851206425 set

Dynamic Management Accountancy. – London : Butterworths, 1983.
ISBN 0406258104 Pbk £8.00

Dynamics of aggression in women's prisons in England / Alexandra Mandaraka-Sheppard. – Aldershot : Gower, 1986.
xiii,272p; 23cm.
Bibliography: p241-260. - Includes index.
ISBN 0566008637 £17.50

Dynamics of development in the European human rights convention system / Clovis C. Morrisson. – The Hague : Martinus Nijhoff, 1981.
xii,176p.
ISBN 9024725461 Hbk £100.00

Dynamics of the one-party state in Zambia / Cherry Gertzel ..., Carolyn Baylies, Morris Szeftel. – Manchester : Manchester University Press, 1984.
xi,262p; 23cm.
Bibliography: p247-258. - Includes index.
ISBN 0719010691 £28.50

Dyson, J. M. → Atkin's Encyclopaedia of Court Forms in Civil Proceedings, 42 Vols.

Dyson, Jacqueline C
Recent tax problems. – London : Sweet & Maxwell, 1986.
ISBN 0420474102 Pbk £16.50
→ Rideout's Principles of labour law.

Dyson, R.
On industrial relations : interprofessional relationships in health care and the role of criminal law in industrial relations / R. Dyson and A.N. Khan. – Leeds : Centre for Social Work and Applied Social Studies, University of Leeds, 1982.
27p. – (Occasional papers).

E.B.C.
Estate Duty Act. – E.B.C. – Lucknow : Eastern Book Company, 1984.
Hbk £8.00
—Prevention of Food Adulteration Act Includes Supplement-1986 / H.D. Trivedi. – 8th ed. – Lucknow : Eastern Book Company, 1983.
838p.
Hbk £115.00

E.C. Act with Central Control Orders. – Allahabad : Orient Law House, 1984.
Hbk £35.00

E.E.C. Consumer Law. – Dordrecht : Kluwer, 1986.
488p.
ISBN 9064394067 Pbk £155.00

E. S. Knight and Company
Review of the Commonwealth Superannuation Scheme : a report to the Minister for Finance / by E.S. Knight & Co. – Canberra : Australian Government Publishing Service, 1983.
28p.
ISBN 0644027363

Eady, David → Law of contempt.

Eagles, Ian
Official Information Bill / by Ian Eagles. – Auckland : Legal Research Foundation Inc., 1982.
31p.
'Paper presented at Auckland Law Faculty Seminar Series 1982 at University of Auckland'.

Eaglestone, F. N.
Building Subsidence / Apted. – Oxford : Blackwell Scientific, 1988.
ISBN 0003834190 Hbk £22.50
—Building Subsidence : Liability and Insurance / Apted. – Oxford : BSP Professional.
ISBN 0632020776 Hbk £22.50
→ Insurance law reports.
—Insurance under the JCT forms / Frank Eaglestone. – London : Collins, 1985.
viii,367p; 24cm.
Includes index. Kept up to date by supplements.
ISBN 0003830225 £20.00

Eales, P. G.
Guide to Bankruptcy / P. A. F. De Vos. – revised 1983 ed. – Abingdon : Professional Books, 1984.
ISBN 0903486482 Hbk £19.00
ISBN 090348644X Pbk £12.00

Earl, Peter
International mergers and acquisitions / Peter Earl and Frederick G. Fisher, III. – London : Euromoney, 1986.
vii,129p.
ISBN 090312193X

Earldom of Annandale and Hartfell : report from the Committee for Privileges together with the proceedings of the Committee and the speeches of Counsel. – London : HMSO, 1985.
xliv,150p.
ISBN 0104961856

Earth-oriented space activities and their legal implications : proceedings of the symposium held on October 15-16, 1981, Centre for Research of Air & Space Law / Les activites spatiales effectuees au service de la terre et leurs implications juridiques. – Montreal : McGill University, 1982.
xii,366p.
English or French texts, English and French preliminaries and closing address.

Easements and restrictive covenants in Australia / Adrian J. Bradbrook and Marcia A. Neave. – Sydney : Butterworths, 1981.
xlv,422p.
Includes index.
ISBN 0409300489 Hbk £65

Easing the Passing. – London : CAPE, 1985.
ISBN 0370306279 Hbk £12.50
ISBN 0571139930 Pbk £4.95

Easing the passing : the trial of Dr John Bodkin Adams / Patrick Devlin. – London : Bodley Head, 1985.
256p; 23cm.
ISBN 0370306279 £9.95

Easson, A J
Cases and Materials On Revenue Law. – Sweet & Maxwell, 1973.
ISBN 0421167807 Pbk £8.75
→ Taxation of foreign investment in the People's Republic of China.

East African Law Reports 1957-1975 20 vols. – Professional Books.
ISBN 0862052688 Hbk £710.00

East Anglia and East Midlands probation hostels : a descriptive study / E.W. Mendelsohn. – Cambridge : Institute of Criminology, 1984.
95p. – (Occasional papers).
Includes bibliographical references.

East Timor : violations of human rights : extrajudicial executions, 'disappearances', torture and political imprisonment, 1975-1984. – Amnesty International. – London : Amnesty International Publications, 1985.
vii,92p.
ISBN 0862100852

East Timor and West Irian / by Keith Suter. – Rev. ed. – London : Minority Rights Group, 1982.
24p. – (Reports).
Previous ed. published 1979, as: West Irian, East Timor and Indonesia. Bibliography: p.24.

East-West Environment and Policy Institute → Shipping, energy, and environment : Southeast Asian perspectives for the eighties : proceedings of a Workshop held in Honolulu, Hawaii, 10-12 December 1980.

Eastaway, Nigel → Practical CTT planning.

Eastaway, Nigel A.
Hong Kong stamp duties / Richards. – London : Longman Professional, 1984.
ISBN 0851208983 Pbk £17.50
→ Intellectual property law and taxation.
—Moores/Rowland's A-Z of Tax Planning / Garlick. – 2nd ed. – London : Longman Professional.
ISBN 0851213235 Pbk £18.95
—Practical share valuation / Neil D Booth. – 2nd ed. – London : Butterworths, 1987.
ISBN 0406190143 Hbk £26.00
—Practical Share Valuation. – 2nd ed. – London : Butterworths, 1987.
ISBN 0406190151 Hbk
—Practical Share Valuation / Harry Booth. – London : Butterworths, 1983.
This book provides a practical guide to valuation questions for purposes of tax assessment for practitioners in the United Kingdom. Share valuation, whether that of a private or a public company, often requires negotiation with the Inland Revenue and this manual explores the many issues raised by such negotiations.
ISBN 0406190143 Hbk
—Rowland's Tax Guide, 1984-1985 / David Trill. – London : Butterworths, 1984.
ISBN 0406359199 Pbk
—Share Valuation Cases / Harry Booth. – London : Butterworths, 1985.
This work is a compendium of extracts from judgements in cases which deal with principles of share valuation in the United Kingdom. The case extracts are presented in alphabetical order.
ISBN 0406009805 Hbk
—Tax and Financial Planning for Medical Practitioners. – 2nd ed. – London : Butterworths, 1987.
ISBN 0406190054 Pbk
—Tax and Financial Planning for Professional Partnerships / Brian Gilligan. – 2nd ed. – London : Butterworths, 1986.
This work explains how the tax liability of United Kingdom professional partnerships can be minimized by effective tax planning. The effects of the Finance Act of 1985 on professional partnerships is discussed in detail.
ISBN 0406501807 Pbk
—Tax planning for medical practitioners / Stephen Burwood. – 2nd ed. – London : Butterworths, 1987.
ISBN 04066190054 Pbk £18.50

—Taxation of Lloyds Underwriters. – 2nd ed. – Croydon : Tolley.
300p.
ISBN 0854593063 Hbk £29.95

—Utilising company tax losses and reliefs / by Nigel A. Eastaway and Edward P. Magrin. – 2nd ed. – London : Institute of Chartered Accountants in England and Wales, 1982.
xxxiv,321p; 21cm.
Previous ed.: 1979. Includes index.
ISBN 0852913133 Pbk

Eastern Africa law review : a journal of law and development. – Dar es Salaam : East African Literature Bureau, 1968-.
TSh50

Eastern Pentecostal Bible College Act, 1983, Bill Pr034 : An Act Respecting Eastern Pentecostal Bible College. – Ontario : Ontario Government Publications Service, 1983.
8p.
Hbk £0.30

Eastern Region of Nigeria
Annual volume of the laws of Eastern Region of Nigeria ... : containing the ordinances of Eastern Region of Nigeria and subsidiary legislation made thereunder. – Eastern Region of Nigeria. – 19 v. – Enugu : Government Printer, 1952.
Originally published as individual supplements to Eastern Nigeria gazette. 1967 volume also contains legislation enacted by the Republic of Biafra. Entitled Laws Eastern Nigeria: 1959-1967.
→ Law reports of the Eastern Region of the Federation of Nigeria : including certain hitherto unreported cases previously decided in the Supreme Court of Nigeria.

Eastham, Nancy E. →Cambridge lectures 1981 : selected papers based upon lectures delivered at the Conference of the Canadian Institute for Advanced Legal Studies, 1981, held at Cambridge University, England.

Easton, Dennis →Introducing the law.

East-West Tensions World Wide. – Exeter : European Atlantic Movement, 1982.
Hbk £0.50

Eberts, Mary →Equality Rights and the Canadian Charter of Rights and Freedom : Carswell's Canadian Legal Classic Series.

Ebrahim, Moosa
Backs Against the Tide : an Evaluation of the President's Council's Report on the Group Areas Act. – Johannesburg : South African Institute of Race Relations, 1987.
Hbk £4.00

—Powder Keg or Damp Squib? : Black Opinion and the Group Areas Act. – Johannesburg : South African Institute of Race Relations, 1987.
Hbk £4.00

EC index : an abstracting and indexing guide to publications and documents of the European Communities. – Maastricht : Europe Data, 1985-.

EC seventh company law directive on consolidated accounts : a consultative document on implementation / Department of Trade and Industry. – London : The Department, 1985.
39,17p.
Includes the text of the directive.

Eccles, George →Tolley's Companies Act : 1980.

—Tolley's Companies Act : 1981 / Jenny Cox. – Croydon : Tolley.
520p.
ISBN 0854590587 Hbk £11.95
ISBN 0854590390 Pbk £8.95

Ecclesiastical Cause papers at York : files transmitted on appeal 1500-1883 / W.J. Sheils. – York : University of York, Borthwick Institute of Historical Research, 1983.
xiv,135p; 25cm.
Includes index.
Pbk

Ecclesiastical Law, 4 Vols. – 8th ed. Repr. of 1824 ed. – Abingdon : Professional Books.
Hbk £75.00

Eckhoff, Torstein →Continuity and development in law and society.

Ecology : political institutions and legislation : environmental law in the USSR / Oleg Kolbasov. – Moscow : Progress, 1983.
215p; 21cm.
Translation of: Ekologia.
ISBN 0714719277 £3.95

Economic analysis of a performers' right / Steven Globerman and Mitchell P. Rothman. – Ottawa, Ont. : Consumer and Corporate Affairs Canada, 1981.
111 p.; 28 cm.
Bibliography: p. 109-111.

Economic and Social Committee of the European Communities →European environment policy : air, water, waste management.

Economic and social powers of the European Union and the member states : subordinate or coordinate relationship? / by John Pinder. – Florence : European University Institute, 1985.
47p.

Economic and Social Research Council → Socio-legal studies and social welfare.

Economic approach to law / edited by Paul Burrows, Cento G. Veljanovski. – London : Butterworths, 1981.
xi,343p; 25cm.
This book of essays provides an introduction to economic aspects of legal analysis. The contributors discuss the economic framework underlying the substance and procedures of the legal system.
ISBN 0408106867 Hbk £27.50
ISBN 0408106859 Pbk £12.95

Economic Approach to Property Value. – Auckland : Legal Research Foundation, 1981.
35p.
Pbk £5.50

Economic Council of
Competition and solvency : a framework for financial regulation / Economic Council of Canada. – Ottawa : Minister of Supply and Services, 1986.
x,46p.
ISBN 0660121921

Economic crime / European Committee on Crime Problems. – Strasbourg : Council of Europe, 1981.
75p.
Recommendation No. R(81)12, adopted by the Committee of Ministers on 25 June 1981. At head of cover title: Council of Europe, Legal Affairs.

Economic crisis and crime / European Committee on Crime Problems. – Strasbourg : Council of Europe, 1985.
157p; 21cm.
At head of cover-title: Council of Europe, Legal affairs.
ISBN 9287107807

Economic crisis, trade unions and the state / edited by Otto Jacobi ... et al. – London : Croom Helm, 1986.
295p; 23cm.
Includes bibliographies and index. Includes papers translated from German and Italian.
ISBN 0709914474 £19.95

Economic History Society →Old Poor Law, 1795-1834.

Economic importance of copyright / Jennifer Phillips. – London : Common Law Institute of Intellectual Property, 1985.
38p.

Economic negligence. – London : Sweet & Maxwell, 1985.
ISBN 0459364707 Hbk £40.00

Economic negligence : the recovery of pure economic loss / by Bruce Feldthusen. – Toronto, Canada : Carswell Legal Publications, 1984.
xxvi, 306 p.; 24 cm.
Includes bibliographical references and indexes.
ISBN 0459364707 Hbk £40

Economic Offences in EEC Law : With Special Reference to English and German Law. – Kehl am Rhein : Norbert Paul Engel, 1983.
228p.
ISBN 3883570273 Hbk £48.00

Economic relationships among states : a further study in international sociology / Evan Luard. – London : Macmillan, 1984.
xiii,328p.
ISBN 0333294777

Economic Rights of Women in Ancient Greece. – Edinburgh : Edinburgh University Press.
180p.
ISBN 0852244231 Pbk £7.50

Economics : ACCA Study Text 1.3. – London : BPP.
ISBN 0862772370 Pbk £12.95

Economics and sociology of rural communities : East-West perspectives / edited by Daniel Thorniley. – Aldershot : Gower, 1987.
229p; 23cm.
Includes bibliographies.
ISBN 0566054299 £19.50

Economics and the Banks' Role in the Economy. – Pitman.
ISBN 0273028820 Pbk £6.95

Economics of 1992 : EC Commission's Assessment of Economic Effects of Completing. – Oxford : Oxford University Press.
ISBN 00198286813 Hbk £27.50
ISBN 00198772947 Pbk £12.95

Economics of Bureaucracy and Statutory Authorities / Warren Hogan. – Turramura : Centre for Independent Studies.
112p.
ISBN 094976910X Hbk £5.95

Economics of consumer protection : a critique of the Chicago School case against intervention / A.J. Duggan. – Adelaide : Adelaide Law Review Association, 1982.
xii,151p.
Includes index.
ISBN 0908448015 Hbk

Economics of Crime and Law Enforcement. – London : Macmillan, 1983.
228p.
ISBN 0333282000 Hbk £33.00

Economics of Foreign Exchange / Sanderson. – Cambridge : Woodhead-Faulkner, 1988.
ISBN 0859413640 Hbk £40.00

Economics of multinational enterprise / Neil Hood, Stephen Young. – 5th impression. – London : Longman, 1984.
xv,412p.
This ed. originally published: 1979. Bibliography: p.393-407. - Includes index.

Economics of Poverty and Income Distribution. – Toronto : Butterworths.
192p.
ISBN 0409834750 Hbk

Economics of the Common Market / Dennis Swann. – 6th ed. – Harmondsworth : Penguin, 1988.
Previous ed.: 1984.
ISBN 0140227814

Economics of the Euro-market : history, theory and policy / R. B. Johnston. – London : Macmillan, 1983.
x,321p.
Bibliography: p308-316.
ISBN 0333334183

Economides, Kim →Legal services in rural Britain : access, accessibility and need.

—Spatial analysis of legal systems : towards a geography of law? / Kim Economides, Mark Blacksell and Charles Watkins. – Exeter : University of Exeter, 1985.
49p. – (Working paper).
Includes bibliographical references.

—Studying rural lawyers : research strategy and context / Kim Economides, Charles Watkins and Mark Blacksell. – Exeter : University of Exeter, 1985.
66,9p. – (Working paper).
→ Use of the law list to assess the distribution and characteristics of solicitors in England and Wales.

Economist Publications Pocket Guide Business Taxes. – London : Edward Arnold.
ISBN 0340499138 Hbk £15.00

Economy of the Principality of Liechtenstein / edited by Walter Kranz : translated from the German by John Anthony Nicholls. – Liechtenstein : Government Press and Information Office, 1982.
154 p.

Ecrits Juridiques du Moyen Age Occidental. – London : Variorum.
ISBN 086078228X Hbk £32.00

Eddey, K. J.
English legal system / by Keith J. Eddey. – 4th ed. – London : Sweet & Maxwell, 1987.
xv,196p. – (Concise college texts).
Previous ed.: 1982. Bibliography: p189-190. - Includes index.
ISBN 0421354003 Hbk £13.50
ISBN 0421354100 Pbk £7.50

Edelman, D.
Statistics for property people. – London : Estates Gazette, 1986.
ISBN 0728200929 Pbk £14.00

Edeson, W.R.
Legal Regime of Fisheries in the Caribbean Region / J.F. Pulvenis. – Berlin : Springer-Verlag, 1983.
x, 204p.
Pbk £43.00

Edey, Harold C. →Companies Act 1981 : text and commentary.

Edgar →Statutes Law.

Edginton
Legal Structures for Voluntary Organisations / Bates. – London : Bedford Square Press, 1984.
ISBN 0719911168 Pbk £1.95

Edicts. – 8 v. – Calabar : Min. of Home Affairs and Information, 1968.
Published as supplements to the South-Eastern State of Nigeria gazette. Includes subsidiary legislation. This library lacks 1975. Numbering begins anew each year.

Edinburgh for lawyers. – 2nd. – Edinburgh : Green (W.) & Son.
Includes a map of legal Edinburgh, historical background, the courts with diagrams of the court system, solicitors, and other related matters.
ISBN 0414008561 Pbk

Edinburgh University →Fourteen to Eighteen : The Changing Pattern of Schooling in Scotland.

Edinger, Elizabeth →Office of sheriff.

Edited versions of selected papers from the international conference on 'Logic, Informatics, Law', Florence, Italy, April 1981
Vol.1 : Artificial intelligence and legal information systems : Constantino Ciampi, editor / Constantino Ciampi. – Amsterdam : North Holland Publishing, 1982.
xii,476p.
Bibliographies.
vol.2 : Deontic logic, computational linguistics, and legal information systems : Antonio A. Martino; editor. – 1982.
xli,518p.
Bibliographies.

Edlund, Sten →Labour law research in twelve countries.

Edmonds, Gerhard
Guidelines for National Implementation of the Convention on International Trade in Endangered Species of Wild Fauna and Flora-Cities. – Gland : International Union for Conservation of Nature and Natural Resources, 1981.
148p.
Hbk £18.00

Edmonds, James
International timesharing. – 2nd ed. – London : Services to Lawyers, 1986.
xix,591p.
Previous ed.: 1984. Bibliography: p.579-581. - Includes index. Includes precedents. Subtitle on cover: a review of United Kingdom law and that of other relevant jurisdictions in relation to timeshare schemes and purchases, including extensive precedents.
ISBN 095041767X

—International timesharing / by James Edmonds. – 1st ed. – London : Services To Lawyers, 1984.
374p.
Bibliography: p.363-365. - Includes index. Includes precedents. Subtitle on cover: a review of United Kingdom law and that of other relevant jurisdictions in relation to timeshare schemes and purchases, including extensive precedents for use in the United Kingdom.
ISBN 0950417653

—International timesharing. – 2nd ed. – London : Sweet & Maxwell, 1986.
ISBN 095041767X Pbk £24.50

—Time-Sharing . – London : Kogan Page.
ISBN 185091463X Pbk £6.95

Edmund-Davies, Herbert Edmund
Bulwark of the law / the Right Honourable Lord Edmund-Davies. – Cardiff : Law Department, UWIST, 1984.
20p.

Edmunds → Alteration/Conversion Of Houses.

Ednie, H. H. → Australian Company Law, 4 Vols.
→ Australian Company Law Reports (ACLR).

EDP systems for court adminstration : proceedings of the 3rd Colloquy on the Use of Computers in the Administration of Justice, Strasbourg, 3-5 November. – Strasbourg : Council of Europe, 1983.
222,viiip; 30cm.
At head of cover title: Legal Affairs.
ISBN 9287102902

EDP systems for the administration of courts and related systems : proceedings of the fifth Colloquy on the Use of Computers in the Administration of Justice, Madrid, 14-16 October 1986. – Strasbourg : Council of Europe, 1987.
314p; 29cm.
At head of cover title: Legal affairs.
ISBN 9287110816

Edstein, John V. → Superannuation and Retirement Benefits in Australia.

Education Act : Elementary and Secondary Schools and Schools for Trainable Retarded Pupils. – Office of the Legislative Assembly (Ontario). – Ontario : Ontario Government Publications Service, 1983.
15p.
Hbk £0.75

Education Act : Supervised Alternative Learning for Excused Pupils. – Office of the Legislative Assembly (Ontario). – Ontario : Ontario Government Publications Service, 1983.
3p.
Hbk £0.50

Education Act : Supervisory Officers. – Office of the Legislative Assembly (Ontario). – Ontario : Ontario Government Publications Service, 1983.
6p.
Hbk £0.50

Education and information in the field of human rights : activities of the Council of Europe / Secretariat memorandum prepared by the Directorate of Human Rights. – Strasbourg : Council of Europe, 1987.
11p. – (H (87) 5).
At head of cover title: Committee of Experts for the Promotion of Education and Information in the Field of Human Rights (DH-ED).

Education and Poverty in the United Kingdom : A Background Paper. – London : Policy Studies Institute, 1981.
Hbk £3.60

Education and the law. – London : Longman Professional, 1986.
ISBN 090031320X Pbk £10.95

Education law : an outline of the law relating to the public system of education in England and Wales / K.P. Poole. – London : Sweet & Maxwell, 1988.
lviii,355p; 26cm.
Sets out the framework of the education system, and gives an account of the law on central and local administration. Deals with schools from nursery onwards, up to further education establishments. Considers issues such as awards, and grants, the Manpower Services Commission, adult education and freedom of speech. Includes the Education (no 2) Act 1986, and the Teachers Pay and Conditions Act 1987.
ISBN 0421328304 £30.00

Education law in Canada / A. Wayne MacKay. – Toronto : Emond-Montgomery, 1984.
xxiv,416p.
Bibliography: p.397-407. - Includes index.
ISBN 0920722121 Hbk £45.00

Educational conflict and the law / David Milman. – London : Croom Helm, 1986.
160p; 23cm.
Includes index.
ISBN 0709935218 £16.95

Educational Law in Canada. – Aurora : Canada Law Book Co, 1984.
250p. – (Text Books-Civil).
Hbk £45.00

Educational Rights of Exceptional Children in Canada. – Agincourt : Carswell, 1988.
144p.
Hbk £25.00

Edward, David
Draft Treaty establishing the European Union : report on the United Kingdom / by David Edward, Richard McAllister, Robert Lane. – Florence : European University Institute, 1985.
40p.

Edwards
Accountancy : Study Text for Banking Students / Mellett. – Folkestone : Bankers Books.
ISBN 0852972091 Pbk £14.60
→ Cassell's UK Tax Guide 1988-89 : Comprehensive Aspects of Taxation.
→ Common Man's Guide to the Common Market.
—Credit Insurance / Briggs. – Cambridge : Woodhead-Faulkner, 1987.
ISBN 0859411761 Hbk £40.00
—International trade finance / Weston. – North Ryde : Law Book Co, 1986.
ISBN 0455203504 Pbk £11.25
—Introduction to Accountancy / Mellett. – London : Chapman Publishers.
ISBN 1853960209 Pbk £13.95

Edwards, B.
Conflict of Laws. – Durban : Professional Publishers, 1984.
ISBN 0409026743 Pbk

Edwards, Chris
Fragmented world : competing perspectives on trade, money and crisis / Chris Edwards. – London : Methuen, 1985.
xvi,350p; 23cm.
Bibliography: p310-333. - Includes index.
ISBN 0416733905 Hbk £14.95
ISBN 0416734006 Pbk £6.95
→ Guide to the Data Protection Act : its implications for business.
→ Information technology & the law.

Edwards, Eric
Police and complaints / Eric Edwards. – London : G.L.C., 1983.
12p. – (Research documents guide).
ISBN 0716813661
—Police and the community / Eric Edwards. – London : G.L.C., 1983.
20p. – (Research documents guide).
ISBN 0716813688
—Race and the police / Eric Edwards. – London : G.L.C., 1983.
21p. – (Research documents guide).
ISBN 071681367X
→ Urban riots and public order : a select bibliography, 1975-1985.

Edwards, Eric J.
Cases on evidence in Australia / by Eric J. Edwards. – 3rd ed. – Sydney : Law Book Co., 1981.
xxix,795p.
Includes index.
ISBN 0455202443 Pbk
ISBN 0455202435
—Cases on the Criminal Code / R.A. Hayes. – North Ryde : Law Book Co, 1984.
xxiii, 739p.
ISBN 0455204276 Hbk £70.50
ISBN 0455204284 Pbk £54.50

Edwards, Gwen M. → Environmental Law, British Columbia Handbook, 1984.

Edwards, J.R.
History of Financial Accounting. – Routledge.
ISBN 0415004322 Pbk £35.00

Edwards, John
Positive discrimination, social justice and social policy : moral scrutiny of a policy practice / John Edwards : foreword by Lord Scarman. – London : Tavistock, 1986.
x,243p; 22cm.
Bibliography: p222-235. - Includes index.
ISBN 0422614009 Hbk £19.95
ISBN 0422789909 Pbk £8.95

Edwards, John Ll. J.
Attorney general, politics and the public interest / by John Ll. J. Edwards. – London : Sweet & Maxwell, 1984.
xxxi,533p; 26cm.
Bibliography: p491-498. - Includes index.
ISBN 0421301805 £30.00

Edwards, M.
Executive Survival : To Your Legal Rights. – London : Kogan Page.
ISBN 1850913641 Hbk £12.95
—Understanding computer contracts. – London : Waterlow, 1983.
ISBN 0803091346 Pbk £7.95

Edwards, Martin → Computer contracts : the deeper issues : conference organised by the Society for Computers and Law on Monday 19th November 1984 at the Royal Garden Hotel, London, W.8.
—Understanding dismissal law / Martin Edwards. – London : Waterlow, 1984.
xiv,188p; 21cm. – (Waterlow's business library).
Includes index.
ISBN 0080391745 Pbk £7.95

Edwards, P. K.
Industrial relations : challenges and prospects : a report on the Warwick conference of March 1986 / P.K.Edwards. – Coventry : Industrial Relations Research Unit, School of Industrial and Business Studies, University of Warwick, 1986.

Edwards, Ray
Model Procedural Agreements. – London : Industrial Society.
Hbk £3.20

Edwards, Richard
Tax for the Self-Employed. – 2nd ed. – London : Oyez Longman, 1983.
ISBN 085120712X Hbk £3.50

Edwards, Susan S. M.
Female sexuality and the law : a study of constructs of female sexuality as they inform statute and legal procedure / Susan S.M. Edwards. – Oxford : Robertson, 1981.
195p; 23cm.
Bibliography: p183-190. - Includes index.
ISBN 085520382X Hbk £12.50
ISBN 0855203854 Pbk £4.95
→ Gender, sex and the law.
—Women on trial : a study of the female suspect, defendant and offender in the criminal law and criminal justice system / Susan S.M. Edwards. – Manchester : Manchester University Press, 1984.
1v.
Bibliography: p227-236. - Includes index.
ISBN 0719009952 £14.50

Edwards, Valerie → Manes Organized Advocacy : a Manual for the Litigation Practitioner.

EEC and intellectual property / Diana Guy and Guy I.F. Leigh. – London : Sweet & Maxwell, 1981.
xxiv,375p; 25cm.
Includes index.
ISBN 0421234202 £30.00

EEC Anti-Dumping and other Trade Protection laws / Bellis. – London : CCH, 1985.
ISBN 0863250602 Pbk £16.50

EEC Antitrust Compliance. – London : European Business, 1986.
ISBN 094262055 Pbk £36.00

EEC antitrust procedure / by C.S. Kerse. – 2nd ed. – London : European Law Centre, 1988.
xlii,398p; 26cm.
Previous ed.: 1981. Includes index.
ISBN 0907451160

EEC banking law / by Marc Dassesse and Stuart Isaacs. – London : Lloyd's of London, 1985.
xix,184p; 23cm.
ISBN 0907432808

EEC competition law / D.G. Goyder. – Oxford : Clarendon Press, 1988.
xxxi,447p.
Account of the substantive law, and an assessment of the historical development and overall effectiveness of the competition policy. Suggests ways of improving co-ordination and implementation of competition policy. Examines the foundations of the last thirty years, and how they can be built upon.
ISBN 0198254032 Pbk £18.95
ISBN 0198255357 Hbk £45

EEC competition law : business issues and legal principles in Common Market antitrust cases / Utz Toepke. – 1. – New York : Wiley, 1982.
27cm.
Bibliography: p907-909. - Includes index.
ISBN 0471093661 Llf

EEC consumer law. – Bruxelles : Story-Scientia, 1986.
xviii, 432p.
Bibliography: p.391-424. - Includes index.
ISBN 9065442820

EEC Customs Law / Ivo Onkelinx. – Oxford : ESC Publishing Ltd, 1986.
ISBN 0906214297 Llf £90.00

EEC Employment Cases from Common Market Law Reports. – London : European Law Centre.
ISBN 0907451217 Hbk £95.00

EEC environmental policy and Britain / Nigel Haigh. – 2nd ed. – Harlow : Longman, 1987.
250p; 24cm.
Previous ed.: 1984.
ISBN 0582016096 Pbk £25.00

EEC Financial Services Cases from Common Market Law Reports. – London : European Law Centre.
ISBN 0907451241 Hbk £105.00

EEC fisheries law / R.R. Churchill. – Dordrecht : M. Nijhoff, 1987.
xxviii, 299 p.; 25 cm.
Includes index. Bibliography: p. 285-289.
ISBN 9024735459 Hbk £165.00

EEC Law / James Dinnage. – 2nd ed. – London : Sweet & Maxwell, 1981.
lvi,531p; 25cm.
Previous ed.: 1973. Includes index.
ISBN 0421260904 Hbk £25.00
ISBN 0421261005 Pbk £16.00

EEC law and Nordic commercial relations with the Communities / edited by Zacharias Sundstrom ... et al. – Helsinki : Finnish Asssociation for European Law, 1985.
358p.
Proceedings of a seminar held at Hanasaari, Helsinki, 2-4 May 1984. Includes bibliographical references.
ISBN 9519960309

EEC Law in Ireland. – London : Butterworths, 1988.
ISBN 0862052378 Hbk £35.00

EEF Employment Guide. – London : Engineering Employers Federation, 1986.
203p.
Hbk £20.00

Eekelaar, John → Divorce mediation and the legal process.

Eekelaar, John M, et al
Aging world : dilemmas and challenges for law and social policy / edited by John Eekelaar and D. Pearl. – Oxford : OUP, 1989.
900.
Critical examination on an international basis of the problems facing legal and social systems due to an increasing number of elderly within the world's population.
Lawyers, demographers, economists, sociologists and political scientists interested in problems of aging populations
ISBN 0198254091 Pbk £39.50
→ Care proceedings : a practical guide for social workers, health visitors and others.

→ Children and divorce : economic factors.

—Family law and social policy / John Eekelaar. – 2nd ed. – London : Weidenfeld and Nicolson, 1984.
xviii,263p.
Includes index. Bibliography: p241-255.
ISBN 0297782746

—Hague Convention on the Civil Aspects of International Child Abduction : explanatory documentation / prepared for Commonwealth jurisdictions by J.M. Eekelaar in association with the Commonwealth Secretariat. – London : Commonwealth Secretariat, 1981.
v,70p.
ISBN 0850921961

—Maintenance after divorce / John Eekelaar and Mavis Maclean. – Oxford : Clarendon, 1985.
x,171p; 22cm.
Bibliography: p161-168. - Includes index.
ISBN 0198255306 Pbk £19.50
ISBN 0198255292 £8.95

—Maintenance after Divorce / Mavis Maclean. – Oxford : Oxford University Press, 1986.
ISBN 0198255292 Pbk £9.95
ISBN 0198255306 Hbk £22.50

→ Oxford essays in jurisprudence : third series.

→ Protection of children : state intervention and family life.

→ Resolution of family conflict : comparative legal perspectives.

Eenvormige hofreels / deur C.J.M. Nathan, M. Barnett, A. Brink. – 3e uitg. / deur C.J.M. Nathan en M. Barnett. – Kaapstad : Juta, 1984.
lxii, 794 p.; 26 cm.
Title on added t.p.: Uniform rules of court. Afrikaans and English. Includes indexes.
ISBN 0702114154 R84.00

Effect of a caveat on a mortgagee's power of sale : report of the Property Law and Equity Reform Committee. – Wellington : Government Printer, 1981.
7,2p.

Effect of disputed debts, set-offs and counterclaims on winding-up and bankruptcy petitions / by R. J. Calnan. – Auckland : Legal Research Foundation, 1981.
55p.
ISBN 0908581165

Effect of treaties in domestic law / the United Kingdom National Committee of Comparative Law : edited by Francis G. Jacobs. – London : Sweet & Maxwell, 1987.
250p; 22cm.
Survey of the effects of treaties in the domestic law of Belgium, Denmark, France, Germany, Italy, the Netherlands, the United Kingdom and the United States. Examines the problem of a states individual treaty responsibilities in conflict with its collective responsibility within the framework of an international organisation. Covers the Hague Convention on Private International Law.
ISBN 0421378700

Effect on English domestic law of membership of the European Communities and of ratification of the European Convention on Human Rights / edited by M.P. Furmston, Roger Kerridge, B.E. Sufrin. – The Hague : M. Nijhoff, 1983.
viii, 428p.
Papers by members of the University of Bristol Faculty of Law in celebration of the fiftieth anniversary of the Faculty.
ISBN 9024728118 Hbk £130.00

Effective Communication for the Accountant. – London : Kogan Page.
ISBN 1850915202 Pbk £5.95

Effective dispute resolution for the international commercial lawyer / Dennis Campbell, Peter Summerfield. – Kluwer Law and Taxation, 1989.
240.
Covers practical remedies under German law, arbitration and the enforcement of arbitration awards, mediation-arbitration and other alternatives for resolving international commercial disputes, and government litigation.
ISBN 9065444157 Pbk £31/Dfl 98

Effective Insurance : A Guide For Buyer and Seller / Paul Braithwaite. – Toronto : Butterworths, 1984.
352p.
Topics covered include insurers, agents, brokers, reinsurers, various types of coverage, policies, riders, endorsements (with appropriate illustrations) and specific advice on minimizing corporate insurance costs.
ISBN 0409872857 Hbk £39.95

Effective Parliamentary Control of European Finances. – European Parliament. – 3rd ed. – Kirchberg : European Parliament, 1989.
Hbk

Effective Planning Appeals. – Oxford : Blackwell Scientific, 1988.
ISBN 0632021241 Hbk

Effective Retention of Title Clauses. – Oxford : Blackwell Scientific, 1986.
ISBN 0003830748 Hbk £19.95

Effectiveness of Judicial Protection and the Constitutional Order. – Dordrecht : Kluwer.
228p.
ISBN 9065441522 Pbk £70.00

Effectiveness of the Forensic Science Service / by Malcolm Ramsay. – London : H.M.S.O., 1987.
v,93p; 25cm.
Examines the extent to which the work of the FSS assists the police and courts in solving crimes.
ISBN 0113408420

Effects of crime and the work of victims support schemes / Mike Maguire and Claire Corbett. – Aldershot : Gower, 1987.
xiii,276p; 23cm.
Bibliography: p263-276.
ISBN 0566054124 £17.50

Effects of Monetary and Fiscal Policy : A Contribution to Pure Theory. – Stockholm : Almqvist & Wiksell.
74p.
Hbk £2850.00

Effects of the various international human rights instruments providing a mechanism for individual communications on the machinery of protection established under the European Convention on Human Rights : Secretariat memorandum / prepared by the Directorate of Human Rights of the Council of Europe. – Strasburg : Council of Europe, 1985.
25p. – (H(85)3).

Egan, Patricia
Alberta Legal Telephone Directory : 1986. – Aurora : Canada Law Book Co.
This telephone directory is arranged by name, listing every lawyer and law firm in Alberta. Each listing includes address, telephone number and firm association. Additional entries include, among others, listings for: Courts, Judges, and Court Officials; Land Registration Districts; Legal Services; Law Libraries and Universities; and Provincial Government Departments.
Pbk For 1-5 Copies 9.00 each

—Atlantic Legal Directory : 1985-1986. – Aurora : Canada Law Book Co, 1985.
Hbk For 1-5 copies 8.50

—Atlantic Legal Telephone Directory. – Aurora : Canada Law Book Co.
– (Directories).
The Atlantic Legal Telephone Directory unifies law-related offices of the four Atlantic Provinces into a single means of access. Included are listings for lawyers, law firms, law societies, courts, legal aid offices, provincial government departments and other key departments and offices.
Hbk £1-5 copies 8.50 ea.

—British Columbia Legal Telephone Directory : 1985. – Aurora : Canada Law Book Co.
This volume, arranged by name, lists every lawyer and law firm in British Columbia. Each listing includes name, firm association, address and telephone. Listings are also provided for, among others: Courts, Judges and Court Officials; Land Registration Districts; Legal Services; and Law Libraries and Universities.
Hbk For 1-5 Copies 9.50 each

—Canadian Law List. – Aurora : Canada Law Book Co.
1882p.
Hbk £63.50

—Lawyer's Phone Book (Ontario). – Aurora : Canada Law Book Co.
– (Directories).
This directory, published each year in the early spring, lists every individual lawyer and law office in Ontario, complete with telephone number, street address and postal code. Also included are the addresses and telephone numbers of all Provincial, County, and District judicial offices, Legal Aid Offices, Ontario Government Officials and others.
Hbk £1-5 copies 26.50 ea.

Egger, Sandra J. → Issues in Criminal Justice Administration.

Eggleston, Richard
Evidence, proof and probability / Sir Richard Eggleston. – 2nd ed. – London : Weidenfeld and Nicolson, 1983.
xiv,274p; 22cm.
Previous ed.: 1978. Bibliography: p262-266. - Includes index.
ISBN 0297782622 Hbk £16.50
ISBN 0297782630 Pbk £7.95
→ Well and truly tried : essays on evidence in honour of Sir Richard Eggleston.

Egypt : violations of human rights / an Amnesty International report. – London : Amnesty International Publications, 1983.
38p.
ISBN 0862100526

Ehindero, S. G.
Police and the law in Nigeria / S.G. Ehindero. – Lagos : Times Press, 1986.
xxv,158p.
Bibliography: p.155. - Includes index.
ISBN 9783023608

Ehrlich, David S.
Nova Scotia Annotated Rules of Practice. – Agincourt : Carswell.
This single volume looseleaf is arranged in eight sections and is published in cooperation with the Law Foundation of Nova Scotia. It consists of a Table of Contents, Judicature Act, Rules of Practice, Forms, Practice Memoranda, Index to Rules, and Index to Forms.
Pbk £71.50

Eide, Asbjrn
Frontiers of Human Rights Education / Marek Thee. – Oslo : Norwegian University Press, 1985.
148p.
ISBN 8200067769 Pbk £95.00

Eight Peak Index of Mass Spectra of Compounds of Forensic Interest / C. Brown. – Edinburgh : Scottish Academic Press Ltd, 1983.
296p.
ISBN 0707303419 Hbk £50.00

Eighth Annual Report of the Lay Observer 1982 : Solicitor's Act 1974. – London : HMSO, 1983.
ISBN 0102323836 Hbk £2.25

Eighth report : oil pollution of the sea / Royal Commission on Environmental Pollution : chairman: Sir Hans Kornberg. – London : HMSO, 1981.
ISBN 0101835809

Eighth report to Parliament on subordinate legislation : concerning Metropolitan Fire Brigades Superannuation (Board Scheme) (Further Amendment) Regulations 1986 ... / Legal and Constitutional Committee. – Melbourne : Government Printer, 1987.
v,4p.

Einhorn, N.
Patent Licensing Transactions. – Matthew Bender, 1968.
ISBN 0000999079 Hbk £112.00

Eirenarcha (1581). – Reprint. – Professional Books, 1986.
– (Classical English Law Texts Ser.).
ISBN 0862053242 Hbk £24.75

Eisenschitz, Tamara S.
Inventors' information guide / by Tamara S. Eisenschitz and Jeremy Phillips. – 2nd edition. – London : The Intellectual Property Law Unit Centre for Commercial Law Studies, 1985.
viii, 100p.
ISBN 0951066404

Eissen, Marc-Andre
Case-law on Article 5 of the Convention for the Protection of Human Rights and Fundamental Freedoms / by Marc-Andre Eissen. – Strasbourg : European Court of Human Rights, 1986.
40p.
ISBN 9287107769

Ejaz
Code of Criminal Procedure, 3 Vols. – Allahabad : Orient Law House, 1984.
Hbk £135.00
—Motor Vehicles Act, 1939 : With All State Amendments, 2 Vols. – Allahabad : Ashoka Law House, 1987.
1,600p.
Hbk £320.00

Ejectment for non-payment of rent / by J. A. Dowling : with a supplement for the Republic of Ireland by G. McCormack. – Belfast : Faculty of Law, the Queen's University of Belfast, 1986.
xvii,84p.
ISBN 0853892695

Ejectments in Ireland. – London : Butterworths.
ISBN 0862053366 Hbk £35.50

Ekblom, Paul →Contacts between police and public : findings from the British crime survey.
—Police response to calls from the public / Paul Ekblom and Kevin Heal. – London : Home Office, 1982.
v,95p; 30cm.
Bibliography: p85-88.
ISBN 0862520657 Pbk
→ Police-public encounters.

Ekstedt, John W.
Corrections in Canada : Policy and Practice / Griffiths. – Toronto : Butterworths, 1984.
432p.
ISBN 0409834548 Pbk £23.95

El-Gemayel, A.E.
Lebanese Legal System. – London : Eurospan.
ISBN 0935328289 Hbk £107.50

El-Sayed, Hussein M.
Maritime regulations of Saudi Arabia / Hussein M. El-Sayed. – London : Graham & Trotman, 1987.
250p; 24cm.
Includes bibliography and index.
ISBN 0860107361 £70.00

El Sheikh, Fath el Rahman Abdalla
Legal regime of foreign private investment in the Sudan and Saudi Arabia : a case study of developing countries / Fath el Rahman Abdalla El Sheikh. – Cambridge : Cambridge University Press in association with Khartoum University Press, 1984.
xxxix,462p; 23cm. – (Cambridge studies in international and comparative law).
Bibliography: p446-458. - Includes index.
ISBN 0521252865

Elagab, Omer Yousif
Legality of non-forcible counter-measures in international law / Omer Yousif Elagab. – Oxford Oxfordshire : Clarendon Press, 1988.
Includes index. Bibliography: p.
ISBN 019825590X
—Non forcible counter measures in international law. – Oxford : Oxford University Press, 1988.
ISBN 019825590X Hbk

Elbra, R. A.
Implications of the Data Protection Act / R.A. Elbra. – Manchester : NCC Publications, 1985.
75p.
Includes bibliography.
ISBN 085012476X Pbk £5.95

Elder, A J
Guide to Building Regulations 1985. – London : Architectural Press, 1986.
ISBN 0851398448 Pbk £16.95
—Guide to the Building Regulations 1985. – 8th ed. – London : Architectural Press, 1986.
256p : Illus.
ISBN 0851398448 Pbk £19.95
—Guide to the Building Regulations 1985 for England and Wales : Butterworths Architecture Library of Building Control. – 2nd ed. – London : Butterworths.
ISBN 0408500131 Pbk £25.00
—Guide to the Building Regulations Nineteen Seventy-Six. – 7th ed. – London : Architectural Press, 1981.
224p : Illus.
ISBN 0851398502 Pbk £11.95
—Guide To The Second Amendment Nineteen Eighty-One : Supplement to Guide to the Building Regulations 1976. – 7th ed. – London : Architectural Press, 1982.
32p : Illus.
ISBN 0851398499 Pbk £4.50

Eldon, Ruth
International Business Lawyer. – London : Sweet & Maxwell.
Hbk £70.00
—International Legal Practitioner. – London : Sweet & Maxwell.
Hbk £40.00

Election Law / Little. – London : Shaw & Sons, 1984.
ISBN 0721903444 Hbk £85.00

Election Law in Canada : the Law and Procedure of Federal, Provincial and Territorial Elections, 2 Vols. – Butterworths, 1987.
1,632p.
Examines legal status and registration of political parties and candidates, electoral boundaries and representation, the calling of elections, election officials, compiling and revising the lists of voters, general conduct of elections, voting procedures, election results and recounts, election offences and corrupt practices, and controverted elections.
ISBN 0409816000 Hbk £170.00

Elections Laws of Malaysia. – Kuala Lumpur : International Law Books Services.
Hbk £25.00

Electrical Inspectorate Act, 1983 (Act 277) and Electrical Inspectorate Regulations, 1984 (P.U.(A) 313/1984). – Kuala Lumpur : International Law Books Services.
Hbk £15.00

Electricity Act, 1949 (Act 116). – Kuala Lumpur : International Law Books Services.
Hbk £10.00

Electricity Laws and Rules. – 2nd ed. – Allahabad : Law Publishers, 1983.
Hbk £13.50

Electronic banking : the legal implications / edited by R.M. Goode. – London : Institute of Bankers, 1985.
xxi,142p; 22cm.
Conference proceedings.
ISBN 0852971303 £9.95

Electronic Banking and the Consumer : the European Dimension. – Policy Studies Institute.
ISBN 0853744394 Pbk £4.95

Electronic banking and the law / by Anu Arora. – London : IBC Financial, 1988.
188p.
Includes index.
ISBN 1852710403 £65.00

Electronic funds transfer / Dimitris N. Chorafas. – London : Butterworths, 1988.
xi,361p; 24cm.
Includes index.
ISBN 0406101000 £38.00

Electronic library : the international journal for minicomputer, microcomputer and software applications in libraries. – Oxford : Learned Information, 1983.
ISBN 02640473

Electronic Pirates : DIY Crime of the Century / Lipman. – Routledge.
ISBN 0415007399 Pbk £7.95
ISBN 0415007380 Hbk £25.00

Electronic surveillance / Law Reform Commission of Canada. – Ottawa : The Commission, 1986.
109,121p; 25cm. – (Working paper).
Added t.p. in French: La surveillance electronique. Cover title: Criminal law - electronic surveillance. Pages numbered in opposite directions. English and French.
ISBN 0662538862

Electronic trade payments / by Michael Rowe. – London : International Business Communications, 1987.
256p; 25cm. – (The IBC financial technology series).
Includes bibliography and index.
ISBN 1852710152 Pbk £65.00

Electronic treasury management. – Cambridge : Woodhead-Faulkner, 1984.
ISBN 0859412733 Hbk £40.00

Elementary statistical methods / G. Barrie Wetherill. – 3rd ed. – London : Chapman and Hall, 1982.
356p; 24cm. – (Science paperbacks).
Previous ed.: 1972. Bibliography: p348-351. - Includes index.
ISBN 0412240009 Pbk £7.95

Elements of Banking 1 and 2. – 2nd ed. – London : Financial Training.
ISBN 0906322999 Pbk £7.95

Elements of Banking / Ford. – 2nd ed. – Pitman.
ISBN 0273029525 Pbk £9.95

Elements of Banking. – 5th ed. – Routledge.
ISBN 0415034752 Hbk £6.95

Elements of Banking. – 5th ed. – London : Sweet & Maxwell, 1986.
ISBN 0416383009 Pbk £5.95

Elements of Banking. – 3rd ed. – Plymouth : Macdonald & Evans, 1985.
ISBN 071210657X Pbk £4.95

Elements of Banking Law. – Delhi : Dhanpat Rai and Sons.
Hbk £10.00

Elements of Banking Law. – New Delhi : Kalyani Publishers, 1987.
ISBN 8170960185 Hbk £25.00

Elements of Cargo Insurance / Geoffrey Whitehead. – Cambridge : Woodhead-Faulkner, 1983.
ISBN 085941227X Pbk £5.25

Elements of Company Law / K.C. Garg. – New Delhi : Kalyani Publishers.
Hbk £18.00

Elements of drafting / by E.L. Piesse. – 6th ed. – Sydney : Law Book Co., 1981.
xv,154p; 19cm.
Bibliography: p.ix-x. - Includes index.
ISBN 0455202559

Elements of export law / Geoffrey Whitehead. – Cambridge : Woodhead-Faulkner, 1983.
xiv,255p; 22cm.
Bibliography: p246. - Includes index.
ISBN 0859412288 Hbk

Elements of Export Marketing. – Cambridge : Woodhead-Faulkner, 1984.
ISBN 0859412334 Pbk £7.95

Elements of Export Marketing and Management. – London : Sweet & Maxwell, 1984.
Hbk £17.50

Elements of Export Marketing and Management. – London : Chapman & Hall, 1984.
ISBN 0412163500 Pbk £9.95

Elements of Export Practice. – 2nd ed. – London : Chapman & Hall, 1985.
ISBN 0412270005 Pbk £9.95

Elements of Family Law. – London : Sweet & Maxwell, 1987.
ISBN 0421352302 Hbk £19.50
ISBN 042135240X Pbk £13.50

Elements of Income Tax Law. – Allahabad : Law Book Company.
Hbk £200.00

Elements of Insurance. – 4th ed. – Plymouth : Macdonald & Evans, 1985.
ISBN 0712106723 Pbk £5.95

Elements of International Trade and Payments. – Cambridge : Woodhead-Faulkner, 1983.
ISBN 0859412261 Pbk £6.25

Elements of land law / Kevin Gray. – London : Butterworths, 1987.
lxxi,1094p; 25cm.
Includes index.
ISBN 0406501602 Hbk £38.00
ISBN 0406501610 Pbk £23.95

Elements of Mercantile Law : Including Company and Industrial Law. – 15th ed. – New Delhi : Sultan Chand and Sons, 1984.
xxviii, 880p.
Pbk £40.00

Elements of Roman Law. – 4th ed. – London : Sweet & Maxwell, Reprint 1986.
ISBN 042107805 Pbk £15.50

Elements of Shipping. – 5th ed. – London : Chapman & Hall, 1981.
ISBN 0412237008 Hbk £20.00
ISBN 0412237105 Pbk £9.95

Elements of the Law and Practice of Legislative Assemblies in the U.S.A. – Dublin : Irish Academic Press.
560p.
ISBN 0716520206 Hbk £55.00

Elements of the Law of Evidence. – 3rd ed. – Lucknow : Eastern Book Company, 1984.
411p.
Pbk £15.00

Eleventh report : managing waste : the duty of care / Richard Southwood. – London : HMSO, 1986.
Chairman: Sir Richard Southwood.
ISBN 0101967500

Eleventh report to Parliament on subordinate legislation concerning Freedom of Information (Exemption Offices) Regulations 1987 (SR NO.266/1987 ... / Legal and Constitutional Committee. – Melbourne : Government Printer, 1987.
ix,58p.
Includes text of legislation.

Elgey, Christine →Sweet & Maxwell's Statutes for the Law Society finals.

Elgie, R. G.
Central Trust Company Act, 1983, Bill 097 : An Act Respecting Central Trust Company and Crown Trust Company. – Ontario : Ontario Government Publications Service, 1983.
5p.
Hbk £0.30
—Extra-Provincial Corporations Act, 1983, Bill 103 : An Act in Respect of Extra-Provincial Corporations. – Ontario : Ontario Government Publications Service, 1983.
12p.
Hbk £0.50
—Land Registration Reform Act, 1983, Bill 156 : An Act Respecting Conveyancing Documents and Procedures and the Recording of Title to Real Property. – Ontario : Ontario Government Publications Service, 1983.
33p.
Hbk £0.70
—Residential Complex Sales Representation Act, 1983, Bill 113 : An Act to Regulate Conveyances of Dwelling Units in Residential Complexes. – Ontario : Ontario Government Publications Service, 1983.
3p.
Hbk £0.30

Elias, Patrick
Cambridge-Tilbury Law Lectures
Vol. 4 /. – Dordrecht : Kluwer, 1983.
92p.
ISBN 9065441085 Pbk £30.00
—Labour Law - Cases and Materials. – 2nd ed. – London : Butterworths, 1988.
ISBN 0406577501 Hbk £19.95
ISBN 0406577593 Pbk
—Trade union democracy, members' rights and the law / Patrick Elias and Keith Ewing. – London : Mansell, 1987.
300p; 24cm.
Includes bibliography and index.
ISBN 0720107296 Hbk £30.00 :
ISBN 0720118719 Pbk £16.00
—Transfer of undertakings : the legal pitfalls : a specially commissioned report / by Patrick Elias and John Bowers. – London : Longman Professional, 1985.
54 leaves.
ISBN 0851208061

Elias, T.
Nigerian Land Law. – 4th ed. – Sweet & Maxwell, 1971.
ISBN 0421160608 Pbk £19.00

Elias, T. O. → Essays in honour of Judge T.O. Elias.
—International Court of Justice and some contemporary problems : essays on international law / Taslim O. Elias. – The Hague : Nijhoff, 1983.
ix,374p; 25cm.
Bibliography: p361-364. - Includes index.
ISBN 902472791X Hbk £150.00
—Judicial Process in Commonwealth Africa. – Accra : Ghana Universities Press.
124p.
Hbk £5.00
—New horizons in international law / by T. O. Elias. – Alphen aan den Rijn : Sijthoff & Noordhoff, .
xxii,260p.
ISBN 9028600396
—New trends in contemporary international law / T.O. Elias. – Hull : Hull University Press, 1985.
14p; 21cm. – (Josephine Onoh memorial lecture).
ISBN 0859584496
—Some aspects of international law considered in relation to apartheid, racism and racial discrimination / by T.O. Elias. – Lagos : Nigerian Institute of Advanced Legal Studies, 1986.
27p. – (Occasional paper).
ISBN 9782353043

Eliasoph, E.R.
Law and Business Practice in Shanghai. – London : Longman Professional, 1988.
ISBN 0582997550 Hbk £25.00

Elkind, Jerome B.
Interim protection : a functional approach / Jerome B. Elkind. – The Hague : Martinus Nijhoff, 1981.
xxiv,287p.
Bibliography: p263-266.
ISBN 9024725399
—Non-appearance before the International Court of Justice : functional and comparative analysis / Jerome B. Elkind. – Dordrecht : Martinus Nijhoff, 1984.
xiv,233p.
Bibliography: 207-213.
ISBN 9024729211 Hbk £110.00
—Standard for justice : a critical commentary on the proposed Bill of Rights for New Zealand / Jerome Elkind and Antony Shaw : with a foreword by P.T. Mahon. – Auckland : Oxford University Press, 1986.
xvi,238p.
Includes index.
ISBN 019558144X

Ellen, Eric
International maritime fraud / by Eric Ellen, and Donald Campbell. – London : Sweet & Maxwell, 1981.
viii,174p; 22cm.
Bibliography: p160. - Includes index.
ISBN 0421271507 Pbk £8.00

Ellenberger, E. Louis
Valuer. – Durban : Professional Publishers, 1983.
ISBN 0409027103 Hbk £64.00

Ellinger, E. P.
Modern banking law / E.P. Ellinger. – Oxford : Clarendon, 1987.
400p; 24cm.
Includes index.
ISBN 0198761562 Hbk £35.00 :
ISBN 0198761570 Pbk £12.00

Ellinghaus, M. P. → High Court of Australia on contract, 1950-1980 : cases.

Elliot → 1688-1988 : Time for a New Constitution.

Elliot, John
Conflict or cooperation? : the growth of industrial democracy. – 2nd ed. – London : Kogan Page, 1983.
350p.
Previous ed.: 1978.
ISBN 0850387477 Hbk £12.00
ISBN 0850387582 Pbk £6.95

Elliot, Michael J
Role of Law in Central-Local Relations. – Oxford : Social Science Research Council, 1981.
105p.
ISBN 0862260248 Pbk £2.50

Elliot Montague, J.
Legally yours - law and the individual / Reed. – 2nd ed. – Maidenhead : McGraw-Hill, 1985.
ISBN 0070848777 Pbk £5.95

Elliot, Robin M. → Litigating the Values of a Nation : The Canadian Charter of Rights and Freedoms.

Elliott → Doing Business in Canada, 3 Vols.

Elliott and Phipson manual of the law of evidence / D. W. Elliott, Sidney L. Phipson. – 12th ed. – London : Sweet & Maxwell, 1987.
380p; 24cm.
Previous ed.: published as Phipson and Elliott manual of the law of evidence. 1980. Includes index.
ISBN 0421338105 Hbk £20.00
ISBN 0421338202 Pbk £15.00

Elliott and Wood's casebook on criminal law / John C. Wood, Celia Wells. – 4th ed. – London : Sweet & Maxwell, 1982.
xlii,666p; 24cm.
Previous ed.: 1974. Bibliography: pxli-xlii. - Includes index.
ISBN 0421277408 Hbk £24.50
ISBN 0421277505 Pbk £14.50

Elliott, D. W. → Elliott and Phipson manual of the law of evidence.
—Elliott and Wood's casebook on criminal law / John C. Wood, Celia Wells. – 4th ed. – London : Sweet & Maxwell, 1982.
xlii,666p; 24cm.
Previous ed.: 1974. Bibliography: pxli-xlii. - Includes index.
ISBN 0421277408 Hbk £24.50
ISBN 0421277505 Pbk £14.50

Elliott, Michael J.
Role of law in central-local relations / by Michael J. Elliott. – London : Social Science Research Council, 1981.
105p; 30cm.
ISBN 0862260248 Pbk £2.50

Elliott, P.
Bank Manager's Handbook. – Cambridge : Woodhead-Faulkner, 1987.
ISBN 085941342X Hbk £25.00
—Learning Banking : Guide Study Revis. Exam. Techniques / Kelly. – 2nd ed. – Folkestone : Bankers Books.
ISBN 0852972164 Pbk £3.95
—Questions and answers on practical banking. – Cambridge : Woodhead-Faulkner, 1984.
ISBN 085941258X Pbk £8.95

Elliott, Paul → Indexation of Capital Gains : Computations and Examples.
→ Indexation of Capital Gains : Examples etc (83).

Elliott, Robert Fenwick
Building contract litigation / Robert Fenwick Elliott. – 2nd ed. – London : Longman, 1985.
xx,206p.
Bibliography: p.200 - Includes index.
ISBN 0851208908

Ellis, A. A. → Philippines: human rights after martial law.

Ellis, Colin → Computer contracts : the deeper issues : conference organised by the Society for Computers and Law on Monday 19th November 1984 at the Royal Garden Hotel, London, W.8.

Ellis, Hadyn → Identification evidence : a psychological evaluation.

Ellis, Jane → Religious minorities in the Soviet Union : a report.

Ellis, John W. → Law relating to firearms.

Ellis, Maarten J. → Business law in Europe : legal, tax and labour aspects of business operations in the ten European Community countries and Switzerland.

Ellis, T. Henry → Regulation of insurance in the United Kingdom and Ireland.

Ellison, R.
Pension fund reform. – London : Longman Professional, 1986.
ISBN 0851211828 Pbk £10.95

Elphinstone → Conveyancing, Vol. 1.

Elsevier's Fiscal and Customs Dictionary / Bauduin. – Amsterdam : Elsevier, 1988.
ISBN 0444428917 Hbk

Elton, G. R.
F.W. Maitland / G.R. Elton. – London : Weidenfeld and Nicolson, 1986.
viii,118p; 22cm.
Includes index.
ISBN 0297786148 Pbk £12.95
ISBN 029778885X £4.95
—Parliament of England 1559-1581. – Cambridge : Cambridge University Press, 1986.
411.
Study of functions of parliament, political and legislative. Finds that legislative capacity was far more important. Discusses the interests involved in promoting bills and problems associated with making them law.
ISBN 0521328357 Hbk £32.50

Elucidations Respecting the Common and Statute Law of Scotland. – Repr. of 1800 ed. – Abingdon : Professional Books.
56p.
Hbk £180.00

Elwyn-Jones, Frederick
In my time : an autobiography / Lord Elwyn-Jones. – London : Weidenfeld, 1983.
319p.
Includes bibliography and index.
ISBN 0297781596

Ely, P.
Control Without Custody / A. Swift. – Edinburgh : Scottish Academic Press Ltd, 1987.
256p : Illus.
ISBN 0707304571 Hbk £15.00

Elzaburu, Alberto de → Present and the future of the profession : (the Elzaburu survey).

Emefiene, Andrew
Principles of business law / Andrew Emefiene. – Akoka, Lagos : Management Science Centre, 1985.
i,194p.
ISBN 9782404098

Emergency Applications to Magistrates. – London : Fourmat, 1986.
ISBN 1851900012 Pbk £13.00

Emergency Family Remedies. – London : Longman Professional, 1987.
ISBN 0851211143 Pbk £12.50

Emergency Laws in Malaysia. – Singapore.
160p.
Pbk £27.00

Emergency powers / by H. P. Lee. – Sydney : Law Book Company, 1984.
xl,334p.
Includes index. Bibliography: pxxxiii-xl.
ISBN 0455202729

Emergency powers in peacetime / by David Bonner. – London : Sweet & Maxwell, 1985.
220p; 22cm.
Includes index.
ISBN 0421310707 Hbk £14.00 :
ISBN 0421310804 Pbk £8.00

Emergency Procedures for Ships Carrying Dangerous Goods : Group Emergency Schedules English Edition. – International Maritime Organization. – London : International Maritime Organization, 1981.
Hbk £3.00

Emergency Procedures Handbook. – London : Legal Action Group, 1986.
ISBN 0905099109 Pbk

Emergency Protection in the Footwear Industry. – London : Trade Policy Research Centre, 1983.
99p. – (Thames Essays Ser.: No. 36).
ISBN 0900842652 Hbk £3.00

Emerging issues in Commonwealth abortion laws, 1982 / by Rebecca J. Cook and Bernard M. Dickens. – London : Commonwealth Secretariat, 1983.
135p; 30cm.
ISBN 0850922305

Emerging Securities Markets. – London : Euromoney, 1984.
ISBN 090312162X Pbk £75.00

Emerson, Garfield
Canadian Corporation Precedents. – 3rd ed. – Agincourt : Carswell, 1987.
440p.
This third edition text provides corporation and securities law precedents. Sample forms utilized from incorporation to dissolution are included. Information pertaining to both private and public corporations are included. Additionally, selected forms and precedents have commentaries analyzing the legal history.
Hbk £75.75

Emery, C. T.
Judicial review : legal limits of official power / by C.T. Emery and B. Smythe : foreword by Sir Gordon Slynn. – London : Sweet & Maxwell, 1986.
xxxi,330p; 23cm.
Includes index.
ISBN 0421345209 Hbk £16.00
ISBN 0421345306 Pbk £11.95

Emery Wilks
Principle and Practice of Rating Valuation. – 4th ed. – London : Estates Gazette, 1984.
ISBN 0728200694 Pbk £22.00

Emily Murphy. – Markham : Fitzhenry and Whiteside.
ISBN 0889022348 Pbk £3.75

Emiola, Akintunde
Nigerian labour law / by Akintunde Emiola. – 2nd ed. – Ibadan : Ibadan University Press, 1982.
xxxviii,599p.
Previous ed.: 1979. Bibliography: p.599. - Includes index.
ISBN 9781211377

—Public servant and the law / by Akintunde Emiola. – Ile-Ife : University of Ife Press, 1985.
xxii,225p.
Includes bibliographical references and index.
ISBN 9781360658

Emmet, L. E.
Emmet on title : Emmet's notes on perusing titles and on practical conveyancing / J.T. Farrand : assisted by Jane M. Milward. – 19th ed. 2 v. – London : Longman Professional, 1986.
looseleaf.
Includes index.
ISBN 0851211488

—Emmet on title : Emmet's notes on perusing titles and on practical conveyancing / J. T. Farrand. – 18th ed. – London : Oyez Longman, 1983.
clxxxviii,1262p.
Previous ed.: 1978. Includes index.
ISBN 0851207332

Emmet on title : Emmet's notes on perusing titles and on practical conveyancing / J.T. Farrand : assisted by Jane M. Milward. – 19th ed. 2 v. – London : Longman Professional, 1986.
looseleaf.
Includes index.
ISBN 0851211488

Emmet on title : Emmet's notes on perusing titles and on practical conveyancing / J. T. Farrand. – 18th ed. – London : Oyez Longman, 1983.
clxxxviii,1262p.
Previous ed.: 1978. Includes index.
ISBN 0851207332

Emmett Hall : Establishment Radical. – Toronto : Macmillan of Canada, 1985.
256p.
ISBN 0771596898 Hbk £27.95

Emmins, Christopher J.
Guide to the Criminal Justice Act 1982 / Christopher J. Emmins. – London : Financial Training, 1982.
iv, 98p.
ISBN 0906322227

—Guide to the Criminal Justice Act 1988 / Scanlan. – London : Blackstone Press.
ISBN 1854310224 Pbk £15.50

—Practical Approach to Criminal Procedure. – 3rd ed. – London : Blackstone Press.
ISBN 0906322774 Hbk £14.95

—Practical approach to sentencing / Christopher J. Emmins. – London : Financial Training, 1985.
xxvii,350p; 23cm.
ISBN 0906322669 Pbk
ISBN 0906322715

Emp. Consultation and Information in Multinational Corps. – Oxford : Croom Helm, 1986.
ISBN 0709926243 Hbk £19.95

Emperors and lawyers / Tony Honore. – London : Duckworth, 1981.
xv,190p; 26cm.
Bibliography: p183-187. - Includes index.
ISBN 0715614495

Empirical analysis of changes in personal income taxes / a report by the Committee on Fiscal Affairs. – Paris : Organisation for Economic Co-operation and Development, 1986.
38p.
ISBN 926412778X

Employee ownership / Nuttall. – London : Fourmat, 1987.
ISBN 1851900330 Pbk £14.95

Employee participation / Terence P. Kenny. – 1 sound cassette. – London : Instructional Dynamics, 1974.

Employee participation : practice and attitudes in north-west manufacturing industry / by M.J. Dowling...et al. – London : Department of Employment, 1981.
44p. – (Research paper).

Employee-Employer Rights : a Complete Guide for the Ontario Work Force. – 6th ed. – North Vancouver : International Self-Counsel Press, 1988.
113p.
ISBN 0889083681 Hbk

Employee-Employer Rights : a Guide for the British Columbia Work Force. – 7th ed. – North Vancouver : International Self-Counsel Press, 1984.
137p.
ISBN 0889081522 Hbk £7.95

Employee-Employer Rights in Alberta : a Guide to Alberta Labour Law / Tim Christian. – 2nd ed. – North Vancouver : International Self-Counsel Press, 1984.
95p.
ISBN 0889082324 Hbk £6.95

Employees Cost of Living Relief Act. – 8th ed. – Karachi : Bureau of Labour Publications, 1987.
Pbk £2.40

Employees' inventions : a comparative study / edited by Jeremy Phillips. – Sunderland : MANS.
212p; 21cm.
ISBN 0950762601 Pbk £14.50

Employees' inventions in the United Kingdom : law and practice / by Jeremy Phillips and Michael J. Hoolahan. – Oxford : ESC, 1982.
xviii,164p; 22cm.
ISBN 0906214114 Pbk £9.50
ISBN 0906214106

Employees' Misconduct : As Cause for Discipline and Dismissal in India and the Commonwealth. – Allahabad : Law Book Company, 1987.
900p.
Hbk £130.00

Employees Provident Fund Act, 1951 (Act 272) and Employees Provident Fund Regulations 1969 and Rules. – Kuala Lumpur : International Law Books Services.
Hbk £10.00

Employees' Social Security Act, 1969 (Act 4). – Kuala Lumpur : International Law Books Services.
Hbk £12.00

Employees' State Insurance Act. – 2nd ed. – Calcutta : Eastern Law House, 1984.
Hbk £142.00

Employer and employee : a complete and practical guide to the modern law of employment / by G. Barrie Marsh. – 2nd ed. – London : Shaw, 1981.
lix, 616p.
ISBN 0721907415

Employer, the employee and the law in Malaysia / Dunston Ayadurai. – Singapore : Butterworths, 1985.
xxiv,335p.
Discusses the Malaysian industrial relations system in the context of the laws in force. Deals with employer-employee relationships, covering both the collective and the individual relationship between employers and workers. Also covers trade unions, and other similar organisations.
ISBN 0409995045

Employer-employee relations in the public service of Canada : proposals for legislative change / J. Finkelman. – 4 v. – Ottawa : Information Canada, 1974.
Includes bibliographical references. Contents: Parts 1-3 - Supplementary observations and recommendations. Parallel English and French texts, Part 3 and Supplementary observations and recommendations.

Employers Guide to Equal Pay Legislation in Great Britain. – London : Engineering Employers Federation, 1984.
32p.
Hbk £4.00

Employers' Guide to the Closed Shop. – London : Engineering Employers Federation, 1983.
20p.
Hbk £2.00

Employers Guide to the Employment Act 1982. – London : Engineering Employers Federation, 1982.
16p.
Hbk £2.00

Employers Guide to the Trade Union Act 1984. – London : Engineering Employers Federation, 1984.
16p.
Hbk £3.00

Employer's Liability at Common Law. – 10th ed. – London : Butterworths, 1985.
ISBN 0406311072 Hbk £48.00

Employers' use of outwork : a study using the 1980 Workplace industrial relations survey and the 1981 National survey of homeworking / by Catherine Hakim. – London : Department of Employment, 1985.
107p. – (Research paper).
Bibliography: p.104-107.

Employing People in Voluntary Organisations : An NCVO Practical Guide. – London : Bedford Square Press, 1984.
ISBN 0719911095 Hbk £2.95

Employment. – London : HMSO.
ISBN 0118102710 Hbk £105.00

Employment : Its Terms and Conditions in Public and Private Sectors. – Lucknow : Eastern Book Company, 1981.
1,322p.
Hbk £150.00

Employment Act, 1955 (Act 265) and Regulations and Orders. – Kuala Lumpur : International Law Books Services.
Hbk £15.00

Employment Act 1982. – Croydon : Tolley, 1983.
ISBN 085459082X Pbk £7.95

Employment Acts 1974-1980, with commentary / by Charles D. Drake and Brian Bercusson. – London : Sweet & Maxwell, 1981.
ca.500p.
ISBN 0421282509

Employment and safety in the offshore oil industry / Brenda Barrett, Brian Hindley and Richard Howells. – London : Kogan Page, 1987.
200p; 24cm.
ISBN 1850910707 £45.00

Employment bill. – London : HMSO, 1987.
vi,45p. – (H.C. Bill 1987-88 17).
ISBN 0103017887

Employment Claims in the County Court / Lloyd-Jones. – London : Low Pay Unit, 1988.
ISBN 0905211413 Pbk £1.00

Employment Digest. – New Malden : Croner Publications.
Hbk £50.90

Employment Equality Law. – Dublin : Round Hall Press, 1988.
ca 140p.
ISBN 0947686045 Hbk £25.00

Employment Equity Act and reporting requirements / Employment and Immigration Canada. – Ottawa : Ministry of Supplies and Services Canada, 1986.
Various pagings.
' ... provided to assist employers to meet their obligations under the Act'. - p.1.
ISBN 0662149777

Employment Handbook. – 4th ed. – Croydon : Tolley, 1987.
ISBN 0854592091 Pbk £15.95

Employment in Alberta : a Guide to Conditions of Work and Employee Benefits, 1 Vol. – Butterworths.
Llf £85.00

Employment in British Columbia : a Guide to Conditions of Work and Employee Benefits, 1 Vol. – Butterworths.
Llf £85.00

Employment law / Hepple & O'Higgins. – 4th ed. – London : Sweet & Maxwell, 1981.
lvii,430p; 25cm.
Previous ed.: 1979. Bibliography: p401-402. - Includes index.
ISBN 0421288302 Pbk £13.25

Employment Law / Painter. – London : Blackstone Press.
ISBN 1854310089 Pbk £8.50

Employment Law / Holmes. – London : Financial Training, 1988.
– (SWOT).
ISBN 1851850848 Pbk £7.50

Employment Law : the New Basics. – North Ryde : C.C.H. Australia.
384p.
ISBN 0887964648 Pbk £19.95

Employment Law Handbook. – 4th ed. – London : Butterworths, 1987.
ISBN 0406142637 Pbk £23.00

Employment Law (ILT). – 2nd ed. – London : Sweet & Maxwell, 1988.
ISBN 0421380705 Pbk

Employment Law in Canada. – 2nd ed. – London : Butterworths.
ISBN 0409823988 Hbk

Employment Law in Western Canada. – Agincourt : Carswell.
This work provides an in-depth analysis of the common and statutory law of employment in Western Canada. Also included is a comprehensive review of federal and Western Canadian collective bargaining law.

Employment Law Manual / Robert Parsons. – London : Sweet & Maxwell, 1988.
ISBN 0421370505 updat £85.00

Employment Law Statutes : Statute Books for Students. – London : Blackstone Press.
ISBN 1854310216 Pbk £10.95

Employment legislation : statutes (as amended to 16 August 1983) / compiled by Sir Arnold de Montmorency, Bart. – 1. – S.l. : s.n., 1983.
loose-leaf.
Contents on publication: Trade Union and Labour Relations Act 1974 - Employment Protection Act 1975 - Employment Proection (Consolidation) Act 1975 - Employment Act 1980. Spine title: Integration of employment legislation. Kept up to date by loose-leaf supplements.

Employment Standards Handbook. – Aurora : Canada Law Book Co, 1986.
– (Text Book-Civil).
Llf £95.00

Employment, trade, and north-south co-operation / edited by Geoffrey Renshaw. – Geneva : International Labour Office, 1981.
xiv, 263 p.; 25 cm. – (A WEP study / ILO).
Working documents in revised and condensed form which formed the basis for discussions at a Tripartite Symposium on Employment, International Trade, and North-South Co-operation, convened in Geneva in May 1980 by the International Labour Organisation. Includes bibliographical references and index.
ISBN 9221025306 Pbk £27.50

Emsley, Kenneth
Courts of the County Palatine of Durham from earliest times to 1971 / by Kenneth Emsley and C.M. Fraser. – Durham City : Durham County Local History Society, 1984.
ix,112p; 21cm.
ISBN 0902958070

Emslie, I.S.
Regional Levies Handbook. – Durban : Professional Publisher.
Hbk £12.50

Emslie, T.S.
Tax Practitioner's Pocketbook. – Durban : Professional Publisher.
ISBN 0409064068 Hbk £45.00

Encountering diversity : observations on the social work assessment of black children / Richard Pinder. – Leeds : Centre for Social Work and Applied Social Studies, 1982.
32p. – (Occasional paper).
Bibliography: p.31-32.

Encounters with the Australian Constitution sound recording . – South Yarra : Louis Braille Productions Ltd..
ISBN 14ac £68.00

Encyclopaedia Financial Services. – Sweet & Maxwell, 1988.
ISBN 0421368802 Hbk £265.00

Encyclopaedia of Banking Law. – London : Butterworths, 1982.
Service to Date.
ISBN 0406569835 Hbk £220.00

Encyclopaedia of Carriage Law Sources (Service). – London : Lloyd's of London Press.
ISBN 1850441081 updat £130.00

Encyclopaedia of Competition Law. – London : Sweet & Maxwell, 1988.
ISBN 0421368705 updat £195.00

Encyclopaedia of Compulsory Purchase Service. – London : Sweet & Maxwell, 1988.
ISBN 0421007508 Hbk £195.00

Encyclopaedia of Consumer Credit Law. – London : Sweet & Maxwell, 1988.
ISBN 0421208104 £175.00

Encyclopaedia of court forms in civil proceedings. – 2nd edition. – LLondon : Butterworths, 1961.

Encyclopaedia of Crimes and Justice. – 4 vols. – London : Macmillan, 1983.
ISBN 0029181100 Hbk £300.00

Encyclopaedia of environmental health law and practice
Service. – Sweet & Maxwell, 1988.
ISBN 0421133600 £190.00

Encyclopaedia of forms and precedents / Raymond Walton. – 5th ed. – London : Butterworths, 1985.
Includes bibliographical references. - Index included in each volume. Partially supersedes 4th ed., entitled: The encyclopaedia of forms and precedents other than court forms. Kept up to date by looseleaf service volume.
ISBN 0406023603

Encyclopaedia of forms and precedents other than court forms / L. G. Jory. – 4th ed. 28 v. – London : Butterworths, 1964-.
Includes bibliographical references and index. Managing editor L.G. Jory. Partially superseded by 5th ed., entitled: The encyclopaedia of forms and precedents.

Encyclopaedia of Health and Safety at Work. – London : Sweet & Maxwell, 1988.
ISBN 0421007109 Hbk £220.00

Encyclopaedia of Health Services/Medical Law. – London : Sweet & Maxwell, 1988.
ISBN 0421315008 Hbk £180.00

Encyclopaedia of highway law and practice Service. – Sweet & Maxwell, 1988.
ISBN 0421044500 Hbk £195.00

Encyclopaedia of housing law and practice Service. – Sweet & Maxwell, 1988.
ISBN 0421007303 Hbk £210.00

Encyclopaedia of Information Technology Law. – London : Sweet & Maxwell, 1988.
ISBN 0421372109 Hbk

Encyclopaedia of Insurance Law. – London : Sweet & Maxwell, 1988.
ISBN 0421281502 Hbk £165.00

Encyclopaedia of International Telecommunications Law. – London : Butterworths, 1987.
Pbk

Encyclopaedia of Investor Protection. – London : Butterworths, 1987.
Hbk

Encyclopaedia of labour relations law Service. – Sweet & Maxwell, 1988.
ISBN 0421169605 Hbk £265.00

Encyclopaedia of Local Government Law. – London : Sweet & Maxwell, 1988.
ISBN 0421260505 Hbk £195.00

Encyclopaedia of Oil and Natural Gas Law. – London : Lloyd's of London Press.
ISBN 1850440980 updat £165.00

Encyclopaedia Of Planning Law and Practice Service. – Sweet & Maxwell, 1988.
ISBN 0421007400 Hbk £265.00

Encyclopaedia of Professional Partnerships. – London : Sweet & Maxwell, 1988.
ISBN 0421332905 Hbk £195.00

Encyclopaedia of Road Traffic Law and Practice. – London : Sweet & Maxwell, 1988.
ISBN 0421007605 Hbk £210.00

Encyclopaedia Of Shipping Law Sources (UK) (Service). – London : Lloyd's of London Press.
ISBN 1850440115 updat £145.00

Encyclopaedia of Social Services Law. – London : Sweet & Maxwell, 1988.
ISBN 0421254505 Hbk £195.00

Encyclopaedia of UK and European Patent Law. – London : Sweet & Maxwell, 1988.
ISBN 0421233508 Hbk £165.00

Encyclopaedia of Value Added Tax. – London : Sweet & Maxwell, 1988.
ISBN 0421178604 Llf £190.00

Encyclopaedia Rating Law and Practice Service. – Sweet & Maxwell, 1988.
ISBN 0421263105 Hbk £95.00

Encyclopedia of arbitration law / Eric Lee. – 1 v. – London : Lloyd's, 1984.
looseleaf.
Includes index.
ISBN 1850440263

Encyclopedia of data protection / edited by Simon Chalton, Shelagh Gaskill. – 1. – London : Sweet & Maxwell, 1988.
Includes index.
ISBN 0421369000 Llf £185

Encyclopedia of European Community Law : Volume B : European Community Treaties. – Edinburgh : W Green.
Llf £290.50
Service. –
Llf £147.50

Encyclopedia of financial services law / editors Eva Z. Lomnicka, John L. Powell. – 2. – London : Sweet & Maxwell, 1987.
loose-leaf; 26cm.
Includes index.
ISBN 0421368802 £100.00

Encyclopedia of Health and Safety at Work : Law and Practice, 3 Vols.
Service only. – London : Sweet & Maxwell.
£74.00

Encyclopedia of health and safety at work : Law and practice. – 3. – London : Sweet & Maxwell, 1962.
loose-leaf.
Includes indexes.

Encyclopedia of Insurance Law, 1 Vol.
Service for 1985 only (post-free). – London : Sweet & Maxwell.
£55.00

Encyclopedia of insurance law / general editor Anthony O'Dowd : assistant general editor John Birds. – 1. – London : Sweet & Maxwell, 1983.
loose-leaf; 25cm.
Includes index.
ISBN 0421281502 £85.00

Encyclopedia of international commercial arbitration / by Eric Lee. – London : Lloyd's of London Press, 1986.
412p; 24cm.
Includes index.
ISBN 185044059X £50.00

Encyclopedia of Labour Law. – Karachi : Bureau of Labour Publications, 1988.
ca 800p.
Hbk £72.00

Encyclopedia of Northern Ireland labour law and practice / editor, Sir John Wood. – Belfast : Labour Relations Agency, 1983.
Looseleaf.
Includes bibliographical references and index.

Encyclopedia of Petroleum Laws. – Allahabad : Universal Book Agency, 1982/83.
Hbk £250.00

Encyclopedia of professional partnerships / by R.C. I'Anson Banks. – London : Sweet & Maxwell, 1987.
1000p; 25cm.
Includes index.
ISBN 0421332905 £165.00

Encyclopedia of Public International Law. – 1st repr. 1985 (nos. 1-6). – Amsterdam : Elsevier Science Publishers, 1981.
Hbk £4,700.00
2: Decisions of International Courts and Tribunals. – 1981.
ISBN 0444862129 Hbk
3: Use of Force, A.-M.. – 1982.
xvi, 300p.
ISBN 044486234X Hbk
4: Use of Force, N-Z. – 1982.
xvi, 370p.
ISBN 0444862358 Hbk
5: International Organizations. – 1983.
xvi, 428p.
ISBN 0444862366 Hbk
6: Regional Cooperation, Organizations and Problems. – 1983.
xvi, 382p.
Hbk £0444862374
7: History of International Law. Foundations and Principles of International Law. Sources of International Law. Law of Treaties. – 1985.
x, 556p.
ISBN 0444862382 Hbk
8: Human Rights and the Individual in International Law. International Economic Relations. – 1985.
xvi, 55p.
ISBN 0444879110
9: International Relations and Legal Cooperation in General Diplomacy and Consular Relations. – 1986.
xvi, 426p.
ISBN 0444862404
10. States - Responsibility of States - International Law and Municipal Law - 10. –
xvi, 544p.
ISBN 0444862412 Hbk

Encyclopedia of public international law / published under the auspices of the Max Planck Institute for Comparative Public Law and International Law : under the direction of Rudolf Bernhardt. – Amsterdam : North-Holland Pub. Co., 1981.
Issued in parts. Includes index.
ISBN 0444861408

Encyclopedia of rating and local taxation : law and practice / Harry Sales, Christopher Lewsley, J.H. Emlyn Jones, V.G. Wellings. – 1. – London : Sweet & Maxwell, 1988.
Contains the relevant legislation on rating, primary and subordinate, set out in full and amended where necessary. Also includes court rules, circulars, and a digest of cases. Annotated and cross-referenced. Supersedes the Encyclopedia of Rating Law and Practice.
ISBN 0421236105 Llf £130.00

Encyclopedia of road traffic law and practice / R Hosking, M Brealey. – 4 looseleaf volumes. – London : Sweet & Maxwell, 1989.
Contains annotated versions of the relevant statutes and statutory instruments, a revised EEC section and a section on general procedure in Britain. Includes tables of Statutes, SLs and cases, and an index. Three updating issues per year and 'stop press' bulletins.
ISBN 0421007605 Llf £210.00

Encyclopedia of Shipping Law Sources UK. – London : LLoyd's of London Press, 1988.
ISBN 1850440115 Hbk £175.00

Encyclopedia of social services law and practice. – 2. – London : Sweet & Maxwell, 1985.
loose-leaf.
Includes indexes. Updated by loose-leaf supplements.

Encyclopedia of Soviet law / edited by F.J.M. Feldbrugge, Ger P. van den Berg, William B. Simons. – 2nd rev. ed. – Dordrecht : M. Nijhoff Publishers, 1984.
1,012p.
Bibliography.
ISBN 9024730759 Hbk £450.00

Encyclopedia of the Law of Compulsory Purchase and Compensation, 2 Vols. – London : Sweet & Maxwell, 1985.
– (Local Government Library).
Includes tables of statutes and cases covered by the encyclopaedia, and a guide to the general principles of compulsory purchase law and practice. Covers rates of interest after entry regulations, and includes the Local Government Act 1988. Also contains a new section with details of major cases.
ISBN 0421007508 Hbk £125.00
Service only. –
£52.00

Encyclopedia of U.K. and European patent law / edited by T.A. Blanco White and others. – London : Sweet & Maxwell, 1977-.
Loose-leaf with up-dating service.
ISBN 0421233508

Encyclopedia of value added tax / consulting editor: G.S.A. Wheatcroft : general editor: J.F. Avery Jones. – London : Sweet & Maxwell, 1973-.
loose-leaf.
Includes index.

End of Law? / Timothy O'Hagan. – Oxford : Blackwell, 1985.
vii,183p; 23cm.
ISBN 0631145354 Pbk £7.50

Ending Lives / Collinson. – Oxford : Blackwell Scientific, 1988.
ISBN 0631153314 Pbk £6.95

Endorsement and Disqualification / Baker. – London : Butterworths.
ISBN 040613801X Pbk £24.50

Endorsement of Driving Licence and Disqualification from Driving / Cooper. – 3rd ed. – Chichester : Barry Rose, 1984.
ISBN 0859923428 Pbk £7.50

Endowments and Deferred Giving sound recording : a Detailed Explanation of Legalities and Procedures. – Toronto : Association of Canadian Orchestras/Ontario Federation of Symphony Orchestras.
ISBN 1ac (60 min) £8.00

Energy and mineral resources law in Ireland / Edward J. Donelan : with a foreword by A.J.F. O'Reilly. – Blackrock : Round Hall in association with Irish Academic, 1985.
214p; 25cm.
Includes index.
ISBN 0950872547

Energy Finance. – London : Euromoney, 1983.
ISBN 0903121476 Pbk £75.00

Energy law '88 : proceedings of the advanced seminar on petroleum, minerals and energy resources law organised by the IBA's Section on Energy and Natural Resources Law in Sydney, Australia, March 1988. – London : Graham & Trotman and International Bar Association, 1988.
xii,865p.
ISBN 1853330973

Energy Laws of Asia. – Kowloon : Petroleum News Southeast Asia Ltd.
Hbk £55.00

Energy strategy in Europe : the legal framework / by Terence Daintith and Leigh Hancher. – Berlin : W. de Gruyter, 1986.
ix,190p. – (Series A, Law).
Includes bibliographical references and index.
ISBN 0899251730

Eneverm, N.
Valuation of property investments. – 3rd ed. – London : Estates Gazette, 1984.
ISBN 0728200732 Pbk £10.00

Enforcement and stop notices : a practical guide / Felix Bourne. – London : Sweet & Maxwell, 1986.
175p; 24cm.
Contains, in chronological order, the relevant information from a variety of statutes, statutory instruments and circulars. Follows procedure from the preliminary points of consideration to the questions arising on appeal, both from the perspective of the local authority, and that of the private developer.
ISBN 0421364106 Pbk £15.00

Enforcement in the Magistrates Courts : a Guide to Enforcing Money Payments / Reynolds. – London : Fourmat.
ISBN 1851900454 Pbk £12.95

Enforcement of a Judgement (LPPN4). – 7th ed. – London : Longman Professional, 1986.
ISBN 0851210236 Pbk £15.50

Enforcement of human rights in peace and war and the future of humanity / Nagendra Singh. – Dordrecht : Nijhoff, 1986.
ISBN 9024733022 Hbk

Enforcement of maritime claims / by D.C. Jackson. – London : Lloyd's of London Press, 1985.
lxi,483p; 26cm.
ISBN 1850440018

Enforcement of Money Judgments Abroad. – Matthew Bender, 1988.
ISBN 0000999070 Hbk £53.00

Enforcement of Natural Resources Legislation : A Handbook. – Agincourt : Carswell, 1988.

Enforcement of Planning Control. – London : Longman Professional, 1988.
ISBN 0851214096 Pbk £14.95

Enforcement of the law relating to social security / report of a NACRO working party. – London : NACRO, 1986.
114p.
Chairman: Sir Norman Price.
ISBN 0850690412

Enforcing antitrust against foreign enterprises : procedural problems in the extraterritorial application of antitrust laws / general rapporteur, Cornelis Canenbley, with the assistance of Amanda Dalton. – Deventer, Netherlands : Kluwer, 1981.
xiii,125p.
'Report submitted to Committee C–Antitrust Law and Monopolies during the IBA Berlin Conference, August 1980.'.
ISBN 9065440143

Enforcing Debenture Security. – Vancouver : British Columbia Continuing Legal Education Society, 1984.
ISBN 086504144X Hbk £60.00

Enforcing international law : a way to world peace : a documentary history and analysis / by Benjamin B. Ferencz. – 2 v. – London : Oceana, 1983.
xix,890p.
Includes bibliographies and index.
ISBN 0379121476

Enforcing Regulation / John M. Thomas. – Dordrecht : Kluwer, 1984.
208p.
ISBN 0898381487 Hbk £95.00

Engelbrecht, Anne-Marie
Commentary on the Industrial Court. – Durban : Professional Publishers, 1984.
Hbk £0409027189

Engineer, Asgher Ali
Shah Bano Controversy. – Allahabad : Orient Law House, 1987.
253p.
Hbk £165.00

Engineering and construction law : with illustrations and cases / P.C. Loots. – Cape Town : Juta, 1985.
xxxv, 431 p.; 26 cm.
'Being a commentary on the General conditions of contract for works of civil engineering construction (fifth edition) 1982.'. Includes indexes.
ISBN 0702115630

Engineering Contract Casebook / Michael P Furmston. – Oxford : Blackwell Scientific, 1988.
ISBN 0003832627 Hbk £30.00

Engineering Tenders, Sales and Contracts. – Spon, 1982.
ISBN 0419125302 Hbk £42.00

Engineer's liability to the contractor : papers presented at the Conference of the International Bar Association's Section on Business Law Conference, Toronto 1983 / International Construction Contracts Committee of the Section on Business Law of the International Bar Assoication. – London : International Bar Association, 1983.
iv,162p.
Includes bibliographical references.

England and its rulers 1066-1272 : foreign lordship and national identity / M.T. Clanchy. – Oxford : Basil Blackwell in association with Fontana, 1983.
317p; 23cm.
First published by Fontana Paperbacks in the 'Fontana history of England', 1983. Bibliography: p299-308. - Includes index.
ISBN 0631133720 £15.00

England, Geoffrey
Essays in Labour Relations Law. – Don Mills : CCH Canadian Ltd.
290p.
ISBN 0887963153 Pbk £16.00
—Negotiating, Writing and Administering Contracts. – Ottawa : Canadian Library Association, 1981.
28p.
Pbk £2.75

Englander, David
Landlord and tenant in urban Britain 1838-1918 / David Englander. – Oxford : Clarendon Press, 1983.
xviii,342p; 23cm.
Bibliography: p318-335. - Includes index.
ISBN 0198226802 £22.50

England's Balme : Proposals By Way of Grievance and Remedy Presented to His Highness and the Parliament Towards the Regulation of the Law and Better Administration of Justice. – Repr. of 1657 ed. – Abingdon : Professional Books.
251p.
Hbk £150.00

Englefield, Dermot J. T.
Parliament and information : the Westminster scene / Dermot Englefield. – London : Library Association, 1981.
vii,132p; 24cm.
Includes index.
ISBN 0853655707 Hbk
ISBN 0853659931 Pbk
—Whitehall and Westminster : Government informs Parliament : the changing scene / Dermot Englefield. – Harlow : Longman, 1985.
x,218p; 24cm.
Includes index.
ISBN 058290272X Pbk £15.00

English administrative system 1780-1870 / Sir Norman Chester. – Oxford : Clarendon Press, 1981.
398p; 23cm.
Bibliography: p385-389. - Includes index.
ISBN 0198226438 £22.50

English and Colonial bars in the nineteenth century / Daniel Duman. – London : Croom Helm, 1983.
228p; 23cm.
Bibliography: p212-221. - Includes index.
ISBN 0856644684 £13.95

English and Empire digest, with complete and exhaustive annotations. – Green band ed. – London : Butterworth, 1971-.
Previous (Blue band) ed.: 1951-71. Includes indexes. From vol.21 (1981) title changes to The digest. Vol.28, Income tax and related taxes (1971), first vol. to be re-issued in new ed.. Kept up to date by continuation vols. and cumulative supplements.
ISBN 0406025002

English, Barbara
Strict settlement : a guide for historians / Barbara English and John Saville. – Hull : University of Hull Press, 1983.
144p. – (Occasional papers in economic and social history).
Bibliography: p.132-137. - Includes index.
ISBN 0859584399

English Business Law : ICSA Study Text. – London : BPP.
ISBN 0862772079 Pbk £12.95

English Business Law Q & A. – London : Financial Training, 1986.
ISBN 1851850104 Pbk £7.95

English church and its laws 12th-14th centuries / C.R. Cheney. – London : Variorum Reprints, 1982.
348p in various pagings; 23cm. – (Collected studies series).
Includes index. Text in English and Latin.
ISBN 0860781089

English Constitution. – Reprint. – London : Fontana, 1983.
ISBN 0006327583 Pbk £2.50

English Criminal Justice. – London : Gabbay (E & J).
ISBN 0950144894 Pbk £15.00

English criminal process : a review of empirical research / Andrew Ashworth. – Oxford : Centre for Criminological Research, University of Oxford, 1984.
135p. – (Occasional paper).
Bibliography: p131-135.
ISBN 094781101X

English Encyclopedia of Forms and Precedents / Robert B Roper. – 5th ed. – Wellington : Butterworths.
Hbk

English, J.
Butterworths' Police Law. – 2nd ed. – London : Butterworths.
ISBN 0406840008 Pbk £14.95
—Police law / Card. – 2nd ed. – London : Butterworths, 1988.
ISBN 0406840008 Pbk £15.95
—Police training manual / Houghton. – 5th ed. – Maidenhead : McGraw-Hill, 1986.
ISBN 0070847975 Pbk £12.95
—Summonses and Charges / R. Houghton. – 4th rev. ed. – London : Police Review Publishing, 1983.
ISBN 085164001X Pbk £4.25

English, J. T., et al
Debt Security Instruments : Creation and Perfection, Pt. 1. – Vancouver : British Columbia Continuing Legal Education Society, 1981.
430p.
ISBN 0865040168 Hbk £22.00

English Judicial Review. – London : Gabbay (E & J).
ISBN 0950144878 Pbk £17.00

English judiciary in the age of Glanvill and Bracton c.1176-1239. – Cambridge : Cambridge University Press, 1985.
335.
Study of the evolution of the professional judiciary in medieval England. Describes the growth of a professional civil service.
ISBN 052126510X Hbk £30.00

English Law / Keenan. – 8th ed. – London : Pitman Publishing, 1986.
ISBN 027302342X Pbk £11.95
ISBN 0406677611 Hbk £19.50

English Law and Ethnic Minority Customs. – London : Butterworths, 1986.
xxviii,300p; 25cm.
ISBN 040618008 Pbk £27.95

English Law for GCSE / Marianne Giles. – 5th ed. – London : Butterworths, 1987.
ISBN 0406653070 Pbk £5.50

English Law in India. – New Delhi : Abhinav Publications, 1984.
viii, 295p.
ISBN 8170171830 Hbk £120.00

English Law-The New Dimension (Hamlyn 26). – Sweet & Maxwell, 1975.
ISBN 0420227008 Pbk £6.95

English Lawyer. – Reprint. – Abingdon : Professional Books, 1986.
– (Classical English Law Texts Ser.).
ISBN 0862053145 Hbk £27.00

English Legal Manuscripts
Vol. 1: Catalogue of the Manuscript Year Books, Readings and Law Reports in the Library of the Harvard Law School. – Zug : Inter Documentation Company.
ISBN 3857500093 Hbk £50.00
Vol. 2: Catalogue of the Manuscript Year Books, Readings, and Law Reports in Lincoln's Inn, the Bodleian Library and Gray's Inn. –
ISBN 3857500247 Hbk £118.00

English legal process / Terence Ingman. – London : Financial Training, 1983.
xxxiv,267p.
ISBN 0906322243

English legal system / by Keith J. Eddey. – 4th ed. – London : Sweet & Maxwell, 1987.
xv,196p. – (Concise college texts).
Previous ed.: 1982. Bibliography: p189-190. - Includes index.
ISBN 0421354003 Hbk £13.50
ISBN 0421354100 Pbk £7.50

English Legal System. – London : Financial Training, 1988.
– (SWOT).
ISBN 1851850449 Pbk £7.50

English legal system / A.K.R. Kiralfy. – 7th ed. – London : Sweet & Maxwell, 1984.
xli,301p; 22cm.
Previous ed.: 1978. Includes index.
ISBN 0421313706 Pbk £16.50
ISBN 0421313803 Pbk £7.50

English legal system / Walker & Walker. – 6th ed. – London : Butterworths, 1985.
li,709p; 25cm.
ISBN 0406677603

English Parliament in the Middle Ages / H.G. Richardson and G.O. Sayles. – London : The Hambledon Press, 1981.
560p in various pagings; 25cm.
Includes bibliographical references and index.
ISBN 0950688215

English Reports : 1220-1865, 178 Vols. – Abingdon : Professional Books.
Hbk £12950.00
Individual vols.. –
Hbk £95.00
Wall chart. –
£105.00
Index Vols. 177 and 178. –
Hbk £110.00 ea.

English Reports Reprint Vols 1-178 (1220-1865). – Professional Books.
ISBN 0862052696 Hbk £10,250.00

English sentencing system / Andrew Ashworth. – 3rd ed. – London : Butterworths, 1981.
xvii,244p; 23cm.
Previous ed.: 1975. Bibliography: p235-236. - Includes index.
ISBN 0406570140 Hbk
ISBN 0406570159 Pbk

English Utilitarians : by Leslie Stephen Vol. 1-3. – 1. – s.l. : Micro-Offset Books, 1900.
Various pagings.
Complete in 3 vols.. Reproduction of 1950 reprint (New York: Peter Smith) of 1900 original published by Duckworth and Co., London. Includes bibliographical references and index. 3 vols. in one.

English Village Constable 1580-1642. – Oxford : Oxford University Press, 1986.
ISBN 0198229135 Hbk £27.50

English-French-Spanish-Russian Manual of the Terminology of Public International Law (Law of Peace) and International Organizations. – Brussels : Emile Bruylant, 1983.
xlviii, 846p.
ISBN 2802702831 Hbk £6,360.00

English-Italian Law Dictionary. – London : Sweet & Maxwell, 1985.
ISBN 0421357401 Hbk £50.00

English-Speaking Justice. – Toronto : Anansi Press, 1985.
64p.
ISBN 0887841414 Pbk £5.95

Enquiries before contract / Ruth Annand, Brian Cain. – London : Sweet & Maxwell, 1986.
xvii,207p; 26cm.
Includes index.
ISBN 0421348100 £16.50

Enquiry Cases of Late Increase in Robbers & Related Writing. – Oxford : Oxford University Press.
ISBN 0198185162 Hbk £50.00

Ensor, K. →PEBCO : a Black Mass Movement.

Enterprise corporatism : new industrial policy and the 'essence' of the legal person / by Gunther Teubner. – Florence : European University Institute, 1987.
47p.

Entertainment Expenses and Substantiation : the New Tax Rules. – Touch Ross. – North Ryde : C.C.H. Australia, 1986.
94p.
ISBN 0869038656 Hbk

Entertainment Industry Contracts. – Matthew Bender, 1987.
ISBN 0000999069 Hbk £197.00

Entrapment in Canadian Criminal Law. – Agincourt : Carswell, 1985.
250p.
Hbk £35.75

Entrapment in Canadian Criminal Law. – Agincourt : Carswell, 1985.
250p.
This book focuses on the problems inherent in the investigations of victimless crimes and sets out the theoretical bases for the defense of entrapment in criminal cases under Canadian law.
ISBN 045937060X Hbk £19.80

Entry Search and Seizure. – London : Butterworths, 1986.
ISBN 0406199108 Pbk £33.00

Entry, search and seizure / Richard Stone. – London : Sweet & Maxwell, 1985.
lii,326p; 26cm.
Takes into account changes enacted by the Drug Trafficking Offences Act 1986, with a discussion of the application of the Police and Criminal Evidence Act 1985. Considers case law for Anton Piller orders, and Mareva injunctions. Defines the categories of persons and authorities who may lawfully exercise entry powers.
ISBN 0421298901 £35.00

Environment and enforcement : regulation and the social definition of pollution / Keith Hawkins. – Oxford : Clarendon Press, 1983.
xvi,253p.
Includes index. Bibliography: p235-247.
ISBN 0198275145 Pbk

Environment Law Handbook : Planning and Land Use in New South Wales. – Redfern : Redfern Legal Centre Publishing, 1988.
350p.
Hbk £24.95

Environment Protection : Problems, Policy Administration Law. – New Delhi : Deep and Deep Publications, 1987.
568p.
ISBN 8171000037 Hbk £350.00

Environmental assessment procedures : a study which focuses on certain oil and gas developments in Scotland in light of the proposed EEC directive : final report August 1984 / prepared by Centre for Environmental Management and Planning, University of Aberdeen. – Aberdeen : Centre for Environmental Management and Planning, 1984.
x, 68p, 6p.

Environmental cooperation between the North Sea states : success or failure? / Sunneva Saetevik. – London : Belhaven Press, 1988.
xiv,173p.
Revision of thesis (cand. polit.): University of Oslo, 1986. Bibliography: p.161-165..
ISBN 1852930489 £22.50

Environmental groups in politics / Philip Lowe & Jane Goyder with additional contributions from Richard Bate, Sarah Buchanan and John McBride. – London : Allen & Unwin, 1983.
xii,208p; 24cm.
Bibliography: p186-197. - Includes index.
ISBN 0043290434 Hbk £
ISBN 0043290442 Pbk

Environmental health law / by Charles A.R. Webster. – London : Sweet & Maxwell, 1981.
xxiii,177p; 22cm.
Includes index.
ISBN 0421266201 Hbk £11.50
ISBN 0421266309 Pbk £1.50

Environmental health procedures / W.H. Bassett. – London : H.K. Lewis, 1983.
xiv,266p; 25cm.
ISBN 0718604709 £13.00

Environmental health standards in housing / David Ormandy & Roger Burridge. – London : Sweet & Maxwell, 1988.
xlv,373p.
Covers the initial inspection of a house, the assessment of conditions (including particular problems of dampness), the application of the various standards, the drafting of the notices and the steps involved in the enforcement of statutory standards.
ISBN 0421365501 £25.00

Environmental Law. – North Vancouver : International Self-Counsel Press.
Hbk

Environmental Law. – Agincourt : Carswell, 1984.
460p.
This text is structured around the various aspects of the environment to be controlled by Canadian regulations. Sections on air, water, waste management, pits and quarries, noise, and other environmental hazards are included in the book. A large appendix of relevant statutes and regulations is provided.
Pbk £40.50

Environmental law / David Hughes. – London : Butterworths, 1986.
400p; 22cm.
Includes bibliographies and index.
ISBN 0406016909 Hbk £ :
ISBN 0406016917 Pbk £9.95

Environmental Law and Chemical Substance. – Berlin : Erich Schmidt, 1982.
ISBN 3503021280 Hbk £48.00

Environmental law and policy in the Pacific basin area / edited by Ichiro Kato, Nobuo Kumamoto, and William H. Matthews. – Tokyo : University of Tokyo Press, 1981.
ix, 229 p.; 24 cm.
Includes bibliographical references and index.
ISBN 0860082857 Y5400

Environmental Law and Practice. – Vancouver : British Columbia Continuing Legal Education Society, 1983.
309p.
ISBN 0865041245 Hbk £60.00

Environmental Law, British Columbia Handbook, 1984 / Gwen M. Edwards. – Butterworths, 1984.
285p.
ISBN 0409988642 Pbk £40.00

Environmental law in Australia / by G.M. Bates. – Sydney : Butterworths, 1983.
xxvi,236p.
Bibliography: p.224-231. - Includes index.
ISBN 0409495182

Environmental Law in the 1980s : a New Beginning / Alastair R. Lucas. – Calgary : Canadian Institute of Resources Law.
233p.
Hbk £13.50

Environmental law of the European communities : Droit de l'environnement des communautes Europeennes Umweltrecht der Europaischen Gemeinschaften / edited by Wolfgang E. Burhenne. – Berlin : E. Schmidt, 1976-.
22 cm.
English and/or French and/or German. Loose-leaf for updating. 'FUST-Project Nr. 75.'.
ISBN 3503014802 Llf

Environmental law of the sea / by Douglas M. Johnston. – Berlin : E. Schmidt, 1981.
419 p.; 21 cm.
Includes bibliographical references.
ISBN 3503021116 Pbk

Environmental Law of the Sea. – Gland : International Union for Conservation of Nature and Natural Resources, 1981.
419p.
Hbk £39.00

Environmental Laws and Water Resources Management. – New Delhi : Radiant Pulbishers, 1986.
xii, 355p.
ISBN 8170270952 Hbk £20.00

Environmental Laws in India. – Madhya Pradesh : Lawyers Home, 1986.
663p.
Hbk £300.00

Environmental Legislation in Indonesia. – Yogyakarta : Gadjah Mada University Press, 1985.
41p.
ISBN 9794200468 Pbk £4.00

Environmental Noise Control Legislation in Australia. – Australian Environment Council-Environmental Noise Control Committee. – Canberra : Australian Government Publishing Service, 1982.
27p.
ISBN 064401914X Hbk £2.50

Environmental planning and development law (NSW) / by A.J. Nott. – Sydney : Penman, 1982.
xlix,417p.
Includes index.
ISBN 0959431608

Environmental policy in the USSR / Charles E. Ziegler. – London : Pinter, 1987.
195p; 24cm.
Includes index.
ISBN 0861879015 £18.50

Environmental policy of the European Communities / Guy Corcelle. – London : Graham & Trotman, 1989.
336. – (International environmental law and policy).
Survey of the legislation on environmental policy introduced by the European Community in recent years. Covers pollution control, environmental impact assessment, and nature conservation. Gives the full text of the Declaration on the Environment adopted by the European Council meeting at Rhodes in 1988.
ISBN 1853332259 Hbk £45

Environmental protection and coastal zone management in Asia and the Pacific / edited by Ichiro Kato ... et al. – Tokyo : University of Tokyo Press, 1985.
xi,244p.
Includes bibliographies and index.
ISBN 0860083926

Environmental protection and sustainable development : legal principles and recommendations / R.D. Munro, J.G. Lammers : adopted by the Experts Group on Environmental Law of the World Commission on Environment and Development, June 1986 ; with a foreword by Nagendra Singh. – London : Graham & Trotman, 1987.
xxi, 196 p.; 25 cm.
Bibliography: p. 133-143.
ISBN 0860109100 Hbk

Environmental Regulation : Its Impact on Major Oil and Gas Projects / Alastair R. Lucas. – Calgary : Canadian Institute of Resources Law.
167p.
Hbk £12.95

Environmental Regulation in Canada : an Assessment of the Regulatory Process. – Vancouver : University of British Columbia, Westwater Research Center, 1981.
134p.
ISBN 0920146090 Pbk £6.95

Environmental Resources Ltd →Law and practice relating to pollution control in Belgium and Luxembourg.

—Resource recovery : a report for the Royal Commission on Environmental Pollution / prepared by Environmental Resources Limited. – 1. – London : HMSO, 1986.
various pagings.
ISBN 0117301329

Environmental rights in Canada / Canadian Environmental Law Research Foundation : edited by John Swaigen. – Toronto : Butterworths, 1981.
vii,447p.
ISBN 0409818801

Epilepsy and human rights. – Canberra : Australian Government Publishing Service, 1985.
144p. – (Occasional paper).
ISBN 0644038462

Epilepsy and the law : a medical symposium on the current law / proceedings of a symposium sponsored by Labaz Sanofi UK Ltd., held at the Royal College of Physicians, London on 18 June 1984 : edited by Peter Fenwick and Elizabeth Fenwick. – London : Royal Society of Medicine, 1985.
viii,88p; 24cm. – (International congress and symposium series).
Bibliography: p79-80.
ISBN 0199220220 Pbk £9.00

Epstein, Gloria J.
Divorce Guide for Ontario : Step-By-Step Guide to Obtaining Your Own Divorce. – 7th ed. – North Vancouver : International Self-Counsel Press, 1988.
Hbk

Equal justice : report of a joint working party. – Hebden Bridge, W. Yorks. : Hebden Royd Publications, 1986.
25p.
The report of a joint working party set up by the Social Democratic Lawyers Association and the Association of Liberal Lawyers.
ISBN 1851870296

Equal Justice and Forensic Process : Truth and Myth. – Lucknow : Eastern Book Company, 1986.
146p.
Hbk £80.00

Equal Opportunities. – Oxford : Blackwell Scientific, 1988.
ISBN 0631159754 Pbk £8.95

Equal pay and opportunities : a study of the implementation and effects of the Equal Pay and Sex Discrimination Acts in 26 organizations / by M.W. Snell, P. Glucklich and M. Povall. – London : Department of Employment, 1981.
7,110p. – (Research paper).
Bibliography: p108-110.

Equal pay and the industrial tribunals. – London : Sweet & Maxwell, 1984.
80p.
ISBN 0421328002 Pbk £7.15

Equal pay for work of equal value. – London : Macmillan, 1984.
ISBN 0333375572 Hbk £22.50

Equal Pay In Northern Ireland. – Belfast : Queen's University of Belfast, 1986.
60p.
Pbk

Equal treatment for men and women. – Equal Opportunities Commission, 1988.
26p.
ISBN 1870358015 Pbk

Equalisation of diligences / Scottish Law Commission. – Edinburgh : The Commission, 1988.
vii,146p. – (Discussion paper).

Equality and discrimination : essays in freedom and justice : papers presented at the United Kingdom Association for Legal and Social Philosophy eleventh annual conference at University College London, 6th-8th April 1984 / edited by Stephen Guest and Alan Milne. – Stuttgart : Steiner, 1985.
102p; 24cm.
Bound with Beihefte nos. 22 and 23..

Equality and discrimination under international law / Warwick McKean. – Oxford : Clarendon, 1983.
ix,333p; 23cm.
Includes index.
ISBN 0198253117 Hbk £30.00
ISBN 0198255195 Pbk £12.50

Equality and judicial neutrality / Sheilah L. Martin and Kathleen E. Mahoney, editors. – Toronto : Carswell, 1986.
xxvii, 430 p.; 24 cm.
Papers presented at a conference held in Banff, Alta., May 22-24, 1986. Includes bibliographical references.
ISBN 0459308319

Equality and prohibition of discrimination in employment / editor R. Blanpain. – Deventer, The Netherlands : Klwver, 1985.
244p.
ISBN 9065442154

Equality and sex discrimination law / Katherine O'Donovan and Erika Szyszczak. – Oxford : Blackwell, 1988.
xiv,254p.
Includes bibliographical references and index.
ISBN 0631147713 Hbk £29.50
ISBN 0631155988 Pbk £10.95

Equality issues in federal law : a discussion paper. – Ottawa : Minister of Supply and Services Canada, 1985.
65,79p.
With French title-page: Les droits et l'egalite et la legislation federale. Pages numbered in opposite directions. English and French text.
ISBN 0662534956

Equality, markets and the state / Raymond Plant. – London : Fabian Society, 1984.
28p.
ISBN 0716304945

Equality now! : a magazine of the Equal Opportunities Commission. – Manchester : Equal Opportunities Commission, 1983-.
Continues: EOC news.

Equality Rights. – Vancouver : Continuing Legal Education Society of British Columbia, 1985.
248p.
ISBN 0865042217 Hbk £60.00

Equality Rights and the Canadian Charter of Rights and Freedom : Carswell's Canadian Legal Classic Series / Mary Eberts. – Agincourt : Carswell, 1985.
600p.
This work is a collection of essays examining section 15 of the Canadian Charter of Rights concerning equality rights. Decisions under the Canadian Bill of Rights, federal and provincial human rights statutes are discussed in the book.
ISBN 045932210 Hbk £38.50

Equality Rights and their Limitations. – Agincourt : Carswell, 1987.
ISBN 0459398407 Hbk £36.00

Equality Rights and Their Limitations in the Charter. – Agincourt : Carswell, 1987.
450p.
This book is a practitioner's sourcebook to Section 15 of the Canadian Charter. The history of the equality rights section of the Charter and Key Canadian decisions touching on equality issues are presented and criticized in the work.
Hbk £63.00

Equity. – North Ryde : Butterworths (Australia).
ISBN 0409494801 Pbk £7.00

Equity / by George W. Keeton and L.A. Sheridan. – 3rd ed. – Chichester : Barry Rose, 1987.
cxxvi,576p.
Previous ed.: 1976. Includes index.
ISBN 1870080300

Equity and Commercial Relationships. – North Ryde : Law Book Co, 1987.
ca 288p.
ISBN 0455207259 Hbk

Equity and the law of trusts / Philip H. Pettit. – 5th ed. – London : Butterworths, 1984.
lvii,649p; 26cm.
Previous ed.: 1979. Includes index.
ISBN 0406641676 Hbk £25.00
ISBN 0406641684 Pbk £21.95

Equity and the law of trusts in the Republic of Ireland / Ronan Keane. – London : Butterworths, 1988.
liii,387p.
Includes index.
ISBN 0406102708 Hbk £27.50

Equity and Trusts. – Plymouth : Macdonald & Evans, 1985.
304p. – (M and E Handbook Ser.).
ISBN 0712106685 Hbk £5.50

Equity and Trusts. – London : Financial Training, 1986.
– (SWOT).
ISBN 1851850457 Pbk £7.95

Equity and trusts in Nigeria / by J.O. Fabunmi. – Ile-Ife : University of Ife Press, 1986.
lii,301p.
Includes bibliographical references and index.
ISBN 9781360453

Equity, doctrines, and remedies / R.P. Meagher, W.M.C. Gummow, J.R.F. Lehane : with a foreword from the first edition by Sir Frank Kitto. – 2nd ed. – Sydney : Butterworths, 1984.
xciii, 912 p.; 25 cm.
Includes bibliographical references and index.
ISBN 040949142X Hbk A$52.10
ISBN 0409491527 Pbk A$39.30

Equity - Practice and Procedure in New South Wales. – Woolloomooloo : International Business Communications, 1987.
Hbk £135.00

Equity proceedings with precedents (New South Wales) / by A.G. Nevill and A.W. Ashe : consultant A.V. Ritchie : with a foreword by M.M. Helsham. – Sydney : Butterworths, 1981.
lii,379p.
Includes index.
ISBN 0409490393 Hbk A$77

Equity, Trusts and Specific Relief. – Lucknow : Eastern Book Company, 1983.
624p.
Hbk £45.00

Equity, trusts, specific relief / Durga Das Basu. – 5th ed. – New Delhi : Prentice-Hall, 1983.
xxiv,336p.
Includes index.
ISBN 0876922329

Erasmus, H.J. → Family, Things and Succession.

Erasmus Universiteit Rotterdam → Appellate decision making in the common law world.

Erickson, Rica
Dempsters. – Nedlands : University of Western Australia Press, 1978.
xiv, 297p.
ISBN 0855641266 Hbk £18.95

Ericson, Richard V.
Making crime a study of detective work / Richard V. Ericson. – Toronto : Butterworths, 1981.
xiii,257p.
Bibliography: p243-254.

—Ordering of justice : a study of accused persons as dependants in the criminal process / Richard V. Ericson, Patricia M. Baranek. – Toronto : Published in association with the Centre of Criminology, University of Toronto by University of Toronto Press, 1982.
xvi, 268 p.; 25 cm.
Includes index. Bibliography: p. 253-261.
ISBN 0802064639 Pbk

—Reproducing order : a study of police patrol work / Richard V. Ericson. – Toronto : Published in association with the Centre of Criminology, University of Toronto, by University of Toronto Press, 1982.
xii,243p; 24cm. – (Canadian studies in criminology).
Bibliography: p225-236. - Includes index.
ISBN 0802055699 Hbk
ISBN 0802064752 Pbk £9.90

Ermisch, John
Housing Finance : Who Gains?. – London : Policy Studies Institute, 1984.
83p.
Hbk £3.50

Ernst & Whinney → Cross-border transactions between related companies : a summary of tax rules.
→ International bank accounting.
→ Tax Reform Around the World.

Errabbi, B.
Right to Travel Under the Constitution. – Lucknow : Eastern Book Company, 1986.
272p.
Hbk £50.00

Error of judgment. – Aurora : Cape, 1986.
ISBN 0701129786 Hbk £10.95

Error of judgment : the Birmingham bombings / by Chris Mullin. – London : Chatto & Windus, 1986.
224p; 23cm.
ISBN 0701129786 £10.95

Erskine, John
Institute of the Law of Scotland, 2 Vols. – Repr of 1773 ed. – Abingdon : Professional Books.
Hbk £200.00

—Principles of the Law of Scotland, 2 Vols. – Repr. of 1754 ed. – Abingdon : Professional Books.
Hbk £160.00

Erskine May's treatise on the law, privileges, proceedings and usage of Parliament / Charles Gordon. – 20th ed. – London : Butterworths, 1983.
xlviii,1200p.
This book is a comprehensive work on the law, privileges, proceedings, and usage of the British Parliament. The book gives accurate and detailed information on the constituent parts of Parliament, its powers and jurisdiction, membership of either House, financial procedure, and the process of debate.
ISBN 0406291039 Hbk £55.00

Erythrae Decree. – Repr. of 1936 ed. – Aalen Wuertt : Scientia, 1981.
viii, 107p.
ISBN 3511024390 Hbk £28.00

Esiemokhai, Emmanuel Omoh
Colonial legal heritage in Nigeria / by Emmanuel Omoh Esiemokhai. – Akure, Nigeria : Fagbamigbe, 1986.
xii,82p.
Bibliography: p.79. - Includes index.
ISBN 9781642483

Eso, Kayode
Nigerian Grundnorm / delivered by Hon. Justice Kayode Eso on Thursday, 31st January 1985 at the University of Benin, Nigeria. – Lagos : Nigerian Law Publications, 1986.
92p.
Bibliography: p.89-90. - Includes index. Published under the auspices of Idigbe Memorial Lectures.

Espiritu, S.C.
Philippine Agrarian Reform and The New Taxation / A.O. Yoingco. – Quezon City : Katha Publishing Co., 1983.
Hbk £3.50

ESRC newsletter. – London : Economic and Social Research Council, 1984-.
Continues SSRC newsletter.

Essay on the Learning of Contingent Remainers and Executory Devises. – 2nd ed. Repr. of 1773 ed. – Abingdon : Professional Books.
491p.
Hbk £85.00

Essayan, Michael → Adkin's landlord and tenant.

Essays for Clive Schmitthoff / edited by John Adams. – Abingdon : Professional Books, 1983.
xviii,174p.
ISBN 0862050596

Essays in air law / edited by Arnold Kean. – The Hague : Nijhoff, 1982.
xvi, 369 p.; 25 cm.
Includes index.
ISBN 9024725437 Hbk £170.00

Essays in Classical and Modern Hindu
Vol. 1: Dharmasastra and Related Ideas. – Leiden : E.J. Brill, 1976.
ISBN 9004044752 Hbk £96.00
Vol. 2: Consequences of the Intellectual Exchange with the Foreign Powers. – 1977.
ISBN 9004048081 Hbk £128.00
Vol. 3: Anglo-Hindu Legal Problems. – 1977.
ISBN 9004054243 Hbk £112.00
Vol. 4: Current Problems and the Legacy of the Past. – 1978.
ISBN 9004057536 Hbk £128.00

Essays In Constitutional Law. – 2nd ed. – Sweet & Maxwell, 1964.
ISBN 042042640X Pbk £9.50

Essays in constitutional law of Nigeria / by R.S. Bhalla. – s.l. : s.n., 1984.
v,112p.
Includes bibliographical references and index.
ISBN 9781660139

Essays in Criminal Law. – Stockholm : Almqvist & Wiksell, 1988.
152p.
ISBN 9176781186 Hbk £170.00

Essays in equity / edited by P.D. Finn. – Sydney : Law Book Company, 1985.
xxv,256p; 25cm.
ISBN 045520585X

Essays in European law and integration : to mark the silver jubilee of the Europa Institute, Leiden, 1957-1982 / edited by David O'Keeffe and Henry G. Schermers. – Deventer, Netherlands : Kluwer Law and Taxation Publishers, 1982.
208 p.; 25 cm.
Includes bibliographical references.
ISBN 9065441107 : est.

Essays in family law 1985 / edited by M.D.A. Freeman. – London : Stevens, 1986.
xiv,118p; 22cm.
Includes index.
ISBN 0420475109 Pbk £18.50

Essays in honour of Judge T.O. Elias / edited by J.A. Omotola. – Lagos : Faculty of Law, University of Lagos, 1987.
xxvii,258p.
Includes index.

Essays in international law in honour of Judge Manfred Lachs / Etudes de droit international en l'honneur du Juge Manfred Lachs : edited by Jerzy Makarczyk. – The Hague : M. Nijhoff, 1984.
760p.
Bibliography: p.18-23. At head of title: Institute of State and Law of the Polish Academy of Sciences Institut de l'Etat et de Droit de l'Academie Polonaise des Sciences. English or French text.
ISBN 9024730716 Hbk £295.00

Essays in Irish Legal History / Paul O'Higgins. – Dublin : Irish Academic Press, 1988.
ca 220p.
ISBN 0716523973 Hbk £27.50

Essays in Jurisprudence 1931. – London : Wildy & Sons.
Hbk £10.50

Essays in Jurisprudence and Philosophy. – Oxford : Oxford University Press, 1983.
ISBN 0198253877 Hbk £19.50
ISBN 0198253885 Pbk £8.95

Essays in Labour Relations Law. – Don Mills : CCH Canadian Ltd.
290p.
ISBN 0887963153 Pbk £16.00

Essays in Law and Society / Geoff Mungham. – London : Sweet & Maxwell, 1986.
Hbk £10.50

Essays in Legal Theory. – Copenhagen : Samfundsvidenskaberne.
Hbk £19.10

Essays in legal theory : a collaborated work / edited by D.J. Galligan : editorial advisers Colin Howard and Michael Crommelin. – Melbourne : Melbourne University Press, 1984.
viii,256p; 22cm.
ISBN 0522842836

Essays in Medieval diplomacy and administration / Pierre Chaplais. – London : Hambledon, 1981.
496p in various pagings,16p of plates; 25cm.
Includes index. English and French text.
ISBN 0950688223

Essays in memory of Professor F.H. Lawson / edited by Peter Wallington, Robert M. Merkin. – London : Butterworths, 1986.
ix,200p; 26cm.
Includes index.
ISBN 0406500304 Hbk £21.00

Essays in the history of Canadian law
Vol.1 : edited by David H. Flaherty / David H. Flaherty. – Toronto : Published for the Osgoode Society by University of Toronto Press, 1981.
xvi,428p; 23cm.
Includes index.
ISBN 0802033822
Vol.2. – 1983.
ISBN 0802033911 Hbk £45.00

Essays on Administrative Law. – Colombo : Lake House Investments.
Pbk £7.15

Essays on Bentham : studies on jurisprudence and political theory / by H.L.A. Hart. – Oxford : Clarendon, 1982.
272p; 23cm.
Includes index.
ISBN 0198253486 Hbk £17.50
ISBN 0198254687 Pbk £4.95

Essays on Civil Proceedings, 4 Vols. – Enugu : Fourth Dimension Publishing, 1981.
ISBN 9781561637 Hbk
Vol. 1. –
240p.
ISBN 9781562277 Hbk £25.00
Vol. 2. –
168p.
ISBN 9781562447 Hbk £15.00

Essays on Constitutional Law : Alladi Krishnaswami Aiyer Memorial Volume. – New Delhi : Concept Publishing Company, 1986.
xvi, 285p.
Hbk £175.00

Essays on contract. – Oxford : Clarendon Press, 1988.
364.
A collection of essays concerned with the theory and foundations of contractual liability, which have been published over the last twenty years. The author has tken the opportunity to revise, and rewrite some of them, and to answer previously made criticisms of his work.
ISBN 0198256418 Pbk £11.95

Essays on human rights in the Helsinki process / edited by A. Bloed and P. van Dijk. – Dordrecht : M. Nijhoff, 1985.
285p.
At head of title: TMC Asser Instituut. Contents: Detente and the concluding document of Madrid / by Arie Bloed – The Madrid Meeting, 1980-1983 / by Harm J. Hazewinkel – Some aspects of the socialist view of human rights / by Arie Bloed & Fried van Hoof – Human rights and non-intervention / by Arie Bloed & Pieter van Dijk – Trade union freedom in socialist states and the Madrid Meeting, with special reference to the Soviet Union / by Ger P. van den Berg – The right to work in East and West / by Ger P. van den Berg & Rene M.A. Guldenmund – Helsinki, Madrid, and the working conditions for western journalists in Eastern Europe / by Andre Gerrits & Joanka Prakken – Jamming of foreign radio broadcasts / by Arie Bloed & Pascale C.A.E. de Wouters d'Oplinter – The boycott of the 1980 Moscow Olympic Games and detente / by Rob C.R. Siekmann.
ISBN 9024732115 Hbk £145.00

Essays on International and Comparative Law : In Honour of Judge Erades. – Institute T.M.C. Asser. – Dordrecht : Kluwer, 1983.
285p.
ISBN 902472838X Hbk £95.00

Essays on international commercial arbitration. – London : Graham & Trotman, 1989.
256.
Focuses on Model Law as prepared by the United Nations Commission on International Trade Law, accepted by the General Assembly in 1985. Also discusses ICSID arbitration and the New York Convention of 1958.
ISBN 0860107051 Hbk £46.50

Essays on International Law. – Bombay : Tripathi, 1981.
Hbk £120.00

Essays on International Law and Organization, 2 Vols. – Dordrecht : Kluwer.
1,230p.
ISBN 9024729106 Hbk £450.00

Essays on Kelsen / edited by Richard Tur and William Twining. – Oxford : Clarendon, 1986.
288p; 22cm.
Includes index.
ISBN 0198254709 £30.00

Essays on law and social practice in South Africa / edited by Hugh Corder. – Cape Town : Juta, 1988.
xii,368p.
Inlcudes bibliographical references and index.
ISBN 0702120057

Essays on Law, Equality and Education. – London : Sweet & Maxwell, 1984.
ISBN 0710098804 Hbk £49.00

Essays on legal education / Centre for Studies in Canadian Legal Education : Neil Gold, editor. – Toronto : Butterworths, 1982.
xi,143p.
Includes bibliographical references.
ISBN 0409822248

Essays on Taxation / J. Prebble. – Wellington : Victoria University of Wellington, 1982.
ISBN 0705508307 Hbk £20.00

Essays on the future of local government / edited by Michael Goldsmith. – S.l. : s.n., 1986.
139p.
Includes bibliographies. 'Sponsored by West Yorkshire Metropolitan County Council' - Preface.

Essays on Third World Perspectives in Jurisprudence / W.E. Conklin. – Singapore : Malayan Law Journal, 1984.
xvii, 442p.
Collection of jurisprudentially-orientated essays with particular reference to the problems and issues peculiar to the third world. Covers constitutional obligation in the third world, liberal conceptions and their applicability to the third world. and the jurisprudence of indigenous law.
ISBN 9971700352 Pbk £45.00

Essays upon several subjects concerning British antiquities. – Repr. of 1747 ed. – Abingdon : Professional Books.
58p.
Hbk £125.00

Essenberg, Bert →Labour courts in Europe : proceedings of a meeting organised by the International Institute for Labour Studies.

Essential Accounting for Managers. – 5th ed. – London : Cassell, 1988.
ISBN 0304314714 Pbk £6.95

Essential cases in insurance law / Kenneth Cannar. – Cambridge : Woodhead-Faulkner, 1985.
240p.
ISBN 0859412849 £25.00

Essential Commodities Act ... – 7th ed. – Allahabad : Law Book Company, 1988.
1,000p.
Hbk £300.00

Essential Law for Horseowners. – Oxford : Blackwell Scientific, 1987.
ISBN 0003832864 Pbk £9.95

Essential Law for Journalists. – 9th ed. – London : Butterworths, 1985.
ISBN 0406772819 Pbk £8.95

Essential Law for Landowners and Farmers / Parrish. – 2nd ed. – Oxford : Blackwell Scientific, 1987.
ISBN 0003832694 Pbk £9.95

Essential Law for Social Workers. – 2nd ed. – London : Oyez Longman, 1981.
ISBN 0851205143 Hbk £9.95

Essentials of Accounting. – 4th ed. – London : Addison-Wesley.
ISBN 0201000172 Pbk £13.95

Essentials of Amateur Sports Law. – London : Eurospan.
ISBN 0865691312 Hbk £30.95

Essentials of Business Law in Australia. – Carleton : Pitman Pty Ltd, 1983.
ISBN 0858966697 Hbk £22.95

Essex County Newspapers Limited : a report by the Director General of Fair Trading on an investigation under Section 3 of the Competition Act 1980 / Office of Fair Trading. – London : Office of Fair Trading, 1983.
41p; 30cm.

Establishing a business in the United Kingdom / by R. M. Cooke and D. C. Borer. – 2nd ed. – London : Institute of Chartered Accountants, 1983.
viii,215p.
ISBN 0852913370

Establishing the validity of contractual claims. – King's Ride : Institute of Building, 1983.
28p.
ISBN 0901822191 Hbk £3.85

Establishment of an independent element in the investigation of complaints against the police : report of a working party appointed by the Home Secretary / Home Office. – London : H.M.S.O., 1981.
ii,12p; 25cm.
ISBN 0101819307 unbound £1.70

Estate Administration : A Solicitor's Reference Manual, 1 Vol. – Agincourt : Carswell, 1984.
700p.
This book is a guide for the solicitor dealing with all aspects of estate administration in Ontario, Canada. The text includes all relevant statutes and regulations. Numerous forms, letters, and checklists are provided.
Llf £109.25

Estate Administration : the Basics for Legal Assistants and Legal Secretaries. – Vancouver : Continuing Legal Education Society of British Columbia, 1988.
224p.
ISBN 0865043787 Hbk £75.00

Estate Agency Law and Practice in New South Wales. – 2nd ed. – North Ryde : Law Book Co, 1985.
xxix, 481p.
ISBN 0455205817 Pbk £33.00

Estate Agency Practise in New South Wales. – North Ryde : Law Book Co, 1985.
xxix, 363p.
ISBN 0455202931 Pbk £33.00

Estate Agents Act 1979. – 2nd ed. – London : Estates Gazette, 1982.
ISBN 0728200430 Pbk £7.60

Estate agents and auctioneers / Law Reform Commission of Victoria. – Melbourne : Government Printer, 1988.
x,46p. – (Report).
At head of cover title: Regulation Review Unit.
ISBN 0724167145

Estate and Trusts Reports. – Agincourt : Carswell.
These volumes contain the key decisions in estates and trust law from Canadian jurisdictions. Topics include wills, estate administration, devolution of estate, dependents relief, and tax matters relating to trusts. Wills are covered in depth.
Hbk £75.75

Estate Conveyancing. – London : Waterlow, 1984.
ISBN 0080391370 Hbk £19.50

Estate duty : principles and planning / by Aubrey S. Silke and Michael L. Stein. – Kenwyn : Juta in association with Divaris Stein, 1984.
369 p.; 23 cm.
Includes indexes.
ISBN 0702115347

Estate Duty Act. – E.B.C. – Lucknow : Eastern Book Company, 1984.
Hbk £8.00

Estate Duty Act. – 4th ed. – Bombay : Tripathi.
Hbk

Estate Duty Law. – 2nd ed. – Nagpur : Wadhura & Co, 1983.
Hbk £220.00

Estate Litigation. – Vancouver : Continuing Legal Education Society of British Columbia, 1986.
96p.
ISBN 0865042683 Hbk £55.00

Estate Litigation. – Agincourt : Carswell, 1987.
400p.
This is an in-depth guide to various types of proceedings which can arise when dealing with an estate. Discussions include committeeship proceedings, proceedings related to mental incapability, and the role of the Official Guardian in estate matters related to children. Also included is a comprehensive discussion of the entire process of estate litigation.
Hbk £46.25

Estate management practice. – 2nd ed. – London : Estates Gazette, 1986.
ISBN 0728200945 Pbk £14.50

Estate Planning. – Croydon : Tolley, 1987.
ISBN 0854592725 Pbk £17.95

Estate Planning. – Vancouver : British Columbia Continuing Legal Education Society, 1983.
77p.
ISBN 0865040915 Hbk £45.00

Estate Planning and Administration. – Agincourt : Carswell, 1987.
406p. – (Bar Admission Course Material Ser.).
This text discusses will planning and drafting, administration of an estate and how to advise the executor on applications for probate or distribution of the estate.
ISBN 045938050 Hbk £30.00

Estate Planning Handbook. – Agincourt : Carswell, 1985.
176p.
This practitioner's handbook of Canadian estate planning law presents numerous precedents and discussions of relevant law. Planning mechanisms to deal with incapacity, terminal illness, and the owner-managed business are addressed in depth.
Pbk £29.50

Estate Planning Law Locator 1988. – New York : Bowker, 1988.
ISBN 0835223507 Hbk £30.00

Estate Tax Planning : Including Will Drafting. – London : Law Society.
– (Nineteen Eighty-Five Crash Course Transcripts).
Hbk £2.05

Estates and interests and family dealings in land / Land Law Working Group. – Belfast : H.M.S.O., 1981.
v,60p; 21cm. – (Discussion document).
ISBN 0337233438 Pbk £3.50

Estates and Trusts Quarterly (E. & T.Q.)
1974-Present. – Aurora : Canada Law Book Co.
Hbk £65.00
Current subscription-Outside Canada. –
Hbk £70.00
Back Vols.. –
Hbk £35.00

Estates & trusts reports. – Agincourt, Ont. : Carswell, 1978-.
24cm.
Cumulative indexes published at intervals.

Estates Gazette Digest of Cases : 1902-1980. – Abingdon : Professional Books.
Hbk £2800.00

Estates Gazette Journal : 1858-1980. – Abingdon : Professional Books.
Hbk £5500.00

Estates gazette law reports. – London : Estates Gazette, 1986-.
Continues : The Estates gazette : digest of land and property cases. Cumulative index published annually as a supplement.

Estates Gazette Planning Law Reports
1988 Vol. 1. – London : Estates Gazette.
ISBN 0728201194 Hbk £23.50
1988 Vol. 2. –
ISBN 0728201208 Hbk £23.50

Estes, James Martin
Christian Magistrate and State Church. – Toronto : University of Toronto Press, 1982.
ISBN 0802055893 Hbk £30.00

Estreicher
Labor Law and Business Change : Theoretical and Transactional Perspectives / Collins. – Quorum Press.
ISBN 0899302076 Hbk £33.50
—Redefining the Supreme Courts' Role : A Theory of Managing the Federal Judicial Process / Sexton. – Yale University Press.
ISBN 0300037341 Pbk £8.95

Estrin, David
Environmental Law. – Agincourt : Carswell, 1984.
460p.
This text is structured around the various aspects of the environment to be controlled by Canadian regulations. Sections on air, water, waste management, pits and quarries, noise, and other environmental hazards are included in the book. A large appendix of relevant statutes and regulations is provided.
Pbk £40.50
—Handle with Caution : Liability in the Production, Transportation and Disposal of Dangerous Substances. – Agincourt : Carswell, 1986.
280p.
This book explains the responsibilities and liabilities, under new Canadian federal and Ontario provincial laws, of generating, transporting, hauling, and disposing of waste and dangerous goods. The new governmental powers, enforcement provisions, and compensation schemes are described in the work.
Hbk £41.75

Etal →Legal System and Social Systems.

Ethical and Legal Issues in Guardianship Options for Intellectually Disadvantaged People / Peter Singer. – Kingston : Australian Government Publishing Service, 1986.
124p.
ISBN 0644034335 Hbk £14.95

Ethics and mental retardation / edited by Loretta Kopelman and John C. Moskop. – Dordrecht : D. Reidel, 1984.
xvi, 258p.
Includes index.
ISBN 9027716307

Ethics and the rule of law / David Lyons. – Cambridge : Cambridge University Press, 1984.
x,229p; 21m.
Bibliography: p220-226. - Includes index.
ISBN 0521257859 Hbk £17.50
ISBN 0521277124 Pbk £4.95

Ethics of Legal Coercion / John D. Hodson. – Dordrecht : Kluwer, 1985.
192p.
ISBN 9027718431 Pbk £52.00

Ethnic minorities and complaints against the police / Philip Stevens and Carole Willis with the assistance of Clare Oxby. – London : Home Office, 1981.
v,40p. – (Research and Planning Unit paper).
Bibliography: p.33-34.
ISBN 0862520266

Ethnic minorities, crime and policing : a survey of the experiences of West Indians and whites / by Mary Tuck and Peter Southgate. – London : H.M.S.O., 1981.
iv,50p.
Bibliography: p50. A Home Office Research and Planning Unit report.
ISBN 0113407653

Ethnic minorities in Britain : a study of trends in their position since 1961 / by Simon Field ... et al. – London : H.M.S.O., 1981.
v,44p.
Bibliography: p42-44. A Home Office Research Unit report.
ISBN 0113407084

Etikerentse
Nigerian petroleum law / G. Etikerentse. – London : Macmillan, 1985.
x,356p; 24cm.
Includes index.
ISBN 0333393570 Pbk £7.95

Etor
Keep Account : Guide to Profitable Bookkeeping / Muspratt. – London : Macmillan.
– (Breakthrough Series).
ISBN 0333481593 Pbk £4.25

Etudes et essais sur le droit international humanitaire et sur les principes de la Croix-Rouge en l'honneur de Jean Pictet : Studies and essays on international humanitarian law and Red Cross principles in honour of Jean Pictet / Christophe Swinarski, redacteur. – The Hague : Martinus Nijhoff, 1984.
English and French. Bibliography.
ISBN 9024730791 Pbk £150.00

Etuk, Efiong J.
Nigerian business law : a guide for students, managers and foreign investors / Efiong J. Etuk, E.K. Quansah. – Basingstoke : Macmillan, 1986.
208p; 22cm.
Includes index.
ISBN 0333435079 Pbk £5.95

Euro-Arab Chambers of Commerce →
Proceedings of the First Euro Arab Arbitration Conference.

Euro DM. – London : Butterworths.
ISBN 0406194009 Hbk £35.00

Eurobond Market. – Cambridge : Woodhead-Faulkner, 1988.
ISBN 0859413373 Hbk £40.00

Eurobonds / by F.G. Fisher, III. – London : Euromoney, 1988.
v,231p.
A 'revised work'. - Preface. Previous ed. entitled: International bonds. Bibliography: p.227. - Includes index.
ISBN 1870031512

Euromoney
International Finance Yearbook 1987. – Euromoney. – London : Euromoney.
ISBN 0903121857 Pbk £75.00

Euromoney issues : papers presented to the Section on Business Law Committee Q (Issues and Trading in Securities) at the International Bar Association 20th biennial conference, Vienna, September 1984. – London : International Bar Association, 1985.
xvi,112p.

Euronotes : RUFs, TRUFs, NIFs, SNIFs and BONUSes / edited by Lloyd Bankson and Michael Lee. – London : Euromoney, 1985.
viii,183p.
ISBN 0903121743

Euronotes and euro-commercial paper / Gareth Bullock. – London : Butterworths, 1987.
vii,136p; 23cm.
Includes index.
ISBN 0406104107 £32.00

European banking law : a guide to Community and member state legislation / Belmont European Community Law Office. – London : Financial Times Business Information Ltd, 1987.
xviii,296p.
ISBN 0902101951

European Banking Law : An Analysis of Community and Member State Legislation / Margie Lindsay. – London : Financial Times Ltd, 1983.
Hbk £85.00

European challenge, 1992 : the benefits of a single market / Paolo Cecchini : with Michel Catinat and Alexis Jacquemin. – English ed. – Aldershot : Gower, 1988.
xxi, 127 p.; 23 cm.
Spine title: 1992, the European challenge. Bibliography: p. 110-111.
ISBN 0704506130 Pbk

European Challenge : 1992. – Wildwood House, 1988.
ISBN 0704506130 Pbk £6.95

European Commission of Human Rights. Decisions and Reports, 26 Vols. – Strasbourg : Council of Europe.
Hbk £3.10

European Commission's Powers of Investigation in the Enforcement of Competition Law. – Luxembourg : Office for Official Publications of the European Communities, 1985.
81p.
ISBN 9282553612 Pbk

European Committee on Legal Co-operation →
Foster families : recommendation no. R(87)6 adopted by the Committee of Ministers of the Council of Europe on 20 March 1987 and Explanatory memorandum.

→ Measures to prevent and reduce the excessive workload in the courts : recommendation no. R (86)12 adopted by the Committee of Ministers of the Council of Europe on 16 September 1986 and Explanatory memorandum.

→ Model agreement to enable members of the family forming part of the household of a member of a diplomatic mission or consular post to engage in a gainful occupation : recommendation no. R (87)2 adopted by the Committee of Ministers of the Council of Europe on 12 February 1987 and Explanatory memorandum.

→ Parental responsibilities : recommendation no.R (84)4 adopted by the Committee of Ministers of the Council of Europe on 28 February 1984, and Explanatory memorandum.

European Communities in the international order / Jean Groux, Philippe Manin. – Luxembourg : Office for Official Publications of the European Communities, 1985.
163p.
At head of title: Commission of the European Communities.
ISBN 9282551377

European Communities legislation : current status. – London : Butterworths, 1988-.
Each annual supersedes preceding year's. Cumulative index wuth each quarterly supplement. Annual index published separately.

European Communities publications : a guide to British Library resources. – British Library. – London : British Library, 1983.
iii,46p.
ISBN 0712320156

European Community : bibliographical excursions / edited by Juliet Lodge. – London : Pinter, 1983.
259p; 24cm.
Includes bibliographies.
ISBN 0861872444 Hbk £17.00
ISBN 0861872460 Pbk £7.50

European Community : law in action / Stanley Clinton Davis. – Exeter : University of Exeter, 1986.
11p.

European Community : The Practical Guide for Business and Government. – London : Macmillan, 1983.
ISBN 0333262050 Hbk £18.50

European Community and GATT / edited by Meinhard Hilf, Francis G. Jacobs, and Ernst-Ulrich Petersmann. – Deventer, the Netherlands : Kluwer, 1986.
xvii, 398 p.; 25 cm.
Includes bibliographical references and index.
ISBN 9065442332

European Community and the Developing World : The Role of the Lorne Convention. – Aldershot : Avebury.
ISBN 0566056097 Hbk £29.50

European Community and the Mediterranean Basin : study on the consequences of the process of enlargement both for the Mediterranean zone and for the Community itself and the conditions necessary for the definition of a global and forward-looking policy of the Community towards the Mediterranean basin / Francois Duchene ... et al. – Luxembourg : Office for Official Publications of the European Communities, 1984.
175p.
At head of title page: Commission of the European Communities.
ISBN 9282547582

European Community Customs Valuation. – 8th ed. – Kirchberg : Commission of the European Communities, 1984.
Hbk

European Community environmental policy in practice
Vol. 1 : Comparative report : water and waste in four countries : a study of the implementation of the EEC directives in France, Germany, Netherlands and United Kingdom : by Nigel Haigh with Graham Bennett ... et al. / Nigel Haigh, Graham Bennett. – London : Graham & Trotman, 1986.
106p.
ISBN 0860105490
Vol. 2 : Netherlands : water and waste : a study of the implementation of the EEC directives : by Graham Bennett. – 1986.
96p.
ISBN 0860105571 Hbk
Vol. 3 : France : water and waste : a study of the implementation of the EEC directives : by Thierry Lavoux. – 1986.
vi,104p.
ISBN 0860106322 Hbk
Vol. 4 : Federal Republic of Germany : water and waste : a study of the implementation of the EEC directives : by Pascale Kromarek. – 1986.
x,133p.
A series of studies by the Institute for European Environmental Policy.
ISBN 0860106330 Hbk

European Community, International Organizations and Multilateral Agreements. – 3rd ed. – London : HMSO, 1983.
285p.
Describes relationships established between the European Community and world and regional intergovernmental organisations.
ISBN 9282537757 Pbk £3.90

European Community Law : Encyclopedia of, 3 Vols.
Incl. Vol. A. United Kingdom Sources. – Abingdon : Professional Books.
Llf

European Community law and national law : the irreversible transfer? / John Usher. – London : University Association for Contemporary European Studies, 1981.
96p; 23cm.
Bibliography: p85-91. - Includes index.
ISBN 0043410170 Pbk £6.95
ISBN 0043410189

European Community law in the United Kingdom / Lawrence Collins. – 3rd ed. – London : Butterworths, 1984.
xxxvi,233p; 22cm.
Previous ed.: 1980. Includes index.
ISBN 040626922X Hbk £17.50
ISBN 0406269238 Pbk £13.95

European Community Treaties, 3 Vols.
Vol. 2. – Edinburgh : W Green, 1985.
– (Encyclopedia of European Community Law Ser.).
ISBN 0421193603 Llf £170.00
Service for 1985 only (post-free). – Llf £105.00

European Community Treaties. – Edinburgh : W Green, 1983.
– (Encyclopedia of European Community Law Ser.: Vol. 2).
Llf £155.00

European Community's legal system. – 2nd ed. – Luxembourg : Office for Official Publications of the European Communities, 1984.
43p.
Bibliography: p.43.
ISBN 928254432X

European company law : a guide to Community and member state legislation / Belmont European Community Law Office. – London : Financial Times Business Information Ltd., 1986.
xviii,215p.
ISBN 090319998X

European Competition Law Review
Vol. 9. – Oxford : ESC Publishing Ltd, 1988.
Hbk £68.00

European Conference of Ministers of Transport
Principal Actions of ECMT in the Field of Road Safety. – European Conference of Ministers of Transport. – Paris : European Conference of Ministers of Transport, 1986.
443p.
Hbk

European consumer law : prospects for integration of consumer law and policy within the European Community : proceedings of the seminar held in Louvain-la-Neuve on May 14 and 15, 1981 / Th. Bourgoignie, ed. – Louvain-la-Neuve : Cabay, 1982.
x,425p. – (Collection droit et consommation).
Includes bibliographical references. At head of title: Centre de Droit de la Consommation.
ISBN 2870770901

European Convention for the Prevention of Torture and Inhuman or Degrading Treatment or Punishment : the text of the Convention and explanatory report. – Strasbourg : Council of Europe, 1987.
30p. – (H(87)4).
At head of front cover: Council of Europe, Human Rights.

European Convention of Human Rights. – 2nd ed. – Oxford : Oxford University Press, 1987.
ISBN 00198255098 Pbk £15.00
ISBN 00198255101 Hbk £35.00

European Convention on Human Rights : Cases and Materials. – 4th ed. – Cologne : Carl Heymanns Verlag, 1981.
440p.
Pbk £40.00

European Convention on Human Rights : collected texts / Convention Europeenne des Droits de l'Homme. – Dordrecht : Nijhoff, 1986.
xi,228p; 25cm.
Previous ed.: 1981. Published for the Council of Europe. Parallel English and French texts.
ISBN 9024732662 Hbk
ISBN 9024734010 Pbk

European Convention on Human Rights International Conference Proceedings. – Council of Europe. – Martinus Nijhoff.
ISBN 9024735394 Hbk £167.50

European Council and Agreements
Vol. 4, 1975-1982 /. – Strasbourg : Council of Europe, 1983.
Collection of international treaties concluded within the Council of Europe. Includes conventions on the legal status of children born out of wedlock, extradition, the suppression of terrorism and conservation of European wildlife.
ISBN 9287102031 Hbk £12.00

European Court of Human Rights
Bilingual Editions of Cases
1961: Lawless. – European Court of Human Rights. – Cologne : Carl Heymanns Verlag.
—European Court of Human Rights : its organisation and working. – European Court of Human Rights. – 1. – Strasbourg : Council of Europe, 1984.
various pagings. – (Press release).
'Information document issued by the Registrar of the Court'.
—Revised rules of court (adopted on 24 November 1982) / European Court of Human Rights : Cour Europeenne des Droits de l'Homme. – Strasbourg : Council of Europe, 1983.
90p.
—Summaries of the judgements delivered in ... / document prepared by the registry of the Court. – Strasbourg : Council of Europe, 1983.
Contains summary judgements not binding on the Court.

European Court of Human Rights : its organisation and working. – European Court of Human Rights. – 1. – Strasbourg : Council of Europe, 1984.
various pagings. – (Press release).
'Information document issued by the Registrar of the Court'.

European Court of Justice Practice and Procedure. – London : Butterworths, 1984.
ISBN 040626810X Hbk £56.00

European Court of Justice Reporter. – Oxford : ESC Publishing Ltd, 1982.
Pbk £140.00

European court practice / by John A. Usher. – London : Sweet & Maxwell, 1983.
xli,357p; 26cm.
Discusses industrial and intellectual property rights, external relations with the UN, the OECD, and North America, Euratom, ECSC, the financing of Community activities including a discussion of the background to Britain's budget rebate. Bibliography annexed to each chapter.
ISBN 0421267801 £32.00

European Democratic Group →Why do we sell butter to Russia? : and other common questions from the Common Market.

European Economic Community : Trade and Investment. – Matthew Bender, 1986.
ISBN 0000999064 Hbk £50.00

European Employment Handbook. – 3rd ed. – London : Engineering Employers Federation, 1985.
Hbk £25.50

European environment policy : air, water, waste management. – Brussels : Economic and Social Committee, 1987.
48 p.; 30 cm.
'Document prepared by the Studies and Research Division of the General Secretariat of the Economic and Social Committee.'. Includes bibliographies.
ISBN 9283001087

European environment review : the journal of European Community and international environmental policy and law. – English ed. – Brussels : Environmental Law Forum, 1986-.
Also published in French and German.

European Free Trade Association →Convention establishing the European Free Trade Association.

European human rights convention in domestic law : a comparative study / Andrew Z. Drzemczewski. – Oxford : Clarendon, 1983.
xiv,372p; 23cm.
Bibliography: p348-360. - Includes index.
ISBN 0198253966

European Human Rights Convention on Domestic Law. – Oxford : Oxford University Press, 1983.
ISBN 019825525X Pbk £12.50

European human rights reports. – London : European Law Centre, 1979-.
Irregular.

European immigration policy : a comparative study / edited by Tomas Hammar. – 1. – Cambridge : Cambridge University Press, 1985.
Includes bibliography and index.
ISBN 0521263263 £30.00

European insolvency practitioners' handbook : the AEPPC compendium of insolvency law and practice / edited by Sir Kenneth Cork and G.A. Weiss. – London : Macmillan, 1984.
xix,291p; 23cm.
Includes index.
ISBN 0333366158 £40.00

European Institute for Social Security
Balance Development of Long-Term Benefits : Proceedings of the European Institute for Social Security. – European Institute for Social Security. – Dordrecht : Kluwer, 1987.
392p.
ISBN 9065442898 Hbk £85.00

European insurance law : a guide to Community and member state legislation / Belmont European Community Law Office. – London : Financial Times Business Information, 1987.
ix,147p.
'The first edition of this report was published in 1982 and revised in 1983'. - T.p. verso.
ISBN 090210196X

European Insurance Law : An Analysis of Community and Member State Legislation / Margie Lindsay. – Rev. ed. – London : Financial Times Ltd, 1983.
Hbk £80.00

European integration : select international bibliography of theses and dissertations Europaische Integration : Internationales Auswahlverzeichnis von Dissertationen und Diplomarbeiten Integration europeenne : bibliographie internationale selective de theses et memoires, 1957-1980 / J.P. Siemers, E.H. Siemers-Hidma : preface, Ralf Dahrendorf. – 2nd rev. and enl. ed. – The Hague : Martinus Nijhoff, 1981.
xx, 412 p.; 24 cm.
English, French, German, and Italian. Includes indexes.
ISBN 9024725429

European inter-state co-operation in criminal matters/la cooperation inter-etatique europeenne en matiere penale / M.Cherif Bassiouni. – London : Graham & Trotman, 1988.
1500.
Contains the texts of the 18 European penal Conventions and Explanatory Reports, the lists of signatory states and status of ratifications, reservations and declarations by states, and resolutions and recommendations adopted by the Committee of Ministers of the Council of Europe on the application of these conventions.
ISBN 9024734657 £345

European Law and Institutions. – Edinburgh : Edinburgh University Press.
60p.
Hbk £2.00

European Law Centre →European human rights reports.

European law review. – London : Sweet & Maxwell, 1975.
Index in each vol.
ISBN 03075400

European monetary system--past, present, and future / by Peter Coffey. – 2nd rev. ed. – Dordrecht : Kluwer, 1987.
x,163p.
Includes bibliographical references and index.
ISBN 9024734460

European Parliament. – Kirchberg : Commission of the European Communities, 1984.
24p.
Hbk

European Parliament
Effective Parliamentary Control of European Finances. – European Parliament. – 3rd ed. – Kirchberg : European Parliament, 1989.
Hbk
—Fact Sheets on the European Parliament and the Activities of the European Community. – European Parliament. – 2nd ed. – Kirchberg : European Parliament, 1989.
ISBN 9282301265 Hbk
—Growing Together : European Parliament Resolutions on Inter-Institutional Relations. – European Parliament. – Kirchberg : European Parliament, 1983.
Hbk
—Rules of procedure / European Parliament. – Strasbourg : European Parliament, 1981.
108p.

European Parliament : Its Powers. – Kirchberg : Commission of the European Communities, 1983.
22p.
Hbk

European Parliament : towards a uniform procedure for direct elections / Sasse ... et al. : with contributions by Roland Bieber and Howard C. Yourow. – Luxembourg : Office for Official Publications of the European Communities, 1981.
viii, 449p.
At head of title page: European University Institute.
ISBN 9282525279

European Parliament and Article 173 of the EEC Treaty / by John Barnard. – Florence : European University Institute, 1987.
59p.

European Parliament, Directorate General for Research
Forging ahead : thirty years of the European Parliament 1952- 1982 / European Parliament. – S.l. : Directorate-General for Research and Documentation, 1982.
237p.
Bibliography: p.215-220. - Includes index.

European Patent Applications Questions and Answers. – London : Oyez Longman, 1984.
ISBN 085120855X Hbk £32.00

European Patent Office →How to get a European patent : guide for applicants.
→ Official journal of the European Patent Office.

European Patent Office reports. – Oxford : ESC Publishing Ltd., 1986-.

European Patent Sourcefinder. – London : Longman Professional.
ISBN 0851214517 Llf £95.00

European Patents Handbook, 3 Vols. – Chartered Institute of Patent Agents. – London : Oyez Longman, 1983.
ISBN 0851203299 Hbk £145.00

European Patents Handbook. – Matthew Bender.
ISBN 0000999075 Hbk £205.00

European prison rules : recommendation no. R (87)3 adopted by the Committee of Ministers of the Council of Europe on 12 February 1987 and Explanatory memorandum. – Council of Europe. – Strasbourg : Council of Europe, 1987.
92p.
At head of cover title : Council of Europe, Legal Affairs.
ISBN 9287110352

European regulation of advertising : supranational regulation of advertising in the European economic community / by Rein Rijkens, Gordon E. Miracle. – Amsterdam : North-Holland, 1986.
xxxiv, 375 p.; 25 cm.
Includes index. Bibliography: p. 337-358.
ISBN 0444879722

European Science Foundation →Medical responsibility in Western Europe : research study of the European Science Foundation.

European Social Charter. – Strasbourg : Council of Europe, 1961.
ISBN 9287100888 Hbk £1.00
Addendum to Conclusions 6: Iceland's First Report. – 1983.
ISBN 9287102287
Case-Law on the European Social Charater. – 1982.
Hbk £4.50

European Social Charter. – Council of Europe. – Strasbourg : Directorate of Press and Information, 1981.
36p.

European tax law for companies / Charles Ferrier. – London : Financial Times Business Information, 1985.
xii,130p; 30cm.
ISBN 0903199890 spiral

European trade unions in figures. – Kluwer Law and Taxation, 1989.
Presents a comparative set of data and sources on union membership in ten European countries - Austria, Denmark, France, West Germany, Italy, the Netherlands, Norway, Sweden, Switzerland and the UK. Gives emphasis to comparative definitions of union membership and union density, that is, the ratio of actual to potential memberships.
ISBN 9065444092 Pbk £24.50/Dfl 79

European Treaties Vocabulary. – Luxembourg : Office for Official Publications of the European Communities, 1984.
311p.
ISBN 9282540456 Pbk £800.00

European Treaties Vocabulary, Part 1. – Luxembourg : Office for Official Publications of the European Communities, 1985.
683p.
ISBN 9282546950 Pbk £1,000.00

European union : one character in search of an author / by Giulio Andreotti. – Luxembourg : Office for Official Publications of the European Communities, 1985.
24p.

European union or decline : to be or not to be / by Gaston Thorn. – Luxembourg : Office for Official Publications of the European Communities, 1984.
23p; 23cm.
Seventh Jean Monnet lecture delivered at the European University Institute, Florence, 24 May 1984.

European Union treaty : commentary on the draft adopted by the European Parliament on 14 February 1984 / by Francesco Capotorti ... et al. – Oxford : Clarendon, 1986.
xii,327p; 23cm.
Bibliography: p325-327. Translation of: Le Traite d'union europeenne.
ISBN 0198255489 £35.00

European University Institute →Change and stability in international law-making.
→ Draft Treaty establishing the European Union : constitutional and political implications in Denmark.
→ European Parliament : towards a uniform procedure for direct elections.
→ Institutions and the decision-making process in the Draft Treaty establishing the European Union.
→ Integration through law : Europe and the American federal experience : a series.
→ Legal and economic analyses on multinational enterprises.

European Yearbook in the Sociology of Law 1988 see under 306. – Luxembourg : Office for Official Publications of the European Communities.

European-Atlantic Movement
All-in-One Guide to European-Atlantic Organisations : Intergovernmental and Supporting Voluntary Bodies : What They Are, What They Do, and Where to Get Further Information. – European-Atlantic Movement. – 9th ed., revised ed. – Exeter : European Atlantic Movement, 1985.
ISBN 0854500057 Hbk £0.25

Europeans, You Have Rights. – Luxembourg : Office for Official Publications of the European Communities, 1987.
48p.
ISBN 9282566854 Pbk

Eurovoc : annex to the index of the Official journal of the European Communities. – 2nd ed. 2. – Luxembourg : Office for Official Publications of the European Communities, 1987.
Previous ed.: 1984. Contents: 1 Alphabetical thesaurus - 2 Subject-oriented thesaurus. Also published in eight other languages.
ISBN 9277258314

EUSIDIC database guide. – Oxford : Learned Information, 1983.
ISBN 0904933377

Evaluating competencies : forensic assessments and instruments / Thomas Grisso. – New York : Plenum, 1986.
x,404p; 24cm.
Bibliography: p365-383. - Includes index.
ISBN 0306421267

Evaluating Police Work : An Action Research Project / Horton. – Policy Studies Institute.
ISBN 0853743533 Pbk £7.95

Evaluating witness evidence : recent psychological research and new perspectives / edited by Sally M.A. Lloyd-Bostock and Brian R. Clifford. – Chichester : Wiley, 1983.
x,305p; 24cm.
Includes bibliographies and index.
ISBN 0471104639 Hbk

Evaluation in the Criminal Justice Services. – Canberra : Australian Institute of Criminology.
free

Evaluation of fines enforcement / written and researched by Robert Brown ... et al. – Wellington : Department of Justice, 1985.
xiv,316,98p. – (Study series).
Bibliography: p.313-316. - Includes index.

Evaluation of legal aid : final report. – 1 v. – Montreal? : Ministere de la justice du Quebec, Service de la statistique, 1983.
various pagings.
Includes bibliographical references.

Evaluation of the Canadian gun control legislation : final report / by Elisabeth Scarff. – Ottawa : Ministry of the Solicitor General, 1983.
xxiv,217p.
Includes English and French parallel texts of the Criminal Law Amendment Act 1977. 'A research report prepared under contract with the Research Division of the Programs Branch, Ministry of the Solicitor General of Canada' - t.p. verso.
ISBN 0660114046 Hbk
Executive summary / by Elisabeth Scarff. – 1983.
14,17p.
With French t.p.: L'Evaluation des mesures legislatives canadiennes relatives au controle des armes a feu: rapport final: resume. English and French text.
ISBN 0662526015 Hbk

Evaluation of the children's advocate scheme pilot in the Auckland Children and Young Persons Court / by Dr. Terrence Loomis : a study commissioned by the Department of Justice. – Auckland : Social Research and Development Trust, 1985.
88,26p.
'Carried out for the Department of Justice by the Social Research and Development Trust of Auckland'. - Abstract.

Evans
Negotiating shorter working hours / Palmer. – London : Macmillan, 1985.
ISBN 0333388585 Hbk £29.50

Evans, Alastair
How to comply with the Data Protection Act : policies, practice and procedures / Alastair Evans and Anthony Korn in association with Percom Limited. – Aldershot : Gower, 1986.
vii,211p; 31cm.
Includes index.
ISBN 0566026325 £22.50

Evans, David Lloyd →Butterworths landlord and tenant handbook.
—Landlord and Tenant / Smith. – 2nd ed. – London : Butterworths, 1985.
ISBN 0406577323 Hbk £28.00
ISBN 0406577331 Pbk £17.95
—Law of landlord and tenant / Evans. – 2nd ed. – London : Butterworths, 1985.
xlvii,505p.
Previous ed.: 1974. Includes index.
ISBN 0406577323 Hbk £22.00
ISBN 0406577331 Pbk £14.50

Evans, Dennis
Tolley's trading within the European Community : a United Kingdom executive guide / Dennis Evans. – Croydon : Tolley, 1983.
xviii,212p; 30cm.
Bibliography: p206-208. - Includes index. Cover title: Trading within the European Community.
ISBN 085459132X Pbk

Evans, E. P.
Criminal prosecution and capital punishment of animals / E.P. Evans. – London : Faber, 1987.
xxxi,336p; 20cm.
Facsimile of: ed. published London : Heinemann, 1906. Bibliography: p314-323. - Includes index.
ISBN 057114893X Pbk £4.95

Evans, J. M. →Administrative law : cases, text, and materials.
—Administrative Law : Cases, Text and Materials / H. N. Janisch. – 2nd ed. – Aurora : Canada Law Book Co, 1984.
1100p. – (Case Books).
This text deals with the complex problems that arise in a wide range of governmental and regulatory contexts. Among other topics, the text discusses the impact of the Charter on administrative procedure, the emergence of the 'rational basis' test in jurisdiction cases and its relevance in other contexts, and the Constitutional right to judicial review.
Hbk £90.00

—Immigration law / by J.M. Evans. – 2nd ed. – London : Sweet & Maxwell, 1983.
xxx,452p; 19cm.
Previous ed.: 1976. Includes index.
ISBN 0421299509 Hbk £
ISBN 0421299606 Pbk £7.50

Evans, Keith
Advocacy at the Bar : a beginner's guide / written and illustrated by Keith Evans. – London : Financial Training, 1983.
ix,201p.
ISBN 0906322235

Evans, Keith R.
Law of defamation in Singapore and Malaysia. – Singapore : Malayan Law Journal, 1988.
ca 200p.
Gives a thorough discussion of the principle aspects of a defamation action, with precedents, and a review of the principles expounded in the local cases and legislation. Appendices cover the relevant statutory provision, cases judicially considered, statutes judicially considered, and a damage digest.
ISBN 9971700611 Hbk £90.00

Evans, Malcolm D
Relevant Circumstances and Maritime Delimitation. – Oxford : Clarendon Press. – (Oxford Monographs in International Law).
ISBN 0198252404 Hbk £30.00

Evans, Michael
Equity. – North Ryde : Butterworths (Australia).
ISBN 0409494801 Pbk £7.00
—Outline of Equity and Trusts. – Butterworths, 1988.
xlii, 365p.
This introductory text covers such areas as the nature of equity, equity assignments, fiduciary obligations, marshalling, contribution, subrogation, discretionary trusts, charitable trusts, and the rights of beneficiaries.
ISBN 0409493767 Hbk £45.00
ISBN 0409493546 Pbk £35.00

—Trusts . – Butterworths, 1989.
ca 98p.
ISBN 040949481X Pbk £10.95

Evans, Michael B.
Sources of English Legal and Constitutional History / R. Ian Jack. – Sydney : Butterworths.
This book gives a collection of prominent sources of the legal and constitutional history of England for students of the subject. The work includes materials ranging from the Dooms of the Anglo-Saxon Kings to the Equal Franchise Act of 1928.
ISBN 0409493821 Hbk

Evans, P.J.
Statutory interpretation : problems in communication. – Auckland : Oxford University Press (NZ), 1989.
256.
An introduction to statutory interpretation, dealing with common problems in the application of statutes to particular cases and with the common law method of statutory interpretation.
ISBN 019558189X Pbk £20.00

Evans, Robert G. →Lawyers and the consumer interest : regulating the market for legal services.

Evans, W. D.
Collection of Statutes Connected With the General Administration of Law, 8 Vols. – Repr. of 1817 ed. – Abingdon : Professional Books.
116p.
Hbk £40.00

Evatt, Herbert Vere
Guide to Family Law. – Kensington : Bay Books.
Pbk £3.95
—Royal prerogative / by H.V. Evatt : commentary by Leslie Zines : foreword by Sir Ninian Stephen. – Sydney : Law Book Co. Ltd, 1987.
xviii, 34, 282 p.; 25 cm.
Includes bibliographical references and index.
ISBN 0455207569

Eve in the East. – Bombay : Jaico Publishing House.
Hbk £20.00

Eve, Judith
Divorce : The Financial Consequences. – Belfast : Queen's University of Belfast, 1986.
30p.
Pbk
—Domestic Proceedings in Magistrates' Courts. – Belfast : Queen's University of Belfast, 1984.
26p.
Pbk £1.95

Ever closer union : a critical analysis of the draft treaty establishing the European Union / Roland Bieber, Jean-Paul Jacque, Joseph H. H. Weiler. – Luxembourg : Office for Official Publications of the European Communities, 1985.
345p.
At head of title page: Commission of the European Communities.
ISBN 9282552209

Everett, D.
Financial Institutions Law / S.A. McCracken. – Wamberal : Serendip Publications.
ISBN 0949379034 Hbk £19.00

Everton
Public Law and the Retail Sector Oxford Reports on Retailing / Hughes. – London : Longman Professional.
ISBN 0582037352 Pbk £40.00

Every Man His Own Income Tax Consultant. – Cape Town : Legal & Financial Publishing.
Hbk £17.50

Every Man's Own Lawyer. – 71st ed. – London : Macmillan, 1981.
896p.
ISBN 0333218493 Hbk £15.00
ISBN 0333318358 Pbk £7.95

Every Woman's Guide to the Law. – Markham : Fitzhenry and Whiteside.
256p.
ISBN 0889026459 Pbk £9.95

Everybody's Book of Law. – 3rd rev. ed. – Allahabad : Orient Law House.
ca 256p.
ISBN 0861314573 Hbk £90.00
ISBN 0861314581 Pbk £45.00

Everyday Law : a Survival Guide for Canadians / Marjorie Harris. – Toronto : Key Key Porter Books, 1987.
224p.
ISBN 1550130412 Pbk £14.95

Everywoman Guide to Consumer Rights. – Unwin Paperbacks.
ISBN 0044402945 Pbk £3.50

Evidence
Research paper no. 1 : Comparison of evidence legislation applying in federal courts and courts of the territories / Australian Law Reform Commission. – Sydney : The Commission, 1981.
xiii,468p.
Research paper no. 2 : Common law evidence : areas of disagreement and uncertainty / Australian Law Reform Commission. – 1981.
viii,233p.
Bibliography: p.228-233.

Evidence. – Vancouver : Continuing Legal Education Society of British Columbia, 1987.
230p.
ISBN 0865043078 Hbk £70.00

Evidence / Law Reform Commission. – 2 v. – Canberra : Australian Government Publishing Service, 1985.
– (Report).
Interim report.
ISBN 0644013028

Evidence / Law Reform Commission. – Canberra : Australian Government Publishing Service, 1987.
xliii,320p. – (Report).
Includes index.
ISBN 0644013710

Evidence. – 6th ed. – London : Butterworths, 1985.
ISBN 0406570078 Pbk £21.95

Evidence /. – North Ryde : Law Book Co, 1984.
x, 78p.
ISBN 0455203423

Evidence / S.E. van der Merwe ... et al. – Cape Town : Juta, 1983.
xxxviii,450p.
Includes index.
ISBN 0702113778

Evidence. – Butterworths, 1988.
xxiii, 243p.
ISBN 0409995355 Pbk £60.00

Evidence : blood group tests, DNA tests and related matters / Scottish Law Commission. – Edinburgh : The Commission, 1988.
i,45p. – (Discussion paper).

Evidence : cases and argument / Peter Murphy and John Beaumont. – London : Financial Training, 1982.
xxv,469p; 23cm.
ISBN 0906322103

Evidence : cases and materials / J.D. Heydon. – 2nd ed. – London : Butterworths, 1984.
510p.
Previous ed: published as Cases and materials on evidence. 1975. Includes index.
ISBN 0406594872 Hbk £
ISBN 0406594880 Pbk £18.95

Evidence : common law and federal rules of evidence / Paul R. Rice. – New York : Matthew Bender, 1987.
xlvi,1212p.
Bibliography : pp.LR1-5. - Includes index. With a separate 'Teacher's guide'.

Evidence : Principles and Problems. – Agincourt : Carswell, 1984.
416p.
This textbook explores the historical background of existing Canadian Rules of Evidence and analyzes the rules in terms of underlying policy considerations. Numerous concrete examples drawn from hypothetical fact situations illustrate the general principles of the rules of evidence.
ISBN 0459364200 Hbk £34.50

Evidence : report on corroboration, hearsay and related matters in civil proceedings / Scottish Law Commission. – Edinburgh : H.M.S.O., 1986.
vi,63p.
Includes bibliographical references.
ISBN 010237886X

Evidence : report on evidence in cases of rape and other sexual offences / Scottish Law Commission. – Edinburgh : H.M.S.O., 1983.
vi,33p.
Includes bibliographical references. Includes Draft Evidence in Sexual Offences (Scotland) Bill.
ISBN 0102028842

Evidence Act, 1950 (Act 56). – Kuala Lumpur : International Law Books Services.
Hbk £12.50

Evidence & advocacy / Peter Murphy and David Barnard. – 2nd ed. – London : Published for Temple Lectures by Financial Training, 1986.
xi,227p; 22cm.
Previous ed.: 1984. Includes index.
ISBN 0906322960 Pbk £7.95

Evidence and Advocacy. – Butterworths, 1988.
327p.
ISBN 040949349X Hbk £59.00

Evidence and Procedure in Magistrates' Courts / Stephen Knapp. – London : Oyez Longman, 1982.
– (Oyez Longman Practitioner Ser.).
ISBN 0851202926 Hbk £12.95

Evidence and Procedure in Magistrates Courts / Knapp. – 2nd ed. – London : Longman Professional, 1985.
ISBN 0851208681 Pbk £19.95

Evidence and related subjects : specific proposals for Alberta legislation / Institute of Law Research and Reform. – Edmonton : The Institute, 1982.
iii,177p. – (Report).

Evidence in a nutshell / Stephen Seabrooke. – London : Sweet & Maxwell, 1981.
vii,84p; 18cm. – (New nutshells).
Includes index.
ISBN 042127820X Pbk £1.75

Evidence in Queensland : the Statute Law. – North Ryde : Law Book Co, 1986.
xxxix, 236p.
ISBN 045520618X Pbk £32.50

Evidence in Singapore. – London : Butterworths, 1988.
– (Singapore Law Series).
ISBN 0409995355 Pbk

Evidence in the litigation process / by Stanley A. Schiff. – 2nd ed. 2. – Toronto : Carswell, 1983.
xxxiv,1211p.
Previous ed.: 1978. Includes bibliographical references and index.
ISBN 045935650X

Evidence Law and Practice / Clegg. – 2nd ed. – London : Longman Professional, 1985.
ISBN 0851213502 Pbk £15.95

Evidence law of Liberia : statutes, cases and materials
Vol.1 / by Tuan Wreh. – 2nd ed. – Monrovia, Liberia : Wreh Agency, 1981.
vii,357p.

Evidence Law Reform Committee
Report on business records and computer output / Evidence Law Reform Committee. – Wellington, N.Z. : The Committee, 1987.
58p.
Includes bibliographical references. Includes extract from Evidence Amendment Act (No. 2) 1980.
—Report on corroboration / Evidence Law Reform Committee, New Zealand. – Wellington : The Committee, 1984.
59p.
Includes bibliographical references.

Evidence law reform stage 2. – Sydney : Law Reform Commission, 1985.
18p. – (Discussion paper).

Evidence of children and other potentially vulnerable witnesses / Scottish Law Commission. – Edinburgh : The Commission, 1988.
iv,160p. – (Discussion paper).

Evidence of the Society for Computers and Law and Technology and Law Limited to The Farrand Conveyancing Committee. – Society for Computers and Law. – S.l. : The authors?, 1984.
10p; 30cm.

Evidence, proof and probability / Sir Richard Eggleston. – 2nd ed. – London : Weidenfeld and Nicolson, 1983.
xiv,274p; 22cm.
Previous ed.: 1978. Bibliography: p262-266. - Includes index.
ISBN 0297782622 Hbk £16.50
ISBN 0297782630 Pbk £7.95

Evidence reference
Research paper no. 3 : Hearsay evidence proposal / Australian Law Reform Commission. – Sydney : The Commission, 1981.
v,174p.
Includes bibliographical references.
Research paper no. 4 : Secondary evidence of documents / Australian Law Reform Commission. – 1982.
v,87p.
Includes bibliographical references.
Research paper no. 5 : Competence and compellability of witnesses / Australian Law Reform Commission. – 1982.
vii,141p.
Includes bibliographical references.
Research paper no. 6 : Sworn and unsworn evidence / Australian Law Reform Commission. – 1982.
vii,133p.
Includes bibliographical references.
Research paper no. 7 : Relevance / Australian Law Reform Commission. – 1982.
iv,80p.
Includes bibliographical references.
Research paper no. 8 : Manner of giving evidence / Australian Law Reform Commission. – 1982.
x,255p.
Includes bibliographical references.
Research paper no. 9 : Hearsay evidence : which approach? / Australian Law Reform Commission. – 1982.
33p.
Includes bibliographical references.
Research paper no. 10 : The judge : adducing evidence and judicial notice / Australian Law Reform Commission. – 1982.
vii,154p.
Includes bibliographical references.
Research paper no. 11 : Character and conduct / Australian Law Reform Commission. – 1982.
xi,269p.
Bibliography: p.267-269.
Research paper no. 12 : Identification evidence / Australian Law Reform Commission. – 1982.
viii,96p.
Includes bibliographical references.
Research paper no. 13 : Opinion evidence / Australian Law Reform Commission. – 1983.
xiv,340p.
Bibliography: p.328-340.
Research paper no. 14 : Aspects of proof / Australian Law Reform Commission. – 1983.
xxi,119p.
Includes bibliographical references.
Research paper no. 15 : Admissions / Australian Law Reform Commission. – 1983.
xxxviii,340p.
Bibliography: p.334-340.

Evidence report / New South Wales Law Reform Commission. – Sydney : Government Printer, 1988.
xv,179p. – (L.R.C.).
Includes text of draft bill.
ISBN 0730555410

Evolution of Central Banks. – London : MIT Press.
ISBN 0262071118 Hbk £20.25

Evolution of giant firms in Britain : a study of the growth of concentration in manufacturing industry in Britain 1909-70 / by S.J. Prais. – 2nd impression. – Cambridge : Cambridge University Press, 1981.
xxii,321p; 23cm. – (NIESR students' edition).
Originally published: 1976. Bibliography: p302-315. - Includes index.
ISBN 052128273X Pbk £7.50

Evolution of law / Alan Watson. – Oxford : Blackwell, 1985.
xi,155p; 23cm.
Discusses theory that legal tradition is the most important factor in legal development.
ISBN 0631142983 £17.50

Evolution of Ocean Property Rights. – London : Trade Policy Research Centre.
Hbk

Evolution of rights in liberal theory / Ian Shapiro. – Cambridge : Cambridge University Press, 1986.
x,326p; 24cm.
Bibliography: p307-320. - Includes index.
ISBN 0521320437 Hbk £27.50
ISBN 0521338530 Pbk £8.95

Evolution of the British financial system / by D.T. Llewellyn. – London : Institute of Bankers, 1985.
59p.
Bibliography: p.59.
ISBN 0852971362

Evolution of the British welfare state : a history of social policy since the Industrial Revolution / Derek Fraser. – 2nd ed. – London : Macmillan, 1984.
xxxii,326p; 22cm.
Previous ed.: 1973. Bibliography: p303-322.
ISBN 0333359992

Evolution of the Constitutional History of India (1773-1947) : With Special Reference to the Role of the Indian Congress and the Minorities. – Delhi : Mittal Publications, 1987.
272p.
ISBN 8170990106 Hbk £160.00

Evolution of the international monetary system, 1945-85 / Brian Tew. – 3rd ed. – London : Hutchinson, 1985.
256p; 22cm.
Previous ed.: 1982. Includes bibliography and index.
ISBN 0091615615 Pbk £7.95

Evolution of the law of the sea : a study of resources and strategy with special regard to the polar regions / Bo Johnson Theutenberg. – Dublin : Tycooly International, 1984.
viii,261p; 25cm.
Bibliography: p97-111. Includes full text of United Nations Convention on the Law of the Sea. Spine title : The law of the sea.
ISBN 0863460410 Hbk
ISBN 0863460429 Pbk

Evolution of the modern Commonwealth : 1902-80 / Denis Judd and Peter Slinn. – London : Macmillan, 1982.
xiii,171p.
Bibliography: p153-157.
ISBN 0333308409

Evolving Indian Administrative Law. – Bombay : Tripathi, 1983.
xxii, 293p.
Pbk £45.00

Evolving Role of Statistical Assessments as Evidence in the Courts. – Berlin : Springer-Verlag, 1989.
ca 375p.
Hbk £68.00

Ewart, J. Douglas
Criminal fraud / J. Douglas Ewart. – Toronto : Carswell, 1986.
xv, 182 p.; 24 cm.
Includes bibliographical references and index.
ISBN 045938550X
—Documentary evidence in Canada / by J. Douglas Ewart in association with Michael Lomer and Jeff Casey. – Canada : Carswell Legal Publications, 1984.
xxxvii, 389 p.; 24 cm.
Includes bibliographical references and indexes.
ISBN 0459359509

Ewaschuk, E.G.
Criminal Pleadings and Practice in Canada. – 2nd ed. – Aurora : Canada Law Book, 1987.
Llf £82.50

Ewelukwa, D. I. O.
Nigerian electoral law / by D.I.O. Ewelukwa. – Lagos : Shelters International, 1983.
xii,252p.

Ewens, Douglas S. →Income Tax Law in Canada.

Ewing, K. D.
Civil liberties in Scotland : cases & materials / K.D. Ewing & W. Finnie. – Edinburgh : Green, 1982.
xiv,285p.
Includes index.
ISBN 0414007069
—Civil liberties in Scotland: cases and materials / W Finnie. – 2nd. – Edinburgh : Green (W.) & Son, 1988.
Covers law on liberty and police powers, freedom from discrimination, freedom of religion, of expression and of assembly. There are special chapters on the European Convention on Human Rights and Privacy.
ISBN 0414008448 Pbk
→ Right to strike in Britain/ the English floating charge.
→ Trade union democracy, members' rights and the law.
—Trade unions, the Labour Party and the law : a study of the Trade Union Act 1913 / K. D. Ewing. – Edinburgh : Edinburgh University Press, 1982.
x,249p; 22cm.
ISBN 0852244533

Ewing, Winifred Crum →Case studies on human rights and fundamental freedoms : a world survey.

Exact Abridgment of All Statutes : Magna Carta, 1641-1666. – 3rd ed. – Abingdon : Professional Books.
566p.
Hbk £45.00

Examination of Witnesses 2. – Vancouver : Continuing Legal Education Society of British Columbia, 1986.
202p.
ISBN 0865043000 Hbk £55.00

Examination of Witnesses. – Vancouver : Continuing Legal Education Society of British Columbia, 1985.
241p.
ISBN 0865042438 Hbk £45.00

Examination of witnesses in criminal cases / Earl J. Levy. – Toronto : Carswell, 1987.
xxxv,263p.
Includes index.
ISBN 0459308211

Excellence in diversity : towards a new strategy for higher education : the Leverhulme report. – Guildford : Society for Research into Higher Education, 1983.
79p; 21cm.
ISBN 0900868996 Pbk £3.75

Exchange Control Act, 1953 (Act 17). – Kuala Lumpur : International Law Books Services.
Hbk £6.50

Exchange of Information on Research in European Law. – Directorate of Legal Affairs. – London : HMSO, 1983.
112p.
Provides information on research projects in law currently underway in various European and non-European states. Gives publication dates and information on how to obtain copies of final reports.
ISBN 0119836300 Pbk £1.25

Excise Laws on Medical Preparations. – Allahabad : Orient Law House, 1983.
Hbk £130.00

Excluding Liability in Contracts. – Butterworths, 1985.
227p.
Examines the English and Australian models, and discusses the popular common law concepts of reasonableness and unconscionability. Includes a review of the major cases and legislation aimed at evolving acceptable solutions to the dilemma of exception clauses.
ISBN 0409995002 Hbk £48

Exclusion clauses / Richard Lawson. – 3rd ed. – London : Longman Professional (UK), 1990. – (Practitioner Series).
Guide to the use of exclusion clauses (as limited by the Unfair Contract Terms Act). Discusses ways in which an exclusion clause can become a contractual term, what loss or damage it covers, and how likely it is to be interpreted by the courts.

Exclusion clauses / Richard Lawson. – 2nd ed. – London : Oyez Longman, 1983.
xx,180p; 22cm.
Previous ed.: 1978. Includes index.
ISBN 0851207294 Pbk

Exclusion clauses in contracts / by David Yates. – 2nd ed. – London : Sweet & Maxwell, 1982.
xxvi,338p; 18cm.
Previous ed.: 1978. Includes index.
ISBN 0421286806 Hbk £9.75
ISBN 0421286903 Pbk £4.85

Exclusion of improperly obtained evidence : with special reference to the Police and Criminal Evidence Act / by David Wolchover. – Chichester : Barry Rose, 1986.
v,260p.
Includes bibliographical references and index.
ISBN 0859923800

Exclusion of Judicial Review : Administrative Efficiency Confronts Legitimacy of Power. – Delhi : Metropolitan Book Co, 1987.
349p.
ISBN 8120002679 Hbk £200.00

Exclusive dealing agreements in the E.E.C. : Regulation 67/67 replaced / by Valentine Korah. – London : European Law Centre, 1984.
xv,101p; 25cm.
ISBN 090745111X Pbk £17.50

Exclusive economic zone : proceedings of the 7th International Ocean Symposium October 21-22, 1982, the Japan Shipping Club, Tokyo. – Tokyo : Ocean Association of Japan, 1983.
82p.
Edited by the Ocean Association of Japan. Title also in Japanese.

Exclusive Economic Zone Claims : an Analysis and Primary Documents. – Dordrecht : Kluwer, 1986.
600p.
ISBN 9024732506 Hbk £350.00

Exclusive economic zone in international law / David Joseph Attard. – Oxford : Clarendon, 1987.
256p; 24cm. – (Oxford monographs in international law).
Includes index.
ISBN 0198255411 £27.50

Execution against shares / Law Reform Commission of British Columbia. – Vancouver : The Commission, 1987.
iii,88p. – (Working paper).

Executive Firing Line : Wrongful Dismissal and the Law. – Agincourt : Carswell, 1982.
240p.
Hbk £27.00

Executive instruments. – Accra : Ghana Publishing Corporation, .
Issued with: Ghana gazette.

Executive Law-Making Under the Economic Stabilisation Act 1948. – Auckland : Legal Research Foundation, 1984.
Hbk £13.50

Executive power of the Commonwealth of Australia / by H.E. Renfree. – Sydney : Legal books, 1984.
xxxvii,599p.
Includes index.
ISBN 0949553093

Executive Survival : To Your Legal Rights. – London : Kogan Page.
ISBN 1850913641 Hbk £12.95

Executorship and Administration. – London : Fourmat, 1986.
ISBN 1851900039 Pbk £12.95

Executorship and Trust Law and Accounts / Suresh Tanna. – Plymouth : Macdonald & Evans, 1985.
360p. – (M and E Professional Studies Ser.).
ISBN 0712104585 Hbk £13.95

Executorship and Trust Law and Accounts (FA88) : Account Study Text. – London : BPP.
ISBN 0862772443 Pbk £13.95

Executorship Law and Accounts. – 8th ed. – London : Butterworths.
ISBN 0409600733 Pbk £18.80

Executorship Law and Accounts / Ernest E Spicer. – 23rd ed. – London : Butterworths, 1987.
ISBN 0406679010 Hbk £45.00

Executorship, Trust Law and Accounts 2.5A. – London : BPP.
– (ACCA Practice and Revision Kits Series).
ISBN 0862772729 Pbk £7.95

Executorship/Trust Law and Accounts. – 2nd ed. – London : Pitman Publishing, 1986.
ISBN 0712107517 Pbk £14.95

Exemption Clauses and Implied Obligations in Contracts. – North Ryde : Law Book Co, 1986.
xxxviii, 290p.
ISBN 0455206813 Pbk £45.00

Exhaustion of Local Remedies in International Law. – Cambridge : Cambridge University Press, 1983.
ISBN 0521229472 Hbk £42.50

Exhaustive and Critical Commentary on the Customs Act, 1962, Vol. 1 : With Notifications. – Delhi : Vinod Prakashan, 1987.
1,121p.
Hbk £250.00

Exhaustive Guide to the Factories Act, 1948. – Delhi : Metropolitan Book Co, 1987.
424p.
ISBN 812000275X Hbk £150.00

Existential Phenomenology of Law, Maurice Merleau-Ponty. – Dordrecht : Kluwer, 1987.
256p.
ISBN 9024735203 Hbk £135.00

Existing and new forms of financing, University of Auckland, 27 May 1982 : papers presented at seminar / by David Ross, Rudolf A. de Monchy, Barry J. McWilliams. – Auckland : Legal Research Foundation Inc., 1982.
44p.
ISBN 0908581173

Existing legislative protection of the cultural and natural heritage of the Pacific region / Patrick O'Keefe, Lyndel V. Prott. – s.l. : UNESCO, 1982.
v,140p.

Expanding circle : ethics and sociobiology / Peter Singer. – Oxford : Clarendon Press, 1981.
xii,190p; 22cm.
Includes index.
ISBN 0198246463 £6.95

Expanding jurisdiction of the United Nations / M.S. Rajan. – Bombay : Tripathi, 1981.
xii,252p.
ISBN 0379207273 £30.00

Expansion of international society / edited by Hedly Bull and Adam Watson. – Oxford : Clarendon, 1984.
xi,479p; 24cm.
Bibliography: p453. - Includes index.
ISBN 0198219423 £25.00

Expatriate Tax Manual. – London : Butterworths, 1985.
ISBN 0406259968 Pbk £15.00

Expatriates Guide. – 2nd ed. – London : Longman Professional, 1986.
ISBN 0851212107 Hbk £13.50

Expediting Civil Litigation : A Study of Commonwealth Jurisdictions. – London : Commonwealth Secretariat, 1983.
ISBN 0850922313 Hbk £5.00

Expenditure budget process of the Government of Canada : a public choice rent-seeking perspective / Douglas G. Hartle. – Toronto : Canadian Tax Foundation, 1988.
xxvii,316p.
Includes index.
ISBN 0888080301

Expense of Time. – Law Society (United Kingdom). – 4th ed. – London : Law Society, 1986.
ISBN 0901064734 Hbk £3.00

Expenses in the Supreme and Sheriff Coourts of Scotland. – Edinburgh : Green (W.) & Son, 1989.
A follow on as opposed to a revision of Maclaren except where the position has changed since 1912. Unlike Maclaren, it includes all relative material regarding expenses relating to non-contentious business. With chapters on legal aid and additional discretionary fees. Also examines difference between a client or fund paying expenses and an unsuccessful party paying, as well as the extent to which Scottish solicitors 'subsidise' legal aid.
ISBN 0414008928 Hbk

Expensive Health Technologies : Regulatory and Administrative Mechanisms in Europe. – Oxford : Oxford University Press.
ISBN 0192617141 Hbk £25.00

Experience at a clinical research ethical review committee / Ethical Committee, University College Hospital. – London : British Medical Association, 1981.
7p.
Reprinted from: British medical journal, 14 No 1981, 283, 1312-1314.

Experiment in the Use of Citation Vectors in the Area of Legal Data. – Oslo : Norwegian University Press, 1982.
112p.
ISBN 8200064794 Hbk £61.00

Expert Evidence : Perspectives on Science and Law / Wynne. – Routledge.
ISBN 0415009413 Hbk £29.95

Expert Evidence, Expert Opinion and Evidence of Third Persons. – 2nd ed. – Allahabad : Law Publishers, 1982.
Hbk £22.50

Expert evidence in actions for personal injuries / Supreme Court Rule Committee. – London : Supreme Court Rule Committee, 1987.
4,1 leaves.

Expert systems : principles and case studies / edited by Richard Forsyth. – London : Chapman and Hall, 1984.
xii,231p; 24cm. – (Chapman and Hall computing).
Bibliography: p227-228. - Includes index.
ISBN 0412262703 Hbk £
ISBN 0412262800 Pbk

Expert systems and scholarly publications / Jean-Claude Gardin. – London : British Library, 1987.
30pin various pagings; 30cm. – (The Fifth British Library Annual Research Lecture).
Includes the text in French, printed t$ete-b$eche, under the title Systemes experts et publications savantes.
ISBN 071233114X Pbk ree

Expert Systems in Banking and Securities / Jeffcoate. – Ovum, 1988.
ISBN 090396936X Hbk £465.00

Expert systems in law : a jurisprudential inquiry / Richard E. Susskind. – Oxford : Clarendon, 1987.
xvi,300p; 23cm.
Bibliography: p271-292. - Includes index.
ISBN 0198255829 £30.00

Expert witness / R. H. Mildred : with a foreword by the Right Honourable Lord Diplock. – London : Godwin, 1982.
x,131p; 24cm.
ISBN 0711456801

Expert witness and his evidence / Michael P. Reynolds and Philip S.D. King. – London : BSP Professional, 1988.
x,160p; 24cm.
Includes index.
ISBN 0632018542 £17.95

Explanatory Handbook on the Water Supply Rules. – Kuala Lumpur : International Law Books Services.
Hbk £10.00

Explanatory Notes to the Customs Tariff of the European Communities : 23rd Amending Supplement. – Kirchberg : Commission of the European Communities, 1984.
44p.
Hbk

Explanatory Report on Protocol No. 6 to the Convention for the Protection of Human Rights and Fundamental Freedoms Concerning the Abolition of the Death Penalty. – Strasbourg : Council of Europe, 1983.
ISBN 9287102163

Explanatory report on the Convention for the Protection of Individuals with regard to Automatic Processing of Personal Data. – Strasbourg : Council of Europe, 1981.
41p; 22cm.
Includes the text of the convention.

Explanatory Report on the European Convention for the Protection of Individuals with Regard to Automatic Processing of Personal Data. – Strasbourg : Council of Europe, 1981.
Hbk £1.25

Explanatory report on the European Convention for the Protection of Vertebrate Animals used for Experimental and other Scientific Purposes. – Council of Europe. – Strasbourg : Council of Europe, 1986.
75p.
Includes the text of the convention.
ISBN 9287108633

Explanatory report on the European Convention on Offences relating to Cultural Property. – Strasbourg : Council of Europe, 1985.
35 p.; 21 cm.
'The text of the European Convention on Offences relating to Cultural Property is also reproduced in this publication'–P. 3.
ISBN 9287107955 Pbk

Explanatory report on the European Convention on the Recognition of the Legal Personality of International Non-Governmental Organisations. – Strasbourg : Council of Europe, 1986.
17p.
Includes text of the Convention. Drawn up within the Council of Europe by a select committee of experts under the authority of the European Committee on Legal Co-operation.
ISBN 9287108978

Exploitation of science and technology : a world force / by Sir Henry Chilver. – Southampton : University of Southampton, 1985.
At head of title page: The Fawley Foundation.

Exploiting the Business Expansion Scheme. – London : Longman Professional, 1987.
ISBN 0851212484 Pbk £17.50

Explosives Act, 1884. – 4th ed. – Lucknow : Eastern Book Company.
288p.
Hbk £48.00

Explosives, Malaysian Legislation On. – Kuala Lumpur : International Law Books Services.
Hbk £15.00

Explosives Manual. – Allahabad : Orient Law House, 1984.
Hbk £100.00

Export credit financing systems in OECD member countries. – 3rd ed. – Paris : OECD, 1987.
285p.
ISBN 9264129472

Export finance / by Angus Dunn and Martin Knight. – London : Euromoney Publications, 1982.
vi,154p.
ISBN 0903121328

Export Finance. – London : Sweet & Maxwell.
ISBN 0421333103 Pbk

Export For The Small Business. – London : Kogan Page, 1984.
ISBN 085038771X Pbk £5.95

Export (Incentives and Miscellaneous Provisions) Decree 1986 : with explanatory note on its provisions / prepared by International Trade Development Centre (ITDC). – Lagos, Nigeria : The Centre, 1986.
20p.

Export Trade, Law and Practice. – 8th ed. – London : Sweet & Maxwell, 1986.
ISBN 0420466509 Pbk £29.00

Exporting goods from the United Kingdom : export co-operatives and contract warehousing / by Paul Vaughan, with John Sykes and Derek Pool. – London : Thames Polytechnic, School of Business, 1986.
22 p.
ISBN 0948296046

Expression of consent by states to be bound by a treaty / Council of Europe Directorate of Legal Affairs. – Strasbourg : Council of Europe, 1987.
122p.
ISBN 9287110441

Expropriation Act. – Vancouver : Continuing Legal Education Society of British Columbia, 1988.
173p.
ISBN 0865043639 Hbk £75.00

Expulsion in international law : a study in international aliens law and human rights with special reference to Finland / by Matti Pellonpaa. – Helsinki : Suomalainen Tiedeakatemia, 1984.
xiii, 508 p.; 25 cm.
Includes index. Bibliography: p. 489-506.
ISBN 9514104730

Extension of customs jurisdiction over the Canadian Continental Shelf : a background paper / issued by the Honourable Paul Cosgrove, Minister of State (Finance). – Ottawa : Minister of Supply and Services Canada, 1982.
14,16p.
Added t.p. in French. English and French text.
ISBN 066252229X

Extension of the Statutory Sick Pay Scheme in April 1986. – London : Engineering Employers Federation, 1985.
Hbk £4.00

Extensions of Time. – King's Ride : Institute of Building, 1983.
22p.
ISBN 0906600685 Hbk £6.60

External auditor as privacy inspector : a study / by Deloitte Haskins & Sells and the National Computing Centre. – Manchester : The Centre, 1982.
38,7,5leaves; 30cm.
ISBN 085012381X Pbk £6.50

External debt rescheduling / Roland Plan. – Vienna : Manzsche Verlags-und Universitatsbuchhandlung, 1985.
x,276p. – (Law, economics, international trade).
Bibliography: p254-266.
ISBN 3214065572

Extortions under terrorist threats. – Council of Europe. – Strasbourg : Council of Europe, 1986.
14p; 21cm. – (Legal affairs).
'... prepared by a select committee of experts under the authority of the European Committee on Crime Problems ... The committee of Ministers of the Council of Europe authorised its publication' - p.3.
ISBN 9287108412

Extradition / presented to Parliament by the Secretary of State for the Home Department. – London : H.M.S.O., 1985.
23p.
ISBN 0101942109

Extradition : a review of the law and practice of extradition in the United Kingdom : comments on the report of an interdepartmental working party / Justice. – London : Justice, 1985.
4 leaves.

Extradition for Drug-Related Offences : A Study. – London : HMSO, 1986.
ISBN 9211480698 Hbk £9.00

Extradition law in Ireland / Michael Forde : with a foreword by Niall McCarthy. – Dublin : Round Hall Press, 1988.
xviii,260p; 24cm.
Includes index.
ISBN 094768624X £35.00

Extrajudicial dispute settlement / Clive M. Schmitthoff. – Deventer : Kluwer Law and Taxation, 1985.
18p.
Includes bibliographical references.
ISBN 9065442340

Extrajudicial executions in El Salvador : report of an Amnesty International mission to examine post-mortem and investigative procedures in political killings, 1-6 July 1983. – Amnesty International. – London : Amnesty International, 1984.
48p; 30cm.
ISBN 0862100704 Pbk

Extra-Provincial Corporations Act, 1983, Bill 103 : An Act in Respect of Extra-Provincial Corporations. – Ontario : Ontario Government Publications Service, 1983.
12p.
Hbk £0.50

Extra-territorial application of laws and responses thereto / edited by Cecil J. Olmstead. – Oxford : International Law Association in association with ESC Publishing Ltd, 1984.
xv,236p.
Proceedings of an International Law Association Conference, 11-12 May 1983.
ISBN 0906214289 £28.00

Extraterritorial Application of National Laws / G. Born. – Dordrecht : Kluwer, 1987.
72p.
ISBN 9065443061 Pbk £50.00

Extraterritorial control of competition under international law, with special regard to US antitrust law / Erik Nerep. – 2. – Stockholm : Norstedt, 1983.
xxvii,xvii,733p.
Thesis (doctoral) - University of Stockholm 1982?.
Bibliography: p.665-716. - Includes index.
ISBN 9118373127

Extraterritorial Effect of Antitrust Law on Transfer of Technology. – Veinheim : VCH.
– (IIC Studies in Industrial Property and Copyright Law).
ISBN 0895738279 Pbk £36.00

Extraterritorial jurisdiction / Law Reform Commission of Canada. – Ottawa : the Commission, 1984.
210p. – (Working paper).
Bibliography: p.209-210.
ISBN 0662136039

Extraterritorial jurisdiction : an annotated collection of legal materials / by A.V. Lowe. – Cambridge : Grotius Publications, 1983.
xxiii,273p.
Bibliography: p.269-270. - Includes index.
ISBN 0906496357

Extraterritoriality in International Trade : Canada and the United States of America Practices Compared. – Butterworths, 1988.
288p.
Study of conflicts of jurisdiction involving international busness transactions. Attempts to define the permissible limits to the assertion of jurisdiction to prescribe, to adjudicate and to enforce a rule of law under traditional principles of public international law and what these limits should be today in the economic field.
ISBN 0409805025 Hbk

Extrinsic aids to statutory interpretation / Attorney-General's Department. – 2nd impression. – Canberra : Australian Government Publishing Service, 1982.
v,25p. – (Policy discussion paper).
Includes bibliographical references.
ISBN 0644020083

Eyewitness identification : a system handbook / Gary L. Wells. – Toronto : Carswell, 1988.
xiv,142p. – (The Carswell law enforcement series).
Bibliography: pp.105-115. - Includes index.
ISBN 0459311611

Eyre of Northamptonshire : 3-4 Edward III, A.D. 1329-1330
Vol.1 / edited for the Selden Society by Donald W. Sutherland. – London : Selden Society, 1983.
lxxv,498,498p; 26cm.
Opposite pages of main sequence bear duplicate numbering. French text with parallel English translation.
Vol.2 / edited for the Selden Society by Donald W. Sutherland. – 1983.
vi,499-770,499-770,771-922p; 26cm.
Opposite pages of main sequence bear duplicate numbering. French text with parallel English translation.

Ezaj
Ezaj on Law of Crimes, 2 Vols. – 3rd ed. – Allahabad : Ashoka Law House, 1987.
Hbk £230.00 ea.

Ezaj on Law of Crimes, 2 Vols. – 3rd ed. – Allahabad : Ashoka Law House, 1987.
Hbk £230.00 ea.

Ezejiofor, Gaius
Nigerian business law / by Gaius Ezejiofor and C.O. Okonkwo and C.U. Ilegbune. – London : Sweet & Maxwell, 1982.
lxvii,531p; 22cm.
Includes index.
ISBN 0421301201 Hbk £32.00
ISBN 042129230X Pbk £16.00

Ezer, S.
Goods in Transit. – London : Matthew Bender, 1985.
ISBN 0000999058 Hbk £53.00

F.W. Maitland / G.R. Elton. – London : Weidenfeld and Nicolson, 1986.
viii,118p; 22cm.
Includes index.
ISBN 0297786148 Pbk £12.95
ISBN 029778885X £4.95

Fabian Society →Who controls training? : the rise of the Manpower Services Commission.

Fabiano, Elizabeth A. →Cognitive model of crime and delinquency prevention and rehabilitation, 2 Vols., Vol. 1 : assessment procedures.
→ Cognitive Model of Crime and Delinquency Prevention and Rehabilitation : Intervention Techniques, 2 Vols., Vol. 2 : intervention techniques.

Fabric of English civil justice / by Sir Jack I.H. Jacob. – London : Stevens, 1987.
100p; 18cm.
Includes index.
ISBN 0420475303 Hbk £18.50
ISBN 0420475400 Pbk £9.95

Fabunmi, J. O.
Equity and trusts in Nigeria / by J.O. Fabunmi. – Ile-Ife : University of Ife Press, 1986.
lii,301p.
Includes bibliographical references and index.
ISBN 9781360453

Faces, cases and places / memoirs by Fatayi Williams. – London : Butterworths, 1983.
xv,185p,16p of plates; 23cm.
Includes index.
ISBN 0406514771

Faces of justice and state authority : a comparative approach to the legal process / Mirjan R. Damaska. – New Haven : Yale University Press, 1986.
288p; 24cm.
Includes index.
ISBN 0300035675 £26.00

Facilitations of Proof in Medical Malpractice Cases : a Comparative Analysis of American and German Law. – Bern : Peter Lang, 1981.
approx 140p.
ISBN 3820470042 Pbk £31.00

Facing the future : a discussion paper on the ground for divorce / the Law Commission. – London : H.M.S.O., 1988.
51p. – (HC).
ISBN 0102479887

Fact Sheets on the European Parliament and the Activities of the European Community. – European Parliament. – 2nd ed. – Kirchberg : European Parliament, 1989.
ISBN 9282301265 Hbk

Factories Act, 1948. – 4th ed. – Lucknow : Eastern Book Company, 1984.
Hbk

Factories Act. – 2nd ed. – Allahabad : Law Book Company, 1967.
500p.
With 1986 supplement.
Hbk £100.00

Factories and Machinery Act, 1967 (Act 139) and Regulations and Rules. – Kuala Lumpur : International Law Books Services.
Hbk £25.00

Factoring. – Croydon : Tolley, 1984.
ISBN 0854591648 Pbk £17.50

Factoring and The Accountant In Practice. – Tolley Publishing.
ISBN 0854592857 Pbk £4.95

Factoring and the Lending Banker. – Tolley Publishing, 1986.
ISBN 0854592539 Pbk £4.95

Factors Affecting Sentencing Decisions In Rape Cases. – Canberra : Australian Institute of Criminology.
Hbk £0.60

Facts in law / Association for legal and social philosophy : ninth annual conference at Hatfield College, University of Durham, 2nd-4th April 1982 : edited by William Twining. – Wiesbaden : Franz Steiner, 1983.
ix,157p.
Bibliography: p156-157.
ISBN 3515038973

Factsheet / Public Information Office, House of Commons. – London : The Office, 1985.
No. 1 is revised ed., No 1984.
ISBN 01444689

Factums in Civil Appeals 1985. – Vancouver : Continuing Legal Education Society of British Columbia, 1985.
235p.
ISBN 0865042454 Hbk £55.00

Faculty Decisions : Three Series, 1752-1841, 37 Vols.
Incl. First Series, 1752-1801, 14 Vols. – Abingdon : Professional Books.
Hbk

Fagbohun, Funke
You and the law : layman's guide to rights and liabilities / by Funke Fagbohun. – Lagos : MIJ Professional Publishers, 1986.
xxii,211p.
ISBN 9782486035

Fage, John
Supreme Court Practice and Procedure. – 4th ed. – London : Fourmat, 1987.
ISBN 1851900365 Pbk £12.95

Failures of the Legal Imagination. – Witney : Academic & University Publishing Group.
ISBN 081228089X Hbk £23.70

Fair and efficient selection : guidance on equal opportunities policies in recruitment and selection procedures. – London : H.M.S.O., 1986.
50p.
ISBN 0117013013

Fair charges? : a review of controls over solicitors' costs / by M.R. Ludlow. – London : Waterlow Publishers, 1982.
x,64p.
ISBN 0900791802 Pbk £4.50

Fair cop : reforming the police complaints procedure / Patricia Hewitt. – London : National Council for Civil Liberties, 1982.
48p; 20cm.
ISBN 0946088012

Fair rents : a practical guide to the law relating to the rents of residential tenancies including the work of rent officers, rent assessment committees and rent tribunals / by John Prophet. – 3rd ed. – London : Shaw and Sons, 1985.
xxxi,243p.
ISBN 0721907024 Pbk £7.50

Fair to the family : a conciliation approach to divorce and separation / by Clare Dyer : illustrated by Claudia Aaron. – East Twickenham : Mediation in Divorce, 1988.
40p.
ISBN 0951313606

Fair Trading in New Zealand : the Fair Trading Act 1986 / Jones. – Butterworths, 1989.
198p.
ISBN 040978771X Pbk £65.00

Fairall, P.A. →Criminal Defences.

Fairest, Paul
Guide to the Consumer Protection Act 1987. – London : CCH, 1988.
ISBN 0863251358 Pbk

Fairhead, Suzan
Day centres and probation / S. Fairhead with the the assistance of J. Wilkinson-Grey. – London : Home Office, 1981.
v,39p. – (Research Unit paper).
Bibliography: p.34.
ISBN 0862520185
—Persistent petty offenders / by Suzan Fairhead. – London : H.M.S.O., 1981.
vi,74p.
Bibliography: p74. A Home Office Research Unit report.
ISBN 0113407068

Faithful Councellor or Marrow of the Law in English. – 2nd ed. Repr. of 1653 ed. – Abingdon : Professional Books.
278p.
Hbk £175.00

Falconbridge, John Delatre
Conflict of Laws. – Aurora : Canada Law Book, 1954.
Hbk £15.00

Falconbridge on Mortgages / McLaren. – 4th ed. – Aurora : Canada Law Book, 1977.
Hbk £27.50

Falk, Ze'ev W.
Law and religion : the Jewish experience / Ze'ev W. Falk. – Jerusalem : Mesharim, 1981.
238p.
Bibliography: p.237-238.

Falkland Islands dispute in international law and politics : a documentary sourcebook / edited by Raphael Perl : with an historic chronology and bibilography by Everette E. Larson. – London : Oceana Publications, 1983.
xiii,722p.
Bibliography: p. 691-722.
ISBN 0379112515

Falkland Islands gazette. – Stanley : Goverment Printing Office, 1891.
Contains proclamations and regulations. Vol. 1, no. 1 published as: Falkland gazette.

Falklands/Malvinas conflict : a spur to arms build-ups / Jozef Goldblat and Victor Millan. – Stockholm : SIPRI, 1983.
vii,63p; 23cm.
Originally published as: World armaments and disarmament in SIPRI Yearbook : London and New York, 1983.
ISBN 9185114308

Falklands war : lessons for strategy, diplomacy, and international law / edited by Alberto R. Coll and Anthony C. Arend. – Boston : Allen & Unwin, 1985.
xiv,252p; 22cm.
Includes index.
ISBN 0043270751 Hbk £18.00
ISBN 004327076X Pbk £7.95

Fallows, S.J.
Food Legislative System of the UK. – London : Butterworths.
ISBN 040701540X Pbk £16.95

Families in the future / final report of the Study Commission. – London : Study Commission on the Family, 1983.
56p; 21cm.
ISBN 0907051170 Pbk £3.25

Family : Australian family studies database Vol. 2 1985 / edited by Deborah Whithear. – Melbourne : Family Information Centre, Insitute of Family Studies, 1985.
xv,246p.
First annual volume published in 1984. Includes indexes.

Family and child law statutes / compiled by Oyez Longman Editorial Staff. – London : Oyez Longman, 1984.
x,711p; 23cm.
ISBN 0851208894

Family and child law statutes / Paul H. Niekirk. – 2nd ed. 1. – London : Longman, 1987.
23cm.
Previous ed.: compiled by Oyez Longman editorial staff. 1984.
ISBN 0851213480 Pbk £19.95

Family and child law statutes. – 3rd. – London : Longman Professional (UK), 1990.
Updated with 1988 and 1989 legislative changes including the Children Act 1989, plus the Adoption Act 1976.
ISBN 0851215750 Pbk £24.50

Family Assessment and Early Intervention / Simeonsson. – Merrill.
ISBN 067520996X Hbk £19.25

Family at Law. – Police Review, 1985.
ISBN 085164051X Pbk £2.50

Family at Law : In which the Hendersons find out what to do after an accident / Campbell. – London : Fourmat.
ISBN 1851900446 Pbk £5.95

Family breakdown, children and the law / by Gilliam Kerr. – Belfast : SLS Legal Publications, 1985.
xii,68p.
Includes index.
ISBN 0853892555

Family Company : Law and Taxation. – London : P..
ISBN 00851208258 Pbk £35.00

Family Court : the Legal Jungle. – Ashburton : Patrick Tennison Enterprises.
Pbk £8.95

Family Court Code. – Butterworths, 1983.
Discusses the Family Courts Act 1980, the Family Proceedings Act 1980, the Guardianship Act 1968 as amended in 1980, the Status of Children Act 1969, the Domestic Protection Act 1969, the Family Proceedings Rules 1981, and the Domestic Protection Rules 1983.
ISBN 0409601276 Hbk

Family court in action / David Barnard. – London : Butterworths, 1983.
xiv,281p; 26cm.
Includes index.
ISBN 0406556504 Hbk £
ISBN 0406556512 Pbk

Family Court reporter. – Chicester : Justice of the Peace Ltd., 1987-.

Family Day Care Services Act, 1983, Bill Pr019 : An Act Respecting Family Day Care Services. – Ontario : Ontario Government Publications Service, 1983.
1p.
Hbk £0.30

Family Dispute Resolution : Litigation and Its Alternatives. – Agincourt : Carswell, 1987.
118p.
Hbk £30.25

Family Finance. – Cambridge : Woodhead-Faulkner, 1987.
ISBN 0859414205 Pbk £4.95

Family home / by W.T. Murphy and Hilary Clark. – London : Sweet & Maxwell, 1983.
229p; 19cm. – (Modern legal studies).
Includes index.
ISBN 0421287403 Hbk £
ISBN 0421287500 Pbk £6.95

Family Home and Income Tax. – Agincourt : Carswell, 1986.
245p.
This work is a guide to the tax consequences of home ownership in Canada for tax practitioners. The book treats the subject of capital gains exemptions, home improvements, mixed use properties, recreational dwellings, and other tax issues.
Hbk £40.50

Family Income Support Part 4 : Widow Benefits. – London : Policy Studies Institute, 1984.
119p.
Hbk £3.85

Family jurisdiction of the High Court and County Courts : consultation paper. – London : Lord Chancellor's Department, 1983.
12p.

Family law 1981 / by P.R.H. Webb and J.G. Adams. – New Zealand : Legal Research Foundation Inc., 1981.
128p; 21cm. – (Seminar Papers Ser.).
Includes bibliographical references. At head of title: Legal Research Foundation Inc. Seminar.
ISBN 0908581122

Family law 1984 style / by P.R.H. Webb and J.G. Adams. – Auckland : Legal Research Foundation, 1984.
182p.
Includes bibliographical references. At head of title: Legal Research Foundation Inc. Seminar.
ISBN 0908581327

Family law 1986 style / by Professor P.R.H. Webb and J.G. Adams. – 4th ed. – Auckland : Legal Research Foundation, 1986.
i,207p.
Previous edition: 1984. Includes bibliographical references.
ISBN 0908581416

Family law / P.M. Bromley, N.V. Lowe. – 7th ed. – London : Butterworths, 1987.
lvi,793p; 25cm.
Previous ed. 1981. Includes index. Cover title: Bromley's family law.
ISBN 0406560145 Hbk £38.00
ISBN 0406560153 Pbk £23.95

Family Law / Daniel J. Baum. – Toronto : IPI Publishing, 1982.
84p. – (You and the Law Ser.).
Pbk £7.95

Family Law. – North Ryde : Law Book Co, 1985.
lxxxvi, 685p.
ISBN 0455203075 Hbk £66.00
ISBN 0455203083 Pbk £49.50

Family law / Grant and Levin. – 4th ed. – London : Sweet & Maxwell, 1982.
xxi,146p; 23cm.
Previous ed.: 1977. Includes index.
ISBN 0421302402 Hbk £9.75
ISBN 0421282800 Pbk £5.50

Family Law. – 3rd ed. – Plymouth : Macdonald & Evans, 1986.
– (M and E Handbook Ser.).
ISBN 0712107584 Pbk £6.50

Family law : an interdisciplinary perspective / Howard H. Irving, editor. – Toronto : Carswell, 1981.
xi,215p.
Includes bibliographical references. Subtitle on cover: Law for the helping professions.
ISBN 0459333801

Family Law : Cases Notes Materials. – 2nd ed. – Agincourt : Carswell, 1987.
ISBN 045930261 Hbk £33.00

Family law : declarations in family matters / The Law Commission. – London : H.M.S.O., 1984.
iv,82p; 25cm. – (H.C.).
ISBN 0102263841

Family law : dimensions of justice : selected papers presented at the Judicial Conference on Family Law, 1981 / edited by Rosalie S. Abella and Claire L'Heureux-Dube. – Toronto : Butterworths, 1983.
xxxi,330p.
The Canadian Institute for the Administration of Justice brought together judges to consider developments in family law and its social milieu. Includes essays by judges, psychiatrists, an economist and a tax specialist.
ISBN 0409819700

Family law : financial relief after foreign divorce / the Law Commission. – London : H.M.S.O., 1982.
iii,115p. – (HC).
ISBN 0102514828

Family law : illegitimacy / Scottish Law Commission. – Edinburgh : The Commission, 1982.
170p. – (Consultative memorandum).

Family law : law of marriage and divorce in India / by Paras Diwan. – New Delhi : Sterling Publishers, 1983.
xxviii,470p.
Authors name on spine: Paras Diwan.
ISBN 8120702417 Hbk £150.00

Family law : matrimonial property / the Law Commission. – London : HMSO, 1988.
iii,30p. – (H.C. 1988-89).
ISBN 0102009899

Family law : report on financial provision after foreign divorce / Scottish Law Commission. – Edinburgh : H.M.S.O., 1982.
47p.
ISBN 0102515824

Family law : report on illegitimacy / Scottish Law Commission. – Edinburgh : H.M.S.O., 1984.
vii,134p.
Includes bibliographical references.
ISBN 0102186847

Family law : report on matrimonial property / Scottish Law Commission. – Edinburgh : H.M.S.O., 1984.
v,35p.
Includes draft Bill.
ISBN 0102467846

Family law : report on outdated rules in the law of husband and wife / Scottish Law Commission. – Edinburgh : H.M.S.O., 1983.
vi,53p.
ISBN 0102330832

Family law : review of child law : Care, supervision and interim orders in custody proceedings / The Law Commission. – London : H.M.S.O., 1987.
v,80p; 21cm. – (Working paper).
Examines the power of the courts to commit a child to local authority care. Makes proposals to reconcile existing inconsistency, simplify and improve the system.
ISBN 0117301825

Family law : review of child law : custody / The Law Commission. – London : H.M.S.O., 1986.
viii,233p; 21cm. – (Working paper).
Includes bibliographical references.
ISBN 0117301779

Family law : review of child law : guardianship / The Law Commission. – London : H.M.S.O., 1985.
viii,205p; 21cm. – (Working paper).
Includes bibliographical references.
ISBN 0117301728

Family law : review of child law : guardianship and custody / The Law Commission. – London : HMSO, 1988.
iv,112p. – (1987-88 HC).
Includes text of a proposed children bill.
ISBN 0102594880

Family law : review of child law : wards of court / the Law Commission. – London : H.M.S.O., 1987.
v,86p. – (Working paper).
ISBN 0117301833

Family Law : Solicitors' Considerations. – Vancouver : Continuing Legal Education Society of British Columbia, 1986.
165p.
Hbk £55.00

Family law : the Commonwealth experience / by Gloria Cumper. – London : Commonwealth Secretariat, 1984.
v,109p.
Includes bibliographies.
ISBN 0850922569

Family law : the financial consequences of divorce : the response to the Law Commission's Discussion paper, and recommendations on the policy of the law / the Law Commission. – London : H.M.S.O., 1981.
iii,23p; 25cm.
ISBN 0102068828

Family law : time restrictions on presentation of divorce and nullity petitions : laid before Parliament ... pursuant to section 3(2) of the Law Commissions Act 1965 / The Law Commission. – London : H.M.S.O., 1982.
iv,77p. – (HC).
ISBN 0102513821

Family law : transfer of money between spouses : the Married Women's Property Act 1964 / the Law Commission. – London : H.M.S.O., 1985. iii,29p; 21cm. – (Working paper).
ISBN 011730171X

Family Law Act, Rules and Regulations. – Sydney : Butterworths, 1988.
470p.
Pbk £29.00

Family Law Act, Rules and Regulations : Students Edition. – Butterworths, 1989.
ca 600p.
ISBN 0409303224 Llf £39.00

Family Law Agreements Manual. – Vancouver : Continuing Legal Education Society of British Columbia, 1986.
418p.
ISBN 0865042780 Hbk £135.00

Family Law and Population in the Pacific Islands. – Suva : University of the South Pacific, Institute of Pacific Studies.
Pbk £5.00

Family law and practice / Peter D. Reekie and Richard Tuddenham. – London : Sweet & Maxwell, 1988.
xxxv,415p; 22cm.
Sections cover divorce and other decrees; financial provision (including property adjustment); children; and family violence. Also contains a chapter on legal aid and legal advice and assistance, and discusses the courts and conciliation.
ISBN 0421360003 Pbk £13.50

Family Law and Practice for Legal Assistants. – Vancouver : British Columbia Continuing Legal Education Society, 1983.
208p.
ISBN 0865041040 Hbk £50.00

Family Law and Social Change. – Bombay : Tripathi, 1975.
168p.
bd £30.00

Family law and social policy / John Eekelaar. – 2nd ed. – London : Weidenfeld and Nicolson, 1984.
xviii,263p.
Includes index. Bibliography: p241-255.
ISBN 0297782746

Family law and social welfare legislation in Canada / Ivan Bernier and Andree Lajoie, research coordinators. – Toronto : University of Toronto Press, 1986.
xv, 133 p.; 23 cm.
'Published by the University of Toronto Press in cooperation with the Royal Commission on the Economic Union and Development Prospects for Canada and the Canadian Government Publishing Centre, Supply and Services Canada.'. Includes bibliographies. Contents: Family law in Canada and the financial consequences of marriage breakdown and divorce / Julien D. Payne – Family law and social welfare in Canada / Mary Jane Mossman – Development and trends in Canadian social law, 1940-1984 / Robert D. Bureau, Katherine Lippel, and Lucie Lamarche.
ISBN 0802072941 Pbk

Family Law and Society : Cases and Materials / David Pearl. – 2nd ed. – London : Butterworths, 1987.
ISBN 0406595925 Hbk £38.00
ISBN 0406595933 Pbk £23.95

Family law and the immigrant communities / David Pearl. – Bristol : Family law, 1986.
xxi,104p; 21cm. – (Guide and practice series).
ISBN 0853081026

Family Law Appeals and Injunctions. – Vancouver : British Columbia Continuing Legal Education Society, 1984.
152p.
ISBN 0865041679 Hbk £55.00

Family Law Awards : In Canada. – Toronto : Butterworths, 1987.
328p.
ISBN 0409843938 Hbk £65.00

Family Law Awards in Canada. – Butterworths, 1987.
304p.
ISBN 0409409843938 Hbk £70.00

Family law casebook / by Frank Bates and J. Neville Turner. – North Ryde, N.S.W. : Law Book Co., 1985.
xxxvii,732p.
Includes bibliographical references and index.
ISBN 0455203946

Family Law Council; 1982-1983 Annual Report. – Canberra : Australian Government Publishing Service, 1983.
70p.
Hbk £4.00

Family Law Council
Administration of Family Law in Australia : Report to the Attorney-General. – Family Law Council. – Canberra : Australian Government Publishing Service, 1985.
185p : Illus.
ISBN 0644039892 Hbk £7.50

Family Law Cumulative Index 1971-1982. – Bristol : Jordan & Sons Ltd, 1985.
Pbk £15.00

Family law, custody of children - jurisdiction and enforcement within the United Kingdom : report on a reference under section 3(1)(e) of the Law Commissions Act 1965 / The Law Commission and the Scottish Law Commission. – London : H.M.S.O., 1985.
x,277p; 25cm.
'Report on a reference under section 3(1)(e) of the Law Commissions Act 1985'.
ISBN 0101941900

Family law - illegitimacy / the Law Commission. – London : H.M.S.O., 1982.
x,379p.
ISBN 0102098832

Family law - illegitimacy (second report) / the Law Commission. – London : H.M.S.O., 1986.
iii,82p.
ISBN 0101991304

Family Law In 1985 : A New Look At Some Old Problems. – London : Law Society, 1985.
23p. – (Nineteen Eighty-Five Crash Course Transcripts).
Hbk £2.05

Family Law in Australia / Rebecca Bailey-Harris. – 4th ed. – Butterworths, 1989.
ca 517p.
This book, intended primarily for law students, places its greatest emphasis on matrimonial property, maintenance, and constitutional issues. Coverage is also given to areas which fall outside Commonwealth jurisdiction and differences in the laws of the various Australian states and territories.
ISBN 0409495212 Hbk £69.00
ISBN 0409495220 Pbk £49.00

Family law in Canada / by Christine Davies. – 4th ed. – Toronto : Carswell Legal Publications, 1984.
cl, 681 p.; 26 cm.
Re ed. of: Power on divorce and other matrimonial causes / W. Kent Power. 'Table of cases': p. xvii-cxx 'Table of statutes': p. cxxviii-cl. Includes bibliographical references, legislation, and index.
ISBN 045936300X Pbk

Family law in Hong Kong / Leanard Pegg. – 2nd ed. – Singapore : Butterworths (Asia), 1986.
vii,256.
Explains the current law relating to the family in Hong Kong. Deals with the transition from customary to enacted law, and notes the problems that have arisen, and could arise in the future. Covers marriage and concubinage, matrimonial causes, financial obligations to the family, and adoption.
ISBN 040999524X Hbk £80

Family law in Malaysia and Singapore / by Tan Sri Datuk Professor Ahmad Ibrahim. – 2nd ed. – Singapore : Malayan Law Journal, 1984.
xxvi,359p.
Covers the family law of non-muslims, marriage, and its effects on status and property, divorce and matrimonial proceedings, inheritance rights, the effect of marriage on the legal status of women under Islamic law, the dissolution of Muslim marriage, and inheritance rights.
ISBN 9971700395 Hbk

Family law in Scotland / J.M. Thomson. – London : Butterworths, 1987.
xxiv,232p; 22cm.
Includes index.
ISBN 0406261903 Pbk £20

Family law in the family courts. – 2nd ed. – Toronto : Carswell, 1981.
Previous ed.: 1973, edited by H.T.G. Andrews. Includes index.
ISBN 0459337300

Family law in the last two decades of the twentieth century : being a series of articles by a distinguished team of authors, first published in 'Acta juridica' 1983 / editorial board, T.W. Bennett ... et al. – Cape Town : Juta, 1983.
ix,243p.
Includes bibliographical references.
ISBN 0702114650

Family Law Journal / Elizabeth Walsh. – Bristol : Jordan & Sons Ltd, 1986.
Hbk £37.50

Family law, report on aliment and financial provision / Scottish Law Commission. – Edinburgh : H.M.S.O., 1981.
x,239p; 25cm. – (H.C.).
ISBN 0102002827 Pbk £8.40

Family law reports : incorporating Family law notes. – Sydney : Butterworths, 1976-.
Contains reports and digests of judgments of the High Court of Australia, the Family Court of Australia, the Family Court of Western Australia, the Supreme Courts of the States and Territories.

Family Law Reports Cumulative Index 1980-1984. – Bristol : Jordan & Sons Ltd, 1985.
Pbk £15.00

Family Law Reports. Vol. 6 / I. W. Crompton. – Bristol : Jordan & Sons Ltd, 1986.
Pbk £75.00

Family Law Review : 1981. – Vancouver : British Columbia Continuing Legal Education Society, 1981.
277p.
ISBN 0865040249 Hbk £50.00

Family Law (Scotland) Act 1985. – Edinburgh : Green (W.) & Son, 1986.
Full text of the Act with annotations reprinted from Scottish Current Law Statutes. The Act provides a new statement of the obligations of aliment and a new code for the settling of property and financial claims on a divorce.
ISBN 0414007840 Pbk

Family Law Service. – Butterworths. – London : Butterworths.
Service to Date.
ISBN 040610719X Llf £120.00

Family Law Service. – Durban : Professional Publisher.
ISBN 0409015547 £245.00 with binder
ISBN 0409015539 £25.00 binder only

Family Law Statutes. – Butterworths of New Zealand. – 2nd ed. – Butterworths, 1988.
516p.
ISBN 0409788627 Pbk £54.00

Family Law (SWOT). – London : Blackstone Press, 1985.
ISBN 0906322901 Pbk £7.50

Family Law Update. – Vancouver : British Columbia Continuing Legal Education Society, 1982.
226p.
ISBN 0865040869 Hbk £55.00

Family Laws of Islam. – Lahore : Kazi Publications.
Hbk £85.00

Family Mediation : Theory and Practice of Dispute Resolutions / Michael Benjamin. – Agincourt : Carswell, 1987.
320p.
This work is a comprehensive guide to family mediation, the process of resolving property support and custody issues with the aid of a third party in Canada. The effectiveness of various mediation efforts based on empirical studies is presented in the work.
Hbk £40.50

Family Planning Legislation : Euro Reports and Studies No. 85. – London : HMSO, 1984.
86p.
Report on a survey of family planning legislation in Greece, Italy, Morocco, Portugal, Spain, Tunisia and Turkey.
ISBN 928901251X Hbk £3.20

Family Practice in Provincial Court : Custody, Access, and Maintenance. – Vancouver : Continuing Legal Education Society of British Columbia, 1987.
306p.
ISBN 0865043450 Hbk £80.00

Family property / by Thomas G. Anderson and Michael Karton. – Victoria : Queen's Printer, 1986.
189p.
Date on front cover: 1985. 'A study paper prepared for the Law Reform Commission of British Columbia'. Includes bibliographical references.
ISBN 0771884931

Family property and financial provision / by J.G. Miller. – 2nd ed. – London : Sweet & Maxwell, 1983.
xlvi,517p; 26cm.
Previous ed.: 1974. Includes index.
ISBN 0421282401 £36.00

Family property in Scotland : an enquiry carried out on behalf of the Scottish Law Commission by the Social Survey Division of the Office of Population Censuses and Surveys in 1979 / A.J. Manners, I. Rauta. – London : H.M.S.O., 1981.
iv,45p.
ISBN 0116907797

Family Protection and Testamentary Promises in New Zealand. – Butterworths, 1985.
Discusses the principles behind the statutory provisions, and the cases in support of the Law of Family Protection and the Law of Testamentary Promises. Considers the amendments to the text if the statutory provisions dealing with Family Protection, particularly those which have given rights to new classes of claimants such as grandchildren.
ISBN 0409701432 Hbk £36.00

Family provision : law and practice / by John G. Ross Martyn. – 2nd ed. – London : Sweet & Maxwell, 1985.
xviii,187p; 22cm.
Previous ed.: published as The modern law of family provision. 1978. Includes index.
ISBN 0421342803 £14.50

Family Provision on Death (LPPN33). – 6th ed. – London : Longman Professional, 1987.
ISBN 0851210694 Pbk £14.95

Family Provision Practice. – 5th ed. – London : Oyez Longman, 1983.
– (Oyez Longman Practice Note Ser.: No. 33).
ISBN 0851207243 Hbk £8.95

Family Rights Group →Accountability in child care - which way forward?.

—Care cases : proposals for legal reform. – Family Rights Group. – London : Family Rights Group, 1985.
54p.
Includes bibliographical references.

Family Separation. – Butterworths, 1988.
192p.
ISBN 0409788708 Pbk £40.00

Family, sex and marriage in England 1500-1800 / Lawrence Stone. – Abridged ed. – Harmondsworth : Penguin, 1982.
446p,16p of plates; 20cm. – (A Peregrine book).
Previous ed.: London : Weidenfeld & Nicolson, 1977. Includes index.
ISBN 0140551670 Pbk £3.50

Family, state and law in Britain today. – 1 v. – London : Institute of Advanced Legal Studies, University of London, 1983.
various pagings. – (W.G. Hart Legal Workshop).
Includes bibliographical references.

Family Story. – London : Butterworths, 1981.
ISBN 0406176094 Hbk £14.50

Family Taxation Planning. – Monash University, Faculty of Law. – Clayton : Monash University Press, 1984.
ISBN 0867463422 Hbk £18.00

FAMILY thesaurus : Australian family studies indexing terms / prepared by the Australian Institute of Family Studies : edited by Deborah Whithear. – 2nd ed. – Melbourne : Australian Institute of Family Studies, 1987.
98p.
ISBN 0642118515

Family, Things and Succession / H.J. Erasmus. – 2nd ed. – Durban : Professional Publishers, 1983.
xvii,615p.
ISBN 0409040525 Pbk £79.00

Family violence : law & practice / Joanne Foakes. – London : Hemstal Press, 1984.
xvi,176p.
Includes index.

Famiy Law Reform Act, 1983, Bill 093 : An Act to Amend the Family Law Reform Act. – Ontario : Ontario Government Publications Service, 1983.
1p.
Hbk £0.30

Famous Advocates and Their Speeches. – Sweet & Maxwell, 1921 Reprint.
ISBN 0421376104 Hbk £15.75

Famous Criminal Cases of Sri Lanka, Vol. 4. – Colombo : Colombo Apothecaries Company, 1981.
Hbk £20.00

Famous trials / edited by Harry Hodge and James H. Hodge : selected and introduced by John Mortimer. – Harmondsworth : Viking, 1984.
375p; 23cm.
ISBN 0670803200 £8.95

Famous Trials sound recording . – South Yarra : Louis Braille Productions Ltd..
ISBN 12ac £60.00

Fanshawe, Elizabeth- → Disability and compensation claims.
→ Special damages for disability 1988.

FAO-ILO-IMO Voluntary Guidelines for the Design, Construction and Equipment of Fishing Vessels
French Edition /. – London : International Maritime Organization.
Hbk £3.00

Farano, Ronald J.
Farano's Income Tax Cases. – Aurora : Canada Law Book Co, 1981.
506p.
Pbk £42.50

Farano's Income Tax Cases. – Aurora : Canada Law Book Co, 1981.
506p.
Pbk £42.50

Farber, D.C.
Entertainment Industry Contracts. – Matthew Bender, 1987.
ISBN 0000999069 Hbk £197.00

Faribault, Genevieve → Life Insurance Laws of Canada.

Farm Bankruptcies in Ontario. – Ontario : Ontario Government Publications Service, 1983.
5p. – (Research Review: No. 13).
Hbk £0.50

Farmer, J.
Creditor and Debtor Law in Australia and New Zealand. – 3rd ed. – North Ryde : C.C.H. Australia, 1986.
333p.
ISBN 0869035908 Hbk £35.00

Farmer, Penny
Acid rain and the environment 1980-84 : a select bibliography / compiled and edited by Penny Farmer. – Letchworth : Technical Communications, 1984.
xx,108p; 30cm.
Includes index.
ISBN 0946655049 Pbk

Farming Futures. – Cambridge : Woodhead-Faulkner, 1984.
ISBN 0859412830 Hbk £12.50

Farnsworth
Contract Law in the USSR and the United States : History and General Concept / Mozolin. – London : Eurospan.
ISBN 0935328475 Hbk £26.50

Farrand Conveyancing Committee → Evidence of the Society for Computers and Law and Technology and Law Limited to The Farrand Conveyancing Committee.
→ Memorandum of evidence to Farrand Committee on Conveyancing Procedure and Practice.

Farrand, J. T.
Contract and Conveyance. – 4th ed. – London : Oyez Longman, 1983.
ISBN 0851207715 Hbk £15.95
→ Emmet on title : Emmet's notes on perusing titles and on practical conveyancing.
→ Introduction to New Zealand Law.
→ Non-solicitor conveyancers : competence and consumer protection : (the first report of the Conveyancing Committee).
—Rent acts and regulations amended and annotated / Andrew Arden, J. T. Farrand. – 2nd ed. – London : Sweet & Maxwell, 1981.
xl,435p; 26cm.
ISBN 0421282207 £16.50
→ Stamp duties for conveyancers.
→ Sweet & Maxwell's tax statutes 1984/85.

Farrand, Julian
Stamp Duty for Conveyancers / Roger Gregory. – 3rd ed. – London : Oyez Longman, 1983. – (Oyez Longman Practice Note Ser.: No. 48).
ISBN 0851206352 Hbk £7.95

Farrar, John H
Butterworth's Commercial Law. – Wellington : Butterworths, 1985.
Hbk
—Butterworths Commercial Law in New Zealand. – Butterworths, 1986.
Contains 48 chapters covering general principles of contract and quasi-contract, specific contracts, secured transactions and hire purchase, competition law, insolvency and dispute resolution. The law is as stated at January 1 1986. Appendices cover interests in land, New Zealand Courts, the present court structure in England and Wales, and a glossary of latin terms.
ISBN 0409702145 Pbk £86.90
ISBN 0409787574 Hbk £107.80
—Company Law. – 2nd ed. – London : Butterworths, 1988.
ISBN 0406581622 Hbk £38.00
ISBN 0406581630 Pbk £22.50
—Company law / John H. Farrar assisted by Nigel Furey, Brenda Hannigan with a chapter on company taxation by O.P. Wylie. – London : Butterworths, 1985.
xlvii,636p; 25cm.
Includes index.
ISBN 0406581606 Hbk £18.50
ISBN 0406581614 Pbk £12.50
—Company Law and Securities Regulation in New Zealand / Mark W Russell. – London : Butterworths, 1984.
ISBN 0409701688 Pbk £38.00
—Company Law in Australia / J. P. Hambrook. – Sydney : Butterworths, 1988.
544p.
Pbk £40.00
→ Hahlo's cases and materials on company law.
—Introduction to legal method / Anthony M. Dugdale. – 2nd ed. – London : Sweet & Maxwell, 1984.
xxiii,307p; 22cm.
Previous ed.: 1977. Bibliography: p296-298. - Includes index.
ISBN 0421297700 Hbk £10.75
ISBN 0421297808 Pbk £6.50

Farrell, Brian
DeValera's Constitution and Ours. – Dublin : Gill and Macmillan, 1988.
ISBN 0717116123 Pbk £9.95

Farrell, John → Irish Landlord and Tenant Law.

Farrell, Leonie → Compendium of human rights courses in Australian tertiary institutions.

Farrington, D. P. → Reactions to crime : the public, the police, courts, and prisons.

Farthing, Bruce
International shipping. – London : Lloyds of London Press, 1988.
Examines the framework that shipping operates in, including the institutions and bodies of both governments and the shipping industry. Includes the Liner conference system, and freedom and cooperation versus protectionism and confrontation. The historical background of sea law is also covered.
ISBN 1850441510 Hbk

Faruki, Kemal A.
Islamic Jurisprudence. – New Delhi : Deep and Deep Publications, 1988.
338p.
Hbk £280.00

Farwell's Rule of Nautical Road. – 6th ed. – Spon (E & FN), 1983.
ISBN 0870212559 Hbk £14.95

Fatayi-Williams, A.
Faces Cases and Places. – London : Butterworths, 1983.
ISBN 0406514771 Hbk £18.20

Fathoming Meech Lake. – Winnipeg : University of Manitoba, Legal Research Institute, 1987.
Hbk £18.00

Fattah, Ezzat A. → From crime policy to victim policy : reorienting the justice system.

Faulkner → Financial Services Act: Index.

Faull, Joathan
Joint ventures and Article 85 / Jonathan Faull. – London : Law Society Solicitors' European Group, 1985.
26p.
'Transcript of a talk given to the Solicitor's European Group on March 19th 1984'.

Favre, David S
International trade in endangered species. – Dordrecht : Nijhoff (Martinus), 1989.
424.
Discusses each article of the Convention on International Trade in Endangered Species, each with a separate chapter. Gives background information on the drafting of the treaty, problems of implementation and economic consequences of world trade in wildlife and plants.
ISBN 0792301145 Hbk £75

Fawcett, J. E. S.
Application of the European Convention on Human Rights / by J.E.S. Fawcett. – 2nd ed. – Oxford : Clarendon, 1987.
xiii,444p; 22cm.
Previous ed.: 1969. Includes index.
ISBN 0198255101 Hbk £25.00
ISBN 0198255098 Pbk £15.00
—European Convention of Human Rights. – 2nd ed. – Oxford : Oxford University Press, 1987.
ISBN 00198255098 Pbk £15.00
ISBN 00198255101 Hbk £35.00
—Human rights : our country in Europe : a public lecture / delivered by J.E.S. Fawcett. – London : Inns of Court School of Law, 1983.
11p; 23cm.
—Law and international resource conflicts / by J.E.S. Fawcett and Audrey Parry. – Oxford : Issued under the auspices of the Royal Institute of International Affairs by Clarendon Press, 1981.
xiv, 254p; 23cm.
Bibliography: p244-246. - Includes index.
ISBN 0198253591 £20.00
—Law and power in international relations / James Fawcett. – London : Faber and Faber, 1982.
140p; 23cm.
ISBN 0571105378 £9.50
—Lights on human rights / by Sir James Fawcett. – Strasbourg : Council of Europe, 1987.
13p. – (H(87)1).
'Prepared at the request of the Committee of Experts for the Promotion of Education and Information in the Field of Human Rights of the Council of Europe'. - t.p..
—Outer space : new challenges to law and policy / J.E.S. Fawcett. – Oxford : Clarendon, 1984.
vi,169p; 22cm.
Bibliography: p161. - Includes index.
ISBN 0198253982 £16.00

Fawcett, J. J. → Cheshire and North private international law.

Fawcett, Julian → Industrial relations : an international and comparative bibliography.

Fawehinmi, Gani
Bend and Bar in Nigeria. – Lagos : Nigerian Law Publications.
ISBN 9782325244 Hbk £100.00
—Cumulative and Comprehensive Index to (1985) NWLR. – Lagos : Nigerian Law Publications.
ISBN 9782325335 Hbk £25.00
—Law of Contempt in Nigeria. – Lagos : Nigerian Law Publications.
ISBN 9782325263 Hbk £15.00
—Murder of Dele Giwa : The Right of a Private Prosecutor. – Lagos : Nigerian Law Publications.
ISBN 9782325236 Hbk £20.00
—Nigerian law of habeas corpus. – Lagos : Nigerian Law Publications, 1986.
lxvi,457p.
Contains cases on habeas corpus.
ISBN 9782325163
—Nigerian Law of Libel and the Press. – Lagos : Nigerian Law Publications.
ISBN 9782325198 Hbk £90.00
—Quick Reference Index to NWLR Parts 1-67. – Lagos : Nigerian Law Publications.
ISBN 09782325334 Hbk £25.00
—Supreme Court of Nigeria Law Reports Vol. 1. – Lagos : Nigerian Law Publications, 1983.
ISBN 9782325010 Hbk £40.00

Fawehinmi, Fawehinmi, Gani, Gani
Nigerian Constitutional Law Reports Vol. 1. – Lagos : Nigerian Law Publications, 1981.
ISBN 9782325000 Hbk £60.00
ISBN 9782325007 Hbk £20.00

Fawhinmi, Gani
Digest of the Supreme Court Cases 10 volumes. – Lagos : Nigerian Law Publications, 1956-1984.
ISBN 09782325023 Hbk £1,500.00
—High Court of Nigeria Law Reports. – Lagos : Nigerian Law Publications, 1985.
ISBN 978232518X Hbk £100.00

Fawley Foundation → Exploitation of science and technology : a world force.

Fay, Edgar
Official referees' business / by Edgar Fay : Foreword by Sir John Stephenson. – 2nd ed. – London : Sweet & Maxwell, 1988.
xviii,170p; 25cm.
Looks at the developments in the Official Referees' Courts since 1983. Chapters cover the trying of cases outside London, the use of expert witnesses, and Scott Schedules. Contains a new chapter on the position of the Users' Committee, and how to make use of it, and one on construction litigation procedures.
ISBN 0421396903 £29.00

Fazal, M.P.
Judicial Control of Adminstrative Action. – 2nd ed. – Allahabad : Law Book Company.
Hbk £175.00

FCO press conference. – London : Foreign and Commonwealth Office, 1987.

Fear of crime in England and Wales / by Michael J. Maxfield. – London : H.M.S.O., 1984.
v,46p; 25cm.
'A Home Office Research and Planning Unit report'.
ISBN 0113407726

Fearne, Charles
Contingent Remainders. – Reprint 1986. – Professional Books, 1844.
ISBN 0862053161 Hbk £53.75
—Essay on the Learning of Contingent Remainers and Executory Devises. – 2nd ed. Repr. of 1773 ed. – Abingdon : Professional Books.
491p.
Hbk £85.00
—Posthumous Works : Consisting of a Reading on the Statute of Inrolments, Arguments in the Case of General Stanwix, and Cases and Opinions / T. M. Shadwell. – 2nd ed. Repr. of 1797 ed. – Abingdon : Professional Books.
338p.
Hbk £25.00

Feaver, George →Lives, liberties and the public good : new essays in political theory for Maurice Cranston.

Federal administrative law / by Geoffrey A. Flick : with a foreword by J.D. Davies. – Sydney : Law Book Co., 1983.
xxvii,251p.
Text of several acts and regulations, with commentary. Includes index.
ISBN 0455204489
ISBN 0455204241

Federal Constitution. – Kuala Lumpur : International Law Books Services.
Hbk £16.50

Federal Constitution (Handbook). – Kuala Lumpur : International Law Books Services.
Hbk £5.90

Federal Constitution of Malaysia : a commentary / by K.V. Padmanabha Rau : assisted by Hamid Ibrahim. – Kuala Lumpur : Malaysian Current Law Journal Sdn. Bhd., 1986.
xlvi,605p.
Includes bibliographical references and index.

Federal constitutional law /. – North Ryde : Law Book Co, 1984.
x, 86p. – (Nutshells).
ISBN 0455203482

Federal Court of Appeal Decisions (1981-Present). – Aurora : Canada Law Book Co.
– (Summary Services, National Series).
Hbk £99.50

Federal Court of Australia
Federal Court reports : the authorised reports of decisions of the Federal Court of Australia / editor C.A. Sweeney. – Sydney : Law Book Co., 1984-.
Indexes.

Federal Court Practice : 1988. – Agincourt : Carswell, 1987.
800p.
This is a comprehensive guide to the Federal Court Act, Federal Court Rules, Forms, Tariffs and related statutes. Also included is a guide to difficult jurisdictional issues such as the choice between Federal and provincial courts for commencing proceedings and locus standi.
Hbk £46.25

Federal Court reports : the authorised reports of decisions of the Federal Court of Australia / editor C.A. Sweeney. – Sydney : Law Book Co., 1984-.
Indexes.

Federal deceptive practices and misleading advertising law : judgements, materials and policy / Warren Pengilley and Alan A. Ransom. – Sydney : Legal Books Pty., 1987.
lxiii,1184p.
Bibliography: pp.1021-1022. - Includes index.
ISBN 0949553344

Federal finance in comparative perspective / Richard M. Bird. – Toronto : Canadian Tax Foundation, 1986.
x,250p.
Includes bibliographical references.
ISBN 0888080247

Federal High Court : law and practice / by A.G. Karibi-Whyte. – Enugu, Nigeria : Fourth Dimension, 1986.
xlvii,344p.
Includes bibliographical references and index.
ISBN 9781562412

Federal Incorporation and Business Guide : How to Form Your Own Federal Corporation Under the Canada Business Corporations Act. – 5th ed. – North Vancouver : International Self-Counsel Press, 1986.
122p.
ISBN 088908632X Hbk £14.95

Federal judicial system of Australia / by Harold Edward Renfree. – Sydney : Legal Books Pty Ltd., 1984.
xxxiii,802p.
Includes bibliographical references and index.
ISBN 0949553085

Federal Limitation Periods : a Handbook of Limitation Periods ad Other Statutory Time Limits, 1 Vol. – Butterworths.
Llf £65.00

Federal Power in Australia's Cities. – Neutral Bay : Hale & Iremonger.
ISBN 0908094043 Hbk £19.00, 015

Federal/Provincial Task Force on Uniform Rules of Evidence
Report of the Federal/Provincial Task Force on Uniform Rules of Evidence / prepared for the Uniform Law Conference of Canada. – Toronto, Canada : Carswell, 1982.
xxxiv, 615 p.; 26 cm.
Includes bibliographical references, legislation, and indexes.
ISBN 0459349309

Federal/provincial/territorial report on wife battering to the meeting of ministers responsible for the status of women, Niagara-on-the Lake, May 28-30, 1984. – Ottawa : Minister of Supply and Services, 1984.
460p.
ISBN 0662133250

Federal State of Canada Service, 2 vols. – Toronto : Butterworths.
Hbk

Federal Taxation : 1989 Corporation, Partnership, Estates and Trusts. – Prentice-Hall.
ISBN 0137032587 Hbk £45.65

Federalism : the founders' design / by Raoul Berger. – Norman : University of Oklahoma Press, 1987.
224p; 24cm.
Includes bibliography and index.
ISBN 0806120592 £16.50

Federalism and judicial review in West Germany / by Philip M. Blair. – Oxford : Clarendon Press, 1981.
xvii, 332p; 23cm.
Bibliography: p314-322. - Includes index.
ISBN 0198274270 £22.50

Federalism in Nigeria under the presidential constitution / by B.O. Nwabueze. – London : Sweet & Maxwell, 1983.
400p.
Includes index.
ISBN 0421316101 Hbk £
ISBN 0421315806 Pbk £16.00

Federation of Law Societies of →Legal profession and quality of service : further report and proposals : report and materials of a National Workshop on Quality of Legal Services held in Toronto in October, 1980, as a sequel to the National Conference on Quality of Legal Services held in Ottawa in October, 1978.

Federation of Nigeria law reports. – Ibadan : Evans Brothers, 1981.
Volume numbering begins anew each year.

Feeney, Thomas G.
Canadian law of wills / Thomas G. Feeney. – 3rd ed. – Toronto : Butterworths, 1987.
Volume 1 focuses on probate, containing new material on the support of dependants, the administration of settled estates, holograph wills and intestate succession. Volume 2 considers the rules affecting construction in relation to recent probate changes.
ISBN 0409810002 Hbk £140.00

Feenstra, R. →Some cases heard in the Hooge Raad.

Fees in Matrimonial Proceedings. – Format. – 4th ed. – London : Fourmat, 1986.
– (LCFS 9).
ISBN 1851900160 Pbk £3.25

Feher, Lenke →Papers : Hungarian-Finnish Penal Law Seminary on Petty Offences.

Feibleman, James Kern
Justice, law, and culture / James K. Feibleman. – Dordrecht : Nijhoff, 1985.
xiii, 208p.
ISBN 9024731054

Feilden, H. St. Clair
Short constitutional history of England / by H. St. Clair Feilden. – 2nd ed., rev. and enl. – Oxford : Blackwell, 1887.
xii,338p.
Includes bibliographical references and index.

Feiler, Herbert →Doing business in the United States.

Feinberg, Joel
Harm to others. – Oxford : Oxford University Press, 1984.
ISBN 0195034090 Hbk £22.50
—Moral limits of the criminal law
Vol.1 : Harm to others / Joel Feinberg. – New York : Oxford University Press, 1984.
xiii,269p; 25cm.
Includes index.
ISBN 0195034090
Vol.2 : Offense to others / Joel Feinberg. – 1985.
xix,328p.
Includes bibliographical references and index.
ISBN 019503449X Hbk
Volume 3 : Harm to self. – 1989.
444.
Looks at the problems associated with the commonly proposed principle of 'legal paternalism'. Evaluates and rejects the principle that it can be right to impose coercion on a person for her own good, regardless of her wishes in the matter.
ISBN 0195059239 Pbk £9.95
—Offence to others. – Oxford : Oxford University Press, 1985.
ISBN 019503449X Hbk £25.00

Feldbausch, F.
Banking Dictionary. – Cambridge : Woodhead-Faulkner, 1984.
ISBN 3478512433 Hbk £25.00

Feldbrugge, F. J. M →Distinctiveness of Soviet law.
→ Encyclopedia of Soviet law.
→ Perspectives on Soviet law for the 1980s.

Feldman, David
Criminal Confiscation Orders : the New Law. – London : Butterworths.
ISBN 0406105294 Pbk £16.95
—Entry Search and Seizure. – London : Butterworths, 1986.
ISBN 0406199108 Pbk £33.00
—Law relating to entry, search and seizure / David Feldman. – London : Butterworths, 1986.
500p; 26cm.
Includes index.
ISBN 0406199108 Pbk £27.50

Feldman, L.
Care Proceedings. – London : Longman Professional.
– (Longham Practitioner Series).
ISBN 085121309X Pbk £22.95

Feldman, Linda
Care Proceedings. – 2nd ed. – London : Oyez Longman, 1983.
– (Oyez Longman Practitioner Ser.).
ISBN 0851207235 Hbk £22.95

Feldman, Martha S. →Reconstructing reality in the courtroom.

Feldman, Philip →Developments in the study of criminal behaviour, Vol.1 : The prevention and control of offending.

Feldthusen, Bruce P. →Cases and Materials on the Law of Torts.
—Economic negligence. – London : Sweet & Maxwell, 1985.
ISBN 0459364707 Hbk £40.00
—Economic negligence : the recovery of pure economic loss / by Bruce Feldthusen. – Toronto, Canada : Carswell Legal Publications, 1984.
xxvi, 306 p.; 24 cm.
Includes bibliographical references and indexes.
ISBN 0459364707 Hbk £40

Felix, Richard →Commercial paper.

Fell, H.R.
On Being a Tenant Farmer : A Guide to the Tenant and Landlord System. – London : Farming Press.
ISBN 0852361815 Hbk £8.95

Fellner, Christine
Future of legal protection for industrial design / Christine Fellner. – Oxford : ESC, 1985.
xxxviii,210p.
A report commissioned by the Common Law Institute of Intellectual Property and the Intellectual Property Unit, Queen Mary College.
ISBN 0906214270

Feltenstein, Mary B
Trading with the Enemy Act. – London : Butterworths, 1988.
ISBN 0880631880 Hbk

Feltham
About You and Fostering / Goodman. – National Foster Care Association.
ISBN 0946015392 Hbk £5.90

Female circumcision, excision and infibulation : the facts and proposals for change / edited by Scilla McLean and Stella Efua Graham : with contributions from Marie Assaad ... et al. – 2nd rev. ed. – London : Minority Rights Group, 1985.
21p. – (Report).
Bibliography: p.11.

Female Criminality. – Lucknow : Eastern Book Company, 1985.
Hbk

Female sexuality and the law : a study of constructs of female sexuality as they inform statute and legal procedure / Susan S.M. Edwards. – Oxford : Robertson, 1981.
195p; 23cm.
Bibliography: p183-190. - Includes index.
ISBN 085520382X Hbk £12.50
ISBN 0855203854 Pbk £4.95

Fenema, H. P. van →International air transport in the eighties : including the proceedings of the first Netherlands Colloquium on International Air Transport, 'The Changing Scene', Wassenaar, August 25-29, 1980.

Fennel, Rosemary
Common agricultural policy of the EEC. – 2nd ed. – Oxford : Blackwell Scientific, 1987.
ISBN 0003833747 Pbk £15.00
ISBN 0632020571 Hbk £19.95

Fennell, Rosemary
Common Agricultural Policy of the European Community : its institutional and administrative organisation / Rosemary Fennell. – 2nd ed. – Oxford : BSP Professional, 1987.
xii,227p; 24cm.
Previous ed.: London : Granada, 1979. Bibliography: p215-220. - Includes index.
ISBN 0632020571 £19.95

Fenton, Steve
Durkheim and modern sociology / Steve Fenton with Robert Reiner and Ian Hamnet. – Cambridge : Cambridge University Press, 1984.
vi,276p; 24cm.
Bibliography: p260-273. - Includes index.
ISBN 0521259231 Hbk £20.00
ISBN 0521277639 Pbk

Fenwick-Elliot, Robert
Building contract litigation. – 3rd. – London : Longman Professional (UK), 1989.
– (Prctitioner series).
Reviews the forms of contract and contractual proceedings, and assesses issues involved between litigation and arbitration.
ISBN 0851214274 Hbk £35.00

Fenwick, Peter →Epilepsy and the law : a medical symposium on the current law.

Ferencz, Benjamin B.
Enforcing international law : a way to world peace : a documentary history and analysis / by Benjamin B. Ferencz. – 2 v. – London : Oceana, 1983.
xix,890p.
Includes bibliographies and index.
ISBN 0379121476

Fergus, T. D. →Introduction to European legal history.

Ferguson →Financial Services Act 1986.

Ferguson, Anthony
AJ Index to 1985 Building Regulations. – London : Architectural Press, 1986.
ISBN 0851398383 Pbk £7.50
—AJ Introduction and Complete Index to the 1985 Building Regulations. – London : Architectural Press.
60p : Illus.
ISBN 0851398383 Pbk £7.50

Ferguson, Marie E.
Carswell's Matrimonial Quantum and Custody Award Service. – Agincourt : Carswell.
Pbk £151.25

Ferguson, Robert A.
Law and letters in American culture / Robert A. Ferguson. – Cambridge, Mass. : Harvard University Press, 1984.
viii,417p; 25cm.
Includes index.
ISBN 0674514653 £22.50

Fergusson, Wilfred K. →Laws of Barbados : subsidiary legislation in force on the 31st day of December, 1978.

Fernandes, Christopher N. →Guide to company formation.

Fernandes, Rui M.
Annotated Canada Shipping Act / Christopher Burke. – Butterworths, 1988.
464p.
Deals with Canadian judicial decisions and Canadian legal literature. Includes recent amendments to the legislation itself and to the regulations. Shows how Canada deals with this form of international commerce.
ISBN 0409811459 Hbk
—Marine Insurance Law of Canada. – Butterworths, 1987.
304p.
Examines the Canadian judicial decisions in marine insurance, using as its basis the Marine Insurance Act, RSO 1980. Includes a table of statute concordance.
ISBN 0409805319 Hbk £48.00

Fernando, T.
Trial of Paulin Croos. – Colombo : Gunasena and Co..
Hbk £10.00

Ferndale : A Caring Repair Service for Elderly Home Owners. – Shelter. – London : Shelter, 1982.
ISBN 0901242632 Pbk £2.50

Ferracuti, Franco →Criminological diagnosis : an international perspective, Vol.2.

Ferrari, Italo →Development of maritime islands as extreme examples of peripheral regions.

Ferrer Vieyra, Enrique
Annotated legal chronology of the Malvinas (Falkland) Islands controversy / Cronologia legal anotada sobre la cuestion Malvinas (resumen) : Enrique Ferrer Vieyra. – Cordoba : Marcos Lerner, 1985.
173p.
Bibliography: p13-15.

Ferrier and Ferrier : UK Money Markets. – London : Butterworths, 1987.
This book describes the operations of the United Kingdom financial sector, concentrating on the principal methods of raising capital. Included in the work is coverage of the key elements in each market together with explanations of the significance of various instruments and forms of finance.
ISBN 0406100306 Hbk

Ferrier, Charles W →Credit Cards.
—European tax law for companies / Charles Ferrier. – London : Financial Times Business Information, 1985.
xii,130p; 30cm.
ISBN 0903199890 spiral
—Ferrier and Ferrier : UK Money Markets. – London : Butterworths, 1987.
This book describes the operations of the United Kingdom financial sector, concentrating on the principal methods of raising capital. Included in the work is coverage of the key elements in each market together with explanations of the significance of various instruments and forms of finance.
ISBN 0406100306 Hbk
—Retail financial services : development and future. – London : Butterworths, 1988.
ISBN 0406259437 Pbk
—UK money markets / David G Ferrier. – London : Butterworths, 1988.
ISBN 0406100306 Hbk
→ Understanding factoring and trade credit.

Ferrier, David G →UK money markets.

Ferrier, Ian →Capital Transfer Tax Act 1984.

Ferrier, Lee K. →Canadian divorce law and practice.

Fettiplace Bellers
Delineation of Universal Law. – Fettiplace Bellers. – 2nd ed. Repr. of 1750 ed. – Abingdon : Professional Books.
592p.
Hbk £15.00

Ffrench, H. Leigh
Casebook on Australian Company Law. – 4th ed. – Butterworths, 1983.
365p.
ISBN 0409491810 Pbk £31.50
—Guide to Company Law. – 2nd ed. – London : Butterworths.
ISBN 0409494534 Pbk £22.80
—Guide to Company Law : Including 1986 Supplement. – 2nd ed. – Butterworths, 1986.
335p.
ISBN 0409491667 Pbk £31.50
—International law of take-overs and mergers : southern Europe, Africa, and the Middle East / H. Leigh Ffrench. – 1. – Westport, Conn. : Quorum, 1987.
23cm.
Includes index.
ISBN 0899302068 £48.50
—International law of take-overs and mergers : the EEC, Northern Europe and Scandinavia / H. Leigh Ffrench. – New York : Quorum, 1987.
416p; 22cm.
Includes bibliography and index.
ISBN 0899300774 £51.75
—Mason's Casebook on Australian Company Law. – 4th ed. – London : Butterworths, 1983.
ISBN 0409491810 Pbk £19.20

Fiat iustitia : essays in memory of Oliver Deneys Schreiner / edited by Ellison Kahn. – Cape Town : Published for School of Law, University of the Witwatersrand, Johannesburg by Juta, 983.
xxii,405p.
Includes bibliographical references.
ISBN 0702113352

FIDIC Conditions of Contract - Commercial Manual. – Waterlow, 1986.
ISBN 0080392342 Hbk £30.00

Fidler, P. J. M. →Practice and law of banking.
→ Sheldon and Fidler's practice and law of banking.

Fiduciary duties of directors : a review / John Lowry. – London : Thames Polytechnic School of Business Administration, 1984.

Field, C.D.
Expert Evidence, Expert Opinion and Evidence of Third Persons. – 2nd ed. – Allahabad : Law Publishers, 1982.
Hbk £22.50
—Field's Law of Evidence in India and Pakistan, 4 Vols. – Allahabad : Law Publishers, 1983.
Hbk £45.00 ea
—Statements, Proofs and Confession. – 2nd ed. – Allahabad : Law Publishers, 1982.
Hbk £24.00

Field, David
Civil Evidence (Scotland) Act 1988. – Edinburgh : Green (W.) & Son, 1989.
Annotated text of the Act from Scottish Current Law Statutes, which introduced far-reaching changes to the law of evidence in civil proceedings, including the abolition of the requirement of cooroboration, the admission of hearsay, and authenticated business records.
ISBN 0414008650 Pbk
—Hotel and catering law in Britain / by David Field. – 5th ed. – London : Sweet & Maxwell, 1988.
xvii,236p; 23cm.
Discusses the legal framework in England, Scotland and Wales. Covers changes in the law effected by the Wages Act 1986, and the Licensing (Restaurant Meals) Act 1987, and also examines the impact of the new Companies legislation on the catering industry.
ISBN 0421392509 Pbk £8.50
—Law of evidence in Scotland / by David Field. – Edinburgh : W. Green, 1988.
xxxv,359p; 22cm.
Includes index.
ISBN 0414008421 Pbk
—Liquor licensing law / by David Field and Matthew Pink. – London : Sweet & Maxwell, 1983.
xxi,206p; 25cm.
Looks at how to obtain a justices licence, including the stages of deciding the relevant licence, the permitted hours in licensed premises, how to renew an existing licence, and its removal and transfer through to the conduct of licensed premises. Also contains a chapter on the nature of a registered club.
ISBN 0421299703 Pbk £11.50

Field-Fisher, T.G.
Dog Problem : A Lawyer's View. – Potters Bar : Universities Federation for Animal Welfare.
ISBN 0900767553 Pbk £1.50

Field, Frank →Diplock courts in Northern Ireland : a fair trial? : an analysis of the law, based on a study commissioned by Amnesty International.
—Policies Against Low Pay : An International Perspective. – London : Policy Studies Institute, 1984.
208p. – (PSI Research Papers).
Hbk £6.50

Field, Simon
Attitudes of ethnic minorities / Simon Field. – London : HMSO, 1984.
49p; 25cm.
Review of currently available research literature on the subject. Indicates the need for caution about accepting commonly expressed judgements on black and Asian attitudes.
ISBN 0113407742
→ Ethnic minorities in Britain : a study of trends in their position since 1961.
—Public disorder : a review of research and a study in one inner city area / by Simon Field and Peter Southgate. – London : H.M.S.O., 1982.
v, 73p.
Bibliographies. Contents: Urban disorders in Britain and America: a review of research/Simon Field - The disturbances of July 1981 in Handsworth, Birmingham: a survey of the views and experiences of male residents/Peter Southgate. A Home Office Research and Planning Unit report.
ISBN 011340767X
—Resettling refugees : the lessons of research / by Simon Field. – London : H.M.S.O., 1985.
vi,60p; 25cm.
Bibliographical references: p55-60. A Home Office Research and Planning Unit report.
ISBN 0113408153 Hbk

Fieldhouse
Taxation Simplified : 1988 Finance Act / Fieldhouse. – Pontefract : Lofthouse Publications.
ISBN 0900370866 Pbk £2.95

Fielding →Consumer Credit Agreements.

Fielding, H.
Enquiry Cases of Late Increase in Robbers & Related Writing. – Oxford : Oxford University Press.
ISBN 0198185162 Hbk £50.00

Fields, Gerald S.
Canadian Mortgage Practice Reporter / Bernard Gershman. – Toronto : DeBoo.
ISBN 0888200870 Llf £375.00

Field's Law of Evidence in India and Pakistan, 4 Vols. – Allahabad : Law Publishers, 1983.
Hbk £45.00 ea

Fienberg, S.E.
Evolving Role of Statistical Assessments as Evidence in the Courts. – Berlin : Springer-Verlag, 1989.
ca 375p.
Hbk £68.00

Fiercest Debate : Caesar Wright, the Benchers, and Legal Education in Ontario / Jerome E. Bickenbach. – Toronto : University of Toronto Press, 1987.
ca 374p.
ISBN 0802039863 Hbk £28

Fife, Ian → Health and safety in factories.
→ Redgrave's health and safety in factories.

Fifoot, C. H. S. → Cheshire, Fifoot and Furmston's Law of contract.
→ Law of Contract : New Zealand Edition.

Fifteen Decisive Battles Of The Law. – Sweet & Maxwell, 1921 Reprint.
ISBN 0421375507 Hbk £15.75

Fifth report from the Energy Committee : session 1984-85 : government oil price policy and the spring supplementary estimate for 20 million in respect of the British National Oil Corporation including Government repsonse to Committee's fourth report of session 1984-85 ... together with minutes of proceedings relating to the report and minutes of evidence and appendices / ordered by the House of Commons to be printed 8 March 1985. – London : H.M.S.O., 1985.
xxiv,72p. – (1984-85 HC).
Includes bibliographical references. Chairman: Ian Lloyd.
ISBN 010223485X

Fifth report from the Environment Committee, session 1985-86 : planning: appeals, call-in and major public inquiries
Vol.1 : Report together with the proceedings of the Committee. – London : H.M.S.O., 1986.
xcvi p. – (H.C. 1985-86).
ISBN 0100110657
Vol. 2 : Minutes of evidence and appendices. – 1986.
viii,466p. – (H.C. 1985-86).
ISBN 0100110754

Fifth report to Parliament on subordinate legislation concerning Film (Amendment) Regulations 1985 ... / Legal and Constitutional Committee. – Melbourne : Government Printer, 1986.
v,4p.

Fifty Years of Labour Law and Social Security. – Dordrecht : Kluwer, 1986.
166p.
ISBN 9031203653 Pbk £90.00

Fifty-Six Schedule. – Cape Town : Legal & Financial Publishing, 1983.
– (Merlen P.A.Y.E. Registers Ser.).
Hbk £7.07

Fighting Asbestos at Work and at Home. – London : Labour Research Department, 1984.
ISBN 0900508639 Pbk £0.85

Fighting Closures / Hugo Levie. – London : Spokesman Books, 1984.
ISBN 0851243614 Hbk £15.00
ISBN 0851243622 Pbk £5.95

Fighting Planning Appeals. – Oxford : Construction Press, 1985.
ISBN 0860957322 Hbk £14.95

Fighting Privatisation : The Victory in Gloucester. – London : Spokesman Books, 1984.
– (IWC Pamphlet: No. 87).
ISBN 0901740861 Pbk £0.90

Fiji / Professor Hugh Tinker et al. – London : Minority Rights Group, 1987.
15p. – (Report).
ISBN 0946690545

Filan, Mark
Police Training in Australia. – Canberra : Australian Institute of Criminology.
free

Filing of Forms, Returns and Applications Under Company Law. – 2nd ed. – New Delhi : Bharat Law House, 1986.
Hbk £220.00

Film Finance : Conference Papers. – Woolloomooloo : International Business Communications, 1987.
ISBN 0949072109 Hbk £34.95

Filmed horse racing / Christopher C. Hallsworth and Barry O. Johnson. – Chichester : Barry Rose, 1983.
26p.

Final Acts of the World Administrative Telegraph and Telephone Conference (Geneva, 1973) Telegraph Regulations, Telephone Regulations. – Geneva : International Telecommunications Union.
Hbk £17.00

Final report / Committee of Inquiry into Crowd Safety and Control at Sports Grounds : Chairman, Mr Justice Popplewell. – London : H.M.S.O., 1984.
85p.
At head of title: Home Office.
ISBN 0101971001

Final report of the Commonwealth Task Force on Occupational Superannuation. – Australia. – Canberra : Australian Government Publishing Service, 1983.
48p.
ISBN 0644026537

Final report on legislation relating to landlord and tenant / report of the Property Law and Equity Reform Committee. – Wellington : The Committee, 1986.
3,105p.

Finance / Townsley. – London : Pitman Publishing, 1986.
ISBN 0273025872 Pbk £6.95

Finance Act 1984. – London : Butterworths, 1984.
ISBN 0406548234 Hbk £60.00

Finance Act 1988. – London : Deloitte Haskins & Sells.
ISBN 0863491375 Pbk £9.95

Finance Act Nineteen Eighty-One. – London : Butterworths, 1981.
ISBN 0406548080 Hbk £38.95

Finance and protection of investments in developing countries / Ingrid Detter De Lupis. – 2nd ed. – Aldershot : Gower, 1987.
xvii,183p; 23cm.
Previous ed.: 1973. Includes index.
ISBN 0566054655 £25.00

Finance Bill / memorandum by the Society's Standing Committee on Revenue Law. – London : Law Society, 1982.
53p.

Finance Companies Act, 1969 (Act 6). – Kuala Lumpur : International Law Books Services.
Hbk £6.00

Finance of Foreign Trade. – 6th ed. – Plymouth : Macdonald & Evans, 1986.
ISBN 0712106618 Pbk £4.95

Finance of International Trade. – 4th ed. – Northwick Publishers.
– (Personal Course for Bankers Series).
ISBN 090713548X Hbk £12.00

Finance of International Trade. – 5th ed. – London : Pitman Publishing, 1987.
ISBN 0273027344 Pbk £8.95

Finance of local government / by N.P. Hepworth. – 7th ed. – London : Allen & Unwin, 1984.
xvi,349p; 20cm.
Previous ed.: 1980. Bibliography: p335-339. - Includes index.
ISBN 0043521118 Hbk £
ISBN 0043521150

Finances of Europe / by Daniel Strasser. – Revised and enlarged edition. – Luxembourg : Office for Official Publications of the European Communities, 1981.
xix,422p.
At head of title: Commission of the European Communities.
ISBN 9282520722

Financial Accounting. – Cambridge : Woodhead-Faulkner, 1986.
ISBN 0859413365 Pbk £12.00

Financial Accounting. – London : VanNostrand Reinhold, 1988.
ISBN 0278000150 Pbk £13.00

Financial Accounting / Holmes. – London : Letts.
ISBN 085097853X Pbk £7.95

Financial Accounting. – Maidenhead : McGraw-Hill, 1988.
ISBN 0070590028 Hbk £27.00

Financial Accounting Cases / Hughes. – New York : Dryden Press.
ISBN 003011778X Pbk £6.95

Financial and Property Problems on Marriage Breakdown / Godfrey Gypps. – London : Law Society, 1982.
– (Oxford Weekend Courses).
Hbk £3.00

Financial apportionment and equalisation / report prepared under the guidance of the members of the Committee of Experts on Local and Regional Finance by Graham Kelly. – Strasbourg : Council of Europe, 1981.
95p.
Up-dated and expanded version of: Financial structures of local and regional authorities in Europe. - Vol. 2. - 1976. - (Study series local and regional authorities in Europe ; no. 13).

Financial Deregulation. – Cambridge : Woodhead-Faulkner, 1986.
ISBN 0859413667 Hbk £30.00

Financial Engineering. – London : Fourmat, 1986.
ISBN 1851900187 Pbk £12.95

Financial futures / by M. Desmond Fitzgerald. – London : Euromoney, 1983.
ix,202p.
Bibliography: p.195-197. - Includes index.
ISBN 0903121433

Financial Institutions Duties : Untangling the Web / J.L. Mansfield. – Butterworths, 1983.
191p.
ISBN 0409492310 Pbk £42.00

Financial Institutions Law / S.A. McCracken. – Wamberal : Serendip Publications.
ISBN 0949379034 Hbk £19.00

Financial Instruments for Corporate Treasurer. – London : Butterworths, 1988.
ISBN 0406103550 Pbk

Financial Law Reports
Vol. 2. – London : Sweet & Maxwell, 1986.
ISBN 0421345004 Hbk £28.00

Financial Management. – London : Butterworths, 1984.
ISBN 0406181160 Pbk £10.00

Financial Management : ACCA Study Text 3.2. – London : BPP.
ISBN 0862772524 Pbk £16.95

Financial Management : Level 3.2. – Witney : A.T.C. Publications.
ISBN 0747700036 Pbk £15.95

Financial Management for Contractors. – Oxford : Blackwell Scientific, 1985.
ISBN 0003830616 Hbk £19.95

Financial Management for Law Firms / M. W. Zwicker. – Vancouver : British Columbia Continuing Legal Education Society, 1982.
82p.
ISBN 0865040451 Hbk £6.50

Financial Management For Solicitors. – 3rd ed. – London : Longman Professional, 1985.
ISBN 0851209998 Pbk £15.95

Financial Marketing and Sales. – Telegraph Publications.
ISBN 0863672930 Hbk £14.95

Financial Planning / Asch. – London : Kogan Page.
ISBN 1850914761 Hbk £25.00

Financial Procedure Act, 1957 (Act 61). – Kuala Lumpur : International Law Books Services.
Hbk £4.00

Financial Reporting in the Public Sector. – London : Butterworths, 1983.
ISBN 0406361401 Pbk £13.50

Financial Reporting Requirements in Australia : a Concise Illustrated Accounting Disclosures Manual. – Butterworths, 1987.
216p.
ISBN 0409492574 Pbk £42.00

Financial reporting requirements of the Companies Act and Codes. – Canberra : Australian Government Publishing Service, 1983.
vi,163p.
ISBN 0644005173

Financial resources for local and regional authorities : report / prepared under the guidance of the Committee of Experts on Local and Regional Finance of the Steering Committee for Regional and Municipal Matters by G. Kelly. – Strasbourg : Council of Europe, 1985.
79p; 30cm.

Financial services : regulating investment business / Simon Morris. – 1st ed. – London : Longman Professional (UK), 1989.
Examines the Financial Services Act 1986, and details its impact on areas of investment business, including the international aspect and the run up to 1992, and civil and criminal liability for operations outside the FSA.
ISBN 0851215572 Hbk £37.50

Financial Services Act 1986 / with annotations by Alan Page and Robert Ferguson. – London : Sweet & Maxwell, 1987.
298,14p; 24cm.
Includes index.
ISBN 0421366907 Pbk £12.00

Financial Services Act 1986 : a guide to the new law / Andrew Whittaker, Geoffrey Morse. – London : Butterworths, 1987.
vii,475p; 26cm.
Includes index.
ISBN 0406551014 £25.00

Financial Services Act. – London : Kogan Page.
ISBN 1850914346 Pbk £12.95

Financial Services Act: Index / Faulkner. – Cambridge : Woodhead-Faulkner, 1986.
ISBN 0859413888 Hbk £16.50

Financial Services Bill : as amended in Committee. – London : H.M.S.O., 1986.
ix,254p.
ISBN 0104238860

Financial services in the United Kingdom : a new framework for investor protection / presented to Parliament by the Secretary of State for Trade and Industry... – London : H.M.S.O., 1985.
iii,43p.
ISBN 0101943202

Financial Services Law / Potts. – London : Sweet & Maxwell, 1988.
ISBN 0421386002 Pbk

Financial services legislation : the auditor's role in the financial services sector : a consultative document. – London : The Division, 1985.
12p.

Financial services legislation : treatment of members od certain professions : a consultative document. – London : The Division, 1985.
16p.

Financial Statements : a Lawyer's Guide. – Vancouver : Continuing Legal Education Society of British Columbia, 1988.
131p.
ISBN 0865049696 Hbk £70.00

Financial Times Business Information → Liability for defective services.

Financial Times law reports. – Brentford : Kluwer Law, 1986-.

Financier's guide to the Credit Contracts Act 1981. – Wellington : Department of Justice, 1982.
17p.

Financing Canadian unemployment insurance / Jonathan R. Kesselman. – Toronto : Canadian Tax Foundation, 1983.
xiii,187p.
Bibliography: p.177-183. - Includes index.
ISBN 0888080166

Financing Consumer Sales and Product Defences in Canada and the United States. – Agincourt : Carswell, 1984.
382p.
This book is a collection of papers and discussion at a Legal Research Institute conference on the question of how well lawyers, police, courts, and lawmakers are perceived to deliver justice and the rule of law to Canadian society.
Hbk £48.75

Financing International Trade. – London : Butterworths, 1988.
ISBN 0880631503 Hbk

Financing of Countertrade. – London : Butterworths, 1986.
ISBN 0406102007 Pbk £32.00

Financing of small business / Desmond L. Hally. – 3rd ed. – London : Sweet and Maxwell, 1982.
xviii,243p; 23cm.
Previous ed.: 1971. Bibliography: p235-238. - Includes index.
ISBN 0421292008 £17.75

Financing the states : the constitutionality of sales tax laws / by Oluwole Akanle. – Lagos : Nigerian Institute of Advanced Legal Studies, 1983.
21p.
Text of a paper presented at the Nigerian Institute of Advanced Legal Studies Staff Seminar Series on Wednesday, June 15, 1983. Includes bibliographical references.

Finch, H.
Law, or a Discourse Thereof. – 4th ed. Repr. of 1661 ed. – Abingdon : Professional Books.
238p.
Hbk £75.00

Finch, John D.
Health services law / by John D. Finch. – London : Sweet & Maxwell, 1981.
xix,338p; 23cm.
Includes index.
ISBN 0421264608 Hbk £11.30
ISBN 0421264705 Pbk £7.30

Findlay, Mark J
Annotated Housing Benefit Legislation 1988-89. – Oxford : Bookspeed.
ISBN 0946744106 Pbk £12.95
—Issues in Criminal Justice Administration / Sandra J. Egger. – North Sydney : Allen & Unwin, 1983.
200p.
ISBN 0868612774 Hbk £29.95
ISBN 0868610542 Pbk £19.95

—Jury Under Attack / Peter Duff. – Butterworths, 1988.
243p.
ISBN 0409493481 Pbk £39.00

—Jury under attack / Peter Duff. – London : Butterworths, 1988.
ISBN 0406503109 Pbk £14.95

Findo, W.M.
Register of Graduate Employment and Training with Legal Prof. 1988. – London : Central Services Unit for University & Polytechnic Careers Advisory Services.
ISBN 0951070045 Pbk £5.75

Fine, Bob
Democracy and the rule of law : liberal ideas and marxist critiques / Bob Fine. – London : Pluto, 1984.
viii,231p; 20cm.
Bibliography: p221-228. - Includes index.
ISBN 0861047842 Pbk £7.95
→ Policing the miners' strike.

Fine enforcement : an evaluation of the practices of individual courts / Paul Softley and David Moxon. – London : Home Office, 1982.
iv,23p; 30cm.
Bibliography: p16.
ISBN 0862520711 Pbk

Fine, Frank L
Mergers and joint ventures in Europe: the law and policy of the EEC. – London : Graham & Trotman, 1989.
220; 240mm.
Explores how articles 85 and 86 of the Treaty of Rome would operate in the context of mergers and production joint ventures, and to non EEC firms seeking to acquire firms in the EEC. Analyses the Draft Regulation for the Control of Mergers, and includes its text in the Annexes.
ISBN 185333314X Hbk £50

Fine in comparative law / by Gerhardt Grebing. – Cambridge : University of Cambridge, Institute of Criminology, 1982.
xvi,279p. – (Institute of Criminology occasional papers).
Includes bibliographical references. Translation of: 'Die Geldstrafe im deutschen und auslandischen Recht', Part II 'Die Geldstrafe in rechtsvergleichender Darstellung' / edited by Hans-Heinrich Jescheck and Gerhardt Grebing.

Fine, J. David
Firearms Laws in Australia. – North Ryde : C.C.H. Australia, 1985.
175p.
ISBN 0869034936 Hbk

Fine, Martin
Butterworths annotations to the New Zealand statutes : 2nd ed. : 1908-1982 / by Martin Fine. – Wellington : Butterworths, 1982.
Previous ed.: Butterworths cases annotations of the New Zealand statutes reprint 1908-1957, published 1960-1961. Looseleaf issues accompanied by monthly Butterworths Automatic Annotations Bulletin.
ISBN 0409701262 Llf

Fingertip Guide to Criminal Law / Hamilton. – London : Butterworths, 1986.
ISBN 0406103801 Pbk £17.50

Finkelman, Jacob
Employer-employee relations in the public service of Canada : proposals for legislative change / J. Finkelman. – 4 v. – Ottawa : Information Canada, 1974.
Includes bibliographical references. Contents: Parts 1-3 - Supplementary observations and recommendations. Parallel English and French texts, Part 3 and Supplementary observations and recommendations.

Finkelmann, P.
The African Slave Trade and the American Courts : the Pamphlet Literature. – London : Garland.
ISBN 0824067223 Hbk
—Statutes on Slavery : the Pamphlet Literature. – London : Garland.
ISBN 082406724X Hbk

Finkelstein, Neil
Charter Issues in Civil Cases / Brian MacLeod Rogers. – Agincourt : Carswell, 1988.
327p.
Hbk £46.25
→ Laskin's Canadian constitutional law.

Finkle, Peter
Environmental Law in the 1980s : a New Beginning / Alastair R. Lucas. – Calgary : Canadian Institute of Resources Law.
233p.
Hbk £13.50

Finland and the international norms of human rights / K. Tornudd. – Dordrecht : M. Nijhoff, 1986.
Bibliography.
ISBN 9024732573

Finlason, W. F. → Reeves' history of the English law, from the time of the Romans to the end of the reign of Elizabeth.

Finlay, H.A.
Family Law in Australia / Rebecca Bailey-Harris. – 4th ed. – Butterworths, 1989.
ca 517p.
This book, intended primarily for law students, places its greatest emphasis on matrimonial property, maintenance, and constitutional issues. Coverage is also given to areas which fall outside Commonwealth jurisdiction and differences in the laws of the various Australian states and territories.
ISBN 0409495212 Hbk £69.00
ISBN 0409495220 Pbk £49.00
—Property and Finance in Family Law / R. Bailey. – Canberra : Australian National University, Research School of Social Sciences, 1981.
ISBN 0909596662 Pbk £9.00

Finlay, Thomas A.
Constitution, fifty years on. – Round Hall, 1988.
16p.
ISBN 094768641X Pbk

Finn, Paul D
Equity and Commercial Relationships. – North Ryde : Law Book Co, 1987.
ca 288p.
ISBN 0455207259 Hbk
→ Essays in equity.

—Essays in Equity. – London : Sweet & Maxwell, 1985.
ISBN 045520585X Hbk £23.00

—Law and government in colonial Australia / Paul Finn. – Melbourne : Oxford University Press, 1987.
xix,216p.
Bibliography: p.207-212. - Includes index.
ISBN 0195547462

→ Professional responsibility, Part 1 : papers presented by Paul Finn ... et al.

Finney, Jarlath
Gaming, lotteries, fundraising and the law / by Jarlath Finney : foreword by Sir David Napley. – London : Sweet & Maxwell, 1982.
xxiv,218p; 25cm.
Includes index.
ISBN 0421299800 Pbk £18.50

Finney, Malcolm J. → Business tax handbook.
—Captive Insurance : A Tax and Financial Analysis. – 2nd ed. – London : Oyez Longman, 1984. – (Oyez Longman Intelligence Report Ser.).
ISBN 085120872X Hbk £65.00

—Companies operating overseas: UK tax, law and practice / John Dixon. – London : Longman Professional (UK), 1986.
– (Commercial series).
Examination of the UK tax implications for any company which trades abroad and is concerned with reducing the risks involved. Looks at problems such as the treatment of double taxation agreements, legislation on controlled foreign companies, and the international VAT implications.
ISBN 0851218770 Pbk £17.50

—UK Companies Operating Overseas : Tax and Financial Strategies / M. J. Packman. – London : Oyez Longman, 1981.
– (Oyez Longman Intelligence Report Ser.).
ISBN 0851205321 Hbk £45.00

—UK Companies Operating Overseas : Tax and Financial Strategies / M. J. Packman. – 2nd ed. – London : Oyez Longman, 1984.
– (Oyez Longman Intelligence Report Ser.).
ISBN 0851208770 Hbk £45.00

Finnie, W. → Civil liberties in Scotland : cases & materials.
→ Civil liberties in Scotland: cases and materials.

Finnis, J. M.
Fundamentals of ethics / by John Finnis. – Oxford : Clarendon, 1983.
x,163p; 23cm.
Includes index.
ISBN 0198246838 Hbk £14.00
ISBN 0198246846 Pbk £4.95
—Nuclear deterrence, morality and realism / John Finnis, Joseph M. Boyle, Jr., Germain Grisez. – Oxford : Clarendon, 1987.
xv,429p; 22cm.
Bibliography: p391-411. - Includes index.
ISBN 0198247923 Hbk £30.00
ISBN 0198247915 Pbk no price

Finnish legal system / edited by Jaakko Uotila : translated by Leena Lehto. – 2nd completely rev. ed. – Helsinki : Finnish Lawyers Pub. Co., 1985.
254p; 22cm.
ISBN 9516402445

Finnish Press Laws. – Helsinki : Suomen valtio, 1984.
45p.
ISBN 951468320X £12.00

Finsinger, Jorg
Insurance: competition or regulation? : a comparative study of the insurance markets in the United Kingdom and the Federal Republic of Germany / Jorg Finsinger, Elizabeth Hammond and Julian Tapp. – London : Institute for Fiscal Studies, 1985.
197p.
Bibliography: p191-197.
ISBN 090299249X

Fire and Motor Insurance. – 4th ed. – London : Butterworths, 1984.
ISBN 040625253X Hbk £49.00

Fire Under the Carpet. – London : CENT, 1986.
ISBN 0853156549 Pbk £4.95

Firearms Act 1968 : proposals for reform / presented to Parliament by the Secretary of State for the Home Department and the Secretary of State for Scotland by command of Her Majesty, December 1987. – London : HMSO, 1987.
9p.
ISBN 0101026129

Firearms Laws in Australia. – North Ryde : C.C.H. Australia, 1985.
175p.
ISBN 0869034936 Hbk

First Asian Congress of Labour Law and Social Security. – Quezon City : University of the Philippines, Law Center, 1982.
608p.
Pbk £60.00

First Book of English Law / Hood. – 8th ed. – London : Sweet & Maxwell, 1988.
ISBN 0421393602 Hbk £16.00
ISBN 042139370X Pbk £11.50

First Joint International Conference on Research in Crime Prevention, Riyad, 23-25 January 1984. – Rome : United Nations Social Defence Research Institute, 1985.
235 p.; 21 cm.
Bibliography: p. 173-174.
ISBN 8876218262 Pbk

First Part of the Institutes of the Lawes of England : Commentary Upon Littleton. – Repr. of 1628 ed. – Abingdon : Professional Books.
449p.
Hbk £1450.00

First Principles : Constitutional Reform with Respect to the Aboriginal Peoples of Canada 1982-1984. – Kingston : Queen's University, Institute of Intergovernmental Relations.
292p.
ISBN 0889114323 Hbk £20.00

First Principles Preparatory to Constitutional Code. – Oxford : Clarendon Press.
ISBN 0198227477 Hbk £40.00

First Report from the Environment Committee 1983-84 : Green Belt and Land for Housing, 3 Vols.
Vol. 1: Report together with the proceedings of the committee relating to the report. – London : HMSO, 1984.
ISBN 0102962847 Hbk £3.75
Vol. 2: Minutes of evidence appendices. – ISBN 0102946841 Hbk £17.20

Vol. 3: Appendices pages 540-664. – ISBN 0102893845 Hbk £7.65

First report from the Foreign Affairs Committee, session 1984-85 : the abuse of diplomatic immunities and privileges : report with an annex; together with the proceedings of the Committee; minutes of evidence taken ... in the last session of Parliament; and appendices. – London : H.M.S.O., 1984.
li,94p; 25cm. – (H.C.).
ISBN 0102127859

First report from the Home Affairs Committee, session 1983-84 : remands in custody
Vol. 1 : Report together with proceedings of the Committee. – London : H.M.S.O., 1984.
xxxiip. – (HC 252-I).
ISBN 0102939845
Vol. 2 : Minutes of evidence and appendices. – 1984.
vii,200p. – (HC252-II).

First report on family law : criminal coversation, enticement and harbouring of a spouse or child, loss of consortium, personal injury to a child, seduction of a child, matrimonial property and breach of promise of marriage / the Law Reform Commission. – Dublin : The Commission, 1981.
iii,32p. – (LRC).

First report on the legal profession : general regulation and structure / New South Wales Law Reform Commission. – Sydney : The Commission, 1982.
242p. – (L.R.C.31).
Bibliography: p.227-229. - Includes index.

First report to Parliament on subordinate legislation / Legal and Constitutional Committee. – Melbourne : Government Printer, 1986.
vii,11p.

First report to Parliament on the operation of section 32 of the Interpretation of Legislation Act 1984 / Legal and Constitutional Committee. – Melbourne : Government Printer, 1986.
vii,10p.

First rights : a guide to legal rights for young people / Maggie Rae, Patricia Hewitt and Barry Hugill : illustrated by Corinne Pearlman. – 3rd ed. – London : National Council for Civil Liberties, 1985.
128p; 20cm.
Previous ed.: 1981. Includes bibliography and index.
ISBN 0946088152 Pbk £1.95

First, Ruth
Black gold : the Mozambican miner, proletarian and peasant / Ruth First : pictures by Moira Forjaz : work-songs and interviews recorded by Alpheus Manghezi. – Brighton : Harvester, 1983.
xxxi,256p,xvip of plates; 23cm.
Bibliography: p207-211. - Includes index.
ISBN 0710803141 £30.00
ISBN 0312083181

First Step in Islamic Law in West Africa / Alexander David Russel. – Lagos : Islamic Publications Bureau, 1986.
ISBN 9782470120 Hbk £7.50

Fiscal policy and tax legislation and administration : technical papers and reports of the 15th General Assembly of the Inter- American Center of Tax Administrators (CIAT), Caracas, Venezuela, 25-27 February 1981. – Inter-American Center of Tax Administrators. – Amsterdam : International Bureau of Fiscal Documentation, 1983.
200p.
'Sponsored by the Government of Venezuela, the German Society for Technical Cooperation (GTZ) and the Inter-American Center of Tax Administrators (CIAT) '.
ISBN 9070125226

Fiscal studies : the journal of the Institute for Fiscal Studies
Vol.1, no.1, Nov. 1979-. – Institute for Fiscal Studies. – London : Institute for Fiscal Studies, 1979-.

Fiscal tiers : the economics of multi-level government / David N. King. – London : Allen & Unwin in association with the Centre for Research on Federal Finance Relations, the Australian National University, 1984.
v,326p; 24cm.
Bibliography: p305-316. - Includes index.
ISBN 0043360815 Hbk £
ISBN 004336084X Pbk £8.95

Fischer, Peter → Collection of international concessions and related instruments : contemporary series.

Fisher → Constitutional History of England.
—Natural Resources Law In Australia 1987. – London : Law Book Co.
ISBN 0455207690 Pbk £28.00

Fisher & Lightwood's law of mortgage / J. M. Lightwood, E. L. G. Tyler, R. D. Oughton. – 10th ed. – London : Butterworths, 1988.
940p; 25cm.
Gives detailed practical presentation of United Kingdom mortgage law for practitioners. Regular supplements will be issued to keep pace with the rapid changes in the field. Copious source references and footnotes are provided throughout the book.
ISBN 0406201064 £90.00

Fisher, D.
Right to Communicate : a New Human Right / L.S. Harms. – Dublin : Boole Press Ltd., 1983.
xxvi, 229p.
ISBN 0906783186 Hbk £45.00
ISBN 0906783194 Pbk £30.00

Fisher, David S.
Juta's index and annotations to the South African law reports 1980-86 / compiled by David S. Fisher and Alan James : assisted by Owen J. Barrow ... et al. – Cape Town : Juta, 1987.
1100p.
Kept up-to-date by supplements.
ISBN 0702118508

Fisher, Frederick G.
Eurobonds / by F.G. Fisher, III. – London : Euromoney, 1988.
v,231p.
A 'revised work'. - Preface. Previous ed. entitled: International bonds. Bibliography: p.227. - Includes index.
ISBN 1870031512
—International bonds / by Frederick G. Fisher, III. – London : Euromoney Publications, 1981.
199p; 30cm.
Bibliography: p195. - Includes index.
ISBN 0903121220 Pbk
→ International mergers and acquisitions.

Fisher, J.
Lindberg case. – Rutgers University Press, 1988.
ISBN 0813512336 Hbk £20.50

Fisher on Matrimonial Property. – 2nd ed. – Butterworths, 1984.
ISBN 0409600393 Hbk £51.00

Fisher, R.
Improving Compliance with International Law. – London : Eurospan.
ISBN 0813908590 Hbk £30.95

Fisher, R.L.
Fisher on Matrimonial Property. – 2nd ed. – Butterworths, 1984.
ISBN 0409600393 Hbk £51.00

Fisher, Roger
Getting to YES : negotiating agreement without giving in / Roger Fisher and William Ury : with Bruce Patton, editor. – London : Business Books, 1986.
xiii,161p; 23cm.
Originally published: Boston, Mass. : Houghton Mifflin, 1981 ; London : Hutchinson, 1982.
ISBN 0091493706 Hbk
ISBN 0091640717 Pbk

Fisher, W. R.
Fisher & Lightwood's law of mortgage / J. M. Lightwood, E. L. G. Tyler, R. D. Oughton. – 10th ed. – London : Butterworths, 1988.
940p; 25cm.
Gives detailed practical presentation of United Kingdom mortgage law for practitioners. Regular supplements will be issued to keep pace with the rapid changes in the field. Copious source references and footnotes are provided throughout the book.
ISBN 0406201064 £90.00

Fisheries Law. – Vancouver : Continuing Legal Education Society of British Columbia, 1985.
384p.
ISBN 0865042039 Hbk £75.00

Fisheries Regime of the Exclusive Economic Zone. – Dordrecht : Kluwer, 1987.
200p.
ISBN 902473374X Hbk £145.00

Fishing in Scotland : law for the angler / by Lord Jauncey. – 2nd ed. – Edinburgh : W. Green, 1984.
vi,17p; 21cm.
Previous ed.: 1952.
ISBN 0414007344 Pbk

Fishwick, C.
General Law for Social Workers. – PEPAR Publications.
ISBN 0948680105 Pbk £7.50

Fitness Interview Test : a Method for Examining Fitness to Stand Trial. – Toronto : University of Toronto, Centre of Criminology, 1984.
£4.50

Fitzgerald, Brendan
Land Registry Practice. – Dublin : Round Hall Press, 1988.
ca 240p.
ISBN 0947686347 Hbk £35.00

Fitzgerald, D.
Elements of Banking 1 and 2. – 2nd ed. – London : Financial Training.
ISBN 0906322999 Pbk £7.95

Fitzgerald et al
Crime and Social Reading In History and Theory. – Routledge.
ISBN 0710009445 Pbk £11.95

Fitzgerald, M. Desmond
Financial futures / by M. Desmond Fitzgerald. – London : Euromoney, 1983.
ix,202p.
Bibliography: p.195-197. - Includes index.
ISBN 0903121433
—Options . – London : Euromoney, 1987.
ISBN 1870031563 Pbk £75.00

Fitzgerald, Mike
British prisons / Mike Fitzgerald and Joe Sim. – 2nd ed. – Oxford : Blackwell (Basil), 1982.
182p; 23cm.
Previous ed.: 1979. Bibliography: p167-170. - Includes index. Previous control number ISBN 0-631-12606-6.
ISBN 0631125299 Hbk £
ISBN 0631126066 Pbk
→ Crime and society : readings in history and theory.

Fitzherbert
Office Aucthoritie. – 2nd ed. – Professional Books, 1986 Reprint.
ISBN 086205317X Hbk £30.00

Fitzherbert, Anthony
New Nature Brevium : With a Table of the Most Material Things Contained Therein, Composed by William Rastal, (also) the Authorities in Law Newly Translated by William Hughes. – Repr. of 1652 ed. – Abingdon : Professional Books.
269p.
Hbk £192.00

Fitzkenton Estate. – London : Sweet & Maxwell, 1984.
640p. – (Sweet and Maxwell's Law Files Ser.: No. 2).
ISBN 0421321504 Hbk £29.50

Fitzmaurice, Catherine
Psychology of judicial sentencing / Catherine Fitzmaurice and Ken Pease. – Manchester : Manchester University Press, 1986.
vii,174p; 22cm.
Bibliography: p159-171. - Includes index.
ISBN 0719018196 £19.95

Fitzmaurice, Gerald
Law and procedure of the International Court of Justice
Vol.1 / by the late Sir Gerald Fitzmaurice. – Cambridge : Grotius, 1986.
xli,427p; 26cm.
An analysis of the decisions of the International Court of Justice given in its formative years. A series of articles, with a consolidated index.
ISBN 0906496330 £95.00
Vol.2 / by the late Sir Gerald Fitzmaurice. – 1986.
pi-xiv,429-860; 26cm.
Includes index.
ISBN 0906496381 Hbk £95.00

Fitzpatrick, Michael M. K. → Canadian forms of wills.

Fitzpatrick, Peter → Critical legal studies.

Fitzroy Legal Service → Legal service bulletin.

Flaherty, David H.
Essays in the history of Canadian law
Vol.2. – Toronto : University of Toronto Press, 1983.
ISBN 0802033911 Hbk £45.00
→ Privacy and data protection : an international bibliography.

—Protecting privacy in two-way electronic services / by David H. Flaherty : foreword by Ronald L. Plasser. – London : Mansell, 1985.
viii,172p; 24cm.
Bibliography: p165-166. - Includes index.
ISBN 0720117445 £23.50

Flanagan
Big Brother or Democracy : The Case for the Abolition of the Australian Security Intelligence Organisation. – London : Spokesman Books, 1983.
161p.
ISBN 085124307X Pbk £2.95

Flanagan, Terence →Modern partnership law.

Flashpoints; Studies in Public Disorder / Jones. – Routledge.
ISBN 0415012384 Hbk £25.00
ISBN 0415012392 Pbk £8.95

Fleming
Deviant Designations : Crime Law and Deviance in Canada / Visano. – Toronto : Butterworths, 1983.
512p.
Examines the reaction of communities to crime; issues involved in creating deviant designations and controlling the careers of those deemed deviant or criminal; the response of formal agents and agencies of social control (courts, police, and prisons) to be discredited, and emerging theoretical concerns.
ISBN 0409829846 Pbk £25.95

Fleming, John G
American tort process / John G. Fleming. – Oxford England : Clarendon Press, 1988.
viii, 271 p.; 23 cm.
Includes bibliographical references and index.
ISBN 0198255977
—Introduction to the Law of Torts. – 2nd ed. – Oxford : Oxford University Press, 1986.
ISBN 0198761546 Hbk £17.50
ISBN 0198761554 Pbk £8.95

—Law of Torts. – 7th ed. – Sweet & Maxwell.
ISBN 0455207534 Hbk £30.00
ISBN 0455207542 Pbk £23.00

—Law of torts / by John G. Fleming. – 6th ed. – Sydney : Law book Company, 1983.
lii,702p; 24cm.
Previous ed.: 1977. Includes bibliographical references and index.
ISBN 0455205477 Hbk £30.00
ISBN 0455205485 Pbk £23.00

Fleming, Thomas →New criminologies in Canada : crime, state and control.

Fletcher, Ian F.
Conflict of laws and European Community law : with special reference to the Community Conventions on private international law / Ian F. Fletcher. – Amsterdam : North-Holland, 1982.
xxix,395p.
Bibliography: p.xxvii-xxix. - Includes index.
ISBN 0444863761

Fletcher, Ian M →Insolvency Act 1985.
→ Law and practice of receivership in Scotland.

Fletcher, K. L. →Higgins and Fletcher the law of partnership in Australia and New Zealand.
—Law Relating to Non-Profit Associations in Australia and New Zealand. – North Ryde : Law Book Co, 1986.
xl, 380p.
ISBN 0455206236 Hbk £48.00

Fletcher, Leonard, et al
Construction Contract Dictionary. – Reading : College of Estate Management, 1981.
120p.
ISBN 0902132652 Hbk £12.30
ISBN 0902132636 Pbk £7.50

Flick, Geoffrey A.
Civil liberties in Australia / by Geoffrey A. Flick. – Sydney : Law Book Company Limited, 1981.
xxxviii,249p.
ISBN 045520084X
—Federal administrative law / by Geoffrey A. Flick : with a foreword by J.D. Davies. – Sydney : Law Book Co., 1983.
xxvii,251p.
Text of several acts and regulations, with commentary. Includes index.
ISBN 0455204489
ISBN 0455204241

—Natural Justice : Principles and Practical Application. – 2nd ed. – Butterworths, 1984.
205p.
ISBN 0409491233 Hbk £49.00

Flint, David
Foreign investment and the new international economic order / by David Flint. – Sydney : International Law Association, 1981.
89p.
ISBN 0949685003
—Foreign investment law in Australia / by David Flint. – Sydney : Law Book Company, 1985.
xxxi,519p.
ISBN 0455204624

—Guide to liquidation in Scotland / David Flint. – Bristol : Jordan & Sons, 1987.
viii,265p; 25cm.
Provides a brief introduction to the Act and rules. With the text of relevant legislation other than the 1986 Insolvency Act.
ISBN 0853080925 Pbk £12.50

Flint, Michael F
Intellectual Property : the New Law / Williams. – London : Butterworths.
ISBN 0406503079 Hbk £27.50
—User's guide to copyright. – 2nd ed. – London : Butterworths, 1985.
ISBN 0406200742 Pbk £18.50

Flinterman, C.
Human rights in Ghana : report of a mission / by Cees Flinterman for the International Commission of Jurists and Netherlands Committee for Human Rights. – Utrecht : SIM, 1984.
47 p.; 21 cm.
ISBN 9290370254 Pbk

Flinterman, K →Transboundary air pollution : international legal aspects of the co-operation of states.

Floating charges and receivers / Scottish Law Commission. – Edinburgh : The Commission, 1986.
iv,151p. – (Consultative memorandum).
Includes bibliographical references. Catalogued from cover.

Floating charges, crystallisation and after-acquired property / by G.C. Thorpe. – Auckland : Legal Research Foundation, 1981.
49p.
ISBN 0908581130

Floating rate notes / by Georges Ugeux : preface by Michael von Clemm. – 2nd ed. – London : Euromoney, 1985.
xix,171p.
Bibliography: p.171.
ISBN 0903121808

Flogging of Phinehas McIntosh : A Tale of Colonial Folly and Injustice, Bechuanaland 1933. – Yale University Press.
ISBN 0300040989 Hbk £20.00

Flood, John A.
Barristers' clerks : the law's middlemen / John A. Flood. – Manchester : Manchester University Press, 1983.
vii,164p; 23cm.
Bibliography: p157-162. - Includes index.
ISBN 0719009286 £17.50

Floor, Willem
Labour unions, law and conditions in Iran (1900-1941) / by Willem Floor. – Durham City : Centre for Middle Eastern and Islamic Studies, University of Durham, 1985.
124p; 21cm. – (Occasional paper series).
Bibliography: p119-124.
Pbk

Floud, Jean
Dangerousness and criminal justice / Jean Floud and Warren Young. – London : Heinemann, 1981.
xvii,228p; 23cm.
Bibliography: p203-221. - Includes index. At head of title : Howard League for Penal Reform.
ISBN 0435823078 £14.50

Floyd, Richard →Company administration orders and voluntary arrangements.

Floyd, Richard E. →Personal insolvency : a practical guide.
→ Voluntary liquidation and receivership : a practical guide.

Flux, David
Hong Kong taxation : law and practice / David Flux. – Rev. ed. – Hong Kong : Chinese University Press, 1982.
xxviii,387p(4 folded); 24cm.
Previous ed.: 1981. Includes index.
ISBN 0421309105 £17.00
—Hong Kong Taxation : Law and Practice. – Sha Tin : Chinese University of Hong Kong Press, 1983-84.
xxviii, 403p.
ISBN 9622013066 Hbk £30.50

Flying off course : the economics of international airlines / Rigas Doganis. – London : Allen & Unwin, 1985.
ix,271p; 23cm.
Bibliography: p260-264. - Includes index.
ISBN 004387004X £18.00

Flynn, William J.
Handbook of Canadian legal terminology : revised and updated / William J. Flynn. – Toronto : Stoddart, 1986.
117p.
ISBN 0773751076

Foakes, Joanne
Family violence : law & practice / Joanne Foakes. – London : Hemstal Press, 1984.
xvi,176p.
Includes index.

Focus on Beirut / by Georg Schwarzenberger. – Leeds : University of Leeds, 1983.
11p.
Bibliography: p.10-11.

Focus on Construction Industry Tax Deduction Scheme. – Croydon : Tolley, 1983.
ISBN 0854591206 Pbk £6.95

Focus on Controlled Foreign Companies. – Croydon : Tolley, 1984.
ISBN 0854591745 Pbk £11.95

Focus on Homelessness : a New Look at Housing Policy / Kennedy. – Oxford : Columbia Press.
ISBN 0948183543 Pbk £5.00

Focus on Purchase & Sale of Private Co's Shares. – 2nd ed. – Croydon : Tolley, 1985.
ISBN 0854591850 Pbk £8.95

Focus on the Administration of Taxes. – Croydon : Tolley, 1983.
ISBN 0854591311 Pbk £5.95

Fogarty, K.H.
Equality Rights and their Limitations. – Agincourt : Carswell, 1987.
ISBN 0459398407 Hbk £36.00

Fogarty, Michael
Retirement Policy : The Next Fifty Years. – London : Policy Studies Institute, 1982.
212p. – (Joint Studies in Public Policy).
Hbk £15.00

Foisy, Claude H., et al
Canada Labour Relations Board Policies and Procedures. – Butterworths, 1986.
640p.
Describes the rules and practices of the Canada Labour Relations Board in the administration of Parts IV and V of the Canada Labour Code. Makes reference to all numbered decisions of the CLRB since 1973, decisions of the Federal Court and the Supreme Court of Canada, reviewing CLRB decisions. Also includes decisions of the Canadian common law courts which have interpreted the code.
ISBN 0409819751 Hbk £95.00

Folsom, Ralph H →Law in the People's Republic of China: commentary, readings and materials.

Fong, Chow Kok
Law Relating to Building Contracts : Cases and Materials. – Singapore : Quins.
Hbk £99.00

Fong, Sng Yok →Index to Singapore/Malaysia legal periodicals 1932-1984.

Fontaine, Marcel
Consumer legislation in Belgium and Luxemburg : a study prepared for the EC Commission / M. Fontaine, Th. Bourgoignie : translated from French by Michael Corkery. – Wokingham, Berkshire : Van Nostrand Reinhold (UK), 1982.
xvi, 229 p.; 24 cm.
Includes bibliographical references and indexes. Translation of: Droit de la consommation en Belgique et Luxembourg.
ISBN 0442304188

Fontana, James A.
Law of Search and Seizure in Canada. – 2nd ed. – Butterworths, 1984.
358p.
Analyses the various processes of issuing and executing search warrants, as well as the different kinds of searches and seizures possible under the Criminal Code and other federal and provincial statutes. Also looks at the effects of the Charter of Rights.
ISBN 0409830283 Hbk £80.00

Food Act, 1983 (Act 281) and Regulations, 1985 (P.U.(A) 437/85). – Kuala Lumpur : International Law Books Services.
Hbk £15.00

Food and Agriculture Legislation
Vol. 33. – Food and Agriculture Organization of the United Nations. – London : HMSO, 1984.
115p.
ISBN 0119410133 Pbk £4.50

Food and Agriculture Organization
Agricultural census legislation / a joint publication by the Statistics Division and the Legislation Branch, Legal Office. – Rome : Food and Agriculture Organization of the United nations, 1984.
v,117p. – (Legislative study).
ISBN 9251013772
→ Agricultural insurance legislation.

→ International groundwater resources law.

→ Legislation on wildlife and protected areas in Africa.

—Regional compendium of fisheries legislation (Indian Ocean Region) / prepared by Legislation Branch, FAO Legal Office, with the assistance of the International Centre for Ocean Development. – Provisional ed. 2. – Rome : Food and Agriculture Organization of the United Nations, 1986.
– (Legislative study).

→ Regional compendium of fisheries legislation West Africa (CECAF region).

—Regional compendium of fisheries legislation (Western Pacific region) / prepared by Legislation Branch, Legal office, FAO, in cooperation with the South Pacific Forum Fisheries Agency. – 2 v. – Rome : F.A.O., 1984. – (Legislative study).
ISBN 925102202X

→ Systematic index of international water resources treaties, declarations, acts and cases by basin.

—Water law in selected European Countries : (Cyprus, Finland, the Netherlands, Union of Soviet Socialist Republics, Yugoslavia). – Food and Agriculture Organization. – Rome : Food and Agriculture Organization of the United Nations, 1983.
ISBN 9251014906

Food and Agriculture Organization of the United Nations
Food and Agriculture Legislation
Vol. 33. – Food and Agriculture Organization of the United Nations. – London : HMSO, 1984.
115p.
ISBN 0119410133 Pbk £4.50

Food and farm policies of the European Community / Simon Harris, Alan Swinbank and Guy Wilkinson. – Chichester : Wiley, 1983.
xii,354p; 24cm.
Includes bibliographies and index.
ISBN 047110261X £12.50

Food Famine and the Legal Order / Julio Menezes. – Colombo : Lake House Investments.
Pbk £10.00

Food Hygiene I: Market Stalls and Delivery Vehicles. – London : Shaw & Sons, 1981. – (Shaway Guide : No. 5).
ISBN 072190873X Pbk £2.50

Food Hygiene II: Food Premises. – London : Shaw & Sons, 1981. – (Shaway Guide: No. 6).
ISBN 0721908748 Pbk £2.50

Food Law in Australia / Gerkens. – North Ryde : Law Book Co, 1985.
ISBN 0455203016 Pbk £16.00

Food Legislation of the UK. – 2nd ed. – London : Butterworths, 1987.
ISBN 0407015507 Pbk £12.50

Food Legislative System of the UK. – London : Butterworths.
ISBN 040701540X Pbk £16.95

Food policy. – Paris : Organisation for Economic Co- operation and Development, 1981.
75 p.; 24 cm.
'This report and five Country Notes were discussed and adopted by the OECD Working Party on Agricultural Policies and by the Committee for Agriculture 28th April 1981.'. Includes bibliographical references.
ISBN 0702216283 Pbk

Fooled again? : the Anglo-Irish Agreement and after / Anthony Coughlan. – Cork : Mercier, 1986.
88p; 21cm.
ISBN 0853427747 Pbk £4.95

Foord, H.
Access : Links Between Children in Care and Their Parents. – Bristol : School of Applied Social Studies, University of Bristol.
ISBN 0862923018 Pbk £3.50

Football Spectator Violence : Report on an Official Working Group. – London : HMSO, 1984.
61p.
Report of an official working group. Examines measures available to deal with football-related violence. Stresses the need for co-operation between football and public authorities such as police and central government.
ISBN 0117517496 Hbk £3.80

Forbes, D
Action on Racial Harrassment : Legal Remedies and Local Authorities. – Sweet & Maxwell.
ISBN 0905099184 Pbk £10.00

Forbes, J.R.S.
Australian Mining and Petroleum Laws / Andrew G Lang. – 2nd ed. – Sydney : Butterworths, 1987.
360p.
This reference describes the Petroleum (Submerged Lands) Act 1982, the Mining Act 1983 (NT), the Petroleum Act 1984 (NT), the Mining Act 1978-81 (WA), the Mining Amendment Act 1985 (WA). Also included are materials on environmental law and joint ventures.
Hbk £55.00

—Evidence in Queensland : the Statute Law. – North Ryde : Law Book Co, 1986.
xxxix, 236p.
ISBN 045520618X Pbk £32.50

—Law of domestic or private tribunals / by J.R.S. Forbes. – Sydney : Law Book, 1982.
xxviii, 247 p.; 22 cm.
Includes index.
ISBN 0455204551 Pbk

—Voluntary but not amateur. – London : London Voluntary, 1988.
ISBN 0901171662 Pbk £6.00

Forbes, Robert E. →Canadian business organizations law.
→ Taxation and estate planning.

Force Majeure and Hardship. – Paris : International Chamber of Commerce.
Hbk £5.00

Ford →Elements of Banking.

Ford, H.A.J.
Cases on Trusts. – 5th ed. – North Ryde : Law Book Co, 1984.
xxxiii, 925p.
ISBN 0455205116 Hbk £73.00
ISBN 0455205124 Pbk £58.50

—Guide to the national companies and securities scheme / by H.A.J. Ford ... et al. – Sydney : Butterworths, 1982.
xxv,406p.
Includes index.
ISBN 040949335X

—Outline of Companies and Securities Law. – Butterworths, 1987.
221p.
ISBN 040949285X Pbk £19.95

—Principles of company law / by H.A.J. Ford. – 3rd ed. – Sydney : Butterworths, 1982.
lxix,650p.
Previous ed.: 1978. Includes index.
ISBN 040930932X

—Principles of company law / H.A.J. Ford. – 4th ed. – Sydney : Butterworths, 1986.
lxxix,774p.
Includes bibliographical references and index.
ISBN 0409490679 Hbk A$59.00
ISBN 0409490687 Pbk A$42.50

—Principles of the law of trusts / by H.A.J. Ford and W.A. Lee. – Sydney : Law Book Co., 1983.
cxvii,1055p.
Includes bibliographical references and index.
ISBN 045520375X

Ford Motor Company Limited : licensing for the manufacture or sale of replacement body parts : a report by the Director General of Fair Trading on an investigation under section 3 of the Competition Act 1980. – London : Office of Fair Trading, 1984.
43p.

Ford, Trowbridge H.
Albert Venn Dicey : the man and his times / by Trowbridge H. Ford. – Chichester : Barry Rose, 1985.
354p.
Bibliography: p322-335.
ISBN 0859923568

Ford, W. J. →Labour law : materials and commentary.

Forde, Michael
Cases on Irish company law / Michael Forde. – Cork : Mercier, 1986.
461p; 23cm.
Includes index.
ISBN 0853427968 £40.00 (Irish)

—Company law in Ireland / Michael Forde. – Cork : Mercier, 1985.
xlix,552p; 23cm.
Includes index.
ISBN 0853427313 Hbk £45.00
ISBN 0853427666 Pbk £22.50

—Constitutional Law of Ireland. – Cork : Mercier Press, 1987.
801p.
ISBN 0853428174 Hbk £60.00

—Extradition law in Ireland / Michael Forde : with a foreword by Niall McCarthy. – Dublin : Round Hall Press, 1988.
xviii,260p; 24cm.
Includes index.
ISBN 094768624X £35.00

Forde, Norma Monica
Women and the law / Norma Monica Forde. – Cave Hill, Barbados : Institute of Social and Economic Research, University of the West Indies, 1981.
x,125p.
Includes bibliographies.

Foreclosure Update 1988. – Vancouver : Continuing Legal Education Society of British Columbia, 1988.
111p.
ISBN 0865043655 Hbk £70.00

Foreclosures : 1987. – Vancouver : Continuing Legal Education Society of British Columbia, 1987.
586p.
ISBN 0865043051 Hbk £85.00

Foreclosures, Debentures, and Bankruptcy for Legal Assistants. – Vancouver : British Columbia Continuing Legal Education Society, 1985.
119p.
ISBN 0865042136 Hbk £55.00

Foreclosures for Legal Assistants. – Vancouver : British Columbia Continuing Legal Education Society, 1983.
177p.
ISBN 0865041350 Hbk £50.00

Foreign affairs in English courts / F.A. Mann. – Oxford : Clarendon, 1986.
300p; 22cm.
ISBN 0198255640 £30.00

Foreign affairs, powers and policy in the draft treaty establishing the European Union / by Peter Bruckner. – Florence : European University Institute, 1985.
30p.

Foreign affiliate system : Canadian taxation after 1982 : a structured overview / by Nathan Boidman. – Don Mills, Ont. : CCH Canadian Ltd., 1983.
ix,218p.
Includes index.
ISBN 0887962092

Foreign Currency Exposure Management. – London : Butterworths, 1987.
ISBN 0406570906 Pbk £22

Foreign Currency Options. – London : Butterworths.
ISBN 0406101604 Pbk £35.00

Foreign Divorces : English Law and Practice. – Aldershot : Avebury.
ISBN 0566053101 Hbk £25.00

Foreign Exchange and Corporate Treasurer. – 4th ed. – London : Black (A & C).
ISBN 0713626712 Hbk £12.50

Foreign Exchange Dealer's Handbook. – 2nd ed. – Cambridge : Woodhead-Faulkner, 1986.
ISBN 0859413438 Hbk £35.00

Foreign Exchange Manual
Supplement. – Cambridge : Woodhead-Faulkner, 1988.
ISBN 0859414396 Hbk £150.00

Foreign Exchange Regulations Act, 1973 / Subodh Markandeya. – Bombay : Jaico Publishing House.
Hbk £95.00

Foreign Exchange Risk : A Tax and Financial Analysis. – London : Oyez Longman, 1983. – (Oyez Longman Intelligence Report Ser.).
ISBN 0851205313 Hbk £45.00

Foreign Investment and Exchange Control. – Woolloomooloo : International Business Communications, 1985.
ISBN 0949072001 Llf

Foreign investment & technology transfer : fiscal and non-fiscal aspects : country profiles on fiscal and non-fiscal regimes affecting two-way flow of investment and technology transfer between the developed countries and the Asian-Pacific region / editor, Ahmad Khan. – Singapore : Asian-Pacific and Investment Research Centre, 1985.
vi,262p.
'A series of contributions ... to the 2nd Asian-Pacific Tax Conference held in Singapore in December 1984 by the Asian-Pacific Tax and Investment Research Centre' - Preface. Includes bibliographical references.

Foreign investment and the new international economic order / by David Flint. – Sydney : International Law Association, 1981.
89p.
ISBN 0949685003

Foreign Investment Debt and Economy / Salazar-Carillo. – London : Macmillan, 1988.
ISBN 0333402081 Hbk £37.50

Foreign investment in mining projects : case studies of recent experiences / Raymond F. Mikesell : a project sponsored and administered by the FMME. – Cambridge, Mass. : Oelgeschlager, Gunn & Hain, 1983.
xv,297p; 24cm.
Bibliography: p281-285. - Includes index.
ISBN 0899461700

Foreign investment law in Australia / by David Flint. – Sydney : Law Book Company, 1985.
xxxi,519p.
ISBN 0455204624

Foreign Investment Review Law in Canada / W.P. Rosenfeld. – Butterworths, 1984.
432p.
Provides practical information and a commentary for those who must deal with the Foreign Investment Review Act (FIRA). Shows the reader how to proceed with applications under the Act, describes the business and political context in which it operates, and clarifies the meaning of its essential concepts. Chapters deal with FIRA-related problems particular to the petroleum and banking industries.
ISBN 0409863009 Hbk £75.00

Foreign Money Liabilities. – Victoria : Government of British Columbia, 1983.
Hbk £6.00

Foreign money liabilities / Law Reform Commission of British Columbia. – Vancouver : Law Reform Commission of British Columbia, 1982.
iv,121p. – (Working paper).

Foreign Policy and Human Rights. – Cambridge : Cambridge University Press, 1986.
ISBN 0521323967 Hbk £25.00

Foreign state immunity / The Law Reform Commission. – Sydney : The Commission, 1983.
8p. – (Discussion paper).
Summary dicussion paper.

Foreign state immunity / the Law Reform Commission. – Canberra : Australian Government Publishing Service, 1984.
xxiv,168p. – (Report).
Bibliography: p.162-5. Includes index.
ISBN 0644012811

Foreign Tax Credits and Foreign Affiliates. – Toronto : Butterworths, 1984.
176p.
Hbk £42.95

Foreign trade, investment, and the law in the People's Republic of China / editor Michael J. Moser : contributors Jesse T.H. Chang ... et al. – 2nd ed. – Hong Kong : Oxford University Press, 1987.
x,603p; 26cm.
An extensively revised and updated second edition. Gives an introduction to the legal framework currently being developed in China with respect to foreign commercial and investment activity.
ISBN 0195840585 Hbk £27.50

Foreman
Trade Description Act 1970. – London : Wildy & Sons.
Hbk £2.25

Foreman, Carol →Australian family law.
—Guide to the De Facto Relationships Act-New South Wales / Stephen O'Ryan. – Butterworths, 1985.
127p.
ISBN 040949075X Pbk £22.00

Foreman, J. C. →Jervis on the office and duties of coroners : with forms and precedents.

Foreman, Tony
Tolley's Focus on the Purchase and Sale of a Private Company's Shares. – 2nd ed. – Croydon : Tolley.
152p.
ISBN 0854591850 Hbk £6.95

Forensic audiology / Chuang Wei Ping : foreword by Ronald Hinchcliffe. – Middlesbrough : Chuang Wei Ping, 1985.
108p in various pagings; 22cm.
ISBN 0951080008 Pbk £6.00

Forensic Fables. – 1985 Reprint. – London : Butterworths.
ISBN 0406201501 Hbk £11.50

Forensic Medicine / Shapiro. – 3rd ed. – Edinburgh : Churchill Livingstone, 1988.
ISBN 0443034400 Hbk £29.50

Forensic Medicine / Knight. – 9th ed. – London : Edward Arnold, 1985.
ISBN 073144521 Pbk £17.50

Forensic Medicine / Johnson. – London : Waterlow, 1987.
ISBN 0080392199 Hbk £30.00

Forensic Medicine for Lawyers. – 2nd ed. – London : Butterworths, 1983.
ISBN 0407013709 Pbk £19.00

Forensic medicine for lawyers / J.K. Mason with chapters by A.K.M. Macrae, J.S. Oliver, A.T. Proudfoot. – 2nd ed. – London : Butterworths, 1983.
xv,418p; 24cm.
Previous ed.: Bristol : J. Wright, 1978. Bibliography: p398-399. - Includes index.
ISBN 0407002448

Forensic Psychologists. – Canberra : Australian Institute of Criminology.
free

Forensic Psychology. – London : Batsford, 1981.
ISBN 0713424753 Hbk £15.00

Forensic science and the expert witness / by J.H. Phillips, J.K. Bowen : with a foreword by Sir Daryl Dawson. – North Ryde, N.S.W. : Law Book Company, 1985.
ix,114p; 22cm.
Introductory guide to forensic science. Contains chapters on forensic science and crime; crime science examiners; continuity of exhibits; photographic evidence; forensic chemistry; forensic biology; firearms and toolmarks; fingerprints; and document examination.
ISBN 0455205914 Pbk £12

Forest Law. – Delhi : Bishen Singh, 1983.
92p.
Hbk £4.00

Forest Law : Containing Commentaries on Indian Forest Act with State Amendments and Rules as Amended... – 6th ed. – Allahabad : Hind Publishing House, 1986.
Hbk £130.00

Forest Legislation in Selected African Countries. – Rome : FAO, Food and Agricultural Organization of the United Nations, 1986.
462p.
ISBN 9251023220 Hbk £28.50

Forfaiting : an alternative approach to export trade finance / Ian Guild and Rhodri Harris. – Cambridge : Woodhead-Faulkner, 1985.
160p.
Includes index.
ISBN 0859413160 £17.50

Forging ahead : thirty years of the European Parliament 1952- 1982 / European Parliament. – S.l. : Directorate-General for Research and Documentation, 1982.
237p.
Bibliography: p.215-220. - Includes index.

Forgotten treaties : a practical plan for world disarmament / Allan McKnight : with an introduction by Keith Suter. – Melbourne : Law Council of Australia, 1983.
xi,136p.
Includes bibliographical references and index. Part II is text of McKnight's Draft Disarmament Treaty.
ISBN 0959660879

Forkosch, Morris D
Outer space and legal liability / by Morris D. Forkosch. – The Hague : Nijhoff, 1982.
xvi,290p.
Includes index. Bibliography: p267-270.
ISBN 9024725828 Hbk £100.00/$43.50

Form and Content of Company Accounts / Lybrand. – 3rd ed. – Oxford : Croner Publications, 1986.
ISBN 1851850325 Pbk £9.95

Form and substance in Anglo-American law : a comparative study of legal reasoning, legal theory, and legal institutions / P.S. Atiyah and Robert S. Summers. – Oxford : Clarendon, 1987.
444p; 24cm.
Includes bibliography and index.
ISBN 0198255772 £35.00

Formal Sittings of the Court of Justice of the European Communities 1982 and 1983. – Kirchberg : Commission of the European Communities, 1984.
64p.
Hbk

Format
Costs in Matrimonial Causes. – Format. – London : Fourmat, 1985.
– (LCFS 2).
ISBN 090684004X Pbk £2.45
—Fees in Matrimonial Proceedings. – Format. – 4th ed. – London : Fourmat, 1986.
– (LCFS 9).
ISBN 1851900160 Pbk £3.25

Formation of the early Meiji legal order : the Japanese code of 1871 and its Chinese foundation / by Paul Heng-Chao Ch'en. – Oxford : Oxford University Press, 1981.
xxii,204p; 23cm.
Bibliography: p187-190. - Includes index.
ISBN 019713601X £12.00

Forms/Agreements Intellectual Property 2 vols. – London : Sweet & Maxwell, 1988.
ISBN 0421253002 Hbk

Forms of Action at Common Law / Chaytor. – Cambridge : Cambridge University Press, 1936.
ISBN 0521091853 Pbk £7.95

Forms of action at international law : the spirit of English law and international law / H.A. Schwarz-Liebermann von Wahlendorf. – Birmingham : Institute of Judicial Administration, University of Birmingham, 1981.
iii,55p.
ISBN 2903642001

Forms of Practical Proceedings in the Courts of King's Bench. – 6th ed. Repr. of 1824 ed. – Abingdon : Professional Books.
357p.
Hbk £45.00

Formulae Bene Placitandi : A Book of Entries Containing Precedents, 2 Vols. – Repr. of 1671 ed. – Abingdon : Professional Books.
264p.
Hbk £95.00

Formulary of old Scots legal documents / compiled by Peter Gouldesbrough : with a supplementary essay on Early Scottish conveyancing by Gordon Donaldson. – Edinburgh : Stair Society, 1985.
viii,196p.
Includes index.
ISBN 0902292110

Forrest, David
Low Pay or No Pay? A Review of the Theory and Practice of Minimum-Wage Laws / S. R. Dennison. – London : Institute of Economic Affairs, 1984.
ISBN 0255361750 Pbk £2.50

Forrest, P.
Introduction to Property. – London : Butterworths, 1988.
ISBN 0406581002 Hbk
ISBN 0406581010 Pbk

Forrester, B.
Travellers' handbook - guide to law affecting gypsies. – TUAR, 1985.
ISBN 0948309008 Pbk £5.95

Forry, John I
Joint Ventures in the United States. – London : Butterworths.
ISBN 0406499616 Hbk £40.00

Forster, Jane
Divorce conciliation : a study of services in England and abroad, with implications for Scotland. – Edinburgh : Scottish Council for Single Parents, 1982.
v,99p.
Includes bibliographies.

Forster, M. J. →Law and practice relating to pollution control in the member states of the European communities : a comparative survey.
→ Law and practice relating to pollution control in the United Kingdom.
—Law Relating to Transport of Dangerous Wastes, United Kingdom / V. di Martino. – Luxembourg : Office for Official Publications of the European Communities, 1987.
104p.
ISBN 9282567524 Pbk £350.00

Forsyth, C. F. →Caney's the law of suretyship in Africa.
—Private international law : the modern Roman-Dutch law including the jurisdiction of the Supreme Court / C.F. Forsyth assisted by T.W. Bennett. – Cape Town : Juta, 1981.
xxxviii,384p.
Bibliography: p.xiii-xvi. - Includes index.
ISBN 0702112305

Forsyth, P.
Accountants Guide to Practise Promotion, The. – London : Kogan Page.
ISBN 1850916292 Pbk £9.95

Forsyth, P. J. →British Airways : Civil Aviation Policy and the Privatisation of British Airways.

Forsyth, Richard S. →Expert systems : principles and case studies.

Forsyth, T. A.
Brief Outline of the Law Relating to Trusts, Wills, Executors, and Administrators. – 2nd ed. – Wellington : Butterworths, 1982.
ISBN 0409627127 Hbk

Forte, A. →Scottish Cases and Materials in Commercial Law.

Fortescue, Edward E. →Australian mercantile law.

Fortier, Laval
Canadian Transport Cases (1966-1977), 7 Vols. – Aurora : Canada Law Book Co.
– (Law Reports).
Hbk £232.00
—Canadian Transport Cases : 1966-77, 7 Vols. – Aurora : Canada Law Book Co.
– (Earlier Series Entitled Canadian Railway and Transport Cases).
Hbk £232.00

Fortson, Rudi
Law on the misuse of drugs. – London : Sweet & Maxwell, 1988.
Refers to the Intoxicating Substances (Supply) Act 1985, and the Drug Trafficking Offences Act 1986 in the context of solvent abuse, drug-kits, and drug-trafficking profits. Lists sentencing examples. Combines an historic perspective of drug misuse with an examination of the legal implications involved.
ISBN 0421396202 Hbk £19

Forum Internationale / Marcus Lutter. – Deventer : Kluwer Law and Taxation Publishers, 1983.

Forward Look at Research and the Child in Care. – Bristol : School of Applied Social Studies, University of Bristol.
ISBN 0862922984 Pbk £4.50

Fosh, Patricia →Industrial relations and the law in the 1980's : issues and future trends.

Foskett, David
Law and practice of compromise / by David Foskett. – 2nd ed. – London : Sweet & Maxwell, 1985.
xlvii,388p.
Covers the significance of an agreement reached, and its consequence, and also the means by which a concluded agreement can, may or should be implemented. Also discusses the role which lawyers play in the negotiating process.
ISBN 0421324708

Fossil in the Sandstone sound recording : the Recollecting Judge. – South Yarra : Louis Braille Productions Ltd..
ISBN 9ac £48.00

Foster, D.
Detention and Torture in South Africa. – DENT, 1987.
ISBN 0852553188 Pbk £7.95

Foster families : recommendation no. R(87)6 adopted by the Committee of Ministers of the Council of Europe on 20 March 1987 and Explanatory memorandum. – Council of Europe. – Strasbourg : Council of Europe, 1987.
15p.
Prepared by the Committee of experts on family law set up under the authority of the European Committee on Legal Co-operation. At head of cover title : Council of Europe, Legal Affairs.
ISBN 9287110875

Foster, John
Capital Taxes Encyclopaedia / Ian A. Marsh. – London : Butterworths.
This looseleaf service provides detailed coverage of capital transfer tax issues and legislation in the United Kingdom. Legislative developments, court decisions, and changes in practice are updated with six service issues per year.
ISBN 0406505101 Llf £150.00

—Crown Law. – Reprint. – Abingdon : Professional Books, 1986.
– (Classical English Law Texts Ser.).
ISBN 0862053196 Hbk £33.50

Foster, Leslie A. →Marine Affairs Bibliography : a Comprehensive Index to Marine Law and Policy Literature, Cumulation 1980-1985.

Foster, T.
Book of Humorous Legal Anecdotes. – Springwood Books.
ISBN 0862541344 Hbk £7.95

Foster, William F.
Real estate agency law / William F. Foster. – Toronto : Carswell, 1984.
xliii,272p.
Includes bibliographical references and index.
ISBN 0459370502

Fotheringham, Allan
Capitol Offences. – Toronto : Key Key Porter Books.
208p.
ISBN 1550130048 Hbk £19.95

Foul Bills and Dagger Money. – Professional Books.
ISBN 0862052483 Hbk £14.50

Foulds
Insect Emblems Act, 1983, Bill 159 : Insect Emblems Act, 1983. – Ontario : Ontario Government Publications Service, 1983.
1p.
Hbk £0.30

Foulkes, David
Administrative law / David Foulkes. – 6th ed. – London : Butterworths, 1986.
xxxv,477p; 25cm.
This text is a thorough discussion of administrative law in the United Kingdom for students of the subject. Recent developments in caselaw and statutes are described.
ISBN 0406584095 Hbk £28.00
ISBN 0406584109 Pbk £17.95

—Welsh Veto : The Wales Act 1978 and the Referendum / J. Barry Jones. – Cardiff : University of Wales, 1983.
238p.
ISBN 0708308317 Hbk £11.95

Foundation for Science and Technology
Technology transfer within the E.E.C. : a summary of papers and discussion of a seminar held in the house of the Royal Society of Arts on Thursday 31 January 1985. – Foundation for Science and Technology. – London : London Science Centre, 1985.
23p.

Foundation for the Study of Plural Societies → Case studies on human rights and fundamental freedoms : a world survey.

Foundations of Canadian Law / Bradford W Morse. – Toronto : Butterworths, 1987.
ISBN 0409811513 Hbk

Foundations of European community law : an introduction to the constitutional and administrative law of the European Community / by T.C. Hartley. – 2nd ed. – Oxford : Clarendon Press, 1988.
li,496p.
Includes bibliographies and index. Revised from the 1981 edition. Discusses the basic principles of European Community law and examines aspects of interes to lawyers. The new edition takes into account changes in treaty, statute and case law since 1981.
ISBN 0198762070 Pbk £17.95
ISBN 0198762089 Hbk £40

Foundations of Justice. – Oxford : Oxford University Press, 1986.
ISBN 0195040767 Hbk £22.50

Foundations of Law Act, 1980 and its implementation. – Jerusalem : The Ministry, 1982.
6p.

Foundations of Real Estate Financing : The Mathematical Basis / David Baxter. – Toronto : Butterworths, 1983.
353p.
Hbk £45.00

Foundations of the law of tort / Glanville Williams, B.A. Hepple. – 2nd ed. – London : Butterworths, 1984.
xxiv,230p; 23cm.
This text for students in the United Kingdom provides an examination of the underlying principles of tort law and liability in the modern context. The function of tort law and its history, the concepts of damage and fault, the effects of insurance and social security, and possibilities for reform are covered.
ISBN 0406683867 Hbk £14.00
ISBN 0406683875 Pbk £10.95

Foundations of the modern Bar / by Raymond Cocks. – London : Sweet & Maxwell, 1983.
vii,257p; 22cm.
Bibliography: p235-249. - Includes index.
ISBN 0421303603 Pbk £9.50

Four Law Drafts to Fight Deflation, Prevent Inflation and Lower Interest Rates microform . – Berrima : Peace Plans.
microform

Four Studies of International Humanitarian Law. – Geneva : Comite International de la Croix-Rouge, 1985.
58p.
Hbk £2.00

Fouracre, Paul →Settlement of disputes in early medieval Europe.

Fourmat Publishing
Conveyancing Fees and Duties. – Fourmat Publishing. – 6th ed. – London : Fourmat, 1986. – (LCFS 5).
ISBN 1851900209 Pbk £4.50

Fourquet, Michele, et al
Legal English 2 : an Introduction to the American Constitution. – Paris : Cujas, 1986.
184p.
Hbk £98.00

Fourteen to Eighteen : The Changing Pattern of Schooling in Scotland. – Aberdeen : Aberdeen University Press, 1983.
192p.
ISBN 0080303749 Pbk £8.75

Fourteenth Report on Competition Policy. – Kirchberg : Commission of the European Communities, 1985.
248p.
Hbk

Fourteenth report to Parliament on subordinate legislation concerning : M.M.B.W. By-law no. 250: Trade Waste / Legal and Constitutional Committee. – Melbourne : Government Printer, 1988.
v,5p.
Includes the text of the By-law.

Fourth Company Law Directive : Implementation by Member States / J.G. Demas. – Luxembourg : Office for Official Publications of the European Communities, 1987.
100p.
ISBN 9282571211 Pbk £400.00

Fourth programme of consolidation and statute law revision / Scottish Law Commission. – Edinburgh : H.M.S.O., 1982.
10p.
ISBN 0102516820

Fourth report from the Energy Committee : session 1984-85 : the winter supplementary estimate for 45 million in respect of the British National Oil Corporation together with minutes of proceedings relating to the report and minutes of evidence and appendices / ordered by the House of Commons to be printed 12 December 1984. – London : H.M.S.O., 1984.
xiv,34p. – (1984-85 HC).
Includes bibliographical references. Chairman: Ian Lloyd.
ISBN 0102126852

Fourth report from the Home Affairs Committee, session 1980-81 : the prison service
Vol. 1 : Report with minutes of proceedings. – London : H.M.S.O., 1981.
lxiiip. – (HC).
ISBN 0100082912
Vol. 2 : Evidence and appendices. – 1981.
vii,282p. – (HC).
ISBN 010008091X

Fourth report from the Home Affairs Committee, session 1981-82 : police complaints procedures
Vol.1 : Report with minutes of proceedings. – London : H.M.S.O., 1982.
xlii; 25cm. – (HC98-I).
ISBN 0100080820 Pbk £3.95
Vol.2 : Evidence and appendices. – 1982.
vii,326p; 25cm. – (HC 98-II).
ISBN 0100080928 Pbk £12.40

Fourth report from the Transport Committee, session 1985-86 : airport security : together with the proceedings of the Committee. – London : H.M.S.O., 1986.
xxiii p. – (H.C. 1985-86).
ISBN 0102597863

Fourth report on the legal profession : solicitors' trust accounts / New South Wales Law Reform Commission. – Sydney : The Commission, 1984.
viii,228p. – (L.R.C. 44).
Bibliography: p.212-214. Includes indexes.

Fourth report to Parliament on subordinate legislation concerning Health (Tobacco packages - warnings) Regulations 1986 ... / Legal and Constitutional Committee. – Melbourne : Government Printer, 1986.
vi,48p.

Fourth report to Parliament on the operation of section 32 of the Interpretation of Legislation Act 1984 concerning : Place Names Committee (Members' Fees and Travelling Allowances) Regulations 1988 (SR No. 251/1988) / Legal and Constitutional Committee. – Melbourne : Government Printer, 1988.
v,6p.
Includes the text of the Regulations.

Fowler →Property Handbook.
—Property Handbook / Fowler. – Sphere Books.
ISBN 074740108X Pbk £10.99

Fowler, David John →Drug Industry : A Case Study in Foreign Control.

Fowler, Stuart G. →Australian family law & practice reporter.

Fowles, A. J. →Crime and penal policy.

Fowlston, B.
Understanding Commercial and Industrial Licensing 1984. – Waterlow.
ISBN 0080391540 Pbk £8.50

Fox, Alan
Man mismanagement / Alan Fox. – 2nd ed. – London : Business Books, 1985.
224p.
Previous ed.: London : Hutchinson, 1974. Includes bibliography and index.
ISBN 0091593808 Pbk £7.95

Fox-Andrews, J.
Business Tenancies. – 3rd ed. – London : Estates Gazette, 1978.
ISBN 0728200392 Hbk £10.00

Fox, H.
Canadian Law Trade Marks and Unfair Competition. – 3rd ed. – Agincourt : Carswell, 1972.
ISBN 045931170 Hbk £59.40

Fox, Hazel →International economic law and developing states : some aspects.

Fox, J C
History Of Contempt Of Court. – Professional Books.
ISBN 0862053668 Hbk £26.50

Fox, R.
Payments on termination of employment. – 2nd ed. – London : Longman Professional, 1984.
ISBN 0851206662 Pbk £9.95

Fox, Richard G.
Research Guide to Criminology Material. – Canberra : Australian Institute of Criminology.
Hbk £1.00

—Sentencing : state and federal law in Victoria / Richard G. Fox, Arie Freiberg. – Melbourne : Oxford University Press, 1985.
lxxv,615p.
ISBN 0195546563 Hbk £50.00

Fox, Robin
Kinship and marriage : an anthropological perspective / Robin Fox. – Cambridge : Cambridge University Press, 1983.
273p; 20cm.
ISBN 0521260736

Foxman, Abraham H. →1987 annual on terrorism.

Fox's Patent Cases : Canada, 22 Vols.
Vols. 1-44 bound in 11 Vols. with Index and Digest Vols. 1-30. – Carswell Legal Publications. – Agincourt : Carswell, 1983.
This multi-volume work covers the years 1940 to 1971 and contains all judgements of the Canadian courts on the patent law published in full. All relevant statutes, statutory amendments, Orders-in-Council, Rules of Practice, and other official acts impacting on patent law are included in the work.
Hbk £579.75

Foy, S.L.
Problems of International Justice. – Wildwood.
ISBN 0813303923 Hbk £31.00

Fractured Federation? / Jennifer Aldred, John Wilkes. – London : Allen and Unwin, 1983.
128p.
ISBN 0868611093 £15.00

Fraenkel, Peter
Namibians / by Peter Fraenkel and Roger Murray : with additional material by Kaye Stearman. – New ed. – London : Minority Rights Group, 1985.
31p. – (Report).
Bibliography: p.31.
ISBN 0946690278

Fragile Freedoms : Human Rights and Dissent in Canada. – Richmond Hill : Irwin Publishing Inc..
298p.
ISBN 0772013586 Hbk £17.95
ISBN 0772013772 Pbk £9.95

Fragmented world : competing perspectives on trade, money and crisis / Chris Edwards. – London : Methuen, 1985.
xvi,350p; 23cm.
Bibliography: p310-333. - Includes index.
ISBN 0416733905 Hbk £14.95
ISBN 0416734006 Pbk £6.95

Framework for evaluating Canada's Trade Marks Act / by Steven Globerman with Mitchell P. Rothman. – Canada : Policy Research, Analysis and Liaison Directorate, Consumer and Corporate Affairs, 1983.
86p.
ISBN 0662124189

Framework of consensus : government, business and trade unions / W. J. Byrt. – Melbourne : Law Book Company Ltd., 1985.
ix,220p.
Bibliography: p211-218.
ISBN 0455205779

Framework of criminal justice / Michael King. – London : Croom Helm, 1981.
159p; 23cm.
Bibliography: p153-156. - Includes index.
ISBN 0709904304 Hbk £10.95
ISBN 0709915004 Pbk £6.50

Framework of Water Rights Legislation in Canada. – Calgary : Canadian Institute of Resources Law.
103p.
ISBN 0919269214 Hbk £20.00

Framing of India's Constitution, 5 Vols. – New Delhi : Indian Institute of Public Administration.
Hbk £125.00

Framing of the Constitution of the United States. – Bombay : Popular Prakashan, 1966.
212p.
Hbk £20.00

Francalanci, Giampiero, et al
Atlas of the Straigth Baselines. – Milan : Giuffre, 1986.
xii, 138p.
Hbk £18,000.00

Francey, Neil
Business Names Guide. – 3rd ed. – North Ryde : C.C.H. Australia, 1985.
154p.
ISBN 0869034413 Hbk £28.00

Franchising 2. – Vancouver : Continuing Legal Education Society of British Columbia, 1985.
699p.
ISBN 0865042071 Hbk £90.00

Franchising. – Vancouver : British Columbia Continuing Legal Education Society, 1981.
703p.
ISBN 0865040303 Hbk £85.00

Franchising : practice and precedents in business format franchising / John Adams, K.V. Prichard Jones. – 2nd ed. – London : Butterworths, 1987.
xxxvii,409p; 25cm.
Previous ed.: 1981. Includes index.
ISBN 0406101043 Hbk £50.00

Franchising in Australia : a legal guide / by David Shannon. – Sydney : Law Book Co., 1982.
xxii,275p.
Includes index.
ISBN 045520456X

Francioni, Francesco
International Law for Antarctica / Tullio Scovazzi. – Milan : Giuffre, 1988.
xiv, 532p.
Hbk L50,000.00

Francis, D.
Countertrade Handbook. – Cambridge : Woodhead-Faulkner, 1987.
ISBN 0859413519 Hbk £40.00

Francis, E.A. → Contract for the Sale of Land in New South Wales.
—Mortgages and Securities / Thomas. – 3rd ed. – Sydney : Butterworths, 1986.
ISBN 0409491633 Hbk £55.00

Franck
Leaders and lawyers / Brownstone. – London : Facts On File, 1986.
ISBN 0816013675 Hbk £7.95

Franey, Ros
Poor law : the mass arrest of homeless claimants in Oxford / by Ros Franey : illustrated by Jim Stanes and Nina Carroll. – London : CHAR, 1983.
93p; 21cm. – (Poverty pamphlet).
ISBN 0906951046 Pbk £1.95

Frank, Andre Gunder
Dependent accumulation and underdevelopment / Andre Gunder Frank. – 1st ed. reprinted. – London : Macmillan, 1982.
xx,226p.
Bibliography: p.202-219. - Includes index.
ISBN 0333239512

Frank, Isaiah
Trade Policy Issues of Interest to the Third World. – London : Trade Policy Research Centre, 1981.
76p.
Hbk £2.00

Frank, W.
General Principles of English Law. – 6th ed. – NELS, 1975.
ISBN 0245526625 Pbk £4.50

Frankel, S. D., et al
Wiretaps and Conspiracy. – Vancouver : British Columbia Continuing Legal Education Society, 1981.
127p.
ISBN 0865040370 Hbk £40.00

Frankenburg, Catherine
Time taken to deal with juveniles under criminal proceedings / Catherine Frankenburg and Roger Tarling. – London : Home Office, 1983.
v,21p.
Bibliography: p.14.
ISBN 0862521025

Frankfurter and Due Process. – London : Eurospan, 1988.
ISBN 0819156159 Hbk £26.25
ISBN 0819156167 Pbk £15.50

Franklin, Blen Lloyd Stuart
Mining and mineral laws of South Africa / by Blen Lloyd Stuart Franklin and Morris Kaplan. – Durban : Butterworths, 1982.
Bibliography: p.lxxvii-lxxviii. - Includes index.
ISBN 0409028983 Hbk R335

Franklin, Bob → Rights of children.

Franklin Dam Case. – Butterworths, 1983.
288p.
ISBN 0409494313 Pbk £175.00

Franklin, David → Introduction to Quebec Law.

Franklin, Martin
Introduction to Quebec Law / David Franklin. – 3rd ed. – Toronto : Copp Clark, 1983.
352p : Illus.
ISBN 0773042903 Pbk £15.37

Franklin, Nicola → Review of administrative action.

Franks, John A.
Company director and the law. – 5th. – London : Longman Professional (UK), 1986.
Explains the legal responsibilities and obligations of the company director. Covers the changes made by the Companies Act 1985, and the Insolvency Act 1986.
ISBN 085121231X Pbk £17.95
→ Guide to perks from shares.
—Management Information Systems. – London : Kogan Page.
ISBN 1850914699 Hbk £18.95

Fransman
Immigration Emergency Procedures / Webb. – London : Legal Action Group, 1986.
ISBN 0905099117 Pbk £11.00

Fransman, Laurie
British Nationality Law. – 2nd ed. – London : Fourmat, 1986.
ISBN 1851900020 Pbk £12.95

Franson, Robert T.
Canadian Environmental Law, 7 Vols. / Alastair R. Lucas. – Scarborough, Ontario : Butterworths (Canada).
Hbk £475.00 (partial)

Frascona et al., J.L.
Principles of Business Law and the Legal Environment. – London : Allyn & Bacon.
ISBN 0205115683 Pbk £35.65

Fraser
Court of Session Cases : Series 1-5, 1821-1906, 63 Vols.
5th Series, 1898-1906, 8 Vols. /. – Abingdon : Professional Books.
Hbk

Fraser, C. M. → Courts of the County Palatine of Durham from earliest times to 1971.

Fraser, Derek
Evolution of the British welfare state : a history of social policy since the Industrial Revolution / Derek Fraser. – 2nd ed. – London : Macmillan, 1984.
xxxii,326p; 22cm.
Previous ed.: 1973. Bibliography: p303-322.
ISBN 0333359992

Fraser et al.
Handbook on Canadian Company Law. – 7th ed. – Agincourt : Carswell, 1975.
ISBN 0459368907 Hbk £41.80

Fraser, Joan N → Law Libraries in Canada.

Fraser, Malcolm → Mission to South Africa : the Commonwealth report.

Fraser, Peter
Conduct of Civil Litigation in British Columbia / John Horn. – London : Butterworths.
ISBN 0409993581 Hbk £292.00

Fraser, T. G.
Partition in Ireland, India and Palestine : theory and practice / T.G. Fraser. – London : Macmillan, 1984.
xiii,225p; 23cm.
Bibliography: p210-213. - Includes index.
ISBN 0333322800 £22.50

Fraser, Vincent → Planning decisions digest.

Fraud / Anthony J. Arlidge and Jacques Parry. – London : Waterlow, 1985.
xlii,368p; 24cm.
Includes index.
ISBN 008039163X £30.00

Fraud. – London : Sweet & Maxwell, 1988.
ISBN 0421365307 Hbk

Fraud in Commercial Transactions. – Vancouver : British Columbia Continuing Legal Education Society, 1982.
192p.
ISBN 086504080X Hbk £17.50

Fraud of the Century : Case of the Supertanker 'Salem'. – Routledge.
ISBN 041500246X Hbk £15.95

Fraud trials : a report / by JUSTICE : chairman of committee Beryl Cooper. – London : JUSTICE, 1984.
vii,47p; 22cm.
ISBN 0907247059

Fraud Trials Committee report / chairman, Lord Roskill. – London : H.M.S.O., 1986.
xi,245p; 25cm.
Examines methods of combating serious commercial fraud. Discusses whether lay juries are capable of understanding evidence in complex fraud trials. Proposes replacement of jury be a Fraud Trials Tribunal in complex cases.
ISBN 0113800088 Pbk £9.00

Fraudulent conveyances and preferences / Law Reform Commission of British Columbia. – Vancouver : The Commission, 1986.
viii,216p. – (Working paper).
Includes bibliographical references.

Frazer, Elizabeth → Lust to kill : a feminist investigation of sexual murder.

Frazer, P.
Plastic and Electronic Money. – Cambridge : Woodhead-Faulkner, 1985.
ISBN 0859412903 Hbk £40.00

Freckelton, Ian R.
Trial of the expert : a study of expert evidence and forensic experts / Ian R. Freckelton. – Melbourne : Oxford University Press, 1987.
xxxii,289p.
A textbook of the rules of expert evidence, and an analysis of the difficulties experienced when experts from non-legal disciplines are called as witnesses. Examines the impact of new scientific disciplines, and looks at how the forensic expert's duties to maintain confidentiality may conflict with the court's need for all the relevant evidence.
ISBN 0195545664 Hbk £30

Fredman, S → Labour law and industrial relations in Great Britain.

Free Movement in European Community Law. – Oxford : Oxford University Press.
ISBN 019825492X Hbk £35.00

Free movement of goods in the EEC. – London : European Law Centre, 1982.
285p.
Supplement 1984.
ISBN 0907451055 £34.00

Free Movement of Goods in the EEC Under Articles 30 to 36 of the Rome Treaty. – London : European Law Centre.
ISBN 0907451209 Hbk £75.00

Free speech : a philosophical enquiry / Frederick Schauer. – Cambridge : Cambridge University Press, 1982.
xiv,.237p; 24cm.
Bibliography: p222-229. - Includes index.
ISBN 0521243408 Hbk £20.00
ISBN 0521286174 Pbk £6.50

Free Trade & Competition in the European Economic Community : Law, Poicy and Practice. – Routledge.
ISBN 0415001102 Hbk £27.50

'Free two pence' Section 137 of the Local Government Act 1972 and Section 83 of the Local Governement (Scotland) Act 1973 / by Colin Crawford and Victor Moore. – London : The Chartered Institute of Public Finance and Accountancy, 1983.
x,218p.
ISBN 0852992556

Freedland, M. R. → Labour law : text and materials.

Freedman
Services charges-Law and practice / Shapiro. – Stewart (Henry), 1986.
ISBN 0946700311 Pbk £17.50

Freedman, Judith → Property and marriage : an integrated approach : property, tax, pensions and benefits in the family.

Freedman, M. D. A. → Lloyd's Introduction to Jurisprudence.

Freedman, Samuel
Chief Justice Samuel Freedman : a great Canadian judge : a collection of the reasons for judgment of the Honourable Samuel Freedman, Justice of the Court of Queen's Bench of Manitobe (1952-60), Justice of the Court of Appeal of Manitoba (1960-83), and Chief Justice of Manitoba (1971-83) / selected and edited by Cameron Harvey : with a bibliographical note by Vivian Rachlis. – Winnipeg : Law Society of Manitoba, 1983.
xi,195p.
ISBN 0969130708

Freedman, W.
Freedom of Speech on Private Property. – Quorum Press.
ISBN 0899303234 Hbk £32.95
—Press and Media Access to the Criminal Court. – Quorum Press.
ISBN 0899303285 Hbk £32.95
—Res Judicata and Collateral Estoppel Tools for Plaintiffs and Defendants. – Westport Publications.
ISBN 0899302777 Hbk £32.95

Freedom and security under the law : second report / Commission of Inquiry Concerning Certain Activities of the Royal Canadian Mounted Police. – 2. – Ottawa : Canadian Government Publishing Centre, 1981.
xxii,1257p; 25cm.
Bibliography: p.1117-1144. Chairman: D.C. McDonald.
ISBN 0660109506 v.2
ISBN 0660109522

Freedom and the Court Civil Rights and Liberties in the United States. – Oxford : Oxford University Press.
ISBN 0195055160 Pbk £12.95

Freedom of Association : a Workers' Education Manual. – Geneva : International Labour Office, 1987.
xi, 149p.
ISBN 9221057828 Hbk £15.00

Freedom of association : digest of decisions and principles of the Freedom of Association Committee of the governing body of the ILO. – International Labour Office. – 3rd ed. – Geneva : International Labour Office, 1985.
xii, 140 i.e. 262 p.; 24 cm.
ISBN 9221050734 Pbk £30.00

Freedom of association and industrial relations : a comparative study / Ferdinand von Prondzynski. – London : Mansell, 1987.
250p; 24cm.
Includes bibliography and index.
ISBN 0720117755 Pbk £30.00 :
ISBN 0720118700 £15.00

Freedom of Association and Procedures for Determining Conditions of Employment in the Public Service : Report 7. Sixty-Third Session of the International Labour Conference, 1977
Part 1: Preliminary Report and Questionnaire. – Geneva : International Labour Office.
iv, 111p.
ISBN 9221015750 Hbk £17.50
Part 1: Proposed Texts Referred to Governments. –
45p.
Hbk £15.00
Part 2: Replies of Governments. –
41p.
ISBN 9221017559 Hbk £12.50
Part 2: Replies of Governments. –
84p.
ISBN 9221015769 Hbk £17.50

Freedom of Association, Industrial Relations and Collective Bargaining Practices in Mines Other than Coal Mines. – Geneva : International Labour Office, 1984.
iv, 79p.
ISBN 9221034577 Hbk £15.00

Freedom of data flows and EEC law / G P V Vandenberghe, Y Poullet. – Kluwer Law and Taxation, 1988.
142. – (Computer/Law Series).
Deals with the legal problems caused by transfrontier flows of information. Includes chapters on the need to speak a common language between partners, data and information in common law, information and data in continental law, and restriction on transborder transmissions of commercial data under EEC law.
ISBN 9065443665 Pbk £32/Dfl 99

Freedom of Information. – North Ryde : Law Book Co, 1984.
xxix, 347p.
ISBN 0455203563 Hbk £36.00

Freedom of Information : Canadian Perspectives. – London : Butterworths.
ISBN 0409857130 Hbk £60.00

Freedom of Information : the Law, the Practice, the Ideal. – Weidenfeld & Nicolson. – (Law in Context Series).
ISBN 0297793446 Hbk £18.00
ISBN 00297793861 Pbk £11.95

Freedom of Information Act 1982 : Annual Report 1984-85. – Kingston : Australian Government Publishing Service, 1985.
481p.
Hbk £20.60

Freedom of information and expression in Poland. – Article 19. – London : Article 19, 1987.
28p.

Freedom of information and expression in Senegal / a commentary by Article 19 on the report submitted to the United Nations Human Rights Committee by the government of the Republic of Senegal. – London : Article 19, 1987.
30p.
Bibliography: p.30.

Freedom of information and expression in Tunisia. – Article 19. – London : Article 19, 1987.
29p.

Freedom of Information Legislation in Nova Scotia, New Brunswick, Newfoundland, and Quebec. – Ontario : Ontario Government Publications Service, 1983.
16p. – (Current Issue Paper: No. 21).
Hbk £0.50

Freedom of information trends in the information age / edited by Tom Riley and Harold C. Relyea. – London : Frank Cass, 1983.
172p; 23cm.
Papers originally presented in the Journal of media law and practice, vol.3, no.1. Bibliography: p169-172.
ISBN 071463221X £15.00

Freedom of interstate trade under the Australian constitution / by Michael Coper. – Sydney : Butterworths, 1983.
xiii,394p.
Bibliography: p.371-380. - Includes index.
ISBN 0409491802

Freedom of Speech. – Oxford : Oxford University Press, 1985.
ISBN 0198253818 Hbk £35.00

Freedom of Speech on Private Property. – Quorum Press.
ISBN 0899303234 Hbk £32.95

Freedom on licence : the development of parole and proposals for reform : report of a Howard League Working Party under the chairmanship of Professor the Lord McGregor of Durris .. – Howard League for Penal Reform. – Sunbury : Quartermaine House, 1981.
xxvi,70p; 22cm.
Bibliography: p70.
ISBN 0905898141 Pbk £4.25

Freedom, peace and their guarantees, from the viewpoint of the Constitution of Japan / Kenji Urata. – s.l. : s.n., 1982.
p.22-45.
'Originally presented as a draft to the Waseda University Centennial International Symposium at Waseda University on August 22 and 23, 1982'. Reprinted from: Waseda bulletin of comparative law, 2 (1982).

Freedom, Public Order and the Law. – Oxford : Basil Blackwell.
ISBN 063115809X Hbk £29.50
ISBN 0631158111 Pbk £10.95

Freedom, State Security and the Rule of Law. – London : Sweet & Maxwell, 1988.
ISBN 0421396407 Hbk £36.00

Freedom, state security and the rule of law : dilemmas of the apartheid society / Anthony S. Mathews. – Cape Town : Juta, 1986.
xxv,312p.
Bibliography: p.xi-xi - Includes index.
ISBN 0702118125

Freedom, the individual and the law / H. Street. – 5th ed. – Harmondsworth, Eng. : Penguin Books, 1982.
352p. – (Pelican Books).
ISBN 0140206469

Freedom Under The Law (Hamlyn No 1). – Sweet & Maxwell, 1949.
ISBN 0420421408 Pbk £7.50

Freeman, M. D. A. → British Nationality Act 1981.
—Cohabitation without marriage : an essay in law and social policy / Michael D.A. Freeman and Christina M. Lyon. – Aldershot : Gower, 1983.
vii,228p; 23cm.
Includes index.
ISBN 0566004550
—Dealing with domestic violence / M.D.A. Freeman. – Bicester : CCH Editions, 1987.
xii,150p; 23cm.
Examines the problem, legal resources, divorce and judicial separation, the criminal law, injunctive relief, Matrimonial Homes Act 1983, Domestic Violence Act 1976, Supreme Court Act 1981/County Court Act 1984, Injunctions ancillary to other proceedings, protection in the Magistrates Court, criminal injuries compensation scheme, and the housing law implications of domestic violence.
ISBN 0863251102 Pbk
→ Essays in family law 1985.
—Guide to the Matrimonial and Family Proceedings Act 1984 / M.D.A. Freeman. – Bicester, Oxfordshire : CCH Editions, 1984.
165p; 23cm.
Contains examination of divorce, the new one year ban, extending time limits of nullity proceedings, financial relief in divorce proceedings, and financial relief after overseas divorces, financial provision in Scotland after overseas divorce, family business, and distribution and transfer.
ISBN 0863250319
—Law and practice of custodianship / by Michael D.A. Freeman. – London : Sweet & Maxwell, 1986.
xviii,156p.
Chapters on the origins of the concept of custodianship, the local authority and custodianship, effects of custodianship orders, adoption of custodianship, custodianship and care, disputes between joint custodians, and on the procedure for application for custodianship.
ISBN 042135500X Pbk £12.00
—Law of residential homes and day-care establishments / M.D.A. Freeman and Christina M. Lyon. – London : Sweet & Maxwell, 1984.
xxvi,239p; 22cm.
Deals with children, the elderly, and the physically handicapped. Includes the Mental Health Act 1983 and the Health and Social Services and Social Security Adjudications Act 1983.
ISBN 0421258608 Pbk
→ Lloyd's Introduction to jurisprudence.
—Medicine, Ethics and the Law. – Sweet & Maxwell.
ISBN 042048020X Pbk £18.00
→ Police and Criminal Evidence Act 1984.
—Rights and wrongs of children / M.D.A. Freeman. – London : Pinter, 1983.
295p; 24cm.
Includes index.
ISBN 0903804204 Hbk £
ISBN 0861872266 Pbk £6.95
—State, law and the family. – London : Sweet & Maxwell, 1984.
ISBN 042279080X Pbk £9.95
→ State, the law, and the family.

Freeman, M. I. → Sheldon and Fidler's practice and law of banking.

Freestone, D. A. C.
Institutional framework of the European Communities / D.A.C. Freestone and J.S. Davidson. – London : Croom Helm, 1988.
17,221p; 23cm.
Includes index.
ISBN 0709910487 Hbk £27.50
ISBN 0709949081 Pbk £9.95

Freethy, N.
Self-administered pensions for directors. – London : Fitzwilliam, 1988.
ISBN 1870555031 Hbk £25.00

Freibert, Arie → Sentencing : state and federal law in Victoria.

Freilich, A. → Commercial Law.
→ Commercial Law II.

Freislich, Ethne
Catalogue of the Van Zyl Collection of Antiquarian Legal Materials at the University of Cape Town. – Rondebosch : University of Cape Town, 1985.
ii, 164p.
ISBN 0799209856 Pbk £5.00

Freitas, Denis de
Copyright system : practice and problems in developing countries / by Denis de Freitas. – London : Commonwealth Secretariat, 1983.
v,87p.
ISBN 085092233X

Freize → Bankruptcy Procedure.

French → Company Insolvency and Liquidation.
→ Company Law 1988-89.

French administrative law / J. F. Garner, Jean-Michel Galabert. – 3rd ed. – London : Butterworths, 1983.
xvii,218p.
Previous ed.: 1973. Bibliography: p.205-207.- Includes index.
ISBN 0406561524

French Canada in crisis : a new society in the making? / Camille Legendre. – Rev. ed. – London : Minority Rights Group, 1982.
20p. – (Report).
Previous ed.: 1980. Bibliography: p.17-18.

French Constitution. – London : Ambassade de France, 1986.
20 p.

French, D.
Dictionary of Accounting Terms. – London : Financial Training, 1985.
ISBN 0906322677 Pbk £8.95
→ Practical approach to company law.

French Labour Code, Part 1: Laws. – Geneva : International Labour Office, 1982.
204p.
ISBN 9221030830 Hbk £20.00

French law of contract / Barry Nicholas. – London : Butterworths, 1982.
xxxviii,253p.
ISBN 040663095X Pbk £16.95
ISBN 0406630968 Hbk £23.00

French multinationals / Julien Savary : foreword by Francois Morin. – London : Pinter, 1984.
220p.
Translation of: Les multinationales francaises.
ISBN 0861873637 £16.50

French, Richard D.
RCMP and the Management of National Security / Andre Beliveau. – Montreal : Institute for Research on Public Policy.
xiii, 79p.
ISBN 0920380182 Hbk

Freshfields → Securities regulation in the UK.

Freshwater fishery law / William Howarth. – London : Financial Training, 1987.
xxiv,311p; 23cm.
Bibliography: p302-304. - Includes index. Includes text of the Salmon and Freshwater Fisheries Act 1975. Originally published: London : H.M.S.O., 1975.
ISBN 1851850309 £17.95

Frewen, Gerard L. →Judgments of the Court of Criminal Appeal 1924-1978.

Frey, R. G.
Rights, killing, and suffering : moral vegetarianism and applied ethics / R.G. Frey. – Oxford : Blackwell, 1983.
xi,256p; 24cm.
Includes index.
ISBN 0631126848 £17.50
→ Utility and rights.

Freyseng, E. J. →Practice in mortgage actions in Ontario : the practice in mortgage actions and in exercising power of sale.

Fricke, Graham L. →Compulsory acquisition of land in Australia.

Fridman, G H L
Introduction to the law of torts. – Scarborough, Ontario : Butterworths (Canada), 1978.
312.
Covers the scope of tortious liability, fundamentals of liability, limitations on liability, personal injuries, negligence, injuries to personality, injuries to property, economic loss, injurious abuse of legal process, remedies, and procedural matters.
ISBN 0409830364 Pbk
—Law of agency / G.H.L. Fridman. – 5th ed. – London : Butterworths, 1983.
xxxvii, 386p.
This text gives an in-depth exploration of the law of agency. Primary emphasis is put on the evolution of agency law in the United Kingdom through the pure common law system into a coherent set of rules.
ISBN 0406584362 Hbk
ISBN 0406584370 Pbk £18.95
—Law of contract in Canada / by G.H.L. Fridman. – 2nd ed. – Toronto : Carswell, 1986.
clii,764p.
Previous ed.: 1976. Includes bibliographical references and index.
ISBN 0459382101
—Restitution / by G.H.L. Fridman, and James G. McLeod. – Toronto, Canada : Carswell Co., 1982.
lxviii, 649 p.; 26 cm.
Includes bibliographical references and index.
—Sale of Goods in Canada. – 3rd ed. – Agincourt : Carswell, 1986.
603p.
This treatise given on the law of sale of goods in Canada has been updated to discuss the recommendations of the Ontario Law Reform Commission's Report on the Sale of Goods, provisions of the International Convention on the Sale of Goods, consumer protection legislation, and related materials on sale of goods.
Hbk £80.00

Fried, Charles
Contract as promise : a theory of contractual obligation / Charles Fried. – Cambridge, Mass. : Harvard University Press, 1981.
162p; 25cm.
Includes index.
ISBN 0674169255 £8.40
→ Minorities : community and identity : report of the Dahlem Workshop on Minorities - Community and Identity, Berlin 1982, Nov. 28 - Dec. 3.

Friedland, Martin L.
Century of criminal justice : perspectives on the development of Canadian law / by Martin L. Friedland. – Toronto : Carswell Legal Publications, 1984.
xxii,245p.
ISBN 0459365800

Friedland, Roger
Class Power and Urban Policy : Corporations and Labour Unions in City Politics. – London : Macmillan, 1982.
256p. – (Sociology, Politics and Cities, Ser.).
ISBN 0333260759 Hbk £12.50
ISBN 0333260767 Pbk £4.95

Friedman, Howard M.
Securities and commodities enforcement : criminal prosecutions and civil injunctions / Howard M. Friedman. – Lexington, Mass. : Lexington Books, 1981.
xiii,238p; 24cm.
Includes index.
ISBN 066903617X £21.50

Friedman, Milton
Taxation, Inflation and the Role of Government. – Turramura : Centre for Independent Studies.
56p.
ISBN 0949769002 Hbk £3.50

Friends in conflict : the Anglo-Icelandic cod wars and the law of the sea / Hannes Jonsson. – London : C.Hurst, 1982.
xi,240p.
Bibliography: p225-233.

Friesen, Connie M.
International bank supervision / by Connie M. Friesen. – London : Euromoney, 1986.
xi,124p.
Includes bibliographical references.
ISBN 1870031105

Frieze, Steven A.
Compulsory winding up procedure. – 2nd ed. – London : Longman Professional, 1987.
ISBN 0851211798 Pbk £3.95
—Compulsory winding-up procedure. – 2nd. – London : Longman Professional (UK), 1987.
Revised following the Insolvency Act 1986. Step by step guide through the process of compulsory winding-up for a limited liability company from the role of the liquidation committee to the proofs of debt and dividend. Appendix contains procedural forms.
ISBN 0851211798 Pbk £14.50
—Handbook Bankruptcy Law and Practice. – 4th ed. – London : Longman Professional, 1988.
ISBN 085120726X Hbk
—Handbook of bankruptcy law and practice / Steven A. Frieze. – 4th ed. – London : Longman Professional (UK), 1988.
– (Practitioner Series).
Discusses the new concepts of statutory demands, individual voluntary arrangements and deeds of arrangement, and sets out the procedure leading to a bankruptcy order. Contains a list of courts with bankruptcy jurisdiction.
ISBN 085120726X Hbk £35
→ Humphreys' Notes on district registry practice and procedure.
—Insolvency law / Steven A. Frieze. – 1st ed. – London : Longman Professional (UK), 1989.
– (Longman Practice Notes).
Covers all forms of insolvency, both corporate and personal. Guidance on voluntary and compulsory winding up, receivership, administration, company voluntary arrangements and deeds of arrangement.
ISBN 0851215114 Pbk £9.95

Fringe benefits : a specially commissioned report / by Robert Maas. – 3rd ed. – London : Oyez Longman, 1984.
xvii,111 leaves; 30cm. – (Oyez Longman intelligence reports).
ISBN 0851209262 spiral

Fritz, Helen
Freedom of Information Legislation in Nova Scotia, New Brunswick, Newfoundland, and Quebec. – Ontario : Ontario Government Publications Service, 1983.
16p. – (Current Issue Paper: No. 21).
Hbk £0.50

Fritz, Linda
Native Law Bibliography. – Saskatoon : University of Saskatchewan, Native Law Centre, 1984.
100p.
ISBN 0888801416 Hbk £20.00
—Subject Guide to Native Law Cases and Annotated Text of the Indian Act of Canada / Zandra MacEachern. – Saskatoon : University of Saskatchewan, Native Law Centre, 1985.
267p.
ISBN 0888801599 Hbk £45.00

From Accident to Liability. – London : Sweet & Maxwell, 1984.
640p. – (Sweet and Maxwell's Law Files Ser.: No. 3).
ISBN 0421321601 Hbk £29.50

From Apology to Utopia : the Structure of International Legal Argument. – Helsinki : Lakimiesliiton Kustannus.
500p.
ISBN 9516404138 Hbk

From contract to status in quest for security : an inaugural lecture delivered at the University of Lagos on Wednesday, 9th April, 1986 / by A.A. Adeogun. – Lagos : Lagos University Press, 1986.
60p. – (Inaugural lecture series).
Includes bibliographical references.
ISBN 9782264709

From crime policy to victim policy : reorienting the justice system / edited by Ezzat A. Fattah. – Basingstoke : Macmillan, 1986.
300p; 22cm.
Conference papers. Includes index.
ISBN 0333399943 £27.50

From Crime to Punishment / David C. Perrier. – Agincourt : Carswell, 1988.
ca 330p.
Hbk

From imported doctrine to municipal law : a sketch history of foreign influences on the growth of the English law of conflict / paper presented at the eigth British Legal History Conference, Cardiff, July 1987, by A. G. Bischoff. – London : Law Notes Lending Library, 1987.
52p.
Bibliography: pp.43-47..
ISBN 0900516100

From plantocracy to nationalisation : a profile of sugar in Guyana / M. Shahabuddeen. – Georgetown? : University of Guyana, 1983.
xiii,440p.
Bibliography: p411-440.

From Punishment To Prevention. – Repr. of 1932 ed. – Aalen Wuertt : Scientia.
xv, 152p.
Hbk £43.00

From Telecommunications to Electronic Services. – Butterworths. – London : Butterworths, 1986.
ISBN 0880631031 Hbk £27.00

From the Waidring Conferences, 4 Vols. – Dordrecht : Kluwer.
ISBN 9065443584 Hbk £275.00
Licensing Agreements: Patents, Know-How, Trade Secrets and Software. –
444p.
ISBN 9065443142
Survey of the International Sale of Goods / edited by Louis Lafili, Franklin Gevurtz, Dennis Campbell. – 1986.
380p.
Includes bibliographies.
ISBN 9065442413 Pbk £95.00
Drafting and Enforcing Contracts in Civil and Common Law Jurisdictions. – 1987.
292p.
ISBN 9065442790 Pbk £85.00

Frontier College Act, 1983, Bill Pr002 : An Act Respecting Frontier College. – Ontario : Ontario Government Publications Service, 1983.
2p.
Hbk £0.30

Frontier of the seas : the problems of delimitation : proceedings of the 5th International Ocean Symposium November 26-27, 1980, the Japan Shipping Club, Tokyo. – Tokyo : Ocean Association of Japan, 1981.
80p; 26cm.
Edited by the Ocean Association of Japan. Title also in Japanese.

Frontiers of Human Rights Education / Marek Thee. – Oslo : Norwegian University Press, 1985.
148p.
ISBN 8200067769 Pbk £95.00

Frost →Quotable lawyer.

Frost, Susan
Union list of law periodicals held in libraries within the City of Liverpool / compiled by Susan Frost, Robert Caley. – Liverpool : Liverpool Polytechnic Library Service, 1985.
30p.
—Union list of law reports and statutes held in libraries within the City of Liverpool / compiled by Susan Frost, Robert Caley. – Liverpool : Liverpool Polytechnic Library Service, 1985.
30p.
—Union list of legal bibliographies and digests and other law-related material held in libraries within the City of Liverpool / compiled by Susan Frost, Robert Caley. – Liverpool : Liverpool Polytechnic Library Service, 1985.
15p.

Frost, Yvonne →Unfair dismissal : a guide to relevant case law.

Fruin, J. A. →Nederlandse wetboeken : zoals zij tot op 1 januari 1984 zijn gewijzigd en aangevuld.

Frundt, H.J.
Refreshing Pauses : Coca-Cola and Human Rights in Guatemala. – Praeger.
ISBN 0275927644 Hbk £29.50

Fry
Computer Appreciation. – 3rd ed. – London : Butterworths, 1981.
ISBN 0408004924 Pbk £7.95
—Data Processing. – London : Butterworths, 1984.
ISBN 0408011718 Pbk £8.50

Fry : A Treatise on the Specific Performance of Contracts. – Repr. of 1921 ed. – London : Sweet & Maxwell.
ISBN 042135190X Hbk £75.00

Fry, E.
Specific Performance of Contracts : Including Those of Public Companies. – 5th ed. Repr. of 1911 ed. – Abingdon : Professional Books.
131p.
Hbk £40.00

Fry, V. C.
Taxing Pensions : The Taxation of Occupational Pension Schemes in the United Kingdom / E. M. Hammond. – London : Institute for Fiscal Studies.
– (Report Ser.).
Hbk £10.00

Fryer, Bob →Law, state and society.

Fryer, James →Moriarty's police law : an arrangement of law and regulations for the use of police officers.

Fuel Rights Handbook. – 6th ed. – SHAC.
ISBN 094885720X Pbk £5.95

Fuels and the national policy / John N. McDougall. – Toronto : Butterworths, 1982.
vi,199p.
Bibliography: p188-194.

Fuerghne, D.K.
But the People in Legal Said Yes ... Guide to Current Legal Issues in Advertising. – Merehurst.
ISBN 01556230915 Hbk £17.95

Fulbeck, William
Fulbeck's direction, or preparative to the study of the law / by William Fulbeck : introduction by Peter Birks. – Godstone : Gregg International, 1987.
xviii,252p;.21cm.
Facsimile ed., first published by J. and W. T. Clarke, London, 1829.
ISBN 057640005X

Fulbeck's direction, or preparative to the study of the law / by William Fulbeck : introduction by Peter Birks. – Godstone : Gregg International, 1987.
xviii,252p; 21cm.
Facsimile ed., first published by J. and W. T. Clarke, London, 1829.
ISBN 057640005X

Fuller, L.
Morality Of Law. – Yale University Press, 1969.
ISBN 0300010702 Pbk £7.95

Fulton, R. D. →Sergeant and Sims on stamp duties and capital duty and stamp duty reserve tax.

Function of bibliography / Roy Stokes. – 2nd ed. – Aldershot : Gower, 1982.
xi,201p; 24cm. – (A Grafton book).
Previous ed.: London : Deutsch, 1969. Includes index.
ISBN 0566034409

Fund for Multinational Management Education
→Foreign investment in mining projects : case studies of recent experiences.

Fundamental legal concepts of China and the West : a comparative study / Hyung I. Kim. – Port Washington : National University Publications, 1981.
xiii,175p; 23cm.
Bibliography: p165-175.
ISBN 0804692750 £14.85

Fundamental Rights and Constitutional Remedies. – 2nd ed. – Lucknow : Eastern Book Company, 1982.
2,452p.
Hbk £150.00

Fundamental Rights and Personal Liberty in India, Pakistan and Bangladesh. – New Delhi : Deep and Deep Publications, 1988.
480p.
Hbk £325.00

Fundamental rights and the EEC / by David Sugarman. – London : Middlesex Polytechnic Faculty of Business Studies and Management, 1981.
34p. – (Working paper).
ISBN 0904804119

Fundamental Rights and the Supreme Court : Reasonableness of Restrictions. – New Delhi : Deep and Deep Publications, 1984.
232p.
Hbk £125.00

Fundamental Rights, Vol. 1 : General Principles of Criminal Liability in Ceylon. – Colombo : Lake House Investments.
Pbk £8.80

Fundamental tax audit considerations : technical papers and reports of the 14th General Assembly of the Inter-American Center of Tax Administrators (CIAT). – Inter-American Center of Tax Administrators. – Amsterdam : International Bureau of Fiscal Documentation, 1981.
198p.
ISBN 9070125188

Fundamentals of Canadian Income Tax. – 2nd ed. – Agincourt : Carswell, 1986.
1288p.
This textbook for students of Canadian income tax law deals with the fundamental structure of the income tax system and the underlying principles and concepts of taxation. Numerous computational examples are provided in the work to illustrate the operation of tax principles.
Hbk £75.75

Fundamentals of ethics / by John Finnis. – Oxford : Clarendon, 1983.
x,163p; 23cm.
Includes index.
ISBN 0198246838 Hbk £14.00
ISBN 0198246846 Pbk £4.95

Fundamentals of Property Management. – London : Butterworths, 1988.
ISBN 0409787787 Pbk

Funds in Court in England and Wales : Account 1981-1982. – London : HMSO, 1983.
Hbk £4.00

Furey, Nigel E. →Company law.

Furlong, Patrick J.
Mixed Marriages Act : a Historical and Theological Study. – Rondebosch : University of Cape Town, 1983.
viii, 108p.
ISBN 0799205206 Pbk £5.00

Furmston, M.
Law of Tort. – London : Duckworth (Gerald), 1986.
ISBN 0715620126 Hbk £29.95
—Sale and supply of goods. – Oxford : Blackwell Scientific, 1987.
ISBN 0003832430 Hbk £20.00

Furmston, M. P. →Contract : cases and materials.

Furmston, Michael P, et al
'A' Level Law. – London : Butterworths, 1988.
ISBN 0406208506 Pbk £9.95
→ Building contract casebook.
—Construction Law Reports 10 vols Vol. 1 / Vincent Powell-Smith. – London : Architectural Press, 1985.
160p.
ISBN 0851397808 Hbk £18.50
—Construction Law Reports / Vincent Powell-Smith. – Vol. 11. – London : Architectural Press, 1988.
ISBN 0851392024 Hbk £25.00
→ Effect on English domestic law of membership of the European Communities and of ratification of the European Convention on Human Rights.
→ Engineering Contract Casebook.
—Sale and Supply of Goods. – London : Collins, 1986.
200p.
ISBN 0003832430 Hbk £20.00

Furnell, M.
Living and Retiring Abroad. – 2nd ed. – London : Kogan Page, 1988.
ISBN 1850914222 Pbk £6.95

Furter, K.R., et al
Morgage Debenture. – 3rd ed. – North Ryde : Law Book Co, 1985.
xii, 108p.
ISBN 0455206031 Pbk £21.50

Further amendments of the Companies Acts 1948-1983 : report under section 116 of the Companies Act 1981 / The Law Commission and The Scottish Law Commission. – London : H.M.S.O., 1984.
iii,7p; 25cm.
ISBN 0101927207

Further aspects of maintenance law : some post 'Family law 1981' chapters / by P.R.H. Webb. – Auckland : Legal Research Foundation, 1981.
44p.
ISBN 0908581157

Further computer contracts. – London : Sweet & Maxwell, 1989.
Includes precedents for shrink-wrap software license, software development agreements, agreements for the supply of a customised computer system, escrow agreement, agreements for provisions of On-Line service and data protection, and software authors agreements.
ISBN 0421403306 Pbk £25.00

Further elaboration and implementation of a strategy for the technological transformation of developing countries : comparative tables of proposals made by regional groups at the first special session of the Committee on Transfer of Technology / prepared by the UNCTAD secretariat. – s.l. : United Nations Conference on Trade and Development, 1984.
43p. – (TD/B/C.6/108).
Item 3 of the provisional agenda for the fifth session of the Committee on Transfer of Technology, Geneva, 22 October 1984.

Further particulars. – Oxford : OUP, 1987.
240. – (Oxford letters and memoirs).
Second volume of C.H. Rolph's memoirs, taking up the story from 'London Particulars' at the end of the First World War. He describes his 25 years with the City Police, rising to the rank of Chief Inspector, his work as a freelance journalist for the New Statesman and at the BBC.
Legal historians, criminologists
ISBN 0192117904 Hbk £12.50
ISBN 0192821431 Pbk £4.95

Future for rented housing? : responses to the Government's proposals / National Housing Forum. – London : National Federation of Housing Associations, 1988.
iv,47p; 30cm.
ISBN 0862971306 Pbk

Future of Community social legislation / Ivor Richard. – Exeter : University of Exeter, 1984.
11p.

Future of European defence : proceedings of the Second International Round Table Conference of the Netherlands Atlantic Commission on May 24 and 25, 1985 / Frans Bletz and Rio Praaning editors. – Dordrecht : M. Nijhoff, 1986.
ISBN 9024732905 Pbk

Future of Health Care and Health Care Systems Industrial Soci. – Praeger.
ISBN 0275924912 Hbk £40.95

Future of International Law in a Multicultural World : Workshop 1983. – Dordrecht : Kluwer, 1984.
510p.
ISBN 9024730708 Hbk £135.00

Future of labour law : two views / Graham Mather, W. E. J. McCarthy. – Coventry : Industrial Relations Research Unit, University of Warwick, 1987.
Contents: The future shape of labour legislation/Graham Mather. - The case for a more balanced framework of labour law/W.E.J. McCarthy.

Future of legal protection for industrial design / Christine Fellner. – Oxford : ESC, 1985.
xxxviii,210p.
A report commissioned by the Common Law Institute of Intellectual Property and the Intellectual Property Unit, Queen Mary College.
ISBN 0906214270

Future of nuclear power. – London : Graham & Trotman, 1988.
ix,213p.
ISBN 0860109879

Future of policing : papers presented to the 15th Cropwood Round-Table Conference, December 1982 / edited by Trevor Bennett. – Cambridge : University of Cambridge Institute of Criminology, 1983.
iii,173p. – (Cropwood Papers Ser.).
Includes bibliographical references.

Future of regionalism in Africa / edited by Ralph I. Onwuka and Amadu Sesay. – London : Macmillan, 1985.
xiii,272p; 22cm. – (Macmillan international college editions).
Bibliography: p259-264.
ISBN 0333345304

Future of sentencing / University of Cambridge Institute of Criminology. – Cambridge : Institute of Criminology, 1982.
i,82p. – (Occasional papers).
Papers delivered at a workshop at Cambridge Criminology Conference, July 1979.

Future of the International Law of the Environment : Workshop 1984. – Dordrecht : Kluwer, 1985.
536p.
ISBN 9024732395 Hbk £155.00

Future of the law in Hong Kong / edited by R.I. Wacks. – Hong Kong : Oxford University Press (Hong Kong), 1989.
320.
Examines the theoretical and procedural aspects of the common law of Hong Kong and evaluates its development up to and beyond 1997 when sovereignty returns to China.
ISBN 0195849183 Hbk £19.50

Futures and Options for Shipping. – London, 1987.
ISBN 1850441367 Lloyd's of London Press £28.00

Futures Game / Jones. – 2nd ed. – Maidenhead : McGraw-Hill, 1986.
ISBN 0070637288 Hbk £39.95

Futures markets : modelling, managing and monitoring futures trading / edited by Manfred E. Streit. – Oxford : Blackwell, in cooperation with the European University Institute, Florence, 1983.
viii,324p; 24cm.
Includes bibliographies and index.
ISBN 0631132945

Fysh, Michael
Industrial property citator / by Michael Fysh and Robert Wilson Thomas. – London : European Law Centre, 1982.
321p; 26cm.
Includes index.
ISBN 0907451047

G.S., Snell, Snell
Nandi Customary Law. – 4th ed. – Nairobi : Kenya Literature Bureau, 1981.
Pbk £16.35

Gabbay, E.
Discretion in Criminal Justice. – 2nd Revised Edition. – London : Gabbay (E & J).
ISBN 095014486X Pbk £15.00
—English Criminal Justice. – London : Gabbay (E & J).
ISBN 0950144894 Pbk £15.00
—English Judicial Review. – London : Gabbay (E & J).
ISBN 0950144878 Pbk £17.00
—Open Criminal Justice. – London : Gabbay (E & J).
ISBN 0950144886 Pbk £3.00

Gabriel, Peter
Legal aspects of syndicated loans / Peter Gabriel. – London : Butterworths, 1986.
xxxvi,276p; 26cm.
Bibliography: p265-267. - Includes index.
ISBN 0406102104 Hbk £50.00

Gabriel, Yiannis
Law as an instrument of state intervention in industrial relations / Yiannis Gabriel. – London : Thames Polytechnic School of Business Administration, 1984.

Gabrielczyk, J.
Financial Engineering. – London : Fourmat, 1986.
ISBN 1851900187 Pbk £12.95

Gadd, R. P.
Peerage law / by R.P. Gadd. – Bristol : ISCA Publishing Ltd., 1985.
viii,178p.
Bibliography: p.163-164. - Includes index.
ISBN 0948343001

Gadsden, G. D.
Law of commons / by G.D. Gadsden. – London : Sweet & Maxwell, 1987.
xlviii,452p; 25cm.
Brings together many aspects of common land, and covers the history and present state of the law. Various types of common, ranging from village greens and urban amenity areas, to upland pastures are examined in the light of rights and obligations concerned.
ISBN 0421365609 £45.00

Gagarin, Michael
Drakon and early Athenian homicide law / Michael Gagarin. – New Haven : Yale University Press, 1981.
xvii,175p; 22cm. – (Yale classical monographs).
Includes index. Includes the Greek text and English translation of Drakon's law.
ISBN 0300026277 Hbk

Gagg, P., et al
Fuel Rights Handbook. – 6th ed. – SHAC.
ISBN 094885720X Pbk £5.95

Gainsborough, J. R.
Arab-Israeli conflict : a politico-legal analysis / J.R. Gainsborough. – Aldershot : Gower, 1987.
xxxv,345p; 23cm.
Bibliography: p319-334. - Includes index.
ISBN 0566008181 £25.00

Gaits, G.
Survey of computing in European local and regional authorities / ... prepared under the guidelines of the Committee of Experts on Management in Local and Regional Government by G.Gaits. – Strasbourg : Council of Europe, 1981.
iii,61p.

Gaitskell, Hugh
Diary of Hugh Gaitskell, 1945-1956 / Philip M. Williams. – London : Jonathan Cape, 1983.
ISBN 0224019112 Hbk £25.00

Gajria, G.T.
Law Relating to Building and Engineering Contracts in India. – 3rd ed. in press. – Bombay : Tripathi.
1060p.
bd £130.00

Galabert, Jean-Michel →French administrative law.

Galan, Beatriz Benilde
Agricultural insurance legislation / by Beatriz Benilde Galan for Land and Water Legislation Section, Legislation Branch, Legal Office. – Rome : Food and Agriculture Organization of the United Nations, 1981.
vii, 149 p.; 27 cm. – (Legislative study).
ISBN 9251010358 £2.50

Galanter, Marc
Competing equalities : law and the backward classes in India / Marc Galanter. – Berkeley : University of California Press, 1984.
xxii,625p; 24cm.
Bibliography: p575-611. - Includes index.
ISBN 0520042891 Pbk £38.25
—Law and society in modern India. – New Delhi : Oxford University Press India, 1989.
430.
Thirteen articles examine the way that modern Indian law operates. Shows the ways that a complex body of formal law adjusts itself to local conditions. The essays cover equality, hierarchy, panchayat justice, caste and policies of discrimination. The introduction by Rajeev Ddhavan traces the history of law in India.
ISBN 0195622944 £15.00

Galaway →Mediation and Criminal Justice : Victims, Offenders and Community.

Galaway, Burt
Restitution imposed on property offenders in New Zealand courts : a study of orders and compliance / Burt Galaway, Walton Walker. – Wellington : Department of Justice, 1985.
v,27p. – (Study series).
Bibliography: p.26.

Gale, Anthony →Polygraph test : lies, truth and science.

Gale, Charles James
Gale on easements / Spencer G. Maurice. – 15th ed. – London : Sweet & Maxwell, 1986.
li,491p; 26cm.
Deals with recent developments in equitable easements, the acquisition and character of easement generally, prescription, registered land, and the extinguishment, release, and disturbance of easements. Includes coverage of the London Building Acts, with annotations in an appendix.
ISBN 0421334606 £55.00

Gale on easements / Spencer G. Maurice. – 15th ed. – London : Sweet & Maxwell, 1986.
li,491p; 26cm.
Deals with recent developments in equitable easements, the acquisition and character of easement generally, prescription, registered land, and the extinguishment, release, and disturbance of easements. Includes coverage of the London Building Acts, with annotations in an appendix.
ISBN 0421334606 £55.00

Galenson, Walter
International Labor Organization : an American view / Walter Galenson. – Madison : University of Wisconsin Press, 1981.
xi,351p; 23cm.
Includes index.
ISBN 0299085406 Hbk £13.95
ISBN 0299085449 Pbk £5.05

Gall, Gerald L
Canadian legal system / Gerald L. Gall. – 2nd ed. – Toronto : Carswell, 1983.
xxiv, 348 p.; 24 cm.
'With Chapter 8, The Quebec legal system, by Mr. Justice Paul Reeves of the Quebec Superior Court.'. Includes bibliographical references and index.
ISBN 0459358103 Pbk
→ Civil liberties in Canada : entering the 1980s.

Gall, Gunter
European Patent Applications Questions and Answers. – London : Oyez Longman, 1984.
ISBN 085120855X Hbk £32.00

Gallafant, Richard J
Intellectual property law and taxation / Nigel A Eastaway. – 3rd ed. – London : Longman Professional, 1988.
ISBN 0851213227 Pbk

Gallant, P.
Electronic treasury management. – Cambridge : Woodhead-Faulkner, 1984.
ISBN 0859412733 Hbk £40.00
—Eurobond Market. – Cambridge : Woodhead-Faulkner, 1988.
ISBN 0859413373 Hbk £40.00

Galletly, G
Big Bang / N Ritchie. – Northcote House, 1988.
ISBN 0746305494 Pbk £4.95
—Crash and The Coming Crisis. – Northcote House, 1988.
ISBN 0746305435 Pbk £4.95

Galligan, D. J.
Discretionary powers : a legal study of official discretion / D.J. Galligan. – Oxford : Clarendon, 1986.
xxi,401p; 22cm.
Bibliography: p383-396. - Includes index.
ISBN 0198254989 £30.00
→ Essays in legal theory : a collaborated work.

Galliner
Criminology of Edwin Sutherland / Gaylord. – Oxford : Clio Distribution.
ISBN 0887381812 Hbk £18.50

Gambia law reports / cyclostyled series. – Banjul : Supreme Court of The Gambia, 1984.
'Cases ... covering the Supreme Court as well as the Court of Appeal' - Preface.

Gambia National Women's Council and Bureau →Women and legal affairs.

Gamble, Helen
Law for parents and children / by Helen Gamble. – 2nd ed. – North Ryde, N.S.W. : Law Book Company, 1986.
vii,392p.
Includes bibliographical references and index.
ISBN 0455206937
—Law relating to parents and children / by Helen Gamble. – Sydney : Law Book Co., 1981.
vii, 341 p.; 19 cm.
'Table of cases': p. 301-308. 'Table of statutes': p. 309-325. Includes bibliographical references and index.
ISBN 0455202540 Pbk

Gamble, R. H.
Working Guide to the Administration of Private Companies. – Durban : Butterworths, 1981.
ISBN 0409029254 Pbk

Game and Fish Act : Revised Statutes of Ontario, 1980. – Office of the Legislative Assembly (Ontario). – Ontario : Ontario Government Publications Service, 1983.
38p.
Hbk £1.75

Gaming, lotteries, fundraising and the law / by Jarlath Finney : foreword by Sir David Napley. – London : Sweet & Maxwell, 1982.
xxiv,218p; 25cm.
Includes index.
ISBN 0421299800 Pbk £18.50

Gammie, Malcolm
Land taxation / by Malcolm Gammie : general editor, Malcolm Gammie : contributing editor, Jeffrey Bailey. – London : Sweet & Maxwell, 1986-.
Includes index.
ISBN 0421275405 Llf
—Stock Relief / David Williams. – London : Oyez Longman, 1981.
– (Oyez Longman Practical Tax Ser.).
ISBN 0851205852 Hbk £9.95
—Tax on company reorganizations / Malcolm Gammie with Susan Ball. – 2nd ed. – London : Taxation Publishing, 1982.
xxvii,518p; 22cm.
Previous ed.: 1980. Includes index.
Pbk £18.00
—Tax Strategies for Directors, Executives and Employees. – London : Oyez Longman, 1983.
ISBN 0851206735 Hbk £15.00
—Tax strategy for companies. – 4th ed. – London : Longman Professional, 1986.
xxviii,511p; 22cm.
Previous ed.: 1983. Includes index.
ISBN 0851209211 Pbk £30.00
—Tax strategy for directors, executives and employers. – 2nd ed. – London : Longman Professional, 1985.
– (Tax Strategy Series).
ISBN 0851210767 Pbk £30.00
→ Whiteman on Capital Gains Tax.

Ganado, Max →Arrest of ships 3 : Malta, Panama, Sweden, United Arab Emirates.

Gandhi, A.L.
Right to Property. – Jodhpur : Scientific Publishers, 1985.
x, 308p.
ISBN 8185046220 Hbk £125.00

Gandhi, B.M.
Equity, Trusts and Specific Relief. – Lucknow : Eastern Book Company, 1983.
624p.
Hbk £45.00
—Law of Tort. – Lucknow : Eastern Book Company, 1987.
Hbk £200.00

Gandhi, Chandrakant R.
Cases and Material on the Urban Land (Ceiling and Regulation) Act, 1976, Act No 33 of 1976 : Along with Rules and Notifications. – Madhya Pradesh : Lawyers Home, 1986.
152p.
Hbk £60.00

Gandhi, Mahatma
Law and the Lawyers. – Ahmedabad : Navajivan Publishing House.
Hbk £15.00

Gane, C H W
Scots criminal law / A J MacLean. – 1st. – London : Butterworths, 1988.
ISBN 0406252696 Hbk

Gane, Christopher H. W.
Casebook on Scottish criminal law / by Christopher H.W. Gane, and Charles N. Stoddart. – 2nd ed. – Edinburgh : Green, 1988.
xxxiv,740p; 22cm.
Previous ed.: 1980. Includes index.
ISBN 041400843X Pbk £25.00
—Criminal procedure in Scotland : cases & materials / C.H.W. Gane & C.N. Stoddart. – Edinburgh : W. Green, 1983.
xxviii,612p.
Includes index.
ISBN 0414007115
—Scots Criminal Law / A. J. Maclean. – London : Butterworths, 1986.
This student text presents the basic principles of Scottish criminal law. The work discusses the general principles of criminal responsibility and examines the principal substantive offenses.
ISBN 0406252696 Hbk

Gangals, V.D.
Bombay Civil Services Rules Explained. – 7th rev. ed. 1980 rep,. – Nagpur : Wadhura & Co, 1984.
Hbk £120.00

Ganguly's Criminal Court Practice and Procedure. – 8th ed. – Calcutta : Eastern Law House, 1984.
Hbk £120.00

Gani, H.A.
Reform of Muslim Personal Law. – New Delhi : Deep and Deep Publications, 1988.
172p.
Hbk £125.00

Ganong, L. R. →Sales and sales financing in Canada : cases and materials.

Ganz, Gabriele →Quasi-legislation : recent developments in secondary legislation.
—Quasi-legislation : recent developments in secondary legislation / by Gabriele Ganz. – 2nd ed. – London : Sweet & Maxwell, 1987.
xiv,114p; 23cm.
New ed. - Previous ed.: published as Administrative procedures. 1974. Includes index.
ISBN 0421370203 Hbk £18.50
ISBN 0421298502 Pbk £10.95

—Understanding public law. – London : Fontana, 1987.
ISBN 0006861180 Pbk £4.95

Garcia, Arthur
Australian Current Law / Jean Malor. – Butterworths, 1987.
ISBN 0409410543 Llf £75.00

Garda Siochana Guide. – 5th ed. – Dublin : Incorporated Law Society of Ireland, 1981.
ISBN 0902027204 Hbk £42.20

Garden law / by Godfrey Sandys-Winsch. – London : Shaw & Sons, 1982.
xiii,245p; 22cm.
Includes index.
ISBN 0721909302 Pbk

Gardies, Jean-Louis →Man, law, and modern forms of life.

Gardin, Jean-Claude
Expert systems and scholarly publications / Jean-Claude Gardin. – London : British Library, 1987.
30pin various pagings; 30cm. – (The Fifth British Library Annual Research Lecture).
Includes the text in French, printed t$ete-b$eche, under the title Systemes experts et publications savantes.
ISBN 071233114X Pbk ree

Gardner, P.
Emergency Family Remedies. – London : Longman Professional, 1987.
ISBN 0851211143 Pbk £12.50

Garg, K.C. →Commercial Law.
—Company Law. – 3rd ed. – New Delhi : Kalyani Publishers, 1987.
ISBN 817096010X Hbk £42.00
→ Elements of Company Law.
→ Indian Mercantile Law and Industrial Law.
→ Industrial and Commercial Law.
→ Mercantile Law.
→ Textbook of Industrial Law.

Garg, S.C.
Delhi and Central Sales Tax / H.P.S. Kohli. – New Delhi : S. Chand and Company.
Hbk £5.50

Garland, David →Power to punish : contemporary penality and social analysis.
—Punishment and welfare : a history of penal strategies / David Garland. – Aldershot : Gower, 1985.
x,297p; 23cm.
Bibliography: p280-290. - Includes index. Previous control number ISBN 0-435-82327-2.
ISBN 0566008556 £21.45

Garlick →Moores/Rowland's A-Z of Tax Planning.

Garner, B.
Dictionary of Modern Legal Usage. – Oxford : Oxford University Press, 1988.
ISBN 0195043774 Hbk £25.00

Garner, J F
Administrative Law. – 6th ed. – London : Butterworths, 1985.
ISBN 0406587981 Hbk £28.00
ISBN 040658799X Pbk £21.95
—Alteration/Conversion Of Houses / Edmunds. – 6th ed. – London : Longman Professional, 1985.
ISBN 0851209971 Pbk £16.95
—Clean Air - Law and Practice. – 4th ed. – Shaw & Sons, 1976.
ISBN 072190680X Pbk £10.00
→ Control of pollution encyclopaedia.
→ French administrative law.
—Garner's administrative law / B. L. Jones, J. F. Garner. – 6th ed. – London : Butterworths, 1985.
552p; 26cm.
Previous ed.: published as Administrative law. 1979. Includes bibliography and index.
ISBN 0406587981 Hbk £ :
ISBN 040658799X Pbk
—Garner's rights of way. – 5th. – London : Longman Professional (UK), 1989.
– (Practitioner series).
Explains how rights of way are created, who is then responsible for them, where to record them and how to get them revoked. New section on the discovery of private rights of way.
ISBN 0851215386 Hbk £17.95
—Law of allotments / by J.F. Garner. – 4th ed. – London : Shaw and Sons, 1984.
xxii,113p; 22cm.
Previous ed.: 1977. Includes index.
ISBN 0721901425 Pbk
—Law of sewers and drains under the Public Health Acts / by J.F. Garner. – 6th ed. – London : Shaw & Sons, 1981.
xxxviii,206p; 22cm.
Previous ed.: 1975. Includes index. .
ISBN 0721905811 Pbk
—Local land charges / by J.F. Garner. – 9th ed. – London : Shaw, 1982.
xxvii,171p; 22cm.
Previous ed.: 1977. Includes index.
ISBN 0721901247 Pbk
—Local land charges / by J.F. Garner. – 10th ed. – London : Shaw & Sons, 1987.
xxv,173p.
Previous ed.: 1982. Includes index.
ISBN 0721901255
—Rights of way and access to the countryside / J.F. Garner. – 4th ed. – London : Oyez Longman, 1982.
xi,122p. – (Oyez Longman practice notes).
Title supersedes: Freeman's rights of way. Includes index.
ISBN 085120466X

Garner, T. G. →Drug addiction research programme 1983.

Garner's administrative law / B. L. Jones, J. F. Garner. – 6th ed. – London : Butterworths, 1985.
552p; 26cm.
Previous ed.: published as Administrative law. 1979. Includes bibliography and index.
ISBN 0406587981 Hbk £ :
ISBN 040658799X Pbk

Garner's rights of way. – 5th. – London : Longman Professional (UK), 1989.
– (Practitioner series).
Explains how rights of way are created, who is then responsible for them, where to record them and how to get them revoked. New section on the discovery of private rights of way.
ISBN 0851215386 Hbk £17.95

Garnett, K. M. →Williams, Mortimer and Sunnucks on executors, administrators and probate.

Garrod, S., et al
Regulation of Toxic and Oxidant Air Pollution in North America. – North Ryde : C.C.H. Australia, 1986.
272p.
ISBN 088796351X Pbk £27.95

Garrow and Caldwell's criminal law in New Zealand / the original text by J.M.E. Garrow. – 6th ed. – Wellington : Butterworths, 1981.
xxxiii,631p; 26cm.
Previous edition: 1968, entitled Garrow and Willis's criminal law. Includes index.
ISBN 040960058X Hbk £106.15

Garrow and Kelly's law of trusts and trustees / the original text by J.M.E. Garrow. – 5th ed. – Wellington : Butterworths, 1982.
lxiii,616p.
Contains a new chapter on the investment of trust funds since the Trustee Amendment Act 1974. Passages from previous editions have been rewritten, and there is comment on the case of Bartlett v Barclays Bank.
ISBN 0409600717

Garrow, J. M. E.
Criminal Law / Caldwell. – 6th ed. – London : Butterworths, 1981.
ISBN 040960058X Hbk £46.70
—Garrow and Caldwell's criminal law in New Zealand / the original text by J.M.E. Garrow. – 6th ed. – Wellington : Butterworths, 1981.
xxxiii,631p; 26cm.
Previous edition: 1968, entitled Garrow and Willis's criminal law. Includes index.
ISBN 040960058X Hbk £106.15
—Garrow and Kelly's law of trusts and trustees / the original text by J.M.E. Garrow. – 5th ed. – Wellington : Butterworths, 1982.
lxiii,616p.
Contains a new chapter on the investment of trust funds since the Trustee Amendment Act 1974. Passages from previous editions have been rewritten, and there is comment on the case of Bartlett v Barclays Bank.
ISBN 0409600717
—Law of Evidence / R A McGechan. – 7th ed. – Wellington : Butterworths (New Zealand), 1984.
ISBN 0409601314 Hbk £34.60
ISBN 0409701742 Pbk £29.10
—Law of Trusts and Trustees in New Zealand / Kelly. – 5th ed. – London : Butterworths, 1981.
ISBN 0409600717 Hbk £44.50

Garsney, John J. →Intellectual Property Reports.

Gart, A.
Handbook of the Money and Capital Markets. – London : Eurospan.
ISBN 089930270X Hbk £40.95

Gaskill, Shelagh →Data protection law.
→ Encyclopedia of data protection.

Gassmann, Hans-Peter →Transborder data flows : proceedings of an OECD conference held December 1983.

Gatenby, John K
Recovery of money. – 7th. – London : Longman Professional (UK), 1989.
– (Practitioner series).
Guide to the law practice and procedure of debt collection from contract to enforcement. Coverage includes contract drafting and formation, preservation of assets pending proceedings, a consideration of the foreign element, mortgage repossession, computer support and office procedure. Takes account of Consumer Credit Act, Insolvency Act and Rules 1986, and Civil Jurisdiction and Judgements Act.
ISBN 0851215165 Hbk £26.50

Gatley, John Clement Carpenter
Gatley on libel and slander / Philip Lewis, J. E. Previte, R. W. Ground. – 8th ed. – London : Sweet & Maxwell, 1981.
cxxxvii,751p; 26cm.
Fifteen of the chapters are new or substantially rewritten, with emphasis on defences and the stages of pleading and settlement. Contains a new chapter on apology, payment into court, and settlement. The relationship between the law of defamation and the law of contempt has been clarified. Developments in Australia, Canada and New Zealand are discussed.
ISBN 0421243406 £60.00

Gatley on libel and slander / Philip Lewis, J. E. Previte, R. W. Ground. – 8th ed. – London : Sweet & Maxwell, 1981.
cxxxvii,751p; 26cm.
Fifteen of the chapters are new or substantially rewritten, with emphasis on defences and the stages of pleading and settlement. Contains a new chapter on apology, payment into court, and settlement. The relationship between the law of defamation and the law of contempt has been clarified. Developments in Australia, Canada and New Zealand are discussed.
ISBN 0421243406 £60.00

Gauch, Peter →Selected problems of construction law : international approach.

Gaucher, Alain John
Stock purchase agreements / by Alain John Gaucher. – Toronto, Canada : Carswell, 1984.
xxvii, 286 p.; 24 cm.
Includes index. Bibliography: p. 275-280.
ISBN 045935910X

Gaulin, R →Need for and the feasibility of an appeals process in regard to municipal grants-in-lieu of taxes : a report prepared for the Minister of Public Works Canada.

Gauntlett, J.
Law of Damages / G.F. Lubbe. – Durban : Professional Publisher.
ISBN 0409029300 Hbk

Gaur, A.N.
Law Relating to Arms, Ammunition and Explosives / K.K. Malik. – 4th rev. ed. – Lucknow : Eastern Book Company, 1985.
920p.
Hbk £125.00

Gaur, K. D.
Law of international telecommunications in India / K.D. Gaur. – Baden-Baden : Nomos, 1988.
219p.
ISBN 3789013102
—Tax Offences, Black Money and the Law. – New Delhi : Deep and Deep Publications, 1987.
416p.
Hbk £250.00

Gaur, V.P.
Delhi Sales Tax and Central Sales Tax Act / D.B. Narang. – New Delhi : Kalyani Publishers.
Hbk £7.50
—Income Tax Law and Practice / D.B. Narang. – 15th ed. – New Delhi : Kalyani Publishers.
Hbk £48.00

Gaus, Gerald F. →Public and private in social life.

Gaustafson, L.S.
Sovereignty Dispute over the Falkland (Malvinas) Islands. – Oxford : Oxford University Press.
ISBN 0195041844 Hbk £32.50

Gavison, Ruth →Issues in contemporary legal philosophy : the influence of H.L.A. Hart.

Gay →Self-Help Groups for Drug Addicts' Families.

Gaylord →Criminology of Edwin Sutherland.

Gays and the law / Paul Crane. – London : Pluto, 1982.
x,244p; 20cm.
Includes index.
ISBN 0861043863 Pbk £4.95

Gazette Law Reports of New Zealand 1898-1952 microform , 54 Vols. – Butterworths.
mf

Gazetteer of European law : case search : European Community law 1953-1983
Vol.1 : Master list of cases / by Neville March Hunnings. – Leeds : European Law Centre, 1983.
xiii,234p; 25cm.
ISBN 0907451098
Vol.2 : Case search and indexes / by Neville March Hunnings. – 1983.
viii,p.237-584; 25cm.
ISBN 0907451101 Hbk

GC/Works/1 Conditions of Contract. – London : Waterlow, 1985.
ISBN 0080392334 Hbk £20.00

GCSE and 'O' level law / by W.J. Brown. – 3rd ed. – London : Sweet & Maxwell, 1986.
280p; 22cm.
Previous ed.: published as O level law. 1982. Includes index.
ISBN 0421352507 Hbk £9.50
ISBN 0421352604 Pbk £6.95

GCSE Law. – London : Financial Training, 1987.
ISBN 1851850546 Pbk £7.95

Geach, Hugh
Providing civil justice for children / Hugh Geach and Elizabeth Szwed. – London : Edward Arnold, 1983.
250p; 22cm.
Includes bibliographies and index.
ISBN 071316400X Pbk £9.95

Geare, A.J.
System of Industrial Relations in New Zealand. – 2nd rev. ed. – Butterworths, 1988.
496p.
ISBN 0409788546 Pbk £70.00

Geary, Roger
Policing industrial disputes: 1893 to 1985 / Roger Geary. – Cambridge : Cambridge University Press, 1985.
vii,171p; 24cm.
Includes index.
ISBN 052130315X £19.50

Gebrehana, Teklewold
Arbitration : an Element of International Law. – Stockholm : Almqvist & Wiksell, 1984.
166p.
ISBN 9122007342 Hbk £119.00

Geddes, S. J. →Court surveys and studies 1978-1984, concerning the civil caseloads of the Supreme Court, the County Court and the Magistrates' Courts of Victoria.

Gee, Stephen
Mareva injunctions : law and practice / Steven Gee and Geraldine Mary Andrews : foreword by Lord Denning. – London : Longman, 1987.
xxvii,143p; 25cm.
Includes index.
ISBN 0851209394 £30.00

Geen, G. K.
Law of pilotage / by G.K. Geen and R.P.A. Douglas. – 2nd ed. – London : Lloyd's of London, 1983.
xx,177p.
Previous ed. published as: The law and administration of pilotage. 1977. Bibliography: p.xxi. - Includes index.
ISBN 0907432662

Gehlen, Monika
Annotated British Columbia Company Act. – Agincourt : Carswell, 1986.
268p.
This annotated edition of the British Columbia Company Act presents an analytical interweaving of case and statute law through the annotations in the work. The text of the Act, the regulations, and forms are included in the book.
Pbk £38.00

—Annotated British Columbia Insurance (Motor Vehicle) Act / Cedric H.L. Hughes. – Agincourt : Carswell, 1987.
ca 220p.
This text contains the Insurance (Motor Vehicle) Act and the Revised Regulations with annotations. Topics include a description of the history of the legislation and the policy that governed its development. Current caselaw and pertinent older cases are discussed.
Hbk £46.00

Geisst, Charles R.
Guide to the financial markets / Charles R. Geisst. – London : Macmillan, 1982.
xv,144p; 23cm.
Includes bibliographies and index.
ISBN 0333309197 £15.00

Geldart, W. M.
Introduction to English law / William Geldart. – 9th ed. – Oxford : Oxford University Press, 1984.
viii,180p; 20cm.
Previous ed.: published as Elements of English law. 1975. Bibliography: p166-170. - Includes index.
ISBN 0192891715 Pbk £3.95

Geller, P.E.
International copyright law and practice. – Matthew Bender, 1988.
ISBN 0000999074 Hbk £53.00

Gelsthorpe, Loraine →Women and crime : papers presented to the 13th Cropwood Round Table Conference, December 1980.

Gender Crime and Justice. – Open University Press, 1988.
ISBN 0335155057 Hbk £25.00

Gender, sex and the law / edited by Susan Edwards. – London : Croom Helm, 1985.
240p.
Includes index.
ISBN 0709909381 £16.95

Genders, D.
Daily Telegraph Guide to Income Tax 1988-89. – Oxford : Collins.
Pbk £2.95

Genders, Elaine
Race relations in prisons / Elaine Player. – Oxford : Clarendon Press, 1989.
200.
Based on a detailed research project undertaken at the request of the Home Office. Examines three institutions and their staff and inmates, and relates their experiences in detail. Demonstrates difficulties arising from trying to isolate race problems, and identifies problems in trying to enforce policies to eradicate discriminating behaviour.
ISBN 0198256175 Hbk £20

General average : the practical problems / Kaj Pineus. – Stockholm, Sweden : Almqvist & Wiksell International, 1985.
58 p.; 21 cm.
Includes bibliographical references.
ISBN 9122007326 Pbk kr150

General Bylaw : Boards of Appeal Bylaw. – Australian National Railways Commission. – Canberra : Australian Government Publishing Service, 1984.
11p.
ISBN 0644031697 Hbk £1.00

General Clauses Act. – 8th ed. – Allahabad : Law Book Company, 1985.
Hbk £160.00

General duty to trade fairly : a discussion paper / Office of Fair Trading. – London : The Office, 1986.
73p.
Bibliography: p.72-73.

General insolvency inquiry / The Law Reform Commission. – Sydney : The Commission, 1987.
xxv,252p. – (Discussion paper).
Accompanied by Appendix: Draft Legislation (99p.).

General Law for Social Workers. – PEPAR Publications.
ISBN 0948680105 Pbk £7.50

General Police Duties / Wilkie. – 7th ed. – London : Butterworths, 1983.
– (Police Promotion Handbook Ser.: No. 3).
This work for United Kingdom police officers discusses the many changes in the law including: the Highways Act of 1980, the Child Care Act, and the Licensed Premises (Exclusion of Certain Persons) Act of 1980; and the effects on the duties of officers.
ISBN 040684142X Pbk £4.95

General Practice Potpourri : 1988. – Vancouver : Continuing Legal Education Society of British Columbia, 1988.
288p.
ISBN 0865049920 Hbk £80.00

General Principles of Administrative Law / D.J. Lanham. – 3rd ed. – Butterworths, 1989.
ca 450p.
ISBN 0409495395 Pbk £55.00
ISBN 0409495387 Hbk £69.00

General Principles of Business Law (Q & A) / De Freitas. – 2nd ed. – London : Castlevale Publishers, 1984.
ISBN 0907235069 Pbk £6.00

General principles of criminal law through the cases / by P.J. Visser and J.P. Vorster. – Durban : Butterworths, 1982.
xxv,523p.
Bibliography: p. 487-501. - Includes index.
ISBN 0409061182

General principles of EEC law and the individual. – Leicester : Leicester University Press, 1989.
320.
Examines the tendency for the European Court to go beyond the application of the written law to regulate the trading of corporations within member states and to apply general principles of law to individual's grievances.
ISBN 0718513193 Hbk £45

General Principles of English Law. – 6th ed. – NELS, 1975.
ISBN 0245526625 Pbk £4.50

General Principles of English Law. – 5th ed. – Plymouth : Macdonald & Evans, 1988.
ISBN 0712107479 Pbk £6.95

General Principles of Insurance Law. – 5th ed. – London : Butterworths, 1986.
ISBN 0406252807 Hbk £80.00

General principles of law / by Clive R. Newton. – 3rd ed. – London : Sweet & Maxwell, 1983.
xix,373p; 22cm.
Previous ed.: 1977. Bibliography: p362-364. - Includes index.
ISBN 042128580X Pbk £7.95

General principles of law in a nutshell / Josephine Dominic. – London : Sweet & Maxwell, 1981.
vii,82p; 18cm. – (New nutshells).
Includes index.
ISBN 0421278307 Pbk £1.75

General principles of Scots law / by Enid A. Marshall. – 4th ed. – Edinburgh : Green, 1982.
xxiv,584p; 22cm. – (Concise college texts).
Previous ed.: 1978. Includes bibliographies and index.
ISBN 041400681X Pbk

General principles of the conflict of laws : with the exclusion of the special principles relative to the law of persons, property, succession and obligations / Erwin Spiro. – Cape Town : Juta, 1982.
xxxiii,145p.
Bibliography: p.xi-xvi. - Includes index.
ISBN 0702112895

General prinicples of the law of contract / D.J. Joubert. – Cape Town : Juta, 1987.
lxvii,344p.
Includes bibliogrpahical references and index.
ISBN 0702118079

General reports to the 10th International Congress of Comparative Law / edited by Zoltan Peteri, Vanda Lamm : publie par Zoltan Peteri, Vanda Lamm. – Budapest : Akademiai Kiado, 1981.
1049p.
ISBN 9630523698

General Survey of Employment Protection Laws in Lesotho. – Maseru : National University of Lesotho, Institute of Labour Studies, 1983.
32p.
Hbk £3.50

General survey on the application of the conventions on freedom of association, the right to organise and collective bargaining and the convention and recommendation concerning rural workers' organisations : third item on the agenda. – International Labour Office. – Geneva : International Labour Office, 1983.
157p.
Cover title: Freedom of association and collective bargaining. Report III (Part 4B).
ISBN 9221031284

General Tariff Principles : Charging and Accounting in International Telecommunications Services - Series D Recommendations. – Geneva : International Telecommunications Union.
ISBN 9261019919 Hbk £38.00

General View of the Criminal Law of England. – Repr. of 1863 ed. – Abingdon : Professional Books.
339p.
Hbk £45.00

Generalised scheme of preferences : a brief summary of the European Community's scheme for 1985 / Department of Trade and Industry. – London : The Department, 1984.
17p.

Generalised system of preferences : review of the first decade: report by the secretary-general. – Organisation for Economic Co-operation and Development. – Paris : Organisation for Economic Co-operation and Development, 1983.
98p.

Genetic manipulation / Law Reform Commission of Victoria. – Melbourne : The Commission, 1987.
ii,41p. – (Discussion paper).
Includes bibliographical references.
ISBN 0724167285

Genetics and the law III / proceedings of the Third National Symposium on Genetics and the Law, held April 2-4, 1984, in Boston, Massachusetts : cosponsored by the American Society of Law and Medicine ... et al. : edited by Aubrey Milunsky and George J. Annas. – New York : Plenum, 1985.
xix,514p; 26cm.
Bibliography: p491-504. - Includes index.
ISBN 0306419831

Geneva Conventions of August 12, 1949. – repr. 1986. – Geneva : Comite International de la Croix-Rouge.
245p.
Hbk £8.00

Genn, Hazel
Hard bargaining. – Oxford : Oxford University Press, 1988.
ISBN 0198255926 Hbk £22.50

—Meeting legal needs? : an evaluation of a scheme for personal injury victims / Hazel Genn. – Oxford : SSRC Centre for Socio-Legal Studies, 1982.
ix,69p; 22cm.
A report commissioned by the Greater Manchester Legal Services Committee.
ISBN 0862260442

Gentleman, Hugh →Scottish Family Conciliation Service (Lothian) : report of an assessment of the first two years of the service, March 1984 - February 1986.

Gentles, I. J.
Confiscation and Restoration : The Archbishopric Estates and the Civil War / W. J. Sheils. – York : St. Anthony's Press, 1981.
– (Borthwick Papers Ser.).
Pbk £3.00

Georgas, M. Stephen
Federal Incorporation and Business Guide : How to Form Your Own Federal Corporation Under the Canada Business Corporations Act. – 5th ed. – North Vancouver : International Self-Counsel Press, 1986.
122p.
ISBN 088908632X Hbk £14.95

George, Arthur →Sale of flats.

George, Edward F. →Brighouse's precedents of wills and life transfers.
—Sale of flats / by Edward F. George and Arthur George. – 5th ed. – London : Sweet & Maxwell, 1984.
xxvii,447p; 23cm.
Expanded section on the treatment of remedies. Covers the 1980 Housing Act, and schedule 19 to the 1980 Act on services and service charges is examined in detail. New chapter on leases demanded by secure tenants from local authorities. Contains precedents, including articles of association of a management company.
ISBN 0421305509 £25.00

George Gavan Duffy 1882-1951 : a legal biography / G.M. Golding. – Blackrock : Irish Academic Press, 1982.
xvi,224p,1leaf of plates; 22cm.
Bibliography: p209-214. - Includes index.
ISBN 0716500787 Hbk £15.00
ISBN 0716502070 Pbk

George Grant and the Twilight of Justice. – Toronto : University of Toronto Press, 1984.
208p.
ISBN 0802056377 Hbk £30.00
ISBN 0802065384 Pbk £12.50

Georges, P. Telford →Vulnerability : small states in the global society.

Gepts, S.J.
Valuation and selection of convertible bonds. – Praeger, 1988.
ISBN 0275924661 Hbk £27.50

Gerard, David
Charities in Britain : conservatism or change? / David Gerard. – London : Bedford Square Press/NCVO, 1983.
187p; 22cm.
Bibliography: p171-179. - Includes index.
ISBN 0719910927 Pbk £5.95

Gerbic
Understanding Commercial Law / Lawrence. – Butterworths, 1988.
476p.
ISBN 0409787876 Pbk £65.00

Gering, Leonard →Law of negotiable instruments in South Africa, Vol.1 : General principles.

Gerkens, M W
Food Law in Australia / Gerkens. – North Ryde : Law Book Co, 1985.
ISBN 0455203016 Pbk £16.00
—Health Act-Victoria. – North Ryde : Law Book Co, 1983.
xxxi, 493p.
ISBN 0455204985 Hbk £65.50

Gerlis, Stephen
Domestic Proceedings in the Magistrates' Court. – 6th ed. – London : Oyez Longman, 1982. – (Oyez Longman Practice Note Ser.: No. 30).
ISBN 0851206514 Hbk £12.50

German administrative law in common law perspective / Mahendra P. Singh. – Berlin : Springer-Verlag, 1985.
xxiv,194p.
Bibliography: p.188-191. - Includes index.
ISBN 0387156186

German Antitrust Law / Hannes Schneider. – 2nd ed. – Plymouth : Macdonald & Evans, 1981.
296p.
ISBN 0712154817 Casebound £23.00

German antitrust law : an introduction to the German antitrust law with German text and synoptic English translation of the Act against Restraints of Competition / Martin H. Heidenhain, Hannes Schneider. – 2nd rev. ed. – Frankfurt am Main : Fritz Knapp, 1981.
291p.
Previous ed., 1973, published as: The German law against restraints of competition. Added t.p. in German: Das Recht gegen Wettbewerbsbeschrankungen.
ISBN 3781928306

German Banking Law : A Synoptical Translation of the Banking with an Introduction in English Gesetz Uber das Kreditwesen : Deutsch-Englische Textausgabe Des Gesetzes Uber das Kreditwesen Mit Einer Englischen Einleitung / Martin Peltzer. – 2nd ed. – Cologne : Otto Schmidt, 1986.
x, 85p.
ISBN 3504400048 Hbk

German Banking System / H. Hellwig. – 2nd ed. – Plymouth : Macdonald & Evans, 1984.
252p.
ISBN 0712154795 Pbk £22.50

German, C.
Your mortgage. – Penguin, 1988.
ISBN 0140105611 Pbk £4.95

German competition law : (legislation and commentary) / by Dietrich Hoffmann in cooperation with Stefan Schaub. – Deventer : Kluwer Law and Taxation Publishers, 1983.
xi,194.
Offprint from Competition law in Western Europe and the USA.
ISBN 9065441425

German Industrial Property, Copyright and Antitrust Laws. – Veinheim : VCH.
ISBN 3527260048 Pbk £41.00

German Insurance Laws : Statutes and Regulations Concerning Insurance Supervision and Insurance Contracts. – 2nd ed. – Wiesbaden : Versicherungswirtschaft, 1986.
viii, 252p.
Hbk £126.00

German Labour Management Relations Act / Rolf Boer. – 3rd ed. Repr. of 1976 ed. – Plymouth : Macdonald & Evans, 1983.
384p.
ISBN 0712154736 Hbk £32.50

German Law of Torts. – Oxford : Oxford University Press, 1986.
ISBN 0198255314 Hbk £55.00

German Law Pertaining to Companies with Limited Liability : A Synoptic Translation Including Comprehensive Introductory Comments on the Laws Affecting the German GmbH / Jermyn Brooks. – Cologne : Otto Schmidt, 1986.
ISBN 3504325321 Hbk

German Monopolies Commission 1973-1983 : summaries of the first five biennial reports / Monopolkommission. – Baden-Baden : Nomos Verlagsgellschaft, 1987.
175p.
ISBN 378901348X

German Patent Law, 1981 : With Annotations. – Cologne : Carl Heymanns Verlag, 1981.
xiii, 99p.
ISBN 3452190005 Pbk £39.00

German private and commercial law : an introduction / by Norbert Horn, Hein Kotz and Hans G. Leser : translated by Tony Weir. – Oxford : Clarendon, 1982.
xvi,355p; 22cm.
Bibliography: p332-334. - Includes index. Translation from the German.
ISBN 0198253826 Hbk £27.00
ISBN 0198253834 Pbk £15.00

German Utility Model Act 1987 : as Promulgated in the Notice of August 28, 1986 and Effective as of January 1, 1987. – Cologne : Carl Heymanns Verlag, 1986.
53p.
ISBN 3452207641 Pbk £28.00

German Yearbook of International Law
Vol. 23 (1980) /. – Berlin : Duncker and Humblot, 1981.
567p.
Hbk £178.00
Vol. 24 (1981). – 1982.
566p.
ISBN 3428051521 Hbk £178.00
Vol. 25 (1982). – 1983.
722p.
Hbk £228.00

Gerrard, P.
Stage One Law. – Northwick Publishers, 1983.
ISBN 0907135102 Pbk £6.00

Gershman, Bernard →Canadian Mortgage Practice Reporter.

Gerstenmaier, Cornelia →Religious minorities in the Soviet Union : a report.

Gertner
Studies in Civil Procedure. – London : Butterworths.
ISBN 0409832502 Hbk £40.00

Gertner, Eric, et al
Debtor and Creditor : Cases and Commentary. – 3rd ed. – Agincourt : Carswell, 1987.
1,150p.
ISBN 0459304712 Hbk £45.00
ISBN 045930481X Pbk £23.00
→ Debtor and Creditor : Cases, Notes and Materials.
→ Debtor-Creditor Law : Practice and Doctrine.
→ New Constitution and the Charter of Rights : Fundamental Issues and Strategies.
→ Supreme Court Law Review, Vol. 1: 1980.

Gertzel, Cherry
Dynamics of the one-party state in Zambia / Cherry Gertzel ..., Carolyn Baylies, Morris Szeftel. – Manchester : Manchester University Press, 1984.
xi,262p; 23cm.
Bibliography: p247-258. - Includes index.
ISBN 0719010691 £28.50

Getting a fair go : case studies of occupational socialization and perceptions of discrimination in a sample of seven Melbourne high schools / Brian M. Bullivant. – Canberra : Australian Government Publishing Service, 1986.
xi,296p. – (Occasional paper).
Bibliographical references: p259-296.
ISBN 0644055243

Getting to YES : negotiating agreement without giving in / Roger Fisher and William Ury : with Bruce Patton, editor. – London : Business Books, 1986.
xiii,161p; 23cm.
Originally published: Boston, Mass. : Houghton Mifflin, 1981 ; London : Hutchinson, 1982.
ISBN 0091493706 Hbk
ISBN 0091640717 Pbk

Getz, W. S. →Gordon and Getz on the South African law of insurance.

Geva, Ben
Financing Consumer Sales and Product Defences in Canada and the United States. – Agincourt : Carswell, 1984.
382p.
This book is a collection of papers and discussion at a Legal Research Institute conference on the question of how well lawyers, police, courts, and lawmakers are perceived to deliver justice and the rule of law to Canadian society.
Hbk £48.75

Geva, Benjamin
Banking and Finance Law Review / Andrew Chant. – Agincourt : Carswell.
This book focuses on issues pertinent to the legal and financial communities. The text is divided into four parts: articles, commentaries on recent developents in banking in Canada and in the world, and casenotes and book reviews.
Hbk £75.75
→ Commercial and consumer transactions : cases, text and materials.

Gevurtz, Franklin →From the Waidring Conferences, 4 Vols., Survey of the International Sale of Goods.

Ghai, Yash
Constitutional Case Studies of Pacific Island States / Peter Bayne. – Suva : University of the South Pacific, Institute of Pacific Studies.
Hbk £7.00
—Law in the Political Economy of Public Enterprise. – Uppsala : Scandinavian Institute of African Studies, 1977.
351p.
ISBN 9171061177 Pbk £15.00 (10.00 in Third World Countries)
ISBN 9171061169 Pbk £10.00 (7.00 Third World Countries)
→ Political economy of law : a third world reader.

Ghaiye, B.R.
Employment : Its Terms and Conditions in Public and Private Sectors. – Lucknow : Eastern Book Company, 1981.
1,322p.
Hbk £150.00
—Law and Procedure of Departmental Enquiries (In Private and Public Sectors). – 2nd ed. 1976 repr. – Lucknow : Eastern Book Company, 1982.
1,747p.
Hbk £165.00
—Law of Simple Discharge (In Private and Public Sectors) / Harminder Singh. – Lucknow : Eastern Book Company, 1984.
1,037p.
Hbk £160.00

Ghana : the people, the laws and the courts / by E.S. Aidoo. – Legon : Institute of Statistical, Social and Economic Research, University of Ghana, 1985.
37p.
'Paper first presented at the Seventh Annual Alumni Lecture of the University of Ghana'.

Ghana income tax law and practice
Vol. 1 / P.O. Andah. – Accra : Sedco, 1987.
xii,252p.
ISBN 9964720718

Ghana law reports digest : being a digest of cases determined by the High Court and the Court of Appeal of the Republic of Ghana. – Accra : Council for Law Reporting, 1980-.
Includes index.
Hbk

Ghana, water supply and control : a record and analysis of legislation / by A.J. Adamson ... et al. – London : Commonwealth Secretariat, 1985.
xv, 133 p.; 30 cm.
Bibliography: p. 113-122. Includes indexes.
ISBN 085092278X Pbk £10.00

Ghana's Income Tax Law and the Investor. – Accra : Ghana Universities Press.
25p.
Hbk £2.50

Ghanem, Isam
Arbitration in the Yemen Arab Republic / Isam Ghanem. – Braunton : Merlin, 1988.
22p; 21cm.
ISBN 0863033784 Pbk £2.00

Gheerbrandt, Philip A
Cases In Banking Law. – 3rd ed. – Plymouth : Macdonald & Evans, 1983.
ISBN 0712104771 Pbk £4.95

Gheerbrant, Philip A.
Cases in Banking Law / D. Palfreman. – 3rd Rev. ed. – Plymouth : Macdonald & Evans, 1983.
160p. – (M and E Handbook Ser.).
ISBN 0712104771 Hbk £4.50

Ghodse, Hamid →Misuse of drugs.

Ghose, T.K.
Banking System of Hong Kong. – London : Butterworths, 1987.
ISBN 0409995320 Pbk £25.00

Ghosh
Commentaries on Payment of Bonus Act with Rules. – 2nd ed. – Allahabad : Law Publishers, 1982.
Hbk £27.00

Ghosh, A.
Law of Benami Transactions. – 6th rev. and enl. ed. – Calcutta : R. Cambray and Company, 1987.
464p.
Hbk £150.00

Ghosh on Principles and Forms of Pleading / H.K. Saharay. – 4th ed. – Calcutta : Eastern Law House, 1984.
Hbk £175.00

Ghosh, S.K.
Aircraft Hijacking and the Developing Law. – New Delhi : Ashish Publishing House, 1985.
160p.
Hbk £100.00
—Law of Monopolies and Restructive Trade Practices in India / T.G. Choudhury. – New Delhi : Prentice-Hall, 1981.
361p.
ISBN 087692075X Hbk £50.00

Ghosh, Shekhar
Law of the Territorial Sea : Evolution and Development. – Calcutta : Naya Prokash, 1988.
280p.
ISBN 8185109699 Hbk £200.00

Ghosh, Sunil Kumar
Ghosh's Land Acquisition Act. – 7th ed. – Calcutta : Eastern Law House, 1984.
Hbk £250.00

Ghosh's Land Acquisition Act. – 7th ed. – Calcutta : Eastern Law House, 1984.
Hbk £250.00

Giannantonio, Ettore
Italian legal information retrieval : a handbook / by Ettore Giannantonio. – Milano : Giuffre, 1984.
xii,181p; 25cm. – (Informatica e ordinamento giuridico).
ISBN 0421239106 Pbk £8.50
ISBN 881400143X

Gibb, Andrew Dewar
Student's glossary of Scottish legal terms / by Andrew Dewar Gibb. – 2nd ed. – Edinburgh : Green, 1982.
100p.
Previous ed.: published as 'Dictionary of words and phrases' by A.W. Dalrymple and Andrew Dewar Gibb, 1946.
ISBN 0414006968

Gibb, S.W. →Company Tax Recoupment Law.

Gibbon, Lewis G.
Blasphemer and Reformer : Study of the works of James Leslie Mitchell. – Aberdeen : Aberdeen University Press.
224p.
ISBN 0080303730 Hbk £12.50

Gibbons, T.
Regulating the media (MLS). – London : Sweet & Maxwell, 1988.
ISBN 0421374500 Hbk
ISBN 0421374608 Pbk

Gibbs, P.
Financial Marketing and Sales. – Telegraph Publications.
ISBN 0863672930 Hbk £14.95

Gibney, R. F.
Container lines : the strategy game / by R.F. Gibney. – Colchester : Lloyd's of London Press, 1984.
87p.
ISBN 0907432840

Gibraltar Law Reports 1812-1979, 3 vols. – London : African Law Reports, 1985.
Hbk £35.00

Gibson, B., et al
Lawyers' Fees. – Vancouver : British Columbia Continuing Legal Education Society, 1981.
154p.
ISBN 0865040397 Hbk £8.00

Gibson, Bryan →Criminal jurisdiction of magistrates.

Gibson, Dale
Law in a Cynical Society? : Opinion and Law in the 1980's / Janet K. Baldwin. – Agincourt : Carswell, 1985.
475p.
Hbk £50.75
—Law of the Charter : general principles / Dale Gibson. – Toronto : Carswell, 1986.
xxxiii,302p.
ISBN 0459389009

Gibson, E.
Codex Ecclesiastici Anglicani : Statutes, Constitutions, Canons, Rubriks, and Articles of the Church of England Digested with a Commentary Historical and Judicial, and Introductory Discourse, and Appendix of Instruments, 2 Vols. – 2nd ed. Repr. of 1761 ed. – Abingdon : Professional Books.
168p.
Hbk £120.00

Gibson, J. →Coal utilisation : technology, economics and policy.

Gibson, J. T. R.
South African mercantile and company law / by J.T.R. Gibson assisted by R. G. Comrie. – 5th ed. – Cape Town : Juta, 1983.
xl,668p.
Previous ed.: 1977. Includes index.
ISBN 070211359X

Gibson, John
Coastal Law. – London : Lloyd's of London Press, 1988.
ISBN 1850441642 Hbk

Gibson, John L.
Canadian Criminal Code Offences, 1 vol. – Agincourt : Carswell, 1986.
ca 350p.
This handbook for the Canadian practitioner presents the fifty most commonly charged Criminal Code offenses in forty-seven chapters. A checklist of all facts that must be proved by the prosecution and a summary of the key features of the offense is included in each chapter.
Hbk £71.50
—Criminal Law Evidence : Practice and Procedure. – Agincourt : Carswell, 1988.
606p.
This looseleaf volume is a practical guide for researching evidentiary, procedural and practice questions arising in criminal law practice. Topics are varied and contain the relevant sections of the Criminal Code, Canada Evidence Act and the Charter of Rights and Freedoms.
Llf £80.00
—Criminal Law Evidence, Practice and Procedure. – Agincourt : Carswell, 1988.
606p.
Llf £80.00

Gibson, Michael S.
Introduction to urban renewal / Michael S. Gibson, Michael J. Langstaff. – London : Hutchinson, 1982.
384p; 24cm.
ISBN 0091475007

Gibson, Robt. W.
Concepts for Financial Statements. – 2nd ed. – North Ryde : Law Book Co, 1984.
viii, 70p.
ISBN 0455202125 Pbk £8.50

Gibson, Kelsen, Andrew, Irene
Essentials of Business Law in Australia. – Carleton : Pitman Pty Ltd, 1983.
ISBN 0858966697 Hbk £22.95

Giddings, Jane
Lawyer-economist extraordinary : the Soviet jurisconsult / Jane Giddings. – s.l. : National Association for Soviet and East European Studies, 1981.
29p; 30cm.

Giesen, Dieter
International medical malpractice law : a comparative law study of civil liability arising from medical care / by Dieter Giesen : with a foreword by Lord Kilbrandon. – Tubingen : Mohr, 1988.
940p; 24cm.
Includes bibliography and index.
ISBN 9024737052 Germany £ :
ISBN 3166453229
—International Medical Malpractice Law : A Comparative Law Study of Civil Liability from Medical Care. – Martinus Nijhoff.
ISBN 9024737052 Hbk £137.00

Giffard, C. Anthony →Press and Apartheid : Repression and Propaganda in South Africa.

Gifford, Anthony Maur
Broadwater Farm Inquiry. – London : CEMT, 1986.
ISBN 094691897 Pbk £4.95

Gifford, Anthony Maurice Gifford →Political policing in Wales.
—Supergrasses : the use of accomplice evidence in Northern Ireland : a report / by Tony Gifford. – London : Cobden Trust, 1984.
38p.
ISBN 0900137215
—Where's the justice ? : a manifesto of law reform / Tony Gifford. – Harmondsworth : Penguin, 1986.
126p. – (A Penguin special).
ISBN 0140523588

Gifford, K.H.
How to Understand An Act of Parliament. – 6th ed. – North Ryde : Law Book Co, 1987.
xxxi, 605p.
Pbk
—Our Legal System. – 2nd ed. 1983. – North Ryde : Law Book Co.
ISBN 0455202680 Pbk £19.00

Gifford, M. N., et al
Indians and the Law. – Vancouver : British Columbia Continuing Legal Education Society, 1982.
420p.
ISBN 0865040524 Hbk £65.00

Gijlstra, D.J.
Competition Law in Western Europe and the USA. – Dordrecht : Kluwer, 1984.
Hbk Gld895.00
—Leading Cases and Materials on the Agricultural Policy of the E.E.C. / H.J. Bronkhorst. – Dordrecht : Kluwer, 1984.
ca 250p.
ISBN 9065440704 Hbk £55.00

→ Leading cases and materials on the competition law of the E.E.C.

→ Leading cases on the law of the European Communities.

→ Materials on the law of the European Communities.

Gilbert, et al
Appeals : Practice and Procedure. – London : Longman Professional, 1986.
ISBN 0851207626 Pbk £18.95

Gilbert, G.
Law of Distresses and Replevins : With Appendix of English Precedents in Replevins. – 3rd ed. Repr. of 1794 ed. – Abingdon : Professional Books.
460p.
Hbk £45.00

Gilbert Islands law reports / compiled by J.A. O'Brien Quinn. – 2 v. – Tarawa : High Court, 1977-.
Continued by: The Kiribati law reports. 'Published by authority'.

Gilbert, J. C.
Keynes's Impact on Monetary Economics. – London : Butterworths, 1982.
This book provides a carefully documented survey of the impact of Keynes on monetary economics. The fundamental concepts of Keynes's theories are considered and related to the work of important critics and followers of Keynes.
ISBN 0408107189 Hbk

Gilbert, Michael →Oxford book of legal anecdotes.

Gilchrist, C.
How to plan your life insurance. – 2nd ed. – Cambridge : Woodhead-Faulkner, 1986.
ISBN 0859413004 Hbk £10.95
ISBN 0859413012 Pbk £4.95
—Unit trusts. – 3rd ed. – Cambridge : Woodhead-Faulkner, 1982.
ISBN 0859412083 Pbk £9.95
ISBN 0959412091 Hbk £17.95

Giles, Marianne
Criminal law in a nutshell / Marianne Giles. – London : Sweet & Maxwell, 1987.
121p; 23cm.
Includes index.
ISBN 0421368209 Pbk £4.95
→ English Law for GCSE.
—Scott's English Law for GCSE. – 5th ed. – London : Butterworths, 1987.
ISBN 0406653070 Pbk £10.50

Giles, O. C. →Chorley and Giles' shipping law.

Giles, W. H
Schools and students : legal aspects of administration / W.H. Giles. – Toronto : Carswell, 1988.
xxix, 206 p.; 24 cm.
Includes index.
ISBN 0459312014

Gilgate Holdings Limited, Raybourne Group Limited, Calomefern Limited, Desadean Properties Limited : investigation under Section 165(b) of the Companies Act 1948 / report by R.A. Morritt and P.L. Ainger. – London : Her Majesty's Stationery Office, 1981.
ca.780p; 30cm.
At head of title: Department of Trade.
ISBN 0115134859 Pbk £23.00

Gill, Brian
Law of agricultural holdings in Scotland / Brian Gill. – Edinburgh : Green, 1982.
xxxiv,451p; 25cm.
Includes index. Includes text of 6 acts.
ISBN 0444996656 SET

Gill, D.
Indoctrination, curriculum and the law. – Southampton : Association for Curriculum Development, 1988.
ISBN 185401066 Pbk £4.00

Gill, Kulwant
Hindu Women's Right to Property in India. – New Delhi : Deep and Deep Publications, 1986.
528p.
Hbk £275.00

Gill, M. L. →Crime victims : needs, services and the voluntary sector.

Gill, Terry D
Litigation strategy at the International Court A case study of the Nicaragua v. United States dispute. – Dordrecht : Nijhoff (Martinus), 1989. 375. – (Legal aspects of international organization 9).
Examines the reasons States have for utilizing or resisting the utilization of the International Court as a means of pursuing and achieving foreign policy goals, and the methods they employ within the scope of the possibilities offered by the Courts Statute and Rule of procedure. This model is applied to the Nicaragua case.
ISBN 0792303326 Hbk £56

—South West Africa and the sacred trust 1919-1972 / T.D. Gill. – The Hague : T.M.C. Asser Instituut, 1984.
ix,107p.
Bibliography: p.106-107.
ISBN 9067040274

Gill, Tess → Rape controversy.
→ Women's rights : a practical guide.

Gill, William H.
Law of arbitration / Gill. – 3rd ed. – London : Sweet & Maxwell, 1983.
xxv,174p; 22cm.
Previous ed.: 1975. Includes index.
ISBN 0421251107 Pbk £7.50

Giller, Henri
Care and discretion : social workers' decisions with delinquents / Henri Giller, Allison Morris. – London : Burnett in association with Deutsch, 1981.
127p; 21cm.
Bibliography: p120-123. - Includes index.
ISBN 0233972943 Hbk £5.95
ISBN 0233973737 Pbk £3.50
→ Juvenile delinquency : trends and perspectives.
→ Providing criminal justice for children.
→ Understanding juvenile justice.

Gilles, P.
Law of Evidence in Australia. – London : Legal Books, 1987.
ISBN 0949553360 Hbk £45.00
ISBN 0959553395 Pbk £30.00

Gillese, E.E. → Text, Commentary and Cases on Trusts.

Gillies
City of Sault Ste. Marie Act, 1983, Bill Pr048 : An Act Respecting the City of Sault Ste. Marie. – Ontario : Ontario Government Publications Service, 1983.
2p.
Hbk £0.30

Gillies, Peter
Australian Evidence : Cases and Commentary. – Sydney : Butterworths, 1988.
608p.
This casebook contains materials on the burden of proof, circumstantial evidence, witnesses, judicial discretion, hearsay, res gestae, admissions, and other topics.
Pbk £55.00

—Criminal law / by Peter Gillies. – Sydney : Law Book Co., 1985.
lvii,668p.
Includes bibliographical references and index.
ISBN 0455205981

—Law in Action. – 2nd ed. – North Ryde : C.C.H. Australia, 1985.
364p.
ISBN 0869035088 Hbk £22.00

—Law of criminal conspiracy / by Peter Gillies. – Sydney : Law Book Co., 1981.
Includes bibliographical references and index.
ISBN 0455200793

—Law of Evidence in Australia. – Woolloomooloo : International Business Communications, 1987.
650p.
ISBN 0949553360 Hbk £85.00

Gilligan, Brian → Tax and financial planning for professional partnerships.

Gilmore, Sheila
Waiting for justice : an SCC survey of facilities in Scotland's Sheriff Courts : results and recommendations by Sheila Gilmore. – Glasgow : Scottish Consumer Council, 1981.
44,A1-A6p,11leaves; 30cm.
ISBN 0907067069 Pbk £1.50

Gilmore, William C.
Grenada intervention : analysis and documentation / William C. Gilmore. – London : Mansell, 1984.
116p; 22cm.
Includes index.
ISBN 0720117232 Pbk £5.95

—Newfoundland and Dominion Status. – Agincourt : Carswell, 1987.
304p.
This work focuses on the pre-Confederation status of Newfoundland from a legal point of view. It is a comprehensive text providing archival sources in documenting the evolution of Newfoundland's external affairs competence between 1855 and 1934. It also provides a review in terms of Imperial constitutional law and international law. Up-to-date decisions of the Supreme Court of Canada and Newfoundland Court of Appeal are reviewed.
Hbk £38.00

Gilpin, Alan
Dictionary of Economics and Financial Markets. – 5th ed. – London : Butterworths, 1986.
This work contains definitions of economic terminology and concepts and topics related to contemporary applied economics and financial institutions. A bibliography is included in the text.
ISBN 0408015705 £19.95

Gilreath, Charles L.
Computerized literature searching research stratagies and databases / Charles L. Gilreath. – Epping : Bowker, 1984.
xiv,177p; 24cm. – (Westview special studies in information science and management).
Includes index.
ISBN 0865315264

Ginsburgs, George
Calendar of Soviet treaties, 1958-1973 / by George Ginsburgs and Robert M. Slusser. – Alphen aan den Rijn : Sijthoff & Noordhoff, 1981.
xx,908p.

—Calendar of Soviet treaties, 1974-1980 / George Ginsburgs. – Dordrecht : Martinus Nijhoff Publishers, 1987.
ISBN 9024736285 Hbk

—Citizenship law of the USSR / by George Ginsburgs. – The Hague : M. Nijhoff Publishers, 1984.
xii,394p.
Includes index. Bibliography: p379-390.
ISBN 9024728630 Hbk

Ginther, K. → New perspectives and conceptions of international law : an Afro-European dialogue.

Ginwala, Frene
Indian South Africans / by Frene Ginwala. – New ed. – London : Minority Rights Group, 1985.
20p. – (Report).
Includes bibliographical references.
ISBN 0946690294

Giri, H.N.
Consumers, Crimes and the Law. – New Delhi : Ashish Publishing House, 1987.
370p.
ISBN 8170240794 Hbk £250.00

Girls and the Law. – Redfern : Redfern Legal Centre Publishing, 1984.
56p.
Hbk £6.00

Girls in the gang : a report from New York City / Anne Campbell. – Oxford : Blackwell, 1984.
vii,277p; 24cm.
Study of girls in New York City gangs.
ISBN 0631133747 Hbk

Gittings, Vera → Conveyancing Practice and Procedure.

Gittins, Vera
Newman's Conveyancing Practice and Procedure / Phyllis E. Newman. – 2nd ed. – London : Fourmat, 1985.
135p.
ISBN 0906840910 Pbk £9.95

Giving desert its due : social justice and legal theory / Wojciech Sadurski. – Dordrecht : D. Reidel, 1985.
xii, 329p.
Includes index. Bibliography: p 309-318.
ISBN 9027719411 Hbk £47.00

Gizzi → Solicitors and VAT.

Gladstone, F. J.
Charity, law and social justice / Francis Gladstone. – London : Bedford Square Press, 1982.
v,211p.
ISBN 0719910846

Gladwin, Philip
Guide to the patent law of the People's Republic of China / by Philip Gladwin in conjunction with Ajmal Hameed. – London : Graham & Trotman, 1985.
70p; 22cm.
ISBN 0860106306

Glasbeek, H J
Cases and Materials on Evidence. – London : Butterworths, 1974.
ISBN 0409436410 Pbk £28.00
→ Labour law and industrial relations in Canada.

Glashoff, H. → Customs Valuation : a Commentary on GATT Customs Valuation Code.

Glass, D
Introduction to the law of carriage of goods / C Cashmore. – London : Sweet & Maxwell, 1989.
Guide to the law of carriage of goods by land, sea and air, with a brief ssummary of the law relating to passengers and their luggage. Explores the principles of UK law, supplemented by Commonwealth, US and European authorities. Provides an examination of international conventions and the standard conditions of carriage in use in the industry.
ISBN 0420397004 Pbk c.14.00

Glass, T. F. → County court procedure in Northern Ireland including a supplement for the Republic of Ireland.

Glassberg, Andrew D.
Representation and Urban Community. – London : Macmillan, 1981.
200p.
ISBN 0333288785 Hbk £20.00

Glassner, Martin Ira → Bibliography on land-locked states.
→ International law of the sea and marine affairs, a bibliography, Supplement to the 1980 edition.

Glasson, E. J → National survey of law libraries in Australia.

Glautier
Cost Accounting / Underdown. – London : Pitman Publishing, 1988.
ISBN 0273025007 Pbk £9.95

Gleeson, V.B. → Law of Education.

Glendinning, J. W.
Management by Objectives in Local Government / R. E. H. Bullock. – Tonbridge : Ernest Benn.
255p.
Hbk £4.00

Glendon, Mary Ann
New family and the new property / Mary Ann Glendon. – Toronto : Butterworths, 1981.
xvii,269p; 23cm.
ISBN 0409834106

Glennester, H.
Paying for Welfare. – Oxford : Blackwell, 1985.
ISBN 0631139729 Pbk £7.95

Glissan, J.L.
Cross Examination Practice and Procedure. – London : Legal Books, 1985.
ISBN 0949553166 Hbk £20.00

Gloag, W. M.
Introduction to the law of Scotland / by W.M. Gloag and R. Candlish Henderson. – 9th ed. – Edinburgh : W. Green, 1987.
clii,1020p.
Previous ed.: 1980. Includes index.
ISBN 0414008189

—Law of Contract. – Edinburgh : W Green, 1985.
Hbk £23.00

Global Investing / Kirzner. – New York : Dow Jones-Irwin, 1988.
ISBN 087094908X Hbk £26.50

Global resources and international conflict : environmental factors in strategic policy and action / edited by Arthur H. Westing : Stockholm International Peace Research Institute, United Nations Environment Programme. – Oxford : Oxford University Press, 1986.
xv,250p; 22cm.
Includes bibliography and index.
ISBN 0198291043 £17.50

Globe, Janet M.
Title Searching in Ontario. – 2nd ed. – Butterworths, 1982.
200p.
Explains the procedure required for a 40-year search of title with a copy of an abstract page and sketches relating to land descriptions, the procedure required under the Land Titles Act, the procedure required under the Condominium Act, under the Registry Act, the Certification of Titles Act, and the provisions allowed under section 29 of the Planning Act.
ISBN 0409834165 Hbk £29.95

Globerman, Steven
Economic analysis of a performers' right / Steven Globerman and Mitchell P. Rothman. – Ottawa, Ont. : Consumer and Corporate Affairs Canada, 1981.
111 p.; 28 cm.
Bibliography: p. 109-111.

—Framework for evaluating Canada's Trade Marks Act / by Steven Globerman with Mitchell P. Rothman. – Canada : Policy Research, Analysis and Liaison Directorate, Consumer and Corporate Affairs, 1983.
86p.
ISBN 0662124189

Glossner, Ottoarndt
Commercial arbitration in the Federal Republic of Germany / by Ottoarndt Glossner. – Deventer : Kluwer Law and Taxation, 1984.
xiv,137p; 25cm.
Bibliography: p113-134. - Includes index.
ISBN 9065441859 Hbk £90.00

Glover, G. N. → Introduction to English law.

Glover, Rupert Granville
New Zealand in Vietnam : a Study of the Use of Force in International Law. – Palmerston North : Dunmore Press Ltd., 1987.
ISBN 0864690584 Pbk £16.45

Glucklich, Pauline → Equal pay and opportunities : a study of the implementation and effects of the Equal Pay and Sex Discrimination Acts in 26 organizations.

GmbH-German Law Concerning Companies with Limited Liabilities. – 4th ed. – Plymouth : Macdonald & Evans, 1981.
176p.
ISBN 0712154809 Casebound £16.00

Gmur, Charles J. → Trade financing.

Gobbo, J.A.
Cross on Evidence : with Supplement 1980 / D. Byrne. – 3rd ed. – Butterworths, 1986.
734p.
ISBN 040949139X Hbk £89.00
ISBN 0409491489 Pbk £65.00

Godana, Bonaya
Africa's shared water resources : legal and institutional aspects of the Nile, Niger and Senegal river systems / by Bonaya Godana. – London : Pinter, 1985.
220p; 23cm.
Includes bibliography and index.
ISBN 086187563X £17.50

Goddard, Kathleen
Shipping Finance : Loans, Ship Mortgages and Other Securities. – Abingdon : Professional Books, 1984.
ISBN 0862050618 Hbk £63.00
ISBN 0862050669 Pbk

Godfrey, Ellen
By Reason of Doubt : the Belshaw Case. – Richmond Hill : Irwin Publishing Inc..
208p.
ISBN 0887801250 Pbk £4.95
ISBN 077201390X Pbk £9.95

Godfrey, G. M.
Saint Piran Limited : investigation under Section 165(b) and Section 172 of the Companies Act 1948 : final report / by G.M. Godfrey and A.J. Hardcastle. – London : H.M.S.O., 1981.
228p; 30cm.
At head of title: Department of Trade.
ISBN 0115134735 Pbk £14.00

Godfrey, Stuart R.
Human Rights and Social Policy in Newfoundland 1832-1982 : Search for a Just Society. – St. John's : Harry Cuff Publications Ltd., 1985.
256p.
ISBN 0919095798 Pbk £14.95

Godin, M.
New Brunswick Court Forms : Formulaire de procedure du Nouveau-Brunswick / Douglas G. Rouse. – Agincourt : Carswell, 1985.
800p.
This looseleaf volume presents in both French and English over two hundred eighty separate forms which document the steps of a civil action in the courts of New Brunswick, Canada.
Pbk £80.00

Goebel, Julius →Law practice of Alexander Hamilton : documents and commentary, Vol.5 : editors Julius Goebel, Jr. and Joseph H. Smith : associate editors Winnifred Bowers ... et al.

—Struggle for the Falkland Islands : a study in legal and diplomatic history / Julius Goebel : with a preface and an introduction by J.C.J. Metford. – New Haven : Yale University Press, 1982.
xxx,482p; 23cm.
Originally published: 1927. Includes index.
ISBN 0300029438 Hbk £12.00
ISBN 0300029446 Pbk £5.95

Goel, C.G. →Military Law in India : a Commentary.

Goff of Chieveley, Robert Goff
Judge, jurist and legislature : a public lecture / delivered by the Right Honourable The Lord Goff of Chieveley. – London : Child & Co., 1986.
17p.

Going bust : inside the bankruptcy business / Stephen Aris. – London : Deutsch, 1985.
194p; 23cm.
Includes index.
ISBN 0233976930 £8.95

Golay, David →Judicial review, transnational and federal : its impact on integration.

Gold, Alan D.
Annual Review of Criminal Law : 1987. – Agincourt : Carswell, Annual, 1986.
304p.
This text, the sixth volume in an annual series, provides a summary and a synopsis of the major issues in Canadian criminal law, practice and evidence. It contains an outline of the trends in judicial interpretations of the Charter. Also included is an index to pertinent periodical literature.
Hbk £40.50

Gold, Edgar
Handbook on marine pollution. – Arendal : Assuranceforeningen Gard, 1985.
247p.
Bibliography: p.174-179.

—New Law of the Sea for the Caribbean : an Examination of Marine Law and Policy Issues in the Lesser Antilles. – Berlin : Springer-Verlag, 1988.
ca 295p.
ISBN 3540968059 Pbk £69.00

→ Problems of development and ocean management in the eastern Caribbean : economic, legal, environmental and planning aspects : proceedings of an international seminar held in Kingstown, St. Vincent & the Grenadines, West Indies, May 11-13, 1981.

Gold, Joseph
Legal and institutional aspects of the International Monetary System : selected essays
Vol 2 : by Joseph Gold. – Washington, D.C. : International Monetary Fund, 1984.
xviii,947p.
Includes bibliographies and index.
ISBN 0939934345

Gold, Neil →Essays on legal education.

Goldberg, A.H. →Real Estate Agency in Victoria.

Goldberg, Julie →Austrian law on companies with limited liability : as of January 1, 1984 with excerpted provisions of other relevant laws and annotations.

Goldberg, V.P.
Readings in the Economics of Contract Law. – Cambridge : Cambridge University Press.
ISBN 0521341205 Hbk £25.00

Goldblat, Jozef
Arms Control Agreements : a Handbook. – Stockholm : Almqvist & Wiksell, 1983.
328p.
ISBN 0850662486 Hbk £139.00

—Falklands/Malvinas conflict : a spur to arms build-ups / Jozef Goldblat and Victor Millan. – Stockholm : SIPRI, 1983.
vii,63p; 23cm.
Originally published as: World armaments and disarmament in SIPRI Yearbook : London and New York, 1983.
ISBN 9185114308

Golden Handshake : Hiring and Firing. – Vancouver : British Columbia Continuing Legal Education Society, 1983.
137p.
ISBN 0865041253 Hbk £45.00

Goldenberg, David M.
Mortgages and Foreclosure : Know Your Rights. – 4th ed. – North Vancouver : International Self-Counsel Press, 1987.
105p.
ISBN 0889086567 Hbk £7.95

Goldhirsch, L.B.
Warsaw Convention Annotated : A Legal Handbook. – Martinus Nijhoff.
ISBN 9024736196 Hbk £82.00

Goldie, R.M.
Image of Man in Human Rights Legislation. – Rome : Herder, 1985.
243p.
Hbk £25,000.00

Golding, C. E.
Golding: The law and practice of reinsurance / by C.E. Golding. – 5th ed. – London : Witherby, 1987.
x,285p; 23cm. – (Monument series).
Previous ed.: 1965. Includes index.
ISBN 094869114X

Golding, G. M.
George Gavan Duffy 1882-1951 : a legal biography / G.M. Golding. – Blackrock : Irish Academic Press, 1982.
xvi,224p,1leaf of plates; 22cm.
Bibliography: p209-214. - Includes index.
ISBN 0716500787 Hbk £15.00
ISBN 0716502070 Pbk

Golding: The law and practice of reinsurance / by C.E. Golding. – 5th ed. – London : Witherby, 1987.
x,285p; 23cm. – (Monument series).
Previous ed.: 1965. Includes index.
ISBN 094869114X

Goldman, Alvin L.
Labour Law and Industrial Relations in the United States of America. – 2nd ed. – Dordrecht : Kluwer, 1984.
374p.
ISBN 9065441689 Pbk £95.00

Goldman, Berthold
Lex mercatoria / Berthold Goldman. – Deventer : Kluwer Law and Taxation Publishers, 1983.
24p.
Includes bibliographical references.
ISBN 9065441948

Goldrein, Iain S.
Commercial litigation : pre-emptive remedies / by Iain S. Goldrein and K.H. P. Wilkinson : with a foreword by Sir John Donaldson. – London : Sweet & Maxwell, 1987.
xlvii,793p; 26cm.
Covers topics in the commercial field where emergency relief may be necessary. Techniques are explained, and relevant reported cases are referred to, including the necessary statutes and court orders. Appendices include forms and precedents, and some Chancery and Queen's Bench Division Practice Directions.
ISBN 0421348003 Hbk £107

—Key to Personal Injury Practice and Compensation / Margaret R De Haas. – London : Longman Professional, 1981.
ISBN 0851206158 Pbk £8.95

—Personal Injury Litigation : Practice and Precedents / Margaret R De Haas. – London : Butterworths, 1985.
This work for personal injury practitioners in the United Kingdom covers a wide range of procedural and practical points. The book includes chapters on deduction of collateral benefits, the Motor Insurers' Bureau, medical examination of plaintiffs, and limitation of damages.
ISBN 0406016607 Llf £105.00

—Property distribution on divorce / Margaret R De Haas. – 2nd ed. – London : Longman Professional, 1985.
ISBN 0851210015 Pbk £14.95

—Ship sale and purchase : law and technique / by Iain S. Goldrein. – London : Lloyd's of London, 1985.
345p; 25cm.
Includes index.
ISBN 1850440522

Goldring
Constitution Of Papua New Guinea : A Study In Legal Nationalism 1978. – London : Law Book Co.
ISBN 0455198403 Pbk £12.00

Goldring, John
Consumer Protection Law in Australia / John Goldring, Laurence W. Maher. – 3rd ed. – London : Butterworths.
Includes index.
ISBN 0409491675 Hbk £56.00
ISBN 0409491683 Pbk £45.00

—Consumers or Victims?. – North Sydney : Allen & Unwin, 1982.
172p.
ISBN 0868610208 Pbk £15.95

Goldsmith, Immanuel
Canadian building contracts / Immanuel Goldsmith. – 3rd ed. – Toronto, Canada : Carswell, 1983.
lxi, 273 p.; 24 cm.
Includes bibliographical references.
ISBN 0459357905

→ Damages for personal injury and death in Canada.

—Patents of Inventions. – 3rd ed. – Agincourt : Carswell, 1981.
This textbook includes the text of the Patent Act of Canada and rules, as well as, an exhaustive summation of case law and statutes pertaining to patent law.
ISBN 045934500 Hbk £25.30

—Trade marks and industrial designs / by Immanuel Goldsmith. – Toronto : Carswell, 1982.
ix,344p.
Reprinted from the Canadian Encyclopedic Digest 3rd ed.
ISBN 0459349805

Goldsmith, Michael →Essays on the future of local government.

Goldstein et al
Nurse's Legal Advisor Your Guide to Legally Safe Practice. – London : Lippincott.
ISBN 0397547005 Pbk £6.95

Goldstein, J.
Aggression and Crimes of Violence. – 2nd ed. – Oxford : Oxford University Press, 1986.
ISBN 0195039440 Pbk £9.00

Goldstein, Laurence
Precedent in law. – Oxford : Oxford University Press, 1988.
ISBN 0198255268 Hbk £27.50

Goldstein, Stephen →Israeli reports to the XI International Congress of Comparative Law.

Goldthorpe, John H. →Order and conflict in contemporary capitalism.

Goldwater, Carmel →Disaster and resolution : two discussion papers dealing with distinct aspects of the aftermath of man-made disasters, the process of litigation, settlement and compensation and the factors affecting the provision of speedy relief and effective rehabilitation.

Golland, R. →Urban riots and public order : a select bibliography, 1975-1985.

Golvan, C.
Writers and the Law / M. McDonald. – North Ryde : Law Book Co, 1986.
xix, 262p.
ISBN 0455207119 Pbk £29.50

Golzen, Godfrey
Taking Up a Franchise / Colin Barrow. – 3rd ed. – London : Kogan Page, 1986.
264p.
ISBN 1850910758 Hbk £12.95

Gomard, Bernhard →Danish law : a general survey.

Gong, Gerrit W.
Standard of 'civilization' in international society / Gerrit W. Gong. – Oxford : Clarendon, 1984.
xvi,267p; 23cm.
Bibliography: p251-261. - Includes index.
ISBN 0198219482 £19.50

Gonski, David M. →Protection of trade secrets : a general guide.

Gonzales, Armando E.
Dominican Republic : divorce law / Armando E. Gonzales. – Washington, D.C. : Law Library, Library of Congress, 1986.
v,43p.

Gooch, Anthony C.
Loan agreement documentation : sample annotated loan agreement for a syndicated Eurodollar transaction / by Anthony C. Gooch, Linda B. Klein. – London : Euromoney Publications, 1986.
iii,93p.
ISBN 1870031407

Good Girls Gone Bad. – London : Futura, 1988.
ISBN 0356151603 Pbk £11.95

Good Practice : A Management Guide for the Profession. – London : Butterworths.
ISBN 0406502803 Pbk

Good Practice : Management Guide for Professions. – London : Butterworths, 1988.
ISBN 0406502803 Pbk

Good Wigging / Hamilton. – London : Butterworths.
ISBN 0406509905 Hbk £20.00

Goodacre, J. Kenneth
Institute time clauses : hulls : a comparison between the 1983 clauses and the 1970 clauses with subsequent amendments / by J. Kenneth Goodacre. – London : Witherby, 1983.
vii,67p.
Includes the text of the Marine Insurance Act, 1906. 'In co-operation with the U.K. Society of Average Adjusters'.
—Marine insurance claims / by J. Kenneth Goodacre. – 2nd ed. – London : Witherby, 1981.
liv,1015p,12p of plates; 23cm. – (Monument series).
Previous ed.: 1974. Includes index.
ISBN 0900886536 £35.00

Goodacre, P.
Delays and Disruptions in Construction : Ascertaining the Cost-A Case Study in Assessing a Contractor's Claim. – King's Ride : Institute of Building, 1987.
68p.
ISBN 0906600928 Hbk £7.75

Goodall
Law and Practice of Conveyancing in New Zealand / Brookfield. – 4th ed. – London : Butterworths, 1981.
ISBN 0409600296 Hbk £41.00

Goodch
Swap agreement documentation / Klein. – London : Euromoney, 1987.
ISBN 1870031717 Pbk £110.00

Goode, R. M.
Commercial law / R.M. Goode. – Harmondsworth : Pelican, 1986.
1119p.
Includes bibliographical references and index.
ISBN 0140226346 Pbk £18.95
→ Conflicts of interest in the changing financial world.
—Consumer Credit Legislation / Yelland. – London : Butterworths, 1977.
Service to Date.
ISBN 0406211612 Llf £130.00
→ Electronic banking : the legal implications.
→ International carriage of goods : some legal problems and possible solutions.
—Legal problems of credit and security / by R.M. Goode. – London : Sweet & Maxwell, 1982.
xviii,133p; 22cm.
Includes index.
ISBN 0421302704 Pbk £10.00
—Legal problems of credit and security / by R.M. Goode. – 2nd ed. – London : Sweet & Maxwell, 1988.
xxxv,218p; 23cm.
Contains chapters on the nature and forms of consensual security and concepts of attachments and perfection. Section on treatment of negative pledges has been expanded. Analysis of the legal nature of subparticipation in loan assessments, and examination of twelve typical priority conflicts and their resolution, and an enlarged chapter on equitable, statutory and contractual set-off and set-off on insolvency.
ISBN 0421384301 Pbk £14.00
—Payment obligations in commercial and financial transactions / by R.M. Goode. – London : Sweet & Maxwell, 1983.
xxiii,151p; 22cm.
Includes index.
ISBN 0421318104 Pbk £11.00
—Proprietary rights and insolvency in sales transactions / by R.M. Goode. – London : Sweet & Maxwell, 1985.
xv,137p; 22cm.
Includes index.
ISBN 0421351403 Pbk £13.00
→ Right to strike in Britain/ the English floating charge.

Goode, Richard → Comparative tax studies : essays in honor of Richard Goode.

Goodfellow, G
Inheritance tax planning / Andrew R Thornhill. – 2nd ed. – London : Longman Professional, 1988.
ISBN 0851213669 Hbk £85.00
→ Potter and Monroe's tax planning with precedents.

Goodhart
Essays in Jurisprudence 1931. – London : Wildy & Sons.
Hbk £10.50

Goodhart, C.A.E.
Evolution of Central Banks. – London : MIT Press.
ISBN 0262071118 Hbk £20.25

Goodhart, William → Divided we stand : a report on the legal profession.
→ Specific performance.

Goodman → About You and Fostering.

Goodman, A.
New Court Guide. – London : Blackstone Press, 1988.
ISBN 185185049X Pbk £5.95

Goodman, J.
Murder In Low Places. – Piatkus Books.
ISBN 0861887514 Hbk £10.95

Goodman, Michael J. → Administration of Justice Act 1982.
—Health & Safety at Work : Law and Practice. – Sweet & Maxwell, 1988.
ISBN 0421376708 Pbk £18.00
—Health and safety at work: law and practice. – London : Sweet & Maxwell, 1988.
Examines claims in industrial tribunals relating to dismissal and constructive dismissal for health and safety reasons, and the rights of safety representatives to times off. Analysis of sickness and invalidity benefits, practice and procedure in social security appeal tribunals, and the grounds for action by the Health and Safety Executive.
ISBN 0421376708
—Industrial tribunals : practice and procedure / by Michael J. Goodman. – 4th ed. – London : Sweet & Maxwell, 1987.
xxv,120p; 22cm.
Overview of the tribunals' principle jurisdictions, and analysis of practice and procedure before industrial tribunals. Covers the changes made by the Wages Act 1986. Contains model forms for application and response to an industrial tribunal, and the text of the Industrial Tribunals (Rules of Procedure) Regulations 1985.
ISBN 0421391200 Pbk

Goodrich, Peter
Legal discourse : studies in linguistics, rhetoric and legal analysis / Peter Goodrich. – London : Macmillan, 1987.
x,266p; 23cm. – (Language, discourse, society series).
Bibliography: p247-258. - Includes index.
ISBN 0333419499 £29.50
—Reading the law : a critical introduction to legal method and techniques / Peter Goodrich. – Oxford : Basil Blackwell, 1986.
ix,229p; 23cm.
Introduction to the study of law. Illustrates how lawyers and students read legal texts.
ISBN 0631146296 Hbk £27.50
ISBN 0631146318 Pbk £9.95

Goods and Services Tax Act 1985 : the Application of the Act / Wayne Mapp. – Butterworths, 1986.
ISBN 0409787663 Pbk £36.30

Goods and services - the new law / by Geoffrey F. Woodroffe. – London : Sweet & Maxwell, 1982.
xviii,164p; 22cm.
Includes index.
ISBN 0421302003 Pbk £9.85

Goods in Transit. – London : Matthew Bender, 1985.
ISBN 0000999058 Hbk £53.00

Goods Operator Licensing / Airey. – London : Kogan Page, 1988.
ISBN 1850914796 Hbk

Goodwin, G A → Criminal Litigation.
—Criminal Litigation / M. S. Iller. – London : Butterworths, 1985.
This work is a factual account of all stages in the practice and procedure of criminal litigation in the United Kingdom from investigation to conclusion of the criminal process. The book is directed at students of criminal evidence and procedure.
Students
ISBN 0406258139 Pbk

Goodwin-Gill, Guy S
Refugee in international law / Guy S. Goodwin-Gill. – Oxford Oxfordshire : Clarendon Press, 1983.
xxvii,318p.
Includes index. Bibliography: p306-311.
ISBN 0198253729

Goonasekara, Savithri
Legal Status of the Female in the Sri Lanka Law on Family Relations. – Colombo : Gunasena and Co..
Hbk £60.00

Goossen, Richard J
Technology transfer in the Peoples' Republic of China : law and practice / Richard J. Goossen. – Dordrecht : M. Nijhoff, 1987.
Bibliography.
ISBN 9024734428

Gopal, B.V.
Video Piracy and the Law. – New Delhi : Deep and Deep Publications, 1986.
160p.
Hbk £100.00

Gopal, Ram
Undemocratic Elements in the Indian Constitution. – New Delhi : Somaiya Publications, 1977.
380p.
Hbk £75.00

Gopal, Shiva
Commentaries on Uttar Pradesh Urban Buildings (Regulation of Letting, Rent and Eviction) Act, 1972. – 4th ed. – Lucknow : Eastern Book Company, 1981.
493p.
Hbk £40.00
—Conveyancing, Precedents and Forms / G.C. Mathur. – 5th ed. – Lucknow : Eastern Book Company, 1983.
704p.
Hbk £70.00
—Law Relating to Electricity in India / Surendra Malik. – 5th rev. ed. – Lucknow : Eastern Book Company, 1986.
1,088p.
Hbk £225.00

Gopalakrishnan
Hindu Adoption and Maintenance Act. – 2nd ed. – Allahabad : Law Book Company, 1985.
Hbk £60.00
→ Hindu Succession Act.

Gopalan, V.R. → Contempt of Court.

Gordon
Contracts of Affreightments and Hybrid Conts / Ivre. – London : Lloyd's of London Press, 1985.
ISBN 1850440603 Hbk £25.85
—Forensic Medicine / Shapiro. – 3rd ed. – Edinburgh : Churchill Livingstone, 1988.
ISBN 0443034400 Hbk £29.50
—Immigration Law and Procedure / Rosenfield. – Matthew Bender, 1966.
ISBN 0000999087 Hbk £409.00
→ Professional Practice for Building Works.
→ Shipbroking and chartering practice.

Gordon and Getz on the South African law of insurance / W. S. Getz, D. M. Davis. – 3rd ed. – Cape Town : Juta, 1983.
xl,624p.
Bibliography: p.ix-xii. - Includes index. Cover title: The South African law of insurance.
ISBN 0702113751

Gordon, Charles → Erskine May's treatise on the law, privileges, proceedings and usage of Parliament.

Gordon, D.
Foreign Divorces : English Law and Practice. – Aldershot : Avebury.
ISBN 0566053101 Hbk £25.00

Gordon, Gerald
Criminal justice (Scotland) Act 1980. – Edinburgh : Green (W.) & Son, 1981.
Annotated copy of this Act which introduced important changes relating to Scotttish criminal law and procedure. With the text of the Act of Adjournal providing for some of the procedures under the Act.
ISBN 0414006747 Pbk
—Gordon and Getz on the South African law of insurance / W. S. Getz, D. M. Davis. – 3rd ed. – Cape Town : Juta, 1983.
xl,624p.
Bibliography: p.ix-xii. - Includes index. Cover title: The South African law of insurance.
ISBN 0702113751

Gordon, Jane → Wills/Probate Procedure for Manitoba and Saskatchewan.

Gordon, Myron J.
Drug Industry : A Case Study in Foreign Control / David John Fowler. – Toronto : Lorimer & Co, 1981.
ISBN 0888625367 Hbk £16.95
ISBN 0888625359 Pbk £8.95

Gordon, Paul
Policing immigration : Britain's internal controls / Paul Gordon. – London : Pluto, 1985.
v,160p.
Includes index.
ISBN 0861046234 Pbk £4.95
—White law : racism in the police courts and prisons / Paul Gordon. – London : Pluto Press, 1983.
159p; 20cm.
ISBN 0861047060 Pbk £3.95

Gordon, R.
Crown Office Proceedings. – London : Sweet & Maxwell, 1988.
ISBN 042137960X Hbk
—Law Relating to Mobile Homes and Caravans. – London : Shaw & Sons, 1985.
ISBN 072190811X Pbk £10.50

Gordon, R. F.
Law Relating to Mobile Homes and Caravans. – 2nd ed. – London : Shaw & Sons, 1985.
Orig. Title : Caravans and the Law.
ISBN 072190811X Pbk £10.50

Gordon, R. J. F.
Judicial review : law and procedure / by R.J.F. Gordon : foreword by the Hon. Mr Justice Mann. – London : Sweet & Maxwell, 1985.
xxxviii,207p; 26cm.
Includes index.
ISBN 0421334908 £19.85

Gordon, Robert →Criminal investigation : a selective literature review and bibliography.

Gordon, William
Scottish land law. – Edinburgh : Green (W.) & Son, 1989.
A fresh treatment of Scottish land law, filling the gap since the last edition of Rankine's 'Landownership' (1909), with particular attention to the very large body of legislation affecting the use of land in the intervening 80 years. The increasing impact of European law, particularly affecting the enviroment, is also noted. With full cross references to Halliday's 'Conveyancing Law and Practice'. Published under the auspices of the Scottish Universities Law Institute.
ISBN 0414008812 Hbk

Gordon, William M. →Introduction to European legal history.

Gore-Browne, Francis
Gore-Browne on companies / general editor A. J. Boyle : consultant editor Richard Sykes. – 44th edition. 2. – Bristol : Jordans, 1986.
looseleaf.
ISBN 0853080828

Gore-Browne on companies / general editor A. J. Boyle : consultant editor Richard Sykes. – 44th edition. 2. – Bristol : Jordans, 1986.
looseleaf.
ISBN 0853080828

Goren, Simon L.
Swiss Federal Code of Obligations : as of January 1, 1984. – Dordrecht : Kluwer, 1987.
318p.
ISBN 9065443231 Hbk £155.00

Gorman, Robertson, C. N., A.
Nelson's Tables : Company Procedure. – 8th ed. – London : Oyez Longman, 1983.
ISBN 0851207154 Hbk £6.95

Gormley, Laurence W.
Prohibiting restrictions on trade within the EEC : the theory and application of Articles 30-36 of the EEC Treaty / by Laurence W. Gormley. – Amsterdam : North-Holland, 1985.
xxv,458p.
Bibliography: p.429-443. - Includes index. At head of title: T.M.C. Asser Instituut - The Hague.
ISBN 0444868488

Gorton, Lars
Practical guide to contracts of affreightment and hybrid contracts / by Lars Gorton and Rolf Ihre. – London : Lloyd's, 1985.
ix,87p; 25cm.
Includes index.
ISBN 1850440603 £45.00
—Shipbroking and chartering practice / by Lars Gorton, Rolf Ihre, Arne Sandevarn. – 2nd ed. – London : Lloyd's of London Press, 1984.
xv,298p; 26cm.
Bibliography: p.247. - Includes index.
ISBN 0907432638
—Shipping and contracting / Lars Gorton. – Lund : Juridiska Foreningen i Lund, 1983.
85p.
Includes bibliographical references and index.
ISBN 9154415012

Gosden, H.
Directory of Personal Financial Services. – London : Macmillan.
ISBN 0333459946 Hbk £95.00

Goslett, Henry M. →Annotated Immigration Act of Canada 1988.

Gosling, P.E.
Sage companion. – Paradigm, 1988.
ISBN 0948825669 Pbk £5.95

Gostin, Larry O →Civil liberties in conflict.
—Court of protection : a legal and policy analysis of the guardianship of the estate / Larry Gostin : foreword by Peter Jefferys. – London : Mind, National Association for Mental Health, 1983.
60p.
Bibliography: p.48.
ISBN 0900557567
—Mental Health : Tribunal Procedure. – London : Oyez Longman, 1984.
– (Oyez Longman Practice Note Ser.: No. 78).
ISBN 0851208444 Hbk
—Mental Health Act, 1983 : Summary of Procedural Requirements in Respect of Compulsory Admission to Hospital and Guardianship, Pt. II. – London : Shaw & Sons, 1983.
ISBN 0721901964 Hbk £0.80
—Mental Health Services : Law and Practice. – London : Shaw & Sons, 1986.
ISBN 0721901972 updat £85.30
—Mental Health Services - Law and Practice. – London : Shaw & Sons, 1986.
912p.
ISBN 0721901972 Hbk £85.00
—Mental Health-Tribunal Procedure. – London : Longman Professional, 1984.
ISBN 0851208444 Pbk £14.95
—Practical guide to mental health law : the Mental Health Act 1983 and related legislation / Larry Gostin : foreword by Lady Bingley : edited by Janet Manning. – Rev ed. – London : MIND, 1983.
xvi,102p; 21cm.
Bibliography: p77-78.
ISBN 0900557591 Pbk
—Secure provision. – Tavistock, 1985.
ISBN 0422784303 Pbk £7.95
—Secure Provision for Mental Patients. – London : Sweet & Maxwell, 1985.
ISBN 0422784206 Hbk £16.95
ISBN 0422784303 Pbk £7.95

Gottfredson, Michael R.
Victims of crime : the dimensions of risk / by Michael R. Gottfredson. – London : H.M.S.O., 1984.
iv,54p; 25cm.
Results of a survey of groups most at risk from crime in England and Wales. Examines lifestyles related to high risks of crime. Provides information for planners of crime-prevention policy.
ISBN 0113407750

Gottselig, Cheryl
Probate Guide for Alberta : a Step-by-Step Guide to Probating an Estate. – 2nd ed. – North Vancouver : International Self-Counsel Press, 1983.
76p.
ISBN 088908226X Hbk £10.95
—Wills for Alberta : How to Make Your Own Will. – 6th ed. – North Vancouver : International Self-Counsel Press, 1985.
108p.
ISBN 0889082294 Hbk £6.50

Goudy, H.
Law of Bankruptcy. – 2nd ed. Repr. of 1895 ed. – Abingdon : Professional Books.
Hbk £35.00

Gouin →Lawyers and the Nuclear Debate.

Gouin, Margaret E. →Lawyers and the Nuclear Debate.

Goup →Companies and Taxes in Liechtenstein.

Gour, Hari Singh
Penal Law of India : Being an Analytical, Critical and Expository Commentary on the Indian Penal Code, 4 Vols. – Allahabad : Law Publishers, 1983.
Hbk £45.00

Gouron, Andre
Science du Droit Dans le Midi de la France au Moyen Age. – Northampton : Variorum, 1984.
360p : Illus.. – – (Collected Studies Ser.: 196).
ISBN 0860781445 Hbk £28.00

Governance of police / Laurence Lustgarten. – London : Sweet & Maxwell, 1986.
xv,197p; 23cm. – (Modern legal studies).
Bibliography: p183-190. - Includes index.
ISBN 0421319003 Hbk £17.00
ISBN 0421319100 Pbk £9.95

Governing the Institute : a study, commissioned by the Institute of Chartered Accountants in England and Wales, on the direction, control and regulation of the Institute / R.I. Tricker. – London : The Institute, 1983.
193p; 25cm.
Bibliography: p191-193.
ISBN 0852913427 Pbk

Government and administration of metropolitan areas in Western democracies : a survey of approaches to the administrative problems of major conurbations in Europe and Canade / Alan Norton. – Birmingham : Institute of Local Government Studies, University of Birmingham, 1983.
60 p.
ISBN 070440690X

Government and law : an introduction to the working of the constitution in Britain / by T.C. Hartley and J.A.G. Griffith. – 2nd ed. – London : Weidenfeld and Nicolson, 1981.
xxxii,472p. – (Law in context).
Bibliography: 464-468p.
ISBN 0297779745

Government & Pressure Groups in Britain / Richardson. – Oxford : Oxford University Press, 1987.
ISBN 0198761678 Hbk £30.00

Government and the governed : BBC Reith Lectures 1983 / Douglas Wass. – London : Routledge and Kegan Paul, 1984.
viii,120p.
ISBN 0710203128

Government and urban poverty : inside the policy-making process / Joan Higgins ... et al. – Oxford : Blackwell, 1983.
vi,215p; 22cm.
Bibliography: p202-206. - Includes index.
ISBN 0631129375 Hbk £
ISBN 063113252X Pbk £5.95

Government Assistance for Businesses. – Croydon : Tolley, 1987.
ISBN 0854593209 Hbk £13.95

Government Assistance for Canadian Business. – Toronto : DeBoo.
This reference work, intended for business owners and financial advisors seeking financial assistance from the Federal and Provincial governments, sets out the eligibility requirements for all Canadian jurisdictions. Subscribers receive a complimentary newsletter and six updates annually.
ISBN 0888201451 Llf £245.00

Government Budgeting in Developing Countries. – Routledge.
– (International Accounting Series).
ISBN 0415004314 Hbk £30.00

Government by Consent : The Principle and Practice of Accountability in Local Government. – London : Bedford Square Press, 1985.
ISBN 0719911400 Hbk £2.95

Government Contracts : Law and Procedure. – Delhi : Eastern Book Corporation, 1984.
xxxv, 532p.
ISBN 8185077010 Hbk £70.00

Government directions to statutory bodies : nineteenth report / Public and Administrative Law Reform Committee. – Wellington : The Committee, 1986.
28p.

Government Financial Assistance Programs in Canada. – 4th ed. – Toronto : Butterworths, 1986.
800p.
ISBN 0409803170 Pbk £31.95

Government gazette index : an index to the Government gazette of the Republic of South Africa. – Pretoria : State Library, 1979 -.
Indexes Gazette no. 6263 onwards.
ISBN 03796078

Government Grants : An NCVO Practical Guide. – 4th ed. – London : Bedford Square Press, 1987.
ISBN 0719912008 Hbk £3.50

Government notices. – Zomba : Government Printer, 1964.
Supplement to: Malawi gazette.

Government of England. – Repr. of 1904 ed. – Abingdon : Professional Books.
220p.
Hbk £25.00

Government Procurement and Judicial Review. – Agincourt : Carswell, 1988.
375p.
Hbk £59.00

Government Regulation for Financial Management of Private Corporate Sector in India. – Bombay : Tripathi, 1987.
330p.
£120.00

Government Regulation of Industry : Proceedings of the Conference held at the University of Newcastle Feb 1981. – Newcastle : University of Newcastle, 1981.
x, 454p.
ISBN 0725904054 Hbk £15.00

Government reply to the first report from the Home Affairs Committee, session 1983-84 HC 252, Remands in custody / presented to Parliament by the Secretary of State for the Home Department. – London : H.M.S.O., 1984.
5p.
ISBN 0101932200

Government reply to the fourth report from the Home Affairs Committee, session 1980-1981 HC 412 : the prison service / presented to Parliament by the Secretary of State for the Home Department. – London : H.M.S.O., 1981.
20p.
ISBN 0101844603

Government reply to the fourth report from the Home Affairs Committee, session 1981-82 HC 98-1 : police complaints procedures / presented to Parliament by the Secretary of State for the Home Department. – London : H.M.S.O., 1982.
19p.
ISBN 0101868103

Government reply to the Sixth report from the Home Affairs Committee, session 1981-82, HC421 : miscarriages of justice. – London : H.M.S.O., 1983.
6p; 25cm.
ISBN 0101885601 unbound £1.30

Government reply to the sixth report from the Home Affairs Committee, session 1984-85 HC277 : Immigration and Nationality Department of the Home Office / presented to Parliament by the Secretary of State for the Home Department. – London : H.M.S.O., 1985.
7p.
ISBN 0101963203

Government reply to the third report from the Home Affairs Committee, session 1986-87 HC 35-1 : sate and the use of prisons / presented to Parliament by the Secretary of State for the Home Department by Command of Her Majesty, December 1987. – London : HMSO, 1987.
10p.
ISBN 0101026323

Government response to the report of the Royal Commission on Legal Services / presented to Parliament by the Lord High Chancellor... – London : H.M.S.O., 1983.
34p.
ISBN 0101907702 Pbk £3.75

Government statistics : a brief guide to sources / Government Statistical Service. – 1983 ed. – London : Press and Information Service, Central Statistical Office, 1983.
20p.

Government views on the report of the Advisory Committee on the Implementation of the Federal Government White Paper of Area Courts Reform / Borno State of Nigeria. – Maiduguri : Government Printer, 1987.
21p.

Governmental Accounting & Auditing : International Comparisons / Jones. – Routledge. – (International Accounting Series).
ISBN 0415012686 Hbk £30.00

Governments and multinationals : policies in the developed countries / A. E. Safarian. – London : British North American Research Organisation, 1983.
x,118p.
Bibliography: p105-110.
ISBN 089068071X

Government's reply to the third report from the Home Affairs Committee, session 1980-1981 HC271, Vagrancy offences / presented to Parliament by the Secretary of State for the Home Department. – London : H.M.S.O., 1981.
3p; 25cm.
ISBN 0101831102 unbound £0.70

Gower, L. C. B. → Auckland Law School centenary lectures.
—Principles of Modern Company Law
2nd Cumulative Supplement to 4th ed. – Stevens & Sons.
ISBN 0420477705 Pbk £5.95
—Review of investor protection : a discussion document / by L.C.B. Gower. – London : H.M.S.O., 1982.
iii,142p.
'Commissioned by the Secretary of State for Trade' - introd.
ISBN 0115135405
—Review of investor protection : report
Part 2 / L. C. B. Gower. – London : H.M.S.O., 1985.
vii,64p.
Part 1 published as Command Paper 9125 in Parliamentary Papers 1983-84.
ISBN 0115138234
—Review of investor protection : report : part 1 / by L.C.B. Gower : presented to Parliament by the Secretary of State for Trade and Industry ... – London : H.M.S.O., 1984.
x,212p.
Includes bibliographical references.
ISBN 0101912501

Gower's Principles of Modern Company Law. – London : Sweet & Maxwell.
ISBN 0420460608 Hbk £2.00

Gowland, D. H.
Modern Economic Analysis 2. – London : Butterworths, 1982.
The objective of this book is to provide an analysis of the economic policy of monetarism. The economics of industrial relations, health, housing, as well as, theories of the firm and central government intervention are discussed.
ISBN 0408107715 Pbk

Goyal, K.N.
Administrative Tribunals Act, 1985. – Lucknow : Eastern Book Company, 1986.
932p.
Hbk £130.00
—Commentaries on Administrative Tribunals Act, 1986. – Lucknow : Eastern Book Company, 1987.
Hbk £165.00

Goybet, Catherine
Second Convention of Lome : EEC aid to the ACP countries (1981-1985) / by Catherine Goybet : with the collaboration of Jane Morrison. – Brussels : Bureau d'Informations Europeennes, 1982.
317 leaves.

Goyder, D. G
EEC competition law / D.G. Goyder. – Oxford : Clarendon Press, 1988.
xxxi,447p.
Account of the substantive law, and an assessment of the historical development and overall effectiveness of the competition policy. Suggests ways of improving co-ordination and implementation of competition policy. Examines the foundations of the last thirty years, and how they can be built upon.
ISBN 0198254032 Pbk £18.95
ISBN 0198255357 Hbk £45

Goyder, Jane → Environmental groups in politics.

Goyle, L.C.
Supreme Court Guide to Words and Phrases. – Calcutta : Eastern Law House, 1986.
Hbk £48.00

Grabar, V E
History of international law in Russia 1647-1917 / Translated by W. E. Butler. – Oxford : Clarendon Press, 1988.
600.
An account of the develoment of the study of international law and the revolution of 1917. A guide to the Russian literature on the law of nations in a contemporary context. The translator's introduction and bibliography are new, and place the work in its historical context.
ISBN 0198254954 Hbk £40

Grabosky, Peter
Of manners gentle : enforcement strategies of Australian business regulatory agencies / Peter Grabosky, John Braithwaite. – Melbourne : Oxford University Press, 1986.
viii,260p.
Includes index.
ISBN 0195546911

Gracie, N.C.
Index and Noter-up to the South African Law Report 1980-1987. – Durban : Professional Publisher, 1988.
ISBN 0409016713 Pbk £68.00
—Index and Noter-up to the South African Law Reports : 1980-1984. – Durban : Butterworths, 1985.
ISBN 0409016675

Graduate Institute of International Studies, Geneva → International regulation of data services: the debate over the trade and development issues.
→ League of Nations in retrospect : proceedings of the symposium.
→ Right of innocent passage and the evolution of the international law of the sea.
→ State responsibility and the direct broadcast satellite.

Grady
British Banking 1960-85 / Weale. – London : Macmillan, 1986.
ISBN 0333375084 Hbk £29.50

Graeff, J. J. de → Law and practice relating to pollution control in the Netherlands.

Graham
Waiving the Rules : The Constitution Under Thatcherism / Tony Prosser. – Open University Press.
ISBN 0355155804 Hbk £25.00

Graham, John
Schools, disruptive behaviour and delinquency : a review of research / by John Graham. – London : H.M.S.O., 1988.
v,69p.
Reviews research on effects of schooling on young people. Concludes that schools can by promoting pro-social and stable patterns of behaviour, help protect children from embarking on criminal careers.
ISBN 0113408870

Graham, John F.
Canadian Insurance Law Review. – Agincourt : Carswell, 1988.
360p.
Hbk £69.50

Graham, Ronald-
Aluminium industry and the Third World : multinational corporations and underdevelopment / Ronald Graham. – London : Zed, 1982.
xii,278p; 22cm.
Bibliography: p263-270. - Includes index.
ISBN 0862320577 Pbk

Graham, Stella Efua → Female circumcision, excision and infibulation : the facts and proposals for change.

Graham, Tony
Precedents in practice / by Tony Graham : illustrated by George Haddon : with a foreword by H. G. Ogden. – Sydney : Law Book Co., 1983.
xiii,263p.
Includes index.
ISBN 0455204926
—Victorian pleading precedents / by Tony Graham : with a foreword by Norman M. O'Bryan. – Sydney : Law Book Co., 1982.
xii,333p.
Includes index.
ISBN 0455203628

Graham, William C. → International business transactions and economic relations : cases, notes and materials on the law as it applies to Canada.
→ New dimensions in international trade law : a Canadian perspective.

Grahl-Madsen, Atle
Status of refugees in international law / Foreword by Felix Schnyder. – Leyden : A. W. Sijthoff, 1966.
v.; 25 cm.
Bibliography: 1, p. 441-458. Contents: 1. Refugee character.

Grain contracts and arbitration for shipments from the United States and Canada / by Albert Slabotzky. – London : Lloyd's, 1984.
x,109p.
Bibliography: p.105-106. - Includes index.
ISBN 0907432883 Hbk £24.00

Grainger, L.
Coal utilisation : technology, economics and policy / L. Grainger and J. Gibson. – London : Graham & Trotman, 1981.
xxii,503p; 25cm.
Bibliography: p489-496. - Includes index.
ISBN 0860102661 £18.00

Gram, Per
Chartering documents / by Per Gram. – London : Lloyd's of London Press, 1981.
xiii,177p.
Includes index.
ISBN 0907432034

Grampian Police
Scottish Criminal Law : Police Duties and Procedure. – Grampian Police. – Aberdeen : Aberdeen University Press.
1590p.
ISBN 0900015454 Hbk

Granados, Eric
Advertising by solicitors : a guide / Eric Granados. – London : Stewart (Henry), 1984.
107p.
ISBN 0946700109 Pbk £12.50

Granger, C.
Trading in commodities. – 4th ed. – Cambridge : Woodhead-Faulkner, 1983.
ISBN 0859411788 Pbk £10.95
ISBN 0859411796 Hbk £19.95

Granger, Christopher
Canadian coroner law : a legal study of coroner and medical examiner systems in Canada / by Christopher Granger. – Toronto, Canada : Carswell, 1984.
xxi, 418 p.; 24 cm.
Includes bibliographical references and indexes.
ISBN 045936460X

Grant → Law of Intellectual Property in New Zealand.
—Legal Education 2000 / Jagtenberg. – Aldershot : Avebury.
ISBN 0566054728 Hbk £27.50

Grant, Brian
Family law / Grant and Levin. – 4th ed. – London : Sweet & Maxwell, 1982.
xxi,146p; 23cm.
Previous ed.: 1977. Includes index.
ISBN 0421302402 Hbk £9.75
ISBN 0421282800 Pbk £5.50

Grant, George
English-Speaking Justice. – Toronto : Anansi Press, 1985.
64p.
ISBN 0887841414 Pbk £5.95

Grant, Kenneth A. → Practical Guide to Law Office Automation : 1988.

Grant, Lawrence
Immigration law and practice / Lawrence Grant, Ian Martin. – London : The Cobden Trust, 1982.
xxxii,410p; 22cm.
Includes index.
ISBN 0900137193 Pbk
ISBN 0900137815

Grant, Malcolm
Planning law handbook / by Malcolm Grant. – London : Sweet & Maxwell, 1981.
xxx,488p; 25cm.
ISBN 0421285702 Pbk £12.50
—Rate capping and the law. – 2nd ed. – London : Sweet & Maxwell, 1986.
ISBN 0902052063 Pbk £9.25
—Urban planning law
Supplement. – 2nd ed. – London : Sweet & Maxwell, 1986.
ISBN 0421395605 Hbk £18.95

Grants From Europe. – 4th ed. – London : Bedford Square Press, 1987.
ISBN 0719912075 Hbk £5.25

Grasing
Achieving Quality in Financial Service Organizations How to Identify and Satisfy Customer Expectations / Hessick. – Quorum Press.
ISBN 0899302319 Hbk £32.95

Gratian and the Schools of Law : 1140-1234. – Northampton : Variorum, 1983.
396p. – (Collected Studies Ser.: CS 185).
ISBN 086078133X Hbk £30.00

Gratuity : Law and Practice. – 4th ed. – Karachi : Bureau of Labour Publications, 1987.
Pbk £2.40

Gratuity Law in India. – Suppl. – Bombay : Tripathi, 1973.
Hbk £8.00

Gravell, Nigel →Sweet & Maxwell's property statutes.

Graves, A.
Concise Criminal Law / D. Pickover. – London : Police Review Publishing, 1984.
ISBN 0851640095 Pbk

Graveson
Status in the Common Law 1953. – London : Wildy & Sons.
Hbk £12.50

Graveson, Ronald Harry
Origins of the conflict of laws / Ronald Graveson. – Tubingen : Mohr, 1981.
p.93-107; 23cm.
Reprinted from: Festschrift fur Konrad Zweigert zum 70. Geburtstag/herausgegeben von Herbert Bernstein, Ulrich Drobnig, Hein Kotz. - Tubingen: Mohr, 1981.

Gray
Ins and outs of immigration and nationality law / Lowe. – London : CENT, 1983.
ISBN 0906072050 Pbk £4.95
—International accounting and transnational decisions. – London : Butterworths, 1983.
ISBN 040810841X Pbk £23.60
—International group accounting / Coenenberg. – Oxford : Croom Helm, 1988.
ISBN 0709938772 Hbk £35.00

Gray, Andrew
Administrative politics in British government / Andrew Gray and William I. Jenkins. – Brighton : Wheatsheaf, 1985.
x,259p; 23cm.
Bibliography: p235-250. - Includes index.
ISBN 0710801432 Hbk £18.95
ISBN 0312004613 £6.95
—Amerindians of South America / by Andrew Gray. – London : Minority Rights Group, 1987.
26p. – (Report).
Includes bibliographical references.
ISBN 0946690529

Gray, Christine D.
Judicial remedies in international law / Christine D. Gray. – Oxford : Clarendon Press, 1987.
300p; 24cm. – (Oxford monographs in international law).
Includes bibliography and index.
ISBN 0198255713 £30.00

Gray, Enid, et al
Social Work (Scotland) Act / Rosemary Gray. – 2nd. – Edinburgh : Green (W.) & Son, 1984.
Full text of the Act as amended and in force, along with prospective amendments as at 25 May 1984. Also with an appendix tabulating legislation, as amended and prospectively amended to the same date, relating to elderly and handicapped persons, welfare rights, children and young persons, mentally ill people and adult offenders.
ISBN 0414007417 Pbk

Gray, J.
Taxation on divorce and separation / J. Gray. – Bicester : CCH Editions, 1987.
xi,103p; 23cm.
Includes index.
ISBN 0863251072 Pbk

Gray, James
Talk to My Lawyer : Great Stories of Southern Alberta's Bar and Bench. – Edmonton : Hurtig.
224p.
ISBN 0888303254 Hbk £24.95

Gray, Jeremy →Police and people in London, vol.4 : The police in action : David J. Smith, Jeremy Gray.

Gray, Kevin J.
Elements of land law / Kevin Gray. – London : Butterworths, 1987.
lxxi,1094p; 25cm.
Includes index.
ISBN 0406501602 Hbk £38.00
ISBN 0406501610 Pbk £23.95
—Property, divorce and retirement pension rights / by K.J. Gray : by C.C. Turpin. – Deventer : Kluwer, 1986.
vii,269p.
Includes bibliographical references.
ISBN 9065442510
—Real property and real people : principles of land law / K.J. Gray, P.D. Symes. – London : Butterworths, 1981.
xxxi,655p; 26cm.
Includes index.
ISBN 0406591105 Hbk
ISBN 0406591113 Pbk
→ Social welfare law.

Gray, Peter L. →Criminal court in action.

Gray, Rosemary →Social Work (Scotland) Act.

Gray, S. J.
Information disclosure and the multinational corporation / S.J. Gray with L.B. McSweeney, J.C. Shaw. – Chichester : Wiley, 1984.
xi,236p; 24cm. – (Wiley/IRM series on multinationals).
Includes index.
ISBN 0471904244 Hbk
—International Accounting and Transnational Decisions. – London : Butterworths, 1983.
This book explores the financial and managerial aspects of international accounting. Among the topics covered are: comparative international accounting, international accounting standards, selected transnational financial reporting issues, and transnational financial decision making and control.
ISBN 040810841X Pbk

Gray, T.
Futures and Options for Shipping. – London, 1987.
ISBN 1850441367 Lloyd's of London Press £28.00

Grayson →Royal Baccarat Scandal.

Grayson, Edward →Sponsorship of sport, arts, and leisure : law, tax and business relationships.
—Sport and the law / by Edward Grayson : with forewords by Lord Havers, Denis Howell. – London : Butterworths, 1988.
xviii,376p; 22cm.
Includes index.
ISBN 0406253005 Pbk £16.95

Graziono, Edward F.
Corporate social responsibility in Papua New Guinea / Law Reform Commission of Papua New Guinea. – Waigani : The Commission, 1981.
ii,17p. – (Occasional paper).
'This paper was researched and written for the Commission by Edward F. Graziono'.

Grbich, Yuri
Institutional Renewal in the Australia Tax Systems. – Clayton : Monash University Press, 1985.
ISBN 0867462752 Hbk £9.50
—Winding Up Trusts. – North Ryde : C.C.H. Australia, 1984.
225p.
ISBN 0869034677 Hbk £50.00

Great Britain
Guide to safety at sports grounds. – London : H.M.S.O., 1986.
75p.
First published 1973.
ISBN 0113408404
→ Law relating to firearms.
→ Succession (Scotland) Act 1964.

Great Britain. Companies Legislation Divsion → Harmonisation of company and related law in the European Community : timetable and progress of draft directives and other proposals.

Great Britain, India Office
Constitutional and National Development in India : Montagu-Chelmsford Report. – Great Britain, India Office. – New Delhi : Ess Ess Publications, 1981.
xix, viii, 243p.
Hbk £110.00

Great Britain Inspectorate of Prisons
HM Prison Brixton : Report. – Great Britain Inspectorate of Prisons. – London : Home Office, 1982.
ii, 32p.
ISBN 0862520614 Hbk £1.10

Great debate : New Zealand, Britain and the EEC : the shaping of attitudes / Robert ,McLuskie. – Wellington : Decision Research Centre, Victoria University of Wellington, 1986.
iv,175p.
Includes bibliographical references and index.
ISBN 0908772009

Great legal fiascos / Stephen Tumim. – London : Barker (Arthur), 1985.
126p.
ISBN 0213169274

Greater Carajas Program : legislation and norms / Presidency of the Republic of Brazil, Secretariat of Planning. – Brailia : The Secretariat, 1984.
55p. – (Publications no 5/84).

Greater Manchester →Meeting legal needs? : an evaluation of a scheme for personal injury victims.

Greaves
Criminal Law-Offences Against Person / D Pickover. – London : Police Review, 1987.
ISBN 085164029X Pbk £5.60
—Police and Criminal Evidence Act 1984 : Guide / D Pickover. – Police Review, 1986.
ISBN 0851640214 Pbk £4.95
→ Working Abroad : You and Tax.

Grebing, Gerhardt
Fine in comparative law / by Gerhardt Grebing. – Cambridge : University of Cambridge, Institute of Criminology, 1982.
xvi,279p. – (Institute of Criminology occasional papers).
Includes bibliographical references. Translation of: 'Die Geldstrafe im deutschen und auslandischen Recht', Part II 'Die Geldstrafe in rechtsvergleichender Darstellung' / edited by Hans-Heinrich Jescheck and Gerhardt Grebing.

Gredley, Ellen
MARC : an introduction / Ellen Gredley. – London : Polytechnic of North London, School of Librarianship and Information Studies, 1983.
47p. – (Occasional publication).
Bibliography: p.45. - Includes index.
ISBN 0900639245

Greek case before the Commission of Human Rights of the Council of Europe. – Athens : R. Ministry of Foreign Affairs, 1970.
v.; 27 cm.
Contents: 1. The report of the Commission of Human Rights: unfounded conclusions based on an illegal procedure.

Greek Charters of Serbian Rulers / V. Mosin. – Repr. of 1936 ed. – Northampton : Variorum.
696p.
ISBN 090208965X Hbk £20.00

Greek Code of Private Maritime Law / Theodoros B. Karatzas and Nigel P. Ready. – The Hague : Nijhoff, 1982.
viii,98p; 25cm.
Includes index.
ISBN 9024725860 Hbk £75.00/$32.50

Green →Principles of Income Taxation.

Green and Henderson: land law / N. Henderson, E. Swinfen Green. – 5th ed. – London : Sweet & Maxwell, 1988.
xvi,217p. – (Concise college texts).
Previous ed.: published as Land law. 1980. Includes index.
ISBN 0421384409 £9.95

Green and pleasant land? : social change in rural England / Howard Newby : cartoons by Thelwell. – Updated ed. – London : Wildwood House, 1985.
324 p.
ISBN 0704505053

Green, B.D.
Reservoirs Act 1975 : A Legal Commentary. – Property Lawyer.
ISBN 00951354701 Pbk £5.75

Green Bans : The Birth of Australian Environmental Politics. – Neutral Bay : Hale & Iremonger.
ISBN 090809423X Hbk £17.95, 015

Green, D.
Splitting Up : Legal & Financial Guide Separation & Divorce. – London : Kogan Page.
ISBN 1850917663 Hbk £5.95

Green, E. Swinfen →Green and Henderson: land law.
—Green and Henderson: land law / N. Henderson, E. Swinfen Green. – 5th ed. – London : Sweet & Maxwell, 1988.
xvi,217p. – (Concise college texts).
Previous ed.: published as Land law. 1980. Includes index.
ISBN 0421384409 £9.95

Green, Jeffrey →Practical commercial precedents.

Green, L. C.
International law : a Canadian perspective / by L.C. Green. – 2nd ed. – Toronto : Carswell Company, 1988.
vii,409p.
'Textbook edition of Title 81 of The Canadian Encyclopedic Digest (Ontario) third edition' - t.p.. Includes index.
ISBN 0459319817

Green, Leslie
Authority of the state / Leslie Green. – Oxford : Clarendon Press, 1988.
x,273p.
: Revision of thesis (D. Phil.)–University of Oxford, 1984. Includes bibliographic references and index.
ISBN 0198249268

Green, Leslie Claude
Law of Nations and the New World. – Edmonton : University of Alberta Press, 1988.
ISBN 088864129X Hbk

Green, N.
International law : law of peace. – 3rd ed. – London : Pitman Publishing, 1987.
ISBN 0273027328 Pbk £25.00

Green, Nathan →Report of the Commission to Review the Police Act & Regulations.

Green, Nicholas
Commercial agreements and competition law : practice and procedure in the UK and EEC / Nicholas Green. – London : Graham & Trotman, 1986.
lxxviii,763p.
Bibliography: p.lxix-lxx - Includes index.
ISBN 0860107884

Green, P. G.
Financial Management for Law Firms / M. W. Zwicker. – Vancouver : British Columbia Continuing Legal Education Society, 1982.
82p.
ISBN 0865040451 Hbk £6.50

Green paper on copyright and the challenge of technology : copyright issues requiring immediate action / communication from the Commission. – Luxembourg : Office for Official Publication of the European Communities, 1988.
vi,237p. – (Document).
ISBN 9277367822

Green, T.A.
Verdict According to Conscience : Perspectives on the English Criminal Trial Jury 1200-1800. – University of Chicago Press.
ISBN 0226306097 Pbk £13.50

Green, W.S.
Traditions of Joashua Ben Hananiah, Part 1 : the Early Legal Traditions. – Leiden : E.J. Brill, 1981.
ISBN 9004063196 Hbk £110.00

Greene, J. H.
Law and practice of receivership in Scotland / J.H. Greene, I.M. Fletcher. – London : Butterworths, 1987.
xxxviii,355p; 26cm.
Includes index.
ISBN 0406005273 £27.50

Greenfield, Roy R. →Dymond's capital transfer tax, Vol.2 : Statutes, etc.

Greenhalgh, Geoffrey
Future of nuclear power. – London : Graham & Trotman, 1988.
ix,213p.
ISBN 0860109879

Greenhill, R.
Profit-sharing and share incentive. – London : Fitzwilliam, 1988.
ISBN 187055504X Hbk £25.00

Greenleaf, G.W., et al
Australasian Computerised Legal Information Handbook. – Butterworths, 1988.
446p.
ISBN 0409494453 Pbk £39.00

—Australasian Legal Information Retrieval Handbook / A. Mowbray. – Sydney : Butterworths, 1988.
208p.
This guide to legal databases includes descriptions of CLIRS, SCALE, LEXIS, MAYNELAW, AUSINET, ESTOPEL, and others. Also contained is an introduction of the principles of computerized legal information retrieval, a set of tutorials for the main retrieval systems, and a directory of all databases containing Australian, New Zealand, and common law.
Pbk £29.50

Greens weekly digest : current Scottish case law. – Edinburgh : W. Green, 1986.
looseleaf.

Greenslade, Richard
Matrimonial Advocacy and Litigation. – London : Butterworths, 1987.
Pbk

—Matrimonial Advocacy and Litigation. – London : Butterworths, 1988.
ISBN 0406103305 Pbk £19.95

—On costs. – Service to Lawyers, 1986.
ISBN 0950417661 updat £69.50

Greenspan : in Defence of / George Jonas. – Toronto : Macmillan of Canada, 1987.
384p.
ISBN 077159495X Hbk £26.95

Greenspan, Edward L. →Canadian Charter of Rights Annotated.

—Canadian Criminal Cases : Index, Annotations, Table of Cases
Vols. 1-26. – Aurora : Canada Law Book Co, 1985.
– (Third Ser.).

—Canadian Criminal Cases : New Series (1963-1970), 30 Vols. – North Ryde : Law Book Co.
Hbk £1,080.00

—Canadian Criminal Cases : Second Series (1971-1983), 70 Vols. – North Ryde : Law Book Co.
Hbk £2,520.00 set

—Canadian Criminal Cases (C.C.C.) 1898-1962, 133 Vols. – Aurora : Canada Law Book Co. – (Old Ser.).
Hbk £3857.00

—Canadian Criminal Cases (C.C.C.) 1963-70, 30 Vols. – Aurora : Canada Law Book Co. – (New Ser.).
Hbk £930.00

—Canadian Criminal Cases (C.C.C.) 1971-83, 70 Vols. – Aurora : Canada Law Book Co. – (Second Ser.).
Hbk £2380.00

—Canadian Criminal Cases (C.C.C.) March 1983-Present. – Aurora : Canada Law Book Co. – (Third Ser.).
Hbk £83.00

—Canadian Criminal Cases Third Series (March 1983-Present). – Aurora : Canada Law Book Co. – (Law Reports).
Hbk £78.00

—Greenspan : in Defence of / George Jonas. – Toronto : Macmillan of Canada, 1987.
384p.
ISBN 077159495X Hbk £26.95

—Martin's Annual Criminal Code. – Aurora : Canada Law Book.
Hbk £21.00

→ Martin's related criminal statutes 1987 : a selection of important statutes and regulations related to the practice of criminal law.

→ Martin's related statutes 1983 : a selection of important statutes and regulations related to the practice of criminal law.

→ Perspectives in Criminal Law : Essays in Honour of John LL.J. Edwards.

Greenstreet, B.
Legal and Contract Procedure for Architects. – 2nd ed. – London : Architectural Press, 1984.
ISBN 0851393691 Pbk £9.95

—Legal and Contractual Procedures for Architects. – 3rd ed. – London : Butterworths.
ISBN 0406004770 Pbk

Greenwich Forum IX : Britain and the sea : future dependence - future opportunities : conference papers delivered 14-16 September, 1983 / conference organizers: A.J. Smith, Lady Elizabeth Kennet, M.B.F. Ranken : editor of proceedings Commander M.B.F. Ranken. – Edinburgh : Scottish Academic Press, 1984.
xxiii,364p; 25cm.
Conference papers.
ISBN 0707303532 Hbk £
ISBN 0707304423 Pbk

Greenwich Health Authority →Child in mind : protection of children in a responsible society : the report of the Commission of Inquiry into the Circumstances Surrounding the Death of Kimberley Carlile.

Greenwood, Walter
McNae's Essential Law for Journalists / Welsh. – 10th ed. – London : Butterworths.
ISBN 0406772827 Pbk £9.50

—McNae's Essential Law for Journalists. – 9th ed. – London : Butterworths, 1985.
This book for working journalists offers information on the ways in which the law effects their professional activities. The work discusses the changes brought about by the Contempt of Court Act of 1981 and recent case in defamation.
ISBN 0406772819 Pbk £17.75

Greer, Desmond S.
Administration of Justice Act 1982 and the Assessment of Damages. – Belfast : Queen's University of Belfast, 1983.
28p.
Pbk £3.25

—Administration of Justice Act 1982 and the assessment of damages for personal injuries in Northern Ireland : the text of a lecture delivered to the Belfast Solicitors' Association on 24 February 1983 / by D.S. Greer. – Belfast : SLS Legal Publications, 1983.
ii,28p.
Includes bibliographical references.

—Compensation for criminal damage to property / by D.S. Greer and V.A. Mitchell. – Belfast : SLS Legal Publications (N.I.), 1982.
xxxviii,345p.
Includes index.

—Compensation for criminal injuries / V A Mitchell. – Sweet & Maxwell, 1988.
ISBN 0421385804 Pbk

—Negligence and Damages for Personal Injuries : Some Recent Developments. – Belfast : Queen's University of Belfast, 1981.
34p.
Pbk £3.25

—Professional negligence today : the text of two lectures delivered to the Belfast Solicitors' Association on 9 and 23 May 1985 / by D.S. Greer and Ethne E. Harkness. – Belfast : SLS Legal Publications, 1985.
61p.
Includes bibiographical references.

—Small claims in Northern Ireland : a step-by-step guide / by D.S. Greer. – 3rd ed. – Belfast : SLS Publications, 1987.
63p. – (The law in action).

Greer, S. C.
Abolishing the Diplock courts : the case for restoring jury trial to scheduled offences in Northern Ireland / S.C. Greer, A. White. – London : Cobden Trust, 1986.
x,133p; 20cm.
Includes index.
ISBN 0900137274 Pbk £5.95

Gregory →Company Law (Q & A).

—Essential Law for Landowners and Farmers / Parrish. – 2nd ed. – Oxford : Blackwell Scientific, 1987.
ISBN 0003832694 Pbk £9.95

Gregory, Denis
Fighting Closures / Hugo Levie. – London : Spokesman Books, 1984.
ISBN 0851243614 Hbk £15.00
ISBN 0851243622 Pbk £5.95

Gregory, Janet
Survey of defenders in debt actions in Scotland / Janet Gregory and Janet Monk. – London : H.M.S.O., 1981.
ix,109p. – (Research report for the Scottish Law Commission).
Includes index.
ISBN 0116907746

Gregory, R.
Bankruptcy of Individuals and Partnerships. – Bicester : CCH.
ISBN 0863251439 Hbk £48.00
ISBN 086325084X Pbk £36.00

Gregory, R.A.
Scientific Identification of Disputed Documents, Fingerprints and Ballistics. – 3rd ed. 1980 repr. – Lucknow : Eastern Book Company, 1984.
155p.
Hbk £35.00

Gregory, R. C. L., et al
Bail : County Court Practice Nineteen Eighty-Seven. – London : Butterworths, 1986.
ISBN 0406163235 Pbk

—County Court Practice 1986 / D. E. Peck. – London : Butterworths, 1986.
ISBN 0406163227 Hbk

Gregory, Roger
Bankruptcy of Individuals and Partnerships. – London : CCH, 1988.
ISBN 0863251439 Hbk £48.00

—Stamp duties for conveyancers / J T Farrand. – 4th ed. – London : Longman Professional, 1986. – (Longman Practice Note. No.48).
ISBN 0851211739 Pbk £15.95

→ Stamp Duty for Conveyancers.

Greig, D W
International Law. – 3rd ed. – London : Butterworths.
ISBN 0406591849 Hbk
ISBN 0406591857 Pbk

—Law of Contract / Davis. – North Ryde : Law Book Co, 1986.
ISBN 0455206198 Hbk £47.50
ISBN 0455206201 Pbk £34.50

Grenada : a study in politics and the limits of international law / Scott Davidson. – Aldershot : Avebury, 1987.
xii,196p; 22cm.
Bibliography: p184-190. - Includes index.
ISBN 0566050528 £18.50

Grenada consolidated index of statutes and subsidiary legislation to 29th July 1983 / compiled at the Faculty of Law Library, University of the West Indies, Barbados. – Barbados : s.n., 1983.
vi,104p.
One of a series in the West Indian Legislation Indexing Project (WILIP) compiled in cooperation with the British Development Division.

Grenada intervention : analysis and documentation / William C. Gilmore. – London : Mansell, 1984.
116p; 22cm.
Includes index.
ISBN 0720117232 Pbk £5.95

Grendler, Paul
Culture and Censorship in Late Renaissance Italy and France. – Northampton : Variorum, 1981.
318p : Illus.. – – (Collected Studies Ser.: No. 138).
ISBN 0860780848 Hbk £24.00

Grenville, Clive
Bankruptcy : Law and Practice. – London : Fourmat, 1987.
ISBN 1851900322 Hbk £28.50

—Bankruptcy: the law and practice. – London : Fourmat, 1988.
534.
Discusses new insolvency legislation as it applies to bankruptcy.
ISBN 1851900322 Hbk £32.50

Grero, Ananda
Selected Legal Essays. – Colombo : Lake House Investments.
Hbk £6.60

Gres, Joachim
Handbook of German employment law : a practical guide to the legal aspects of employment - from hiring through termination : with a bi-lingual selection of relevant German statutes and sample forms / by Joachim Gres and Harald Jung. – Deventer, The Netherlands : Kluwer, 1983.
305p; 26cm.
ISBN 9065441441 Hbk £90.00

→ Starting business operations in Germany : a practical guide with emphasis on sales agency agreements, limited liability companies, branch operations.

Gresty →Practical food law.

Gretton
Crime UK 1988 / Harrison. – Policy Journals.
ISBN 0946967245 Hbk £24.50

Gretton, George Lidderdale
Law of inhibition and adjudication / George Lidderdale Gretton. – London : Butterworths, 1987.
200p; 22cm.
Includes index.
ISBN 0406104336 Pbk £18

Grewal
General Principles of Business Law (Q & A) / De Freitas. – 2nd ed. – London : Castlevale Publishers, 1984.
ISBN 0907235069 Pbk £6.00

Grey, Antony →Reform of the law of sexual offences.

Grey, Julius H
Immigration Law in Canada. – London : Butterworths.
ISBN 0409834505 Hbk £40.00
—Law and the Legal Profession in Canada. – Toronto : Butterworths, 1987.
250p.
ISBN 0409834343 Hbk £55.00

Grice, R. Geoffrey →Japanese banking, securities and anti-monopoly law.

Grieg, D.W.
Commercial Law / N.A. Cunningham. – 3rd ed. – Butterworths, 1988.
582p.
ISBN 0409492485 Pbk £49.50
ISBN 0409492477 Hbk £65.00

Grier, Ian S
Company administration orders and voluntary arrangements / Richard Floyd. – London : Longman Professional (UK), 1988.
– (Practitioner series).
Guide to the law and procedure relating to administration orders, and voluntary arrangements (resulting from the Insolvency Act 1986). Examines corporate administration orders from beginning to end, comparing them to other insolvency proceedings. Includes specimen proposals.
ISBN 0851214800 Hbk £18.95
—Personal insolvency : a practical guide / Ian S. Grier, Richard E. Floyd. – London : Sweet & Maxwell, 1987.
xxiii,224p; 26cm.
Deals with the law and procedure relating to personal insolvency, through the full range of bankruptcy from the pre-petition stage to the closing procedures. Covers changes introduced by the Insolvency Act 1986, and includes forms of available voluntary arrangements, falling short of bankruptcy, and aspects of criminal bankruptcy.
ISBN 0421360100 £19.50
—Voluntary liquidation and receivership : a practical guide / Ian S. Grier and Richard E. Floyd. – London : Oyez Longman, 1985.
xvii,187p.
Includes index.
ISBN 0851209548

Grievance procedures in prisons : a study of prisoners' applications and petitions / by John Ditchfield and Claire Austin. – London : H.M.S.O., 1986.
vi,71p; 25cm.
Study of prisoners' applications and petitions. Examines the operation of grievance procedures in six prisons for adult male offenders to identify differences in practice between prisons and assess the confidence which inmates and staff have in them.
ISBN 0113408390

Grievances, remedies and the state / by Patrick Birkinshaw. – London : Sweet & Maxwell, 1985.
xix,192p; 23cm.
Includes index.
ISBN 042132600X Hbk £9.25
ISBN 0421326107 Pbk £8.95

Grieves, M. →Information handling and the office of the future : report of a seminar.

Griew, Edward
Theft Acts 1968 and 1978 / by Edward Griew. – 5th ed. – London : Sweet & Maxwell, 1986.
xxxiii,269p; 26cm.
For the first time, this edition covers the following major cases; Ghosh, on dishonesty; Morris, on appropriation; Bloxham, on handling; and Wilson, on alternative verdicts. Includes other decisions on theft, taking a conveyance, obtaining property by deception, and the 1978 Act.
ISBN 0421353007 Hbk £21.00
ISBN 0421353104 Pbk £13.95
—Theft Acts 1968 and 1978 / by Edward Griew. – 4th ed. – London : Sweet & Maxwell, 1982.
xxix,240p; 25cm.
Previous ed.: 1978. Includes index. Includes the texts of The Theft Act 1968 and The Theft Act 1978.
ISBN 0421286407 Hbk £
ISBN 0421286504 Pbk £9.50

Griffin, James
Well-being : its meaning, measurement, and moral importance / James Griffin. – Oxford : Clarendon Press, 1988.
xii,412p.
Bibliography: pp.391- 402. - Includes index.
ISBN 0198249039

Griffith, Ernest Stacey
Modern Development of City Government in the United Kingdom and the United States, 2 Vols. – Repr. of 1927 ed. – Aalen Wuertt : Scientia.
764p : Illus.
Hbk £190.00

Griffith, J. A. G. →Government and law : an introduction to the working of the constitution in Britain.
—Politics of the judiciary / J. A. G. Griffith. – 3rd ed. – London : Fontana, 1985.
255p.
ISBN 0006860206
—Public rights and private interests / J. A. G. Griffith. – Trivandrum : Academy of Legal Publications, 1981.
12196,iv.

Griffith, R. G. De B.
Griffith's Probate law and practice in Victoria / Ross A. Sundberg. – 3rd ed. – Sydney : Law Book Company, 1983.
xxv,338p.
Includes index.
ISBN 0455204942

Griffiths
Company Law (Q & A) / Gregory. – 2nd ed. – London : Financial Training.
ISBN 185185018X Pbk £7.50
→ Corrections in Canada : Policy and Practice.
—Questions and answers on English law. – London : Financial Training, 1983.
ISBN 0906322391 Pbk £5.95

Griffiths, A.
Chronicles of Newgate. – New Edition. – New York : Bracken Books.
ISBN 1851701427 Hbk £6.95

Griffiths, Curt T, et al
Criminal justice in Canada: an introductory text / John F Klein, Simon B Verdun-Jones. – Scarborough, Ontario : Butterworths (Canada).
359.
Overview of the Canadian criminal justice system. Coverage includes corectional institutions, policing in Canada, police powers and discretion, the criminal court system, sentencing, the public and criminal justice system, community-based corrections, juvenile justice system, special categories of offenders, and trends in Canadian criminal justice.
ISBN 0409998022 Pbk

Griffiths, David →Restraint of trade and business secrets : law and practice.

Griffiths, Lionel
Legal Aspects of the Care of the Aged / Godrey Gypps. – London : Law Society, 1985.
– (Oxford Weekend Courses).
Hbk £5.00

Griffith's Probate law and practice in Victoria / Ross A. Sundberg. – 3rd ed. – Sydney : Law Book Company, 1983.
xxv,338p.
Includes index.
ISBN 0455204942

Griffiths, William Hugh Griffiths
Developments in the law of product liability : being the presidential address of Lord Griffiths, president of the Holdsworth Club of the Faculty of Laws in the Univeristy of Birmingham, 1986-1987. – birmingham : The Holdsworth Club of the University of Birmingham, 1987.
17p. – (The Holdsworth Club).
ISBN 0704409259

Griggs, Patrick
Limitation of liability for maritime claims / by Patrick Griggs and Richard Williams. – London : Lloyd's, 1986.
122p; 22cm.
ISBN 1850440832 £24.00

Grime, R.
Marine Insurance Clauses / R. Swatton. – London : LLoyd's of London Press, 1985.
ISBN 1850440581 Hbk

Grime, Robert
Law of Marine Insurance. – Abingdon : Professional Books, 1984.
ISBN 086205091X Hbk £63.00
ISBN 0862050960 Pbk £25.50
—Shipping Law (CCT). – Sweet & Maxwell, 1978.
ISBN 042121130X Pbk £8.00

Grimes, R.
Law and the Elderly. – Oxford : Croom Helm, 1988.
ISBN 0709911629 Hbk
—Law and the Elderly. – Routledge.
ISBN 0415005175 Hbk £25.00

Grimes, Richard H.
Introduction to law in the Republic of Ireland : its history, principles, administration & substance / Richard H. Grimes and Patrick T. Horgan. – Portmarnock : Wolfhound, 1981.
368p; 22cm.
Bibliography: p348-351. - Includes index.
ISBN 0905473558 Pbk £15.00
ISBN 0905473566 unpriced

Grimwade, N.
International Trade. – Routledge.
ISBN 0415003962 Hbk £40.00
ISBN 0415003970 Pbk £14.95

Grisso, Thomas
Evaluating competencies : forensic assessments and instruments / Thomas Grisso. – New York : Plenum, 1986.
x,404p; 24cm.
Bibliography: p365-383. - Includes index.
ISBN 0306421267
—Juveniles' waiver of rights : legal and psychological competence / Thomas Grisso. – New York : Plenum, 1981.
xiii,295p; 24cm.
Bibliography: p279-286. - Includes index.
ISBN 0306405261

Grogan, Vincent
Sale of goods and supply of services : a guide to the legislation / Vincent Grogan, Thelma King and Edward J. Donelan. – Dublin : Incorporated Law Society of Ireland, 1983.
xxii,133p.
Includes index.
ISBN 0902027239

Gronfors, Kurt
Cargo key receipt and transport document replacement / Kurt Gronfors. – Goteburg : Akademiforlaget, 1982.
104p. – (Skrifter).
ISBN 9124160555

Groot, John de
Solicitors Checklists / Stephen A. Karas. – Butterworths, 1988.
ca 232p.
ISBN 0409494690 Llf £29.00

Groote Eylandt Prisoners : A Research Report. – Canberra : Australian Institute of Criminology.
free

Grosman, Brian A.
Executive Firing Line : Wrongful Dismissal and the Law. – Agincourt : Carswell, 1982.
240p.
Hbk £27.00

Gross, Hyman →Sentencing.

Gross, Leo
Essays on International Law and Organization, 2 Vols. – Dordrecht : Kluwer.
1,230p.
ISBN 9024729106 Hbk £450.00

Grosskurth, Anne
Housing association allocations : Achieving racial equality : a West Midlands case study : summary of a report by Pat Niner in association with Valerie Karn / Anne Grosskurth. – London : Runnymede Trust, 1985.
20p.
ISBN 0902397540

Grossman, L.
Public Sector Prices and Compensation Review Act, 1983, Bill 111 : An Act to Provide for the Review of Prices and Compensation in the Public Sector and for the Elderly Transition to the Resumption of Full Collective Bargaining. – Ontario : Ontario Government Publications Service, 1983.
18p.
Hbk £0.50

Ground for divorce : should the law be changed? / Scottish Law Commission. – Edinburgh : The Commission, 1988.
23p. – (Discussion paper).

Ground, R. W. →Gatley on libel and slander.

Grounds for divorce / Gwynn Davis and Mervyn Murch. – Oxford : Clarendon Press, 1988.
x,177p.
Bibliography: pp.169-171. - Includes index. Examines, through social research, the legal ending of marriage. Reviews the present law and suggests future reforms. The focus is on the relationship between the personal experience of parties and legal foms of divorce. The 'process over time' reform proposal has been adopted by the Law Commission.
ISBN 019825220X Hbk £20

Grounds of liability : an introduction to the philosophy of law / Alan R. White. – Oxford : Clarendon, 1985.
x,128p; 23cm.
Bibliography: p122-126. - Includes index.
ISBN 0198761910 Hbk £15.00
ISBN 019876197X Pbk £6.95

Groundwork of Nigerian Criminal Law. – Lagos : Nigerian Law Publications.
ISBN 1234525501 Hbk £10.00

Group Accounting. – London : Butterworths, 1988.
ISBN 0406500193 Pbk

Groupe de Bellerive →Nuclear war, nuclear proliferation and their consequences : proceedings of the Vth international colloquium organized by the Groupe de Bellerive, Geneva 27-29 June 1985.

Groups of companies : the law and practice in Britain, France and Germany / by Frank Wooldridge. – London : Institute of Advanced Legal Studies, 1981.
xxvi,159p; 21cm.
Includes bibliographical references.
ISBN 0901190268

Grout, T. J.
Public Law. – 1st ed. – Plymouth : Macdonald & Evans, 1984.
260p.
ISBN 0712117598 Pbk £7.50

Grout, Victor
Grout's value added tax cases 1983 / by Victor Grout : with a foreword by Lord Grantchester : consultant Hugh Mainprice. – 2nd ed. – Croydon : Tolley, 1984.
xv,372p.
Includes index.
ISBN 0854591400
—Tolley's tax cases 1988 / by Victor Grout. – 8th ed. – Croydon : Tolley, 1988.
xxvi,516p.
Includes index.
ISBN 0854591508
—Tolley's Value Added Tax Cases : 1983. – 3rd ed. – Croydon : Tolley.
530p.
ISBN 0854592970 Hbk £29.95

Grout's value added tax cases 1983 / by Victor Grout : with a foreword by Lord Grantchester : consultant Hugh Mainprice. – 2nd ed. – Croydon : Tolley, 1984.
xv,372p.
Includes index.
ISBN 0854591400

Groux, Jean
European Communities in the international order / Jean Groux, Philippe Manin. – Luxembourg : Office for Official Publications of the European Communities, 1985.
163p.
At head of title: Commission of the European Communities.
ISBN 9282551377

Groves, Harry → Constitution of Malaysia.

Growing out of crime / Andrew Rutherford. – Harmondsworth : Penguin Books, 1986.
188p.
Bibliography: p176-182.
ISBN 0140223835

Growing Together : European Parliament Resolutions on Inter-Institutional Relations. – European Parliament. – Kirchberg : European Parliament, 1983.
Hbk

Growth of international business / edited by Mark Casson : contributors; authors Peter J. Buckley ... et al. : reviewers and discussants: Charles E. Harvey ... et al. – London : Allen & Unwin, 1983.
xii,276p; 23cm.
Bibliography: p258-272. - Includes index.
ISBN 0043303331 £15.00

Grozdanic, Stanislav → Workers' management in Yugoslavia : recent developments and trends.

Grubb → Medical Law and Ethics.

Grubb, P.
Patents in chemistry and biotechnology. – 2nd ed. – Oxford : Oxford University Press, 1987.
ISBN 0198552211 Pbk £12.50

Grubel, Herbert G.
International monetary system : efficiency and practical alternatives / Herbert G. Grubel. – 4th ed. – Harmondsworth : Penguin, 1984.
214p.
Bibliography: p201-206.
ISBN 0140808183

Gruending, Dennis
Emmett Hall : Establishment Radical. – Toronto : Macmillan of Canada, 1985.
256p.
ISBN 0771596898 Hbk £27.95

Grundy, Milton
Grundy's Tax havens : a world survey. – 5th ed. – London : Sweet & Maxwell, 1987.
xxiv,100p; 22cm.
Previous ed.: 1983. Includes index.
ISBN 0421379006 Pbk £26.00
—World of international tax planning / Milton Grundy. – Cambridge : Cambridge University Press, 1984.
x,143p; 23cm.
Includes index.
ISBN 052125955X £19.50

Grundy's Tax havens : a world survey. – 5th ed. – London : Sweet & Maxwell, 1987.
xxiv,100p; 22cm.
Previous ed.: 1983. Includes index.
ISBN 0421379006 Pbk £26.00

Grunfeld, Cyril
Law of redundancy. – 3rd. – London : Sweet & Maxwell, 1989.
Covers compulsory consultation with recognised unions, dismissal, lay-off and start-time and the offer of new employment, redundancy payments, employers' rebates, guaranteed payments and unfair dismissal for redundancy.
ISBN 0421339004

Gruson, Michael → Legal opinions in international transactions : foreign lawyers' response to US opinion requests.
→ Sovereign lending : managing legal risk.

GT Guide to World Equity Markets 1987. – 2nd ed. – London : Euromoney.
ISBN 1870031903 Hbk £85.00

Guarantees For New Homes / R Rolfe. – 3rd ed. – London : Longman Professional, 1981.
ISBN 0851295437 Pbk £23.00

Guardian Guide to running a Small Business. – London : Kogan Page, 1986.
ISBN 1850910952 Pbk £6.95

Guardian Law reports. – Lodnon : The Guardian, 1987-.

Guardians and Wards Act, 1980 : Bare Act with Commentary. – Delhi.
Hbk £5.00

Guatemala : a government program of political murder. – Amnesty International. – London : Amnesty International, 1981.
32p; 30cm.
Cover title.
ISBN 0862100267 Pbk

Guelff, Richard → Documents on the Laws of War.

Guest, A. G. → Anson's Law of contract.
→ Benjamin's sale of goods.
→ Chitty on contracts.
→ Law of Contract.

Guest, Stephen → Equality and discrimination : essays in freedom and justice : papers presented at the United Kingdom Association for Legal and Social Philosophy eleventh annual conference at University College London, 6th-8th April 1984.

Guha, D.N.
Civil Litigation. – Calcutta : Eastern Law House.
Hbk

Guidance Memorandum for Expert Witnesses and Their Clients. – Telford (Thomas).
ISBN 0727713345 Pbk £2.00

Guidance notes on Finance (Miscellaneous) Taxation Provisions Decree 1985 / by Zubair Alhaji Abdullahi. – Zaria, Nigeria? : the Author, 1986.
i,92p.
Includes index.

Guide Concerning the Rights and Obligations with Regard to Social Security of Persons Going to Work in Ireland. – Luxembourg : Office for Official Publications of the European Communities, 1985.
28p.
ISBN 9282546519 Pbk

Guide Concerning the Rights and Obligations with Regard to Social Security of Persons Going to Work in the Netherlands. – Luxembourg : Office for Official Publications of the European Communities, 1985.
24p.
ISBN 9282546721 Pbk

Guide Concerning the Rights and Obligations with Regard to Social Security of Persons Going to Work in the United Kingdom of Great Britain and Northern Ireland Including Gibraltar. – Luxembourg : Office for Official Publications of the European Communities, 1986.
32p.
ISBN 9282546799 Pbk

Guide Concerning the Rights and Obligations with Regard to Social Security of Persons Going to Work in Luxembourg. – Luxembourg : Office for Official Publications of the European Communities, 1985.
34p.
ISBN 9282546659 Pbk

Guide Concerning the Rights and Obligations with Regard to Social Security of Persons Going to Work in France. – Luxembourg : Office for Official Publications of the European Communities, 1985.
43p.
ISBN 9282546373 Hbk

Guide Concerning the Rights and Obligations with Regard to Social Security of Persons Going to Work in Belgium. – Luxembourg : Office for Official Publications of the European Communities, 1985.
30p.
ISBN 9282546233 Pbk

Guide Concerning the Rights and Obligations with Regard to Social Security of Persons Going to Work in the FR of Germany. – Luxembourg : Office for Official Publications of the European Communities, 1985.
32p.
ISBN 9282546160 Pbk

Guide for Applicants for Patents. – Patent Trade Marks & Designs Office. – Canberra : Australian Government Publishing Service, 1981.
45p.
ISBN 0642060371 Hbk £2.30

Guide for Articled Clerks and Trainee Legal Executives. – London : Sweet & Maxwell, 1984.
ISBN 0421320508 Pbk £5.50

Guide for Commercial Agencies. – Paris : International Chamber of Commerce.
38p.
Hbk £4.50

Guide for Developing Countries on the Examination of Patent Applications. – Geneva : World Intellectual Property Organization, 1982.
62p.
Hbk £15.00

Guide for guardians ad litem in the juvenile court. – London : Department of Health and Social Security, 1984.
61p.

Guide on Drawing up International Contracts for Services Relating to Maintenance, Repair and Operation of Industrial and Other Works. – Geneva : United Nations Publications.
ISBN 9211163846 Hbk £12.00

Guide on Multi-Party Arbitration. – Paris : International Chamber of Commerce.
8p.
Hbk £4.50

Guide on the Industrial Property Activities of Enterprises in Developing Countries. – Geneva : World Intellectual Property Organization, 1983.
31p.
£15.00

Guide to Accounting Pronouncements and Sources. – Toronto : Butterworths.
152p.
ISBN 0409805130 Pbk £21.95

Guide to allowances under the Costs in Criminal Cases (Allowances) Regulations 1977 / Lord Chancellor's Department. – London : Lord Chancellor's Department, 1984.
12,vp.

Guide to amendments to the Trade Practices Act / Trade Practices Commission. – Canberra : Trade Practices Commission, 1986.
13 leaves.

Guide to Appearing Before the Surface Rights Board of Alberta / Barbara Roulston. – 2nd ed. – Calgary : Canadian Institute of Resources Law, 1986.
124p.
ISBN 0919269192 Hbk £17.00

Guide to arbitration : and related services offered by the International Chamber of Commerce. – International Chamber of Commerce. – Paris : ICC, 1983.
139p; 25cm. – (ICC publication).
Replaces ICC publication; no.301.
ISBN 9284210186

Guide to Bankruptcy / P. A. F. De Vos. – revised 1983 ed. – Abingdon : Professional Books, 1984.
ISBN 0903486482 Hbk £19.00
ISBN 090348644X Pbk £12.00

Guide to Building Control by Local Acts 1987. – London : Architectural Press, 1987.
128p : Illus.
ISBN 0851398413 Pbk £19.50

Guide to Building Control in Inner London 1986. – London : Architectural Press, 1987.
ISBN 0851398421 Pbk £19.50

Guide to Building Regulations 1985. – London : Architectural Press, 1986.
ISBN 0851398448 Pbk £16.95

Guide to Canadian Diplomatic Relations 1925-1983. – Ottawa : Canadian Library Association, 1985.
Hbk £12.00

Guide to Commercial Insolvency in Canada. – Butterworths, 1988.
ca 388p.
Takes the reader through the relevant proceedings and applicable legislation, covering the commencement of bankruptcy proceedings, receiverships, liquidation of asset; to directors' responsibilities on insolvency and annulment of transactions.
ISBN 0409846740 Hbk

Guide to Company Borrowings. – New Delhi : Bharat Law House, 1987.
Hbk £220.00

Guide to Company Flotation. – London : Fitzwilliam, 1988.
ISBN 1870555058 Hbk £40.00

Guide to company formation / by Nandlal H. Bhatter and Christopher N. Fernandes : foreword by V.B. Haribhakti. – Bombay : Tripathi, 1984.
viii,121p.

Guide to company law. – 2nd ed. – Bicester : CCH Editions, 1987.
307p; 23cm.
Explains the basic principles, alerts the leader to potential pitfalls, and provides solutions to frequently encountered problems. Case examples help to illustrate the commentary, appendices include the new Table A, and relevant schedules showing the prescribed format for company accounts, case table, legislation finding list, and comprehensive index.
ISBN 0863250955 Pbk

Guide to Company Law. – New Delhi : Bharat Law House, 1986.
Hbk £250.00

Guide to Company Law. – 2nd ed. – London : Butterworths.
ISBN 0409494534 Pbk £22.80

Guide to Company Law. – 2nd ed. – North Ryde : Law Book Co, 1982.
xi, 270p.
ISBN 0455203709 Pbk £15.00

Guide to Company Law. – New Delhi : S. Chand and Company.
Hbk £18.00

Guide to Company Law : Including 1986 Supplement. – 2nd ed. – Butterworths, 1986.
335p.
ISBN 0409491667 Pbk £31.50

Guide to Company Law Procedures, Vol. 1. – 11th ed. – Nagpur : Wadhura & Co, 1988.
Hbk £330.00

Guide to Company Management. – New Delhi : Bharat Law House, 1985.
Hbk £240.00

Guide To Compliance and Penalty Provisions for VAT. – Tolley Publishing.
ISBN 0854592849 Pbk £6.95

Guide to Consumer Protection Act. – Oxford : Croner Publications, 1987.
ISBN 1851850783 Pbk £11.95

Guide to Consumer Protection Law. – Chichester : Barry Rose.
173p.
ISBN 0859921247 Hbk £5.25

Guide to Contracting for the Sale of Goods. – London : Sweet & Maxwell, 1984.
Hbk £9.95

Guide to contracting, negotiation and the law / R.I. Akroyd. – London : Routledge & Kegan Paul, 1987.
256p; 22cm.
Includes bibliography and index.
ISBN 0710204868 £22.50

Guide to Departmental Promotions Enquiries, Punishments and Appeals. – 4th ed. 1983. – Allahabad : Orient Law House, 1983.
Hbk £90.00

Guide to Development and Planning. – 7th ed. – London : Longman Professional, 1981.
ISBN 0851205496 Hbk £37.00

Guide To Directors' Transactions. – Tolley Publishing.
ISBN 0854591184 Pbk £5.95

Guide to DIY House Buying : Supp. Leasehold Flats and Houses. – London : Castle Books, 1985.
ISBN 0950717096 Pbk £3.50

Guide to DIY House Buying, Selling and Conveyancing. – 2nd ed. – London : Castle Books, 1983.
ISBN 0950717053 Pbk £4.95

Guide to EC court decisions / editors, Alfred E. Kellermann ... et al. – Amsterdam : North-Holland Pub. Co., 1982.
At head of title: T.M.C. Asser Institute–The Hague. Includes index.
ISBN 0444864571

Guide to EEC law in Northern Ireland / by Sylvia E. Paisley. – Belfast : SLS Legal Publications (NI), Queen's University, Belfast, 1986.
xxii,247p; 21cm.
Bibliography: p237. - Includes index.
ISBN 0853892628 Pbk

Guide to EEC-legislation / editors, Alfred E. Kellermann...et al. : T.M.C. Asser Institute, The Hague. – 2nd ed. 3 v. – Amsterdam : North-Holland, 1983.
2522p.
Previous ed.: 1979. Includes index. Kept up to date by supplements.
ISBN 0444853200

Guide to Employment Practices. – London : Industrial Society.
– (Managers Ser.).
Hbk £2.50

Guide To Enquiries Before Contract. – London : Longman Professional, 1978.
ISBN 0851203876 Pbk £5.95

Guide to Enquiries of Local Authorities. – 2nd ed. – London : Longman Professional, 1982.
ISBN 085120645X Pbk £5.95

Guide to Environmental Legislation and Administrative Arrangements in Australia. – 2nd ed. – Kingston : Australian Government Publishing Service, 1987.
363p.
Pbk £29.95

Guide to European Community law / by P.S.R.F. Mathijsen. – 4th ed. – London : Sweet & Maxwell, 1985.
xl,284p; 22cm.
Previous ed.: 1980. Includes bibliographies and index. Includes index.
ISBN 0421339306 Pbk £16.50
ISBN 0421339209 Hbk £22

Guide to Export Finance / Mills. – London : Euromoney, 1987.
ISBN 1870031458 Pbk £75.00

Guide to Family Law. – Kensington : Bay Books.
Pbk £3.95

Guide to Family Law (Scotland) Act 1985. – London : CCH, 1986.
ISBN 0863250629 Pbk £9.00

Guide to Financial Futures. – London : Butterworths, 1988.
ISBN 0406200106 Hbk £35.00

Guide to Foreign Exchange Regulation. – new ed. – Nagpur : Wadhura & Co, 1988.
Hbk £160.00

Guide to Foreign Exchange Regulations. – Lucknow : Eastern Book Company, 1981.
336p.
Hbk £45.00

Guide To Foster Care Allowances. – National Fostêr Care Association.
ISBN 0946015597 Hbk £8.25

Guide to franchising / by Martin Mendelsohn. – 4th ed. – Oxford : Pergamon, 1985.
xvii,319p; 24cm.
Previous ed.: 1982. Includes index.
ISBN 0080312829 £25.00

Guide to General Sales Tax. – Cape Town : Legal & Financial Publishing, 1983.
ISBN 0869940333 Hbk £10.50

Guide to government department and other libraries 1988 / edited by R.T. Adkins. – 28th ed. – London : Science Reference and Information Service, 1988.
100p.
Previous ed.: 1986. Includes indexes.
ISBN 071230746X £20.00

Guide to House Buying, Selling and Conveyancing for All. – London : Castle Books.
ISBN 0951043951 Pbk £6.95

Guide to Housing Benefit 1988-1989 / Zebedee. – 2nd ed. – London : London Housing Aid.
ISBN 0948857196 Pbk £5.95

Guide to Housing Benefit / Nick Raynsford. – Rev. – London : CENT, 1986.
ISBN 0948857056 Pbk £4.95

Guide to housing benefit / by Nick Raynsford, Peter McGurk. – Rev. ed. – London : SHAC, 1987.
xvi,137p.
Includes index.
ISBN 0948857161

Guide to Importing. – Cambridge : Woodhead-Faulkner, 1987.
ISBN 0859413101 Pbk £14.95

Guide to Insurance Professional Negligence Risks. – London : Butterworths, 1982.
ISBN 0406257108 Pbk £21.95

Guide to international human rights practice / edited for the International Human Rights Law Group by Hurst Hannum. – London : Macmillan, 1984.
xvi,310p; 24cm.
ISBN 0333370767

Guide to International Law Periodicals. – Ibadan : University Press.
Hbk

A Guide to International Real Estate Investment. – London : Eurospan.
ISBN 089930205X Hbk £32.95

Guide to joint equity ventures. – 2nd ed. – Beijing : External Services Department of Economic Daily, 1986.
243p.
Includes text of legislation. Includes title in Chinese. Text in English and Chinese.

Guide to Judicial Review. – 2nd ed. – Agincourt : Carswell, 1984.
320p.
This work classifies and categorizes the most important principles of judicial review in Canada. The right to the opportunity to be heard, procedural aspect of judicial review, evidentiary aspect of judicial review, and other topics are discussed in the book.
ISBN 0459366106 Hbk £23.00

Guide to Jurisprudence. – New Delhi : B. Jain Publishers.
Hbk £3.00

Guide to Land Registry Practice / Timothy. – 16th ed. – London : Longman Professional, 1985.
ISBN 0851212840 Pbk £19.95

Guide to Law Society's Conditions of Sale. – London : Longman Professional, 1984.
ISBN 0851209521 Pbk £7.90

Guide to liquidation in Scotland / David Flint. – Bristol : Jordan & Sons, 1987.
viii,265p; 25cm.
Provides a brief introduction to the Act and rules. With the text of relevant legislation other than the 1986 Insolvency Act.
ISBN 0853080925 Pbk £12.50

Guide to Maritime Boundary Delimitation / Adam J. Kerr. – Agincourt : Carswell, 1986.
136p.
This work addresses the technical aspects of maritime boundaries under international law. The book provides commentary on relevant cases which have been refered to the International Court of Justice.
Hbk £25.25

Guide to Mercantile Law. – New Delhi : S. Chand and Company.
Hbk £24.00

Guide to Monopolies and Restrictive Trade Practices Act. – 2nd ed. – Nagpur : Wadhura & Co, 1982.
Hbk £145.00

Guide to National Conditions of Sale. – 20th ed. – London : Oyez Longman, 1981.
ISBN 0851206204 Hbk £2.95

Guide to negotiable instruments and the Bills of Exchange Acts / Dudley Richardson. – 7th ed. – London : Butterworths, 1983.
viii,220p; 22cm.
A student and reference introduction to the law of negotiable instruments in the United Kingdom. The impact of cheque cards and credit cards on the negotiable instrument is discussed in detail.
ISBN 0406648247 Pbk £22.40

Guide to New VAT Exemption Rules. – Tolley Publishing, 1987.
ISBN 0854593071 Hbk £9.95

Guide to official industrial property literature : the Netherlands, Belgium, Luxembourg, Benelux / Brenda M. Rimmer. – London : British Library, Science Reference Library, 1981.
28p; 25cm.
Includes index.
ISBN 090291460X Pbk

Guide to Partnership Problems and Pitfalls. – Young Solicitors Group. – 2nd ed. – London : Law Society, 1983.
Hbk £1.75

Guide to pathological evidence for lawyers and police officers / Frederick A. Jaffe. – 2nd ed. – Toronto : Carswell, 1983.
xv,204p.
Bibliography: p.189-197. - Includes index.
ISBN 0459355406

Guide to perks from shares / John A Franks. – London : Kogan Page, 1988.
ISBN 185095237 Pbk

Guide to Personal Pensions. – Tolley Publishing, 1988.
ISBN 0854593101 Hbk £9.95

Guide to planning legislation in the Republic of Ireland / by Kevin Ingram Nowlan. – Dublin : Incorporated Law Society of Ireland, 1988.
xxiii,375p; 26cm.
Includes index.
ISBN 0902027301

Guide to purchasing law reports / Doug MacEllven, Guy Tanguay, Lorna K. Rees-Potter : edited by L.K. Rees-Potter. – Ottawa, Ont. : Canadian Law Information Council, 1985.
iv, 115 p.; 23 cm.
Includes index.
ISBN 0920358578

Guide to Redundancy Law. – London : Macmillan, 1985.
256p.
ISBN 0333388526 Hbk £25.00

Guide to Revenue Law in U.P., 3 Vols.
1901-1976. – 4th ed. – Lucknow : Eastern Book Company, 1977.
986p.
Hbk £70.00
1901-1982. – 1983.
1,406p.
Hbk £115.00
1976-1982. – 1983.
420p.
Hbk £45.00

Guide to safety at sports grounds. – London : H.M.S.O., 1986.
75p.
First published 1973.
ISBN 0113408404

Guide to Sales Tax Laws in Maharashtra. – 4th ed. – Nagpur : Wadhura & Co, 1987.
Hbk £300.00

Guide to Social Security Tribunals. – Belfast : Queen's University of Belfast, 1986.
200p.
Hbk

Guide to South African Industrial Incentives. – Durban : 0409017000.
ISBN 0409016985 £295.00 (with binder)

Guide to Stamp Duties. – London : CCH, 1987.
ISBN 0863251153 Pbk

Guide To Statistical Sources In Money Banking and Finance. – Oryx Press.
ISBN 0897742656 Hbk £30.00

Guide to Successful Debt Collecting. – 1st ed. – Bristol : Jordan & Sons Ltd, 1982.
Pbk £4.00

Guide to supplementary benefit law / by Jenny Levin. – 3rd ed. – London : Legal Action Group, 1981.
136p.

Guide to the 1985 Companies Act. – London : Longman Professional, 1985.
ISBN 0851210279 Pbk £8.95

Guide to the ACA Form of Building Agreement 1982. – 2nd ed. – London : Architectural Press, 1984.
60p. – (ACA Contract Documents).
ISBN 0851397336 Pbk £8.95

Guide to the benefits of charitable status. – TUAR, 1982.
ISBN 0907164099 Pbk £4.95

Guide to the Building Regulations 1985. – 8th ed. – London : Architectural Press, 1986.
256p : Illus.
ISBN 0851398448 Pbk £19.95

Guide to the Building Regulations 1985 for England and Wales : Butterworths Architecture Library of Building Control. – 2nd ed. – London : Butterworths.
ISBN 0408500131 Pbk £25.00

Guide to the Building Regulations Nineteen Seventy-Six. – 7th ed. – London : Architectural Press, 1981.
224p : Illus.
ISBN 0851398502 Pbk £11.95

Guide to the children's hearings. – Edinburgh : Green (W.) & Son, 1989.
Explains the complex legal and administrative provisions and procedures of those involved: panel members, parents, reporters, social workers and the children themselves.
ISBN 0414009045 Pbk

Guide to the civil jurisdiction and judgments convention / by Alan Dashwood, Richard Hacon & Robin White. – Deventer : Kluwer Law and Taxation, 1986.
648p.
Includes index and bibliography.
ISBN 9065442693 Hbk £265.00

Guide to the Collision Avoidance Rules / J. Lameijer. – London : Stanford Maritime Ltd.
224p.
Pbk £7.95

Guide to the Companies Act. – 11th rev. ed. – Nagpur : Wadhura & Co, 1988.
Hbk £440.00

Guide to the Companies Act of 1982 Vol. 1 / D.C. Jayasuriya. – 1st ed. – Nawala, Sri Lanka : Asian Pathfinder, 1983.
194p.

Guide to the Consumer Protection Act 1987. – Bicester : CCH Editions Ltd, 1988.
Covers what products are covered by the Act, who is liable, and what a defect is, the type of damages recoverable, commencement and limitation, the general safety duty, safety regulations, notices and forfeiture, defences to criminal prosecutions, and civil liability for unsafe goods.
ISBN 0863251358 Pbk £16.00

Guide to the Criminal Justice Act 1982 / Christopher J. Emmins. – London : Financial Training, 1982.
iv, 98p.
ISBN 0906322227

Guide to the Criminal Justice Act 1988 / Scanlan. – London : Blackstone Press.
ISBN 1854310224 Pbk £15.50

Guide to the Data Protection Act : its implications for business / Nigel Savage & Chris Edwards. – London : Financial Training, 1984.
ISBN 0906322537

Guide to the De Facto Relationships Act-New South Wales / Stephen O'Ryan. – Butterworths, 1985.
127p.
ISBN 040949075X Pbk £22.00

Guide to the Deeds. – 4th rev. ed. – Allahabad : Modern Law Publications, 1986.
Hbk £330.00

Guide to the Deposit of Microorganisms under the Budapest Treaty. – Geneva : World Intellectual Property Organization.
Hbk £90.00

Guide to the Employment Act 1988. – London : Butterworths.
ISBN 0406502838 Hbk £17.50

Guide to the Family Law Act. – 4th ed. – Sydney : Butterworths, 1986.
240p.
The fifth edition of this work has been revised to reflect the changes to the Act that have occurred since 1982. It discusses jurisdictional grounds for dissolution and settlement, proceedings relating to children, ancillary property proceedings, preparation for hearings, and other topics.
ISBN 0409491055 Hbk £45.00
ISBN 0409491063 Pbk £32.00

Guide to the Family Law (Scotland) Act 1985. – Bicester : CCH Editions Ltd, 1986.
vi,118p.
Includes the full text of the Act and of the new Rules of Court. Contains useful illustrations of how the principles will operate in practice. Covers obligations of aliment, actions for aliment, financial provisions on divorce, orders for financial provisions on divorce, nullity, agreements on aliment and financial provisions, and matrimonial property.
ISBN 0863250629 Pbk £9.00
ISBN 0863250807 Hbk

Guide to the financial markets / Charles R. Geisst. – London : Macmillan, 1982.
xv,144p; 23cm.
Includes bibliographies and index.
ISBN 0333309197 £15.00

Guide to the Financial Services Act 1986 / A.J. Wedgwood ... et al. – London : Financial Training, 1986.
xi,371p.
Includes index. Includes the text of the Act.
ISBN 1851850503

Guide to the Financial Services Act 1986 / Barry A.K. Rider, David A. Chaikin, Charles Abrams. – Bicester : CCH Editions, 1987.
xxii,472p; 23cm.
Examines Investor protection, the Act and the City revolution, the regulatory structure, the need for authorisation, obtaining authorisation, the conduct of investment business, insider dealing, public issues, marketing of investments, and collective investment schemes.
ISBN 0863250785 Pbk £15.00

Guide to the Hague and Hague-Visby rules. – 2nd. – London : Lloyds of London Press, 1989.
Revised and updated since the 1985 edition. Includes the York-Antwerp Rules related to General Average, and details of the Hague-Visby SDR Convention and the Limitation Convention. Also includes the latest position in the 'Gold Clause Agreement', and a list of signatories to both sets of rules.
ISBN 1850442436 Pbk

Guide to the Heavy Goods Vehicle Driving Test and Licenses. – 5th ed. – London : Kogan Page, 1986.
120p.
ISBN 1850911304 Pbk £5.95

Guide to the Hong Kong Code on Takeovers and Mergers. – London : Longman Professional.
ISBN 0582999006 Hbk £95.00

Guide to the indemnity and insurance aspects of building contracts : based on the JCT Standard Forms of Building Contract / Peter Madge. – London : RIBA, 1985.
285p; 24cm.
ISBN 0900630914

Guide to the Insolvency Act 1985 / W.F. Ratford ... et al. – London : Financial Training Publications, 1985.
xvi,336p.
Includes index. Includes text of the Act. At head of title: Peat Marwick.
ISBN 0906322847

Guide to the Insurance of Professional Negligence Risks. – Wellington : Butterworths, 1982.
This book discusses in detail the coverage provided by the 'basic' United Kingdom professional indemnity policy and some of the more popular extensions in common practice. The work provides a general explanation of the law of professional negligence and insurance law.
ISBN 0406257108 Pbk £35.00

Guide to the International Deposit of Industrial Designs (Hague Union). – Geneva : World Intellectual Property Organization, 1982.
200p.
Hbk £35.00

Guide to the International Registration of Marks (Madrid Union). – rep. 1984. – Geneva : World Intellectual Property Organization.
167p.
Hbk £30.00

Guide to the Investment Canada Act / Gabor S.G. Takach. – Butterworths, 1986.
176p.
ISBN 0409805203 Hbk £50.00

Guide to the Law Society's Conditions of Sale. – London : Oyez Longman, 1981.
ISBN 0851205542 Hbk £2.95

Guide to the Matrimonial and Family Proceedings Act 1984 / M.D.A. Freeman. – Bicester, Oxfordshire : CCH Editions, 1984.
165p; 23cm.
Contains examination of divorce, the new one year ban, extending time limits of nullity proceedings, financial relief in divorce proceedings, and financial relief after overseas divorces, financial provision in Scotland after overseas divorce, family business, and distribution and transfer.
ISBN 0863250319

Guide to the Mental Health (NI) Order 1986. – Belfast : Queen's University of Belfast, 1986.
150p.
Pbk

Guide to the national companies and securities scheme / by H.A.J. Ford ... et al. – Sydney : Butterworths, 1982.
xxv,406p.
Includes index.
ISBN 040949335X

Guide to the new Inheritance Tax. – Tolley Publishing, 1986.
ISBN 0854592563 Pbk £4.95

Guide to the New Law of Family Proceedings in Magistrates Courts, Including Adoption. – Chichester : Barry Rose, 1983.
ii, 49p.
ISBN 0859920631 Hbk £4.60

Guide to the patent law of the People's Republic of China / by Philip Gladwin in conjunction with Ajmal Hameed. – London : Graham & Trotman, 1985.
70p; 22cm.
ISBN 0860106306

Guide to the Patents Act 1977. – 2nd ed. – London : Sweet & Maxwell.
ISBN 042139580X Hbk £35.00

Guide to the Police and Criminal Evidence Act 1984 / Vaughan T. Bevan and Ken W. Lidstone. – London : Butterworths, 1985.
xv,554.
This text gives a comprehensive dissertation on every aspect of the Act. The book includes a full text of the United Kingdom's Police and Criminal Evidence Act of 1984.
ISBN 0406014302 Pbk

Guide to the records of the Lord Chancellor's Department / Patrick Polden. – London : HMSO, 1988.
xxx,376p.
Guide to Lord Chancellor's records on judges, courts and the legal profession and on the making of law on property, divorce, transport and lunacy.
ISBN 0113800150

Guide to the Rome Convention and to the Phonograms Convention. – Geneva : World Intellectual Property Organization, 1981.
145p.
Hbk £40.00

Guide To The Second Amendment Nineteen Eighty-One : Supplement to Guide to the Building Regulations 1976. – 7th ed. – London : Architectural Press, 1982.
32p : Illus.
ISBN 0851398499 Pbk £4.50

Guide to the Trademarks Act 1938. – CIPA. – London : Sweet & Maxwell, 1988.
ISBN 0421381205 Hbk

Guide to the 'travaux preparatoires' of the International Covenant on Civil and Political Rights / Marc J. Bossuyt. – Dordrecht : M. Nijhoff, 1987.
Includes text of the covenant. Includes index. Bibliography.
ISBN 9024734673

Guide to the UNCITRAL model on international commercial arbitration: legislation, history and commentary / J E Neuhaus. – Kluwer Law and Taxation, 1989.
1320.
Gives the legislative history of the new UNCITRAL model arbitration law. Each chapter starts with a commentary on the legislative history of the Article, highlighting the principle issues considered, followed by the legislative history of the article. Text contains documents, including drafts, reports, summary records of debates, government comments and conference room papers.
ISBN 9065443053 Hbk £139/Dfl 450

Guide to the Wages Act 1986 / Fraser P. Davidson. – London : Financial Training, 1986.
136p; 22cm.
Includes index. Includes the text of the Wages Act 1986.
ISBN 1851850473 Pbk £8.50

Guide to United Nations criminal policy / Manuel Lopez-Rey. – Aldershot : Gower, 1985.
xi,142p; 23cm.
Includes index.
ISBN 0566050706 £15.00

Guide to V.A.T. in Europe. – Price Waterhouse. – London : Graham & Trotman, 1989.
144; 216mm.
A guide to VAT systems in operation in Western Europe, including the EC member states. Emphasis is placed on registration requirements, and there is an explanation of how to reclaim input tax incurred in each state under the EC 8th and 13th VAT directive procedure. The law is as stated in 1988.
ISBN 1853333069 Hbk £25

Guide to VAT in Business. – London : CCH, 1988.
ISBN 0863251366 Pbk

Guidebook to Alberta Business Corporations Act / James S. Smeltzer. – North Ryde : C.C.H. Australia, 1984.
134p.
ISBN 0887962556 Hbk £12.00

Guidebook to Australian bankruptcy law / L.G. Priddle and T.G. Matthews. – North Ryde, N.S.W. : CCH Australia, 1982.
vii,255p.
Includes index.
ISBN 0869033727

Guidebook to Australian Company Law. – 9th ed. – North Ryde : C.C.H. Australia, 1986.
320p.
ISBN 0869039962 Hbk £32.00

Guidebook to Australian Family Law. – 6th ed. – North Ryde : C.C.H. Australia, 1985.
302p.
ISBN 086903541X Hbk £38.00

Guidebook to Australian Industrial Law. – 4th ed. – North Ryde : C.C.H. Australia, 1984.
620P.
ISBN 0869036742 Hbk £40.00

Guidebook to Australian Trade Marks Law and Practice. – 2nd ed. – North Ryde : C.C.H. Australia, 1985.
364p.
ISBN 0869035657

Guidebook to Australian Trade Practices Law. – 5th ed. – North Ryde : C.C.H. Australia, 1987.
450p.
ISBN 0869039717 Pbk £38.00

Guidebook to British company law. – Bicester : CCH Editions, 1983.
v,197p; 23cm.
Includes index.
ISBN 0863250084 Pbk

Guidebook to Canada Business Corporations Act / M.I. Wainberg. – 2nd ed. – Don Mills : CCH Canadian Ltd, 1981.
104p.
ISBN 0887961533 Pbk £9.50

Guidebook to Civil Claims in New South Wales. – North Ryde : C.C.H. Australia, 1986.
470p.
ISBN 0869039865 Hbk £38.00

Guidebook to Contract Law in Australia. – 3rd ed. – North Ryde : C.C.H. Australia, 1987.
350p.
ISBN 0869034715 Pbk £35.00

Guidebook to Insurance Law in Australia and New Zealand. – North Ryde : C.C.H. Australia, 1987.
341p.
ISBN 0869036378 Pbk £35.00

Guidebook to New Zealand Companies and Securities Law. – 3rd ed. – North Ryde : C.C.H. Australia, 1987.
400p.
ISBN 0864750188 Hbk

Guidebook to New Zealand's Competition Laws. – North Ryde : C.C.H. Australia, 1987.
250p.
ISBN 0864750676 Hbk

Guidebook to Occupational Health and Safety Laws in Australia. – 2nd ed. – North Ryde : C.C.H. Australia, 1986.
600p.
ISBN 0869036939 Hbk £38.00

Guidebook to Ontario Business Corporations Act / M.I. Wainberg. – 1st ed. – North Ryde : C.C.H. Australia, 1985.
122p.
ISBN 088796267X Pbk £12.00

Guidebook to Partnership Law in Australia. – 2nd ed. – North Ryde : C.C.H. Australia, 1984.
350p.
ISBN 086903457X Pbk £38.00

Guidebook to Taxation and Investment Law in Hong Kong. – 2nd ed. – North Ryde : C.C.H. Australia, 1985.
276p.
ISBN 0869037811

Guidebook to Victorian Real Estate Law and Practice. – North Ryde : C.C.H. Australia, 1986.
557p.
ISBN 0869035118 Hbk

Guidebook to Workers Compensation in Australia. – 5th ed. – North Ryde : C.C.H. Australia, 1986.
624p.
ISBN 086903846X Pbk £38.00

Guideline to Freedom of Information Act. – Attorney-General's Department. – Canberra : Australian Government Publishing Service, 1982.
398p.
ISBN 0644022752 Hbk £14.00

Guidelines for National Implementation of the Convention on International Trade in Endangered Species of Wild Fauna and Flora-Cities. – Gland : International Union for Conservation of Nature and Natural Resources, 1981.
148p.
Hbk £18.00

Guidelines for personal dealings by fund managers / Council for the Securities Industry. – Rev. ed. – London : The Council, 1982.
8p. – (CSI).

Guidelines for the administration and use of part II of the Register of Applications for Planning Permission / prepared by a joint working party of the RICS/RTPI/Law Society. – London : Royal Town Planning Institute, 1987.
3p.
Published as part of The Planner, Jan (1987) p. 21-23.

Guidelines for the Design and Construction of Offshore Supply Vessels. – International Maritime Organization. – London : International Maritime Organization, 1982.
Hbk £1.25

Guidelines for the operation of personal data systems : exposure draft / Privacy Committee. – Sydney : The Committee, 1986.
29p.

Guidelines on Surveys under the Nineteen Seventy-Eighty SOLAS Protocol. – International Maritime Organization. – London : International Maritime Organization, 1982.
Hbk £1.25

Guidelines to Buying and Contract Specifications for Sorghum Malt. – Pretoria : Council for Scientific and Industrial Research.
15p.
ISBN 0798803193

Guidelines to Specifications for Bantu Beer Packaging Contracts. – Pretoria : Council for Scientific and Industrial Research.
19p.
ISBN 0798803207

Guild, Ian
Forfaiting : an alternative approach to export trade finance / Ian Guild and Rhodri Harris. – Cambridge : Woodhead-Faulkner, 1985.
160p.
Includes index.
ISBN 0859413160 £17.50

Guilfoyle
Expert Systems in Banking and Securities / Jeffcoate. – Ovum, 1988.
ISBN 090396936X Hbk £465.00

Gulleford, Kenneth
Data Protection in Practice. – London : Butterworths, 1986.
ISBN 0406177007 Pbk £23.00

Gulshan, S.S.
Handbook of Corporate Laws / G.K. Kapur. – New Delhi : S. Chand and Company.
Hbk £20.00
→ Principles of Company Law.

Gumbley, K. F. W. →Isle of Man Orders in Council : consisting of Orders in Council extending or applying Acts of Parliament and Statutory Instruments to the Isle of Man.

Gummow, W. M. C. →Cases and materials on equity and trusts.
→ Equity, doctrines, and remedies.
→ Jacobs law of trusts in Australia.

Gun Law. – 5th ed. – Shaw & Sons, 1988.
ISBN 0721903630 Pbk £6.00

Gun Owner's Guide to South African Law and the Safe Handling of Firearms. – Cape Town : Struik Publishers.
96p.
Pbk £8.75

Gunderson, Morley
Economics of Poverty and Income Distribution. – Toronto : Butterworths.
192p.
ISBN 0409834750 Hbk

Gunn, B.
Licensing Entertainments in England and Wales. – London : Butterworths, 1985.
ISBN 0406200300 Pbk £24.00

Gunn, J. A. L. →Australian income tax guide 1988.

Gunningham, Neil
Safeguarding the Worker : Job Hazards and the Role of the Law. – North Ryde : Law Book Co, 1984.
xxiv, 426p.
ISBN 0455205043 Pbk £25.00

Gunter, Hans
ILO research on multinational enterprises and social policy : an overview. – 2nd (revised) ed. – Geneva : International Labour Office, 1982.
ii,33p.
Bibliography: p27-33.
ISBN 9221029182
—Tripartite Declaration of Principles concerning Multinational Enterprises and Social Policy : history, contents, follow-up and relationship with relevant instruments of other organisations / Hans Gunter. – Geneva : Interntional Labour Office, 1981.
iii,29p.
ISBN 9221029093

Gupta
Controlling Corporate Sickness : Lessons from Experiences for Managers and Bankers / Sekhar. – Oxford : Oxford University Press.
ISBN 00195621042 Hbk £6.95
—Law of Forgeries, Counterfeiting and Cheating. – 3rd ed. – Allahabad : Law Book Company, 1982.
Hbk £60.00
—Law of Injunctions. – Allahabad : Orient Law House, 1984.
Hbk £100.00
—Powers-of-Attorney Act. – 2nd ed. – Allahabad : Law Book Company, 1988.
94p.
Pbk £40.00

Gupta, Chheda Lal
Law of Partnership : with Tax-Planing at a Glance. – Allahabad : Modern Law Publications, 1987.
Hbk £280.00

Gupta, J.P. →Law of Partnership in India.

Gupta, Janak Raj
Burden of Tax in Punjab. – New Delhi : Concept Publishing Company, 1983.
xiv, 223p.
Hbk £90.00

Gupta, N.H.
Social Security Legislation for Labour in India. – New Delhi : Deep and Deep Publications, 1986.
382p.
Hbk £250.00

Gupta, Ram Lal
Law of Arrest, Bail, Search and Seizure. – 2nd ed. – Lucknow : Eastern Book Company, 1985.
Hbk
—Law Relating to Identification and Expert Opinion / H.D. Trivedi. – 3rd ed. – Lucknow : Eastern Book Company, 1983.
236p.
Hbk £35.00

Gupta, S.C.
Capital Punishment in India. – New Delhi : Deep and Deep Publications, 1986.
240p.
Hbk £175.00

Gupta, S.P.
Commentaries on Uttar Pradesh Public Premises (Eviction of Unauthorised Occupants) Act, 1972. – 2nd ed. – Lucknow : Eastern Book Company, 1983.
154p.
Hbk £20.00

Gupta, Satpal
Constituent Power of the Indian Parliament. – Delhi : Anmol Publications, 1987.
Hbk £125.00

Gupta, V. K.
Kautilyan jurisprudence / by V.K. Gupta. – Delhi : B.D. Gupta, 1987.
xii,356p.
Includes excerpts from Kautilya's Arthasastra in Sanskrit.

Gurry, Francis
Breach of confidence / Francis Gurry. – Oxford : Clarendon, 1984.
xxvii,487p; 22cm.
Includes index.
ISBN 0198253788 Hbk £42.50

Guthrie, Duncan
Disability : Legislation and Practice. – London : Macmillan, 1981.
264p.
ISBN 0333315758 Pbk £8.95

Gutierrez Girardot, Rafael
New Directions in International Law : Essays in Honour of Wolfgang Abendroth. – Frankfurt : Campus Verlag, 1982.
592p.
ISBN 3593330229 Hbk £178.00

Gutteridge, H. C.
Law of bankers' commercial credits / Maurice Megrah. – 7th ed. – London : Europa, 1984.
xxxv,343p; 25cm.
Previous ed.: 1979. Bibliography: pxxxiv-xxx - Includes index.
ISBN 0905118782 £19.50

Gutteridge, William →New terrorism.

Guttieres, M.
Law and practice relating to pollution control in Italy / U. Ruffolo, P. Dell'Anno. – 2nd ed. – London : Published by Graham & Trotman for the Commission of the European Communities, 1982.
200p.
Previous ed: / by P. Dell'Anno. 1976. Bibliography: p197-201. - Includes index.
ISBN 0860103099 £18.00

Guy, Diana
EEC and intellectual property / Diana Guy and Guy I.F. Leigh. – London : Sweet & Maxwell, 1981.
xxiv,375p; 25cm.
Includes index.
ISBN 0421234202 £30.00

Guy, J. A.
Christopher St. German on chancery and statute / by J.A. Guy. – London : Selden Society, 1985.
x,149p.
—Court of Star Chamber and its records to the reign of Elizabeth I / by J. A. Guy. – London : H.M.S.O., 1985.
112 p.
ISBN 0114401918
—Law and Social Change / H. G. Beale. – London : Royal Historical Society, 1984.
– (Studies in History (London) Ser.: Vol. 40).
ISBN 0901050946 Hbk £17.50

Guyana consolidated index of statutes and subsidiary legislation to 1st January 1982 / compiled at the Faculty of Law Library, University of the West Indies, Barbados. – Barbados : s.n., 1983.
x,89p.
One of a series in the West Indian Legislation Indexing Project (WILIP) compiled in cooperation with the British Development Division.

Gwillim, H.
Collection of Acts and Records of Parliament : With Reports of Cases in Courts of Law and Equity (1224-1800) Respecting Tithes, 4 Vols. – Repr. of 1801 ed. – Abingdon : Professional Books.
192p.
Hbk £175.00

Gyan, Chand
Judicial Control of Labour Tribunals. – Bombay : Tripathi, 1983.
xxiv, 335p.
Hbk £130.00

Gyeke-Dako, K.
Role of district tribunals in the administration of criminal justice in the Gambia : a critical appraisal / by K. Gyeke-Dako. – Banjul : Government Printer, 1984.
20 leaves.

Gypps, Godfrey →Financial and Property Problems on Marriage Breakdown.

Gypps, Godrey →Legal Aspects of the Care of the Aged.

H.B. Higgins. – North Sydney : Allen & Unwin, 1984.
248p.
ISBN 0868616818 Hbk £29.95

H.L.A. Hart / Neil MacCormick. – London : Edward Arnold, 1981.
184p; 22cm.
Includes index.
ISBN 071316333X Hbk £
ISBN 0713163348 Pbk £4.95

Haack, R. E.
Splintered Market : Barriers to Interprovincial Trade in Canadian Agriculture / David R. Hughes. – Toronto : Lorimer & Co, 1981.
ISBN 0888625170 Hbk £16.95
ISBN 0888625162 Pbk £7.95

Haakonssen, Knud
Science of a legislator : the natural jurisprudence of David Hume and Adam Smith / Knud Haakonssen. – Cambridge : Cambridge University Press, 1981.
vii,240p; 24cm.
Bibliography: p227-229. - Includes index.
ISBN 0521238919 £17.50

Haanappel, Peter P. C.
Pricing and capacity determination in international air transport : a legal analysis / by P.P.C. Haanappel. – 2nd ed. – Deventer, Netherlands : Kluwer Law and Taxation Publishers, 1984.
xv, 210 p.; 25 cm.
Re ed. of: Ratemaking in international air transport. 1978. Includes index. Bibliography: p. 201-204.
ISBN 9065441549 Pbk

Haas
Challenging Capital Punishment : Legal and Social Science Approaches / Inciardi. – Sage Publications.
ISBN 0803929099 Hbk £32.00
ISBN 0803929102 Pbk £14.95

Haber, Harvey M.
Shopping Centre Leases, 2 Vols.
Vols. 1 and 2. – Aurora : Canada Law Book Co.
1438p.
Hbk £92.50

Haberbeck, Andreas →Maritime laws of the Arabian Gulf Cooperation Council States, Vol.1.

Habitual criminals and the indeterminate sentence / Advisory Committee on Law Reform. – Causeway : The Committee, 1981.
50p. – (Report).

Habitual criminals and the indeterminate sentence / Advisory Committee on Law Reform. – Causeway : The Committee, 1981.
52 leaves. – (Working paper).

HAC Guide to Taxation of Bloodstock Industry. – Stoy Hayward, 1987.
ISBN 0870382005 Hbk £20.00

Hachten, William A.
Press and Apartheid : Repression and Propaganda in South Africa / C. Anthony Giffard. – London : Macmillan, 1984.
336p.
ISBN 0333384350 Hbk £33.00

Hacking
Financial Services Law / Potts. – London : Sweet & Maxwell, 1988.
ISBN 0421386002 Pbk

Hackney, J.
Understanding Equity and Trusts. – London : Fontana.
ISBN 0006860729 Pbk £4.95

Hackwill, G. R. J. →Mackeurtan's sale of goods in South Africa.

Hacon, R. J →Guide to the civil jurisdiction and judgments convention.

Hadden, T.
Company Law and Capitalism. – 3rd ed. – Weidenfeld & Nicolson.
ISBN 029778761 Hbk £25.00
ISBN 029778787X Pbk £15.95

Hadden, Tom B.
Canadian business organizations law / by Tom Hadden, Robert E. Forbes, Ralph L. Simmonds. – Toronto : Butterworths, 1984.
xlix,680p.
Relates common-law rules and statutory provisions to current commercial and industrial practice, distinguishing between the problems of small private businesses and larger public companies. Provides information on current corporate issues; practices and problems in designed instruments of corporate finance, securities law, corporate acquisitions, corporate groups, foreign acquisitions, and lease financing.
ISBN 0409834815 Hbk £95
—Control of corporate groups / by Tom Hadden. – London : Institute of Advanced Legal Studies (University of London), 1983.
75p.,4 charts.
ISBN 0901190284
—Housing Law in Northern Ireland / W. David Trimble. – Belfast : Queen's University of Belfast, 1986.
350p.
Pbk
—Northern Ireland housing law : the public and private rented sectors / by T.B. Hadden and W.D. Trimble. – Belfast : SLS Legal Publications, 1986.
xxxvi,323p.
Includes bibliographical references and index.
ISBN 0853892806

Hadfield, Brigid
Committees of the House of Commons and Northern Ireland Affairs. – Belfast : Queen's University of Belfast, 1984.
32p.
Pbk £2.00
—Northern Ireland Act 1982 : Do-It-Yourself Devolution. – Belfast : Queen's University of Belfast.
25p.
Pbk £2.00

Hadjifotiou, N.
Women and harassment at work. – Pluto Press, 1983.
ISBN 086104729X Pbk £3.95

Hafizullah, M. →Arrest of ships 5 : Bangladesh, Finland, Saudi Arabia, South Africa.

Hagan, J.L.
Structural Criminology. – Polity Press.
ISBN 0745605168 Hbk £29.50

Hagan, John →Law and the Chinese in Canada : a Case Study in Ethnic Perceptions of the Law.
—Victims Before the Law : the Organizational Domination of Criminal Law. – Butterworths, 1983.
304p.
Hbk £55.00

Hagberg, Lennart →Handbook on maritime law, Argentina-Norway.
—Maritime Law
Vol. 1: Arrest of Vessels. – Dordrecht : Kluwer, 1976.
108p.
ISBN 9026808941 Hbk £45.00

Haggerty
Non-Unionized Workers Protection Act, 1983, Bill 115 : An Act Respecting the Rights of Non-Unionized Workers. – Ontario : Ontario Government Publications Service, 1983.
3p.
Hbk £0.30

Hague Academy of International Law
Collected Courses : Recueil des Cours. – Hague Academy of International Law. – Dordrecht : Kluwer.
Hbk
→ Protection du droit a la vie a la lumiere des regles du droit international : bibliographie selective.
→ Statut juridique international des minorites : bibliographie selective.

Hague Conference on Private International Law : Collection of Conventions (1951-1980). – London : Butterworths, 1981.
ISBN 0406658404 Pbk £27.50

Hague Convention on International Access to Justice : Explanatory Documentation Prepared for Commonwealth Jurisdictions. – London : Commonwealth Secretariat, 1982.
ISBN 085092216X Hbk £4.00

Hague Convention on the civil aspects of international child abduction : consultative document. – Edinburgh? : Scottish Courts Administration?, 1983.
10 leaves.

Hague Convention on the Civil Aspects of International Child Abduction : explanatory documentation / prepared for Commonwealth jurisdictions by J.M. Eekelaar in association with the Commonwealth Secretariat. – London : Commonwealth Secretariat, 1981.
v,70p.
ISBN 0850921961

Hague Convention on the Service Abroad of Judicial and Extrajudicial Documents in Civil or Commercial Matters (1965) / the Law Reform Commission. – Dublin : The Commission, 1987.
vii,36p. – (LRC).
Includes the text of the convention. Cover title: Service of documents abroad re civil proceedings.

Hague Convention on the Taking of Evidence Abroad : explanatory documentation prepared for Commonwealth jurisdicitons / by David McClean and Campbell McLachlan : in association with the Commonwealth Secretariat. – Revised. – London : Commonwealth Secretariat (Legal Division), 1986.
30,16p.
Includes the text of the Convention.
ISBN 0850922879

Hague, N. T.
Leasehold enfranchisement / by N.T. Hague. – 2nd ed. – London : Sweet & Maxwell, 1987.
xxxix,519p; 25cm.
Previous ed.: 1967. Includes index.
ISBN 0421283602 £35.00

Hague Rules law digest : a practical digest and comprehensive cross-referenced index to leading British cases governing the interpretation of the Hague Rules : by W.E. Astle. – London : Fairplay Publications, 1981.
ix,90p.
ISBN 0905045246

Hague yearbook of international law : Annuaire de la Haye de droit international / J.G. Lammers. – Dordrecht : Nijhoff (Martinus), 1988.
471. – (A.A.A. Yearbook).
In-depth articles on some of the developments taking place in international law institutions such as the International Court of Justice and the Hague Conference on Private International Law. The articles, and summaries, in both English and French, deal with decisions rendered by these institutions.
ISBN 9024737494 Hbk £80

Hague-Zagreb Essays
2: Product Liability, Road Transport, Foreign Law. – Dordrecht : Kluwer, 1978.
xiii, 255p.
ISBN 9028604782 Hbk £62.00
4: On the Law of International Trade / edited by C.C.A. Voskuil and J.A. Wade. – 1983.
410p.
ISBN 9024728401 Hbk £135.00
5: On the Law of International Trade / edited by C.C.A. Voskuil and J.A. Wade. – 1985.
193p.
At head of title: TMC Asser Instituut. Reports and discussions of the fifth session of the Hague-Zagreb Colloquium, Isle of Krk, Yugoslavia, 1983. Includes bibliographies.
ISBN 9024731704 Hbk £135.00

Hahlo, H. R.
Hahlo's cases and materials on company law / John H. Farrar, H. R. Hahlo. – 3rd ed. – London : Sweet & Maxwell, 1987.
xxxvi,674p; 24cm.
Previous ed: published as Hahlo's casebook on company law, 1977. Includes index.
ISBN 0421317302 Hbk £
ISBN 042131740X Pbk
—South African company law through the cases : a collection of leading South African and English cases on company law, with explanatory notes and comments / H. R. Hahlo. – 4th ed. – Cape Town : Juta, 1984.
xli,673p.
ISBN 0702114316
—South African law of husband and wife / H. R. Hahlo. – 5th ed. – Cape Town : Juta, 1985.
lxx,526p.
ISBN 0702115681

Hahlo's cases and materials on company law / John H. Farrar, H. R. Hahlo. – 3rd ed. – London : Sweet & Maxwell, 1987.
xxxvi,674p; 24cm.
Previous ed: published as Hahlo's casebook on company law, 1977. Includes index.
ISBN 0421317302 Hbk £
ISBN 042131740X Pbk

Haig, P.G.
Butterworths Conveyancing Bulletin. – Butterworths.
ISBN 0409701815 Hbk
—New Zealand Conveyancing and Property Reports. – Wellington : Butterworths, 1983.
ISBN 0409701416 Hbk
—New Zealand Conveyancing Bulletin. – Wellington : Butterworths.
ISBN 0409781428 Pbk
—New Zealand Town Planning Appeals. – Wellington : Butterworths.
Hbk

Haigh, Nigel
EEC environmental policy and Britain / Nigel Haigh. – 2nd ed. – Harlow : Longman, 1987.
250p; 24cm.
Previous ed.: 1984.
ISBN 0582016096 Pbk £25.00
→ European Community environmental policy in practice, Vol. 1 : Comparative report : water and waste in four countries : a study of the implementation of the EEC directives in France, Germany, Netherlands and United Kingdom : by Nigel Haigh with Graham Bennett ... et al.

Hailsham
Hamlyn Revisited (Hamlyn 35) 1983. – Sweet & Maxwell.
ISBN 0420467300 Pbk £6.50

Hailsham of St. Marylebone, Quintin Hogg
Hamlyn revisited : the British legal system today / by Lord Hailsham of St. Marylebone. – London : Published under the auspices of the Hamlyn Trust by Stevens & Sons, 1983.
xii,89p; 18cm.
Includes index.
ISBN 0420467203 Hbk £
ISBN 0420467300 Pbk £4.95

Haines, Paul Douglas →Law on Speeding and Radar.

Hainsworth, Terry W.
Ontario Family Law Act. – Aurora : Canada Law Book Co.
– (Text Books-Civil).
This manual is a working guide to the Ontario Family Law Act of 1986. Divided into four main parts, this manual includes the full text of each section of the Act, insightful author commentary, convenient cross-referencing and case law with unreported decisions.
Hbk £89.00
—Ontario Family Law Reform Act Manual (O.F.L.R.) 1979-Present. – Aurora : Canada Law Book Co.
Llf £89.00

Haiti : Amnesty International briefing. – Amnesty International. – London : Amnesty International, 1985.
14p; ill.
ISBN 086210081X

Haitian refugees in the U.S. / by Alex Stepick : with the assistance of Dale Frederick Swartz. – Updated ed. – London : Minority Rights Group, 1986.
20p. – (Report).
Bibliography: p.18-19.
ISBN 0946690464

Hakapaa, Kari
Marine pollution in international law : material obligations and jurisdiction with special reference to the Third United Nations Conference on the Law of the Sea / by Kari Hakapaa. – Helsinki : Suomalainen Tiedeakatemia, 1981.
341 p.; 25 cm.
Errata slip and notice of public dissertation discussion inserted. Thesis (doctoral)–University of Helsinki, 1981. Includes indexes. Bibliography: p. 299-336.
ISBN 9514104021

Hakeney, D.
Assessing Legal Aid Costs. – London : Longman Professional, 1984.
ISBN 0851209629 Pbk £8.95

Hakim, C.
Employers' use of outwork : a study using the 1980 Workplace industrial relations survey and the 1981 National survey of homeworking / by Catherine Hakim. – London : Department of Employment, 1985.
107p. – (Research paper).
Bibliography: p.104-107.

Haksar, Nandita
Demystification of Law for Women. – New Delhi : Lancer International, 1986.
112p.
Pbk £95.00
→ Nagaland File : A Question of Human Rights.

Halberstadt, R. H.
Data Protection Act 1984 : New Problems For Solicitors and Their Clients. – London : Law Society, 1985.
27p. – (Nineteen Eighty-Five Crash Course Transcripts).
Hbk £2.05

Halberstadt, Richard
Basic book-keeping for solicitors / Richard Halberstadt. – 3rd ed. – London : Sweet & Maxwell, 1985.
300p; 23cm.
Previous ed.: 1982. Includes index.
ISBN 042133830X £12.00
—Basic Bookkeeping for Solicitors. – 2nd ed. – London : Sweet & Maxwell, 1982.
ISBN 0421297603 Pbk £5.95
—Bookkeeping for Solicitors. – 4th ed. – Sweet & Maxwell.
ISBN 0421413700 Pbk £13.00

Haldane journal : a journal of law and socialism. – London : Haldane Society, 1985-.

Haldane Society employment law bulletin. – London : Haldane Society of Socialist Lawyers, 1983.

Haldane Society of Socialist Lawyers
Labour law with a Labour government : a workers' charter / Haldane Society. Employment Law Committee. – London : The Society, 1987.
9p.
→ Police, the law and the people.
→ Socialist lawyer.

Haldane Society of Socialist Lawyers bulletin. – London : The Society, 1970.

Hale, Alan M.
Patenting Manual. – 2nd. – Waterloo, 1983.
381p.
ISBN 094341802X Hbk £48.50

Hale, Ken W
Australian Corporate Law Reference / James G Jackson. – London : Legal Books, 1986.
ISBN 0949553263 Hbk £27.50

Hale, M.
Historia Placitorum Coronae. – Reprint. 2 vols. – Abingdon : Professional Books, 1986.
– (Classical English Law Texts Ser.).
ISBN 086205320X Hbk £53.75
—History of the Common Law of England, 2 Vols. – 5th ed. – Abingdon : Professional Books.
239p.
Hbk £125.00
—Pleas of the Crown 1678. – Reprint. – Abingdon : Professional Books, 1986.
ISBN 0862053218 Hbk £24.75
—Pleas of the Crown : Summary. – Abingdon : Professional Books.
– (Classical English Law Texts Ser.).
Hbk £35.00
—Summary of the Pleas of the Crown : A Brief But Full Account of Whatsoever Can Be Found Relating to That Subject. – Repr. of 1716 ed. – Abingdon : Professional Books.
362p.
Hbk £125.00

Half Open Door / Lynne Strahan. – Neutral Bay : Hale & Iremonger.
ISBN 0868060488 Hbk £24.95, 015
ISBN 0868060496 Pbk £11.95, 015

Half-a-century of commercial law, 1930-1980 / being the presidential address of Lord Roskill ... – Birmingham : Holdsworth Club of the University of Birmingham, 1981.
17p; 21cm. – (Presidential addresses/Holdsworth Club).
ISBN 0704406187

Hall →Business laws of the United Arab Emirates, Federal law No. 8 of 1984 Re: Commercial Companies.
—Company Secretarial Practice 1984 Supplement / Thom. – 6th ed. – Plymouth : Macdonald & Evans, 1984.
ISBN 071210478X Pbk £6.50

Hall, Chris
Hong Kong in International Tax Planning. – London : Oyez Longman, 1983.
– (Oyez Longman Intelligence Report Ser.).
ISBN 085120810X Hbk £55.00

Hall, Clarke
Clarke Hall and Morrison on Children, 2 Vols. / A.C.L. Morrison. – 10th ed. – London : Butterworths, 1986.
ISBN 040615807X Llf

Hall, Geoffrey
Sentencing in New Zealand. – Butterworths.
Hbk £99.00

Hall, J. E., et al
Jury Trials. – Vancouver : British Columbia Continuing Legal Education Society, 1981.
202p.
ISBN 0865040419 Hbk £11.50

Hall, J. L.
Online bibliographic databases : a directory and sourcebook / Marjorie J. Brown. – 3rd ed. – London : Aslib, 1983.
xiv,383p; 24cm.
Previous ed.: 1981. Bibliography: p315-331. - Includes index.
ISBN 0851421679 North America £
ISBN 0810305305

Hall, Jean Graham
Child abuse : procedure and evidence in juvenile courts / by Jean Graham Hall and Douglas F. Martin. – 2nd ed. – London : Barry Rose, 1987.
xv,117p.
ISBN 187008070X
—Towards a unified family court : court orders concerning children : overlapping jurisdictions / Jean Graham Hall, Douglas F. Martin. – s.l. : s.n., 1986.
88p.
—Towards a unified Family Court : the collection of maintenance and the enforcement of court orders for maintenance / research by Jean Graham Hall and Douglas F. Martin. – s.l. : s. n., 1984.
ca.200 leaves.
Includes some French text.

Hall, L.
Meetings. – 3rd ed. – Plymouth : Macdonald & Evans, 1984.
ISBN 0712104496 Pbk £5.95

Hall, Peter →Inner city in context : the final report of the Social Science Research Council Inner Cities Working Party.

Hall, Peter M.
Unconscionable Contracts and Economic Duress. – North Ryde : C.C.H. Australia, 1985.
260p.
ISBN 0869035495

Hall, William Clarke
Law relating to children and young persons / Clarke Hall and Morrison. – 10th ed. 2. – London : Butterworths, 1985.
looseleaf.
Includes index. Includes the text of the relevant legislation. Spine title: Clarke Hall & Morrison on children. Kept up-to-date by supplements.
ISBN 0406158126

Hall Williams, J E
Criminology and criminal justice / by J.E. Hall Williams. – London : Butterworths, 1982.
xvii,266p.
Bibliography: p243-254.
ISBN 0406593205
—Role of the Prosecutor. – London : LSEPS, 1987.
ISBN 0566057239 Hbk £22.50

Hallam, H.
Constitutional History of England : 1485-1760. – 7th ed. Repr. of 1850 ed. – Abingdon : Professional Books.
Hbk £145.00

Halleck, S.L.
Mentally Disordered Offender. – Cambridge : Cambridge University Press.
ISBN 0521357144 Pbk £13.95

Hallen, Lars
International Industrial Purchasing. – Stockholm : Almqvist & Wiksell, 1982.
74p.
ISBN 9155412661 Hbk £51.00

Hallen, Philip
Evidence /. – North Ryde : Law Book Co, 1984.
x, 78p.
ISBN 0455203423

Hallett, Leonard Arthur
Royal commissions and boards of inquiry : some legal and procedural aspects / by Leonard Arthur Hallett. – Sydney : Law Book Company, 1982.
xxxvi,368p.
Bibliography: pxxxi-xxxvi.
ISBN 0455204721

Halliday, John M.
Conveyancing law and practice in Scotland Vol.1 / by John M. Halliday. – Edinburgh : W. Green under the auspices of the Scottish Universities Law Institute, 1985.
xxxviii,491p; 25cm.
Includes index.
ISBN 0414007603
Vol.2 : Feus and dispositions / by John M. Halliday. – 1986.
xxxvii,518p; 25cm.
Includes index.
ISBN 0414007891 Hbk £30.00
Vol.3 : Leases and heritable securities / by John M. Halliday. – 1987.
xxix,550p; 25cm.
Includes index.
ISBN 0414008154
Vol.4. Wills and succession. – 1990.
Deals with testate and intestate succession both before and after the Succession (Scotland) Act 1964, including statutory prior rights and legal rights, completion of title to both heritable and moveable estate, preparation of wills, administration of executries, destination, entails, judicial transmissons, compulsory acuisition, trusts, taxation, and pension schemes. Includes index for Vols. 1 to 4. Published under the auspices of the Scottish Universities law Institute.
ISBN 0414008936 Hbk

Hallmann, Ulrich C. →Industrial property laws of the Federal Republic of Germany : patent, utility model, trademark, design : texts of the laws, orders, regulations, guidelines and index.

Hallsworth, Christopher C.
Filmed horse racing / Christopher C. Hallsworth and Barry O. Johnson. – Chichester : Barry Rose, 1983.
26p.

Hallwood, Paul
International money : theory, evidence and institutions / Paul Hallwood and Ronald MacDonald with contributions from Robert Shaw. – Oxford : Basil Blackwell, 1986.
272p; 23cm.
Includes bibliography and index.
ISBN 0631144455 Hbk £25.00 :
ISBN 0631144463 Pbk £8.95

Hally, Desmond L. →Financing of small business.

Halnan, Patrick
Drunk-Driving : The New Law. – London : Oyez Longman, 1984.
– (Oyez Longman Practice Note Ser.: No. 65).
ISBN 0851208657
—Road traffic / Patrick Halnan. – Chichester : Rose for the Magistrates' Association, 1981.
50p; 21cm.
ISBN 0859922073 Pbk £2.50
→ Wilkinson's road traffic offences.

Halpern, Lionel
Taxes in France. – 4th ed. – London : Butterworths, 1986.
This work is a comprehensive look at French taxation law covering income tax, company tax, value added tax, and stamp and registration duties. The major reforms enacted by the Socialist government in France are included in the text.
ISBN 0406520860 Pbk

Halsbury, Hardinge Stanley Giffard →Halsbury's statutes of England and Wales.

Halsbury's Law of England. – 4th ed. – London : Butterworths.
Service.
ISBN 0990000358 Hbk

Halsbury's Laws of England, 56 Vols. – 4th ed. – London : Butterworths.
Hbk

Halsbury's Laws of England
Incl. 1907-1939, 31 Vols. 1st ed. – Abingdon : Professional Books.
Hbk

Halsbury's Laws of England. – 4th ed. – Abingdon : Professional Books, 1984.
Hbk £1350.00

Halsbury's Laws of England : 1907-1917, 31 Vols. – Abingdon : Professional Books.
Hbk £140.00

Halsbury's Laws of England : 1931-1942, 37 Vols. – 2nd ed. – Abingdon : Professional Books.
Hbk £90.00

Halsbury's Laws of England : 1952-1964, 43 Vols. – 3rd ed. – Abingdon : Professional Books.
Hbk £495.00

Halsbury's Statutes of England, 47 Vols. – 2nd ed. – Abingdon : Professional Books.
Hbk £125.00

Halsbury's Statutes of England. – 4th ed. – London : Butterworths.
Service.
Llf

Halsbury's statutes of England. – 3rd ed. 53. – London : Butterworths, 1968.
Superseded in part by 4th ed.
ISBN 0406042004

Halsbury's statutes of England and Wales / managing editor Paul Brown. – 4th ed. 50 v. – London : Butterworths, 1985.
With Users guide and Alphabetical list of statutes. Updating service.
ISBN 0406214093

Halsbury's Statutory Instruments, 23 Vols. – London : Butterworths.
This 23 volume work provides a complete reference to every statutory instrument in force and of general application in England and Wales. A separate volume of consolidated index is included in the work.
Hbk

Halsbury's Statutory Instruments, 24 Vols. – Abingdon : Professional Books.
Hbk £245.00

Halsbury's Statutory Instruments. – London : Butterworths.
Service.
Llf

Ham, Christopher
Health Policy in Britain : The Organisation and Politics of the NHS. – 2nd ed. – London : Macmillan, 1985.
192p. – (Studies in Social Policy, General Ser.).
ISBN 0333394925 Hbk £20.00
ISBN 0333394933 Pbk £6.95
—Policy process in the modern capitalist state / Christopher Ham and Michael Hill. – Brighton : Wheatsheaf Books Ltd, 1984.
xiii,210p.
Bibliography: p190-204.
ISBN 0710801904

Hamalengwa, M →International law of human rights in Africa : basic documents and annotated bibliography.

Hamblin, C.
Banking law / by Clive Hamblin. – London : Sweet & Maxwell, 1985.
xxvii,377p; 22cm. – (Concises College Texts).
Includes index.
ISBN 0421327502 Hbk £18.50
ISBN 042132760X Pbk £11.50
—Introduction to commercial law / F. B. Wright. – 2nd ed. – London : Sweet & Maxwell, 1982.
240p. – (Concise College Texts).
Previous ed. published as: ONC-OND commercial law. 1976.
ISBN 0421285109 Pbk £10.00

Hambly, D. →Torts : Cases and Commentary.

Hambro Capital Taxes and Estate Planning Guide / P. D. Silke. – London : Oyez Longman, 1982.
ISBN 085120662X Hbk £9.95

Hambro Tax Guide / W. I. Sinclair. – London : Oyez Longman, 1982.
ISBN 0851206700 Hbk £8.95
September 1983 Edition. –
ISBN 0851207464 Hbk £9.95

Hambrook, J. P. →Company Law in Australia.

Hamburg Rules : an appreciation of the cause and effect of the amendments to the Hague Rules and the Hague-Visby Rules / W.E. Astle. – London : Fairplay, 1981.
xii,163p; 25cm.
ISBN 0905045319 Pbk

Hamburger, Joseph →Troubled lives : John and Sarah Austin.

Hamburger, Lotte
Troubled lives : John and Sarah Austin / Lotte and Joseph Hamburger. – Toronto : University of Toronto Press, 1985.
xiii,261p.
Includes index.

Hameed, Ajmal →Guide to the patent law of the People's Republic of China.

Hamilton →Fingertip Guide to Criminal Law.
→ Good Wigging.

Hamilton, Alexander
Law practice of Alexander Hamilton : documents and commentary
Vol.5 : editors Julius Goebel, Jr. and Joseph H. Smith : associate editors Winnifred Bowers ... et al. / Julius Goebel, Joseph H. Smith, Winnifred Bowers. – New York : Published under the auspices of the William Nelson Cromwell Foundation by Columbia University Press, 1981.
xiv,754p; 24cm.
Includes index.
ISBN 0231089295 £52.00

Hamilton, H. M. →Criminal law in New South Wales, Vol. 2 : by Ray Watson and Reg Bartley.

Hamilton, J.
Stockbroking tomorrow. – London : Macmillan, 1985.
ISBN 0333219945 Hbk £27.50

Hamilton, K R
Impaired driving and breathalyzer law: recent case law. – 1 vol. – Scarborough, Ontario : Butterworths (Canada).
Joint publication with the Legal Service Society of British Columbia. The most litigated sections - 234, 235 and 236 - of the Criminal Code are broken into their component aspects and the appropriate case law relating to each aspect is set out in digest form. Contains a table of cases, and covers impaired driving, failing to provide breath samples, driving with more than 80mg of alcohol in blood, and sentencing.
ISBN 0409806471 Loose leaf
—Judicial Interim Release. – 4th ed. – Toronto : Butterworths.
Llf £150.00
—Judicial interim release (Bail manual). – 1 vol. – Scarborough, Ontario : Butterworths (Canada).
Part one provides a one-paragrah summary of the key cases as they relate to specific sections or sub-sections of the Criminal Code or other relevant statutes. Part two contains a digest of the most cited cases in part one, giving the citation, a review of the facts, and the main issues decided. Part three contains references and excerpts for various Acts.
Loose leaf

Hamilton, P.
Administration of Corporate Security. – Cambridge : Woodhead-Faulkner, 1987.
ISBN 0902197258 Hbk £25.00

Hamilton, R.
Foul Bills and Dagger Money. – Professional Books.
ISBN 0862052483 Hbk £14.50
—Guide to Development and Planning. – 7th ed. – London : Longman Professional, 1981.
ISBN 0851205496 Hbk £37.00

Hamilton, R G
All jangle and riot: a legal history of the Bar. – Abingdon : Professional Books, 1986.
ISBN 0862050839 Hbk £14.95

Hamilton, R. N. D.
Guide to development and planning / by R.N.D. Hamilton. – 7th ed. – London : Oyez, 1981.
lxiv,510p; 23cm.
Previous ed.: 1975. Includes index.
ISBN 0851205496
—Planning Procedure Tables. – 4th ed. – London : Oyez Longman, 1981.
ISBN 0851205585 Hbk £9.25

Hamilton, Roger
Foreign Investment and Exchange Control. – Woolloomooloo : International Business Communications, 1985.
ISBN 0949072001 Llf

Hamilton, Stanley
Foundations of Real Estate Financing : The Mathematical Basis / David Baxter. – Toronto : Butterworths, 1983.
353p.
Hbk £45.00

Hamilton, Susan
Modern Law of Highways. – London : Butterworths, 1981.
This book presents detailed coverage of the common law of highways and the Highways Act of 1980 for the practitioner in the United Kingdom. The full text of the Act, along with other relevant legislation, is included in the work along with extensive annotations.
ISBN 0406220808 Hbk

Hamisi, Ruckia →Study on the legislative framework, agreements and financial impositions affecting the mining industry in Pacific Commonwealth countries.

Hamlyn →Investigations manual.

Hamlyn revisited : the British legal system today / by Lord Hailsham of St. Marylebone. – London : Published under the auspices of the Hamlyn Trust by Stevens & Sons, 1983.
xii,89p; 18cm.
Includes index.
ISBN 0420467203 Hbk £
ISBN 0420467300 Pbk £4.95

Hamlyn Revisited (Hamlyn 35) 1983. – Sweet & Maxwell.
ISBN 0420467300 Pbk £6.50

Hamlyn Trust →Development of consumer law and policy - bold spirits and timorous souls.
→ Hamlyn revisited : the British legal system today.
→ Pragmatism and theory in English law.

Hammar, Tomas →European immigration policy : a comparative study.

Hammersmith & Fulham Public Libraries
Law : a guide to the collection of Hammersmith & Fulham / Hammersmith & Fulham Libraries. – 2nd ed. – London : Hammersmith & Fulham Libraries, 1987.
40p.
ISBN 0904038068

Hammond, E. M. →Taxing Pensions : The Taxation of Occupational Pension Schemes in the United Kingdom.

Hammond, Elizabeth →Insurance: competition or regulation? : a comparative study of the insurance markets in the United Kingdom and the Federal Republic of Germany.

Hammond, Robert C. →African tax systems.

Hamnett, Ian →Durkheim and modern sociology.

Hampel, Justice, et al
New Sentencing Options : Penalties and Sentences Act. – Melbourne : Law Institute of Victoria, 1986.
Hbk £15.00

Hampton, Celia
Criminal procedure / Celia Hampton. – 3rd ed. – London : Sweet & Maxwell, 1982.
lxi,472p; 22cm.
Previous ed.: 1977. Includes index.
ISBN 0421286601 Hbk £
ISBN 0421286709 Pbk £8.95

Hamrick, W.S.
Existential Phenomenology of Law, Maurice Merleau-Ponty. – Dordrecht : Kluwer, 1987.
256p.
ISBN 9024735203 Hbk £135.00

Han, K.H.
Financial Management. – Butterworths, 1984.
387p.
ISBN 0406181160 Pbk £30.00

Hanami, T. A. →Industrial conflict resolution in market economics : a study of Australia, the Federal Republic of Germany, Italy, Japan and the USA.

Hanami, Tadashi
Labour law and industrial relations in Japan / by T.A. Hanami. – 2nd ed. – Deventer, Netherlands : Kluwer Law and Taxation, 1985.
171p.
Bibliography: p78-80. Includes index.
ISBN 9065442146

Hanau, P →Handbook on European employee co-maangement, Supplement.

Hanbury, Harold Greville
Modern Equity / R H Maudsley. – 12th ed. – London : Sweet & Maxwell, 1985.
ISBN 0420470506 Hbk £32.00
ISBN 0420470603 Pbk £24.00
—Modern Equity / Harling. – Stevens & Sons.
ISBN 0420481303 Hbk £36.00
ISBN 0420481400 Pbk £26.00
—Modern equity / by Harold Greville Hanbury. – 11th ed. – London : Stevens, 1981.
cvi,796p; 25cm.
Previous ed.: 1976. Includes index.
ISBN 0420461302 Hbk £27.50
ISBN 042046140X Pbk £16.50
—Modern equity / by Harold Greville Hanbury and Ronald Harling Maudsley. – 12th ed. – London : Stevens, 1985.
cxiv,920p; 26cm.
Previous ed.: 1981. Includes index.
ISBN 0420470506 Hbk £30.00
ISBN 0420470603 Pbk £19.75

Hancher, Leigh →Energy strategy in Europe : the legal framework.

Hand book of the Federal Court of Appeal. – Lagos : The Court, 1983.
232p.
At head of title: Federal Republic of Nigeria.

Handbook / The Association of Law Teachers. – Sheffield? : Association of Law Teachers, 1986.
80p.

Handbook Bankruptcy Law and Practice. – 4th ed. – London : Longman Professional, 1988.
ISBN 085120726X Hbk

Handbook Conveyancing Practice in Scotland. – London : Butterworths, 1986.
ISBN 0406206007 Pbk £19.00

Handbook for Local Law Societies. – London : Law Society.
Hbk £1.25

Handbook of administrative tribunals / Sara Blake. – Scarborough, Ontario : Butterworths (Canada), 1988.
256.
Examination of how tribunals should conduct themselves in order to minimize the risks of judicial review. Cover compliance with prescribed rules, Ontario and Alberta Codes of Procedure, specific procedural rules, parties, notice, disclosure of the case to be met, adjournments, effective participation, the in-camers hearing, evidence, witnesses and the right to make submissions.
ISBN 0409806650 Hbk

Handbook of Air Transport Legislation. – Ottawa : Canadian Government Publishing Centre, 1986.
944p.
ISBN 0660533219 Llf £50.00

Handbook of arbitration practice / by Ronald Bernstein, contributors John Tackaberry ... et al. : foreword by Sir John Donaldson : introduction by Sir Michael Kerr. – London : Sweet & Maxwell in conjunction with the Chartered Institute of Arbitrators, 1987.
xxv,575p; 26cm.
Examines the constitution of the tribunal, the range of procedures available, conduct of the hearing, the role of advocates and expert witnesses, techniques of enforcement, and remuneration. Advises on arbitration in rent reviews, commodity contracts, maritime and construction disputes, and documents-only disputes.
ISBN 0421317906 £55.00

Handbook of Australian Corporate Finance. – London : Butterworths.
ISBN 0409302449 Pbk £27.00

Handbook of bankruptcy law and practice / Steven A. Frieze. – 4th ed. – London : Longman Professional (UK), 1988.
– (Practitioner Series).
Discusses the new concepts of statutory demands, individual voluntary arrangements and deeds of arrangement, and sets out the procedure leading to a bankruptcy order. Contains a list of courts with bankruptcy jurisdiction.
ISBN 085120726X Hbk £35

Handbook of business tenancies / D.W. Williams : assisted by C.M. Brand : consultant on valuation and practice C.C. Hubbard. – 1. – London : Sweet & Maxwell, 1985.
looseleaf.
Includes index.
ISBN 0421327901 £75.00

Handbook of Canadian legal terminology : revised and updated / William J. Flynn. – Toronto : Stoddart, 1986.
117p.
ISBN 0773751076

Handbook of Cautions, Oaths and Recognizances, Etc. – 10th ed. – London : Shaw & Sons, 1981.
ISBN 0721904734 Hbk £4.50

Handbook of charities, 1987-1988 ... / edited by Erroll Christie and Anne Frazer Simpson. – London : Charities Data Services, 1987.
128 p.
'... a guide for those involved in the educational field, community service and the selection and search for organisations in need of support'.
ISBN 1870914007

Handbook of Charity Law and Practice. – London : Sweet & Maxwell, 1988.
ISBN 0421358106 Pbk £27.50

Handbook of company administration / Keith Walmsley, John Birds, A. Harding Boulton. – 4th ed. – Bristol : Published under the authority of the Institute of Chartered Secretaries and Administrators by Jordon & Sons, 1981.
xvi,318p; 21cm.
Previous ed.: / by A. Harding Boulton in collaboration with J.E. Neill. 1977. Includes index.
ISBN 0853080658 Pbk £6.00

Handbook of Computer Security. – London : Kogan Page, 1987.
ISBN 185091348X Hbk £14.95

Handbook of conveyancing searches / E.O. Bourne. – 2nd ed. – London : Sweet & Maxwell, 1986.
ix,87p.
ISBN 042136680X

Handbook of Corporate Laws / G.K. Kapur. – New Delhi : S. Chand and Company.
Hbk £20.00

Handbook of Drug Laws : With Appropriate Technology for Drugs and Pharmaceuticals. – Allahabad : Universal Book Agency, 1985.
Hbk £300.00

Handbook of Financial Futures and Options / Krikic. – Cambridge : Woodhead-Faulkner, 1986.
ISBN 0859414116 Hbk £25.00

Handbook of German employment law : a practical guide to the legal aspects of employment - from hiring through termination : with a bi-lingual selection of relevant German statutes and sample forms / by Joachim Gres and Harald Jung. – Deventer, The Netherlands : Kluwer, 1983.
305p; 26cm.
ISBN 9065441441 Hbk £90.00

Handbook of Hong Kong tax statutes : profits tax, salaries tax, property tax, interest tax, estate duty, stamp duty, Board of Review decisions / by Patrick B. Paul, Leonard van Hien. – Singapore : Butterworths, 1986.
931p.
Includes texts of legislation relating to income tax, salaries tax, profits tax, property tax, estate duty, and stamp duty. Sets out Inland Revenue Departmental Interpretation and Practice Notes, and all published Inland Revenue Board of Review decisions, cross-referenced to the legislation.
ISBN 0409995274 Hbk £163.75

Handbook of international joint ventures / John Walmsley. – London : Graham & Trotman, 1983.
viii,161p; 24cm.
Includes index.
ISBN 0860103692 £22.00

Handbook of Irish Case Law 1984. – Dublin : Round Hall Press, 1983.
120p.
ISBN 0950872539 Pbk £5.95
ISBN 0947686002 Hbk £9.50

Handbook of Irish Case Law 1985. – Dublin : Round Hall Press, 1985.
120p.
ISBN 094768610X Hbk £6.95

Handbook of Irish Case Law 1986. – Dublin : Round Hall Press, 1986.
120p.
Pbk £6.95

Handbook of Irish Case Law 1987. – Dublin : Round Hall Press.
ca 120p.
ISBN 0947686266 Pbk £7.95

Handbook of Irish Case Law 1988. – Dublin : Round Hall Press, 1988.
ca 120p.
ISBN 0947686363 Pbk £9.95

Handbook of Irish Case Law 1989. – Round Hall Press.
ISBN 0947686541 Pbk £11.95

Handbook of Labour and Industrial Law. – 3rd ed. – Lucknow : Eastern Book Company, 1986.
Hbk £80.00

Handbook of leasehold reform / C.C. Hubbard and Delyth W. Williams. – 21. – London : Sweet & Maxwell, 1988.
32cm.
Includes index.
ISBN 0421351306 Llf £95.00

Handbook of legal information retrieval / edited by Jon Bing in cooperation with Tove Fjeldvig, Trygve Harvold and Robert Svoboda. – Amsterdam : North-Holland, 1984.
xviii,580p; 23cm.
Bibliography: p505-532.,- Includes index.
ISBN 044487576X £58.82

Handbook of National Agreements. – London : Engineering Employers Federation, 1985.
Hbk £8.00

Handbook of Record Linkage Methods for Health and Statistical Studies, Admin. Business. – Oxford : Oxford University Press.
ISBN 019261732X Hbk £22.50

Handbook of rent review / Ronald Bernstein and Kirk Reynolds : consultant editor on valuation and arbitration practice J.C. Hill. – 1. – London : Sweet & Maxwell in collaboration with the Royal Institution of Chartered Surveyors, 1981.
loose-leaf; 32cm.
Includes index.
ISBN 042127980X

Handbook of Singapore and Malaysian Corporate Finance / Chwee Huat Tan. – London : Butterworths, 1988.
ISBN 0409995487 Pbk £120.00

Handbook of Singapore Employment Law. – 2nd ed. – London : Butterworths, 1986.
ISBN 0409995142 Pbk £65.00

Handbook of Singapore Land Law. – London : Butterworths, 1986.
ISBN 0409995169 Hbk £69.00

Handbook of Singapore Tax Statutes, 1985-86 Edition / Laurence Chan. – Butterworths, 1986.
933p.
Contains the texts of important tax legislation, together with amendments and excerpts from the 1986/87 Budget Statement. Covers income tax, double tax treaties, estate duty, payroll tax, property tax and stamp duty.
ISBN 0409995207 Pbk £99.00

Handbook of Tax on Salaries : Incorporating the Finance Act. – New Delhi : Tata McGraw-Hill Publishing Co, 1988.
354p.
ISBN 0074518291 Pbk £5.00

Handbook of the Companies Inspection System : Inspections and Departmental Enquiries Under the Companies Act 1985. – London : HMSO, 1986.
ISBN 0115138439 Hbk £4.00

Handbook of the Money and Capital Markets. – London : Eurospan.
ISBN 089930270X Hbk £40.95

Handbook of UK Corporate Finance. – London : Butterworths, 1987.
Pbk

Handbook of Written and Oral Pleading in the Sheriff Court and Notes on the Structure of Interlocutors Sheriff Court. – London : Caledonian Books.
ISBN 0950660795 Hbk £29.50

Handbook on Basic Trial Evidence. – 2nd ed. – University Press of America.
ISBN 00819167150 Hbk £23.50
ISBN 00819167169 Pbk £13.50

Handbook on Canadian Company Law. – 7th ed. – Agincourt : Carswell, 1975.
ISBN 0459368907 Hbk £41.80

Handbook on CTT Act 1984. – Butterworths. – London : Butterworths, 1984.
ISBN 0406505349 Pbk £6.00

Handbook on Drug Laws. – Allahabad : Law Publishers, 1983.
£24.00

Handbook on European employee co-maangement / Walter Kolvenbach, P Hanau. – Kluwer Law and Taxation, 1989.
818.
ISBN 90T2802003 Llf £102/Dfl 325
Supplement. – 1989.
308.
Covers the co-determination laws, contractual agreements, and other regulations of European countries, and existing regulations of the OECD and ILO. A comparison with the US is made. Includes participative institutions at shop floor level, employee participation at board level, and selected documentation in each chapter.
ISBN 90T2800019 Llf £73/Dfl 231

Handbook on foreign trade arbitration in the CMEA countries / S. N. Lebedev, A. G. Dmitriev, V. A. Kabatov. – Moscow : s.n., 1983.
112p.
Editors: A.G. Dmitriev, V.A. Kabatov; General Editor, S.N. Lebede Translated from the Russian.

Handbook on Gold Control Act, Rules and Notifications. – 3rd ed. – Allahabad : Law Publishers, 1982.
Hbk £10.50

Handbook on Insurance Laws. – 2nd ed. – Allahabad : Law Publishers, 1983.
Hbk £22.50

Handbook on International Organisations. – Martinus Nijhoff.
ISBN 9024736587 Hbk £86.50

Handbook on marine pollution. – Arendal : Assuranceforeningen Gard, 1985.
247p.
Bibliography: p.174-179.

Handbook on maritime law
Argentina-Norway / edited by Lennart Hagberg : written by members of the Committee on Maritime and Transport Law of the Section on Business Law of the International Bar Association. – Deventer : Kluwer, 1983.
xxvii,401p.
ISBN 9065440577
Pakistan-Yugoslavia / edited by Lennart Hagberg : written by Members of the Committee on Maritme and Transport Law of the Section on Business Law of the International Bar Association. – 1983.
xxvii,296p.
ISBN 9065440585 Hbk

Handbook on Pollution Laws. – Allahabad : Law Publishers, 1983.
Hbk £18.00

Handbook on the Conduct of Public Inquiries in Canada / Alastair R. Lucas. – Butterworths, 1985.
288p.
Brings together the considerations that participants should address in designing and operating an enquiry, and analyzes the legal and organizational options available for achieving the intended goals of the inquiry process.
ISBN 0409846732 Hbk £60.00

Handbook on the Law of War for Armed Forces. – Geneva : Comite International de la Croix-Rouge, 1987.
254p.
Hbk £20.00

Handbook on the Saskatchewan Personal Property Security Act / by Ronald C.C. Cuming and Roderick J. Wood. – Saskatoon? : Law Reform Commission of Saskatchewan, 1987.
xxx,386p.
'Funded by the Law Foundation of Saskatchewan.' - T.p..
ISBN 0921923007

Handbook on the U.S. - German Tax Convention. – International Bureau of Fiscal Documentation. – Amsterdam : International Bureau of Fiscal Documentation, 1988.
Llf £880.00
Supplements-1989 renewal. –
Llf £300.00

Handbook on the United States-German Tax Convention / authors Helmut Debatin, Otto L. Walter : in cooperation with Ernst Weber and Eric Osterweil : general editors Piroska Soos and Eugen Jehle. – 4. – Amsterdam : International Bureau of Fiscal Documentation, 1966.
loose-leaf.
Includes texts of Convention and Protocol. With added title-page in German. Final loose-leaf supplement no. 50 (Dec. 1983). Parallel German and English texts.

Handbook To Marine Insurance. – 8th ed. – Witherby, 1975.
ISBN 0854930736 Hbk £18.00

Handbook to the Ontario Human Rights Code / Connie Nakatsu. – Agincourt : Carswell, 1988.
250p.
This book focuses on issues pertinent to the Ontario Human Rights Code. Topics include policy of the code, prohibited grounds and areas of discrimination, processing a human rights complaint, jurisdiction of the commission, evidence required in human rights cases, findings and awards by Board of Inquiry, review and enforcement of board decisions and alternate remedies.
Pbk

Handle with Caution : Liability in the Production, Transportation and Disposal of Dangerous Substances. – Agincourt : Carswell, 1986.
280p.
This book explains the responsibilities and liabilities, under new Canadian federal and Ontario provincial laws, of generating, transporting, hauling, and disposing of waste and dangerous goods. The new governmental powers, enforcement provisions, and compensation schemes are described in the work.
Hbk £41.75

Handler, L.G. → Wills Probate and Administration Service, New South Wales.

Handling Criminal Cases. – London : Waterlow, 1986.
ISBN 0080391583 Pbk £9.95

Handling of press and public information during the Falklands conflict : observations presented by the Secretary of State for Defence on the First Report from the Defence Committee / presented to Parliament by the Secretary of State for Defence. – London : H.M.S.O., 1983.
5p.
ISBN 0101882009

Hands up for democracy. – Trades Union Congress. – London : Trades Union Congress, 1983.
40p.
ISBN 0900878983

Handsworth Law Centre
Immigration law handbook. – Handsworth Law Centre. – 3rd ed. – TUAR, 1985.
ISBN 0951074504 Pbk £2.50

Handy, Christopher R. → Housing association law.

Handy Hints on Legal Practice / E.J. Kyrou. – North Ryde : Law Book Co, 1985.
xiv, 196p.
ISBN 0455206058 Pbk £19.50

Hanf, Kenneth → International Comparisons in Implementing Pollution Laws.

Hanks, P. J.
Australian constitutional law / by P.J. Hanks. – 3rd ed. – Sydney : Butterworths, 1985.
xxix,792p.
Previous ed.: 1980, published as Fajgenbaum and Hanks' Australian constitutional law. Includes bibliographical references and index.
ISBN 0409494836 Hbk £53.00

Hanks, Peter → Aborigines and the law.
→ Australian social security law, policy and administration.
—Relationship between legal aid agencies and social agencies : research report for the Commonwealth Legal Aid Council / by Peter Hanks, Kate Lavender, Guy Powles. – Canberra : Australian Government Publishing Service, 1983.
51p.
Bibliography: p.48.
ISBN 0644024674

Hanlon, Joseph
Beggar your neighbours : apartheid power in Southern Africa / Joseph Hanlon. – London : Catholic Institute for International Relations in collaboration with Currey, 1986.
xi,352p; 24cm.
Includes index.
ISBN 0852553072 Hbk £25.00
ISBN 0946848270 CIIR (pbk) £8.95

Hannah, Leslie
Rise of the corporate economy / Leslie Hannah. – 2nd ed. – London : Methuen, 1983.
xii,266p; 23cm.
Previous ed.: 1976. Includes index.
ISBN 0416348505 Hbk £
ISBN 0416348602 Pbk

Hannam, Harry → SCOLMA directory of libraries and special collections on Africa in the United Kingdom and Western Europe.

Hanneman, H. W. A. M.
Patentability of computer software : an international guide to the protection of computer-related inventions / by H.W.A.M. Hanneman. – Deventer : Kluwer Law and Taxation Publishers, 1985.
257p; 23cm.
ISBN 9065442251

Hannes Jonsson
Friends in conflict : the Anglo-Icelandic cod wars and the law of the sea / Hannes Jonsson. – London : C.Hurst, 1982.
xi,240p.
Bibliography: p225-233.

Hannigan, Brenda M. → Company law.

Hannikainen, Lauri
Peremptory Norma (Jus Cogens) in International Law : Historical Development, Criteria, Present Status. – Helsinki : Lakimiesliiton Kustannus, 1988.
781p.
ISBN 9516403948 Hbk £519.00

Hannum, Hildegard → Thou shalt not be aware : society's betrayal of the child.

Hannum, Hunter → Thou shalt not be aware : society's betrayal of the child.

Hannum, Hurst → Guide to international human rights practice.
—Right to leave and return in international law and practice / by Hurst Hannum. – Dordrecht : Nijhoff, 1987.
xiii, 189p. – (International studies in human rights).
Includes index.
ISBN 9024734452

Hansaria, B.L.
Writ Jurisdiction Under the Constitution. – Bombay : Tripathi, 1984.
Hbk £90.00

Hansell, D S
Elements of Insurance. – 4th ed. – Plymouth : Macdonald & Evans, 1985.
ISBN 0712106723 Pbk £5.95

Hansen, et al
Canadian Taxation. – Toronto : DeBoo, 1981.
ISBN 0888201001 Hbk £39.95

Hansen, G.
Arizona : Its Constitution and Government. – 2nd ed. – University Press of America, 1988.
ISBN 0819161446 Pbk £9.25

Hanson
Legal Aid - How to use it / Levenson. – London : Legal Action Group, 1985.
ISBN 0905099095 Pbk £11.00

Hanson, Charles G.
Striking out strikes : changing employment relations in the British labour market / Charles G. Hanson and Graham Mather. – London : Institute of Economic Affairs, 1988.
94p; 22cm.
ISBN 0255362080

Hanson, D.
Dictionary of Banking and Finance. – London : Pitman Publishing, 1985.
ISBN 0273018590 Hbk £35.00

Haraszti, Gyorgy → Questions of international law, vol.2 : edited by Gyorgy Haraszti.

Harbison, J. F. A. → Legal aspects of medical practice.

Hard bargaining. – Oxford : Oxford University Press, 1988.
ISBN 0198255926 Hbk £22.50

Hard graft in Hong Kong : scandal; corruption; the ICAC / H. J. Lethbridge. – Hong Kong : Oxford University Press, 1985.
viii,247p.
Bibliography: p232-243.
ISBN 0195838963

Hardcastle, A. J. → Saint Piran Limited : investigation under Section 165(b) and Section 172 of the Companies Act 1948 : final report.

Harden → Introduction to accounting for business studies.

Harden, Ian
Noble lie : the British constitution and the rule of law / Ian Harden and Norman Lewis : foreword by Sir Douglas Wass. – London : Hutchinson, 1986.
xiii,334p; 23cm.
Bibliography: p313-317. - Includes index.
ISBN 0091641306 £25.00

Harden, Sheila → Small is dangerous : micro states in a macro world: report of a Study Group of the David Davies Memorial Institute of International Studies.

Harders, Clarrie W. → Report of the Inquiry into Disclosure of Electoral Expenditure.

Harding, A.J.
Common Law in Singapore and Malaysia. – Butterworths, 1985.
401p.
Series of essays which, by presenting a number of case studies of different aspects of local law, explore the problems raised by the application of the common law in Singapore and Malaysia. Includes discussion of the Privy Council as court of last resort in Singapore and Malaysia 1957-1983, and the abuse of discretion. Also looks at Chinese marriage custom.
ISBN 0409995096 Hbk £110.00

Harding, Alan → Roll of the Shropshire eyre of 1256.

Harding, Andrew J
Judicial review of public duties. – Oxford : Clarendon Press, 1989.
300.
Examines the principles and remedies which have been applied in public duty cases such as postal strikes and licence applications. Argues that public duties should be taken more seriously by the courts.
ISBN 0198256078 Hbk £30

Harding, Christopher → Imprisonment in England and Wales : a concise history.
—Notices and Group Exemptions in EEC Competition Law. – Oxford : ESC Publishing Ltd.
ISBN 0906214041 Llf £45.00
—Sentencing and the penal system : text and materials / by Christopher Harding and Laurence Koffman. – London : Sweet & Maxwell, 1988.
xxvii,401p; 25cm.
Bibliography: p385-396. - Includes index.
ISBN 0421357703 Pbk £13.50

Harding, George R.
Acts and orders relating to joint stock companies / by George R. Harding. – Brisbane : Watson, Ferguson, 1887.
xxviii,239p.
Includes index.
—Acts and rules relating to insolvency / by George R. Harding and P. MacPherson. – Brisbane : Watson, Ferguson, 1887.
lviii,338p.
Includes index.

Harding, Jim
Aboriginal Rights and Government Wrongs : Uranium Mining and Neocolonialism in Northern Saskatchewan. – Regina : Prairie Justice Research, 1988.
ISBN 0773101403 Hbk £12.00

Harding, John → Probation and the community : a practice and policy reader.

Harding, S.B.
Financial Accounting. – London : VanNostrand Reinhold, 1988.
ISBN 0278000150 Pbk £13.00

Harding, T.W. → Human rights and mental patients in Japan : report of a mission by Dr. T. W. Harding, Judge J. Schneider, Dr. H. M. Visotsky and Dr. C. L. Graves on behalf of the International Commission of Jurists and the International Commission of Health Professionals.

Harding, Thomas Garrard → Norwest Holst Limited : investigation under section 165(b) of the Companies Act 1948.

Harding, V. A. → Survey of Documentary Sources for Property-Holding in London Before the Great Fire, Vol. 22.

Hardingham, I. J.
Australian family property law / by I. J. Hardingham and M. A. Neave. – Sydney : Law Book Company, 1984.
liii,647p.
ISBN 0455205132
—Discretionary Trusts : with 1978 Supplement / R. Baxt. – 2nd ed. – Butterworths, 1984.
235p.
ISBN 040949383X Hbk £55.00
—Wills and intestacy in Australia and New Zealand : being a revised and consolidated version of Hardingham, Neave and Ford's The Law of Wills and Hardingham's The Law of Intestate Succession in Australia and New Zealand / by I.J. Hardingham, M.A. Neave, H.A.J. Ford. – Sydney : Law Book Co., 1983.
xliv,518p.
Includes bibliographical references and index.
ISBN 0455204152

Hardjasoemantri, Koesnadi
Environmental Legislation in Indonesia. – Yogyakarta : Gadjah Mada University Press, 1985.
41p.
ISBN 9794200468 Pbk £4.00

Hardless, Shri
Disputed Documents, Handwriting and Thumb-print Identification / Rao Chiyod Seshagiri. – 4th ed. – Allahabad : Law Book Company, 1988.
400p.
Pbk £125.00

Hardman, Anna → Western Europe's migrant workers.

Hardy, Anne E.
Crown priority in insolvency / Anne E. Hardy. – Toronto : Carswell, 1986.
xxxii, 195 p.; 24 cm.
Includes index. Bibliography: p. 179-181.
ISBN 0459391402

Hardy, E.
Encyclopedia of Shipping Law Sources UK. – London : LLoyd's of London Press, 1988.
ISBN 1850440115 Hbk £175.00

Hardy Ivamy, E. R.
Butterworth's Dictionary of Company Law. – 2nd ed. – Wellington : Butterworths, 1985.
A practical guide to company law of the United Kingdom, this book gives brief details of the Companies Act provisions relating to the terms defined within. Technical phrases from business and finance are listed along with legal terms.
ISBN 0406681635 Hbk
ISBN 0406681643 Pbk

Hargreaves
Practitioner's Guide to the Police and Criminal Evidence Act '84 / Levenson. – London : Legal Action Group.
ISBN 0905099079 Pbk £13.00

Hargreaves, J.
Home-owner's guide. – Cambridge : Woodhead-Faulkner, 1987.
ISBN 085941423X Pbk £4.95

Harker, Norman → Commercial leases.

Harkness, Ethne E. → Professional negligence today : the text of two lectures delivered to the Belfast Solicitors' Association on 9 and 23 May 1985.
—Some Aspects of Building Contracts. – Belfast : Queen's University of Belfast, 1982.
31p.
Pbk £2.95

Harland, D. J. → Cases and Materials on Contract Law in Australia.
→ Contract law in Australia.
→ Trade practices and consumer protection : a commentary on the Trade Practices Act 1974.

Harling → Modern Equity.

Harlow, Carol
Compensation and government torts / by Carol Harlow. – London : Sweet & Maxwell, 1982.
xvii,173p; 19cm.
Bibliography: p163-167. - Includes index.
ISBN 0421292504 Hbk £12.50
ISBN 0421292601 Pbk
—Law and administration / Carol Harlow, Richard Rawlings. – London : Weidenfeld and Nicolson, 1984.
xxvi,718p; 22cm.
Bibliography: p686-695. - Includes index.
ISBN 0297782398 Hbk £
ISBN 0297782401 Pbk £15.95
→ Public law and politics.

Harlow, P. A.
Contractual claims : an annotated bibliography / compiled by P.A. Harrow. – 4th ed. – Ascot : Chartered Institute of Building, 1986.
vi,25p; 25cm.
Previous ed.: 1979.
ISBN 0906600847 Pbk

Harm to others. – Oxford : Oxford University Press, 1984.
ISBN 0195034090 Hbk £22.50

Harmer, C
Practical partnership
Supplement / Camp. – London : Longman Professional, 1982.
ISBN 0851210392 Pbk £13.95
—Practical partnership for solicitors / C. Harmer and P. Camp. – 2nd ed. – London : Longman Professional (UK), 1990.
Examines drafting a partnership agreement, taxation, finance, accounts, and matters of professional conduct. Covers the Practice Rules, Publicity Code 1988 and the Introductions and Referrals Code 1988. Includes material on practising abroad, the Overseas Practice Rules 1987, and the effect of the European element and 1992 on the profession. Also deals with Solicitors Incorporated Practice Rules 1988.
ISBN 0851215513 Hbk £29.50

Harmer, C. G.
Family Law In 1985 : A New Look At Some Old Problems. – London : Law Society, 1985.
23p. – (Nineteen Eighty-Five Crash Course Transcripts).
Hbk £2.05

Harmer, Caroline → Law and Practice in Matrimonial Causes.

Harmes, L.T.C.
Amler : Precedents of Pleadings. – Durban : Professional Publishers, 1988.
ISBN 0409011002 Hbk

Harmonisation Measures in the Field of Legal Data Processing in the Member States of the Council of Europe. – Strasbourg : Council of Europe, 1982.
ISBN 9287100365

Harmonisation of company and related law in Europe : timetable and progress of draft directives and other proposals / Companies Division, Department of Trade. – London : Companies Division, Department of Trade, 1982.
13p.

Harmonisation of company and related law in Europe : timetable and progress of draft directives and other proposals / Companies Legislation Division, Department of Trade. – London : The Division, 1983.
15p.
Previous ed.: 1982.

Harmonisation of company and related law in the European Community : progress on draft directives and other proposals / Department of Trade and Industry, Companies Division. – London : The Division, 1987.
13p.

Harmonisation of company and related law in the European Community : progress on draft directives and other proposals / Companies Division, Department of Trade and Industry. – Sept. 1987. – London : The Division, 1987.
27p.

Harmonisation of company and related law in the European Community : timetable and progress of draft directives and other proposals / Companies Legislation Division, Department of Trade and Industry. – London : Companies Legislation Division, Department of Trade and Industry, 1983.
13p.
Previous ed.: published as 'Harmonisation of company and related law in Europe', 1982.

Harmonisation of laws relating to the requirement of written proof and to the admissibility of reproductions of documents and recordings on computers : Recommendation No.R (81) 20 adopted by the Committee of Ministers of the Council of Europe on 11 December 1981 and Explanatory memorandum. – Council of Europe. – Strabourg : Council of Europe, 1982.
21p; 21cm. – (Legal Affairs).
ISBN 9287100446

Harmonisation of National Procedures Relating to Asylum. – Strasbourg : Council of Europe, 1982.
ISBN 9287100497

Harmonization of business law in Canada / Ronald C.C. Cuming, research coordinator. – Toronto : University of Toronto Press, 1986.
xx, 245 p.; 23 cm.
Includes bibliographies. Contents: Harmonization of provincial laws, with particular reference to commercial, consumer, and corporate law / Jacob S. Ziegel – The regulation of the securities market and the harmonization of provincial laws / Philip Anisman – Harmonization of Canadian personal property security law / Ronald C.C. Cuming – Harmonization of Canadian insurance law / Marvin G. Baer.
ISBN 0802073034 Pbk

Harmonization of Laws in the European Communities : Products, Liability, Conflict of Laws and Corporation Law. – London : Eurospan.
ISBN 0813909856 Hbk £17.50

Harms, L.S. → Right to Communicate : a New Human Right.

Harper
Fingertip Guide to Criminal Law / Hamilton. – London : Butterworths, 1986.
ISBN 0406103801 Pbk £17.50

Harper, Patricia
Changing laws for changing families / Patricia Harper. – Melbourne : Institute of Family Studies, 1982.
24p. – (Discussion paper).
Paper prepared for the 3rd Australian Conference on adoption, 'Changing Families', Adelaide, 14-19 May 1982.
ISBN 0642884552
—Children in stepfamilies : their legal and family status / Patricia Harper. – Melbourne : Institute of Family Studies, 1984.
– (Policy background paper).
Bibliography: p.28-29.
ISBN 0642876665

Harpwood
GCSE Law. – London : Financial Training, 1987.
ISBN 1851850546 Pbk £7.95

Harrasim, Mary
Landlord-Tenant Rights in Alberta. – 5th ed. – North Vancouver : International Self-Counsel Press, 1986.
106p.
ISBN 0889082413 Hbk £6.95

Harrington, David
Tolley's capital gains tax 1981-82 / David Harrington and Glyn Saunders. – Croydon : Tolley, 1981.
viii,245p.
Includes index. Up to date to 1 August 1981.
ISBN 0854590315
→ Tolley's corporation tax 1981-82.

Harrington, Dorothy
Knight's Environmental and Public Health Acts. – Tonbridge : Ernest Benn.
5000p.
ISBN 0853140235 Llf £495.00

Harris
Justice Denied. – Toronto : Macmillan of Canada.
ISBN 0771596901 Hbk £24.95
→ Multilateral Treaties : Current Status and Index.

Harris, Amy Bjork
Staying OK / Amy Bjork Harris and Thomas A. Harris. – London : Pan, 1986.
xv,297p; 18cm.
Originally published: London : Cape, 1985. Includes index.
ISBN 033029136X Pbk £2.95

Harris, B.
Rehabilitation of Offenders : a Guide to the Law. – London : Fourmat.
ISBN 1851900578 Pbk £9.95

Harris, B.V.
Executive Law-Making Under the Economic Stabilisation Act 1948. – Auckland : Legal Research Foundation, 1984.
Hbk £13.50

Harris, Brian
Criminal jurisdiction of magistrates / by Brian Harris. – 11th ed. – Chichester? : Barry Rose, 1988.
lxxxi,848p.
Previous ed.: 1986. Includes index.
ISBN 1870080513
—Guide to the New Law of Family Proceedings in Magistrates Courts, Including Adoption. – Chichester : Barry Rose, 1983.
ii, 49p.
ISBN 0859920631 Hbk £4.60
—Magistrate's Companion : Guide for Magistrates in Announcing Sentence and Other Orders of the Court. – 3rd ed. – Chichester : Barry Rose, 1985.
88p.
ISBN 0859922332 Hbk £3.75

Harris, D.
HAC Guide to Taxation of Bloodstock Industry. – Stoy Hayward, 1987.
ISBN 0870382005 Hbk £20.00

Harris, D. J.
Cases and materials on international law / by D.J. Harris. – 3rd ed. – London : Sweet & Maxwell, 1983.
li,810p; 24cm.
Previous ed.: 1979. Includes index.
ISBN 0421292709 Hbk £26.00
ISBN 0421292806 Pbk £19.50
→ Civil liberties : cases and materials.
→ Multilateral treaties : index and current status.

Harris, David
Canadian Cases on Employment Law
Vol. 14. – Agincourt : Carswell, 1987.
Hbk £75.00
—Wrongful Dismissal. – Toronto : DeBoo, 1984.
This treatise presents the Canadian law of wrongful dismissal. Awards for mental distress, constructive dismissal, punitive damages, just cause for dismissal, special status of Crown employees, and other related issues are discussed in depth in the work.
ISBN 0888201613 Hbk £85.00

Harris, Donald →Compensation and support for illness and injury.
—Contract law today: Anglo-French comparisons / Denis Tallon. – Oxford : Clarendon Press, 1989.
400.
The result of a joint research project by two research institutes, one in the UK and one in France. It examines the evolution of contract in England and France.
Contract lawyers, comparative lawyers
ISBN 0198355934 Hbk £40

—Remedies in contract and tort / Donald Harris. – London : Weidenfeld & Nicolson, 1988.
xxxvii,411p.
Includes index.
ISBN 0297793551

Harris, Edwin C.
Canadian income taxation. – 4th ed. – Toronto : Butterworths, 1986.
xxv,776p.
Previous ed.: 1983. Includes index.
ISBN 0409805149

Harris, Garth
Goods and Services Tax Act 1985 : the Application of the Act / Wayne Mapp. – Butterworths, 1986.
ISBN 0409787663 Pbk £36.30

Harris, George
Policeman's Lot. – Repr. of 1979 ed. – London : Police Review Publishing, 1983.
ISBN 0851649939 Pbk £1.95
—Spare a Copper. – London : Police Review Publishing, 1982.
ISBN 0851640001 Pbk £1.95

Harris, J.
Scapegoat Famous Courts Martial. – Severn House.
ISBN 0727821032 Pbk £12.95

Harris, James →Claims to the possession of land : the law and practice.

Harris, John
Consumers : Know Your Rights. – 3rd ed. – London : Oyez Longman, 1983.
– (It's Your Law Ser.).
ISBN 0851207286 Hbk £8.50
ISBN 0851207278 Pbk £4.95
—Your Business and the Law. – 2nd ed. – London : Oyez Longman, 1983.
– (It's Your Law Ser.).
ISBN 0851207251 Hbk £8.50

Harris, Marjorie →Everyday Law : a Survival Guide for Canadians.

Harris, Michael →Lawmakers and Wayward Whigs : Law and Justice in South Australia.

Harris, Nigel H. →Medical negligence.

Harris, Olivia →Latin American Women.

Harris, P.
Introduction to Law. – 3rd ed. – Weidenfeld & Nicolson.
– (Law In Context Series).
ISBN 0297793403 Hbk £18.95
ISBN 0297793411 Pbk £9.50

Harris, Peter J.
Young Offenders Act Manual. – Aurora : Canada Law Book Co.
– (Text Books-Criminal).
Hbk £94.00

Harris, Phil →Welfare law and order : a critical introduction to law for social workers.

Harris, R. P.
Management Contracting / A. C. Sidwell. – London : Collins, 1987.
250p.
ISBN 0003833143 Hbk £17.50

Harris, Ralph
Over-ruled on Welfare / Arthur Seldon. – London : Institute of Economic Affairs.
Pbk £3.00

Harris, Rhodri →Forfaiting : an alternative approach to export trade finance.

Harris, Simon
Food and farm policies of the European Community / Simon Harris, Alan Swinbank and Guy Wilkinson. – Chichester : Wiley, 1983.
xii,354p; 24cm.
Includes bibliographies and index.
ISBN 047110261X £12.50

Harris, Thomas A. →Staying OK.

Harris, William Vernon →Studies in Roman law in memory of A. Arthur Schiller.

Harrison →Crime UK 1988.
—Ejectments in Ireland. – London : Butterworths.
ISBN 0862053366 Hbk £35.50

Harrison, Edward R.
Harrison's Inland Revenue index to tax cases : a judicial dictionary of tax law / prepared on the instructions of the Board of Inland Revenue. – 7th ed. 2 vols. – London : Oyez Longman, 1982.
Loose-leaf.
ISBN 0851206492

Harrison, J.
Hume's Theory of Justice. – Oxford : Oxford University Press, 1983.
ISBN 0198247249 Pbk £8.95
—Remedies for police misconduct (LAG). – London : Sweet & Maxwell, 1987.
ISBN 0905099168 Pbk £12.00

Harrison, John
Police misconduct : legal remedies / John Harrison. – London : Legal Action Group, 1987.
xxix,218p.
Guide to the remedies and procedures available in this area. Covers police complaints, civil actions against the police, the European Convention on Human Rights, police discipline, judicial review, wrongful convictions, criminal proceedings, and legal aid. Appendices include levels of damages and useful names and addresses.
ISBN 0905099168

Harrison, M. L. →Planning control : philosophies, prospects and practice.

Harrison, Margaret →Divorce in Australia.
—Informal marriages / by Margaret Harrison. – Rev. ed. – Melbourne : Institute of Family Studies, 1982.
12 p.; 23 cm. – (Working paper).
Bibliography: p. 10.
ISBN 0642887780 Pbk

Harrison, R. A.
Irish Reports Digests : 1894-1970, 6 Vols.
Vol. 4, 1939-1948 /. – Green. – Abingdon : Professional Books.
Hbk £56.00
Vol. 5, 1949-1958. –
Hbk £56.00

Harrison, T.
Law for Housing Managers. – 2nd ed. – London : Business Education, 1986.
ISBN 0907679145 Pbk £13.95

Harrison, Tim
Access to information in local government / by Tim Harrison. – London : Sweet & Maxwell, 1988.
110p.
Covers the Local Government (Access to Information) Act 1985, including a chapter on access by elected members of councils. Also contains the Data Protection Act 1984 as it relates to councils, the Access to Personal Files Act 1987, and the common law.
ISBN 0421384107 £10.00

Harrison's Inland Revenue index to tax cases : a judicial dictionary of tax law / prepared on the instructions of the Board of Inland Revenue. – 7th ed. 2 vols. – London : Oyez Longman, 1982.
Loose-leaf.
ISBN 0851206492

Harrod
UN Under Attack / Schrijver. – Aldershot : Avebury.
ISBN 056605695X Hbk £18.50

Harrowes, D.
Managing the Partnership Office. – London : Butterworths, 1978.
ISBN 0406221529 Pbk £8.50

Harry, C.B.E.
Law of the Sea and Antarctica. – Hobart : University of Tasmania, Department of Political Science.
£1.50

Harry Sacher Institute for Legislative Research and Comparative Law →Bibliography of Israeli law in European languages.

Hart, C. W. B. →Province of Transvaal ordinances and regulations : including pre-union legislation in force in that province together with a reference to decided cases.

Hart, Geoffrey E. →Copyright law in Australia and the rights of performers, authors and composers in the Pacific region.

Hart, Gerry
Dictionary of taxation / by Gerry Hart : consultant B.E.V. Sabine. – London : Butterworths, 1981.
v,236p; 23cm. – (Butterworths professional dictionaries series).
ISBN 040652159X Hbk £14.00
ISBN 0406521603 Pbk

Hart, H.
Concept Of Law. – Oxford : Oxford University Press, 1961.
ISBN 0198760728 Pbk £6.95
—Essays in Jurisprudence and Philosophy. – Oxford : Oxford University Press, 1983.
ISBN 0198253877 Hbk £19.50
ISBN 0198253885 Pbk £8.95

—Punishment and Responsibility. – Oxford : Oxford University Press, 1968.
ISBN 0198251815 Pbk £6.50

Hart, H. L. A.
Causation in the law / by H.L.A. Hart and Tony Honore. – 2nd ed. – Oxford : Clarendon, 1985.
lxxxi,516p; 23cm.
Previous ed.: 1959. Bibliography: p498-507. - Includes index.
ISBN 019825475X Hbk £25.00
ISBN 0198254741 Pbk £14.50
—Essays in jurisprudence and philosophy / by H.L.A. Hart. – Oxford : Clarendon, 1983.
viii,396p; 23cm.
Collection of essays first published between 1953 and 1981. Includes index.
ISBN 0198253877 Pbk £
ISBN 0198253885 £7.50
—Essays on Bentham : studies on jurisprudence and political theory / by H.L.A. Hart. – Oxford : Clarendon, 1982.
272p; 23cm.
Includes index.
ISBN 0198253486 Hbk £17.50
ISBN 0198254687 Pbk £4.95

Hart, Marilyn →Use of paperbacks in public libraries in the United Kingdom : a review of research.

Hart, R. J.
Copyright & computers / Cliff Dilloway. – London : Gower in association with Institute of Purchasing and Supply, 1985.
xii,126p; 23cm.
Bibliography: p123-126. Includes: Copyright & computers / R.J. Hart. Originally published: London : British Computer Society, 1983.
ISBN 0566025205 £21.45

Harte, J.
Landscape, Land use and the Law. – Spon (E & FN), 1984.
ISBN 0419125205 Pbk £16.95

Harte, Peter J. →Privacy and data protection : an international bibliography.

Harting →Administrative Receivership Law & Practice England & Wales.

Hartle, Douglas G.
Expenditure budget process of the Government of Canada : a public choice rent-seeking perspective / Douglas G. Hartle. – Toronto : Canadian Tax Foundation, 1988.
xxvii,316p.
Includes index.
ISBN 0888080301
—Revenue budget process of the Government of Canada : description, appraisal and proposals / Douglas G. Hartle. – Toronto : Canadian Tax Foundation, 1982.
xii,76p.
Includes index.
ISBN 0888080093

Hartley, M.
Checklists For Solicitors. – 5th ed. – London : Longman Professional, 1987.
ISBN 0851211720 Pbk £15.95

Hartley, Trevor C →Cases and materials on international business transactions.
—Cases and materials on international business transactions / T.C. Hartley. – London : London School of Economics, 1987.
8.
A collection of course material.
—Civil jurisdiction and judgments : the application in England of the convention on jurisdiction and the enforcement of judgments in civil and commercial matters under the Civil Jurisdiction and Judgments Act 1982 / by T.C. Hartley. – London : Sweet & Maxwell, 1984.
xxi,233p; 25cm.
Includes index.
ISBN 0421311800 Pbk £18.00
—Foundations of European community law : an introduction to the constitutional and administrative law of the European Community / by T.C. Hartley. – 2nd ed. – Oxford : Clarendon Press, 1988.
li,496p.
Includes bibliographies and index. Revised from the 1981 edition. Discusses the basic principles of European Community law and examines aspects of interes to lawyers. The new edition takes into account changes in treaty, statute and case law since 1981.
ISBN 0198762070 Pbk £17.95
ISBN 0198762089 Hbk £40
—Government and law : an introduction to the working of the constitution in Britain / by T.C. Hartley and J.A.G. Griffith. – 2nd ed. – London : Weidenfeld and Nicolson, 1981.
xxxii,472p. – (Law in context).
Bibliography: 464-468p.
ISBN 0297779745

Hartley, W.
Matrimonial Conveyancing. – 3rd ed. – London : Longman Professional, 1988.
ISBN 0851212832 Pbk £22.00

Hartley, William M.
Matrimonial Conveyancing : A Draftsman's Handbook. – London : Oyez Longman, 1981.
ISBN 0851206034 Hbk £9.95

Hartmann, Charles
Anglo-American privacy law : an economic analysis / Charles J. Hartmann and Stephen M. Renas. – s.l. : s.n., 1985.
36,12p.
Includes bibliographical references.

Hartrick and Lazor
Annotated Child Welfare Act. – Hartrick and Lazor. – Agincourt : Carswell, 1983.
460p.
Hbk £29.50

Hartrick, Michael D.
Child Welfare Act annotated / by Michael D. Hartrick and Yan Arthur M. Lazor. – Toronto : Carswell, 1983.
xxix,431p.
Includes index. Includes text of the Ontario Child Welfare Act 1980 and related Regulations.
ISBN 0459357107

Harvard Law School → Taxation of corporations and shareholders.

Harvey
British Constitution / Bather. – 4th ed. – London : Macmillan, 1977.
ISBN 0333214706 Pbk £5.95
—Industrial Relations and Employment Law. – London : Butterworths.
Service.
ISBN 0406221731 Llf £120.00

Harvey, Alan Burnside → Damages for personal injury and death in Canada.

Harvey, Audrey
How to Become a Lay Advocate. – 2nd ed. – London : Shelter, 1984.
Hbk £1.00

Harvey, Brian W.
Auctions : law and practice / Brian W. Harvey, Franklin Meisel. – London : Butterworths, 1985.
300p; 25cm.
Includes index.
ISBN 0406526605 Pbk £17.00
—Auctions Law and Practice / Franklin Meisel. – London : Butterworths, 1985.
ISBN 0406526605 Pbk £29.00

→ Consumer and trading law : cases and materials.

→ Consumer and Trading Law - Cases and Materials.

—Law of consumer protection and fair trading / by Brian W. Harvey and Deborah L. Parry. – 3rd ed. – London : Butterworths, 1987.
xxxii,435p; 22cm.
Includes parts 1-4 of the Consumer Protection Act 1987.
ISBN 0406222622 Hbk £25.00
ISBN 0406222630 Pbk £17.95

Harvey, Cameron → Chief Justice Samuel Freedman : a great Canadian judge : a collection of the reasons for judgment of the Honourable Samuel Freedman, Justice of the Court of Queen's Bench of Manitobe (1952-60), Justice of the Court of Appeal of Manitoba (1960-83), and Chief Justice of Manitoba (1971-83).
—Legal Wit and Whimsy : an Anthology of Legal Humour. – Agincourt : Carswell, 1988.
168p.
Hbk £22.00

Harvey, Eric L.
Tolley's capital transfer tax 1981-82 / by Eric L. Harvey. – Croydon : Tolley, 1981.
vii,63p.
Includes index. Up to date to 1 August 1981.
ISBN 0854590366
—Tolley's income tax 1986-87 / by Eric L. Harvey and Glyn Saunders with Patrick Noakes. – 71st ed. – Croydon : Tolley Publishing, 1986.
xi,596p.
Includes index.
ISBN 0854592385

—Tolley's income tax 1988-89 / by Eric L. Harvey and Glyn Saunders : with David Smailes. – 73rd ed. – Croydon, Surrey : Tolley, 1988.
xii,623p.
Includes index.
ISBN 0854593462

→ Tolley's taxation in the Republic of Ireland 1981-82.

→ Tolley's taxation in the Republic of Ireland 1987-88.

Harvey, R. J. → Industrial relations and employment law.

Harvey, Richard → Tax and financial planning for sportsmen and entertainers.

Harvey, Wendy
So, You Have to Go to Court : a Child's Guide to Testifying as a Witness in Child Abuse Cases / Anne Watson-Russell. – Butterworths, 1986.
48p.
ISBN 040980519X Pbk £7.95
—So, You've Been Busted! / Anne Watson-Russell. – Butterworths, 1988.
48p.
Guide to the Youth Court. Discusses what the reader needs to know about court, how to get a lawyer, what to talk about with a lawyer, seeing the youth worker, letters of reference, getting parents ready for court, seeing a psychologist, the trial, taking the oath, witnesses and cross-examination, and the verdict and sentencing.
ISBN 0409809853 Pbk £7.95

Harwood, Michael
Modern English land law / by Michael Harwood. – 2nd ed. – London : Sweet & Maxwell, 1982.
xliii,597p; 23cm.
Previous ed.: published as English land law. 1975. Includes index.
ISBN 0421278900 Hbk £
ISBN 0421279001 Pbk £12.95

Has the Trade Union Movement a Place in Europe?. – Exeter : European Atlantic Movement, 1982.
Hbk £0.50

Hasan, Ahmad
Analogical Reasoning in Islamic Jurisprudence. – Islamabad : Islamic Research Institute, 1986.
viii, 489p.
ISBN 9694080649 Hbk £20.00

Hasan, Askari
Railway Property (Unlawful Possession) Act 1966. – Lucknow : Eastern Book Company, 1983.
471p.
Pbk £45.00

Hasan, S.M.
Socio-Economic Re-evaluation of the Torts Law of Liability for Personal Injuries. – Lucknow : Eastern Book Company, 1962.
115p.
Pbk £5.00

Hasan, Shariful
Supreme Court : Fundamental Rights and Directive Principles. – New Delhi : Deep and Deep Publications, 1984.
120p.
Hbk £60.00

Haskins, Deloitte
Tolley's Accounting Problems of the Companies Acts : Practical Guidance on Recent Legislation / Sells. – Croydon : Tolley, 1984.
136p.
ISBN 0854591478 Hbk £7.95
—Tolley's Double Taxation Relief / Sells. – Croydon : Tolley.
175p.
ISBN 0510493874 Hbk £8.95

Hasselbalch, Ole
Perspective on labour law / Ole Hasselbalch, Alan C. Neal, Anders Victorin. – Stockholm : Almqvist & Wiksell, 1982.
128p.
ISBN 0421307102

Hastings, James
Expenses in the Supreme and Sheriff Coourts of Scotland. – Edinburgh : Green (W.) & Son, 1989.
A follow on as opposed to a revision of Maclaren except where the position has changed since 1912. Unlike Maclaren, it includes all relative material regarding expenses relating to non-contentious business. With chapters on legal aid and additional discretionary fees. Also examines difference between a client or fund paying expenses and an unsuccessful party paying, as well as the extent to which Scottish solicitors 'subsidise' legal aid.
ISBN 0414008928 Hbk

Hastings, R. P.
Poverty and the Poor Law in the North Riding of Yorkshire : Circa 1780-1837. – York : St. Anthony's Press, 1982.
– (Borthwick Papers Ser.).
Pbk £3.00

Haswell, C. K.
Civil Engineering Contracts : Practice and Procedure / D. S. de Silva. – London : Butterworths, 1982.
ISBN 0408005262 Hbk

Hatchard, John
Case book on criminal law / by John Hatchard and Muna Ndulo. – Lusaka : Government Printer, 1983.
viii,425p.
Includes index.
ISBN 0903826585

Hate propaganda / Law Reform Commission of Canada. – Ottawa : The Commission, 1986.
57,63p. – (Working paper).
Includes bibliographies. Added t.p. in French: La propagande haineuse. Pages numbered in opposite directions. Text in English and French.

Hatty, Suzanne → National Conference on Domestic Violence : proceedings, 11-15 November 1985.

Hauser, Wolfgang
Legal Regime for Deep Seabed Mining under the Law of the Sea Convention. – Dordrecht : Kluwer, 1983.
250p.
ISBN 9065441166 Hbk £107.00
—Legal Regime for Deep Seabed Mining under the Law of the Sea Convention. – Frankfurt : Alfred Metzner, 1984.
ISBN 3787540180 Hbk £98.00

Havelock, Keith R. → Concise trade mark law and practice.

Havemann, Paul → Law and order for Canada's indigenous people.
—Law and Order for Canada's Indigenous People : a Review of the Recent Literature Relating to the Operation of the Criminal Justice System and Canada's Indigenous People. – Regina : Prairie Justice Research, 1985.
ISBN 0773100016 Hbk £18.00
—Team Work : Sashatoon's Unified Family Court Project 1978-1981. – Regina : Prairie Justice Research, 1982.
ISBN 0773100385 Hbk £24.00

Havers
Royal Baccarat Scandal / Grayson. – Souvenir Press.
ISBN 0285628526 Hbk £12.95
ISBN 0285628372 Pbk £6.95

Havnevik, Kjell J → IMF and the World Bank in Africa : conditionality, impact, and alternatives.

Havrot
Smyth Town Plot Land Act, 1983, Bill Pr033 : An Act Respecting Certain Land in the Town of Smyth, in the District of Nipissing. – Ontario : Ontario Government Publications Service, 1983.
3p.
Hbk £0.30

Haward, Lionel
Forensic Psychology. – London : Batsford, 1981.
ISBN 0713424753 Hbk £15.00

Hawdon, David → Changing structure of the world oil industry.

Hawk, B.E.
United States and Common Market antitrust policies. – Matthew Bender, 1987.
ISBN 0000999063 Hbk £50.00

Hawke, Neil
Introduction to Administrative Law. – Oxford : ESC Publishing Ltd, 1984.
296p.
ISBN 0906214254 Hbk £19.95
ISBN 0906214246 Pbk £11.95
—Right to buy in rural areas : an investigation of section 19 of the Housing Act 1980 / Neil Hawke. – Leicester : Leicester Polytechnic. School of Law, 1985.
33p. – (Research monographs).

Hawker
Institute of Civil Engineers' arbitration practice / John Uff. – Telford (Thomas), 1986.
ISBN 0727702475 Hbk £18.50

Hawkes
Cash Flow and Credit Management / Slater. – Telegraph Publications, 1988.
ISBN 0863672264 Pbk £6.95

Hawkins, A. J. → Landlord and tenant law.
→ Standard business contracts.

Hawkins, David J. → Boynton's Guide to Compulsory Purchase and Compensation.

Hawkins, Gordon → Capital punishment and the American agenda.
—Prisoners' rights : a study of human rights and Commonwealth prisoners / by Gordon Hawkins. – Canberra : Australian Government Publishing Service, 1986.
vii,102p. – (Occasional paper).
Bibliography: p.95-102.
ISBN 0644054603

Hawkins, Keith
Environment and enforcement : regulation and the social definition of pollution / Keith Hawkins. – Oxford : Clarendon Press, 1983.
xvi,253p.
Includes index. Bibliography: p235-247.
ISBN 0198275145 Pbk

Hawkins, Keith O.
Enforcing Regulation / John M. Thomas. – Dordrecht : Kluwer, 1984.
208p.
ISBN 0898381487 Hbk £95.00

Hawkins, Kevin
Case Studies in Industrial Relations. – London : Kogan Page, 1982.
226p.
ISBN 0850384184 Hbk £13.50

Hawkins, Nigel
Housing Grants. – 2nd ed. – London : Kogan Page, 1983.
172p.
ISBN 0850387108 Hbk £9.95
ISBN 0850387116 Pbk £4.50

Hawley, Donna Lea
Canadian Firearms Law. – Butterworths, 1988.
152p.
Guidance on all aspects of the criminal and civil law relating to gun use and misuse in Canada. Provides an outline of history and purpose of current legislation, and analysis of current legislation and all relevant case law, a discussion of various types of certificates and permits required, contains a step by step procedure to be followed upon, and discussion of the law governing, refusal or revocation of certificates and permits.
ISBN 0409806455 Hbk £42.50
—Indian Act Annotated. – 2nd ed. – Agincourt : Carswell, 1986.
124p.
This work is a section-by-section analysis of the recently amended Canadian Indian Act. Significant treaties are presented in the appendices to the book. The extent of provincial legislative control of Indians in the areas of matrimonial property division, child welfare, and other topics is addressed in the book.
Pbk £27.50

Hawser, Cyril Lewis →Annual members' conference held in the Lord Chief Justice's Court on Saturday 22nd March 1986 : subject, public order.

Hay →Sports Law for Educational Institutions.

Hay, Douglas →Labour, law and crime : an historical perspective.

Hayek, F.
Law, Legislation and Liberty. – Revised edition. – Routledge, 1982.
ISBN 0710092113 Pbk £7.95

Hayes, Mary
Practitioner's Guide to Child Care Law / Vaughan Bevan. – Bristol : Jordan & Sons Ltd, 1986.
– (Family Law Practitioner's Ser.).
ISBN 085308100X Pbk

Hayes, R.A. →Cases on the Criminal Code.

Hayes, Robert
Australian Law Reports (ALR) / J. D. Heydon. – Wellington : Butterworths.
Hbk
→ Mental retardation : law, policy and administration.

Hayes, Susan C.
Mental retardation : law, policy and administration / by Susan C. Hayes and Robert Hayes : with a foreword by M. D. Kirby. – North Ryde : Law Book Co, 1982.
xxviii,428p.
Includes index.
ISBN 0455204691 Pbk
ISBN 0455204705

Hayllar
UK Tax Offshore Oil and Gas / Rouse. – 2nd ed. – London : Butterworths.
Service to Date.
ISBN 0406220719 Hbk £100.00

Hayter, Teresa
Aid : rhetoric and reality / Teresa Hayter, Catharine Watson. – London : Pluto, 1985.
xv,303p; 20cm.
Includes index.
ISBN 0861046269 Pbk £4.95
—Creation of world poverty / Teresa Hayter. – London : Pluto Press, 1981.
128p.
Bibliography: p.124-127.
ISBN 0861043391

Hayton, David J
Butterworth's Handbook on the Value Added Tax Act 1983. – London : Butterworths, 1984.
This handbook contains the full text of the Capital Transfer Tax Act of 1984 for the United Kingdom practitioner. A table of cases, comprehensive index, and a destination table is included in the work.
ISBN 0406505349 Pbk
—Cases and commentary on the law of trusts / Hayton and Marshall. – 8th ed. – London : Stevens, 1986.
796p; 25cm.
Previous ed.: / Nathan and Marshall. 1980. Includes index.
ISBN 042047370X Hbk £36.00
ISBN 0420473807 Pbk £27.00
→ Law relating to trusts and trustees.
→ Manual of the law of real property.
→ Megarry's manual of the law of real property.
—Registered land / by David J. Hayton. – 3rd ed. – London : Sweet & Maxwell, 1981.
xxiii,222p; 20cm.
Previous ed.: 1977. Includes index.
ISBN 042128160X Hbk £10.00
ISBN 0421281707 Pbk £6.50

Hayward, Peter A.
Hayward's Patent Cases 1600-1883 11 vols. – Abingdon : Professional Books, 1988 & Index.
ISBN 0862052793 Hbk £750.00

Hayward, Stoy
Audit Guide. – London : Butterworths, 1983.
A publication for practitioners providing practical explanations of the stages of an audit. The book gives a straightforward discussion of the often confusing topic of the use of statistical sampling methods in the audit. Included are sections on flowcharting, error rate sampling, monetary unit sampling, as well as extracts from standard documentation for an audit.
ISBN 0406270600 Hbk

Hayward's Patent Cases 1600-1883 11 vols. – Abingdon : Professional Books, 1988 & Index.
ISBN 0862052793 Hbk £750.00

Hazard, John N.
Managing change in the USSR : the politico-legal role of the Soviet jurist / John N. Hazard. – Cambridge : Cambridge University Press, 1983.
ix,182p; 23cm.
'The Goodhart lectures 1982'. Bibliography: p175-177. - Includes index.
ISBN 0521253160 £17.50

Hazard unlimited. – 3rd ed. – London, 1987.
ISBN 1850441316 Pbk £5.95
ISBN 1850441375 Hbk £14.50

Hazardous Products : Canada's Right-to-Know Laws. – Don Mills : CCH Canadian Ltd.
310p.
ISBN 0887964524 Pbk £18.95

Hazell's Guide to the Judiciary and the Courts 1989 With Holborn Law Society List of Barristers by Chambers. – Hazell.
ISBN 0901718483 Pbk £17.00

Hazelwood, Steven J. →Introduction of P & I.
—P & I Clubs: law and practice. – London : Lloyds of London Press, 1989.
Discusses the constitution, workings and practice of shipowners' mutual protection and in indemnity associations. Covers the historical development and legal structure of clubs. Issues including the Court of Appeal ruling in the cases of the FANTI and PADRE ISLAND are contained, as is the clubs' method for their own reinsurance.
ISBN 1850442304 Hbk

He Left Them Laughing When He Said Good-Bye : the Life and Times of Frontier Lawyer Paddy Nolan. – Saskatoon : Western Producer Prairie Books, 1987.
ISBN 0888332416 Pbk £12.95

Head, Adrian
Butterworth's County Court Precedents and Pleadings / A. V. B. Bartlett. – London : Butterworths.
Llf

Head, John G. →Taxation issues of the 1980s : papers presented at a conference organised by the Centre of Policy Studies, Monash University.

Head, Nicholas
Nigerian Criminal Reports. – London : Sweet & Maxwell, 1981.
ISBN 090382647X Hbk £201.00

Headlam
Construction refurbishment and design. – London : Estates Gazette, 1986.
ISBN 0728200996 Pbk £15.95

Head's Legal Guide. – New Malden : Croner Publications.
Pbk £29.00

Heal, Kevin →Crime control and the police : a review of research.
→ Police response to calls from the public.
→ Policing today.
→ Situational crime prevention : from theory into practice.

Healey, J.M. →Law-Medicine Relations : a Philosophical Exploration : Proceedings of the 8th Trans-Disciplinary Symposium on Philosophy and Medicine Held at Farmington, Conn., 1978.

Healey, Patsy
Local plans in British land use planning / by Patsy Healey. – Oxford : Pergamon, 1983.
xv,324p; 24cm.
Bibliography: p303-318. - Includes index.
ISBN 0080252427 £16.50

Health Act-Victoria. – North Ryde : Law Book Co, 1983.
xxxi, 493p.
ISBN 0455204985 Hbk £65.50

Health & Safety at Work : Law and Practice. – Sweet & Maxwell, 1988.
ISBN 0421376708 Pbk £18.00

Health and safety at work: law and practice. – London : Sweet & Maxwell, 1988.
Examines claims in industrial tribunals relating to dismissal and constructive dismissal for health and safety reasons, and the rights of safety representatives to times off. Analysis of sickness and invalidity benefits, practice and procedure in social security appeal tribunals, and the grounds for action by the Health and Safety Executive.
ISBN 0421376708

Health and safety in factories / Ian Fife. – 2nd ed. – London : Butterworths, 1982.
ISBN 0406353077 Hbk £52.00
Supplement-1985. –
ISBN 0406353085 Pbk £7.50

Health and safety practice / M Dewis. – London : Pitman Publishing, 1986.
ISBN 0273025996 Pbk £22.50

Health Law in Canada. – Toronto : Butterworths.
Hbk

Health Policy in Britain : The Organisation and Politics of the NHS. – 2nd ed. – London : Macmillan, 1985.
192p. – (Studies in Social Policy, General Ser.).
ISBN 0333394925 Hbk £20.00
ISBN 0333394933 Pbk £6.95

Health protection and drug laws / Educational Services, Health Protection Branch, Department of National Health and Welfare. – Ottawa : The Department, 1982.
45p.
Includes bibliographies.
ISBN 0660112329

Health protection and food laws. – 4th rev ed. – Ottawa : Minister of National Health and Welfare, 1987.
95p.
Includes bibliographical references.
ISBN 0660121808

Health, rights and resources / edited by Peter Byrne. – London : King Edward's Hospital Fund for London, 1988.
201p; 23cm.
Includes index.
ISBN 0197246451 £16.95

Health service development : Mental Health Act 1983 : draft code of practice / Department of Health and Social Security. – London : The Department, 1987.
45p. – (Local authority circular).
Cover title: Mental Health Act 1983.

Health services law / by John D. Finch. – London : Sweet & Maxwell, 1981.
xix,338p; 23cm.
Includes index.
ISBN 0421264608 Hbk £11.30
ISBN 0421264705 Pbk £7.30

Heap, Desmond
Outline of planning law. – 9th. – London : Sweet & Maxwell, 1987.
Examines the Acts and statutory instruments regulating planning law, including the nine new acts introduced since the 1982 edition. Contains discussion of the impact of the abolition of the Metropolitan County Councils, and planning gain, use and misuse of planning conditions, conservation areas, and National Parks.
ISBN 042125459X Pbk £22.50

Hear the other side : Audi alteram partem. – London : Butterworths, 1985.
ISBN 0406502404 Hbk £14.95

Hearken to the Evidence. – Stittsville : Canada's Wings, 1983.
254p.
ISBN 0920002242 Hbk £18.95

Hearn, Patrick
International business agreements : a practical guide to the negotiation and formulation of agency distribution and intellectual property licensing agreements / Patrick Hearn. – Aldershot : Gower, 1987.
viii,222p; 24cm.
Includes index.
ISBN 0566025973 £27.50

Hearnden, K.
Handbook of Computer Security. – London : Kogan Page, 1987.
ISBN 185091348X Hbk £14.95

Heather, D. R. H.
Snow's Annotated Criminal Code, 1 Vol. – Bound Edition. – Agincourt : Carswell, 1988.
This looseleaf service contains the annotated text of the Criminal Code of Canada and its amendments. Extensive case law citations are provided in the work.
Llf £74.00

Heavens, Lewis →Calver's Powers of Arrest : Charges.
→ Constable's Pocket Guide to Powers of Arrest and Charges.

Hebbert
London Government Handbook / Travers. – London : Cassell.
ISBN 0304315745 Hbk £15.00

Hebenton, S., et al
Legal Problems Relating to Shareholders' Agreements. – Vancouver : British Columbia Continuing Legal Education Society, 1982.
106p.
ISBN 0865040613 Hbk £12.50

Hebert, Francoise
Copyright : Proceedings of the Workshop Held at the Annual Conference of the Canadian Library Association June 7, 1984, Toronto, Ontario. – Ottawa : Canadian Library Association, 1985.
72p.
ISBN 0888021925 Hbk £10.00

Hecke, Georges van
Multinational enterprise between hammer and anvil / Georges van Hecke. – Deventer : Kluwer Law and Taxation Publishers, 1984.
16p.
Includes bibliographical references.
ISBN 9065441956

Hedge, Ramakrishna
Judiuciary today : disturbing trends and suggestion for reforms / Ramakrishna Hedge. – s.l. : Government of Karnataka, 1986.
15p.
'Address by Sir Ramakrishna Hedge, Chief Minister of Karnataka, delivered on 27th June, 1986 at the Bar Association of India Conference 1986 held at Bangalore'. - t.p. verso.

Hedley, William
Bills of exchange and bankers' documentary credits / by William Hedley. – London : Lloyd's, 1986.
320p; 25cm.
Includes index.
ISBN 1850440840

Heere, W.P.
International Bibliography of Air Law 1900-1971. Supplements 1972-1976. – Dordrecht : Kluwer, 1976.
xxii, 169p.
ISBN 9028605266 Hbk £64.00

Heertje, Arnold →Investing in Europe's future.

Heffey, Peter G →Cases and materials on contract.

Hegde, Ramaskrishna
Judiciary today : a plea for a collegium / Ramakrishna Hedge. – Bangalore : Governmnet of Karnataka, .
80p.

Heginbotham, Chris
Rights of mentally ill people / Chris Heginbotham. – London : Minority Rights Group, 1987.
12p. – (Report).
ISBN 0946690499

Heidenhain, Martin H. →German antitrust law : an introduction to the German antitrust law with German text and synoptic English translation of the Act against Restraints of Competition.

Heidensohn, Frances
Women and crime / Frances Heidensohn. – Basingstoke : Macmillan, 1985.
xii,216p; 23cm.
Bibliography: p201-213. - Includes index.
ISBN 0333362160 Hbk £20.00
ISBN 0333362179 Pbk £6.95

Heim, B. B.
Heraldry in the Catholic Church : its origin, customs and laws. – 2nd enl. and rev. ed. – Gerrards Cross : Van Duren, 1982.
200p.
ISBN 0905715128 Hbk £25.00

Held, David →New forms of democracy.
→ States and societies.

Hellard, R.B.
Managing Construction Conflict. – London : Longman Scientific, 1988.
ISBN 0582003504 Pbk £18.00

Heller
Beyond Justice. – Oxford : Blackwell, 1987.
ISBN 0631152067 Hbk £25.00

Heller, K
Outline of Austrian constitutional law. – Kluwer Law and Taxation, 1989.
72.
A brief introduction to the law of Austria. Covers leading statutesand commentaries, basic principles of the constitution, neutrality, and legislation of the Federation.
ISBN 9065444041 Pbk £16.25/Dfl 50

Heller, Kurt →Austrian business law : legal, accounting and tax aspects of business in Austria.

Hell-Hole, Robben Island : Reminiscences of a Political Prisoner. – London : Spokesman Books, 1984.
192p.
ISBN 0851244076 Hbk £13.50
ISBN 0851244017 Pbk £4.95

Hellstern, Melany
Nova Scotia Community Legal Needs Survey. – Ottawa : Canadian Law Information Council, 1984.
32p.
ISBN 0920358586 Pbk £7.50

Hellwig, H. →German Banking System.

Hellyer, Bart →Disability and compensation claims.
→ Special damages for disability 1988.

Helme, W.
Handbook of Cautions, Oaths and Recognizances, Etc. – 10th ed. – London : Shaw & Sons, 1981.
ISBN 0721904734 Hbk £4.50

Helmholz, R. H.
Canon law and English common law / by R. H. Helmholz. – London : Selden Society, 1983.
24 p.
'Selden Society lecture delivered in the Old Hall of Lincoln's Inn, July 5th, 1982'.
→ Select cases on defamation to 1600.

Helmore, B. A.
Helmore's personal property and mercantile law in New South Wales / by W. J. Chappenden and J. W. Carter. – 9th ed. – Sydney : Law Book Company, 1985.
xlvi,485p.
ISBN 045520294X

Helmore's personal property and mercantile law in New South Wales / by W. J. Chappenden and J. W. Carter. – 9th ed. – Sydney : Law Book Company, 1985.
xlvi,485p.
ISBN 045520294X

Help : Marketplace Handbook of Consumer Rights in Canada. – Toronto : Canadian Broadcasting Corporation Enterprises.
84p.
Pbk £3.00

Helping the Victim : Your Guide to Claiming Compensation / Marilyn Salkeld. – London : Bedford Square Press.
ISBN 0719912164 Hbk £4.50

Helsby, R., et al
Offshore Survival. – London : Deloitte Haskins & Sells.
– (Trouble with the Taxman Series).
ISBN 0863491324 Pbk £9.95

Henderson
Bankruptcy (Scotland) Act 1985. – Tolley Publishing.
ISBN 854592814 Hbk £17.95
—Securitisation / Scott. – Cambridge : Woodhead-Faulkner, 1988.
ISBN 0859414167 Hbk £40.00

Henderson, A. G., et al
Fraud in Commercial Transactions. – Vancouver : British Columbia Continuing Legal Education Society, 1982.
192p.
ISBN 086504080X Hbk £17.50
—Statements by an accused. – Vancouver : British Columbia Continuing Legal Education Society, 1981.
252p.
ISBN 0865040214 Hbk £45.00

Henderson, Dorothy →New Zealand royal commissions, commissions and committees of inquiry, 1864-1981 : a checklist.

Henderson, G. P. →Directory of British associations & associations in Ireland.

Henderson, Gordon F.
Canadian Patent Reporter Third Series (1985-Present). – Aurora : Canada Law Book Co.
– (Law Reports).
Hbk £190.00
—Canadian Patent Reporter: 1985. – Aurora : Canada Law Book Co, 1985.
– (Third Ser.).
Hbk £195.00

Henderson, Joan
Law on unfair dismissal : guidance for small firms / Joan Henderson. – London : H.M.S.O., 1982.
13p.

Henderson, L. D. J. →Civil procedure.

Henderson, M.J.
Banking Operations. – London : DP Publications.
ISBN 0905435982 Pbk £7.95

Henderson, N. →Green and Henderson: land law.

Henderson, R. Candlish →Introduction to the law of Scotland.

Henderson, Ronald F. →Consultation and government : report of the inquiry into processes of consultation in Victoria with special reference to the case of tenancy law reform.

Henderson, S. P. A. →Directory of British associations & associations in Ireland.

Henderson, Schuyler K →Currency and Interest Rate Swaps.

Hendry, I. D.
Legal status of Berlin / by I.D. Hendry and M.C. Wood. – Cambridge : Grotius, 1987.
xxii,388p.
Describes the unique legal position of Berlin as it emerges from the actual practice and positions adopted by the four Occupying Powers. Deals with the original occupation rights of the four Powers, and their agreements and practices. Makes reference to Allied and German legislation, and includes chapters on the institutional framework and law applicable in Berlin, and the special Berlin area.
ISBN 0949009059

Henham, John Alfred
Magistrates' Summary Jurisdiction : Guide to Sentencing Powers. – 6th ed. – Chichester : Barry Rose, 1983.
ISBN 0859923681 Hbk £4.50

Henke, Dan F. →Automation in the law school, including law libraries.

Hennessy
Ruling performance / Seldon. – Oxford : Blackwell Scientific, 1987.
ISBN 0631156453 Hbk £25.00

Hennessy, Peter →States of emergency : British governments and strikebreaking since 1919.

Henning, J.J.
Partnership / Henning and Delport. – Durban : Professional Publisher, 1984.
ISBN 0409040223 Hbk £33.00

Henochsberg on the Companies Act. – 4th ed. – Durban : Professional Publishers, 1985.
Hbk
Vol. 1. –
ISBN 0409032964 £105.00
Vol. 2. –
ISBN 0409032972 £105.00

Henrik Brenkman (1681-1736). Jurist and Classicist : a Chapter from the History of Roman Law as Part of the Classical Tradition. – Groningen : Egbert Forsten Publishing, 1981.
viii, 141p.
ISBN 9060880757 Hbk £38.50

Henry, Cleopatra Elmira
Carriage of dangerous goods by sea : the role of the International Maritime Organisation in international legislation / by Cleopatra Henry. – London : Pinter, 1985.
iii,184; 23cm.
Includes index. Clarifies the work of the IMO revealing its methods and mandate for enacting maritime controls on the transportation of controversial toxins.
ISBN 0861875699 Hbk £25

Henry, Colin
Teaching, enacting and sticking up for human rights : an evaluation report on the Human Rights Commission's 'Teaching for Human Rights: Activities for Schools'. / Colin Henry, David Hitchcock, Michelle Michie. – Canberra : Australian Government Publishing Service, 1985.
viii,83p. – (Occasional paper).
Includes bibliographical references.
ISBN 0644039639

Henry, Ellen J
Annotated Motor Vehicle Legislation in British Columbia. – Agincourt : Carswell, 1987.
200p.
This compact volume contains the complete text of the Motor Vehicle Act, Motor Dealer Act, and Motor Vehicle (All Terrain) Act of British Columbia, along with selected regulations under the Acts.
Hbk £48.75

Henry, Stuart
Private justice / Stuart Henry. – London : Routledge & Kegan Paul, 1983.
ix,245p.
Includes index. Bibliography: p229-235.
ISBN 0710097034 Pbk

Henshaw, L. G. →Welsh language in the courts.

Hepburn, L.
Limited Partnerships. – Toronto : DeBoo, 1983.
ISBN 0888201192 Hbk £135.00

Hepperle, Winifred →U.S. legal system : a practice handbook.

Hepple, B. A.
Employment law / Hepple & O'Higgins. – 4th ed. – London : Sweet & Maxwell, 1981.
lvii,430p; 25cm.
Previous ed.: 1979. Bibliography: p401-402. - Includes index.
ISBN 0421288302 Pbk £13.25
—Equal pay and the industrial tribunals. – London : Sweet & Maxwell, 1984.
80p.
ISBN 0421328002 Pbk £7.15
→ Foundations of the law of tort.
→ Industrial tribunals : a report.
—Labour law and industrial relations in Great Britain / by B.A. Hepple, S. Fredman. – Deventer : Kluwer Law and Taxation, 1986.
295p.
: 'Originally published as a monograph in the International encyclopaedia for labour law and industrial relations.'. Includes index. Bibliography: p.257-259.
ISBN 9065442626
→ Labour law in Great Britain and Ireland to 1978 : a companion volume to A bibliography of the literature on British and Irish labour law.
→ Making of labour law in Europe : a comparative study of nine countries up to 1945.
→ Sweet and Maxwell's labour relations statutes and materials.
→ Tort : cases and materials.
—Tort : cases and materials / M H Matthews. – 3rd ed. – London : Butterworths, 1985.
ISBN 0406594848 Hbk £32.00
ISBN 0406594902 Pbk £21.95

Heptonstall, S.M.
Making a Case. – Geneva : International Labour Office, 1981.
59p.
ISBN 9221022463 Hbk £5.00

Hepworth, N. P.
Finance of local government / by N.P. Hepworth. – 7th ed. – London : Allen & Unwin, 1984.
xvi,349p; 20cm.
Previous ed.: 1980. Bibliography: p335-339. - Includes index.
ISBN 0043521118 Hbk £
ISBN 0043521150

Her Majesty's Chief Insepctor of Prisons Reports : Her Majesty's Detention Centre Eastwood Park. – London : Home Office, 1982.
Hbk

Her Majesty's Chief Inspector of Prisons Reports : Her Majesty's Prison Cookham Wood. – London : Home Office, 1981.
ISBN 0862520118 Hbk

Her Majesty's Chief Inspector of Prisons Reports : Her Majesty's Prison Erlestoke House. – London : Home Office, 1982.
ISBN 0862520096 Hbk

Her Majesty's Chief Inspector of Prisons Reports : Her Majesty's Prison Featherstone. – London : Home Office, 1981.
ISBN 086252010X Hbk

Her Majesty's Chief Inspector of Prisons Reports : Her Majesty's Prison Gartree. – London : Home Office, 1982.
ISBN 0862520290 Hbk

Her Majesty's Chief Inspector of Prisons Reports : Her Majesty's Prison Glouchester. – London : Home Office, 1981.
ISBN 086252024X Hbk

Her Majesty's Chief Inspector of Prisons Reports : Her Majesty's Prison High Point. – London : Home Office, 1981.
ISBN 0862520363 Hbk

Her Majesty's Chief Inspector of Prisons Reports : Her Majesty's Prison Leeds. – London : Home Office, 1981.
ISBN 0862520282 Hbk

Her Majesty's Chief Inspector of Prisons Reports : Her Majesty's Prison Leyhill. – London : Home Office, 1981.
ISBN 0862520355 Hbk

Her Majesty's Chief Inspector of Prisons Reports : Her Majesty's Prison Raidstone. – London : Home Office, 1981.
ISBN 0862520215 Hbk

Her Majesty's Chief Inspector of Prisons Reports : Her Majesty's Prison Weymouth. – London : Home Office, 1981.
ISBN 086252038X Hbk

Heraldry in the Catholic Church : its origin, customs and laws. – 2nd enl. and rev. ed. – Gerrards Cross : Van Duren, 1982.
200p.
ISBN 0905715128 Hbk £25.00

Herbert
Practical Accounts
Book 1 / Bright. – London : Macmillan. – (New Edition).
ISBN 0333481410 Pbk £4.95

Herbert, A.
Uncommon Law - 66 Misleading Cases. – Methuen, 1969.
ISBN 041338540X Pbk £5.95

Herczegh, Geza
Development of international humanitarian law / by Geza Herczegh. – Budapest : Akademiai Kiado, 1984.
239p.
Bibliography: p231-235.
ISBN 9630534487

Herligy
Introduction to the Criminal Law of Queensland and WQ / Kenny. – 2nd ed. – London : Butterworths, 1984.
ISBN 040949433X Pbk £23.20

Herlihy, J.H.
Introduction to the Criminal Law of Queensland and Western Australia / R.G. Kenny. – 2nd ed. – Butterworths, 1984.
259p.
The new edition of this introductory text covers the changes in the law since July 1977. Contained are materials on the extraterritorial competence of the respective State Parliaments and a table of comparative sections, including provisions of the Tasmanian Criminal Code.
ISBN 040949433X Pbk £38.50

Herman, Amos
Shipping conferences. – London : Lloyd's of London, 1983.
viii,255p.
Bibliography: p.253-255. Bibliography: p253-255. Includes text of the Convention on a Code of conduct for liner conferences (1974).
ISBN 9065440895 Hbk £116.00

Herman, Edward S.
Corporate control, corporate power / Edward S. Herman. – Cambridge : Cambridge University Press, 1981.
xv,432p; 24cm.
Includes index.
ISBN 0521239966 £25.00

Hermann, A. H.
Conflicts of national laws with international business activity : issues of extraterritoriality / by A.H. Hermann. – London : British North American Research Organisation, 1982.
xii,96p.
ISBN 0902594419

—Judges, law, and businessmen / A.H. Hermann. – Deventer, Netherlands : Kluwer Law and Taxation Publishers, 1983.
ISBN 9065440828

—Law Versus Business : Business Law Articles from the Financial Times'. – London : Butterworths.
ISBN 0406177015 Pbk £25.00

Herr, Stanley S.
Advocacy and Mental Handicap / Raquel Schuster-Herr. – Brussels : International League of Societies for Persons with Mental Handicap, 1984.
Hbk £1.50

—Legal rights and mental-health care / Stanley S. Herr, Stephen Arons, Richard E. Wallace. – Lexington, Mass. : Lexington Books, 1983.
xv,180p; 24cm.
Includes index.
ISBN 0669049107 £19.50

Herrup, Cynthia B.
Common peace. – Cambridge : Cambridge University Press.
Examines attitudes behind the enforcement of criminal law in seventeenth-century England. Based on court records but concerned with popular rather than professional legal culture.
ISBN 052133313X Hbk £25.00

Hertner, Peter → Multinationals : theory and history.

Herzberg, A. → Understanding Company Law.

Herzfeld, E. O.
Joint ventures / Edgar Herzfeld. – Bristol : Jordan, 1983.
vii,105p.
Bibliography: p.99-102. - Includes index.
ISBN 0853080704

Herzog, P.E.
Harmonization of Laws in the European Communities : Products, Liability, Conflict of Laws and Corporation Law. – London : Eurospan.
ISBN 0813909856 Hbk £17.50
→ Law Of The European Economic Community.

Heseltine, Richard G. → Information system dynamics : the impact of interactive information networks on the UK library and information system : final report for the period August 1979 - July 1982 : report to the British Library Research and Development Dept., on project SI/G/327.

Hess, Albert G.
History of Juvenile Delinquency, 2 Vols. / Priscilla F. Clement. – Aalen Wuertt : Scientia, 1989.
Hbk

Hesse, J.
Radio Documentary Handbook. – North Vancouver : International Self-Counsel Press, 1987.
ISBN 0889086532 Hbk £8.95

Hessick → Achieving Quality in Financial Service Organizations How to Identify and Satisfy Customer Expectations.

Hetherington, Marion → Mareva injunctions.

Heunis, J. C
United Nations versus South Africa : a legal assessment of United Nations and United Nations related activities in respect of South Africa / Jan C. Heunis. – 1st ed. – Johannesburg : Lex Patria, 1986.
593 p., 1 folded leaf of plates; 25 cm.
: Originally presented as the author's thesis (doctoral–Rand Afrikaans University, 1984). Includes index. Bibliography: p. 583-593.
ISBN 0628030363

Heuston, R F V
Essays In Constitutional Law. – 2nd ed. – Sweet & Maxwell, 1964.
ISBN 042042640X Pbk £9.50

—Lives of the Lord Chancellors (1885-1940). – Oxford : Oxford University Press, 1987.
ISBN 0198213123 Hbk £45.00

—Lives of the Lord Chancellors (1940-1970). – Oxford : Oxford University Press, 1987.
ISBN 0198200749 Hbk £25.00

→ Salmond and Heuston on the law of torts.

Heward, Edmund
Chancery practice / Edmund Heward. – London : Butterworths, 1983.
xx,198p.
Includes index.
ISBN 040622451X

Heward, Roger
Maritime Law Handbook / Hans Christian Albrecht. – Dordrecht : Kluwer, 1987.
350p.
Llf £185.00

Hewitt, E.E.
Judges Through the Years : Being a Chronology of the Judges of the County Court of Victoria from its Inception (1852). – South Yarra : Hyland House, 1984.
176p.
ISBN 0908090676 Hbk £25.00

Hewitt, Patricia
Abuse of power : civil liberties in the United Kingdom / Patricia Hewitt. – Oxford : Robertson, 1982.
xiv,295p; 24cm.
Bibliography: p267-279. - Includes index.
ISBN 085520379X Hbk £15.00
ISBN 0855203803 Pbk £4.95

—Fair cop : reforming the police complaints procedure / Patricia Hewitt. – London : National Council for Civil Liberties, 1982.
48p; 20cm.
ISBN 0946088012

→ First rights : a guide to legal rights for young people.

→ Prevention of Terrorism Act : the case for repeal.

Hewitt, S.
Manufacturers' Liability for Defective Goods. – Oxford : Blackwell Scientific, 1987.
ISBN 0003833623 Hbk £20.00

Heydon, J. D. → Australian Law Reports (ALR).

—Cases and Materials on Equity and Trusts / R.P. Austin. – 3rd ed. – Butterworths, 1989.
1024p.
ISBN 0409495239 Hbk £89.00
ISBN 0409495247 Pbk £69.00

—Cases and materials on equity and trusts / by J.D. Heydon, W.M.C. Gummow, R.P. Austin. – 2nd ed. – Sydney : Butterworths, 1982.
xxxvi,934p.
This book introduces the main principles and remedies of Anglo-Australasian equity. A range of questions have been provided for undergraduate law students.
ISBN 0409309389

—Evidence : cases and materials / J.D. Heydon. – 2nd ed. – London : Butterworths, 1984.
510p.
Previous ed: published as Cases and materials on evidence. 1975. Includes index.
ISBN 0406594872 Hbk £
ISBN 0406594880 Pbk £18.95

Heymann
Decision Support Systems in Finance and Accounting / Bloom. – Quorum Press.
ISBN 0899302696 Hbk £32.95

Heywood, J.
Foreign Exchange and Corporate Treasurer. – 4th ed. – London : Black (A & C).
ISBN 0713626712 Hbk £12.50

Heywood, Margaret
Journal of Social Welfare Law / Christina M. Lyon. – London : Sweet & Maxwell.
Hbk £31.00

Heywood, Nathaniel Arthur
Court of Protection Practice
Supplement 1986 / Arnold Stewart Massey. – 11th ed. – London : Sweet & Maxwell, 1986.
ISBN 0420469206 Hbk £80.00

hfsdjrejiwjkdfgvmlsfdkvnm – 1954.

HGV Law Guide. – London : Butterworths, 1981.
This work is written for those who operate or are responsible for goods vehicles in the United Kingdom. The Construction and Use Regulations of 1978 and the Special Types Order of 1979 are analyzed in the book. Numerous diagrams illustrate the text.
ISBN 0408005696 Pbk £10.00

Hibberd, Peter R.
Sub-contracts under JCT intermediate form. – Oxford : Blackwell Scientific, 1987.
240p.
ISBN 0003831752 Hbk £19.95

—Variations in construction contracts. – Oxford : Blackwell Scientific, 1986.
ISBN 0003831914 Hbk £19.95

Hibbert, Alan A.
Robinson's County Court Costs. – 6th ed. – London : Oyez Longman, 1982.
– (Oyez Longman Practice Note Ser.: No. 24).
ISBN 0851206409 Hbk £7.95

Hickling, M. A., et al
Labor Arbitration : 1982. – Vancouver : British Columbia Continuing Legal Education Society, 1982.
194p.
ISBN 0865040567 Hbk £45.00

Hickling, R.H.
Malaysian Law. – Professional Law, 1988.
ISBN 09679958001 Hbk £35.00

Hickmott, G.
Principles and practice of interruption insurance. – London : Witherby & Co, 1982.
ISBN 0900886560 Hbk £35.00

Hicks, Andrew
Annotation of the Singapore Companies Act / Walter C M Woon. – Singapore : Butterworths (Asia).
700.
Covers the relevant case law with cross-references to rules and other relevant legislation, along with the cross-references to parliamentary reports.
ISBN 0409995681 Hbk

—Hong Kong Company Law Handbook. – London : Butterworths, 1982.
ISBN 0406595607 Pbk

Hickson
Construction Insurance Claims and Management. – Spon (E & FN), 1987.
ISBN 0419138404 Hbk £22.50

Hickson, David J. →Writers on organizations.

Hidayatullah, M.
Constitutional Law of India. Vol 1. – London : Lucas Publications, 1986.
ISBN 1851800123 Hbk £50.00
—Judge's Miscellancy. – New Delhi : Arnold-Heinemann, 1982.
Hbk £85.00
—Judge's Miscellany, 2 Vols. – Bombay : Tripathi.
Hbk £70.00

Hiebert, Marilyn →Small Claims Court Materials : Can They Be Read? Can They Be Understood?.

Hiemstra : Introduction to the Law of Criminal Procedure. – Durban : Professional Publisher, 1985.
ISBN 0409032689 Pbk £35.00

Hiemstra, V.G.
Hiemstra : Introduction to the Law of Criminal Procedure. – Durban : Professional Publisher, 1985.
ISBN 0409032689 Pbk £35.00
—Statutes of the Republic of South Africa / I. Isaacs. – Durban : Butterworths.
Hbk

Hien, Leonard van →Handbook of Hong Kong tax statutes : profits tax, salaries tax, property tax, interest tax, estate duty, stamp duty, Board of Review decisions.

Higgins and Fletcher the law of partnership in Australia and New Zealand / K. L. Fletcher. – 5th ed. – North Ryde, N.S.W. : Law Book Co.,, 1987.
lxvii,394p.
Previous ed.: 1981. Includes index. Spine title: The law of partnership in Australia and New Zealand.
ISBN 0455207097

Higgins, Joan →Government and urban poverty : inside the policy-making process.

Higgins, P. F. P.
Higgins and Fletcher the law of partnership in Australia and New Zealand / K. L. Fletcher. – 5th ed. – North Ryde, N.S.W. : Law Book Co.,, 1987.
lxvii,394p.
Previous ed.: 1981. Includes index. Spine title: The law of partnership in Australia and New Zealand.
ISBN 0455207097

Higgins, Rosalyn →Colloquy: Democracy and Human Rights, Report on human rights and foreign policy : presented by R. Higgins.
—Conceptual thinking about the individual in international law / Rosalyn Higgins. – S.l. : s.n., 1981.
19p; 25cm.
Photocopy from: British Journal of International Studies 4 (1978).

High Court and the Constitution / Leslie Zines. – Sydney : Butterworths, 1981.
xvii, 358 p.; 25 cm.
Includes bibliographical references and index.
ISBN 0409300195

High Court and the Constitution. – 2nd ed. – Butterworths, 1987.
423p.
ISBN 0409491780 Hbk £69.00
ISBN 0409491799 Pbk £49.00

High Court Forms / A.A.P Willy. – Butterworths, 1985.
Contains 167 forms for use with the new High Court Rules. Of those, 114 are completely new. All the forms, including the Schedule forms, are annotated. The book is cross-referenced with Sim and Cain's Practice and Procedure.
ISBN 0409600792 Hbk £89.10

High Court Forms / E. H. J. Wily. – Wellington : Butterworths.
Hbk

High Court Manual. – Butterworths, 1989.
220p.
ISBN 0409787930 Hbk

High Court of Australia : 1982-1983 Annual Report. – Canberra : Australian Government Publishing Service, 1983.
13p.
Hbk £0.90

High Court of Australia on contract, 1950-1980 : cases / edited by M. P. Ellinghaus. – Sydney : Law Book Co., 1983.
xviii,487p.
Includes index.
ISBN 0455205310
ISBN 0455205329

High Court of Nigeria Law Reports. – Lagos : Nigerian Law Publications, 1985.
ISBN 978232518X Hbk £100.00

High Courts of Nigeria law reports. – Lagos : Nigerian Law Publications, 1987-.

Higham, John- →Loose on liquidators : the role of a liquidator in a voluntary winding-up.

Highby, Leo Ingemann
Erythrae Decree. – Repr. of 1936 ed. – Aalen Wuertt : Scientia, 1981.
viii, 107p.
ISBN 3511024390 Hbk £28.00

Highlights of federal initiatives in criminal justice, 1966- 1980 / prepared by Gerald Woods and Heather Sim. – Ottawa : Research Division, Ministry of the Solicitor General of Canada, 1981.
vii,78p.
Bibliography: p.71-78.
ISBN 0662118294

Highway law / by Stephen J. Sauvain. – London : Sweet and Maxwell, 1989.
lxxiv,404p.
Sets out the common law and statutes in their operative context, with the text numbered in paragraphs. Covers civil liability of highway authorities, inquiries, compensation with particular emphasis on areas such as stopping up, and diversion of highways.
ISBN 0421311908 Hbk £36.00

Highways Act 1980 / with annotations by Charles Cross and Stephen Sauvain. – London : Sweet & Maxwell, 1981.
xxix,532p; 25cm.
Includes index.
ISBN 0421281308 £15.00

Higson, C.
Business Finance. – London : Butterworths, 1986.
ISBN 0406501408 Pbk £13.95

Hildesley, Alfred →Case of the Requisition.

Hildreth
Ocean and Coastal Law / Johnson. – Prentice-Hall, 1983.
ISBN 0136292046 Hbk £35.05

Hildreth, R. →Theory of Legislation.

Hilf, M →New GATT round of multilateral trade negotiations: legal and economic problems.

Hilf, Meinhard →European Community and GATT.

Hilgendorf, Linden
Social workers and solicitors in child care cases / by Linden Hilgendorf with the assistance of Deborah Holland, Barrie Irving, Diana Schlaefli. – London : H.M.S.O., 1981.
ix,150p.
ISBN 0113207697

Hill and Redman's law of landlord and tenant / General editor, Michael Barnes. – 18th ed. 2. – London : Butterworths, 1988.
looseleaf.
Includes index. Previous ed.: 1982.
ISBN 0406227403

Hill, Bernard
Competitive Trading in New Zealand : the Commerce Act 1986 / Mark Jones. – Butterworths.
Format of annotated statute; each section of the Act is commented on, with commentary fully integrated with legislation. Appendices cover forms of application for authorisation of prices for controlled goods or services, for authorisation of a restrictive trade practice, form of notification for clearance or authorisation of a merger of takeover proposal, and the Commerce Act (Fees) Regulations 1986.
ISBN 0409787728 Pbk £71.50
—Fair Trading in New Zealand : the Fair Trading Act 1986 / Jones. – Butterworths, 1989.
198p.
ISBN 040978771X Pbk £65.00

Hill, Brian E.
Common Agricultural Policy : past, present and future / Brian E. Hill. – London : Methuen, 1984.
xvi,168p; 23cm. – (The Methuen EEC series).
Bibliography: p160-163. - Includes index.
ISBN 0416321801 Hbk £
ISBN 0416321909 Pbk

Hill, Christopher, et al
Introduction of P & I / Bill Robertson, Steven J. Hazelwood. – London : Lloyds of London Press, 1988.
A practical rather than academic text, covering the origins of P and I clubs, the scope of cover, specialist clubs, and claims and claims handling.
ISBN 1850441634 Hbk
—Maritime law / Christopher Hill. – 2nd ed. – London : Lloyds of London, 1985.
400p; 24cm.
Previous ed.: London : Pitman, 1981. Includes index.
ISBN 185044045X

Hill, D. J.
CMR : contracts for the international carriage of goods by road / by D.J. Hill and A.D. Messent. – London : Lloyd's of London Press, 1984.
xliii,288p; 26cm.
Contains the text of the Carriage of Goods by Road Act 1965 and the French (i.e., definitive) text of the CMR.
ISBN 0907432557

Hill, E. F.
Principles of the law of workers' compensation, particularly in Victoria / by E. F. Hill and J. B. Bingeman. – Sydney : Law Book Company Limited, 1981.
xxiv,276p.
ISBN 0455200882

Hill, G. J. S. →Encyclopaedia of banking law.

Hill, Harold Arthur
Hill and Redman's law of landlord and tenant / General editor, Michael Barnes. – 18th ed. 2. – London : Butterworths, 1988.
looseleaf.
Includes index. Previous ed.: 1982.
ISBN 0406227403
—Landlord and Tenant, 2 Vols. / Joseph Haworth Redman. – 17th ed. – Wellington : Butterworths, 1982.
Llf
—Landlord and Tenants / Joseph Haworth Redman. – 18th ed. – London : Butterworths, 1988.
Service to date.
ISBN 040612987X Hbk £200.00

Hill, J.B.
Weapons Law. – Waterlow.
– (Waterlow's Practitioners Library).
ISBN 0080331041 Pbk £9.95

Hill, J.R.
Arms Control at Sea. – Routledge.
ISBN 0415012805 Hbk £30.00
—Maritime strategy for medium powers / J.R. Hill. – London : Croom Helm, 1985.
247p; 23cm.
ISBN 0709937199 £19.95

Hill, M.J.
Understanding Social Policy. – 3rd ed. – Oxford : Blackwell.
ISBN 0631162259 Pbk £8.50

Hill, Michael →Policy process in the modern capitalist state.

Hill, Peter →Criminal trials : the search for truth. → Rough justice.

Hill, R.
How to survive your articles. – London : Waterlow, 1986.
ISBN 0080330681 Pbk £5.95

Hill, Robert N. →Civil litigation.
—Recent and Prospective Developments in Civil and Criminal Litigation. – London : Law Society, 1985.
32p. – (Nineteen Eighty-Five Crash Course Transcripts).
Hbk £2.05

Hill-Smith, Alexander G. L.
Consumer credit : law and practice / by Alexander G.L. Hill-Smith. – London : Sweet & Maxwell, 1985.
xxxi,330p; 25cm.
Examines the terminology of the 1974 Consumer Credit Act, the agreements to which the regulations apply, withdrawal and cancellation, debtors' and creditors' rights, the provision of security, and the powers of the court as well as enforcement provisions. Appendix contains a model Cancellable Hire-Purchase Agreement.
ISBN 0421342900 Pbk £29

Hiller, Andrew
Public order and the law / by Andrew Hiller : with a foreword by Judge Gibney. – Sydney : Law Book Co., 1983.
xx,230p.
Bibliography: p.xix-xx. - Includes index.
ISBN 0455202761
ISBN 0455204101 Pbk £26.00
—Tolley's Employment Act 1982. – Croydon : Tolley.
256p.
ISBN 085459082X Hbk £7.95

Hillgarth, J. N.
Register Notule Communium 14 of the Diocese of Barcelona (1345-1348) A Calendar with Selected Documents / Julio Silano. – Toronto : Pontifical Institute of Mediaeval Studies, 1983.
x, 365p. – (Subsidia Mediaevalia: No. 13).
ISBN 0888443625 Hbk £30.00

Hilliard, Brian
Nickers : A Gentleman's Guide to Police Duty. – London : Police Review Publishing, 1982.
Illus.
ISBN 085164175X Pbk £2.50

Hillman, William C. →Current problems of letters of credit and bankers' quarantees.

Hills, I.
Corporation Tax. – Telegraph Publications, 1988.
ISBN 0863672280 Pbk £6.95

Hills, J.
Savings and Fiscal Privilege. – 2nd ed. – London : Institute for Fiscal Studies.
– (Report Ser.).
Hbk £6.00

Hills, P. J. →Sources of funding for research and publication.

Hillyard, Simon →International directory of legal aid.

Himsworth, Christopher →Judicial teeth for local ombudsmen? : proceedings of a conference held at the University of Edinburgh, 13th December 1984.
—Public sector housing law in Scotland. – 3rd. – Edinburgh : Green (W.) & Son, 1989.
Describes the functions with regard to housing responsibilities of local authorities, the Scottish Office, Scottish Homes and housing associations. Chapter on public sector secure tenancies, assured tenancies for housing associations, the right to buy, homelessness and the improvement of sub-standard housing.
ISBN 041400891X Pbk
—Scottish community charge / Neil Walker. – Edinburgh : Green (W.) & Son, 1989.
Provides full commentary on every section of the Abolition of Domestic Rates Etc. (Scot) Act 1987 and an analysis of subsequent developments with the full set of regulations.
ISBN 0414008634 Pbk

Hinde, G.W.
Introduction to Land Law / D.W. McMorland. – 2nd ed. – Butterworths, 1987.
708p.
Covers title to land, freehold estates, future interests, leasehold estates, easements and profits, licenses, land as security, mortgages and other charges, the holding of interest in land, the transfer of interest in land, covenants affecting freehold land, and the extent of landholder's rights.
ISBN 0409701726 Pbk £82.50
—Introduction to Land Law / D W McMorland. – 2nd ed. – London : Butterworths, 1987.
ISBN 0409636045 Hbk £111.50
ISBN 0409701726 Pbk £51.00
—Land Law, 2 Vols.
Vol. 1. – Butterworths, 1978.
ISBN 0409636002 Hbk
—New Zealand Law Dictionary / M.S. Hinde. – 3rd rev. ed. – Butterworths, 1986.
ISBN 0409787620 Pbk £60.50

Hinde, M.S. →New Zealand Law Dictionary.

Hindley, Brian →Employment and safety in the offshore oil industry.

Hindu Adoption and Maintenance Act, 1956 : Bare Act with Commentary. – Delhi : SBD Enterprises.
Hbk £5.00

Hindu Adoption and Maintenance Act. – 2nd ed. – Allahabad : Law Book Company, 1985.
Hbk £60.00

Hindu Family Law and Social Change. – Bombay : University of Bombay, Publications Department.
Hbk £21.00

Hindu Law. – 2nd ed. – Allahabad : Law Book Company, 1986.
1,000p.
Hbk £200.00

Hindu Law. – 15th ed. – Bombay : Tripathi. 1982.
£140.00

Hindu law. – 8th ed. – Nagpur : Wadhura & Co, 1987.
Hbk £330.00

Hindu Law and the Constitution. – Calcutta : Eastern Law House, 1983.
Pbk £20.00

Hindu Law and Usage. – 12th ed. repr. 1986. – New Delhi : Bharat Law House.
Hbk £260.00

Hindu Law of Inheritance : As in the Viramitrodaya of Mitramisa. – Delhi : Gian Publishing House, 1986.
xv, 286p.
ISBN 8121200164 Hbk £180.00

Hindu Law of Marriage and Stridhana. – Delhi : Mittal Publications, 1984.
Hbk £300.00

Hindu Law of Partition under Income-Tax Law. – 2nd ed. repr. – Allahabad : Law Book Company, 1983.
Hbk £22.50

Hindu Law (Students Ed.). – 6th ed. – Lucknow : Eastern Book Company, 1982.
354p.
Hbk £20.00

Hindu Marriage Act. – 2nd ed. – Allahabad : Law Book Company, 1986.
Hbk £100.00

Hindu Minority and Guardianship : and Hindu Adoptions and Maintenance Act. – 2nd ed. – Allahad : Law Book Company, 1986.
200p.
Pbk £60.00

Hindu Succession Act / Gopalakrishnan. – 5th ed. – Allahabad : Law Book Company, 1981.
Hbk £45.00

Hindu Succession Act. – 2nd ed. – Allahabad : Law Publishers, 1982.
Hbk £21.00

Hindu Undivided Family : Law, Judiciary and Bankers. – Delhi : UDH Publishers, 1986.
Hbk £100.00

Hindu Women's Right to Property in India. – New Delhi : Deep and Deep Publications, 1986.
528p.
Hbk £275.00

Hines, Colin →Agribusiness in Africa : a study of the impact of big business on Africa's food and agricultural production.

Hines, M.A.
A Guide to International Real Estate Investment. – London : Eurospan.
ISBN 089930205X Hbk £32.95

Hines, Vivian Gerald
Judicial discretion in sentencing by judges and magistrates / by Vivian Gerald Hines. – 1. – Chichester : Rose, 1982.
27cm.
Includes index.
ISBN 0859923169 £42.50

Hines, W. D. →Keyguide to information sources on the international protection of human rights.

Hinge, Gail →Indian acts and amendments 1868-1975 : an indexed collection.

Hingorani, R. C.
Human rights in India / R.C. Hingorani. – New Delhi : Oxford & IBH, 1985.
vii, 181 p.; 22 cm.
Includes bibliographical references and index.
ISBN 8120400208 Rs95.00
—Humanitarian Law. – New Delhi : Oxford University Press.
Hbk £95.00
—Studies in International Law. – New Delhi : Oxford University Press.
Hbk £60.00

Hinsley, F.
Sovereignty. – Cambridge : Cambridge University Press, 1986.
ISBN 052133988X Pbk £8.95

Hinson, J. F. W. →Sergeant and Sims on stamp duties and capital duty and stamp duty reserve tax.

Hinton →Credit Unions.
—Money advice services / Berthoud. – Policy Studies Institute, 1988.
ISBN 0853743789 Pbk £8.95

Hinton, John W. →Dangerousness : problems of assessment and prediction.

Hira, T.K.
Consumer Debt Problems of Scottish Families. – Scottish Association of Citizens Advice Bureau, 1988.
ISBN 0905831063 Pbk £2.00

Hire Purchase Act, 1967 (Act 212) and Regulations, Orders and Guide Lines. – Kuala Lumpur : International Law Books Services.
Hbk £9.00

Hire purchase law and cases / by Olusegun Yerokun. – Jos : Salama Press, 1983.
ix,125p.

Hiring and Leasing : Practice and Precedents / K. V. Prichard Jones. – London : Butterworths, 1986.
A practical guide to the issues of leasing for the business attorney in the United Kingdom. An extensive appendix of caselaw and commentary is provided.
ISBN 0406101140 Pbk

Hiro, Dilip
Untouchables of India / by Dilip Hiro. – New 1982 ed. – London : Minority Rights Group, 1982.
19p. – (Report).
Previous ed.: 1975. Bibliography: p.19.

Hirst, J.M. →Criminal Evidence.

Hirst, Paul Q.
Law, socialism and democracy / Paul Q. Hirst. – London : Allen & Unwin, 1986.
200p; 22cm.
Includes bibliography and index.
ISBN 0043012531 Hbk £15.00 :
ISBN 004301254X Pbk £6.95
—Social relations and human attributes / Paul Hirst and Penny Woolley. – London : Tavistock, 1982.
xi,297p; 24cm.
Bibliography: p274-286. - Includes index.
ISBN 0422772208 Hbk £12.00
ISBN 0422772305 Pbk £4.95

Historia Placitorum Coronae. – Reprint. 2 vols. – Abingdon : Professional Books, 1986. – (Classical English Law Texts Ser.).
ISBN 086205320X Hbk £53.75

Historic buildings : the law and practice. – 2nd ed. – London : Sweet & Maxwell, 1988.
ISBN 0421381302 Hbk £40.00

Historical English Law before Edward I / Frederic William Maitland. – 2nd ed. – Cambridge : Cambridge University Press, 1988.
ISBN 0521095166 Pbk £30.00

Historical foundations of Common Law. – 2nd ed. – London : Butterworths, 1981.
496.
ISBN 0406625025 Hbk £22.50
ISBN 0406625034 Pbk £16.95

Historical foundations of the common law / S.F.C. Milsom. – 2nd ed. – London : Butterworths, 1981.
xiii,475p; 22cm.
Previous ed.: 1969. Includes index. .
ISBN 0406625026 Hbk
ISBN 0406625034 Pbk

Historical Introduction To English Law / A K R Kiralfy. – 4th ed. – Sweet & Maxwell, 1969.
ISBN 0421136308 Pbk £11.50

Historical Introduction to Legal Studies. – Agincourt : Carswell, 1982.
411p.
This textbook for Canadian law students examines the historical development of the Canadian Constitution and the legal institution of Canada from their Anglo-Saxon origins to the present.
Hbk £40.50

Historical Law Tracts, 2 Vols. – Repr. of 1758 ed. – Abingdon : Professional Books.
34p.
Hbk £180.00

Historical research on crime and criminal justice : sixth Criminological Colloquim (PC-CC), Strasbourg 21-23 November 1983. – Council of Europe. – Strasbourg : Council of Europe, 1984.
ii,153p.
Includes bibliographies. 'Secretariat memorandum prepared by the Directorate of Legal Affairs'.

History and practice of the law of mines and minerals / Jean Cantlie Stewart. – Banff : Rowan Books, 1987.
ISBN 0950993212

History and Principles of Roman Private Law. – Durban : Professional Publisher, 1983.
This book presents a systematic approach to the basic principles of Roman law and its history for students of the subject.
ISBN 0409060631 Pbk £72.00

History and Sources of Nigerian Criminal Law. – Enugu : Fourth Dimension Publishing, 1985.
400p.
Pbk £17.00

History, Law and the Human Sciences : Medieval and Renaissance Perspectives. – Northampton : Variorum.
334p.
ISBN 0860781534 Hbk £28.00

History of American City Government : The Emergence of the Metropolis 1920-45. – London : Eurospan.
ISBN 0819166499 Hbk £30.50

History of British criminology / edited by Paul Rock. – Oxford : Clarendon, 1988.
192.
'First appeared as a special issue of the British journal of criminology.' Includes bibliographical references. Focuses on the past and present condition of criminology. Contains a series of essays, some on the history of criminological ideas, some on the formation of particular emphases, methods and problems. Others are personal accounts of major phases in the growth of the discipline.
ISBN 0198256353 Pbk £9.95

History of British industrial relations 1875-1914 / edited by Chris Wrigley. – Brighton : Harvester, 1982.
xv,269p; 23cm.
Includes index.
ISBN 0710803168 £25.00

History of British trade unionism / by Henry Pelling. – 4th ed. – London : Macmillan, 1987.
336p; 22cm.
Previous ed.: 1976. Includes bibliography and index.
ISBN 0333442857 £27.50

History Of Contempt Of Court. – Professional Books.
ISBN 0862053668 Hbk £26.50

History of custodial and related penalties in New Zealand / Patricia M. Webb. – Wellington : Government Printer, 1982.
197p.
ISBN 0477011969

History of English criminal law and its administration from 1750
Vol.5 : The emergence of penal policy : by Sir Leon Radzinowicz, Roger Hood / Roger Hood. – London : Stevens, 1986.
xv,1101p; 26cm.
Bibliography: p781-1039. - Includes index.
ISBN 0420462805 £75.00

History of English law before the time of Edward I
Vol. 1 / by Sir Frederick Pollock and Frederic William Maitland. – 2nd edition. – Cambridge : Cambridge University Press, 1988.
xxxviii,688p.
ISBN 0521095166 Hbk
Vol. 2 / by Sir Frederick Pollock and Frederic William Maitland. – 1988.
xiv,691p.

History of English prison administration
Vol.1 : 1750-1877 / Sean McConville. – London : Routledge & Kegan Paul, 1981.
xvii,534p; 23cm.
Bibliography: p483-505. - Includes index.
ISBN 0710006942 £25.00

History of Financial Accounting. – Routledge.
ISBN 0415004322 Pbk £35.00

History of Freshfields / Judy Slinn. – London : Freshfields, 1984.
208p.
Bibliography: p.181-187. - Includes index.

History of Ideas and Doctrines of Canon Law in the Middle Ages. – Northampton : Variorum.
394p. – (Collected Ser.: CS 113).
ISBN 0860780589 Hbk £22.00

History of international law in Russia 1647-1917 / Translated by W. E. Butler. – Oxford : Clarendon Press, 1988.
600.
An account of the develoment of the study of international law and the revolution of 1917. A guide to the Russian literature on the law of nations in a contemporary context. The translator's introduction and bibliography are new, and place the work in its historical context.
ISBN 0198254954 Hbk £40

History of Juvenile Delinquency, 2 Vols. / Priscilla F. Clement. – Aalen Wuertt : Scientia, 1989.
Hbk

History of Kilmainham Gaol The Dismal House of Little Ease. – Cork : Mercier Press.
ISBN 0853428395 Pbk £5.95

History of Solicitors in New South Wales. – Woolloomooloo : International Business Communications, 1984.
ISBN 094955314X Hbk £39.95

History of the common law of contract. – Oxford : Oxford University Press, 1987.
ISBN 019825573X Pbk £19.50

History of the Common Law of England, 2 Vols. – 5th ed. – Abingdon : Professional Books.
239p.
Hbk £125.00

History of the English Bar 1929. – London : Wildy & Sons.
Hbk £13.75

History of the Eurobond market : the first 21 years / by Ian M. Kerr. – London : Euromoney, 1984.
166p.
ISBN 0903121689

History of the Hong Kong and Shanghai Banking Corporation
Vol. 2 Hong Kong Bank in Period Imperialism 1895-1918 / King. – Cambridge : Cambridge University Press.
ISBN 0521327075 Hbk £60.00
Vol. 4 Hong Kong Bank in Period of Development 1941-1984. –
ISBN 0521327091 Hbk £60.00

History of the land law / A.W.B. Simpson. – 2nd ed. – Oxford : Clarendon, 1986.
316p; 22cm.
Previous ed.: published as An introduction to the history of land law. Oxford : Oxford University Press, 1961. Bibliography: p292-295. - Includes index.
ISBN 0198255365 Pbk £12.50
ISBN 0198255373 Hbk £25.00

History of the Law Reports 1884. – London : Wildy & Sons.
Hbk £11.75

History of the Most Remarkable Trials in Great Britain and Ireland in Capital Cases, 2 Vols. – Repr. of 1715 ed. – Abingdon : Professional Books.
370p.
Hbk £75.00

History of the United Nations Volume 2 : The Age of Decolonization 1955-65. – London : Macmillan.
ISBN 00333244249 Hbk £35.00

Hit and run and uninsured drivers. – 5th ed. – Chichester : Barry Rose, 1987.
ISBN 0870080653 Pbk

Hitchcock, David →Teaching, enacting and sticking up for human rights : an evaluation report on the Human Rights Commission's 'Teaching for Human Rights: Activities for Schools'.

Hitchens, Christopher
Inequalities in Zimbabwe / by Christopher Hitchens and David Stephen : with a foreword by Garfield Todd. – Rev. ed. – London : Minority Rights Group, 1981.
20p. – (Report).
Previous ed.: 1979. Bibliography: p.20.

Hitchins, R. L. →Statutes of Natal.

HM Customs and Excise Official VAT Guides. – London : Oyez Longman, 1983.
ISBN 0851206832 Llf £50.00

HM Land Registry →Registered land practice notes.

HM Prison Brixton : Report. – Great Britain Inspectorate of Prisons. – London : Home Office, 1982.
ii, 32p.
ISBN 0862520614 Hbk £1.10

HM Prison Manchester : Report. – London : Home Office, 1982.
ii, 32p.
ISBN 0862520681 Hbk £1.10

Hoath, David C.
75 years of law at Sheffield, 1909-1984 / edited by David C. Hoath. – Sheffield : University of Sheffield Faculty of Law, 1985.
viii,116p.
Includes bibliographical references.
—Council housing / by David C. Hoath. – 2nd ed. – London : Sweet & Maxwell, 1982.
xxvii,223p; 18cm.
Previous ed.: 1978. Includes index.
ISBN 042127610X Hbk £
ISBN 0421276207 Pbk £6.95
—Homelessness / by David C. Hoath. – London : Sweet & Maxwell, 1983.
xxi,217p; 18cm.
Bibliography: p215-217.
ISBN 0421281804 Hbk £11.50
ISBN 0421281901 Pbk £6.75

Hobbes's Science of Natural Justice / P.J. Johnson. – Dordrecht : Kluwer, 1987.
326p.
ISBN 9024732263 Hbk £195.00

Hobbs, R.
Doing the Business. – Oxford : Clarendon Press. – (Oxford Socio-Legal Studies).
ISBN 0198255985 Hbk £25.00

Hocker, P. J.
Cases and materials on contract / by P.J. Hocker, Ann Dufty and Peter G. Heffey. – 5th ed. – Sydney : Law Book Co., 1985.
xli,983p.
4th ed., 1979 by C.L. Pannam and P.J. Hocker. Includes bibliographical references and index.
ISBN 0455204039

Hocking, B.
International law and aboriginal rights. – Oxford : Croom Helm, 1987.
ISBN 0949614351 Hbk £22.50

Hodes, Lionel H. →Suzman, Gordon and Hodes on the law of compulsory motor vehicle insurance in South Africa.

Hodge, Harry →Famous trials.

Hodge, J.
Vicarious liability. – Witherby, 1986.
ISBN 094869100X Pbk £7.50

Hodge, Ralph A.
Organizing a Law Office : Law Office Management Series. – Agincourt : Carswell, 1988.
160p.
This is a guidebook to correct law office management. The author presents flow charts, sample precedents, effective accounting procedures and, in general, a cost efficient operation.
Hbk £33.75

Hodge, William C.
Criminal Procedure in New Zealand. – 2nd ed. – North Ryde : Law Book Co, 1984.
xxi, 198p.
ISBN 0455203547 Pbk £21.00
—Torts In New Zealand : Cases and Materials / Allin. – Oxford : Oxford University Press.
ISBN 00195581814 Pbk £22.50

Hodges, Lucy →Uprising! : the police, the people and the riots in Britain's cities.

Hodges, Tony
Jehovah's Witnesses in Africa / by Tony Hodges. – New rev. ed. – London : Minority Rights Group, 1985.
16p. – (Report).
Previous ed. published as: Jehovah's Witnesses in Central Africa. Bibliography: p.14.
ISBN 0946690227
—Western Saharans / by Tony Hodges. – London : Minority Rights Group, 1984.
20p. – (Report).
Bibliography: p.19-20.
ISBN 0946690219

Hodgin, R. W.
Insurance intermediaries and the law / by R.W. Hodgin. – 1. – London : Lloyd's of London Press, 1987.
22cm.
Includes bibliography and index.
ISBN 1850441073 Pbk £14.50

Hodgson
Silverstone Oil Company Limited Act, 1983, Bill Pr022 : An Act to Revive Silverstone Oil Company Limited. – Ontario : Ontario Government Publications Service, 1983.
2p.
Hbk £0.30
—Your Legal Position in Teaching / Tingle. – New Education.
ISBN 00946947252 Pbk £2.00

Hodgson, Derek →Justice annual members' conference held in the Lord Chief Justice's Court on Saturday 27 March 1982 : subject, decriminalisation.
→ Profits of crime and their recovery.

Hodgson, Godfrey
Lloyds of London. – Rev ed. – Penguin.
ISBN 0140056467 Pbk £7.95

Hodgson, Maurice →Civil justice review.

Hodgson, T.
Liquor Laws Guide. – Butterworths, 1983.
176p.
ISBN 0409494011 Pbk £27.50

Hodkinson →Law of Trusts.

Hodkinson, Keith
Muslim family law : a sourcebook / Keith Hodkinson. – London : Croom Helm, 1984.
401p; 22cm.
Bibliography: p367-377. - Includes index.
ISBN 0709912560 Pbk £14.95

Hodson, John D.
Ethics of Legal Coercion / John D. Hodson. – Dordrecht : Kluwer, 1985.
192p.
ISBN 9027718431 Pbk £52.00

Hoecke, Mark van →On the Utility of Legal Theory.

Hoffe, Otfried
Political justice : outline of a philosophical theory / by Otfried Hoffe. – Florence : European University Institute, 1985.
20p.

Hoffmann, Dietrich
German competition law : (legislation and commentary) / by Dietrich Hoffmann in cooperation with Stefan Schaub. – Deventer : Kluwer Law and Taxation Publishers, 1983.
xi,194.
Offprint from Competition law in Western Europe and the USA.
ISBN 9065441425

Hoffmann, L. H.
South African law of evidence / D. T. Zeffertt. – 3rd ed. – Durban : Butterworths, 1981.
lxxii,504p.
Previous ed.: 1970. Includes index.
ISBN 0409033227 Pbk
ISBN 0409033235

Hog, R.
Decisions of the Court of Session from 1681-91. – Repr. of 1757 ed. – Abingdon : Professional Books.
51p.
Hbk £90.00

Hogan
Political Violence and the Law in Ireland / Walker. – Manchester : Manchester University Press.
ISBN 00719029104 Hbk £25.00

Hogan, Brian
'A' level law : cases and materials / Brian Hogan, Peter Seago, Geoffrey Bennett. – London : Sweet & Maxwell, 1986.
xxvii,507p; 22cm.
Includes index.
ISBN 0421352906 Pbk £8.95
ISBN 042138820X Hbk £9.95
—Career in law / by Brian Hogan. – London : Sweet & Maxwell, 1981.
vii,98p; 18cm.
Bibliography: p92-95. - Includes index.
ISBN 0421280506 Pbk £1.95
→ Cases and Materials on Criminal Law.
→ Criminal law.
→ Criminal law : cases and materials.

Hogan, Daire
Legal profession in Ireland 1789-1922. – Dublin : Incorporated Law Society of Ireland, 1986.
xii,176p.
Bibliography: p.165-169. - Includes index.
ISBN 090202728X

Hogan, Gerard →Administrative Law.

Hogan, Gerard W. →Prisoners' rights : a study in Irish prison law.

Hogan, Greer
Constitutional and administrative law in a nutshell / Greer Hogan. – London : Sweet & Maxwell, 1987.
122p; 22cm.
Includes index.
ISBN 0421368101 Pbk £3.95

Hogan, Warren →Economics of Bureaucracy and Statutory Authorities.

Hogg et al
Bullion : Brinks-Mat Story Of Britain's Biggest Gold Robbery. – Penguin.
ISBN 014008567X Pbk £3.50

Hogg, Peter W.
Canada Act 1982 annotated / by Peter W. Hogg. – Toronto : Carswell, 1982.
155p.
Includes the Constitution Act, 1982 - the Canadian Bill of Rights - the International Bill of Rights - the International Covenant on Civil and Political Rights. Includes index.
ISBN 0459351303

Hoggett, Brenda M.
Family, law and society : cases and materials / Brenda M. Hoggett, David S. Pearl. – 2nd ed. – London : Butterworths, 1987.
670p; 25cm.
Previous ed.: 1983. Includes bibliography and index.
ISBN 0406595925 Pbk £30.00 :
ISBN 0406595933 £22.50
—Mental health law / Brenda M. Hoggett. – 2nd ed. – London : Sweet & Maxwell, 1984.
xxiv,370p; 22cm.
Account of the basic legal rights of psychiatric patients before, during and after hospital confinement. Explains Mental Health Tribunals, and the Court of Protection. Also covers the Mental Health Act 1983.
ISBN 0421302208 Pbk £12.95
—Parents and children: the law of parental responsibility. – 3rd. – London : Sweet & Maxwell, 1987.
Places legal problems in their social context, and discusses the nature of parental rights and duties, the consequences of marriage breakdown, and the legal response to child abuse. Covers the Family Law Reform Act, the legal implications of surrogacy arrangements, the sterilisation of a mentally handicapped ward of court, the custodianship provision of the Children Act 1975, and the Law Commission's review of the private law relating to children.
ISBN 042136050X Pbk £17
→ White, Carr and Lowe: a guide to the Children Act 1989.
→ Women and the law.

Hoghughi, Masud
Delinquent : directions for social control / Masud Hoghughi. – London : Burnett, 1983.
317p; 24cm.
Bibliography: p295-310. - Includes index.
ISBN 0091506808 Hbk £15.00
ISBN 0091506816 Pbk £6.95

Hogwood, Brian W. →Regional government in England.

Holborn Law Society →List of barristers by chambers, with index.

Holbrook, R. G.
Conveyancing 1985. – London : Law Society, 1985.
15p. – (Nineteen Eighty-Five Crash Course Transcripts).
Hbk £2.05

Holcombe, Lee
Wives and property : reform of the married women's property law in nineteenth-century England / Lee Holcombe. – Oxford : Martin Robertson, 1983.
viii,311p; 24cm.
Bibliography: p275-292. - Includes index.
ISBN 0855206071 £15.00
—Wives and Property : Reform of the Married Women's Property Law in Nineteenth-Century England. – Toronto : University of Toronto Press, 1982.
ISBN 0802055737 Hbk £35.00
ISBN 0802064760 Pbk £12.50

Holdaway, S.
Crime and Deviance : Issues in Sociology. – London : Macmillan.
ISBN 033344051X Pbk £4.25

Holdaway, Simon
Inside the British police : a force at work / Simon Holdaway. – Oxford : Basil Blackwell, 1983.
vi,186p; 23cm.
Bibliography: p176-177. - Includes index.
ISBN 0631131124 £14.95

Holden →Legal Secretary Today.

Holden, J. Milnes
Law and practice of banking
Vol.1 : Banker and customer / J. Milnes Holden. – 4th ed. – London : Pitman, 1986.
lxv,500p; 22cm.
Previous ed.: 1982. Includes index.
ISBN 0273024884 Pbk £12.95
Vol.2 : Securities for bankers' advances / J. Milnes Holden. – 1986.
512p; 22cm.
Previous ed.: 1980. Includes index.
ISBN 0273022954 Pbk £10.95

Holdert, H. M. C.
Collision cases : judgments and diagrams / by H.M.C. Holdert and F.J. Buzek. – London : Lloyd's, 1984.
xvii,190p.
ISBN 0907432964

Holdgate, M. W. →World environment 1972-1982 : a report.

Holdsworth Club →Control of power within the European Communities : being the presidential address of Lord Mackenzie Stuart, president of the Holdsworth Club of the Faculty of Law in the University of Birmingham, 1985-1986.
→ Half-a-century of commercial law, 1930-1980.
→ Preserving freedom under the law : being the presidential address of the Rt. Hon. Lord Bridge of Harwich, President of the Holdsworth Club of the Faculty of Law in the University of Birmingham, 1981-82.
→ Towards a rational criminal law : being the Presidential Address of Professor J. C. Smith, President of the Holdsworth Club of the faculty of Law in the University of Birmingham, 1982-83.

Holes in the Welfare Net. – London : Bedford Square Press.
ISBN 0719909392 Hbk £6.95
ISBN 0719909406 Pbk £3.95

Holland →Landlord and Tenant.

Holland, Richard E. →Advocacy : views from the bench.

Holland, Winifred H.
Unmarried couples : legal aspects of cohabitation / by Winifred H. Holland : Tax aspects, D. Keith McNair. – Toronto : Carswell, 1982.
xxxii,249p.
Includes bibliographical references and index.
ISBN 0459348701

Hollander, Charles →Documentary evidence.

Hollis, M.
Surveying for Delapidations : A Practical Guide to the Law and its Applications. – London : Estates Gazette.
ISBN 0728201046 Pbk £24.50

Hollis, Martin →Rationality and relativism.

Holloway, D. R.
Holloway's Probate Handbook. – 6th ed. – London : Oyez Longman, 1982.
– (Oyez Longman Practitioner Ser.).
ISBN 0851206484 Hbk £15.00
—Probate Handbook. – 8th ed. – London : Longman Professional.
– (Practitioner Series (3 volumes Supplements)).
ISBN 0851214703 Hbk £38.50

Holloway, John
Social policy harmonisation in the European Community / John Holloway. – Farnborough, Hants. : Gower, 1981.
vi,318p; 23cm.
Bibliography: p305-318.
ISBN 0566001969 £10.50

Holloway's Probate Handbook. – 6th ed. – London : Oyez Longman, 1982.
– (Oyez Longman Practitioner Ser.).
ISBN 0851206484 Hbk £15.00

Holme
1688-1988 : Time for a New Constitution / Elliot. – London : Macmillan.
ISBN 0333467019 Hbk £27.50
ISBN 0333467027 Pbk £8.85

Holmes
Employment Law / Painter. – London : Blackstone Press.
ISBN 1854310089 Pbk £8.50
→ Financial Accounting.
—Interpreting company reports and accounts / Sugden. – 3rd ed. – Cambridge : Woodhead-Faulkner, 1986.
ISBN 085941325X Hbk £25.00
ISBN 0859413268 Pbk £14.95
—Serial murder / Deburger. – Sage Publications, 1988.
ISBN 0803928408 Hbk £25.95
ISBN 0803928416 Pbk £12.00

Holmes, D.
Butterworths Student Companions
Family Law /. – Butterworths, 1986.
ISBN 0409491365
Torts. – 1984.
128p.
ISBN 0409494127

Holmes, E. McL.
Managing the water industry : the accounting, reporting and auditing dimension : a report to the Public Bodies Review Committee / from E. McL. Holmes. – Melbourne : Public Bodies Review Committee, 1982.
xi,237p.

Holmes McDougall Ltd. : restriction of advertisements containing prices : a report by the Director General of Fair Trading on an investigation under section 3 of the Competition Act 1980. – London : Office of Fair Trading, 1985.
39p; 30cm.

Holmes, Oliver Wendell
Common law / by O.W. Holmes. – London : Macmillan, 1911.
xvi,422p.
Includes bibliographical references and index.

Holmested
Ontario Civil Procedure, 3 Vols.
Vols. 1-3. – Agincourt : Carswell.
This two volume set provides complete textual analysis on practice and procedure topics arising under the Ontario, Canada Rules of Civil Procedure and Courts of Justice Act. Annotated cases relevant to the Ontario Rules and comparisons to rules in other provinces are included in the work.
Pbk £189.00

Holmstrom, Lynda Lytle
Victim of rape : institutional reactions / Lynda Lytle Holmstrom, Ann Wolbert Burgess. – New ed. – New Brunswick : Transaction, 1983.
xl,293p; 23cm.
Previous ed.: New York ; Chichester : Wiley, 1978.
ISBN 0878559329 Pbk

Holt
Acquisitions & Mergers : Accounting, Financial & Strategic Issues / Reynolds. – Routledge.
ISBN 0415004306 Hbk £27.50

Holt, Laurence James
Compulsory arbitration in New Zealand : the first forty years / James Holt. – Auckland : Auckland University Press, 1986.
247p.
Bibliography: p236-242.
ISBN 1869400062

Holt, Stephen
Democracy and Direct Action in Contemporary Europe. – Exeter : European Atlantic Movement, 1982.
Hbk £0.50
→ Professional negligence.

Holtzman, H M
Guide to the UNCITRAL model on international commercial arbitration: legislation, history and commentary / J E Neuhaus. – Kluwer Law and Taxation, 1989.
1320.
Gives the legislative history of the new UNCITRAL model arbitration law. Each chapter starts with a commentary on the legislative history of the Article, highlighting the principle issues considered, followed by the legislative history of the article. Text contains documents, including drafts, reports, summary records of debates, government comments and conference room papers.
ISBN 9065443053 Hbk £139/Dfl 450

Holyoak, J. H.
Civil liability for defective premises / J. H. Holyoak, David K. Allen. – London : Butterworths, 1982.
xxvii,278p.
This book provides United Kingdom practitioners with a comprehensive guide to liabilities of occupier, owner, builder, and other parties in cases of defective premises. Measure of damages, claims for economic loss, limitation periods, and misrepresentation are also covered.
ISBN 0406233403 Hbk £34.00

Homant, R.J.
Police and Law Enforcement
Vol. 4. – London : Eurospan, 1988.
ISBN 0404112080 Hbk £47.25

Home Office 1848-1914 : from clerks to bureaucrats / Jill Pellew. – London : Heinemann, 1982.
xi,271p; 22cm.
Bibliography: p225-233. - Includes index.
ISBN 0435326856 £12.50

Home Office
Cautioning by the police : a consultative document / Home Office. – London : Home Office, 1984.
47p.
Bibliography: p.47.
ISBN 0862521513
—Criminal justice : plans for legislation : presented to Parliament by the Secretary of State for the Home Department ... / Home Office. – London : HMSO, 1986.
23p; 25cm.
ISBN 010196580X Hbk £2.80
—Custodial sentences for young offenders : a discussion paper / Home Office. – London : Home Office, 1986.
12p.
—Development of cable systems and services / Home Office, Department of Industry. – London : H.M.S.O., 1983.
90p; 25cm.
ISBN 0101886608 Pbk £6.00
—Draft codes of practice for the treatment, questioning and identification of persons suspected of crime / Home Office. – Revised draft. – London : Home Office, 1983.
51p.
ISBN 0862520975
—Establishment of an independent element in the investigation of complaints against the police : report of a working party appointed by the Home Secretary / Home Office. – London : H.M.S.O., 1981.
ii,12p; 25cm.
ISBN 0101819307 unbound £1.70
—Review of appeals under the Immigration Act 1971 : a discussion document / Home Office. – Croydon : Home Office, 1981.
16p.
—Review of the Operation of the Prevention of Terrorism (Temporary Provisions) Act 1984 / by the Viscount Colville of Culross : presented to Parliament by the Secretary of State for the Home Department ... – London : HMSO, 1987.
v,70p.
ISBN 0101026420

—Sentence of the court : a handbook for courts on the treatment of offenders / Home Office. – 4th ed. – London : H.M.S.O., 1986.
109p; 21cm.
ISBN 0113408072

—Tackling drug misuse : a summary of the governments strategy / Home Office. – 2nd ed. – London : Home Office, 1986.
39p.
Includes bibliographical references.
ISBN 086252234X

—Use of video technology at trials of alleged child abusers / Home Office. – London : Home Office, 1987.
14p.
ISBN 0862522749

Home Office : perspectives on policy and administration : bicentenary lectures 1982. – London : Royal Institute of Public Administration, 1983.
98p; 21cm.
ISBN 0900628308 Pbk £6.00

Home, R.
Planning use classes. – Oxford : Blackwell Scientific, 1987.
ISBN 063202125X Pbk £14.95

Homeless persons : the Housing Act 1985 Part III / Andrew Arden. – 2nd ed. – London : Legal Action Group, 1986.
xxiii,200p.
Previous ed.: published as 'The Homeless Persons Act' 1982. Includes index. Includes text of act.

Homeless person's handbook. – London : Allison & Busby, 1988.
ISBN 085031769 Pbk £4.95

Homeless young offenders : an action programme : the Report of a NACRO Group. – NACRO. – London : NACRO, 1981.
69p.
Bibliography: p.67-69.
ISBN 0850690242

Homelessness / by David C. Hoath. – London : Sweet & Maxwell, 1983.
xxi,217p; 18cm.
Bibliography: p215-217.
ISBN 0421281804 Hbk £11.50
ISBN 0421281901 Pbk £6.75

Homelessness among women : report of an Ad Hoc Working Group, Women's National Commission / Norma Nelson. – London : Cabinet Office, 1983.
56p; 30cm.
Report prepared under the chairmanship of Norma Nelson.

Homelessness and the law / by Paul Q. Watchman and Peter Robson. – Glasgow : The Planning Exchange, 1983.
xvi,182p; 21cm.
Bibliography: p148-158. - Includes index.
ISBN 0905011201 Pbk £6.95

Home-owner's guide. – Cambridge : Woodhead-Faulkner, 1987.
ISBN 085941423X Pbk £4.95

Homeowner's guide to the law. – London : Fourmat, 1987.
ISBN 1851900233 Pbk £6.95

Homer, Arnold
Tolley's Tax Guide 1988-89 / Rita Burrows. – Croydon : Tolley.
464p.
ISBN 0854593535 Hbk £15.95

Homes for the future : statement to Annual Comnference 1985 / by the Labour Party National Executive Committee. – London : Labour Party, 1985.
47p.
ISBN 0861171233

Homes Wasted. – Shelter. – London : Shelter, 1982.
ISBN 0901242640 Hbk £2.50

Homicide / Law Reform Commission of Victoria. – Melbourne : The Commission, 1988.
72p. – (Discussion paper).
Includes bibliographical references.
ISBN 0724167137

Homicide / Law Reform Commission of Canada. – Ottawa : Law Reform Commission of Canada, 1984.
117,128p; 25cm. – (Working paper).
At head of cover title: Criminal law. English and French texts bound back to back.
ISBN 0662529871

Homicide : the law and the Proofs / G.K. Jaisimaha Rao. – North Ryde : Law Book 6, 1986.
ca xvi, 210p.
ISBN 0455206740 jb £45.00

Homicide compensation in Papua New Guinea : problems and prospects / edited by Richard Scaglion. – Papua New Guinea : Published by the Office of Information, Papua New Guinea for the Law Reform Commission of Papua New Guinea, 1981.
102p; 23cm. – (Monograph).
Includes bibliographical references.
ISBN 0724707301

Homicide, the law and the proofs. – North Ryde : Law Book Co, 1986.
ISBN 0455206740 Hbk £22.75

Homoud, S. H.
Islamic banking : the adaptation of banking practice to conform with Islamic law / S.H. Homoud. – London : Arabian Information, 1985.
300p; 28cm.
Translated from the Arabic.
ISBN 0860105032 Hbk £75.00 :
ISBN 0860105024 Pbk £35.00

Hon. Dr. T. Akinola Aguda : the man, his works and society / by I.O. Agbede. – Lagos : Nigerian Institute of Advanced Legal Studies, 1986.
v,30p. – (Occasional paper).
Bibliography: pp.21-30..

Honderich, Ted
Punishment : the supposed justifications / Ted Honderich. – Rev.ed. – Harmondsworth : Pelican Books, 1984.
248p.
Revised edition issued in Peregrine Books 1976.
ISBN 0140213120

Hondius, F.
A.A.A. Yearbook
Vol. 45/46: Computer and International Law /. – Dordrecht : Kluwer, 1981.
vi, 196p.
ISBN 902472323X Hbk £65.00

Honeyball, S.
Guide to the Employment Act 1988. – London : Butterworths.
ISBN 0406502838 Hbk £17.50

Honeygold, D.
International financial markets. – Cambridge : Woodhead-Faulkner, 1988.
ISBN 085941440X Hbk £35.00

Hong, Damian C.F. →Singapore Taxation.

Hong Kong Banking Ordinance / Anthony Williams. – London : Butterworths, 1988.
350p.
Contains an annotation of the Banking Ordinance of 1986 and the Amendment Ordinance of 1988, annotations that consider the practical implications of the new provisions with reference to extensive legal authorities in Hong Kong and other countries.
ISBN 0409995398 Hbk

Hong Kong Company Law. – 2nd ed. – Pitman.
ISBN 0273030892 Pbk £8.95

Hong Kong Company Law Handbook. – London : Butterworths, 1982.
ISBN 0406595607 Pbk

Hong Kong company legislation. – London : Butterworths, 1988.
ISBN 0409995525 Llf

Hong Kong conveyancing and property ordinance. – London : Butterworths, 1988.
ISBN 0409995401 Hbk £42.00

Hong Kong Correctional Service
Drug addiction research programme 1983 / Correctional Services Department, Hong Kong. – Hong Kong : The Department, 1983.
40p.

Hong Kong current law. – London : Sweet & Maxwell, 1986.

Hong Kong in International Tax Planning. – London : Oyez Longman, 1983.
– (Oyez Longman Intelligence Report Ser.).
ISBN 085120810X Hbk £55.00

Hong Kong law yearbook. – London : Sweet & Maxwell, 1985-.

Hong Kong private company : a manual of practice. – Singapore : Butterworths (Asia), 1989.
300.
A practical guide to Company Secetarial practice in Hong Kong. Includes forms and precedents, extensive cross-references, and coverage of topics such as future legal developments.
ISBN 0409995703 Hbk

Hong Kong revenue law. – Matthew Bender, 1981.
ISBN 0000999046 Hbk £140.00

Hong Kong stamp duties / Richards. – London : Longman Professional, 1984.
ISBN 0851208983 Pbk £17.50

Hong Kong tax cases. – Hong Kong : Government Printer, 1983.
looseleaf.
Kept up to date by supplements.

Hong Kong taxation : law and practice / David Flux. – Rev. ed. – Hong Kong : Chinese University Press, 1982.
xxviii,387p(4 folded); 24cm.
Previous ed.: 1981. Includes index.
ISBN 0421309105 £17.00

Hong Kong Taxation : Law and Practice. – Sha Tin : Chinese University of Hong Kong Press, 1983-84.
xxviii, 403p.
ISBN 9622013066 Hbk £30.50

Hong Kong tenancy law : an introduction to the law of landlord and tenant / Malcolm Merry. – Singapore : Butterworths, 1985.
xix,343p.
Includes index. English and Chinese forms.
ISBN 0409995126 Pbk £24.00

Hong, Peter Owyong Gim
Handbook of Singapore Tax Statutes, 1985-86 Edition / Laurence Chan. – Butterworths, 1986.
933p.
Contains the texts of important tax legislation, together with amendments and excerpts from the 1986/87 Budget Statement. Covers income tax, double tax treaties, estate duty, payroll tax, property tax and stamp duty.
ISBN 0409995207 Pbk £99.00

Honnold, John O
Documentary history of the 1980 uniform law for international sales. – Kluwer Law and Taxation, 1989.
896.
Covers the United Nations Commission on International Trade Law (1969-1977) and the Vienna Diplomatic Conference (1980). Compiled from documents in the nine volumes of the UNCITRAL yaerbook and the Official Records on the 1980 Conference.
ISBN 9065443738 Hbk £105/Dfl 350

—On the road to unification of the law of sales / John Honnold. – Deventer : Kluwer Law and Taxation Publishers, 1983.
31p.
ISBN 9065441662

Honore, Anthony Maurice →Causation in the law.

—Emperors and lawyers / Tony Honore. – London : Duckworth, 1981.
xv,190p; 26cm.
Bibliography: p183-187. - Includes index.
ISBN 0715614495

—Justinian's Digest. – Repr. of 1971 ed. – Aalen Wuertt : Scientia, 1983.
35p.
ISBN 3511091284 Hbk £15.00

—Making law bind : essays legal and philosophical / Tony Honore. – Oxford : Clarendon, 1987.
288p; 22cm.
Includes index.
ISBN 0198254670 Hbk £30.00

—Quest for security : employees, tenants, wives / by Tony Honore. – London : Stevens, 1982.
xiv,128p; 19cm.
Includes index.
ISBN 0420464107 Hbk £12.00
ISBN 0420464204 Pbk £5.80

—South African law of trusts / by Tony Honore. – Cape Town : Juta, 1985.
lxvi,551p.
Previous ed.: 1976. Includes bibliographical references and index.
ISBN 0702115320

—Ulpian / Tony Honore. – Oxford : Clarendon Press, 1982.
ix,303p; 24cm.
Bibliography: p285-294. - Includes index.
ISBN 0198253583

Honsberger, John D.
O'Brien's Encyclopedia of Forms : Division One-Commercial & General
Vols. 1-3. – Aurora : Canada Law Book Co. – (Abridgments and Encyclopedias).
Hbk £150.00

Honsberger, John David →Anger and Honsberger: law of real property.
→ O'Briens encyclopedia of forms.

—O'Brien's Encyclopedia of Forms : 1893-Present, 9 Vols.
Vols. 1-9. – Aurora : Canada Law Book Co. – (Divisions 1-5 Covering All Ser.).
Hbk £451.50

Hood →First Book of English Law.

Hood, Neil
Economics of multinational enterprise / Neil Hood, Stephen Young. – 5th impression. – London : Longman, 1984.
xv,412p.
This ed. originally published: 1979. Bibliography: p.393-407. - Includes index.

—Multinationals in retreat : the Scottish experience / by Neil Hood and Stephen Young. – Edinburgh : Edinburgh University Press, 1982.
xi,193p; 24cm.
Includes index.
ISBN 0852244282 Pbk £10.00

Hood, Roger
Death penalty: a worldwide perspective. – Oxford : Clarendon Press, 1989.
200; 21.5.
Survey of practice literature covering the death penalty, by analysis of the law and practice of all states where the death penalty is, or has been, used in recent years. Discusses whether or not the claimed deterrent effect of the death penalty has any basis in known fact.
ISBN 0198252722 Hbk £20.00
→ History of English criminal law and its administration from 1750, Vol.5 : The emergence of penal policy : by Sir Leon Radzinowicz, Roger Hood.

Hoof, G. J. H. van
Rethinking the sources of international law / by G. J. H. van Hoof. – Deventer : Kluwer, 1983.
xiv,322p; 25cm.
Dutch summary, p.313-321.
ISBN 9065440852 Pbk £121.00
→ Theory and practice of the European convention on human rights.

Hoogan, W.P. → Regulation, Investor/Depositor Protection and the Campbell Report.

Hooker, I → Non-means tested benefits: the legislation.

Hooker, Michael Barry
Islamic law in South-East Asia / M.B. Hooker. – Singapore : O.U.P., 1984.
xxx,330p.
Bibliography: p.281-296. - Includes index.
ISBN 0195825039
→ Laws of South-East Asia, Vol. 1 : The pre-modern texts.
→ Malaysian legal essays : a collection of essays in honour of Professor Emeritus Datuk Ahmad Ibrahim.

Hookway, Harry
Can knowledge survive? / Sir Harry Hookway. – London : British Library, 1986.
8p; 30cm. – (The Fourth British Library Annual Research Lecture).
ISBN 0712330747 Pbk ree

Hoolahan → Law of Breach of Confidence.

Hoolahan, Michael J. → Employees' inventions in the United Kingdom : law and practice.

Hooligan : a history of respectable fears / Geoffrey Pearson. – London : Macmillan, 1983.
xi,283p.
Bibliography: p244-275.
ISBN 0333233999

Hooligans abroad : the behaviour and control of English fans in Continental Europe / John Williams, Eric Dunning and Patrick Murphy. – London : Routledge & Kegan Paul, 1984.
xiv,230p,12p of plates; 22cm.
Includes index.
ISBN 0710201435 Pbk £8.95

Hooper, D.
Official Secrets : the Use and Abuse of the Act. – New edition. – Oxford : Coronet Books.
ISBN 0340426500 Pbk £3.95

Hoorn, J. van → Taxation in European socialist countries.

Hope, J → Rent (Scotland) Act 1984.

Hope, Tim
Burglary in schools : the prospects for prevention / Tim Hope. – London : Home Office, 1982.
iv,47p.
Bibliography: p.38-41.
ISBN 0862520703
—Implementing crime prevention measures / by Tim Hope. – London : H.M.S.O., 1985.
vi,75p; 25cm.
Examines practicality of crime prevention methods. Considers situational measures aimed at dealing with specifically defined offences and community involvement in prevention of crime. Illustrates difficulties by case histories.
ISBN 0113408129

Hopkins, Andrew
Crime, Law and Business : The Sociological Sources of Australian Monopoly Law. – Canberra : Australian Institute of Criminology.
Hbk £3.00
—Impact of Prosecutions Under the Trade Practices Act. – Canberra : Australian Institute of Criminology.
Hbk £2.00

Hopkins, Leon
Audit Report. – London : Butterworths, 1984.
A review of the current state of audit reporting which outlines legal and other requirements of the audit. The book surveys a wide range of reporting styles and provides many examples, drawn from published reports, to illustrate problems in modern auditing.
ISBN 040601650X Pbk £15.00

Hopkins, Michael
Policy formation in the European Communities : a bibliographic guide to Community documentation 1958-1978 / Michael Hopkins. – London : Mansell, 1981.
xx,339p; 24cm.
Includes index.
ISBN 0720115973 £24.50
—Publications, documentation and means for their dissemination in the Commission of the European Communities / M. Hopkins. – London : British Library, 1981.
iv,28p; 30cm.
ISBN 0905984692 Pbk

Hopkins, Richard
Approach to Searching for Research and Evaluation Reports in the Field of Public Legal Education and Information (PLEI). – Ottawa : Canadian Law Information Council, 1984.
28p.
ISBN 0920358608 Pbk £7.50

Hopper → Critical Accounts.

Hopt, Klaus J. → Corporate governance and directors' liabilities : legal, economic, and sociological analyses on corporate social responsibility.
→ Legal and economic analyses on multinational enterprises.
→ Legal harmonization and the business enterprise : corporate and capital market law, harmonization policy in Europe and the U.S.A.

Hopwood, Charles Henry
Inns of Court : Middle Temple Records (1501-1703). – Repr. of 1905 ed. – Abingdon : Professional Books.
214p.
Hbk £75.00
→ Middle Temple records.

Horgan, M.
Competitive Tendering for Engineering Contracts. – London : Sweet & Maxwell, 1983.
Hbk £18.95
—Competitive Tendering For Engineering Contracts. – Spon (E & FN), 1983.
ISBN 0419116303 Hbk £19.95

Horgan, Patrick T. → Introduction to law in the Republic of Ireland : its history, principles, administration & substance.

Horle, C.W.
Quakers and the English Legal System 1660-68. – Witney : Academic & University Publishing Group.
ISBN 0812281012 Hbk £33.20

Horn, Frank
Reservations and Interpretative Declarations to Multilateral Treaties. – Amsterdam : Elsevier Science Publishers, 1988.
xxviii, 514p.
ISBN 0444703985 Hbk £250.00

Horn, John → Conduct of Civil Litigation in British Columbia.

Horn, Norbert → Adaptation and renegotiation of contracts in international trade and finance.
—German private and commercial law : an introduction / by Norbert Horn, Hein Kotz and Hans G. Leser : translated by Tony Weir. – Oxford : Clarendon, 1982.
xvi,355p; 22cm.
Bibliography: p332-334. - Includes index. Translation from the German.
ISBN 0198253826 Hbk £27.00
ISBN 0198253834 Pbk £15.00
→ Transnational law of international commercial transactions.

Horne, A.
Book Called the Mirror of Justices : With the Book (By Sir Anthony Fitzherbert), Called the Divinity of Courts and Their Jurisdictions / William Hughes. – Repr. of 1646 ed. – Abingdon : Professional Books.
40p.
Hbk £125.00

Horne, Donald → Changing the system : political and constitutional reform, some options and difficulties.

Horne, Frederic T. → Cordery's law relating to solicitors.

Horne, Jennifer
Trade unionists and the law / Jennifer Horne. – London : Shaw, 1983.
xii,84p; 21cm.
ISBN 072190940X Pbk

Horner, S.
Parallel imports. – Oxford : Blackwell Scientific, 1987.
ISBN 0003833666 Hbk £20.00

Horner, Simon A.
Isle of Man and the Channel Islands : a study of their status under constitutional, international and European law / by Simon A. Horner. – Florence : European University Institute, 1984.
142p.
At head of title: European University Institute, Florence, Law Department.

Horowitz, E.
World trademark law and practice. – 2nd ed. – Matthew Bender, 1985.
ISBN 0000999080 Hbk £141.00

Horse and the law. – London : David & Charles, 1987.
ISBN 0715388134 Hbk £10.95

Horse law. – Shaw & Sons, 1988.
ISBN 0721911307 Pbk

Horsley
Law of Meetings / Paul. – New Zealand ed. – London : Butterworths, 1981.
ISBN 040963560X Pbk £23.50

Horsman → Matrimonial proceedings before Magistrates.

Horsman, J. Basil → Pugh's matrimonial proceedings before magistrates.

Horst, M. H. J. van den
Roman Dutch law in Sri Lanka / by Marleen H.J. van den Horst. – Amsterdam : Free University Press, 1985.
154 p.; 24 cm.
Re translation of: Het Rooms Hollandse recht in Sri Lanka. : Originally presented as the author's thesis (M.A.–Free University, Amsterdam) in 1984. Includes index. Bibliography: p. 138-144.
ISBN 9062562361 Pbk

Horstman, A.
Victorian divorce. – Oxford : Croom Helm, 1985.
ISBN 0709937652 Hbk £17.95

Horton → Evaluating Police Work : An Action Research Project.

Horwath and Horwath International
International tax planner's manual / Horwath & Horwath International. – Rev. impression. – North Ryde, N.S.W. : CCH Australia, 1985.
xvi,547p.
Includes index.
ISBN 0869038273
→ International tax planning manual.

Hosen, F.E.
Unfolding Westward in Treaty and Law Land Documents US History-Appalachians to Pacific. – Folkestone : Bailey Bros., 1783-1934.
ISBN 089950308X Hbk £33.75

Hoskin
Financial Accounting Cases / Hughes. – New York : Dryden Press.
ISBN 003011778X Pbk £6.95

Hoskin, E.J.
Community Law and United Kingdom Value Added Tax. – London : Deloitte Haskins & Sells, 1988.
ISBN 0863491235 Hbk £45.00

Hosking, Gordon A.
Hosking's Pension schemes and retirement benefits / K. Muir McKelvey, Tony Round, Michael Fairclough, Gordon A. Hosking. – 5th ed. – London : Sweet & Maxwell, 1985.
272p.
Previous ed: published as Pension schemes and retirement benefits. 1977. Includes index.
ISBN 0421309601 Pbk £16.00

Hosking, R → Encyclopedia of road traffic law and practice.

Hosking's Pension schemes and retirement benefits / K. Muir McKelvey, Tony Round, Michael Fairclough, Gordon A. Hosking. – 5th ed. – London : Sweet & Maxwell, 1985.
272p.
Previous ed: published as Pension schemes and retirement benefits. 1977. Includes index.
ISBN 0421309601 Pbk £16.00

Hoskins, E.J.
Appearing before a Value Added Tax Tribunal. – London : Deloitte Haskins & Sells.
ISBN 0863491227 Pbk £20.00

Hossain, Kamal → Permanent sovereignty over natural resources in international law.
—Petroleum Development : Law and Policy, a Comparative Study. – London : Commonwealth Secretariat.
Hbk £15.00

Hosten Edwards Nathan and Bosman : Introduction to South African Law and Legal Theory
Supplement 1984. – Durban.
ISBN 0409033545 Hbk £16.00

Hosten, W. J. → Treatise on the quasi-contract called promutuum and on the condictio indebiti.

Hotel and catering law in Britain / by David Field. – 5th ed. – London : Sweet & Maxwell, 1988.
xvii,236p; 23cm.
Discusses the legal framework in England, Scotland and Wales. Covers changes in the law effected by the Wages Act 1986, and the Licensing (Restaurant Meals) Act 1987, and also examines the impact of the new Companies legislation on the catering industry.
ISBN 0421392509 Pbk £8.50

Hotop, S. D.
Cases and materials on review of administrative action / by S.D. Hotop. – 2nd ed. – Sydney : Law Book Co., 1983.
xxxiii,1219p.
Previous ed.: 1979. Includes bibliographical references and index.
ISBN 0455203776

Hough, Mike
British crime survey : first report / by Mike Hough and Pat Mayhew. – London : H.M.S.O., 1983.
v,57p; 25cm.
'A Home Office Research and Planning Unit report'.
ISBN 0113407866 Pbk £4.35
→ Crime and police effectiveness.
→ Crime and public housing : proceedings of a workshop held in September 1980.

—Taking account of crime : key findings from the second British crime survey / Mike Hough and Pat Mayhew. – London : H.M.S.O., 1985.
vi,110p.
Reports on extent, risks and nature of selected crime, including incidents neither reported to nor recorded by police. Examines changing trends in crime between 1981 and 1983. Discusses differences between reported and unreported crime, the impact of crime on victims and public attitudes to crime.
ISBN 0113408102

Houghton → Land Law.
→ Police training manual.

Houghton, Anthony R.
Tolley's European insolvency guide / Anthony R. Houghton, Neil H. Cooper. – Croydon : Tolley Publishing Co., 1984.
xv,364p; 23cm. – (An Extel Group publication).
Includes index.
ISBN 0854590978 Pbk £19.95

Houghton, R. → Summonses and Charges.

Houlden, L. W.
Bankruptcy law of Canada / by L.W. Houlden and C.H. Morawetz. – New ed. 2 v. – Toronto : Carswell, 1984.
looseleaf.
Previous ed.: 1960. Includes text of Bankruptcy Act.

Houndsditch Murders and the Siege of Sidney Street. – Allan (WH).
ISBN 0491031785 Hbk £12.95

Hours of Work and Over Time. – 3rd ed. – Karachi : Bureau of Labour Publications, 1987.
Pbk £2.40

House Construction and Renovation : a Solicitor's Guide. – Vancouver : Continuing Legal Education Society of British Columbia, 1988.
310p.
ISBN 0865049688 Hbk £80.00

House of Care : Prisons and Prisoners in England 1500-1800. – Nottingham : Department of Adult Education, University of Nottingham.
ISBN 1850410216 Hbk £18.50

House of Commons Weekly Information Bulletin. – London : HMSO.
Hbk £51.00
Single Issue. –
Hbk £1.50

House of Lords. – Allan (Philip), 1988.
ISBN 086003402X Hbk £34.50
ISBN 0860037029 Pbk £14.95

House of Lords
Copyright, Designs and Patents Bill H.L. : as amended by Standing Committee E. – House of Lords. – London : HMSO, 1988.
xiii,217p. – (H.L. Bill 1987-88 (176)).
ISBN 0103176888

House of Lords Appeals : 1821-1873, 28 Vols. Incl. 1821-1824, 2 Vols. – Abingdon : Professional Books.
Hbk

House of Representatives Practice
Making an Act of Parliament : Legislative Process. – House of Representatives Practice. – Canberra : Australian Government Publishing Service, 1981.
Hbk £1.40

House of Representatives Standing Committee on Road Safety
Impact of Advertising Standards on Road Safety : Report, November 1983. – House of Representatives Standing Committee on Road Safety. – Canberra : Australian Government Publishing Service, 1983.
58p.
ISBN 0644029706 Hbk £3.30

House selling the Scottish way for England and Wales / an explanatory guide by the Conveyancing Standing Committee. – London : The Law Commission, Conveyancing Standing Committee, 1985.
20 leaves.

Household insurance / a report by the Director General of Fair Trading. – London : Office of Fair Trading, 1985.
58p.

Houseman and Davies law of life assurance / B. P. A. Davies. – 10th ed. – London : Butterworths, 1984.
xxiv,378p; 26cm.
This work for practitioners covers general United Kingdom contract law, law relating to insurance policies, legislation on insurance supervision, and relevant EEC developments in insurance law. Model contracts and trust agreements are included in the appendix.
ISBN 0406597073 Hbk £68.75

Houseman, David
Houseman and Davies law of life assurance / B. P. A. Davies. – 10th ed. – London : Butterworths, 1984.
xxiv,378p; 26cm.
This work for practitioners covers general United Kingdom contract law, law relating to insurance policies, legislation on insurance supervision, and relevant EEC developments in insurance law. Model contracts and trust agreements are included in the appendix.
ISBN 0406597073 Hbk £68.75

Housing : the government's proposals / presented to parliament by the Secretaries of State for the Environment and Wales by command of Her Majesty, September 1987. – London : HMSO, 1987.
iii,18p.
ISBN 0101021429

Housing : the New Law. – London : Butterworths.
ISBN 0406503214 Pbk £16.50

Housing Act 1980, as amended by the Housing and Building Control Act 1984 / Trevor M. Aldridge. – London : Longman Professional (UK), 1984.
xxxix,334p.
Previous ed.: 1980, titled The Housing Act 1980: a practical guide. Includes index.
ISBN 0851207650 Pbk £27.00

Housing Act 1985 / with annotations by Andrew Arden. – 1. – London : Sweet & Maxwell, 1986.
various pagings.
Includes index.
ISBN 0421353708

Housing Act 1988. – London : Blackstone Press.
ISBN 1854310453 Pbk £16.95

Housing Act 1988 : A Shelter Guide. – Shelter.
ISBN 0901242853 Pbk £2.50

Housing Act Nineteen Eighty : The Tenant's Charter. – Shelter. – London : Shelter, 1981.
ISBN 0901242578 Pbk £1.75

Housing Act Nineteen-Eighty. – London : Butterworths, 1981.
This book gives an extensive narrative exposition of the Act followed by the text of the Act with extensive annotations. The work is a thorough guide to the provisions of the United Kingdom's Housing Act of 1980.
ISBN 0406657904 Hbk

Housing alternatives for the elderly / Alan Butler and Anthea Tinker. – Leeds : Centre for Applied Social Studies, 1983.
28p. – (Occasional paper).
Includes bibliographical references.

Housing and Building Control Act 1984 / with annotations by Andrew Arden and Charles Cross. – London : Sweet & Maxwell, 1984.
127p; 24cm.
ISBN 0421330805 Pbk £7.50

Housing and Campaigning. – Shelter. – London : Shelter, 1983.
ISBN 0901242667 Pbk £3.00/Members 1.25

Housing and the Whitehall Bulldozer. – London : Institute of Economic Affairs.
Hbk £0.50

Housing association allocations : Achieving racial equality : a West Midlands case study : summary of a report by Pat Niner in association with Valerie Karn / Anne Grosskurth. – London : Runnymede Trust, 1985.
20p.
ISBN 0902397540

Housing association law / by John Alder and Christopher R. Handy. – London : Sweet & Maxwell, 1987.
xlii,330p; 21cm.
Text examines the partnership between public and private sector in providing low-cost housing, 'new' forms of tenure as a means of extending owner-occupation and tenant self-management, and tenants' rights and accountability to the Housing Corporation.
ISBN 042134430X Pbk £15.00

Housing Associations Act 1985 / James Ramage. – London : Sweet & Maxwell, 1986.
ISBN 0421359005 Pbk £7.50

Housing Benefit review : report of the review team. – London : H.M.S.O., 1985.
43 p.
ISBN 0101952007

Housing Consolidation 1985. – London : Sweet & Maxwell, 1986.
ISBN 0421360801 Pbk £25.00

Housing Developers (Control and Licensing) Act, 1966 (Act 118) and Regulations 1982. – Kuala Lumpur : International Law Books Services.
Hbk £9.00

Housing disrepair / Nicholas C. Martyn and Edward Lloyd-Jones. – London : Longman Professional, 1985.
xxv,187p; 22cm. – (Longman professional practitioner series).
Includes index.
ISBN 0851209904 Pbk £13.50

Housing Economics and Public Policy. – London : Macmillan.
176p. – (Studies in Planning Ser.).
ISBN 0333211073 Pbk £4.95

Housing finance. – 2nd ed. – Turnaround Press, 1986.
ISBN 090120273X Pbk £3.95

Housing Finance : Who Gains?. – London : Policy Studies Institute, 1984.
83p.
Hbk £3.50

Housing Grants. – 2nd ed. – London : Kogan Page, 1983.
172p.
ISBN 0850387108 Hbk £9.95
ISBN 0850387116 Pbk £4.50

Housing (Homeless Persons) Act 1977 : code of guidance (England and Wales). – 2nd ed. – London : H.M.S.O., 1983.
42p.
First published 1977. Includes index.
ISBN 0117516945

Housing improvement and repair / Christopher J. Wright. – London : Sweet & Maxwell, 1986.
xiv,130p; 26cm.
Bibliography: p125. - Includes index.
ISBN 0421358203 £16.50

Housing inequality and deprivation / Alan Murie. – London : Heinemann Educational, 1983.
250p; 23cm.
Bibliography: p237-246. - Includes index.
ISBN 0435826263 £13.50

Housing law / Martin Partington. – London : Sweet & Maxwell, 1983.
ISBN 0421242108 Hbk £110.00
Supplement 2 (1986). –
Defines legal statues likely to affect all classes of occupiers of residential accomodation, deals with the law relating to housing finance, the private and public law relating to housing conditions, the rights of occupation in housing, and special categories of occupier such as agricultural workers and occupiers of mobile homes.
ISBN 0421362006 Pbk £22.00

Housing Law for the Elderly. – London : Oyez Longman, 1982.
– (Oyez Longman Practice Note Ser.: No. 72).
ISBN 0851206875 Pbk £12.95

Housing Law in Northern Ireland / W. David Trimble. – Belfast : Queen's University of Belfast, 1986.
350p.
Pbk

Housing Law Reports. – London : Sweet & Maxwell.
Hbk £89.00
Vol. 19. –
ISBN 0421394501 Hbk £35.00
Bound Vol.. –
Hbk £18.50
Back Vols.. –
Hbk £16.00
Single copies. –
Hbk £23.00

Housing law reports / edited by Andrew Arden. – Harlow : G. Godwin, 1982-.
Annual indexes.

Housing Policy and Housing Needs. – London : Macmillan.
160p. – (Building and Survey Ser.).
ISBN 0333307011 Hbk £14.00
ISBN 0333236955 Pbk £6.95

Housing Policy and Practice / Alan Murie. – London : Macmillan, 1982.
216p. – (Public Policy and Politics, General Ser.).
ISBN 0333328426 Hbk £15.00
ISBN 0333328434 Pbk £5.95

Housing rights guide. – 2nd ed. – Turnaround Press, 1987.
ISBN 0948854145 Pbk £4.95

Housing (Scotland) Act 1988. – Edinburgh : Green (W.) & Son, 1988.
The annotated Act reprinted from Scottish Current Law Statutes with an introduction and the text of the regulations made under the Act which introduced new categories of tenancies in the private sector with corresponding effects on security of tenure. Rights of succession were also curtailed.
ISBN 0414008960 Pbk

Housing (Scotland) Bill : report on the consolidation of certain enactments relating to housing in Scotland ... / Scottish Law Commission. – Edinburgh : H.M.S.O., 1987.
11p.
ISBN 0101010427

Houtte, J. van → Sociology of law and legal anthropology in the Dutch speaking countries.

Hovius, Berend
Family Law : Cases Notes Materials. – 2nd ed. – Agincourt : Carswell, 1987.
ISBN 045930261 Hbk £33.00

How Criminal Law Protects You. – Bombay : Jaico Publishing House.
Hbk £30.00

How Ottawa Spends Your Tax Dollars : The Liberals, The Opposition and Federal Priorities 1983. – Toronto : Lorimer & Co, 1983.
264p.
ISBN 0888626428 Pbk £12.95

How Protection Taxes Exporters / Larry A. Sjaastad. – London : Trade Policy Research Centre, 1985.
87p.
Hbk £8.00

How the City of London Works : An Introduction to its Financial Markets. – 2nd ed. – Waterlow.
ISBN 008033105X Pbk £6.95

How to account for foreign currencies / Jeff Pearcy. – London : Macmillan, 1984.
x,264p; 22cm.
ISBN 0333365461 £30.00

How to Become a Lay Advocate. – 2nd ed. – London : Shelter, 1984.
Hbk £1.00

How to Become an Immigrant to Canada and the United States of America. – Lucknow : Eastern Book Company, 1985.
Hbk £50.00

How to claim state benefits. – 2nd ed. – Northcote House, 1988.
ISBN 0746305311 Pbk £5.95

How to Combat Hijacking. – Canberra : Australian Institute of Criminology.
free

How to comply with the Data Protection Act : policies, practice and procedures / Alastair Evans and Anthony Korn in association with Percom Limited. – Aldershot : Gower, 1986.
vii,211p; 31cm.
Includes index.
ISBN 0566026325 £22.50

How to conduct arbitrations / Smith. – London : Architectural Press, 1988.
ISBN 0851392164 Hbk

How to Cope with Personal Taxes. – Ward Lock. – (Your and Your Money Series).
ISBN 0706365700 Hbk £4.99

How to deal with your bank manager. – London : Kogan Page, 1988.
ISBN 1850915962 Hbk £12.95
ISBN 1850915970 Pbk £5.95

How to do things with rules : a primer of interpretation / William Twining, David Miers. – 2nd ed. – London : Weidenfeld and Nicholson, 1982.
xx,387p; 23cm.
Previous ed. 1976.
ISBN 0297780832 Hbk £18.50
ISBN 0297780840 Pbk

How to Fight for What's Right : the Citizen's Guide to Public Interest Law. – Toronto : James Lorimer & Co.
ISBN 0888624220 Pbk £12.95
ISBN 0888624239 Hbk £24.95

How to Frame a Charge. – 1981 repr. – Lucknow : Eastern Book Company, 1985.
174p.
Hbk £30.00

How to get a European patent : guide for applicants / European Patent Office. – 6th ed. – Munchen : European Patent Office, 1983.
72p.
Accompanied by Schedule of fees (13p).

How to live with VAT. – Daily Mail. – Maidenhead : McGraw-Hill, 1987.
ISBN 0670849439 Pbk £6.75

How to make meetings work. – London : Kogan Page, 1988.
ISBN 0850915077 Pbk

How to Make Money from Your Software : Legal and Business Aspects. – Oxford : ESC Publishing Ltd, 1985.
108p.
ISBN 0906214319 Pbk £9.50

How to patent without a lawyer. – Spon (E & FN), 1984.
ISBN 0915586088 Hbk £18.00

How to pay less income tax. – London : Pitman Publishing, 1986.
ISBN 0712108254 Pbk £2.95

How to Pay Less Malaysian Income Tax. – Singapore, 1982.
Hbk £36.00

How to Pay Less Singapore Income Tax. – Singapore : Quins, 1982.
Pbk £27.00

How to plan your life insurance. – 2nd ed. – Cambridge : Woodhead-Faulkner, 1986.
ISBN 0859413004 Hbk £10.95
ISBN 0859413012 Pbk £4.95

How to Re-Organise Your Affairs so as to Pay the Least Amount of Tax. – Cape Town : Legal & Financial Publishing, 1983.
ISBN 0869940139 Hbk £13.50

How to run committees and meetings. – London : Macmillan, 1982.
ISBN 0333207533 Hbk £33.00
ISBN 0333290356 Pbk £4.95

How to study law. – London : Sweet & Maxwell, 1986.
ISBN 042134380X Hbk £9.50
ISBN 0421343907 Pbk £7.50

How to Study Law in Canada. – Butterworths, 1988.
72p.
Examines how to approach research problems and exam questions. Also includes brief outlines of major subject areas, and tactical tips on how to best structure your time and select the most appropriate courses for career development. Looks at extra-curricular activities, and contains a glossary of legal words and phrases.
ISBN 0409806056 Pbk £5.00

How to Survive Practicing Law in the 80's. – Vancouver : British Columbia Continuing Legal Education Society, 1982.
77p.
ISBN 0865040761 Hbk £7.50

How to survive your articles. – London : Waterlow, 1986.
ISBN 0080330681 Pbk £5.95

How to turn round a company. – London : Fitzwilliam, 1988.
ISBN 1870555023 Hbk £35.00

How to Understand An Act of Parliament. – 6th ed. – North Ryde : Law Book Co, 1987.
xxxi, 605p.
Pbk

How to use a law library / by Jean Dane and Philip A. Thomas. – 2nd ed. 1. – London : Sweet & Maxwell, 1987.
23cm.
Previous ed.: 1979. Includes bibliography and index.
ISBN 0421360305 Hbk £12.50
ISBN 0421360402 Pbk £8.50

How wars end : the United Nations and the termination of armed conflicts, 1946-1964 Vol.1. – Oxford : Clarendon Press, 1982.
400p.
ISBN 0198274246 £35.00
Vol.2. – 1982.
720p.
ISBN 0198274629 £45.00

Howard → AIDS and Employment Law.
→ Currency Problems in Maritime Disputes.
→ Principles of Business Law.

Howard, Colin
Australian federal constitutional law / by Colin Howard. – 3rd ed. – Sydney : Law Book Company, 1985.
lxxviii,611p.
Bibliography: pxliii-li.
ISBN 0455205736
→ Essays in legal theory : a collaborated work.
—Law of Commercial Companies. – 3rd ed. – North Ryde : Law Book Co, 1987.
xlix, 379p.
ISBN 0455207291 Hbk £59.50
ISBN 0455207305 Pbk £35.00

Howard, Gillian
Statutory Sick Pay - Practical Guide. – 2nd ed. – London : Longman Professional, 1986.
ISBN 0851212336 Pbk £11.95

Howard, J. Woodford
Courts of appeals in the federal judicial systems : a study of the Second, Fifth, and District of Columbia Circuits / J. Woodford Howard, Jr. – Princeton : Princeton University Press, 1981.
xxvi,415p; 25cm.
Includes index.
ISBN 0691076235 Hbk £18.10
ISBN 0691101000 Pbk £7.00

Howard journal : a review of modern methods for the prevention and treatment of crime and juvenile delinquency. – London : Howard League for Penal Reform, 1921.
Continued by: The Howard journal of penology and crime prevention. Subtitle varies.

Howard journal of criminal justice. – Oxford : Basil Blackwell for the Howard League, 1984.
Continues: The Howard journal of penology and crime prevention.

Howard journal of penology and crime prevention. – Howard League for Penal Reform. – London: Scottish Academic Press, 1965-1983, 1965-.
Continues: The Howard journal; continued by: The Howard journal of criminal justice.

Howard, K.
Trusts /. – North Ryde : Law Book Co, 1985.
ix, 102p. – (Nutshells).
ISBN 0455206317

Howard, Keith
Management of a student research project / Keith Howard & John A. Sharp. – Aldershot : Gower, 1983.
xiii,238p; 23cm.
Bibliography: p219-232. - Includes index.
ISBN 0566004623 Hbk £
ISBN 0566006138 Pbk

Howard, L.R.
Auditing. – Pitman, 8th ed.
– (M & E Handbook Series).
ISBN 0712107932 Pbk £6.95

Howard League for Penal Reform → Community service order : a first decade of promise.
→ Dangerousness and criminal justice.
—Freedom on licence : the development of parole and proposals for reform : report of a Howard League Working Party under the chairmanship of Professor the Lord McGregor of Durris .. – Howard League for Penal Reform. – Sunbury : Quartermaine House, 1981.
xxvi,70p; 22cm.
Bibliography: p70.
ISBN 0905898141 Pbk £4.25
→ Howard journal : a review of modern methods for the prevention and treatment of crime and juvenile delinquency.
—Howard journal of penology and crime prevention. – Howard League for Penal Reform. – London: Scottish Academic Press, 1965-1983, 1965-.
Continues: The Howard journal; continued by: The Howard journal of criminal justice.
—Unlawful sex : offences, victims and offenders in the criminal justice system of England and Wales / the report of a Howard League working party. – London : Waterlow, 1985.
xvi,264p. – (Waterlow's legal and social policy library).
Includes bibliography and index.
ISBN 0080392202 Pbk £9.95
→ Women in the penal system.

Howard, M.N → Phipson on evidence.

Howard, Michael
Causes of wars : and other essays / Michael Howard. – London : Temple Smith, 1983.
190p.
ISBN 0851172229 £10.00
—Lessons of history : an inaugural lecture delivered before the vice-chancellor and Fellows of the University of Oxford on Friday 6 March 1981 / by Michael Howard. – Oxford : Clarendon, 1981.
21p; 22cm.
ISBN 0199515328 Pbk £1.95

Howarth, D.
English Legal System. – London : Financial Training, 1988.
– (SWOT).
ISBN 1851850449 Pbk £7.50

Howarth, William
Freshwater fishery law / William Howarth. – London : Financial Training, 1987.
xxiv,311p; 23cm.
Bibliography: p302-304. - Includes index. Includes text of the Salmon and Freshwater Fisheries Act 1975. Originally published: London : H.M.S.O., 1975.
ISBN 1851850309 £17.95
—Land law in a nutshell / William Howarth. – London : Sweet & Maxwell, 1987.
117p; 22cm.
Includes index.
ISBN 0421368306 Pbk £3.95
—Salmon and Freshwater Fisheries Act 1975 / William Howarth. – London : Financial Training, 1987.
xxiv,311p; 23cm.
Bibliography: p302-304. - Includes index. Includes text of the Salmon and Freshwater Fisheries Act 1975. Originally published: London : H.M.S.O., 1975.
ISBN 1851850309 £17.95
—Water pollution law / by William Howarth. – London : Shaw, 1988.
xxxvii,608p.
Bibliography: p.580-594. - Includes index.
ISBN 0721911005 £19.95

Howcroft → Banking Law.
—Retail Banking / Lavis. – Oxford : Blackwell.
ISBN 0631149325 Hbk £29.50

Howe & Hummel / Richard H. Rovere. – London : Arlington, 1986.
xvii,169p; 22cm.
Originally published: New York : Farrar, Straus and Giroux, 1985.
ISBN 0851406890 £9.95

Howe, Betsy-Ann
New Zealand Current Taxation. – Wellington : Butterworths.
Hbk

Howell, Arthur H.
Industrial tribunal : a guide to the jurisdiction of industrial tribunals within the provisions of the following Acts : The Employment Act 1975, The Employment Protection (Consolidation) Act 1978, The Employment Act 1980, The Equal Pay Act 1970, The Sex Discrimination Act 1975, The Race Relations Act 1976 / Arthur H. Howell. – Chichester : Barry Rose, 1981.
38p; 26cm.
Cover title.
ISBN 0859922189 spiral £7.75

Howell James
Notes on need for planning permission. – 3rd ed. – London : Longman Professional, 1984.
ISBN 0851207146 Pbk £16.95

Howell James' Notes on the Need for Planning Permission / D. W. Williams. – 3rd ed. – London : Oyez Longman, 1984.
ISBN 0851207146 Hbk

Howell, T. J. → Howell's State Trials : 1163-1820, 34 Vols.

Howells, John
Mediation in New Zealand : the Attitudes of the Mediated / Susan Cathro. – Palmerston North : Dunmore Press Ltd..
126p.
ISBN 0864690541 Pbk £28.55

Howells, Richard → Employment and safety in the offshore oil industry.

Howell's State Trials : 1163-1820, 34 Vols. / T. J. Howell. – Repr. – Abingdon : Professional Books.
Hbk

Hoyle, Mark S. W.
Cases and Materials On International Trade. – 2nd ed. – London : Laureate-Thomson Press, 1983.
ISBN 0907392105 Pbk £17.00
—Cases and materials on the law of international trade / edited by Mark S. W. Hoyle. – 2nd ed. – London : Laureate-Thomson, 1983.
xviii,342p; 25cm.
Previous ed.: 1980. Includes index.
ISBN 0907392105 Pbk £18.50
—Law of international trade / Mark S.W. Hoyle. – 2nd ed. – Bicester : CCH Editions, 1985.
vii,518p; 23cm.
Previous ed.: 1981?. Bibliography: p471-472. - Includes index.
ISBN 0863250726 Pbk
—Mareva injunction and related orders. – 2nd. – London : Lloyds of London Press, 1989.
Sets out the framework for applications in court for Mareva injunctions, Anton Pillar orders and similar and ancillary relief. The position in EEC countries is given, including the implications of the Civil Jurisdiction and Judgements Act 1982. The international section covers developments in Commonwealth and other jurisdictions.
ISBN 1850441618 Hbk
—Mareva injunction and related orders / by Mark S.W. Hoyle. – London : Lloyd's of London Press, 1985.
viii,141p; 22cm.
ISBN 1850440441
→ Private international law : cases and materials.

Hoyle, S.W., et al
Immigraton and Nationality : Statutes and Rules. – Shaw & Sons.
ISBN 072191120X Pbk £17.95

Hoysted, P.A.
Content and Historical Development of Forestry Legislation in Tasmania. – Hobart : University of Tasmania, Centre for Environmental Studies, 1981.
38p.
Hbk £5.00

Hribar, Z.
Guide to Company Law. – 2nd ed. – North Ryde : Law Book Co, 1982.
xi, 270p.
ISBN 0455203709 Pbk £15.00

Huang, Paul Te-Hsien
World oceans : a selected bibliography of social and natural sciences / Des oceans du monde: une selection bibliographique des sciences sociales et naturelles : compiled by Paul Te-Hsien Huang. – Halifax : Huang, 1985.
xii,754p.
ISBN 0969218109

Hubbard, C. C. →Handbook of business tenancies.
—Handbook of leasehold reform / C.C. Hubbard and Delyth W. Williams. – 21. – London : Sweet & Maxwell, 1988.
32cm.
Includes index.
ISBN 0421351306 Llf £95.00

Hucker, Stephen J. →Mental disorder and criminal responsibility.

Huda, Shamsul
Principles of the Law of Crimes / O.P. Srivastava. – Lucknow : Eastern Book Company, 1982.
505p.
Hbk £75.00

Huddy, Grenfell →Huddy: Introduction to legal practice, Vol.1.
→ Introduction to legal practice, Vol.2 : edited by Charles Blake and Grenfell Huddy.

Huddy: Introduction to legal practice
Vol.1 / Grenfell Huddy, Charles Blake. – 2nd ed. – London : Published in association with the Institute of Legal Executive by Sweet & Maxwell, 1985.
xx,323p.
Previous ed.: published as Introduction to legal practice. 1982. Includes index.
ISBN 0421332204 Pbk £14.50

Hudec, Albert J.
Guidebook to Alberta Business Corporations Act / James S. Smeltzer. – North Ryde : C.C.H. Australia, 1984.
134p.
ISBN 0887962556 Hbk £12.00

Hudec, Robert E
Developing countries in the GATT legal system / by Robert E. Hudec. – Aldershot : Gower for the Trade Policy Research Centre, 1987.
xix,259p.
Bibliography: p.236-250..
ISBN 0566056976

Hudson, A. H.
Dictionary of commercial law / by A.H. Hudson. – London : Butterworths, 1983.
289p; 23cm. – (Butterworths professional dictionaries series).
A reference source on commercial law of the United Kingdom. Entries are arranged in alphabetical order, and all terms are fully described, rather than merely defined.
ISBN 0406681597 Hbk £17.00
ISBN 0406681600 Pbk £10.95

Hudson, Andy →Children : rights and responsibilities.

Hudson, N.G.
Insurance of average disbursements. – London : Lloyd's of London Press, 1988.
ISBN 1850441693 Pbk £8.95
—Marine claims handbook / by N.G. Hudson and J.C. Allen. – 4th ed. – London : Lloyds of London Press, 1984.
vi,102p.
ISBN 0907432913
—New Institute clauses : a commentary on the new standard policy forms for marine risks issued by the London insurance market / by N.G. Hudson and J.C. Allen. – London : Lloyd's, 1986.
217p; 24cm.
ISBN 185044093X £47.50

Hudson, Richard
Butterworth's Annotated Legislation Service. – London : Butterworths.
This service for practitioners provides a working guide to the text of new statutes in the United Kingdom.
ISBN 040654834X Pbk
→ Butterworths insurance law handbook.

Hugessen, James K. →Report of formal investigation into the fire aboard and abandonment of the Canadian tanker Hudson Transport in the St. Lawrence River on December 25, 1981.

Huggett, Donald R.
Canadian Tax News. – Agincourt : Carswell, 1987.
Hbk £105.00

Hughes
Computer Contracts : Principles and Practice 1987 / A. Sharpe. – London : Law Book Co.
ISBN 0455207364 Hbk £38.00
→ Financial Accounting Cases.
→ Public Law and the Retail Sector Oxford Reports on Retailing.

Hughes : Federal Court of Canada Service, 2 Vols. – Butterworths.
Llf £150.00

Hughes and Woodley on patents / John M Woodley. – 1 vol. – Scarborough, Ontario : Butterworths (Canada).
Covers the requirements for patentability, infringement actions (the grounds, defences, parties, procedure, remedies and jurisdiction), Patent Office procedure and practice, and conflicting applications.
Loose leaf

Hughes, Cedric H.L. →Annotated British Columbia Insurance (Motor Vehicle) Act.

Hughes, Christopher →Receivership manual.

Hughes, D. J.
Public sector housing law / D.J. Hughes. – 2nd ed. – London : Butterworths, 1987.
xxxix,329p.
Previous ed.: 1981. Includes bibliographies and index.
ISBN 0406600627 Pbk £16.95

Hughes, David
Environmental law / David Hughes. – London : Butterworths, 1986.
400p; 22cm.
Includes bibliographies and index.
ISBN 0406016909 Hbk £ :
ISBN 0406016917 Pbk £9.95

Hughes, David R. →Splintered Market : Barriers to Interprovincial Trade in Canadian Agriculture.

Hughes, G. →Accident Compensation Handbook (Vic.).
—Building and Civil Engineering Claims In Perspective. – 2nd ed. – London : Longman Professional, 1986.
ISBN 0582494702 Hbk £29.00

Hughes, H G
Textbook of commerce / J W Loveridge. – 3rd ed. – London : Butterworths, 1981.

Students
ISBN 0408709286 Pbk £6.95

Hughes, Margaret E.
National Themes in Family Law / Diane Pask. – Agincourt : Carswell, 1988.
320p.
Hbk £45.50

Hughes on copyright and industrial design. – 1 vol. – Scarborough, Ontario : Butterworths (Canada).
Covers registration procedures, assignment and licensing, infringement, and remedies.
Loose leaf

Hughes on trade marks. – 1 vol. – Scarborough, Ontario : Butterworths (Canada).
Looks at registability, the procedures for registering, amending, assigning and licensing marks, infringement, trade names and passing off actions at common law and under statute.
Loose leaf

Hughes Parry, D.
Sanctity Of Contracts In English Law. – Sweet & Maxwell, 1959 Reprint.
ISBN 0421376007 Hbk £14.75

Hughes, Peter H. →New Zealand royal commissions, commissions and committees of inquiry, 1864-1981 : a checklist.

Hughes, Robert T
Federal State of Canada Service, 2 vols. – Toronto : Butterworths.
Hbk

Hughes, Roger T.
Hughes : Federal Court of Canada Service, 2 Vols. – Butterworths.
Llf £150.00
—Hughes and Woodley on patents / John M Woodley. – 1 vol. – Scarborough, Ontario : Butterworths (Canada).
Covers the requirements for patentability, infringement actions (the grounds, defences, parties, procedure, remedies and jurisdiction), Patent Office procedure and practice, and conflicting applications.
Loose leaf
—Hughes on copyright and industrial design. – 1 vol. – Scarborough, Ontario : Butterworths (Canada).
Covers registration procedures, assignment and licensing, infringement, and remedies.
Loose leaf
—Hughes on trade marks. – 1 vol. – Scarborough, Ontario : Butterworths (Canada).
Looks at registability, the procedures for registering, amending, assigning and licensing marks, infringement, trade names and passing off actions at common law and under statute.
Loose leaf

Hughes, Rupert →Review of child care law : report to ministers of an interdepartmental working party : published by the government as a consultative document.

Hughes, Sally →Social security law in Britain and Ireland : a bibliography.

Hughes, T.
International Tax Planning for United Kingdom Companies. – 2nd ed. – London : Deloitte Haskins & Sells.
ISBN 0863491308 Pbk £4.95

Hughes, W.
Concise Precedents in Modern Conveyancing, 2 Vols. – Repr. of 1853 ed. – Abingdon : Professional Books.
175p.
Hbk £45.00

Hughes, William →Book Called the Mirror of Justices : With the Book (By Sir Anthony Fitzherbert), Called the Divinity of Courts and Their Jurisdictions.

Hugill, Barry →First rights : a guide to legal rights for young people.

Hugill, Christopher
Business tenancies. – London : Longman Professional (UK), 1989.
– (Longman practice notes).
Examines the law pertaining to assigning, subletting, parting with possession and repairs, with specimen letters. Contains details of time limits, costs and fees, and precedent forms for termination of a tenancy under s.25 and a request for a new tenancy under s.26 of the Landlord and Tenant Act 1954.
ISBN 0851215319 Pbk £9.95

Hull, Rodney →Canadian forms of wills.
—Probate Practice : MacDonell, Sheard and Hull / Maurice C Cullity. – 3rd ed. – Agincourt : Carswell, 1981.
774p.
This is a comprehensive volume for estate law practitioners in Ontario, Canada. The text covers valid wills, the recognition of holographic wills, survivorship, ancillary letters probate, conflict of laws relating to wills and estates, and numerous other probate topics.
Hbk £80.00

Human and peoples' rights in Africa and the African Charter : report of a conference held in Nairobi from 2 to 4 December 1985 convened by the International Commission of Jurists. – International Commission of Jurists. – Geneva : International Commission of Jurists, 1986.
101p.
Includes the text of the African charter on Human and Peoples' Rights.
ISBN 9290370289

Human artificial insemination / New South Wales Law Reform Commission. – Sydney : Government Printer, 1984.
xxvi,138p. – (Artificial conception discussion paper).
Includes bibliographical references.

Human Body and the Law. – Edinburgh : Edinburgh University Press.
215p.
ISBN 0852241739 Hbk £10.00

Human fertilisation and embryology : a framework for legislation / presented to Parliament by the Secretary of State for Social Services ...et al. by Command of Her Majesty November 1987. – London : H.M.S.O., 1987.
20p.
ISBN 0101025920

Human life and medical practice / J.K. Mason. – Edinburgh : Edinburgh University Press, 1988.
192p; 22cm.
Includes bibliography and index.
ISBN 0852245602 Hbk £15.00 :
ISBN 085224584X Pbk £7.50

Human rights / Miller. – Oxford : Blackwell, 1984.
ISBN 0631136991 Pbk £6.95

Human rights / Pike. – Bradford : Mary Glasgow, 1988.
ISBN 01852341688 Hbk £16.95

Human Rights : A Compilation of International Instruments. – United Nations. – London : HMSO, 1983.
ISBN 0119078589 Hbk £13.50

Human rights : from rhetoric to reality / edited by Tom Campbell ... et al. – Oxford : Blackwell, 1986.
vi,280p; 23cm.
Discusses issues involved in the argument for a British bill of rights.
ISBN 0631143610 Hbk £25.00 :
ISBN 0631143629 Pbk £9,50

Human rights : information sheet. – Strasbourg : Council of Europe, 1982-.

Human Rights : Myth and Reality. – Kuala Lumpur : Intellectual Book Corner, 1987.
xxviii, 188p.
Hbk £100.00

Human rights : our country in Europe : a public lecture / delivered by J.E.S. Fawcett. – London : Inns of Court School of Law, 1983.
11p; 23cm.

Human Rights : the Australian Debate. – Redfern : Redfern Legal Centre Publishing, 1987.
270p.
Hbk £19.95

Human rights and conditions of the people of East Timor / Senate Standing Committee on Foreign Affairs and Defence, the Parliament of the Commonwealth of Australia. – Canberra : Australian Government Publishing Service, 1983.
xvii,106p.
Includes bibliographical references.
ISBN 0644027800

Human Rights and Disarmament / Vaclav Racek. – London : Spokesman Books, 1983.
60p.
Pbk individual 4.00

Human rights and foreign policy / Evan Luard. – S.l. : s.n., 1986.
p.579-606.
Photocopy from: International affairs, vol. 56, no. 4 (Autumn 1980).

Human Rights and Freedoms in Canada : Cases, Notes and Materials / William F Pentney. – Butterworths, 1987.
672p.
ISBN 0409813087 Pbk £80.00

Human rights and human diversity : an essay in the philosophy of human rights / A.J.M. Milne. – London : Macmillan, 1986.
240p; 22cm.
Includes index.
ISBN 0333406184 £25.00

Human rights and humanitarian norms as customary law. – Oxford : OUP, 1989.
320.
Looks at the relationship between human rights/humanitarian norms and customary law, also between human rights/humanitarian norms and the law of state responsibility. Examines how contemporary human rights mesh with the general principles of international law and particularly with the principles governing the international responsibility of states.
International lawyers, international organizations, scholars and students of international law
ISBN 0198252390 Hbk £30.00

Human rights and international relations. – Cambridge : Cambridge University Press, 1987.
ISBN 0521327989 Hbk £20.00
ISBN 0521339952 Pbk £7.95

Human rights and mental patients in Japan : report of a mission by Dr. T. W. Harding, Judge J. Schneider, Dr. H. M. Visotsky and Dr. C. L. Graves on behalf of the International Commission of Jurists and the International Commission of Health Professionals / T.W. Harding. – Geneva : International Commission of Jurists, 1985.
94p.
Bibliography: p.87-93.
ISBN 9290370327

Human Rights and Social Policy in Newfoundland 1832-1982 : Search for a Just Society. – St. John's : Harry Cuff Publications Ltd., 1985.
256p.
ISBN 0919095798 Pbk £14.95

Human rights and the deportation of convicted aliens and immigrants. – Canberra : Australian Government Publishing Service, 1983.
vii,31p. – (Report).
ISBN 0644026367

Human Rights and the Migrant Act. – Kingston : Australian Government Publishing Service.
209p.
Hbk £11.95

Human rights and the police / by J. Alderson. – Strasbourg : Council of Europe, Directorate of Human Rights, 1984.
207p.
Illustrates how awareness of concepts of human rights defined by the European Convention should affect the way police carry out duties. Training guidelines and case law examples are considered.
ISBN 9287103666 Pbk £10.90

Human rights and the rule of law / Geoffrey Brindman. – Pinter, 1988.
164.
Report of a mission sent to South Africa by the Internaitonal Commission of Jurists. Gives a detailed account of the legislation used to frustrate human rights.
ISBN 0861879791 Hbk £30
ISBN 0861877799 Pbk £9.95

Human Rights and World Peace
Vol. 2. – Enstone : Ditchley Foundation, 1981. – (Ditchley Conference Reports).
Hbk

Human Rights Commission
Australian Citizenship Act, 1948. – Human Rights Commission. – Canberra : Australian Government Publishing Service, 1982.
27p.
ISBN 0644021373 Hbk £1.80
—Proposed A.C.T. Mental Health Ordinance 1981 / Human Rights Commission. – Canberra : Australian Government Publishing Service, 1982.
vii,44p. – (Report).
ISBN 0644022477
—Review of Crimes Act 1914 and other crimes legislation of the Commonwealth / Human Rights Commission. – Canberra : Australian Government Publishing Service, 1983.
viii,44p. – (Report).
Includes extracts from legislation.
ISBN 0644027207
—Testamentary guardianship in the Australian Capital Territory / Human Rights Commission. – Canberra : Australian Government Publishing Service, 1983.
vii,10p. – (Report).
ISBN 0644024593

Human Rights Commission of British Columbia
Recommendations for changes to the Human Rights Code of British Columbia / Human Rights Commission of British Columbia. – Victoria, B.C. : The Commission, 1981.
22p.

Human Rights First : the Child. – Dandenong : Society of Those Who Have Less, 1982.
Hbk £2.00

Human Rights for Australia : Survey of Literature and Developments, and a Select and Annotated Bibliography of Recent Literatue in Australia and Abroad. – Kingston : Australian Government Publishing Service, 1986.
360p.
ISBN 0644034327 Hbk £6.00

Human Rights Guarantees in the Administration of Criminal Justice / Leslie T Wilkins. – Canberra : Australian Institute of Criminology.
Hbk £2.00

Human rights in a state of emergency. – London : Pinter, 1989.
288.
Illustrates the International Law Association's attempt to develop minimum standards for a rule of law during a state of emergency.
ISBN 0861877373 Hbk £35

Human Rights in Africa. – Apapa : Heritage Books.
Hbk £8.50

Human Rights in B.C. – Vancouver : Continuing Legal Education Society of British Columbia, 1985.
132p.
ISBN 086504239X Hbk £55.00

Human rights in criminal procedure : a comparative study / edited by J.A. Andrews. – The Hague : M. Nijhoff, 1981.
451p.
Revisions of papers presented at a conference organized by the United Kingdom National Committee of Comparative Law held at Manchester in Sept., 1978. Includes index.
ISBN 9024725526 Hbk £195.00

Human Rights in Europe : Being an Account of the European Convention for the Protection of Human Rights and Fundamental Freedoms Signed in Rome on 4 November 1950 of the Protocol Thereto and of the Machinery Created Thereby : The European Commission of Human Rights and the European Court of Human Rights. – Amsterdam : University Press.
Hbk

Human rights in Ghana : report of a mission / by Cees Flinterman for the International Commission of Jurists and Netherlands Committee for Human Rights. – Utrecht : SIM, 1984.
47 p.; 21 cm.
ISBN 9290370254 Pbk

Human rights in India / R.C. Hingorani. – New Delhi : Oxford & IBH, 1985.
vii, 181 p.; 22 cm.
Includes bibliographical references and index.
ISBN 8120400208 Rs95.00

Human rights in internal strife : their international protection / by Theodor Meron. – Cambridge : Grotius, 1987.
xiii,172p.
An examination of the problem of protecting human rights in internal strife and of developing adequate safeguards in areas beyond the scope of the Geneva Conventions.
ISBN 0949009040

Human Rights in International Law. – New Delhi : Deep and Deep Publications, 1986.
212p.
Hbk £150.00

Human rights in International law. – rep 1986. – Oxford : Oxford University Press, 1984.
ISBN 0198255403 Pbk £17.50

Human rights in international law : basic texts. – Strasbourg : Council of Europe, 1985.
261p.
ISBN 9287103992

Human rights in international law : legal and policy issues / edited by Theodor Meron. – 2 vols. – Oxford : Clarendon Press, 1983.
Includes bibliographies and index.
ISBN 0198254881 v. 2

Human rights in Islam : report of a seminar held in Kuwait, December 1980 / organised by the International Commission of Jurists, University of Kuwait and Union of Arab Lawyers. – Geneva : International Commission of Jurists, 1982.
ii,95p.

Human rights in Ontario / by Judith Keene. – Toronto : Carswell, 1983.
xxxv,367p.
Includes bibliographical references and index. Includes text of the Human Rights Code, 1981.
ISBN 0459354604

Human rights in prisons / by A. Reynaud. – Strasbourg : Council of Europe, Directorate of Human Rights, 1986.
218p.
Describes human rights problems prison establishments may encounter. Outlines the relevant international human rights law, in particular the European Convention on Human Rights and its case law.
ISBN 9287108811

Human rights in Sweden : the annual reports 1982-1984 from the national correspondent for Sweden to the Documentation Center for Human Rights at the Directorate for Human Rights, Council of Europe / Jacob W.F. Sundberg. – Stockholm : Institutet for offentlig och internationell ratt, 1985.
ix,118p. – (Publications).
Includes bibliographical references and index.
ISBN 9103487806

Human Rights in the Administration of Criminal Justice : Report on the United Nations Course. – Canberra : Australian Institute of Criminology.
Hbk £1.50

Human rights in the Israeli-occupied territories, 1967-1982 / Esther Rosalind Cohen. – Manchester : Manchester University Press, 1985.
xxii,500p.
Bibliography: p470-498. - Includes index.
ISBN 0719017262 £30.00

Human rights in the People's Republic of China. – Westview Press, 1988.
ISBN 0813374391 Hbk £29.95

Human Rights in the U.N. Declaration. – Stockholm : Almqvist & Wiksell, 1984.
209p.
ISBN 9155415482 Pbk £110.00

Human rights in the United Kingdom / prepared by Reference Division, Central Office of Information. – London : H.M.S.O., 1984.
3,50p; 24cm.
Bibliography: p.49-50.
ISBN 0117009857 sd £1.25

Human Rights in the United Kingdom. – Pinter.
ISBN 0861877454 Hbk £22.50
ISBN 0861877500 Pbk £6.95

Human rights in the world : an introduction to the study of the international protection of human rights / by A.H. Robertson. – 2nd ed. – Manchester : Manchester University Press, 1982.
viii,243p; 23cm.
Previous ed.: 1972. Includes index.
ISBN 0719008638 £17.50

Human Rights in Urban Areas. – Paris : UNESCO, 1983.
169p.
ISBN 923101983X Hbk £35.00

Human Rights International Documentation System →Directory of human rights information and documentation facilities in the field of human rights in western Europe.

Human rights law journal. – Kehl am Rhein : Engel, 1980-.
Absorbed: Human rights review, 1982.

Human rights law-making in the United Nations. – Oxford : Oxford University Press, 1986.
ISBN 0198255497 Hbk £35.00

Human rights law-making in the United Nations : a critique of instruments and process / Theodor Meron. – Oxford : Clarendon, 1986.
350p; 22cm.
Includes index.
ISBN 0198255497 £35.00

Human rights missions : a study of the fact-finding practice of non-governmental organizations / Hans Thoolen and Berth Verstappen. – Dordrecht : M. Nijhoff, 1986.
ISBN 9024733642 Pbk

Human rights of aliens in contemporary international law / Richard Lillich. – Manchester : Manchester University Press, 1984.
xii,177p; 24cm.
Includes index.
ISBN 0719009146 £27.50

Human rights of aliens in Europe : proceedings of the Colloquy on 'Human Rights of Aliens in Europe' / organised by the Secretariat General of the Council of Europe in co-operation with the Ministries of Justice and for Foreign Affairs of Portugal and with the Regional Government of Madeira, Funchal-Madeira (Portugal) 17-19 October 1983. – Dordrecht : Martinus Nijhoff Publishers, 1985.
x, 474p.
At head of title: Council of Europe, Human Rights Conseil de l'Europe, Droits de l'homme.
ISBN 9024732158 Hbk £225.00

Human rights or a way of life in a democracy / by Jean-Bernard Marie. – Strasbourg : Council of Europe, 1985.
114p.
Studies the extent to which respect for human rights depends on the public and the impact of those rights on daily life.
ISBN 9287103852 Pbk £3.80

Human rights reports : an annotated bibliography of fact-finding missions / by Berth Verstappen. – London : Zell, 1987.
400p; 21cm.
Includes index.
ISBN 0905450353 Hbk £45.00

Humanism and the law : the case of the shari'ah / by Isma'il R. Al Faruqi. – Lagos : Nigerian Institute of Advanced Legal Studies, 1983.
17p. – (Occasional paper).

Humanitarian good offices in international law : the good offices of the United Nations Secretary General in the field of human rights : the 1981 Reid Lectures delivered at Acadia University, Wolfville, Nova Scotia, Canada / B.G. Ramcharan. – The Hague : Nijhoff, 1983.
xii,220p; 25cm.
Bibliography: p217-218. - Includes index.
ISBN 9024728053 Hbk £95.00

Humanitarian Law. – New Delhi : Oxford University Press.
Hbk £95.00

Humanity in warfare : International law conflicts. – Methuen, 1983.
ISBN 0416348106 Pbk £7.50

Hume, D.
Commentaries on the Law of Scotland Respecting Trial for Crimes. – Repr. of 1800 ed. – Abingdon : Professional Books.
52p.
Hbk £35.00
—Decisions of the Court of Session : 1781-1822. – Repr. of 1839 ed. – Abingdon : Professional Books.
52p.
Hbk £70.00

Hume, Gavin H.
Labour Law and Practice : Materials Prepared for a Continuing Legal Education Seminar Held in Vancouver, B. C., April 14-15, 1983 / Allan E. Black. – Vancouver : British Columbia Continuing Legal Education Society, 1983.
ISBN 086504094X Llf

Hume, L. J.
Bentham and bureaucracy / L.J. Hume. – Cambridge : Cambridge University Press, 1981.
xii,320p; 23cm. – (Cambridge studies in the history and theory of politics).
Bibliography: p303-309. - Includes index.
ISBN 0521235421 £22.50

Humerus of the long arm of the law. – Stockwell, 1988.
ISBN 0722322194 Pbk £6.60

Hume's Theory of Justice. – Oxford : Oxford University Press, 1983.
ISBN 0198247249 Pbk £8.95

Humphreys' matrimonial causes / D. A. Salter. – 17th ed. – London : Longman Professional (UK), 1989.
22cm. – (Longman practitioner series).
ISBN 0851211445 £19.95

Humphreys' Notes on district registry practice and procedure / Steven A. Frieze, Parr Richard N. – 24th ed. – London : Longman Professional, 1987.
Includes index..
ISBN 0851213138 Pbk £18.50

Humphreys, Richard F.
Index to Irish statutory instruments / Richard F. Humphreys. – 3. – Dublin : Butterworths, 1988.
Contents: 1 Statutory instruments - 2 Enabling Acts - 3 Subject index.
ISBN 0862052327

Humphreys, S. C. →Discourse of law.

Humphreys, Thomas Stanworth
Humphreys' matrimonial causes / D. A. Salter. – 17th ed. – London : Longman Professional (UK), 1989.
22cm. – (Longman practitioner series).
ISBN 0851211445 £19.95
—Humphreys' Notes on district registry practice and procedure / Steven A. Frieze, Parr Richard N. – 24th ed. – London : Longman Professional, 1987.
Includes index..
ISBN 0851213138 Pbk £18.50

Hungarian Canadian Cultural Centre (Hungarian House) Act, 1983, Bill Pr054 : An Act Respecting the Hungarian Canadian Cultural Centre (Hungarian House). – Ontario : Ontario Government Publications Service, 1983.
4p.
Hbk £0.30

Hungarian perspectives on questions of international law / edited by Hanna Bokor-Szego. – Dordrecht : M. Nijhoff, 1986.
276p.
ISBN 902473293X Hbk £125.00

Hungarian-Finnish Penal Law Seminary on Petty Offences
Papers : Hungarian-Finnish Penal Law Seminary on Petty Offences / editor, Lenke Feher. – Budapest : Geza Kilenyi, 1984.
199 leaves.

Hunnings, Neville March
Antitrust Cases from Common Market Law Reports : Cartels
Vol. 2. – London : European Law Centre.
Hbk £55.50
—EEC Employment Cases from Common Market Law Reports. – London : European Law Centre.
ISBN 0907451217 Hbk £95.00
—EEC Financial Services Cases from Common Market Law Reports. – London : European Law Centre.
ISBN 0907451241 Hbk £105.00
→ Gazetteer of European law : case search : European Community law 1953-1983, Vol.1 : Master list of cases.

Hunt, Alan →Critical legal studies.

Hunt, Constance D.
Environmental Regulation : Its Impact on Major Oil and Gas Projects / Alastair R. Lucas. – Calgary : Canadian Institute of Resources Law.
167p.
Hbk £12.95

Hunt, D. Peter →Distribution of matrimonial assets on divorce.

Hunt, P. M. A. →South African criminal law and procedure, Vol. 2 : Common-law crimes : by P.M.A. Hunt.

Hunter, C →Quiet enjoyment : remedies for harassment and illegal eviction.

Hunter, John M.
Northern Ireland bankruptcy law and practice / by John M. Hunter. – Belfast : SLS Legal Publications, 1984.
lvii,466p.
Includes index.
—Notes on procedure by originating summons and in actions by mortgagees / by Master Hunter. – 2nd ed. – Belfast : SLS Legal Publications, 1985.
37p.
Cover title: Revised notes on procedure by originating summons and in actions by mortgagees.
—Revised Notes on Procedure by Originating Summons and In Actions By Mortgages. – Belfast : Queen's University of Belfast.
35p.
Pbk £3.25
—Winding up of companies in Northern Ireland : a practitioner's guide / by John M. Hunter. – Belfast : SLS Legal Publications, 1984.
xxxvi,142p.
Bibliography: p.135. - Includes index.
ISBN 0853892482

Hunter, Martin →Law and practice of international commercial arbitration.

Hunter, Muir
Muir Hunter on personal insolvency / Muir. Hunter and John Briggs. – 1. – London : Stevens, 1987.
looseleaf.
Supersedes 19th ed. of Williams and Muir Hunter on bankruptcy. Includes index.
—Personal insolvency. – London : Sweet & Maxwell, 1986.
ISBN 0420475605 Hbk £220.00

Hunter, Robert L. C.
Law of arbitration in Scotland / Robert L.C. Hunter. – Edinburgh : T & T Clark, 1987.
384p; 24cm.
A comprehensive account of the modern law of arbitration in Scotland, the ordinary submission to arbitration clauses, the appointment of arbiters, proceedings, the 'stated case' under the Administration of Justice (Scotland) Act 1972, and the decree-arbitral. The final part contains chapters on quasi-arbitral and equitable procedures, agricultural and industrial arbitrations. There is consideration of the impact of Community law and comparison with the practice of other countries. Includes bibliography and index.
ISBN 0567094804 Hbk £29.95

Hunting law. – London : Shaw & Sons, 1988.
ISBN 0721911404 Pbk

Huock
Legal Environment for Foreign Direct Investment / Caywood. – London : Eurospan.
ISBN 093532805X Hbk £26.00

Hurd, Douglas
Prospects for the European Community in 1982 : the Exeter Lecture in European Community law, delivered in the University on 19 February 1982 / by Douglas Hurd. – Exeter : University of Exeter, Centre for European Legal Studies, 1982.
12p.

HURIDOCS standard formats for the recording and exchange of information on human rights / by Bjrn Stormorken : with the assistance of Annie McMorris. – Dordrecht : M. Nijhoff, 1985.
112p.
ISBN 9024731879 Hbk £80.00

Hurlburt, William H.
Law reform commissions in the United Kingdom, Australia and Canada / by William H. Hurlburt. – Edmonton : Juriliber, 1986.
vii,514p.
Bibliography: p.498-514.
ISBN 0919311032
→ Legal profession and quality of service : further report and proposals : report and materials of a National Workshop on Quality of Legal Services held in Toronto in October, 1980, as a sequel to the National Conference on Quality of Legal Services held in Ottawa in October, 1978.

Hurley, J.D.
Children or Brethren : Aboriginal Rights in Colonial Iroquoia. – Saskatoon : University of Saskatchewan, Native Law Centre, 1985.
338p.
ISBN 0888801718 Hbk £75.00

Hursthouse, R.
Beginning Lives. – Oxford : Blackwell, 1987.
ISBN 0631153284 Pbk £8.95

Hurwitz, Bruce A.
Legality of space militarization / Bruce A. Hurwitz. – Amsterdam : North-Holland, 1986.
xii,252p; 25cm.
Bibliography: p243-252.
ISBN 0444700412 £48.83

Hurwitz, Leon
State as defendant : governmental accountability and the redress of individual grievances / Leon Hurwitz. – London : Aldwych Press, 1981.
xv,211p.
Bibliography: p.197-203.
ISBN 0861720172

Hurwitz, Stephan
Criminology / Karl O. Christiansen. – 2nd ed. – London : Allen & Unwin, 1983.
xvi,454p; 24cm.
Previous ed.: 1952. Bibliography: p417-443. - Includes index.
ISBN 0043640125 £.

Husain, Mazhar
Immoral Traffic (Prevention) Act, 1956. – 4th ed. – Lucknow : Eastern Book Company, 1987.
Hbk £90.00
—Law Relating to Drugs and Cosmetics in India / P.L. Malik. – 3rd ed. – Lucknow : Eastern Book Company, 1984.
1,248p.
Hbk £200.00
—Law Relating to Foreigners, Passports and Citizenship in India. – 6th ed. – Lucknow : Eastern Book Company, 1985.
Hbk
—Supreme Court Cases 1987, Vol. 1. – Lucknow : Eastern Book Company, 1987.
Hbk £110.00

Husain, S.M.
Commentaries on Indian Stamp Act as Applicable to Uttar Pradesh. – 7th ed. – Lucknow : Eastern Book Company, 1985.
Hbk

—Uttar Pradesh Land Revenue Act, 1901 / P.L. Malik. – 7th ed. – Lucknow : Eastern Book Company, 1983.
243p.
Hbk £25.00

—Uttar Pradesh Local Acts in about 12 Volumes / Surendra Malik. – 5th rev. ed. – Lucknow : Eastern Book Company.
ca 800p per vol.
Hbk £90.00 ea.

Husband and wife business partnership: what the law says / Margot Owles. – London : Graham & Trotman, 1989.
116; 215mm.
Deals with the legal aspects of a business partnership between husband and wife, and examines the nature and formation of a partnership, the partners, liabilities, how to avoid major pitfalls, the present income tax procedure with reference to the separate taxation of spouses due to be implemented in 1990, and how to provide for the future in retirement.
ISBN 1853330574 Hbk £14.95
ISBN 1853333131 Pbk £7.50

Hussain, Altav
Workers' Children Ordinance 1972 / Javed Altaf. – Lahore : Pakistan Law Times.
Hbk

Hussain, Ashiq
Principles of English Law Including Mercantile Law. – Nairobi : Heinemann Educational Books (East Africa), 1982.
276p.
Hbk £75.00

—Questions and Answers Company Law. – Nairobi : Heinemann Educational Books (East Africa).
196p.
Hbk £55.00

Hussain, Ijaz
Dissenting and separate opinions at the World Court / Ijaz Hussain. – The Hague : M. Nijhoff Publishers, 1984.
xv,335p.
Revision of thesis (doctorate)–University of Nice, 1974 under title: Le role dialectique des opinions dissidentes et individuelles dans le developpement du droit international a la CIJ. Bibliography: p309-321. Includes index.
ISBN 9024729203 Hbk £145.00

Hussain, Sayed Tassadque
Customary Law and Indian Constitution : With Sant Ram Dogra's Code of Tribal Custom. – New Delhi : Rima Publishing House, 1987.
250p.
Hbk £175.00

Hussey, Roger → Keeping employees informed.

Huston
Japanese international taxation / Miyatake. – Matthew Bender, 1983.
ISBN 0000999083 Hbk £50.00

Hutchesson et al., P. → All England Law Reports : 1936-1985, 143 Vols.

Hutchinson, Allan C.
Dwelling on the threshold. – London : Sweet & Maxwell, 1988.
ISBN 0459305611 Hbk £32.00

—Dwelling on the threshold : critical essays on modern legal thought / Allan C. Hutchinson. – Toronto : Carswell, 1988.
ix,326p.
Bibliography: pp.324-325..
ISBN 0421400501

—Rule of Law : Ideal or Ideology / Patrick J Monahan. – Agincourt : Carswell, 1987.
ISBN 0459395408 Hbk £20.50

—Rule of Law : Ideal or Ideology / Patrick J. Monahan. – Agincourt : Carswell, 1987.
224p.
This work contains a series of essays responding to recent attacks on the concept of 'Rule of Law'. These essays evaluate the present predicament of the 'Rule of Law' and offer prognosis for the future prospects of the ideal in modern society.
Hbk £40.50

Hutchinson, Scott C. → Presumption of innocence.

Hutchinson, W.B. → Sale of Real Property and Law of Agency in Queensland.

Hutley, F.C.
Cases and Materials on Succession / R.A. Woodman. – 3rd ed. – North Ryde : Law Book Co, 1984.
xxxix, 794p.
ISBN 0455202826 Hbk £73.00
ISBN 0455202834 Pbk £60.00

Hutley's Australian Wills Precedents / Gary Tamsitt. – 4th ed. – 1989.
ca 240p.
This text, intended for both student and practitioners, includes materials on wills and trusts and examples of complete wills. The fourth edition changes the form of the precedents to the legislative drafting style.
ISBN 0409494887 Hbk £49.00

Hutter, Bridget
Reasonable arm of the law? : the law enforcement procedures of environmental health officers / Bridget M. Hutter. – Oxford : Clarendon Press, 1988.
Includes index. Bibliography.
ISBN 0198255942

Hutton, N. R. → Lay justice?.

Hyam, Alan A.
Law affecting the valuation of land in Australia / by Alan A. Hyam : with a foreword by R. Else-Mitchell. – North Ryde, N.S.W. : Law Book Co., 1983.
xxxii,246p.
Includes index.
ISBN 0455202079

Hybrid corporate securities : international legal aspects / editors Roger McCormick, Harriet Creamer. – London : Sweet & Maxwell, 1987.
xxi,218p; 22cm.
Analysis of hybrid securities arising from a conference of the International Bar Association. Covers the law applicable to the UK, Canada, the USA, Switzerland, the Netherlands, the Federal Republic of Germany, Austria and France. Looks at the practical and technical aspects of taxation, issuance, and stock exchange regulation in each of these jurisdictions.
ISBN 0421379405 Pbk £17.50

Hyde, Gordon V
Local Authority Licensing and Registration / Rosson. – London : Longman Professional, 1985.
ISBN 085120886X updat £125.00
→ Metropolitan problem : papers from a conference held at Oxford, September 1984, organised by the Bar Council, the Law Society, and the Royal Institution of Chartered Surveyors.

→ Planning inquiries.

Hyman, S.
Law, Justice and the Common Good : The Great Debate and a Search for Meaning. – University Press of America.
ISBN 0819166502 Hbk £31.50
ISBN 0819166510 Pbk £13.75

Hyndman, Patricia
Democracy in peril : Sri Lanka : a country in crisis : report to the LAWASIA Human Rights Standing Committee / by Patricia Hyndman. – Sydney : LAWASIA, 1985.
xi,483p.
→ Meeting of Experts on the Exploitation of the Child, November 12-13, 1984, Singapore and the Conference on Child Labour and Child Prostitution, February 21-23, 1986, Kuala Lumpur.

Hywel
Law of Hywel Dda : law texts of medieval Wales / translated and edited by Dafydd Jenkins. – Llandysul : Gomer, 1986.
xlvii,425p; 22cm.
Bibliography: pxliii-xlvii. - Includes index.
ISBN 0863832776 £14.95

I.C.B.C. Claims and Impaired Driving. – Vancouver : British Columbia Continuing Legal Education Society, 1985.
310p.
ISBN 0865042462 Hbk £65.00

I.Mech.E/I.E.E. conditions of contract : a commentary on five I.Mech.E./I.E.E. model forms of general conditions of contract and on the BEAMA contract price adjustment clauses and formulae / by Andrew Pike. – London : Sweet & maxwell, 1984.
xix,333p; 26cm.
Includes index.
ISBN 0421299908 £38.00

Iacobucci, F
Canadian Business Corporations / Pilkington. – Aurora : Canada Law Book, 1977.
Hbk £25.00

IAEA Notification and Assistance Conventions in Case of a Nuclear Accident : Landmarks in the History of the Multilateral Treaty-Making Process. – Dordrecht : Kluwer, 1987.
226p.
ISBN 9024736161 Hbk £125.00

IATA review. – Geneva : International Air Transport Association, 1985-.
Supersedes: IATA world airline cooperation review.

Ibadan University law review : the journal of the Faculty of Law, University of Ibadan. – Ibadan, Nigeria : Evans Brothers, 1986.

Ibrahim, Ahmad
Distribution of estates according to Shafii law. – Singapore : Malayan Law Journal, 1976.
vi,72.
Guide to the Islamic law of inheritance as it is practised in Malaysia and Singapore. Gives a summary of the law, and includes distribution of estates according to Shafii law, the Quranic heirs, the Agnatic heirs, the Bair-ul-mal, MINHAJ ET TALIBIN, a table of Quranic heirs, Quranic verses, and Hadith on the law of inheritance.
Hbk

—Family law in Malaysia and Singapore / by Tan Sri Datuk Professor Ahmad Ibrahim. – 2nd ed. – Singapore : Malayan Law Journal, 1984.
xxvi,359p.
Covers the family law of non-muslims, marriage, and its effects on status and property, divorce and matrimonial proceedings, inheritance rights, the effect of marriage on the legal status of women under Islamic law, the dissolution of Muslim marriage, and inheritance rights.
ISBN 9971700395 Hbk

—Income tax case law of Malaysia and Singapore Vol. 1. – Singapore : Malayan Law Journal, 1984.
xix,1031.
Collection of cases containing decisions on the relevant legislation since the introduction of income tax law in Malaysia and Singapore. Decisions include those of the old Boards of Review of Singapore and in the Federation of Malaya.
ISBN 9971700425 Hbk £230.00

—The legal status of the Muslims in Singapore. – Singapore : Malayan Law Journal, 1965.
95.
Intends to set out the legal position of the Muslims, including the Malays, in Singapore. Contains a historical introduction, a summary of the existing statute and the case law relating to the family law, the law of property and the law relating to the construction of wills and trust instruments as they affect the Muslims in Singapore, and the history of Muslim endowments.

→ Malaysian legal essays : a collection of essays in honour of Professor Emeritus Datuk Ahmad Ibrahim.

—Sources and development of Muslim law. – Singapore : Malayan Law Journal, 1965.
142.
Studies the sources of Muslim law, and attempts to bring together the views of the 'Orientalists' and the Muslim authorities. Traces the development of Muslim law from the year 13 before Hijrah to the present day, and also looks to the future of Muslim law. Looks at the writing of Muslim jurists.
Hbk

—Survey of Malaysian Law
1981. – Singapore : Malayan Law Journal, 1983.
xvi, 304p.
ISBN 9971700328 Spiral bound £46
1982. – 1984.
xvi, 306p.
ISBN 9971700360 Spiral bound £50

Ibrahim, Hamid → Federal Constitution of Malaysia : a commentary.

ICSA
Administration of Insurance. – ICSA. – Cambridge : Woodhead-Faulkner, 1987.
ISBN 0902197428 Hbk £25.00

—Administration of Property. – ICSA. – Cambridge : Woodhead-Faulkner, 1986.
ISBN 0902197371 updat £45.00

—Charities Administration. – ICSA. – Cambridge : Woodhead-Faulkner, 1986.
ISBN 0902197274 updat £55.00

Idea of law. – Rev Ed. – Pelican, 1981.
ISBN 0140206884 Pbk £4.95

Identification evidence : a psychological evaluation / John W. Shepherd, Hadyn D. Ellis and Graham M. Davies : foreword by Lord Devlin. – Aberdeen : Aberdeen University Press, 1982.
xii,155p; 26cm.
Bibliography: p140-149. - Includes index.
ISBN 0080284418 £12.50

Idra and Industrial Licensing : With Rules Forms Notifications, Press Notes, Guidelines, Policies. – New Delhi : Bharat Law House, 1987.
Hbk £260.00

If You Are Arrested... – Redfern : Redfern Legal Centre Publishing, 1987.
52p.
Hbk £2.50

Iffland et al, C.
International Banking. – London : Macmillan.
ISBN 0333447123 Hbk £35.00

IFLA International Office for UBC
Names of states : an authority list of language forms for catalogue entries / compiled by the IFLA International Office of UBC. – London : The Office, 1981.
viii,49p; 30cm.
At head of title: International Federation of Library Associations and Institutions.
ISBN 0903043327 Pbk

IFRB Handbook on Radio Regulatory Procedures
French. – Geneva : International Telecommunications Union.
ISBN 9261018327 Hbk £395.00
English. –
ISBN 9261018319 Hbk £395.00

Spanish. –
ISBN 9261018335 Hbk £395.00

Igbinedion, Igbinewedo Albert
Impeachment under the Nigerian Constitution / Igbinewedo Albert Igbinedion. – Benin City : Benfranco Printers, 1983.
76p.

Ignarski, Jonathan
Underwriters bedside book. – London : Lloyd's of London Press, 1987.
ISBN 1850441332 Hbk £16.50

Igweiko, K.I.
Law of Banking. – Onitsha : Africana-FEP.
Hbk
—Nigerian Commercial Law. – Onitsha : Africana-FEP.
Hbk

Ihre, Rolf →Practical guide to contracts of affreightment and hybrid contracts.

—Shipbroking and chartering practice / Gordon. – 2nd ed. – London : Lloyd's of London Press, 1984.
ISBN 0907432638 Hbk £39.00

Ilersic, A. R., et al
Tax Avoision. – London : Institute of Economic Affairs.
Pbk £2.50

Iles, Susan →Community constables : a Study of a policing initiative.
→ Punishment practice by prison Boards of Visitors.

ILEX
Introduction to Law. – ILEX. – 2nd ed. – London : Sweet & Maxwell, 1987.
ISBN 0421367601 Pbk £17.00

Ill conceived : law and abortion practice in New Zealand / Jocelyn Brooks et al. – Dunedin : Caveman Press, 1981.
169p.
Bibliography: p.160-166.
ISBN 0908562462

Illegal aliens under Nigerian law / R.C. Chhangani. – Jodhpur : Associated Law Publications, 1983.
91p.
Includes index.

Illegal contracts / Law Reform Commission of British Columbia. – Vancouver : The Commission, 1982.
vi,179p. – (Working paper).
Includes bibliographical references.

Illegal Transactions. – Victoria : Government of British Columbia, 1983.
Hbk £12.00

Illegality of nuclear warfare
Pamphlet 1 / Lawyers for Nuclear Disarmament. – London : Lawyers for Nuclear Disarmament, 1983.
26p.
Originally published: 1982. Bibliography: p.19.
ISBN 0946499004

Iller, M. S. →Criminal Litigation.
—Criminal Litigation / G A Goodwin. – London : Butterworths, 1985.
ISBN 0406258139 Hbk £33.00
ISBN 0406500002 Pbk £18.95

Illusions about crime & justice / Leon Radzinowicz. – London : Encounter, 1981.
p.31-39.
Extracted from: Encounter, Feb./March 1981.

ILO and the world of work. – International Labour Organisation. – Geneva : International Labour Organisation, 1984.
74p.
ISBN 9221031500

ILO research on multinational enterprises and social policy : an overview. – 2nd (revised) ed. – Geneva : International Labour Office, 1982.
ii,33p.
Bibliography: p27-33.
ISBN 9221029182

I'M : information market, marche d'information, Informationsmarkt. – Luxembourg : Commission of the European Communities, 1985.
Continues: Euronet Diane news. Multilingual text.

Image of Man in Human Rights Legislation. – Rome : Herder, 1985.
243p.
Hbk £25,000.00

IMCO news : the magazine of the Inter-Govermental Maritime Consultative Organization. – London : IMCO, 1979 - 1982.
n v.
Continued by: IMO news.

IMF and stabilisation : developing country experiences / directed and edited by Tony Killick : contributors : Graham Bird ... et al. – London : Gower in association with the Overseas Development Institute, 1985.
viii,216p; 22cm.
Originally published: London : Heinemann Educational in association with the Overseas Development Institute, 1984. Includes bibliographies.
ISBN 0566050412 £13.45

IMF and the debt crisis : a guide to the Third World's dilemma / Peter Korner ... et al. : translated from the German by Paul Knight. – London : Zed, 1987.
226p; 23cm.
Bibliography: p210-219. - Includes index. Translation of: Im Teufelskreis der Verschuldung.
ISBN 0862324874 Hbk £18.95
ISBN 0862324882 Pbk £6.95

IMF and the World Bank in Africa : conditionality, impact, and alternatives / edited by Kjell J. Havnevik. – Uppsala : Scandinavian Institute of African Studies, 1987.
177 p.; 23 cm.
Includes bibliographies.
ISBN 9171062645

Immigrant workers in Europe : their legal status : a comparative study / Eric-Jean Thomas, study director. – Paris : Unesco Press, 1982.
245 p.; 25 cm.
Includes bibliographies.
ISBN 9231018671 Hbk £50

Immigrants and the Welfare State. – NACAB. – London : CENT, 1983.
ISBN 0906072069 Pbk £4.80

Immigrant's Handbook : a Critical Guide. – Law Union of Ontario. – Montreal : Black Rose Books, 1981.
263p.
Pbk £9.95

Immigrating to Canada : Who is Allowed? What is Required? How to Do It. – 6th ed. – North Vancouver : International Self-Counsel Press, 1986.
179p.
ISBN 0889086133 Hbk £14.95

Immigrating to the U.S.A. – 4th ed. – North Vancouver : International Self-Counsel Press, 1983.
208p.
ISBN 0889089124 Hbk £14.95

Immigration. – Vancouver : British Columbia Continuing Legal Education Society, 1985.
302p.
ISBN 0865042322 Hbk £70.00

Immigration : Law and Practice / John Cavanagh. – 2nd ed. – London : Longman Professional. – (Longman Practitioner Series).
ISBN 0851213898 Pbk £19.95

Immigration Act, 1959/1963, (Act 155) Regulations and Orders. – Kuala Lumpur : International Law Books Services.
Hbk £12.50

Immigration and Nationality Department report, July 1985. – London, 1985.
30p. – (A Home Office publication).
'Second published report on the work of the Immigration and Nationality Department of the Home Office' -Foreword.

Immigration and nationality law and practice. – London : Frank Cass, 1986-.

Immigration and the judiciary : law and politics in Britain and America / Stephen H. Legomsky. – Oxford : Clarendon, 1987.
xxxix,345p; 24cm.
Bibliography: p327-345.
ISBN 0198255616 £35.00

Immigration Appeal Reports. – London : HMSO, 1984.
ISBN 0113407939 Hbk £9.95

Immigration control procedures : report of a formal investigation. – London : CRE, 1985.
xiv,188p.
ISBN 0907920543

Immigration Decree 1979. – Seychelles Government. – Mahe : Seychelles National Printing Co.
Hbk £8.00

Immigration Emergency Procedures / Webb. – London : Legal Action Group, 1986.
ISBN 0905099117 Pbk £11.00

Immigration Into Britain. – 2nd ed. – London : HMSO.
ISBN 0117012548 Hbk £3.00

Immigration law / by J.M. Evans. – 2nd ed. – London : Sweet & Maxwell, 1983.
xxx,452p; 19cm.
Previous ed.: 1976. Includes index.
ISBN 0421299509 Hbk £
ISBN 0421299606 Pbk £7.50

Immigration Law : 1987. – Vancouver : Continuing Legal Education Society of British Columbia, 1987.
386p.
ISBN 0865043582 Hbk £85.00

Immigration Law and Practice Supplement-1985. – London : CENT.

Immigration law and practice / Lawrence Grant, Ian Martin. – London : The Cobden Trust, 1982.
xxxii,410p; 22cm.
Includes index.
ISBN 0900137193 Pbk
ISBN 0900137815

Immigration law and practice in the United Kingdom / Ian A. Macdonald. – 2nd ed. – London : Butterworths, 1987.
560p; 25cm.
Previous ed.: 1983. Includes index.
ISBN 0406283141 £50.55

Immigration Law and Procedure / Rosenfield. – Matthew Bender, 1966.
ISBN 0000999087 Hbk £409.00

Immigration law handbook. – Handsworth Law Centre. – 3rd ed. – TUAR, 1985.
ISBN 0951074504 Pbk £2.50

Immigration Law in Canada. – London : Butterworths.
ISBN 0409834505 Hbk £40.00

Immigration Practice and Procedure. – Vancouver : British Columbia Continuing Legal Education Society, 1982.
436p.
ISBN 0865040516 Hbk £75.00

Immigraton and Nationality : Statutes and Rules. – Shaw & Sons.
ISBN 072191120X Pbk £17.95

Immoral Traffic (Prevention) Act, 1956. – 4th ed. – Lucknow : Eastern Book Company, 1987.
Hbk £90.00

Immoral Traffic (Prevention) Act. – 4th ed. – Allahabad : Law Book Company, 1988.
600p.
Hbk £175.00

IMO Grain Rules
English Edition. – International Maritime Organization. – London : International Maritime Organization, 1982.
Hbk £1.25
French Edition. –
Hbk £1.50

IMO news : the magazine of the International Maritime Organization. – London : IMO, 1982.
Continues: IMCO news.

Imo State law reports. – Ibadan : Evans Brothers (Nigeria Publishers) for Law Reporting Committee, Ministry of Justice, Imo State of Nigeria, 1977.

Imo State of Nigeria
Annual volume of the laws of Imo State of the Federal Republic of Nigeria containing edicts and subsidiary legislation. – Imo State of Nigeria. – Owerri : Government Printer, 1976.
Consolidated index 1976-1985 published separately, 1986.

IMO-UNEP Guidelines on Oil Spill Disperant Application and Environmental Considerations : Practical Information On the Use of Disperants for Dealing With Oil Spills at Sea. – International Maritime Organization Staff. – London : International Maritime Organization, 1982.
Hbk £2.00

Impact. – Ottawa : Ministry of the Solicitor General, 1982-.
Contents: 'a periodical which presents research and statistics about crime and criminal justice'.

Impact of Advertising Standards on Road Safety : Report, November 1983. – House of Representatives Standing Committee on Road Safety. – Canberra : Australian Government Publishing Service, 1983.
58p.
ISBN 0644029706 Hbk £3.30

Impact of European Community law on the implementation of the European Convention on Human Rights / by Maurice Mendelson. – Strasbourg : Council of Europe, 1984.
43p.
ISBN 928710350X

Impact of Prosecutions Under the Trade Practices Act. – Canberra : Australian Institute of Criminology.
Hbk £2.00

Impact of reprography on the copyright system / S.J. Liebowitz. – Ottawa : Research and International Affairs Branch, Bureau of Corporate Affairs, Consumer and Corporate Affairs Canada, 1981.
82 p.; 28 cm.
Bibliography: p. 81-82.
ISBN 0662113969 Pbk

Impact of residual disability from illness and injury on the distribution of household income : a lognormal approach / by Yvonne Brittan and Ioannis G. Vlachonikolis. – Oxford : SSRC-Social Science Research Council, 1981.
23p. – (Working paper).

Impact of sociology of law on government action: proceedings of a conference on sociology of law, Saarbrucken, Federal Republic of Germany, September 5th-8th, 1977. – Bern : Peter Lang, 1981.
448p.
ISBN 3820461736 Pbk £57.00

Impacts of the UN Convention on the Law of the Sea on tuna regulation / by W.T. Burke. – Rome : Food and Agriculture Organization of the United Nations, 1982.
v,19p. – (Norway funds-in-trust).
Discusses impact of the Third United Nations Convention on the Law of the Sea on tuna management, especially Article 64 concerning conservation.
ISBN 925101292X

Impaired Driving 1987. – Vancouver : Continuing Legal Education Society of British Columbia, 1987.
109p.
ISBN 0865043353 Hbk £65.00

Impaired Driving. – Vancouver : British Columbia Continuing Legal Education Society, 1984.
ISBN 0865041253 Hbk £45.00

Impaired driving and breathalyzer law: recent case law. – 1 vol. – Scarborough, Ontario : Butterworths (Canada).
Joint publication with the Legal Service Society of British Columbia. The most litigated sections - 234, 235 and 236 - of the Criminal Code are broken into their component aspects and the appropriate case law relating to each aspect is set out in digest form. Contains a table of cases, and covers impaired driving, failing to provide breath samples, driving with more than 80mg of alcohol in blood, and sentencing.
ISBN 0409806471 Loose leaf

Impeachment under the Nigerian Constitution / Igbinewedo Albert Igbinedion. – Benin City : Benfranco Printers, 1983.
76p.

Imperial appeal : the debate on the appeal to the Privy Council, 1833-1986 / David B. Swinfen. – Manchester : Manchester University Press, 1987.
viii,268p; 23cm.
Bibliography: p255-260. - Includes index.
ISBN 0719018951 £35.00

Impey, Ken → Internal Audit.

Implementation of EC directive on product liability : an explanatory and consultative note / Department of Trade and Industry. – London : The Department, 1985.
18,xivp.

Implementation of human rights covenants : with special reference to India / H.O. Agarwal. – Allahabad : Kitab Mahal, 1983.
x,210p.
Includes index. Includes the text of the International Covenant on Economic, Social and Cultural Rights and the International Covenant on Civil and Political Rights.

Implementation of international humanitarian law / Yves Sandoz. – Dordrecht : Nijhoff (Martinus), 1989.
488.
A collection of articles resulting from the 1986 session of the Centre for Studies and Research in International Law and International Relations of the Hague Academy. Explores humanitarian law from the viewpoint of implementation and enforcement, and offers suggestions for improvement.
ISBN 9024737842 Hbk £85

Implementation of Labour Enactments. – Bombay : Popular Prakashon.
Hbk £60.00

Implementation of the European Convention on Human Rights in respect of young persons and children placed in care or in institutions following a decision of the administrative or judicial authorities : replies of Governments to the Secretary General's enquiry under Article 57 of the European Convention on Human Rights / Council of Europe. – Strasbourg : Council of Europe, 1986.
196p; 30cm. – (H (86) 1).
At head of cover title: Human rights.

Implementation of the sixth EC directive on company law : an explanatory and consultative note / Department of Trade and Industry. – 1. – London : The Department, 1984.
various pagings.

Implementation of the third E.C. directive : Department of Trade explanatory and consultative note : memorandum / by the Society's Standing Committee on Company Law. – London : Law Society, 1982.
10p.

Implementation of the third EC directive on company law : an explanatory and consultative note / Department of Trade. – 1. – London : The Department, 1982.
various pagings.
Includes the text of the directive.

Implementing crime prevention measures / by Tim Hope. – London : H.M.S.O., 1985.
vi,75p; 25cm.
Examines practicality of crime prevention methods. Considers situational measures aimed at dealing with specifically defined offences and community involvement in prevention of crime. Illustrates difficulties by case histories.
ISBN 0113408129

Implementing Networks In Banking and Financial Services. – London : Macmillan.
ISBN 0333440692 Hbk £35.00

Implementing the European Convention on Human Rights in Sweden : the Boll discussion / by Jacob W. F. Sundberg. – Stockholm : s.n., 1983.
14,9 leaves.
Includes bibliographical references.

Implementing the Law. – London : Edward Arnold.
ISBN 0340423110 Pbk £26.00

Implications of marital separation for young children / compiled by the Australian Institute of Family Studies from a report of a survey conducted in 1982-83 by G.W. Smiley, E.R. Chamberlain and L.I. Dalgleish. – Melbourne : Australian Institute of Family Studies, 1987.
ix,45p. – (Working paper).
Bibliography: p.33-45.

Implications of the Data Protection Act / R.A. Elbra. – Manchester : NCC Publications, 1985.
75p.
Includes bibliography.
ISBN 085012476X Pbk £5.95

Implied terms in the law of contract in England and South Africa / submitted for the degree of PhD by Jacob Petrus Vorster. – S.l. : s.n., 1987.
xii,240p.
Thesis (PhD): St. John's College, Cambridge, 1987. Bibliography: pp.204-212. - Includes index.
ISBN 0620113057

Importation of patented products in the Andean group / by German Cavelier. – Bogota, Columbia : Cavelier Abogados, 1985.
11 leaves.

Importation of products with the same trademark / by German Cavelier. – Bogota, Colombia : Cavelier Abogados, 1985.
9 leaves.

Importing for the Small Business. – London : Kogan Page, 1985.
128p.
ISBN 0850388694 Pbk £6.95

Imprisonent Today : Current Issues in the Prison Debate / McNeill. – London : Macmillan.
ISBN 0333421957 Hbk £29.50

Imprisonment in England and Wales : a concise history / Christopher Harding ... et al. – London : Croom Helm, 1985.
xiii,308p,8p of plates; 23cm.
Includes index.
ISBN 0709912943 £25.00

Imprisonment of women. – Oxford : Blackwell, 1986.
ISBN 063114319X Pbk £7.95

Imprisonment: the legal status and rights of prisoners. – London : Sweet & Maxwell, 1989.
Describes the history and structure of the prison system, focusing on the various categories of prisons and prisoners within it. Analyses the body of case law, including issues such as disciplinary hearings, prisoners' correspondence, visits, and access to the courts. Summarises the law on remission and parole. Contains the European Prison Rules as an appendix.
ISBN 0421322306 Pbk £25.00

Improving access to civil justice : the report of the Law Society's Working Party on the Funding of Litigation. – Law Society. – London : Law Society, 1987.
11p.
Supplement to the Law Society's Gazette. Includes bibliographical references.

Improving Compliance with International Law. – London : Eurospan.
ISBN 0813908590 Hbk £30.95

Improving the presentation of information to juries in fraud trials : a report of four research studies / by the MRC Applied Psychology Unit, Cambridge. – London : H.M.S.O., 1986.
vii,63p; 25cm.
Presents the results of research by the Roskill Fraud Trials Committee on the presentation of evidence to juries.
ISBN 0113800096

Imputation systems : objectives and consequences : proceedings of a seminar held in Montreal 1982 during the 36th Congress of the International Fiscal Association / organized by the International Fiscal Association. – Deventer : Kluwer, 1983.
129p. – (IFA congress seminar series).
ISBN 9065441212

In memoriam J.D.B. Mitchell / editors St. John Bates ... et al. : foreword Lord Cameron. – London : Sweet & Maxwell, 1983.
xxxix,247p,1leaf of plates; 23cm.
Includes index.
ISBN 042129700X £19.50

In my time : an autobiography / Lord Elwyn-Jones. – London : Weidenfeld, 1983.
319p.
Includes bibliography and index.
ISBN 0297781596

In Place of a Parent. – Bristol : Jordan & Sons Ltd, 1986.
– (Family Law Practitioner's Ser.).
ISBN 0853081018 Pbk

In search of law : sociological approaches to law / Vilhelm Aubert. – Oxford : Martin Robertson, 1983.
180p; 22cm.
Bibliography: p174-175. - Includes index.
ISBN 0855204915

In the child's best interest? / Vincent. – London : Sweet & Maxwell, 1987.
ISBN 042261260X Hbk £22.00
ISBN 0422612707 Pbk £10.95

In Whose Interest? International Banking and American Foreign Policy. – Yale University Press.
ISBN 0300042051 Pbk £9.95

Inamullah, Jan
Tribal Law of the Pathans in Historical Perspective. – Islamabad : Quaid-i-Azam University.
Hbk

Incapacitated principal : report on a reference under section 3(1)(e) of the Law Commissions Act 1965 / the Law Commission. – London : H.M.S.O., 1983.
v,104p; 25cm.
ISBN 0101897707

Incapacity. – Vancouver : Continuing Legal Education Society of British Columbia, 1988.
205p.
ISBN 0865049750 Hbk £70.00

Ince, John
Environmental Law, British Columbia Handbook, 1984 / Gwen M. Edwards. – Butterworths, 1984.
285p.
ISBN 0409988642 Pbk £40.00
—Land Use Law : B.C. Handbook / Z. Pereboom. – Toronto : Butterworths, 1984.
310p.
ISBN 0409988634 Pbk £26
—Land Use Law : British Columbia Handbook. – Butterworths, 1984.
310p.
ISBN 0409988634 Pbk £40.00

Ince, Noel J.
Tax and Financial Planning for Family Businesses / George J. Bell. – London : Butterworths, 1984.
This book addresses the tax problems faced by owners of small and medium sized family business in the United Kingdom. The work examines the benefits to be gained from allowances, reliefs, exemptions, and Revenue concessions.
ISBN 0406557306 Pbk £16.00
—Year End and Accounting Period Tax Planning / G. J. Bell. – 2nd ed. – London : Oyez Longman, 1984.
– (Oyez Longman Practical Tax Ser.).
ISBN 0851208398 Hbk £10.50

Incest : a family pattern / Jean Renvoize. – London : Routledge & Kegan Paul, 1982.
viii,224p; 23cm.
Bibliography : p217-220. - Includes index.
ISBN 0710090730 £7.95

Inciardi → Challenging Capital Punishment : Legal and Social Science Approaches.

Incitement to racial hatred : issues and analysis. – Canberra : Australian Government Publishing Service, 1982.
31,2p. – (Occasional paper).
ISBN 0644021926

Incitement to racial hatred : the international experience. – Canberra : Australian Government Publishing Service, 1982.
65p. – (Occasional paper).
ISBN 0644022221

Income and Corporation Act 1988. – London : Butterworths, 1988.
ISBN 0406008000 Pbk £18.00

Income and Corporation Taxes Act 1988. – Bicester : CCH.
ISBN 0863251595 Pbk £18.00
ISBN 086325148X Hbk £32

Income, Corporation and Capital Gains Taxes and Petrole. – Bicester : CCH.
ISBN 0863251633 Pbk £18.00

Income Support and Housing Benefit for Single People. – Turnaround Press.
ISBN 0906951399 Pbk £5.95

Income Tax 1980
Supplement 1987. – Sweet & Maxwell.
ISBN 0421389702 Pbk £21.00

Income Tax, 1983-84. – 13th ed. Repr. of 1981 ed. – Plymouth : Macdonald & Evans, 1984.
xi, 192p. – (M and E Handbook Ser.).
ISBN 0712109706 Hbk £3.95

Income Tax 1986/87. – Pitman.
ISBN 0712109749 Pbk £7.95

Income Tax
1988-89. – Tolley Publishing.
ISBN 0854593462 Pbk £17.95
Nineteen Eighty-Six Supplement. –
ISBN 0421369108 Pbk

Index to legal essays : English language legal essays in festschriften, memorial volumes, conference papers and other collections, 1975-1979 / compiled for the British and Irish Association of Law Librarians under the editorship of Barbara Tearle. – London : Mansell, 1983.
xii,430p; 26cm.
Bibliography: pxii.
ISBN 0720116538 £25.00

Index to New Zealand legal writing / J.F. Northey. – 2nd ed. – Auckland : Legal Research Foundation, 1982.
ix,260p.
Previous ed.: 1977.
ISBN 090858119X

Index to Nigerian legal periodicals, 1946-1981 / compiled by the Library, Nigerian Institute of Advanced Legal Studies. – Lagos : NIALS Library, 1983.
v,33p.

Index to Reports of Tax Cases : 1875-1981, 52 Vols. – Abingdon : Professional Books, 1984.
ISBN 0862050707 Hbk £63.00

Index to Sheriff Court districts of Scotland. – Edinburgh : Green (W.) & Son, 1981.
Lists alphabetically each Scottish city, town, village and hamlet giving the appropriate sheriffdom and sheriff court for the place.
ISBN 0414006666 Pbk

Index to Singapore/Malaysia legal periodicals 1932-1984 / Compiled by the staff of the Law Library, National University of Singapore Library : edited by Molly Cheang, Sng Yok Fong, Carolyn Wee. – Singapore : Malayan Law Journal Pte., 1986.
xvi,431p.
ISBN 9971700506 Hbk £160.00

Index to statutes in force. – London : Sweet & Maxwell, 1988.
ISBN 0421317809 Hbk

Index to the Companies (South Australia) Code. – Adelaide : Government Printer, 1982.
97p.
' ... prepared by the Law Book Company'. - t.p..

Index to the Decisions Rendered By the Immigration Appeal Board. – Agincourt : Carswell, 1987.
168p.
This is a comprehensive index to the decisions of the Immigration Appeal Board from 1976 through to 1987. Special legal research features include a key word index, and alphabetical listing by style of case, and a case citator.
Pbk £33.25

Index to the Decisions Rendered by the Immigration Appeal Board. – Agincourt : Carswell, 1988.
174p.
Hbk £33.25

Index to the opinions of Roman-Dutch lawyers and the decisions of the courts of the Netherlands which have been digested in the Algemeen Beredeneerd Register of Nassau La Leck (1741-1795) / by the late Alfred Adrian Roberts : edited byt S.I.E. van Tonder. – 8. – Pretoria : Government Printer on behalf of the South African Law Commission, 1985.
– (Research series).

Index to the South African Law Reports : 1828-1946, 2 vols. / F. R. Malan. – Durban : Butterworths.
ISBN 0409040770 Hbk

Index to the Southern African Law Reports 1828-1946, 4 Vols. / F.R. Malan. – Durban : Professional Publishers, 1981-1982.
Hbk

Index to the Southern African law reports 1828-1946
Vol. 1 : Transvaal / editors, F.R. Malan, J.C. Van der Walt. – Durban : Butterworths, 1981.
729p.
Covers the major law reports published in Southern Africa prior to 1947.
ISBN 0409040789
Vol. 2 : Cape / editors, F.R. Malan, J.C. Van der Walt. – 1983.
1006p.
Covers the major law reports published in Southern Africa prior to 1947.
ISBN 0409040797 Hbk
Vol. 3: Natal. – 1985.
ISBN 0409040800 £80.00
Vol 4: Griqueland West, OFS, SWA. – 1987.
ISBN 0409016691 £90.00

Index to the statutes of Alberta, including Spring sitting 1983 / prepared for the Province of Alberta by Canadian Law Information Council. – Edmonton : Queen's Printer, 1983.
vii,876p.

Index to the Treaty Series
No. 84, 1983. – London : HMSO.
ISBN 0101920903 Hbk £3.15
No. 63, 1982. –
ISBN 0101899203 Hbk £2.70
No. 96, 1981. –
ISBN 0101856601 Hbk £2.95
No. 97, 1980. –
ISBN 0101817606 Hbk £2.40

Indexation of Capital Gains : Computations and Examples / Paul Elliott. – London : Butterworths, 1983.
This work is designed to assist United Kingdom tax practitioners with the new rules for indexing of capital gains. Worked examples are provided throughout the work to explain the subject matter.
ISBN 0406256101 Pbk

Indexation of Capital Gains : Examples etc (83) / Paul Elliott. – London : Butterworths.
ISBN 0406256101 Pbk £9.00

Indexes to the legislation of Tasmania. – Hobart : Office of the Parliamentary Counsel, 1984.
104,124,79p.
Originally published in 3 parts. Contents: Alphabetical table of Tasmanian Acts 1826-1983 - Subject index to statute law - Subject index to subordinate legislation.

Index-Linked Gilts. – Cambridge : Woodhead-Faulkner, 1985.
ISBN 085941289X Hbk £30.00

India Stamp Act / Pratt. – 7th ed. – Bombay : Tripathi.

Indian Act Annotated. – 2nd ed. – Agincourt : Carswell, 1986.
124p.
This work is a section-by-section analysis of the recently amended Canadian Indian Act. Significant treaties are presented in the appendices to the book. The extent of provincial legislative control of Indians in the areas of matrimonial property division, child welfare, and other topics is addressed in the book.
Pbk £27.50

Indian Act of Canada, Second Edition. – 2nd ed. – Saskatoon : University of Saskatchewan, Native Law Centre, 1988.
48p.
ISBN 0888802048 Hbk £10.00

Indian acts and amendments 1868-1975 : an indexed collection / Sharon Helen Venne. – Saskatchewan : University of Saskatchewan Native Law Centre, 1981.
lxvii,460p.
Includes index. Includes: Consolidation of Indian legislation / prepared by Gail Hinge for the Office of Native Claims, Dept. of Indian and Northern Affairs. Vol.2: Indian acts and amendments, 1868-1975.
ISBN 0888801041

Indian Arbitration Act. – 5th ed. – Allahabad : Law Book Company, 1984.
xxxiv, 864p.
Hbk £220.00

Indian Company Law, 2 Vols. – 10th ed. – Nagpur : Wadjura & Co, 1987.
1,360p.
Hbk £525.00

Indian Company Law. – 9th ed. – Delhi : SBD Enterprises.
Hbk £21.00

Indian Constitution. – Madras : Ramaswami Aiyar Foundation.
Hbk £5.00

Indian Constitution and its Working. – rev. ed. – Allahabad : Orient Law House.
236p.
ISBN 0861316118 Pbk £40.00

Indian Constitutional Law. – 3rd ed. 1978 with Supplement. – Bombay : Tripathi, 1983.
799p.
bd £95.00

Indian Contract Act, 3 Vols. / E.S. Subrahmanyam. – 3rd ed. – Allahabad : Law Book Company, 1989.
Hbk £550.00

Indian Contract and Specific Relief Acts / Mulla. – 10th ed. in press. – Bombay : Tripathi.
bd

Indian Direct Taxes Law and Practice. – Nagpur : Wadhura & Co, 1983.
Hbk £125.00

Indian Divorce Act, 1869 : Bare Act with Commentary. – Delhi : SBD Enterprises.
Hbk £5.00

Indian Explosives Act, 1884 and Explosive Rules, 1983 : Together with Explosive Substances Act, 1908, Gas Cylinders Rules, 1981 and Static Mobile Pressure Vessels (Unfired) Rules, 1981. – 3rd ed. – Lucknow : Eastern Book Company, 1984.
255p.
Hbk £40.00

Indian Hunting, Trapping and Fishing Rights in the Prairie Provinces of Canada. – Saskatoon : University of Saskatchewan, Native Law Centre, 1983.
64p.
ISBN 0888801254 Hbk £20.00

Indian Income Tax Law and Practice. – 14th ed. – Nagpur : Wadhura & Co, 1982.
ca 1,050p.
Pbk £70.00

Indian Law of Marriage and Divorce. – 4th ed. – Bombay : Tripathi, 1981.
660p.
bd £125.00

Indian Mercantile Law and Industrial Law / K.C. Garg. – New Delhi : Kalyani Publishers, 1984.
Hbk £25.00

Indian Ocean as a zone of peace : Workshop on the Indian Ocean as a Zone of Peace, Dhaka, People People's Republic of Bangladesh, November 23-25, 1985. – Dordrecht : Martinus Nijhoff, 1986.
Sponsored and organized by the Bangladesh Institute of International and Strategic Studies in association with the International Peace Academy.
ISBN 0898389178 Pbk

Indian Partnership Act. – 5th ed. – Bombay : Tripathi, 1987.
264p.
Hbk £80.00

Indian Partnership Act : With a Special Reference to Taxation Laws. – 5th ed. – Allahabad : Law Book Company, 1986.
1,700p.
Hbk £320.00

Indian Penal Code, 1860, 2 Vols. – 4th ed. – Lucknow : Eastern Book Company.
Hbk £220.00

Indian Penal Code / Dhirajlal. – 26th ed. – Nagpur : Wadhura & Co, 1987.
Hbk £220.00

Indian Penal Code. – 2nd ed. – Lucknow : Eastern Book Company, 1981.
406p.
Hbk £30.00

Indian Penal Code in 2 Vols. – 7th ed. – Allahabad : Law Book Company, 1981-83.
Hbk £280.00

Indian Presidency. – New Delhi : Deep and Deep Publications, 1988.
124p.
Hbk £75.00

Indian Private International Law. – New Delhi : Sterling Publishers, 1982.
248p.
ISBN 8120702409 Hbk £75.00
ISBN 812070438X Pbk £25.00

Indian Registration Act. – 9th ed. in prep. – Bombay : Tripathi.
Hbk

Indian Reserves in Quebec. – Saskatoon : University of Saskatchewan, Native Law Centre, 1984.
44p.
ISBN 0888801408 Hbk £20.00

Indian Reserves in the Atlantic Provinces of Canada. – Saskatoon : University of Saskatchewan, Native Law Centre, 1986.
92p.
ISBN 088880167X Hbk £25.00

Indian South Africans / by Frene Ginwala. – New ed. – London : Minority Rights Group, 1985.
20p. – (Report).
Includes bibliographical references.
ISBN 0946690294

Indian Stamp Act : With State Amendments. – 6th ed. – Allahabad : Law Book Ccompany, 1986.
800p.
Hbk £180.00

Indian Succession Act. – 5th ed. – Allahabad : Law Book Company, 1985.
Hbk £220.00

Indian Title in Canada. – Agincourt : Carswell, 1987.
154p.
This work focuses on the basis of Indian land claims in Canada and provides a thorough discussion of the court's responses to these claims. The author integrates history and law in explaining the issues.
Hbk £39.50

Indian Trade and Merchandise Marks Act. – 3rd ed. in prep. – Bombay : Tripathi.
Hbk

Indian Trusts Act : With Special Reference to Taxation Laws. – 3rd ed. – Allahabad : Law Book Company, 1987.
ca 900p.
Hbk £200.00

Indians and Taxation in Canada, Second Edition. – 2nd ed. – Saskatoon : University of Saskatchewan, Native Law Centre, 1987.
88p.
ISBN 0888801823 Hbk £25.00

Indians and the Law 2. – Vancouver : Continuing Legal Education Society of British Columbia, 1985.
181p.
ISBN 0865041334 Hbk £60.00

Indians and the Law 3. – Vancouver : Continuing Legal Education Society of British Columbia, 1986.
243p.
ISBN 0865042675 Hbk £60.00

Indians and the Law. – Vancouver : Continuing Legal Education Society of British Columbia, 1982.
420p.
ISBN 0865040524 Hbk £70.00

Indigenous Resource Rights and Mining Companies in North America and Australia, February 1986 / G.J. Crough. – Kingston : Australian Government Publishing Service, 1986.
132p.
ISBN 0644046392 Hbk £7.60

Individual and Democratic Rights : Report of the Advisory Committee to the Constitutional Commission. – Kingston : Australian Government Publishing Service, 1987.
xx, 148p.
Pbk £9.95

Individual Cases Reports : 1972-1981. – Abingdon : Professional Books.
Hbk £190.00

Individual Freedom, Social Welfare and Islamic Economic Order. – Islamabad : Pakistan Institute of Development Economics, 1982.
40p.
Pbk £5.00

Individual Income Taxes 1989 : Federal Taxation. – Prentice-Hall.
ISBN 0137032668 Hbk £48.15

Individual Property Rights Conceptions Privacy in Family / Emmanuel Lazega. – Cambridge : Cambridge University, Department of Social Science Research Council.
ISBN 094877410X Pbk £2.50

Individual under African law : proceedings of the first All-Africa Law Conference, October 11-16, 1981, Royal Swazi Spa, Swaziland / edited by Peter Nanyenya Takirambudde. – Kwaluseni (Sq) : University of Swaziland Department of Law, 1982.
iv,209p.

Individual's Petition in International Law. – New Delhi : Deep and Deep Publications, 1985.
287p.
Hbk £150.00

Indoctrination, curriculum and the law. – Southampton : Association for Curriculum Development, 1988.
ISBN 185401066 Pbk £4.00

Indonesia and the rule of law: twenty years of 'New Order' government / Hans Thoolen. – Pinter, 1987.
224.
Sets out the constitutional provisions and legislation relating to human rights and assesses their practical application.
ISBN 0861879198 Hbk £29.50

Indonesian legal history 1602-1848. – Sydney : Oughtershaw Press, 1982.
viii,300p.
Bibliography: p.275-293. - Includes index.
ISBN 0959342001

Indonesian legal history : British West Sumatra, 1685-1825 / John Ball. – Sydney : Oughtershaw Press, 1984.
viii, 307 p.; 21 cm.
Includes index. Bibliography: 296-299.
ISBN 095934201X Pbk

Indrayan, N.K.
Law and Public Opinion in India. – New Delhi : Deep and Deep Publications, 1985.
311p.
Hbk £175.00

Industrial Accidents : Employer Liability for Monetary Damages / Audrey Balla. – North Ryde : C.C.H. Australia, 1987.
180p.
ISBN 0869038664 Hbk

Industrial air pollution : health and safety 1983 / Health & Safety Executive. – London : H.M.S.O., 1985.
33p.
ISBN 0118837877

Industrial and Commercial Law / K.C. Garg. – 7th ed. 1986 repr. – New Delhi : Kalyani Publishers, 1987.
ISBN 8170960932 Hbk £60.00

Industrial and Commercial Law : For I.C.W.A. Students / Saxena. – Delhi : SBD Enterprises.
Hbk £35.00

Industrial and Labour Law. – Calcutta : Eastern Law House.
1,298p.
Hbk £65.00

Industrial and Labour Laws of India, Second Edition. – New Delhi : Prentice-Hall, 1986.
704p.
ISBN 0876924259 Hbk £95.00

Industrial conflict resolution in market economics : a study of Australia, the Federal Republic of Germany, Italy, Japan and the USA / T. Hanami editor : R. Blanpain associate editor. – Deventer : Kluwer Law and Taxation, 1984.
xiv,321p; 25cm.
Includes bibliographies and index.
ISBN 9065441808 Pbk

Industrial democracy and participation : a Scottish survey / by Peter Cressey...et al. – London : Department of Employment, 1981.
62p. – (Research paper).

Industrial design law in Australia and New Zealand. – Sydney : Butterworths, 1986.
256p.
Chapters include the role of design in modern society, recent changes in design law, design basics, application for registration, the registrar of design, the owner, the scope of legal protection for designs, design duration and fees, specific features of the New Zealand law of industrial designs, and design legislation in Australia and New Zealand.
ISBN 0409490482 Hbk £55.00

Industrial Development Act 1982. – London : HMSO, 1983.
ISBN 0102072841 Hbk £8.60

Industrial Disputes : a Guide to the Industrial Disputes Act, 1947, Revised Edition. – 3rd repr. 1985. – New Delhi : Prentice-Hall.
120p.
ISBN 0876923686 Hbk £25.00

Industrial Disputes Law in Malaysia. – Singapore : Malayan Law Journal, 1984.
393p.
Reproduces the Industrial Relations Act with annotations from the decisions of the Industrial Court and the superior courts of Malaysia. Covers protection of rights of workmen and employers and their trade unions, collective bargaining and collective agreement, representation on dismissals, Industrial Relations Regulations 1967, and 1980.
ISBN 967962000X Hbk £90.00

Industrial Employment Injuries : an Overview of the Legal Protection System. – New Delhi : Deep and Deep Publications, 1986.
388p.
Hbk £250.00

Industrial hazardous waste management. – Paris : United Nations Environment Programme, 1983.
79p.
Includes bibliogrpahical references.

Industrial injuries benefits scheme / Mark Rowland. – London : Legal Action Group, 1983.
xxvii,122p.
Includes index.
ISBN 0905099052

Industrial Innovation and Public Policy : Preparing for the 1980's and the 1990's / Walter Zegveld. – London : Pinter Publishers Ltd, 1981.
251p.
ISBN 0903804921 Hbk £17.50
ISBN 0861872509 Pbk £7.75

Industrial Law / Narang. – Delhi : Dhanpat Rai and Sons.
Hbk £23.75

Industrial Law. – 14th ed. – Lucknow : Eastern Book Company, 1985.
1,774p.
Hbk £225.00

Industrial law / Wood. – 3rd ed. – London : Butterworths, 1986.
ISBN 0406381453 Pbk £17.95

Industrial law / I.T. Smith, Sir John C. Wood. – 3rd ed. – London : Butterworths, 1986.
516p; 25cm.
Previous ed.: 1983. Includes index.
ISBN 0406381445 Hbk £
ISBN 0406381453 Pbk

Industrial Law / Stepensons. – 7th ed. – Wellington : Butterworths.
ISBN 0409667706 Hbk

Industrial Law : For B Com. and I.C.W.A. Students / Saxena. – Delhi : SBD Enterprises.
Hbk £35.00

Industrial Law Bulletin / Alexander Szakats. – Wellington : Butterworths.
ISBN 040978107X Pbk

Industrial law journal. – London : Sweet & Maxwell for the Industrial Law Society, 1972-.
Supersedes: Bulletin of the Industrial Law Society. Index in each vol..

Industrial Law Society →Industrial law journal.

Industrial Law, Victoria. – Butterworths, 1981.
ISBN 0409490415 Llf

Industrial policies in the European Community / Victoria Curzon Price. – London : Macmillan for the Trade Policy Research Centre, 1981.
xvi,141p.
Bibliography: p132-135.
ISBN 0333319117

Industrial property citator / by Michael Fysh and Robert Wilson Thomas. – London : European Law Centre, 1982.
321p; 26cm.
Includes index.
ISBN 0907451047

Industrial property laws and treaties / compiled and published by the World Intellectual Property Organization. – Geneva : WIPO, 1976-.
Llf Sfr110.00

Industrial property laws of the Federal Republic of Germany : patent, utility model, trademark, design : texts of the laws, orders, regulations, guidelines and index / translated and edited by Volker Vossius and Ulrich C. Hallmann. – 2nd ed. – Munchen : Wila Verlag fur Wirtschaftswerbung Wilhelm Lampl, 1985.
278p.
Includes index.
ISBN 3879101477

Industrial relations. – 3rd ed. – Oxford : Croom Helm, 1985.
ISBN 0709914741 Pbk £9.95

Industrial relations. – Routledge, 1986.
ISBN 0710097964 Hbk £16.95

Industrial relations : an international and comparative bibliography / compiled by John Bennett and Julian Fawcett for the British Universities Industrial Relations Association. – London : Mansell, 1985.
200p; 23cm.
Includes index.
ISBN 0720117879 £20.00

Industrial relations : challenges and prospects : a report on the Warwick conference of March 1986 / P.K.Edwards. – Coventry : Industrial Relations Research Unit, School of Industrial and Business Studies, University of Warwick, 1986.

Industrial relations and employment law / editor in chief R. J. Harvey. – 2 vols. – London : Butterworths, 1984.
Cover title: Harvey on Industrial relations and employment law. Loose leaf.
ISBN 0406221731

Industrial relations and the law in the 1980's : issues and future trends / edited by Patricia Fosh and Craig R. Littler. – Aldershot : Gower, 1985.
xv,199p; 23cm.
Includes bibliographies and index.
ISBN 0566009781 Hbk £20.45
ISBN 0566009811 Pbk £9.50

Industrial relations in Britain / edited by George Sayers Bain. – Oxford : Blackwell, 1983.
xii,516p; 24cm.
Bibliography: p457-487. - Includes index.
ISBN 0631131388 Hbk £
ISBN 0631132953 Pbk £9.95

Industrial relations in West Germany : a case study of the car industry / Wolfgang Streeck. – London : Heinemann, 1984.
178p; 23cm.
Bibliography: p170-172. - Includes index. At head of title: Policy Studies Institute.
ISBN 0435838393 £16.50

Industrial relations law reports. – London : Eclipse Publications, 1972-.
Annual cumulative indexes.

Industrial Relations Legislation : Interim Report, September, 1982. – Industrial Relations Legislation (Senate Select) Committee. – Canberra : Australian Government Publishing Service, 1982.
Hbk £2.15

Industrial Relations Legislation (Senate Select) Committee
Industrial Relations Legislation : Interim Report, September, 1982. – Industrial Relations Legislation (Senate Select) Committee. – Canberra : Australian Government Publishing Service, 1982.
Hbk £2.15

Industrial Relations Reform Act. – Vancouver : Continuing Legal Education Society of British Columbia, 1987.
157p.
ISBN 0865043329 Hbk £70.00

Industrial Relations Society of Australia
International issues in industrial relations / Industrial Relations Society of Australia. – Gordon, N.S.W. : The Society, 1983.
vi,125p.
Convention proceedings. Includes bibliographical references.

Industrial tribunal / Ian McLean. – Chichester : Barry Rose, 1982.
ISBN 0859922243 Hbk £20.00

Industrial tribunal : a guide to the jurisdiction of industrial tribunals within the provisions of the following Acts : The Employment Act 1975, The Employment Protection (Consolidation) Act 1978, The Employment Act 1980, The Equal Pay Act 1970, The Sex Discrimination Act 1975, The Race Relations Act 1976 / Arthur H. Howell. – Chichester : Barry Rose, 1981.
38p; 26cm.
Cover title.
ISBN 0859922189 spiral £7.75

Industrial tribunal : a practical guide to employment law and tribunal procedure / by John Mulhern and Ian McLean. – Chichester : Rose, 1982.
280p; 23cm.
Includes index.
ISBN 0859922243 £19.50

Industrial tribunal practice. – London : Longman Professional (UK), 1988.
– (Practitioner series).
Analysis of the expanding case law on procedure with practical hints. Takes account of the procedures ofr equal value claims, with worked examples, precedents and statutory materials.
ISBN 0851213766 Pbk £16.95

Industrial tribunal practice / Walker. – 2nd ed. – Stewart (Henry), 1985.
ISBN 0946700184 Pbk £24.00

Industrial tribunal practice in Scotland / by William Leslie. – Edinburgh : Green, 1981.
xxxxi,323p; 21cm.
Includes index.
ISBN 0414006801 Pbk

Industrial Tribunal Reports 1966-1978 13 vols. – Professional Books.
ISBN 086205270X Hbk £750.00

Industrial Tribunal Reports : 1966-1978, 13 Vols. – Abingdon : Professional Books, 1984.
Hbk £535.00

Industrial tribunals
Supplement 1985. – Tolley Publishing, 1984.
ISBN 0854591540 Pbk £14.95

Industrial tribunals. – Pluto Press, 1983.
ISBN 0861043685 Pbk £6.95

Industrial tribunals : a report / by JUSTICE : chairman of committee Bob Hepple. – London : JUSTICE, 1987.
72p.
ISBN 0907247105

Industrial tribunals : practice and procedure / by Michael J. Goodman. – 4th ed. – London : Sweet & Maxwell, 1987.
xxv,120p; 22cm.
Overview of the tribunals' principle jurisdictions, and analysis of practice and procedure before industrial tribunals. Covers the changes made by the Wages Act 1986. Contains model forms for application and response to an industrial tribunal, and the text of the Industrial Tribunals (Rules of Procedure) Regulations 1985.
ISBN 0421391200 Pbk

Industrial Tribunals in Northern Ireland / John McKee. – 2nd ed. – Belfast : Queen's University of Belfast, 1986.
125p.
Pbk

Industrial tribunals in Northern Ireland : a practical guide / by Phyllis Bateson and John McKee. – Belfast : SLS Publications, Faculty of Law, Queen's University, Belfast, 1981.
xi,146p; 21cm.
Includes index.
ISBN 0853891915 Pbk

Industrialisation and reproductive rights / by Paulin sic Jackson. – Florence : European University Institute, 1986.
ii,24p.
Bibliography: p.22-24.

Industrialization and developing countries / Alan B. Mountjoy. – 5th ed. – London : Hutchinson, 1982.
256p; 22cm. – (Hutchinson university library).
Previous ed.: 1975. Bibliography: p243-246. - Includes index.
ISBN 0091468019 Pbk £4.95

Industries Development and Regulation. – 3rd ed. – Lucknow : Eastern Book Company, 1985.
337p.
Hbk

Industry and the regulatory agencies : a collection of the papers given at the fourth seminar organised by Committee F of the International Bar Association's Section on Business Law in April 1985 at Stratford-upon-Avon / edited by John H. Bates. – 4. – London : International Bar Association, 1985.
Includes bibliographical references.

Inequalities and the Law. – Lucknow : Eastern Book Company, 1984.
192p.
Hbk £60.00

Inequalities in Zimbabwe / by Christopher Hitchens and David Stephen : with a foreword by Garfield Todd. – Rev. ed. – London : Minority Rights Group, 1981.
20p. – (Report).
Previous ed.: 1979. Bibliography: p.20.

Inequality of bargaining power : judicial intervention in improvident and unconscionable bargains / Robert W. Clark. – Toronto : Carswell, 1987.
xxxvii,255p.
ISBN 0459388401

Inert Gas Systems for Ships Carrying Petroleum Products in Bulk
English Edition. – International Maritime Organization. – London : International Maritime Organization, 1982.
Hbk £2.50
French Edition. –
Hbk £3.00

Informal marriages / by Margaret Harrison. – Rev. ed. – Melbourne : Institute of Family Studies, 1982.
12 p.; 23 cm. – (Working paper).
Bibliography: p. 10.
ISBN 0642887780 Pbk

Information chain : proceedings of the UK Serials Group conference, held at Christ Church College Canterbury, 29 March - 1 April 1982 / edited by John A. Urquhart. – London : UK Serials Group, 1983.

Information computer communication policy
8 : An exploration of legal issues in information and communication technologies / Organisation for Economic Co-operation and Development. – Paris : O.E.C.D., 1983.
136p; 24cm.
Discusses the development of computer and communications technologies with relation to the existing legal regulations.
ISBN 9264125272 Pbk £7.00

Information disclosure and the multinational corporation / S.J. Gray with L.B. McSweeney, J.C. Shaw. – Chichester : Wiley, 1984.
xi,236p; 24cm. – (Wiley/IRM series on multinationals).
Includes index.
ISBN 0471904244 Hbk

Information, freedom and censorship : the Article 19 world report 1988 / prepared by the staff of Article 19. – Harlow : Longman, 1988.
xii,340p; 24cm.
Bibliography: p324-326. - Includes index.
ISBN 0582026245 Pbk £12.95

Information handling and the office of the future : report of a seminar / M. Grieves, editor. – London : British Library Research and Development Department, 1984.
ii,84p.

Information on LEXIS Prepared Specifically for Tax Specialist. – London : Butterworths.
Hbk

Information service 1986 : accounting and time recording systems for solicitors / the Law Society. – 1. – London : Law Society, 1986.
various pagings.

Information service 1986 : technology for solicitors / the Law Society. – 1. – London : Law Society, 1986.
various pagings.

Information sources in law / editor R.G. Logan. – London : Butterworths, 1986.
xiv,370p; 23cm. – (Butterworths guides to information sources).
Commentary on specialist legal literature and electronic data bases. Refers to source materials, textbooks, reference books, journal articles, and visual reports and bibliographies. Covers social law, employment law, United States of America law, European Community law, computer-assisted research, and law books for non-lawyers.
ISBN 0408114746 Hbk £43.00

Information system dynamics : the impact of interactive information networks on the UK library and information system : final report for the period August 1979 - July 1982 : report to the British Library Research and Development Dept., on project SI/G/327 / Brian C. Vickery, Richard G. Heseltine, Carolyn S. Brown. – London : School of Library, Archive and Information Studies, University College London, 1982.
392p; 30cm.

Information technology : the challenge to copyright / by James Lahore, Gerald Dworkin, Yvonne M. Smyth. – London : Sweet & Maxwell, 1984.
vii,116p; 22cm.
Includes index.
ISBN 0421322608 Pbk £11.00

Information Technology Advisory Panel
Learning to live with IT : an overview of the potential of information technology for education and training. – Information Technology Advisory Panel. – London : H.M.S.O., 1986.
44p.
ISBN 0116308311
→ Making a business of information : a survey of new opportunities.
—Report on cable systems. – Information Technology Advisory Panel. – London : H.M.S.O., 1982.
54p; 20cm.
At head of title: Cabinet Office. Information Technology Advisory Panel.
ISBN 0116308214 Pbk £3.60

Information technology and polytechnic libraries : discussion papers / Council of Polytechnic Librarians. – S.l. : COPOL, 1984.
28p.
ISBN 0907130062

Information technology & the law / edited by Chris Edwards and Nigel Savage. – Basingstoke : Macmillan, 1986.
viii,283p; 24cm.
Includes index.
ISBN 0333413938 £35.00

Informative Labelling in Some European Countries : Proceedings of the 1st Symposium of the Committee on Producer-Consumer Relations, 1981. – Bern : European Office for Quality Control.
Hbk £25.00

Informed consent to medical treatment / Law Reform Commission of Victoria. – Melbourne : The Commission, 1987.
iv,45p. – (Discussion paper).
Includes bibliographical references. 'Issued in conjunction with Australian Law Reform Commission and New South Wales Law Reform Commission' - cover.
ISBN 0724166467

Inglis, B.D.
Family Court Code. – Butterworths, 1983.
Discusses the Family Courts Act 1980, the Family Proceedings Act 1980, the Guardianship Act 1968 as amended in 1980, the Status of Children Act 1969, the Domestic Protection Act 1969, the Family Proceedings Rules 1981, and the Domestic Protection Rules 1983.
ISBN 0409601276 Hbk
—Practice and procedure in the Family Court : papers presented at the Family Law Seminar, University of Auckland, 26 May, 1984 / by B.D. Inglis. – Auckland : Legal Research Foundation, 1984.
22p.
At head of title: Legal Research Foundation Inc. Family Law Seminar.
ISBN 0908581351

Inglis, Michael W. →Australian Capital Gains Tax.

Ingman, Terence
English legal process / Terence Ingman. – London : Financial Training, 1983.
xxxiv,267p.
ISBN 0906322243

Ingram, Collingwood William Malcolm
Dunlop Holdings Limited : investigation under Section 172 of the Companies Act 1948 : interim report / by Collingwood William Malcolm Ingram and Francis Herbert Pulling for the Department of Trade. – London : H.M.S.O., 1981.
50p; 30cm.
ISBN 0115131817 Pbk £6.00

Ingram, Peter →Jurisprudence of orthodoxy : Queen's University essays on H.L.A. Hart.

Inheritance : who should have a claim to a persons property on death? : is the present law fair? / Scottish Law Commission. – Edinburgh : The Commission, 1986.
35p.

Inheritance Tax 1988-89 / John Newth. – Belfast : Tolley Publishing.
ISBN 0854593497 Hbk £13.95

Inheritance tax. – London : Longman Professional, 1988.
ISBN 0851213812 Hbk

Inheritance tax. – 7th ed. – London : Longman Professional, 1987.
ISBN 085121326X Hbk £48.00
ISBN 0851214673 Pbk

Inheritance tax / by John Coombes and Gordon Channon. – London : Sweet & Maxwell, 1987.
xxxiv,305p; 22cm.
Includes index.
ISBN 0421370300 Pbk £18.00

Inheritance tax. – 3rd ed. – London : Sweet & Maxwell, 1988.
ISBN 042139790X Pbk £110.00

Inheritance tax. – London : Pitman Publishing, 1986.
ISBN 0712106928 Pbk £7.95

Inheritance tax guide. – Butterworths. – London : Butterworths, 1986.
ISBN 0406500347 Pbk £16.50

Inheritance tax on lifetime gifts / by Thomas Ivory ... et al. – London : Sweet & Maxwell, 1987.
xix,181p; 26cm.
Includes index.
ISBN 0421379103 £25.00

Inheritance tax on lifetime gifts / T P G Ivory. – London : Sweet & Maxwell, 1987.
ISBN 04212379103 Hbk £24.50

Inheritance tax planning / Andrew R Thornhill. – 2nd ed. – London : Longman Professional, 1988.
ISBN 0851213669 Hbk £85.00

Iniuria Types in Roman Law. – Budapest : Akademiai Kiado, 1986.
226p.
ISBN 9630544598 Hbk £24.00

Injunctions. – Vancouver : British Columbia Continuing Legal Education Society, 1985.
155p.
ISBN 0865041989 Hbk £55.00

Injunctions / David Bean. – 3rd ed. – London : Oyez Longman, 1984.
xxvi,149p; 22cm. – (Oyez Longman practice notes).
Previous ed.: 1982. Includes index.
ISBN 0851208576 Pbk £9.95

Injunctions : A Practical Handbook. – Agincourt : Carswell, 1985.
725p.
This manual is a practitioners' guide to the preparation and presentation of injunction motions in Canadian courts. Sample forms and model motions are provided in the book.
ISBN 0459376500 Hbk £19.80

Injunctions and specific performance / Phil. – Aurora : Canada Law Book, 1983.
Hbk £35.75

Injunctions and specific performance / by Robert J. Sharpe. – Toronto : Canada Law Book Ltd., 1983.
lxxiv,450p.
ISBN 0888040172

Injunctions (LPPN66). – 4th ed. – London : Longman Professional, 1984.
ISBN 0851212980 Pbk £14.95

Injustice, inequality and ethics : a philosophical introduction to moral problems / Robin Barrow. – Brighton, Sussex : Wheatsheaf, 1982.
xii,204p.
Includes index. Bibliography: p199-202.
ISBN 038920269X Barnes & Noble

Inland Revenue
Company's purchase of own shares : Section 53 and Schedule 9 Finance Act 1982 / Inland Revenue. – London : Inland Revenue, 1982.
2,vp. – (Statement of practice).

—Consultation on valuation and pricing proposals / Inland Revenue. – London : Inland Revenue Press Office, 1987.
3,8p. – (Press release).

—Petroleum revenue tax : valuation and pricing / Inland Revenue. – London : Inland Revenue Press Office, 1986.
3p. – (Press release).

Inland Revenue and the taxpayer : proposals in response to the recommendations of the Keith Committee on income tax, capital gains tax and corporation tax : a consultative document / Board of Inland Revenue. – London : H.M.S.O., 1986.
170p.
ISBN 0116413646

Inland Revenue Clearances / Michael Wyatt. – London : Oyez Longman, 1984.
ISBN 0851207499 Hbk £50.00

Inland Revenue Official Tax Guides. – London : Oyez Longman, 1983.
ISBN 0851206174 Llf £45.00

Inland Revenue Practices and Concessions. – London : Oyez Longman, 1983.
ISBN 0851204988 Llf £45.00

Inland Revenue press release. – London : Inland Revenue Press Office, 1943.

Inman, William
Loss of the 'City of Boston' : Inman v. Jenkins : an action for libel, tried at the Liverpool Assizes, before Mr. Justice Lush amd a special jury, on Tuesday and Wednesday, August 30th and 31st, 1870 / Benjamin George Jenkins. – Liverpool : Reported and printed by Lee and Nightingale, 1870.
85p.

Inner city in context : the final report of the Social Science Research Council Inner Cities Working Party / edited by Peter Hall. – London : Heinemann, 1981.
viii,175p; 23cm.
Bibliography: p154-163. - Includes index.
ISBN 0435357174 Hbk £12.50
ISBN 0435357182 Pbk

Inner London Education Authority →Contract law.

Innes, William I.
Tax evasion in Canada / William I. Innes. – Toronto : Carswell, 1987.
xxvi,326p.
Includes index.
ISBN 0459305719

Innovative approaches to juvenile justice : executive summaries of four juvenile diversion project reports / by Therese Lajeunesse. – Ottawa, Ont. : Consultation Centre, Solicitor General Canada, 1982.
35, 38 p.; 22 cm.
English and French. Title on added t.p.: Approches innovatrices en matiere de justice pour adolescents. .
ISBN 0662518160 Pbk

Inns of Court. – Wildy & Sons, 1971.
ISBN 0854900012 Pbk £1.95

Inns of Court : Middle Temple Records (1501-1703). – Repr. of 1905 ed. – Abingdon : Professional Books.
214p.
Hbk £75.00

Inns of Court and Chancery / Railton. – Southampton : Ashford Press, 1985.
ISBN 090706910X Hbk £24.95

Inquests and Inquiries. – Vancouver : Continuing Legal Education Society of British Columbia, 1988.
89p.
ISBN 0865049858 Hbk £65.00

Inquiry and Accounting. – Quorum Press, 1988.
ISBN 089930222X Hbk £40.95

Inquiry into Motor Vehicle Accident Compensation in Ontario
Report of Inquiry into Motor Vehicle Accident Compensation in Ontario / Coulter A. Osborne, commissioner. – Toronto : Ontario Ministry of the Attorney General, 1988.
2 v.; 25 cm.
Title from cover. Co-published by: Ministry of Financial Institutions. Bibliography: p. 667-712 (2.). Contents: 1. Report – 2. Research studies and 1 appendices.
ISBN 0772938466 (v.2)

—Report of Inquiry into Motor Vehicle Accident Compensation in Ontario : summary of findings and recommendations / Coulter A. Osborne, Commissioner. – Toronto : Ontario Ministry of the Attorney General, 1988.
68, 79 p.; 25 cm.
Title from cover. Co-published by: Ministry of Financial Institutions. Text in English and French with French text on inverted pages. Title on added t.p.: Rapport de l'enquete sur l'indemnisation des victimes d'accidents d'automobiles en Ontario.
ISBN 0772938474

Inquiry into the substantive law of rape / by Ngaire Naffin. – Adelaide : Women's Adviser's Office, Department of the Premier and Cabinet, 1984.
iii,80p.
Includes bibliographical references.

Inquisition Unmasked, 2 Vols. – Repr. of 1816 ed. – Aalen Wuertt : Scientia.
lxxxviii, 362p.
Hbk £230.00

Ins and outs of immigration and nationality law / Lowe. – London : CENT, 1983.
ISBN 0906072050 Pbk £4.95

Insall, H.K.
Law of Fences and Pastures Protection, NSW. – 2nd ed. – North Ryde : Law Book Co, 1984.
xxi, 208p.
ISBN 0455202788 Pbk £37.00

Insanity Defense : A Critical Assessment of Law and Policy in Post-Hinckley Era / Aaronson. – Praeger.
ISBN 0275927849 Hbk £38.65
ISBN 00275928306 Hbk £32.95
ISBN 0275928314 Pbk £12.50

Insect Emblems Act, 1983, Bill 159 : Insect Emblems Act, 1983. – Ontario : Ontario Government Publications Service, 1983.
1p.
Hbk £0.30

Inside Investment Banking. – 2nd ed. – Merehurst.
ISBN 01556231288 Hbk £30.50

Inside the British police : a force at work / Simon Holdaway. – Oxford : Basil Blackwell, 1983.
vi,186p; 23cm.
Bibliography: p176-177. - Includes index.
ISBN 0631131124 £14.95

Inside the city : a guide to London as a financial centre / William M. Clarke. – Rev. ed. – London : Allen & Unwin, 1983.
xii,283p; 22cm.
Previous ed.: 1979. Includes index.
ISBN 0043320910 Pbk £6.95

Inside the new gilt-edged market. – 2nd ed. – Cambridge : Woodhead-Faulkner, 1987.
ISBN 0859413462 Hbk £25.00

Inside the over-the-counter market. – Cambridge : Woodhead-Faulkner, 1985.
ISBN 08593413095 Hbk £25.00

Inside Third World cities / Stella Lowder. – London : Routledge, 1988.
xii,292p.
Originally published: London : Croom Helm, 1986. Bibliography: pp.270-286. - Includes index.
ISBN 0415027756

Insider dealing. – London : Butterworths, 1988.
ISBN 1862052573 Hbk

Insider dealing : guidance for members following the Companies Act 1980. – London : Institute of Directors, 1981.
21p; 22cm.
Pbk £3.95

Insider trading / Barry A. K. Rider. – Bristol : Jordan and Sons, 1983.
xix, 338p.
ISBN 0853080755

Insider Trading Legislation for Australia : an Outline on the Issues and Alternatives. – Kingston : Australian Government Publishing Service.
Hbk £19.95

Insolvency. – London : Collins, 1986.
200p.
ISBN 0003832937 Hbk £17.50

Insolvency / Peter Totty and Michael Jordan. – London : Longman Professional (UK).
Covers areas such as the disqualification of directors, wrongful trading, voluntary arrangements, appointment of administrators, and antecedent transactions. Contains statutes, statutory instruments and guidance notes, forms and practice directions, tables of destination, derivations and special definitions. New chapters cover the Government Insolvency Service, the construction industry and insurance companies.
ISBN 0851211429 Llf £205

Insolvency : ACCA Study Text 2.5F. – London : BPP.
ISBN 0862772850 Pbk £14.95

Insolvency : Disqualification and personal liability of directors. – London : CCH, 1986.
ISBN 0863250920 Pbk £6.00

Insolvency : law and taxation / Timothy J. Lyons. – 1st ed. – London : Longman Professional (UK), 1988.
– (Law and Taxation).
Examines legal aspects and tax implications of both company and partnership insolvency. Chapters deal with the enforcement powers of the Inland Revenue and tax planning opportunities prior to and during an insolvency. Contains worked examples, precedents, forms and non-statutory material.
ISBN 0851214193 Hbk £35

Insolvency Act 1985 / with annotations by Ian Fletcher. – London : Sweet & Maxwell, 1986.
various pagings.
Includes index. Includes text of the Act.
ISBN 0421347007

Insolvency - Introduction to the 1985 Act / Jordan. – London : Longman Professional, 1986.
ISBN 0851212166 Pbk £7.95

Insolvency law / Steven A. Frieze. – 1st ed. – London : Longman Professional (UK), 1989.
– (Longman Practice Notes).
Covers all forms of insolvency, both corporate and personal. Guidance on voluntary and compulsory winding up, receivership, administration, company voluntary arrangements and deeds of arrangement.
ISBN 0851215114 Pbk £9.95

Insolvency law & practice. – London : F. Cass, 1985-.

Insolvency law and practice : report of the Review Committee / Chairman Sir Kenneth Cork : presented to Parliament by the Secretary of State for Trade ... – London : H.S.M.O., 1982.
xvi,460p.
ISBN 010185580X

Insolvency law handbook. – London : Butterworths, 1987.
ISBN 0406500061 Pbk £23.50

Insolvency Service of the Department of Trade and Industry
Companies in 1983 Annual Report. – Insolvency Service of the Department of Trade and Industry. – London : HMSO, 1984.
ISBN 0115137025 Hbk £4.75

Insolvency - Understanding the new law. – London : Financial Training, 1987.
ISBN 1851850627 Pbk £9.95

Inspectorates in British government : law enforcement and standards of efficiency / Gerald Rhodes. – London : Allen & Unwin for the Royal Institute of Public Administration, 1981.
xiii,281p; 23cm.
Includes index.
ISBN 0043510566 £15.00

Instead of the Dole : Enquiry into Integration of Tax and Benefit Systems. – Routledge.
ISBN 0415009618 Hbk £35.00

Institut fur Auslandisches und Internationales Wirtschaftsrecht →Bibliography on transnational law of natural resources.

Institute cargo clauses 1982 / by Robert H. Brown. – 2nd ed. – London : Witherby, 1983.
v,59p; 30cm.
Previous ed.: 1982. Includes index.
ISBN 0900886846 Pbk

Institute Cargo Clauses (Air). – Witherby, 1986.
ISBN 0900886277 Pbk £9.00

Institute for Christian Studies Act, 1983, Bill Pr021 : An Act Respecting the Institute for Christian Studies. – Ontario : Ontario Government Publications Service, 1983.
12p.
Hbk £0.50

Institute for Fiscal Studies →Corporation tax : the impact of the 1984 budget.

—Fiscal studies : the journal of the Institute for Fiscal Studies
Vol.1, no.1, Nov. 1979-. – Institute for Fiscal Studies. – London : Institute for Fiscal Studies, 1979-.

→ North Sea taxation for the 1990s.

→ Report of the Working Party on Company Residence, Tax Havens, and Upstream Loans.

—Report of the Working Party on Company Residence, Tax Havens, and Upstream Loans / Edmund Dell. – London : Institute for Fiscal Studies, 1982.
35p; 22cm.
ISBN 0902992309 Pbk

→ Structure of tobacco taxes in the European Community.

Institute for the Study of Conflict →New terrorism.

Institute of Advanced Legal Studies
List of current legal research topics : being topics forming the subject of research by students for degrees in Universities and Polytechnics in the United Kingdom / Institute of Advanced Legal Studies. – 35th ed. – London : the Institute, 1987.
vii,111p.
Supplements: Legal research in the United Kingdom 1905-1984. Includes indexes.

Institute of Bankers →Electronic banking : the legal implications.

Institute of Chartered Accountants →Family Taxation Planning.

Institute of Chartered Accountants in England and Wales
Governing the Institute : a study, commissioned by the Institute of Chartered Accountants in England and Wales, on the direction, control and regulation of the Institute / R.I. Tricker. – London : The Institute, 1983.
193p; 25cm.
Bibliography: p191-193.
ISBN 0852913427 Pbk

Institute of Chartered Secretaries and Administrators →Handbook of company administration.
—Pensions and Insurance Administration : ICSA Study Text. – Institute of Chartered Secretaries and Administrators. – London : BPP.
ISBN 0862772168 Pbk £14.95
—Taxation : ICSA Study Text. – Institute of Chartered Secretaries and Administrators. – Rev. ed. – London : BPP.
ISBN 086277215X Pbk £15.95

Institute of Chartered Shipbrokers
Shipbroker's manual
Vol. 1 / compiled by the Institute of Chartered Shipbrokers. – London : Lloyd's of London Press, 1983.
xix,167p.
Includes index.
ISBN 090743259X

Institute of Civil Engineers
Conditions of contract for minor works. – Institute of Civil Engineers. – Telford (Thomas), 1988.
ISBN 0727713299 Pbk £5.00

Institute of Civil Engineers' arbitration practice / John Uff. – Telford (Thomas), 1986.
ISBN 0727702475 Hbk £18.50

Institute of Directors
Deregulation for small private companies / Institute of Directors. – London : Institute of Directors, 1986.
13 leaves.
→ Insider dealing : guidance for members following the Companies Act 1980.
—Trade union law and the pursuit of prosperity - the next step : submission to the Secretary of State for Employment in response to the green paper on trade union immunities / prepared by Roderick Thomas. – London : Director Publications, 1981.
66p; 30cm.
At head of title: Institute of Directors.
Pbk £4.95

Institute of Economic Affairs →Choice by cable : the economics of a new era in television.
→ Striking out strikes : changing employment relations in the British labour market.

Institute of Family Studies
Annual report/Institute of Family Studies, Australia. – Institute of Family Studies. – Melbourne : Australian Institute of Family Studies, 1980-.

Institute of Financial Management / Sarrat. – Prentice-Hall.
ISBN 0137097751 Pbk £16.95

Institute of International Business Law and Practice →Arbitration and state enterprises : a survey on the national and international state of law and practice.
→ Performance bonds and contract guarantees : with special reference to the risk of unfair calling and injunction procedures : proceedings of the seminar held in Paris in January, 1982.

Institute of Law Research and Reform
Compensation for security interests in expropriated land / Institute of Law Research and Reform. – Edmonton : The Institute, 1984.
iii,30p. – (Report).
—Compensation for security interests in expropriated land : memorandum for discussion. – Institute of Law Research and Reform. – Edmonton, Alta. : The Institute, 1982.
48p.
—Debt collection practices / Institute of Law Research and Reform. – Edmonton : The Institute.
vi,161p. – (Report no 42).
—Defences to provincial charges / Institute of Law Research and Reform. – Edmonton : The Institute, 1984.
ii,123p. – (Report).
—Evidence and related subjects : specific proposals for Alberta legislation / Institute of Law Research and Reform. – Edmonton : The Institute, 1982.
iii,177p. – (Report).
→ International Invitational Conference on Matrimonial and Child Support, May 27-30, 1981, Edmonton, Alberta, Canada : conference materials.
—Judicial review of administrative action : application for judicial review / Institute of Law Research and Reform. – Edmonton : Institute of Law Research and Reform, 1984.
v,125p. – (Report).
—Limitations / Institute of Law Research and Reform. – Edmonton : The Institute, 1986.
vii,370p. – (Report for discussion).
—Matrimonial property : division of pension benefits upon marriage breakdown / Institute of Law Research and Reform. – Edmonton : The Institute, 1985.
ii,127,25,13p. – (Report for discussion).
—Matrimonial property : division of pension benefits upon marriage breakdown / Institute of Law Research and Reform. – Edmonton : Institute of Law Research and Reform, 1986.
viii,115p. – (Report).
—Operation of the unsecured creditors' remedies system in Alberta / Institute of Law Research and Reform. – Edmonton : The Institute, 1986.
vii,188p. – (Research paper).
Includes bibliographical references.
—Proposals for a new Alberta Arbitration Act / Institute of Law Research and Reform, Edmonton, Alberta. – Edmonton : The Institute, 1988.
iv,166p. – (Report).
Includes draft legislation and the text of the Convention on the Recognition and Enforcement of Foreign Arbitral Awards.
ISBN 0888648669
—Proposals for a new Alberta Incorporated Associations Act / Institute of Law Research and Reform, Edmonton, Alberta. – Edmonton : The Institute, 1987.
i,223p. – (Report).
—Protection of children's interests in custody disputes / Institute of Law Research and Reform. – Edmonton : The Institute, 1984.
ii,42p. – (Report no 43).
—Protection of trade secrets / Institute of Law Research and Reform. – Edmonton : The Institute, 1984.
159p. – (Report for discussion).
Includes bibliographical references.
—Remedies of unsecured creditors / Institute of Law Research and Reform. – Edmonton : The Institute, 1986.
xiv,370p. – (Report for discussion).
Includes bibliographical references.
—Status of children : revised report, 1985 / Institute of Law Research and Reform. – Edmonton : The Institute, 1985.
137p. – (Report).
—Statute of Frauds and related legislation / Institute of Law Research and Reform. – Edmonton : The Institute, 1985.
iv,88p. – (Report).
—Survey of adult living arrangements : a technical report / Institute of Law Research and Reform. – Edmonton : The Institute, 1984.
v,93,19p. – (Research paper).
—Survivorship / Institute of Law Research and Reform, Edmonton, Alberta. – Edmonton : The Institute, 1986.
65p. – (Report).
—Towards a new Arbitration Act for Alberta / Institute of Law Research and Reform. – Edmonton, Alberta : Institute of Law Research and Reform, 1987.
xvi,199p.
—Trade secrets / Institute of Law Research and Reform, Edmonton, Alberta and a Federal Provincial Working Party. – Edmonton : The Institute, 1986.
284p. – (Report).
Includes bibliographical references.
—Uniform Evidence Act 1981 : a basis for uniform evidence legislation / Institute of Law Research and Reform. – Edmonton : The Institute, 1982.
ii,109p. – (Report).
—Uniform Sale of Goods Act / Institute of Law Research and reform. – Edmonton : The Institute, 1982.
iii,323p. – (Report).

Institute of Legal Executives →Huddy: Introduction to legal practice.
→ Introduction to law.
→ Introduction to legal practice.

Institute of London Underwriters
Companies' marine policy : attached clauses. – Institute of London Underwriters. – London : The Institute, 1982.
26p.
Contents: Insurance cargo clauses (A), (B), and (C) - Institute war clauses (Cargo) - Institute strikes clauses (Cargo) - Institute war clauses (sendings by post) - Institute war clauses (Air cargo) (excluding sendings by post) - Institute cargo clauses (Air) (excluding sendings by post) - Institute strikes clauses (Air cargo) - Institute standard conditons for cargo contracts - Companies' marine policy form.

Institute of Management Consultants of Ontario Act, 1983, Bill Pr026 : An Act Respecting the Institute of Management Consultants of Ontario. – Ontario : Ontario Government Publications Service, 1983.
4p.
Hbk £0.30

Institute of Personnel Management →Twenty years of statutory redundancy payments in Great Britain.

Institute of Public Administration → Administrative law in Ireland.

Institute of Public Administration of →Judicial administration in Canada.

Institute of Public International Law and International Relations of Thessaloniki → Communications : (includes telecommunications).

Institute of Purchasing and Supply →Copyright & computers.

Institute of Taxation in Ireland →Capital acquisitions tax.

Institute of the Law of Scotland, 2 Vols. – Repr of 1773 ed. – Abingdon : Professional Books.
Hbk £200.00

Institute of the Laws of Scotland in Civil Rights with Observations upon the Agreement or Diversity Between Them and the Laws of England, 3 Vols. – Repr. of 1753 ed. – Abingdon : Professional Books.
Hbk £75.00

Institute T.M.C. Asser
Essays on International and Comparative Law : In Honour of Judge Erades. – Institute T.M.C. Asser. – Dordrecht : Kluwer, 1983.
285p.
ISBN 902472838X Hbk £95.00

Institute time clauses : hulls : a comparison between the 1983 clauses and the 1970 clauses with subsequent amendments / by J. Kenneth Goodacre. – London : Witherby, 1983.
vii,67p.
Includes the text of the Marine Insurance Act, 1906. 'In co-operation with the U.K. Society of Average Adjusters'.

Institute time clauses - Hulls 1983 : full conditions / by Robert H. Brown. – London : Witherby, 1983.
vi,45p; 30cm.
ISBN 0900886897 Pbk

Institution of Civil Engineers →Basic crucial issues in major construction projects : papers presented at a seminar held jointly with the Institution of Civil Engineers, London, June 1985.
→ Engineering and construction law : with illustrations and cases.

Institution of Ombudsman in the English legal system and especially that of Cyprus / by Criton G. Tornaritis. – Nicosia : s.n., 1983.
27 leaves.

Institutional framework of the European Communities / D.A.C. Freestone and J.S. Davidson. – London : Croom Helm, 1988.
17,221p; 23cm.
Includes index.
ISBN 0709910487 Hbk £27.50
ISBN 0709949081 Pbk £9.95

Institutional Renewal in the Australia Tax Systems. – Clayton : Monash University Press, 1985.
ISBN 0867462752 Hbk £9.50

Institutional theory of law : new approaches to legal positivism / Neil MacCormick and Ota Weinberger. – DordrechtHolland : Reidel, 1986.
xiv, 229p. – (Law and philosophy library).
ISBN 9027720797

Institutions and the decision-making process in the draft treaty / by Gianfranco Pasquino and Luciano Bardi. – Florence : European University Institute, 1985.
66p.

Institutions and the decision-making process in the Draft Treaty establishing the European Union / by Roland Bieber. – Badia Fiesolana : European University Institute, 1985.
26,3p.
Paper presented at a conference organised by the European Policy Unit of the European University Institute, in colloboration with the University of Strasbourg and TEPSA, October 1984. Includes bibliographical references.

Institutions of Private Law and Their Social Functions. – London : Sweet & Maxwell.
ISBN 0710083025 Hbk £16.95

Institutions of the law of Scotland : deduced from its originals, and collated with the civil, canon and feudal laws, and with the customs of neighbouring nations in iv books / by James, Viscount of Stair : edited by David M. Walker. – Edinburgh : University Presses of Edinburgh and Glasgow, 1981.
xvii,1186p,1leaf of plates; 24cm.
Originally published: Edinburgh : s.n., 1693. Includes index.
ISBN 0852243979 £40.00

Institutions of the Law of Scotland : Deduced From its Originals and Collated With the Civil, Canon, and Feudal Laws and With the Customs of Neighbouring Nations. – Repr. of 1681 ed. – Abingdon : Professional Books.
108p.
Hbk £295.00

Institutions of the Laws of Scotland. – 5th ed. Repr. of 1723 ed. – Abingdon : Professional Books.
73p.
Hbk £110.00

Insurance Act, 1963 (Act 89) and Insurance Regulations and Orders. – Kuala Lumpur : International Law Books Services.
Hbk £17.50

Insurance case law digest: property and casualty. – 2 vols. – Scarborough, Ontario : Butterworths (Canada).
Coverage of automobile and property insurance cases in Canada. Each part has a table of cases, and the case digests are arranged to reflect the organizational categories of the standard automobile and home insurance policies.
Loose leaf

Insurance contract law / Robert M. Merkin and Andrew McGee : editorial advisors, John S. Butler, Alison A. Green. – 2. – London : Kluwer, 1988.
looseleaf.
Includes index.
ISBN 1870080475

Insurance contracts / Law Reform Commission. – Canberra : Australian Government Publishing Service, 1982.
xxxx,372p. – (Report).
Bibliography: p.352-357. - Includes index.
ISBN 064401217X

Insurance development in the Arab world : retention relationship capacity and the demand for international reinsurance / by Abdul Zahra Abdullah Ali. – London : Graham & Trotman, 1985.
369p; 25cm.
Bibliography: p352-362. - Includes index.
ISBN 0860107078 £73.00

Insurance handbook. – 1st ed. – London : Legal Books, 1985.
ISBN 0949553182 Pbk £12.00

Insurance in Rabbinic Law. – Edinburgh : Edinburgh University Press.
230p.
ISBN 0852242581 Hbk £10.00

Insurance in the Arab world : a Lloyd's List conference-London. – 1. – London : Lloyd's of London Press, 1982.
various pagings.
ISBN 0907432492

Insurance Institute of London →Operation and management of protection and indemnity clubs.

Insurance intermediaries and the law / by R.W. Hodgin. – 1. – London : Lloyd's of London Press, 1987.
22cm.
Includes bibliography and index.
ISBN 1850441073 Pbk £14.50

Insurance Law 1988. – Vancouver : Continuing Legal Education Society of British Columbia, 1988.
150p.
ISBN 0865049823 Hbk £70.00

Insurance Law : 1982. – Vancouver : British Columbia Continuing Legal Education Society, 1982.
115p.
ISBN 0865040745 Hbk £45.00

Insurance law handbook. – 2nd ed. – London : Butterworths, 1985.
ISBN 040617637X Pbk £23.00

Insurance law in Africa. – Witherby, 1987.
ISBN 0948691255 Hbk £35.00

Insurance law in Australia and New Zealand / by P. E. Joske and Robert Brooking. – Sydney : Butterworths, 1975.
xxxix, 302 p.; 25 cm.
Includes index. Sets out insurance law both in terms of general principles and explains how these principles have been applied to particular aspects of insurance in the courts of Australia and New Zealand. Refers to decisions of the UK.
ISBN 0409436305 £20.00

Insurance law in Canada : a treatise on the principles of indemnity insurance as applied in the common law provinces of Canada / by Craig Brown and Julio Menezes. – Toronto, Canada : Carswell, 1982.
lxxix, 518 p.; 26 cm.
Includes bibliographical references and indexes.
ISBN 0459339605

Insurance law in New Zealand / by A.A. Tarr. – Sydney : Law Book Co., 1985.
xxxv,257p.
Includes bibliographical references and index.
ISBN 0455205698

Insurance Law of Malaysia. – rev ed. – Singapore : Quins, 1982.
Hbk £81.00

Insurance law reports / edited by F.N. Eaglestone and K.S. Cannar. – Harlow : G. Goodwin, 1982-.
Annual index.

Insurance Legislation Manual / Minhael Ball. – Butterworths, 1986.
131p.
ISBN 0409491195 Pbk £33.00

Insurance of average disbursements. – London : Lloyd's of London Press, 1988.
ISBN 1850441693 Pbk £8.95

Insurance of commercial risks : law and practice / Digby C. Jess. – London : Butterworths, 1986.
445p; 26cm.
Includes index.
ISBN 0406257116 Hbk £36.00

Insurance under the JCT forms / Frank Eaglestone. – London : Collins, 1985.
viii,367p; 24cm.
Includes index. Kept up to date by supplements.
ISBN 0003830225 £20.00

Insurance: competition or regulation? : a comparative study of the insurance markets in the United Kingdom and the Federal Republic of Germany / Jorg Finsinger, Elizabeth Hammond and Julian Tapp. – London : Institute for Fiscal Studies, 1985.
197p.
Bibliography: p191-197.
ISBN 090299249X

Insurances of Liability. – Witherby.
ISBN 0948691670 Pbk £4.95

Integration of marine space in national development strategies of small island states : the case of the Caribbean states of Grenada and St. Lucia / Carlyle L. Mitchell and Edgar Gold. – Halifax, N.S. : Dalhousie Ocean Studies Programme, 1982.
x,346p.
Bibliography: p338-345.

Integration through law : Europe and the American federal experience : a series
Vol. 1 : Methods, tools and institutions : edited by Mauro Cappelletti, Monica Seccombe, Joseph Weiler / under the general editorship of Mauro Cappelletti, Monica Seccombe, Joseph Weiler. – 3 v. – Berlin, : W. de Gruyter, 1986.
– (Series A, Law).
Includes bibliographical references and index. Contents: bk.1. A political, legal and economic overview - bk.2. Political organs, integration techniques and judicial process - bk.3. Forces and potential for a European identity.
Vol. 2 : Environmental protection policy : by Eckard Rehbinder and Richard Stewart : associate editor Patrick del Duca / under the general editorship of Mauro Cappelletti, Monica Seccombe, Joseph Weiler. – 1985.
xxiv,350p. – (Series A, Law).
Includes bibliographical references and indexes.

Vol.3 : Consumer law, common markets and federalism in Europe and the United States : by Thierry Bourgoignie and David Trubek : (with Louise Trubek and Denis Stingl) / under the general editorship of Mauro Cappelletti, Monica Seccombe and Joseph Weiler. – 1987.
xxiii,271p. – (Series A, Law).
Bibliographical references.

Vol. 4: Legal Harmonization and the Business Enterprise. –
ISBN 3110107422 Hbk £20.00

Vol. 5 : The legal integration of energy markets : by Terence Daintith and Stephen F. Williams / under the general editorship of Mauro Cappelletti, Monica Seccombe, Joseph Weiler. – 1987.
xxvii,176p. – (Series A, Law).
Includes bibliographical references and index.
ISBN 3110107430 Hbk

Intellectual Property. – Sydney : Butterworths, 1988.
144p. – (Student Companion Ser.).
This guide contains over 200 summaries of cases in the area of intellectual property. It is intended for use in conjunction with lecture notes, textbooks, and other working documents.
Pbk £9.95

Intellectual Property : Commentary and Materials / J P McKeough. – North Ryde : Law Book Co, 1986.
xlviii, 741p.
ISBN 0455206945 Hbk A$80.00
ISBN 0455206953 Pbk A$59.50

Intellectual property : patents, copyright, trade marks and allied rights / by W.R. Cornish. – London : Sweet & Maxwell, 1981.
lxi,630p; 23cm.
Includes index.
ISBN 0421243104 Hbk £26.50
ISBN 0421243309 Pbk £16.50

Intellectual Property : the New Law / Williams. – London : Butterworths.
ISBN 0406503079 Hbk £27.50

Intellectual property and innovation / presented to Parliament by the Secretary of State for Trade and Industry. – London : H.M.S.O., 1986.
iv,78p.
Bibliography: p.77-78.
ISBN 0101971206

Intellectual Property and Technology Transfer in the People's Republic of China. – Hong Kong : Hong Kong University Press, 1988.
ISBN 9622092020 Hbk

Intellectual property case books
1 : Patents and confidential information / edited by W.R. Cornish. – Oxford : ESC, 1985.
212p.
ISBN 0906214335
3 : Trade marks and names / edited by W.R. Cornish. – 1985.
185p.
ISBN 0906214351

Intellectual Property Colloquium of Judges in Asia and the Pacific. – Geneva : World Intellectual Property Organization, 1984.
260p.
Hbk £30.00

Intellectual property in Australia
Patents, designs, trade marks, confidential information, unfair competition / editor, James Lahore. – 2. – Sydney : Butterworths, 1981.
looseleaf.
ISBN 0409300373

Intellectual Property in Australia : Copyright. – London : Butterworths, 1984.
Hbk

Intellectual Property in Australia : Patents, Designs, Trade Marks, Confidential Information and Unfair Competition / James W. Dwyer. – Wellington : Butterworths.
This looseleaf service provides exhaustive coverage of the law in Australia relating to copyright in literary and artistic works, sound recordings, film, television and radio broadcasts, and published editions of books and other works. The full text of relevant statutes is provided.
Llf

Intellectual property in New Zealand and Australia / papers presented by M.P. Crew ... et al. – Auckland : Legal Research Foundation, 1985.
227p.
ISBN 0908581378

Intellectual Property Journal. – Agincourt : Carswell, 1985.
Hbk £75.75

Intellectual property law and taxation / Nigel A Eastaway. – 3rd ed. – London : Longman Professional, 1988.
ISBN 0851213227 Pbk

Intellectual Property Law in New Zealand and Australia. – Auckland : Legal Research Foundation, 1985.
Hbk £27.50

Intellectual property law in the People's Republic of China : a guide to patents, trade marks and technology transfer / Michael D.Pendleton. – Singapore : Butterworths, 1986.
xvii,138p.
ISBN 0409995193 Pbk £17.00

Intellectual Property Law in the PRC. – London : Longman Professional.
ISBN 0582999685 Hbk

Intellectual property laws of Korea / by Kyung Jae Park. – Seoul : Lee & Ko, 1986.
xx,372p.

Intellectual Property Reports. – London : Butterworths.
Hbk

Intellectual Property Reports / John J. Garsney. – Wellington : Butterworths.
These comprehensive reports are complete with headnotes, catchwords, holdings, court hearings, and final judgement dates for all major decisions in field of intellectual property in Australia.
Hbk

Intellectual property reports : being reports of judgments of the High Court of Australia, the Federal Court of Australia, the Supreme Courts of the states and territories of Australia, the Patent, Trade Marks and Designs Office, the Copyright Tribunal and incorporating reports of signficant cases decided by the courts in the United Kingdom, the United States of America and other international jurisdictions / editor, James Lahore. – Vol. 1, pt.1 (Oct. 1983)-. – Sydney : Butterworths, 1983-.

Intellectual Property Reports, Vol. 1, 1989 / edited by Brown. – Wellington : Butterworths (New Zealand).
435p.
ISBN 0409787361 Hbk £190.00

Intellectual property rights and innovation : presented to Parliament by the Prime Minister ... December 1983. – London : H.M.S.O., 1983.
45p; 25cm.
ISBN 010191170X Pbk £4.65

Intellectual property rights in biotechnology worldwide / Stephen A. Bent ... et al. – London : Macmillan, 1985.
300p.
Includes index.
ISBN 0333392884 Pbk £40.00
ISBN 094381815X

Intelligence report : inheritance tax. – London : Longman Professional, 1986.
ISBN 085121245X Hbk £75.00

Intelligence report : the film business. – London : Longman Professional, 1986.
ISBN 0851212387 Hbk £95.00

Intentional interference with domestic relations / Law Reform Commission of British Columbia. – Vancouver : The Commission, 1983.
iii,55p. – (Working paper).
Includes bibliographical references.

Intentional Interference with Domestic Relations. – Victoria : Government of British Columbia, 1983.
Hbk £4.75

Intepretation of Statutes. – 7th ed. – Allahabad : Law Book Company, 1984.
400p.
Hbk £250.00

Inter-American Commercial Arbitration Commission. →Proceedings of a seminar on commercial arbitration held in Ottawa, 19 June 1985.

Inter-Governmental Maritime Consultative Organization →IMCO news : the magazine of the Inter-Governmental Maritime Consultative Organization.

Inter-American Center of Tax Administrators
Fiscal policy and tax legislation and administration : technical papers and reports of the 15th General Assembly of the Inter-American Center of Tax Administrators (CIAT), Caracas, Venezuela, 25-27 February 1981. – Inter-American Center of Tax Administrators. – Amsterdam : International Bureau of Fiscal Documentation, 1983.
200p.
'Sponsored by the Government of Venezuela, the German Society for Technical Cooperation (GTZ) and the Inter-American Center of Tax Administrators (CIAT) '.
ISBN 9070125226

—Fundamental tax audit considerations : technical papers and reports of the 14th General Assembly of the Inter-American Center of Tax Administrators (CIAT). – Inter-American Center of Tax Administrators. – Amsterdam : International Bureau of Fiscal Documentation, 1981.
198p.
ISBN 9070125188

—Measures for improving the level of voluntary compliance with tax obligations : technical papers and reports of the 18th General Assembly of the Inter-American Center of Tax Administrators (CIAT) Cartagena, Colombia, 21-25 May 1984. – Inter-American Center of Tax Administrators. – Amsterdam : International Bureau of Fiscal Documentation, 1985.
168 p.; 25 cm. – (Publications of the International Bureau of Fiscal Documentation).
Includes bibliographical references.
ISBN 9070125277 Pbk

Inter-American system : treaties, conventions & other documents : a compilation / annotated by F.V. Garcia-Amador. – London : Oceana Publications for the Secretariat for Legal Affairs, General Secretariat of the Organization of American States, 1983.
Includes bibliographical references.

Inter-American Yearbook on Human Rights. – Organization of American States. – Dordrecht : Kluwer, 1987.
1,276p.
ISBN 0898389232 Hbk £450.00

Interception of Communications Act 1985 : chapter 56 : report of the Commissioner for ... – London : HMSO, 1987-.

Interception of communications in Great Britain : report / by Lord Diplock. – London : H.M.S.O., 1981.
7p; 25cm.
ISBN 0101819102 unbound £1.10

Interdepartmental review of family and domestic jurisdiction : a consultation paper. – London : Lord Chancellors Department, 1986.
96p.

Interest and Jurisdictional Limits in the County and Provincial Courts. – Victoria : Government of British Columbia, 1982.
Hbk

Interest arbitration : measuring justice in employment / Joseph M. Weiler, editor. – Toronto : Carswell, 1981.
iv,283p.
Papers presented at a conference sponsored by the Continuing Legal Education Society of British Columbia, in Vancouver B.C., April 1980.
ISBN 0459339206

Interest On Unpaid Or Overpaid Tax. – VANN, 1977.
ISBN 0852911858 Pbk £6.50

Interference or Internationalism : The Extraterritorial Application of National Laws Regulating Business Activities
Vol. 4. – Enstone : Ditchley Foundation.
1982p.
Hbk

Interference or Internationalism? Conference Report No. 3. – Entstone : Ditchley Foundation, 1982.
Hbk

Inter-Governmental Conference on the Convention on the Dumping of Wastes at Sea French Edition /. – London : International Maritime Organization.
Hbk £1.75

Interights. – London : International Human Rights Law Centre, 1983.
Continued by: Interights bulletin. Only one issue published.

Interights bulletin. – London : International Centre for the Protection of Human Rights, 1985.
Continues: Interights.
ISBN 02683709

Interim Measures in the Hague Court : an Attempt at a Scrutiny. – Dordrecht : Kluwer, 1983.
350p.
ISBN 9065440933 Hbk £104.00

Interim policy guide : Access to Information Act and the Privacy Act / Treasury Board of Canada Secretariat. – 1. – Ottawa : Minister of Supply and Services, 1983.
loose-leaf.
English and French text.
ISBN 0660522551

Interim protection : a functional approach / Jerome B. Elkind. – The Hague : Martinus Nijhoff, 1981.
xxiv,287p.
Bibliography: p263-266.
ISBN 9024725399

Interim report / Home Office Committee of Inquiry into Crowd Safety and Control at Sports Grounds : Chairman Mr Justice Popplewell. – London : H.M.S.O., 1985.
92p.
Popplewell Inquiry following the Bradford fire, May 1985. Recommends improved police involvement, stricter safety measures, membership-only games and making missile-throwing an offence at sports grounds.
ISBN 0101958501

Interim report on legislation relating to landlord and tenant / report of the Property Law and Equity Reform Committee. – Wellington : The Committee, 1983.
29p.

Interjurisdictional Issues in Canadian Water Management. – Calgary : Canadian Institute of Resources Law.
127p.
ISBN 0919269273 Hbk £22.00

Intermediate Accounting Step by Step. – London : Edward Arnold.
ISBN 0713176660 Pbk £7.50

Intermediate Education Act, 1921 : Together with Amending Acts, Regulations and Notifications. – Lucknow : Eastern Book Company, 1982.
173p.
Hbk £25.00

Intermediate examination in laws
Constitutional law : subject guide 1986 / University of London. External System. – London : University of London, 1986.
46p.
ISBN 0718707516
Criminal law : subject guide 1986 / University of London. External System. – 1986.
60p.
ISBN 0718707524
English legal system : subject guide 1987 / University of London External system. – 1987.
33p.
ISBN 0718707761

Intermittent custody / presented to Parliament by the Secretary of State for the Home Department. – London : H.M.S.O., 1984.
17p.
ISBN 0101928106

Internal audit / Impey. – London : Butterworths, 1985.
ISBN 0406013802 Pbk £18.50

Internal conflict of law problems in African legal systems / Fafa E M'Bai. – Banjul : Xam Xam, 198?.

Internal Security Act, 1960 (Act 82). – Kuala Lumpur : International Law Books Services.
Hbk £7.50

International accounting and transnational decisions. – London : Butterworths, 1983.
ISBN 040810841X Pbk £23.60

International action against genocide / by Leo Kuper. – Rev. 1984 ed. – London : Minority Rights Group, 1984.
19p. – (Report).
Bibliography: p.18.

International agency, distribution and licensing agreements. – London : Longman Professional, 1986.
ISBN 0851211887 Hbk £45.00

International Agreement on Jute and Jute Products, 1982 : New York, 3 January-30 June 1983. – London : H.M.S.O., 1983.
27p; 25cm.
ISBN 0101882505 unbound £2.95

International Air Transport : Law, Organization and Policies for the Future. – Montreal : Centre for Research of Air and Space Law.
172p.
Hbk £30.00

International Air Transport Association
Act of incorporation, articles of association, rules and regulations / International Air Transport Association. – 16th ed. 1. – Montreal : The Association, 1986.
looseleaf.
Previous ed.: 1981. Act of incorporation in English and French, articles of association and rules of procedure in English, French and Spanish.
→ IATA review.

—Minutes / Annual General Meeting, International Air Transport Association. – Montreal : IATA, 1981.
Continues: Reports and proceedings.
→ Principal instruments of the Warsaw system.

International air transport in the eighties : including the proceedings of the first Netherlands Colloquium on International Air Transport, 'The Changing Scene', Wassenaar, August 25-29, 1980 / edited by H.A. Wassenbergh and H.P. van Fenema : a colloquium organized by the Netherlands Instiute of Transport and the Netherlands Civil Aviation Authority under the auspices of the University of Leyden, Faculty of Law (Air and Space). – Deventer : Kluwer, 1981.
ix,250p; 25cm.
Bibliography: p.248-250.
ISBN 9065440267 Hbk £104.00

International and interstate conflict of laws / Edward I. Sykes, Michael C. Pryles. – 2nd ed. – Sydney : Butterworths, 1981.
lv,966p.
Bibliography; p.943-950. - Includes index.
ISBN 0409455342 Pbk
ISBN 0409300438

International and legal problems of the gulf / S.H. Amin. – London : Middle East and North African Studies Press, 1981.
235p.
Bibls.
ISBN 0906559057

International anti-trust law
Vol. 1 : A review of national laws / edited by Julian Maitland-Walker. – Oxford : ESC Publishing, 1984.
viii,178p.
Includes bibliographical references.
ISBN 090621419X
vol.2 : Recent developments in EEC and US anti-trust / edited by Julian Maitland-Walker. – 1984.
10,116p.
Contains contributions to the 1st International Anti-trust Law Conference, Oxford, 1982.
ISBN 0906214203

International arbitration : 60 years of ICC arbitration : a look at the future. – Paris : ICC, 1984.
421p.
Papers given at a conference in Paris, October 1983, to mark the 60th anniversary of the ICC Court of Arbitration. Includes index. Spine title: ICC Court of Arbitration 60th anniversary: a look at the future.
ISBN 9284210208

International Arbitration : a Look at the Future. – Paris : International Chamber of Commerce.
421p.
Hbk £27.00

International arbitration : a practical study with specific reference to the petroleum industry / a collection of papers presented by the Section of Energy and Natural Resources Law at the International Bar Association's Twentieth Biennial Conference held in Vienna, 2-7 September 1984. – London : International Bar Association, 1984.
Various pagings.

International arbitration : three salient problems / by Stephen M. Schwebel. – Cambridge : Grotius Publications, 1987.
xviii,303p.
At head of title: University of Cambridge. Research Centre for International Law.
ISBN 0949009024

International aspects of tax expenditures : a comparative study / Paul R. McDaniel, Stanley S. Surrey, editors. – Deventer, the Netherlands : Kluwer Law and Taxation, 1984.
ISBN 9065441638

International Association for Philosophy of Law and Social Philosophy → Man, law, and modern forms of life.
→ Social justice and individual responsibility in the welfare state.

International Association of Democratic Lawyers → International review of contemporary law.

International Association of Energy Economists
International energy options : an agenda for the 1980s : selected papers from leading contributors to the 1980 Annual Conference of the International Association of Energy Economists in Cambridge, UK / edited by Paul Tempest. – Cambridge, Mass. : Oelgeschlager, Gunn & Hain, 1981.
xv,304p.
Includes bibliographical references and index.
ISBN 086010303X Oelschlager, Gunn & Hain
ISBN 0899460895

International Association of Judges → Role of the judge in contemporary society.

International Association of Law Libraries → Courts, law libraries and legal information in a changing society : 25. IALL Anniversary, Freiburg i. Br., July 15-20, 1984.

International Association of Legal Science → International encyclopedia of comparative law.
—International enforcement of human rights : reports submitted to the Colloquium of the International Association of Legal Science, Heidelberg, 28-30 August 1985 / edited by Rudolf Bernhardt, John-Anthony Jolowicz. – Berlin : Springer-Verlag, 1987.
Includes index.
ISBN 0387175741

International Association of Universities → International handbook of universities and other institutions of higher education.

International Atomic Energy Agency
Agreements registered with the International Atomic Energy Agency : definitive entries up to 31 December 1980; provisional entries up to 31 December 1982. – International Atomic Energy Agency. – 9th ed. – Vienna : IAEA, 1985.
262p. – (Legal series).
ISBN 920176085X
—Agreements registered with the International Atomic Energy Agency (up to 31 December 1978). – International Atomic Energy Agency. – 8th ed. – Vienna : International Atomic Energy Agency, 1981.
253p; 24cm. – (Legal series).
ISBN 9201760817
→ Convention on Early Notification of a Nuclear Accident and Convention on Assistance in the Case of a Nuclear Accident or Radiological Emergency.
→ Convention on the physical protection of nuclear material.

International audit in public sector / Simpson. – Cambridge : Woodhead-Faulkner, 1985.
ISBN 0859412725 Pbk £11.95

International Aviation Law Seminar : the Mount Irvine Bay Hotel, Tobago, West Indies March 16, 17, 18, 19, 1981 / organised by Lloyd's of London Press : sponsored by the Royal Aeronautical Society. – London : Lloyd's of London Press, 1982.
349p; 31cm.
ISBN 0907432271

International bank accounting. – 2nd ed. – London : Euromoney, 1987.
ISBN 1870031016 Pbk £75.00

International bank supervision / by Connie M. Friesen. – London : Euromoney, 1986.
xi,124p.
Includes bibliographical references.
ISBN 1870031105

International Banking. – London : Macmillan.
ISBN 0333447123 Hbk £35.00

International banking : management and strategies / David B. Zenoff ... et al. – London : Euromoney, 1985.
xv,207p.
ISBN 0903121786

International banking centres / edited by Bowman Brown. – London : Euromoney, 1982.
v,277p.
ISBN 0903121271

International Banking Set-Off. – London : Sweet & Maxwell.
ISBN 0421324503 Pbk

International Bar Association
Arab comparative & commercial law : the international approach : proceedings : International Bar Association first Arab Regional Conference, Cairo 15-19 February 1987. – International Bar Association. – London : Graham & Trotman, 1987.
Contents: 1. The Sharia and its relevance to modern transnational transactions. The settlement of disputes through arbitration. Joint ventures. – 2. Energy law.
ISBN 086010978X v. 2
—Arbitration : the IBA rules of evidence : supplementary rules governing the presentation and reception of evidence in international commercial arbitration / International Bar Association, Section on Business Law. – London : The Association, 1986.
8p.
ISBN 0948711043
—Avoidance of fraudulent transfers and related bankruptcy crimes : papers delivered at the meetings of Committee J - Creditor's Rights, Insolvency, Liquidation and Reorganizations, Vienna, 2-7 September 1984 / Barrett. – London : International Bar Association, 1984.
166p.
Chairman: John A. Barrett.
—Challenges to the Legal Profession : Law and Investment in Developing Countries. – International Bar Association. – Lucknow : Eastern Book Company, 1985.
807p.
Hbk £200.00
—Challenges to the legal profession : law and investment in developing countries : addresses, committee papers and reports of the 19th biennial conference of the International Bar Association at New Delhi. – International Bar Association. – Lucknow : Eastern Book Co. in co-ordination with the International Bar Association and the Bar Association of India, 1984.
xx,787p.
→ Comparative survey of corporate investments.
—Current problems of letters of credit and bankers' quarantees / William C. Hillman. – London : International Bar Association, 1985.
iii,404p.
Papers presented at the seminar in Amsterdam, 8-9 May 1984. Seminar Chairman: Judge William C. Hillman.
→ Energy law '88 : proceedings of the advanced seminar on petroleum, minerals and energy resources law organised by the IBA's Section on Energy and Natural Resources Law in Sydney, Australia, March 1988.
→ Enforcing antitrust against foreign enterprises : procedural problems in the extraterritorial application of antitrust laws.
→ Engineer's liability to the contractor : papers presented at the Conference of the International Bar Association's Section on Business Law Conference, Toronto 1983.
—Engineer's liability to the contractor : papers presented at the Conference of the International Bar Association's Section on Business Law Conference, Toronto 1983 / International Construction Contracts Committee of the Section on Business Law of the International Bar Assoication. – London : International Bar Association, 1983.
iv,162p.
Includes bibliographical references.
→ Euromoney issues : papers presented to the Section on Business Law Committee Q (Issues and Trading in Securities) at the International Bar Association 20th biennial conference, Vienna, September 1984.
→ Handbook on maritime law.
—Industry and the regulatory agencies : a collection of the papers given at the fourth seminar organised by Committee F of the International Bar Association's Section on Business Law in April 1985 at Stratford-upon-Avon / edited by John H. Bates. – 4. – London : International Bar Association, 1985.
Includes bibliographical references.
—International arbitration : a practical study with specific reference to the petroleum industry / a collection of papers presented by the Section of Energy and Natural Resources Law at the International Bar Association's Twentieth Biennial Conference held in Vienna, 2-7 September 1984. – London : International Bar Association, 1984.
Various pagings.
→ International Bar Association, Section on Energy & Natural Resources Law : seminar topics index 1975-84 : Stavanger, 1975; Cambridge 1, 1978; Cambridge II, 1979; Banff, 1981; Singapore, 1982; Houston, 1984; Oslo, 1984.
→ International business lawyer : journal of the Section on Business Law of the International Bar Association.
→ International franchising - an overview.
→ Interplay of contracts : papers presented at the International Bar Association's 20th Biennial Conference, Vienna 1984.
—Interplay of contracts : papers presented at the International Bar Association's 20th Biennial Conference, Vienna 1984 / International Bar Assoication. Section on Business Law. International Construction Contracts Committee. – London : International Bar Association, 1984.
102p.
Includes bibliographical references.
→ Joint development of resources projects : a comparison : proceedings of the Regional Energy Law Seminar, Singapore, 30 September 1985.
→ Joint ventures in the construction industry : papers presented at the 7th Conference of the International Bar Association's Section on Business Law, Singapore 1985.
→ Land and the law : report of the proceedings of the International Bar Association Section on General Practice seminar in Rome , May 1983.
→ Legal opinions in international transactions : foreign lawyers' response to US opinion requests.
→ Proceedings of Seminar : Protection of Sellers in Transnational Sales - Beyond Letters of Credit, at the Cafe Royal, London, 2- 3 June 1982.
→ Proceedings of the Seminar on Middle East Law, with reference to Bahrein, Egypt, Iran, Kuwait, Oman, Qatar, Saudi Arabia, U.A.E., 1-4 July 1981, Hamburg, Germany.
→ Proceedings of the seminar on planning law for industry : March 29th-April 2nd 1981, Churchill College, Cambridge, England.
→ Tax avoidance, tax evasion : a survey of the treatment of tax aviodance and tax evasion in the main industrialised countries of the world.
→ Tax avoidance, tax evasion : a survey of the treatment of tax avoidance and tax evasion in the main industrialized countries of the world.
→ World coal mining law : a comparative survey.

International Bar Association, Section on Energy & Natural Resources Law : seminar topics index 1975-84 : Stavanger, 1975; Cambridge 1, 1978; Cambridge II, 1979; Banff, 1981; Singapore, 1982; Houston, 1984; Oslo, 1984. – S.l. : International Bar Association, Section on Energy & Natural Resources Law, 1986.
24p.
ISBN 0948711027

International Bibliography of Air Law 1900-1971.
Supplements
1972-1976. – Dordrecht : Kluwer, 1976.
xxii, 169p.
ISBN 9028605266 Hbk £64.00
1977-1980. – 1981.
394p.
ISBN 9024725550 Hbk £160.00
1981-1984. – 1985.
284p.
ISBN 9065442308 Hbk £104.00

International bonds / by Frederick G. Fisher, III. – London : Euromoney Publications, 1981.
199p; 30cm.
Bibliography: p195. - Includes index.
ISBN 0903121220 Pbk

International Buffer Stocks : Theory and Practice. – Bern : Peter Lang, 1983.
xxix, 342p.
ISBN 3261033185 Pbk £66.00

International Bureau of Fiscal Documentation
→ Analysis of the German tax system : general principles, taxation of income and capital, unilateral measures for the avoidance of double taxation.
—Handbook on the U.S. - German Tax Convention. – International Bureau of Fiscal Documentation. – Amsterdam : International Bureau of Fiscal Documentation, 1988.
Llf £880.00
→ Handbook on the United States-German Tax Convention.
→ International tax glossary.
—Taxation of Companies in Europe. – International Bureau of Fiscal Documentation. – Amsterdam : International Bureau of Fiscal Documentation, 1988.
– (Guides to European Taxation Ser.: Vol. 2).
Llf £1800.00
—Taxation of Patent Royalties, Dividends, and Interest in Europe. – International Bureau of Fiscal Documentation. – Amsterdam : International Bureau of Fiscal Documentation, 1988.
– (Guides to European Taxation Ser.: Vol. 1).
Llf £690.00

—Taxation of Private Investment Income. - International Bureau of Fiscal Documentation. - Amsterdam : International Bureau of Fiscal Documentation, 1988.
- (Guides to European Taxation Ser.: Vol. 3).
Llf £690.00

—Value Added Taxation in Europe. - International Bureau of Fiscal Documentation. - Amsterdam : International Bureau of Fiscal Documentation, 1988.
- (Guides to European Taxation Ser.: Vol. 4).
Llf £950.00

International business agreements : a practical guide to the negotiation and formulation of agency distribution and intellectual property licensing agreements / Patrick Hearn. - Aldershot : Gower, 1987.
viii,222p; 24cm.
Includes index.
ISBN 0566025973 £27.50

International business and national jurisdiction / A.D. Neale and M.L. Stephens. - Oxford : Clarendon Press, 1988.
xix,216p.
Examines the relationship between issues in international and municipal law, specifically the relationship between historically exclusive spheres of sovereign interest, and legal and practical requirements of the modern international commercial environment. Concentrates on US antitrust law, but some EEC and English decisions are included.
ISBN 0198255322 Hbk £52.00

International Business Lawyer. - London : Sweet & Maxwell.
Hbk £70.00

International business lawyer : journal of the Section on Business Law of the International Bar Association. - London : International Bar Association, 1973.
Index in each vol., 1979-.
ISBN 03097676

International business transactions and economic relations : cases, notes and materials on the law as it applies to Canada / J.G.Castel, A.L.C. deMestral, W.C.Graham. - Toronto(Ont.) : Edmond Montgomery Publications Ltd, 1986.
xxii,925p.
ISBN 0920722067 Hbk £119.50

International capital markets 1984 / prepared by Orion Royal Bank Limited. - London : Euromoney, 1984.
vi,207p.
ISBN 0903121638

International cargo carriers' liabilities : the determination of some current contractual problems arising from the international carriage of goods / W.E. Astle. - London : Fairplay, 1983.
viii,140p; 25cm.
ISBN 0905045416 Pbk

International carriage of goods : some legal problems and possible solutions / edited by C.M. Schmitthoff, R.M. Goode. - London : Centre for Commercial Law Studies, 1988.
xxvii,135p.
Includes index. Includes the text of the Uniform Rules of Conduct for Interchange of Trade Data by Teletransmission (UNCID) and of the United Nations Convention on International Multimodal Transport of Goods.
ISBN 0951066455

International carriage of goods by road : CMR / by Malcolm A. Clarke. - London : Stevens, 1982.
xxvi,212p; 26cm.
Includes index. Appendix in French.
ISBN 0420464905 £19.50

International carriage of goods by road (CMR) / general editor Jan Theunis. - London : Published under the auspices of the International Road Transport Union by Lloyd's of London, 1987.
353p; 24cm.
Conference proceedings.
ISBN 1850441456 £48.00

International carriage of goods by road - CMR / by Malcolm A. Clarke. - Sweet & Maxwell, 1982.
ISBN 0420464905 Hbk £38.00

International Center for Law in Development → Law and social enquiry : case studies of research.
→ Lawyers in the Third World : comparative and developmental perspectives.

International Centre for Ocean Development → Regional compendium of fisheries legislation (Indian Ocean Region).

International Centre for Parliamentary Documentation → Parliaments of the world : a comparative reference compendium.

International Centre for Technical Expertise. - Paris : International Chamber of Commerce.
22p.
Hbk £4.50

International Centre of Sociological and Penitentiary Research and Studies → Protection of the individual with reagard sic to the acts of the tax and customs administrations : proceedings of the colloquy organised by the Council of Europe in co-operation with the International Centre of Sociological and Penitentiary Research and Studies in Messina 25-27 March 1986.

International Chamber of Commerce → Arbitration law in Europe.
→ Banker's documentary credits : issued in accordance with the Uniform customs and practice (1974 revision) of the International Chamber of Commerce.
→ Commercial arbitration and the law throughout the world : summary of the rules concerning arbitration agreements, procedure, arbitral awards, enforcement of awards, means of recourse.
→ Commercial arbitration in the Arab Middle East : a study in Shara and statute law.

—Guide to arbitration : and related services offered by the International Chamber of Commerce. - International Chamber of Commerce. - Paris : ICC, 1983.
139p; 25cm. - (ICC publication).
Replaces ICC publication; no.301.
ISBN 9284210186

→ International arbitration : 60 years of ICC arbitration : a look at the future.

—Introduction to ICC rules on international contracts. - International Chamber of Commerce. - Paris : ICC Services S.A.R.L., 1981.
49p.

—Rules for the ICC court of arbitration / International Chamber of Commerce. - 1980 ed. - Paris : International Chamber of Commerce, 1981.
32p.
Previous ed.: 1975. The Rules of the ICC Court of Arbitration were first published in April 1975 as Publication 291. The text of the Rules remains unchanged in the present edition but a new section called 'the Internal Rules of the Court' has been added to it. 'The schedule of costs' has also been revised..

International Chamber of Commerce Arbitration. - Paris : International Chamber of Commerce.
704p.
Hbk £75.00

International Civil Aviation Organization Aeronautical agreements and arrangements : tables of agreements and arrangements registered with the Organization, 1 January 1946 - 31 December 1985. - International Civil Aviation Organization. - 14th ed. - Montreal : International Civil Aviation Orgainization, 1986.
vi,373p. - (Doc 9460-LGB/382).
Kept up to date by supplements and lists. Supplements held: 1st, 1986; 2nd, 1987.

—Assembly resolutions in force : (as of 10 May 1984) / International Civil Aviation Organization. - 1 v. - Montreal : I.C.A.O., 1984.
various pagings. - (Doc).
Includes index.

—Assembly resolutions in force : (as of 10 October 1986). - International Civil Aviation Organization. - 1. - Montreal : International Civil Aviation Organization, 1986.
various pagings. - (Doc.).
Published by authority of the Secretary General.

—Assembly resolutions in force : (as of 7 October 1980) / International Civil Aviation Organization. - 1. - Montreal : International Civil Aviation Organization, 1981.
various pagings. - (Doc).

—Aviation security : digest of current ICAO policies and actions on the subject of unlawful interference with international civil aviation and its facilities. - International Civil Aviation Organization. - 4th ed. - Montreal : International Civil Aviation Organization, 1987.
iii,36p. - (Doc 8849-C/990/4).
Decisions taken and work done by ICAO on the subject of unlawful interference with international civil aviation and its facilities. Includes the texts of three international conventions.

→ International Conference on Air Law, Montreal, September 1978 : minutes and documents.

—International standards : aircraft nationality and registration marks : annex 7 to the Convention on International Civil Aviation. - International Civil Aviation Organization. - 4th ed. - July 1981. 1. - Montreal : International Civil Aviation Organization, 1981.
loose-leaf.
Kept up to date by amendments and supplements.

—International standards : rules of the air : annex 2 to the Convention on International Civil Aviation. - International Civil Aviation Organization. - 8th ed. - July 1986. 1. - Montreal : International Civil Aviation Organization, 1986.
looseleaf.
Kept up to date by amendments and supplements.

—International standards : units of measurement to be used in air and ground operations : annex 5 to the Convention on International Civil . Aviation. - International Civil Aviation Organization. - 4th ed. - July 1979. 1. - Montreal : International Civil Aviation Organization, 1979 -.
loose-leaf.
Kept up to date by amendments and supplements.

—International standards and recommended practices : aerodromes : annex 14 to the Convention on International Civil Aviation. - International Civil Aviation Organization. - 8th ed. - March 1984. 1. - Montreal : International Civil Aviation Organization, 1983.
looseleaf.
Kept up to date by amendments and supplements.

—International standards and recommended practices : aeronautical charts : annex 4 to the Convention on International Civil Aviation. - International Civil Aviation Organization. - 8th ed. 1 v. - Montreal : International Civil Aviation Organization, 1985.
looseleaf.
Kept up to date by amendments and supplements.

—International standards and recommended practices : aeronautical information services : annex 15 to the Convention on International Civil Aviation. - International Civil Aviation Organization. - 7th ed. - July 1987. 1. - Montreal : International Civil Aviation Organization, 1987.
looseleaf.
Kept up to date by amendments and supplements.

—International standards and recommended practices : air traffic services ... : annex 11 to the Convention on International Civil Aviation. - International Civil Aviation Organization. - 8th ed. - July 1987. 1. - Montreal : International Civil Aviation Organization, 1987.
looseleaf.
Kept up to date by amendments and supplements.

—International standards and recommended practices : aircraft accident investigation : annex 13 to the Convention on International Civil Aviation. - International Civil Aviation Organization. - 7th ed. 1. - Montreal : International Civil Aviation Organization, 1988.
looseleaf.
Kept up to date by amendments and supplements.

—International standards and recommended practices : airworthiness of aircraft : annex 8 to the Convention on International Civil Aviation. - International Civil Aviation Organization. - 7th ed. - April 1983. 1. - Montreal : International Civil Aviation Organization, 1983.
looseleaf.
Kept up to date by amendments and supplements.

—International standards and recommended practices : environmental protection : annex 16 to the Convention on International Civil Aviation Vol. 1 : Aircraft noise. - International Civil Aviation Organization. - 1st ed - 1981. 1. - Montreal : International Civil Aviation Organization, 1981.
loose-leaf; 28cm.
Supersedes: International standards and recommended practices: aircraft noise: annex 16 to the Convention on International Civil Aviation. 3rd ed. - July 1978. Current edition only kept. Kept up to date by amendments and supplements.

Vol. 2 : Aircraft engine emissions. - 1981.
loose-leaf; 28cm.
Supersedes: International standards and recommended practices : aircraft noise : annex 16 to the Convention on International Civil Aviation. 3rd ed. - July 1978. Kept up to date by amendments and supplements.

—International standards and recommended practices : meteorological service for international air navigation : annex 3 to the Convention on International Civil Aviation. - International Civil Aviation Organization. - 10th ed. - July 1986. 1. - Montreal : International Civil Aviation Organisation, 1986.
looseleaf.
Kept up to date by amendments and supplements.

—International standards and recommended practices : operation of aircraft : annex 6 to the Convention on International Civil Aviation Part 1 : International commercial air transport. - International Civil Aviation Organization. - 4th ed. - July 1983. 1. - Montreal : International Civil Aviation Organization, 1983.
looseleaf.
Kept up to date by amendments and supplements.

Part 2 : International general aviation. - 1983.
looseleaf.
Kept up to date by amendments and supplements.

Part 3 : International operations - helicopters. - 1986.
looseleaf.
Kept up to date by amendments and supplements.

—International standards and recommended practices : personnel licensing : annex 1 to the Convention on International Civil Aviation. – International Civil Aviation Organization. – 7th ed. - September 1982. 1. – Montreal : International Civil Aviation Organization, 1982. looseleaf.
Kept up to date by amendments and supplements.

—International standards and recommended practices : security : safeguarding international civil aviation against acts of unlawful interference : annex 17 to the Convention on International Civil Aviation. – International Civil Aviation Organization. – 3rd ed. 1. – Montreal : International Civil Aviation Organization, 1986. looseleaf.
Kept up to date by amendments and supplements.

—International standards and recommended practices : the safe transport of dangerous goods by air : annex 18 to the Convention on International Civil Aviation. – International Civil Aviation Organization. – 1st ed. - January 1983. 1 v. – Montreal : International Civil Aviation Organization, 1983.
looseleaf.

—International standards, recommended practices and procedures for air navigation services : aeronautical telecommunications : annex 10 to the Convention on International Civil Aviation. – International Civil Aviation Organization. – 4th ed. 1 v. – Montreal : International Civil Aviation Organization, 1985.
looseleaf.
Kept up to date by amendments and supplements.

—Report / International Civil Aviation Organization Legal Committee. – Montreal : I.C.A.O., 1983-.
Continues: Report and minutes.

—Report . – International Civil Aviation Organization. – s.l. : International Civil Aviation Organaization, 984.
19p. – (LC/SC-ICA-Report 1984 10 03).
'The Sub-Committee met at Montreal and held eleven meetings between 25 September and 3 October 1984' - Introduction.

—Report and minutes / International Civil Aviation Organization Legal Committee. – Montreal : I.C.A.O., 1983.
v,202p.
Continues: Minutes and documents. - Continued by: Report.

International Civil Engineering Contract. – Sweet & Maxwell, 1974.
ISBN 0421201606 Hbk £58.00
Supplement 1980. –
ISBN 042126800X Pbk £21.00

International civil litigation in United States courts: commentary and materials / David Westin. – Kluwer Law and Taxation, 1989.
720.
A treatment of international civil litigation in US courts. Covers personal jurisdiction over foreign defendants, services outside the US, discovery of materials outside the US including the Hague Evidence Convention and the Aerospatiale decision.
ISBN 9065443800 Hbk £54/Dfl 168

International Claims : Adjudications by National Commission. – London : Eurospan.
ISBN 0813908345 Hbk £17.50

International Claims : Contemporary European Practice / Weston. – London : Eurospan.
ISBN 0813909279 Hbk £21.95

International Claims : Postwar British Practice. – London : Eurospan.
ISBN 0813908507 Hbk £17.50

International Claims : Settlement by Lump Sum Agreement / Weston. – London : Eurospan.
ISBN 0813906423 Hbk £39.50

International Claims : Their Preparation and Presentation / Christenson. – London : Eurospan.
ISBN 0813908353 Hbk £17.50

International Classification of Goods and Services for the Purposes of the Registration of Marks. – 5th ed. – Geneva : World Intellectual Property Organization, 1986.
Hbk £110.00
Part 1: Alphabetical List of Goods and Services. –
Pbk £100.00

International Code for the Construction and Equipment of Ships Carrying Dangerous Chemicals in Bulk (IBC, Vol. 2)
English. – International Maritime Organization. – London : International Maritime Organization.
ISBN 9280111620 Hbk £3.75
French. –
ISBN 9280121294 Hbk £3.75
Russian. –
ISBN 9280140442 Hbk £3.75
Spanish. –
ISBN 9280130870 Hbk £3.75
Chinese. –
Hbk £3.75

International Code for the Construction and Equipment of Ships Carrying Liquified Gases in Bulk (IGC)
English. – International Maritime Organization. – London : International Maritime Organization.
ISBN 9280111639 Hbk £4.50
French. –
ISBN 9280121308 Hbk £4.50
Russian. –
ISBN 9280140450 Hbk £4.50
Spanish. –
ISBN 9280130889 Hbk £4.50
Chinese. –
Hbk £4.50

International code of signals. – London : IMO, 1985.
vii,175p; 31cm.
Includes index.
ISBN 9280111841 £14.00

International Coffee Agreement 1983 : New York, 1 January-30 June 1983. – London : H.M.S.O., 1986.
49p; 25cm.
ISBN 0101977506 unbound £4.90

International commercial and maritime arbitration / edited by F.D. Rose. – London : Sweet & Maxwell, 1988.
118p; 22cm.
Explains aspects of international arbitration, and includes chapters on commercial arbitration, transnational arbitration and English laws, soviet maritime arbitration, arbitral immunity, and salvage arbitration.
ISBN 0421392207 Pbk £15.00

International Commercial Arbitration. – Vancouver : British Columbia Continuing Legal Education Society, 1983.
216p.
ISBN 0865041415 Hbk £50.00

International commercial crime : second international commercial crime symposium / organised under the auspices of the Commonwealth Secretariat's Commercial Crime Unit, the ICC-International Maritime Bureau and the Centre for Commercial Law Studies, Queen Mary College ... : documentation edited by Susan G. Lie. – London : Queen Mary College. Faculty of Laws, Centre for Commercial Law Studies, 1984.
502p.

International Commercial Crime Conference. – Vancouver : British Columbia Continuing Legal Education Society, 1981.
275p.
ISBN 0865040362 Hbk £25.00

International commercial litigation / Stephen Cromie; consulting editor: William Park. – London : Butterworths, 1990.
600; 24cm.
Focuses on national commercial litigation in its international context. Covers procedural and substantive law of England and Wales, USA, Canada, Frane, Germany, Switzerland, Japan and Australia. The conduct of simultaneous proceedings in the various countries and how decisions may be enforced are also treated.
ISBN 0406290024 Hbk £120

International Commission of Health Professionals → Human rights and mental patients in Japan : report of a mission by Dr. T. W. Harding, Judge J. Schneider, Dr. H. M. Visotsky and Dr. C. L. Graves on behalf of the International Commission of Jurists and the International Commission of Health Professionals.

International Commission of Jurists → Academic freedom under Israeli military occupation : report of WUS/ICJ mission of enquiry into higher education in the West Bank and Gaza.
→ Development, human rights and the rule of law : report of a conference held in The Hague on 27 April-1 May 1981.

—Human and peoples' rights in Africa and the African Charter : report of a conference held in Nairobi from 2 to 4 December 1985 convened by the International Commission of Jurists. – International Commission of Jurists. – Geneva : International Commission of Jurists, 1986.
101p.
Includes the text of the African charter on Human and Peoples' Rights.
ISBN 9290370289

→ Philippines: human rights after martial law.
→ Rule of law in the areas administered by Israel.
→ States of emergency : their impact on human rights.

International Committee for Soviet and East European Studies → Perspectives on Soviet law for the 1980s.

International Committee 'Justice for Massimo Carlotto'
Carlotto affair : a terrible injustice / International Committee 'Justice for Massimo Carlotto'. – London : the Committee, 1987.
40p.

International Committee of the Red Cross. – Dordrecht : Kluwer, 1984.
300p.
ISBN 9024730643 Hbk £120.00
→ Etudes et essais sur le droit international humanitaire et sur les principes de la Croix-Rouge en l'honneur de Jean Pictet : Studies and essays on international humanitarian law and Red Cross principles in honour of Jean Pictet.

International Comparisons in Implementing Pollution Laws / Kenneth Hanf. – Dordrecht : Kluwer, 1983.
352p.
ISBN 089838110X Hbk £78.00

International computer law issues / Keustermans. – Matthew Bender, 1988.
ISBN 0000999059 Hbk £53.00

International Conference on Air Law, Montreal, September 1978 : minutes and documents. – Montreal : International Civil Aviation Organization, 1982.
viii,383p. – (Doc. 9357-LC/183).
Includes documents in English, French, Russian and Spanish.

International Conference on Liability and Compensation for Damage in Connection with the Carriage of Certain Substances By Sea : 1984
English. – International Maritime Organization. – London : International Maritime Organization.
ISBN 9280111922 Hbk £4.50
French. –
ISBN 9280121537 Hbk £4.50
Russian. –
ISBN 9280140507 Hbk £4.50
Spanish. –
ISBN 9280134078 Hbk £4.50
Arabic. –
ISBN 9280150030 Hbk £4.50
Chinese. –
ISBN 9280160044 Hbk £4.50

International conference on liability and compensation for damage in connexion with the carriage of certain substances by sea, 1984 : final act of the conference with resolutions : Protocol of 1984 to amend the International Convention on Civil Liability for Oil Pollution Damage, 1969 : Protocol of 1984 to amend the International Convention on the Establishment of an International Fund for Compensation for Oil Pollution Damage, 1971 ... – London : International Maritime Organization, 1985.
iv,90p.
Includes the text of the International Convention on Civil Liability for Oil Pollution Damage, 1984 and of the International Convention on the Establishment of an International Fund for Compensation for Oil Pollution Damage, 1984.

International conflicts of labour law : a survey of the law applicable to the international employment relation / Felice Morgenstern. – Geneva : International Labour Office, 1986.
ix,129p; 25cm.
ISBN 922103593X

International construction contracts. – London : Butterworths, 1988.
ISBN 0406009007 Hbk

International construction law review. – London : Lloyd's of London, 1983-.

International contract law & finance review yearbook. – 1981. 2 v. – London : Euromoney, 1981.
ISBN 0903121360

International conventions concerning applications for and awards of maintenance : explanatory documentation / prepared for Commonwealth Jurisdictions by David McClean in association with the Commonwealth Secretariat. – London : Commonwealth Secretariat, 1981.
v,83p.
ISBN 0850922003

International cooperation in marine science and technology in the Pacific region : proceedings of the 6th International Ocean Symposium November 5-6, 1981, the Japan Shipping Club, Tokyo, Japan. – Tokyo : Ocean Association of Japan, 1982.
69p.
Edited by the Ocean Association of Japan. Title also in Japanese.

International copyright and neighbouring rights / Stephen M. Stewart. – London : Butterworths, 1983.
xii,740p; 26cm.
This book covers the underlying general principles of both international and national copyright laws with particular reference to neighbouring rights including coverage of corporate ownership rights. This work is directed at the international law student and practitioner.
ISBN 0406662207 Hbk £73.50

International copyright law and practice. – Matthew Bender, 1988.
ISBN 0000999074 Hbk £53.00

International Council for Commercial Arbitration → Comparative arbitration practice and public policy in arbitration.
→ International handbook on commercial arbitration.

→ UNCITRAL's project for a model law on international commercial arbitration.

International Court of Justice
Bibliography of the International Court. – International Court of Justice. – London : HMSO, 1984.
ISBN 0119836971 Hbk £1.90

—Reports of Judgments, Advisory Opinions and Orders
ICJ No 521: Yearbook No 40, 1985-1986. – International Court of Justice. – Geneva : United Nations Publications.
Hbk £12.00

—Yearbook 1982-83. – International Court of Justice. – London : HMSO, 1984.
ISBN 0119080028 Hbk £9.00

International Court of Justice and some contemporary problems : essays on international law / Taslim O. Elias. – The Hague : Nijhoff, 1983.
ix,374p; 25cm.
Bibliography: p361-364. - Includes index.
ISBN 902472791X Hbk £150.00

International Court of Justice and the Western Tradition of International Law. – Dordrecht : Kluwer, 1987.
172p.
ISBN 9024735246 Hbk £125.00

International courts and international politics / Robert Yewdall Jennings. – Hull : Hull University Press, 1986.
17p.
Josephine Onoh Memorial Lecture.
ISBN 0859584550

International Crimes of State : a Critical Analysis of the ILC's Draft Article 19 on State Responsibility. – Berlin : De Gruyter, 1989.
xii, 368p.
ISBN 3110116197 Hbk £152.00

International criminal responsibility of states : a study on the evolution of state responsibility with particular emphasis on the concept of crime and criminal responsibility / by Farhad Malekian. – Stockholm : s.n., 1985.
xviii,234p.
Thesis (Doctor of Laws) - University of Stockholm, 1985. Bibliography: p.198-209. - Includes index.
ISBN 9171465022

International debt game / by Brian Kettell and George Magnus. – London : Graham & Trotman, 1985.
384p; 23cm.
Includes index.
ISBN 0860105717 Pbk £18.75
ISBN 0860108104 £12.50

International Dictionary of the Securities Industry. – 2nd ed. – London : Macmillan.
ISBN 0333449738 Hbk £45.00

International Digest of Health Legislation. – World Health Organization. – London : HMSO.
Hbk £48.00

International directory of legal aid / edited by Judy Lane and Simon Hillyard. – London : International Bar Association, 1985.
244p; 21cm.
ISBN 0421325607 Hbk £30

International dispute settlement / by J.G. Merrills. – London : Sweet & Maxwell, 1984.
xvi,211p; 19cm.
Includes index.
ISBN 0421303700 Hbk £
ISBN 0421303808 Pbk £6.95

International economic law. – Dordrecht : Nijhoff (Martinus), 1989.
274.
Updated and extended version of the General Course held by the author at the Hague Academy of International Law in 1986. References to literature have been increased, and a detailed keyword index and an index of cases cited are included. Contains chapters on various aspects on international law.
ISBN 9024737990 Hbk £47

International economic law and developing states : some aspects / Gillian M. White ... et al. : edited by Hazel Fox. – London : British Institute of International & Comparative Law, 1988.
x,148p.
'Based on revised papers originally given at the Commonwealth Law Students' Conference held by the British Institute of International and Comparative Law at Manchester University in April 1987'. - T.p.. Includes index.
ISBN 0903067293 £15.00

International Economic Sanctions : Improving the Haphazard US Legal Regime. – Cambridge : Cambridge University Press.
ISBN 0521342589 Hbk £25.00

International economics / Sidney J. Wells. – 3rd ed. – London : Allen & Unwin, 1985.
xxiii,369p; 25cm.
Previous ed.: by Sidney J. Wells. 1973. Bibliography: p343-362. - Includes index.
ISBN 0043303498 Hbk £20.00
ISBN 0043303501 Pbk £9.95

International employment tax handbook / Reading. – Cambridge : Woodhead-Faulkner, 1982.
ISBN 0859411915 Hbk £115.00

International encyclopaedia for labour law and industrial relations / editor in chief: R. Blanpain. – n. – Deventer : Kluwer, 1977.
25cm.
Updated periodically by loose leaf supplement.

International Encyclopaedia for Labour Law and Industrial Relations. Supplements
45. – Dordrecht : Kluwer.
Hbk £135.25
46. –
Hbk £81.40
47. –
Hbk £58.50
48. –
Hbk £100.00
49. – 1985.
Pbk £134.00
50. – 1985.
96p.
Pbk £54.00
51. – 1985.
208p.
Hbk £115.00
52. – 1985.
264p.
Pbk £147.00
53. – 1985.
224p.
Pbk £124.00
54. – 1985.
168p.
Pbk £94.25
55. – 1985.
120p.
Pbk £66.00

International encyclopedia of comparative law / under the auspices of the International Association of Legal Science. – Tubingen : Mohr, 1971.

International energy markets / edited by Paul Tempest. – Cambridge Mass. : Oelgeschlager, Gunn & Main, 1983.
xxi,353p; 24cm.
Conference proceedings - papers and abstracts. Includes bibliographies and index.
ISBN 0860104028 £18.00
ISBN 0899462014

International energy options : an agenda for the 1980s : selected papers from leading contributors to the 1980 Annual Conference of the International Association of Energy Economists in Cambridge, UK / edited by Paul Tempest. – Cambridge, Mass. : Oelgeschlager, Gunn & Hain, 1981.
xv,304p.
Includes bibliographical references and index.
ISBN 086010303X Oelschlager, Gunn & Hain
ISBN 0899460895

International enforcement of human rights : reports submitted to the Colloquium of the International Association of Legal Science, Heidelberg, 28-30 August 1985 / edited by Rudolf Bernhardt, John-Anthony Jolowicz. – Berlin : Springer-Verlag, 1987.
Includes index.
ISBN 0387175741

International environment law : multilateral treaties Droit international de l'environnement : traites multilateraux Internationales Umweltrecht : multilaterale Vertrage / editor, W. E. Burhenne : compiled by Robert Muecke. – Berlin : E. Schmidt, 1974-.
1 v.; 32 cm.
Cover title: Internationales Umweltrecht. Loose-leaf for updating. Parallel text in English and/or French and/or German. 'FUST-Projekt nr. 51.'.
ISBN 3503011048 Hbk

International Environmental Law Information System. – Berlin : Erich Schmidt.
354p. – (BZU Ser.: Vol. B3).
ISBN 3503010181 Pbk £39.00

International factoring / by Anthony N. Cox and John A. MacKenzie. – London : Euromoney Publications, 1986.
xv,112p.
ISBN 0903121913

International Federation of Commercial Arbitration Institutions →Commercial arbitration institutions : an international directory and guide.

International Federations of Industrial Property Attorneys →Present and the future of the profession : (the Elzaburu survey).

International Finance Yearbook 1987. – Euromoney. – London : Euromoney.
ISBN 0903121857 Pbk £75.00

International financial law / edited by Robert S. Rendell. – 2nd ed. 2. – London : Euromoney Publications, 1983.
ISBN 0903121557

International financial law review. – London : Euromoney, 1983-.
Supersedes: The international contract law & finance review.

International financial markets. – Cambridge : Woodhead-Faulkner, 1988.
ISBN 085941440X Hbk £35.00

International financial policy and economic development : a disaggregated approach / Graham Bird. – Basingstoke : Macmillan, 1987.
xvi,348p; 23cm.
Bibliography: p338-343. - Includes index.
ISBN 033340890X £29.50

International Firm. – Carleton : Pitman Pty Ltd, 1984.
ISBN 0273011197 Hbk £29.95, 015

International Fiscal Association →Adjustments for tax purposes in highly inflationary economics : proceedings of a seminar held in Buenos Aires in 1984 during the 38th Congress of the International Fiscal Association.
→ Disregard of a legal entity fortax purposes.

—Imputation systems : objectives and consequences : proceedings of a seminar held in Montreal 1982 during the 36th Congress of the International Fiscal Association / organized by the International Fiscal Association. – Deventer : Kluwer, 1983.
129p. – (IFA congress seminar series).
ISBN 9065441212

—International tax problems of charities and other private institutions with similar tax treatment : proceedings of a seminar held in 1985 during the 39th Congress of the International Fiscal Association. – International Fiscal Association. – Deventer Netherlands : Kluwer Law and Taxation Publishers, 1986.
Conference held in London, England.
ISBN 9065442707

→ International tax treatment of common law trusts : proceedings of a seminar held in New York in 1986 during the 40th Congress of the International Fiscal Association.

—Recent International Developments to Counter Tax Avoidance and Evasion. – International Fiscal Association. – Toronto : DeBoo, 1982. – (IFA Seminars Ser.).
ISBN 0888201168 Hbk £35.00

—Recourse to tax havens : use and abuse : proceedings of a seminar held in Paris during the 34th Congress of the International Fiscal Association... / organised by the International Fiscal Association. – Deventer : Kluwer on behalf of the IFA, 1981.
147p; 21cm. – (IFA congress seminar series).
Bibliography: p.141-148.
ISBN 9065440054

→ Tax policy towards the national heritage : proceedings of a seminar held in Venice, 1983, during the 37th Congress of the International Fiscal Association.

→ Taxation and human rights : proceedings of a seminar held in Brussels in 1987 during the 41st Congress of the International Fiscal Association.

→ Taxation of domestic shareholders on undistributed income of foreign corporate affiliates : objectives, techniques, and consequences : proceedings of a seminar held in New York in 1986 during the 40th Congress of the International Fiscal Association.

International franchising - an overview / papers presented to the International Franchising Committee at the SBL Conferences, held in Toronto, October, 1983 : organized by SBL Section on Business Law of the International Bar Association : edited by Martin Mendelsohn. – Amsterdam : North-Holland, 1984.
xxvii,407p; 23cm.
ISBN 0444875484 Hbk £49.95

International groundwater resources law / by Julio A. Barberis for the Legislation Branch, FAO Legal Office. – Rome : Food and Agriculture Organization of the United Nations, 1986.
vii,67p. – (Legislative study).
ISBN 925102507X

International group accounting / Coenenberg. – Oxford : Croom Helm, 1988.
ISBN 0709938772 Hbk £35.00

International Guide to Capital Markets 1988. – Cambridge : Woodhead-Faulkner.
ISBN 1870031172 Hbk £75.00

International handbook of universities and other institutions of higher education / editor, D.J. Aitken : assistant editor, Ann C.M. Taylor. – 9th ed. – London : Macmillan for the International Association of Universities, 1983.
ix, 1131p.
ISBN 0333274466

International handbook on commercial arbitration / general editor Pieter Sanders : with the cooperation of the T.M.C. Asser Institute for International Law, The Hague. – 2. – Deventer : Kluwer Law and Taxation Publishers, 1984.
At head of title page: International Council for Commercial Arbitration.
ISBN 906544999X Llf

International handbook on pensions law and similar employee benefits. – London : Graham & Trotman, 1989.
352.
On behalf of the International Association for Insurance Law, examines pension laws in over 17 countries. Topics include surplus reversion and the recapture of assets, predator proofing, the national and international nomad, human rights and sex equality in retirement pensions, share incentive, and stock option plans.
ISBN 0860109941 Hbk £85

International Health Regulations (1969). – World Health Organization. – 3rd ed. – London : HMSO, 1983.
ISBN 9241580070 Hbk £4.40

International human rights instruments of the United Nations 1948-1982 / collected and arranged by the UNIFO editorial staff. – London : Mansell, 1984.
ix,175p; 29cm.
Originally published: Pleasantville, N.Y. : UNIFO Publishers, 1983. Includes index.
ISBN 0720116988 £25.00

International Human Rights Law Group → Guide to international human rights practice.

International human rights law in the Commonwealth Caribbean / edited for the International Center for the Legal Protection of Human Rights (Interights) by Angela D. Byre. – Dordrecht : Nijhoff (Martinus), 1989.
408. – (International Studies in Human Rights).
Collection of papers concerning the protection of human rights under Bills of Rights in Commonwealth Carribean countries and under regional and international human rights treaties. Demonstrates the relevance of international human rights law in domestic cases and considers practical ways of strengthening human rights protection.
ISBN 9024737850 Hbk Gld150.00

International humanitarian assistance : disaster relief actions in international law and organization / Peter Macalister-Smith. – Hague : M. Nijhoff Publishers, 1985.
260p.
ISBN 9024729939 Hbk £130.00

International Implications of New Telecommunications Technology
Vol. 4. – Enstone : Ditchley Foundation. – (Ditchley Conference Reports).
Hbk

International Industrial Purchasing. – Stockholm : Almqvist & Wiksell, 1982.
74p.
ISBN 9155412661 Hbk £51.00

International Institute for Labour Studies
Labour courts in Europe : proceedings of a meeting organised by the International Institute for Labour Studies / edited by Bert Essenberg. – Geneva : International Institute for Labour Studies, 1986.
68p.
ISBN 9290144076 Hbk £10.00

International Institute of Administration Sciences
Public administration in Japan / edited by IIAS Tokyo Round Table organizing committee. – Tokyo : Institute of Administrative Management, 1982.
299p.
Proceedings of a conference.

International Institute of Air and Space Law → Regulatory reform in international air transport : address by H.A. Wassenbergh on the occasion of the introduction of the International Institute of Air and Space Law of the State University at Leyden 17 March 1986.

International Institute of Higher Studies in Criminal Sciences → Penal protection of works of art.

International Institute of Human Rights → Development and principles of international humanitarian law : course given in July 1982 at the University of Strasbourg as part of the courses organized by the International Institute of Human Rights.

International Institute of Management → Law and economics and the economics of legal regulation.

International institutional law / Henry G. Schermers. – 3. – Leiden : Sijthoff, 1972.
Volumes 1 and 2 superseded by later edition in one volume. Includes bibliography and index.
ISBN 9028603948 v.3

International institutions in trade and finance / A.I. MacBean and P.N. Snowden. – London : Allen & Unwin, 1981.
xiv,255p; 23cm.
Bibliography: p249-252. - Includes index.
ISBN 0043820328 Hbk
ISBN 0043820336 Pbk

International Insurance, Industry Guide. – Coopers & Lybrand Associates. – 4th ed. – London : Lloyd's of London Press.
ISBN 1850441936 Hbk £19.50

International interbank market : a descriptive study. – Basle : Bank for International Settlements, 1983.
44p; 21cm.
'... written by a study group ... under the auspices of the Bank for International Settlements' - inside front cover.

International Invitational Conference on Matrimonial and Child Support, May 27-30, 1981, Edmonton, Alberta, Canada : conference materials. – Edmonton : Institute of Law Research and Reform, University of Alberta, 1982.
xv,146p. – (Research paper).
Conference convened by the Institute of Law Research and Reform.

International issues in industrial relations / Industrial Relations Society of Australia. – Gordon, N.S.W. : The Society, 1983.
vi,125p.
Convention proceedings. Includes bibliographical references.

International issues in taxation : the Canadian perspective / Donald J.S. Brean. – Toronto : Canadian Tax Foundation, 1984.
xiii,180p.
Bibliography: p.166-176. - Includes index.
ISBN 0888080190

International journal of comparative labour law and industrial relations. – Leicester : University of Leicester, 1985.

International journal of estuarine and coastal law. – London : Graham & Trotman, 1986-.

International journal of law and the family. – Oxford : Oxford University Press, 1987-.

International jurisdiction and the recognition and enforcement of foreign judgements in the LAWASIA region : a comparative study of the laws of eleven Asian countries inter-se and with the E.E.C. countries / Bradford A. Caffrey. – Sydney : CCH Australia, 1985.
xxxii,407p.
Cover title: Enforcement of foreign judgements.
ISBN 0869037897

International Labor Organization : an American view / Walter Galenson. – Madison : University of Wisconsin Press, 1981.
xi,351p; 23cm.
Includes index.
ISBN 0299085406 Hbk £13.95
ISBN 0299085449 Pbk £5.05

International labour conventions and national law : the effectiveness of the automatic incorporation of treaties in national legal systems / Virginia A. Leary. – The Hague : M. Nijhoff, 1982.
xiv,191p.
Revision of thesis (doctoral)–Graduate Institute of International Studies at Geneva. Bibliography: p171-179.
ISBN 9024725518

International labour conventions and recommendations, 1919-1981 : arranged by subject-matter. – Geneva : International Labour Office, 1982.
xxxiv, 1167 p.; 25 cm.
'Conventions and recommendations adopted by the International Labour Conference'–Pref. At head of title: International Labour Organisation.
ISBN 9221029344

International Labour Law : a Comparative Survey of the Conflict Rules Affecting Labour Legislation and Regulations / A.W. Sijthoff. – Budapest : Akademiai Kiado, 1968.
465p.
Hbk £24.00

International labour law reports
Volume 7 / Benjamin Aaron, Thilo Ramm, Tore Sigeman, Jean-Maurice Verdier, Felice Morgenstern, Kenneth William Wedderburn of Charlton. – Dordrecht : Nijhoff (Martinus), 1989.
688. – (International labour law reports).
A volume in the series of annual publications of labour law judgements by the highest courts in a number of jurisdictions. Each judgement reprinted has Headnotes and usually an Annotation setting out the legal issues involved, and basic facts of the case if not included in the judgement. Judgements are normally printed in extenso.
ISBN 0792300998 Hbk £105
Vol. 1 (1974-1975). – 1978.
398p.
ISBN 9028608982
Vol. 3 (1976-1977). –
xix, 399p.
ISBN 9028600604 Hbk £200.00
Vol. 4. – 1986.
462p.
ISBN 9024733073 Hbk £225.00
Vol. 5. – 1987.
442p.
ISBN 9024734738 Hbk £225.00
Vol. 6. – 1988.
444p.
ISBN 9024736056 Hbk £225.00

International Labour Office → Black migration to South Africa : a selection of policy-oriented research.
→ Collective bargaining in industrialised market economies : a reappraisal.
→ Deterrence and compensation : legal liability in occupational safety and health.
—Freedom of association : digest of decisions and principles of the Freedom of Association Committee of the governing body of the ILO. – International Labour Office. – 3rd ed. – Geneva : International Labour Office, 1985.
xii, 140 i.e. 262 p.; 24 cm.
ISBN 9221050734 Pbk £30.00
—General survey on the application of the conventions on freedom of association, the right to organise and collective bargaining and the convention and recommendation concerning rural workers' organisations : third item on the agenda. – International Labour Office. – Geneva : International Labour Office, 1983.
157p.
Cover title: Freedom of association and collective bargaining. Report III (Part 4B).
ISBN 9221031284
→ ILO research on multinational enterprises and social policy : an overview.
→ International conflicts of labour law : a survey of the law applicable to the international employment relation.
→ International labour standards : the case of freedom to strike.
→ International labour standards : their nature, their working, their value.
—Safety and health in the construction of fixed offshore installations in the petroleum industry. – International Labour Office. – Geneva : International Labour Office, 1981.
135 p.; 18 cm.
Includes index.
ISBN 922102900X Pbk £20.00
→ Workers' management in Yugoslavia : recent developments and trends.
→ Workforce reductions in undertakings : policies and measures for the protection of redundant workers in seven industrialised market economy countries.

International Labour Organisation → Employment, trade, and north-south co-operation.
—ILO and the world of work. – International Labour Organisation. – Geneva : International Labour Organisation, 1984.
74p.
ISBN 9221031500
→ International labour conventions and recommendations, 1919-1981 : arranged by subject-matter.

International labour standards : the case of freedom to strike / by Ruth Ben-Israel. – Deventer : Kluwer Law and Taxation Publishers, 1988.
vii,133p.
'A study prepared for the International Labour Office.' - T.p.. Includes index.
ISBN 9065443177

International labour standards : their nature, their working, their value. – Geneva : International Labour Office, 1981.
49p.

International Law, 2 Vols. – Calcutta : Mukherjee & Co.
Hbk £43.00

International Law. – 3rd ed. – London : Butterworths.
ISBN 0406591849 Hbk
ISBN 0406591857 Pbk

International law / N.A. Maryan Green. – 3rd ed. – London : Pitman, 1987.
384p; 22cm.
Previous ed.: Plymouth : Macdonald and Evans, 1982. Includes bibliography and index.
ISBN 0273027328 £25.00

International Law / by Malcolm N. Shaw. – 2nd ed. – Cambridge : Grotius, 1986.
39,627p; 23cm.
A revised and updated edition. An introduction to international law, setting the subject in the context of world political events. Also examines the importance of the political, cultural and economic influences that affect international law. Student text, also for private practitioners, governmental and civil servants.
ISBN 0906496373 Pbk £10.95

International Law. – 3rd ed. – Delhi : SBD Enterprises.
Hbk £35.00

International law / by Rebecca M.M. Wallace. – London : Sweet and Maxwell, 1986.
275p; 18cm.
Includes index.
ISBN 0421335009 Hbk £15.00
ISBN 0421335106 Pbk £10.00

International law : a Canadian perspective / by L.C. Green. – 2nd ed. – Toronto : Carswell Company, 1988.
vii,409p.
'Textbook edition of Title 81 of The Canadian Encyclopedic Digest (Ontario) third edition' - t.p.. Includes index.
ISBN 0459319817

International law : chiefly as interpreted and applied in Canada / Hugh M. Kindred ... et al. – 4th ed. – Toronto : Emond Montgomerry Publications, 1987.
xlix,958p.
Includes bibliographical references and index, as well as the texts of the Charter of the United Nations and the Statute of the International Court of Justice.
ISBN 0920722210 Hbk £96.00

International law : chiefly as interpreted and applied in Canada / Castel. – 4th ed. – Aurora : Canada Law Book, 1986.
Hbk £53.00

International law : law of peace. – 3rd ed. – London : Pitman Publishing, 1987.
ISBN 0273027328 Pbk £25.00

International law : law of peace / N. A. Maryan Green. – 2nd ed. – Plymouth : Macdonald & Evans, 1982.
xxxiv,254p.
ISBN 0712109560

International Law : the Essential Treaties. – Berlin : De Gruyter, 1985.
ca 832p.
ISBN 3110101122 Hbk £158.00

International law and aboriginal rights. – Oxford : Croom Helm, 1987.
ISBN 0949614351 Hbk £22.50

International law and Australian sovereignty in Antarctica / by Gillian D. Triggs. – Sydney : Legal Books, 1986.
xxix,403p.
Bibliography: p.379-391. - Includes index.
ISBN 0949553239

International Law and Development. – Martinus Nijhoff.
ISBN 9024737184 Hbk £58.00

International Law and Economic Development and Cooperation. – Dordrecht : Kluwer.
ISBN 9065441921

International law and fact - finding in the field of human rights / edited by B.G. Ramcharan. – The Hague : Nijhoff, 1982.
x,259p; 25cm.
Bibliography: p255-256. - Includes index.
ISBN 9024730422 Hbk £110.00

International Law and Municipal Law : Deutsch-Argentinisches Verfassungsrechtskolloquium, Buenos Aires, April 1979. – Berlin : Duncker and Humblot.
322p.
ISBN 3428050738 Pbk £116.00

International Law and Municipal Law : Proceedings of the German-Soviet Colloquy on International Law at the Institut fur Internationales Recht an der Universitat Kiel 4 to 8 May 1987 / Rudiger Wolfrum. – Berlin : Duncker and Humblot, 1988.
210p.
ISBN 3428064267 Hbk £96.00

International law and struggle for the freedom and welfare of man in Africa / by Itsejuwa E. Sagay. – Ile-Ife : University of Ife Press, 1983.
41p. – (Inaugural lecture series).
'An inaugural lecture delivered at the University of Ife on 3rd June, 1982'.

International law and the developing countries : confrontation or cooperation? / R.P. Anand. – Dordrecht : Martinus Nijhoff, 1987.
xii, 274p.
Includes index and bibliographies.
ISBN 902473438X Hbk £125.00

International Law and the International System. – Dordrecht : Kluwer, 1987.
208p.
ISBN 9024735343 Hbk £125.00

International law and the new states of Africa : a study of the international legal problems of state succession in the newly independent states of Eastern Africa / by Yilma Makonnen : with a foreword by T.O. Elias. – Addis Ababa : Ethiopian National Agency for UNESCO, 1983.
xxvi, 575 p.; 23 cm.
'Published with the assistance of UNESCO under the Regional Participation Programme for Africa.'. Includes index. Bibliography: p. 541-564.
ISBN 0961193409 Pbk

International law and the use of force by national liberation movements / Heather A. Wilson. – Oxford : Clarendon, 1988.
208p; 24cm.
Includes bibliography and index.
ISBN 0198255705 Hbk £25.00

International Law and World Revolution. – Toronto : Canadian Broadcasting Corporation Enterprises.
116p.
Pbk £2.50

International Law as Applied by International Courts and Tribunals
Vol. 4. – London : Sweet & Maxwell, 1985.
ISBN 0420446109 Hbk £85.00

International Law Association → Extra-territorial application of laws and responses thereto.
→ Prospects for a new Law of the Sea : papers read at a seminar conducted by the International Law Association in Sydney on 19 June 1982.

International law at a time of perplexity / Mala Tabory. – Dordrecht : Nijhoff (Martinus), 1989.
1040.
A collection of essays in honour of the seventieth birthday of Professor Rosenne. The contributions from friends and colleagues deal with humanitarian law, human rights, the law of treaties, and dispute settlement.
ISBN 9024736544 Hbk £142.50

International Law Commission / by Sir Ian Sinclair. – Cambridge : Grotius, 1987.
viii,177p.
Examines the constitution and working methods of the International Law Commission, and reviews the activity of the Commission since 1949 in the codification process. Analyses the contribution it has made to the development of general international law.
ISBN 0949009105

International Law Commission
Yearbook 1982, 2 Vols.
Vol. 2, Part 1. – International Law Commission. – London : HMSO.
ISBN 0119080702 Hbk £18.05

International Law for Antarctica / Tullio Scovazzi. – Milan : Giuffre, 1988.
xiv, 532p.
Hbk L50,000.00

International law governing communications and information : a collection of basic documents / prepared by Edward W. Ploman. – London : Pinter, 1982.
xvi,367p; 25cm.
Includes index.
ISBN 0861872045 £25.00

International law in a divided world / Antonio Cassese. – Oxford : Clarendon, 1986.
xiii,420p; 24cm.
Includes bibliography and index.
ISBN 0198761945 £40.00

International law in Australia / K. W Ryan. – 2nd ed. – North Ryde, N.S.W. : Published for the Australian Institute of International Affairs by the Law Book Co., 1984.
xliii, 523 p.; 25 cm.
Includes bibliographical references.
ISBN 0455202699 Pbk

International Law in Australia. – 2nd ed. – Deakin : Australian Institute of International Affairs, 1985.
Hbk £59.50

International law in historical perspective / By J. H. W. Verzijl. – Rockville : Sijthoff & Noordhoff, 1968-.
v.; 24 cm. – (Nova et vetera iuris gentium. Series A, Modern international law, no. 4, 6-9, 12-14).
Contents: 1. General subjects.– 2. International persons.– 3. State territory.– 4. Stateless domain.– 5. Nationality and other matters relating to individuals.– 6. Juridical facts as sources of international rights and obligations.– 7. State succession.– 8. Inter-state disputes and their settlements.–pt. 9a. The laws of war.–pt. 9b. The law of neutrality.
fl 62.50 (v. 1)

International law in the Netherlands / edited by H.F. van Panhuys...et al. – Alphen aan den Rijn : Sijthoff & Noordhoff, 1978.
v; 25 cm.
Organised by the T.M.C. Asser Institute. Includes bibliographical references and index.

International Law Institute → Default and rescheduling : corporate and sovereign borrowers.

International Law of Development / Francis G Snyder. – London : Butterworths.
ISBN 0862052408 Pbk £19.50

International law of development : comparative perspectives / edited by Francis Snyder and Peter Slinn. – Abingdon : Professional Books, 1987.
ix,322p; 22cm.
ISBN 0862052580

International law of diplomacy. – Dordrecht : Nijhoff (Martinus), 1989.
672. – (New Haven studies in international law and world public order 5).
A legal study from a policy-orientated perspective, which examines new patterns of diplomacy and their influence on the traditional ones. Looks at what world policies have so far regulated the use of the diplomatic process, and whether those policies are needlessly restrictive. Suggests what policies should guide the regulation in future.
ISBN 0792300831 Hbk £95

International Law of Fisheries : a Framework for Policy-Oriented Inquiries. – Dordrecht : Kluwer, 1987.
632p.
ISBN 089838902X Hbk £225.00

International law of human rights. – Oxford : Oxford University Press, 1984.
ISBN 0198760973 Pbk £21.00

International law of human rights in Africa : basic documents and annotated bibliography / compiled by M. Hamalengwa, C. Flinterman, E.V.O. Dankwa. – Dordrecht : M. Nijhoff, 1988.
xii, 427 p.; 25 cm.
Includes bibliographical references and index.
ISBN 9024735874

International Law of International Welfare : The Politics of Law-Making. – London : Pinter Publishers Ltd, 1984.
200p.
ISBN 0861872894 Hbk £21.00

International Law of Ocean Development, 2 Vols.
Vol. 1. – Leiden : Sijthoff, 1975-1982.
Bibliography: 1, p.515-519; 2, 629-631.
ISBN 9028601228 Llf £10.00
Vol. 2. –
ISBN 9028601775 Hbk £578.00

International Law of State Responsibility for Injuries to Aliens. – London : Eurospan.
ISBN 0813909619 Hbk £30.95

International law of take-overs and mergers : southern Europe, Africa, and the Middle East / H. Leigh Ffrench. – 1. – Westport, Conn. : Quorum, 1987.
23cm.
Includes index.
ISBN 0899302068 £48.50

International law of take-overs and mergers : the EEC, Northern Europe and Scandinavia / H. Leigh Ffrench. – New York : Quorum, 1987.
416p; 22cm.
Includes bibliography and index.
ISBN 0899300774 £51.75

International law of the ocean development : basic documents / by Shigeru Oda. – 2nd ed. 2. – Leiden : Sijthoff, 1977.
looseleaf.

International law of the sea
Vol.1 : by D.P. O'Connell : edited by I.A. Shearer / D. P. O'Connell, I. A. Shearer. – Oxford : Clarendon Press, 1982.
xxxiii,633p; 24cm.
Bibliography: p582-607. - Includes index.
ISBN 019825346X
Vol. 2. – 1984.
Hbk £45.00
Vol.2 : by D.P. O'Connell : edited by I.A. Shearer. – 1984.
xxvi,p.636-1201; 24cm.
Bibliography: p1159-1170. - Includes index.
ISBN 0198254695 £40.00

International Law of the Sea. – London : Central Books.
ISBN 0714727695 Hbk £6.95

International law of the sea and marine affairs, a bibliography
Supplement to the 1980 edition / edited by Nikos Papadakis, Martin Glassner. – The Hague : M. Nijhoff, 1983.
xxvi,579p.
Supplement to: International law of the sea / N. Papadakis. Includes indexes.
ISBN 9024728150 Hbk £350.00

International law quarterly. – 4 v. – London : Stevens, 1947.
Merged with Journal of the Society of Comparative Legislation to form International and comparative law quarterly. Index in each vol..

International law teaching and practice / edited by Bin Cheng. – London : Stevens, 1982.
xxix,287p; 25cm.
Conference papers. Includes index.
ISBN 042046350X £23.00

International Legal Context of Petroleum Operations in Canadian Arctic Waters. – Calgary : Canadian Institute of Resources Law.
76p.
Hbk £9.00

International Legal Environment. – Toronto : University of Toronto Press, 1986.
288p.
ISBN 0802072984 Hbk £18.95

International Legal Practitioner. – London : Sweet & Maxwell.
Hbk £40.00

International legal structures / David Kennedy. – Baden-Baden : Nomos, 1987.
294p.
Includes bibliographical references.
ISBN 3789013676

International Light, Shape and Sound Signals. – London : Stanford Maritime Ltd.
ISBN 0540072710 Pbk £6.95

International Literary Artistic Association → Public lending right : reports of an ALAI symposium and additional materials.

International Maritime Arbitration. – Vancouver : Continuing Legal Education Society of British Columbia, 1988.
338p.
ISBN 0865043663 Hbk £100.00

International Maritime Arbitration Organization. – Paris : International Chamber of Commerce.
64p.
Hbk £5.50

International Maritime Committee →Court appointed experts in maritime cases : a comparative law study.

International Maritime Dangerous Goods Code : Amendment 19-80
English. – International Maritime Organization. – London : International Maritime Organization, 1981.
ISBN 9280111264 Llf £11.00
French. –
ISBN 9280121073 Llf £11.00

International Maritime Dangerous Goods Code : Amendment 20-82
English. – International Maritime Organization. – London : International Maritime Organization.
ISBN 9280111507 Hbk £12.50
French. –
ISBN 9280121200 Hbk £12.50

International Maritime Dangerous Goods Code : Amendment 22-84
English. – International Maritime Organization. – London : International Maritime Organization.
Hbk £18.00
French. –
ISBN 9280121553 Hbk £18.00

International Maritime Dangerous Goods Code : Amendment 22-86
English. – International Maritime Organization. – London : International Maritime Organization.
ISBN 9280112031 Hbk £2.50
French. –
ISBN 9280121618 Hbk £2.50

International Maritime Dangerous Goods Code : Amendments 21-83 and 21-84
English. – International Maritime Organization. – London : International Maritime Organization.
ISBN 9280111698 Hbk £8.00
French. –
ISBN 9280121340 Hbk £8.00

International Maritime Dangerous Goods Code : Indexes to Amendment 22-84
English. – International Maritime Organization. – London : International Maritime Organization.
ISBN 9280111957 Hbk £4.00
French. –
ISBN 9280121561 Hbk £4.00

International Maritime Dangerous Goods Code (IMDG, 5 Vols.)
English. – International Maritime Organization. – London : International Maritime Organization, 1981.
ISBN 9280111256 Llf £60.00
French. –
ISBN 9280121057 Llf £55.00

International maritime fraud / by Eric Ellen, and Donald Campbell. – London : Sweet & Maxwell, 1981.
viii,174p; 22cm.
Bibliography: p160. - Includes index.
ISBN 0421271507 Pbk £8.00

International Maritime Law Conv (BSL) 4 vols. – London : Sweet & Maxwell, 1983.
ISBN 042066002 Hbk £310.00

International maritime law conventions / compiled by Mahararj Nagendra Singh. – Updated ed. 4. – London : Stevens, 1983.
xxvii,,3305p; 26cm.
Previous ed.: published in 1 as International conventions of maritime shipping. 1973. Includes index.
ISBN 0420466002 £24.00

International Maritime Organization
Vol.1 : International shipping rules / Samir Mankkabady. – 2nd ed. – London : Croom Helm, 1986.
xxi,450p; 23cm.
Previous ed.: published in 1 vol. 1984. Includes index.
ISBN 0709935919 £45.00
Vol.2 : Accidents at sea / Samir Mankabady. – 1987.
xxvii,452p; 23cm.
Previous ed.: published in 1 vol. 1984. Includes index.
ISBN 0709946406 Hbk £50.00

International Maritime Organization
Amendments to the Convention on the International Regulations for Preventing Collisions at Sea: 1972
English. – International Maritime Organization. – London : International Maritime Organization, 1983.
Hbk £1.50

—Amendments to the International Convention for the Safety of Life at Sea : 1974
English Edition. – International Maritime Organization. – London : International Maritime Organization, 1982.
Hbk £3.50

—Basic documents
Vol. 1 / International Maritime Organization. – London : I.M.O., 1983.
107p.
ISBN 9280111531

—Code of Safety for Nuclear Merchant Ships
English Edition. – International Maritime Organization. – London : International Maritime Organization, 1982.
Hbk £3.00

—Dedicated Clean Ballast Tanks. – International Maritime Organization. – London : International Maritime Organization, 1982.
Hbk £2.50

—Emergency Procedures for Ships Carrying Dangerous Goods : Group Emergency Schedules
English Edition. – International Maritime Organization. – London : International Maritime Organization, 1981.
Hbk £3.00

—Guidelines for the Design and Construction of Offshore Supply Vessels. – International Maritime Organization. – London : International Maritime Organization, 1982.
Hbk £1.25

—Guidelines on Surveys under the Nineteen Seventy-Eighty SOLAS Protocol. – International Maritime Organization. – London : International Maritime Organization, 1982.
Hbk £1.25

—IMO Grain Rules
English Edition. – International Maritime Organization. – London : International Maritime Organization, 1982.
Hbk £1.25

→ IMO news : the magazine of the International Maritime Organization.

—Inert Gas Systems for Ships Carrying Petroleum Products in Bulk
English Edition. – International Maritime Organization. – London : International Maritime Organization, 1982.
Hbk £2.50

—International Code for the Construction and Equipment of Ships Carrying Dangerous Chemicals in Bulk (IBC, Vol. 2)
English. – International Maritime Organization. – London : International Maritime Organization.
ISBN 9280111620 Hbk £3.75

—International Code for the Construction and Equipment of Ships Carrying Liquified Gases in Bulk (IGC)
English. – International Maritime Organization. – London : International Maritime Organization.
ISBN 9280111639 Hbk £4.50

→ International code of signals.

—International Conference on Liability and Compensation for Damage in Connection with the Carriage of Certain Substances By Sea : 1984
English. – International Maritime Organization. – London : International Maritime Organization.
ISBN 9280111922 Hbk £4.50

→ International conference on liability and compensation for damage in connexion with the carriage of certain substances by sea, 1984 : final act of the conference with resolutions : Protocol of 1984 to amend the International Convention on Civil Liability for Oil Pollution Damage, 1969 : Protocol of 1984 to amend the International Convention on the Establishment of an International Fund for Compensation for Oil Pollution Damage, 1971.

—International Maritime Dangerous Goods Code : Amendment 19-80
English. – International Maritime Organization. – London : International Maritime Organization, 1981.
ISBN 9280111264 Llf £11.00

—International Maritime Dangerous Goods Code : Amendment 20-82
English. – International Maritime Organization. – London : International Maritime Organization.
ISBN 9280111507 Hbk £12.50

—International Maritime Dangerous Goods Code : Amendment 22-84
English. – International Maritime Organization. – London : International Maritime Organization.
Hbk £18.00

—International Maritime Dangerous Goods Code : Amendment 22-86
English. – International Maritime Organization. – London : International Maritime Organization.
ISBN 9280112031 Hbk £2.50

—International Maritime Dangerous Goods Code : Amendments 21-83 and 21-84
English. – International Maritime Organization. – London : International Maritime Organization.
ISBN 9280111698 Hbk £8.00

—International Maritime Dangerous Goods Code : Indexes to Amendment 22-84
English. – International Maritime Organization. – London : International Maritime Organization.
ISBN 9280111957 Hbk £4.00

—International Maritime Dangerous Goods Code (IMDG, 5 Vols.)
English. – International Maritime Organization. – London : International Maritime Organization, 1981.
ISBN 9280111256 Llf £60.00

—Nineteen Seventy-Eight Protocol Relating to the International Convention for the Prevention of Pollution from Ships, 1973 : Regulations for the Prevention of Pollution by Oil-'86 Consolidated Version. – International Maritime Organization. – London : International Maritime Organization.
ISBN 9280111981 Hbk £7.00

—Noise Levels on Board Ships
English Edition. – International Maritime Organization. – London : International Maritime Organization, 1982.
Hbk £1.75

→ Official records of the International Conference on the Limitation of Liability for Maritime Claims, 1976.

—Oily-Water Separating and Monitoring Equipment. – International Maritime Organization. – English Edition. – London : International Maritime Organization, 1982.
Hbk £2.25

—Pesticides : Recommendations on the Safe Use of Pesticides in Ships
English Edition. – International Maritime Organization. – Rev. ed. – London : International Maritime Organization, 1981.
Hbk £1.25

—Procedures for the Control of Ships. – International Maritime Organization. – English Edition. – London : International Maritime Organization, 1982.
Hbk £2.00

—Regulations for the Prevention of Pollution by Oil. – International Maritime Organization. – London : International Maritime Organization, 1982.
Hbk £5.50

—Resolutions and Other Decisions of the Assembly : 11th Session 1979 (Res. 410-462)
English. – International Maritime Organization. – London : International Maritime Organization.
ISBN 9280111027 Hbk £10.00

—Resolutions and Other Decisions of the Assembly : 12th Session 1981 (Res. 463-512)
English. – International Maritime Organization. – London : International Maritime Organization, 1982.
ISBN 9280111477 Hbk £12.00

—Resolutions and Other Decisions of the Assembly : 13th Session 1983 (Res. 513-557)
English. – International Maritime Organization. – London : International Maritime Organization.
ISBN 9280111752 Hbk £12.00

International Maritime Organization Staff
IMO-UNEP Guidelines on Oil Spill Disperant Application and Environmental Considerations : Practical Information On the Use of Disperants for Dealing With Oil Spills at Sea. – International Maritime Organization Staff. – London : International Maritime Organization, 1982.
Hbk £2.00

—Prevention, 4 Vols.
Vol. 1. – International Maritime Organization Staff. – rev. ed. – London : International Maritime Organization, 1983.
– (Manual on Oil Pollution Ser.).
Hbk £3.75

—Supplement Relating to the International Convention for the Prevention of Pollution of the Sea by Oil : 1954 (As Amended in 1962 and 1969). – International Maritime Organization Staff. – London : International Maritime Organization, 1981.
Hbk £1.25

International media law : a monthly bulletin on rights, clearances and legal practice. – London : Oyez Longman, 1982.
ISBN 02636395

International medical malpractice law : a comparative law study of civil liability arising from medical care / by Dieter Giesen : with a foreword by Lord Kilbrandon. – Tubingen : Mohr, 1988.
940p; 24cm.
Includes bibliography and index.
ISBN 9024737052 Germany £ :
ISBN 3166453229

International Medical Malpractice Law : A Comparative Law Study of Civil Liability from Medical Care. – Martinus Nijhoff.
ISBN 9024737052 Hbk £137.00

International Mergers and Acquisitions. – Oxford : Blackwell Scientific.
ISBN 0631142489 Hbk

International mergers and acquisitions / Peter Earl and Frederick G. Fisher, III. – London : Euromoney, 1986.
vii,129p.
ISBN 090312193X

International migration law / Richard Plender. – Rev. 2nd ed. – Dordrecht, Netherlands : M. Nijhoff, 1987.
xxvii,587p.
Includes index.
ISBN 9024736048

International Monetary Fund 1972-1978 : Cooperation on trial / edited by Margaret Garritsen de Vries. – 3 v. – Washington, D.C. : International Monetary Fund, 1985.
Vols.I and II: Narrative and analysis. Vol.III: Documents.
ISBN 0939934434

International Monetary Fund → International Monetary Fund 1972-1978 : Cooperation on trial.
→ Legal and institutional aspects of the International Monetary System : selected essays.
→ Recent multilateral debt restructurings with official and bank creditors.

International monetary system. – 2nd ed. – Matthew Bender, 1984.
ISBN 0000999050 Hbk £26.50

International monetary system : efficiency and practical alternatives / Herbert G. Grubel. – 4th ed. – Harmondsworth : Penguin, 1984.
214p.
Bibliography: p201-206.
ISBN 0140808183

International monetary system and the less developed countries / Graham Bird. – 2nd ed. – London : Macmillan, 1982.
xi,352p.
Bibliography: p331-350.
ISBN 0333330021

International money : theory, evidence and institutions / Paul Hallwood and Ronald MacDonald with contributions from Robert Shaw. – Oxford : Basil Blackwell, 1986.
272p; 23cm.
Includes bibliography and index.
ISBN 0631144455 Hbk £25.00 :
ISBN 0631144463 Pbk £8.95

International money and finance / Michael Melvin. – New York : Harper & Row, 1985.
xiii,200p; 25cm.
Includes bibliographies and index.
ISBN 0060444177 £12.95

International money and the real world / Paul Davidson. – London : Macmillan, 1982.
XI,312p.

International money game. – 5th ed. – London : Macmillan, 1988.
ISBN 0333467817 Hbk £29.50
ISBN 0333467825 Pbk £9.95

International mutual asssistance in criminal matters : a discussion paper. – London : Criminal Department, Home Office, 1988.
6,24p.
Includes the text of the European Convention on Mutual Assitance in Criminal Matters.
ISBN 0862523362

International oil industry : an interdisciplinary perspective / edited by Judith Rees and Peter Odell. – Basingstoke : Macmillan, 1987.
xii,181p; 23cm.
Includes bibliographies and index.
ISBN 0333436601 £25.00

International Ombudsman Institute → Directory of ombudsmen and other complaint-handlers.
→ Seventh annual conference of Canadian legislative ombudsmen, Saskatoon, Saskatchewan, August 30 - September 3, 1981 : the ombudsman in the eighties : new challenges.

International Organisation for the Elimination of All Forms of Racial Discrimination → Witness of war crimes in Lebanon.

International organization and integration → International organization and integration : annotated basic doucments of international organizations and arrangements.

International organization and integration : annotated basic documents and descriptive directory of international organizations and arrangements / board of editors, P.J.G. Kapteyn ... et al. : with a foreword by Louis B. Sohn. – 2nd, completely rev. ed. n v. – The Hague : Martinus Nijhoff Publishers, 1981.
25cm.
Tables inserted in each volume. Includes indexes. Contents: 1A: The United Nations Organization - 2A: European Communities - 2B-2K.
ISBN 9024725798

International organization and integration : annotated basic doucments of international organizations and arrangements / selected by Louis B. Sohn. – Student ed. – Dordrecht Netherlands : Martinus Nijhoff, 1986.
xxviii, 1082 p.; 24 cm.
Includes index. Based on the five-volume set International organization and integration.
ISBN 0898389151 Pbk

International organizations / Clive Archer. – London : Allen & Unwin, 1983.
xii,193p; 23cm.
Bibliography: p180-188. - Includes index.
ISBN 0043201563 Hbk
ISBN 0043201571 Pbk

International organizations and the law of the sea. – Netherlands Institute for the Law of the Sea (NILOS). – Dordrecht : Nijhoff (Martinus), 1989.
712. – (ILOS yearbook 3).
An annual publication. Reproduces the most important documents related to the law of the sea that are issued each year by international organisations.
ISBN 1853331627 Hbk £97

International Organizations and the Law of the Sea : Documentary Yearbook 1985. – Netherlands Institute for the Law of the Sea (NILOS). – Dordrecht : Kluwer, 1987.
650p.
ISBN 9024734886 Hbk £275.00

International Patent Classification : Valid by the 1st January 1985, 9 Vols. – World Intellectual Property Organization. – 4th ed. – Cologne : Carl Heymanns Verlag, 1984.
ISBN 3452185990 Pbk DM618.00
Vol. 1, Section A: Human Necessities. –
133p.
ISBN 3452194140 Pbk DM69.00
Vol. 2, Section B: Performing Operations, Transporting. –
314p.
ISBN 3452194159 Pbk £143.00
Vol. 3, Section C: Chemistry; Metallurgy. –
213p.
ISBN 3452194167 Pbk £98.00
Vol. 4, Section D: Textiles and Paper. –
57p.
ISBN 3452194175 Pbk £40.00
Vol. 5, Section E: Fixed Constructions. –
71p.
ISBN 3452194183 Pbk £46.00
Vol. 6, Section F: Mechanical Engineering, Lighting, Heating, Weapons, Blasting. –
167p.
ISBN 3452194191 Pbk £88.00
Vol. 7, Section G: Physics. –
145p.
ISBN 3452194205 Pbk £77.00
Vol. 8, Section H: Electricity. –
137p.
ISBN 3452194213 Pbk £77.00
Vol. 9: Guide, Survey of Classes and Summary of Maingroups. –
xxx, 279p.
ISBN 3452194221 Pbk £46.00

International Peace Academy → Indian Ocean as a zone of peace : Workshop on the Indian Ocean as a Zone of Peace, Dhaka, People People's Republic of Bangladesh, November 23-25, 1985.

International petroleum exploration and exploitation agreements : legal, economic and policy aspects / by Keith W. Blinn ... et al. : preface by Ibrahim F.I. Shihata. – London : Euromoney Publications, 1986.
431p.
Bibliography: p.322-323.
ISBN 0903121921

International private law : cases and statutes / G. Maher. – Edinburgh : Green, 1985.
xx,294p; 22cm. – (Concise College Texts).
Bibliography: p.xx. - Includes index.
ISBN 0414007611 Pbk £17.50

International private trade. – 2nd ed. – Matthew Bender, 1981.
ISBN 0000999048 Hbk £26.50

International production and the multinational enterprise / John H. Dunning. – London : Allen & Unwin, 1981.
viii,439p; 23cm.
Includes bibliographies and index.
ISBN 0043303196 Hbk
ISBN 004330320X Pbk

International Protection of Minorities. – Delhi : Mittal Publications, 1986.
Hbk £160.00

International protection of the environment on a regional level. – Thessaloniki : Institute of Public International Law and International Relations, 1982.
xii,768p.
Includes bibliographies. English or French text.

International recognition of national identity cards : recommendation no.R(83)11 adopted by the Committee of Ministers of the Council of Europe on 23 September 1983 and Explanatory memorandum. – Council of Europe. – Strasbourg : Council of Europe, 1984.
10p; 21cm.
'... prepared by the ad hoc Committee of experts for identity documents and movement of persons (CAHID)'. At head of cover title: Legal Affairs.
ISBN 9287103186

International Register of Potentially Toxic Chemicals, 2 Vols. – United Nations. – London : HMSO, 1984.
Provides information on the danger to humans and the environment of chemicals and details of individual nations' controlling legislation.
ISBN 0119079860 Hbk £58.50

International regulation of data services: the debate over the trade and development issues. – London : Pinter, 1990.
250.
Bibliography and index included.
ISBN 0861878531 Hbk £30

International Regulation of Internal Resources : a Study of Law and Policy. – London : Eurospan.
ISBN 0813908795 Hbk £32.95

International Regulation Of Salvage At Sea. – London : Lloyd's of London Press.
ISBN 1850441502 Hbk £32.00

International reinsurance : the law and market practice : an RRG seminar. – 1. – Colchester : Lloyd's of London Press, 1982.
various pagings.

International review of contemporary law. – Brussels : International Association of Democratic Lawyers, 1982-.
Continues: Review of contemporary law.

International review of law and economics. – Sevenoaks : Butterworths, 1981.

International Road Transport Union → International carriage of goods by road (CMR).

International rules of law relating to bills of lading / compiled by W.E. Astle. – London : Fairplay, 1982.
72p; 25cm.
ISBN 0905045343 Pbk

International sanctions in contemporary perspective / Margaret P. Doxey. – Basingstoke : Macmillan, 1987.
xi,175p; 23cm.
Includes index.
ISBN 033338945X Hbk £27.50
ISBN 0333389468 Pbk £9.50

International securities : Law and practice / edited by J. Michael Robinson. – London : Euromoney, 1985.
xx,303p.
ISBN 0903121751

International Ship Arrest : A Practical Guide. – London : Lloyd's of London Press.
ISBN 1850441901 Hbk £40.00

International shipping. – London : Lloyds of London Press, 1988.
Examines the framework that shipping operates in, including the institutions and bodies of both governments and the shipping industry. Includes the Liner conference system, and freedom and cooperation versus protectionism and confrontation. The historical background of sea law is also covered.
ISBN 1850441510 Hbk

International Society for Military Law and Law of War → Protocol additional to the Geneva conventions for the protection of victims of international armed conflicts and the United Nations Convention on the Law of the Sea : repercussions on the law of naval warfare : report to the Committee for the Protection of Human Life in Armed Conflict of the International Society for Military Law and Law of War.

International space policy / McIntyre. – Quorum Press, 1988.
ISBN 0899302157 Hbk £39.25

International standards : aircraft nationality and registration marks : annex 7 to the Convention on International Civil Aviation. – International Civil Aviation Organization. – 4th ed. - July 1981. 1. – Montreal : International Civil Aviation Organization, 1981.
loose-leaf.
Kept up to date by amendments and supplements.

International standards : rules of the air : annex 2 to the Convention on International Civil Aviation. – International Civil Aviation Organization. – 8th ed. - July 1986. 1. – Montreal : International Civil Aviation Organization, 1986.
looseleaf.
Kept up to date by amendments and supplements.

International standards : units of measurement to be used in air and ground operations : annex 5 to the Convention on International Civil Aviation. – International Civil Aviation Organization. – 4th ed. - July 1979. 1. – Montreal : International Civil Aviation Organization, 1979 -.
loose-leaf.
Kept up to date by amendments and supplements.

International standards and recommended practices : aerodromes : annex 14 to the Convention on International Civil Aviation. – International Civil Aviation Organization. – 8th ed. - March 1984. 1. – Montreal : International Civil Aviation Organization, 1983.
looseleaf.
Kept up to date by amendments and supplements.

International standards and recommended practices : aeronautical charts : annex 4 to the Convention on International Civil Aviation. – International Civil Aviation Organization. – 8th ed. 1 v. – Montreal : International Civil Aviation Organization, 1985.
looseleaf.
Kept up to date by amendments and supplements.

International standards and recommended practices : aeronautical information services : annex 15 to the Convention on International Civil Aviation. – International Civil Aviation Organization. – 7th ed. - July 1987. 1. – Montreal : International Civil Aviation Organization, 1987.
looseleaf.
Kept up to date by amendments and supplements.

International standards and recommended practices : air traffic services ... : annex 11 to the Convention on International Civil Aviation. – International Civil Aviation Organization. – 8th ed. - July 1987. 1. – Montreal : International Civil Aviation Organization, 1987.
looseleaf.
Kept up to date by amendments and supplements.

International standards and recommended practices : aircraft accident investigation : annex 13 to the Convention on International Civil Aviation. – International Civil Aviation Organization. – 7th ed. 1. – Montreal : International Civil Aviation Organization, 1988.
looseleaf.
Kept up to date by amendments and supplements.

International standards and recommended practices : airworthiness of aircraft : annex 8 to the Convention on International Civil Aviation. – International Civil Aviation Organization. – 7th ed. - April 1983. 1. – Montreal : International Civil Aviation Organization, 1983.
looseleaf.
Kept up to date by amendments and supplements.

International standards and recommended practices : environmental protection : annex 16 to the Convention on International Civil Aviation Vol. 1 : Aircraft noise. – International Civil Aviation Organization. – 1st ed - 1981. 1. – Montreal : International Civil Aviation Organization, 1981.
loose-leaf; 28cm.
Supersedes: International standards and recommended practices: aircraft noise: annex 16 to the Convention on International Civil Aviation. 3rd ed. - July 1978. Current edition only kept. Kept up to date by amendments and supplements.
Vol. 2 : Aircraft engine emissions. – 1981.
loose-leaf; 28cm.
Supersedes: International standards and recommended practices : aircraft noise : annex 16 to the Convention on International Civil Aviation. 3rd ed. - July 1978. Kept up to date by amendments and supplements.

International standards and recommended practices : meteorological service for international air navigation : annex 3 to the Convention on International Civil Aviation. – International Civil Aviation Organization. – 10th ed. - July 1986. 1. – Montreal : International Civil Aviation Organisation, 1986.
looseleaf.
Kept up to date by amendments and supplements.

International standards and recommended practices : operation of aircraft : annex 6 to the Convention on International Civil Aviation Part 1 : International commercial air transport. – International Civil Aviation Organization. – 4th ed. - July 1983. 1. – Montreal : International Civil Aviation Organization, 1983.
looseleaf.
Kept up to date by amendments and supplements.
Part 2 : International general aviation. – 1983.
looseleaf.
Kept up to date by amendments and supplements.
Part 3 : International operations - helicopters. – 1986.
looseleaf.
Kept up to date by amendments and supplements.

International standards and recommended practices : personnel licensing : annex 1 to the Convention on International Civil Aviation. – International Civil Aviation Organization. – 7th ed. - September 1982. 1. – Montreal : International Civil Aviation Organization, 1982.
looseleaf.
Kept up to date by amendments and supplements.

International standards and recommended practices : security : safeguarding international civil aviation against acts of unlawful interference : annex 17 to the Convention on International Civil Aviation. – International Civil Aviation Organization. – 3rd ed. 1. – Montreal : International Civil Aviation Organization, 1986.
looseleaf.
Kept up to date by amendments and supplements.

International standards and recommended practices : the safe transport of dangerous goods by air : annex 18 to the Convention on International Civil Aviation. – International Civil Aviation Organization. – 1st ed. - January 1983. 1 v. – Montreal : International Civil Aviation Organization, 1983.
looseleaf.

International standards, recommended practices and procedures for air navigation services : aeronautical telecommunications : annex 10 to the Convention on International Civil Aviation. – International Civil Aviation Organization. – 4th ed. 1 v. – Montreal : International Civil Aviation Organization, 1985.
looseleaf.
Kept up to date by amendments and supplements.

International Stock Exchange of the United Kingdom and Republic of Ireland
Regulations of the International Stock Exchange, 31st May 1988. – International Stock Exchange of the United Kingdom and Republic of Ireland. – London : International Stock Exchange, 1988.
ca. 175p.
Supersedes The Sock Exchange regulations.
—Rules of the International Stock Exchange, 31st May 1988. – International Stock Exchange of the United Kingdom and Republic of Ireland. – London : International Stock Exchange, 1988.
ca. 100p.
Supersedes the Stock Exchange rules.

International syndicated loans / by Robert P. McDonald. – London : Euromoney, 1982.
ix,264p.
Bibliography: p.261-262. - Includes index.
ISBN 0903121441

International Tax Agreements : Supplement No. 40. – United Nations. – London : HMSO, 1985.
ISBN 0119083663 Hbk £5.70

International tax avoidance / Board of Inland Revenue. – London : Board of Inland Revenue, 1981.
66 leaves.

International tax avoidance and evasion : colloquy of 5-7 March 1980 (Strasbourg), compendium of documents. – Amsterdam : International Bureau of Fiscal Documentation, 1981.
184p.
ISBN 9070125196

International tax avoidance and evasion : four related studies. – Paris : O.E.C.D., 1987.
112p.
ISBN 9264129251

International tax glossary / W. G Kuiper. – Amsterdam : International Bureau of Fiscal Documentation, 1988.
xii, 322 p.; 19 cm.
'Prepared by a working group ... headed by Mr. W.G. Kuiper'–P. i 'The first volume of a new series of books, entitled 'International tax manuals''–P. vi.
ISBN 9070125366

International tax planner's manual / Horwath & Horwath International. – Rev. impression. – North Ryde, N.S.W. : CCH Australia, 1985.
xvi,547p.
Includes index.
ISBN 0869038273

International tax planning / Barry Spitz. – 2nd ed. – London : Butterworths, 1983.
xxiii,178p.
This book for the tax planner dealing with international tax issues analyzes the methods of international tax planning and explains the basic techniques. Statutes and treaties in conjunction with case law are used to illustrate the analysis.
ISBN 0406382379 Hbk £18.00

International Tax Planning for United Kingdom Companies. – 2nd ed. – London : Deloitte Haskins & Sells.
ISBN 0863491308 Pbk £4.95

International tax planning manual / by Horwath & Horwath International. – 2. – North Ryde, N.S.W. : CCH Australia, 1986.
looseleaf.
Includes index.
ISBN 0869037595

International tax problems of charities and other private institutions with similar tax treatment : proceedings of a seminar held in 1985 during the 39th Congress of the International Fiscal Association. – International Fiscal Association. – Deventer Netherlands : Kluwer Law and Taxation Publishers, 1986.
Conference held in London, England.
ISBN 9065442707

International Tax Systems and Planning Techniques. – London : Oyez Longman, 1984.
ISBN 085120760X Llf £75.00

International tax treatment of common law trusts : proceedings of a seminar held in New York in 1986 during the 40th Congress of the International Fiscal Association. – Deventer Netherlands : Kluwer Law and Taxation Publishers, 1987.
ISBN 9065443460

International taxation encyclopaedia. – London : Butterworths, 1988.
Service.
Hbk

International Technology Joint Ventures in the Countries of the Pacific Rim. – Butterworths, 1988.
xvii, 211p.
Discusses the legal forms best suited for a joint venture in particular countries, how the operation is affected by the country's tax laws, and the available protection for intellectual property. Studies Australia, Canada, China, Taiwan, Hong Kong, Japan, Korea, New Zealand, Singapore, Thailand and the United States of America.
ISBN 0880632364 Hbk £125.00

International technology licensing : compensation, costs, and negotiation / Farok J. Contractor. – Lexington : Lexington Books, 1981.
xiv,193p; 24cm.
Bibliography: p185-189. - Includes index.
ISBN 0669043591 £22.50

International Telecommunication Convention : Final Protocol, Additional Protocols, Compulsory Settlement of Disputes - Nairobi 1982
French. – Geneva : International Telecommunications Union.
ISBN 9261016529 Hbk £27.00
English. –
ISBN 9261016510 Hbk £27.00
Spanish. –
ISBN 9261016537 Hbk £27.00

International timesharing. – 2nd ed. – London : Sweet & Maxwell, 1986.
ISBN 095041767X Pbk £24.50

International timesharing / by James Edmonds. – 1st ed. – London : Services To Lawyers, 1984.
374p.
Bibliography: p.363-365. - Includes index. Includes precedents. Subtitle on cover: a review of United Kingdom law and that of other relevant jurisdictions in relation to timeshare schemes and purchases, including extensive precedents for use in the United Kingdom.
ISBN 0950417653

International timesharing. – 2nd ed. – London : Services to Lawyers, 1986.
xix,591p.
Previous ed.: 1984. Bibliography: p.579-581. - Includes index. Includes precedents. Subtitle on cover: a review of United Kingdom law and that of other relevant jurisdictions in relation to timeshare schemes and purchases, including extensive precedents.
ISBN 095041767X

International Trade. – Routledge.
ISBN 0415003962 Hbk £40.00
ISBN 0415003970 Pbk £14.95

International trade : law and practice / edited by Julian D.M. Lew and Clive Stanbrook. – London : Euromoney Publications, 1983.
xxiii,213p.
Includes bibliographical references and index.
ISBN 0903121468

International Trade Development Centre → Export (Incentives and Miscellaneous Provisions) Decree 1986 : with explanatory note on its provisions.

International trade finance / Weston. – North Ryde : Law Book Co, 1986.
ISBN 0455203504 Pbk £11.25

International trade in endangered species. – Dordrecht : Nijhoff (Martinus), 1989.
424.
Discusses each article of the Convention on International Trade in Endangered Species, each with a separate chapter. Gives background information on the drafting of the treaty, problems of implementation and economic consequences of world trade in wildlife and plants.
ISBN 0792301145 Hbk £75

International trade in service : securities. – Paris : OECD, 1987.
125p.

International trade law and practice of the European Community : EEC anti-dumping and other trade protection laws / Ivo van Bael, Jean-Francois Bellis. – Bicester : CCH, 1985.
viii,438p.
Discusses the Community's four main methods of trade protection; anti-dumping rules, anti-subsidy rules, safe-guard measures, and the 'New Commercial Policy Instrument', and comments on the EEC and ECSC Anti-dumping Regulations. Contains tables and annexes.
ISBN 0863250602

International trade regulation : GATT, the United States and the European Community / Edmond McGovern. – 2nd ed. – Exeter : Globefield, 1986.
xliv,629p; 25cm.
Previous ed. 1982. Bibliography: p599-619. - Includes index.
ISBN 0950846341 £36.00

International transactions and Australian income tax : being a commentary on Division 13 of the Income Tax Assessment Act 1936 together with the text of the Legislation / by E. F. Mannix. – Sydney : Butterworths, 1982.
x,46p.
Includes index.
ISBN 0409493554

International Transportation : Law of Carriage by Air. – New Delhi : Deep and Deep Publications, 1987.
328p.
ISBN 8171000010 Hbk £110.00

International treasury management. – Cambridge : Woodhead-Faulkner, 1987.
ISBN 0859413632 Hbk £45.00

International Treaties and Conventions 1983, Vol. 2. – Kingston : Australian Government Publishing Service, 1986.
360p.
ISBN 0644047143 Hbk £18.70

International Treaties and Conventions 1984. – Kingston : Australian Government Publishing Service, 1986.
ISBN 0644047402 Hbk £2.20

International Union for Conservation of Nature and Natural Resources →International wildlife law : an analysis of international treaties concerned with the conservation of wildlife.
—IUCN bulletin : a quarterly journal of the International Union for Conservation of Nature and Natural Resources. – International Union for Conservation of Nature and Natural Resources. – Gland, Switzerland : The Union, 1953 -.
ISBN 00209058
→ Legal measures for the conservation of marine mammals.

International Union for the Protection of Industrial Property →Committee of Experts on Biotechnological Inventions and Industrial Property : third session, Geneva, June 29 to July 3, 1987 : report prepared by the International Bureau.
→ Committee of Experts on Biotechological Inventions and Industrial property : first session, Geneva, November 5 to 9, 1984.
→ Report.

International wildlife law : an analysis of international treaties concerned with the conservation of wildlife / by Simon Lyster. – Cambridge : Grotius Publications, 1985.
xxiii,470p.
Covers the international conventions on whaling, wetlands, protection of cultural and natural heritage, international trade in endangered species, and Antarctic marine living resources.
ISBN 0906496225

Internationalisation of banking : the policy issues / by R.M. Pecchioli. – Paris : O.E.C.D., 1983.
221p.
Includes bibliographical references.
ISBN 9264124888

Internationalizing the seabed / Roderick Ogley. – Aldershot : Gower, 1984.
vii,256,9p; 23cm.
Bibliography: p248-256. - Includes index.
ISBN 0566006294 £17.95

Internatioinal law in a divided world. – Oxford : Oxford University Press, 1988.
ISBN 019876233X Pbk £16.95

Internoscia, Jerome
New Code of International Law. – Berrima : Peace Plans.

Interpersonal Conflict of Laws in India, Pakistan and Bangladesh. – Bombay : Tripathi, 1981.
350p.
bd £50.00

Interpersonal conflict of laws in India, Pakistan and Bangladesh / David Pearl. – London : Stevens, 1981.
xxviii,176p; 25cm.
Bibliography: p.165-69. Includes index.
ISBN 0420457704

Interplay of contracts : papers presented at the International Bar Association's 20th Biennial Conference, Vienna 1984 / International Bar Assoication. Section on Business Law. International Construction Contracts Committee. – London : International Bar Association, 1984.
102p.
Includes bibliographical references.

Interpretation Act, 1967 (Act 23 of 1967). – Kuala Lumpur : International Law Books Services.
Hbk £6.00

Interpretation of contracts. – London : Sweet & Maxwell, 1989.
Covers the object of integration, implied terms, the canons of construction, ambiguity and uncertainty, mistakes and inconsistencies, preliminary parts of the deed, parcels and subject matter of the contract, exemption clauses, certificates, consents and similar clauses, stipulations as to time, penalties, terminations and forfeiture clauses.
ISBN 042136940X Hbk £45.00

Interpretation of Statues. – 3rd ed. – Lucknow : Eastern Book Company, 1986.
704p.
Hbk £180.00

Interpretation of Statutes. – Bombay : Tripathi, 1981.
Hbk £45.00

Interpretation of Statutes. – 2nd ed. – Calcutta : Eastern Law House, 1983.
Hbk £108.00

Interpretation of statutes / Gail-Maryse Cockram. – 3rd ed. – Cape Town : Juta, 1987.
xvi,181p.
Previous ed.: 1983. Includes index.
ISBN 0702118346

Interpretation of Statutes. – Durban : Butterworths.
Hbk

Interpretation of Statutes. – 2nd ed. – Lahore : Pakistan Law Times, 1981.
Hbk £44.00

Interpretation of Taxing Statutes. – Allahabad : Law Publishing House, 1984.
Hbk £90.00

Interpretation of wills / Law Reform Commission of British Columbia. – Vancouver : Law Reform Commission of British Columbia, 1981.
iv,164p. – (Working paper).

Interpretation of Wills. – Victoria : Government of British Columbia, 1982.
Hbk £2.50

Interpreting bilingual legislation / Michael Beaupre. – 2nd ed. – Toronto : Carswell, 1986.
xvi, 236 p.; 24 cm.
Re ed. of: Construing bilingual legislation in Canada. Includes index. Bibliography: p. 223-227.
ISBN 0459390600

Interpreting company reports and accounts / Sugden. – 3rd ed. – Cambridge : Woodhead-Faulkner, 1986.
ISBN 085941325X Hbk £25.00
ISBN 0859413268 Pbk £14.95

Interpreting US Financial Statements. – London : Butterworths.
ISBN 0406502412 Hbk £45.00

Interprovincial product liability litigation / Robert J. Sharpe. – Toronto : Butterworths, 1982.
xxi,145p.
Includes bibliographical references and index.
ISBN 0409866423

Interspousal immunity in tort / Law Reform Commission of British Columbia. – Vancouver : The Commission, 1982.
iii,42p. – (Working paper).
Includes bibliographical references.

Interspousal Immunity in Tort. – Victoria : Government of British Columbia, 1983.
Hbk £1.35

Intervention in world politics / edited by Hedley Bull. – Oxford : Clarendon, 1984.
198p; 23cm.
Includes index.
ISBN 019827467X £12.50

Interviewing and Counselling : Skills for Legal Practitioners. – Toronto : Butterworths, 1987.
168p.
ISBN 0409873454 Hbk

Intestate succession and legal rights / Scottish Law Commission. – Edinburgh : The Commission, 1986.
v,241p. – (Consultative memorandum).
Includes bibliographical references. Catalogued from cover.

Intimate Fragments : Private Writings of a Supreme Court Judge. – Halifax : Nimbus, 1985.
140p.
ISBN 0920852424 Pbk £12.95

Into the 1990's : Voluntary Organisations and Public Sector. – Royal Institute of Public Administration.
ISBN 0900628464 Pbk £3.00

Intolerable inquisition? : reflections on the law of tax / by Hubert Monroe. – London : Stevens published under the auspices of Hamlyn Trust, 1981.
xiii,84p; 19cm.
ISBN 0420461906 Hbk £11.25
ISBN 0420462007 4.60

Intra-Group Arrangements under Articles 85 and 86 of the Treaty Establishing the European Economic Community : with a Comparative Survey. – Bern : Peter Lang, 1984.
xii, 173p.
ISBN 3820451668 Pbk £41.00

Introducing Police Work. – Unwin Hyman.
ISBN 004363012X Hbk £25.00
ISBN 0043630081 Pbk £9.95

Introducing the law / Dennis Easton ... et al. – 2nd ed. – North Ryde : CCH Australia, 1985.
x,374p.
Includes bibliographical references.
ISBN 0869035002

Introduction of P & I / Bill Robertson, Steven J. Hazelwood. – London : Lloyds of London Press, 1988.
A practical rather than academic text, covering the origins of P and I clubs, the scope of cover, specialist clubs, and claims and claims handling.
ISBN 1850441634 Hbk

Introduction to Accountancy / Mellett. – London : Chapman Publishers.
ISBN 1853960209 Pbk £13.95

Introduction to Accounting. – Pitman.
ISBN 0273028804 Pbk £6.95

Introduction to accounting for business studies / Harden. – 4th ed. – London : Butterworths, 1985.
ISBN 040801542 Pbk £11.50

Introduction to administrative law / Peter Cane. – Oxford : Clarendon, 1986.
xxii,325p; 23cm. – (Clarendon law series).
Includes index.
ISBN 0198254849 Hbk £22.50
ISBN 0198254857 Pbk £ 9.50

Introduction to Administrative Law. – Oxford : ESC Publishing Ltd, 1984.
296p.
ISBN 0906214254 Hbk £19.95
ISBN 0906214246 Pbk £11.95

Introduction to air law / by I.H.Ph. Diederiks-Verschoor. – 3rd rev. & enl. ed. – Deventer : Kluwer Law and Taxation, 1988.
xxiv, 197p.
Bibliography: pp.177-189. - Includes index. Translation of: Inleiding tot het luchtrecht.
ISBN 9065443754

Introduction to air law / by I.H. Ph. Diederiks-Verschoor. – Deventer, Netherlands : Kluwer Law and Taxation Publishers, 1983.
Includes index and bibliography. Translation of: Inleiding tot het luchtrecht.
ISBN 9065440976 : est.

Introduction to animal law. – London : Academic Press, 1987.
ISBN 0121880303 Hbk

Introduction to British constitutional law. – London : Blackstone Press, 1985.
ISBN 0906322685 Pbk £9.95

Introduction to British constitutional law / D.C.M. Yardley. – 6th ed. – London : Butterworths, 1984.
xviii, 180p; 23cm.
Previous ed.: 1978. Includes index.
ISBN 0406690073 Hbk £12.00
ISBN 0406690081 Pbk £10.50

Introduction to business associations in Canada : cases, notes, and materials / by R.L. Simmonds and Peter P. Mercer. – Toronto, Canada : Carswell Legal Publications, 1984.
xxviii, 778 p.; 25 cm.
Spine title: Business associations in Canada.
ISBN 0459365304 Pbk

Introduction to Business Law / Dawson. – Plymouth : Macdonald & Evans.
ISBN 0071211173 Pbk £6.95

Introduction to Business Law / K.E. Lindgren. – 4th ed. – North Ryde : Law Book Co, 1984.
xv, 285p.
ISBN 0455202117 Pbk £7.50

Introduction to Canadian Law of Trusts. – London : Butterworths.
ISBN 0409868108 Hbk £22.00

Introduction to Capital Gains Tax. – Butterworths.
ISBN 0409493066 Pbk £7.95

Introduction to civil procedure in Malaysia and Singapore / by Grace Chang. – Singapore : Malayan Law Journal Pte., 1986.
iii,165p.
Includes index.
ISBN 997170045X

Introduction to commercial law / F. B. Wright. – 2nd ed. – London : Sweet & Maxwell, 1982.
240p. – (Concise College Texts).
Previous ed. published as: ONC-OND commercial law. 1976.
ISBN 0421285109 Pbk £10.00

Introduction to Company Law. – 3rd ed. – North Ryde : Law Book Co, 1985.
xx, 271p.
ISBN 0455204663 Pbk £25.00
ISBN 0455205655 Hbk £38.00
1986 Supplement. –
35p.
ISBN 0455207240 Pbk £5.00

Introduction to company law. – North Ryde : Law Book Co, 1987.
ISBN 0455207720 Hbk
ISBN 0455207739 Pbk

Introduction to company law in New Zealand / by J.F. Northey. – 9th ed. – Wellington : Butterworths, 1981.
xxxvi,452p.
Previous ed.: 1976. Includes index.
ISBN 0409600911

Introduction to comparative law / Konrad Zweigert and Hein Kotz : translated from the German by Tony Weir. – 2nd rev ed. 2. – Oxford : Clarendon Press, 1987.
Previous edition: 1977. Includes indexes. Contents: 1 The framework. - 2 The institutions of private law. German title: Einfuhrung in die Rechtsvergleichung auf dem Gebiete des Privatsrechts.

Introduction to Conflict of Laws. – 2nd ed. – Butterworths, 1986.
240p.
ISBN 0409805920 Pbk £38.95

Introduction to conveyancing. – 2nd ed. – London : Longman Professional, 1983.
ISBN 0851207383 Pbk £14.95

Introduction to criminal and civil litigation / Brian Raymond. – London : Oyez, 1981.
170p; 24cm.
ISBN 0851205569 Pbk

Introduction to criminal law / Jones. – 10th ed. – London : Butterworths, 1984.
ISBN 0406570507 Hbk £20.00
ISBN 0406570515 Pbk £15.95

Introduction to criminal law / Philip Asterley Jones, Richard Card. – 11th ed. 1 (various pagings). – London : Butterworths, 1988. 22cm.
Previous ed.: 1984. Includes index.
ISBN 0406570523 Hbk £20.00
ISBN 0406570531 Pbk £13.95

Introduction to English Canon Law / Briden. – 2nd ed. – London : Dent (J M) & Sons, 1985.
ISBN 0264668545 Pbk £11.95

Introduction to English law / William Geldart. – 9th ed. – Oxford : Oxford University Press, 1984.
viii,180p; 20cm.
Previous ed.: published as Elements of English law. 1975. Bibliography: p166-170. - Includes index.
ISBN 0192891715 Pbk £3.95

Introduction to English Law. – 11th ed. – London : Butterworths, 1985.
ISBN 0406605017 Hbk £18.00
ISBN 0406605025 Pbk £12.95

Introduction to English Law : ICSA Study Text. – London : BPP.
ISBN 0862772044 Pbk £12.95

Introduction To Equity In Nigeria. – Sweet & Maxwell, 1975.
ISBN 0421205709 Pbk £12.50

Introduction to European legal history. – London : Butterworths, 1985.
ISBN 086205107X Hbk £35.00
ISBN 0862051088 Pbk £16.95

Introduction To Family Law 1987. – London : Law Book Co.
ISBN 0455207607 Pbk £20.00

Introduction to Family Law. – Butterworths, 1983.
180p.
Outlines how the law operates in each common law province. Coverage includes marriage, rights and duties, marriage and property, termination of marriage, children, and reform in children's law.
ISBN 040984828X Pbk £21.95

Introduction to Family Law. – Toronto : Butterworths, 1983.
180p.
Pbk £21.95

Introduction to Fitzherbert's Abridgement / by Frederick Lister Boersma. – Abingdon : Professional Books, 1981.
6,117p; 23cm.
ISBN 0862050413

Introduction to Foreign Exchange. – 2nd ed. – Cambridge : Woodhead-Faulkner, 1984.
ISBN 0859412865 Pbk £9.95

Introduction To French Law / Walton. – 3rd ed. – Oxford : Oxford University Press, 1967.
ISBN 0198251785 Hbk £17.00

Introduction to General Average. – Witherby, 1986.
ISBN 0948691107 Pbk £6.00

Introduction to GST : a Practical Guide. – 2nd ed. – North Ryde : C.C.H. Australia, 1986.
ca 100p.
ISBN 0864750625 Hbk

Introduction to ICC rules on international contracts. – International Chamber of Commerce. – Paris : ICC Services S.A.R.L., 1981.
49p.

Introduction to insurance / G.C.A. Dickson, J.T. Steele. – 2nd ed. – London : Pitman, 1984.
xii,212p.
Includes index.
ISBN 0273027905

Introduction to intellectual property law / Jeremy Phillips. – London : Butterworths, 1986.
230p; 22cm.
Includes index.
ISBN 0406258325 Hbk £18.00
ISBN 0406258333 Pbk £12.50

Introduction to International Law French /. – Toronto : Butterworths.
ISBN 0409824852 Pbk £31.95

Introduction to international law / J.G. Starke. – 9th ed. – London : Butterworths, 1984.
xxviii,664p; 23cm.
Previous ed.: 1977. Includes index.
ISBN 0406659575 Hbk £
ISBN 0406659583 Pbk

Introduction to International Law / Armand L.C. de Mestral. – 2nd ed. – Butterworths, 1987.
472p.
Contains new material on the treaty-implementation power in Canada, recognition of foreign states and governments, sovereign immunity, the international protection of human rights, the international protection of the environment, the law of the sea, fisheries, international crimes, and extraterritoriality.
ISBN 0409875597 Pbk £70.00

Introduction To Islamic Law. – Oxford : Oxford University Press, 1964.
ISBN 0198251610 Hbk £9.50

An Introduction to Labour Arbitration. – Praeger.
ISBN 0275930475 Pbk £39.50

Introduction to Land Law / D W McMorland. – 2nd ed. – London : Butterworths, 1987.
ISBN 0409636045 Hbk £111.50
ISBN 0409701726 Pbk £51.00

Introduction to Land Law / D.W. McMorland. – 2nd ed. – Butterworths, 1987.
708p.
Covers title to land, freehold estates, future interests, leasehold estates, easements and profits, licenses, land as security, mortgages and other charges, the holding of interest in land, the transfer of interest in land, covenants affecting freehold land, and the extent of landholder's rights.
ISBN 0409701726 Pbk £82.50

Introduction to Land Law. – 4th ed. – London : Butterworths, 1988.
ISBN 0406648395 Pbk £14.95
ISBN 0406648441 Hbk £30.00

Introduction to land law / J.G. Riddall. – 4th ed. – London : Butterworths, 1988.
547p; 25cm.
Previous ed.: 1983. Includes index.
ISBN 0406648441 Hbk £24.00 :
ISBN 040664845X Pbk £16.00

Introduction to land law / J.G. Riddall. – 3rd ed. – London : Butterworth, 1983.
xxxii,487p; 26cm.
Previous ed.: 1979. Includes index.
ISBN 0406648344 Hbk £
ISBN 0406648395 Pbk unpriced

Introduction to Law. – ILEX. – 2nd ed. – London : Sweet & Maxwell, 1987.
ISBN 0421367601 Pbk £17.00

Introduction to Law. – 3rd ed. – Weidenfeld & Nicolson.
– (Law In Context Series).
ISBN 0297793403 Hbk £18.95
ISBN 0297793411 Pbk £9.50

Introduction to law / by L.A. Rutherford, I.A. Todd and M.G. Woodley. – 2nd ed. – London : Sweet & Maxwell published in association with the Institute of Legal Executives, 1987.
400p; 26cm.
Previous ed.: 1982. Includes index.
ISBN 0421367601 Pbk £17.50

Introduction to law / by L.A. Rutherford, I.A. Todd, M.G. Woodley. – London : Sweet and Maxwell published in association with the Institute of Legal Executives, 1982.
xxiii,379p; 25cm.
Includes index.
ISBN 0421293802 Pbk £14.50

Introduction to law in the Republic of Ireland : its history, principles, administration & substance / Richard H. Grimes and Patrick T. Horgan. – Portmarnock : Wolfhound, 1981.
368p; 22cm.
Bibliography: p348-351. - Includes index.
ISBN 0905473558 Pbk £15.00
ISBN 0905473566 unpriced

Introduction to Law of Trusts. – London : Financial Training, 1986.
ISBN 185185021X Pbk £9.95

Introduction to legal method / Anthony M. Dugdale. – 2nd ed. – London : Sweet & Maxwell, 1984.
xxiii,307p; 22cm.
Previous ed.: 1977. Bibliography: p296-298. - Includes index.
ISBN 0421297700 Hbk £10.75
ISBN 0421297808 Pbk £6.50

Introduction to legal practice
Vol.2 : edited by Charles Blake and Grenfell Huddy / Charles Blake, Grenfell Huddy. – London : Published in association with the Institute of Legal Executives by Sweet & Maxwell, 1983.
xii,287p; 25cm.
Includes index.
ISBN 0421293004 Pbk £14.50
Vol.2 : edited by Craig Osborne. – 1987.
300p; 26cm.
Previous ed.: 1983. Includes index.
ISBN 0421367903 Pbk £16.50

Introduction to Legal Studies. – 4th ed. – Butterworths, 1984.
456p.
ISBN 0409494038 Pbk £22.50

Introduction to Legislative Drafting. – 2nd ed. in prep. – Bombay : Tripathi.

Introduction to Mercantile Law / Swanepoel, Makins, Lapping and Reynecke. – Durban : Professional Publisher, 1984.
ISBN 0409057800 Pbk £39.00

Introduction to Negotiable Instrument Act. – Bombay : Universal Book Corporation.
Hbk £6.00

Introduction to New Zealand Law / J T Farrand. – 4th ed. – London : Butterworths, 1981.
ISBN 0409655376 Pbk £34.00

Introduction to Nigerian Company Law. – London : Sweet & Maxwell.
ISBN 0421312203 Hbk
ISBN 0421312300 Pbk

Introduction To Nigerian Law. – Sweet & Maxwell.
ISBN 0421239409 Hbk £17.50
ISBN 0421239506 Pbk

Introduction to ordinary civil procedure in the sheriff court / Brian Kearney. – Edinburgh : Law Society of Scotland, 1982.
xvi,233,1p.
Bibliography: p.233-234.
ISBN 0902023071

Introduction to partnership law / Geoffrey Morse. – London : Financial Training, 1986.
xiv,176p; 23cm.
Includes index.
ISBN 1851850252 Pbk £6.95

Introduction To Philosophy Of Law. – Rev Ed. – Yale University Press, 1954.
ISBN 0300001886 Pbk £7.95

Introduction to Property. – London : Butterworths, 1988.
ISBN 0406581002 Hbk
ISBN 0406581010 Pbk

Introduction to Property Law / B. M. Dwyer. – Sydney : Butterworths, 1988.
240p.
This volume, intended for student use, describes concepts of property, tenure and estates, registration, the Torrens system, gifts, leases, covenants, mortgages, and other topics.
ISBN 0409493082 Pbk £29.00

Introduction to Property Valuation. – 2nd ed. – London : Estates Gazette, 1982.
ISBN 0728200589 Pbk £6.50

Introduction to Quebec Law / David Franklin. – 3rd ed. – Toronto : Copp Clark, 1983.
352p : Illus.
ISBN 0773042903 Pbk £15.37

Introduction to Quebec legal bibliography : 1980 CALL pre- conference workshop, May 20, 1980 - Montreal, Quebec. – 1 (various pagings). – Toronto : Canadian Association of Law Libraries, 1981.

Introduction to real property gains taxation in Malaysia / by Arjunan Subramaniam. – Kuala Lumpur : Malayan Law Journal, 1982.
x,121p.
Bibliography: p.x. - Includes index.

Introduction to real property gains taxation in Malaysia. – Singapore : Malayan Law Journal, 1982.
121.
Outlines the provisions of the Real Property Gains Tax Act 1976, giving the background and general principles of the tax computation, and examine specific cases. Discusses the administration involved in the returns and assessments, recovery and collection, the offence, and penalties indicated. Appendix reproduces the Real Property Gains Tax Act 1976, and other Acts.
Hbk

Introduction to Real Property Law. – 3rd ed. – Butterworths, 1987.
120p.
Covers the doctrine of the estate in land, concurrent ownership, a prologue to modern law, and the statutes of uses and modern law. Takes into account recent changes in this area, including family law, easements, and water rights.
ISBN 0409808849 Hbk £23.95

Introduction to revenue law / F.R. Davies. – 2nd ed. – London : Sweet & Maxwell, 1985.
xxii,416p; 22cm.
Previous ed. by F.R. Davies. 1980. Includes index.
ISBN 0421334304 Hbk £18.00
ISBN 0421334401 Pbk £13.95

Introduction to risk management. – 2nd ed. – Cambridge : Woodhead-Faulkner, 1986.
ISBN 0859413322 Hbk £19.95

Introduction To Roman Law. – Oxford : Oxford University Press, 1962.
ISBN 0198760639 Pbk £7.95

Introduction to Roman law / by Ph. J. Thomas. – Deventer Netherlands : Kluwer Law and Taxation Publishers, 1986.
xv, 168 p.; 25 cm.
Bibliography: p. 168.
ISBN 9065442456 Pbk

Introduction to Shii law : a bibliographical study / Hossein Modarressi Tabatabai. – London : Ithaca Press, 1984.
258p; 24cm.
Bibliography: p218-237. - Includes index.
ISBN 0863720153 £18.00

Introduction to Social Administration in Britain. – 6th ed. – London : Hutchinson, 1985.
– (Politics Ser.).
ISBN 0091599717 Hbk £7.95

Introduction to Swedish law / edited by Stig Stromholm. – 2nd ed. – Stockholm, Sweden : Norstedts, 1988.
532 p.; 23 cm.
Includes bibliographies and index.
ISBN 9118771521 Hbk £382.00

Introduction to Swedish law / edited by Stig Stromholm. – 2 vols. – Deventer : Kluwer, 1981.
436p; 23cm.
Includes bibliographies.
ISBN 9065440194 Hbk £212.00

Introduction to Swedish Law. – 2nd ed. – Stockholm : Almqvist & Wiksell.
ISBN 9118771521 Hbk

Introduction to Swiss law / edited by F. Dessemontet and T. Ansay. – Deventer : Kluwer law and taxation, 1981.
x,292p.
Bibliography: p.273-286. - Includes index.
ISBN 9065440208

Introduction to tax appeals in Malaysia : notes on practice and procedure in appeals to the Special Commissioners of Income Tax / by Sim Ewe Eong : with a foreword by Tun Dr. Mohamed Suffian. – Kuala Lumpur : Malayan Law Journal, 1981.
xii,88p.
ISBN 9971700182

Introduction to Taxation in New Zealand. – Butterworths, 1988.
470p.
ISBN 0409788570 Pbk £45.00

Introduction to the Australian Constitution. – 4th ed. – North Ryde : Law Book Co, 1987.
x, 264p.
Pbk

Introduction to the Australian constitution. – 3rd ed. – London : Law Book Co, 1983.
ISBN 0455202109 Pbk £10.00

Introduction to the Conflict of Laws. – London : Butterworths.
ISBN 0406500487 Pbk £14.95

Introduction to the Constitution of India, Eleventh Edition. – 7th repr. 1985. – New Delhi : Prentice-Hall.
478p.
ISBN 0986924194 Hbk £35.00

Introduction to the Criminal Law of Queensland and Western Australia / R.G. Kenny. – 2nd ed. – Butterworths, 1984.
259p.
The new edition of this introductory text covers the changes in the law since July 1977. Contained are materials on the extraterritorial competence of the respective State Parliaments and a table of comparative sections, including provisions of the Tasmanian Criminal Code.
ISBN 040949433X Pbk £38.50

Introduction to the Criminal Law of Queensland and WQ / Kenny. – 2nd ed. – London : Butterworths, 1984.
ISBN 040949433X Pbk £23.20

Introduction to the Criminal Process in Canada. – Agincourt : Carswell, 1988.
246p.
This is a comprehensive guide to Canadian criminal procedure. The various stages of the criminal process are outlined.
Hbk £40.50

Introduction to the history of Mexican law / Guillermo Floris Margadant S. – 1st English ed. – London : Oceana Publications, 1981.
Includes bibliographical references and index. Translation of: Introduccion a la historia del derecho mexicano, 4th ed.
ISBN 0379207443

Introduction to the Hong Kong legal system / Peter Wesley-Smith. – Hong Kong : Oxford University Press, 1987.
ix, 118 p.; 22 cm.
An overview of the Hong Kong legal system; the constitution, imported law and law made in Hong Kong, literary sources, structure of the courts, operation of judge-made laws, the process of legislative law-making, and the institutions of the law.
ISBN 0195840577 Pbk £10.00

Introduction to the law and institutions of the European Communities / by D. Lasok and J.W. Bridge. – 4th ed. – London : Butterworths, 1987.
Includes index. Bibliography: p422-436.
ISBN 0406268800 Hbk £28
ISBN 0406268819 Pbk £21.95

Introduction to the law in Papua New Guinea / by D.R.C. Chalmers and A.H. Paliwala. – 2nd ed. – North Ryde, N.S.W. : Law Book Co, 1984.
xxiv,236p.
Includes bibliographies and index.
ISBN 0455203806

Introduction to the law of carriage of goods / C Cashmore. – London : Sweet & Maxwell, 1989.
Guide to the law of carriage of goods by land, sea and air, with a brief ssummary of the law relating to passengers and their luggage. Explores the principles of UK law, supplemented by Commonwealth, US and European authorities. Provides an examination of international conventions and the standard conditions of carriage in use in the industry.
ISBN 0420397004 Pbk c.14.00

Introduction to the law of contract / by P.S. Atiyah. – 3rd ed. – Oxford : Clarendon, 1981.
x,335p; 23cm. – (Clarendon law series).
Previous ed.: 1971. Includes index.
ISBN 0198761406 Hbk £
ISBN 0198761414 Pbk £5.95

Introduction to the Law of Contract. – 2nd ed. – Lucknow : Eastern Book Company, 1983.
419p.
Pbk £30.00

Introduction to the Law of Employment. – 3rd ed. – Butterworths, 1988.
435p.
ISBN 0409787922 Pbk

Introduction to the law of employment / by Alexander Szakats. – 2nd ed., completely revised. – Wellington : Butterworths, 1981.
li,522p.
Previous ed.: 1975. Includes bibliographical references and index.
ISBN 0409601063

Introduction to the Law of International Trade. – Oxford : BSP Professional.
ISBN 0632023767 Pbk £14.95

Introduction to the law of obligations / A.M. Tettenborn. – London : Butterworths, 1984.
xxv,238p; 23cm.
Includes index.
ISBN 0406260672 Hbk £19.50
ISBN 0406260680 Pbk £13.95

Introduction to the Law of Restitution. – Oxford : Oxford University Press, 1985.
ISBN 0198760744 Hbk £45.00
ISBN 0198256450 Pbk £20.00

Introduction to the law of Scotland / by W.M. Gloag and R. Candlish Henderson. – 9th ed. – Edinburgh : W. Green, 1987.
clii,1020p.
Previous ed.: 1980. Includes index.
ISBN 0414008189

Introduction to the Law of Tenures. – Repr. of 1730 ed. – Abingdon : Professional Books.
460p.
Hbk £95.00

Introduction to the law of the European Communities: after the coming into force of the Single European Act / Edited by L. W. Gormley. – 2nd. – Kluwer Law and Taxation, 1989.
850.
A revised second edition, taking into account the Single European Act. As well as basic sources and material of the law of the European Communities, deals with the increased case law of the Court of Justice.
ISBN 9065444009 Hbk £65/Dfl 230

Introduction to the law of torts / by John G. Fleming. – 2nd ed. – Oxford : Clarendon, 1985.
viii,236p; 23cm. – (Clarendon law series).
Previous ed.: 1967. Includes index.
ISBN 0198761546 Hbk £17.50
ISBN 0198761554 Pbk £8.95

Introduction to the law of torts. – Scarborough, Ontario : Butterworths (Canada), 1978.
312.
Covers the scope of tortious liability, fundamentals of liability, limitations on liability, personal injuries, negligence, injuries to personality, injuries to property, economic loss, injurious abuse of legal process, remedies, and procedural matters.
ISBN 0409830364 Pbk

Introduction to the legal system of Zimbabwe / by John Redgment. – 2nd ed., rev. and enl. – Salisbury Rhodesia : Book Centre, 1981.
107p.
Bibliography: p.106-107.

Introduction to the Malaysian legal system / Wu Min Aun. – Rev. 3rd ed. – Kuala Lumpur : Heinemann Educational (Asia), 1982.
xii,196p.
Previous ed.: 1978. Bibliography: p.189-196.

Introduction to the Matrimonial Property Act 1984 / June D. Sinclair. – Cape Town : Juta, 1984.
ix,102p.
ISBN 0702115096

Introduction to the New Zealand Legal System. – 6th ed. – London : Butterworths, 1986.
ISBN 0409702285 Pbk £31.00

Introduction to the Principles of Morals and Legislation. – London : Loughton.
ISBN 0879754346 Pbk £4.45

Introduction to the Principles of Morals and Legislation. – Repr. of 1879 ed. – Abingdon : Professional Books.
Hbk £55.00

Introduction to the Scots law of contract. – Edinburgh : Green (W.) & Son, 1987.
An introduction to the basic principles at student level.
ISBN 0414008197 Pbk

Introduction to the Scots law of delict. – Edinburgh : Green (W.) & Son, 1989.
An introduction to the most important principles and rules, with coverage of negligence, defamation, occupiers' liability, employers' liability and other forms of liability. Case summaries and statutory extracts provided along with references to other sources such as journal articles.
ISBN 0414008901 Pbk

Introduction to the Scottish Law of Leases. – London : Butterworths, 1988.
ISBN 0406105898 Pbk

Introduction to the Securities Industry Codes / C.M. Maxwell. – Sydney : Butterworths, 1988.
256p.
Pbk £37.50

Introduction to the Singapore legal system / by Helena H.M. Chan. – Singapore : Malayan Law Journal Pte., 1986.
vi,140p.
Covers the legal history of Singapore, sources of law, structure of government, legal institutions, civil and criminal procedure, and a chapter devoted to legal culture and the future development of the law.
ISBN 9971700549

Introduction to the Social Services. – 4th ed. – London : Macmillan, 1983.
208p.
ISBN 0333335430 Pbk £4.95

Introduction to the Study of Law. – 3rd ed. – Agincourt : Carswell, 1987.
ISBN 0459302418 Hbk £11.50

Introduction To The Study Of The Constitution / Wade. – London : Macmillan, 1959.
ISBN 0333052552 Pbk £9.95

Introduction to the World conservation strategy / prepared for the International Union for Conservation of Nature and Natural Resources by its Commission on Education : text and selection of photographs, Stan Croner. – Gland, Switzerland : IUCN, 1984.
28 p.; 30 cm.
ISBN 2880327024 Pbk £7.95

Introduction to Torts. – North Ryde : Law Book Co, 1985.
xxxiv, 307p.
ISBN 0455205574 Hbk £41.50
ISBN 0455205582 Pbk £23.50

Introduction to town and country planning / John Ratcliffe. – 2nd ed. – London : Hutchinson, 1981.
506p; 22cm.
Previous ed.: 1974. Bibliography: p483-487. - Includes index.
ISBN 0091440203 Hbk £15.00
ISBN 0091440211 Pbk £6.95

Introduction to trade mark law in the Benelux / W. Mak, H. Molijn : translated by M.V. Snoxall, M.O. Snoxall. – Deventer, The Netherlands : Kluwer, 1982.
Includes index. Bibliography. Translation of: Merkenbescherming in de Benelux.
ISBN 9065440216

Introduction to Trademark Law and Practice : the Basic Concepts. – Geneva : World Intellectual Property Organizations, 1987.
99p.
Hbk £35.00

Introduction to Turkish law / edited by Tugrul Ansay and Don Wallace, Jr. – 3rd ed. – Deventer : Kluwer, 1987.
xiv,279p; 25cm.
Previous ed.: Ankara: Society of Comparative Law, Turkey and Middle East Technical University, Faculty of Administrative Sciences, 1966. Bibliography: p261-269. - Includes index.
ISBN 9065442987

Introduction to United States international taxation / by Paul R. McDaniel, Hugh J. Ault. – 2nd rev. ed. – Deventer : Kluwer, 1981.
209p; 25cm.
Previous ed.: 1977. Includes index.
ISBN 9065440046

Introduction to urban renewal / Michael S. Gibson, Michael J. Langstaff. – London : Hutchinson, 1982.
384p; 24cm.
ISBN 0091475007

Introduction to Valuation. – 2nd ed. – London : Macmillan, 1985.
ISBN 0333384377 Pbk £5.95

Introduction to working in the Lloyds Market / Wormell. – Witherby, 1987.
ISBN 0948691387 Pbk £10.00

Introductory essays on Scots law / by W.A. Wilson. – 2nd ed. – Edinburgh : Green, 1984.
ix,156p; 21cm.
Previous ed.: 1978. Includes index.
ISBN 0414007298 Pbk

Introductory guide to EEC competition law and practice / Valentine Korah. – 2nd ed. – Oxford : ESC, 1981.
xxii,160p; 22cm.
ISBN 0906214084 Pbk

Introductory guide to EEC Competition law and practice / Valentine Korah. – 3rd ed. – Oxford : ESC Publishing, 1986.
xxi,177p; 21cm.
Includes bibliographies and index. Cover title: EEC competition law and practice.
ISBN 0906214394

Inuit (Eskimo) of Canada / by Ian Creery. – London : Minority Rights Group, 1983.
16p. – (Report).
Bibliography: p.16.

Invasion of Privacy : Police and Electric Surveillance in Canada. – Agincourt : Carswell, 1983.
250p.
This book analyzes the legal and ethical dimensions of police surveillance in Canada and discusses the question of the extent of police surveillance powers.
Hbk £42.00

Inventors' information guide / by Tamara S. Eisenschitz and Jeremy Phillips. – 2nd edition. – London : The Intellectual Property Law Unit Centre for Commercial Law Studies, 1985.
viii, 100p.
ISBN 0951066404

Inventory of current legal research in Canada / l'inventaire des activites de recherche juridique courantes au Canada : compilers, Catherine M. Parker, Laurie A. Davidson. – Ottawa : Canadian Law Information Council, 1986.
vi,169p.
Includes index.
ISBN 0920358888

Investigating burglary : the measurement of police performance / by John Burrows. – London : H.M.S.O., 1986.
v,30p; 25cm.
Examines differences in clear-up rates in areas with similar problems. Finds that clear-up rates are not necessarily a reflection of success in arresting burglars, but involve questioning about previous offences.
ISBN 0113408242

Investigating into the legal position of illegitimate children / South African Law Commission. – Pretoria : The Commission, 1984.
viii,167 leaves. – (Project).
Bibliography: p.161-167.

Investigating Rape : New approaches for the Police. – Oxford : Croom Helm, 1985.
ISBN 0709920989 Hbk £14.95

Investigating robbery / Michael Banton. – Aldershot : Gower, 1985.
vii,126p; 22cm.
Bibliography: p109-110. - Includes index.
ISBN 0566051141 £16.50

Investigating sexual assault / Gerry Chambers, Ann Millar. – Edinburgh : H.M.S.O., 1983.
viii,142p. – (A Scottish Office social research study).
Bibliography: p.141-142.
ISBN 0114923272

Investigation and prosecution of criminal offences in England and Wales : the law and procedure / the Royal Commission on Criminal Procedure : Chairman: Sir Cyril Philips. – London : H.M.S.O., 1981.
vii,229p; 25cm.
ISBN 0101809212 Pbk £7.50

Investigation into the advancement of the age of majority / South African Law Commission. – Pretoria : The Commission, 1985.
xviii,63p. – (Report).
Includes bibliographical references.
ISBN 0621102466

Investigation into the advancement of the age of majority / South African Law Commission. – Pretoria : The Commission, 1984.
iv,36p. – (Project).
Bibliography: p.30-34.

Investigation into the courts' powers of review of administrative acts / South African Law Commission. – Pretoria : The Commission, 1986.
v,110p. – (Project).

Investigation into the legal consequences of suspensive conditions in contracts of sales / South African Law Commission. – Pretoria : The Commission, 1986.
vi,32p. – (Report).
Includes text of draft legislation.
ISBN 0621113506

Investigation into the legal position of illegitimate children / South African Law Commission. – Pretoria : The Commission, 1985.
xx,157p. – (Report).
Includes bibliographical references.
ISBN 0621102059

Investigation into the limits for the institution of actions against the state / South African Law Commission. – Pretoria : The Commission, 1985.
iv,50p. – (Report).
Includes bibliographical references. Includes draft of Bill.

Investigation into the possibility of making provision for a divorced woman to share in the pension benefits of her former husband / South African Law Commission. – Pretoria : The Commission, 1984.
v,67leaves. – (Project).
Bibliography: p.66-67.

Investigation into the possiblity of making provision for a divorced woman to share in the pension benefits of her former husband / South African Law Commission. – Pretoria : The Commission, 1986.
x,77p. – (Report).
Bibliography: pp.vi-x. Includes draft legislation.
ISBN 0621113573

Investigations by Adminstrative Agencies. – North Ryde : Law Book Co, 1987.
ca 1,250p.
ISBN 0455205868 Hbk £125.00

Investigations Manual. – Binder Hamlyn Staff. – London : Butterworths, 1985.
Based on an in-house manual for investigation work, this book provides a reference for the preparation and conduct of an investigation. It is intended for use in the opening stages of an investigation to develop the quickest and most productive approach to the work.
ISBN 0406142580 Pbk

Investigative tests / Law Reform Commission of Canada. – Ottawa : Law Reform Commission of Canada, 1984.
166,186p; 25cm. – (Working paper).
At head of cover title: Criminal law. English and French texts bound back to back.
ISBN 066253039X

Investing in Britain : jobs and industry / Labour Party. – London : Labour Party, 1985.
23p.

Investing in Europe's future / edited by Arnold Heertje : contributors Michel Albert ... et al. : preface by Yves Le Portz. – Oxford : Blackwell, for the European Investment Bank, 1983.
x,218p; 24cm.
ISBN 0631134050

Investing in the Oil and Gas Industry in Canada. – Vancouver : British Columbia Continuing Legal Education Society, 1981.
222p.
ISBN 0865040354 Hbk £40.00

Investment. – London : Pitman Publishing, 1988.
ISBN 0273028944 Pbk £9.95

Investment Appraisals Guide for Managers. – London : Kogan Page.
ISBN 1850914680 Pbk £8.95

Investment Guide 1987-1988s (LIC). – London : Longman Professional.
ISBN 0851212905 Hbk £13.50

Investment in Shares and Securities. – London : Butterworths, 1988.
ISBN 0406504504 Pbk £40.00

Investment in US Real Estate. – London : Oyez Longman, 1984.
– (Oyez Longman Intelligence Report Ser.).
ISBN 0851208495 Hbk

Investment incentives worldwide. – London : Butterworths, 1988.
ISBN 040800900X Hbk £55.00

Investment Institutions. – 4th ed. – Plymouth : Macdonald & Evans, 1984.
180p.
ISBN 0712155074 Pbk £4.75

Investment Laws and Opportunities in Africa. – Apapa : Heritage Books.
Hbk £8.50

Investment trusts explained / A.A. Arnaud. – 2nd ed. – Cambridge : Woodhead-Faulkner in co-operation with the Association of Investment Trust Companies, 1983.
xiii,.145p; 24cm.
Previous ed.: 1977. Includes index.
ISBN 0859412431 Hbk
ISBN 0859412490 Pbk £6.95

Investments. – 3rd ed. – Prentice-Hall, 1985.
ISBN 0135047137 Pbk £18.50

Investor Prot., Corp. Disclosure and Insider Dealing in HK. – London : Butterworths, 1988.
ISBN 0409995460 Hbk

Investors' Guide to Commodities Futures Markets / Bettelheim. – London : Butterworths, 1986.
ISBN 0406101906 Hbk £17.95

Invitation to law / by A.W.B. Simpson. – Oxford : Blackwell, 1988.
227p.
Includes index.
ISBN 0631145389 Pbk

Invitation to the law / by C.G. Weeramantry. – Sydney : Butterworths, 1982.
xiv,369p.
Includes bibliographies and index.
ISBN 0409309346 Pbk

Inward investment : policy options for the United Kingdom / Michael Brech and Margaret Sharp. – London : Routledge and Kegan Paul, 1983.

Ioffe, O. S
Soviet civil law / by Olimpiad S. Ioffe. – Dordrecht : M. Nijhoff, 1988.
392p.
Includes index.
ISBN 9024736765 Hbk £205.00
→ Soviet law and economy.
—Soviet law and Soviet reality / Olimpiad S. Ioffe. – Dordrecht : M. Nijhoff, 1985.
240p. – (Law in Eastern Europe).
Includes bibliographies and index.
ISBN 9024731062 Hbk £135.00

Iosipescu, Michael
Comparison of automated and manual legal research : a computer study / by Michael Iosipescu and John Yogis. – Ottawa : Canadian Law Information Council, 1981.
ii, 86 p.; 28 cm. – (Canadian Law Information Council working paper).
Cover title: Legal research.
ISBN 092035808X Pbk £13.50

Iran - United States Claims Tribunal 1981-83. – London : Eurospan.
ISBN 0813910420 Hbk £21.95

Iran-Iraq war : legal implications / S.H. Amin. – Glasgow : Royston, 1982.
26p.
Reprinted from Marine Policy, vol. 6, no. 3 (July 1982).

Iran-United States Claims Tribunal Reports. – Cambridge : Grotius Publications, 1983.

Iraq : evidence of torture : an Amnesty International report. – London : Amnesty International Publications, 1981.
44p; 30cm.
ISBN 0862100321 unbound

Iredale, Martin
Receivership manual / Martin Iredale, Christopher Hughes. – 3rd ed. – Croydon : Tolley, 1987.
xiv,178p.
Guide to receivership including recent Insolvency Acts and company law changes.
ISBN 0854592202 Hbk £21.95

Ireland and the European Communities : Ten Years of Membership. – Dublin : Gill & MacMillan, 1983.
ISBN 0717113264 Hbk £20.00

Irish Association of Civil Liberty
Your Rights as an Irish Citizen. – Irish Association of Civil Liberty. – Dublin : Poolbag Press, 1982.
80p.
ISBN 0907085210 Pbk £1.50

Irish at law : a selection of famous and unusual cases / James Comyn. – London : Sphere, 1983.
ix,261p; 18cm.
Originally published: London : Secker & Warburg, 1981.
ISBN 0722125615 Pbk £1.95

Irish cases on evidence / by J.S.R. Cole. – 2nd ed. – Dublin : Incorporated Law Society of Ireland, 1982.
xxi, 264 p.; 22 cm.
Includes index.
ISBN 0902027190

Irish Commercial Law. – 2nd ed. – Dublin : Round Hall Press, 1988.
200p.
ISBN 0947686398 Pbk £12.95
ISBN 0947686320 Hbk £20.00

Irish conflict of laws / by William Binchy. – Dublin? : Butterworths (Ireland), 1988.
lxxiv,691p.
Bibliography: p.lxxi-lxxi - Includes index.
ISBN 0862052203 Pbk £65.00
ISBN 0862052211 £25.00

Irish constitution / J.M. Kelly. – 2nd ed. – Dublin : Jurist Publishing, 1984.
xxxi,741p.
Previous ed.: 1980. Includes index. Kept up to date by supplements.

Irish conveyancing law. – London : Butterworths, 1982.
ISBN 0903486458 Hbk £41.00

Irish criminal process / Edward F. Ryan and Philip P. Magee. – Dublin : Mercier Press, 1983.
lxxi,595p.
Includes index.
ISBN 0853427003

Irish Current Law Statutes Annotated. – London : Sweet & Maxwell, 1984.
ISBN 0421327405 Hbk £250.00

Irish Employment Equality Law. – Round Hall Press.
ISBN 0947686045 Hbk £55.00

Irish Income Tax. – London : Butterworths.
Service to Date.
ISBN 0406678707 Hbk £118.00

Irish income tax and corporation profits tax by F.N. Kelly and K.S. Carmichael / K. S. Carmichael. – 8th ed. 1 v. – London : HFL, 1975.
looseleaf.
Includes index.
ISBN 0372016529

Irish Justice of the Peace and Treatise on the Powers and Duties of Justices of the Peace in Ireland, 2 Vols.
Vol. 2 /. – Abingdon : Professional Books.
Hbk £79.00

Irish Justice Pease. – London : Butterworths.
ISBN 0862053463 Hbk £52.75

Irish land law / by J.C.W. Wylie : consultant editor for the Republic of Ireland, The Hon. Mr. Justice Kenny. – 2nd ed. – Abingdon, Oxon. : Professional Books, 1986.
cxxi,1004p.
Previous ed.: 1975. Includes index.
ISBN 0862052173

Irish Landlord and Tenant Law / John Farrell. – Abingdon : Professional Books, 1984.
ISBN 0862050626 Hbk £63.00
ISBN 0862050677 Pbk

Irish law of defamation / Marc McDonald : with a foreword by Thomas A. Finlay. – Dublin : Round Hall in association with Irish Academic Press, 1987.
xx,304p; 24cm.
Includes index.
ISBN 0947686150 £30.00

Irish law of torts / by Bryan M.E. McMahon and William Binchy. – Abingdon, Oxon. : Professional Books, 1981.
lxxvi,620p; 24cm.
Bibliography: p.lxiii. - Includes index.
ISBN 0862050405

Irish Law Reform Commission Reports
Vols. 1-5. – Professional Books.
ISBN 0862052777 Hbk £250.00

Irish Law Reports Monthly 1978 : Selected Previously Unreported Judgments. – Dublin : Round Hall Press, 1988.
ca 300p.
ISBN 0947686355 Hbk £90.00

Irish Law Reports Monthly 1979 : Selected Previously Unreported Judgments. – Dublin : Round Hall Press.
ca 320p.
ISBN 0947686193 Hbk £85.00

Irish Law Reports Monthly 1980 : Selected Previously Unreported Cases. – Dublin : Round Hall Press.
310p.
ISBN 0947686029 Hbk £85.00

Irish Law Reports Monthly
Vol. 1. – Dublin : Round Hall Press, 1981.
534p.
ISBN 0950872563 Hbk £90.00
Vol. 2. – 1982.
62p.
ISBN 0950872571 Hbk £90.00
Vol. 3. – 1983.
650p.
ISBN 095087258X Hbk £90.00
Vol. 4. – 1984.
732p.
ISBN 0947686061 Hbk £90.00
Vol. 5. – 1985.
732p.
ISBN 0947686096 Hbk £90.00
Vol. 6 12 issues index. – 1986.
Hbk £135.00

Irish law reports monthly. – Dublin : Irish Academic Press, 1981.
From vol. 1, - vol. 3, no. 2 (1981-83) incorporates Irish law times.
ISBN 03323293

Irish Law Times and Solicitors' Journal : New Series
Vol 1. – Round Hall Press, 1983.
148p.
ISBN 0947686207 £40.00
Vol 2.. – 1984.
240p.
ISBN 0947686215 Hbk £40.00
Vol 3.. – 1985.
262p.
ISBN 0947686223 Hbk £40.00
Vol 4.. – 1986.
Hbk £55.00

Irish Legal System : Cases and Materials / J P McCutcheon. – London : Butterworths, 1986.
ISBN 086205222X Hbk £22.50
ISBN 0862052238 Pbk £12.50

Irish, Maureen
Customs Valuation in Canada. – Don Mills : CCH Canadian Ltd, 1985.
292p.
ISBN 088796284X Hbk £45.00
→ Legal framework for Canada-United States trade.

Irish Notary. – London : Butterworths, 1987.
ISBN 0862052386 Hbk £35.00

Irish Reports 1838-1986. – Professional Books.
ISBN 0862052718 Hbk

Irish Reports : 1838-1979, 233 Vols. – Abingdon : Professional Books, 1984.
Hbk

Irish Reports : 1894-1979, 118 Vols. – Repr. – Abingdon : Professional Books.
Hbk £5160.00
1894-1925 (Ser. V). –
Hbk £2525.00
1926-1979 (Ser. VI). –
Hbk £3030.00
Individual vols. Ser. V. –
Hbk £52.50
Individual vols. Ser. VI. –
Hbk £67.00

Irish Reports Digests : 1894-1970, 6 Vols.
Incl. Vol. 1. Irish Reports Digests : 1894-1918. – Abingdon : Professional Books.
Hbk £105.00
Vol. 2, 1919-1928. –
Hbk £46.00
Vol. 3, 1929-1938. –
Hbk £56.00
Vol. 6, 1959-1970. –
Hbk £46.00

Irish Society for European Law →Journal of the Irish Society for European Law.

Irish Society for Labour Law →Journal of the Irish Society for Labour Law.

Irish Trade Marks Law and Practice : Introduction by Mr Justice Declan Costello. – Dublin : Gill and Macmillan, 1987.
ISBN 0717114406 Hbk £30.00

Irish trade union law / Tony Kerr and Gerry Whyte. – Abingdon : Professional Books, 1985.
lxiv,383p.
ISBN 0862050510 Hbk £31.50
ISBN 0862050936 Pbk £22.50

Irlicht, T.
Assignments, Arrangements and Compositions by Debtors with Precedents. – 2nd ed. – Butterworths, 1986.
176p.
ISBN 0409490652 Hbk £45.00

IRPTC Legal File, 2 Vols. – Geneva : United Nations Publications, 1987.
1,345p.
ISBN 9280711636 Pbk £98.00

Irrigation users' organizations in the legislation and administration of certain Latin American countries / by Miguel Solanes. – Rome : Food and Agriculture Organization of the United Nations, 1983.
vii,87p. – (Legislative study).
Includes bibliographical references.
ISBN 9251011702

Irritancies in leases / Scottish Law Commission. – Edinburgh : Scottish Law Commission, 1981.
42p. – (Memorandum).

Irritancies in leases : report on a reference under section 3(1)(e) of the Law Commissions Act 1965 / Scottish Law Commission. – Edinburgh : H.M.S.O., 1983.
vi,41p.
ISBN 0101876009

Irukwu
Insurance law in Africa. – Witherby, 1987.
ISBN 0948691255 Hbk £35.00

Irvine, John
Canadian Cases on the Law of Torts
Vols. 1-31. – Agincourt : Carswell.
Hbk £734.75

Irving, B.L.
Regulating custodial interviews. – Police Foundation, 1988.
ISBN 0947692088 Pbk £6.95

Irving, Barrie
Police interrogation: the effects of the Police and Criminal Evidence Act 1984 / Ian McKenzie. – London : Policy Studies Institute, 1989.
250; 21.
A comparison of research data from 1979 with new research data from 1986 in one police station in Brighton.
ISBN 0947692118 Hbk £18.95

Irving, Howard H. →Family law : an interdisciplinary perspective.
—Family Mediation : Theory and Practice of Dispute Resolutions / Michael Benjamin. – Agincourt : Carswell, 1987.
320p.
This work is a comprehensive guide to family mediation, the process of resolving property support and custody issues with the aid of a third party in Canada. The effectiveness of various mediation efforts based on empirical studies is presented in the work.
Hbk £40.50

Is divorce the answer? : an examination of no-fault divorce against the background of the Irish debate / William Binchy. – Blackrock, C. Dublin : Irish Academic, 1984.
115p; 22cm.
Bibliography: p111-115.
ISBN 071650314X Pbk £2.95

Is it in force?. – London : Butterworths, 1988.
ISBN 0406072833 Pbk £15.00

Is It In Force? 1987. – Butterworths Editorial Staff. – London : Butterworths, 1987.
ISBN 0406072825 Pbk £33.00

Is retributivism analytic? / Igor Primorac. – s.l. : s.n., 1981.
9 leaves.
Photo-copy of an article in Philosophy, vol. 56 (1981), p.203-211. Includes bibliographical references.

Isaacs : Beck's Theory and Principles of Pleadings in Civil Actions
Supplement. – Durban : Professional Publisher, 1985.
ISBN 0409012378 £20.00

Isaacs, I. →Beck's theory and principles of pleading in civil actions.
→ Statutes of the Republic of South Africa.

Isaacs, Stuart →EEC banking law.

Isaacson
Lawyers Remembrancer 1989 / Roskamus. – London : Butterworths.
ISBN 0406269319 Hbk £13.00

Isaacson, Isabel →Lawyer's Remembrancer 1988.

Ish, Daniel
Law of Canadian co-operatives / by Daniel Ish. – Toronto : Burroughs, 1981.
xxvi, 294 p.; 24 cm.
This book reviews co-operative corporation legislation of provincial and federal jurisdictions in Canada. The work analyzes the principles of corporate common law in the context of co-operative corporations, in addition to corporate statutory materials.
ISBN 0459336800 Hbk £46.25

Islahi, Amin Ahsan
Juristic Differences and How to Solve Them in an Islamic State. – Lagos : Islamic Publications Bureau.
Pbk £30.00

Islamic banking : the adaptation of banking practice to conform with Islamic law / S.H. Homoud. – London : Arabian Information, 1985.
300p; 28cm.
Translated from the Arabic.
ISBN 0860105032 Hbk £75.00 :
ISBN 0860105024 Pbk £35.00

Islamic banking and finance / Butterworths editorial staff. – London : Butterworths, 1986.
xii,149p; 24cm.
Conference papers. Includes index.
ISBN 0406100349 £65.00

Islamic banking and finance : the experience of Iran / by Sayed Hassan Amin. – Glasgow : Royston, 1986.
128p; 22cm.
Includes bibliography and index.
ISBN 0946706301 £27.00

Islamic conception of justice / Majid Khadduri. – Baltimore : Johns Hopkins University Press, 1984.
xvi,256p; 24cm.
Bibliography: p243-249. - Includes index.
ISBN 0801832454 £22.20

Islamic criminal justice system / M. Cherif Bassiouni, editor. – London : Oceana Publications, 1981.
Primarily selected papers from the 1st International Conference on the Protection of Human Rights in the Islamic Criminal Justice System held May 1979 at the International Institute of Higher Studies in Criminal Sciences, Syracuse, Sicily, and sponsored by the International Association of Penal Law and the Arab Organization for Social Defense against Crime.
Appendices : A. Summary report of the first International Conference on the Protection of Human Rights in the Islamic Criminal Justice System, May 1979, International Institute of Higher Studies in Criminal Sciences, Siracusa, Italy – B. List of conference participants – C. Final resolution adopted by conference.
ISBN 0379207451 Hbk £30.00

Islamic Criminal Law and Procedure : An Introduction / McConville. – Praeger.
ISBN 0275930092 Hbk £29.95

Islamic family law / Jane Connors. – London : Graham & Trotman, 1989.
350; 240mm.
Covers current research into areas of Islamic family law in the form of articles. Addresses historical issues such as the development of the law of succession in Islamic law, the colonial encounter and its impact on Islamic family law in India, as well as contemporary law of the family in Egypt, the sub-continent, Iran and Europe, and the law of minorities in their relation to the state.
ISBN 1853333018 Hbk £35

Islamic Family Law (Federal Territory) Act, 1984 (Act 303). – Kuala Lumpur : International Law Books Services.
Hbk £10.00

Islamic government and the revolution in Iran / by Ayatollah Allama Yahya Noori. – 2nd ed. – Glasgow : Royston, 1985.
74,xip; 23cm.
New ed. - Previous ed.: 1984. Includes index.
ISBN 0946706255 £18.95

Islamic Jurisprudence. – New Delhi : Deep and Deep Publications, 1988.
338p.
Hbk £280.00

Islamic Jurisprudence. – Islamabad : Islamic Research Institute.
ca 500p.
Hbk

Islamic jurisprudence : an international perspective / C.G. Weeramantry : foreword by M. Hidayatullah : message from His Eminence the Grand Sheikh of Al-Azhar University, Cairo. – Basingstoke : Macmillan, 1988.
xix,207p; 23cm.
Bibliography: p189-200. - Includes index.
ISBN 0333446682 £29.50

Islamic Law : Social and Historical Contexts. – Oxford : Croom Helm.
ISBN 0709905882 Hbk £22.50

Islamic law and finance / edited by Chibli Mallat. – London : Graham & Trotman, 1988.
xiv,196p.
Includes bibliographical references and index.
ISBN 185333121X

Islamic Law and its Implications for the Modern World. – Royston.
ISBN 0946706492 Pbk £15.00

Islamic Law in Nigeria. – Lagos : Islamic Publications Bureau, 1988.
ISBN 9782470376 Hbk £25.00

Islamic law in South-East Asia / M.B. Hooker. – Singapore : O.U.P., 1984.
xxx,330p.
Bibliography: p.281-296. - Includes index.
ISBN 0195825039

Islamic law in the contemporary world : introduction, glossary and bibliography / by Sayed Hassan Amin. – Glasgow : Royston, 1985.
ix,190p; 22cm.
Bibliography: p153-172. - Includes index.
ISBN 0946706247 Pbk £15.00

Islamic law of bequest / Abdulaziz Mohammed Zaid. – London : Scorpion Publishing, 1986.
296p.
Bibliography: p.291-294. - Includes index.
ISBN 090590642X

Islamic law of personal status / Jamal J. Nasir. – London : Graham & Trotman, 1986.
xiv,328p; 25cm.
Bibliography: p314-319. - Includes index.
ISBN 0860108252 deluxe £45.00
ISBN 0860108260 £75.00

Isle of Man : a low-tax area / by Mark Solly. – Croydon : Tolley, 1984.
ix,458p.
Includes index.
ISBN 0854591397

Isle of Man and the Channel Islands : a study of their status under constitutional, international and European law / by Simon A. Horner. – Florence : European University Institute, 1984.
142p.
At head of title: European University Institute, Florence, Law Department.

Isle of Man Orders in Council : consisting of Orders in Council extending or applying Acts of Parliament and Statutory Instruments to the Isle of Man / edited and annotated with an introduction by K.F.W. Gumbley. – Douglas : Government Printer, 1987-.
looseleaf.

Isle of Man statutes in force. – Douglas : Isle of Man Government, 1985.
loose-leaf.

Islington crime survey : crime, victimization and policing in inner-city London / Trevor Jones, Brian MacLean and Jock Young. – Aldershot : Gower, 1986.
xiv, 265p; 23cm.
ISBN 0566052644

Ison, Terence G.
Workers' compensation in Canada / by Terence G. Ison. – Toronto : Butterworths, 1983.
xxvii,179p.
Includes index.
ISBN 040984005X

—Workers' Compensation in Canada. – Butterworths, 1983.
208p.
Hbk £43.95

Israel and Palestine. – Preparatory Committee for the Russell Hearings on Lebanon and the Occupied Territories. – London : Spokesman Books, 1984.
– (End Papers: No. 9).
ISBN 0851244041 Hbk £3.95

Israel Yearbook on Human Rights 1987. – Martinus Nijhoff.
ISBN 9024736463 Hbk £39.00

Israel yearbook on human rights. – Tel Aviv : Published under the auspices of the Faculty of Law, Tel Aviv University, 1971.
ISBN 03335925

Israel yearbook on human rights / Mala Tabory. – Dordrecht : Nijhoff (Martinus), 1989.
312. – (Israel yearbook on human rights 18).
Published under the auspices of the Faculty of Law of Tel Aviv University. Contains studies on human rights in peace and war, . with particular emphasis on problems relevant to the State of Israel, and the Jewish people. Summaries of judicial decisions, and military proclamations are included.
ISBN 0792300173 Hbk £42

Israeli reports to the XI International Congress of Comparative Law / edited by Stephen Goldstein. – Jerusalem : Harry Sacher Institute for Legislative Research and Comparative Law, 1982.
363p.
Cover titles in English and Hebrew.

Issacs
The Law of Collisions in Africa / Leveson. – 5th ed. – London : Butterworths, 1974.
ISBN 0409034207 Hbk £27.40

Issacs, I.
Beck's Theory and Principles of Pleading in Civil Actions. – London : Butterworths.
ISBN 0409012351 Hbk £37.90

Isserlis, A. R.
Conversations on Policy. – London : Policy Studies Institute, 1984.
88p. – (PSI's Discussion Papers).
Hbk £3.75

Issues and offers of company securities : the new regimes / by John L. Powell : with a foreword by Clive M. Schmitthoff. – London : Sweet & Maxwell, 1988.
xxvii,154p; 26cm.
Based on: Palmer's company law. 24th ed., ch.23 and 27. Includes index.
ISBN 042139630X £25.00

Issues in Computing, Telecommunications and Information Policy. – Paris : International Chamber of Commerce.
24p.
Hbk £5.00

Issues in contemporary legal philosophy : the influence of H.L.A. Hart / edited by Ruth Gavison. – Oxford : Clarendon, 1988.
368p; 22cm.
Includes bibliography and index. A collection of essays on legal philosophy themes, influenced by the work of H L A Hart. Pays tribute to Hart as a teacher, rather than being an introduction to his work.
ISBN 0198255179 Hbk £35.00
ISBN 0198256566 Pbk £12.95

Issues in Criminal Justice Administration / Sandra J. Egger. – North Sydney : Allen & Unwin, 1983.
200p.
ISBN 0868612774 Hbk £29.95
ISBN 0868610542 Pbk £19.95

Issues in Environmental Impact Assessment. – Downsview : York University, Faculty of Environmental Studies, 1983.
128p.
ISBN 0919762220 pb

Issues in reproductice health law in the Commonwealth / by Rebecca J. Cook and Bernard M. Dickens. – London : Commonwealth Secretariat, 1986.
109p.
ISBN 085092295X

Issues in Tort Law / Sanda Rodgers-Magnet. – Agincourt : Carswell, 1983.
388p.
This book is a collection of papers on key issues in Canadian tort law by leading scholars in the field.
Hbk £43.75

Issues regarding the reform of Canada's private pensions system / James E. Pesando. – Canada : Policy Research, Analysis and Liaison Directorate, Consumer and Corporate Affairs, 1983.
ISBN 0662121643

Italian Agency Agreements. – London : Longman Professional, 1977.
– (ECLL).
ISBN 0851203019 Pbk £26.00

Italian legal information retrieval : a handbook / by Ettore Giannantonio. – Milano : Giuffre, 1984.
xii,181p; 25cm. – (Informatica e ordinamento giuridico).
ISBN 0421239106 Pbk £8.50
ISBN 881400143X

Italian Legal System. – Sydney : Butterworths, 1985.
ISBN 0409490849 Hbk £37.00

Italian legal system / G. Leroy Certoma. – London : Butterworths, 1985.
xxiv,520p; 23cm. – (Butterworths' legal systems of the world).
Bibliography: p493-500. - Includes index.
ISBN 040639993X Hbk £43.00

Italian patent law / Guido Jacobacci, Giuseppe Sena. – Milano : Giuffre, 1985.
vii, 156p.
ISBN 8814007179

Italian yearbook of international law. – Napoli : Editoriale Scientifica, 1975.
Index in each vol..
ISBN 0379008254

Italian Yearbook of International Law. – Milan : Giuffre, 1986.
xii, 467p.
Hbk £65,000.00

Italy's Knights of St. George : The Historical Development and Juridical Position of the Sacred and Military Constantinian Order of St. George. – Gerrards Cross : Van Duren.
ISBN 0905715284 Hbk £12.00

It's All Quite Legal. – Butterworths, 1982.
48p.
ISBN 0409491500 Pbk £21.50

ITT-CIA Subversion in Chile : A Case Study of U.S. Corporate Intrigue in the Third World. – Spokesman University. – London : Spokesman Books, 1983.
114p.
ISBN 0851240402 Pbk £2.50

IUCN bulletin : a quarterly journal of the International Union for Conservation of Nature and Natural Resources. – International Union for Conservation of Nature and Natural Resources. – Gland, Switzerland : The Union, 1953 -.
ISBN 00209058

Ivamy
Merchant Shipping Act 1970. – London : Lloyd's of London Press.
ISBN 1850441103 Pbk £17.50

Ivamy, E R Hardy →Carriage of Goods by Sea.

—Casebook on agency / E.R. Hardy Ivamy. – 3rd ed. – London : Lloyd's, 1987.
160p; 22cm.
Previous ed.: 1980. Includes index.
ISBN 185044112X Pbk £15.00

—Casebook on carriage by sea / by E.R. Hardy Ivamy. – 6th ed. – London : Lloyd's of London, 1985.
256p; 25cm.
Previous ed.: 1982. Includes index.
ISBN 1850440549 Pbk

—Casebook on carriage by sea / by E.R. Hardy Ivamy. – 5th ed. – London : Lloyd's of London Press, 1982.
xxvii,203p.
Previous ed.: 1979. Includes index.
ISBN 0907432360

—Casebook on Insurance Law. – 4th ed. – London : Butterworths, 1984.
ISBN 0406602638 Pbk £14.95

—Casebook on partnership / by E.R. Hardy Ivamy. – 2nd ed. – Abingdon, Oxfordshire : Professional Books, 1982.
xv,99p; 23cm.
ISBN 086205043X Hbk £13.20

—Casebook on sale of goods / E.R. Hardy Ivamy. – 5th ed. – London : Lloyd's of London, 1987.
ix,200p; 22cm.
Previous ed.: 1980. Includes index.
ISBN 1850441170 Pbk

—Casebook on shipping law / E.R. Hardy Ivamy. – 4th ed. – London : Lloyd's of London Press, 1987.
210p; 22cm.
Previous ed.: 1982. Includes index.
ISBN 1850441308 Pbk £14.50

→ Chalmers' Marine Insurance Act 1906.

—Dictionary of company law / by E.R. Hardy Ivamy. – London : Butterworths, 1983.
265p; 23cm. – (Butterworths professional dictionary series).
ISBN 0406681619 Hbk £
ISBN 0406681627 Pbk

—Dictionary of insurance law / by E.R. Hardy Ivamy. – London : Butterworths, 1981.
– (Butterworths professional dictionary series).
This work contains terms in general use in marine as well as in non-marine insurance which have been legally defined in statute or case law. Many entries are accompanied by extracts from cited cases and statutes.
ISBN 0406603014 Pbk £14.95

—Dictionary of shipping law / by E.R. Hardy Ivamy. – London : Butterworths, 1984.
179p; 23cm. – (Butterworths professional dictionaries series).
ISBN 0406623996 Hbk £
ISBN 0406624003 Pbk

—Encyclopaedia of Carriage Law Sources (Service). – London : Lloyd's of London Press.
ISBN 1850441081 updat £130.00

—Encyclopaedia of Oil and Natural Gas Law. – London : Lloyd's of London Press.
ISBN 1850440980 updat £165.00

—Encyclopaedia Of Shipping Law Sources (UK) (Service). – London : Lloyd's of London Press.
ISBN 1850440115 updat £145.00

—Fire and Motor Insurance. – 4th ed. – London : Butterworths, 1984.
ISBN 040625253X Hbk £49.00

—General principles of insurance law / E.R. Hardy Ivamy. – 5th ed. – London : Butterworths, 1986.
1050p; 26cm.
This text provides an account of insurance law procedure from contract drafting to the final settlement of claims in the United Kingdom. The impact of the Insurance Companies Act of 1982 is fully discussed.
ISBN 0406252807 Hbk £70.00

—Marine Insurance. – 4th ed. – London : Butterworths, 1985.
ISBN 0406253137 Hbk £68.00

→ Merchant Shipping (Linear Conferences) Act 1982.

—Mozley and Whiteley : Law Dictionary. – 10th ed. – London : Butterworths, 1988.
ca 500p.
Explains the precise meaning of words and phrases, giving where relevant an historical account of the term, and if further information is required, a reference to either statutory case law or other authority.
ISBN 0406625255 Hbk £15.00
ISBN 0406625263 Pbk £7.95

→ Payne and Ivamy's Carriage of goods by sea.

Ivan-Smith, Edda
Women in sub-Saharan Africa / Edda Ivan-Smith, Nidhi Tandon and Jane Connors. – London : Minority Rights Group, 1988.
18p. – (Report).
Includes bibliographical references.
ISBN 094669057X

Ives, E. W.
Common lawyers of pre-Reformation England : Thomas Kebell : a case study / by E.W. Ives. – Cambridge : Cambridge University Press, 1983. xxx,536p; 23cm. – (Cambridge studies in English legal history).
Includes index.
ISBN 0521240115 £40.00
→ Law, litigants and the legal profession.

IVF and the status of children / report by the Senate Standing Committee on Constitutional and Legal Affairs on National Uniformity in Laws Relating to the Status of Children Born through the Use of In Vitro Fertilisation. – Canberra : Australian Government Publishing Service, 1985. xvi,84p. – (Parliamentary paper).
Includes bibliographical references. Chairman: Senator Michael Tate.
ISBN 0644046104

Ivory, T P G → Inheritance tax on lifetime gifts.

Ivre → Contracts of Affreightments and Hybrid Conts.

Iwasaki, K. → Dispute Resolutions in Australia-Japan Transactions.

Iyengar, Sampath
Law of Income Tax, 5 Vols. – 7th ed. – New Delhi : Bharat Law House.
Hbk £200.00 ea.

Iyengar, T.R. Srinivasa
Companies Act. – 2nd ed. – Allahabad : Law Book Company, 1986.
2,500p.
Hbk £425.00
—Companies' Directors. – 2nd ed. – Allahabad : Law Book Company, 1988.
800p.
Hbk £200.00
—Companies Winding-up. – 2nd ed. – Allahabad : Law Book Company, 1988.
700p.
Hbk £200.00
—Copyright Act. – 5th ed. – Allahabad : Law Book Company, 1985.
435p.
Hbk £125.00
—Law Relating to Private Limited Companies. – Allahabad : Law Book Company, 1986.
1,422p.
Hbk £275.00

Iyenger, T.R. Srinivasa
Company Meetings, Accounts, Audit and Investigation. – 2nd ed. – Allahabad : Law Book Company, 1987.
Hbk £200.00
—Law Relating to Companies Administration : With several Useful Appendices. – 2nd ed. – Allahabad : Law Book Company, 1987.
443p.
ISBN 8185029245 Hbk £150.00

Iyer, N. Suryanarayana
Indian Trusts Act : With Special Reference to Taxation Laws. – 3rd ed. – Allahabad : Law Book Company, 1987.
ca 900p.
Hbk £200.00

Iyer, Ramaswamy
Everybody's Book of Law. – 3rd rev. ed. – Allahabad : Orient Law House.
ca 256p.
ISBN 0861314573 Hbk £90.00
ISBN 0861314581 Pbk £45.00

Iyer, V.H. Krishna
Indian Presidency. – New Delhi : Deep and Deep Publications, 1988.
124p.
Hbk £75.00

Iyer, V.R.
Twin Acts Simplified : Company and M.R.T.P. Law / P.C. Jain. – New Delhi : S. Chand and Company.
Hbk £25.00

Iyer, V.R. Krishna
Constitutional Miscellany. – Lucknow : Eastern Book Company, 1986.
256p.
Hbk £80.00
—Equal Justice and Forensic Process : Truth and Myth. – Lucknow : Eastern Book Company, 1986.
146p.
Hbk £80.00
—Law and Social Change : an Indian Overview. – Patiala : Punjab University, Publication Bureau.
Hbk £25.00
—Law, Freedom and Change. – New Delhi : Affiliated East-West Press.
Hbk £28.50
—Our Courts on Trial. – Delhi : B.R. Publishing Corporation, 1987.
174p.
ISBN 8170184487 Hbk £75.00

Iyer, Venkatesa
Law of Contracts, 2 Vols. – 4th ed 1983-84. – Allahabad : Orient Law House.
Hbk £350.00
—Sale of Goods and Partnership. – 4th ed. – Allahabad : Orient Law House, 1984.
Hbk £100.00

Jack, R. Ian → Sources of English Legal and Constitutional History.

Jack the Ripper : A Casebook 1976. – London : Wildy & Sons.
Hbk £6.50

Jackaman, Peter → Law : a guide to the collection of Hammersmith & Fulham.

Jackson
Understanding tort law / Powell. – London : Sweet & Maxwell, 1987.
Pbk £4.95

Jackson, Bernard S
Law, Fact and Narrative Coherence. – London : Deborah Charles.
ISBN 0951379305 Hbk £18.00
ISBN 0951379631 Pbk £12.00
—Semiotics and legal theory / Bernard S. Jackson. – London : Routledge and Kegan Paul, 1985.
xii,373p; 22cm.
Bibliography: p.349-373.
ISBN 0710097190
→ Semiotics, law and social science.

Jackson, David C.
Civil jurisdiction and judgements : maritime claims / by D.C. Jackson. – London : Lloyds of London Press, 1987.
386p; 22cm.
Includes index.
ISBN 1850441448 £17.50
—Enforcement of maritime claims / by D.C. Jackson. – London : Lloyd's of London Press, 1985.
lxi,483p; 26cm.
ISBN 1850440018

Jackson, Harold
Two Irelands : the problem of the double minority / by Harold Jackson and Anne McHardy. – 3rd rev. ed. – London : Minority Rights Group, 1984.
16p. – (Report).
Bibliography: p.16.

Jackson, Hilary
Recruiting volunteers / Hilary Jackson. – London : Home Office, 1985.
iv,50p.
Bibliography: p.49-50.
ISBN 0862521769
→ Residential burglary : the limits of prevention.
—Unlocking community resources : four experimental government small grants schemes / Hilary Jackson. – London : Home Office, 1986.
iv,61p; 30cm.
Bibliography: p61.
ISBN 0862522617 Pbk

Jackson, James G → Australian Corporate Law Reference.
—Australian Corporate Law Reference / Ken W. Hale. – Woolloomooloo : International Business Communications, 1986.
ca 600p.
ISBN 0949553263 Hbk £49.50

Jackson, John D.
Northern Ireland Supplement to Cross on Evidence. – 5th ed. – Belfast : Queen's University of Belfast, 1984.
xli, 194p.
ISBN 0853892253 Pbk £9.75

Jackson, Joseph
Jackson's matrimonial finance and taxation / D. T. A. Davies. – 4th ed. 1. – London : Butterworths, 1986.
Previous ed.: 1980. Includes index.
ISBN 0406254478 Hbk £52.00
→ Rayden and Jackson's law and practice in divorce and family matters.

Jackson, M.
Industrial relations. – 3rd ed. – Oxford : Croom Helm, 1985.
ISBN 0709914741 Pbk £9.95
—Matters of Justice. – Oxford : Croom Helm, 1986.
ISBN 0709914709 Hbk £22.50

Jackson, Margaret A. → Clinical assessment before trial : legal issues and mental disorder.

Jackson, P.
Law of Easements and Proits. – London : Butterworths, 1978.
ISBN 0406253838 Hbk £29.00

Jackson, Paul → O. Hood Phillips' Constitutional and administrative law.

Jackson, Pauline
Industrialisation and reproductive rights / by Paulin sic Jackson. – Florence : European University Institute, 1986.
ii,24p.
Bibliography: p.22-24.

Jackson, R.
Machinery of Justice in England. – 8th ed. – Cambridge : Cambridge University Press, 1987.
ISBN 052129231X Pbk £19.50

Jackson, Rupert M.
Professional negligence / by Rupert M. Jackson and John L. Powell. – 2nd ed. – London : Sweet & Maxwell, 1987.
xlvii,472p; 25cm.
Considers the reported cases on professional negligence, with particular emphasis on recent developments. Uses cases reported in established law reports, but also those appearing in individual professional journals. Commonwealth cases are also included.
ISBN 0421341602 £36.00

Jackson, T.
Legitimate pursuit. – Southampton : Ashford Press, 1988.
ISBN 1852531045 Hbk £12.95

Jackson, Tudor
Law of Kenya : Cases and Statutes. – Nairobi : Kenya Literature Bureau, 1986.
Hbk £120.00

Jackson's Machinery of Justice. – 8th ed. – Cambridge : Cambridge University Press.
ISBN 0521362571 Hbk £75.00
ISBN 0521317673 Pbk £25.00

Jackson's matrimonial finance and taxation / D. T. A. Davies. – 4th ed. 1. – London : Butterworths, 1986.
Previous ed.: 1980. Includes index.
ISBN 0406254478 Hbk £52.00

Jacob, H.
Silent Revolution : Transformation of divorce law in the United States. – University of Chicago Press.
ISBN 0022639510 Hbk £15.90

Jacob, J. M. → Civil procedure including courts and evidence.
—Doctors and Rules : A Sociology of Professional Values. – Routledge.
ISBN 0415006880 Hbk £35.00

Jacob, Jack
White Books, 2 Vols. – London : Sweet & Maxwell, 1984.
ISBN 0421302801 Hbk £150.00

Jacob, Jack I. H.
Atkin's Encyclopaedia of Court Forms in Civil Proceedings, 42 Vols. / J. M. Dyson. – 2nd ed. – Wellington : Butterworths.
Hbk
→ Chitty and Jacob's Queen's Bench forms.
—Civil procedure including courts and evidence / J. M. Jacob. – 1. – London : Butterworths, 1966.
various pagings.
Photocopies of articles from Annual survey of Commonwealth Law 1965-1977 bound together in one volume. Includes bibliographical references. 1972 article onwards by I.H. Jacob and J.M. Jacob. 1976 and 1977 articles entitled: Civil procedure including courts.
—Fabric of English civil justice / by Sir Jack I.H. Jacob. – London : Stevens, 1987.
100p; 18cm.
Includes index.
ISBN 0420475303 Hbk £18.50
ISBN 0420475400 Pbk £9.95
—Outline of English civil procedure / by Sir Jack Jacob. – s.l. : Jack Jacob, 1984.
44p in various pagings.
'Prepared for lectures for delivery at the Faculty of Law of the Universities of Florence, Sienna, Milan, Pavia, Rome and Macerata, April 1984.'.
→ Private international litigation.
—Reform of civil procedural law and other procedure / Sir Jack I.H. Jacob. – London : Sweet & Maxwell, 1982.
xii,359p; 26cm.
ISBN 0421301104 £18.50

Jacob, Robin → Kerly's law of trade marks and trade names.
→ Patents, trade marks, copyright and industrial designs.

Jacobacci, Guido
Italian patent law / Guido Jacobacci, Giuseppe Sena. – Milano : Giuffre, 1985.
vii, 156p.
ISBN 8814007179

Jacobi, Otto → Economic crisis, trade unions and the state.
→ Technological change, rationalisation and industrial relations.

Jacobs, Francis G. → Court of Justice of the European Communities.
→ Effect of treaties in domestic law.

Jacobs, J.H.A.
Butterworths Student Companions Criminal Law /. – Butterworths, 1984.
142p.
ISBN 0409491829

Jacobs, Kenneth Sydney
Jacobs law of trusts in Australia / R P Meagher, W. M. C. Gummow. – 5th ed. – Sydney : Butterworths, 1986.
lxxxiv,1106p.
Previous ed.: 1977. Includes index. Includes texts of Acts.
ISBN 0409490768 Hbk A$94.00
ISBN 0409490792 Pbk A$72.00

Jacobs law of trusts in Australia / R P Meagher, W. M. C. Gummow. – 5th ed. – Sydney : Butterworths, 1986.
lxxxiv,1106p.
Previous ed.: 1977. Includes index. Includes texts of Acts.
ISBN 0409490768 Hbk A$94.00
ISBN 0409490792 Pbk A$72.00

Jacobs, Louis
Tree of life : diversity, flexibility, and creativity in Jewish law / Louis Jacobs. – Oxford : Published for the Littman Library by Oxford University Press, 1984.
310p; 25cm.
Bibliography: p278-293. - Includes index.
ISBN 0197100392 £18.00

Jacobs, Marcus
Law of expropriation in South Africa / Marcus Jacobs. – Cape Town : Juta, 1982.
xxxiv,700p.
Bibliography: p.xv-xvi. - Includes index.
ISBN 0702112550

Jacobs, T.
Yearbook of European law
Vol. 1. – Oxford : Oxford University Press, 1981.
ISBN 0198253842 Hbk £50.00

Jacomy-Millette, Anne-Marie
Treaty Law in Canada. – Ottawa : University of Ottawa Press, 1975.
xvii, 432p.
ISBN 0776620134 Hbk £17.00

Jacque, Jean-Paul →Ever closer union : a critical analysis of the draft treaty establishing the European Union.

Jacquemin, Alex →European challenge, 1992 : the benefits of a single market.

Jaedicke →Managerial Accounting.

Jaenicke, G.
Joint Venture Agreement for Seabed Mining. – Dordrecht : Kluwer.
127p.
ISBN 9065440135 Hbk £44.00

Jaffe, Frederick A.
Guide to pathological evidence for lawyers and police officers / Frederick A. Jaffe. – 2nd ed. – Toronto : Carswell, 1983.
xv,204p.
Bibliography: p.189-197. - Includes index.
ISBN 0459355406

Jaffey, A. J. E.
Introduction to the conflict of laws / A.J.E. Jaffey. – London : Butterworths, 1988.
300p; 22cm.
Includes bibliography and index.
ISBN 0406500487 Pbk £13.95

Jaganmohan Reddy, Pingle
Law and society : lectures and writings of Justice P. Jaganmohan Reddy / edited by M.V.K. Sivamohan. – Delhi : Ajanta Publications, 1986.
xii, 163 p.; 22 cm.
'Continuation of the anthology of lectures and writings of Justice P. Jaganmohan Reddy ... published ... under the title, 'Quest for justice'–Pref. Includes bibliographies and index.
ISBN 8120201566 Rs60.00

Jager, M. →Law and Practice of Company Accounting in Australia.

Jager, M O →Law and Practice of Company Accounting in Australia.

Jaggi
Motor Vehicles Act, 2 Vols. – 5th ed. – Allahabad : Law Publishers, 1982.
Hbk £67.50

Jagota, S. P
Maritime boundary / S.P. Jagota. – Dordrecht : M. Nijhoff, 1985.
388p.
Bibliography.
ISBN 902473133X Hbk £175.00

Jagtenberg →Legal Education 2000.

Jahan, Rounaq →Women in Asia.

Jain, D.C.
Military Law in India : a Commentary / C.G. Goel. – New Delhi : Deep and Deep Publications, 1984.
450p.
Hbk £250.00

Jain, H.C.
Law Library Administration and Reference. – Delhi : Metropolitan Book Co.
182p.
bd £25.00

Jain, Harrish C.
Anti-discrimination staffing policies : implications of human rights legislation for employers and trade unions / by Harrish C. Jain. – Ottawa : Department of the Secretary of State of Canada, 1985.
iv,100p.
Includes bibliographical references.
ISBN 0662141474

Jain, K.C.
Income Tax Law and Practice : Jabalpur Edition. – New Delhi : Kalyani Publishers.
Hbk £13.50

Jain, L.R.
Banking Law and Practice / S.P. Jain. – New Delhi : Kalyani Publishers.
Hbk £25.00

Jain, M.P.
Evolving Indian Administrative Law. – Bombay : Tripathi, 1983.
xxii, 293p.
Pbk £45.00
—Indian Constitutional Law. – 3rd ed. 1978 with Supplement. – Bombay : Tripathi, 1983.
799p.
bd £95.00
—Law and Practice of Restrictive Trade Practices in India. – New Delhi : Deep and Deep Publications, 1988.
360p.
Hbk £275.00
—Principles of Administrative Law / S.N. Jain. – 4th ed. – Bombay : Tripathi, 1986.
1138p.
Hbk £200.00

Jain, Mahabir Prasad
Outlines of Indian Legal History. – 4th ed. – Bombay : Tripathi, 1981.
xxiii, 640p.
Hbk £60.00

Jain, N.N.
Manual of Banking and Public Financial Institutions : Laws with Allied Acts, 2 Vols. – Madhya Pradesh : Lawyers Home, 1986.
Hbk £175.00 ea

Jain, P.C.
Income Tax Ready Reckoner, 1987-88. – New Delhi : Konark, 1987.
Hbk £75.00
→ Twin Acts Simplified : Company and M.R.T.P. Law.

Jain, S.C.
Child Marriage Restraint (Amendment) Act, 1978. – Delhi : SBD Enterprises.
Hbk £5.00
—Hindu Adoption and Maintenance Act, 1956 : Bare Act with Commentary. – Delhi : SBD Enterprises.
Hbk £5.00
—Indian Divorce Act, 1869 : Bare Act with Commentary. – Delhi : SBD Enterprises.
Hbk £5.00
—Law Relating to Marriage and Divorce. – 4th ed. – Delhi : SBD Enterprises, 1988.
Hbk £150.00
—Special Hindu Marriage Act, 1942 : Bare Act with Commentary. – Delhi : SBD Enterprises.
Hbk £5.00

Jain, S.N. →Principles of Administrative Law.

Jain, S.P. →Banking Law and Practice.

Jain, Subhash C.
Nationalization of foreign property : a study in North-South dialogue / Subhash C. Jain : foreword by B. Sen. – New Delhi : Deep & Deep, 1983.
298p.
Bibliography: p.268-298 - Includes index.

Jain, Jain, Suresh, Vimala
Environmental Laws in India. – Madhya Pradesh : Lawyers Home, 1986.
663p.
Hbk £300.00

Jaisimaha Rao, G.K. →Homicide : the law and the Proofs.

Jaiswal, J.N.
Cattle Trespass Act, 1871 / Vijay Malik. – 2nd ed. – Lucknow : Eastern Book Company, 1982.
138p.
Hbk £20.00

Jakhu, Ram S. →Law of international telecommunications in Canada.

Jakob, Karen
Complete Guide to Police Writing. – Agincourt : Carswell, 1984.
190p.
This work for law enforcement students offers an examination of the areas of written communication that are most problematic to police officers. On-the-job police writing and academic essay writing are discussed in the work.
Pbk £11.00

Jakovljevic, Bosko
New international status of civil defence : as an instrument for strengthening the protection of human rights / Bosko Jakovljevic. – The Hague : M. Nijhoff Publishers, 1982.
142p.
Includes bibliographical references and index.
ISBN 9024725674

Jamaica : the death penalty : report of an Amnesty International mission to Jamaica. – Amnesty International. – London : Amnesty International Publications, 1984.
63p.
ISBN 0862100763

Jamaica consolidated index of statutes and subsidiary legislation to 1st January 1982 / compiled at the Faculty of Law Library, University of the West Indies, Barbados. – Barbados : s.n., 1983.
v,104p.
One of a series in the West Indian Legislation Indexing Project (WILIP) compiled in cooperation with the British Development Division.

Jamaica consolidated index of statutes and subsidiary legislation to 1st January 1983 / compiled at the Faculty of Law Library, University of the West Indies, Barbados. – Barbados? : s.n., 1984.
v,146p.
Previous ed.: 1st January 1982. One of a series in the West Indian Legislation Indexing Project (WILIP) compiled in cooperation with the British Development Division.

James, Alan →Juta's index and annotations to the South African law reports 1980-86.

James, D W B
Safe place of work. – London : Butterworths, 1983.
ISBN 0406013044 Hbk £9.50

James, Desmond A. G.
Reciprocal enforcement : a practical guide to magistrates' courts' jurisdiction & procedure in international domestic proceedings / Desmond A.G. James : with a foreword by Dewi E. Davies. – Chichester : Rose, 1984.
133p; 22cm.
Includes index.
ISBN 0859923320 £17.75

James, Donna
Emily Murphy. – Markham : Fitzhenry and Whiteside.
ISBN 0889022348 Pbk £3.75

James Fitzjames Stephen : Portrait Victorian Rationalist. – Cambridge : Cambridge University Press.
ISBN 0521340292 Hbk £30.00

James, Jack D.
Incorporation and Business Guide for British Columbia : How to Form Your Own Corporation. – 13th ed. – North Vancouver : International Self-Counsel Press, 1988.
ISBN 0889084319

James, Jennifer →Law for Accountancy Students.

James, John S. →Strouds judicial dictionary of words and phrases.

James, Michael
Constitutional Challenge : Essays on the Australian Constitution, Constitutionalism and Parliamentary Practice / G. S. Reid. – Turramura : Centre for Independent Studies, 1982.
viii, 166p. – (CIS Readings Ser.).
ISBN 0949769010 Hbk £7.95

James, Philip S
Introduction to English Law. – 11th ed. – London : Butterworths, 1985.
ISBN 0406605017 Hbk £18.00
ISBN 0406605025 Pbk £12.95

James, R. W.
Land law and policy in Papua New Guinea : by R.W. James. – Port Moresby : Papua New Guinea Law Reform Commission, 1985.
xix,204p. – (Monograph).
Includes bibliographical references.
ISBN 998055004X
—Nigerian Land Use Act : policy and principles / by R.W. James. – Ife-Ife, Nigeria : University of Ife Press, 1987.
xxxi,195p.
Includes bibliographical references and index.
ISBN 9781360690

James, Simon →Dictionary of legal quotations.

Jameson, Grant A. →Canadian Customs and Excise Reports.

Jameson, M.
Practical guide to creative accounting. – London : Kogan Page, 1988.
ISBN 1850913013 Hbk £16.95
ISBN 185091611X Pbk £6.95

Jamieson, George
Competency of Interdict in the Enforcement of Planning Control. – Glasgow : Planning Exchange, 1983.
41p. – (Scottish Planning Law and Practice Ser.).
Hbk £8.00

Jamieson, Wanda
Native criminal justice : research issues and data sources / Wanda Jamieson and Carol Laprairie. – Ottawa : Solicitor General Canada, 1987.
iii,84p. – (User report).
Bibliography: p.78-84. On cover: Programs Branch.

Janisch, Alice
Profile of published legal research : a report to the Consultative Group on Research and Education in Law based on a survey of Canadian legal publications / Alice Janisch. – Ottawa : Consultative Group on Research and Education in Law, 1982.
39p.

Janisch, H. N. →Administrative Law : Cases, Text and Materials.
—Canadian Telecommunications Regulation Bibliography. – Ottawa : Canadian Law Information Council.
ISBN 0921481063 £25.00

Janner, G.
Building Your Business : Know Your Law. – London : Business Books, 1984.
ISBN 0091518113 Pbk £6.95

Janner, Greville
Sex and ethnic monitoring, discrimination and equal pay : new codes and regulations / by Greville Janner. – New Malden : Croner Publications, 1984.
vi,120p.
Includes index.
ISBN 0900319321

Jansen, Erna →Current Law.

Japan Securities Research Institute
Securities market in Japan 1986. – Japan Securities Research Institute. – 7th ed. – Tokyo : Japan Securities Research Institute, 1986.
xiii,215p.
Previous edition: 1985.
ISBN 4890328068

Japanese banking, securities and anti-monopoly law / edited by Hiroshi Oda, R. Geoffrey Grice. – London : Butterworths, 1988.
174p.
Includes index. '...a selection of papers delivered at the first Japanese Law Conference held at the Faculty of Law, University College London in September 1987'. - Preface.
ISBN 0406106851 £45.00

Japanese finance : Deregulation. – London : Euromoney, 1986.
ISBN 1870031253 Hbk £110.00

Japanese international taxation / Miyatake. – Matthew Bender, 1983.
ISBN 0000999083 Hbk £50.00

Japan's minorities : Burakumin, Koreans, Ainu and Okinawans / by George A. De Vos and William O. Wetherall. – New ed. – London : Minority Rights Group, 1983.
18p. – (Report).
Previous ed.: 1974. Bibliography: p. 17-18.
ISBN 0946690022

Jaque, Colin →Chancery practice handbook.

Jarashow, Richard L. →Oil pollution from ships : international, United Kingdom and United States law and practice.

Jareborg, Nils
Essays in Criminal Law. – Stockholm : Almqvist & Wiksell.
ISBN 9176781186 Hbk

Jarman
Jarman On Wills. – 8th ed. – Sweet & Maxwell, 1951 Reprint.
ISBN 0421355301 Hbk £160.00

Jarman on Wills. – Repr. of 1951 ed. – London : Sweet & Maxwell, 1986.
– (Sweet and Maxwell Library Reprints).
ISBN 0421355301 Hbk £150.00

Jarvie, Elizabeth →Computer contracts handbook : precedents of contracts for the sale, purchase, support, distribution and licence of computers and computer software.

Jarvis, F.
Probation officer's manual. – 4th ed. – London : Butterworths, 1987.
ISBN 040625608X Pbk £14.95

Jauncey, Charles Eliot Jauncey
Fishing in Scotland : law for the angler / by Lord Jauncey. – 2nd ed. – Edinburgh : W. Green, 1984.
vi,17p; 21cm.
Previous ed.: 1952.
ISBN 0414007344 Pbk

Javillier, J.-C. →Comparative dismissal law.

Jayasuriya →Management of Correctional Institutions.

Jayasuriya, D. C.
Guide to the Companies Act of 1982
Vol. 1 / D.C. Jayasuriya. – 1st ed. – Nawala, Sri Lanka : Asian Pathfinder, 1983.
194p.
—Mechanics of constitutional change : the Sri Lankan style / by D.C. Jayasuriya. – Nawala, Sri Lanka : Asian Pathfinder Publishers, 1982.
130p.
Bibliography: p.103-125. - Includes index.
—Regulation of pharmaceuticals in developing countries : legal issues and approaches / by D.C. Jayasuriya. – Geneva : World Health Organization, 1985.
118p.
Includes bibliographical references.
ISBN 9241560894

Jayewardene
Management of Correctional Institutions. – Jayewardene. – Toronto : Butterworths, 1981.
208p.
Analyses the aims and objectives of a correctional institution, the context in which it must operate, and the material and human resources available for it to operate, using the framework of extant sociological and physiological theory. Illustrates how from this analysis an efficient program of activity could be derived, using the framework of managerial theory.
ISBN 0409840513 Pbk £21.95

JCT 80 and the Builder : An Introduction. – King's Ride : Institute of Building, 1985.
211p.
ISBN 0906600774 Hbk £12.75

JCT Agreement For Minor Building Works. – Spon (E & FN).
ISBN 0728200767 Pbk £15.00

JCT Intermediate Form of Contract : An Architectural Press Legal Guide / Vincent Powell-Smith. – London : Architectural Press, 1985.
232p : Illus.
ISBN 0851398855 Hbk £19.95

JCT Minor Works Form of Contract : An Architectural Press Legal Guide / Vincent Powell-Smith. – London : Architectural Press, 1986.
176p : Illus.
ISBN 0851398863 Hbk £18.00

Jeevanandam, C.
Objective Type Questions in Banking Law and Practice. – 6th rev. ed. – New Delhi : Sultan Chand and Sons, 1985.
iv, 124p.
Hbk £10.00

Jeffcoate →Expert Systems in Banking and Securities.

Jeffery, Keith
States of emergency : British governments and strikebreaking since 1919 / Keith Jeffery and Peter Hennessy. – London : Routledge & K. Paul, 1983.
312p.
Includes index. Bibliography: p300-304.
ISBN 0710094647

Jegede, M. I.
Land law and development : an inaugural lecture delivered at the University of Lagos on Thursday, 17th January, 1980 / by M.I. Jegede. – Lagos : University of Lagos Press, 1981.
39p. – (Inaugural lecture series).
Includes bibliographical references.
ISBN 978226413X
—Principles of equity / by M. I. Jegede. – Benin City, Nigeria : Ethiope Publishing Corporation, 1981.
xxv,262p. – (Ethiope law series).
Includes bibiographical references and index.

Jegede, Oluremi →Basic resourses on Nigerian law.
—Bibliography on the constitutions of Nigeria / compiled by Oluremi Jegede. – London : Oceana, 1981.
vi,72p; 26cm.
Includes index.
—Bibliography on the writings of the Hon. Judge T. O. Elias / by Oluremi Jegede. – 2nd ed. – Lagos : Nigerian Institute of Advanced Legal Studies, 1986.
viii, 51p. – (Occasional paper).
Includes index.
ISBN 9782353027

Jehoram, H. Cohen →Public lending right : reports of an ALAI symposium and additional materials.

Jehovah's Witnesses in Africa / by Tony Hodges. – New rev. ed. – London : Minority Rights Group, 1985.
16p. – (Report).
Previous ed. published as: Jehovah's Witnesses in Central Africa. Bibliography: p.14.
ISBN 0946690227

Jelf
Fifteen Decisive Battles Of The Law. – Sweet & Maxwell, 1921 Reprint.
ISBN 0421375507 Hbk £15.75

Jellicoe, George Patrick John Rushworth

Jellicoe →Review of the operation of the Prevention of Terrorism (Temporary Provisions) Act 1976.

Jenkins
Conduct of Canadian Meetings : Company Law and Common Law. – London : Butterworths.
ISBN 0409840653 Hbk £36.00
—Racism and equal opportunity policy in the 1980's / Solomos. – Cambridge : Cambridge University Press, 1987.
ISBN 0521330130 Hbk £25.00

Jenkins, Benjamin George →Loss of the 'City of Boston' : Inman v. Jenkins : an action for libel, tried at the Liverpool Assizes, before Mr. Justice Lush amd a special jury, on Tuesday and Wednesday, August 30th and 31st, 1870.

Jenkins, C.
Practical timeshare and group ownership. – London : Butterworths, 1987.
ISBN 0406103283 Pbk £26.95

Jenkins, Dafydd →Law of Hywel Dda : law texts of medieval Wales.

Jenkins, David Llewelyn Jenkins →Minutes of evidence taken before the Company Law Committee.

Jenkins, John J.
Understanding Locke : an introduction to philosophy through John Locke's Essay / John J. Jenkins. – Edinburgh : Edinburgh University Press, 1983.
xviii,256p; 21cm.
Bibliography: p241-252. - Includes index.
ISBN 0852244428 Hbk £15.00
ISBN 0852244495 Pbk

Jenkins, John R.G.
Canadian Cases in Marketing Communications. – Butterworths, 1983.
480p.
ISBN 0409840645 Hbk £36.95

Jenkins, W. I. →Administrative politics in British government.

Jenner Wily, H.
Abridgment of New Zealand Case Law : 1861-1967, 16 Vols. – Wellington : Butterworths.
ISBN 0409600008 Hbk

Jennings
Corporate Communications / Churchill. – London : Fitzwilliam, 1988.
ISBN 1870555066 Hbk £25.00

Jennings, A.R.
Advanced Accounting Practice : ACCA Study and Revision Manual 2.9. – London : BPP.
ISBN 1870941047 Pbk £19.90

Jennings, Ivor
British Constitution. – 5th ed. – Cambridge : Cambridge University Press, 1966.
ISBN 0521091365 Pbk £7.95
—Modern Theories of Law 1933. – London : Wildy & Sons.
Hbk £8.25

Jennings, R.J.
What is International Law and How Do We Tell it When We See It? / J.R. Spencer. – Dordrecht : Kluwer.
66p.
Hbk £26.00

Jennings, Robert Yewdall
International courts and international politics / Robert Yewdall Jennings. – Hull : Hull University Press, 1986.
17p.
Josephine Onoh Memorial Lecture.
ISBN 0859584550

Jennings, Y.
Cambridge-Tilburg Law Lectures
Vol. 3 / J.R. Spencer. – Dordrecht : Kluwer, 1983.
68p.
ISBN 9065441077 Pbk £25.00

Jensen, C. H.
Law and practice relating to pollution control in Denmark / prepared by C.H. Jensen for Environmental Resources Limited. – 2nd ed. – London : Graham & Trotman for the Commission of the European Communities, 1982.
200p.
Previous ed: 1976. Includes index.
ISBN 0860103129 £18.00

Jeremy Bentham and representative democracy : a study of the Constitutional code / Frederick Rosen. – Oxford : Clarendon Press, 1983.
vi,255p; 23cm.
Bibliography: p243-248. - Includes index.
ISBN 019822656X £19.50

Jeremy, David J.
Dictionary of Business Biography. – London : Butterworths.
This work contains over 1000 biographies of British businessmen from 1860 to 1980. Each subject is treated in terms of his major successes and failures, innovations, and management style and policies.
Pbk

Jersey : a low tax area / by Mark Solly. – Croydon : Tolley, 1982.
iv,323p; 24cm.
Includes index.
ISBN 0854590536 Hbk
ISBN 0854590544 Pbk £15.00

Jersey law of trusts / by Paul Matthews and Terry Sowden : foreword by Justice Hoffmann. – London : Key Haven, 1988.
102p; 30cm.
Includes index. English text with statutory material in French.
ISBN 1870070070 spiral

Jersey Law Reports 1985-86 Part 3. – London : Law Reports International.
ISBN 0903826933 Hbk £20.00

Jersey law reports. – Oxford : Law Reports International, 1987-.
Continues : Judgments of the Royal Court of Jersey and of the Court of Appeal of Jersey.

Jervis, John →Jervis on the office and duties of coroners : with forms and precedents.
—Jervis on the office and duties of coroners : with forms and precedents / Paul- Matthews, J. C. Foreman, John Jervis. – 10th ed. – London : Sweet & Maxwell, 1986.
xl,539p.
Examines the field of the coroner's work; the classification, appointment, office, jurisdiction and powers of the coroner; matters pertaining to the inquest from prehearing to verdict and review of the inquisition and coronial decision, medical matters such as special cases including notifiable accidents and prescribed diseases with reference to the Social Security (Industrial Injuries) Regulations 1985.
ISBN 0421329602 £55.00

Jervis on Coroners
Supplement 1 / Matthews. – 10th ed. – Sweet & Maxwell.
ISBN 00421403802 Pbk £8.50

Jervis on the office and duties of coroners : with forms and precedents / Paul- Matthews, J. C. Foreman, John Jervis. – 10th ed. – London : Sweet & Maxwell, 1986.
xl,539p.
Examines the field of the coroner's work; the classification, appointment, office, jurisdiction and powers of the coroner; matters pertaining to the inquest from prehearing to verdict and review of the inquisition and coronial decision, medical matters such as special cases including notifiable accidents and prescribed diseases with reference to the Social Security (Industrial Injuries) Regulations 1985.
ISBN 0421329602 £55.00

Jervis, Jervis, John
Jervis on Coroners
Supplement 1 / Matthews. – 10th ed. – Sweet & Maxwell.
ISBN 00421403802 Pbk £8.50

Jess, Digby Charles
Guide to Insurance Professional Negligence Risks. – London : Butterworths, 1982.
ISBN 0406257108 Pbk £21.95
—Guide to the Insurance of Professional Negligence Risks. – Wellington : Butterworths, 1982.
This book discusses in detail the coverage provided by the 'basic' United Kingdom professional indemnity policy and some of the more popular extensions in common practice. The work provides a general explanation of the law of professional negligence and insurance law.
ISBN 0406257108 Pbk £35.00
—Insurance of commercial risks : law and practice / Digby C. Jess. – London : Butterworths, 1986.
445p; 26cm.
Includes index.
ISBN 0406257116 Hbk £36.00

Jessep, Owen
Custody jurisdiction in Papua New Guinea / by Owen Jessep. – Waigani : Law Reform Commission of Papua New Guinea, 1987.
37p. – (LRC working paper).
Includes text of the Infants Act.
—Principles of family law in Papua New Guinea / by Owen Jessep and John Luluaki. – Waigani : University of Papua New Guinea Press, 1985.
205p.
Bibliography: pp.194-197. - Includes index.
ISBN 9980840137

Jessop, Bob
Capitalist state : Marxist theories and methods / Bob Jessop. – Oxford : Robertson, 1982.
xvi,296p; 24cm.
Bibliography: p260-281. - Includes index.
ISBN 0855202696 Hbk £17.00
ISBN 0855202688 Pbk £5.95

Jessup, C.N.
Industrial Law, Victoria. – Butterworths, 1981.
ISBN 0409490415 Llf

Jessup, G. A.
Jessup's Forms and practice of the Lands Titles Office of South Australia / J. G. Maher. – 6th ed. – Sydney : Law Book Co., 1982.
xii,444p.
Includes index.
ISBN 0455205345

Jessup's Forms and practice of the Lands Titles Office of South Australia / J. G. Maher. – 6th ed. – Sydney : Law Book Co., 1982.
xii,444p.
Includes index.
ISBN 0455205345

Jewish law annual. – Leiden : Brill, 1978-.

Jews of Africa and Asia : contemporary anti-semitism and other pressures / Tudor Parfitt. – London : Minority Rights Group, 1987.
15p. – (Report).
Bibliography: p.15.
ISBN 0946690561

Jhala, H. M.
Law of monopolies and restrictive trade practices in India / H.M. Jhala. – 2nd ed. – Bombay : Tripathi (N. M.), 1984.
xxxvii,456p.
Includes index.

Jhala, J.M.
Assessment of Medical Impairment and Disability. – Madhya Pradesh : Lawyers Home, 1987.
Hbk £100.00
—Medical Jurisprudence / Raju. – 4th ed. 1981 repr. – Lucknow : Eastern Book Company, 1982.
681p.
Hbk £45.00

Jhirad, E.E.
Law Relating to Private Companies / Avtar Singh. – 4th ed. – Lucknow : Eastern Book Company, 1983.
651p.
Hbk £125.00

Jindal, K.B.
Income Tax Past and Present, Vol 1. – 4th ed. – Allahabad : Orient Law House, 1984.
Hbk £180.00

Jinyan, L →Taxation of foreign investment in the People's Republic of China.

Job evaluation schemes free of sex bias / Equal Opportunities Commission. – Manchester : The Commission, 1981.
ISBN 0905829395

Jobs in Local Authorities. – London : Kogan Page, 1985.
95p. – (Jobs In...Ser.).
ISBN 085038978X Pbk £2.95

Joel, Adrian
Insurance handbook. – 1st ed. – London : Legal Books, 1985.
ISBN 0949553182 Pbk £12.00
—Practical Guide to Accepting Insurance Risks. – Woolloomooloo : International Business Communications, 1986.
ISBN 0949553255 Hbk £13.50
—Practical Guide to Obtaining Permanent Residence in Australia. – 3rd ed. – Woolloomooloo : International Business Communications, 1987.
ISBN 0949553387 Hbk £14.50

Joelson, Mark R. →Joint ventures in the United States.

Joergensen, Boel →Academic freedom under Israeli military occupation : report of WUS/ICJ mission of enquiry into higher education in the West Bank and Gaza.

Johansson, Eve →Official publications of Western Europe, Vol.2 : Austria, Belgium, Federal Republic of Germany, Greece, Norway, Portugal, Sweden, Switzerland and United Kingdom.

John Austin. – London : E. Arnold, 1982.
192p.
ISBN 0713163593 Hbk £11.00
ISBN 0713163607 Pbk £5.50

John Locke's moral philosophy / John Colman. – Edinburgh : Edinburgh University Press, 1983.
viii,282p; 22cm.
Bibliography: p270-276. - Includes index.
ISBN 0852244452 £20.00

John, M.
Politics and the Law in Late 19th Century Germany. – Oxford : Clarendon Press.
ISBN 0198227485 Hbk £35.00

John Stuart Mill's On liberty / John C. Rees : constructed from published and unpublished sources by G.L. Williams. – Oxford : Clarendon, 1985.
xi,210p; 22cm.
Bibliography: p204-207. - Includes index.
ISBN 0198247664 £19.50

Johns, Richard Anthony
Tax havens and offshore finance : a study of transnational economic development / Richard Anthony Johns. – London : Frances Pinter, 1983.
xiv,259p.
Bibliography: p248-255.

Johnson
'A' Level Law / Pannett. – London : Financial Training, 1988.
– (SWOT).
ISBN 1851850651 Pbk £7.50
→ Forensic Medicine.
→ Ocean and Coastal Law.

Johnson, Barry O. →Filmed horse racing.

Johnson, C.
Lloyds Bank Annual Review. – Pinter, 1988.
ISBN 0861879740 Hbk £20.00

Johnson, J. Peter
Canadian Industrial Incentives Legislation, 2 Vols. / Janice A. Lacke. – Scarborough, Ontario : Butterworths (Canada).
Llf £150.00

Johnson, Lannes →Sexual violence : a case for law reform : papers presented at seminar, University of Auckland, 27 August 1982.

Johnson, Nicholas L.
Soviet military strategy in space / Nicholas L. Johnson. – London : Jane's, 1987.
287p.
ISBN 0710604491

Johnson, P.J. →Hobbes's Science of Natural Justice.

Johnson, Samuel →Course of lectures on the English law : delivered at the University of Oxford, 1767-1773.

Johnson, Stanley P, et al
Environmental policy of the European Communities / Guy Corcelle. – London : Graham & Trotman, 1989.
336. – (International environmental law and policy).
Survey of the legislation on environmental policy introduced by the European Community in recent years. Covers pollution control, environmental impact assessment, and nature conservation. Gives the full text of the Declaration on the Environment adopted by the European Council meeting at Rhodes in 1988.
ISBN 1853332259 Hbk £45

Johnson, Tony →Development Land Tax Guide.

Johnston, Christine →Role of an auditor in detecting fraud and other irregularities : a study.

Johnston, D.
Design Protection. – 2nd ed. – London : Design Council Books, 1986.
ISBN 0850721652 Hbk £8.95
Guide to Law on Plagiarism for Manufacturers and Designers. –
ISBN 0850722489 Hbk £15.00

Johnston, David
On a Singular Book of Cervidius Scaevola. – Berlin : Duncker and Humblot, 1987.
103p.
ISBN 3428062922 Hbk £54.00
—Roman law of trusts / David Johnston. – Oxford : Clarendon Press, 1988.
xiii,306p.
Discusses the Roman equivalent of a trust, a fideicommissum, which affected the strategies of succession open to testators. Provides an illustration of the emperor's involvement in building private law. Relates Roman law to social history and uses the development of the trust as a case study in legal evolution.
ISBN 0198252161 Hbk £37.50

Johnston, David L.
Canadian Securities Regulation. – Butterworths, 1977.
528p.
ISBN 0409841226 Hbk £95.00

Johnston, Douglas M.
Canada and the new international law of the sea / Douglas M. Johnston. – Toronto : University of Toronto Press in cooperation with the Royal Commission on the Economic Union and Development Prospects for Canada and the Canadian Government Publishing Centre, 1985.
xviii,124p. – (Collected research studies).
Includes bibliographical references.
ISBN 0802073018
—Environmental Law of the Sea. – Gland : International Union for Conservation of Nature and Natural Resources, 1981.
419p.
Hbk £39.00
—Environmental law of the sea / by Douglas M. Johnston. – Berlin : E. Schmidt, 1981.
419 p.; 21 cm.
Includes bibliographical references.
ISBN 3503021116 Pbk
—International Law of Fisheries : a Framework for Policy-Oriented Inquiries. – Dordrecht : Kluwer, 1987.
632p.
ISBN 089838902X Hbk £225.00
—Ocean Boundary Making / Saunders. – Oxford : Croom Helm, 1988.
ISBN 0709914954 Hbk £35.00
→ Structure and Process of International Law : Essays in Legal Philosophy, Doctrine and Theory.
—Theory and History of Ocean Boundary Making. – Witney : Academic & University Publishing Group.
ISBN 0773506241 Hbk £37.95
—Theory and History of Ocean Boundary-Making. – Montreal : McGill-Queen's University Press, 1988.
ISBN 0773506241 Hbk £39.95

Johnston, J.
Government Financial Assistance Programs in Canada. – 4th ed. – Toronto : Butterworths, 1986.
800p.
ISBN 0409803170 Pbk £31.95

Johnston, R. B.
Economics of the Euro-market : history, theory and policy / R. B. Johnston. – London : Macmillan, 1983.
x,321p.
Bibliography: p308-316.
ISBN 0333334183

Johnston, T R
Law and Practice of Company Accounting in Australia / M O Jager, R B Taylor. – 6th ed. – North Ryde : Butterworths (Australia), 1983.
Analysis of the law of company accounting and reporting. Includes aspects of practice as necessary to interpret the law and explain its significance and application. Incorporates developments including the changes effected by the Companies Act 1981 (the National Act), and the latest Accounting Standards.
ISBN 0409493902 Pbk £27.60
—Law and Practice of Company Accounting in Australia / M. Jager. – 6th ed. – Sydney : Butterworths, 1987.
669p.
ISBN 0409491853 Hbk
—Law and Practice of Company Accounting in New Zealand. – 6th ed. – Butterworths, 1982.
Treatment of the law relating to company accounting and reporting and of the professional pronouncements and accounting practices which stem from or assist in the application of such law. All SSAPS including the CCA Standard are reproduced in the appendix.
ISBN 040960089X Pbk £82.50

Johnstone, D.
The Roman Law of Trusts. – Oxford : Clarendon Press.
ISBN 0198252161 Hbk £25.00

Joint Committee on Western Europe →Order and conflict in contemporary capitalism.

Joint development of resources projects : a comparison : proceedings of the Regional Energy Law Seminar, Singapore, 30 September 1985 / International Bar Association. Section on Energy and Natural Resources Law. – London : International Bar Assocation, 1985.
Various pagings.

Joint enterprise : roles and relationships of the public and private sectors in the provision of library and information services / report of Library and Information Services Council and British Library Research and Development Department Working Party. – London : H.M.S.O., 1987.
vii, 49p.
On cover: Office of Arts and Libraries.
ISBN 011430016X

The Joint Operating Agreement : Oil and Gas Law. – London : Longman Professional.
ISBN 0851212395 Hbk £50.00

Joint Operating Agreements 1988. – London : Longman Professional.
ISBN 08512112395 Hbk

Joint Venture Agreement for Seabed Mining. – Dordrecht : Kluwer.
127p.
ISBN 9065440135 Hbk £44.00

Joint ventures / Edgar Herzfeld. – Bristol : Jordan, 1983.
vii,105p.
Bibliography: p.99-102. - Includes index.
ISBN 0853080704

Joint ventures. – London : Longman Professional, 1988.
ISBN 0851213189 Hbk

Joint ventures and Article 85 / Jonathan Faull. – London : Law Society Solicitors' European Group, 1985.
26p.
'Transcript of a talk given to the Solicitor's European Group on March 19th 1984'.

Joint ventures in the construction industry : papers presented at the 7th Conference of the International Bar Association's Section on Business Law, Singapore 1985 / International Construction Contracts Committee of the Section on Business Law of the International Bar Association. – 1. – London : International Bar Association, 1985.
Various pagings.
Includes bibliographical references.

Joint ventures in the Kingdom of Saudi Arabia / John Walmsley. – 2nd ed. – London : Graham & Trotman, 1985.
388p; 25cm.
Previous ed.: 1979. Bibliography: p381. - Includes index.
ISBN 0860106799 £43.00

Joint ventures in the United States / edited by John I. Forry, Mark R. Joelson. – London : Butterworths, 1988.
200p; 24cm.
Includes index.
ISBN 0406499616 £40.00

Joint Working Party of the Law Reform Committees of the Senate of the Inns of Court and the Bar and the Law Society
Reservation of title : draft Council of Europe Convention (CDCJ(82)15) / memorandum by a Working Party of the Senate of the Inns of Court and the Bar and the Law Society. – London? : the Working Party?, 1983.
4p.
Bound with 'Draft proposal for a Council Directive on the legal consequences of agreements creating simple reservation of title (III/872/79-EN)'.

Joint Working Party on Banking Law
UNCITRAL Draft Convention on international bills of exchange and internnational promissory notes, and Draft Convention on international cheques / memorandum by the Joint Working Party of the Law Reform Committees of the Senate of the Inns of Court and the Bar and the Law Society. – London? : the Joint Working Party?, 1983.
7p.

Joint Working Party on Competition Law
Submission by the Joint Working Party on Competition Law to the House of Lords Select Committee on the European Communities on procedures for administering EEC competition policy. – Joint Working Party on Competition Law. – London : Senate of the Inns of Court and the Bar, 1981.
10p; 30cm.
At head of title: The Senate of the Inns of Court and Bar, The Law Society.

Joint Working Party on Intellectual Property
Memorandum by the Joint Working Party on Intellectual Property : on proposals by the European Commission for a first Council directive to approximate the laws of the member states relating to trade marks and for a Council regulation on Community trade marks : Com (80) 635 Final/2 (published (1981) XXX Common Market Law Reports 357 & 365). – Joint Working Party on Intellectual Property. – London : Senate of the Inns of Court and the Bar, 1981.
13,4,3p; 30cm.
At head of title: The Senate of the Inns of Court and the Bar, The Law Society.

Jois, Rama
Legal and Constitutional History of India, 2 Vols. – Bombay : Tripathi.
Hbk

Jolly, Brian
Property Development Library, 4 Vols. – London : Sweet & Maxwell, 1984.
Hbk £135.00
—Property Development Library
Vol. 1, 5 titles. – Reading : College of Estate Management, 1983.
– (College of Estate Management Handbooks Ser.).
Hbk £25.00

Jolly, Julius
Naradiya Dharmasastra : Judicial System in Ancient India. – Delhi : Ajanta Books International, 1981.
180p.
ISBN 8120200578 Hbk £70.00

Jolowicz, John Anthony →Winfield and Jolowicz on tort.

Jonas, George →Greenspan : in Defence of.
—Scales of Justice : Seven Famous Criminal Cases Recreated. – Toronto : Canadian Broadcasting Corporation Enterprises, 1984.
256p.
ISBN 0887941206 Pbk £10.95
ISBN 0887941249 Hbk £16.95

Jones
Disorderly Conduct : Real Life Comedy from the Courtrooms / Victor J Sevilla. – London : Angus & Robertson.
ISBN 0207160007 Hbk £4.95
→ Fair Trading in New Zealand : the Fair Trading Act 1986.
→ Flashpoints; Studies in Public Disorder.
→ Futures Game.
→ Governmental Accounting & Auditing : International Comparisons.
→ Introduction to criminal law.
—Malton Memorial Recreation Association Act, 1983, Bill Pr030 : An Act to Revive the Malton Memorial Recreation Association. – Ontario : Ontario Government Publications Service, 1983.
2p.
Hbk £0.30
→ Memoirs of Edwin Waterhouse.
—Public Sector Accounting / N Pendlebury. – 2nd ed. – Pitman.
ISBN 0273029304 Pbk £12.95
—Tax and Interest Tables / Nuttall. – London : Fourmat.
ISBN 1851900470 Hbk £6.95

Jones, Alan
Jury Service. – London : Hale, 1983.
142p.
ISBN 0709012845 Hbk £7.95

Jones, B. L. →Garner's administrative law.

Jones, Barry
A-Level Law. – Plymouth : Macdonald & Evans, 1984.
240p. – (M and E Handbook Ser.).
ISBN 0712101608 Pbk £3.25
Supplement 1987. – 1984.
– (M and E Handbook Ser.).
ISBN 0712101926 Pbk £4.95

Jones, D. R. →Underhill's principles of the law of partnership.

Jones, D.S.
Regulation of Building Standards Queensland / D.K. Woodhead. – Butterworths, 1988.
ISBN 0409300942 Llf

Jones, David
Crime, protest, community and police in nineteenth-century Britain / David Jones. – London : Routledge & Kegan Paul, 1982.
xi, 247p.
Includes index. Includes bibliography.
ISBN 0710090080

Jones, David Lloyd →Three international conventions on hijacking and offences on board aircraft : (i) Convention on Offences and Certain Other Acts Committed on Board Aircraft ... 1963. (ii) Convention for Suppression of Unlawful Seizure of Aircraft ... 1970. (iii) Convention for the Suppression of Unlawful Acts Against the Safety of Civil Aviation ... 1971 : explanation documentation prepared for Commonwealth jurisdictions by David Lloyd Jones in association with the Commonwealth Secretariat.

Jones, David Phillip
Principles of administrative law / by David Philip Jones and Anne S. de Villars. – Toronto : Carswell, 1985.
xlv,489p.
ISBN 0459377604

Jones, G.
New Approach I.C.I. Conditions of Contract Vol. 1. – Oxford : Construction Press, 1975.
ISBN 0904406075 Hbk £27.00
—New Approach to (Dom/1) Standard Form Building Contract 1983. – Oxford : Construction Press.
ISBN 0860957225 Hbk £42.50
—New approach to JCT design/building contract. – Oxford : Construction Press, 1984.
ISBN 086095904X Hbk £38.00

Jones, Gareth
Specific performance / Gareth Jones, William Goodhart. – London : Butterworths, 1986.
lxvi,274p; 25cm.
Bibliography: plxv-lxvi. - Includes index.
ISBN 0406258090 £35.00

Jones, Gregory
Law : a Guide to Select Law Sources in the Canberra College of Advanced Education Library / Peter Stone. – 4th ed. – Belconnen : Canberra College of Advanced Education, 1982.
2, 73p.
ISBN 0858892065 Hbk £4.00

Jones, Gregory Philip
Aboriginal land rights legislation : an examination of the publications associated with Commonwealth legislation / Gregory P. Jones. – Belconnen, A.C.T., Australia : Canberra College of Advanced Education, Library, 1983.
iii, 196 p.; 25 cm.
Includes bibliographical references.
ISBN 0858892391 Pbk £9.00

Jones, Harold E. →Surveying offshore Canada lands for mineral resource development.

Jones, Howard
Crime, race and culture : a study in a developing country / Howard Jones. – Chichester : Wiley, 1981.
xv,184p; 24cm.
Bibliography: p175-179. - Index.
ISBN 047127996X £12.75
→ Society against crime : penal practise sic in modern Britain.

Jones, J. Barry →Welsh Veto : The Wales Act 1978 and the Referendum.

Jones, J. F. Avery →Encyclopedia of value added tax.

Jones, J.H. Emlyn →Encyclopedia of rating and local taxation : law and practice.

Jones, Janet →Shareholders' agreements.

Jones, John Mervyn
British Nationality Law. – Repr. of 1956 ed. – Aalen Wuertt : Scientia.
xxviii, 306p.
Hbk £85.00

Jones, K. V. Prichard →Franchising : practice and precedents in business format franchising.

Jones, Kelvin
Law and economy : the legal regulation of corporate capital / Kelvin Jones. – London : Academic Press, 1982.
xvi,190p; 24cm.
Bibliography: p179-184. - Includes index.
ISBN 0123900409 £16.00

Jones, M.
Textbook on torts. – London : Financial Training, 1986.
ISBN 1851850260 Pbk £13.95

Jones, Maggie
Voluntary Organisations and the Media : An NCVO Practical Guide. – London : Bedford Square Press, 1984.
ISBN 0719911206 Hbk £3.50

Jones, Margrave
Butterworth's Inheritance Tax Guide. – London : Butterworths, 1986.
ISBN 0406500347 Pbk £31.50

Jones, Mark →Competitive Trading in New Zealand : the Commerce Act 1986.

Jones, Martyn, et al
Revenue law in Scotland / Simon Mackintosh. – London : Butterworths, 1986.
Starts with an introduction to the Scottish legal system and a discussion of applying UK revenue law in Scotland. Chapters on taxation of persons, property, charities and partnership with longer chapters on trusts and succession. Styles for discretionary and accumulation and maintenance trusts provided.
ISBN 040650170X Pbk £18.50

Jones, Mervyn
Sami of Lapland / by Mervyn Jones. – London : Minority Rights Group, 1981.
15p. – (Report).
Bibliography: p.15.

Jones, Neil F.
Commentary on the JCT Intermediate Form of Building Contract / Neil F. Jones and David Bergman. – London : Collins, 1985.
viii,351; 25cm.
Includes index.
ISBN 0003830241 Pbk

Jones, Noragh
Staff management in library and information work / Noragh Jones, Peter Jordan. – Aldershot : Gower, 1982.
vii,215p; 23cm. – (A Grafton book).
Bibliography: p205-212. - Includes index.
ISBN 0566034301

Jones, Peter →Juvenile sentencing : is there a tariff?.

Jones, Peter R.
Staff resource implications of an independent prosecution system / Peter R. Jones. – London : Home Office, 1983.
v,39p.
Bibliography: p.32.
ISBN 086252119X

—Vietnamese refugees : a study of their reception and resettlement in the United Kingdom. – London : Home Office, 1982.
iv,63p.
Bibliography: p.56.
ISBN 0862520789

Jones, Philip Asterley →Introduction to criminal law.

Jones, Pickett
Understanding child abuse. – 2nd ed. – London : Macmillan, 1987.
ISBN 0333428935 Pbk £7.95

Jones, R.
Adoption Act Manual. – London : Sweet & Maxwell, 1988.
ISBN 0421393505 Pbk £18.00

—Local Government Audit Law. – London : HMSO, 1985.
ISBN 0117012599 Hbk £19.50

Jones, R.G.
Unsolved : classic true murder cases. – Star Books, 1988.
ISBN 0352321741 Pbk £2.95

Jones, R. J. M →Conveyancing in South Africa.

—Conveyancing in South Africa / R.J.M. Jones. – 3rd ed. – Cape Town : Juta, 1985.
xix, 540 p.; 26 cm.
Re ed. of: The law and practice of conveyancing in South Africa. 2nd ed. 1976. Includes indexes.
ISBN 0702115967

Jones, Reginald →Local Government Finance Act 1982.

Jones, Richard M.
Adoption act manual / Richard M. Jones. – London : Sweet & Maxwell, 1988.
vii,263p.
Includes the amended form of the 1976 Act, relevant statutory instruments, and DHSS circulars, and annotated version of the Adoption Rules 1984, the Magistrates Court (Adoption Rules) 1984.
ISBN 0421393505 £15.00
→ Mental Health Act manual.
→ Registered Homes Act 1984.
→ Sweet & Maxwell's social work statutes.

Jones, Rod
United Kingdom Offshore Legislation Guide. – Tonbridge : Ernest Benn.
300p.
ISBN 0854591524 Hbk £110.00

Jones, S.
Banking and Business in South Africa. – London : Macmillan.
ISBN 0333444655 Hbk £29.50

—Policewoman and Equality (1988). – London : Macmillan, 1988.
ISBN 0333424417 Pbk £8.95

Jones, Sally
Share Capital : Company Law and Taxation / David Bellringer. – London : Butterworths, 1984.
ISBN 0406258163 Hbk

Jones, Trevor
Islington crime survey : crime, victimization and policing in inner-city London / Trevor Jones, Brian MacLean and Jock Young. – Aldershot : Gower, 1986.
xiv, 265p; 23cm.
ISBN 0566052644

Jonker, A. J.
Property valuation in South Africa. – Cape Town : Juta, 1984.
x,181p.
ISBN 0702114855

Jonsson, Christer
Cooperation and Conflict : Nordic Journal of International Politics. – Oslo : University of Forlag.
Hbk

Jordan
Government & Pressure Groups in Britain / Richardson. – Oxford : Oxford University Press, 1987.
ISBN 0198761678 Hbk £30.00
→ Insolvency - Introduction to the 1985 Act.

Jordan, Alan
Permanent incapacity : invalid pension in Australia / Alan Jordan. – Canberra : Department of Social Security, 1984.
264p. – (Research paper).
ISBN 0642515565

Jordan, Bill
State : authority and autonomy / Bill Jordan. – Oxford : Blackwell, 1985.
vi,352p.
Includes bibliography and index.
ISBN 0631142738 £19.50

Jordan, Frederick
Select Legal Papers. – limited ed. – Woolloomooloo : International Business Communications, 1983.
ISBN 0949553050 Hbk £34.95

Jordan, Michael →Insolvency.

Jordan, Peter →Staff management in library and information work.

Jordan's Guide to Companies Legislation : 1985. – Bristol : Jordan & Sons Ltd, 1985.
ISBN 0853080798 Pbk £10.00

Jorde
Foreign Investment Debt and Economy / Salazar-Carillo. – London : Macmillan, 1988.
ISBN 0333402081 Hbk £37.50

Jory, L. G. →Encyclopaedia of forms and precedents other than court forms.

Joseph, Bruce G. →Protection for semiconductor chip masks in the United States : analysis of the Semiconductor Chip Protection Act of 1984.

Joseph, Philip A.
Judicial Perspective on Industrial Conciliation and Arbitration in New Zealand. – Repr. of 1980 ed. – Auckland : Legal Research Foundation, 1982.
49p.
ISBN 0908581076 Pbk £5.50

Josey, Alex
Trial of Sunny Ang. – Singapore : Times Booker International.
160p.
ISBN 9971651548 Pbk £6.50

Joshi
Maharashtra Local Laws, 14 Vols. – Allahabad : Ashoka Law House, 1987.
Hbk £125.00 ea.

Joshi et al, Ram
Indian Constitution and its Working. – rev. ed. – Allahabad : Orient Law House.
236p.
ISBN 0861316118 Pbk £40.00

Joshi, G.N.
Constitution of India. – 7th ed. – New Delhi : Macmillan India.
422p.
ISBN 0333900588 Pbk £25.00

Joshua, Harris
To ride the storm : the 1980 Bristol 'riot' and the state / Harris Joshua, Tina Wallace and Heather Booth. – London : Heinemann, 1983.
vii,221p.
Bibliography: p211-216.
ISBN 0435824813

Joske, Percy Ernest
Australian Federal Government. – 3rd ed. – London : Butterworths.
ISBN 0409372056 Pbk £11.80

—Insurance law in Australia and New Zealand / by P. E. Joske and Robert Brooking. – Sydney : Butterworths, 1975.
xxxix, 302 p.; 25 cm.
Includes index. Sets out insurance law both in terms of general principles and explains how these principles have been applied to particular aspects of insurance in the courts of Australia and New Zealand. Refers to decisions of the UK.
ISBN 0409436305 £20.00

—Joske's law and procedure at meetings in Australia / by W.J. Chappenden. – 7th ed. – Sydney : Law Book Co., 1982.
xxiii,211p.
Includes index.
ISBN 0455205388

Joske's law and procedure at meetings in Australia / by W.J. Chappenden. – 7th ed. – Sydney : Law Book Co., 1982.
xxiii,211p.
Includes index.
ISBN 0455205388

Josling
Adoption Of Children / Levy. – 10th ed. – London : Longman Professional, 1985.
ISBN 0851208665 Pbk £24.00

Josling, J.
Change of name. – 13th ed. – London : Longman Professional, 1985.
ISBN 0851209890 Pbk £11.95

Josling, J. F.
Law of clubs : with a note on unincorporated associations / J.F. Josling, Lionel Alexander. – 4th ed. – London : Oyez, 1981.
xl,235p; 24cm. – (Oyez practitioner series).
Previous ed.: 1975. Includes index.
ISBN 0851205828 Pbk

—Law of clubs : with a note on unincorporated associations / J.F. Josling, Lionel Alexander. – 6th ed. – London : Longman, 1987.
242p; 24cm. – (Longman practitioner series).
Previous ed.: London : Oyez Longman, 1984. Includes index.
ISBN 0851212972 Pbk £26.50

—Periods of limitation : with practical notes / J.F. Josling. – 6th ed. – London : Longman Professional, 1986.
144p; 22cm. – (Longman professional practice notes).
Previous ed.: London : Oyez, 1981.
ISBN 0851211453 Pbk £12.95

Joss, Jean
Careers in the Police Force. – 2nd ed. – London : Kogan Page, 1986.
96p.
ISBN 18500911703 Hbk £2.95

Joubert, D. J.
General prinicples of the law of contract / D.J. Joubert. – Cape Town : Juta, 1987.
lxvii,344p.
Includes bibliogrpahical references and index.
ISBN 0702118079

Joubert, J. J.
Current Law / Erna Jansen. – Durban : Butterworths.

Joubert, W.A.
Law of South Africa / T.J. Scott. – To be completed in ca 29 vols and 2 index vols. Vols 1-12, 14-15, 17-21, 23, 24, 26, 28 and index to vols. 1-10 now available. – Durban : Professional Publishers, 1982.
ISBN 0409003387 Hbk £2,205.00 (set)

Journal of African law. – London : Butterworth, 1957-.

Journal of applied philosophy : journal of the Society for Applied Philosophy. – Abingdon : Carfax, 1984.

Journal of Business Law. – London : Sweet & Maxwell.
Hbk £41.00
Bound Vol.. –
Hbk £18.50
Back Vols. avail.. –
Hbk £29.00
Single copy. –
Hbk £10.45

Journal of business law. – London : Stevens, 1957.
Index in each vol. - Index, 1957-1976. 1977.
ISBN 00219460

Journal of Contemporary Roman-Dutch law. – Durban : Butterworths.
– (Eng. and Afrikaans).
Hbk

Journal of energy & natural resources law. – London : Sweet & Maxwell, 1983-.
Co-sponsored by the Section on Energy and Natural Resources Law (S.E.R.L) of the International Bar Association and the Centre for Petroleum and Mineral Law Studies, University of Dundee, Scotland.

Journal of international arbitration. – Geneva : D. Thompson and J. Werner, 1984-.

Journal of international banking law. – Oxford : ESC Publishing Ltd., 1986-.

Journal of international franchising & distribution law. – London : Frank Cass, 1986-.

Journal of Islamic and comparative law : journal of the Centre of Islamic Legal Studies, Faculty of Law, Ahmadu Bello University, Zaria, Nigeria. – Zaria : The Centre, 1968.
Continues: Journal of the Centre of Islamic Legal Studies.

Journal of law and society. – Oxford : Blackwell (Basil), 1974-.
Continues: British journal of law and society.

Journal of Planning and Environment Law. – London : Sweet & Maxwell.
Pbk £45.00
Single copies. –
Pbk £5.65
Back Vols.. –
Pbk £29.00

Journal of Planning and Environmental Law : 1948-1981, 34 Vols. – Abingdon : Professional Books.
Hbk £395.00

Journal of private & property law. – Lagos : Department of Private & Property Law, University of Lagos, 1984-.

Journal of professional legal education. – Sydney, 1983-.
Index published every two years.

Journal of Social Welfare Law / Christina M. Lyon. – London : Sweet & Maxwell.
Hbk £31.00
Bound Vol.. –
Hbk £18.50
Single copy. –
Hbk £8.50
Back Vols. avail.. –
Hbk £32.00

Journal of the Irish Society for European Law. – Dublin : Irish Society for European Law, 1977 -.
ISBN 03324753

Journal of the Irish Society for Labour Law. – Dublin : The Society, 1982.

Journal of the Society of Public Teachers of Law : 1924-date. – Abingdon : Professional Books.
Hbk £575.00

Journal of the Society of Public Teachers of Law : New Series, 1946-1980, 14 Vols. – Abingdon : Professional Books, 1984.
Hbk £575.00

Journal of world trade law. – London : Vincent Press, 1967-.
Index in each vol.

Journalist's Legal Guide. – Agincourt : Carswell, 1986.
266p.
This legal manual for working journalists in Canada addresses a variety of relevant legal subjects, including: access to information, contempt, defamation, police powers, court structure, and procedure. A glossary of legal terms is included in the text.
Hbk £33.75

Journey from the Gallows : Historical Evolution of the Penal Philosophies and Practices. – London : Eurospan.
ISBN 0819167231 Hbk £24.75

Jowell, Jeffrey L → Changing constitution.
—Judicial review / Dawn Oliver. – London : Sweet & Maxwell, 1988.
– (Current Legal Problems).
ISBN 0421478000 Pbk
→ Lord Denning : the judge and the law.
→ New directions in judicial review.

Jowett → Rivalry in Retail Financial Services.

Jowitt, William Allen Jowitt
Dictionary of English Law / Burke. – 2nd ed. – Sweet & Maxwell, 1977.
ISBN 0421230908 Hbk £160.00
—Jowitt's dictionary of English law / by the late Earl Jowitt and Clifford Walsh. – 2nd ed. – London : Sweet and Maxwell, 1977.
2v.(11,1935p); 26cm.
Gives a definition and explanation of old and new legal terms in English law. Covers arbitration, trade descriptions, latin maxims and the writings of Glanvil, Bracton, Fitzherbert, Coke, Hale and Blackstone. Also examines the organisation of relevant Ministries, and all new law and statutes of recent years.
ISBN 0421230908 £45.00

Jowitt's dictionary of English law / by the late Earl Jowitt and Clifford Walsh. – 2nd ed. – London : Sweet and Maxwell, 1977.
2v.(11,1935p); 26cm.
Gives a definition and explanation of old and new legal terms in English law. Covers arbitration, trade descriptions, latin maxims and the writings of Glanvil, Bracton, Fitzherbert, Coke, Hale and Blackstone. Also examines the organisation of relevant Ministries, and all new law and statutes of recent years.
ISBN 0421230908 £45.00

Joyce, Joe
Blind Justice / Peter Murtagh. – Dublin : Poolbag Press, 1984.
448p.
£6.50

Joyce, M. A. S.
Spending on law and order : the police service in England and Wales / M. A. S. Joyce. – London : National Institute of Economic and Social Research, 1985.
64p. – (Discussion paper).

Joyce, Roger B.
Samuel Walker Griffith. – St. Lucia : University of Queensland Press, 1984.
448p.
ISBN 0702216887 Hbk £45.00

Joynson-Hicks on copyright / Paul Mitchell. – London : Sweet & Maxwell, 1989.
Covers works protected by Copyright Protection, qualifying for protection, first ownership, duration of copyright protection, restricted acts, secondary infringement, permitted acts, subsequent ownership, licensing and exploitation, remedies, moral rights, design rights, performance in rights, and Peter Pan.
ISBN 0421409606 Hbk

JPEL occasional papers : challenging decisions. – London : Sweet & Maxwell, 1986.
ISBN 0421361301 Pbk £22.00

JPEL occasional papers : planning for growth and decline. – London : Sweet & Maxwell, 1987.
ISBN 0421382600 Pbk £25.00

Jrgensen, Stig
Reason and reality / Stig Jrgensen. – Aarhus : Aarhus University Press, 1986.
159p.
Includes bibliographical references.
ISBN 8772880023
→ Tradition and progress in modern legal cultures.

Jubilee lectures celebrating the foundation of the Faculty of Law, University of Birmingham / edited by I.R. Scott. – London : Wildy & Sons Ltd, 1981.
viii,215p. – (Wildy's texts in law and jurisprudence).
Contents include: Restraining the misuse of power/by Lord Denning.
ISBN 0854900039

Judd, Denis
Evolution of the modern Commonwealth : 1902-80 / Denis Judd and Peter Slinn. – London : Macmillan, 1982.
xiii,171p.
Bibliography: p153-157.
ISBN 0333308409
—Lord Reading : Rufus Isaacs, First Marquess of Reading, Lord Chief Justice and Viceroy of India, 1860-1935 / Denis Judd. – London : Weidenfeld and Nicolson, 1982.
x,316p.
Bibliography: p303-307.
ISBN 029778014X

Judge, discretion, and the criminal trial / by Rosemary Pattendon. – Oxford : Clarendon, 1982.
xv,299p; 23cm.
Includes index.
ISBN 0198253737 £20.00

Judge, jurist and legislature : a public lecture / delivered by the Right Honourable The Lord Goff of Chieveley. – London : Child & Co., 1986.
17p.

Judge, N.
Irish Income Tax. – London : Butterworths.
Service to Date.
ISBN 0406678707 Hbk £118.00

Judge or Jury? : the Jury Trial for Personal Injury Cases in Ireland. – Cork : Cork University Press, 1985.
35p.
ISBN 0902561383 Pbk £1.50

Judgements and How to Write Them. – 3rd ed. – Lucknow : Eastern Book Company, 1974.
216p.
Hbk £40.00

Judges. – Markham : Penguin Books Canada.
ISBN 0140100717 Pbk £6.95

Judges. – Toronto : Macmillan of Canada.
ISBN 0771597290 Hbk £24.95

Judges / David Pannick. – Oxford : Oxford University Press, 1987.
224p; 22cm.
Includes index.
ISBN 0192159569 £10.95

Judges. – Oxford : Oxford University Press.
ISBN 0192822365 Pbk £4.95

Judges and the judicial power : essays in honour of Justice V.R. Krishna Iyer / edited by Rajeev Dhavan, R. Sudarshan and Salman Khurshid. – London : Sweet & Maxwell, 1985.
xii,340p; 25cm.
Includes index.
ISBN 0421288604

Judges at work : the role and attitudes of the South African appellate judiciary, 1910-50 / by Hugh Corder. – Cape Town : Juta, 1984.
xxxii,252p.
Bibliography: pxxi-xxvi.
ISBN 0702114359

Judges I Have Known. – Cape Town : Legal & Financial Publishing, 1983.
Hbk £8.04

Judges, law, and businessmen / A.H. Hermann. – Deventer, Netherlands : Kluwer Law and Taxation Publishers, 1983.
ISBN 9065440828

Judges, legislators and professors : chapters in European legal history / R.C. van Caenegem. – Cambridge : Cambridge University Press, 1987.
x,205p; 23cm.
Examines how continental and common law have come to differ substantially. Describes how European law developed through power struggles between various groups representing certain political and social ambitions.
ISBN 0521340772 £19.50

Judge's Miscellancy. – New Delhi : Arnold-Heinemann, 1982.
Hbk £85.00

Judge's Miscellany, 2 Vols. – Bombay : Tripathi.
Hbk £70.00
Vol. 1. – 1972.
xi, 324p.
bd £30.00

Judges of New Brunswick and Their Times / D.G. Bell. – Fredericton : Acadiensis Press, 1985.
552p.
ISBN 0919107044 Hbk £45.00

Judges Through the Years : Being a Chronology of the Judges of the County Court of Victoria from its Inception (1852). – South Yarra : Hyland House, 1984.
176p.
ISBN 0908090676 Hbk £25.00

Judging inequality : the effectiveness of the tribunal system in sex discrimination and equal pay cases / Alice M. Leonard. – London : Cobden Trust, 1987.
160p; 20cm.
Includes bibliography.
ISBN 0900137282 Pbk £7.95

Judging judges / Simon Lee. – London : Faber, 1988.
350p; 22cm.
Includes bibliography and index.
ISBN 0571148301 £12.95

Judgments. – Income Tax Appeals Special Court of Zimbabwe. – Zimbabwe : The Court, 1980-.
Continues: Income tax appeal: judgment / Income Tax Appeals Special Court, Southern Rhodesia.

Judgments and Orders. – 3 vols. – London : Sweet & Maxwell, 1981 Reprint.
ISBN 0421346000 Hbk £150.00

Judgments and orders in the Gambia court of Appeal. – Banjul : The Court, 1982.

Judgments of Justice Lionel Murphy. – Leichhardt : Primavera Press.
352p.
ISBN 0958949433 Hbk £19.95

Judgments of the Court of Criminal Appeal 1924-1978 / edited by Gerard L. Frewen. – Dublin : Law Library, Incorporated Council of Law Reporting for Ireland, 1983.
xxxi,619p.
Includes indexes.
ISBN 0946738009

Judgments of the Supreme Court of Nigeria. – Lagos : Department of Information Printing Division, 1981-.
Continues: Reserved judgments of the Supreme Court of Nigeria. 'Published by authority of the Supreme Court'.

Judical Settlement of International Disputes : International Court of Justice; Other Courts and Tribunals : Arbitration and Conciliation : an International Symposium / R. Bernhardt. – Berlin : Springer-Verlag.
xii, 572p.
ISBN 3540067566 Hbk £94.00

Judicial administration in Canada / Perry S. Millar and Carl Baar. – Kingston : McGill-Queen's University Press, 1981.
xxiii,452p.
ISBN 0773503676

Judicial appointments : the Lord Chancellors policies and procedures. – London : Central Office of Information, 1986.
iv,20p.

Judicial attitudes to freedom of speech and the press with particular reference to contempt of court / by Isabella E. Adi. – Lagos : Nigerian Institute of Advanced Legal Studies, 1983.
23p.
Seminar paper presented at the Institute on Wednesday, April 20, 1983.

Judicial Bay : Its Designation and Delimitation In Int Law. – Oxford : Oxford University Press.
ISBN 019503998X Pbk £29.50

Judicial Bench in England, 1727-1875 : The Reshaping of a Professional Elite. – London : Royal Historical Society, 1982.
– (Studies in History (London) Ser.: Vol. 29).
ISBN 0901050806 Hbk £19.60

Judicial Control of Adminstrative Action. – 2nd ed. – Allahabad : Law Book Company.
Hbk £175.00

Judicial Control of Labour Tribunals. – Bombay : Tripathi, 1983.
xxiv, 335p.
Hbk £130.00

Judicial Dictionary, 6 Vols.
Supplement 1. – London : Sweet & Maxwell.
ISBN 042137120X Pbk £5.00

Judicial discretion and criminal litigation. – 2nd. – Oxford : Clarendon Press, 1989.
350; 23.5.
Examines the discretions exercised by criminal trial courts both at Crown Court and Magistrates level, and discretion in the criminal appellate process. Intends to provide a theoretical framework within which to discuss and assess the discretions. Concentrates on the law and practice in England and Wales, but also refers to statutes and decision in Australia, New Zealand and Canada.
ISBN 0198255675 Pbk £14.95

Judicial discretion in sentencing by judges and magistrates / by Vivian Gerald Hines. – 1. – Chichester : Rose, 1982.
27cm.
Includes index.
ISBN 0859923169 £42.50

Judicial Enforcement of International Debt Obligations / Bradlow. – London : Eurospan.
ISBN 0935328483 Hbk £38.75

Judicial independence : the contemporary debate / edited by Shimon Shetreet and Jules Desch$enes. – Dordrecht, the Netherlands : M. Nijhoff, 1985.
720p.
Includes index.
ISBN 9024731828 Hbk £245.00

Judicial Interim Release. – 4th ed. – Toronto : Butterworths.
Llf £150.00

Judicial interim release (Bail manual). – 1 vol. – Scarborough, Ontario : Butterworths (Canada).
Part one provides a one-paragrah summary of the key cases as they relate to specific sections or sub-sections of the Criminal Code or other relevant statutes. Part two contains a digest of the most cited cases in part one, giving the citation, a review of the facts, and the main issues decided. Part three contains references and excerpts for various Acts.
Loose leaf

Judicial Panorama. – Allahabad : Law Book Company, 1981.
Hbk £10.00

Judicial Perspective on Industrial Conciliation and Arbitration in New Zealand. – Repr. of 1980 ed. – Auckland : Legal Research Foundation, 1982.
49p.
ISBN 0908581076 Pbk £5.50

Judicial Politics in Europa : an Impact Analysis. – Bern : Peter Lang, 1986.
xii, 325p.
ISBN 0820402893 Hbk £35.05

Judicial Process in Commonwealth Africa. – Accra : Ghana Universities Press.
124p.
Hbk £5.00

Judicial protection in the European Communities / Henry G. Schermers. – 3rd ed. – Deventer, 1983.
xvi,495p.
ISBN 9065440518

Judicial protection in the European Communities / Denis Waelbroeck. – 4th ed. – Deventer : Kluwer Law and Taxation Publishers, 1987.
xviii,510p; 25cm.
Previous ed.: 1983. Includes index. At head of title: Europa Instituut, University of Leiden.
ISBN 9065443274 Pbk

Judicial reform : working paper : Conference on the Reform on sic the Indian Legal System. – New Delhi : Indian Law Institute, 1983.
53p.
Caption title: Judicial reforms.

Judicial remedies in international law / Christine D. Gray. – Oxford : Clarendon Press, 1987.
300p; 24cm. – (Oxford monographs in international law).
Includes bibliography and index.
ISBN 0198255713 £30.00

Judicial review. – Profex, 1985.
ISBN 095102860X Pbk £10.95

Judicial review / Dawn Oliver. – London : Sweet & Maxwell, 1988.
– (Current Legal Problems).
ISBN 0421478000 Pbk

Judicial review : law and procedure / by R.J.F. Gordon : foreword by the Hon. Mr Justice Mann. – London : Sweet & Maxwell, 1985.
xxxviii,207p; 26cm.
Includes index.
ISBN 0421334908 £19.85

Judicial review : legal limits of official power / by C.T. Emery and B. Smythe : foreword by Sir Gordon Slynn. – London : Sweet & Maxwell, 1986.
xxxi,330p; 23cm.
Includes index.
ISBN 0421345209 Hbk £16.00
ISBN 0421345306 Pbk £11.95

Judicial review in comparative perspective. – Oxford : Clarendon Press, 1989.
300.
Applies the comparative method to the analysis of basic features of the judicial process, and their evolution in modern societies, especially Europe and America.
ISBN 0198256345 Hbk £30.00

Judicial Review in Corporate Law. – Cambridge : Cambridge University Press.
– (Cambridge Studies in International and Comparative Law).
ISBN 0521333873 Hbk £50.00

Judicial Review in India. – Sangam Books.
ISBN 0861321766 Hbk £12.95

Judicial review in Scotland / John St. Clair, Neil F. Davidson. – Edinburgh : W. Green, 1986.
xxi,94p; 22cm.
Includes index.
ISBN 0414007743 £8.00

Judicial review of administrative action : application for judicial review / Institute of Law Research and Reform. – Edmonton : Institute of Law Research and Reform, 1984.
v,125p. – (Report).

Judicial review of administrative action in the 1980's : problems and prospects : papers presented at a Conference held by the Legal Research Foundation Inc. at the University of Auckland on 20 and 21 February 1986 / edited by Michael Taggart : with a foreword by Lord Wilberforce. – Auckland : Oxford University Press, in association with the Legal Research Foundation Inc, 1986.
xx,208p; 24cm.
ISBN 0195581512

Judicial review of Community administrative acts / Sir Gordon Slynn. – Exeter : University of Exeter, 1985.
16p.
Includes bibliographical references.

Judicial review of public duties. – Oxford : Clarendon Press, 1989.
300.
Examines the principles and remedies which have been applied in public duty cases such as postal strikes and licence applications. Argues that public duties should be taken more seriously by the courts.
ISBN 0198256078 Hbk £30

Judicial review of the death penalty / David Pannick. – London : Duckworth, 1982.
245p; 23cm.
Includes index.
ISBN 0715615947 £18.00

Judicial review, transnational and federal : its impact on integration / by Mauro Cappelletti and David Golay. – Florence : European University Institute, 1981.
143p.

Judicial Review Update. – Vancouver : Continuing Legal Education Society of British Columbia, 1984.
184p.
ISBN 0865041563 Hbk £55.00

Judicial Role Under Constitutions of Ceylon (Sri Lanka). – Colombo : 16.00.
Pbk £13.00

Judicial Separation : A Research Study. – Oxford : Social Science Research Council, 1983.
102p.
ISBN 0862260574 Pbk £2.50

Judicial Statistics Annual Report 1983. – Lord Chancellor's Department. – London : HMSO, 1984.
ISBN 0101937008 Hbk £9.10

Judicial system envisaged in the draft treaty / by Thijmen Koopmans. – Florence : European University Institute, 1985.
57p.

Judicial teeth for local ombudsmen? : proceedings of a conference held at the University of Edinburgh, 13th December 1984 / edited by Chris Himsworth. – Edinburgh : Department of Constitutional and Administrative Law, University of Edinburgh, 1985.
63p.
Bibliography: p.60.

Judicialism in Commonwealth Africa. – London : Dent (J M) & Sons, 1977.
ISBN 0903983567 Hbk £15.00

Judiciary and the 1983 elections / by T. Akinola Aguda. – Lagos : Nigerian Institute of Advanced Legal Studies, 1983.
19p.
Notes of a seminar presented at the Institute on Wednesday, February 23, 1983.

Judiciary in the government of Nigeria / by T. Akinola Aguda. – Ibadan : New Horn Press, 1983.
xii,183p.
Bibliography: p.183.
ISBN 9782266051

Judiciary in the second republic of Nigeria, 1979-1983 / by F. Olisa Awogu. – Onitsha : Pacific Colege Press, 1984.
x,176p.
Bibliography: p.163-164. - Includes index.
ISBN 9782347108

Judiciary today : a plea for a collegium / Ramakrishna Hedge. – Bangalore : Governmnet of Karnataka,
80p.

Judiuciary today : disturbing trends and suggestion for reforms / Ramakrishna Hedge. – s.l. : Government of Karnataka, 1986.
15p.
'Address by Sir Ramakrishna Hedge, Chief Minister of Karnataka, delivered on 27th June, 1986 at the Bar Association of India Conference 1986 held at Bangalore'. - t.p. verso.

Jukes, D J
Food Legislation of the UK. – 2nd ed. – London : Butterworths, 1987.
ISBN 0407015507 Pbk £12.50

Julyan, Alan
Service Agreements. – 5th ed. – London : Longman Professional (UK), 1986.
– (Practitioner Series).
Guidance on drafting service agreements. Looks at different types of agreement showing benefits designed to protect compant interests and to offer security to the employee.
ISBN 0851212212 Pbk £22.50

Jung, Harald →Handbook of German employment law : a practical guide to the legal aspects of employment - from hiring through termination : with a bi-lingual selection of relevant German statutes and sample forms.
—Starting business operations in Germany : a practical guide with emphasis on sales agency agreements, limited liability companies, branch operations / by Harald Jung and Joachim Gres. – Deventer : Kluwer, 1984.
79p.
Bibliography: p.73-74. - Includes index.
ISBN 9065441794
ISBN 3787540229

Jurado, Desiderio P.
Personal and Family Law. – Manila : National Book Store, 1984.
602p.
ISBN 9710805282 Hbk £35.00

Juridical law and physical law : towards a realist foundation for human law / by Thomas F. Torrance. – Edinburgh : Scottish Academic Press, 1982.
xii,70p.
ISBN 0707303141

Juridical Yearbook 1981. – London : HMSO, 1985.
Contains legal documents concerning the United Nations including legislative texts, treaty provisions and a review of the United Nations' legal activities.
ISBN 0119086506 Hbk £25.00

Juridification of social spheres : a comparative analysis in the areas of labor, corporate, antitrust, and social welfare law / edited by Gunther Teubner. – Berlin : De Gruyter, 1987.
viii, 446 p.; 24 cm.
Includes bibliographies and index.
ISBN 0899252729

Juries and Prac. Co. Court Ireland. – London : Butterworths.
ISBN 0862053323 Hbk £36.50

Juris and Practice Eng Courts / Bruce. – Professional Books.
ISBN 0862053080 Hbk £53.75

Jurisdiction in Criminal Law. – Agincourt : Carswell, 1985.
275p.
This work for the practitioner examines all aspects of the exercise of jurisdiction by Canadian criminal courts and discusses the remedies available in cases of error. The book provides a theoretical approach to analyzing the validity of the exercise of jurisdiction.
Hbk £43.75

Jurisdiction to tax in international law: theory and practice of legislative fiscal jurisdiction. – Kluwer Law and Taxation, 1989.
238. – (Series on International Taxation 9).
Deals with the bases and the limits of the right of states under international lw to create tax obligations on persons within and outside their territory. Describes the practice of states on matters of taxation in terms of the doctrine of jurisdiction in international law. Examines topics such as the taxation of mining activities on the continental shelf.
ISBN 9065444165 Hbk £51/Dfl 160

Jurisprudence 1987. – London : Financial Training.
ISBN 1851850481 Pbk £7.95

Jurisprudence / R.W.M. Dias. – 5th ed. – London : Butterworths, 1985.
505p; cased.
Previous ed.: 1976. Includes index.
ISBN 0406574324 Pbk £24.50 :
ISBN 0406574316 £16.95

Jurisprudence : a descriptive and normative analysis of law / Anthony D'Amato. – Dordrecht, The Netherlands : Nijhoff, 1984.
xiv, 334 p.; 25 cm.
Includes bibliographical references and index.
ISBN 902472919X Hbk £140.00

Jurisprudence and Legal Theory. – 3rd ed. – Lucknow : Eastern Book Company, 1986.
358p.
Hbk £25.00

Jurisprudence and Legal Theory. – 9th ed. 1975 repr. – Lucknow : Eastern Book Company, 1985.
Pbk £18.00

Jurisprudence of orthodoxy : Queen's University essays on H.L.A. Hart / edited by Philip Leith and Peter Ingram. – London : Routledge, 1988.
216p.
Bibliography: pp.201-210. - Includes index.
ISBN 0415003059

Jurisprudence of the living oracles / Tunji Braithwaite. – Benin City, Nigeria : Ethiope, 1987.
xviii,308p. -
Bibliography: p.296-297 . - Includes index. Includes the texts of the Charter of the United Nations and Statute of the International Court of Justice, and the Universal Declaration of Human Rights.
ISBN 9781233176

Juristic Differences and How to Solve Them in an Islamic State. – Lagos : Islamic Publications Bureau.
Pbk £30.00

Jurists : Profiles in Legal Theory. – London : Edward Arnold.

Jury Service. – London : Hale, 1983.
142p.
ISBN 0709012845 Hbk £7.95

Jury Trials - 1985. – Vancouver : British Columbia Continuing Legal Education Society, 1985.
165p.
ISBN 0865041903 Hbk £60.00

Jury Trials. – Vancouver : British Columbia Continuing Legal Education Society, 1981.
202p.
ISBN 0865040419 Hbk £11.50

Jury under attack / Peter Duff. – London : Butterworths, 1988.
ISBN 0406503109 Pbk £14.95

Jury Under Attack / Peter Duff. – Butterworths, 1988.
243p.
ISBN 0409493481 Pbk £39.00

Just and painful : a case for corporal punishment of criminals / Graeme Newman. – New York : Macmillan, 1983.
163p; 23cm.
Includes index.
ISBN 0029231302 £11.95

JUSTICE
Administration of the courts : JUSTICE / a report by John Macdonald, Chairman of committee. – London : JUSTICE, 1986.
46p.
ISBN 0907247083

—Administrative justice : some necessary reforms / (report of the Committee of the JUSTICE-ALL Souls Review of Administrative law in the United Kingdom). – Oxford : Clarendon, 1988.
xxxv,449p; 23cm.
Includes index.
ISBN 019825587X Hbk £25.00
ISBN 0198255861 Pbk £12.50

—Annual members' conference held in the Lord Chief Justice's Court on Saturday 22nd March 1986 : subject, public order / Chairman His Hon. Judge Hawser. – London : Justice, 1986.
38 leaves.

—Annual members' conference held in the Lord Chief Justice's Court on Saturday, 30th March, 1985 : subject, the future of the legal profession / Chairman, Sir Nicholas Browne-Wilkinson. – London : Justice, 1985.
55 leaves.

—Civil justice review : consultation paper no. 6 : general issues / response by JUSTICE. – London : JUSTICE, 1987.
19p.

—Codification of the criminal law : memorandum on the Law Commission report / Justice. – London : Justice, 1986.
3 leaves.
A commentary on a Law Commission report entitled: Criminal law: codification of the criminal law: a report to the Law Commission.

—Comments by JUSTICE on the white paper 'A revised framework for insolvency law' (Cmnd. 9175). – JUSTICE. – S.l. : JUSTICE, 1984.
7 leaves; 30cm.

—Comments on civil justice review of housing cases / JUSTICE. – London : JUSTICE, 1987.
7 leaves.

—Comments on consultation paper on personal injuries litigation : civil justice review / JUSTICE. – London : JUSTICE, 1986.
9p.

—Comments on the consultation paper no. 3 from the civil justice review relating to the commercial court / JUSTICE. – London : JUSTICE, 1987.
5p.

—Comments on the Home Office discussion document : Review of appeals under the Immigration Act, 1971 / Justice. – London : Justice, 1981.
5p; 33cm.

—Compensation for wrongful imprisonment : a report / by JUSTICE : Chairman of Committee : Charles Wegg-Prosser. – London : JUSTICE, 1982.
35p; 22cm.
ISBN 0907247024

—Coroners courts in England and Wales : a report / by JUSTICE : Chairman of Committee Evan Stone. – London : JUSTICE, 1986.
28p.
ISBN 0907247075

—Extradition : a review of the law and practice of extradition in the United Kingdom : comments on the report of an interdepartmental working party / Justice. – London : Justice, 1985.
4 leaves.

—Fraud trials : a report / by JUSTICE : chairman of committee Beryl Cooper. – London : JUSTICE, 1984.
vii,47p; 22cm.
ISBN 0907247059

—Industrial tribunals : a report / by JUSTICE : chairman of committee Bob Hepple. – London : JUSTICE, 1987.
72p.
ISBN 0907247105

—Justice : annual members conference held in the Lord Chief Justice's Court on Saturday 30th May 1987 : subject: judicial review of administrative action / Chairmen, Lord Scarman, Sir Patrick Neill. – London : Justice, 1987.
39 leaves.

—Justice in prison : a report / by Justice. – London : Justice, 1983.
v,96p.
Chairman of committee: Sir Brian MacKenna.
ISBN 0907247032

—JUSTICE's response to the Lord Chancellor's civil justice review consultation paper no. 4 : enforcement of debt. – JUSTICE. – London? : JUSTICE, 1987.
8p.

—Memorandum of evidence to Farrand Committee on Conveyancing Procedure and Practice / Justice. – London : Justice, 1984.
17p.

—Memorandum on guardianship : Law Commission working paper no. 91 / Justice. – London : Justice, 1986.
6 leaves.
A commentary on the Law Commission's working paper no. 91 entitled Family law: review of child law: guardianship.

—Memorandum on Law Commission working paper no. 92: Formalities for contracts for sale of land and Law Commission working paper no. 93: Formalities for deeds and esrows / Justice. – London : Justice, .
9 leaves.

—Memorandum on the White Paper on Criminal Justice / Justice. – London : Justice, 1986.
7 leaves.

—Memorandum to the Lord Chancellor's Advisory Committee on Legal Aid / JUSTICE. – S.l. : JUSTICE, 1984.
9p; 30cm.

—Public defender : a report / by JUSTICE : chairman of committee James Morton. – London : JUSTICE, 1987.
51p.
ISBN 0907247091

—Remands in custody : evidence on House of Commons Home Affairs Committee / Justice. – London : Justice, 1984.
3 leaves.

—Response to 'Small claims in the County Court' / JUSTICE. – London : JUSTICE, 1987.
20p.

—Road traffic law review : memorandum to the Department of the Environment / Justice. – London : Justice, 1986.
7 leaves.

—Wards of court : Law Commission working paper no. 101 / JUSTICE. – London : JUSTICE, 1987.
3 leaves.

—Witnesses in the criminal courts : a report / by Justice : chairman of committee Peter Crawford. – London : Justice, 1986.
25p.
ISBN 0907247067

Justice : annual members conference held in the Lord Chief Justice's Court on Saturday 30th May 1987 : subject: judicial review of administrative action / Chairmen, Lord Scarman, Sir Patrick Neill. – London : Justice, 1987.
39 leaves.

Justice and comparative law : Anglo-Soviet perspectives on criminal law, evidence, procedure, and sentencing policy / edited by W.E. Butler. – Dordrecht : M. Nijhoff, 1986.
246p.
Includes index.
ISBN 9024733758 Hbk £125.00

Justice and politics in People's China : legal order or continuing revolution? / James P. Brady. – London : Academic Press, 1982.
xiii,268p; 24cm.
Includes index.
ISBN 0121247503 £17.80

Justice and predictability / Antony Cutler and David Nye. – London : Macmillan, 1983.
xi,169p.
Includes index. Bibliography.
ISBN 0333315154

Justice and the Law in Britain. – United Kingdom Central Office of Information. – London : Central Office of Information, 1982.
– (References Services Ser.).
ISBN 0117010340 Hbk £3.15

Justice annual members' conference held in the Lord Chief Justice's Court on Saturday 24th March 1984 : subject time and crime / chairman Sir George Waller. – London : Justice, 1984.
58 leaves.

Justice annual member's conference held in the Lord Chief Justice's Court on Saturday 26th March, 1983 : subject family law / chairman Lord McGregor. – London : Justice, 1983.
44p.

Justice annual members' conference held in the Lord Chief Justice's Court on Saturday 27 March 1982 : subject, decriminalisation / Chairman, Sir Derek Hodgson. – London : Justice, 1982.
35 leaves.

Justice at Home. – 3rd ed. – Chichester : Barry Rose, 1983.
21p.
ISBN 0859923592 Hbk £3.50

Justice beyond Orwell / edited by Rosalie S. Abella and Melvin L. Rothman : Institut canadien dadministration de la justice : Canadian Institute for the Administration of Justice. – Montreal : Yvon Blais, 1985.
516p.
Includes bibliographical references.
ISBN 2890735540

Justice Delayed : Nazi War Criminals in Canada / Susan Charendoff. – Toronto : Summerhill Press.
220p.
ISBN 0920197426 Hbk £21.95

Justice Denied. – Toronto : Macmillan of Canada.
ISBN 0771596901 Hbk £24.95

Justice for Aboriginal Australians : Report to the World Council of Churches Team Visit to the Aborigines, June 15 to July 3, 1981. – Sydney : Australian Council of Churches.
Hbk £3.50

Justice for Some : a Discussion Book on Law for People with Mental Handicap. – Downsview : Roeher Institute, 1983.
95p.
£10.00

Justice for the Common Man / M.C. Setalvad. – Lucknow : Eastern Book Company, 1964.
97p.
Hbk £7.50

Justice Hidayatullah on Commercial Laws. – New Delhi : Deep and Deep Publications, 1982.
130p.
Hbk £60.00

Justice in prison : a report / by Justice. – London : Justice, 1983.
v,96p.
Chairman of committee: Sir Brian MacKenna.
ISBN 0907247032

Justice in South Africa. – Ibadan : Heinemann Educational Books (Nigeria).
Hbk £5.53

Justice in Wartime. – London : Spokesman Books, 1983.
232p.
ISBN 0851240895 Hbk £6.00

Justice, law, and culture / James K. Feibleman. – Dordrecht : Nijhoff, 1985.
xiii, 208p.
ISBN 9024731054

Justice, Law and Method in Plato and Aristotle. – London : Biblios.
ISBN 092098018X Hbk £27.95
ISBN 0920980201 Pbk £14.50

Justice, Lord Denning and the constitution / edited by Peter Robson and Paul Watchman. – Farnborough, Hants. : Gower, 1981.
xvi,253p; 23cm.
Bibliography: px-xi. - Includes index.
ISBN 0566003996 Hbk £10.50
ISBN 0566004542 Pbk £5.95

Justice of the peace reports. – Chichester : Justice of the Peace Ltd., 1983-.
Continues: Justice of the peace and local government reports.

Justice, rights and tort law / edited by Michael D. Bayles and Bruce Chapman. – Dordrecht : Reidel, 1983.
vii,272p; 23cm.
Reprinted from Law and Philosophy; 1, no.3 and 2, no.1.
ISBN 9027716390 Hbk £90.00

Justice Studies and Research : a Three Year Review. – Regina : Prairie Justice Research, 1988.
ISBN 0773101306 Hbk £9.50

Justice-All Souls Review of Administrative Law in the United Kingdom
Discussion paper / J-AS Review of Administrative Law in the United Kingdom. – London : The Review, 1981.
97p.
ISBN 0907247016

Justices' Clerks' Society
Case for summary trial : proposals for a redistribution of criminal business / the Justices' Clerks' Society. – Bristol : The Society, 1982.
26p.

—Observations on the Criminal Justice Bill / the Justices' Clerks' Society. – Bristol b The Society, 1982.
21 leaves.

—Observations on the Mental Health (Amendment) Bill / the Justices' Clerks' Society. – Bristol : The Society, 1982.
8p.

—Observations on the Police and Criminal Evidence Bill / the Justices' Clerks' Society. – Bristol : The Society, 1983.
34p.

—Resolving family conflict in the 1980s : a unified family court / Justices' Clerks' Society. – Bristol : The Society, 1982.
88p.

Justices of the Supreme Court. – Quezon : New Day.
Hbk
Vol. 1 1901-1942: From Justice Cayetano Arellano to Justice Jose Lopez Vito. – 1984.
280p.
ISBN 9711001330 £18.50
Vol. 2 1944-1964: From Justice Delfin Jaranilla to Justice Jose P. Bengzon. – 1985.
225p.
ISBN 9711001365 £17.85
Vol. 3 1966-Present. – 1985.
304p.
ISBN 9711001381 £16.25

JUSTICE's response to the Lord Chancellor's civil justice review consultation paper no. 4 : enforcement of debt. – JUSTICE. – London? : JUSTICE, 1987.
8p.

Justiciability of constitutional adjudication / a paper presented by Owolabi Kolawole at the Seminar on the Constitutional Adjudication in a Presidential System of Government, a comparative American and Nigerian experience, held at the Nigerian Institute of Advanced Legal Studies, University of Lagos, on Wednesday September 2, 1981. – Lagos : Nigerian Institute of Advanced Legal Studies, 1981.
20p.

Justification and excuse in the criminal law. – London : Stevens & Sons, 1989.
– (Hamlyn lectures).
Examines the distinction between justification and excuse, asks whether circumstances unknown to the defendant may amount to a defence, looks at judicial interpretation of statutory 'let-out' clause, necessity and duress, and the future of justification and excuse, in case law, legislation, and codification.
ISBN 0420478108 Hbk £17.50
ISBN 0420478205 Pbk £8.95

Justification and Excuse in the Criminal Law. – Stevens & Sons.
ISBN 00420478205 Pbk £11.00
ISBN 0420478108 Hbk £15.00

Justinian's Digest. – Repr. of 1971 ed. – Aalen Wuertt : Scientia, 1983.
35p.
ISBN 3511091284 Hbk £15.00

Justyces of Peas. – 1st ed. 1986 Reprint. – London : Butterworths.
ISBN 0862053099 Hbk £17.15

Juta's index and annotations to the South African law reports 1980-86 / compiled by David S. Fisher and Alan James : assisted by Owen J. Barrow ... et al. – Cape Town : Juta, 1987.
1100p.
Kept up-to-date by supplements.
ISBN 0702118508

Juvenile court : a guide to law and practice / by Terence G. Moore and Tony P. Wilkinson. – Chichester : Barry Rose, 1984.
xiii,231p; 23cm.
Includes index.
ISBN 0859923355

Juvenile courts in Canada / by Larry C. Wilson. – Toronto, Canada : Carswell, 1982.
xx, 272 p.; 24 cm.
Includes index. 'Table of cases': p. vii-xx.
ISBN 0459352709

Juvenile delinquency : trends and perspectives / Michael Rutter and Henri Giller. – Harmondsworth : Penguin, 1983.
432p; 20cm. – (Penguin education).
Bibliography: p363-415. - Includes index. Also published: New York, Guilford Press, 1984.
ISBN 0140804625 Pbk £5.95

Juvenile Delinquency and Indian Justice System. – New Delhi : Deep and Deep Publications, 1988.
516p.
Hbk £375.00

Juvenile delinquency in the Netherlands / edited by Josine Junger-Tas and Richard L. Block. – Amstelveen, The Netherlands : Kugler Publications BV, 1988.
xiii, 242 p.; 23 cm.
Includes bibliographies.
ISBN 9062990363

Juvenile justice in South Australia / by John Seymour. – Sydney : Law Book Company in association with the Australian Institute of Criminology, 1983.
xix,146p.
Includes bibliographical references and index.
ISBN 0455204853

Juvenile justice in the United Kingdom : comparisons and suggestions for change / Sarah McCabe and Phyllis Treitel. – London : New Approaches to Juvenile Crime, 1983.
81p.
Includes bibliographical references.
ISBN 0950929905

Juvenile justice policy : analyzing trends and outcomes / edited by Scott H. Decker. – Beverly Hills : Sage in cooperation with the Academy of Criminal Justice Sciences, 1984.
168p; 23cm.
Includes bibliographies.
ISBN 0803921977 Hbk
ISBN 0803921985 Pbk £7.95

Juvenile sentencing : is there a tariff? / David Moxon, Peter Jones and Roger Tarling. – London : Home Office, 1985.
v,19p.
Bibliography: p.19.
ISBN 0862521874

Juvenile social maladjustment and human rights in the context of urban development. – United Nations Social Defence Research Institute. – Rome : Fratelli Palombi, 1984.
504p. – (Publication).
'Funded by the United Nations Development Programme'. Parallel Spanish and French titles. English, Spanish and French text.
ISBN 8876218289

Juveniles' waiver of rights : legal and psychological competence / Thomas Grisso. – New York : Plenum, 1981.
xiii,295p; 24cm.
Bibliography: p279-286. - Includes index.
ISBN 0306405261

Juxon, John
Lewis and Lewis / John Juxon. – London : Collins, 1983.
320p,12p of plates; 23cm.
Bibliography: p310-312. - Includes index.
ISBN 0002164760 £10.95

Kabatov, V. A. →Handbook on foreign trade arbitration in the CMEA countries.

Kably, Haroon S.
Customs Act, 1962 / Subodh Markandeya. – Bombay : Jaico Publishing House.
Hbk £69.00

—Foreign Exchange Regulations Act, 1973 / Subodh Markandeya. – Bombay : Jaico Publishing House.
Hbk £95.00

Kadish
Encyclopaedia of Crimes and Justice. – 4 vols. – London : Macmillan, 1983.
ISBN 0029181100 Hbk £300.00

Kagzi, Mangal Chandra J, Mangal Chandra
Constitution of India. – 3rd ed. – Delhi : Metropolitan Book Co.
850p.
bd £80.00

—Present Constitutional Issues and Views. – Delhi : Metropolitan Book Co, 1987.
378p.
ISBN 8120002598 Hbk £200.00

Kahn
Child Support : From Debt Collection To Social Policy / Kamerman. – Sage Publications, 1988.
ISBN 080392979X Hbk £29.95

Kahn, Ellison
Businessman's Law. Vol. 16 / P. Q. R Boberg. – Kenwyn : Juta & Co, 1986.
Hbk £7900.00

—Contract and mercantile law : a source book Vol. 1 : General principles of contract, agency and representation : edited by Ellison Kahn, Carole Lewis and Coenraad Visser / by Ellison Kahn. – 2nd ed. – Cape Town : Juta, 1988.
lix,926p.
Includes index.
ISBN 0702119962

—Contract and mercantile law through the cases Vol.2 : Specific contracts and mercantile law, security : by Ellison Kahn ... et al. / by Ellison Kahn. – 2nd ed. – Cape Town : Juta, 1985.
lix,970p.
Bibliography: p.xxv-xxxviii. - Includes index.
ISBN 0702116548

→ Fiat iustitia : essays in memory of Oliver Deneys Schreiner.

—Life and works of Hugo Grotius (1583-1645) : address delivered to members of the South African Law Commission and other dignitaries on 26 July 1983 at the University of Pretoria to commemorate the 400th birthday of Hugo Grotius / by Ellison Kahn. – Pretoria : South African Law Commission, 1983.
iii,21p. – (Research series).

Kahn-Freund, Otto
Kahn-Freund's Labour and the law / P. L. Davies, M. R. Freedland. – 3rd ed. – London : Stevens, 1983.
xxvii,375p; 23cm. – (Hamlyn lecture series).
Previous ed.: published as Labour and the law. 1977.
ISBN 0420462201 Hbk £
ISBN 0420462309 Pbk £10.50

—Law of Carriage by Inland Transport. – 5th ed. – London : Sweet & Maxwell.
ISBN 042046820X Hbk

Kahn, Peggy →Picketing : industrial disputes, tactics and the law.

Kahn-Freund's Labour and the law / P. L. Davies, M. R. Freedland. – 3rd ed. – London : Stevens, 1983.
xxvii,375p; 23cm. – (Hamlyn lecture series).
Previous ed.: published as Labour and the law. 1977.
ISBN 0420462201 Hbk £
ISBN 0420462309 Pbk £10.50

Kaikobad, Kaiyan Homi
Shatt Al-Arab Boundary Question : A Legal Reappraisal. – Oxford : Oxford University Press.
ISBN 0198255918 Hbk £25.00

—Shatt-al-Arab Boundary question : a legal reappraisal / Kaiyan Homi Kaikobad. – Oxford : Clarendon, 1988.
160p; 24cm. – (Oxford monographs in international law).
Includes bibliography and index.
ISBN 0198255918 £20.00

Kalaiah, A.B.
Human Rights in International Law. – New Delhi : Deep and Deep Publications, 1986.
212p.
Hbk £150.00

Kalderen, Lars →Sovereign borrowers : guidelines on legal negotiations with commercial lenders.

Kalkobad, K.
Shatt-Al-Arab questions. – Oxford : Oxford University Press, 1988.
ISBN 0198255918 Hbk

Kalkundrikar, A.B., et al
Banking Law and Practice. – New Delhi : Himalaya Publishing House, 1987.
200p.
Hbk £80.00

Kalley, Jacqueline Audrey
South Africa by Treaty 1806-1986 : a Chronological and subject index. – Braam Fontein : South African Insitute of International Affairs, 1987.
Hbk £40.00

Kalley, Jaqueline Audrey
Chronological and subject analysis of South Africa's multilateral and bilateral treaties, 1806-1979 / Jaqueline Audrey Kalley. – Johannesburg : s.n., 1985.
xvi,677 leaves.
Thesis (M.A.) - University of Witwatersrand 1985. Bibliography: p.659-677. - Includes index.

Kalshoven, Frits
Assisting the victims of armed conflict and other disasters. – Dordrecht : Nijhoff (Martinus), 1989.
264.
Contains papers given at the conference, with brief summaries, and annexes giving the text of treaty provisions and other documents. Goes beyond armed conflict, and looks at other disasters as well, including problems of offering humanitarian assistance in such situations.
ISBN 0792301633 Hbk £47.50

—Constraints on the Waging of War. – Dordrecht : Kluwer, 1987.
175p.
ISBN 0898389240 Pbk Gld85.00

—Implementation of international humanitarian law / Yves Sandoz. – Dordrecht : Nijhoff (Martinus), 1989.
488.
A collection of articles resulting from the 1986 session of the Centre for Studies and Research in International Law and International Relations of the Hague Academy. Explores humanitarian law from the viewpoint of implementation and enforcement, and offers suggestions for improvement.
ISBN 9024737842 Hbk £85

Kamali, Mohammad Hashim
Law in Afghanistan : a study of the Constitutions, matrimonial law and judiciary / by Mohammad Hashim Kamali. – Leiden : E. J. Brill, 1985.
viii,265p.
Bibliography: p254-259.
ISBN 9004071288

Kamba Customary Law. – 3rd ed. – Nairobi : Kenya Literature Bureau, 1983.
Pbk £24.50

Kamerman → Child Support : From Debt Collection To Social Policy.

Kamerschen
Money and Banking / Klise. – 9th ed. – London : Eurospan.
ISBN 0538082712 Hbk £29.95

Kames
Decisions of the Court of Session : Abridged in Form of a Dictionary / Woodhouselee. – Repr. of 1741 ed. – Abingdon : Professional Books.
57p.
Hbk £60.00
—Elucidations Respecting the Common and Statute Law of Scotland. – Repr. of 1800 ed. – Abingdon : Professional Books.
56p.
Hbk £180.00
—Essays upon several subjects concerning British antiquities. – Repr. of 1747 ed. – Abingdon : Professional Books.
58p.
Hbk £125.00
—Remarkable Decisions in the Court of Session : 1716-52, 2 Vols. – 2nd ed. Repr. of 1799 ed. – Abingdon : Professional Books.
57p.
Hbk £225.00
—Statute Law of Scotland : Abridged with Historical Notes. – Repr. of 1757 ed. – Abingdon : Professional Books.
57p.
Hbk £225.00

Kames, H. H.
Historical Law Tracts, 2 Vols. – Repr. of 1758 ed. – Abingdon : Professional Books.
34p.
Hbk £180.00

Kampuchea : politics, economics and society / Michael Vickery. – London : Pinter, 1986.
xviii,211p; 23cm.
Bibliography: p199-205. - Includes index.
ISBN 0861874226 Hbk £17.50
ISBN 0931477743 : Pbk £5.95

Kanaks of New Caledonia / by Ingrid A. Kircher. – London : Minority Rights Group, 1986.
20p. – (Report).
Bibliography: p.20.
ISBN 0946690405

Kandel, Randy Frances
Legislation on foods for infants and small children. – Rome : Food and Agriculture Organization of the United Nations, 1983.
v,104p. – (Legislative study).
Includes bibliographical references.
ISBN 9251014876

Kane, L.
Legal Rights of Citizens with Mental Retardation. – London : Eurospan.
ISBN 0819171107 Hbk £16.50

Kanga, J.B.
Law and Practice of Income Tax, 2 Vols. / N.A. Palkhivala. – 7th ed. – Bombay : Tripathi, 1977.
2872p.
bd £280.00

Kanger, Helle
Human Rights in the U.N. Declaration. – Stockholm : Almqvist & Wiksell, 1984.
209p.
ISBN 9155415482 Pbk £110.00

Kant, Immanuel
Philosophy of law : an exposition of the fundamental principles of jurisprudence as the science of right / translated from the German by W. Hastie. – Edinburgh : Clark, 1887.
xxxvi, 265p.
Translation of Metaphysische Anfangsgrunde der Rechtslehre, pr.1 of the author's Die Metaphysik der Sitten.

Kapardis, Andreas
Sentencing by English magistrates as a human process / by Andreas Kapardis. – Nicosia : Asselia, 1985.
xi,288p.
Bibliography: p.270-286. - Includes index.
ISBN 9963750079

Kaplan, Morris → Mining and mineral laws of South Africa.

Kaplan, William E.
Practice and Procedure Under the Access to Information and Privacy Acts. – Toronto : Butterworths, 1986.
128p.
ISBN 0409811645 Hbk
→ Prevention and prosecution of computer and high-tech crime.

Kapoor
Industrial Law / Narang. – Delhi : Dhanpat Rai and Sons.
Hbk £23.75

Kapoor, A.C.
Constitutional History of India 1765-1984. – New Delhi : S. Chand and Company.
Hbk £65.00

Kapoor, D. C.
Guide to Maritime Boundary Delimitation / Adam J. Kerr. – Agincourt : Carswell, 1986.
136p.
This work addresses the technical aspects of maritime boundaries under international law. The book provides commentary on relevant cases which have been refered to the International Court of Justice.
Hbk £25.25

Kapoor, N.D.
Elements of Mercantile Law : Including Company and Industrial Law. – 15th ed. – New Delhi : Sultan Chand and Sons, 1984.
xxviii, 880p.
Pbk £40.00
—Principles of Law : for Company Secretaries Exam. – 4th ed. – New Delhi : Sultan Chand and Sons, 1986.
xiii, 776p.
Pbk £35.00

Kapteyn, P. J. G → International organization and integration : annotated basic documents and descriptive directory of international organizations and arrangements.
—Introduction to the law of the European Communities: after the coming into force of the Single European Act / Edited by L. W. Gormley. – 2nd. – Kluwer Law and Taxation, 1989.
850.
A revised second edition, taking into account the Single European Act. As well as basic sources and material of the law of the European Communities, deals with the increased case law of the Court of Justice.
ISBN 9065444009 Hbk £65/Dfl 230

Kapur, Anup Chand
Select Constitutions. – New Delhi : S. Chand and Company, 1983.
Hbk £80.00

Kapur, G.K. → Handbook of Corporate Laws.

Kapur, Harish
China and the European Economic Community : the new connection / Harish Kapur. – Dordrecht : Nijhoff, 1986.
xv, 351p.
Includes index. Bibliography: p.99-110.
ISBN 9024732301

Karas, Stephen A. → Solicitors Checklists.

Karasek, Colin
Oil and gas in Canada : a new environment for development / Colin and Pamela Karasek. – London : Financial Times Business Information, 1985.
ix,206p.
Bibliography: p.201-206.
ISBN 0903199939

Karasek, Pamela → Oil and gas in Canada : a new environment for development.

Karatzas, Theodoros B. → Greek Code of Private Maritime Law.

Karibi-Whyte, A.G.
Criminal Policy, Traditional and Modern Trends. – Lagos : Nigerian Law Publications.
ISBN 9782325332 Hbk £10.00
—Federal High Court : law and practice / by A.G. Karibi-Whyte. – Enugu, Nigeria : Fourth Dimension, 1986.
xlvii,344p.
Includes bibliographical references and index.
ISBN 9781562412
—Groundwork of Nigerian Criminal Law. – Lagos : Nigerian Law Publications.
ISBN 1234525501 Hbk £10.00
—History and Sources of Nigerian Criminal Law. – Enugu : Fourth Dimension Publishing, 1985.
400p.
Pbk £17.00
—Relevance of the judiciary in the polity : in historical perspective / by A.G. Karibi-Whyte. – Lagos : Nigerian Institute of Advanced Legal Studies, 1987.
100p.
ISBN 9782353051

Karl Llewellyn and Realist Movement (LIC). – Weidenfeld & Nicolson, 1985.
ISBN 0297786679 Pbk £12.95
ISBN 0297994828 Hbk £20.00

Karmali, A.E.
Maharashtra Cooperative Societies Act, 1960. – Bombay : Tripathi, 1981.
Hbk £85.00
—Rent Act : Including Ownership of Old Buildings. – Bombay : Universal Book Corporation.
Hbk £125.00

Karpinski
Consumer Credit Agreements / Fielding. – London : Waterlow, 1985.
ISBN 0080392008 Pbk £18.50

Karrer, Pierre A → Switzerland's private international law statute.

Karton, Michael → Family property.

Karwat, Hans
Regulation of Expert's Fees in the European Community. – 3rd rev. exp. ed. – Dusseldorf : VDI-Verlag, 1986.
70p.
ISBN 3184007405 Pbk £28.00

Kasbekar, A.V.
Taxation of Companies : a Handbook. – Calcutta : Eastern Law House, 1969.
260p.
Hbk £15.00

Kaser, M.
Roman Private Law. – 4th rev. ed. – Pretoria : University of South Africa, 1984.
455p.
ISBN 0869813161 Pbk £18.50

Kassas, Mohammed → World environment 1972-1982 : a report.

Kassin
American Jury on Trial : Psychological Perspectives / Wrightsman. – Taylor & Francis.
ISBN 0891167374 Hbk £25.00

Kastantin, J.T.
Professional Accounting Practice Management. – Quorum Press.
ISBN 0899302904 Hbk £36.90

Katholieke Universititeit te Leuven →
Restructuring labour in the enterprise : law and practice in France, F.R. of Germany, Italy, Sweden and the United Kingdom.

Katiyar, B.B.
Law of Easements and Licences. – 10th ed. – Allahabad : Law Book Company, 1984.
1,200p.
Hbk £250.00

Katju, M.
Domestic Enquiry. – 3rd ed. in prep. – Bombay : Tripathi.
Hbk

Katju, S.N.
Handbook on Drug Laws. – Allahabad : Law Publishers, 1983.
£24.00

Kato, Ichiro → Environmental law and policy in the Pacific basin area.
→ Environmental protection and coastal zone management in Asia and the Pacific.
→ Water management and environmental protection in Asia and the Pacific.

Katz, Sanford N. → Resolution of family conflict : comparative legal perspectives.

Katzman → Carriage Of Goods By Sea.

Kaufman, Donna Soble
Broadcasting Law in Canada : Fairness in the Administrative Process. – Agincourt : Carswell, 1987.
120p.
This book provides a rigorous analysis of the legal problems inherent in the regulation of broadcasting in Canada. The work comprehensively reviews the application of the principles of procedural fairness to the administrative process of the C.T.R.C.
Hbk £33.00

Kausar's Ready Referencer of Legal Words, Phrases and Maxims. – Lahore : Pakistan Law Times.
Hbk £15.00

Kautilyan jurisprudence / by V.K. Gupta. – Delhi : B.D. Gupta, 1987.
xii,356p.
Includes excerpts from Kautilya's Arthasastra in Sanskrit.

Kavanagh, Giles
Coroners' rules and statutes / by Giles Kavanagh. – London : Sweet & Maxwell, 1985.
xviii,135p; 25cm.
Includes index.
ISBN 0421338806 Pbk £6.50

Kavanagh, John
Guide to Judicial Review. – 2nd ed. – Agincourt : Carswell, 1984.
320p.
This work classifies and categorizes the most important principles of judicial review in Canada. The right to the opportunity to be heard, procedural aspect of judicial review, evidentiary aspect of judicial review, and other topics are discussed in the book.
ISBN 0459366106 Hbk £23.00

Kaw, Vun-Ping → Arrest of ships 4 : People's Republic of China, Nigeria, Oman, Scotland.

Kay, J. A.
British tax system / J.A. Kay, M.A. King. – 4th ed. – Oxford : Oxford University Press, 1986.
viii,261p; 23cm.
Previous ed.: 1983. Bibliography: p241-250. - Includes index.
ISBN 0198772637 Hbk £17.50
ISBN 0198772629 Pbk £6.95
—Practical approach to contract and consumer law / Sewell. – London : Financial Training, 1984.
ISBN 0906322456 Pbk £12.95

—Privatisation and regulation. – Oxford : Oxford University Press, 1986.
ISBN 019877253X Pbk £9.95
ISBN 0198772548 Hbk £25.00

→ Reform of social security.

—Structure of tobacco taxes in the European Community / J.A. Kay, M.J. Keen. – London : Institute for Fiscal Studies, 1982.
44p; 22cm.
Bibliography: p44.
ISBN 0902992295 Pbk

—Taxing Currency Fluctuations? / J. R. King. – London : Institute for Fiscal Studies. – (Report Ser.).
Hbk £10.00

Kay, Neil M.
Approach to the analysis of joint ventures / by Neil Kay, Jean-Philippe Robe and Patrizia Zagnoli. – Florence : European University Institute, 1987.
39p.

—Markets and false hierarchies : some problems in transaction cost economics / Neil Kay. – San Domenico, Florence : European University Institute, 1987.
52p.
Bibliography: pp.50-52..

Kay, Reginald
Burundi since the genocide / by Reginald Kay. – London : Minority Rights Group, 1987.
12p. – (Report).
'This report was first published under the title Selective genocide in Burundi by Professor Rene Lemarchand and David Martin in July 1974'. - Front cover verso.
ISBN 0946690472

Kay, W.
Big Bank. – Weidenfeld & Nicolson, 1986.
ISBN 0297789848 Hbk £9.95

Kaye
Financial Planning / Asch. – London : Kogan Page.
ISBN 1850914761 Hbk £25.00

Kaye, Peter
Civil jurisdiction and enforcement of foreign judgments : the application in England and Wales of the Brussels Convention of 1968 on Jurisdiction and Enforcement of Judgments in Civil and Commercial Matters under the Civil Jurisdiction and Judgments Act 1982 / by Peter Kaye. – Abingdon : Professional Books, 1987.
cxvi, 1949p; 24cm.
Includes the text of the Civil Jurisdiction and Judgments Act 1982.
ISBN 0862050812

Kazmi, Farred
Human Rights : Myth and Reality. – Kuala Lumpur : Intellectual Book Corner, 1987.
xxviii, 188p.
Hbk £100.00

Kean, Arnold → Essays in air law.

Keane, Adrian
Modern law of evidence / by Adrian Keane. – Abingdon : Professional Books, 1985.
lxv,544p.
ISBN 0862051037 Pbk
ISBN 0862051045

Keane, Ronan
Company Law in the Republic of Ireland. – London : Butterworths, 1985.
ISBN 0406272905 Hbk £22.00

—Equity and the law of trusts in the Republic of Ireland / Ronan Keane. – London : Butterworths, 1988.
liii,387p.
Includes index.
ISBN 0406102708 Hbk £27.50

—Law of Equity in Republic of Ireland. – London : Butterworths, 1988.
ISBN 0406102708 Hbk £29.50

—Law of local government in the Republic of Ireland / by Ronan Keane. – Dublin : Incorporated Law Society of Ireland, 1982.
xliv,423p.
Includes index.
ISBN 0902027212

→ Planning and development law.

Kearney, Brian
Children's Hearings and the Sheriff Court. – London : Butterworths, 1987.
ISBN 0406105650 Hbk £41.00

—Introduction to ordinary civil procedure in the sheriff court / Brian Kearney. – Edinburgh : Law Society of Scotland, 1982.
xvi,233,1p.
Bibliography: p.233-234.
ISBN 0902023071

Kearney, James
Action for breach of confidence in Australia / by James Kearney. – Sydney : Legal Books, 1985.
xiv,97p.
Bibliography: p.91-93. - Includes index.
ISBN 0949553204

Kearns, John → Australian company law.

Keat, Russell
Social theory as science / Russell Keat and John Urry. – 2nd ed. – London : Routledge & K. Paul, 1982.
xi,301p.
Includes index. Bibliography: p278-295.
ISBN 0710094310

Keating, D.
Building Contracts. – 4th ed. – Sweet & Maxwell, 1978.
ISBN 042119720X Hbk £70.00

Keating, H. M. → Criminal law : text and materials.

Keating, Michael → Regional government in England.

Kee, Robert
Trial and error : the Maguires, the Guildford pub bombings and British justice / Robert Kee. – London : Hamish Hamilton, 1986.
284p; 22cm.
Includes index.
ISBN 0241119588 £10.95

Keeble, L.
Fighting Planning Appeals. – Oxford : Construction Press, 1985.
ISBN 0860957322 Hbk £14.95

Keen, M. J. → Structure of tobacco taxes in the European Community.

Keenan
Business Law / Riches. – Pitman, 1987.
ISBN 0273024159 Pbk £7.95

→ English Law.

→ Mercantile Law.

Keenan, D.
ACCA Study and Revision Pack. – Pitman.
ISBN 0273028022 Pbk £10.95

Keenan, Denis → Mercantile law.

→ Smith and Keenan's company law.

→ Smith and Keenan's mercantile law.

Keenan, Dennis → Company Law.

Keenan, Pat
Helping the Victim : Your Guide to Claiming Compensation / Marilyn Salkeld. – London : Bedford Square Press.
ISBN 0719912164 Hbk £4.50

Keene, D. J.
Survey of Documentary Sources for Property-Holding in London Before the Great Fire / V. A. Harding. – London : London Record Society, 1985.
ISBN 0900952229 Hbk £12.00

Keene, Judith
Human rights in Ontario / by Judith Keene. – Toronto : Carswell, 1983.
xxxv,367p.
Includes bibliographical references and index. Includes text of the Human Rights Code, 1981.
ISBN 0459354604

Keep Account : Guide to Profitable Bookkeeping / Muspratt. – London : Macmillan. – (Breakthrough Series).
ISBN 0333481593 Pbk £4.25

Keeping employees informed / Roger Hussey. – Sydney : Butterworths, 1982.
175p.
Discusses various forms of employee communication, including noticeboards, mass meetings and discussion groups. Aims at assisting the manager to assess and improve the standard of his own employee communications by presenting a detailed picture of the current practice in Australia.
ISBN 0409309435 Pbk

Keeping Offenders Out of Court : Further Alternatives to Prosecution. – Committee on Alternatives to Prosecution. – London : HMSO, 1983.
ISBN 0101895801 Hbk £6.00

Keeping pace with change / papers from a conference held at Oxford, September 1987, organised by the Bar Council, the Law Society and the Royal Institution of Chartered Surveyors. – London : Sweet & Maxwell, 1988.
85p.
ISBN 042140390X £25.00

Keeping the Estate in the Family : Inheritance Tax. – Oxford : BSP Professional.
ISBN 063202505 Pbk £99.50

Keeton → Auditor's Manual.

→ Company Law and Company Taxation in South Africa.

—Digest English Law Trust / L A Sheridan. – London : Butterworths.
ISBN 0862056504 Hbk £22.00

Keeton, George W.
Equity / by George W. Keeton and L.A. Sheridan. – 3rd ed. – Chichester : Barry Rose, 1987.
cxxvi,576p.
Previous ed.: 1976. Includes index.
ISBN 1870080300

→ Law of trusts.

→ Modern law of charities.

Keith, K. J.
Resolution of disputes under the Official Information Act 1982 / by K. J. Keith. – Wellington : Information Authority, 1984.
12p. – (Occasional paper).

Keley, P.
Interest On Unpaid Or Overpaid Tax. – VANN, 1977.
ISBN 0852911858 Pbk £6.50

Kelkar, R.V.
Outlines of Criminal Procedure. – 2nd ed. – Lucknow : Eastern Book Company, 1984.
692p.
Hbk £75.00

Kellerhals
Individual Property Rights Conceptions Privacy in Family / Emmanuel Lazega. – Cambridge : Cambridge University, Department of Social Science Research Council.
ISBN 094877410X Pbk £2.50

Kellermann, Alfred E → Guide to EC court decisions.

→ Guide to EEC-legislation.

Kelley, Donald R.
History, Law and the Human Sciences : Medieval and Renaissance Perspectives. – Northampton : Variorum.
334p.
ISBN 0860781534 Hbk £28.00

Kelley, Patrick
EEC Customs Law / Ivo Onkelinx. – Oxford : ESC Publishing Ltd, 1986.
ISBN 0906214297 Llf £90.00

Kellock, Jane
Layman as a magistrate / prepared for the Commonwealth Secretariat by Jane Kellock. – London : The Secretariat, 1988.
viii,32p.

Kellough, H. J., et al
Lawyer's Use of Financial Statements : 1982. – Vancouver : British Columbia Continuing Legal Education Society, 1983.
464p.
ISBN 0865040508 Hbk £14.50

Kellough, Howard J.
Taxation of private corporations and their shareholders / Howard J. Kellough, Peter E. McQuillan. – Toronto : Canadian Tax Foundation, 1983.
ix,825p.
ISBN 0888080174

Kells
Canadian National Exhibition Association Act, 1983, Bill Pr017 : An Act Respecting the Canadian National Exhibition Association. – Ontario : Ontario Government Publications Service, 1983.
9p.
Hbk £0.50

Kelly
Famous Advocates and Their Speeches. – Sweet & Maxwell, 1921 Reprint.
ISBN 0421376104 Hbk £15.75

—Kelly's Draftsman / R. W. Ramage. – 15th ed. – Wellington : Butterworths, 1986.
This book is a guide to drafting documents in a variety of commercial law settings. Carefully annotated model contracts are provided in a well organized manner. For the United Kingdom practitioner.
ISBN 0406263159 Hbk

→ Law of Trusts and Trustees in New Zealand.

→ Learning Banking : Guide Study Revis. Exam. Techniques.

→ Practice of banking.

Kelly, D.
Probation and Parole : Interstate Supervision and Enforcement / Mary W. Daunton-Fear. – Canberra : Australian Institute of Criminology.
Hbk £1.40

Kelly, David
Insurance Legislation Manual / Minhael Ball. – Butterworths, 1986.
131p.
ISBN 0409491195 Pbk £33.00

Kelly, F.
History of Kilmainham Gaol The Dismal House of Little Ease. – Cork : Mercier Press.
ISBN 0853428395 Pbk £5.95

Kelly, F. N.
Irish income tax and corporation profits tax by F.N. Kelly and K.S. Carmichael / K. S. Carmichael. – 8th ed. 1 v. – London : HFL, 1975.
looseleaf.
Includes index.
ISBN 0372016529

Kelly, G.M.
Sport and the Law. – North Ryde : Law Book Co, 1987.
350p.
ISBN 0455207127 Pbk £27.50

Kelly, Graham
Financial apportionment and equalisation / report prepared under the guidance of the members of the Committee of Experts on Local and Regional Finance by Graham Kelly. – Strasbourg : Council of Europe, 1981.
95p.
Up-dated and expanded version of: Financial structures of local and regional authorities in Europe. - Vol. 2. - 1976. - (Study series local and regional authorities in Europe ; no. 13).

—Financial resources for local and regional authorities : report / prepared under the guidance of the Committee of Experts on Local and Regional Finance of the Steering Committee for Regional and Municipal Matters by G. Kelly. – Strasbourg : Council of Europe, 1985.
79p; 30cm.

—Management structures in local and regional government : report / prepared under the guidance of the Committee of Experts on Management in Local and Regional Government of the Steering Committee for Regional and Municipal Matters, by G. Kelly. – Strasbourg : Council of Europe, 1985.
54p.

Kelly, J. E.
Banking Points From Case and Statute Law / F. E. Perry. – London : Waterlow, 1982.
122p.
ISBN 0080390277 Pbk £4.95

—Practice of banking/1. – Pitman, 1984.
ISBN 0712116796 Pbk £9.95

Kelly, John Maurice
Irish constitution / J.M. Kelly. – 2nd ed. – Dublin : Jurist Publishing, 1984.
xxxi,741p.
Previous ed.: 1980. Includes index. Kept up to date by supplements.

Kelly, John S.
Lending and Recovery : Benefits and Pitfalls of Consulting Engagements / Peter W. Aykroyd. – Agincourt : Carswell, 1985.
150p.
This work addresses the problems faced by Canadian corporations, financial institutions, insolvency consultants, and attorneys as they deal with questions of the solvency of a corporation to whom a loan has been made.
Hbk £40.50

Kelly, N. C. → Garrow and Kelly's law of trusts and trustees.

Kelly's Draftsman / R. W. Ramage. – 15th ed. – Wellington : Butterworths, 1986.
This book is a guide to drafting documents in a variety of commercial law settings. Carefully annotated model contracts are provided in a well organized manner. For the United Kingdom practitioner.
ISBN 0406263159 Hbk

Kelman, Alistair → Computer generated output as admissible evidence in civil and criminal cases : a report.

—Computer in court : a guide to computer evidence for lawyers and computing professionals / Alistair Kelman, Richard Sizer. – Aldershot : Gower, 1982.
viii,104p; 22cm.
Bibliography: p99. - Includes index.
ISBN 0566034190

Kelsen, Irene
Victorian Law of Real Estate. – Woolloomooloo : International Business Communications, 1986.
ISBN 094955328X Hbk £19.50

Kemelfield, Roger L.
Law for Architects, Builders and Engineers. – 2nd ed. – Butterworths, 1983.
355p.
ISBN 0409493422 Pbk £29.50

Kemp
Asian Capital and Money Markets / Message. – London : Butterworths, 1988.
ISBN 0406103607 Hbk

Kemp, Alexander G.
Petroleum Tax Analysis : North Sea : A Comparative Study of the Oil Exploitation Taxation System of the United Kingdom, Norway, Denmark and the Netherlands / David Rose. – London : Financial Times Ltd, 1983.
Hbk £130.00

Kemp and Message : Asian Capital and Money Markets. – London : Butterworths, 1987.
ISBN 0406103607 Hbk

Kemp, David
Authority and politics in Australia : some key dynamics of Australian politics. – Victoria : Oxford University Press, 1988.
320.
Argues that a few basic principles underlie many features of Australian politics and government. It is maintained that in the Australian setting these processes have resulted in continuing restrictive features in Australian law and institutions.
ISBN 0195547446 Pbk £15.00

—Damages For Personal Injury and Death. – 3rd ed. – London : Longman Professional, 1986.
ISBN 0851211178 Pbk £18.95

—Quantum of damages in personal injury and fatal accident claims
Vol. 1 : Law and practice - fatal accident awards / Kemp & Kemp. – Special ed. by David A. McI. Kemp assissted by Derrick Turriff ... et al. 1. – London : Sweet & Maxwell, 1986.
various pagings.
Includes index.
ISBN 0421366001

Kemp, David A. McI.
Quantum of damages in personal injury and fatal accident claims
Vol.2 : law and practice - personal injury reports / Kemp & Kemp. – 4th ed. 1. – London : Sweet & Maxwell, 1975-.
Volume 1 collects the law and practice applicable to personal injury and to fatal injury claims. Appendices set out the Fatal Accident Acts and other texts. Volume 2 deals with case reports classified according to injury, and the damages awarded.
ISBN 0421216808 Llf

Kemp, John A
Patent claim : drafting and interpretation. – London : Longman Professional, 1983.
ISBN 0851206859 Hbk £58.00

→ Patent claim drafting and interpretation.

Kemp, K.J.
Law of Delict / A.D.J. van Rensburg. – Durban : Professional Publisher, 1983.
ISBN 0409037087 Pbk

Kemp, Lynette
Kemp and Message : Asian Capital and Money Markets. – London : Butterworths, 1987.
ISBN 0406103607 Hbk

Kemp, Lynette J.
Wardley guide to world money and securities markets / by Lynette J. Kemp. – London : Euromoney Publications, 1984.
xvii,472p.
ISBN 0903121662

Kemp, Margaret Sylvia → Quantum of damages in personal injury and fatal accident claims, Vol. 1 : Law and practice - fatal accident awards.

Kemp, Peter
Cost of chaos : a survey of the housing benefits scheme / Peter Kemp. – London : SHAC, 1984.
85p; 22cm. – (SHAC research report).
ISBN 0903113759

Kempson, Elaine
Legal advice and assistance. – London : Policy Studies Institute, 1989.
160; 21.
A study commissioned by the Law Society to examine social welfare advice. Surveys the nature of the work of solicitors and advice services and their inter-relationship in thre areas - the London Borough of Newham, the Metropolitan Borough of Oldham, and Cornwall.
ISBN 0853744769 Pbk £6.95

Kenkel, Joseph
Small Claims Litigation. – Butterworths, 1988.
160p.
Guide to the conduct of small claims court actions. Takes the reader step by step from the initial client interview and preliminary issues such as limitations, parties and forums, to drafting effective pleadings. Shows how to handle interlocutory proceedings and how to effectively negotiate settlement. Contains annotated Court Rules, and a set of sample forms.
ISBN 0409806528 Pbk £24.95

Kennedy → Focus on Homelessness : a New Look at Housing Policy.

—Medical Law and Ethics / Grubb. – London : Butterworths, 1988.
ISBN 0406500401 Hbk

Kennedy, Cormie
Sterk's Alberta Conveyancing Law and Practice. – 2nd ed. – Agincourt : Carswell, 1987.
300p.
This practitioner's quick reference text provides materials on real estate transactions practice in Alberta, Canada. Forms, checklist, precedents, and other items needed to conduct the typical real estate transaction are included.
Hbk £46.25

Kennedy, David
International legal structures / David Kennedy. – Baden-Baden : Nomos, 1987.
294p.
Includes bibliographical references.
ISBN 3789013676

Kennedy, Ian, et al
Medical Law and Ethics Commentary and Materials. – London : Butterworths.
ISBN 0406500401 Hbk

—Treat me right : essays on medical law and ethics. – Oxford : Oxford University Press, 1988.
xvii,375p.
Brings together a wide selection of the author's work in the field of medical law and ethics. Many of the articles contained have already been published in journals, but some appear for the first time.
Lawyers, doctors, students of law, ethics and medicine
ISBN 0198255586 Pbk
ISBN 0198255594 Hbk £35

—Unmasking of medicine / Ian Kennedy. – London : Allen & Unwin, 1981.
xiii,189p; 23cm.
Bibliography: p169-182. - Includes index.
ISBN 0046100164

Kennedy, Ludovic
Airman and the carpenter : the Lindbergh kidnapping / Ludovic Kennedy. – London : Collins, 1985.
x,438p,32p ofplates; 24cm.
Bibliography: p425-428. - Includes index.
ISBN 0002170604 £12.95

Kennedy, William Rann
Kennedy's law of salvage / F. D. Rose, David Steel, William Rann Kennedy. – 5th ed. – London : Stevens, 1985.
lxii,833p; 26cm.
Deals with the practical and legal developments that have taken place in the last thirty years. Discusses the widespread acceptance and use of the terms of Lloyd's standard form of salvage agreement (no cure no pay), the preparation in Montreal of a new draft International Convention on salvage, and the effect of legislative activity in the area of oil pollution.
ISBN 0420434305 £70.00

—Law of Salvage (BSL). – 5th ed. – London : Sweet & Maxwell, 1985.
ISBN 0420434305 Hbk £98.00

Kennedy's law of salvage / F. D. Rose, David Steel, William Rann Kennedy. – 5th ed. – London : Stevens, 1985.
lxii,833p; 26cm.
Deals with the practical and legal developments that have taken place in the last thirty years. Discusses the widespread acceptance and use of the terms of Lloyd's standard form of salvage agreement (no cure no pay), the preparation in Montreal of a new draft International Convention on salvage, and the effect of legislative activity in the area of oil pollution.
ISBN 0420434305 £70.00

Kennett, B. → Law of Nature and Nations.

Kenny → Introduction to the Criminal Law of Queensland and WQ.

—Sweet & Maxwell Law
File 1, Land law (Co Habiting). – London : Sweet & Maxwell, 1984.
ISBN 0421321407 Pbk £29.50

Kenny, Anthony
Road to Hillsborough : the shaping of the Anglo-Irish agreement / by Anthony Kenny. – Oxford : Pergamon, 1986.
xi,141p; 21cm.
ISBN 0080347754 Pbk £12.95
ISBN 0080342485 £6.50

Kenny, P. H.
Conveyancing Law / C. Bevan. – 3rd. – Plymouth : Macdonald & Evans, 1986.
– (M and E Handbook Ser.).
ISBN 071210755X Pbk £6.50

Kenny, Phillip H
Fitzkenton Estate. – London : Sweet & Maxwell, 1984.
640p. – (Sweet and Maxwell's Law Files Ser.: No. 2).
ISBN 0421321504 Hbk £29.50

—From Accident to Liability. – London : Sweet & Maxwell, 1984.
640p. – (Sweet and Maxwell's Law Files Ser.: No. 3).
ISBN 0421321601 Hbk £29.50

—Land Law : Cohabitating Owners. – London : Sweet & Maxwell, 1984.
640p. – (Sweet and Maxwell's Law Files Ser.: No. 1).
ISBN 0421321407 Hbk £29.50

—Liability of an Industrialist. – London : Sweet & Maxwell, 1985.
– (Sweet and Maxwell's Law Files Ser.: No. 6).
ISBN 0421340304 Llf £29.50

→ Licensed conveyancing : the new legislation.

—Neighbours in Law. – London : Sweet & Maxwell, 1985.
– (Sweet and Maxwell's Law Files Ser.: No. 4).
ISBN 042134010X Llf £29.50

—Striking a Bargain?. – London : Sweet & Maxwell, 1985.
– (Sweet and Maxwell's Law Files Ser.: No. 7).
ISBN 0421340401 Llf £29.50

—Studying law. – London : Butterworths, 1985.
ISBN 0406016089 Hbk £9.50
ISBN 0406016097 Pbk £5.50

—Trustees of the Fitzkenton Estate. – London : Sweet & Maxwell, 1985.
– (Sweet and Maxwell's Law Files Ser.: No. 5).
ISBN 0421340207 Llf £29.50

Kenny, R.G. → Introduction to the Criminal Law of Queensland and Western Australia.

Kenny, Terence
Employee participation / Terence P. Kenny. – 1 sound cassette. – London : Instructional Dynamics, 1974.

Kent, C.
Everywoman Guide to Consumer Rights. – Unwin Paperbacks.
ISBN 0044402945 Pbk £3.50

Kent, D.
Who's Who in International Banking 1988-89. – London : Cedar Tree House.
ISBN 1852710233 Pbk £95.00

Kent, J.
English Village Constable 1580-1642. – Oxford : Oxford University Press, 1986.
ISBN 0198229135 Hbk £27.50

Kent, Tom → Royal Commission on Newspapers.

Kenya Law Reports. – Nairobi : East African Publishing House, 1976.
Hbk £60.00

Kenya law reports. – Nairobi : Published under the authority of the Attorney- General of the Republic of Kenya by East African Publishing House, 1981.
v.
Continues in part: East Africa law reports.

Keown, J.
Abortion, Doctors and the Law : Aspects of Legal Regulation of Abortion England 1802-1982. – Cambridge : Cambridge University Press.
ISBN 052134574X Hbk £22.50

Kercher, Bruce
Remedies / by Bruce Kercher and Michael Noone. – Sydney : Law Book Co., 1983.
xxxvi,408p.
Includes index.
ISBN 0455204454 Hbk £62

Kerimov, Dzhangir Ali-Abbasovich → Social justice and individual responsibility in the welfare state.

Kerly, Duncan M.
Kerly's law of trade marks and trade names / Robin Jacob. – 12th ed. – London : Sweet & Maxwell, 1986.
830p.
Incorporates developments through legislation and case law, including the provisions of the Trademarks (Amendment) Act 1984, and the Patents, Designs and Marks Act 1986.
ISBN 0421350601 £65.00

Kerly's law of trade marks and trade names / Robin Jacob. – 12th ed. – London : Sweet & Maxwell, 1986.
830p.
Incorporates developments through legislation and case law, including the provisions of the Trademarks (Amendment) Act 1984, and the Patents, Designs and Marks Act 1986.
ISBN 0421350601 £65.00

Kernaghan, Kenneth → Public administration in Canada : selected readings.

Kerr
Law and Practice as to Receivers / Anthony Walton. – 17th ed. – London : Sweet & Maxwell, 1988.
ISBN 0421296909 Hbk
—Law Of Fraud and Mistake. – Sweet & Maxwell, 1952 Reprint.
ISBN 0421355409 Hbk £50.00

Kerr, Adam J. → Guide to Maritime Boundary Delimitation.

Kerr, Alastair James
Law of Lease. – 2nd ed. – Durban : Professional Publisher, 1976.
ISBN 0409037389 Hbk £0409037370
—Law of sale and lease / by A.J. Kerr. – Durban, South Africa : Butterworth Publishers, 1984.
xxxii, 352 p.; 25 cm.
Includes indexes.
ISBN 0409037494 Hbk £27.40
ISBN 0409037508 Pbk £19.50

Kerr, Gillian → Custody of children on breakdown of marriage in Northern Ireland : report of the proceedings of a seminar held in the Queen's University, Belfst, on 12 June 1981.
—Family breakdown, children and the law / by Gilliam Kerr. – Belfast : SLS Legal Publications, 1985.
xii,68p.
Includes index.
ISBN 0853892555

Kerr, Ian M.
Big Bang / by Ian M. Kerr. – London : Euromoney Publications, 1986.
180p.
ISBN 187003130X
—History of the Eurobond market : the first 21 years / by Ian M. Kerr. – London : Euromoney, 1984.
166p.
ISBN 0903121689

Kerr, M. Kaye
Procedures for meetings and organizations / M. Kaye Kerr and Hubert W. King. – Agincourt, Ont. : Carswell Legal Publications, 1984.
xv, 313 p.; 24 cm.
Includes index. Bibliography: p. 276.
ISBN 0459361503

Kerr on the Law of Fraud and Mistake. – London : Sweet & Maxwell, 1986.
– (Sweet and Maxwell Library Reprints).
ISBN 0421355409 Hbk £50.00

Kerr, Tony
Irish trade union law / Tony Kerr and Gerry Whyte. – Abingdon : Professional Books, 1985.
lxiv,383p.
ISBN 0862050510 Hbk £31.50
ISBN 0862050936 Pbk £22.50

Kerridge, Roger → Effect on English domestic law of membership of the European Communities and of ratification of the European Convention on Human Rights.

Kerrigan, Herbert → Law of contempt.

Kerse, C. S.
EEC antitrust procedure / by C.S. Kerse. – 2nd ed. – London : European Law Centre, 1988.
xlii,398p; 26cm.
Previous ed.: 1981. Includes index.
ISBN 0907451160

Kersley → Legal Maxims.

Kess, Joseph F.
Psycholinguistic Principles Applicable to the Formulation of Jury Instructions : an Annotated Bibliography. – Ottawa : Canadian Law Information Council, 1985.
60p.
ISBN 0920358853 Pbk £5.00

Kesselman, Jonathan R.
Financing Canadian unemployment insurance / Jonathan R. Kesselman. – Toronto : Canadian Tax Foundation, 1983.
xiii,187p.
Bibliography: p.177-183. - Includes index.
ISBN 0888080166

Kessler, Charles → Austrian Federal Constitution : as revised in 1929 together with subsequent additions and amendments and other important constitutional provisions including the Constitutional Law on the Neutrality of Austria.

Kettell, Brian
International debt game / by Brian Kettell and George Magnus. – London : Graham & Trotman, 1985.
384p; 23cm.
Includes index.
ISBN 0860105717 Pbk £18.75
ISBN 0860108104 £12.50

Kettl, D.F.
Leadership at the Fed. – Yale University Press.
ISBN 0300043635 Pbk £8.95

Kettle, Martin
Uprising! : the police, the people and the riots in Britain's cities / Martin Kettle and Lucy Hodges. – London : Pan Books, 1982.
271p; 18cm.
ISBN 0330268457

Keustermans
International computer law issues / Keustermans. – Matthew Bender, 1988.
ISBN 0000999059 Hbk £53.00

Key
Conveyancing
Vol. 1 / Elphinstone. – London : Butterworths.
ISBN 086205334X Hbk £64.50

Key Issues in Irish Family Law. – Dublin : Round Hall Press, 1988.
ca 192p.
ISBN 0947686312 Hbk £22.50

Key to Personal Injury Practice and Compensation / Margaret R De Haas. – London : Longman Professional, 1981.
ISBN 0851206158 Pbk £8.95

Keyguide to information sources on the international protection of human rights / J.A. Andrews and W.D. Hines. – London : Mansell, 1987.
xiii,169p; 24cm.
Includes index.
ISBN 0720118735 £25.00

Keynes's Impact on Monetary Economics. – London : Butterworths, 1982.
This book provides a carefully documented survey of the impact of Keynes on monetary economics. The fundamental concepts of Keynes's theories are considered and related to the work of important critics and followers of Keynes.
ISBN 0408107189 Hbk

Keys, Donald → Disarmament : the human factor : proceedings of a colloquium on the societal context for disarmament.

Khadduri, Majid
Islamic conception of justice / Majid Khadduri. – Baltimore : Johns Hopkins University Press, 1984.
xvi,256p; 24cm.
Bibliography: p243-249. - Includes index.
ISBN 0801832454 £22.20

Khan, A. N. → On industrial relations : interprofessional relationships in health care and the role of criminal law in industrial relations.

Khan, Ahmad → Foreign investment & technology transfer : fiscal and non-fiscal aspects : country profiles on fiscal and non-fiscal regimes affecting two-way flow of investment and technology transfer between the developed countries and the Asian-Pacific region.
→ Taxation in the Asian-Pacific region : a country by country survey.

Khan, Kabir-ur-Rahman
Law and organisation of international commodity agreements / Kabir-ur-Rahman Khan. – The Hague : M. Nijhoff, 1982.
xxv,416p.
Includes index. Bibliography: p394-400.
ISBN 9024725542 Hbk £170.00

Khan Kausar, Alhaj Mauj Mohammad
Kausar's Ready Referencer of Legal Words, Phrases and Maxims. – Lahore : Pakistan Law Times.
Hbk £15.00

Khan, M.S.
Law of Retrenchment in India. – New Delhi : Deep and Deep Publications, 1982.
130p.
Hbk £55.00

Khan, M.Y.
Law, Procedure and Ready Reckoner of Bonus, E.S.I. Gratuity and Provident Fund / Abha Kulshreshtha. – Delhi : Metropolitan Book Co, 1987.
370p.
ISBN 812000258X Hbk £150.00

Khan, Ursula
Recent personal injury awards made in the Supreme Court of Judicature of Jamaica / compiled by Ursula Khan. – s.l. : s.n., 1981.
xxvii,200p.

Khanna, A.N.
Law of Court Fees and Suits Valuation in India / H.N. Seth. – 6th ed. – Allahabad : Universal Book Agency, 1988.
ca 1,000p.
Hbk £250.00

Khanna, H. R.
Law, men of law and education / H. R. Khanna. – Bombay : Tripathi, 1981.
184p.
—Making of India's Constitution. – Lucknow : Eastern Book Company, 1982.
vii, 121p.
Hbk £40.00
—Neither Roses Nor Thorns : an Autobiography by the Retired Judge of the Supreme Court of India. – Lucknow : Eastern Book Company, 1985.
208p.
Hbk

Kharbanda, et al
Corporate failure. – Maidenhead : McGraw-Hill, 1986.
ISBN 0070847940 Hbk £17.50

Kharbanda, V.K. → Supreme Court Labour Digest, 1950-82. 2 Vols.

Khaw, Lake Tee → Land Law in Malaysia : Cases and Commentary.

Khoo, D. S.
Parent-Child Law in Singapore. – Singapore : Butterworths, 1984.
The book provides a discussion of legitimacy, maintenance, guardianship, and adoption under the law of Singapore. The 1980 amendments to the Women's Charter pertaining to maintenance, welfare and custody of children are analyzed in depth.
ISBN 0406181217 Pbk

Khoo, O.S.
Parent-Child Law in Singapore. – London : Butterworths, 1984.
ISBN 0406181217 Pbk £25.00

Khoo, Siew-Ean
Living together : young couples in de facto relationships : a report using Australian Family Formation Project Data / prepared for the Australian Institute of Family Studies. – Melbourne : Australian Institute of Family Stuides, 1986.
ii,50p. – (Working paper).
ISBN 0859244466

Khosha, G.U.
Know Your Copyright. – Allahabad : Orient Law House.
ISBN 0861251318 Hbk £30.00

Khosla, N.M.
Civil Service Rules : With Classified Extracts from Judgements and Decisions of the Supreme Court and High Courts in India, Govt of India's Orders, Instructions and Interpretations with Index. – Bombay : N.M. Khosla & Co., 1988.
Hbk £100.00

Khoury
Butterworths Student Companions
Tax /. – Butterworths, 1987.
117p.
ISBN 0409492469

Khoury, Daniel
Understanding Contract Law / Yvonne Yamouni. – 2nd ed. – Butterworths, 1988.
312p.
ISBN 0409302538 Pbk £32.00

Khublall, N.
Law of Company Purchase and Compensation-Singapore and Malaysia. – London : Butterworths, 1984.
ISBN 0406181225 Pbk £22.50
—Law of compulsory purchase and compensation - Singapore and Malaysia / N. Khublall. – Singapore : Butterworths, 1984.
xxviii,310p.
Account of the main provisions relating to powers, procedures and appeals, and discusses the concept of market value as the basis for compensation. Cases and statutory provisions are drawn from both Singapore and Malaysia, as well as from England and India.
ISBN 0406181225 Pbk £55.00

Khumalo, J. A. M.
Civil practice of all courts for blacks in Southern Africa / J.A.M. Khumalo. – 3rd ed. – Cape Town : Juta, 1984.
xli,300p.
Previous ed. (1975) has title: Civil practice and procedure in all Bantu courts in Southern Africa. Bibliography: p.xix. - Includes index.
ISBN 0702114677

Khurshid, Salman →Judges and the judicial power : essays in honour of Justice V.R. Krishna Iyer.

Khushalani, Yougindra
Dignity and honour of women as basic and fundamental human rights / by Yougindra Khushalani. – The Hague : Martinus Nijhoff Publishers, 1982.
153p.
Includes index.
ISBN 9024725852 Hbk £105.00

Kidder, Robert L.
Connecting law and society : an introduction to research and theory / Robert L. Kidder. – Englewood Cliffs, N.J. : Prentice-Hall, 1983.
xv,286p; 24cm.
Includes bibliographies and index.
ISBN 0131678094

Kidner, Richard
Trade union law / Richard Kidner. – 2nd ed. – London : Stevens, 1983.
xl,290p; 25cm.
Previous ed.: London : Sweet & Maxwell, 1979. Includes index.
ISBN 0420465502 £25.00

Kiernan, Anne
Butterworths Family Law Bulletin. – Butterworths.
Hbk £44.00
—Butterworth's Family Law Bulletin / Hellen Papadopoulos. – Wellington : Butterworths.
Hbk
—Butterworth's Family Law Reports / Hellen Papadopoulos. – Wellington : Butterworths.
Hbk
—Butterworths Family Law Reports. – Butterworths.
Llf
—Butterworth's Family Law Service / H. K. Bevan. – Wellington : Butterworths, 1986.
ISBN 0406107203 Llf

Kieve, Jeffrey L. →Urban land economics.

Kilby, R L
Notes on the Mental Health Act 1983. – London : Shaw & Sons, 1983.
ISBN 0721902049 Pbk £1.95

Killen, Diana
Negotiating a Database Contract. – Hawthorn : Australian Database Development Agency, 1987.
ISBN 0959096736 Hbk £5.00

Killick, Tony →Adjustment and financing in the developing world : the role of the International Monetary Fund.
→ IMF and stabilisation : developing country experiences.
→ Quest for economic stabilisation : the IMF and the Third World.

Killing of Justice Godfrey : an investigation into England's most remarkable unsolved murder / Stephen Knight. – London : Granada, 1984.
280p,8p of plates; 24cm.
Bibliography: p259-270. - Includes index.
ISBN 0246123516 £10.95

Kiln, R.
Reinsurance in practice. – 2nd ed. – London : Witherby & Co, 1986.
ISBN 0900886986 Hbk £30.00

Kilty, B.J.
Building and Civil Engineering Contracts in Ireland. – London : Butterworths.
ISBN 0406132011 Hbk

Kim, Chan-jin →Business laws in Korea : investment, taxation, and industrial property.

Kim, Chin
Criminal Procedure Code of the People's Republic of China. – London : Sweet & Maxwell, 1982.
– (American Series of Foreign Penal Codes: No. 25).
ISBN 0421300108 Hbk £33.00

Kim, Hyung I.
Fundamental legal concepts of China and the West : a comparative study / Hyung I. Kim. – Port Washington : National University Publications, 1981.
xiii,175p; 23cm.
Bibliography: p165-175.
ISBN 0804692750 £14.85

Kime's international law handbook : brief facts about legal practice in most of the countries of the world / editor : James M. Matthews ; research and compilation : Roderick N. Matthews. – London : Kime's International Law Directory Limited, 1981.
266p.
ISBN 0900503149

Kindred, Hugh M
International law : chiefly as interpreted and applied in Canada / Castel. – 4th ed. – Aurora : Canada Law Book, 1986.
Hbk £53.00

King
History of the Hong Kong and Shanghai Banking Corporation
Vol. 2 Hong Kong Bank in Period Imperialism 1895-1918 / King. – Cambridge : Cambridge University Press.
ISBN 0521327075 Hbk £60.00
—Solicitors and their business clients / Barlow. – 3rd ed. – London : Financial Training, 1986.
ISBN 1851850317 Pbk £16.50

King, Alexander
Coming information society. – London : British Library, 1984.
1v.
ISBN 0712330364 Pbk

King, Andrew J. →Papers of Daniel Webster, Vol.1 : The New Hampshire practice : Alfred S. Konefsky and Andrew J. King.

King, Anthony →Wills administration and taxation: a practical guide.

King, David N.
Fiscal tiers : the economics of multi-level government / David N. King. – London : Allen & Unwin in association with the Centre for Research on Federal Finance Relations, the Australian National University, 1984.
v,326p; 24cm.
Bibliography: p305-316. - Includes index.
ISBN 0043360815 Hbk £
ISBN 004336084X Pbk £8.95

King Edward's Hospital Fund for London → Rights and wrongs in medicine : King's College studies 1985-6.

King, F.H.H.
History of the Hong Kong and Shanghai Banking Corporation
Vol. 4 Hong Kong Bank in Period of Development 1941-1984. – Cambridge : Cambridge University Press.
ISBN 0521327091 Hbk £60.00

King-Hamilton, Alan
And nothing but the truth / Alan King-Hamilton : foreword by Lord Diplock. – London : Weidenfeld and Nicolson, 1982.
xvi,237p,8p of plates; 24cm.
Includes index.
ISBN 0297780530 £12.50

King, Hubert W. →Procedures for meetings and organizations.

King, J. R. →Taxing Currency Fluctuations?.

King, Lesley →Wills administration and taxation: a practical guide.

King, Mervyn A. →British tax system.

King, Michael
Framework of criminal justice / Michael King. – London : Croom Helm, 1981.
159p; 23cm.
Bibliography: p153-156. - Includes index.
ISBN 0709904304 Hbk £10.95
ISBN 0709915004 Pbk £6.50

King, Michael Sandford
Natural Law and Consciousness. – West Perth : Gantheaume Press, 1987.
ISBN 0958861013 Hbk £8.95

King, Philip S. D. →Expert witness and his evidence.
—VAT on construction and development work / Philip S.D. King. – London : Granada, 1984.
194p; 24cm.
Includes index.
ISBN 0246122501 Hbk £17.95
—Watts Pocket Guide to Building Cases 1989. – Watts & Partners.
ISBN 01870776011 Hbk £2.50

King, R. M.
Manual on Legislative Drafting. – London : Commonwealth Secretariat, 1984.
free

King Taylor, Lynda
Good Practice : A Management Guide for the Profession. – London : Butterworths.
ISBN 0406502803 Pbk
—Good Practice : Management Guide for Professions. – London : Butterworths, 1988.
ISBN 0406502803 Pbk

King, Thelma →Sale of goods and supply of services : a guide to the legislation.

Kingcombe Turner, Alexander
New Zealand Commentary to Halsbury's Laws of England. – Wellington : Butterworths.
Hbk

Kings Bench Decision upon Settlement Cases : From 1732-76. – Repr. of 1776 ed. – Abingdon : Professional Books.
286p.
Hbk £95.00

King's College, London →Lending in booms and slumps.

Kingsbury, Benedict →United Nations, divided world : the UN's roles in international relations.

Kingshort, Maureen
Alcohol and Crime. – Canberra : Australian Institute of Criminology.
Hbk £3.60

Kingshott, M. A.
Alternatives to Imprisonment. – Canberra : Australian Institute of Criminology.
free

Kingston, Robert A.
Canada Corporation Manual, 3 Vols. – Toronto : DeBoo, 1984.
ISBN 0888201346 Hbk £325.00
—Ontario Corporation Manual. – Toronto : DeBoo.
ISBN 088820132X Llf £325.00

Kinkeldey, Hermann →New German Patent Law (1981) in English and German.

Kinsella, Janet →Online public access to library files : conference proceedings.

Kinsey, Richard
Losing the fight against crime / Richard Kinsey, John Leo, Jock Young. – Oxford : Basil Blackwell, 1986.
viii,221p; 23cm.
Bibliography: p216-218. - Includes index.
ISBN 063113719X Hbk £22.50
ISBN 0631137211 Pbk £6.95
→ Police powers and politics.

Kinship and marriage : an anthropological perspective / Robin Fox. – Cambridge : Cambridge University Press, 1983.
273p; 20cm.
ISBN 0521260736

Kiralfy, A. K. R. →Burden of proof.
—Burden of Proof. – London : Butterworths, 1987.
ISBN 0862052157 Hbk £26.50
—English legal system / A.K.R. Kiralfy. – 7th ed. – London : Sweet & Maxwell, 1984.
xli,301p; 22cm.
Previous ed.: 1978. Includes index.
ISBN 0421313706 Pbk £16.50
ISBN 0421313803 Pbk £7.50
→ Historical Introduction To English Law.
→ New perspectives in Scottish legal history.

Kirby, Keith →Preventing rent arrears.

Kirby, Michael
Reform the law : essays on the renewal of the Australian legal system / Michael Kirby. – Melbourne, Oxford : Oxford University Press, 1983.
xii,284p; 21cm.
ISBN 0195543955 Pbk £12.99
ISBN 0195543955 Hbk £27.50
→ Right to know.

Kirby, Michael G.
Domestic Airline Regulation : Australian Debate. – Turramura : Centre for Independent Studies.
120p.
ISBN 0959648593 Hbk £5.50

Kircher, Ingrid A.
Kanaks of New Caledonia / by Ingrid A. Kircher. – London : Minority Rights Group, 1986.
20p. – (Report).
Bibliography: p.20.
ISBN 0946690405

Kirchheimer, Otto
Social democracy and the rule of law / Otto Kirchheimer and Franz Neumann : edited by Keith Tribe : translated by Leena Tanner and Keith Tribe. – London : Allen & Unwin, 1987.
224p; 22cm.
Includes bibliography and index. Translated from the German.
ISBN 0043013007 £25.00

Kirgis, F.L.
Prior Consultation in International Law : a Study of State Practice. – London : Europspan.
ISBN 0813909716 Hbk £30.95

Kirkby, Diane →Law and history in Australia : selected papers from the fourth and fifth Law in History Conferences held at La Trobe University, 1985 and 1986, Vol. 3.

Kirkwood, J.
Social Security Law and Policy. – North Ryde : Law Book Co, 1986.
xxvi, 272p.
ISBN 0455206155 Pbk £29.50

Kirsh : a Guide to Construction Liens in Ontario. – Butterworths, 1984.
480p.
Overview of the flow of funds on construction projects. Covers preserving and protecting the lien, practice and procedure in the lien action, the statutory holdbacks, the new trust fund provisions and liability for breach of trust, liens against Crown lands and municipal streets, labour and material bonds, and the appointment of trustee.
ISBN 0409842869 Hbk £80.00

Kirsh : Selected Bibliography of Construction Law Writings in Canada. – Agincourt : Carswell, 1988.
43p.
Hbk £21.00

Kirsh, Harvey J.
Construction Law Reports
Vols. 1-19. – Agincourt : Carswell, 1985.
—Kirsh : a Guide to Construction Liens in Ontario. – Butterworths, 1984.
480p.
Overview of the flow of funds on construction projects. Covers preserving and protecting the lien, practice and procedure in the lien action, the statutory holdbacks, the new trust fund provisions and liability for breach of trust, liens against Crown lands and municipal streets, labour and material bonds, and the appointment of trustee.
ISBN 0409842869 Hbk £80.00

—Kirsh : Selected Bibliography of Construction Law Writings in Canada. – Agincourt : Carswell, 1988.
43p.
Hbk £21.00

Kirzner →Global Investing.

Kiss, A -Ch
A.A.A. Yearbook
Vol. 47/48 (1977/78): Foreign Investments Today and Tomorrow /. – Dordrecht : Kluwer, 1986.
160p.
ISBN 9024725704 Pbk £75.00
Vol. 54/55/56: Natural Resources in International Law. – 1987.
320p.
ISBN 902473469X Pbk £150.00

—Hague yearbook of international law : Annuaire de la Haye de droit international / J.G. Lammers. – Dordrecht : Nijhoff (Martinus), 1988.
471. – (A.A.A. Yearbook).
In-depth articles on some of the developments taking place in international law institutions such as the International Court of Justice and the Hague Conference on Private International Law. The articles, and summaries, in both English and French, deal with decisions rendered by these institutions.
ISBN 9024737494 Hbk £80

Kiss, Charles
Selected Multilateral Treaties in the Field of the Environment. – Geneva : United Nations Publications.
525p.
Pbk £38.00

Kitchen, Harry M.
Local government finance in Canada / Harry M. Kitchen. – Toronto : Canadian Tax Foundation, 1984.
xvii,495p.
Includes bibliographical references and index.
ISBN 0888080204

Kitchin, L.D.
Road transport law. – 26th ed. – London : Butterworths, 1988.
ISBN 0406106738 Pbk £19.95

Kitchin, Leslie Deans
Kitchin's road transport law : a summary of the legislation affecting the construction, equipment and use of motor vehicles / James Duckworth. – 26th ed. – London : Butterworths, 1988.
400p; 22cm.
Previous ed.: 1985. Includes index.
ISBN 0406106738 Pbk £20.00

Kitchin's road transport law : a summary of the legislation affecting the construction, equipment and use of motor vehicles / James Duckworth. – 26th ed. – London : Butterworths, 1988.
400p; 22cm.
Previous ed.: 1985. Includes index.
ISBN 0406106738 Pbk £20.00

Kivivuori, Antti →Law drafting and sociology : a seminar report.

Kjonstad, A.
Norwegian social law / Asbjrn Kjnstad. – Oslo : Norwegian University Press, 1987.
303p; 23cm.
Presents Norwegian social law as an example of the Nordic model. Discusses social security legislation, its history and administration, financing of social security measures, disablement, and some health and welfare issues.
ISBN 8200059030 £30.00

Klami, Hannu Tapani
Legalists : Finnish legal science in the period of autonomy, 1809-1917 / by Hannu Tapani Klami. – Helsinki : Societas Scientiarum Fennica, 1981.
153 p., 4 leaves of plates; 24 cm.
Includes index. Bibliography: p. 141-150. Translation with revisions of: Oikeustaistelijat.
ISBN 9516531008 Pbk
—Private international law in Finland : an outline / by Hannu Tapani Klami. – Turku : Turun yliopiston offsetpaino, 1986.
67 p.; 21 cm. – (Turun yliopiston oikeustieteellisen tiedekunnan julkaisuja. Yksityisoikeuden sarja A).
Bibliography: p. 64-65. Includes index.
ISBN 9516427871
—Three Essays on the Theory of Legal Norms. – 1986. – Helsinki : Suomalainen Tiedeakatemia.
54p.
Hbk £46.00

Klar, L.
Remedies in Tort, 4 Vols. / A M Linden. – Agincourt : Carswell, 1987.
This multi-volume set of looseleaf books provides an in-depth coverage of the area of torts. There are 23 chapters. Discussions include related proceedings, elements the plaintiff must establish to succeed in an action, available defenses, remedies, necessary and proper parties to an action, and practice issues pertaining to tort law. Special features include a legal research guide and sample statements of claims.
Hbk £159.75
—Studies in Canadian Tort Law. – London : Butterworths.
ISBN 0409843008 Hbk £60.00

Klein
Family Law Awards : In Canada. – Toronto : Butterworths, 1987.
328p.
ISBN 0409843938 Hbk £65.00
→ Swap agreement documentation.

Klein, David A.
Family Law Awards in Canada. – Butterworths, 1987.
304p.
ISBN 0409409843938 Hbk £70.00

Klein, Gerald →Dictionary of banking.

Klein, John F →Criminal justice in Canada: an introductory text.

Klein, Linda B. →Loan agreement documentation : sample annotated loan agreement for a syndicated Eurodollar transaction.

Klein, Malcolm W. →Western systems of juvenile justice.

Klein, Rudolf →Accountabilities : five public services.

Kling, Allan →Applications of computer technology to law (1979-1982) : a selected bibliography.
—Computer-Assisted Legal Research : a Guide for Canadian Law Students. – Ottawa : Canadian Law Information Council, 1984.
103p.
ISBN 0920358551 Pbk £15.00

Klinghoffer, A.J.
Fraud of the Century : Case of the Supertanker 'Salem'. – Routledge.
ISBN 041500246X Hbk £15.95

Klippert, George B.
Unjust enrichment / George B. Klippert. – Toronto : Butterworths, 1983.
xlix,389p.
Explains how Canadian restitution law has developed its own independent and unique voice: increasingly relying less on English authority and more on American jurisprudence. Recognises that the Supreme Court of Canada, in the process of affirming the concept of restitution as a distinct head of civil liability, has also carved a way to an independent interpretation of unjust enrichment.
ISBN 0409842931

Klise →Money and Banking.

Klunker, Hans-Friedrich, et al
German Utility Model Act 1987 : as Promulgated in the Notice of August 28, 1986 and Effective as of January 1, 1987. – Cologne : Carl Heymanns Verlag, 1986.
53p.
ISBN 3452207641 Pbk £28.00

Kluver, J.B.
Powers of Investigation in Revenue, Companies and Trade Practices Law / R.H. Woellner. – Butterworths, 1983.
486p.
ISBN 0409493813 Pbk £65.00

Knafla, Louis A.
Law and Justice in a New Land : Essays in Western Canadian Legal History. – Agincourt : Carswell, 1986.
300p.
This work is a collection of essays incorporating primary historical research on topics relating to aboriginal and Indian land and resource law; law, politics, and justice in frontier communities; and legal and social problems in urban settings of Western Canada.
Hbk £46.25

Knapman, Paul →Thurston's coronership : the law and practice on coroners.

Knapp →Demonstrating Successful Community Care.
→ Evidence and Procedure in Magistrates Courts.

Knapp, Stephen →Evidence and Procedure in Magistrates' Courts.

Knetch, Jack L.
Property Rights and Compensation : Compulsory Acquisition and Other Losses. – Butterworths, 1983.
192p.
Includes alternative bases for assessing economic losses, compulsory acquisition of business, compensation for goodwill and licences, economic value and property, reservation values and compulsory acquisitions, compensation claims and the taking of public property.
ISBN 0409843059 Hbk £45.00

Knight →Forensic Medicine.

Knight, Bernard
Legal aspects of medical practice / Bernard Knight. – 4th ed. – Edinburgh : Churchill Livingstone, 1987.
336p; 22cm.
Previous ed.: 1982. Includes bibliography and index.
ISBN 0443037817 Pbk £4.95
—Legal aspects of medical practice / Bernard Knight. – 3rd ed. – Edinburgh : Churchill Livingstone, 1982.
viii,302p; 22cm. – (Churchill Livingstone medical text).
Previous ed.: 1976.
ISBN 0443025584

Knight, Martin →Export finance.

Knight, Stephen
Killing of Justice Godfrey : an investigation into England's most remarkable unsolved murder / Stephen Knight. – London : Granada, 1984.
280p,8p of plates; 24cm.
Bibliography: p259-270. - Includes index.
ISBN 0246123516 £10.95

Knight, W
Acquisition of private companies. – 5th. – London : Longman Professional (UK), 1989.
New edition covers Financial Services Act 1986, the Finance Act 1986, the Income and Corporatin Taxes Act 1988, and the implications of the 1989 Budget. New section on merger control and competition, and includes precedents of agreements for sale both for individual and corporate vendors.
ISBN 085121438X Hbk £35.00
—Hunting law. – London : Shaw & Sons, 1988.
ISBN 0721911404 Pbk

Knight, W D →Structuring foreign investment in US real estate.

Knight, W.J.L.
Acquisition of Private Companies. – 5th ed. – London : Longman Professional.
ISBN 085121438X Pbk £28.00

Knighton, William M →National laws and international commerce : the problem of extraterritoriality.

Knight's Environmental and Public Health Acts. – Tonbridge : Ernest Benn.
5000p.
ISBN 0853140235 Llf £495.00

Knight's Industrial and Commercial Reports : 1966-75, 17 Vols. – Abingdon : Professional Books, 1984.
Hbk £595.00

Knights Industrial Law Reports 1-17. – Professional Books, 1966-1975.
ISBN 0862052750 Hbk £435.00

Knight's Local Government and Magisterial Reports, Statutes and Orders : 1903-date, 234 Vols. – Abingdon : Professional Books.
Hbk

Knights, Philip
Public liberty and the police role / Philip Knights. – S.l. : University of Wales. Institute of Science and Technology, 1985.
23p.
Bibliography: p22-23.

Knoll, Patrick J.
Criminal Law Defences. – Agincourt : Carswell.
200p.
This text contains a comprehensive summary of the 40 defenses used in Canadian criminal law. Principles for application of the defenses and more in-depth information is also included. The main topic headings include exemptions, justifications, excuses, procedural and other defenses.
Hbk £35.75

Knoppers, Bartha Maria →Contemporary Trends in Family Law : A National Perspective.

Knots and Crime. – London : Police Review, 1985.
ISBN 0851640176 Pbk £3.95

Knott
Currency Problems in Maritime Disputes / Howard. – London : Lloyd's of London Press.
ISBN 1850441677 Hbk

Knott, G.
Practical Cost and Management Accounting. – London : Macmillan.
– (New Edition Breakthrough Series).
ISBN 0333481399 Pbk £5.95

Know how : to find out your rights / Grainne Morby. – London : Pluto, 1982.
188p; 20cm.
Includes index.
ISBN 0861043596 Pbk £3.95

Know Your Copyright. – Allahabad : Orient Law House.
ISBN 0861251318 Hbk £30.00

Know Your Rights When You Retire. – Kensington : Bay Books.
Pbk £3.95

Know-how contract in Germany, Japan, and the United States / edited by Herbert Stumpf. – Deventer, The Netherlands : Kluwer Law and Taxation, 1984.
309 p.; 25 cm.
Includes bibliographies.
ISBN 9065441379 Pbk

Knowles
Partnership. – London : Butterworths.
ISBN 0409843156 Hbk £30.00

Knowles, Henry J., et al
So You Want a Fight! : Shareholder Rights and Remedies in Canada. – North Ryde : C.C.H. Australia, 1986.
195p.
ISBN 0887963668 Pbk £16.95

Knowles, R.
Law & Prac Of Local Authority Meetings. – Cambridge : Woodhead-Faulkner.
ISBN 0902197517 Hbk £32.50

Kobrin, D.
Agency. – Stockholm : Anderson Keenan, 1981.
– (Law Unit).
ISBN 0906501237 Pbk £3.00

Kobrin, David
Negotiable Instruments / Vanessa Stott. – Winchester : DP Publications.
ISBN 0905435583 Hbk £3.50

Koch, H. W.
Constitutional history of Germany : in the nineteenth and twentieth centuries / H.W. Koch. – London : Longman, 1984.
xiv,400p; 22cm.
Includes index.
ISBN 0582491827 Pbk £7.95

Koch, Robert J.
Damages for lost income / Robert J. Koch. – Cape Town : Juta, 1984.
xxxii,367p.
Bibliography: pxvii-xix.
ISBN 0702115126

Kodilinye, G.
Introduction To Equity In Nigeria. – Sweet & Maxwell, 1975.
ISBN 0421205709 Pbk £12.50

Koffman, Laurence →Sentencing and the penal system : text and materials.

Koh, Kheng Lian →Current developments in international securities commodities and financial futures markets.

Koh, Peter Soon Kwang →Carriage of goods by sea.
—Carriage of Goods by Sea. – London : Butterworths, 1986.
ISBN 0409995150 Hbk £38.00

Kohli, H.P.S. →Delhi and Central Sales Tax.

Kohona, Palitha Tikiri Bandara
Regulation of international economic relations through law / by Palitha Tikiri Bandara Kohona. – Dodrecht : M. Nijhoff Publishers, 1985.
Based on author's thesis (Ph. D.)–Cambridge University.
ISBN 9024731046

Kolawole, Owolabi
Justiciability of constitutional adjudication / a paper presented by Owolabi Kolawole at the Seminar on the Constitutional Adjudication in a Presidential System of Government, a comparative American and Nigerian experience, held at the Nigerian Institute of Advanced Legal Studies, University of Lagos, on Wednesday September 2, 1981. – Lagos : Nigerian Institute of Advanced Legal Studies, 1981.
20p.

Kolbasov, O. S.
Ecology : political institutions and legislation : environmental law in the USSR / Oleg Kolbasov. – Moscow : Progress, 1983.
215p; 21cm.
Translation of: Ekologia.
ISBN 0714719277 £3.95

Kolhatkar, D.D.
Commentary on the University Laws in India. – Madhya Pradesh, 1986.
220p.
Hbk £90.00

Koltveit, J.M.
Accounting For Banks. – Matthew Bender, 1982.
ISBN 0000999082 Hbk £55.00

Kolvenbach, Walter
Cooperation between management and labor : a survey of co-determination mechanisms in European corporations / Walter Kolvenbach. – Deventer, Netherlands : Kluwer Law and Taxation Publishers, 1982.
89 p.; 25 cm.
ISBN 9065440666 Pbk £.
→ Handbook on European employee co-maangement.
—Protection of foreign investments: a private law study of safeguarding devices in international crisis situations. – Kluwer Law and Taxation, 1989.
500.
Deals primarily with the situation in the USA, but also summarises the discussions and ideas developed from twenty years of practical studies. Includes chapters on the Canadian Trading with the Enemy Act, the treatment of Private Enemy Property in the USA, proof of ownershihp and documentation.
ISBN 9065443827 Hbk £54/Dfl 165

Kome, Penny
Taking of 28 : Women Challenge the Constitution. – Toronto.
124p.
ISBN 0889610835 Pbk £6.95

Konefsky, Alfred S. →Papers of Daniel Webster, Vol.1 : The New Hampshire practice : Alfred S. Konefsky and Andrew J. King.

Konold et al., W.G.
What Every Engineer Should Know about Patents. – London : European Book Service.
ISBN 0824780108 Hbk £47.50

Kononewsky, Anatole
Cost of Criminal Justice : An Analysis. – Canberra : Australian Institute of Criminology.
Hbk £2.30

Koopmans, Thijmen
Judicial system envisaged in the draft treaty / by Thijmen Koopmans. – Florence : European University Institute, 1985.
57p.

Kopelman, Loretta M →Ethics and mental retardation.

Korah, Valentine
Competition law of Britain and the Common Market / by Valentine Korah. – 3rd ed. – The Hague : Martinus Nijhoff, 1982.
xxvii,352p.
Bibliography: p321-326. Includes index.
ISBN 9024726158 Hbk £140.00
—Exclusive dealing agreements in the E.E.C. : Regulation 67/67 replaced / by Valentine Korah. – London : European Law Centre, 1984.
xv,101p; 25cm.
ISBN 090745111X Pbk £17.50
—Introductory guide to EEC Competition law and practice / Valentine Korah. – 3rd ed. – Oxford : ESC Publishing, 1986.
xxi,177p; 21cm.
Includes bibliographies and index. Cover title: EEC competition law and practice.
ISBN 0906214394
—Introductory guide to EEC competition law and practice / Valentine Korah. – 2nd ed. – Oxford : ESC, 1981.
xxii,160p; 22cm.
ISBN 0906214084 Pbk
—Patent licensing and EEC competition rules : Regulation 2349/84 / Valentine Korah. – Oxford : ESC Publishing, 1985.
xiv,126p. – (European competition law monographs).
Includes bibliographies.
ISBN 090621436X
—R & D and the EEC competition rules : Regulation 418/85 / Valentine Korah. – Oxford : ESC Publishing, 1986.
xxi,114p. – (European competition law monographs).
Bibliography: p.xxi.
ISBN 0906214459
→ Recent developments in EEC competition law : seminar documentation : Monday 8th December 1986, Cavendish Conference Centre, London W1.

Korean Straits. – Martinus Nijhoff.
ISBN 9024737249 Hbk £42.00

Korff, Douwe
Diplock courts in Northern Ireland : a fair trial? : an analysis of the law, based on a study commissioned by Amnesty International / by Douwe Korff. – Utrecht : Studie-en Informatiecentrum Mensenrechten, 1984.
115p.

Korn, Anthony →How to comply with the Data Protection Act : policies, practice and procedures.

Korner, Peter →IMF and the debt crisis : a guide to the Third World's dilemma.

Kos, J. Stephen →Law and You : a Practical Guide for New Zealanders.

Kos-Rabcewicz-Zubkowski, Ludwik
Commercial arbitration institutions : an international directory and guide / Ludwik Kos-Rabcewicz-Zubkowski and Paul J. Davidson. – London : Oceana Publications, 1986.
ix, 186p.
Published under the auspices of the International Federation of Commercial Arbitration Institutions.
ISBN 0379207893

Koskenniemi, Martti
From Apology to Utopia : the Structure of International Legal Argument. – Helsinki : Lakimiesliiton Kustannus.
500p.
ISBN 9516404138 Hbk

Kothari, A.G. →Study of Industrial Law, Vol 1 : Law Relating to Industrial Disputes, Trade Unions, Wages and Workmen's Compensation.

Kothari, G.M.
Drafting, Conveyancing and Pleadings. – 2nd ed. – Bombay : Tripathi, 1982.
460p.
bd £80.00
—Study of Industrial Law, Vol 1 : Law Relating to Industrial Disputes, Trade Unions, Wages and Workmen's Compensation / A.G. Kothari. – Bombay : Tripathi, 1987.
404p.
bd £90.00

Kothary, P. →Central Sales Tax Laws.
→ Principles of Sales Tax Laws, 2 Vols.

Kotz, Hein →German private and commercial law : an introduction.
→ Introduction to comparative law.

KPMG Peat Marwick →Tax Practitioner 1989.

Kramer, J.L.
Federal Taxation : 1989 Corporation, Partnership, Estates and Trusts. – Prentice-Hall.
ISBN 0137032587 Hbk £45.65

Kramer, L.
E.E.C. Consumer Law. – Dordrecht : Kluwer, 1986.
488p.
ISBN 9064394067 Pbk £155.00
—EEC consumer law. – Bruxelles : Story-Scientia, 1986.
xviii, 432p.
Bibliography: p.391-424. - Includes index.
ISBN 9065442820

Kranz, Walter →Economy of the Principality of Liechtenstein.
→ Principality of Liechtenstein : a documentary handbook.

Kreiger, Ian
Arthur Andersen: management buy-outs. – London : Butterworths, 1990.
ix,240; 248.
Sets out some of the main considerations investors and bankers take into account when deciding whether to back buy-outs. Contributions by legal, tax, and pension experts. Contains an executive guide, financing the deal, structuring the finance, buying the company, tax aspects of buy-outs, and legal aspects of buy-outs.
ISBN 0406518904 Hbk £65.00

Kreindler, L.S.
Aviation Accident Law. – Matthew Bender, 1963.
ISBN 0000999056 Hbk £123.50

Krever, R.
Mastering Law Studies and Law Exam Techniques. – Sydney : Butterworths, 1986.
184p.
This book is designed to show students how to learn law and organize their study habits using exam-oriented techniques. Sample exam questions and answers are included. Other sections discuss study hints and how to read and brief a case.
Pbk £18.00

Kriangsak Kittichaisaree
Law of the sea and maritime boundary delimitation in South-East Asia / Kriangsak Kittichaisaree. – Singapore : Oxford University Press, 1987.
xv, 209 p.; 23 cm.
Discusses maritime boundary delimination in international law. Concentrates on South-East Asia, but legal analyses are examined in a global context, using South-East Asian practice as concrete instances to elaborate particular legal problems.
ISBN 0195888626 Hbk £20.00

Kriefman →Work out accounting.

Krikic →Handbook of Financial Futures and Options.

Krishen, Kumar
Delhi Police Law : Containing Commentaries on Delhi Police Act, 1978 with Up-to-date Rules and Regulations. – Delhi : Allied Book Co., 1987.
303p.
Hbk £120.00

Krishna, Vern, et al
Canadian Current Tax, 1 Vol. – Butterworths.
Llf £175.00
—Fundamentals of Canadian Income Tax. – 2nd ed. – Agincourt : Carswell, 1986.
1288p.
This textbook for students of Canadian income tax law deals with the fundamental structure of the income tax system and the underlying principles and concepts of taxation. Numerous computational examples are provided in the work to illustrate the operation of tax principles.
Hbk £75.75
—Taxation of capital gains / by Vern Krishna. – Toronto : Butterworths, 1983.
xxiii,251p.
Includes index.
ISBN 0409843776 Hbk £51.95

Krishnamurthi, K.
Police Investigations and Prosecutions. – 5th ed. 1986 repr. 1987. – Allahabad : Law Book Company, 1987.
900p.
Hbk £200.00

Krishnamurthi, S.
Guide to Foreign Exchange Regulation. – new ed. – Nagpur : Wadhura & Co, 1988.
Hbk £160.00
—Law and Practice Relating to Government Companies. – New Delhi : Bharat Law House, 1987.
Hbk £180.00

Krishnan, P. Leela
Consumer Protection and Legal Control : Essays and Papers of the U.G.C. National Seminar at University of Cochin. – Lucknow : Eastern Book Company, 1984.
346p.
Hbk £60.00

Krishnan, Rengan
Simon's Weekly Tax Service : Simon's Tax Cases. – London : Butterworths.

Krishnapuram, R.M.
Sovereignty of Parliament in India. – New Delhi : Deep and Deep Publications, 1985.
212p.
Hbk £150.00

Krishnaswami
Law of Adverse Possession. – 11th ed. – Allahabad : Law Book Company, 1988.
650p.
Hbk £180.00

Krivy, Boris →Cambridge lectures 1981 : selected papers based upon lectures delivered at the Conference of the Canadian Institute for Advanced Legal Studies, 1981, held at Cambridge University, England.

Kroll, Robert
Intimate Fragments : Private Writings of a Supreme Court Judge. – Halifax : Nimbus, 1985.
140p.
ISBN 0920852424 Pbk £12.95

Kromarek, Pascale →European Community environmental policy in practice, Vol. 4 : Federal Republic of Germany : water and waste : a study of the implementation of the EEC directives : by Pascale Kromarek.

Kronby, Malcolm C.
Ontario Family Law Reports / Jeffery Wilson. – Butterworths.
ISBN 0409809136 Llf £135.00

Kronman, Anthony T.
Max Weber / Anthony T. Kronman. – London : Edward Arnold, 1983.
214p; 22cm.
Includes bibliographies and index.
ISBN 0713163615 Pbk £9.95
ISBN 0713163623 Pbk £4.95

Kruzeniski, G.
Divorce Guide for Saskatchewan. – North Vancouver : International Self-Counsel Press, 1987.
ISBN 0889085129 Hbk £12.95

Kruzeniski, Ronald
Wills/Probate Procedure for Manitoba and Saskatchewan / Jane Gordon. – 3rd ed. – North Vancouver : International Self-Counsel Press, 1985.
81p.
ISBN 088908503X Hbk £5.95

Kshirsagar, R.K.
Untouchability in India : Implementation of the Law and Abolition. – New Delhi : Deep and Deep Publications, 1986.
368p.
Hbk £250.00

Kudla, R.J.
Voluntary Corporate Liquidations. – Quorum Press.
ISBN 0899302750 Hbk £32.50

Kuiper, W. G →International tax glossary.

Kukubo, Robert J. W.
Cumulative index to the statute law of Lesotho 5 March 1960 to 31 December 1982 : including tables of repealed/amended statutes between 5 March 1960 and December 1982, statutes of Lesotho (including Cape statutes) in force on the 31 December 1982 / by Robert J.W. Kukubo. – Roma, Lesotho : University Press of Lesotho, 1983.
xiv,351p.
Includes an appendix for 1983.

Kulashrestha, V.D.
Government Regulation for Financial Management of Private Corporate Sector in India. – Bombay : Tripathi, 1987.
330p.
£120.00

Kulcsar, Kalman →Disputes and the law.
—Modernization and law : theses and thoughts / Kalman Kulcsar. – Budapest : Institute of Sociology, Hungarian Academy of Sciences, 1987.
198p.
Bibliography: pp.181-198..
ISBN 9638301686

Kulshreshtha, Abha
Exhaustive Guide to the Factories Act, 1948. – Delhi : Metropolitan Book Co, 1987.
424p.
ISBN 812000275X Hbk £150.00
→ Law, Procedure and Ready Reckoner of Bonus, E.S.I. Gratuity and Provident Fund.

Kulshreshtha, V.D.
Landmarks in Indian Legal Constitutional History. – 5th ed. – Lucknow : Eastern Book Company, 1981.
546p.
Hbk £40.00
—Textbook of English Legal History. – 2nd ed. – Lucknow : Eastern Book Company, 1983.
296p.
Pbk £12.00
—Trade and Merchandise Marks Act, 1958 / V.P. Sarathi. – 2nd rev. and enl. ed. – Lucknow : Eastern Book Company, 1982.
789p.
Hbk £140.00

Kulshrestha, Abha
Workmen's Compensation Act, 1923 : Commentary and Case-Law. – Delhi : Metropolitan Book Co, 1987.
296p.
ISBN 8120002601 Hbk £150.00

Kumar, Arun
Cultural and Educational Rights of the Minorities under Indian Constitution. – New Delhi : Deep and Deep Publications, 1985.
286p.
Hbk £150.00

Kumar, H.L.
Retrenchment, Lay-Off and Closure Based on Latest Amendments and Up-to-date Case-Laws. – Allahabad : Law Publishing House, 1982.
ca 400p.
Hbk £60.00
—Supreme Court on Constitutional Aspects of Labour Laws. – Allahabad : Law Publishing House, 1987.
1,400p.
Hbk £350.00

Kumar, M.
Control of Exclusion Clauses England and India. – Ravenswood, 1985.
ISBN 0901812595 Hbk £31.00

Kumar, Naresh
Constitutional Rights of Prisoners. – Delhi : Mittal Publications, 1986.
Hbk £95.00

Kumar, Shellendra
Law of Textiles in India. – Delhi : Periodical Experts Book Agency, 1986.
387p.
£275.00

Kuper, Leo
International action against genocide / by Leo Kuper. – Rev. 1984 ed. – London : Minority Rights Group, 1984.
19p. – (Report).
Bibliography: p.18.

Kurds / by David McDowall. – New ed. – London : Minority Rights Group, 1985.
32p. – (Report).
Previous ed.: by Martin Short and Anthony McDermott. 1981. Bibliography: p.24.
ISBN 094669026X

Kurkela, Matti →Comparative report on force majeure in Western Europe.
—Liability of banks under letters of credit / Matti Kurkela. – Helsinki : Union of the Finnish Lawyers Pub. Co., 1982.
85 p.; 22 cm.
Bibliography: p. 84-85.
ISBN 9516401503 mk70.00
—On International Construction and Project Export Contracts. – Helsinki : Lakimiesliiton kustannus, 1982.
168p.
Hbk £102.00

Kurland, Richard T.
Cumulative Index to the Decisions of the Immigration Appeal Board. – Agincourt : Carswell, 1987.
180p.
Pbk £31.25
—Index to the Decisions Rendered by the Immigration Appeal Board. – Agincourt : Carswell, 1988.
174p.
Hbk £33.25
—Index to the Decisions Rendered By the Immigration Appeal Board. – Agincourt : Carswell, 1987.
168p.
This is a comprehensive index to the decisions of the Immigration Appeal Board from 1976 through to 1987. Special legal research features include a key word index, and alphabetical listing by style of case, and a case citator.
Pbk £33.25

Kurowska, Sheila
Employing People in Voluntary Organisations : An NCVO Practical Guide. – London : Bedford Square Press, 1984.
ISBN 0719911095 Hbk £2.95

Kusumowidagdo, Judo Umarto
Consultation clauses as means of providing for treaty obedience : a study in the law of treaties / by Judo Umarto Kusumowidagdo. – Stockholm : Almqvist & Wiksell, 1981.
321p; 25cm.
Bibliography: p.311-321.
ISBN 9122004629 Pbk
ISBN 9122004602

Kutschera, Michael →Legal opinions in international transactions : foreign lawyers' response to US opinion requests.

Kuttab, Jonathan
Civilian administration in the occupied West Bank : analysis of Israeli Military Government Order no. 947 / by Jonathan Kuttab and Raja Shehadeh. – Ramallah : Law in the Service of Man, 1982.
44p.
ISBN 9290370181

Kutten, L J
Overview of US export controls / B C Murphy. – Kluwer Law and Taxation, 1989.
160.
A general overview of the US laws controlling the export of goods and technology from the US. Covers individual validated licenses, special licenses, technical data, Nuclear Short Supply Controls, restrictive trade practices and boycotts, and common exporting terms and acronyms.
ISBN 9065443967 Pbk £28/Dfl 85

Kuttner, Stephan
Gratian and the Schools of Law : 1140-1234. – Northampton : Variorum, 1983.
396p. – (Collected Studies Ser.: CS 185).
ISBN 086078133X Hbk £30.00
—History of Ideas and Doctrines of Canon Law in the Middle Ages. – Northampton : Variorum.
394p. – (Collected Ser.: CS 113).
ISBN 0860780589 Hbk £22.00

Kuwabara, Sachiko
Legal regime of the protection of the Mediterranean against pollution from land-based sources. – Dublin : Tycooly International, 1984.
256p.
ISBN 0907567827 Hbk £19.50
ISBN 0907567835 Pbk £11.50

Kwan, Kuen Chor
Handbook of Singapore and Malaysian Corporate Finance / Chwee Huat Tan. – London : Butterworths, 1988.
ISBN 0409995487 Pbk £120.00

Kwiatkowska, Barbara
200 mile exclusive economic zone in the new law of the sea. – Dordrecht : Nijhoff (Martinus), 1989.
408. – (Publications on ocean development 14).
Examines the rights and duties of states with regard to activities such as fisheries and navigation. Also evaluates the existing and potential impact of the EEZ upon the socioeconomic development of states and the reduction of disparities between the developing and industrialised countries.
ISBN 0792300742 Hbk £60
→ Transboundary air pollution : international legal aspects of the co-operation of states.

Kyer, C. Ian
Fiercest Debate : Caesar Wright, the Benchers, and Legal Education in Ontario / Jerome E. Bickenbach. – Toronto : University of Toronto Press, 1987.
ca 374p.
ISBN 0802039863 Hbk £28

Kyle, Keith
Cyprus / by Keith Kyle. – New 1984 ed. – London : Minority Rights Group, 1984.
23p. – (Report).
Bibliography: p.23.
ISBN 0946690103

Kyriakides, R.
Liquidation of Insolvent Private Companies. – London : Butterworths, 1988.
ISBN 0406267006 Pbk

Kyrou, E.J. →Handy Hints on Legal Practice.

Labaz Sanofi UK →Epilepsy and the law : a medical symposium on the current law.

Labelling of chemical products : Swedish regulations and general advice with regard to the classification and labelling of chemical products hazardous to health, flammables and explosives / National Chemicals Inspectorate, National Inspectorate of Explosives and Flammables. – Solna : National Chemicals Inspectorate, 1987.
224p.
ISBN 9138098873

Labor Arbitration : 1982. – Vancouver : British Columbia Continuing Legal Education Society, 1982.
194p.
ISBN 0865040567 Hbk £45.00

Labor Law and Business Change : Theoretical and Transactional Perspectives / Collins. – Quorum Press.
ISBN 0899302076 Hbk £33.50

Labor relations in 17 countries / Christian Bratt : translated by David Jenkins. – Stockholm : Swedish Employers' Confederation, 1982.
134p.
Translated from 'Arbetsmarknaden i 16 lander' by David Jenkins.
ISBN 9171522514

Labour Arbitration, 1983. – Vancouver : British Columbia Continuing Legal Education Society, 1983.
130p.
ISBN 0865041121 Hbk £45.00

Labour Arbitration, 1984. – Vancouver : British Columbia Continuing Legal Education Society, 1984.
ISBN 0865041636 Hbk £50.00

Labour Arbitration 1984. – Vancouver : Continuing Legal Education Society of British Columbia, 1987.
161p.
ISBN 0865043302 Hbk £65.00

Labour Arbitration - 1985. – Vancouver : British Columbia Continuing Legal Education Society, 1985.
116p.
ISBN 0865042063 Hbk £55.00

Labour Arbitration 1988. – Vancouver : Continuing Legal Education Society of British Columbia, 1988.
156p.
ISBN 0865049971 Hbk £70.00

Labour Arbitration : Boon or Bane for Unions?. – Toronto : Butterworths.
70p.
ISBN 0409988618 Pbk £29.95

Labour Arbitration Cases : Consolidated Index Vols. 1-24 of Third Series. – Aurora : Canada Law Book Co, 1985.
– (Law Reports).
Hbk £17.00

Labour Arbitration Cases (L.A.C.) 1948-72, 24 Vols.
Back Vols. – Aurora : Canada Law Book Co.
Hbk £52.00 each

Labour Arbitration Cases (L.A.C.) 1973-81, 30 Vols. – Aurora : Canada Law Book Co.
– (Second Ser.).
Hbk £1530.00
Back Vols.. –
Hbk £51.00 each

Labour Arbitration Cases (L.A.C.) 1982-Present. – Aurora : Canada Law Book Co.
– (Third Ser.).
Hbk £78.00
Back Vols.. –
Hbk £52.00 ea.
Current subscription-Outside Canada. –
Hbk £83.00

Labour Arbitration Cases (Second Series) Consolidated Index, List of Awards Vols. 1-30. – Aurora : Canada Law Book Co, 1982.
400p.
Pbk £30.00

Labour Arbitrations and All That. – 2nd ed. – Aurora : Canada Law Book Co, 1985.
146p. – (Text Books-Civil).
Pbk £17.50

Labour Campaign for Criminal Justice →Law and order : theft of an issue.

Labour Code of Pakistan. – 12th ed. – Karachi : Bureau of Labour Publications, 1987.
1,439p.
Hbk £102.00

Labour courts in Europe : proceedings of a meeting organised by the International Institute for Labour Studies / edited by Bert Essenberg. – Geneva : International Institute for Labour Studies, 1986.
68p.
ISBN 9290144076 Hbk £10.00

Labour Housing Group
Right to a Home. – Labour Housing Group. – London : Spokesman Books, 1984.
165p.
ISBN 0851243991 Hbk £15.00
ISBN 0851244009 Pbk £4.95

Labour injunctions. – Chichester : Wiley (John), 1990.
104; 25.
ISBN 0471515868 Pbk £44.35

Labour law / by Charles D. Drake. – 3rd ed. – London : Sweet & Maxwell, 1981.
278p; 23cm. – (Concise college texts).
Previous ed.: 1973. Includes index.
ISBN 0421281006 Hbk £
ISBN 0421281103 Pbk £7.50

Labour law / M. Wright and C.J. Carr. – 4th ed. – Plymouth : MacDonald and Evans, 1984.
xx,211p. – (The M & E handbook series).
Bibliography: p.195. - Includes index.
ISBN 0712101918

Labour law : materials and commentary / by W. B. Creighton, W. J. Ford, R. J. Mitchell. – North Ryde, N.S.W. : Law Book Co., 1983.
liii,944p; 25cm.
ISBN 0455204136

Labour law : text and materials / Paul Davies, Mark Freedland. – 2nd ed. – London : Weidenfeld and Nicolson, 1984.
xlii,964p; 24cm.
Previous ed.: 1979. Includes index.
ISBN 0297780891 Hbk £30.00
ISBN 0297780905 Pbk £17.95

Labour Law : the Rights and Responsibilities of Employer-Employee. – Haryana : PB Publications, 1987.
515p.
Hbk £180.00

Labour, law and crime : an historical perspective / edited by Francis Snyder and Douglas Hay. – London : Tavistock, 1987.
x,309p; 23cm.
Bibliography: p292-297. - Includes index.
ISBN 0422608408 £30.00

Labour law and industrial relations : building on Kahn-Freund / edited by Lord Wedderburn of Charlton, Roy Lewis, Jon Clark. – Oxford : Clarendon Press, 1983.
vii,250p; 23cm.
Includes index.
ISBN 0198253931 Hbk £
ISBN 0198254822 Pbk £8.95

Labour law and industrial relations in Canada / by H.W. Arthurs, D.D. Carter, H.J. Glasbeek. – 2nd ed. – Deventer : Kluwer Law and Taxation, 1984.
316p; 25cm.
Deals with Canadian labour movement, the individual employment relationship, legal status and democratic rule in trade unions, the collective bargaining process, industrial conflict and collective agreements. Presents policy themes and typical legal solutions as well as recording significant departures.
ISBN 9065441905
ISBN 0409811858 Hbk

Labour law and industrial relations in Finland / by A.J. Suviranta. – Helsinki : Finnish Lawyers, 1987.
187p; 25cm.
Bibliography: p57-61. - Includes index.
ISBN 9065443444 Pbk
ISBN 9516403573 Finland

Labour law and industrial relations in France / by Michel Despax and Jacques Rojot. – Deventer : Kluwer Law and Taxation, 1987.
314p.
Includes index.
ISBN 9065443436

Labour law and industrial relations in Great Britain / by B.A. Hepple, S. Fredman. – Deventer : Kluwer Law and Taxation, 1986.
295p.
: 'Originally published as a monograph in the International encyclopaedia for labour law and industrial relations.'. Includes index. Bibliography: p.257-259.
ISBN 9065442626

Labour law and industrial relations in Ireland / Mary Redmond. – Dublin : Bridgefoot Press, 1984.
188p.
Includes index. Cover title: Redmonds guide to Irish labour law.

Labour law and industrial relations in Japan / by T.A. Hanami. – 2nd ed. – Deventer, Netherlands : Kluwer Law and Taxation, 1985.
171p.
Bibliography: p78-80. Includes index.
ISBN 9065442146

Labour law and industrial relations in the Federal Republic of Germany / Manfred Weiss. – Deventer : Kluwer, 1987.
190p; 25cm.
Bibliography: p37. - Includes index.
ISBN 9065443002 Pbk

Labour Law and Industrial Relations in the United States of America. – 2nd ed. – Dordrecht : Kluwer, 1984.
374p.
ISBN 9065441689 Pbk £95.00

Labour Law and Practice : Materials Prepared for a Continuing Legal Education Seminar Held in Vancouver, B. C., April 14-15, 1983 / Allan E. Black. – Vancouver : British Columbia Continuing Legal Education Society, 1983.
ISBN 086504094X Llf

Labour law and the community : perspectives for the 1980's / Editors, Lord Wedderburn of Charlton and W.T. Murphy. – London : Institute of Advanced Legal Studies, University of London, 1982.
viii,189p.
Includes bibliographical references. Papers presented at a workshop for law teachers held in 1982 at the Institute of Advanced Legal Studies.
ISBN 0901190276

Labour Law and Urban Law in Canada / Andree Lajoie. – Toronto : University of Toronto Press, 1986.
232p.
ISBN 0802072976 Hbk £16.95

Labour Law Cases : 1981-1988. – Karachi : Bureau of Labour Publications.
400p.
Hbk £36.00

Labour law cases and materials / by Roger Benedictus & Brian Bercusson. – London : Sweet & Maxwell, 1987.
700p; 25cm.
Includes index.
ISBN 0421278609 Hbk £
ISBN 0421278706 Pbk

Labour Law - Cases and Materials. – 2nd ed. – London : Butterworths, 1988.
ISBN 0406577501 Hbk £19.95
ISBN 0406577593 Pbk

Labour Law Cases LLC (Pakistan) : Decisions of Supreme Court, High Courts and Labour Courts on Labour Laws, 21 Vols. – Karachi : Bureau of Labour Publications, 1947-1980.
Hbk £597.00

Labour Law Digest, 6 Vols. – Agincourt : Carswell, 1985.
This multi-volume set digests over fifteen thousand reported Canadian labor law cases under federal and provincial law. A cumulative supplement is supplied every six months to keep the work up-to-date.
Hbk £332.00

Labour law in Britain / edited by Roy Lewis. – Oxford : Blackwell, 1986.
700p; 23cm.
Examines legal aspects of industrial relations in Britain today.
ISBN 0631137548 Hbk £37.50 :
ISBN 0631137556 Pbk £10.00

Labour law in Great Britain and Ireland to 1978 : a companion volume to A bibliography of the literature on British and Irish labour law / B.A. Hepple ... et al. – London : Sweet & Maxwell, 1981.
xxii,131p; 25cm.
Includes index.
ISBN 0421288000

Labour Law Journal Digest 1949-1982, 9 Vols. – Nagpur : Wadhura & Co.
Hbk £400.00

Labour law research in twelve countries / editor: Sten Edlund. – Stockholm : Arbetarskyddsfonden & Arbetslivscentrum, 1986.
296p; 25cm.
ISBN 9122008004

Labour law with a Labour government : a workers' charter / Haldane Society. Employment Law Committee. – London : The Society, 1987.
9p.

Labour Laws in Uttar Pradesh / Kamlesh Chopra. – 3rd ed. – Lucknow : Eastern Book Company, 1985.
2,131p.
Hbk £330.00

Labour Manual, 2 Vols. – Allahabad : Law Publishers, 1983.
Hbk £33.00

Labour market structure, industrial organisation and low pay / DAE Labour Studies Group : Christine Craig ... et al. – Cambridge : Cambridge University Press, 1982.
xi,165p; 24cm. – (Occasional paper).
Bibliography: p160-165.
ISBN 0521245796

Labour Party
Homes for the future : statement to Annual Comnference 1985 / by the Labour Party National Executive Committee. – London : Labour Party, 1985.
47p.
ISBN 0861171233

—Investing in Britain : jobs and industry / Labour Party. – London : Labour Party, 1985.
23p.

Labour protection and labour relations in ASEAN : the impact of protective labour laws on labour relations. – Geneva : International Labour Office, 1986.
v,204p.
Papers presented at ' ... the ASEAN Tripartite Symposium on Labour Protection and Labour Relations held in Kuala Lumpur, Malaysia on 16-19 September 1986 ... '. - p. 'Published ... under the auspices of the joint ILO/UNDP/ASEAN Programme on Industrial Relations for Development.' - T.p..
ISBN 922105893X

Labour Protection Laws in ASEAN. – Geneva : International Labour Office, 1987.
vii, 481p.
ISBN 9221058913 Hbk £30.00

Labour Relations Act : Rules of Procedure, Regulations and Practice Notes. – Office of the Legislative Assembly (Ontario). – Ontario : Ontario Government Publications Service, 1983.
177p.
Hbk £4.50

Labour Relations Agency → Encyclopedia of Northern Ireland labour law and practice.

Labour Relations Amendment Act. – Johannesburg : South African Institute of Race Relations, 1984.
Hbk £2.00

Labour relations and the collective bargaining cycle / Gerald E. Phillips. – 2nd ed. – Toronto : Butterworths, 1981.
xiii,333p.
Previous ed.: published as 'The practice of labour relations and collective bargaining in Canada', 1977. Includes bibliographies and index.

Labour Relations and the Law. – London : Butterworths, 1988.
ISBN 0406015503 Hbk

Labour Relations Board → Canadian Labour Relations Board Reports.

Labour Relations Board of British Columbia
Canadian Labour Relations Board Reports. – Labour Relations Board of British Columbia. – Butterworths.
Hbk £115.00

Labour Relations Board Practice. – Vancouver : British Columbia Continuing Legal Education Society, 1985.
193p.
ISBN 0865042144 Hbk £55.00

Labour Relations Laws in ASEAN : a Collection of Current Labour Laws in Six Asean States. – Geneva : International Labour Office, 1986.
vii, 365p.
ISBN 9221054349 Hbk £17.50

Labour Relations Statutes and Materials. – 2nd ed. – London : Sweet & Maxwell, 1983.
ISBN 0421320109 Pbk £17.50

Labour Research Department
Our unions, our democracy : LRD's response to the Tory green paper. – Labour Research Department. – London : LRD Publications, 1983.
24p.

Labour unions, law and conditions in Iran (1900-1941) / by Willem Floor. – Durham City : Centre for Middle Eastern and Islamic Studies, University of Durham, 1985.
124p; 21cm. – (Occasional paper series).
Bibliography: p119-124.
Pbk

Labour Welfare and Social Security Legislation in India. – New Delhi : Deep and Deep Publications, 1984.
302p.
Hbk £150.00

Labour Welfare Laws and Employment Conditions in India. – New Delhi : Deep and Deep Publications, 1985.
235p.
Hbk £140.00

Lacey, Nicola
State punishment : political principles and community values / Nicola Lacey. – London : Routledge, 1988.
xiii, 222 p.; 23 cm.
Includes index. Bibliography: p. 202-218.
ISBN 0415001714

Lachmann, Per
Draft Treaty establishing the European Union : constitutional and political implications in Denmark / by Per Lachmann. – Badia Fiesolana : European University Institute, 1985.
39p.
Paper presented at a conference organised by the European Policy Unit of the European University Institute, in collaboration with the University of Strasbourg and TEPSA, October 1984.

Lachs, Manfred → Essays in international law in honour of Judge Manfred Lachs.
—Teacher in international law : (teachings and teachers) / Manfred Lachs. – The Hague : Nijhoff, 1982.
236p; 25cm.
Bibliography: p211-225. - Includes index.
ISBN 9024725666
—Teacher in international law : teachings and teaching / Manfred Lachs. – Rev. 2nd ed. – Dordrecht : M. Nijhoff, 1986.
Includes index. Bibliography.
ISBN 9024733138 Pbk

Lack of Discretion of Judgment because of Schizophrenia : Doctrine and Recent Rotal Jurisprudence. – Rome : Editrice Pontificia Universitana Gregoriana, 1986.
256p.
Hbk L35,000.00

Lacke, Janice A. → Canadian Industrial Incentives Legislation, 2 Vols.

Lacugna, C.S.
An Introduction to Labour Arbitration. – Praeger.
ISBN 0275930475 Pbk £39.50

Ladd, David
Protection for semiconductor chip masks in the United States : analysis of the Semiconductor Chip Protection Act of 1984 / David Ladd, David E. Leibowitz and Bruce G. Joseph. – Weinheim : VCH, 1986.
vi,99p.
ISBN 0895734842

Laddie
Modern law of copyright / Prescott. – 2nd ed. – London : Butterworths, 1988.
ISBN 0406616973 Hbk

Lady in the Lords. – Weidenfeld & Nicolson.
ISBN 0297793217 Hbk £14.95

Lafili, Louis → From the Waidring Conferences, 4 Vols., Survey of the International Sale of Goods.

LaForest, G. V.
Allocation of taxing power under the Canadian constitution / G.V. La Forest. – 2nd ed. – Toronto : Canadian Tax Foundation, 1981.
viii,219p.

Laguette, Serge-Pierre
Lawyers in the European Community. – London : Alan Armstrong & Associates Ltd.
ISBN 9282569780 Hbk £9.60

Lahey, Kathleen A.
Corporate taxation / Kathleen A. Lahey. – Toronto : Emond Montgomery Publications, 1984.
lx,540p.
Includes bibliographical references and index.
ISBN 0920722113
—Corporate Taxation. – Aurora : Canada Law Book Co, 1984.
585p. – (Text Books-Civil).
Hbk £75.00

Lahiri, N.M.
Lahiri's Transfer of Property Act. – 11th ed. – Calcutta : Eastern Law House, 1986.
1,047p.
Hbk £155.00

Lahiri's Transfer of Property Act. – 11th ed. – Calcutta : Eastern Law House, 1986.
1,047p.
Hbk £155.00

Lahore, James C
Information technology : the challenge to copyright / by James Lahore, Gerald Dworkin, Yvonne M. Smyth. – London : Sweet & Maxwell, 1984.
vii,116p; 22cm.
Includes index.
ISBN 0421322608 Pbk £11.00
→ Intellectual property in Australia, Patents, designs, trade marks, confidential information, unfair competition.
—Intellectual Property in Australia : Copyright. – London : Butterworths, 1984.
Hbk
—Intellectual Property in Australia : Patents, Designs, Trade Marks, Confidential Information and Unfair Competition / James W. Dwyer. – Wellington : Butterworths.
This looseleaf service provides exhaustive coverage of the law in Australia relating to copyright in literary and artistic works, sound recordings, film, television and radio broadcasts, and published editions of books and other works. The full text of relevant statutes is provided.
Llf
—Intellectual Property Reports / John J. Garsney. – Wellington : Butterworths.
These comprehensive reports are complete with headnotes, catchwords, holdings, court hearings, and final judgement dates for all major decisions in field of intellectual property in Australia.
Hbk
—Intellectual Property Reports. – London : Butterworths.
Hbk
→ Intellectual property reports : being reports of judgments of the High Court of Australia, the Federal Court of Australia, the Supreme Courts of the states and territories of Australia, the Patent, Trade Marks and Designs Office, the Copyright Tribunal and incorporating reports of signficant cases decided by the courts in the United Kingdom, the United States of America and other international jurisdictions.
→ Patent co-operation treaty : a new era : papers prepared for presentation at a seminar held at the Brewery Conference Centre...November 11, 1985.

Lajeunesse, Therese
Innovative approaches to juvenile justice : executive summaries of four juvenile diversion project reports / by Therese Lajeunesse. – Ottawa, Ont. : Consultation Centre, Solicitor General Canada, 1982.
35, 38 p.; 22 cm.
English and French. Title on added t.p.: Approches innovatrices en matiere de justice pour adolescents. .
ISBN 0662518160 Pbk

Lajoie, Andree → Labour Law and Urban Law in Canada.
→ Regulations, Crown Corporations, and Adminstrative Tribunals.
→ Supreme Court of Canada as an Instrument of Political Change.

Lake, Ralph B.
Letters of intent. – London : Butterworths, 1990.
310; 24cm.
Deals with the legal aspects of letters of intent and other pre-contractual documents. It addresses the problem of enforceability of such contracts to contract from the point of view of both common law and civil law jurisdictions as well as their effective use and drafting. Includes specimen documentation and forms.
Lawyers, businessmen and women
ISBN 0880632305 Hbk £50

Lakhani → National welfare benefits handbook.

Lakshminarayanan, S.
Guide to Company Borrowings. – New Delhi : Bharat Law House, 1987.
Hbk £220.00

Lal, B.B.
Income Tax Law and Practice. – 7th ed. – New Delhi : Allied Publishers, 1984.
Hbk £60.00

Lal, Jagadish
Civil Procedure Code / Lal Jagadish. – 2nd ed. – Allahabad : Law Publishers, 1982.
Hbk £12.00
—Code of Criminal Procedure. – 2nd ed. – Allahabad : Law Publishers, 1983.
Hbk £12.00
—Constitution of India. – Allahabad : Law Publishers, 1982.
Hbk £10.50
—Electricity Laws and Rules. – 2nd ed. – Allahabad : Law Publishers, 1983.
Hbk £13.50
—Handbook on Gold Control Act, Rules and Notifications. – 3rd ed. – Allahabad : Law Publishers, 1982.
Hbk £10.50
—Labour Manual, 2 Vols. – Allahabad : Law Publishers, 1983.
Hbk £33.00
—Police Handbook. – Allahabad : Law Publishers, 1982.
Hbk £45.00
—Statutory Changes in Hindu Law. – Allahabad : Law Publishers, 1982.
Hbk £12.00
—Supreme Court Rules, 1950 : as Intepreted by Supreme Court. – Allahabad : Law Publishers, 1982.
vi, 199p.
Hbk £7.50

Lal, Jai
Law and Practice of Conveyancing. – Allahabad : Universal Book Agency.
Hbk £225,00

Lal, Nand
Comments on Civil Procedure Code, 4 Vols. – 2nd ed. – Allahabad : Law Publishers, 1983.
Hbk £30.00

Lal, Nathuni
Law of Arbitration. – 4th ed. – Lucknow : Eastern Book Company, 1983.
826p.
Hbk £85.00

Lal Reform Commission of Victoria
Murder : mental element and punishment / Law Reform Commissioner, Victoria. – Melbourne : The Commission, 1984.
52p. – (Working paper no 8).
Includes bibliographical references.

Lall, S.K.
Digest of Wealth Tax Cases 1957 to 1986. – Allahabad : Modern Law Publications, 1986.
Hbk £125.00

Lalouette, M. J. Gerard → Seychelles digest.

Lambard, W.
Eirenarcha (1581). – Reprint. – Professional Books, 1986.
– (Classical English Law Texts Ser.).
ISBN 0862053242 Hbk £24.75

Lambden, David W.
Boundaries and Surveys / Izaak de Rijcke. – Agincourt : Carswell, 1985.
235p.
This text covers the law of Ontario, Canada relating to boundaries and surveys. Relevant Ontario statutes and digests of cases from other provinces are provided in the appendices.
Hbk £38.00

Lambert, Francis J. D.
Cortes and the King : Constitutional Monarchy in the Iberian World. – Glasgow : University of Glasgow, Institute of Latin American Studies, 1981.
– (Occasional Paper: No. 32).
Hbk £3.00

Lambert, J.
Police powers and accountability. – Oxford : Croom Helm, 1986.
ISBN 0709916604 Hbk £16.95

Lambert, John
Motor vehicle safety standards and product liability in the USA / by John Lambert. – London : Economist Intelligence Unit, 1982.
131p.

Lambert, Nigel A. D. →Tolley's Social security and state benefits 1983/84.
→ Tolley's social security and state benefits 1985.

Lambeth, R. J. →Templeman on marine insurance : its principles and practice.

Lameijer, J. →Guide to the Collision Avoidance Rules.

Lament for the Law Commission / R.T. Oerton. – Chichester : Countrywise Press, 1987.
v,117p.

Lamm →Legal Development and Comparative Law 1986 : Selected Essays for the 12th Congres International de Droit Compare.

Lamm, Vanda
Utilization of nuclear energy and international law / Vanda Lamm. – Budapest : Akademiai Kiado, 1984.
155p.
ISBN 963053892X

Lammers, J.G. →A.A.A. Yearbook, Vol. 54/55/56: Natural Resources in International Law.
→ Environmental protection and sustainable development : legal principles and recommendations.
→ Hague yearbook of international law : Annuaire de la Haye de droit international, 1988.
—Pollution of international watercourses : search for substantive rules and principles of law / by J.G. Lammers. – The Hague : M. Nijhoff, 1984.
xxvi, 724 p.; 25 cm.
Includes indexes. Bibliography: p. 663-703.
ISBN 9024729556 Hbk £275.00
→ Transboundary air pollution : international legal aspects of the co-operation of states.

Lamont, C.
Prescription and Limitation of Actions. – Durban : Professional Publishers, 1984.
ISBN 0409040134 Hbk

Lamont, Donald H. L.
O'Brien's Encyclopedia of Forms : Division Three-Conveyancing and Mortgages
Vol. 7. – Aurora : Canada Law Book Co.
– (Abridgments and Encyclopedias).
Hbk £45.00
—Residential Tenancies. – 4th ed. – Agincourt : Carswell, 1983.
366p.
This textbook is a comprehensive treatment of the Canadian law of landlord and tenant in the residential tenancy. Numerous reported and unreported decisions from courts across Canada are summarized in the work.
Hbk £40.50

Lamont, W. D.
Law and the moral order / W.D. Lamont. – Aberdeen : Aberdeen University Press, 1981.
xxviii,115p.
Includes bibliography.
ISBN 0080257429 flexi
ISBN 0080257461

Lamson, Amy
Psychology of juvenile crime / Amy Lamson. – New York : Human Sciences, 1983.
123p; 22cm.
Includes index.
ISBN 0898850606

Land acquisition. – 2nd ed. – London : Butterworths, 1983.
ISBN 0409490911 Hbk £31.30

Land Acquisition Act, 1960 (Act No. 34 of 1960). – Kuala Lumpur : International Law Books Services.
Hbk £9.00

Land and Tax Planning. – 2nd ed. – London : Longman Professional, 1984.
ISBN 0851208800 Pbk £22.00

Land and Tax Planning. – 3rd ed. – London : Longman Professional.
– (Practical Tax Series).
ISBN 0851214541 Hbk £32.50

Land and Tax Planning. – London : Oyez Longman, 1982.
300p. – (Oyez Longman Practical Tax Ser.).
ISBN 0851206077 Hbk £15.00

Land and the law : report of the proceedings of the International Bar Association Section on General Practice seminar in Rome , May 1983. – London : IBA, 1984.
150p.
ISBN 0950587680

Land Aquisition. – Allahabad : Universal Book Agency, 1985.
Hbk £350.00

Land compensation : a study of compensation determination / Barry P.D. Denyer-Green. – Cambridge : Granta Editions, 1986.
xi,124p. – (Occasional paper).
Includes bibliographical references.
ISBN 0906782228

Land compensation and valuation law in Hong Kong / Gordon N. Cruden. – Singapore : Butterworths, 1986.
xxxii,476p.
Collation and analysis of relevant statutory and case law. References are made to Hong Kong cases, as well as English, Scottish, Australian, Canadian, and New Zealand cases.
ISBN 0409995258 Hbk £78.00

Land Compensation Reports : Consolidated Index, Tables of Cases
Vols. 1-30 of Current Series. – Aurora : Canada Law Book Co, 1985.
382p. – (Law Reports).
Pbk £37.50

Land Compensation Reports Current Series (1971-Present). – Aurora : Canada Law Book Co.
– (Law Reports).
Hbk £80.00
Back Vols.. –
Hbk £46.00 ea.

Land Compensation Reports (L.C.R.)
1971-Present. – Aurora : Canada Law Book Co.
Hbk £80.00
Back Vols.. –
Hbk £46.00 ea.

Land development and the infrastructure Lottery / J. Rowan-Robinson, M.G. Lloyd. – Edinburgh : T. & T. Clark, 1988.
xvi,160p; 22cm.
Includes index. Examines the relationship between local authorities and the private sector in the provision of supporting services and 'infrastructure' for private development. Looks at the discretionary powers of local authorities, at the legislation conferring this discretion and at how this is exercised.
ISBN 0567291499 Pbk £12.50

Land for housing the poor / edited by Shlomo Angel ... et al. – Singapore : Select Books, 1983.
ix,556p; 22cm.
Papers from a seminar, 'Land for Housing the Poor: Towards Positive Action in Asian Cities' held in Bangkok, 18th and 31st Jan. 1982.
ISBN 9971835517

Land, Hilary
Women won't benefit : the impact of the Social Security Bill on women's rights / Hilary Land and Sue Ward. – London : National Council for Civil Liberties. Rights for Women Unit, 1986.
48p.
ISBN 0946088268

Land Law, 2 Vols.
Vol. 1. – Butterworths, 1978.
ISBN 0409636002 Hbk
with Supplement-1981. –
ISBN 0409636045

Land Law / Houghton. – London : Financial Training, 1987.
– (SWOT).
ISBN 1851850465 Pbk £7.50

Land Law. – 4th ed. – Plymouth : Macdonald & Evans, 1982.
ISBN 0712112596 Pbk £6.50

Land law / Patrick J. Dalton. – 3rd ed. – London : Pitman, 1983.
xliii,377p; 22cm.
Previous ed.: London : Oyez, 1975. Includes index.
ISBN 0273018582 Pbk £9.95

Land law / by Robert A. Pearce. – London : Sweet & Maxwell, 1985.
200p; 22cm.
Includes index.
ISBN 0421312009 Pbk £17.25

Land Law. – Singapore : University of Singapore, 1985.
– (Singapore Law Series).
The text discusses the structure of Singapore land law and considers the various basic land law concepts. Topics covered include: types of land transfer and registration, consideration of commercial interests in land, and land planning and the planning acts.
ISBN 0409995010 Hbk £25.00

Land Law. – Stockholm : Anderson Keenan, 1982.
– (Law Unit).
ISBN 0906501288 Pbk £4.30

Land Law : Cohabitating Owners. – London : Sweet & Maxwell, 1984.
640p. – (Sweet and Maxwell's Law Files Ser.: No. 1).
ISBN 0421321407 Hbk £29.50

Land law and development : an inaugural lecture delivered at the University of Lagos on Thursday, 17th January, 1980 / by M.I. Jegede. – Lagos : University of Lagos Press, 1981.
39p. – (Inaugural lecture series).
Includes bibliographical references.
ISBN 978226413X

Land law & landscape / Philip Britton and Ian Thompson. – 1 videocassette. – London : Sweet & Maxwell in association with the University of Warwick, 1986.
– (Sweet & Maxwell's lawfilms).

Land law and policy in Papua New Guinea : by R.W. James. – Port Moresby : Papua New Guinea Law Reform Commission, 1985.
xix,204p. – (Monograph).
Includes bibliographical references.
ISBN 998055004X

Land Law and Policy in Zambia. – Lusaka : University of Zambia, Publications Office, 1982.
112p.
Hbk £5.50

Land law in a nutshell / William Howarth. – London : Sweet & Maxwell, 1987.
117p; 22cm.
Includes index.
ISBN 0421368306 Pbk £3.95

Land Law in Malaysia : Cases and Commentary / Lake Tee Khaw. – 1987. – Butterworths.
539p.
Covers the Malaysian Torrens system, rights and powers of the State authority, the nature and extent of private ownership, the registration of dealings, transfers, leases and tenancies, security transactions, restraints of dealings, planning law use under the national code, and powers of the court.
ISBN 0409995312 Hbk £130.00

Land law in Nigeria / M. G. Yakubu. – London : Macmillan, 1985.
xxvi,270p. – (Macmillan international college edition).
Bibliography: p.260-261. - Includes index.
ISBN 0333350901

Land law lecture notes / Angela Sydenham. – London : Polytechnic of North London Students' Union, 1981.
224p; 21cm.
Bibliography: p221-222. Cover title.
ISBN 0906513014 Pbk £3.00

Land mortgages / the Law Commission. – London : HMSO, 1986.
xv,254,48p. – (Working paper).
ISBN 0117301809

Land options. – 2nd. – London : Longman Professional (UK), 1990.
– (Practitioner series).
Covers the law relating to the creation, transfer and exercise of options to purchase, rights of pre-emption, options to renew and determine leases and rent review clauses. Comments on relevant precedents, and considers the tax implications.

Land Reform Commission
Criminal Investigation : Interim Report. – Land Reform Commission. – Repr. of 1977 ed. – Canberra : Australian Government Publishing Service, 1983.
224p. – (ALRC Report: No. 2).
ISBN 0642017921 Hbk £13.00

Land registration forms / Christopher West. – 3rd ed. – London : Sweet & Maxwell, 1983.
xv,261p; 23cm.
Previous ed.: 1973. Includes index.
ISBN 0421287608 £19.50

Land Registration Reform Act, 1983, Bill 156 : An Act Respecting Conveyancing Documents and Procedures and the Recording of Title to Real Property. – Ontario : Ontario Government Publications Service, 1983.
33p.
Hbk £0.70

Land Registry Practice. – Round Hall Press.
ISBN 0947686347 Hbk £37.50

Land Registry Practice in Northern Ireland. – Belfast : Queen's University of Belfast, 1984.
xxiii, 142p.
Hbk £11.95
Main work only. –
ISBN 085389194X Hbk £10.95
Supplement only. –
Hbk £1.50

Land registry practice in Northern Ireland / by Herbert Wallace : assisted by James Derek Reade. – 2nd ed. – Belfast : SLS Legal Publications, 1987.
xxviii,167p.
Previous ed.: 1981. Includes index.
ISBN 0853892938

Land (Settled Estate) Act. – Law Reform Commission of British Columbia. – Vancouver : The Commission, 1988.
iii,38p. – (Working paper).
ISBN 077188625X

Land taxation / by Malcolm Gammie : general editor, Malcolm Gammie : contributing editor, Jeffrey Bailey. – London : Sweet & Maxwell, 1986-.
Includes index.
ISBN 0421275405 Llf

Land, the central human settlement issue / H. Peter Oberlander. – Vancouver : University of British Columbia Press, 1985.
x, 103 p., 4 p. of plates; 24 cm.
Bibliography: p. 93-101.
ISBN 0774802359

Land Titles Reform / Andrew G Lang. – Auckland : Legal Research Foundation, 1983.
Hbk £12.50

Land Transfer Conveyancing Kit. – Nunawading : Harrison-Ede Book Publishing.
Hbk £20.00

Land Use Act. – Zaria : Ahmadu Bello University Press.
Hbk £10.00

Land Use Act : issues and controversies / by Hari C. Chand. – Jos, Nigeria : University of Jos, 1985.
22p. – (Postgraduate open lectures series).
Includes bibliographical references.

Land Use Act : report of a National Workshop held at the University of Lagos, May 25 - May 28, 1981 / edited by J.A. Omotola. – Lagos : Lagos University Press, 1982.
178p.

Land Use Act revisited
Vol. 2 / by Alhaji Isa Alabi. – Kano, Nigeria : Alhaji Isa Alabi, 1984.
v,63p.

Land Use Control Handbook. – Reading : College of Estate Management, 1981.
400p. – (College of Estate Management Handbooks Ser.).
Hbk £24.00

Land Use Law : B.C. Handbook / Z. Pereboom. – Toronto : Butterworths, 1984.
310p.
ISBN 0409988634 Pbk £26

Land Use Law : British Columbia Handbook. – Butterworths, 1984.
310p.
ISBN 0409988634 Pbk £40.00

Land use planning / Robert Macaulay. – Scarborough, Ontario : Butterworths (Canada).
Survey of Ontario Municipal Board cases, precedents, pointers on the impact of the Charter of Rights, and relevant legislation, regulations, guidelines and interpretation bulletins. Covers planning authorities, provincial planning, official plans, zoning and development control, development levies and municipal finance, and the conduct of a planning application.
Llf

Land Use Planning : Practice Procedure and Policy / Robert Macaulay. – Toronto : Butterworths.
Hbk

Landau, Barbara →Children's rights in the practice of family law.

Landau, Eve C.
Rights of working women in the European Community / by Eve C. Landau. – Luxembourg : Office for Official Publications of the European Communities, 1985.
244p.
At head of title: Commission of the European Communities.
ISBN 9282553418 Hbk £3.00

Land-based marine pollution : international law development / by Meng Qing-nan. – London : Graham & Trotman, 1987.
xvi,254p.
Bibliography: p464-476. - Includes index.
ISBN 0860109097

Landfilling wastes. – London : HMSO, 1986.
ISBN 0117518913

Landlord and Tenant, 2 Vols. / Joseph Haworth Redman. – 17th ed. – Wellington : Butterworths, 1982.
Llf

Landlord and tenant. – Belfast : H.M.S.O., 1982.
vi,88p. – (Discussion document).
At head of title page: Department of Finance and Personnel for Northern Ireland, Office of Law Reform.
ISBN 0337233853

Landlord and Tenant / Smith. – 2nd ed. – London : Butterworths, 1985.
ISBN 0406577323 Hbk £28.00
ISBN 0406577331 Pbk £17.95

Landlord and Tenant / Holland. – 4th ed. – Agincourt : Casdec.
ISBN 0907595464 Hbk £15.95
ISBN 0907595448 Pbk £8.95

Landlord and Tenant. – London : Butterworths, 1988.
– (Singapore Law Series).
ISBN 0409995347 Pbk

Landlord and Tenant. – 1st ed. – Plymouth : Macdonald & Evans, 1982.
304p. – (M and E Handbook Ser.).
ISBN 0712112510 Hbk £3.95

Landlord and Tenant. – 2nd ed. – Plymouth : Macdonald & Evans, 1985.
304p. – (M and E Handbook Ser.).
ISBN 0712128050 Hbk £6.50

Landlord and tenant : compensation for tenants' improvements / The Law Commission. – London : H.M.S.O., 1987.
iv,104p; 22cm. – (Working paper).
ISBN 0117301841

Landlord and tenant : privity of contract and estate : duration of liability of parties to leases / the Law Commission. – London : HMSO, 1986.
iv,101p. – (Working paper).
Includes bibliographical references.
ISBN 0117301760

Landlord and Tenant Act 1985 / with annotations by Andrew Arden and Siobhan McGrath. – London : Sweet & Maxwell, 1986.
75p.
Includes index.
ISBN 0421358904

Landlord and Tenant Act 1987. – London : Shaw & Sons, 1987.
ISBN 072191070X Pbk £10.95

Landlord and Tenant Casebook. – London : Estates Gazette, 1985.
ISBN 0728200880 Pbk £12.00

Landlord and Tenant Handbook. – Butterworths. – 2nd ed. – London : Butterworths, 1987.
ISBN 0406253714 Pbk £22.95

Landlord and tenant in urban Britain 1838-1918 / David Englander. – Oxford : Clarendon Press, 1983.
xviii,342p; 23cm.
Bibliography: p318-335. - Includes index.
ISBN 0198226802 £22.50

Landlord and Tenant Law. – Oxford : Blackwell Scientific, 1986.
ISBN 0003831183 Pbk £12.95

Landlord and tenant law / by David Yates and A.J. Hawkins. – 2nd ed. – London : Sweet & Maxwell, 1986.
cviii,839p; 26cm.
Includes legislation enacted between 1980 and 1985. Covers the common law framework of landlord and tenant, the Rent Acts, protected tenants, council tenants, housing associations, the Housing Act 1985, the Landlord and Tenant Act 1985, the Housing Associations Act 1985, and the Housing (Consequential Provisions) Act 1985. The law applying to business tenants, and agricultural tenants is also discussed.
ISBN 0421354208 Hbk £36.50
ISBN 0421354305 Pbk £26.50

Landlord and tenant law : privity of contract and estate / the Law Commission. – London : HMSO, 1988.
v,67p. – (H.C. 1988-89).
Includes the text of a draft Landlord and Tenant (Covenants) bill.
ISBN 0102008892

Landlord and tenant - reform of the law / The Law Commission. – London : H.M.S.O., 1987.
iv,35p; 30cm.
ISBN 010101452X

Landlord and Tenant Up-to-Date. – London : Law Society, 1985.
23p. – (Nineteen Eighty-Five Crash Course Transcripts).
Hbk £2.05

Landlord and Tenants / Joseph Haworth Redman. – 18th ed. – London : Butterworths, 1988.
Service to date.
ISBN 040612987X Hbk £200.00

Landlord-Tenant Rights in Alberta. – 5th ed. – North Vancouver : International Self-Counsel Press, 1986.
106p.
ISBN 0889082413 Hbk £6.95

Landlord-Tenant Rights in British Columbia. – 4th ed. – North Vancouver : International Self-Counsel Press, 1985.
ISBN 0889081565 Hbk £7.95

Landlord-Tenant Rights in Ontario. – 6th ed. – North Vancouver : International Self-Counsel Press, 1986.
168p.
ISBN 0889083592 Hbk £7.95

Landmarks in Indian Legal Constitutional History. – 5th ed. – Lucknow : Eastern Book Company, 1981.
546p.
Hbk £40.00

Landmarks in the Development of the Contractual System. – Budapest : Akademiai Kiado.
192p.
ISBN 9630536668 Hbk £19.00

Landmarks in the Law. – London : Butterworths, 1984.
ISBN 0406176035 Hbk £14.95
ISBN 0406176140 Pbk £9.95

Landon, P.
VAT and the City. – London : CCH, 1987.
ISBN 086325120X Pbk £19.50

Lands Law. – Lahore : Pakistan Law Times, 1981.
Hbk £36.00

Landscape and External Works Price Book 1987. – Spon (E & FN).
ISBN 0419144309 Hbk £29.50

Landscape, Land use and the Law. – Spon (E & FN), 1984.
ISBN 0419125205 Pbk £16.95

Land-use planning in Hong Kong : history, policies and procedures / Roger Bristow. – Hong Kong : Oxford University Press, 1984.
xii, 328p, 8 leaves of plates.
Bibliography: p299-317.
ISBN 0195814967

Lane →Child Care and the Courts.
—Newspaperman's guide to the law. – 4th ed. – Wellington : Butterworths (New Zealand), 1986.
ISBN 040903457 Hbk £33.00
ISBN 040905764 Pbk £23.00

→ Practical Social Work.

Lane, David
Landlord-Tenant Rights in British Columbia. – 4th ed. – North Vancouver : International Self-Counsel Press, 1985.
ISBN 0889081565 Hbk £7.95

Lane, E.
Hear the other side : Audi alteram partem. – London : Butterworths, 1985.
ISBN 0406502404 Hbk £14.95

Lane, Judy →International directory of legal aid.

Lane, P.H.
Digest of Australian Constitutional Cases. – 2nd ed. – North Ryde : Law Book Co, 1982.
xvi, 359p.
ISBN 0455204748 Hbk £49.00
ISBN 0455204756 Pbk £37.50
—Introduction to the Australian Constitution. – 4th ed. – North Ryde : Law Book Co, 1987.
x, 264p.
Pbk

—Introduction to the Australian constitution. – 3rd ed. – London : Law Book Co, 1983.
ISBN 0455202109 Pbk £10.00

—Lane's Commentary on the Australian Constitution. – North Ryde : Law Book Co, 1986.
xxxvii, 766p.
ISBN 0455207011 Hbk £111.00

—Manual of Australian Constitutional Law. – 3rd ed. – North Ryde : Law Book Co, 1984.
xx, 554p.
ISBN 0455202893 Hbk £67.50
ISBN 0455202907 Pbk £48.00

Lane, Robert →Draft Treaty establishing the European Union : report on the United Kingdom.

Lane, V.
Security computer based information systems. – London : Macmillan, 1985.
ISBN 0333364376 Pbk £7.95

Lane's Commentary on the Australian Constitution. – North Ryde : Law Book Co, 1986.
xxxvii, 766p.
ISBN 0455207011 Hbk £111.00

Lang, Andrew G →Australian Mining and Petroleum Laws.
—Estate Agency Law and Practice in New South Wales. – 2nd ed. – North Ryde : Law Book Co, 1985.
xxix, 481p.
ISBN 0455205817 Pbk £33.00

—Estate Agency Practise in New South Wales. – North Ryde : Law Book Co, 1985.
xxix, 363p.
ISBN 0455202931 Pbk £33.00

→ Land Titles Reform.

—Sale of Land : Commentary and Cases / Diane Skapinker. – Woolloomooloo : International Business Communications, 1986.
488p.
ISBN 0949553220 Pbk £39.95

Lang, David Marshall
Armenians / by David Marshall Lang and Christopher J. Walker. – New rev ed. – London : Minority Rights Group, 1987.
20p. – (Report).
Previous ed.: 1981. Bibliography: p.20.
ISBN 094669043X

Lang, John Temple
Duties of national courts under the constitutional law of the European Community / John Temple Lang. – Exeter : University of Exeter, 1987.
40p; 21cm.
The Dominik Lasok lecture in European Community law delivered in the University on 23rd January 1987.

Lang, Kathy
Data base management packages / by Kathy Lang. – Southampton : Ashford Press, 1987.
350p.
ISBN 1852530235 unbound £80.00

Langan, P. St. J.
Civil procedure / L. D. J. Henderson. – 3rd ed. – London : Sweet & Maxwell, 1983.
xlvii,448p; 23cm.
Previous ed.: 1976. Includes index.
ISBN 0421289104 Hbk £
ISBN 0421289201 Pbk £9.45
→ Snell's Principles of equity.

Langdon
Book Keeping and Accounting Examinations Explained / Rizvi. – Croydon : Telles Langdon, 1988.
ISBN 0904467147 Pbk £6.75

Langdon, A. J. →Managing the long-term prison system : the report of the...Committee.

Lange
Administrative Receivership Law & Practice England & Wales / Harting. – Sweet & Maxwell.
ISBN 0421409908 Hbk £20.00

Lange, C.E.
Humerus of the long arm of the law. – Stockwell, 1988.
ISBN 0722322194 Pbk £6.60

Lange, D.
Extraterritorial Application of National Laws / G. Born. – Dordrecht : Kluwer, 1987.
72p.
ISBN 9065443061 Pbk £50.00

Lange, Peter
Unions, change and crisis : French and Italian union strategy and the political economy, 1945-1980 / Peter Lange, George Ross, Maurizio Vannicelli. – London : Allen & Unwin, 1982.
viii,295p; 25cm.
Includes index.
ISBN 0043310885

Langevad, E.J. →Mines and Minerals Act, 1969, and the Mineral Tax Act, 1970.

Langford, J. Stuart
Law of Your Land : a Practical Guide to the New Canadian Constitution. – Toronto : Canadian Broadcasting Corporation Enterprises, 1984.
ISBN 0887941079 Pbk £5.95

Langley
Introduction to accounting for business studies / Harden. – 4th ed. – London : Butterworths, 1985.
ISBN 040801542 Pbk £11.50
—Workbook in accounting / Caldicott. – 3rd ed. – London : Butterworths, 1981.
ISBN 0408106808 Pbk £10.50

Langman
Litigation Practice And Service. – London : Longman Professional.
ISBN 085121083X Llf

Langstaff, Michael J. →Introduction to urban renewal.

Langton, M. →Aborigines, Land and Land Rights.

Language and Law / Rajul Bhargava. – New Delhi : Macmillan India.
224p.
Hbk £30.00

Langworthy →Older Offenders : Perspectives, Criminology, Criminal Justice.

Lanham
Criminal Fraud 1987 / Weinberg. – London : Law Book Co.
ISBN 0455207453 Hbk £37.50

Lanham, D.J. →General Principles of Administrative Law.

Lansdown, Alfred V. →South African criminal law and procedure, Vol.5 : Criminal procedure : by Alfred V. Lansdown : Evidence : Jean Campbell.

Lantin, Barbara
Service please : services and the law : a consumer view / prepared for the National Consumer Council by Barbara Lantin and Geoffrey Woodroffe. – London : National Consumer Council, 1981.
35p; 30cm.
ISBN 0905653386 Pbk

Laprairie, Carol →Native criminal justice : research issues and data sources.

Larceny Act, 1916. – Dublin : Round Hall Press, 1988.
ca 156p.
ISBN 0947686185 Hbk £17.50

Lariviere, Richard W.
Dvystattva of Raghunandana Bhattacharya : Ordeals in Classical Hindu Law. – New Delhi : Manohar Publications, 1981.
280p.
Hbk £110.00

Larmour, Constance
Sex discrimination legislation in Australia / Constance Larmour. – Canberra : Legislative Research Service, Department of the Parliamentary Library, 1985.
29p. – (Basic paper).

Larnani
National welfare benefits / Read. – London : Central Books, 1988/89.
ISBN 0946744084 Pbk £5.50

Larsen →Modern Advanced Accounting.

Larson, Everette E. →Falkland Islands dispute in international law and politics : a documentary sourcebook.

Laskar, S.I.
Directive Principles of State Policy in Indian Constitution. – New Delhi : Deep and Deep Publications, 1988.
200p.
Hbk £150.00

Laskin, Bora
Laskin's Canadian constitutional law / Neil Finkelstein. – 5th ed. – Toronto : Carswell, 1986.
2 v. (1501 p.); 26 cm.
'Canadian Bill of Rights': p. 1495-1497. 'American Bill of Rights': p. 1500-1501.
ISBN 0459384406 v. 2

Laskin, John B.
Canadian Charter of Rights Annotated / Edward L. Greenspan. – Aurora : Canada Law Book Co. – (Text Books-Civil).
Pbk £127.00
—Debtor and Creditor : Cases, Notes and Materials / Eric Gertner. – 2nd ed. – Aurora : Canada Law Book Co, 1982.
1200p. – (Case Books).
Hbk £89.50

Laskin's Canadian constitutional law / Neil Finkelstein. – 5th ed. – Toronto : Carswell, 1986.
2 v. (1501 p.); 26 cm.
'Canadian Bill of Rights': p. 1495-1497. 'American Bill of Rights': p. 1500-1501.
ISBN 0459384406 v. 2

Lasok, Dominik
Conflict of Law in the European Community / Stone. – London : Butterworths.
ISBN 0862050715 Hbk £25.95
—Conflict of laws in the European Community / D. Lasok and P. A. Stone. – Abingdon : Professional Books, 1987.
xx,460p.
Bibliography: p xviii-xx.
ISBN 0862050715
—Customs law of the European Economic Community / by D. Lasok and W. Cairns. – Deventer : Kluwer, 1983.
xxiii,292p.
Includes bibliography: p.287-289. - Includes index.
ISBN 9065440771
—Introduction to the law and institutions of the European Communities / by D. Lasok and J.W. Bridge. – 4th ed. – London : Butterworths, 1987.
Includes index. Bibliography: p422-436.
ISBN 0406268800 Hbk £28
ISBN 0406268819 Pbk £21.95
—Law and institutions of the European Communities / D. Lasok, J.W. Bridge. – 4th ed. – London : Butterworths, 1987.
570p; 22cm.
Previous ed.: published as An introduction to the law and institutions of the European communities. 1982. Includes index.
ISBN 0406268800 Hbk £23.00 :
ISBN 0406268819 Pbk £16.00
—Private international law in the European Community / Stone. – London : Butterworths, 1987.
ISBN 0862050812 Hbk £28.00
—Professions and services in the European Economic Community / by D. Lasok. – Deventer, The Netherlands : Kluwer Law and Taxation Publishers, 1986.
ISBN 9065442537 Hbk

Lasok, K.
European Court of Justice Practice and Procedure. – London : Butterworths, 1984.
ISBN 040626810X Hbk £56.00

Laszlo, Ervin →Disarmament : the human factor : proceedings of a colloquium on the societal context for disarmament.

Latent damage : consultative document / Law Reform Committee. – 1. – London : Law Reform Committee 1981, 1981.
various pagings.

Latent Damage Act 1986. – London : LEST, 1987.
ISBN 1852710080 Pbk £28.50

Latham, C. T.
Family Law Reports. Vol. 6 / I. W. Crompton. – Bristol : Jordan & Sons Ltd, 1986.
Pbk £75.00

Latham, Patrick →Lawyers in the European Community.

Latimer, P
Cases and text on insurance law: Australia and New Zealand. – North Ryde : Butterworths (Australia).
Explains the insurance law of Australia and New Zealand, and illustrates how the law is interpeted with a selection of modern cases as well as relevant statutory material.
ISBN 0409308706 Pbk

Latin American urbanization / Douglas Butterworth, John K. Chance. – Cambridge : Cambridge University Press, 1981.
xi,243p; 24cm.
Bibliography: p216-237. - Includes index.
ISBN 0521237130 Hbk £15.00
ISBN 052128175X Pbk £5.50

Latin American Women / edited by Olivia Harris. – London : Minority Rights Group, 1982.
22p. – (Report).
Bibliography: p.21. - List of films: p.22.

Laundy, K. H. C.
Accounting in a Law Office. – Toronto : Law Society of Upper Canada.
Hbk

Laundy, Philip
Office of Speaker in the Parliaments of the Commonwealth / Philip Laundy. – London : Quiller Press, 1984.
xiii,274p.
Bibliography: p261-269.
ISBN 0907621317

Laursen, F.
Towards a New International Marine Order : conference of the Youth Movement for a New International Order (1980, Amsterdam). – Dordrecht : Kluwer, 1982.
224p.
ISBN 9024725976 Hbk £100.00

Lausche, Barbara J.
UNEP Environmental Law In-Depth Review 1981
Vol. VII. – Berlin : Erich Schmidt, 1982.
ISBN 3503021213 Hbk £24.00

Lauterpacht, Hersch
Development of International Law by the International Court. – Cambridge : Grotius.
408p.
ISBN 0906496306 Hbk £30.00

Lavender, Kate →Relationship between legal aid agencies and social agencies : research report for the Commonwealth Legal Aid Council.

Lavers, Anthony P. →Construction Law in Singapore and Malaysia.

Lavery, David
Motoring Law in Northern Ireland. – Belfast : Queen's University of Belfast, 1986.
350p.
Hbk

Lavis →Retail Banking.

Lavoux, Thierry →European Community environmental policy in practice, Vol. 3 : France : water and waste : a study of the implementation of the EEC directives : by Thierry Lavoux.

Law / Emile Woolf, Suresh Tanna, Karam Singh. – Plymouth : Macdonald & Evans, 1985.
1v.
ISBN 0712104860 Pbk

Law : a Guide to Select Law Sources in the Canberra College of Advanced Education Library / Peter Stone. – 4th ed. – Belconnen : Canberra College of Advanced Education, 1982.
2, 73p.
ISBN 0858892065 Hbk £4.00

Law : a guide to the collection of Hammersmith & Fulham / Hammersmith & Fulham Libraries. – 2nd ed. – London : Hammersmith & Fulham Libraries, 1987.
40p.
ISBN 0904038068

Law : ACCA Study Text 1.4. – London : BPP.
ISBN 0862772389 Pbk £11.95

Law : Level 1.4. – Witney : A.T.C. Publications.
ISBN 0747700028 Pbk £11.95

Law : Level 1.4. – London : BPP. – (ACCA Practice and Revision Kits Series).
ISBN 0862772648 Pbk £5.95

Law affecting the valuation of land in Australia / by Alan A. Hyam : with a foreword by R. Else-Mitchell. – North Ryde, N.S.W. : Law Book Co., 1983.
xxxii,246p.
Includes index.
ISBN 0455202079

Law among nations : an introduction to public international law / Gerhard von Glahn. – 4th ed. – New York : Macmillan, 1981.
xv,810p; 25cm.
Previous ed.: 1976. Includes bibliographies and index.
ISBN 0024231606 £15.95

Law and administration / Carol Harlow, Richard Rawlings. – London : Weidenfeld and Nicolson, 1984.
xxvi,718p; 22cm.
Bibliography: p686-695. - Includes index.
ISBN 0297782398 Hbk £
ISBN 0297782401 Pbk £15.95

Law and Administration of Incorporated Societies. – 2nd ed. – Butterworths, 1986.
276p.
Covers the nature of societies, the procedure of incorporation, branches, the registrar and assistant registrar, rules, members and membership, the secretary and other officers, secretarial and administrative duties, accounts taxation, dissolution and winding up, conduct of meetings, conventions and conferences, public relations, and the law of defamation.
ISBN 0409787442 Pbk £49.50

Law and Business Practice in Shanghai. – London : Longman Professional, 1988.
ISBN 0582997550 Hbk £25.00

Law and Commercial Dictionary - 5 Languages 2 vols. – West, 1985.
ISBN 0314805028 Hbk £170.00

Law and commercial dictionary in five languages : definitions of the legal and commercial terms and phrases in American, English and civil law jurisdictions : English to German, Spanish, French, Italian. – 2 v. – Munchen : Beck, 1985.
ISBN 031495502X

Law and democracy in Africa / by Richard Akinjide. – Lagos : Office of the President, Department of Information, 1981.
22p.

Law and development / edited by J.A. Omotola and A.A. Adeogun. – Lagos : Lagos University Press, 1987.
xviii,336p.
Includes index.
ISBN 9782264822

Law and disorder / John Alderson. – London : Hamilton, 1984.
vii,247p; 23cm.
Includes index.
ISBN 0241112591 £8.95

Law and Economic Organization. – Cambridge : Cambridge University Press, 1985.
ISBN 0512128966 Pbk £7.95

Law and economics / edited by Ross Cranston and Anne Schick. – Canberra : Department of Law, Research School of Social Sciences, Australian National University, 1982.
v,220p.
ISBN 0909596727 Pbk £9

Law and economics and the economics of legal regulation / edited by J.-Matthias Graf v.d. Schulenburg, Goran Skogh. – Dordrecht : M. Nijhoff, 1986.
248p. – (International studies in economics and econometrics).
'Selected papers of a conference of the International Institute of Management Wissenschaftszentum Berlin.'. Includes index. Contents: Law and economics and the economics of legal regulation / Goran Skogh – Efficiency, equity, and inalienability / Susan Rose-Ackerman – Negotiated settlement / Gordon Tullock – Economic efficiency and the common law / Peter H. Aranson – Default risk and the optimal pricing of court enforcement services / Hugh Gravelle – Transaction cost and communincation / Michael Hutter – Regulatory measures to enforce quality production of self-employed professinals / J.-Matthias Graf d. Schulenburg – Controlling insider trading in Europe and America / David D. Haddock, Jonathan R. Macey – The regulatin of shop opening hours in the United Kingdom / Susan M. Jaffer, John A. Kay Belgian public policy towards the retailing trade / Roger Van den Bergh – Assessing the effectiveness of economic efficiency of an E.E.C. pollution control directive / John Ashworth, Ivy Papps, David J. Storey.
ISBN 9024733774 Hbk £135.00

Law and economics of transborder telecommunications : a symposium / edited by Ernst-Joachim Mestmacker. – Baden-Baden : Nomos, 1987.
450p.
Includes bibliographical references.
ISBN 3789013684

Law and economy : the legal regulation of corporate capital / Kelvin Jones. – London : Academic Press, 1982.
xvi,190p; 24cm.
Bibliography: p179-184. - Includes index.
ISBN 0123900409 £16.00

Law and Ethics in the Medical Office incl. Bioethical Issues / Warden. – Second Revised Edition. – London : European Book Service.
ISBN 0803656173 Pbk £11.96

Law and Finance for the Farmer / Davis. – Cape Town : Legal and Financial Publishing Co.
Hbk £17.47

Law and government in colonial Australia / Paul Finn. – Melbourne : Oxford University Press, 1987.
xix,216p.
Bibliography: p.207-212. - Includes index.
ISBN 0195547462

Law and Government under the Tudors : Essays Presented to Sir Geoffrey Elton on his Retirement. – Cambridge : Cambridge University Press.
ISBN 0521335108 Hbk £25.00

Law and Health Visitors. – London : B Edsall, 1982.
72p.
ISBN 0902623354 Pbk £3.00

Law and history in Australia : selected papers from the fourth and fifth Law in History Conferences held at La Trobe University, 1985 and 1986
Vol. 3 / edited by Diane Kirkby. – Melbourne : Legal Studies Department, La Trobe University, 1987.
136p.
Includes bibliographical references.
Vol. 4 / edited by Diane Kirkby. – 1987.
133p.
Includes bibliographical references.

Law and Inflation. – London : HMSO, 1986.
32p.
Reviews the European provision for inflation in law. Includes details of current legislation in most Western European countries.
ISBN 9287108323 Hbk £3.30

Law and institutions of the European Communities / D. Lasok, J.W. Bridge. – 4th ed. – London : Butterworths, 1987.
570p; 22cm.
Previous ed.: published as An introduction to the law and institutions of the European communities. 1982. Includes index.
ISBN 0406268800 Hbk £23.00 :
ISBN 0406268819 Pbk £16.00

Law and international resource conflicts / by J.E.S. Fawcett and Audrey Parry. – Oxford : Issued under the auspices of the Royal Institute of International Affairs by Clarendon Press, 1981.
xiv, 254p; 23cm.
Bibliography: p244-246. - Includes index.
ISBN 0198253591 £20.00

Law and its limitations in the GATT multilateral trade system / Olivier Long. – Dordrecht : M. Nijhoff, 1985.
158p.
'An adaptation in English, brought up to date to the end of 1984, of a series of lectures delivered at the Hague Academy of International Law and published in French in its 'Collected courses' 1983, IV, volume 182'–Pref. Includes index. Bibliography.
ISBN 9024731895 Hbk £100.00

Law and its presuppositions : actions, agents and rules / S.C. Coval and J.C. Smith. – London : Routledge & Kegan Paul, 1986.
viii, 141p. – (International library of philosophy).
ISBN 0710204469

Law and Jurisdiction in the Middle Ages. – London : Variorum.
– (Variorum Collected Studies Series).
ISBN 086078231X Hbk £34.00

Law and justice / Australian Labor Party. – s.l. : The Party, 1983.
iii,24p.
'Policy launched by Senator Gareth Evans, ... Melbourne, 23 February, 1983'.

Law and Justice in a New Land : Essays in Western Canadian Legal History. – Agincourt : Carswell, 1986.
300p.
This work is a collection of essays incorporating primary historical research on topics relating to aboriginal and Indian land and resource law; law, politics, and justice in frontier communities; and legal and social problems in urban settings of Western Canada.
Hbk £46.25

Law and justice in contemporary Yemen : the People's Democratic Republic of Yemen and the Yemen Arab Republic by S.H. Amin. – Glasgow : Royston, 1987.
v,159p; 23cm.
Bibliography: p129-140. - Includes index.
ISBN 0946706360 £18.75

Law and justice in Tokugawa Japan : materials for the history of Japanese law and justice under the Tokugawa Shogunate 1603-1867
Part IV-C : Contract : commercial customary law / edited by John Henry Wigmore. – Tokyo : University of Tokyo Press, 1986.
xxix,443p.
Translated and published under the auspices of the Japan Foundation.

Law and learning : report to the Social Science and Humanities Research Council of Canada / by the Consultative Group on Research and Education in Law. – Ottawa : The Council, 1983.
ix, 186, 212, x p.; 23 cm.
English and French. Title on added t.p.: Le droit et le savoir. Includes bibliographies.
ISBN 0662524365 Pbk

Law and Legality : Materials on Legal Decision Making. – Butterworths, 1982.
592p.
Describes the institutions of law and identifies the decision makers, and poses questions about the limits of decision making authority. Cases have been selected to increase awareness of the interactions amongst legal decision makers, giving an understanding of the attributes, limits and potential of the legal system.
ISBN 0409824003 Pbk £50.00

Law and Leisure Services Management. – London : Longman Professional.
ISBN 0582021928 Pbk £7.95

Law and letters in American culture / Robert A. Ferguson. – Cambridge, Mass. : Harvard University Press, 1984.
viii,417p; 25cm.
Includes index.
ISBN 0674514653 £22.50

Law and Management of Water Resources and Supply / L. Skeet. – London : Shaw & Sons, 1981.
ISBN 0721909108 Pbk £16.00

Law and Medical Ethics / McCall-Smith. – 2nd ed. – London : Butterworths, 1987.
ISBN 0406501300 Hbk £18.00
ISBN 0406501319 Pbk £14.50

Law and Medicine in Canada / Glenn Ivan Sawyer. – 2nd ed. – Butterworths, 1987.
704p.
Analysis of recent case law and a review of statutory developments. Covers consent, the confidentiality of health records, artificial reproduction, biomedical research involving human subjects. Separate chapters discuss in more detail experimentation, organ transplants, determination of death, and a completely new chapter on abortion.
ISBN 0409865907 Hbk £85.00

Law and modern society / P.S. Atiyah. – Oxford : Oxford University Press, 1983.
viii,158p; 23cm.
Bibliography: p150-155. - Includes index.
ISBN 0192191667 £9.95

Law and morals : Warnock, Gillick and beyond / Simon Lee. – Oxford : Oxford University Press, 1986.
144p; 22cm.
Includes bibliography and index.
ISBN 0192177532 Hbk £12.50 :
ISBN 019283052X Pbk £4.95

Law and order / by Ralf Dahrendorf. – London : Stevens, 1985.
160p. – (Hamlyn lectures).
Includes index.
ISBN 0420472401 Hbk £14.00
ISBN 0420472509 Pbk £8.25

Law and order : arguments for socialism / Ian Taylor. – London : Macmillan, 1981.
xxii,234p.
Bibliography: p224-234.

Law and order : theft of an issue / David Downes. – London : Fabian Society in association with Labour Campaign for Criminal Justice, 1983.
33p.
Bibliography: p32-33.
ISBN 0716304902

Law and order and British politics / edited by Philip Norton. – Aldershot : Gower, 1984.
viii,224p; 23cm.
Bibliography: p215-217. - Includes index.
ISBN 056600688X £16.45

Law and order for Canada's indigenous people / Paul Havemann, Keith Couse, Lori Foster, Rae Matonovich : Prairie Justice Research Consortium, School of Human Justice, University of Regina. – Ottawa : Ministry of the Solicitor General, 1984.
xxxi,187p. – (User report).
Bibliography: p.178-187.

Law and Order for Canada's Indigenous People : a Review of the Recent Literature Relating to the Operation of the Criminal Justice System and Canada's Indigenous People. – Regina : Prairie Justice Research, 1985.
ISBN 0773100016 Hbk £18.00

Law and Order in India. – New Delhi : Abhinav Publications, 1987.
359p.
ISBN 8170172160 Hbk £190.00

Law and organisation of international commodity agreements / Kabir-ur-Rahman Khan. – The Hague : M. Nijhoff, 1982.
xxv,416p.
Includes index. Bibliography: p394-400.
ISBN 9024725542 Hbk £170.00

Law and philosophy : an international journal for jurisprudence and legal philosophy. – Dordrecht : D. Reidel, 1982-.

Law & policy. – Oxford : Blackwell for the Baldy Center for Law and Social Policy, State University of New York at Buffalo, 1984-.
Continues: Law & policy quarterly. Includes bibliographies.

Law and policy in the space stations' era. – Dordrecht : Nijhoff (Martinus), 1989.
352. – (Utrecht studies in air and space law 2).
Addresses the policy implications for all current participants in the Space Stations Era. Deals with a constitutional perspective of the treaty-making process in the space field, the optimum framework for management of the US/International Space Station based on a review of the most significant cooperative agreements, and a presentation of commercial issues involved.
ISBN 9024737222 Hbk £52

Law and policy of producers' associations / D.E. Pollard. – Oxford : Clarendon, 1984.
xii,372p; 23cm.
Includes index.
ISBN 0198254806 Hbk £40.00

Law and politics in Aztec Texcoco. – Cambridge : Cambridge University Press, 1984.
354.
Analyses the Aztec legal system. Discusses land tenure, inheritance, kinship relations, business trade and local and imperial administration.
ISBN 0521234751 Hbk £35.00

Law and politics of abortion / edited by Carl E. Schneider, Maris A. Vinovskis. – Lexington : Lexington, 1981.
xlvii,268p; 24cm.
Includes index.
ISBN 0669033863 £11.50

Law and population growth in Lesotho / Sebastian Poulter...et al. – Roma, Lesotho : Law and Population Project, Faculty of Law, National University of Lesotho, 1981.
96p.

Law and power in international relations / James Fawcett. – London : Faber and Faber, 1982.
140p; 23cm.
ISBN 0571105378 £9.50

Law & Prac Of Local Authority Meetings. – Cambridge : Woodhead-Faulkner.
ISBN 0902197517 Hbk £32.50

Law and Practice as to Receivers / Anthony Walton. – 17th ed. – London : Sweet & Maxwell, 1988.
ISBN 0421296909 Hbk

Law and practice concerning occupational health in the member states of the European Community
Vol. 1 / Environmental Resources Limited for the Commission of the European Communities. – London : Graham & Trotman for The Commission, 1985.
22cm. – (EUR).
Includes index.
ISBN 0860106268 Hbk £55

Vol. 2 / Environmental Resources Limited for the Commission of the European Communities. – 1985.
22cm. – (EUR).
Includes index.
ISBN 0860106276 Hbk £55

Vol. 3 / Environmental Resources Limited for the Commission of the European Communities. – 1985.
22cm. – (EUR).
Includes index.
ISBN 0860106284 Hbk £45

Vol. 4 / Environmental Resources Limited for the Commission of the European Communities. – 1985.
22cm. – (EUR).
Includes index.
ISBN 0860107949 Hbk £45

Vol. 5 / Environmental Resources Limited for the Commission of the European Communities. – 1985.
22cm. – (EUR).
Includes index.
ISBN 0860107957 Hbk £50

Law and Practice In Bankruptcy
Supplement 1986. – Sweet & Maxwell.
ISBN 0420475508 Pbk £15.00

Law and Practice in Matrimonial Causes / Caroline Harmer. – 4th ed. – London : Butterworths, 1985.
This text is an introduction to matrimonial law and a guide to developments in the area for students of the subject in England. All forms and model pleadings reflect the Matrimonial and Family Proceedings Act of 1984 and the Matrimonial Homes Act of 1983.
ISBN 0406637075 Pbk £21.95
ISBN 0406637083 Hbk £38.00

Law and Practice in the Termination of Employment in ASEAN : a Collection of Papers and the Laws from Six Member States. – Geneva : International Labour Office, 1986.
147p.
ISBN 9221054357 Hbk £10.00

Law and Practice of Arms and Explosives : With Explosives Rules 1988. – 10th ed. – Allahabad : Law Book Company, 1988.
1,000p.
Hbk £275.00

Law and practice of banking
Vol.1 : Banker and customer / J. Milnes Holden. – 4th ed. – London : Pitman, 1986.
lxv,500p; 22cm.
Previous ed.: 1982. Includes index.
ISBN 0273024884 Pbk £12.95

Vol.2 : Securities for bankers' advances / J. Milnes Holden. – 1986.
512p; 22cm.
Previous ed.: 1980. Includes index.
ISBN 0273022954 Pbk £10.95

Law and Practice of Banking in Nigeria. – Ile-Ife : Obafemi Awolowo Unviversity.
Hbk £15.00

Law and Practice of Close Corporations including Income Tax Aspects. – Cape Town : Legal and Financial Publishing Co.
£27.50

Law and practice of commercial arbitration / by Richard H. McLaren and Earl Edward Palmer. – Toronto, Canada : Carswell, 1982.
xlii, 422 p.; 24 cm.
Includes bibliographical references and index.
ISBN 0459349902

Law and practice of commercial arbitration in England / Sir Michael J. Mustill, Stewart C. Boyd. – London : Butterworths, 1985.
lxxiv,727p.
An extensive and detailed treatment of the subject of commercial arbitration is given in this work. The book covers appointment of arbitrators, the arbitration process, the award, and appeals in the United Kingdom.
ISBN 0406311218

Law and Practice of Company Accounting in Australia / M. Jager. – 6th ed. – Sydney : Butterworths, 1987.
669p.
ISBN 0409491853 Hbk

Law and Practice of Company Accounting in Australia / M O Jager, R B Taylor. – 6th ed. – North Ryde : Butterworths (Australia), 1983.
Analysis of the law of company accounting and reporting. Includes aspects of practice as necessary to interpret the law and explain its significance and application. Incorporates developments including the changes effected by the Companies Act 1981 (the National Act), and the latest Accounting Standards.
ISBN 0409493902 Pbk £27.60

Law and Practice of Company Accounting in New Zealand. – 6th ed. – Butterworths, 1982.
Treatment of the law relating to company accounting and reporting and of the professional pronouncements and accounting practices which stem from or assist in the application of such law. All SSAPS including the CCA Standard are reproduced in the appendix.
ISBN 040960089X Pbk £82.50

Law and practice of compromise / by David Foskett. – 2nd ed. – London : Sweet & Maxwell, 1985.
xlvii,388p.
Covers the significance of an agreement reached, and its consequence, and also the means by which a concluded agreement can, may or should be implemented. Also discusses the role which lawyers play in the negotiating process.
ISBN 0421324708

Law and Practice of Conveyancing. – Allahabad : Universal Book Agency.
Hbk £225,00

Law and Practice of Conveyancing in New Zealand / Brookfield. – 4th ed. – London : Butterworths, 1981.
ISBN 0409600296 Hbk £41.00

Law and Practice of Conveyancing Precedents in New Zealand
Supplement-1986. – Butterworths.
ISBN 040970167X

Law and practice of custodianship / by Michael D.A. Freeman. – London : Sweet & Maxwell, 1986.
xviii,156p.
Chapters on the origins of the concept of custodianship, the local authority and custodianship, effects of custodianship orders, adoption of custodianship, custodianship and care, disputes between joint custodians, and on the procedure for application for custodianship.
ISBN 042135500X Pbk £12.00

Law and Practice of Deeds Registration
Supplement. – Durban : Butterworths.
ISBN 0409045527 Hbk

Law and practice of employment / by H.G. Ringrose. – 2nd ed. – Cape Town : Juta, 1983.
xi,275p.
Previous ed.: 1976. Includes index.
ISBN 0702114057

Law and Practice of Estate Duty : with Rules and Forms. – 4th ed. 1982 repr. 1983. – New Delhi : Bharat Law House.
Hbk £150.00

Law and Practice of Franchising / John Drysdale. – Pergamon, 1989.
ISBN 0080240356 Hbk

Law and Practice of Futures and Options / Cregan. – London : Sweet & Maxwell, 1988.
ISBN 04213914006 Hbk

Law and Practice of Income Tax, 2 Vols. / N.A. Palkhivala. – 7th ed. – Bombay : Tripathi, 1977.
2872p.
bd £280.00
Supplement 1982. –
Hbk £180.00
Vol. 3. –
£180.00

Law and practice of international commercial arbitration / by Alan Redfern, Martin Hunter : foreword by Sir Robert Jennings. – London : Sweet & Maxwell, 1986.
xliii,462p; 24cm.
Reviews the process of international commercial arbitration, from the drafting of the arbitration agreement to the enforcement of the arbitral tribunal's award. Describes the role of the main international arbitral institutions, and comments on institutional and international rules of arbitration.
ISBN 0421324902 £64.00

Law and practice of intestate succession / by C.H. Sherrin, R.C. Bonehill. – London : Sweet & Maxwell, 1987.
xliii,515p; 25cm.
Areas such as social security benefits, private pension entitlements, bank accounts, small estates and the tax position and law relating to marital homes are covered. Reference has been made within the text to the usually more modern Commonwealth codes, where a contrast can elucidate the English law.
ISBN 0421326301 £39.00

Law and Practice of Legal Aid in Scotland. – 2nd ed. – Edinburgh : W Green, 1985.
ISBN 0414007638 Llf £18.00

Law and Practice of Life Insurance in India. – New Delhi : Deep and Deep Publications, 1987.
448p.
Hbk £275.00

Law and practice of marine insurance and average / by Alex L. Parks. – 2 v. – London : Stevens, 1988.
Concentrates on United States marine insurance law, and practice, and includes relevant case citations, extending to those not directly concerned with marine insurance, but of fundamental importance in understanding the liabilities which underwriters insure, such as collision wreck removal, personal injury and cargo damage.
ISBN 0420476504 £140.00

Law and practice of receivership in Scotland / J.H. Greene, I.M. Fletcher. – London : Butterworths, 1987.
xxxviii,355p; 26cm.
Includes index.
ISBN 0406005273 £27.50

Law and Practice of Restrictive Trade Practices in India. – New Delhi : Deep and Deep Publications, 1988.
360p.
Hbk £275.00

Law and practice of sentencing in Scotland / C.G.B. Nicholson. – Edinburgh : W. Green, 1981.
xxxi,274p; 22cm.
Includes index.
ISBN 0414006844 Pbk

Law and Practice of the District Courts of Queensland. – 2nd ed. – Butterworths, 1983.
608p.
ISBN 040949240X Hbk £102.00

Law and practice of the International Court / Shabtai Rosenne. – Dordrecht : Martinus Nijhoff, 1985.
xxv, 811p.
Reprint. Originally published: Leyden : A.W. Sijthoff, 1965. Includes index.
ISBN 9024729866 Hbk £350.00

Law and Practice of Wealth Tax and Gift Tax : with Rules and Forms. – 4th ed. – New Delhi : Bharat Law House, 1983.
Hbk £120.00

Law and Practice of Wealth Tax, Gift Tax. – 9th ed. – Nagpur : Wadhura & Co, 1982.
ca 425p.
Pbk £35.00

Law and practice relating to banking / F.E. Perry. – 4th ed. – London : Methuen, 1983.
x,566p; 20cm.
Previous ed.: 1981. Includes index.
ISBN 041635680X Pbk £7.50

Law and Practice Relating to Government Companies. – New Delhi : Bharat Law House, 1987.
Hbk £180.00

Law and practice relating to pollution control in Belgium and Luxembourg / Dirk Soetemans. – 2nd ed. – London : Graham & Trotman for the Commission of the European Communities, 1982.
200p.
Previous ed: /by J.M. Didier and Associates for Environmental Resources Limited. 1976. Includes index.
ISBN 0860103102 £18.00

Law and practice relating to pollution control in Denmark / prepared by C.H. Jensen for Environmental Resources Limited. – 2nd ed. – London : Graham & Trotman for the Commission of the European Communities, 1982.
200p.
Previous ed: 1976. Includes index.
ISBN 0860103129 £18.00

Law and practice relating to pollution control in France / William Coulet, Claude Albert Colliard. – 2nd ed. – London : Graham & Trotman for the Commission of the European Communities, 1982.
xxvii,150p; 23cm.
Previous ed.: / by Claude-Albert Colliard. 1976. Bibliography: p141-144. - Includes index.
ISBN 0860103072 £21.00

Law and practice relating to pollution control in Greece / prepared by J. Timagenis, B Pavlopoulos for Environmental Resources Limited. – 2nd ed. – London : Graham & Trotman for the Commission of the European Communities, 1982.
200p.
Previous ed.: 1976. Bibliography: p139-140. - Includes index.
ISBN 0860103145 £18.00

Law and practice relating to pollution control in Ireland / prepared by Yvonne Scannell for Environmental Resources Limited. – 2nd ed. – London : Graham & Trotman for the Commission of the European Communities, 1982.
xxix,215p; 22cm.
Previous ed. : 1976. Includes index.
ISBN 0860103137 £18.00

Law and practice relating to pollution control in Italy / U. Ruffolo, P. Dell'Anno. – 2nd ed. – London : Published by Graham & Trotman for the Commission of the European Communities, 1982.
200p.
Previous ed: / by P. Dell'Anno. 1976. Bibliography: p197-201. - Includes index.
ISBN 0860103099 £18.00

Law and practice relating to pollution control in the Federal Republic of Germany / Heinhard Steiger. – 2nd ed. – London : Graham & Trotman for the Commission of the European Communities, 1982.
xxvii,308p; 23cm.
Previous ed.: 1976 / by Heinhard Steiger and Otto Kimminich. Bibliography: p301-302. Includes index.
ISBN 0860103080 £21.00

Law and practice relating to pollution control in the member states of the European communities : a comparative survey / M. J. Forster. – 2nd ed. – London : Graham & Trotman for the Commission of the European Communities, 1982.
545p.
Previous ed: 1976.
ISBN 0860103153 £18.00

Law and practice relating to pollution control in the member states of the European Communities : recent developments / prepared by Environmental Resources Limited. – London : Graham & Trotman for the Commission of the European Communities, 1986.
144p; 22cm.
ISBN 0860108066 £21.00

Law and practice relating to pollution control in the Netherlands / J. J. de Graeff. – 2nd ed. – London : Graham & Trotman for the Commission of the European Communities, 1982.
200p.
Previous ed: / by J.J. de Graeff and J.M. Polack i.e. Polak for Environmental Resources Limited. 1976. Includes index.
ISBN 0860103110 £18.00

Law and practice relating to pollution control in the United Kingdom / M. J. Forster. – 2nd ed. – London : Graham & Trotman for the Commission of the European Communities, 1982.
200p.
Previous ed: 1976. Includes index.
ISBN 0860103064 Hbk £18.00
ISBN 0860104400 Pbk £9.00

Law and Practice Under the Family Law Act of Ontario. – Revised Edit. – Agincourt : Carswell, 1986.
This looseleaf work provides analysis of the Family Law Act of Ontario for the practitioner, along with summaries of relevant case law. Problems in preparation and drafting of domestic documents are discussed in the work, as well as, income tax implications and the valuation of family property.
Llf £75.75

Law and Procedure / Alan Willis. – London : Butterworths, 1987.
ISBN 0406104816 Pbk

Law and Procedure of Departmental Enquiries and Disciplinary Actions : Public and Private Servants. – Allahabad : Law Book Company, 1985.
Hbk £240.00

Law and Procedure of Departmental Enquiries (In Private and Public Sectors). – 2nd ed. 1976 repr. – Lucknow : Eastern Book Company, 1982.
1,747p.
Hbk £165.00

Law and Procedure of Meetings. – London : Sweet & Maxwell, 1983.
– (Concise College Texts Ser.).
ISBN 0421253401 Pbk £7.50

Law and procedure of the International Court of Justice
Vol.1 / by the late Sir Gerald Fitzmaurice. – Cambridge : Grotius, 1986.
xli,427p; 26cm.
An analysis of the decisions of the International Court of Justice given in its formative years. A series of articles, with a consolidated index.
ISBN 0906496330 £95.00
Vol.2 / by the late Sir Gerald Fitzmaurice. – 1986.
pi-xiv,429-860; 26cm.
Includes index.
ISBN 0906496381 Hbk £95.00

Law and psychiatry : rethinking the relationship / Michael S. Moore. – Cambridge : Cambridge University Press, 1984.
xiv,527p; 24cm.
Bibliography: p495-513. - Includes index.
ISBN 0521255988 £35.00

Law and psychology : papers presented at SSRC Law and Psychology Conferences 1979-1980 / edited by Sally LLoyd-Bostock. – Oxford : SSRC Centre for Socio-Legal Studies, 1981.
x,165p; 21cm. – (Conference papers).
Includes bibliographical references. 'The papers in this collection were originally presented at two meetings of the SSRC Law and Psychology Seminar Group, held in Oxford during 1979-1980'.
ISBN 0862260752

Law and Public Opinion in India. – New Delhi : Deep and Deep Publications, 1985.
311p.
Hbk £175.00

Law and Records in Medieval England Studies on the Medieval Papacy. – London : Varorium.
ISBN 00860782263 Hbk £34.00

Law and Regulation of International Space Communication : The Artech Telecommunication Library. – London : Artech House.
ISBN 0890062749 Hbk

Law and religion : the Jewish experience / Ze'ev W. Falk. – Jerusalem : Mesharim, 1981.
238p.
Bibliography: p.237-238.

Law and Social Change / H. G. Beale. – London : Royal Historical Society, 1984.
– (Studies in History (London) Ser.: Vol. 40).
ISBN 0901050946 Hbk £17.50

Law and Social Change : an Indian Overview. – Patiala : Punjab University, Publication Bureau.
Hbk £25.00

Law and social change in Papua New Guinea / editors David Weisbrot, Abdul Paliwala, Akilagpa Sawyerr. – Sydney : Butterworths, 1982.
xxiv, 319p.
'A successor to Fashion of law in New Guinea, edited for Butterworths by B.J. Brown in 1969' - Pref.. Bibliography: p291-301 - Includes index.
ISBN 0409309184

Law and social conflict / by Hans-Martin Pawlowski. – Florence : European University Institute, 1983.
19p.
At head of title page: European University Institute, Florence, Department of Political and Social Sciences.

Law and social enquiry : case studies of research / edited by Robin Luckham. – Uppsala : Scandinavian Institute of African Studies, 1981.
290p.
Includes bibliographical references.
ISBN 9171061819 Pbk
ISBN 9171061789

Law and social policy : some current problems in Irish law / edited by William Duncan. – Dublin : Dublin University Law Journal, 1987.
133p.
Includes bibliographical references.
ISBN 0951226908

Law and society : lectures and writings of Justice P. Jaganmohan Reddy / edited by M.V.K. Sivamohan. – Delhi : Ajanta Publications, 1986.
xii, 163 p.; 22 cm.
'Continuation of the anthology of lectures and writings of Justice P. Jaganmohan Reddy ... published ... under the title, 'Quest for justice'–Pref. Includes bibliographies and index.
ISBN 8120201566 Rs60.00

Law and society east and west / dharma, li and nomos : by Reinhard May. – Wiesbaden : Franz Steiner, 1985.
251p,9p.
Revised version of the London Doctoral Theses 'An enquiry in comparative jurisprudene. Similarity and disparity between dharma, li, and nomos.'. Bibliography p.227-250. - Includes index.
ISBN 3515045376

Law and Society in Medieval Europe. – London : Variorum, 1988.
ISBN 0860782190 Hbk £32.00

Law and society in modern India. – New Delhi : Oxford University Press India, 1989.
430.
Thirteen articles examine the way that modern Indian law operates. Shows the ways that a complex body of formal law adjusts itself to local conditions. The essays cover equality, hierarchy, panchayat justice, caste and policies of discrimination. The introduction by Rajeev Ddhavan traces the history of law in India.
ISBN 0195622944 £15.00

Law and Tax for the Family Company. – London : Oyez Longman, 1982.
– (Law and Tax Ser.).
ISBN 085120614X Hbk £15.00

Law and Tax for the Layman. – Bombay : India Book House.
Pbk £25.00

Law and teachers today / Neil Adams. – London : Hutchinson, 1983.
285p; 24cm.
Includes index.
ISBN 0091516102

Law and the Chinese in Canada : a Case Study in Ethnic Perceptions of the Law / John Hagan. – Toronto : University of Toronto, Centre of Criminology, 1982.
viii, 103p.
ISBN 0919584551 Pbk £6.00

Law and the citizen : looking to the '80s : a Colloquium on Public Legal Education held on April 29 and 30, 1977 / edited, updated and with present conclusions and recommendations by Frederick B. Sussmann and Bradford W. Morse. – Ottawa, Ont. : University of Ottawa Press, 1981.
ix, 135 p.; 23 cm.
Includes index.
ISBN 2760322297 Pbk

Law and the countryside. – Abingdon : Professional Books, 1987.
ISBN 0862052564 Hbk £37.50

Law and the cultural heritage
Vol. 1 : Discovery and excavation / by Lyndel V. Prott and P.J. O'Keefe : foreword by Henry Cleere. – Abingdon : Professional Books, 1983.
xxvii,434p.
Bibliography: p.371-386. - Includes index. Cover title: Law and the cultural heritage/ by P.J. O'Keefe and Lyndel V. Prott.
ISBN 086205060X
ISBN 0862050650

Law and the economy / Roger Bowles. – Oxford : Martin Robertson, 1982.
xvi,239p; 22cm.
Introduction to law and economics, relating the two subjects to each other.
ISBN 0855204656 Hbk £
ISBN 0855204745 Pbk £6.95

Law and the Elderly. – Routledge.
ISBN 0415005175 Hbk £25.00

Law and the Elderly. – Oxford : Croom Helm, 1988.
ISBN 0709911629 Hbk

Law and the electoral process / by H.F. Rawlings. – London : Sweet & Maxwell, 1988.
xix,252p; 23cm.
Bibliography: p243-248. - Includes index.
ISBN 0421376406 Pbk £13.50

Law and the Gorbachev era : essays in honor of Dietrich Andre Loeber / edited by Donald D. Barry ... et al. – Dordrecht : M. Nijhoff, 1988.
xix,426p.
Chiefly English; some German. 'List of publications of Dietrich Andre Loeber' included.
ISBN 9024736781

Law and the Individual. – 1st ed. – Plymouth : Macdonald & Evans, 1982.
144p : Illus.. – – (M and E Handbook Ser.).
ISBN 071211260X Hbk £4.50

Law and the Lawyers. – Ahmedabad : Navajivan Publishing House.
Hbk £15.00

Law and the Legal Profession in Canada. – Toronto : Butterworths, 1987.
250p.
ISBN 0409834343 Hbk £55.00

Law and the media in Canada / Clare F. Beckton. – Toronto, Canada : Carswell, 1982.
xvi, 161 p.; 24 cm.
Includes index. Bibliography: p. xi-xvi.
ISBN 0459344501 Pbk

Law and the moral order / W.D. Lamont. – Aberdeen : Aberdeen University Press, 1981.
xxviii,115p.
Includes bibliography.
ISBN 0080257429 flexi
ISBN 0080257461

Law and the other sex : the legal position of women in Swaziland / by Alice Kavanagh Armstrong and Ronald Thandabantu Nhlapo. – Mbabane : Webster, 1985.
150p.
Bibliography: p148-150.

Law and the Software Marketeer. – Prentice-Hall.
ISBN 0135266335 Hbk £41.75

Law and the twin pillars of justice / by C.A. Oputa. – Owerri Nigeria : Government Printer, 1981.
146p.
Collection of law lectures and papers presented by the author at various seminars and symposia.

Law and the weaker party : an Anglo-Swedish comparative study
Vol. 1 : The Swedish experience, edited by Alan C. Neal / general editors: Steve Anderman...et al. – Abingdon : Professional Books, 1981.
Vol. 2 : The English experience, edited by Steve Anderman / general editors: Steve Anderman...et al.. – 1981.
Vol. 3 : Swedish statutory material : edited by Alan C. Neal and Anders Victorin / general editors: Steve Anderman...et al.. – 1981.

Law and treatment of drug- and alcohol- dependent persons : a comparative study of existing legislation / by L. Porter, A. E. Arif, W. J. Curran. – Geneva : World Health Organization, 1986.
216p.
Bibliography: p209-216.
ISBN 9241560932

Law and vulnerable elderly people. – Mitcham : Age Concern, 1986.
144p.
Bibliography: p.141-143.
ISBN 0862420504

Law and You. – Toronto : Canadian Broadcasting Corporation Enterprises.
64p.
Pbk £1.50

Law and You : a Practical Guide for New Zealanders / J. Stephen Kos. – Birkenhead : Reed Methuen.
ISBN 0589013807 Hbk £9.95

Law as a moral judgment / Deryck Beyleveld, Roger Brownsword. – London : Sweet & Maxwell, 1986.
xxix,483p; 24cm.
Bibliography: p457-462. - Includes index.
ISBN 0421329203 £30.00

Law as an academic discipline : a response to the Leverhulme Report and the UGC letter on a strategy for Higher Education into the 1990's / the Committee of Heads of University Law Schools. – S.l. : The Committee, 1984.
iii,20 leaves.

Law as an instrument of economic policy : comparative and critical approaches / edited by Terence Daintith. – Berlin : W. de Gruyter, 1987.
– (Series A–Law).
Includes index. Bibliography. Based on papers presented at a colloquium held in Florence, Mar. 1985.
ISBN 0899254179

Law as an instrument of state intervention in industrial relations / Yiannis Gabriel. – London : Thames Polytechnic School of Business Administration, 1984.

Law as Process : An Anthropological Approach. – London : Sweet & Maxwell, 1983.
ISBN 0710200218 Pbk £6.95

Law Association for Asia and the Western Pacific →Lawasia newsletter.

Law at play. – T.A.K. – Edinburgh : W Green, 1984.
ISBN 0414007433 Hbk £2.50

Law Book Publisher
All Canada Weekly Summaries-National (A.C.W.S.) 1977-79, 9 Vols. – Law Book Publisher. – Aurora : Canada Law Book Co. – (First Ser.).
Hbk £261.00

—All Canada Weekly Summaries-National (A.C.W.S.) 1980-1986, 39 Vols. – Law Book Publisher. – Aurora : Canada Law Book Co. – (Second Ser.).
Hbk £1365.00

—All Canada Weekly Summaries-Ontario Edition (A.C.W.S. ONT) June 1981-1986, 30 Vols. – Law Book Publisher. – Aurora : Canada Law Book Co.
Hbk £780.00

—Annual Statutes of Canada : 1984, 2 Vols. – Law Book Publisher. – Aurora : Canada Law Book Co.
Hbk £185.00

—Consolidated Regulations of Canada, 1978, 18 Vols.
Regulations and Index. – Law Book Publisher. – Aurora : Canada Law Book Co.
Hbk £520.00
ISBN Pbk £320.00

—Ontario Statute Citator Current Bills Service. – Law Book Publisher. – Aurora : Canada Law Book Co.
Llf £85.00

—Revised Statutes of Canada, 1985. – Law Book Publisher. – Aurora : Canada Law Book Co.
Llf £550.00

Law books 1876-1981 : books and serials on law and its related subjects. – 4. – New York : R R Bowker, 1981.
xviii,5039p; 29cm.
Includes index.
ISBN 0835213978 Hbk £413.00

Law books and serials in print, 1989. – New York : R R Bowker, 1989.
ISBN 0835225593 Set
Vol. 1. Books (Subjects). – 1989.
1265.
ISBN 0835225607 Hbk
Vol. 2. Books (Titles). – 1989.
912.
ISBN 0835225615 Hbk
Vol. 3.. – 1989.
1144.
ISBN 0835225623 Hbk

Law, Capitalism and Democracy : a Sociology of Australian Legal Order. – North Sydney : Allen & Unwin, 1983.
180p.
ISBN 0868613819 Pbk £16.95

Law centre staff research project / Francis Stevens. – London : Law Centres Federation, 1983.
34p.
Summary of a report commissioned by the Law Centres Federation Evaluation Sub-Committee.

Law Centres Federation →Law centre staff research project.
→ Law centres news.

Law centres news / quarterly bulletin of the Law Centres Federation. – London : The Federation, 1979 -.

Law Commission
Annual report / the Law Commission. – London : HMSO, 1986.
v,71p.
ISBN 0102247862

—Chronological table of local legislation / the Law Commission and the Scottish Law Commission. – 2 v. – London : Law Commission, 1985.
Contents: Part 1. Local and personal acts 1797-1908 - Part 2. Local and personal acts 1909-1973, private acts 1539-1973.

—Computer misuse / the Law Commission. – London : HMSO, 1988.
viii,130p. – (Working paper).
Law Commission Working Paper, examines activities which might constitute computer misuse. Concludes present criminal law is sufficient to deal with computer misuse excepting unauthorised access which might require the creation of a new computer crime.
ISBN 0117301922

—Criminal law : report on criminal libel / by the Law Commission. – London : HMSO, 1985.
iv,80p.
ISBN 0101961804

—Distribution on intestacy / the Law Commission. – London : HMSO, 1988.
vii,54p. – (Working paper).
ISBN 0117301906

—Family law : matrimonial property / the Law Commission. – London : HMSO, 1988.
iii,30p. – (H.C. 1988-89).
ISBN 0102009899

—Family law : review of child law : guardianship and custody / The Law Commission. – London : HMSO, 1988.
iv,112p. – (1987-88 HC).
Includes text of a proposed children bill.
ISBN 0102594880

—Incapacitated principal : report on a reference under section 3(1)(e) of the Law Commissions Act 1965 / the Law Commission. – London : H.M.S.O., 1983.
v,104p; 25cm.
ISBN 0101897707

—Land mortgages / the Law Commission. – London : HMSO, 1986.
xv,254,48p. – (Working paper).
ISBN 0117301809

—Landlord and tenant : privity of contract and estate : duration of liability of parties to leases / the Law Commission. – London : HMSO, 1986.
iv,101p. – (Working paper).
Includes bibliographical references.
ISBN 0117301760

—Landlord and tenant law : privity of contract and estate / the Law Commission. – London : HMSO, 1988.
v,67p. – (H.C. 1988-89).
Includes the text of a draft Landlord and Tenant (Covenants) bill.
ISBN 0102008892

—Law under review : a quarterly bulletin of law reform projects. – Law Commission. – London : Law Commission, 1987.
Includes index.

—Part II of the Landlord and Tenant Act 1954 / the Law Commission. – London : HMSO, 1988.
viii,144p. – (Working paper).
Includes sections from the Act.
ISBN 0117301930

—Property law : fourth report on land registration / the Law Commission. – London : HMSO, 1988.
iii,147p. – (H.C. 1987-88).
ISBN 0102680884

—Property law : liability for chancel repairs / the Law Commission. – London : HMSO, 1985.
v,48p.
ISBN 0102039860

—Transfer of land : formalities for contracts for sale etc. of land / the Law Commission. – London : H.M.S.O., 1987.
37p. – (1987/88 HC2).
ISBN 0102002886

—Transfer of land : implied covenants for title / the Law Commission. – London : HMSO, 1988.
v,57,11p. – (Working paper).
Includes excerpts from relevant acts.
ISBN 0117301892

—Transfer of land : liability for chancel repairs / The Law Commission. – London : H.M.S.O., 1983.
vi,62p; 21cm. – (Working paper).
ISBN 0117301663

—Transfer of land : passing of risk from vendor to purchaser / the Law Commission. – London : HMSO, 1988.
v,87p. – (Working paper).
ISBN 0117301914

—Transfer of land : the rule in Bain v. Fothergill / The Law Commission. – London : H.M.S.O., 1986.
iv,49p; 21cm. – (Working paper).
Includes bibliographical references.
ISBN 0117301795

—Transfer of land : the rule in Bain v. Fothergill / the Law Commission. – London : H.M.S.O., 1987.
iv,28p.
ISBN 010101922X

—Transfer of land : title on death / the Law Commission. – London : HMSO, 1987.
viii,106p. – (Working paper).
ISBN 0117301876

—Transfer of land, the law of positive and restrictive covenants ... / the Law Commission. – London : H.M.S.O., 1984.
x,331p; 25cm. – (H.C.1983-84).
ISBN 0102201846

—Trustee savings banks bill : report on the consolidation of the Trustee Savings Banks Acts 1969 to 1978 / the Law Commission and the Scottish Law Commission. – London : H.M.S.O., 1981.
11p; 25cm.
ISBN 0101825706

—Trusts of land / the Law Commission. – London : H.M.S.O., 1985.
iv,76p. – (Working paper).
ISBN 0117301752

—Trusts of Land : overreaching / the Law Commission. – London : H.M.S.O., 1988.
iv,42,20p. – (Working paper).
ISBN 0117301884

Law Commission and law reform / edited by Graham Zellick. – London : Sweet & Maxwell, 1988.
xiii,157p.
Includes index. Includes a list of Law Commission publications.
ISBN 0421404604 £32.00

Law Commission Digest. – London : Butterworths.
ISBN 0903486512 Hbk £37.75

Law Commission Reports 1-18. – Professional Books.
ISBN 0862050251 Hbk £769.50

Law Commission Reports, 13 Vols.
Nos. 1-120. – Repr. – Abingdon : Professional Books.
Hbk £680.00
Individual vols.. –
Hbk £68.00

Law Commission Working Papers
Vols. 1-13. – Professional Books.
ISBN 0862052769 Hbk £479.00

Law Courts. – London : MIT Press, 1984.
ISBN 0262021994 Hbk £37.50

Law, custom and social order : the colonial experience in Malawi and Zambia / Martin Chanock. – Cambridge : Cambridge University Press, 1985.
xi,286p; 24cm. – (African studies series).
Examines development of customary law in African law during the colonial period. Studies how customary law developed alongside criminal law in Malawi and Zambia.
ISBN 0521301378 £25.00

Law Dictionary. – 10th ed. – London : Butterworths, 1988.
ISBN 0406625255 Hbk £6.50
ISBN 0406625263 Pbk

Law Dictionary : Explaining the Rise, Progress, and Present State of the British Law, 2 Vols. – 3rd ed. Repr. of 1820 ed. – Abingdon : Professional Books.
259p.
Hbk £90.00

Law Dictionary : Interpreting Difficult and Obscure Words and Terms in Common or Statute, Ancient or Modern Laws. – 2nd ed. Repr. of 1691 ed. – Abingdon : Professional Books.
Hbk £175.00

Law dictionary : technical dictionary of the Anglo-Americal legal terminology including commercial and political terms : English-German / von Beseler/Jacobs-Wustefeld. – 4th rev. and enl. ed. – Berlin : W. de Gruyter, 1986.
ISBN 0899251773

Law drafting and sociology : a seminar report / edited by Antti Kivivuori. – Helsinki : Ministry of Justice, Law Drafting Dept., 1985.
122 p.; 25 cm. – (Publication series / Ministry of Justice, Law Drafting Department).
Includes bibliographical references.
ISBN 9514686764 Pbk

Law, economy and society, 1750-1914 : essays in the history of English law / edited by G.R. Rubin, David Sugarman. – Abingdon : Professional Books, 1984.
iv,503,xxviii p; 24cm.
ISBN 0861050855 Hbk £32.40
ISBN 0862050987 Pbk £19.25

Law England Reports Annual Review Nineteen Eighty-Six. – Leading Academic Lawyers. – London : Butterworths, 1987.
ISBN 040687963X Pbk

Law, Ethics and Medicine : Studies in Medical Law. – New Edition. – Oxford : Oxford University Press.
ISBN 00198256426 Pbk £11.95

Law, ethics and medicine : studies in medical law / by P.D.G. Skegg. – Oxford : Clarendon, 1984.
xii,268p; 23cm.
Includes index.
ISBN 0198253656 £25.00

Law, Fact and Narrative Coherence. – London : Deborah Charles.
ISBN 0951379305 Hbk £18.00
ISBN 0951379631 Pbk £12.00

Law Firm of the Future - Today : Materials Prepared for a Continuing Legal Education Seminar Held February 5, 1983 / Phil Baudin. – Vancouver : British Columbia Continuing Legal Education Society, 1983.
ISBN 0865041008 Llf £45.00

Law for Accountancy Students / Jennifer James. – 3rd ed. – London : Butterworths, 1986.
ISBN 0406708835 Pbk

Law for Architects, Builders and Engineers. – 2nd ed. – Butterworths, 1983.
355p.
ISBN 0409493422 Pbk £29.50

Law for Cinemas and Videos. – 4th ed. – Lucknow : Eastern Book Company, 1985.
Hbk £45.00

Law for Civil Engineers. – London : Collins, 1987.
280p.
ISBN 0003832570 Hbk £19.50

Law for Commercial Retailers. – London : Sweet & Maxwell.
ISBN 0421347902 Hbk

Law for councillors / by Barbara Turner. – London : Sweet & Maxwell, 1986.
xii,146p; 21cm.
ISBN 0421353600 Pbk £5.00

Law for Doctors and Nurses / Tingle. – London : Financial Training, 1988.
ISBN 1851851011 Pbk £15.00

Law for Estate Management Students / John R Murdoch, Peter Schofield. – London : Butterworths, 1986.
A review of the basics of United Kingdom law for students of estate management. The English legal system, including elements of constitutional law, contracts, torts, and land law, are outlined in this book.
ISBN 0406562911 Pbk £18.95

Law for Everyman. – Onitsha : Africana-FEP.
Hbk £10.00

Law for GCSE / Collins. – London : Pitman Publishing, 1987.
ISBN 0273028367 Pbk £5.95

Law for Housing Managers. – 2nd ed. – London : Business Education, 1986.
ISBN 0907679145 Pbk £13.95

Law for Licensed Conveyancers. – London : Financial Training, 1988.
ISBN 1851850724 Pbk £7.95

Law for Migrant Welfare Workers. – North Sydney : Allen & Unwin, 1983.
112p.
ISBN 0868610380 Hbk £19.95
ISBN 0868610461 Pbk £12.95

Law for Nurses. – 3rd ed. – North Ryde : Law Book Co, 1983.
xi, 282p.
ISBN 0455204950 Pbk £28.50

Law for parents and children / by Helen Gamble. – 2nd ed. – North Ryde, N.S.W. : Law Book Company, 1986.
vii,392p.
Includes bibliographical references and index.
ISBN 0455206937

Law for retailers / Jennifer Brave. – London : Sweet & Maxwell, 1983.
xii,207p; 23cm.
Bibliography: p195-197. - Includes index.
ISBN 0421298103 Hbk £
ISBN 0421298200 Pbk £7.50

Law for social workers : a Canadian guide / by Elaine J. Vayda, Mary T. Satterfield. – Toronto, Canada : Carswell, 1984.
xxi, 292 p.; 24 cm.
This second edition text reviews the structure of the Canadian legal system. Discussions include the rights of persons living in common law relationships, criteria for awarding support, possible courses of legal action for situations of family violence, basic grounds and procedure for obtaining divorce, custody and access, child protection proceedings, adoption and children that break the law. Also included in the new edition is divorce, custody, support, family property, and young offenders. Includes bibliographies and index.
ISBN 0459366602 Pbk

Law for the Haulier. – London : Kogan Page, 1987.
250p.
ISBN 1850911479 Hbk £11.95

Law for the Medical Profession. – Butterworths, 1988.
356p.
ISBN 040949318X Hbk £39.00

Law for the Psychotherapist. – Norton.
ISBN 039370033X Hbk £25.00

Law for the Small Business. – 5th ed. – London : Kogan Page, 1987.
ISBN 0850912157 Pbk £7.50

Law for the Small Business : 'The Daily Telegraph' Guide. – 4th ed. – London : Kogan Page, 1985.
264p.
ISBN 0850388937 Hbk £11.95
ISBN 0850388945 Pbk £6.95

Law for the Small Business (Daily Telegraph Guide). – 6th ed. – London : Kogan Page.
ISBN 1850916438 Pbk £7.95

Law for the world ocean / by Gerard J. Mangone. – London : Stevens, 1981.
ii,313p; 19cm.
Bibliography: p292-300. - Includes index.
ISBN 0421284803 £12.00

Law for Youth Workers. – North Sydney : Allen & Unwin, 1983.
124p.
ISBN 0868610305 Pbk £12.95

Law, force and diplomacy at sea / Ken Booth. – London : Allen & Unwin, 1985.
xiii,231p,1p folded leaf of plates; 24cm.
ISBN 0043410278 Hbk £18.00
ISBN 0043410286 Pbk £7.95

Law Foundation of New South Wales → Continuing legal education in the 1980's : papers and proceedings of the Conference on Continuing Legal Education in the 1980's, conducted by the Law Society of New South Wales and the Law Foundation of New South Wales at the College of Law, Sydney, 13-15 November 1980.

Law, Freedom and Change. – New Delhi : Affiliated East-West Press.
Hbk £28.50

Law from anarchy to Utopia : an exposition of the logical, epistemological and ontological foundations of the idea of law, by an inquiry into the nature of legal propositions and the basis of legal authority / Chhatrapati Singh. – Delhi : Oxford University Press, 1986.
xxi,299p; 22cm.
Bibliography: p278-292. - Includes index.
ISBN 0195617045 £30.00

Law, Government and Business in Kuwait. – Royston.
ISBN 0946706522 Hbk £87.00

Law, Government and Public Policy. – Oxford : Oxford University Press.
ISBN 0195548485 Hbk £25.00
ISBN 0195548507 Pbk £13.95

Law Handbook. – 3rd ed. – Redfern : Redfern Legal Centre Publishing, 1988.
976p.
Hbk £34.95

Law Has Long Ears. – Fitzroy : Wildgrass Books, 1986.
256p.
Hbk £24.96

Law in a Cynical Society? : Opinion and Law in the 1980's / Janet K. Baldwin. – Agincourt : Carswell, 1985.
475p.
Hbk £50.75

Law in Action. – 2nd ed. – North Ryde : C.C.H. Australia, 1985.
364p.
ISBN 0869035088 Hbk £22.00

Law in Afghanistan : a study of the Constitutions, matrimonial law and judiciary / by Mohammad Hashim Kamali. – Leiden : E. J. Brill, 1985.
viii,265p.
Bibliography: p254-259.
ISBN 9004071288

Law in Colonial Society : The Nova Scotia Experience. – Agincourt : Carswell, 1984.
300p.
ISBN 0459364200 Hbk £36.50

Law in Hong Kong. – 2nd ed. – London : Federal, 1986.
ISBN 9623020015 Pbk £15.00

Law In Modern Society. – London : Macmillan, 1976.
ISBN 0029328802 Pbk £13.95

Law in Relation to Children / A C L Morrison. – 10th ed. – London : Butterworths, 1985.
Service to 31.3.89.
ISBN 0406158126 Llf £145.00

Law in Singapore on carriage of goods by sea / by Tan Lee Meng. – Singapore : Malayan Law Journal Pte., 1986.
lv,509p.
Deals with voyage charterparties, time charterparties, demise charterparties, bills of lading, the Carriage of Goods by Sea Act 1872, exclusion of liability, limitation of liability, and limitation of action, loading, proceeding on the voyage, discharge and delivery, laytime and demurrage, salvage and wreck, and remedies for breach of contract.
ISBN 9971700492

Law in the balance : legal services in the 1980s / edited by Philip A. Thomas. – Oxford : Robertson, 1982.
x,245p; 23cm.
Includes bibliographies and index.
ISBN 0855204443 Hbk £18.50
ISBN 0855204826 Pbk £6.50

Law In The Making. – 7th ed. – Oxford : Oxford University Press, 1964.
ISBN 0198810296 Pbk £8.50

Law in the Making : a Comparative Survey. – Berlin : Springer-Verlag, 1987.
ca 410p.
ISBN 3540184457 Hbk £198.00

Law in the People's Republic of China: commentary, readings and materials / Ralph H Folsom, John H Minan. – Dordrecht : Nijhoff (Martinus), 1989.
1100.
Reviews the Chinese legal tradition. Each chapter focuses on the emerging law as related to a selected topic, giving an overview, and then edited excerpts selected from a wide range of legal materials.
ISBN 0792300556 Hbk £159/Dfl495

Law in the Political Economy of Public Enterprise. – Uppsala : Scandinavian Institute of African Studies, 1977.
351p.
ISBN 9171061177 Pbk £15.00 (10.00 in Third World Countries)
ISBN 9171061169 Pbk £10.00 (7.00 Third World Countries)

Law in the Service of Man → Civilian administration in the occupied West Bank : analysis of Israeli Military Government Order no. 947.

Law in transition : contracts. – Don Mills : R. De Boo, 1984.
193p.
Includes bibliographical references and index.
ISBN 0888201826

Law in transition : evidence. – Don Mills : R. De Boo, 1984.
196p.
Includes bibliographical references and index.
ISBN 0888201877

Law Institute of Victoria → Supreme court rules : guide to time limits, civil proceedings.

Law is an Ass. – London : Pan Books Ltd, 1984.
ISBN 0330282107 Hbk £1.95

Law is for all / by Hon. Justice Akin. Apara. – Enugu : Fourth Dimension Publishers, 1982.
x,118p.
Includes index.

Law Journal County Court Reports : 1934-1947, 14 Vols. – Abingdon : Professional Books.
Hbk £275.00

Law journals / Middlesex Polytechnic Library Services. – Hendon : The Polytechnic, 1982.
11p.
'List of law related journals and law reports taken by Middlesex Polytechnic libraries'.

Law, justice and democracy / Lord McCluskey. – London : Sweet & Maxwell, 1987.
116p; 21cm.
Includes index.
ISBN 0421378905 Hbk £9.95
ISBN 0563205490 Pbk £5.95

Law, Justice and the Common Good : The Great Debate and a Search for Meaning. – University Press of America.
ISBN 0819166502 Hbk £31.50
ISBN 0819166510 Pbk £13.75

Law, Justice and the Judiciary : Transitional / Dato' Visu Sinnadurai. – Professional Law, 1988.
ISBN 09679958002 Hbk £95.00

Law Landlord and Tenant Service 1988 / Wellings. – 28th ed. – Sweet & Maxwell, 1978.
ISBN 0421228202 Hbk £255.00

Law, Legislation and Liberty. – Revised edition. – Routledge, 1982.
ISBN 0710092113 Pbk £7.95

Law, legitimacy and the constitution : essays marking the centenary of Dicey's Law of the Constitution / edited by Patrick McAuslan and John F. McEldowney. – London : Sweet & Maxwell, 1985.
xiv,219p; 22cm.
Includes index.
ISBN 0421331208 Hbk £19.50
ISBN 0421331305 Pbk £13.50

Law Lexicon. – rep. 1987. – Nagpur : Wadhura & Co.
£330.00

Law Librarian : Bulletin of the British and Irish Association of Law Librarians. – London : Sweet & Maxwell, 1986.
Hbk £13.50

Law Libraries in Canada / Joan N Fraser. – Agincourt : Carswell, 1988.
This work presents a series of articles written about Canadian law library services and delivery of legal information in Canada. Topics include the types of primary legal materials and law libraries found in Canada, development of law collections, library automation and the impact of bilingualism. Information as to Canadian universities, courthouses, legislative law libraries, government publishing agencies, and more, are also included.
Hbk £46.25

Law Library Administration and Reference. – Delhi : Metropolitan Book Co.
182p.
bd £25.00

Law Library manual / by N.O. Obi. – Lagos : Law Library, Federal Ministry of Justice, 1984.
23p.
Includes a list of commonly used author and title abbreviations.

Law, litigants and the legal profession / papers presented to the Fourth British Legal History Conference at the University of Birmingham, 10-13 July, 1979 : edited by E.W. Ives and A.H. Manchester. – London : Royal Historical Society, 1983.
xii,233p; 26cm.
Includes index.
ISBN 0901050911 £11.25
ISBN 0391029258

Law lords / Alan Paterson. – London : Macmillan, 1982.
x,288p; 23cm.
ISBN 0333238869

Law machine / Marcel Berlins and Clare Dyer. – 2nd rev ed. – Harmondsworth : Penguin Books, 1986.
185p.
ISBN 0140226958

Law machine / Marcel Berlins and Clare Dyer. – Harmondsworth : Penguin, 1982.
191p.
Includes index.
ISBN 0140224815

Law, men of law and education / H. R. Khanna. – Bombay : Tripathi, 1981.
184p.

Law, morality, and rights / edited by M.A. Stewart. – Dordrecht, Holland : Reidel, 1983.
xii,452p. – (Synthese library).
Includes index.
ISBN 902771519X

Law, norms and authority / George C. Christie. – London : Duckworth, 1982.
x,181p; 23cm.
Includes index.
ISBN 0715615939 £18.00

Law of Adverse Possession. – 11th ed. – Allahabad : Law Book Company, 1988.
650p.
Hbk £180.00

Law of Adverse Possession. – 2nd ed. – Allahabad : Law Publishers, 1983.
Hbk £27.00

Law of agency / G.H.L. Fridman. – 5th ed. – London : Butterworths, 1983.
xxxvii, 386p.
This text gives an in-depth exploration of the law of agency. Primary emphasis is put on the evolution of agency law in the United Kingdom through the pure common law system into a coherent set of rules.
ISBN 0406584362 Hbk
ISBN 0406584370 Pbk £18.95

Law of Agency. – Lucknow : Eastern Book Company, 1985.
784p.
Hbk £175.00

Law of Agency. – 2nd ed. – Allahabad : Law Book Company, 1986.
918p.
Hbk £200.00

Law of agency in South Africa / De Villiers and Macintosh. – 3rd ed. – Cape Town : Juta, 1981.
lxviii,684p.
Previous ed.: 1956. Includes index.
ISBN 0702112542

Law of Agricultural Holdings / H. A. C. Densham. – 7th ed. – London : Butterworths, 1987.
A thorough treatment of the United Kingdom law of agricultural holdings is included in this text. The work presents a commentary on the law, statutes and statutory instruments, and useful forms and precedents.
ISBN 0406368139 Hbk

Law of agricultural holdings in Scotland / Brian Gill. – Edinburgh : Green, 1982.
xxxiv,451p; 25cm.
Includes index. Includes text of 6 acts.
ISBN 0444996656 SET

Law of allotments / by J.F. Garner. – 4th ed. – London : Shaw and Sons, 1984.
xxii,113p; 22cm.
Previous ed.: 1977. Includes index.
ISBN 0721901425 Pbk

Law of arbitration / Gill. – 3rd ed. – London : Sweet & Maxwell, 1983.
xxv,174p; 22cm.
Previous ed.: 1975. Includes index.
ISBN 0421251107 Pbk £7.50

Law of Arbitration. – 4th ed. – Lucknow : Eastern Book Company, 1983.
826p.
Hbk £85.00

Law of arbitration in Scotland / Robert L.C. Hunter. – Edinburgh : T & T Clark, 1987.
384p; 24cm.
A comprehensive account of the modern law of arbitration in Scotland, the ordinary submission to arbitration clauses, the appointment of arbiters, proceedings, the 'stated case' under the Administration of Justice (Scotland) Act 1972, and the decree-arbitral. The final part contains chapters on quasi-arbitral and equitable procedures, agricultural and industrial arbitrations. There is consideration of the impact of Community law and comparison with the practice of other countries. Includes bibliography and index.
ISBN 0567094804 Hbk £29.95

Law of Arms and Explosives : Acts and Rules. – 3rd ed. – Allahabad : Ashoka Law House, 1987.
657p.
Hbk £160.00

Law of Arms and Explosives : with Act Rules and Notifications. – 4th ed. – Allahabad : Law Publishers, 1982.
Hbk £30.00

Law of Arrest, Bail, Search and Seizure. – 2nd ed. – Lucknow : Eastern Book Company, 1985.
Hbk

Law of bail : practice, procedure and principles / by Brian Harrie Kevin Donovan : foreword by Mr Justice Roden : introduction by Roger Court. – Sydney : Legal Books, 1981.
xxi,186p.
Includes index.
ISBN 0959656855

Law of Bails. – 5th ed. – Allahabad : Law Book Company, 1986.
750p.
Hbk £180.00

Law of Bails, Forfeiture of Bonds and Habeas Corpus / A.N. Saha. – 2nd ed. – Lucknow : Eastern Book Company, 1985.
391p.
Hbk £75.00

Law of bankers' commercial credits / Maurice Megrah. – 7th ed. – London : Europa, 1984.
xxxv,343p; 25cm.
Previous ed.: 1979. Bibliography: pxxxiv-xxx - Includes index.
ISBN 0905118782 £19.50

Law of Banking
Supplement 1987. – 3rd ed. – Plymouth : Macdonald & Evans, 1986.
ISBN 0712106820 Pbk £6.50

Law of banking / by Ian F.G. Baxter. – 3rd ed. – Toronto : Carswell, 1981.
xl,574p.
Previous eds. entitled: The law of banking and the Canadian Bank Act. Includes bibliographical notes and index. Includes text of Banks and Banking Law Revision Act, 1980.
ISBN 0459337408

Law of Banking. – Onitsha : Africana-FEP.
Hbk

Law of Banking / Maurice Megrah. – 10th ed. – London : Butterworths, 1988.
ISBN 040633353X Hbk

Law of Banking. – 2nd ed. – Plymouth : Macdonald & Evans, 1982.
336p. – (M and E Handbook Ser.).
ISBN 0712112588 Hbk £4.95

Law of Banking and Negotiable Instruments in Singapore and Malaysia. – 2nd ed. – Singapore : Quins, 1983.
Hbk £99.00

Law of Bankruptcy. – 2nd ed. Repr. of 1895 ed. – Abingdon : Professional Books.
Hbk £35.00

Law of Benami Transactions. – 6th rev. and enl. ed. – Calcutta : R. Cambray and Company, 1987.
464p.
Hbk £150.00

Law of Betting, Gaming and Lotteries / Stephen P Monkcom. – London : Butterworths, 1987.
ISBN 0406296596 Hbk £85.00

Law of Bias and Malafides. – 3rd ed. – Lucknow : Eastern Book Company, 1985.
298p.
Hbk

Law of borrowing. – London : Sweet & Maxwell, 1989.
Account of the institutional framework within which borrowing takes place, and consideration of the regulation and supervision of banks, building societies, the securities market, the wholesale money market, and consumer credit transactions. Chapter dealing with the characteristics of a loan, and types of loan.
ISBN 0421000000 Llf

Law of Breach of Confidence / Hoolahan. – London : Butterworths, 1984.
ISBN 0406120102 Hbk

Law of Burial, Cremation and Exhumation. – 6th ed. – London : Shaw & Sons, 1988.
ISBN 072190064X Pbk

Law of Canadian Companies : 1931. – Repr. of 1980 ed. – Agincourt : Carswell.
1226p.
This book is a reprint of the 1931 text on the Companies Act of Canada and the case law applicable to companies incorporated under the Act.
Hbk £92.50

Law of Canadian co-operatives / by Daniel Ish. – Toronto : Burroughs, 1981.
xxvi, 294 p.; 24 cm.
This book reviews co-operative corporation legislation of provincial and federal jurisdictions in Canada. The work analyzes the principles of corporate common law in the context of co-operative corporations, in addition to corporate statutory materials.
ISBN 0459336800 Hbk £46.25

Law of Canadian municipal corporations / by Ian MacF. Rogers. – 2d ed. – Toronto : Carswell, 1971.
2 v. (loose-leaf); 25 cm.
ISBN 0459307606

Law of Carriage by Inland Transport. – 5th ed. – London : Sweet & Maxwell.
ISBN 042046820X Hbk

Law of Central Excise. – 2nd ed. – Bombay : Tripathi, 1983.
Hbk £220.00

Law of Central Sales Tax, 2 Vols. – Allahabad : Orient Law House, 1984.
Hbk £280.00

Law of Central Sales Tax. – 4th ed. – Lucknow : Eastern Book Company, 1985.
859p.
Hbk £150.00

Law of Charitable Trusts. – Butterworths, 1983.
212p.
ISBN 0409490709 Hbk £52.00

Law of charities - cases & materials : Singapore & Malaysia / Ter Kah Leng. – Singapore : Butterworths, 1985.
xxvii,353p; 23cm.
Covers trusts for the relief of property, trusts for the advancement of education, religion, and other purposes beneficial to the community, 'Sin Chew' (ancestor worship) and ceremonies in memory of souls, and trusts for graves, memorials, and burial grounds.
ISBN 0409995037 Hbk

Law of Child Care. – London : Pitman Publishing, 1982.
ISBN 0712112529 Hbk £12.95

Law of Cinematograph (Central and States), 1987. – 3rd ed. – Allahabad : Law Book Company, 1987.
Hbk £250.00

Law of Citizenship and Passports : with All Allied Laws. – 5th ed. – Allahabad : Law Book Company, 1987.
400p.
Hbk £120.00

Law of Citizenship, Foreigners and Passports. – Allahabad : Orient Law House, 1984.
Hbk £150.00

Law of Claims. – Allahabad : Law Book Company, 1981.
Includes 1986 supplement.
Hbk £160.00

Law of clubs : with a note on unincorporated associations / J.F. Josling, Lionel Alexander. – 6th ed. – London : Longman, 1987.
242p; 24cm. – (Longman practitioner series).
Previous ed.: London : Oyez Longman, 1984. Includes index.
ISBN 0851212972 Pbk £26.50

Law of clubs : with a note on unincorporated associations / J.F. Josling, Lionel Alexander. – 4th ed. – London : Oyez, 1981.
xl,235p; 24cm. – (Oyez practitioner series).
Previous ed.: 1975. Includes index.
ISBN 0851205828 Pbk

Law of Collective Agreements in the Countries of the European Community. – Kirchberg : Commission of the European Communities.
47p.
Hbk

Law of collective agreements in the countries of the European Community / report submitted by Gian Carlo Perone : with the assistance of Antonio Vallebona. – Luxembourg : Office for Official Publications of the European Communities, 1985.
47p.
Describes the tasks given to the Commission of the European Communities in the social sector, particularly under Articles 117 and 118 of the Treaty of Rome.
ISBN 9282550125 Pbk £3.30

Law of Collision at Sea. – Amsterdam : Elsevier Science Publishers, 1987.
xxxviii, 608p.
ISBN 0444703071 Hbk £250.00

The Law of Collisions in Africa / Leveson. – 5th ed. – London : Butterworths, 1974.
ISBN 0409034207 Hbk £27.40

Law of Commercial Companies. – 3rd ed. – North Ryde : Law Book Co, 1987.
xlix, 379p.
ISBN 0455207291 Hbk £59.50
ISBN 0455207305 Pbk £35.00

Law of commons / by G.D. Gadsden. – London : Sweet & Maxwell, 1987.
xlviii,452p; 25cm.
Brings together many aspects of common land, and covers the history and present state of the law. Various types of common, ranging from village greens and urban amenity areas, to upland pastures are examined in the light of rights and obligations concerned.
ISBN 0421365609 £45.00

Law of companies and meetings / B.A. Masodkar. – Bombay : Tripathi, 1984.
xxxii,263p.

Law of Companies in Australia. – 2nd ed. – North Ryde : C.C.H. Australia, 1986.
670p.
ISBN 0869039814 Hbk £54.00
ISBN 086903930X Pbk £42.00

Law of company litigation : being the law relating to liquidation of limited liability companies / by B. H. McPherson. – 3rd ed. – Sydney : Law Book Co., 1987.
lxxxii,501p.
Previous ed.: 1980. Bibliography: pp.lxxix-lxxx. - Includes index.
ISBN 0455207410

Law of Company Purchase and Compensation-Singapore and Malaysia. – London : Butterworths, 1984.
ISBN 0406181225 Pbk £22.50

Law of company receiverships in Australia and New Zealand / by Peter Blanchard. – Sydney : Butterworths, 1983.
xxvi,213p.
Includes index.
ISBN 0409491632

Law of company receiverships in New Zealand and Australia / by Peter Blanchard. – Wellington : Butterworths, 1982.
xxvi,213p.
Covers the law governing receiverships initiated by the holders of charges over corporate assets in New Zealand and Australia.
ISBN 0409601330

Law of Compromises / S.K. Argawal. – 4th ed. – Allahabad : Law Book Company, 1986.
600p.
Hbk £140.00

Law of compulsory purchase and compensation / Keith Davies. – 4th ed. – London : Butterworths, 1984.
xxxv,364p; 23cm.
Previous ed.: 1978. Includes index.
ISBN 0406571872 Hbk £21.00
ISBN 0406571880 Pbk £17.95

Law of compulsory purchase and compensation - Singapore and Malaysia / N. Khublall. – Singapore : Butterworths, 1984.
xxviii,310p.
Account of the main provisions relating to powers, procedures and appeals, and discusses the concept of market value as the basis for compensation. Cases and statutory provisions are drawn from both Singapore and Malaysia, as well as from England and India.
ISBN 0406181225 Pbk £55.00

Law of Confessions Approvers and Accomplices. – 7th ed. – Allahabad : Law Book Company, 1988.
ca 600p.
Hbk £200.00

Law of Conflicts and Foreign Trade / L. Vekas. – Budapest : Akademiai Kiado.
xiv, 379p.
ISBN 9630542749 Hbk £38.00

Law of consent / by Peter W. Young. – Sydney : Law Book Company, 1986.
xxxvi,228p.
ISBN 0455206791

Law of consumer protection and fair trading / by Brian W. Harvey and Deborah L. Parry. – 3rd ed. – London : Butterworths, 1987.
xxxii,435p; 22cm.
Includes parts 1-4 of the Consumer Protection Act 1987.
ISBN 0406222622 Hbk £25.00
ISBN 0406222630 Pbk £17.95

Law of contempt / by Anthony Arlidge and David Eady : consulting editor - (Scotland) Herbert Kerrigan : with a foreword by Lord Justice Lawton. – London : Sweet & Maxwell, 1982.
xxxvi,479p; 26cm.
Intends to reduce the law to basic principles, consonant with the common law and modern statutes. Chapter on the impact of the 1981 Contempt of Court Act on the law of Scotland and Northern Ireland. Considers the effect of the European Convention on Human Rights on the development of the contempt jurisdiction.
ISBN 0421259205 £30.00

Law of Contempt in Nigeria. – Lagos : Nigerian Law Publications.
ISBN 9782325263 Hbk £15.00

Law of Contempt of Court. – Allahabad : Universal Book Agency.
Hbk £225.00

Law of Contempt of Courts, Legislatures and Public Servants. – 8th ed. – Allahabad : Law Book Company, 1989.
1,000p.
Hbk £300.00

Law of Contract / A G Guest. – 26th ed. – Oxford : Oxford University Press, 1984.
ISBN 0198761481 Hbk £32.50
ISBN 019876149X Pbk £16.95

Law of contract / Hugh Collins. – London : Weidenfeld and Nicolson, 1986.
xi,236p; 23cm.
Bibliography: p210-224. - Includes index.
ISBN 0297787845 Hbk £14.95
ISBN 0297787853 Pbk £7.50

Law of Contract. – Edinburgh : W Green, 1985.
Hbk £23.00

Law of Contract / Davis. – North Ryde : Law Book Co, 1986.
ISBN 0455206198 Hbk £47.50
ISBN 0455206201 Pbk £34.50

Law of Contract. – 4th ed. – Lucknow : Eastern Book Company, 1985.
526p.
Hbk £65.00

Law of contract / by G.H. Treitel. – 7th ed. – London : Stevens, 1987.
850p; 25cm.
Previous ed.: 1983. Includes index.
ISBN 0420474900 Hbk £30.00 :
ISBN 0420475001 Pbk £22.00

Law of contract : implied terms in contracts for the supply of services Report on a reference under Section 3(1)(e) of the Law Commissions Act 1965 / by the Law Commission. – London : H.M.S.O., 1986.
v, 49p.
ISBN 0101977301

Law of contract : minors' contracts / Law Commission. – London : H.M.S.O., 1984.
v,42p.
ISBN 0102494843

Law of contract : minors' contracts / the Law Commission. – London : H.M.S.O., 1982.
vi,179p. – (Working paper).
ISBN 0117301612

Law of Contract : New Zealand Edition / C. H. S. Fifoot. – 6th ed. – Wellington : Butterworths, 1984.
ISBN 0409701645 Hbk
ISBN 0409701564 Pbk

Law of contract : pecuniary restitution on breach of contract / The Law Commission. – London : H.M.S.O., 1983.
iv,56p; 25cm.
ISBN 0102034842

Law of contract : the parol evidence rule / the Law Commission. – London : H.M.S.O., 1986.
iv,31p.
ISBN 0101970005

Law of Contract and related obligations in Scotland. – 2nd ed. – London : Butterworths, 1985.
ISBN 0406677875 Hbk £44.50

Law of contract in Canada / by G.H.L. Fridman. – 2nd ed. – Toronto : Carswell, 1986.
clii,764p.
Previous ed.: 1976. Includes bibliographical references and index.
ISBN 0459382101

Law of Contract in India, 3 Vols. – 2nd ed. – Lucknow : Eastern Book Company, 1983-1985.
Hbk £150.00 ea.

Law of Contract in India. – New Delhi : Deep and Deep Publications, 1985.
326p.
Hbk £175.00

Law of Contract in Malaysia and Singapore : Cases and Commentary. – 2nd ed. – Butterworths, 1987.
900p.
Chapters cover interpretation of contracts, conditional contracts, collateral contracts, economic duress, contracting out of a statute, the application of the doctrine of frustration to contracts for the sale of land, rescission under the Contract Act, equitable relief against forfeiture of deposits and part payments, and Foreign Investment Committee regulations.
ISBN 0409995290 Hbk £78.00

Law of contract in Scotland. – Edinburgh : Green (W.) & Son, 1987.
The most comprehensive analysis of the practical and theoretical aspects of contract law since Gloag on Contract in 1929. Practical guidance is also provided on drafting some of the commonly found contract clauses.
ISBN 041400793X Hbk

Law of contract in South Africa / by R.H. Christie. – Durban : Butterworths, 1981.
lxxiv,575p.
ISBN 0409018317

Law of Contract (SWOT). – 2nd ed. – London : Blackstone Press.
ISBN 1851850910 Pbk £7.50

Law of Contracts, 2 Vols. – 4th ed 1983-84. – Allahabad : Orient Law House.
Hbk £350.00

Law of Contracts. – New Delhi : Association of Indian Universities.
229p.
Pbk £11.00

Law of contracts / S.M.Waddams. – 2nd edition. – Toronto : Canada Law Book Co.Inc, 1984.
cxli,614p.
ISBN 0888040237

Law of co-operatives / Ian Snaith. – London : Waterlow, 1984.
xxviii,218p; 22cm.
Bibliography: p210-213. - Includes index.
ISBN 0080391591 Hbk £31.00

Law of Copyright. – Repr. of 1912 ed. – Aalen Wuertt : Scientia.
xxxii, 351p.
Hbk £115.00

Law of corporate insolvency. – London : Waterlow, 1990.
912; 23.
ISBN 0080392059 Hbk £70

Law of corporate insolvency in Scotland / by John B. St. Clair and J.E. Drummond Young. – Edinburgh : W. Green & Son Ltd., 1988.
xxix,381p; 25cm.
Includes index. A comprehensive guide to the law of corporate insolvency in the light of the reforming legislation of 1986. Deals with winding-up, receivership, administration and related problems such as trust and retention of title.
ISBN 0414008170 Pbk

Law of costs / A.C. Cilliers. – 2nd ed. – Durban : Butterworths, 1984.
lvii, 330 p.; 25 cm.
Includes indexes. Bibliography: p. lvi-lvii.
ISBN 0409019097 R52.50

Law of Costs. – 2nd ed. – Aurora : Canada Law Book, 1987.
Llf £49.50

Law of Court Fees and Suits Valuation in India / H.N. Seth. – 6th ed. – Allahabad : Universal Book Agency, 1988.
ca 1,000p.
Hbk £250.00

Law of credit agreements and hire-purchase in South Africa / P. J. Aronstam. – 5th ed. – Cape Town : Juta, 1982.
lii,505p.
Previous ed., 1978, entitled: The law of hire-purchase in South Africa. Bibliography: p.xxi-xxiii. - Includes index.
ISBN 070211250X

Law of Crimes, 2 Vols. / Dhirajlal. – 23rd ed. – New Delhi : Bharat Law House, 1987.
Hbk £280.00 ea.

Law of Crimes / by Kharisu Sufiyan Chukkol. – Zaria : Ahmadu Bello University Press.
Hbk £15.00

Law of Crimes. – 3rd ed 1984. – Allahabad : Orient Law House, 1984.
Hbk £200.00

Law of crimes in Nigeria : skeletal notes and important references / Kharisu Sufiyan Chukkol. – Zaria : Ahmadu Bello University Press, 1981.
iv, 51 leaves.

Law of Criminal Appeals and Revisions. – 4th ed. – Allahabad : Law Book Company, 1986.
ca 1000p.
Hbk £200.00

Law of Criminal Attempt. – Agincourt : Carswell, 1984.
330p.
This text examines the law of criminal attempt as set out in legislation and interpreted by the courts around the world, with an emphasis on Canadian law. The book includes numerous comparisons of differing legal responses to similar fact situations in attempt cases.
Hbk £54.75

Law of criminal conspiracy / by Peter Gillies. – Sydney : Law Book Co., 1981.
Includes bibliographical references and index.
ISBN 0455200793

Law of Culpable Homicide, Murder and Punishment in India. – New Delhi : Deep and Deep Publications, 1988.
464p.
Hbk £250.00

Law of Customs. – Bombay : Tripathi.
Hbk

Law of Damages / G.F. Lubbe. – Durban : Professional Publisher.
ISBN 0409029300 Hbk

Law of damages / by S.M. Waddams. – Toronto : Canada Law Book Ltd., 1983.
cx,755p.
ISBN 0888040164

Law of Damages and Compensation, 3 Vols. – 5th ed. – Allahabad : Law Publishers, 1983.
Hbk £30.00

Law of Declaratory Judgments. – 2nd ed. – Agincourt : Carswell, 1988.
300p.
Hbk £50.50

Law of Declaratory Judgments. – Agincourt : Carswell, 1978.
ISBN 045932200 Hbk £22.00

Law of Deep Sea-Bed Mining : a Study of the Progressive Development of International Law Concerning the Management of the Polymetallic Nodules of the Deep Sea-Bed. – Stockholm : Almqvist & Wiksell, 1987.
356p.
ISBN 9122011560 Hbk £525.00

Law of Defamation. – Agincourt : Carswell, 1987.
1540p.
This treatise provides a thorough treatment of the Canadian law of defamation. All significant Canadian cases, as well as, major cases from the Commonwealth and U.S. on defamation are included in the work. The practice and procedure for defamation cases is discussed in the book.
ISBN 045939630 Hbk £55.00

Law of Defamation : Some Aspects. – Bombay : Tripathi, 1986.
151p.
Hbk £60.00

Law of Defamation and Malicious Prosecution. – 9th ed. – Allahabad : Law Publishers, 1987.
500p.
Hbk £150,000

Law of Defamation and Malicious Prosecution (Civil and Criminal). – 2nd ed. – Allahabad : Law Publishers, 1982.
Hbk £22.50

Law of Defamation in Canada, 2 Vols. – Agincourt : Carswell, 1987.
1,540p.
Hbk £122.50

Law of defamation in Singapore and Malaysia. – Singapore : Malayan Law Journal, 1988.
ca 200p.
Gives a thorough discussion of the principle aspects of a defamation action, with precedents, and a review of the principles expounded in the local cases and legislation. Appendices cover the relevant statutory provision, cases judicially considered, statutes judicially considered, and a damage digest.
ISBN 9971700611 Hbk £90.00

Law of defamation in South Africa / Jonathan M. Burchell. – Cape Town : Juta, 1985.
xxxii, 359 p.; 26 cm.
Includes bibliographical references and index.
ISBN 0702115673

Law of defective premises / Anthony Speight, Gregory Stone : foreword by the Honourable Mr Justice Wood. – London : Pitman, 1982.
xxi,205p; 23cm.
Includes index.
ISBN 0273017705 Hbk £15.95

Law of delict / by P.Q.R. Boberg. – Cape Town : Juta, 1984.
v. 1; 26 cm.
Includes indexes. Bibliography: 1, p. xvii-xx. Contents: 1. Aquilian liability.
ISBN 070211426X

Law of Delict / A.D.J. van Rensburg. – Durban : Professional Publisher, 1983.
ISBN 0409037087 Pbk

Law of delict in Scotland / by David M. Walker. – 2nd ed., rev. – Edinburgh : Published under the auspices of the Scottish Universities Law Institute by W. Green, 1981.
cxli,1111p; 26cm.
Previous ed.: 1966. Includes index.
ISBN 0414006690

Law of Dilapidations. – 9th ed. – London : Estates Gazette, 1988.
ISBN 0728200449 Pbk £11.00
ISBN 0728201151 Hbk £18.50

Law of Discovery 1885. – Woolloomooloo : International Business Communications, 1985.
872p.
ISBN 0949553212 Hbk £85.00

Law of discovery in Australia : documents, interrogatories and property / by Bernard C. Cairns. – Sydney : Law Book Co., 1984.
xxv,199p.
Bibliography: p.xx - Includes index.
ISBN 0455202842

Law of Dismissal in Canada. – Aurora : Canada Law Book Co, 1985.
403p. – (Text Books-Civil).
Hbk £55.00

Law of Dismissals. – 7th ed. – Allahabad : Law Book Company, 1985.
1,000p.
Hbk £250.00

Law of Distresses and Replevins : With Appendix of English Precedents in Replevins. – 3rd ed. Repr. of 1794 ed. – Abingdon : Professional Books.
460p.
Hbk £45.00

Law of domestic or private tribunals / by J.R.S. Forbes. – Sydney : Law Book, 1982.
xxviii, 247 p.; 22 cm.
Includes index.
ISBN 0455204551 Pbk

Law of Dying Declaration. – Allahabad : Law Book Company, 1988.
60p.
Pbk £40.00

Law of Easements
Includes Supplement-1986 / Sastri. – 5th rev. ed. – Lucknow : Eastern Book Company, 1984.
846p.
Hbk £130.00

Law of Easements. – Allahabad : Orient Law House, 1984.
Hbk £75.00

Law of Easements and Licences. – 10th ed. – Allahabad : Law Book Company, 1984.
1,200p.
Hbk £250.00

Law of Easements and Proits. – London : Butterworths, 1978.
ISBN 0406253838 Hbk £29.00

Law of Education / V.B. Gleeson. – Butterworths, 1982.
211p.
ISBN 0409309230 Pbk £39.00

Law of Education and Educational Institutions in India, 3 Vols. – Allahabad : Law Book Company, 1982-83.
With 1988 supplement.
Hbk £600.00

Law of Electricity in Uttar Pradesh. – 2nd ed. – Lucknow : Eastern Book Company, 1985.

Law of Employees State Insurance / Dwivedi. – 2nd ed. – Allahabad : Law Book Company.
700p.
With 1987 supplement.
Hbk £150.00

Law of Employment. – 2nd ed. – North Ryde : Law Book Co, 1984.
xix, 351p.
ISBN 0455205108 Pbk £30.00
ISBN 0455205094 Hbk £42.00

Law of Employment. – 6th ed. – London : Butterworths.
ISBN 0406653461 Pbk £16.95

Law of Employment. – 5th ed. – London : Butterworths, 1985.
ISBN 0406653445 Pbk £15.95

Law of employment / N.M. Selwyn. – 6th ed. – London : Butterworths, 1988.
xlv,582p.
Previous ed.: 1985. Includes index. Cover title: Selwyn's law of employment.
ISBN 0406653461 £14.95

Law Of Employment The. – 2nd ed. – London : Law Book Co.
ISBN 0455205094 Hbk £19.00

Law of Equity in Republic of Ireland. – London : Butterworths, 1988.
ISBN 0406102708 Hbk £29.50

Law of Essential Services in India : a Critical Study of the Essential Services Maintenance Act 1981. – New Delhi : Deep and Deep Publications, 1983.
211p.
Hbk £70.00

Law of estate agency and auctions / by J.R. Murdoch. – 2nd ed. – London : Estates Gazette, 1984.
xlii,576p.
Includes bibliographical references and index.

Law of Estate and Gift Duties in New Zealand / Richardson. – 5th ed. – London : Butterworths.
ISBN 0409606030 Hbk £30.80

Law of Evidence. – 13th ed. – London : Sweet & Maxwell, 1982.
– (Common Law Library : No. 10).
Hbk £89.00
South Australian Supplement. – 1985.
41p.
ISBN 0409491942 £11.00
Supplement only. –
Pbk

Law of Evidence / Beaumont. – London : Financial Training, 1985.
– (SWOT).
ISBN 090632274X Pbk £7.50

Law of Evidence. – 2nd ed. – Plymouth : Macdonald & Evans, 1986.
ISBN 0712106758 Pbk £6.50

Law of Evidence / R A McGechan. – 7th ed. – Wellington : Butterworths (New Zealand), 1984.
ISBN 0409601314 Hbk £34.60
ISBN 0409701742 Pbk £29.10

Law of Evidence. – Allahabad : Orient Law House.
ISBN 0861254104 Hbk £30.00

Law of Evidence / Dhirajlal. – 17th ed. – Nagpur : Wadhura & Co, 1987.
Hbk £180.00

Law of Evidence. – Calcutta : Eastern Law House, 1987.
Hbk £158.00

Law of Evidence in Australia. – London : Legal Books, 1987.
ISBN 0949553360 Hbk £45.00
ISBN 0959553395 Pbk £30.00

Law of Evidence in Civil Cases / W R Lederman. – London : Butterworths.
ISBN 0409868507 Hbk £68.00

Law of Evidence in Criminal Trials in Hong Kong / Gerard McCoy. – Butterworths, 1987.
ca 350p.
Examines the principles which govern in Hong Kong the reception of evidence in criminal proceedings: trial, sentence, and appeal. Covers facts which need not be proved, burden and standard of proof, the rule against hearsay and its exceptions, similar fact evidence and other evidence of criminal conduct probative of the guilt of the accused.
ISBN 0409995479 Hbk £97.50

Law of Evidence in Malaysia and Singapore. – Singapore : Quins, 1983.
Hbk £81.00

Law of Evidence in Nigeria. – 3rd ed. – London : Sweet & Maxwell, 1987.
ISBN 0421378506 Pbk £20.00

Law of evidence in Scotland / by David Field. – Edinburgh : W. Green, 1988.
xxxv,359p; 22cm.
Includes index.
ISBN 0414008421 Pbk

Law of evidence in Scotland / N M L Walker. – Edinburgh : Clark (T. & T.) Ltd, 1986.
A practical handbook for practitioners and for situations in which questions of evidence arise. Where the law is undecided, the authors indicate the general principle which should be applied. There is a concluding chapter on international private law.
ISBN 0852791208 Pbk

Law of Evidence in Sri Lanka. – Colombo : Lake House Investments.
Hbk £6.60

Law of evidence in the Sudan / by Krishna Vasdev. – London : Butterworths, 1981.
xlviii,486p; 22cm.
Includes index.
ISBN 0406406103 Pbk

Law of Evidence. Short Edition in One Volume. – Allahabad : Universal Book Agency, 1984.
Hbk £175.00

Law of Execution. – 3rd ed. – Allahabad : Law Book Company, 1987.
1,600p.
ISBN 8185029431 Hbk £340.00

Law of expropriation in South Africa / Marcus Jacobs. – Cape Town : Juta, 1982.
xxxiv,700p.
Bibliography: p.xv-xvi. - Includes index.
ISBN 0702112550

Law of Factories. – 5th ed. – Karachi : Bureau of Labour Publications, 1987.
60p.
Pbk £4.50

Law of Fences and Pastures Protection, NSW. – 2nd ed. – North Ryde : Law Book Co, 1984.
xxi, 208p.
ISBN 0455202788 Pbk £37.00

Law of fiduciaries / by J.C. Shepard. – Toronto, Canada : Carswell, 1981.
xxix, 386 p.; 24 cm.
Includes bibliographical references and index.
ISBN 0459343009 Hbk £33

Law of Flats. – London : Longman Professional, 1982.
ISBN 085101388X Pbk £25.50

Law of flats. – 2nd. – London : Longman Professional (UK), 1989.
– (Practitioner series).
New edition takes account of the Landlord and Tenant Acts of 1985 and 1987 and changes resulting from the Housing Act 1988, including assured tenancies. Includes new chapters on disposition, the landlord's identity and the right of first refusal.
ISBN 085121388X Hbk £27.50

Law of Food and Drugs. – London : Butterworths.
Service to Date.
ISBN 0406115591 Hbk £425.00

Law of Foreigners and Citizenship ... – 3rd ed. – Allahabad : Law Publishers, 1983.
£33.00

The Law of Foreigners and Registration of Foreigners, 1987 : Containing Commentaries on Foreigners Act, Registration of Foreigners Act and Orders, Rules, Notifications and Allied Laws. – 5th ed. – Allahabad : Law Book Company, 1987.
466p.
Hbk £140.00

Law of Forests : Central and States. – 5th ed. – Allahabad : Law Book Company.
Hbk £200.00

Law of Forgeries, Counterfeiting and Cheating. – 3rd ed. – Allahabad : Law Book Company, 1982.
Hbk £60.00

Law Of Fraud and Mistake. – Sweet & Maxwell, 1952 Reprint.
ISBN 0421355409 Hbk £50.00

Law of Fundamental Rights / Chaudhari. – 2nd ed. – Allahabad : Law Book Company, 1984.
Hbk £225.00

Law Of General Average and York-Antwerp Rules (BSL) / Rudolf. – Sweet & Maxwell.
ISBN 0420429808 Hbk £75.00

Law of Groups of Companies in Europe : a Challenge for Jurisprudence. – Dordrecht : Kluwer, 1984.
ISBN 9065441654 Pbk £25.00

Law of Guarantee. – London : Sweet & Maxwell, 1986.
ISBN 0459383906 Hbk £45.00

Law of guarantee : a treatise on guarantee, indemnity and the standby letter of credit / by Kevin Patrick McGuinness. – Toronto : Carswell, 1986.
lxv,456p.
This text on the Canadian law pertaining to various secondary obligations used to secure debt and other contract loss gives a detailed survey of the modern law as it has developed in the courts of both Canada and England.
ISBN 0459383906

Law of guarentees / Thomas Putnam and Julienne Walker. – 2nd ed. – London : Longman Professional (UK), 1989.
– (Commercial Series).
Discusses the law relating to contracts where one party agrees to be answerable for the debts or obligations of another to a third party. Deals with guarentees in loans, consumer credit, hire purchase, landlord and tenant (to guarentee payment of rent), building contracts, and commercial contracts. Contains specimen pleadings.
ISBN 0851215395 Hbk £40

Law of habeas corpus. – Oxford : Clarendon Press, 1989.
300; 21.5.
Updated to include references to current developments in the law of habeas corpus. Examines the nature of the judicial reivew exercised on habeas corpus, and explores the past, present, and potential uses of the writ. Also contains discussions on the law in Commonwealth countries.
ISBN 0198254040 Hbk £30.00

Law of health and safety at work / Norman Selwyn. – London : Butterworths, 1982.
xxviii,354p; 22cm.
Includes index.
ISBN 0406667500 Pbk

Law of health and safety at work : the new approach / by Charles D. Drake and Frank B. Wright : with a foreword by John H. Locke. – London : Sweet & Maxwell, 1983.
xii; 25cm.
Includes index.
ISBN 0421286202 Hbk £22.00
ISBN 042128630X Pbk £13.85

Law of Health Care Facility Administration. – Butterworths, 1988.
ca 224p.
Deals with issues such as quality assurance – payment for services, physicians privileges, liability issues and employment relations.
ISBN 0409801747 Hbk

Law of Hindi Religious and Charitable Endowments. – 3rd ed. – Lucknow : Eastern Book Company, 1985.
Hbk £200.00

Law of Homicide in the Sudan. – London : Butterworths, 1978.
ISBN 040640609X Pbk £17.60

Law of homicide in Victoria : the sentence for murder / Law Reform Commission of Victoria. – Melbourne : The Commission, 1985.
viii,27p. – (Report v no 1).
Bibliography: p.25-27.

Law of husband and wife in Scotland / by Eric M. Clive. – 2nd ed. – Edinburgh : Green (W.) & Son, 1982.
lxxiv,756p. – (Scottish Universities' Law Institute Ser.).
Chapters describe the general development of the law from before the Reformation to the present day, the formation and termination of marriage and the legal effects of marriage. Bibliography: plxxi-lxxi Published under the auspices of the Scottish Universities Law Institute.
ISBN 0414006682 Hbk £47

Law of Hywel Dda : law texts of medieval Wales / translated and edited by Dafydd Jenkins. – Llandysul : Gomer, 1986.
xlvii,425p; 22cm.
Bibliography: pxliii-xlvii. - Includes index.
ISBN 0863832776 £14.95

Law of Identification and Discovery. – 6th ed. – Allahabad : Law Book Company, 1988.
500p.
Hbk £150.00

Law of incest in Scotland : report of a reference under Section 3(1)(e) of the Law Commissions Act 1965 / Scottish Law Commission. – Edinburgh : H.M.S.O., 1981.
vii,74p; 25cm.
ISBN 0101842201 Pbk £4.80

Law of Income Tax, 5 Vols. – 7th ed. – New Delhi : Bharat Law House.
Hbk £200.00 ea.

Law of Income Tax. – 3rd ed. – Lucknow : Eastern Book Company, 1982.
350p.
Hbk £30.00

Law of Industrial and Commercial Employment. – 5th ed. – Karachi : Bureau of Labour Publications, 1987.
44p.
Pbk £3.00

Law of Industrial Conflict. – London : Macmillan, 1987.
ISBN 0333419138 Hbk £35.00

Law of Industrial Disputes, 2 Vols. – 4th ed. in press. – Bombay : Tripathi.
Hbk £4238p

Law of Industrial Disputes : as Amended by Amendment Act No. 46 of 1982, 2 Vols. – 2nd ed. – New Delhi : Bharat Law House, 1986.
Hbk £135.00 ea.

Law of industrial relations / by J.G. Riddall. – London : Butterworths, 1981.
xxiv,319p; 25cm.
Includes index. Supplement for 1982 covers the Employment Act 1982.
ISBN 0406648107 Pbk

Law of Industrial Relations. – 8th ed. – Karachi : Bureau of Labour Publications, 1987.
102p.
Pbk £6.00

Law of industrial relations in Pakistan : commentary on the Industrial Relations Ordinance 1969 / Obaidur Rahman. – Karachi : Asia Law House, 1984.
v,43p.
Bibliography: p.44.

Law of inhibition and adjudication / George Lidderdale Gretton. – London : Butterworths, 1987.
200p; 22cm.
Includes index.
ISBN 0406104336 Pbk £18

Law of Injunctions, 2 Vols. – 6th ed. – Allahabad : Law Book Company, 1985.
2,200p.
Hbk £400.00

Law of Injunctions. – Allahabad : Orient Law House, 1984.
Hbk £100.00

Law of Insolvency / P D McKenzie. – 2nd ed. – London : Butterworths, 1981.
ISBN 0409667900 Hbk £25.50

Law of Insolvency. – 2nd ed. – London : Butterworths, 1982.
ISBN 0409056022 Hbk £38.30
ISBN 0409056030 Pbk £30.30

Law of Insolvency (In Nutshell). – repr. 1983. – Lucknow : Eastern Book Company.
82p.
Pbk £6.00

Law of insurance / by Poh Chu Chai. – Singapore : Malayan Law Journal Pte., 1986.
xxv,289p.
Covers the principles of insurance law with regard to insurable interest, duty of disclosure, formation of the contract of insurance, insurance agents, construction of policies, proximate cause of loss, subrogation and contribution, and assignment of policies. Three chapters cover motor insurance and the Motor Insurers' Bureau.
ISBN 9971700484

Law of insurance / by Raoul Colinvaux. – 5th ed. – London : Sweet & Maxwell, 1984.
xci,553p; 26cm.
Deals with policies of insurance, parties to insurance contracts, and special types of insurance. New chapter on marine insurance. Covers the Insurance Companies Act 1982, and the Insurance Companies Regulations. Implications of EEC membership, New York law, Lloyd's standard policy terms and the Marine Insurance Act are also included.
ISBN 042131110X £42.00

Law of Intellectual and Industrial Property in Hong Kong. – London : Butterworths, 1984.
ISBN 0406181179 Pbk £50.00

Law of intellectual and industrial property in Hong Kong : a guide to trade marks, copyright, patents, registered designs and other protected commercial information / Michael D. Pendleton. – London : Butterworth, 1984.
xxxix,556p.
Deals with Hong Kong's intellectual property law, including both civil and criminal remedies. Discusses passing off, registered trademarks, trade descriptions, legislation, copyright, patents, registered designs, and trade secrets.
ISBN 0406181179

Law of Intellectual Property. – Bombay : Tripathi.
Hbk

Law of intellectual property / by Staniforth Ricketson. – North Ryde : Law Book Co., 1985.
clxxv,1201p.
Bibliography: p.cxxxix-clxx - Includes index.
ISBN 0455204179

Law of Intellectual Property in New Zealand / Grant. – Butterworths, 1989.
715p.
ISBN 0409787981 Hbk £130.00

Law of Interdict. – London : Butterworths, 1987.
ISBN 040610445X Pbk

Law of International Air Transport. – Sweet & Maxwell, 1962.
ISBN 0420354808 Hbk £95.00

Law of international institutions / D.W. Bowett. – 4th ed. – London : Sweet & Maxwell, 1982.
xv,431p; 23cm.
Published under the auspices of the London Institute for World Affairs by Stevens & Sons Previous ed.: 1975. Includes index.
ISBN 0420460101 Hbk £30
ISBN 0420460209 Pbk £21

Law of international telecommunications in Canada / Nicolas Mateesco Matte, Ram S. Jakhu. – Baden-Baden : Nomos, 1987.
131p.
Includes bibliographical references.
ISBN 3789013099

Law of international telecommunications in India / K.D. Gaur. – Baden-Baden : Nomos, 1988.
219p.
ISBN 3789013102

Law of international telecommunications in the United States / Stephen R. Barnett, Michael Botein, Eli M. Noam. – Baden-Baden : Nomos, 1988.
271p.
ISBN 3789013080

Law of international trade / by D.M. Day. – London : Butterworths, 1981.
xxii,254p,2p of plates; 22cm.
This book is an introduction to the law of international trade. Carriage of goods, insurance of goods in transit, government controls, EEC law, and statutory material are discussed in the work.
ISBN 040657202X Hbk
ISBN 0406572011 Pbk

Law of international trade / Mark S.W. Hoyle. – 2nd ed. – Bicester : CCH Editions, 1985.
vii,518p; 23cm.
Previous ed.: 1981?. Bibliography: p471-472. - Includes index.
ISBN 0863250726 Pbk

Law of international transactions / by Ferenc Madl : translated by J. Decsenyi. – Budapest : Akademiai Kiado, 1982.
206p.
Bibliography: p199-206. Translation of: Osszehasonlito nemzetkozi maganjog.
ISBN 9630529327

Law of Kenya : Cases and Statutes. – Nairobi : Kenya Literature Bureau, 1986.
Hbk £120.00

Law of Kidnapping and Sexual Offences / Singh. – Allahabad : Law Book Company, 1988.
500p.
Hbk £180.00

Law of Land Acquisition and Compensation, 2 Vols. – 7th ed. – Lucknow : Eastern Book Company, 1986.
2,144p.
Hbk £400.00

Law of Land Acquisition and Compensation, 2 Vols. – 7th ed. – Allahabad : Law Book Company, 1984.
With 1987 supplement.
Hbk £360.00

Law of landlord and tenant / Evans. – 2nd ed. – London : Butterworths, 1985.
xlvii,505p.
Previous ed.: 1974. Includes index.
ISBN 0406577323 Hbk £22.00
ISBN 0406577331 Pbk £14.50

Law of Lease. – 2nd ed. – Durban : Professional Publisher, 1976.
ISBN 0409037389 Hbk £0409037370

Law of Leases. – London : Estates Gazette, 1970.
ISBN 0900361174 Hbk £3.50

Law of Libel. – Sweet & Maxwell, 1912 Reprint.
ISBN 0421375604 Hbk £18.40

Law of libel and slander in Canada / Jeremy S. Williams. – 2nd ed. – Toronto : Butterworths, 1988.
xxxi, 145 p.; 24 cm.
Analysis of the law of defamation as it applies in each common law province of Canada, covering both jurisdictions which retain libel and slander as distinct torts, and jurisdictions which have adopted the Uniform Defamation Act. Covers the publication requirements, credit reporting and other commercial representations, limitation periods, damages and injunctions.
ISBN 0409876410 Hbk £57

Law of lien / Alfred H. Silvertown. – London : Butterworth, 1988.
190p; 25cm.
Includes index.
ISBN 040610395X Hbk £29.00

Law of Limitation, 3 Vols. – Lucknow : Eastern Book Company, 1984.
Hbk £450.00

Law of local government in the Republic of Ireland / by Ronan Keane. – Dublin : Incorporated Law Society of Ireland, 1982.
xliv,423p.
Includes index.
ISBN 0902027212

Law of Marine Insurance. – Abingdon : Professional Books, 1984.
ISBN 086205091X Hbk £63.00
ISBN 0862050960 Pbk £25.50

Law of Marine Insurance and Average Supplement. – London : Sweet & Maxwell, 1988.
ISBN 0420445005 Hbk £150.00

Law of Marine Insurance and Average (BSL). – 16th ed. 2 vols. – London : Sweet & Maxwell, 1981.
ISBN 0420445005 Hbk £170.00

Law of maritime delimitation - reflections. – Cambridge : Grotius, 1989.
343.
Assesses the scope and meaning of the solutions already reached to the problem of maritime delimitation and submits them to critical analysis. Also intends to identify the directions in which the evolution of the law is heading and to advance some suggestions as to desirable developments.
ISBN 0949009407 Hbk £55.00

Law of Maritime Liens. – Reprint of 1940 edition. – Abingdon : Professional Books.
Hbk

Law of markets and fairs. – Croydon : Tolley, 1984.
ISBN 0853143188 Hbk £45.00

Law of marriage / Susan M. Blake. – Chichester : Rose, 1982.
liii,280p; 20cm.
Includes index.
ISBN 0859923142 Hbk £14.00
ISBN 0859923088 Pbk £10.50

Law of Marriage and Divorce in India. – Lucknow : Eastern Book Company, 1982.
xxxii, 718p.
Hbk £100.00

Law of Meetings / Paul. – New Zealand ed. – London : Butterworths, 1981.
ISBN 040963560X Pbk £23.50

Law of mental health. – London : Fourmat, 1990.
244; 22.
ISBN 1851900837 Pbk uk19.95

Law of monopolies and restrictive trade practices in India / H.M. Jhala. – 2nd ed. – Bombay : Tripathi (N. M.), 1984.
xxxvii,456p.
Includes index.

Law of Monopolies and Restructive Trade Practices in India / T.G. Choudhury. – New Delhi : Prentice-Hall, 1981.
361p.
ISBN 087692075X Hbk £50.00

Law of Monopolies, Restrictive and Unfair Trade Practices. – Lucknow : Eastern Book Company, 1984.
134p.
Pbk £20.00

Law of Mortgages. – Sweet & Maxwell. – (Property and Conveyancing Library).
ISBN 0421344105 Hbk £65.00

Law of Motor Vehicles in U.P. – 3rd ed. – Lucknow : Eastern Book Company, 1984.
820p.
Hbk £100.00

Law of Municipalities and Municipal Corporations. – 3rd ed. – Allahabad : Law Book Company, 1987.
1,800p.
Hbk £380.00

Law of Muslim Marriage, Dissolution and Maintenance. – 2nd ed. – Allahabad : Law Book Company, 1988.
600p.
Hbk £175.00

Law of Nations and the New World. – Edmonton : University of Alberta Press, 1988.
ISBN 088864129X Hbk

Law of Nature and Nations / B. Kennett. – Repr. of 1703 ed. – Abingdon : Professional Books.
597p.
Hbk £450.00

Law of Naval Warfare : A Collection of Agreements and Documents with Commentaries. – Martinus Nijhoff.
ISBN 9024736528 Hbk £117.00

Law of Negotiable Instruments. – Singapore : Malayan Law Journal, 1984.
139p.
Discusses what constitutes a valid negotiable instrument, problems arising in cases of forgery and material alterations, concepts of holder and holder in due course, and provisions relating to cheques under the Singapore provisions that are in line with the English Cheques Act 1957.
ISBN 9971700417 Pbk £28.00

Law of Negotiable Instruments in Australia. – 2nd ed. – Butterworths, 1989.
256p.
ISBN 0409495271 Hbk £59.00
ISBN 040949528X Pbk £39.00

Law of negotiable instruments in Singapore and Malaysia. – Singapore : Malayan Law Journal, 1984.
xxviii,225.
Account of the basic law governing negotiable instruments, covering the curent practice where relevant. Includes status of parties to the bill upon its enforceability. Relevant Asian and English cases are discussed including some of the leading Commonwealth authorities from Australia and Canada.
ISBN 9971700409 Hbk £50.00

Law of negotiable instruments in South Africa Vol.1 : General principles / Denis V. Cowen and Leonard Gering. – Cape Town : Juta, 1985.
xxiv,587.
ISBN 0702115703

Law of non-international armed conflict : Protocol II to the 1949 Geneva conventions / edited by Howard S. Levie. – Dordrecht : M. Nijhoff, 1987.
xiii, 635 p.; 25 cm.
'A record of certain of the proceedings of the 1974-1977 Geneva Diplomatic Conference on the Reaffirmation and Development of International Humanitarian Law Applicable in Armed Conflicts which drafted the 1977 Protocol additional to the Geneva conventions of 12 August 1949, and relating to the protection of victims of non-international armed conflicts (Protocol II)'–T.p. verso. Includes indexes.
ISBN 9024734916 Hbk £275.00

Law of Notices : Civil and Criminal, with Model Forms. – 4th ed. – Allahabad : Law Book Co, 1984.
Hbk £150.00

Law of Nuisance. – Wellington : Butterworths, 1981.
This work on torts and the law of nuisance in United Kingdom is directed at practitioners and academics. The book presents a lengthy discussion of recent developments in the law on liability for natural occurrences.
ISBN 040614110X Hbk

Law of Obscenity : a Comparative Study. – Delhi : Mittal Publications, 1988.
Hbk £300.00

Law of Ownership of Property and Investigation of Title. – New Delhi : Bharat Law House, 1985.
Hbk £100.00

Law of parent and child / by Erwin Spiro. – 4th ed. – Cape Town : Juta, 1985.
lxv, 661 p.; 26 cm.
Includes bibliographical references and indexes.
ISBN 0702115746

Law of Partnership. – 3rd ed. – Lucknow : Eastern Book Company, 1982.
828p.
Hbk £110.00

Law of Partnership. – Durban : Professional Publishers, 1984.
ISBN 0409023620 Pbk

Law of partnership / by Charles D. Drake. – 3rd ed. – London : Sweet & Maxwell, 1983.
xxx,391p; 22cm.
Previous ed.: 1977. Includes index.
ISBN 0421298405 Pbk £10.50

Law of Partnership / Ernest H Scammell. – 15th ed. – London : Sweet & Maxwell, 1984.
ISBN 042129860X Hbk £92.00

Law of Partnership : Including Limited Partnership. – 15th ed. – London : Sweet & Maxwell, 1984.
ISBN 042129860X Hbk £82.00

Law of Partnership : Principles, Practice, Taxation. – Lucknow : Eastern Book Company, 1981.
627p.
Hbk £60.00

Law of Partnership : with Tax-Planing at a Glance. – Allahabad : Modern Law Publications, 1987.
Hbk £280.00

Law of Partnership in India / J.P. Gupta. – 2nd ed. – Allahabad : Orient Law House, 1983.
Hbk £200.00

Law of Partnership with Central and All State Rules, 2 Vols. – 2nd ed. – Allahabad : Law Publishers, 1983.
Hbk £66.00 set

Law of pilotage / by G.K. Geen and R.P.A. Douglas. – 2nd ed. – London : Lloyd's of London, 1983.
xx,177p.
Previous ed. published as: The law and administration of pilotage. 1977. Bibliography: p.xxi. - Includes index.
ISBN 0907432662

Law of Pre-Emption. – Lahore : Pakistan Law Times, 1981.
Hbk £36.00

Law of Prescription and Limitation of Actions in Scotland. – 3rd ed. – Edinburgh : W Green, 1981.
ISBN 0414006674 Hbk £12.50

Law of Pre-Trial Statements, Depositions and Police Diaries / Y.R. Rao. – 2nd ed. – Nagpur : Wadhura & Co, 1987.
763p.
Hbk £220.00

Law of Prints and Impressions. – 2nd ed 1972 2nd repr. – Allahabad : Law Book Company, 1988.
400p.
With supplement.
Pbk £100.00

Law of Private Defence / B.L. Yadav. – 5th ed. – Allahabad : Universal Book Agency, 1987.
Hbk £175.00

Law of Procedure and Justice in Ancient India. – New Delhi : Deep and Deep Publications, 1986.
320p.

Law of property / Bernard Rudden, F. H. Lawson. – 2nd ed. – Oxford : Clarendon, 1982.
ix,247p; 23cm. – (Clarendon law series).
Previous ed.: published as Introduction to the law of property. 1958. Includes index.
ISBN 0198761287 Hbk £14.00
ISBN 0198761295 Pbk £6.95

Law of property / A.J. Oosthuizen. – Cape Town : Juta, 1981.
xiii,105p.
Bibliography: p.
ISBN 0702111937

Law of Property / J Schoeman. – 2nd ed. – London : Butterworths, 1983.
ISBN 0409053120 Hbk £49.50
ISBN 0409053139 Pbk £35.40

Law of Property in Sri Lanka, Vol 1. – Colombo : Lake House Investments.
Pbk £15.50

Law of Property-the Transfer of Property Act, 1882 : a Commentary. – Allahabad : Orient Law House.
ISBN 086125516X Hbk £35.00

Law of Psychiatry and Morality. – Cambridge : Cambridge University Press, 1986.
ISBN 0521339545 Pbk £12.95

Law of Public Company Finance / R. Vann. – North Ryde : Law Book Co, 1986.
xxix, 593p.
ISBN 0455206856 Hbk £89.50

Law of public leisure services / by Michael Scott : foreword by Charles Cross. – London : Sweet & Maxwell, 1985.
lvii,352p; 26cm.
Draws together the spectrum of legal rights and duties arising out of the public leisure services, from the taking on of staff, to licensing activities and safety procedures. Includes sections on employment law, duties in tort, commons, open spaces, National Parks, and libraries and museums.
ISBN 0421326808 £25.00

Law of Railway Servants. – 2nd ed. – Allahabad : Law Book Company, 1984.
With 1987 supplement.
Hbk £120.00

Law of real property / Sir Robert Megarry and H.W.R. Wade. – 5th ed. – London : Stevens, 1984.
cxxviii,123p; 24cm.
Previous ed.: 1975. Includes index.
ISBN 0420467106 Hbk £
ISBN 0420470301 Pbk £26

Law of Real Property : Quebec. – Repr. of 1932 ed. – Agincourt : Carswell, 1986.
686p.
This work originally published in 1932, is a detailed English language reference guide to the law of 'unmovable property' under the Quebec Civil Code. The book offers a basic understanding of the Quebec law of real property.
Hbk £59.00

Law of Real Property in New South Wales. – North Ryde : Law Book Co.
xli, 372p.
ISBN 0455202397 Hbk £38.00

Law of Receivers / P.M.K. Nair. – 3rd ed. – Allahabad : Law Book Company, 1988.
1,000p.
Hbk £275.00

Law of receivers of companies / by Gavin Lightman and Gabriel Moss : with a foreword by Sir John Vinelott. – London : Sweet & Maxwell, 1986.
xlix,358p; 24cm.
Guide to the law relating to administrative receiverships, covering all aspects of practice and procedure. Includes sections on administrators, title retention clauses, and the role of the receiver in the winding up of a company.
ISBN 0421300906 £38.00

Law of Redundancy. – 3rd ed. – Sweet & Maxwell.
ISBN 0421339004 Hbk £40.00
ISBN 0421339101 Pbk £30.00

Law of Rent Control, Eviction and Leases in India, 3 Vols. – 2nd ed. 1980-1 repr. – Allahabad : Law Book Company, 1982.
Hbk £360.00

Law of residential homes and day-care establishments / M.D.A. Freeman and Christina M. Lyon. – London : Sweet & Maxwell, 1984.
xxvi,239p; 22cm.
Deals with children, the elderly, and the physically handicapped. Includes the Mental Health Act 1983 and the Health and Social Services and Social Security Adjudications Act 1983.
ISBN 0421258608 Pbk

Law of Restrictive Trade Practices in New Zealand. – 2nd. ed. – Butterworths, 1982.
ISBN 040960125X Hbk £33.10

Law of Retrenchment in India. – New Delhi : Deep and Deep Publications, 1982.
130p.
Hbk £55.00

Law of sale and lease / by A.J. Kerr. – Durban, South Africa : Butterworth Publishers, 1984.
xxxii, 352 p.; 25 cm.
Includes indexes.
ISBN 0409037494 Hbk £27.40
ISBN 0409037508 Pbk £19.50

Law of Sales Tax in Uttar Pradesh, 2 Vols. / G.C. Mathur. – 5th ed. – Lucknow : Eastern Book Company, 1986.
Hbk £175.00

Law of Salvage (BSL). – 5th ed. – London : Sweet & Maxwell, 1985.
ISBN 0420434305 Hbk £98.00

Law of Scotland relating to debt / W.A. Wilson. – Edinburgh : Green (W.) & Son, 1982.
lxxvii,380p; 22cm.
Deals with ways in which debts arise out of common transactions such as sale and hire purchase, debt recovery and defences such as payment and compensation. Full treatment of relevant sections of the Consumer Credit Act 1974, with discussion of securities, diligence, insolvency and documents on debt. Includes index.
ISBN 0414006828 Pbk

Law of Search and Seizure in Canada. – 2nd ed. – Butterworths, 1984.
358p.
Analyses the various processes of issuing and executing search warrants, as well as the different kinds of searches and seizures possible under the Criminal Code and other federal and provincial statutes. Also looks at the effects of the Charter of Rights.
ISBN 0409830283 Hbk £80.00

Law of securities : an account of the law pertaining to securities over real and personal property under the laws of the Australian States / Edward I.Sykes. – 4th edition. – Sydney : Law Book Company, 1986.
xcv,1043p.
ISBN 0455206287

Law of Set-Off. – London : Sweet & Maxwell, 1988.
ISBN 0421324503 Pbk

Law of Set-Off. – London : Sweet & Maxwell, 1986.
ISBN 0421348607 Hbk

Law of sewers and drains under the Public Health Acts / by J.F. Garner. – 6th ed. – London : Shaw & Sons, 1981.
xxxviii,206p; 22cm.
Previous ed.: 1975. Includes index. .
ISBN 0721905811 Pbk

Law of shipping and carriage in South Africa / by B.R. Bamford. – 3rd ed. – Cape Town : Juta, 1983.
xlvi,389p.
Previous ed.: 1973. Includes index.
ISBN 070211376X

Law of Shops and Establishments. – 12th ed. – Karachi : Bureau of Labour Publications, 1987.
20p.
Pbk £3.00

Law of Simple Discharge (In Private and Public Sectors) / Harminder Singh. – Lucknow : Eastern Book Company, 1984.
1,037p.
Hbk £160.00

Law of social security / A.I. Ogus ... et al. – 3rd ed. – London : Butterworths, 1988.
lxxii,634p.
Includes index. At head of cover title: Ogus & Barendt.
ISBN 040663372X

Law of Social Security. – Karachi : Bureau of Labour Publications, 1986.
40p.
Pbk £3.00

Law of South Africa / T.J. Scott. – To be completed in ca 29 vols and 2 index vols. Vols 1-12, 14-15, 17-21, 23, 24, 26, 28 and index to vols. 1-10 now available. – Durban : Professional Publishers, 1982.
ISBN 0409003387 Hbk £2,205.00 (set)

Law of Speaking Orders. – 3rd ed. – Lucknow : Eastern Book Company, 1985.
Hbk

Law of Special Educational Needs. – Oxford : Croom Helm, 1985.
ISBN 070993498X Pbk £7.95

Law of Specific Relief. – 8th ed. – Allahabad : Law Publishers, 1982.
£72.00

Law of Specific Reliefs : an Exhaustive Commentary on The Specific Relief Act 1887 : with Ammendments and Case Law Up-to-date. – Lahore : Pakistan Law Times.
Hbk £75.00

Law of Subdivision Control in Ontario : a Practical Guide to Section 49 of the Planning Act. – Agincourt : Carswell, 1988.
350p.
Hbk £48.75

Law of Succession. – 2nd ed. – Plymouth : Macdonald & Evans, 1981.
272p. – (M and E Handbook Ser.).
ISBN 0712112561 Hbk £4.95

Law of succession / Anthony R. Mellows. – 4th ed. – London : Butterworths, 1983.
lv,619p; 26cm.
Previous ed.: 1977. Includes index.
ISBN 0406623775 Hbk £
ISBN 0406623783 Pbk £23.95

Law of succession / A.J. Oosthuizen. – Cape Town : Juta, 1982.
xiv,96p.
Bibliography: p. Includes the text of the Wills Act 7 of 1953.
ISBN 0702112879

Law of succession : intestate succession. – South African Law Commission. – Pretoria : South African Law Commission, 1983.
vii,49p. – (Working paper).
Project 22. Bibliography: pv-vi.

Law of Succession Certificate. – 6th ed. – Allahabad : Law Book Company, 1987.
Hbk £75.00

Law of Superannuation in Australia. – Woolloomooloo : International Business Communications.
476p.
ISBN 0959029001 Hbk £60.00

Law of supplementary benefits / M. S. Rowell, A. M. Wilton. – London : Butterworths, 1982.
xxxi,239p; 22cm.
ISBN 0406649103

Law of Surtax in India. – Bombay : Tripathi, 1983.
xx, 191p.
Pbk £60.00

Law of Suspension. – 2nd ed. – Lucknow : Eastern Book Company, 1985.
145p.
Hbk £30.00

Law of Textiles in India. – Delhi : Periodical Experts Book Agency, 1986.
387p.
£275.00

Law of the carriage of goods by land, sea and air / by Jasper Ridley. – 6th ed. – London : Shaw, 1982.
xlviii,328p; 22cm.
Previous ed.: 1978. Includes index.
ISBN 0721906222 Pbk £9.50

Law of the Charter : general principles / Dale Gibson. – Toronto : Carswell, 1986.
xxxiii,302p.
ISBN 0459389009

Law of the Common Agricultural Policy / by Francis G. Snyder. – London : Sweet & Maxwell, 1985.
130p; 22cm.
Includes index.
ISBN 0421318805 Hbk £11.50 :
ISBN 0421318902 Pbk £6.50

Law of the European Communities, 2 Vols. – London : Butterworths, 1986.
ISBN 0406003009 Hbk £140.00

Law Of The European Economic Community / P E Herzog. – Matthew Bender, 1976.
ISBN 0000999047 Hbk £247.00

Law of the International Civil Service: as applied by internatinal administrative tribunals. – Oxford : Clarendon Press.
686.
ISBN 0198255608 Hbk £60

Law of the International Civil Service: as applied by internatinal administrative tribunals. – Oxford : Clarendon Press.
1350.
On the law as applied by international administrative tribunals in the area of employment relations between international organisations and their staff. Analyses the way in which obligations and rights are enforced and recognised.
ISBN 0198256108 Hbk £60

Law of the investment markets. – Oxford : Blackwell Scientific, 1990.
672. – (Blackwell Law Library).
A detailed guide to the complex rules and procedures prescribed by the Financial Services Act 1986; covers the history, structure, and regulation of investment markets. Further chapters cover finacial, accounting and reporting rules, the marketing of unlisted securities, unit trusts, investment schemes and overseas aspects of investments.
Investment practitioners, Lawyers, Investors, Financial advisors
ISBN 0632023724 Hbk £85

Law of the Parish Church. – 5th ed. – London : Butterworths, 1975.
ISBN 0406174016 Pbk £10.95

Law of the Prerogatives of the Crown. – Repr. of 1820 ed. – Abingdon : Professional Books.
64p.
Hbk £40.00

Law of the Press, Second Edition : Asutosh Lectures, Calcutta University. – 2nd ed. – New Delhi : Prentice-Hall, 1986.
606p.
ISBN 0876924186 Hbk £75.00

Law of the sea / R.R. Churchill and A.V. Lowe. – Manchester : Manchester University Press, 1983.
xxxiii,321p; 24cm.
Includes bibliographies and index.
ISBN 0719009367 £19.50

Law of the Sea : a Select Bibliography. – Geneva : United Nations Publications.
ISBN 9210330633 Hbk £9.50

Law of the Sea : A Select Bibliography. – London : HMSO, 1985.
ISBN 9211333350 Hbk £12.00

Law of the Sea : Current Developments in State Practice. – Geneva : United Nations Publications.
ISBN 9211332850 Hbk £23.00

Law of the Sea : Problems of Conflict and Management of Fisheries in Southeast Asia. – Metro Manila : International Center for Living Aquatic Resources Management.
68p.
Hbk £4.00 (surface)

Law of the Sea : Status of the UN Convention on the Law of the Sea. – London : HMSO, 1986.
52p.
Contains declarations explaining the understanding and interpretation of the Law of the Sea by its international signatories.
ISBN 9211332699 Hbk £8.00

Law of the Sea : Text of U.N. Conventions. – Delhi : Mittal Publications, 1985.
Hbk £190.00

Law of the Sea and Antarctica. – Hobart : University of Tasmania, Department of Political Science.
£1.50

Law of the sea and maritime boundary delimitation in South-East Asia / Kriangsak Kittichaisaree. – Singapore : Oxford University Press, 1987.
xv, 209 p.; 23 cm.
Discusses maritime boundary delimination in international law. Concentrates on South-East Asia, but legal analyses are examined in a global context, using South-East Asian practice as concrete instances to elaborate particular legal problems.
ISBN 0195888626 Hbk £20.00

Law of the Sea Convention 1982 : Text and Commentary. – London : Butterworths, 1985.
ISBN 0406252610 Hbk

Law of the Sea Zones in the Pacific Ocean. – Singapore : Institute of Southeast Asian Studies, 1987.
120p.
ISBN 9971988739 Hbk £26.00

Law of the Territorial Sea : Evolution and Development. – Calcutta : Naya Prokash, 1988.
280p.
ISBN 8185109699 Hbk £200.00

Law of theft / J.C. Smith. – 5th ed. – London : Butterworths, 1984.
xxxii,257p; 26cm.
Previous ed.: 1979. Includes index.
ISBN 0406379084 Hbk £
ISBN 0406379092 Pbk £13.95

Law of Tort. – London : Duckworth (Gerald), 1986.
ISBN 0715620126 Hbk £29.95

Law of Tort. – Lucknow : Eastern Book Company, 1987.
Hbk £200.00

Law of Torts
Supplement 1987. – 4th ed. – Plymouth : Macdonald & Evans, 1982.
ISBN 0712127046 Pbk £6.50
Supplement-1987. –
ISBN 0421378409

Law of Torts. – 5th ed. – Allahabad : Law Book Company, 1985.
lxxx, 103p.
Hbk £220.00

Law of torts / Margaret Brazier. – 8th ed. – London : Butterworths, 1988.
lix,562p.
Previous ed.: / by Harry Street. 1983. Includes index.
ISBN 0406662118 Hbk £34
ISBN 0406662126 Pbk £19.95

Law of Torts / Stephenson. – London : Financial Training, 1985.
– (SWOT).
ISBN 0906322731 Pbk £7.50

Law of Torts / Kumud Desai. – 8th ed. – Bombay : Tripathi, 1987.
744p.
bd £220.00

Law of Torts. – 7th ed. – Sweet & Maxwell.
ISBN 0455207534 Hbk £30.00
ISBN 0455207542 Pbk £23.00

Law of torts / by John G. Fleming. – 6th ed. – Sydney : Law book Company, 1983.
lii,702p; 24cm.
Previous ed.: 1977. Includes bibliographical references and index.
ISBN 0455205477 Hbk £30.00
ISBN 0455205485 Pbk £23.00

Law of torts / by John G. Fleming. – 7th ed. – Sydney : Law Book Company, 1987.
lxix,706p; 25cm.
Previous ed.: 1983. Includes index.
ISBN 0455207534 Hbk
ISBN 0455207542 Pbk

Law of Torts / Dhirajlal. – 21st ed. – Nagpur : Wadhura & Co, 1987.
£250.00

Law of Torts. – 4th ed. 1976 repr. – Lucknow : Eastern Book Company, 1981.
528p.
Pbk £22.50

Law of Torts. – 8th ed. – London : Butterworths, 1988.
ISBN 0406662118 Hbk £34.00
ISBN 0406662126 Pbk £19.95

Law of Torts. – 4th ed. – Plymouth : Macdonald & Evans, 1982.
– (M and E Handbook Ser.).
ISBN 0712127046 Hbk £5.95

Law of torts in Australia / F.A. Trindade, Peter Cane. – Melbourne : Oxford University Press, 1985.
lxv, 763 p.; 24 cm.
Includes indexes.
ISBN 0195544633 Pbk £39.00
ISBN 0195544641 Hbk £55.00

Law of Torts, Tenth Edition. – 4th repr. 1984. – New Delhi : Prentice-Hall.
232p.
ISBN 0876920253 Hbk £25.00

Law of Town and Country Planning. – 3rd ed. – Butterworths, 1981.
ISBN 0409600377 Hbk £103.95
Supplement. –
ISBN 0409701513 Hbk £35.75

Law Of Treaties. – Reprint. – Oxford : Oxford University Press, 1961.
ISBN 0198251521 Hbk £70.00

Law of Trespass / Birts. – London : Butterworths, 1987.
ISBN 040614816 Pbk £15.95

Law of trusts. – South African Law Commission. – Pretoria : South African Law Commission, 1983.
vi,63p. – (Working paper).
Project 9. Bibliography: pv-vi.

Law of Trusts. – 2nd ed. Repr. of 1980 ed. – Plymouth : Macdonald & Evans, 1982.
352p. – (M and E Handbook Ser.).
ISBN 0712112553 Hbk £4.95

Law of Trusts / J. Mowbray. – 18th ed. – London : Sweet & Maxwell.
– (Property and Conveyancing Library).
ISBN 0421233907 Hbk

Law of trusts / J.G. Riddall. – 3rd ed. – London : Butterworths, 1987.
420p; 24cm.
Previous ed.: 1982. Includes index.
ISBN 0406648425 Hbk £27.00
ISBN 0406648433 Pbk £17.95

Law of trusts / J.G. Riddall. – 2nd ed. – London : Butterworths, 1982.
xxxi, 371p.
This textbook for United Kingdom students of trusts deals with the creation of trusts; the appointment, powers, and duties of trustees; and beneficiaries. Hypothetical examples, tables, and diagrams are included in the book.
ISBN 0406648379

Law of trusts / George W. Keeton. – 11th ed. – Chichester : Rose, 1983.
lxiv,578p; 26cm.
Previous ed.: 1974. Includes index.
ISBN 085992369X £45.00

Law of Trusts / Hodkinson. – London : CCH, 1984.
ISBN 086325019X Pbk £20.00

Law of Trusts and Trustees in New Zealand / Kelly. – 5th ed. – London : Butterworths, 1981.
ISBN 0409600717 Hbk £44.50

Law of Trusts in Canada. – Agincourt : Carswell, 1984.
ISBN 045936200 Hbk £41.80

Law of Tug, Tow and Pilotage. – 2nd ed. – London : Chapman & Hall, 1982.
ISBN 0412250209 Hbk £60.00

Law of Unfair Dismissal / John H. Angel. – 2nd ed. – Wellington : Butterworths, 1985.
xlv,444; 22cm.
This book provides a detailed discussion of the law of unfair dismissal in the United Kingdom. The work includes references to the changes brought about by recent legislation, such as, the Employment Protection (Consolidation) Act of 1978 and the Employment Acts of 1980 and 1982.
ISBN 0406107076 Pbk

Law of unjust contracts : including the Contracts Review Act 1980 (NSW) with detailed annotations, procedure, and pleadings / by John R. Peden. – Sydney : Butterworths, 1981.
xix, 187 p.; 22 cm.
Includes bibliographical references and index.
ISBN 0409309311 Hbk £28.00

Law of war / Ingrid Detter de Lupis. – Cambridge : Cambridge University Press, 1987.
xx,411p; 23cm.
Bibliography: p367-406. - Includes index.
ISBN 0521343372 Hbk £40.00
ISBN 0521348382 Pbk £15.00

Law of War and the Armed Forces. – 2nd ed. – Geneva : Comite International de la Croix-Rouge, 1981.
44p.
Hbk £3.00

Law of Weights and Measures. – 2nd ed. – London : Butterworths, 1977.
Service.
ISBN 0406326452 Llf £125.00

Law of wills
Supplement 1984 / J.B. Clark. – 4th ed. – Sweet & Maxwell.
ISBN 0420452508 Hbk £120.00
Supplement/ 1984. –
ISBN 0420469400 Pbk

Law of Wills along with Model Forms. – 3rd ed. – Allahabad : Law Publishers, 1982.
Hbk £40.50

Law of Wills and Administration. – 5th ed. – Butterworths, 1984.
Takes into account the significant developments made by the Wills Amendment Act 1977, and amendments to the Administration Act 1969, and the Status of Children Act 1969.
ISBN 0409601306 Hbk £90.75

Law of Workers' Children Education. – Karachi : Bureau of Labour Publications, 1986.
54p.
Pbk £4.50

Law of Workers' Participation in Companies Profits. – Karachi : Bureau of Labour Publications, 1986.
Pbk £3.00

Law of Workmen's Compensation. – 2nd ed. – Karachi : Bureau of Labour Publications, 1986.
48p.
Pbk £23.00

Law of Writs. – 3rd ed. – Lucknow : Eastern Book Company, 1983.
1,070p.
Hbk £155.00

Law of Your Land : a Practical Guide to the New Canadian Constitution. – Toronto : Canadian Broadcasting Corporation Enterprises, 1984.
ISBN 0887941079 Pbk £5.95

Law office practice management guide. – Scarborough, Ontario : Butterworths (Canada), 1988.
350.
Guide to the operation and management of a law office practice. Provides information on starting the practice, human resource planning, interviewing process selection and salary determination, avoiding wrongful dismissal, financing the practice, law firm recruitment, performance appraisal techniques, training and development, and marketing of professional services.
ISBN 0409805610 Hbk

Law Officers' opinions to the Foreign Office 1793-1860 : a reproduction of the manuscript series with index and commentaries / prepared and edited by Clive Parry. – 97. – Farnborough, Hants. : Gregg International, 1970.
25cm.
Later printed reports published in microfilm under the title: Great Britain Law Officers' opinions. - Dobbs Ferry, N.Y.: Trans-Media, 1976.
ISBN 0576012009

Law on child care and family services / Department of Health and Social Security...et al. : presented to Parliament by the Secretary of State for Social Services... – London : H.M.S.O., 1987.
iv,22p.
ISBN 0101006225

Law on Speeding and Radar / Paul Douglas Haines. – Toronto : Macmillan of Canada, 1988.
120p.
ISBN 077159531X Pbk £6.95

Law on Speeding and Radar / Paul Douglas Haines. – Butterworths, 1985.
136p.
States the law relating to speeding and examines all relevant authorities on speeding and the use of radar in speeding. Examines the identification of speeding as an absolute liability offence and presents a comprehensive picture of how the law has evolved.
ISBN 0409811793 Hbk £36.95

Law on the Federal Constitutional Court : documents on politics and society in the Federal Republic of Germany / Oguz Akalin. – Bonn : Inter Nationes, 1982.
69p.
Bibliography: p.69. Prepared by Oguz Akalin.

Law on the misuse of drugs. – London : Sweet & Maxwell, 1988.
Refers to the Intoxicating Substances (Supply) Act 1985, and the Drug Trafficking Offences Act 1986 in the context of solvent abuse, drug-kits, and drug-trafficking profits. Lists sentencing examples. Combines an historic perspective of drug misuse with an examination of the legal implications involved.
ISBN 0421396202 Hbk £19

Law on unfair dismissal : guidance for small firms / Joan Henderson. – London : H.M.S.O., 1982.
13p.

Law, or a Discourse Thereof. – 4th ed. Repr. of 1661 ed. – Abingdon : Professional Books.
238p.
Hbk £75.00

Law, Order and the Authoritarian State. – Open University Press.
ISBN 0353155111 Hbk £25.00

Law, Politics and the Judicial Process in Canada. – 4th repr. – Calgary : University of Calgary Press, 1987.
356p.
ISBN 0919813038 Pbk £16.95

Law practice of Alexander Hamilton : documents and commentary
Vol.5 : editors Julius Goebel, Jr. and Joseph H. Smith : associate editors Winnifred Bowers ... et al. / Julius Goebel, Joseph H. Smith, Winnifred Bowers. – New York : Published under the auspices of the William Nelson Cromwell Foundation by Columbia University Press, 1981.
xiv,754p; 24cm.
Includes index.
ISBN 0231089295 £52.00

Law, Procedure and Ready Reckoner of Bonus, E.S.I. Gratuity and Provident Fund / Abha Kulshreshtha. – Delhi : Metropolitan Book Co, 1987.
370p.
ISBN 812000258X Hbk £150.00

Law Provincial Insolvency Act. – 5th ed. – Allahabad : Universal Book Agency, 1988.
212p.
Hbk £150.00

Law publishing and legal information : small jurisdictions of the British Isles / edited by William Twining and Jennifer Uglow. – London : Sweet & Maxwell, 1981.
181p; 22cm.
Bibliography: p150-178. - Includes index.
ISBN 0421289309 Pbk £10.00

Law Quarterly Review. – London : Sweet & Maxwell, 1982.
Hbk £37.00

Law Reform Commission
Insurance contracts / Law Reform Commission. – Canberra : Australian Government Publishing Service, 1982.
xxxx,372p. – (Report).
Bibliography: p.352-357. - Includes index.
ISBN 064401217X

—Law Reform Commission, Annual Report, 1981. – Law Reform Commission. – Canberra : Australian Government Publishing Service, 1981.
69p. – (ALRC Report: No. 19).
Hbk £3.00

—Law Reform Commission, Annual Report, 1982. – Law Reform Commission. – Canberra : Australian Government Publishing Service, 1982.
73p. – (ALRC Report: No. 21).
Hbk £4.60

—Law Reform Commission, Annual Report, 1983. – Law Reform Commission. – Canberra : Australian Government Publishing Service, 1983.
73p. – (ALRC Report: No. 23).
Hbk £4.30

—Matrimonial property / Law Reform Commission. – Canberra : Australian Government Publishing Service, 1987.
xxxiv,382p. – (Report).
Bibliography: p.367-372. - Includes index.

—Privacy : Proposals
Vol. 2. – Law Reform Commission. – Canberra : Australian Government Publishing Service, 1983.
xvi, 443p. – (ALRC Report Ser.: No. 22).
ISBN 0644012501 Hbk £10.40

—Privacy : Summary of Report. – Law Reform Commission. – Canberra : Australian Government Publishing Service, 1983.
v, 50p. – (ALRC Report Ser.).
ISBN 0644012544 Hbk £2.90

—Report on certificates of lis pendens / Law Reform Commission. – Winnipeg : Queen's Printer, 1983.
28p. – (Report).

—Report on investment provisions under The Trustee Act / Law Reform Commission. – Winnipeg : Queen's Printer, 1982.
i,38p. – (Report).

—Report on prejudgment compensation on money awards : alternatives to interest / Law Reform Commission. – Winnipeg : Queen's Printer, 1982.
iv,108p. – (Report).

—Report on the rules against accumulations and perpetuities / Law Reform Commission. – Winnipeg : Queen's Printer, 1982.
i,105p. – (Report).

—Report on the structure of the courts Part 1 : Amalgamation of the Court of Queen's Bench and the County Courts of Manitoba / Law Reform Commission. – Winnipeg : Queen's Printer, 1982.
iii,38,6p. – (Report).

—Report on The Survivorship Act / Law Reform Commission. – Winnipeg : Queen's Printer, 1982.
ii,44p. – (Report).

—Sentencing / Law Reform Commission. – Canberra : Australian Government Publishing Service, 1988.
lv,203p. – (Report).
Bibliography: p.197-203. Includes draft legislation.
ISBN 0644069104

—Service and execution of process / Law Reform Commission. – Canberra : Australian Government Publishing Service, 1987.
lix,539p. – (Report).
Bibliography: pp.527-531. - Includes index. Includes draft legislation.
ISBN 0644013796

Law Reform Commission, Annual Report, 1981. – Law Reform Commission. – Canberra : Australian Government Publishing Service, 1981.
69p. – (ALRC Report: No. 19).
Hbk £3.00

Law Reform Commission, Annual Report, 1982. – Law Reform Commission. – Canberra : Australian Government Publishing Service, 1982.
73p. – (ALRC Report: No. 21).
Hbk £4.60

Law Reform Commission, Annual Report, 1983. – Law Reform Commission. – Canberra : Australian Government Publishing Service, 1983.
73p. – (ALRC Report: No. 23).
Hbk £4.30

Law Reform Commission of British Columbia
Authority of a guardian / Law Reform Commission of British Columbia. – Vancouver : Law Reform Commission of British Columbia, 1985.
13p.
ISBN 0771884664

—Breach of promise of marriage. – Law Reform Commission of British Columbia. – Vancouver : Law Reform Commission of British Columbia, 1983.
iii,67p. – (Working paper).

—Bulk sales legislation / Law Reform Commission of British Columbia. – Vancouver : The Commission, 1983.
v,115p. – (Working paper).
Includes bibliographical references.

—Buyer's lien : a new consumer remedy / Law Reform Commission of British Columbia. – Vancouver : The Commission, 1986.
iii,52p. – (Working paper).
Includes bibliographical references.

—Commercial Tenancy Act. – Law Reform Commission of British Columbia. – Vancouver : Law Reform Commission of British Columbia, 1988.
v,185p. – (Working paper).
Includes extracts from legislation.
ISBN 0771886624

—Compensation for non-pecuniary loss / Law Reform Commission of British Columbia. – Vancouver : The Commission, 1983.
iii,53p. – (Working paper).
Includes bibliographical references.

—Competing rights to mingled property tracing and the rule in Clayton's case / Law Reform Commission of British Columbia. – Vancouver : Law Reform Commission of British Columbia, 1982.
iv,122p. – (Working paper).
Includes bibliographical references and index.

—Co-ownership of land / Law Reform Commission of British Columbia. – Vancouver : The Commission, 1987.
ii,75p. – (Working paper).
Caatalogued from cover. Includes bibliographical references. Includes Draft Property Law Amendment Act.
ISBN 0771886071

—Court Order Interest Act / Law Reform Commission of British Columbia. – Vancouver : The Commission, 1985.
xi,409p. – (Working paper).

—Covenants in restraint of trade / Law Reform Commission of British Columbia. – Vancouver : The Commission, 1983.
iii,69p. – (Working paper).
Includes bibliographical references.

—Crown as creditor : priorities and privileges. – Law Reform Commission of British Columbia. – Vancouver : Law Reform Commission of British Columbia, 1981.
v,179p. – (Working paper).

—Deeds and seals / Law Reform Commission of British Columbia. – Victoria : Government of British Columbia, 1987.
ii,39p. – (Working paper).
Includes bibliographical references.
ISBN 0771886020

—Execution against shares / Law Reform Commission of British Columbia. – Vancouver : The Commission, 1987.
iii,88p. – (Working paper).

→ Family property.

—Foreign money liabilities / Law Reform Commission of British Columbia. – Vancouver : Law Reform Commission of British Columbia, 1982.
iv,121p. – (Working paper).

—Fraudulent conveyances and preferences / Law Reform Commission of British Columbia. – Vancouver : The Commission, 1986.
viii,216p. – (Working paper).
Includes bibliographical references.

—Illegal contracts / Law Reform Commission of British Columbia. – Vancouver : The Commission, 1982.
vi,179p. – (Working paper).
Includes bibliographical references.

—Intentional interference with domestic relations / Law Reform Commission of British Columbia. – Vancouver : The Commission, 1983.
iii,55p. – (Working paper).
Includes bibliographical references.

—Interpretation of wills / Law Reform Commission of British Columbia. – Vancouver : Law Reform Commission of British Columbia, 1981.
iv,164p. – (Working paper).

—Interspousal immunity in tort / Law Reform Commission of British Columbia. – Vancouver : The Commission, 1982.
iii,42p. – (Working paper).
Includes bibliographical references.

—Land (Settled Estate) Act. – Law Reform Commission of British Columbia. – Vancouver : The Commission, 1988.
iii,38p. – (Working paper).
ISBN 077188625X

—Mortgages of land : the priority of further advances / Law Reform Commission of British Columbia. – Vancouver : The Commission, 1985.
iv,76p. – (Working paper).
Includes bibliographical references.

→ Office of sheriff.

—Peremptory challenges in civil jury trials / Law Reform Commission of British Columbia. – Vancouver : The Commission, 1982.
ii,31p. – (Working paper).
Includes bibliographical references.

—Performance under protest / Law Reform Commission of British Columbia. – Vancouver : The Commission, 1984.
ii,35p. – (Working paper).
Includes bibliographical references.

—Personal liability under a mortgage or agreement for sale / Law Reform Commission of British Columbia. – Vancouver : The Commission, 1985.
ii,52p. – (Working paper).
Includes bibliographical references.

—Report on arbitration / Law Reform Commission of British Columbia. – Vancouver : The Commission, 1982.
149p.
ISBN 0771883110

—Report on breach of promise of marriage. – Law Reform Commission of British Columbia. – Victoria : Queen's Printer, 1983.
36p.
ISBN 0771883811

—Report on bulk sales legislation / Law Reform Commission of British Columbia. – Victoria : Queen's Printer, 1983.
45p.
Includes bibliographical references.
ISBN 0771883943

→ Report on cable television and defamation.

—Report on compensation for non-pecuniary loss / Law Reform Commission of British Columbia. – Vancouver : Law Reform Commission of British Columbia, 1984.
40p.
ISBN 0771884567

—Report on co-ownership of land / Law Reform Commmission of British Columbia. – Vancouver : The Commission, 1988.
Includes bibliographical references. Includes draft legislation and text of the Partition of Property Act.
ISBN 0771887256

—Report on covenants in restraint of trade. – Law Reform Commission of British Columbia. – Victoria : Queen's Printer, 1984.
76p.
Includes bibliographical references.
ISBN 077188429X

—Report on deeds and seals / Law Reform Commission of British Columbia. – Vancouver : The Commission, 1988.
ii,47p.
Includes bibliographical references.
ISBN 0771886799

→ Report on distress for rent.

—Report on foreign money liabilities / Law Reform Commission of British Columbia. – Vancouver : The Commission, 1983.
64p.
Includes bibliographical references.
ISBN 0771883919

—Report on fraudulent conveyances and preferences : Law Reform Commission of British Columbia. – Law Reform Commission of British Columbia. – Vancouver : The Commission, 1988.
vii,180p.
Includes bibliographical references. Includes draft legislation.
ISBN 0771886314

—Report on illegal transactions. – Law Reform Commission of British Columbia. – Victoria : Queen's Printer, 1983.
115p.
ISBN 077188401X

—Report on international interference with domestic relations / Law Reform Commission of British Columbia. – Victoria : Queen's Printer, 1983.
27p.
Includes bibliographical references.
ISBN 0771883986

—Report on interpretation of wills. – Law Reform Commission of British Columbia. – Victoria : Queen's Printer, 1982.
58p.
ISBN 0771883455

—Report on interspousal immunity in tort / Law Reform Commission of British Columbia. – Victoria : Queen's Printer, 983.
21p.

—Report on mortgages of land : the priority of further advances / Law Reform Commission of British Columbia. – Vancouver : The Commission, 1986.
60p.
Includes bibliographical references.
ISBN 0771885067

—Report on obsolete remedies against estate property : Estate Administration Act, Part 9 / Law Reform Commission of British Columbia. – Vancouver : The Commission, 1987.
22p.
Includes bibliographical references.
ISBN 0771885695

—Report on peremptory challenges in civil jury trials. – Law Reform Commission of British Columbia. – Victoria : Queen's Printer, 1983.
22p.
ISBN 0771883773

—Report on performance under protest / Law Reform Commission of British Columbia. – Vancouver : The Commission, 1985.
21p.
Includes bibliographical references.
ISBN 077188477X

—Report on personal liability under a mortgage or agreement for sale. – Law Reform Commission of British Columbia. – Victoria : Queen's Printer, 1986.
37p.
Date on front cover: 1985. Includes bibliographical references.
ISBN 0771884982

—Report on presumptions of survivorship. – Law Reform Commission of British Columbia. – Victoria : Queen's Printer, 1982.
29p.
ISBN 0771883382

—Report on review of civil jury awards / Law Reform Commission of British Columbia. – Vancouver : The Commission, 1984.
60p.
Includes bibliographical references.
ISBN 0771884478

—Report on settlement offers / Law Reform Commission of British Columbia. – Vancouver : Law Reform Commission of British Columbia, 1984.
47p.
ISBN 0771884494

—Report on spousal agreements / Law Reform Commission of British Columbia. – Victoria : Queens Printer, 1986.
37p.
Includes bibliographical references.
ISBN 0771885326

—Report on statutory succession rights / Law Reform Commission of British Columbia. – Vancouver : The Commission, 1983.
209p.
Date on title page 1983.
ISBN 0771884087

—Report on the action per quod servitium amisit / Law Reform Commission of British Columbia. – Victoria : Queens Printer, 1986.
20p.
Includes bilbiographical references.
ISBN 0771885490

—Report on the buyer's lien : a new consumer remedy / Law Reform Commission of British Columbia. – Vancouver : The Commission, 1987.
iv,62p.
Includes bibliographical references.
ISBN 0771885954

—Report on the Court Order Interest Act / Law Reform Commission of British Columbia. – Vancouver : The Commission, 1987.
139p.
Includes bibliographical references.
ISBN 077188561X

—Report on the Crown as creditor : priorities and privileges. – Law Reform Commission of British Columbia. – Victoria : Queen's Printer, 1982.
99p.
ISBN 0771883404

—Report on the Land (Settled Estate) Act / Law Reform Commission of British Columbia. – Vancouver : The Commission, 1988.
41p.
Includes text of the Land (Settled Estate) Act and Trust Variation Act.
ISBN 0771887248

—Review of civil jury awards / Law Reform Commission of British Columbia. – Vancouver : The Commission, 1983.
iii,104p. – (Working paper).
Includes bibliographical references.

—Set-off / Law Reform Commission of British Columbia. – Vancouver : The Commission, 1987.
iv,81p. – (Working paper).
Includes bibliographical references.

—Settlement offers / Law Reform Commission of British Columbia. – Vancouver : The Commission, 1984.
iii,92p. – (Working paper).
Includes bibliographical references.

—Shared liability / Law Reform Commission of British Columbia. – Vancouver : The Commission, 1985.
iv,62p. – (Working paper).
Includes bibliographical references.

—Spousal agreements / Law Reform Commission of British Columbia. – Vancouver : The Commission, 1985.
iii,74p. – (Working paper).
Includes bibliographical references.

—Statutory succession rights / Law Reform Commission of British Columbia. – Vancouver : The Commission, 1982.
vii,401p. – (Working paper).

—Testamentary intent and unexpected circumstances / Law Reform Commission of British Columbia. – Vancover : The Commission, 1987.
iv,77p. – (Working paper).
Includes bibliographical references.
ISBN 0771886047

—Vicarious liability under the Motor Vehicle Act. – Law Reform Commission of British Columbia. – Vancouver : The Commission, 1988.
ii,60p. – (Working paper).
ISBN 0771886241

Law Reform Commission of Canada
Arrest / Law Reform Commission of Canada. – Ottawa : The Commission, 1985.
143,161p. – (Working paper).
Includes bibliographical references. Added t.p. in French: L'arrestation. Cover title: Criminal law : arrest. Pages numbered in opposite directions. Text in English and French.
ISBN 0662538013

—Assault / Law Reform Commission of Canada. – Ottawa : the Commission, 1984.
59,68p. – (Working paper).
Includes bibliographical references. Added t.p. in French: Les voies de fait. Pages numbered in opposite directions. Text in English and French.
ISBN 0662534174

—Behaviour alteration and the criminal law / Law Reform Commission of Canada. – Ottawa : The Commission, 1985.
48,56p. – (Working paper).
Bibliography: p.44-48. Added t.p. in French: Les techniques de modification du comportement et de droit penal. Cover title: Protection of life : behaviour alteration and the criminal law. Pages numbered in opposite directions. Text in English and French.
ISBN 0662538579

—Bigamy / Law Reform Commission of Canada. – Ottawa : The Commission, 1985.
32,34p. – (Working paper).
Includes bibliographical references. Added t.p. in French: La bigamie. Cover title: Criminal law : bigamy. Pages numbered in opposite directions. Text in English and French.
ISBN 0662538560

—Charge document in criminal cases. – Law Reform Commission of. – Ottawa : The Commission, 1987.
57,63p. – (Working paper).
Includes bibliographical references. Added t.p. in French: Le document d'inculpation. Pages numbered in opposite directions. Text in English and French.
ISBN 0662549635

—Classification of offences / Law Reform Commission of Canada. – Ottawa : The Commission, 1986.
92,98p. – (Working paper).
Includes bibliographical references. Pages numbered in opposite directions. Text in English and French.
ISBN 0662545699

—Compelling appearance, interim release and pre-trial detention / Law Reform Commission of Canada. – Ottawa : The Commission, 1988.
138,150p. – (Working paper).
Added t.p. in French: Les mesures assurant la comparution, la mise en liberte provisoire et la detention avant le proces. Pages numbered in opposite directions. Text in English and French.
ISBN 0662558960

—Contempt of Court / Law Reform Commission of Canada. – Ontario : Law Reform Commission of Canada, 1982.
67,69p; 25cm. – (Report).
English and French texts bound in reverse.
ISBN 0662512995

—Crimes against the environment / Law Reform Commission of Canada. – Ottawa : The Commission, 1985.
75,85p. – (Working paper).
Bibliography: p.71-72. Cover title: Protection of life: crimes against the environment. Added t.p. in French: Les crimes contre l'environment. Pages numbered in opposite directions. Text in English and French.
ISBN 0662539907

—Crimes against the state / Law Reform Commission of Canada. – Ottawa : The Commission, 1986.
72,76p. – (Working paper).
Includes bibliographies. Added t.p. in French: Les crimes contre l'etat. Pages numbered in opposite directions. Text in English and French.

—Criminal intrusion / Law Reform Commission of Canada. – Ottawa : The Commission, 1986.
25,30p. – (Working paper).
Includes bibliographical references. Added t.p. in French: L'intrusion criminelle. Pages numbered in opposite directions. Text in English and French.
ISBN 0662542061

—Criminal law : the general part : liability and defences / Law Reform Commission of Canada. – Ottawa : Law Reform Commission of Canada, 1982.
12,204,239,10p; 25cm. – (Working paper).
Parallel text in French and English bound in reverse.
ISBN 0662514297

—Damage to property : arson / Law Reform Commission of Canada. – Ottawa : The Commission, 1984.
44,52p. – (Working paper).
Includes bibliographical references. Added t.p. in French: Les dommages aux biens : le crime d'incendie. Added t.p. in French: Les dommages aux biens : le crime d'incendie. Pages numbered in opposite directions. Text in English and French.
ISBN 0662532457

—Damage to property - vandalism / Law Reform Commission of Canada. – Ottawa : the Commission, 1984.
65,77p; 25cm. – (Working paper).
Cover title: Criminal law - damage to property - vandalism. Added t.p. in French: Les dommages aux biens - le vandalisme. Pages numbered in opposite directions. In English and French.
ISBN 0662528956

—Electronic surveillance / Law Reform Commission of Canada. – Ottawa : The Commission, 1986.
109,121p; 25cm. – (Working paper).
Added t.p. in French: La surveillance electronique. Cover title: Criminal law - electronic surveillance. Pages numbered in opposite directions. English and French.
ISBN 0662538862

—Extraterritorial jurisdiction / Law Reform Commission of Canada. – Ottawa : the Commission, 1984.
210p. – (Working paper).
Bibliography: p.209-210.
ISBN 0662136039

—Hate propaganda / Law Reform Commission of Canada. – Ottawa : The Commission, 1986.
57,63p. – (Working paper).
Includes bibliographies. Added t.p. in French: La propagande haineuse. Pages numbered in opposite directions. Text in English and French.

—Homicide / Law Reform Commission of Canada. – Ottawa : Law Reform Commission of Canada, 1984.
117,128p; 25cm. – (Working paper).
At head of cover title: Criminal law. English and French texts bound back to back.
ISBN 0662529871

—Investigative tests / Law Reform Commission of Canada. – Ottawa : Law Reform Commission of Canada, 1984.
166,186p; 25cm. – (Working paper).
At head of cover title: Criminal law. English and French texts bound back to back.
ISBN 066253039X

—Legal status of the federal administration / Law Reform Commission of Canada. – Ottawa : The Commission, 1985.
106,111p. – (Working paper).
Includes bibliographical references. Added t.p. in French: Le statut juridique de l'administration federale. Pages numbered in opposite directions.

—Obtaining reasons before applying for judicial scrutiny : Immigration Appeal Board / Law Reform Commission of Canada. – Ottawa : Law Reform Commission of Canada, 1982.
21,25p; 25cm. – (Report).
English and French text, in reverse.
ISBN 0662521064

—Omissions, negligence and endangering / Law Reform Commission of Canada. – Ottawa : The Commission, 1985.
42,48p. – (Working paper).
Includes bibliographical references. Added t.p. in French: L'omission, la negligence et la mise en danger. Pages numbered in opposite directions. Text in English and French.
ISBN 0662540824

→ Parliament and administrative agencies : a study paper prepared for the Law Reform Commission of Canada.

→ Pesticides in Canada : an examination of federal law and policy.

—Police powers - search and seizure in criminal law enforcement / Law Reform Commission of Canada. – Ottawa : The Commission, 1983.
356,403p; 25cm. – (Working paper).
Added t.p. in French: Les pouvoirs de la police : les fouilles, les perquisitions et les saisies en droit penal. Pages numbered in opposite directions. In English and French.
ISBN 066252277X

—Policy implementation, compliance and administrative law / Law Reform Commission of Canada. – Ottawa : Law Reform Commission of Canada, 1986.
105,115p; 25cm. – (Working paper).
Cover title: Administrative law - policy implementation, compliance and administrative law. Added t.p. in French: Droit, objectifs publics et observation des normes. Pages numbered in opposite directions. Text in English and French.
ISBN 0662540832

→ Political economy of environmental hazards : a study paper prepared for the Law Reform Commission of Canada.

—Post-seizure procedures / Law Reform Commission of Canada. – Ottawa : the Commission, 1985.
77,84p. – (Working paper).
Includes bibliographical references. Added t.p. in French: Les procedures posterieures a la saisie. Cover title: Criminal law: post-seizure procedures. Pages numbered in opposite directions. Text in English and French.
ISBN 0662534603

—Private prosecutions / Law Reform Commission of Canada. – Ottawa : Law Reform Commission of Canada, 1986.
51,59p; 25cm. – (Working paper).
Cover title: Criminal law - private prosecutions. Added t.p. in French: Les poursuites privees. Pages numbered in opposite directions. Text in English and French.
ISBN 0662544595

—Public and media access to the criminal process / Law Reform Commission of Canada. – Ottawa : The Commission, 1987.
106,120p. – (Working paper).
Includes bibliographical references. Added t.p. in French: L'acces du public et des medias au processus penal. Pages numbered in opposite directions. Text in English and French.
ISBN 0662551168

—Questioning suspects / Law Reform Commission of Canada. – Ottawa : The Commission, 1984.
25,28p. – (Report).
Added t.p. in French: L'interrogatoire des suspects. Pages numbered in opposite directions. Text in English and French.
ISBN 0662533208

—Questioning suspects / Law Reform Commission of Canada. – Ottawa : the Commission, 1984.
104,112p; 25cm. – (Working paper).
Cover title: Criminal law - questioning suspects. Added t.p. in French : L'interrogatoire des suspects. Pages numbered in opposite directions. In English and French.
ISBN 0662529162

—Report on arrest / Law Reform Commission of Canada. – Ottawa : the Commission, 1986.
65,71p. – (Report).
Pages numbered in opposite directions. Text in English and French.
ISBN 0662544757

—Report on disclosure by the prosecution / Law Reform Commission of Canada. – Ottawa : the Commission, 1984.
38,36p. – (Report).
Pages numbered in opposite directions. Text in English and French.
ISBN 0662530942

—Report on disposition of seized property : post-seizure procedures / Law Reform Commission of Canada. – Ottawa : The Commission, 1986.
76,83p. – (Report).
Includes bibliographical references. Added t.p. in French : La facon de disposer des choses saisies. Pages numbered in opposite directions. Text in English and French.
ISBN 0662540816

—Report on independent administrative agencies : a framework for decision making. – Law Reform Commission of. – Ottawa : Law Reform Commission of Canada, 1985.
101,11p. – (Working paper).
Bibliography: p.87-94. Added t.p. in French: Rapport sur organismes administratifs autonomes. Pages numbered in opposite directions. Text in English and French.
ISBN 0662537483

—Report on investigative tests - alcohol, drugs and driving offences / Law Reform Commission of Canada. – Ottawa : Law Reform Commission of Canada, 1983.
33,34p; 25cm. – (Report).
English and French texts back to back. French title: L'alcool, la drogue et la conduit des vehicules.
ISBN 0662527259

—Report on obtaining forensic evidence : investigative procedures in respect of the person / Law Reform Commission of Canada. – Ottawa : The Commission, 1985.
45,48p; 25cm. – (Report).
Added t.p. in French: Rapport sur les techniques d'investigation policiere et les droits de la personne. Cover title: Obtaining forensic evidence. Pages numbered in opposite directions. In English and French.
ISBN 0662537351

—Report on our criminal procedure. – Law Reform Commission of. – Ottawa : Law Reform Commission of Canada, 1988.
56,60p. – (Report).
Includes t.p. in French. Pages numbered in opposite directions. Text in English and French.
ISBN 0662557360

—Report on recodifying criminal law / Law Reform Commission of Canada. – Rev. and enl. ed. – Ottawa : The Commission, 1987.
213,233p; 25cm. – (Report).
Includes text of draft legislation. 'Revised and enlarged edition of Report 30' - t.p.. Added t.p. in French: Rapport pour une nouvelle codification du droit penal. Cover title: Recodifying criminal law. Pages numbered in opposite directions. Pages numbered in opposite directions. In English and French.
ISBN 0662547578

—Report on recodifying criminal law / Law Reform Commission of Canada. – Ottawa : the Commission, 1986.
– (Report).
Pages numbered in opposite directions. Text in English and French.
ISBN 0662547322

—Report on search and seizure / Law Reform Commission of Canada. – Ottawa : The Commission, 1984.
78,86p; 25cm. – (Report).
Added t.p. in French: Rapport sur les fouilles, les perquisitions et les saises. Cover title: Searches and seizures. Pages numbered in opposite directions. Text in English and French.
ISBN 0662532872

—Report on some aspects of medical treatment and criminal law / Law Reform Commission of Canada. – Ottawa : The Commission, 1986.
19,19p. – (Report).
Pages numbered in opposite directions. Text in English and French.
ISBN 0662543793

—Report on the jury. – Law Reform Commission of. – Ottowa : Minister of Supply and Services, 982.
86p,91p. – (Report).
Added t.p. in French: Rapport sur le jury. Pages numbered in opposite directions. Text in English and French.
ISBN 0662518667

—Report on writs of assistance and telewarrants / Law Reform Commission of Canada. – Ottawa : The Commission, 1983.
110,124p; 25cm. – (Report).
Cover-title: Writs of assistance and telewarrants. Added t.p. in French: Rapport sur le mandat de main-forte et le telemandat. Pages numbered in opposite directions. In English and French.
ISBN 0662525159

—Secondary liability : participation in crime and inchoate offences / Law Reform Commission of Canada. – Ottawa : The Commission, 1985.
53,61p. – (Working paper).
Includes bibliographical references. Added t.p. in French: La responsabilite secondaire: complicite et infractions inchoatives. Cover title: Criminal law - secondary liability. Pages numbered in opposite directions. English and French text.
ISBN 0662537491

→ Sentencing in environmental cases : a study paper.

→ Tariff Board : a study prepared for the Law Reform Commission of Canada.

—Workplace pollution / Law Reform Commission of Canada. – Ottawa : The Commission, 1986.
94,106p. – (Working paper).
Includes bibliographical references. Added t.p. in French: La pollution en milieu de travail. Pages numbered in opposite directions. Text in English and French.
ISBN 0662545702

Law Reform Commission of Hong Kong
Report : young persons : effects of age in civil law / the Law Reform Commission of Hong Kong. – Hong Kong : The Commission, 1986.
various pagings. – (Topic 11).

—Report on competence and compellability of spouses in criminal proceedings / the Law Reform Commission of Hong Kong. – Hong Kong : The Commission, 1988.
viii,181p. – (Topic).
Bibliography:pp. 180-181.

—Report on contempt of court / the Law Reform Commission of Hong Kong. – Hong Kong : The Commission, 1986.
v,102p. – (Topic).
Includes bibliographical references.

—Report on coroners / the Law Reform Commission of Hong Kong. – Hong Kong : The Commission, 1987.
viii,176p. – (Topic).
Includes bibliographical references.

—Report on laws on insurance / the Law Reform Commission of Hong Kong. – Hong Kong : The Commission, 1986.
vi,172p. – (Topic 9).
Bibliography: p.97-102. Summary in Chinese.

—Report on the adoption of the UNCITRAL model law of arbitration / the Law Reform Commission of Hong Kong. – Hong Kong : The Commisssion, 1987.
v,121p. – (Topic).
Includes bibliographical references.

—Report on the control of exemption clauses / the Law Reform Commission of Hong Kong. – Hong Kong : The Commission, 1986.
vi,98p. – (Topic).
Includes bibliographical references.

Law Reform Commission of Papua New Guinea
Consumer protection / Law Reform Commission of Papua New Guinea. – Waigani : The Commission, 1981.
18p. – (LRC working paper).
Includes summary in Papuan.

→ Corporate social responsibility in Papua New Guinea.

→ Custody jurisdiction in Papua New Guinea.

→ Customary law in Papua New Guinea : a Melanesian view.

→ Domestic violence in Papua New Guinea.

—Marriage and domestic violence in rural Papua New Guinea / results of a research project conducted by the Law Reform Commission of Papua New Guinea : by Susan Toft and Susanne Bonnell. – Waigani : Law Reform Commission of Papua New Guinea, 1985.
v,116p. – (Occasional paper).
Bibliography: p.111.
ISBN 9980550007

—Motor Vehicles (Third Party Insurance) (Basic Protection Compensation) Act, (revised laws of Papua New Guinea, chapter no. 296) : a fourth review / Law Reform Commission of Papua New Guinea. – Waigani : Law Reform Commission of Papua New Guinea, 1983.
12p. – (LRC working paper).
Includes bibliographical references.

—Seminar on a legal profession act for Papua New Guinea : Port Moresby, 4th & 5th of May 1982 / Law Reform Commission and Legal Training Institute. – 1. – Waigani : Law Reform Commission of Papua New Guinea, 1982.
various pagings. – (LRC Working Paper).

—What should be done about corruption and bribery? / Law Reform Commission of Papua New Guinea. – Waigani : The Commission, 1982.
24p. – (LRC working paper).
Prepared for the Commission by Ross DeVere.

Law Reform Commission of Saskatchewan
Annual report and review / Law Reform Commission of Saskatchewan. – Saskatoon : The Commission, 1988.
Supersedes: Yearly review.

→ Handbook on the Saskatchewan Personal Property Security Act.

—Proposals for a compulsory mental health care act : report to the Minister of Justice / Law Reform Commission of Saskatchewan. – Saskatoon : The Commission, 1985.
40p.
Includes bibliographical references.

—Proposals for a Frustrated Contracts Act : report to the Minister of Justice / Law Reform Commission of Saskatchewan. – Saskatoon : The Commission, 1988.
31p.

—Proposals for a guardianship act : Report to the Attorney General
Part 1 : personal guardianship / Law Reform Commission of Saskatchewan. – Saskatoon : Law Reform Commission of Saskatchewan, 1983.
19p.

—Proposals for a Human Artificial Insemination Act / Law Reform Commission of Saskatchewan. – Saskatoon : The Commission, 1987.
12p.

—Proposals for a new coroners act : report to the Minister of Justice / Law Reform Commission of Saskatchewan. – Saskatoon : The Commission, 1984.
62p.
Includes bibliographical references.

—Proposals for a survival of actions act : report to the Minister of Justice / Law Reform Commission of Saskatchewan. – Saskatoon : The Commission, 1985.
19p.
Includes bibliographical references.

—Proposals for an Equality of Status of Married Persons Act : report to the Attorney General / Law Reform Commission of Saskatchewan. – Saskatoon : The Commission, 1982.
17p.

—Proposals for defences to provincial offences : report to the Minister of Justice / Law Reform Commission of Saskatchewan. – Saskatoon : The Commission, 1986.
18p.
Includes bibliographical references.

—Proposals for restoring civil remedies lost upon forfeiture under the Automobile Accident Insurance Act : report to the Minister of Justice / Law Reform Commission of Saskatchewan. – Saskatoon : The Commission, 1984.
11p.
Includes bibliographical references.

—Proposals on custody, parental guardianship, and the civil rights of minors : report to the Attorney General / from the Law Reform Commission of Saskatchewan. – Saskatoon : Law Reform Commission of Saskatchewan, 1981.
iv,40p.

—Proposals relating to ademption by equitable conversion / Law Reform Commission of Saskatchewan. – Saskatoon : The Commission, 1984.
12p.
Includes bibliographical references.

—Proposals relating to joint obligations : report to the Minister of Justice / Law Reform Commission of Saskatchewan. – Saskatoon : The Commission, 1985.
13p.

—Proposals relating to matrimonial property legislation / Law Reform Commission of Saskatchewan. – Saskatoon : The Commission, 1985.
22p.

—Proposals relating to the change of name of children of divorced parents : report to the Minister of Justice / Law Reform Commission of Saskatchewan. – Saskatoon : The Commission, 1985.
8p.

—Proposals relating to the rules against perpetuities and accumulations : report to the Minister if Justice / Law Reform Commission of Saskatchewan. – Saskatoon : The Commission, 1987.
29p.

—Tentative proposals for a compulsory mental health care act / Law Reform Commission of Saskatchewan. – Saskatoon : Law Reform Commission of Saskatchewan, 1981.
46,xlixp.

—Tentative proposals for a Frustrated Contracts Act / Law Reform Commission of Saskatchewan. – Saskatoon : The Commission, 1987.
55p.
Includes text of proposed Act.

—Tentative proposals for a human artificial insemination act / Law Reform Commission of Saskatchewan. – 1. – Saskatoon : Law Reform Commission of Saskatchewan, 1981.
various pagings.
Includes bibliographical references.

—Tentative proposals for a Lieutenant Governor's Review Board in Saskatchewan / Law Reform Commission of Saskatchewan. – Saskatoon : The Commission, 1984.
28p.
Includes text of proposed Act.

—Tentative proposals for an Enforcement of Maintenance Orders Act / Law Reform Commission of Saskatchewan. – Saskatoon : The Commission, 1982.
100,xiiip.

—Tentative proposals for an equality of status of married persons act / Law Reform Commission of Saskatchewan. – Saskatoon : Law Reform Commission of Saskatchewan, 1981.
68p.
Includes bibliographical references.

—Tentative proposals for changes in limitations legislation
Part 1 : The effect of limitations on title to real property / Law Reform Commission of Saskatchewan. – Saskatoon : Law Reform Commission of Saskatchewan, 1981.
27p.
Part 2 : The Limitation of Actions Act / Law Reform Commission of Saskatchewan. – 1986.
149p.

—Tentative proposals for compensation of accused on acquittal / Law Reform Commission of Saskatchewan. – Saskatoon : The Commission, 1987.
38p.
Includes bibliographical references. Includes text of proposed Act.

—Tentative proposals for reform of the Matrimonial Property Act / Law Reform Commission of Saskatchewan. – Saskatoon : The Commission, 1984.
167p.
Includes bibliographical references.

—Tentative proposals relating to testamentary custody and guardianship of children / Law Reform Commission of Saskatchewan. – Saskatoon : The Commission, 1984.
58p.
Includes texts of proposed Acts.

Law Reform Commission of Tasmania →Child witnesses in sexual assault.

—Compensation for victims of motor vehicle accidents / Law Reform Commission of Tasmania. – Hobart : Acting Government Printer, 1987.
76p. – (Report).

—Occupiers' liability / Law Reform Commission of Tasmania. – Hobart : Government Printer, 1988.
6p. – (Report).

—Report and recommendations for reform on fifteen conveyancing matters / Law Refrom Commission of Tasmania. – Hobart : Government Printer, 1984.
20p. – (Report).

—Report and recommendations on rape and sexual offences / Law Reform Commission of Tasmania. – Hobart : Government Printer, 1982.
44p. – (Report).

—Report and recommendations on the law and procedure relating to the sale of land by instalments / Law Reform Commission of Tasmania. – Hobart : Government Printer, 1983.
25p. – (Report).

—Report and recommendations on the use of tranquillizer guns / Law Reform Commission of Tasmania. – Hobart : Government Printer, 1982.
16p. – (Report).

—Report and recommendations relating to consumer claims and small debts / Law Reform Commission of Tasmania. – Hobart : Government Printer, 1982.
55p. – (Report).

—Report and recommendations relating to exclusion clauses and implied obligations in contracts for the supply of goods and services / Law Reform Commission of Tasmania. – Hobart : Government Printer, 1983.
23p. – (Report).

—Report and recommendations upon perpetuities and accumulations / Law Reform Commission of Tasmania. – Hobart : Government Printer, 1983.
25p. – (Report).

—Report on computer misuse / Law Reform Commission of Tasmania. – Hobart : Government Printer, 1986.
37p. – (Report v no 47).

—Report on contracts and the disposition of property by minors / Law Reform Commission of Tasmania. – Hobart : Acting Government Printer, 1987.
14p. – (Report).
Includes text of the Infants' Relief Act 1875.

—Report on fines / Law Reform Commission of Tasmania. – Hobart : Government Printer, 1985.
12p. – (Report v no 41).

—Report on interest on pre- and post-judgment debts / Law Reform Commission of Tasmania. – Hobart : Government Printer, 1985.
17p. – (Report v no 44).

—Report on local courts / Law Reform Commission of Tasmania. – Hobart : Government Printer, 1985.
29p. – (Report v no 45).

—Report on powers of attorney / Law Reform Commission of Tasmania. – Hobart : Government Printer, 1984.
21p. – (Report v no 39).

—Report on private rights of access to neighbouring land / Law Reform Commission of Tasmania. – Hobart : Government Printer, 1985.
23p. – (Report v no 42).

—Report on reform in the law of wills / Law Reform Commission of Tasmania. – Hobart : Government Printer, 1983.
17p. – (Report v no 35).

—Report on section 9(7), (8) and (9) of the Worker's Compensation Act 1927 / Law Reform Commission of Tasmania. – Hobart? : Goverment Printer?, 1985.
17p. – (Report).

—Report on succession rights on intestacy / Law Reform Commission of Tasmania. – Hobart : Government Printer, 1985.
21p. – (Report v no 43).

—Report on suretyship and guarantee / Law Reform Commission of Tasmania. – Hobart : Government Printer, 1987.
30p. – (Report v no 50).

—Report on the Boundary Fences Act 1908 / Law Reform Commission of Tasmania. – Hobart : Government Printer, 1984.
19p. – (Report v no 37).

—Report on the burden of proof in criminal proceedings and statutory offences / Law Reform Commission of Tasmania. – Hobart : Government Printer, 1987.
26p. – (Report v no 49).

—Report on the rule in Hollington v. Hewthorn / Law Reform Commission of Tasmania. – Hobart : Government Printer, 1982.
7p. – (Report v no 29).

—Report on the variation of private trusts / Law Reform Commission of Tasmania. – Hobart : Acting Government Printer, 1987.
28p. – (Report).
Includes text of Model Bill.

—Report on variations of charitable trusts / Law Reform Commission of Tasmania. – Hobart? : Government Printer?, 1984.
23p. – (Report).

→ Research paper on computer misuse.

→ Research paper on fines.

→ Research paper on occupiers' liability law.

→ Research paper on the variation of private trusts.

→ Working paper on the law relating to contracts and the disposition of property by minors.

Law Reform Commission of the Gambia
Memoranda and draft : bills re : christian marriage, matrimonial causes, offences relating to property and lands (Banjul and Kombo St. Mary) / Law Reform Commission of the Gambia. – Banjul : The Commission?, 1985.
xv,112p.
Includes the text of draft legislation.

Law Reform Commission of Victoria
Annual report / Law Reform Commission of Victoria. – Melbourne : The Commission, 1985. v.
Published as part of the report series of the Commission.

—Criminal responsibility : intention and gross intoxication / Law Reform Commission of Victoria. – Melbourne : The Commission, 1986.
v,31p. – (Report no 6).
Includes bibliographical references.

—Deregulation of hire-purchase / Law Reform Commission of Victoria. – Melbourne : The Commission, 1986.
x,22p. – (Report no 4).
Bibliography: p.21-22. Includes text of Hire-purchase (Deregulation) Bill 1986.

—Diminshed responsibility as a defence to murder / Law Reform Commissioner, Victoria. – Melbourne : The Commission, 1981.
40p. – (Working paper no 7).
Includes bibliographical references.

—Estate agents and auctioneers / Law Reform Commission of Victoria. – Melbourne : Government Printer, 1988.
x,46p. – (Report).
At head of cover title: Regulation Review Unit.
ISBN 0724167145

—Genetic manipulation / Law Reform Commission of Victoria. – Melbourne : The Commission, 1987.
ii,41p. – (Discussion paper).
Includes bibliographical references.
ISBN 0724167285

—Homicide / Law Reform Commission of Victoria. – Melbourne : The Commission, 1988.
72p. – (Discussion paper).
Includes bibliographical references.
ISBN 0724167137

—Informed consent to medical treatment / Law Reform Commission of Victoria. – Melbourne : The Commission, 1987.
iv,45p. – (Discussion paper).
Includes bibliographical references. 'Issued in conjunction with Australian Law Reform Commission and New South Wales Law Reform Commission' - cover.
ISBN 0724166467

—Law of homicide in Victoria : the sentence for murder / Law Reform Commission of Victoria. – Melbourne : The Commission, 1985.
viii,27p. – (Report v no 1).
Bibliography: p.25-27.

—Legislation, legal rights and plain English / Law Reform Commission of Victoria. – Melbourne : The Commission, 1986.
iv,56p. – (Discussion paper).
Includes bibliographical references.

—Liquidated damages and penalties / Law Reform Commission of Victoria. – Melbourne : The Commission, 1988.
i.20p. – (Discussion paper).
Includes bibliographical references.
ISBN 0724167293

—Mental malfunction and criminal responsibility / Law Reform Commission of Victoria. – Melbourne : The Commission, 1988.
95p. – (Discussion paper).
Includes bibliographical references.
ISBN 0724167307

—Mortgagee sales and judgment debts / Law Reform Commission of Victoria. – Melbourne : The Commission, 1986.
iii,10p. – (Discussion paper of Victoria).
Includes bibliographical references.

—Mortgagee sales and judgment debts / Law Reform Commission of Victoria. – Melbourne : The Commission, 1987.
iv,17p. – (Report no 8).
Includes bibliographical references.

—Plain English and the law : a report / Law Reform Commission of Victoria. – Melbourne : The Commission, 1987.
xvi,109p. – (Report no 9).
Includes bibliographical references and index. Accompanied by appendices 1-8 (3).

—Principles for occupational regulation / Law Reform Commission of Victoria. – Melbourne : The Commission, 1988.
iv,35p. – (Report no 17).
At head of cover title: Regulation Review Unit.
ISBN 0724167234 Hbk

—Priorities / Law Reform Commission of Victoria. – Melbourne : The Commission, 1988.
iv,19p. – (Discussion paper).
ISBN 0724167129

—Provocation and diminished responsibility as defences to murder / Law Reform Commissioner, Victoria. – Melbourne : The Commission, 1982.
48p. – (Report no 12).
Includes bibliographical references.

—Rape and allied offences : procedure and evidence / Law Reform Commission of Victoria. – Melbourne : The Commission, 1988.
v,62p. – (Report no 13).
ISBN 0724166351 Hbk

—Rape and allied offences : procedure and evidence / Law Reform Commission of Victoria. – Melbourne : The Commission, 1987.
iii,31p. – (Discussion paper).
Calatogued from cover. Includes bibliographical references.
ISBN 072414319X

—Rape and allied offences : substantive aspects / Law Reform Commission of Victoria. – Melbourne : The Commission, 1986.
iv,55p. – (Discussion paper).
Includes bibliographical references.

—Rape and allied offences : victims with impaired mental functioning / Law Reform Commission of Victoria. – Melbourne : The Commission, 1987.
39p. – (Discussion paper).
Includes bibliographical references.
ISBN 0724167064

—Rape and alllied offences : substantive aspects / Law Reform Commission of Victoria. – Melbourne : The Commission, 1987.
viii,40p. – (Report no 7).
Includes bibliographical references.

—Role of the jury in criminal trials / Law Reform Commission of Victoria. – Melbourne : The Commission, 1985.
xxvi,220p. – (Background paper).
Bibliography: pp.185-220.. With appendices in separate vol..

—Sale of land / Law Reform Commission of Victoria. – Melbourne : The Commission, 1988.
iv,40p. – (Discussion paper).
Includes bibliographical references.
ISBN 0724166947

—Sexual offences against children / Law Reform Commission of Victoria. – Melbourne : The Commission, 1988.
iv,80p. – (Discussion paper).
Includes bibliographical references.
ISBN 0724167218

—Sexual offences against people with impaired mental functioning / Law Reform Commission of Victoria. – Melbourne : The Commission, 1988.
ii,52p. – (Report no 15).
ISBN 0724167153 Hbk

—Torrens register book / Law Reform Commision of Victoria. – Melbourne : The Commission, 1986.
iv,19p. – (Discussion paper).
Includes bibliographical references.

—Unsworn statements in criminal trials / Law Reform Commission of Victoria. – Melbourne : The Commission, 1985.
x,43p. – (Report no 2).
Includes bibliographical references.

—Unsworn statements in criminal trials / Law Reform Commissioner, Victoria. – Melbourne : The Commission, 1981.
43p. – (Report no 11).
Includes bibliographical references.

Law Reform Commission of Western Australia

Alteration of ground levels / the Law Reform Commission of Western Australia. – Perth the Commission, 1984.
89p. – (Discussion paper).

—Criminal process and persons suffering from mental disorder / Law Reform Commission of Western Australia. – Perth : Law Reform Commission of Western Australia, 1987.
i,146p. – (Discussion paper).

—Medical treatment for minors / the Law Reform Commission of Western Australia. – Perth : the Commission, 1988.
111p. – (Discussion paper).

—Medical treatment for the dying / the Law Reform Commission of Western Australia. – Perth : the Commission, 1988.
66p. – (Discussion paper).

—Payment of witnesses in civil proceedings / the Law Reform Commission of Western Australia. – Perth : Law Reform Commission of Western Australia, 1988.
iii,11 leaves. – (Discussion paper).

—Problem of old convictions / the Law Reform Commission of Western Australia. – Perth : Law Reform Commission of Western Australia, 1984.
97,vip. – (Discussion paper).

—Report on alteration of ground levels / the Law Reform Commission of Western Australia. – Perth : The Commission, 1986.
94p. – (Project).
Includes bibliographical references.

—Report on judicial review of administrative decisions : procedural aspects and the right to reasons / Law Reform Commission of Western Australia. – Perth : The Commission, 1986.
77p. – (Project).
Includes bibliographical references.

—Report on liability for stock straying on to the highway / Law Reform Commission of Western Australia. – Perth : Law Reform Commission of Western Australia, 1981.
51p. – (Project).

—Report on limitation and notice of actions : latent disease and injury / Law Reform Commission of Western Australia. – Perth : The Commission, 1982.
125p. – (Project).

—Report on minors' contracts / the Law Reform Commission of Western Australia. – Perth : Law Reform Commission of Western Australia, 1988.
117p. – (Project).

—Report on pre-judgment interest / Law Reform Commission of Western Australia. – Perth : Law Reform Commission of Western Australia, 1981.
38p. – (Project v no 70 part 1).

—Report on recognition of interstate and foreign grants of probate and administration / the Law Reform Commission of Western Australia. – Perth : The Commission, 1984.
128p. – (Project).
Includes bibliographical references.

—Report on review of administrative decisions : part 1, appeals / the Law Reform Commission of Western Australia. – Perth : The Commission, 1982.
114p. – (Project).

—Report on the administration of assets of the solvent estates of deceased persons in the payment of debts and legacies / Law Reform Commission of Western Australia. – Perth : Law Reform Commission of Western Australia, 1988.
50p. – (Project).

—Report on the jurisdiction, procedures and administration of local courts / Law Reform Commission of Western Australia. – Perth : Law Reform Commission of Western Australia, 1988.
262p. – (Project).
Cover title: Report on local courts.

—Report on the liability of highway authorities for non-feasance / Law Reform Commission of Western Australia. – Perth : Law Reform Commission of Western Australia, 1981.
116p. – (Project v no 62).

—Report on the Pawnbrokers Act 1860-1984 / the Law Reform Commission of Western Australia. – Perth : The Commission, 1985.
82p. – (Project).

—Report on the problem of old convictions / the Law Reform Commission of Western Australia. – Perth : Law Reform Commission of Western Australia, 1986.
267p. – (Project).

—Report on the Strata Titles Act / the Law Reform Commission of Western Australia. – Perth : Law Reform Commission of Western Australia, 1982.
387p. – (Project).

—Report on trustees' powers of investment / Law Reform Commission of Western Australia. – Perth : Government Printer, 1984.
141p. – (Project v no 34 part 5).
Includes bibliographical references.

—Report on wills : substantial compliance / Law Reform Commission of Western Australia. – Perth : The Commission, 1985.
60p. – (Project).
Includes bibliographical references.

—Review of the Justices Act 1902-1982 : constitution, powers and procedure of Courts of Petty Sessions / the Law Reform Commission of Western Australia. – Perth : Law Reform Commission of Western Australia, 1984.
ii,253p. – (Discussion paper).
Cover title: Courts of Petty Sessions: constitution, powers and procedure.

—Review of the Pawnbrokers Act, 1860 : proposals paper / the Law Reform Commission of Western Australia. – Perth : The Commission, 1985.
46 leaves. – (Project).

—Wills : substantial compliance / the Law Reform Commission of Western Australia. – Perth : Law Reform Commission of Western Australia, 1984.
37p. – (Discussion paper).

—Working paper : the judicial review of administrative decisions / Law Reform Commission of Western Australia. – Perth : Law Reform Commission of Western Australia, 1981.
178p. – (Project).
Includes bibliographical references.

—Working paper and survey : privacy and statutory powers of intrusion / Law Reform Commission of Western Australia. – Perth : Law Reform Commission of Western Australia, 1981.
25,ii,112p. – (Project v no 26 part 2).

—Working paper on Local Courts Act 1904-1982, and rules / the Law Reform Commission of Western Australia. – Perth : Law Reform Commission of Western Australia, 1983.
307p. – (Project).
Bibliography: p.276-279.

Law reform commissions in the United Kingdom, Australia and Canada / by William H. Hurlburt. – Edmonton : Juriliber, 1986.
vii,514p.
Bibliography: p.498-514.
ISBN 0919311032

Law Reform Committee

Latent damage : consultative document / Law Reform Committee. – 1. – London : Law Reform Committee 1981, 1981.
various pagings.

—Powers and duties of trustees : presented to parliament ... October 1982 / Law Reform Committee. – London : H.M.S.O., 1982.
iv,71p; 25cm. – (Report).
ISBN 0101873301 Hbk £5.25

—Twenty-fourth report (latent damage) / Law Reform Committee. – London : H.M.S.O., 1984.
iv,34p; 25cm. – (Report).
ISBN 0101939000

Law Reform Committee of South Australia

Report ... dealing with disparate subjects in the inherited imperial law / Law Reform Committee of South Australia. – Adelaide : Government Printer, 1984.
56p. – (68th report).

—Report ... dealing with the inherited imperial law / Law Reform Committee of South Australia. – Adelaide : Government Printer, 1984.
28p. – (79th report).

—Report ... dealing with the inherited imperial law between 1751 and 1780 / Law Reform Committee of South Australia. – Adelaide : Government Printer, 1984.
46p. – (85th report).

—Report ... dealing with the inherited imperial law between 1781 and 1800 / Law Reform Committee of South Australia. – Adelaide : Government Printer, 1984.
41p. – (86th report).

—Report ... dealing with the inherited imperial law between 1801 and 1820 / Law Reform Committee of South Australia. – Adelaide : Government Printer, 1984.
41p. – (89th report).

—Report ... dealing with the inherited imperial law between 1821 and 1836 / Law Reform Committee of South Australia. – Adelaide : Government Printer, 1985.
32p. – (91st report).

—Report ... on the further consideration of the Contracts Review Bill 1978 / Law Reform Committee of South Australia. – Adelaide : Government Printer, 1986.
73p. – (74th report).
Bibliography: p.51-52.

—Report ... on the inherited imperial statute law with regard to proceedings in summary jurisdiction. – Law Reform Committee of South Australia. – Adelaide : Government Printer, 1981.
16p. – (58th report).

—Report ... relating to a general rule of standing in environmental matters / Law Reform Committee of South Australia. – Adelaide : Government Printer, 1987.
141,5,4p. – (97th report).
Bibliography: p.1-2. Includes text of draft bill..

—Report ... relating to administrative appeals / Law Reform Committee of South Australia. – Adelaide : Government Printer, 1984.
67p. – (82nd report).
Bibliography: p.65-68.

—Report ... relating to civil actions for perjury committed in criminal proceedings and to the tort of malicious prosecution / Law Reform Committee of South Australia. – Adelaide : Government Printer, 1984.
13p. – (83rd report).
Bibliography: p.14.

—Report ... relating to claims for injuries from toxic substances and radiation effects / Law Reform Committee of South Australia. – Adelaide : Government Printer, 1985.
96p. – (87th report).

—Report ... relating to group defamation. – Law Reform Committee of South Australia. – Adelaide : Government Printer, 1982.
13p. – (69th report).

—Report ... relating to locus standi : prisoners' rights. – Law Reform Committee of South Australia. – Adelaide : Government Printer, 1982.
6p. – (70th report).

—Report ... relating to maintenance, champerty, embracery and barratry, malicious prosecution and abuse of process / Law Reform Committee of South Australia. – Adelaide : Government Printer, 1987.
86,3p. – (101st report).
Includes text of the Abolition of Obsolete Offences Act (1969).

—Report ... relating to owners or occupiers of land and trespassers on that land / Law Reform Committee of South Australia. – Adelaide : Government Printer, 1985.
13p. – (48th report).

—Report ... relating to powers of attorney. – Law Reform Committee of South Australia. – Adelaide : Government Printer, 1981.
17p. – (47th report).

—Report ... relating to prescription and limitation of actions / Law Reform Committee of South Australia. – Adelaide : Government Printer, 1987.
59,14p. – (76th report).

—Report ... relating to problems of proof of survivorship as between two or more persons dying at about the same time in one accident / Law Reform Committee of South Australia. – Adelaide : Government Printer, 1985.
37p. – (88th report).
Bibliography: p.29.

—Report ... relating to proceedings by and against the crown / Law Reform Committee of South Australia. – 1. – Adelaide : Government Printer, 1987.
Various pagings. – (104th report).

—Report...relating to qui tam and penal actions and common informers / Law Reform Committee of South Australia. – Adelaide : Government Printer, 1985.
16p. – (94th report).

—Report ... relating to the amendment of the law of escheat. – Law Reform Committee of South Australia. – Adelaide : Government Printer, 1983.
7p. – (64th report).

—Report ... relating to the demise of the Crown / Law Reform Committee of South Australia. – Adelaide : Government Printer, 1984.
13p. – (81st report).

—Report relating to the doctrine of frustration in the law of contract / Law Reform Committee of South Australia. – Adelaide : Government Printer, 1983.
40p. – (71st report).

—Report ... relating to the effect of mistake upon contracts / Law Reform Committee of South Australia. – Adelaide : Government Printer, 1987.
112p. – (106th report).
Bibliography: p.109-112.

—Report ... relating to the fatal accidents provisions of the Wrongs Act 1936. – Law Reform Committee of South Australia. – Adelaide : Government Printer, 1981.
9p. – (56th report).

—Report ... relating to the inherited imperial law / Law Reform Committee of South Australia. – Adelaide : Government Printer, 1984.
38p. – (80th report).

—Report ... relating to the inherited imperial law and constitutional statutes / Law Reform Committee of South Australia. – Adelaide : Government Printer, 1985.
9p. – (96th report).

—Report ... relating to the inherited imperial law and to statutes previously covered by the Colonial Laws Validity Act 1865. – Law Reform Committee of South Australia. – Adelaide : Government Printer, 1986.
22p. – (102nd report).

—Report ... relating to the inherited imperial law on gaming and wagering in South Australia. – Law Reform Committee of South Australia. – Adelaide : Government Printer, 1982.
9p. – (68th report).

—Report ... relating to the inherited imperial law regarding the Crown. – Law Reform Committee of South Australia. – Adelaide : Government Printer, 1981.
15p. – (65th report).

—Report ... relating to the inherited imperial observance of Lord's Day Acts / Law Reform Committee of South Australia. – Adelaide : Government Printer, 1987.
40p. – (92nd report).
Bibliography: p.40.

—Report ... relating to the irrecoverability of benefits obtained by reason of mistake of law / Law Reform Committee of South Australia. – Adelaide : Government Printer, 1984.
40p. – (84th report).

—Report ... relating to the law governing locus standi : non-party interventions and amici curiae in relation to proceedings in civil jurisdiction. – Law Reform Committee of South Australia. – Adelaide : Government Printer, 1982.
9p. – (67th report).

—Report ... relating to the law of detinue, conversion and trespass to goods / Law Reform Committee of South Australia. – Adelaide : Government Printer, 1987.
100p. – (95th report).
Bibliography: p.99-100.

—Report ... relating to the reform of the law of distress. – Law Reform Committee of South Australia. – Adelaide : Government Printer, 1983.
8p. – (66th report).

—Report relating to the reform of the law of set-off / Law Reform Committee of South Australia. – Adelaide : Government Printer, 1983.
11p. – (75th report).
Includes draft Act.

—Report ... relating to the reform of the law on wills and intestacies / Law Reform Committee of South Australia. – Adelaide : Government Printer, 1983.
7p. – (72nd report).

—Report ... relating to the reform of the law regarding entire contracts and the rule usually known as the rule in Cutter v. Powell / Law Reform Committee of South Australia. – Adelaide : Government Printer, 1986.
29p. – (90th report).

—Report ... relating to the review and reappraisal of the twenty-fifth report of this committe sic on the subject of misfeasance and non-feasance / Law Reform Committee of South Australia. – Adelaide : Government Printer, 1986.
48p. – (51st report).
Bibliography: p.39-40.

Law Reform Digest. – Abingdon : Professional Books, 1984.
Hbk

Law reform digests : a digest of the reports of law reform agencies in Australia, New Zealand and Papua New Guinea, 1910-1980. – Canberra : Australian Government Publishing, 1983.
xviii,754p.
Includes index.
ISBN 0644016280

Law reform in Guyana / address delivered by Attorney General to Guyana Bar Association on 21st September 1981. – S.l. : s.n., 1981.
43p.
At head of title: 'Extracts printed in the Guyana Bar Association journal'.. Includes bibliographical references.

Law Reform in the Commonwealth : A Report on the 1983 Meeting of Commonwealth Law Reform Agencies. – London : Commonwealth Secretariat.
free

Law reform in the Commonwealth : law reform proposals and their implementation / Commonwealth Secretariat. – London : Commonwealth Secretariat, 1981.
Pilot issue published Oct. 1979.

Law Reform in the Muslim World. – London : Athlone Press, 1976.
ISBN 048513411X Hbk £18.00

Law Reform (Miscellaneous Provisions) (Scotland) Act 1985. – Edinburgh : Green (W.) & Son, 1986.
Annotated text of the Act from Scottish Current Law Statutes.
ISBN 0414007883 Pbk

Law reforms in a democratic society / the Rt. Hon. Lord Scarman. – New Delhi : National Publishing House, 1985.
114p.
Includes index.

Law Reforms Ordinance 1972. – Lahore : Pakistan Law Times.
Hbk £16.00

Law Relating to Appointment : Enquiry and Disciplinary Action of Workmen, with Model Forms. – 2nd ed. – Allahabad : Law Publishers, 1982.
Hbk £18.00

Law Relating to Arms, Ammunition and Explosives / K.K. Malik. – 4th rev. ed. – Lucknow : Eastern Book Company, 1985.
920p.
Hbk £125.00

Law Relating to Bankers Letters of Credit. – Allahabad : Indian Press.
290p.
Hbk £1.50

Law Relating to Banking. – London : Checkmate Gold.
ISBN 1853130397 Pbk £10.95

Law Relating to Banking. – 5th ed. – London : Butterworths, 1985.
ISBN 0406647682 Hbk £19.50
ISBN 0406647690 Pbk £16.50

Law Relating to Banking (Q & A). – London : Financial Training, 1984.
ISBN 090632257X Pbk £6.50

Law Relating to Bills of Lading and Charterparties. – Allahabad : Indian Press.
253p.
Hbk £1.50

Law Relating to Building and Engineering Contracts in India. – 3rd ed. in press. – Bombay : Tripathi.
1060p.
bd £130.00

Law Relating to Building Contracts : Cases and Materials. – Singapore : Quins.
Hbk £99.00

Law Relating to Business Tenancies in Germany. – Plymouth : Macdonald & Evans, 1985.
72p.
ISBN 0712154701 Hbk £10.75

Law Relating to C.I.F. Contracts. – New Delhi : Deep and Deep Publications, 1982.
142p.
Hbk £60.00

Law relating to charities / D.G. Cracknell. – 3rd ed. – London : Longman Professional (UK), 1987.
ISBN 0851213006 Hbk £29.50

Law Relating to Children. – 2nd ed. – London : Butterworths.
ISBN 0406117004 Hbk £8.50
ISBN 0406117012 Pbk £7.50

Law relating to children and young persons / Clarke Hall and Morrison. – 10th ed. 2. – London : Butterworths, 1985.
looseleaf.
Includes index. Includes the text of the relevant legislation. Spine title: Clarke Hall & Morrison on children. Kept up-to-date by supplements.
ISBN 0406158126

Law relating to cohabitation / by Martin L. Parry. – 2nd ed. – London : Sweet & Maxwell, 1988.
xxxiii,263p.
Changes effected by the Family Law Reform Act 1987 and the Social Security Act 1986 are included. Discusses home ownership, home occupation, money, tax, children, violence, death, and contracts, and contains an appendix of precedents.
ISBN 0421371102 £20.00

Law Relating to Companies Administration : With several Useful Appendices. – 2nd ed. – Allahabad : Law Book Company, 1987.
443p.
ISBN 8185029245 Hbk £150.00

Law Relating to Drugs and Cosmetics in India / P.L. Malik. – 3rd ed. – Lucknow : Eastern Book Company, 1984.
1,248p.
Hbk £200.00

Law Relating to Electricity in India / Surendra Malik. – 5th rev. ed. – Lucknow : Eastern Book Company, 1986.
1,088p.
Hbk £225.00

Law relating to entry, search and seizure / David Feldman. – London : Butterworths, 1986.
500p; 26cm.
Includes index.
ISBN 0406199108 Pbk £27.50

Law Relating to Execution of Decrees : Along with Executability of the Orders of Tribunals. – Allahabad : Hind Publishing House, 1986.
Hbk £100.00

Law relating to firearms / by P. J. Clarke and John W. Ellis. – London : Butterworths, 1981.
xxvi,272p.
ISBN 0406158207

Law Relating to Foreigners, Passports and Citizenship in India. – 6th ed. – Lucknow : Eastern Book Company, 1985.
Hbk

Law Relating to Forests in Uttar Pradesh. – 1981 repr. ed. – Lucknow : Eastern Book Company, 1984.
206p.
Hbk £25.00

Law Relating to Government Contracts 1979. – Bombay : Tripathi.
500p.
bd £100.00
Supplement 1982. –
Hbk £40.00

Law Relating to Identification and Expert Opinion / H.D. Trivedi. – 3rd ed. – Lucknow : Eastern Book Company, 1983.
236p.
Hbk £35.00

Law Relating to Marine Insurance. – Allahabad : Indian Press.
371p.
Hbk £3.00

Law Relating to Marriage and Divorce. – 4th ed. – Delhi : SBD Enterprises, 1988.
Hbk £150.00

Law Relating to Mobile Homes and Caravans. – London : Shaw & Sons, 1985.
ISBN 072190811X Pbk £10.50

Law Relating to Non-Profit Associations in Australia and New Zealand. – North Ryde : Law Book Co, 1986.
xl, 380p.
ISBN 0455206236 Hbk £48.00

Law Relating to Notaries Act / Bhatnagar. – Allahabad : Ashoka Law House, 1987.
300p.
Hbk £80.00

Law relating to parents and children / by Helen Gamble. – Sydney : Law Book Co., 1981.
vii, 341 p.; 19 cm.
'Table of cases': p. 301-308. 'Table of statutes': p. 309-325. Includes bibliographical references and index.
ISBN 0455202540 Pbk

Law Relating to Private Companies / Avtar Singh. – 4th ed. – Lucknow : Eastern Book Company, 1983.
651p.
Hbk £125.00

Law Relating to Private Limited Companies. – Allahabad : Law Book Company, 1986.
1,422p.
Hbk £275.00

Law Relating to Protected Lincensees. – Bombay : Tripathi, 1975.
416p.
bd £30.00

Law Relating to Provident Funds. – Bombay : Tripathi, 1974.
Hbk £50.00
Supplement 1979. –
Hbk £8.00

Law Relating to Receivers and Managers. – London : Butterworths, 1984.
ISBN 0406337608 Hbk £66.00

Law relating to social security : the statutes, regulations and orders as now in force. – London : HMSO, 1988.
looseleaf.
Supersedes : The law relating to social security and child benefit (the Brown Books); and The law relating to supplementary benefits and family income supplements (the Yellow Books). At head of title : Department of Health and Social Security. Popular title : the Blue Volumes.

Law Relating to Social Security and Child Benefit, 4 Vols. – London : HMSO.
Sets out the current legislation, both statutes and regulations with footnotes and sidenotes giving the origin of amendments.
ISBN 0117609102 Pbk £95.00

Law Relating to Supplementary Benefit and Family Income Supplement. – London : HMSO, 1984.
Sets out current legislation, both statutes and regulations with footnotes and sidenotes giving the origin of amendments.
ISBN 0117609242 Pbk £41.00

Law relating to supplementary benefits and family income supplements : the statutes, regulations and orders as now in force / H. V. Roberts. – 3rd ed. 2. – London : HMSO, 1980-.
looseleaf.
Superseded by: The law relating to social security (the Blue volumes). Popular title: the Yellow Books. With supplements of amendments.

Law Relating to the Sugar Industries in Uttar Pradesh, with Case-Law and Comments as Amended Up-to-Date / Gyan Prakash. – 3rd ed. – Allahabad : Hind Publishing House, 1982.
iv, 340p.
Hbk £40.00

Law Relating to Trade Descriptions / Smith. – London : Butterworths, 1971.
Service.
ISBN 0406326347 Llf £110.00

Law Relating to Trade Unions in India. – 2nd ed. – Lucknow : Eastern Book Company, 1982.
831p.
Hbk £110.00

Law Relating to Traffic. – London : Police Review Publishing, 1982.
ISBN 0851649920 Pbk £3.50

Law relating to transport of dangerous wastes : Ireland. – Shankill, Co. Dublin : European Foundation for the Improvement of Living and Working Conditions, 1987.
vii,58p. – (Research report).
ISBN 9282567605

Law Relating to Transport of Dangerous Wastes, Netherlands / V. di Martino. – Luxembourg : Office for Official Publications of the European Communities, 1987.
132p.
ISBN 9282567575 Pbk £450.00

Law Relating to Transport of Dangerous Wastes, United Kingdom / V. di Martino. – Luxembourg : Office for Official Publications of the European Communities, 1987.
104p.
ISBN 9282567524 Pbk £350.00

Law Relating to Trusts and Trustees
Nineteen Eighty-Two supplement only. – Wellington : Butterworths.
This book for practitioners in the United Kingdom covers express or declared trusts, trusts implied by law, the administration of a trust, and the consequences of a breach of trust.
ISBN 0406405891 Pbk

Law relating to trusts and trustees / Underhill and Hayton. – 14th ed. – London : Butterworths, 1987.
cxxxv,858p; 26cm.
Previous ed.: published as Underhill's law relating to trusts and trustees. 1979. Includes index.
ISBN 040640593X Hbk £110.00

Law relating to water courses : interim report / Property Law and Equity Reform Committee. – Wellington : The Committee, 1983.
15,9,2,8p.

Law, religion and the Jewish community / by Graham Zellick. – London : Jews' College, 1987.
Delivered at Jews' College on April 2 1986. Revised February 1987.

Law Report. – Seychelles Government. – Mahe : Seychelles National Printing Co.
Pbk £20.00

Law Report : Teaching Assessment of Law in Social Work Education. – London : Central Council for Education & Training in Social Work.
ISBN 0904488217 Pbk £7.00

Law Reporting : Pre-Confederation to the Computer Era. – Aurora : Canada Law Book Co.

Law Reports : 1865-date. – Abingdon : Professional Books, 1984.
Hbk

Law Reports Digest : 1951-1980, 3 Vols. – Abingdon : Professional Books, 1984.
Hbk

Law Reports Digests : 1865-1950, 12 Vols. – Abingdon : Professional Books.
Hbk £680.00
Individual vols.. –
Hbk £72.00

Law Reports of Nigeria, 3 Vols. / F. A. Ajayi. – London : Butterworths.
Hbk

Law Reports of Nigeria : 1980-date. – Abingdon : Professional Books, 1984.
This series of law reports provides information and guidance arising from the interpretation of common law principles and customary law by the Nigerian courts. The reports cover all the major Federal courts of Nigeria.
Hbk

Law reports of the Commonwealth
Constitutional and administrative law reports. – Abingdon : Professional Books, 1985.
Includes indexes.

Law reports of the Eastern Region of the Federation of Nigeria : including certain hitherto unreported cases previously decided in the Supreme Court of Nigeria. – 2 v. – Enugu? : Government Printer, 1956.
Continued by: Law reports of Eastern Nigeria. Bound with vols. 3-6 of the Law reports of Eastern Nigeria. Popular title: Eastern Region law reports.

Law reports of the Kwara State of Nigeria ... / compiled by the Law Reporting Committee. – Ilorin : Government Printer, 1979-.

Law Reports Reprint : 1865-1971, 565 Vols. – Wellington : Butterworths.
Hbk

Law, rights and the welfare state / edited by C.J.G. Sampford and D.J. Galligan. – London : Croom Helm, 1986.
xv,215p; 23cm.
Bibliography: p200-207. - Includes index.
ISBN 0709938381 £25.00

Law School Orientation : Cases and Materials. – Agincourt : Carswell, 1986.
341p.
This work for law students provides a series of introductory readings, cases, and materials for students beginning their studies at American law schools.
Pbk £18.75

Law, socialism and democracy / Paul Q. Hirst. – London : Allen & Unwin, 1986.
200p; 22cm.
Includes bibliography and index.
ISBN 0043012531 Hbk £15.00 :
ISBN 004301254X Pbk £6.95

Law Society

Accounting for goodwill : Accounting Standards Committee exposure draft no. 30 : memorandum / by the Society's Standing Committee on Company law. – London : Law Society, 1983.
4p.

—Annual report of the Council of the Law Society : intended to be presented to the general meeting of the members on ... – Law Society. – London : Spottiswoode, 1903.
Continues: Annual report of the Council of the Incorporated Law Society. 1975 onwards incorporates the interim report and accounts of the Solicitors Benevolent Association. Cover title, 1966/67 onwards: Annual report of the Council and accounts. Published by the Law Society, 1945 onwards.

—Better way out reviewed : memorandum / by the Society's Standing Committee on Family Law. – London : Law Society, 1982.
41p.

—Breach of confidence : comments on Law Commission report on breach of confidence (Law Com. no. 110) : memorandum / by the Council's Law Reform Committee. – London : Law Society, 1982.
5p.

—Briefing memorandum on the Police and Criminal Evidence Bill / the Law Society. – London : Law Society, 1982.
5 leaves.

—Capital transfer tax : discretionary trusts : memorandum by the Society's Standing Committee on Revenue Law commenting on draft clauses published by the Inland Revenue. – Law Society. – London : Law Society, 1982.
9p; 30cm.

—Child care law : proposals for reform / the Law Society. – London : Law Society, 1983.
14 leaves.
'Prepared by the Law Society's Standing Committee on Criminal Law' - Introduction.

—Comments on the Justice-All Souls discussion paper on administrative law (April 1981) : memorandum / by the Council's Law Reform Committee. – London : Law Society, 1981.
13,2p.

—Companies Act 1980, sections 54 and 55 : transactions or arrangements in which a director has a material interest : memorandum / by the Society's Standing Committee on Company Law. – London : Law Society, 1981.
6p; 30cm.

—Companies purchasing their own shares : memorandum / by the Society's Standing Committee on Revenue Law. – London : Law Society, 1981.
9p; 30cm.
Submitted in reply to the Inland Revenue's consultative document: Companies purchasing their own shares.

—Data Protection Bill : notes on the passage of the Bill from the House of Lords to the House of Commons / by the Council's Law Reform Committee. – London : The Committee, 1983.
8p.

—Finance Bill / memorandum by the Society's Standing Committee on Revenue Law. – London : Law Society, 1982.
53p.

→ Guidelines for the administration and use of part II of the Register of Applications for Planning Permission.

—Implementation of the third E.C. directive : Department of Trade explanatory and consultative note : memorandum / by the Society's Standing Committee on Company Law. – London : Law Society, 1982.
10p.

—Improving access to civil justice : the report of the Law Society's Working Party on the Funding of Litigation. – Law Society. – London : Law Society, 1987.
11p.
Supplement to the Law Society's Gazette. Includes bibliographical references.

—Information service 1986 : accounting and time recording systems for solicitors / the Law Society. – 1. – London : Law Society, 1986.
various pagings.

—Information service 1986 : technology for solicitors / the Law Society. – 1. – London : Law Society, 1986.
various pagings.

→ Joint ventures and Article 85.

—Lawyers and the courts : time for some changes / a discussion paper issued by the Law Society's Contentious Business Committee : an appraisal published by the Council of the Law Society of the effect of the Building Societies Bill on the solicitors' profession. – London : Law Society, 1986.
10 leaves.
Supplement to the Law Society's 'Gazette', 22 January (1986). Includes bibliographical references.

→ Legal aid handbook 1981.

→ Legal aid handbook 1983.

→ Legal aid handbook 1984.

—Legal aid handbook 1986 / prepared by the Law Society. – 7th ed. – London : HMSO, 1986.
v,460p.
Contains eligibility tables, a list of legal aid forms with explanatory notes, all Acts and Regulations covering legal aid, notes for guidance issued by the Council of the Law Society, practice directions and articles on criminal legal aid.
ISBN 0113800010 Pbk £7.95

→ Multidisciplinary partnerships and allied topics.

—N.V. Slavenburg's Bank v. Intercontinental Natural Resources Ltd. : (1980) 1 All E.R. 955 : memorandum / by the Society's Standing Committee on Company Law. – London : Law Society, 1981.
12p; 30cm.

—Occupiers' liability and access to the countryside / memorandum by the Council's Law Reform Committee. – London : Law Society, 1982.
7p.

—Pension scheme accounts : a discussion paper by the Accounting Standards Committee : memorandum / by the Society's Standing Committee on Company Law. – London : Law Society, 1982.
4p.

—Proceedings and resolutions of the ... provincial meeting of the members of the Society / the Law Society. – 25 v. – London : The Law Society, 1903.
Continues: Proceedings and resolutions / Incorporated Law Society. Continued by: Annual conference of the Law Society, 1st(1948). Bound with the annual reports of the Council of the Law Society.

→ Proceedings of Forum London : a seminar organised by the International Bar Association, Section on Business Law, in conjunction with the Solicitors' European Group of the Law Society of England and Wales, 23-26 September 1981, London.

—Professional conduct of solicitors / Law Society. – 1. – London : The Society, 1986.
loose-leaf; 23cm.

—Proposal for a Council regulation on the European Co-operation Grouping (COM (78) 139 Final) : memorandum / by the Society's Standing Committee on Company Law. – London : Law Society, 1981.
4p; 30cm.

—Reform of revenue law : memorandum / by the Law Society. – London : Law Society, 1983.
38p.

—Registered land practice notes. – Law Society. – 2nd ed. – London : Longman Professional, 1986.
ISBN 0851212573 Pbk £5.95

→ Reservation of title : draft Council of Europe Convention (CDCJ(82)15).

—Review of criminal procedure / the Law Society. – London : Law Society, 1981.
24p.

—Rights of access to neighbouring land : Law Commission Working paper no. 78 : memorandum / by the Council's Law Reform Committee. – London : Law Society, 1981.
9p; 30cm.

—Royal Commission on Criminal Procedure : memorandum by the Council of the Law Society on the Royal Commission's Report. – Law Society. – London : Law Society, 1981.
38p; 30cm.

—Solicitors Accounts Rules 1976, The Solicitors Trust Accounts Rules 1986, The Accountants Reports Rules 1986, The Solicitors Accounts (Deposit Interest) Rules 1986. – Law Society. – London : Law Society.
Hbk £5.00

→ Solicitors' and barristers' directory and diary : an almanac and directory incorporating the Law Society list of practising solicitors and the Senate of the Inns of Court and the Bar list of members.

—Survey of the structure and finances of the legal profession in private practice 6th January 1986 / Law Society, Special Committee on Remuneration. – 3. – London : Law Society, 1986.
Contents: 1 Commentary - 2 Major tables - 3 Detailed tables.

—Tax law in the melting pot / a study by the Revenue Law Committee of the Law Society of the 'Ramsay' doctrine after 'Furniss v. Dawson', with proposals. – London : Law Society, 1985.
iii,119p.
Bibliography: p.119.

—Taxation of international business : memorandum / by the Society's Standing Committee on Revenue Law. – London : Law Society, 1983.
21p.

—UNIDROIT : Draft Convention on Agency in the International Sale of Goods : memorandum / by a working party of the Council's Law Reform Committee. – London : Law Society, 1983.
2p.

Law, society, and the economy / Ivan Bernier and Andree Lajoie, research coordinators. – Toronto : University of Toronto Press, 1986.
xv, 230 p.; 23 cm.
Includes bibliographies.
ISBN 0802072917 Pbk

Law Society of Northern Ireland
Legal aid : annual reports of the Law Society and of the Lord Chancellor's Advisory Committee. – Law Society of Northern Ireland. – Belfast : H.M.S.O., 1983.
Continues: Report of the Incorporated Law Society of Northern Ireland on the Legal Aid Scheme; and, Report of the Legal Aid Advisory Committee on the Report of the Incorporated Law Society of Northern Ireland. 1981/1982 issue includes 16th (final) Report of the Law Society of Northern Ireland on legal aid in criminal proceedings.

Law Society of Scotland →Aspects of agricultural law.

—Response by the Law Society of Scotland to Consultative Paper on Conveyancing by Employed Solicitors in Scotland. – Law Society of Scotland. – Edinburgh : The Society, 1984.
20p.

Law Society of Upper
Advocacy. – Law Society of Upper. – Toronto : DeBoo, 1982.
ISBN 0888201117 Hbk £100.00

→ Charter of Rights and administrative law, 1983-1984.

—Costs, Party and Party : Updated. – Law Society of Upper. – Toronto : Law Society of Upper Canada.
ISBN 0887590608 Hbk

—Law Society of Upper Canada - Special Lectures Series. – Law Society of Upper. – Toronto : DeBoo, 1980-83.
ISBN 0888201729 Hbk Four vol. set 175.00

—Ontario Law Reports (O.L.R.) 1901-1931, 66 Vols. – Law Society of Upper. – Aurora : Canada Law Book Co.
– (Predecessor to the Ontario Reports (O.R.)).
Hbk £2178.00

→ Recent developments in administrative law.

→ Torts in the 80s.

Law Society of Upper Canada - Special Lectures Series. – Law Society of Upper. – Toronto : DeBoo, 1980-83.
ISBN 0888201729 Hbk Four vol. set 175.00
Thirty-One vol. set incl. index. –
Hbk £395.00

Law Society (United Kingdom)
Expense of Time. – Law Society (United Kingdom). – 4th ed. – London : Law Society, 1986.
ISBN 0901064734 Hbk £3.00

Law Society's Criminal Law Committee
Advising a suspect in the police station : guidelines for solicitors. – Law Society's Criminal Law Committee. – London : Law Society.
Hbk £2.00

Law, state and society / edited by Bob Fryer ... et al. – London : Croom Helm, 1981.
234p; 23cm.
Conference papers. Includes bibliographies and index.
ISBN 0709910045 £14.95

Law, state and the working class in Tanzania : c.1920-1964 / Issa G. Shivji. – London : Currey, 1986.
xix,268p; 24cm.
Bibliography: p253-260. - Includes index.
ISBN 0852553021 Hbk £25.00
ISBN 043508013X £9.95

Law, State and Working Class in Tanzania. – London : Dent (J M) & Sons, 1986.
ISBN 085255303X Pbk £9.95

Law Suit : A Study in Damages (U.S.A.) 1980. – London : Wildy & Sons.
Hbk £12.95

Law Teacher : Journal of the Association of Law Teachers / John Tilotson. – London : Sweet & Maxwell, 1986.
Hbk £22.00

Law Technology Centre
Newsletter / Law Technology Centre & BILETA. – Warwick : LTC, School of Law, University of Warwick, 1987-.

Law Times : 1843-1965, 235 Vols. – Abingdon : Professional Books, 1984.
Hbk

Law under review : a quarterly bulletin of law reform projects. – Law Commission. – London : Law Commission, 1987.
Includes index.

Law Union of Ontario
Immigrant's Handbook : a Critical Guide. – Law Union of Ontario. – Montreal : Black Rose Books, 1981.
263p.
Pbk £9.95

Law Unit : Torts / Lucas. – Stockholm : Anderson Keenan, 1981.
ISBN 0906501245 Pbk £3.70

Law Versus Business : Business Law Articles from the 'Financial Times'. – London : Butterworths.
ISBN 0406177015 Pbk £25.00

LAWASIA →Conference on prospects for the establishment of an inter-governmental human rights commission in the South Pacific.

→ Democracy in peril : Sri Lanka : a country in crisis : report to the LAWASIA Human Rights Standing Committee.

→ Meeting of Experts on the Exploitation of the Child, November 12-13, 1984, Singapore and the Conference on Child Labour and Child Prostitution, February 21-23, 1986, Kuala Lumpur.

—Recent trends in human rights / Lawasia Human Rights Standing Committee. – Sydney : Law Association for Asia and the Western Pacific, 1982.
viii,112p.

Lawasia directory. – Sydney : Lawasia, 1979-.

Lawasia human rights bulletin. – Sydney : Lawasia, 1982-.

Lawasia newsletter. – Sydney : Law Association for Asia and the Western Pacific, 1977-.

Lawdata Papers. – Oslo : Norwegian University Press, 1982.
48p.
ISBN 8200059650 Hbk £26.00

Lawes and Acts of Parliament Made by King James the First and His Successours Kinges of Scotland : 1424-1597. – Repr. of 1597 ed. – Abingdon : Professional Books.
116p.
Hbk £350.00

Lawford, Peter E
Canadian Mining Law. – London : Butterworths.
ISBN 0409802794 Hbk £132.00

Lawful and the Prohibited in Islam. – London : Shorouk International, 1985.
ISBN 1850240027 Pbk £6.50

Lawful rights of mankind : an introduction to the international legal code of human rights / Paul Sieghart. – Oxford : Oxford University Press, 1985.
xiii,252p; 23cm.
Bibliography: p247-248. - Includes index.
ISBN 019219190X £9.95

Lawless, Paul
Britain's inner cities / Paul Lawless. – London : Harper and Row, 1981.
224p.
ISBN 0063181843 Hbk £8.95
ISBN 0063181851 Pbk £4.95

Lawlor, William R →Cross-border transactions between related companies : a summary of tax rules.

Lawmakers and Wayward Whigs : Law and Justice in South Australia / Michael Harris. – Cowandilla : Wakefield Press, 1986.
256p.
ISBN 0949268607 Pbk £50.00
ISBN 0949268615 40.00 £75.00
ISBN 0949268623 Hbk

Lawmaking by the people : referendums and plebiscites in Canada / J. Patrick Boyer. – Toronto : Butterworths, 1982.
xxxii,304p.
Outlines the laws which make possible the existence of political rights in Canada by exploring constitutional conventions such as responsible government, parliamentary democracy, and the role of political parties. It examines municipal and provincial laws regarding signs, posters and parades, as well as federal broadcasting laws governing provincial elections.
ISBN 0409816019

Law-making process... / Michael Zander. – 2nd. ed. – London : Weidenfeld, 1985.
xxiv, 416p.
ISBN 0297786628 Pbk
ISBN 0297786636

Law-Medicine Relations : a Philosophical Exploration : Proceedings of the 8th Trans-Disciplinary Symposium on Philosophy and Medicine Held at Farmington, Conn., 1978 / J.M. Healey. – Dordrecht : Kluwer, 1981.
319p.
ISBN 9027712174 Hbk £75.00

Lawrence →Understanding Commercial Law.

Lawrence, Joseph Wilson
Judges of New Brunswick and Their Times / D.G. Bell. – Fredericton : Acadiensis Press, 1985.
552p.
ISBN 0919107044 Hbk £45.00

Laws. – Rev. ed. – Valletta : Legal (Publishing) Enterprises, 1978.

Laws and Acts Made in the First Parliament of Queen Anne. – Repr. of 1702 ed. – Abingdon : Professional Books.
115p.
Hbk £85.00

Laws and Acts of Parliament : James VII-Anne (1685-1707). – Repr. of 1731 ed. – Abingdon : Professional Books.
117p.
Hbk £180.00

Laws and Acts of Parliament Made by James I-Charles II : 1424-1681. – Repr. of 1681 ed. – Abingdon : Professional Books.
116p.
Hbk £200.00

Laws and Acts of Parliament Made by King James I and Royal Successors : 1424-1621. – Repr. of 1682 ed. – Abingdon : Professional Books.
116p.
Hbk £250.00

Laws and Customs of Scotland in Matters Criminal : Wherein is to be Seen How the Civil Law and Laws and Customs of Other Nations Do Not Agree With and Supply Ours. – Repr. of 1678 ed. – Abingdon : Professional Books.
74p.
Hbk £275.00

Laws and policies affecting adolescent health / by John M. Paxman and Ruth Jane Zuckerman. – Geneva : World Health Organization, 1987.
x,300p.
Includes bibliographical references.
ISBN 9241560959

Laws and Statutes for Production and Marketing of Nutrition. – Oslo : Fabritius og Sonners, 1984.
804p. – (Food).
ISBN 8207009020 Hbk £230.00

Law's Disposal of a Person's Estate Who Dies Without Will or Testament : The Disposal of Estates of Will, Form of Wills, and Directions for Executors etc. – 10th ed. Repr. of 1809 ed. – Abingdon : Professional Books.
492p.
Hbk £60.00

Laws of Anguilla : printed by authority. – Anguilla. – St. Michael, Barbados : Coles Printery, appointed as Government Printer for Anguilla, 1982.
Continues in part: Laws of Saint Christopher, Nevis and Anguilla, 1961-1970. Half title, 1972 onwards: Anguilla ordinances and statutory rules and orders.

Laws of armed conflicts : a collection of conventions, resolutions and other documents / edited by Dietrich Schindler and Jiri Toman. – 2nd rev. ed. – Alphen aan den Rijn : Sitjhoff & Noordhoft, 1981.
xxxiv,933p.
ISBN 9028601996

Laws of armed conflicts : a collection of conventions, resolutions and other documents / edited by Dietrich Schindler and Jiri Toman. – 3rd rev. ed. – Dordrecht : Nijhoff, 1986.
xxxix,1033p.
Includes index.
ISBN 9024733065

Laws of Barbados : subsidiary legislation in force on the 31st day of December, 1978 / prepared under the authority of the Law Revision Act cap. 2 by Wilfred K. Fergusson. – 3. – Bridgetown : Government Printer, 1982.
looseleaf.

Laws of Cross River State of Nigeria : containing the laws of the State in force on 30th September 1979 together with certain subsidiary legislation and Federal acts and decrees / Lionel Brett. – Rev. ed. 7 v. – s.l. : s.n., 1981.
Includes index. Printed by Eyre and Spottiswoode, London, authorised by the Government of Cross River State of Nigeria.

Laws of Federation of Nigeria, 12 Vols. – Abingdon : Professional Books, 1984.
Hbk

Laws of Indo-European. – Amsterdam : John Benjamins Publishing Co., 1985.
xviii, 273p.
ISBN 9027235309 Hbk £100.00
ISBN 0915027755 Pbk £16.00
ISBN 9027221022 Pbk £44.00

Laws of Saint Christopher, Nevis and Anguilla : printed by authority. – Saint Christopher, Nevis and Anguilla. – St. Michael, Barbados : Coles Printer, appointed Government Printer, 1982.
Continued in part by: Laws of Anguilla, 1971-. Includes ordinances and statutory rules and orders.

Laws of Scotland : Stair memorial encyclopaedia / James Dalrymple Stair. – Edinburgh : The Law Society of Scotland, 1987.
Includes indexes.
ISBN 040623700X

Laws of South-East Asia
Vol. 1 : The pre-modern texts / edited by M.B. Hooker. – Singapore : Butterworth, 1986.
xvi,624p.
Introduction to the pre-modern laws of South-East Asia. Analyses the nature, problems and difficulties of the Burmese Dhammathat, the Thai Thammasat, the epigraphy of Angkorian Cambodia, the law texts of Java and Bali, and the law texts of Muslim South-East Asia.
ISBN 0409995061
Vol. 2: European Laws in South-East Asia. – 1988.
ca 680p.
Essays studying the introduction and adaptation of European and 'Europeanized' legal systems into South-East Asia. Examines what these laws were in the late eighteenth and all of the nineteenth and twentieth century, and what has become of them in South-East Asia. Looks at the Portuguese, Spanish, Dutch, English, Siamese, and American systems.
ISBN 0409995444 Hbk £280.00

Laws of the Australian Capital Territory made during the year ... – Australian Capital Territory. – Canberra : Commonwealth Government Printer, 1964.
Contains ordinances and regulations.

Laws of the Federation of Nigeria and Lagos : 1958, 12 Vols. – Abingdon : Professional Books.
Hbk

Laws of the Straits Settlements : a Commentary. – Singapore : Oxford University Press, 1982.
308p.
ISBN 0195825594 Hbk £49.50

Laws of Trinidad and Tobago
Vols. 1-17. – London : Sweet & Maxwell, 1981.
ISBN 0421287306 Hbk £245.00

Laws of Tuvalu. – London : Sweet & Maxwell, 1982.
ISBN 0421330503 Hbk £40.00

Laws on the defense of the consumer / German Cavelier. – Bogota : Cavelier Abogados, 1985.
41 leaves.
Contains the text of relevant laws, decrees and resolutions in English.

Laws Relating to Notices. – 5th ed. – Calcutta : Eastern Law House, 1982.
Hbk £90.00

Lawson
Tortious Liability for Unintentional Harm
Vol. 1 / B S Markesinis. – Cambridge : Cambridge University Press.
ISBN 0521272092 Pbk £17.50

Lawson, F. H. →Law of property.
—Law of property / Bernard Rudden, F. H. Lawson. – 2nd ed. – Oxford : Clarendon, 1982.
ix,247p; 23cm. – (Clarendon law series).
Previous ed.: published as Introduction to the law of property. 1958. Includes index.
ISBN 0198761287 Hbk £14.00
ISBN 0198761295 Pbk £6.95
—Tortious liability for unintentional harm in the common law and the civil law / by F.H. Lawson, B.S. Markesinis. – 2. – Cambridge : Cambridge University Press, 1982.
Includes index.
ISBN 0521235863 v. 2

Lawson, Richard
Butterworth's Trading Law Cases. – London : Butterworths.
This comprehensive looseleaf service covers cases dealing with such topics as trade descriptions, weights and measures, food and advertising, consumer credit, hallmarking, prices, and product safety in the United Kingdom.
Pbk
—Exclusion clauses / Richard Lawson. – 3rd ed. – London : Longman Professional (UK), 1990. – (Practitioner Series).
Guide to the use of exclusion clauses (as limited by the Unfair Contract Terms Act). Discusses ways in which an exclusion clause can become a contractual term, what loss or damage it covers, and how likely it is to be interpreted by the courts.

Lawson, Richard G
Advertising Law. – Pitman, 1978.
ISBN 0712112391 Hbk £13.95
—Consumer Credit. – Plymouth : Macdonald & Evans, 1981.
ISBN 0712103996 Pbk £4.95
—Exclusion Clauses. – 2nd ed. – London : Longman Professional, 1983.
ISBN 0851207294 Pbk £21.00
—Sales promotion law. – Oxford : Blackwell Scientific, 1987.
ISBN 0003833941 Hbk £25.00
—Supply of Goods and Services Act 1982 : a practical guide / R.G. Lawson. – London : Oyez Longman, 1982.
xix,136p; 22cm.
Includes index.
ISBN 0851206727 Pbk £16.50

Lawton
Meetings : Law and Practice / Rigby. – 4th ed. – Plymouth : Macdonald & Evans, 1987.
ISBN 0712113002 Pbk £6.50

Lawyer : a quarterly journal of the Trinidad & Tobago Bar Association. – Port of Spain : Trinidad and Tobago Bar Association, 1977.
28cm.
Includes: Digest of cases with editorial notes. Subtitle varies.

Lawyer : journal of the Law Society, University of Lagos, Lagos, Nigeria. – Lagos : Faculty of Law, University of Lagos, 1960-.

Lawyer Incorporation. – Vancouver : Continuing Legal Education Society of British Columbia, 1988.
146p.
ISBN 0865049963 Hbk £70.00

Lawyer-economist extraordinary : the Soviet jurisconsult / Jane Giddings. – s.l. : National Association for Soviet and East European Studies, 1981.
29p; 30cm.

Lawyers. – Markham : Penguin Books Canada.
ISBN 0140073906 Pbk £9.95

Lawyers. – North Ryde : Law Book Co, 1986.
xli, 944p.
ISBN 0455206538 Hbk £37.50
ISBN 0455206546 Pbk £29.50

Lawyers : Meet the Computer!. – Vancouver : British Columbia Continuing Legal Education Society, 1983.
200p.
ISBN 0865041091 Hbk £55.00

Lawyers and laymen / edited by T.M. Charles-Edwards, Morfydd E. Owen and D. B. Walters. – Cardiff : University of Wales Press, 1986.
394,1p of plates; 23cm.
Bibliography: p355-368. - Includes index. Festschrift in honour of Professor Dafydd Jenkins. Includes two papers in Welsh.
ISBN 0708309259 £25.00

Lawyers and public administrators : separate and unequal : a public lecture / delivered by Lousi Blom-Cooper on ... 1st March 1984. – London : Inns of Court School of Law, 1984.
20p; 23cm.

Lawyers and the consumer interest : regulating the market for legal services / edited by Robert G. Evans, Michael J. Trebilcock. – Toronto : Butterworths, 1982.
xxiii,459p.
Includes bibliographical references.
ISBN 0409873543

Lawyers and the courts : the response of the Bar to a discussion paper issed bu the Law Society's Contentious Business Committee. – Senate of the Inns of Court and the Bar. – London : Senate of the Inns of Court and the Bar, 1986.
14p.
Includes bibliographical references. At head of p.3: Seanate of the Inns of Court and the Bar.

Lawyers and the courts : time for some changes / a discussion paper issued by the Law Society's Contentious Business Committee : an appraisal published by the Council of the Law Society of the effect of the Building Societies Bill on the solicitors' profession. – London : Law Society, 1986.
10 leaves.
Supplement to the Law Society's 'Gazette', 22 January (1986). Includes bibliographical references.

Lawyers and the Nuclear Debate / Margaret E. Gouin. – Ottawa : University of Ottawa Press, 1988.
xvi, 420p.
ISBN 0776602098 Hbk £65.00
ISBN 0776601997 Pbk £35.00

Lawyers' Etiquette. – 2nd ed. – Allahabad : Law Book Company, 1988.
Hbk £50.00

Lawyers' Fees. – Vancouver : Continuing Legal Education Society of British Columbia, 1987.
133p.
ISBN 0865043108 Hbk £65.00

Lawyers' Fees. – Vancouver : British Columbia Continuing Legal Education Society, 1981.
154p.
ISBN 0865040397 Hbk £8.00

Lawyers for Nuclear Disarmament
Illegality of nuclear warfare
Pamphlet 1 / Lawyers for Nuclear Disarmament. – London : Lawyers for Nuclear Disarmament, 1983.
26p.
Originally published: 1982. Bibliography: p.19.
ISBN 0946499004

Lawyer's Guide to Financial Statements - 1985. – Vancouver : British Columbia Continuing Legal Education Society, 1985.
125p.
ISBN 0865041938 Hbk £65.00

Lawyer's Guide to Financial Statements. – Vancouver : British Columbia Continuing Legal Education Society, 1984.
ISBN 0865041490 Hbk £45.00

Lawyer's Guide to Software. – Pinter, 1985.
ISBN 0861874978 Hbk £15.00

Lawyers in business : and the law business / Karl J. Mackie. – Basingstoke : Macmillan, 1988.
viii,289p.
Includes bibliography and index.
ISBN 0333419081 £29.50

Lawyers in early modern Europe and America / edited by Wilfrid Prest. – London : Croom Helm, 1981.
216 p.

Lawyers in Society
Volume 1 The Common Law World / Lewis. – University of California Press.
ISBN 0520056035 Hbk

Lawyers in the European Community / from the French original by Serge-Pierre Laguette : updated for this Engish language version in collaboration with Patrick Latham. – Luxembourg : Office for Official Publications of the European Communities, 1987.
293p.
At head of title: Commission of the European Communities.
ISBN 9282569780

Lawyers in the Third World : comparative and developmental perspectives / edited by C.J. Dias ... et al. – Uppsala : Scandinavian Institute of African Studies, 1981.
400p; 22cm.
Bibliography: p.382-399. Sponsored by the Scandinavian Institute of African Studies and the International Center for Law in Development.
ISBN 9171061797 Hbk £25.00 (20.00 in Third World Countries)
ISBN 9171061762 Pbk £16.00 (8.00 in Third World countries)

Lawyers in the United Kingdom / Richard Abel. – 1st draft. – S.l. : s.n., 1983.
xvi,209p.
'Prepared for the meeting of the Working Group for Comparative Study of Legal Professions of the ISA Research Committee on Sociology of Law, to be held at the Villa Serbelloni, Bellagio, Italy, July 16-21, 1984'. Bibliography: p.199-209.

Lawyers' law books : a practical index to legal literature / by Donald Raistrick. – 2nd ed. – Milton, Oxon. : Professional Books, 1985.
xxxv,604p. – (Professional Books law reference library).
ISBN 0862050723 Hbk £32.50

Lawyers' Law Directory, 1984-85. – Abingdon : Professional Books, 1985.
ISBN 0862050995 Hbk £45.00

Lawyers Law Directory 1988. – London : Butterworths.
ISBN 086205000 Hbk £36.00

Lawyer's Peregrination. – 2nd ed. – London : Sweet & Maxwell, 1987.
ISBN 0421391804 Pbk £1.95

Lawyer's Phone Book (Ontario). – Aurora : Canada Law Book Co.
– (Directories).
This directory, published each year in the early spring, lists every individual lawyer and law office in Ontario, complete with telephone number, street address and postal code. Also included are the addresses and telephone numbers of all Provincial, County, and District judicial offices, Legal Aid Offices, Ontario Government Officials and others.
Hbk £1-5 copies 26.50 ea.

Lawyer's Pocketbook. – Durban : Professional Publishers, 1982.
ISBN 0409034533 Hbk

Lawyer's Pocketbook. – Durban : Butterworths, 1985.
ISBN 0409034568 Hbk

Lawyer's Remembrancer 1987. – London : Butterworths.
ISBN 040626919X Hbk £11.50

Lawyer's Remembrancer 1988 / Isabel Isaacson, Julian Roskams. – London : Butterworths, 1987.
This book is a concise encyclopedia of United Kingdom practice and legislation, together with a diary section running from November, 1985 to January, 1987. Each week in the diary is given two full pages. The references section includes names, addresses, phone numbers, and relevant abbreviations.
ISBN 0406269300 Hbk £12.50

Lawyers Remembrancer 1989 / Roskamus. – London : Butterworths.
ISBN 0406269319 Hbk £13.00

Lawyers' Trust Accounts. – Vancouver : Continuing Legal Education Society of British Columbia, 1988.
54p.
ISBN 0865049998 Hbk £40.00

Lawyer's Use of Financial Statements : 1982. – Vancouver : British Columbia Continuing Legal Education Society, 1983.
464p.
ISBN 0865040508 Hbk £14.50

Lawyers Versus the Bomb → Trade union powers and the anti-nuclear campaign.

Lawyers Weekly : Consolidated Digest
Vol. 5. – Butterworths.
ISBN 0409806048 Pbk £39.75
Vol. 6. –
ISBN 0409809411 Pbk £59.95
Vols. 1 and 2 combined. –
ISBN 0409856657 Pbk £37.95
Vols. 3 and 4 combined. –
ISBN 0409811653 Pbk £37.95

Laxmi et al
Public Enterprise and Fundamental Rights. – Bombay : Tripathi.

Lay Advocacy Service → Rent arrears and the courts : a report by the Lay Advocacy Service.

Lay justice? / Z.K. Bankowski, N.R. Hutton and J.J. McManus. – Edinburgh : T. & T. Clark, 1987.
xi,187p; 22cm.
Includes index. An analysis of the work of lay justice and a comprehensive study of the structure, operation and criteria of the Scottish District Courts.
ISBN 0567291391 Pbk £9.95

Laycock, Gloria → Situational crime prevention : from theory into practice.

Laying Down the Law : The Foundations of Legal Reasoning Research and Writing in Australia and New Zealand / C. Cook. – 2nd ed. – Sydney : Butterworths, 1988.
304p.
This workbook contains exercises which require students to find cases and statutes, analyze legal problems, interpret judicial decisions and legislation, and use basic research tools such as digests and encyclopedias. Additional material has been included to cover New Zealand.
Pbk £22.00

Layman as a magistrate / prepared for the Commonwealth Secretariat by Jane Kellock. – London : The Secretariat, 1988.
viii,32p.

Layman's Dictionary of English Law. – London : Waterlow, 1984.
ISBN 0080391613 Hbk £12.95

Layman's Guide to Pesticide Legislation. – National Turfgrass Council.
ISBN 1871140013 Pbk £3.00

Layperson's Guide to Treaty Rights in Canada. – Saskatoon : University of Saskatchewan, Native Law Centre, 1985.
59p.
ISBN 0888801610 Hbk £15.00

Laytime / Michael Brynmor Summerskill. – 4th ed. – London : Sweet & Maxwell, 1988.
ISBN 042079708 Hbk

Laytime and demurrage / by John Schofield. – London : Lloyds of London, 1985.
393p; 24cm.
Include index.
ISBN 1850440573

Layton, A. → Manual of European Practice, Vol. 1.

Layton, Alexander → Recent Developments in the Law Relating to Damages With Particular Reference to Professional Claims.

Layton, Christopher
One Europe: one world : a first exploration of Europe's potential contribution to world order / a report by Christopher Layton in conjunction with a gorup sponsored by the Federal Trust for Education and Research, the Wyndham Place Trust and the One World Trust. – London : Journal of World Trade Law, 1986.
70p.
Special supplement no. 4 to the Journal of World Trade Law, vol. 20 (1986).

Lazar, Fed
New Protectionism : Non-Tariff Barriers and Their Effects for Canada. – Toronto : Lorimer & Co, 1981.
ISBN 0888624425 Hbk £16.95
ISBN 0888624417 Pbk £7.95

Lazega, Emmanuel → Individual Property Rights Conceptions Privacy in Family.

Lazor, Yan Arthur M. → Child Welfare Act annotated.

Le Docte, E
Legal dictionary in four languages. – 3rd. – London : Sweet & Maxwell, 1987.
Over 13,000 legal expressions are translated, or given corresponding meanings, in the four European languages of English, French, German, and Spanish.
ISBN 0421378204 Hbk £77

Lea, John → Losing the fight against crime.
—What is to be done about law and order? / John Lea and Jock Young. – Harmondsworth : Penguin Books in association with the Socialist Society, 1984.
284p.
Includes index. Bibliography: p275-284.
ISBN 0140065938

Leach → Rule Against Perpetuities.

Leach, S. → Urban riots and public order : a select bibliography, 1975-1985.

Lead in the environment : the government response to the ninth report of the Royal Commission on Environmental Pollution. – London : H.M.S.O., 1983.
v,19p.
ISBN 0117517143

Leaders and lawyers / Brownstone. – London : Facts On File, 1986.
ISBN 0816013675 Hbk £7.95

Leadership at the Fed. – Yale University Press.
ISBN 0300043635 Pbk £8.95

Leading Academic Lawyers
Law England Reports Annual Review Nineteen Eighty-Six. – Leading Academic Lawyers. – London : Butterworths, 1987.
ISBN 040687963X Pbk

Leading Cases and Materials on the Agricultural Policy of the E.E.C. / H.J. Bronkhorst. – Dordrecht : Kluwer, 1984.
ca 250p.
ISBN 9065440704 Hbk £55.00

Leading cases and materials on the competition law of the E.E.C. / edited by D.G. Gijlstra and D.F. Murphy. – 3rd ed. – Deventer : Kluwer, 1984.
xviii,679p; 25cm.
Previous ed: 1979. At head of title: Europa Institute, University of Amsterdam.
ISBN 9065441115 Pbk

Leading cases and materials on the external relations law of the European Community, with emphasis on the common commercial policy / by E.L.M. Volker and J. Steenbergen. – Deventer, The Netherlands : Kluwer Law and Taxation Publishers, 1985.
At head of title: Europa Institute, University of Amsterdam.
ISBN 9065442219

Leading cases and materials on the social policy of the EEC. – Dordrecht : Kluwer, 1989.
556.
Guide to the scope of community law, using basic sources, such as treaty provisions and directives. Examines the problem of the direct effect on, and the relationship between, national and community law.
ISBN 9065443126 Pbk £39/Dfl 125

Leading Cases in Negligence for 'A' Level. – 2nd ed. – London : Butterworths, 1986.
ISBN 0406016828 Pbk £5.50

Leading Cases in the Law of Negligence for 'A' Level. – London : Butterworths, 1981.
This book provides the student in the United Kingdom taking the AEB 'A' level optional paper on negligence with all required cases as originally reported in the All England Law Reports.
ISBN 0406016801 Pbk

Leading Cases on Australian Income Tax / Mannix. – 5th ed. – North Ryde : Butterworths (Australia), 1984.
ISBN 0409493929 Pbk £31.30
Supplement-1986. –
ISBN 0409491160 Pbk £3.40

Leading cases on the law of the European Communities / edited by D.J. Gijlstra ... et al. – 4th ed. – Deventer, Netherlands : Kluwer Law and Taxation Publishers, 1982.
xxi, 599 p.
At head of title: Europa Institute, University of Amsterdam. Includes bibliographies and indexes.
ISBN 9065440682 Pbk £28.00

Leading constitutional decisions : cases on the British North America Act / edited and with an introduction by Peter H. Russell. – 3rd ed. – Ottawa : Carleton University Press, 1982.
vii,578p. – (The Carleton Library series).
Bibliography: p575-578.
ISBN 0886290058

League of Nations : its life and times 1920-1946 / F.S. Northedge. – Leicester : Leicester University Press, 1985.
viii,342p; 22cm.
Bibliography: p311-316. - Includes index.
ISBN 0718511948 £28.00

League of Nations in retrospect : proceedings of the symposium / organized by the United Nations Library and the Graduate Institute of International Studies, Geneva, 6-9 November 1980 La Societe des Nations, retrospective : actes du colloque / organise par la Bibliotheque des Nations Unies et l'Institut universitaire de hautes etudes internationales, Geneve 6-9 novembre 1980. – Berlin : W. de Gruyter, 1983.
xii, 427 p.; 24 cm. – (Serial publications / United Nations Library, Geneva. Series E, Guides and studies).
Includes bibliographical references and index.
ISBN 3110087332 £77.00 : est. DM154.00

Learning Banking : Guide Study Revis. Exam. Techniques / Kelly. – 2nd ed. – Folkestone : Bankers Books.
ISBN 0852972164 Pbk £3.95

Learning Canadian criminal law / by Don Stuart and Ronald Joseph Delisle. – Toronto : Carswell, 1982.
xix,913p.
ISBN 0459348205

Learning Canadian Criminal Procedure / Ronald Joseph Delisle. – Agincourt : Carswell, 1986.
798p.
This work for law students in Canada discusses the principles and policies underlying criminal procedure. Full coverage is given to the Canadian Charter of Rights and Freedoms and its impact on criminal procedure in the text.
Hbk £80.00

Learning the law / by Glanville Williams. – 11th ed. – London : Stevens, 1982.
viii,241p; 19cm.
Previous ed.: 1978. Includes index. .
ISBN 0420462902 Hbk £
ISBN 0420463003 Pbk £4.50

Learning to live with IT : an overview of the potential of information technology for education and training. – Information Technology Advisory Panel. – London : H.M.S.O., 1986.
44p.
ISBN 0116308311

Leary, Virginia A
International labour conventions and national law : the effectiveness of the automatic incorporation of treaties in national legal systems / Virginia A. Leary. – The Hague : M. Nijhoff, 1982.
xiv,191p.
Revision of thesis (doctoral)–Graduate Institute of International Studies at Geneva. Bibliography: p171-179.
ISBN 9024725518
—Philippines: human rights after martial law / report of a mission by Virginia Leary, A.A. Ellis, Kurt Madlener. – Geneva : International Commission of Jurist, 1984.
123p.
Includes bibliographical references.
ISBN 9290370238

Lease Drafting. – Vancouver : Continuing Legal Education Society of British Columbia, 1985.
252p.
ISBN 0865042004 Hbk £55.00

Lease Financing (Concept, Law and Procedure). – repr. 1986. – New Delhi : Bharat Law House, 1986.
Hbk £200.00

Lease or Licence. – London : Longman Professional, 1985.
ISBN 0851211240 Pbk £10.50

Leasehold conveyancing : laid before Parliament by the Lord High Chancellor pursuant to section 3(2) of the Law Commissions Act 1965 / the Law Commission. – London : H.M.S.O., 1987.
iii,37p. – (H.C.).
ISBN 0102360871

Leasehold enfranchisement / by N.T. Hague. – 2nd ed. – London : Sweet & Maxwell, 1987.
xxxix,519p; 25cm.
Previous ed.: 1967. Includes index.
ISBN 0421283602 £35.00

Leasehold Law (Service to Date). – London : Longman Professional.
ISBN 0851204716 Hbk £195.00

Leasing, 1984. – Vancouver : British Columbia Continuing Legal Education Society, 1984.
ISBN 0865041598 Hbk £60.00

Leasing finance / edited by Tom Clark. – London : Euromoney Publications, 1985.
ix,147p.
ISBN 0903121778

Leasing for General Practitioners. – Vancouver : Continuing Legal Education Society of British Columbia, 1986.
166p.
ISBN 0865042942 Hbk £65.00

Leasing in Canada : A Business Guide. – Toronto : Butterworths, 1986.
ISBN 0409805041 Pbk £35.00

Leave and Holidays. – 3rd ed. – Karachi : Bureau of Labour Publications, 1987.
Pbk £3.00

Leaves from My Library / by Lord Denning. – London : Butterworths, 1986.
ISBN 0406176159 Hbk £13.95

Leaving Money to Charity. – TUAR, 1983.
ISBN 0907164129 Pbk £1.95

Lebanese Legal System. – London : Eurospan.
ISBN 0935328289 Hbk £107.50

Lebedev, S. N. → Handbook on foreign trade arbitration in the CMEA countries.

LeBlanc, Marc → Current Issues in Juvenile Justice.

Lectures on Company Law. – 18th ed. 1981 repr. – Bombay : Tripathi, 1983.
Hbk £65.00

Lectures on English Commercial Law. – Dordrecht : Kluwer.
64p.
ISBN 9065441506 Pbk £30.00

Leder, M. J.
Consumer law / M.J. Leder. – 2nd ed. – London : Pitman, 1986.
xxxiii,220p; 22cm. – (M & E handbook series).
Previous ed.: Plymouth : Macdonald & Evans, 1980.
Includes index.
ISBN 0712106774 Pbk £4.95

Lederman, W R → Canadian Constitutional Law.
—Continuing Canadian constitutional dilemmas : essays on the constitutional history, public law and federal system of Canada / W.R. Lederman. – Toronto : Butterworths, 1981.
xx,442p.
Includes bibliographical references.
ISBN 0409844616 Hbk 55.00
ISBN 0409844608 Pbk 35.00
→ Law of Evidence in Civil Cases.

Lee and Nightingale → Loss of the 'City of Boston' : Inman v. Jenkins : an action for libel, tried at the Liverpool Assizes, before Mr. Justice Lush amd a special jury, on Tuesday and Wednesday, August 30th and 31st, 1870.

Lee, Eric H. K.
Commercial Arbitration Worldwide Guide. – London : LLoyd's of London Press, 1985.
ISBN 1850440530 Hbk
—Commercial disputes settlement in China / Eric Lee. – London : Lloyds of London, 1985.
152p; 22cm.
Includes index.
ISBN 1850440638 Pbk
—Dictionary of arbitration law & practice / Eric Lee. – London : Mansfield Law Publishers, 1986.
185p.
—Encyclopedia of arbitration law / Eric Lee. – 1 v. – London : Lloyd's, 1984.
looseleaf.
Includes index.
ISBN 1850440263
—Encyclopedia of international commercial arbitration / by Eric Lee. – London : Lloyd's of London Press, 1986.
412p; 24cm.
Includes index.
ISBN 185044059X £50.00

Lee, G.
Planned practice development. – London : Longman Professional, 1984.
ISBN 0851208673 Pbk £13.95

Lee, H. P. → Constitution of Malaysia : further perspectives and developments : essays in honour of Tun Mohamed Suffian.
—Emergency powers / by H. P. Lee. – Sydney : Law Book Company, 1984.
xl,334p.
Includes index. Bibliography: pxxxiii-xl.
ISBN 0455202729

Lee, Hock Lock
Central Banking in Malaysia. – Singapore : Butterworths (Asia), 1987.
520.
Deals with powers over finance companies, merchant banks, Islamic banks and other deposit takers, issue of currency, monetary policy and regulation of the quantity and direction of credit, and the relationship with the government.
ISBN 0409995339 Hbk

Lee, Li Kuo
Worldwide Space Law Bibliography. – Montreal : De Daro Publishing.
Hbk £120.00

Lee, Michael → Euronotes : RUFs, TRUFs, NIFs, SNIFs and BONUSes.
—Securitisation in international finance. – London : Butterworths, 1988.
ISBN 0406100616 Pbk

Lee, R.
Building Maintenance Management. – 3rd ed. – Oxford : Blackwell Scientific, 1987.
ISBN 0003833755 Pbk £14.95
—Elements of Roman Law. – 4th ed. – London : Sweet & Maxwell, Reprint 1986.
ISBN 042107805 Pbk £15.50

Lee, R G → Blackstones Statutes on Public Law.
—Constitutional and Administrative Law (SWOT). – London : Blackstone Press, 1985.
ISBN 0906322723 Pbk £7.95

Lee, Simon
Judging judges / Simon Lee. – London : Faber, 1988.
350p; 22cm.
Includes bibliography and index.
ISBN 0571148301 £12.95
—Law and morals : Warnock, Gillick and beyond / Simon Lee. – Oxford : Oxford University Press, 1986.
144p; 22cm.
Includes bibliography and index.
ISBN 0192177532 Hbk £12.50 :
ISBN 019283052X Pbk £4.95

Lee, W. A.
Manual of Queensland succession law / by W. A. Lee. – 2nd ed. – Sydney : Law Book Company, 1985.
xlix,268p.
ISBN 0455205620
→ Principles of the law of trusts.

Leedham-Green, E.
Books in Cambridge Inventories
Vol. 1. – Cambridge : Cambridge University Press.
ISBN 0521308739 Hbk £75.00

Leeding, A.
Child Care Manual. – 4th ed. – London : Butterworths.
ISBN 04062070031 Pbk £11.75

Lees, J.M.
Handbook of Written and Oral Pleading in the Sheriff Court and Notes on the Structure of Interlocutors Sheriff Court. – London : Caledonian Books.
ISBN 0950660795 Hbk £29.50

Left and rights : a conceptual analysis of the Socialist rights / Tom Campbell. – London : Routledge & Kegan Paul, 1982.
253p.
Includes bibliographical references and index.
Bibliography: p216-249.
ISBN 0710090854 Pbk

Legacies - Practical Guide for Charities. – Turnaround Press, 1983.
ISBN 0907164110 Pbk £3.95

Legal 500 : the major law firms in England, Wales and Scotland / John Pritchard. – London : Legalease, 1988.
352p.

Legal Acceptance of International Trade Data Transmitted by Electronic Means : CompLex 10/83. – Oslo : Norwegian University Press, 1983.
90p.
Hbk £131.00

Legal action : the bulletin of the Legal Action Group. – London : Legal Action Group, 1984.
Continues: LAG bulletin.

Legal Action Group → Legal action : the bulletin of the Legal Action Group.
→ Police misconduct : legal remedies.

Legal advice and assistance. – London : Policy Studies Institute, 1989.
160; 21.
A study commissioned by the Law Society to examine social welfare advice. Surveys the nature of the work of solicitors and advice services and their inter-relationship in thre areas - the London Borough of Newham, the Metropolitan Borough of Oldham, and Cornwall.
ISBN 0853744769 Pbk £6.95

Legal aid : annual reports of the Law Society and of the Lord Chancellor's Advisory Committee. – Law Society of Northern Ireland. – Belfast : H.M.S.O., 1983.
Continues: Report of the Incorporated Law Society of Northern Ireland on the Legal Aid Scheme; and, Report of the Legal Aid Advisory Committee on the Report of the Incorporated Law Society of Northern Ireland. 1981/1982 issue includes 16th (final) Report of the Law Society of Northern Ireland on legal aid in criminal proceedings.

Legal aid : efficiency scrutiny / Lord Chancellors Department. – 2 v. – London : The Department, 1986.

Legal Aid : the New Framework. – London : Butterworths.
ISBN 0406502951 Pbk £12.50

Legal Aid and Advice : Replies made by Governments to the Questionnaire on Legal Aid and Advice. – Strasbourg : Council of Europe, 1978.
Hbk £3.10

Legal aid and law clinics in South Africa : proceedings of a conference held at the Howard College School of Law, University of Natal, Durban, from 11-13 July 1983. – Durban : School of Law, Howard College, University of Natal, 1985.
ix,163p.
ISBN 0869804251

Legal aid cost comparison : salaried and private lawyers / by G.G. Meredith. – Canberra : Australian Government Publishing Service, 1983.
viii,61p.
Bibliography: p.61. At head of title: Commonwealth Legal Aid Council, Attorney-General's Department.
ISBN 0644025441

Legal aid handbook 1981 / prepared by the Law Society. – 5th ed. – London : H.M.S.O., 1981.
329p; 25cm.
ISBN 0113906307

Legal aid handbook 1983 / prepared by the Law Society. – 5th i.e. 6th ed. – London : H.M.S.O., 1983.
v,351p.
Includes index.
ISBN 0113906331

Legal aid handbook 1984
1984 / prepared by the Law Society. – London : HMSO, 1984.
v,404p; 25cm.
ISBN 0113906358 Pbk £6.95

Legal aid handbook 1986 / prepared by the Law Society. – 7th ed. – London : HMSO, 1986.
v,460p.
Contains eligibility tables, a list of legal aid forms with explanatory notes, all Acts and Regulations covering legal aid, notes for guidance issued by the Council of the Law Society, practice directions and articles on criminal legal aid.
ISBN 0113800010 Pbk £7.95

Legal Aid - How to use it / Levenson. – London : Legal Action Group, 1985.
ISBN 0905099095 Pbk £11.00

Legal aid in England and Wales : a new framework / presented to Parliament by the Lord Chancellor .. – London : H.M.S.O., 1987.
ii,22p; 30cm.
ISBN 0101011822

Legal Aid Summary. – New ed. – London : Oyez Longman, 1983.
ISBN 0851205879 Hbk

Legal analysis of economic policy / by Terence C. Daintith. – Florence : European University Institute, 1982.
13p.

Legal and Commercial Looseleaf Services Available in Australia and New Zealand. – Melbourne : , 1987.
Loose £99.00

Legal and Constitutional History of India, 2 Vols. – Bombay : Tripathi.
Hbk

Legal and Contract Procedure for Architects. – 2nd ed. – London : Architectural Press, 1984.
ISBN 0851393691 Pbk £9.95

Legal and Contractual Procedures for Architects. – 3rd ed. – London : Butterworths.
ISBN 0406004770 Pbk

Legal and economic analyses on multinational enterprises / edited by Klaus J. Hopt. – 2 V. – Berlin : Walter de Gruyter, 1982.
At head of title: European University Institute. Vol. 2, English and French, with summaries for each item in the other language, has also parallel title: Analyses legales et economiques sur les entreprises multinationales. Includes indexes. Contents: 1. European merger control – 2. Groups of companies in European laws.
ISBN 3110087049 v. 2

Legal and Economic Regulation in Marketing. – Quorum Press.
ISBN 0899302874 Hbk £34.95

Legal and ethical aspects of the management of newborns with severe disabilities. – Canberra : Australian Government Publishing Service, 1985.
71p. – (Occasional paper).
Includes bibliographical references.
ISBN 0644043849

Legal and institutional arrangements in minerals developments : a study based on an international workshop organised in Berlin (West) in August 1980 by the Department of Technical Co-operation for Development, United Nations, and the Development Policy Forum of the German Foundation for International Development. – London : Mining Journal Books, 1982.
xi,224p; 23cm.
ISBN 090011729X Pbk

Legal and institutional aspects of the International Monetary System : selected essays
Vol 2 : by Joseph Gold. – Washington, D.C. : International Monetary Fund, 1984.
xviii,947p.
Includes bibliographies and index.
ISBN 0939934345

Legal and Management Guides. – London : Architectural Press.

Legal and political structure of an Islamic state : implications for Iran and Pakistan / by Y. Noori and S.H. Amin. – Glasgow : Royston, 1986.
144p; 22cm.
Includes bibliography and index.
ISBN 094670631X £30.00

Legal and practical effects of the Transport Licensing Act (No. 2) 1983 : papers presented by R.J. Craddock ... et al., University of Auckland, 23 February 1984 / R. J. Craddock. – Auckland : Legal Research Foundation, 1984.
46p.
At head of title: Legal Research Foundation Inc. seminar.
ISBN 0908581335

Legal aspect of money : with special reference to comparative private and public international law / by F.A. Mann. – 4th ed. – Oxford : Clarendon, 1982.
lvi,602p; 25cm.
Previous ed.: Oxford : Oxford University Press, 1971. Bibliography: pli - Includes index.
ISBN 0198253672 Hbk £45.00

Legal aspects of agriculture in the European Community / J.A. Usher. – Oxford : Clarendon Press, 1988.
xxxvi,170p.
Includes index. Examines legal issues arising from the Common Agricultural Policy, and sets out the principles underlying changing legislation. Includes agricultural legislation which is behind European Court case law on the relationship between Community law and national law.
ISBN 0198255659 Hbk £30

Legal aspects of business transactions and investment in the Far East / Dennis Campbell, A Wolff. – Kluwer Law and Taxation, 1989.
400.
Describes the legal framework for trading with, licensing to, and investing in China, Hong Kong, Indonesia, Japan, Korea, Malaysia, Singapore, Taiwan and Thailand. Includes legal aspects of entering the Japanese market, parallel imports in Japan and legal aspects of trade and investment in Singapore, and forms of foreign investment in the People's Republic of China.
ISBN 9065443150 Pbk £63/Dfl 195

Legal aspects of doing business in Africa / edited by Dennis Campbell. – Deventer, The Netherlands : Kluwer Law and Taxation Publishers, 1986.
– (International business series).
Includes index.
ISBN 9065442685

Legal aspects of doing business in Asia and the Pacific / edited by Dennis Campbell. – Deventer, Netherlands : Kluwer Law and Taxation Publishers, 1984.
– (International business series).
Includes index. Kept up to date by supplements.
ISBN 9065449825

Legal aspects of doing business in Eastern Europe and the Soviet Union / edited by Dennis Campbell. – Deventer, The Netherlands : Kluwer Law and Taxation Publishers, 1986.
– (International business series).
Includes index and bibliography.
ISBN 9065442634

Legal aspects of doing business in Latin America / edited by Dennis Campbell. – Deventer, The Netherlands : Kluwer Law and Taxation Publishers, 1984.
vii, 351 p.; 25 cm. – (International business series).
Includes index.
ISBN 9065441026

Legal aspects of doing business in the Middle East / edited by Dennis Campbell. – Deventer, Netherlands : Kluwer Law and Taxation Publishers, 1986.
– (International business series).
Includes index.
ISBN 9065442642

Legal aspects of doing business in Western Europe / edited by Dennis Campbell. – Deventer, Netherlands : Kluwer Law and Taxation Publishers, 1983.
viii, 451 p.; 25 cm. – (International business series).
Includes index.
ISBN 0314792899 West Pub. Co.

Legal aspects of geology / Ronald W. Tank. – New York : Plenum, 1983.
xii,583p; 24cm.
Includes bibliographies and index.
ISBN 0306411598 Hbk
ISBN 0306412152 Pbk

Legal aspects of international business transactions : the Edinburgh Institute on International Business Transactions 1983 : a project of University of the Pacific McGeorge School of Law international programs / edited by D. Campbell and C. Rohwer. – Amsterdam : North-Holland, 1984.
x,463p; 24cm.
ISBN 0444875069 £34.88

Legal aspects of international drug control / S.K. Chatterjee. – The Hague : Nijhoff, 1981.
xxiv,587p.
Includes index. Bibliography: p547-555. Based on the author's thesis (doctoral–University of London).
ISBN 9024725569 Hbk £285.00

Legal aspects of joint ventures in Eastern Europe / edited Dennis Campbell. – Deventer : Kluwer, 1981.
133p; 25cm.
Includes index.
ISBN 9065440348

Legal aspects of medical practice / Bernard Knight. – 3rd ed. – Edinburgh : Churchill Livingstone, 1982.
viii,302p; 22cm. – (Churchill Livingstone medical text).
Previous ed.: 1976.
ISBN 0443025584

Legal aspects of medical practice / Bernard Knight. – 4th ed. – Edinburgh : Churchill Livingstone, 1987.
336p; 22cm.
Previous ed.: 1982. Includes bibliography and index.
ISBN 0443037817 Pbk £4.95

Legal Aspects of Starting a Business in Quebec. – Montreal : McGill Campus Legal Aid Clinic, 1984.
139p.
Hbk £8.50

Legal aspects of syndicated loans / Peter Gabriel. – London : Butterworths, 1986.
xxxvi,276p; 26cm.
Bibliography: p265-267. - Includes index.
ISBN 0406102104 Hbk £50.00

Legal Aspects of the Care of the Aged / Godrey Gypps. – London : Law Society, 1985.
– (Oxford Weekend Courses).
Hbk £5.00

Legal Aspects of the ECU / Dierciex. – London : Butterworths, 1988.
ISBN 0406112002 Hbk

Legal Aspects of the Namibian Dispute. – Ile-Ife : Obafemi Awolowo University Press.
xxli, 402p.
Hbk £10.00

Legal aspects of the problem of refugees in Cyprus / by Criton G. Tornaritis. – Nicosia : s.n., 1975.
25 leaves.

Legal aspects of trade preferences for developing states : a study in the influence of development needs on the evolution of international law / by Abdulqawi Yusuf. – The Hague : Nijhoff, 1982.
xx,185p; 25cm.
Bibliography: p169-181. - Includes index.
ISBN 9024725836

Legal Basis of Probation. – Canberra : Australian Institute of Criminology.
Hbk £0.60

Legal Bibliography, 3 Vols. – Repr. of 1925 ed. – Abingdon : Professional Books.
Hbk £45.00

Legal capacity and responsibility of minors and pupils / Scottish Law Commission. – Edinburgh : The Commission, 1985.
280p. – (Consultative memorandum).
Includes bibliographical references.

Legal Change : Essays in Honour of Julius Stone. – London : Butterworths, 1982.
Hbk £70.00

Legal change : essays in honour of Julius Stone / edited by A.R. Blackshield : on behalf of the Committee to honour Professor Julius Stone, OBE : with an introduction by Sir Zelman Cowen. – Sydney : Butterworths, 1983.
xxiv,367p.
Bibliography: p.335-344. - Includes index. Contains contributions from former students and colleagues of Professor Stone, from Australia and around the world. The essays represent broad areas of growth and change in the law, with emphasis on development and prospects for the last quarter of this century.
ISBN 0409491306

Legal character of petroleum licences : a comparative study / edited by Terence Daintith. – Dundee : University of Dundee, Centre for Petroleum and Mineral Law Studies, 1981.
xv,225p; 21cm.
Conference papers.
ISBN 0906343089 Pbk £13.00

Legal Control of Casinos. – Canberra : Australian Institute of Criminology.
free

Legal control of the multinational enterprise : national regulatory techniques and the prospects for international controls / Cynthia D. Wallace. – The Hague : Martinus Nijhoff, 1983.
354p.
Originally presented as the author's thesis (Ph.D.)–Cambridge University. Includes index. Bibliography: p331-355.
ISBN 9024726689 Hbk £135.00

Legal Cooperation in Europe in the Fields of Civil, Commercial and International Law (1957-82). – Strasbourg : Council of Europe, 1983.
ISBN 9287101698

Legal co-operation in Europe in the fields of civil, commercial, public and international law, 1957-1982. – Strasbourg : Council of Europe, 1983.
112p; 21cm.
Preface by Erik Harremoes, Director of Legal Affairs. - 'This brochure was produced according to a classification plan devised by the Secretariat' - pref.. At head of cover title: Legal Affairs.
ISBN 9287101698 Pbk £3.90

Legal Costs, New South Wales / Kingsley Siebel. – Butterworths.
Llf

Legal Counselling in Canada-Japan Business Transactions - II. – Vancouver : British Columbia Continuing Legal Education Society, 1983.
425p.
ISBN 0865041016 Hbk £65.00

Legal databases in Europe : user attitudes and supplier strategies / Michael Lloyd. – Amsterdam : North-Holland, 1986.
xiii, 218 p.; 24 cm.
At head of title: Commission of the European Communities. 'Report no. EUR 10439 of the Commission of the European Communities'–T.p. verso. Bibliography: p.205.
ISBN 044470048X

Legal Decisions Affecting Bankers Vols. 1-11 / P E Smart. – Professional Books.
ISBN 0862052459 Hbk £395.00

Legal Decisions on Special Banking Laws. – Karachi : Royal Book, 1986.
235p.
Hbk £200.00

Legal Deskbook : 1988. – Agincourt : Carswell.
530p.
This softcover text provides a summary of resources and factual information pertinent to legal and non-legal researchers. It includes directories of courts, judges, law associations, government bodies, sources of legal information, etc. Special features include a legal information directory for business law, criminal law, family law and social services, litigation and real estate.
Hbk £58.50

Legal Development and Comparative Law 1986 : Selected Essays for the 12th Congres International de Droit Compare / Lamm. – Budapest : Akademiai Kiado, 1986.
330p.
ISBN 9630544342 Hbk £29.00

Legal developments in maritime commerce : matters of general interest and importance arising out of selected legal issues / W.E. Astle. – London : Fairplay, 1983.
viii,125p; 25cm.
ISBN 0905045432 Pbk

Legal dictionary in four languages. – 3rd. – London : Sweet & Maxwell, 1987.
Over 13,000 legal expressions are translated, or given corresponding meanings, in the four European languages of English, French, German, and Spanish.
ISBN 0421378204 Hbk £77

Legal discourse : studies in linguistics, rhetoric and legal analysis / Peter Goodrich. – London : Macmillan, 1987.
x,266p; 23cm. – (Language, discourse, society series).
Bibliography: p247-258. - Includes index.
ISBN 0333419499 £29.50

Legal Division, Commonwealth Secretariat
Commonwealth Developments in Health Law. – Legal Division, Commonwealth Secretariat. – London : Commonwealth Secretariat, 1984.
324p.
ISBN 0850922283 Hbk £6.00
ISBN 0850922070 Pbk £6.00
—Commonwealth Law Bulletin. – Legal Division, Commonwealth Secretariat. – London : Commonwealth Secretariat, 1983.
– (Quarterly).
Pbk £5.00

Legal drafting / by Robert C. Dick. – 2nd ed. – Toronto : Carswell, 1985.
xiii,234p.
Includes bibliographical references and index.
ISBN 045937740X

Legal Duties. – Repr. of 1931 ed. – Aalen Wuertt : Scientia.
xvi, 318p.
ISBN 3511090318 Hbk £80.00

Legal Education 2000 / Jagtenberg. – Aldershot : Avebury.
ISBN 0566054728 Hbk £27.50

Legal education and lawyer competency : curricula for change / Fernand N. Dutile, editor. – Notre Dame : University of Notre Dame Press, 1981.
viii,155p; 21cm.
Conference proceedings.
ISBN 0268012644 £10.50

Legal education for Canadian youth : proceedings of a conference held at the College of Law, University of Saskatchewan, May 22-24, 1980 / edited by Edward R. Myers. – Ottawa : Canadian Law Information Council, 1981.
v,98p. – (Occasional paper).
Bibliography: p.47.
ISBN 0920358144

Legal Education in Virginia 1779-1979 : a Bibliographical Approach. – London : Eurospan.
ISBN 0813909015 Hbk £41.25

Legal Education Society of Alberta & Butterworth & Co. () Ltd.
Alberta Law for the Nineteen Eighties Vol. 3. – Legal Education Society of Alberta & Butterworth & Co. () Ltd. – Toronto : Butterworths, 1981.
250p.
ISBN 0409987034 Pbk £21.00

Legal effect of resolutions and codes of conduct of the United Nations. – Deventer : Kluwer, 1986.
16p.
Includes bibliographical references.
ISBN 9065442421

Legal English 2 : an Introduction to the American Constitution. – Paris : Cujas, 1986.
184p.
Hbk £98.00

Legal environment : business law. – 2nd. – London : Cassell plc.
Introductory text-book on business law.
ISBN 0039106020

Legal Environment for Foreign Direct Investment / Caywood. – London : Eurospan.
ISBN 093532805X Hbk £26.00

Legal Environment of Business / Reed. – 7th ed. – Maidenhead : McGraw-Hill, 1987.
ISBN 0070132569 Hbk £29.95

Legal environment of the business world / R.B. Buchanan. – Cheltenham : Stanley Thornes, 1982.
xix,230p; 22cm.
Includes index.
ISBN 0859503054 Pbk £3.75

Legal ethics : a guide to professional conduct for South African attorneys / E.A.L. Lewis. – Cape Town : Juta, 1982.
xix,339p.
Bibliography: p.xiii-xi - Includes index.
ISBN 0702113026

Legal foundations of the Welfare State. – London : Weidenfeld & Nicolson, 1984.
400p.
ISBN 0297784870 Hbk £16.00
ISBN 0297785346 Pbk £9.00

Legal Foundations of the Welfare State (LIC). – Weidenfeld & Nicolson, 1985.
ISBN 0297784870 Hbk £18.95
ISBN 0297785346 Pbk £12.95

Legal framework for Canada-United States trade / edited by Maureen Irish and Emily F. Carasco. – Toronto : Carswell, 1987.
xxxviii,275p.

Legal Framework of English Feudalism. – Cambridge : Cambridge University Press, 1976.
ISBN 0521209471 Hbk £30.00

Legal harmonization and the business enterprise : corporate and capital market law, harmonization policy in Europe and the U.S.A. / by Richard M. Buxbaum and Klaus J. Hopt. – Berlin : De Gruyter, 1988.
– (Series A–Law).
Includes index. Bibliography.
ISBN 0899251277 Hbk £96.00

Legal History : Does it Still Deserve Its Place in the Curriculum?. – Rondebosch : University of Cape Town, 1981.
10p.
ISBN 0799204153 Pbk £0.30

Legal history of Scotland
Vol.1 : The beginnings to A.D. 1286 / by David M. Walker. – Edinburgh : Green (W.) & Son, 1988.
xxi,435p; 24cm.
A systematic examination of the development of public, criminal and private law up to the death of Alexander III, with attention to the emerging lawmaking institutions, the deciding of cases and the procedure and principles of substantive law. Bibliography: p408-420. - Includes index.
ISBN 0414008162

Legal impact of the Constitution (Suspension and Modification) Decree, 1984 : on the constitution of the Federal Republic of Nigeria, 1979 / Niki Tobi. – Calabar, Nigeria : Centaur Press, 1985.
xi,110p.
Includes the text of the Constitution (Suspension and Modification) Decree 1984.

Legal implications of disclosure in the public interest : an analysis of prohibitions and protections with particular reference to employers and employees / Yvonne Cripps. – Oxford : ESC, 1986.
xx,299p; 24cm.
Bibliography: p289-296. - Includes index.
ISBN 0906214408 Pbk £32.50

Legal implications of the creation of more states in Nigeria : being a paper presented at the National Conference on Creation of States in Nigeria / by T. Akinola Aguda. – Ile Ife : Nigerian Institute of Advanced Legal Studies, 1981.
20p; 25cm.

Legal institutions : the development of dispute settlement / Peter Stein. – London : Butterworths, 1984.
ix,236p; 23cm.
Includes index.
ISBN 0406400253 Hbk £16.00
ISBN 0406400261 Pbk £12.95

Legal issues in human reproduction / edited by Sheila McLean. – Aldershot, Hants. : Gower, 1989.
vii,238p.
Includes bibliographical references and index.
ISBN 0566053934

Legal issues in medicine / edited by Sheila A.M. McLean. – Aldershot : Gower, 1981.
xiv,219p; 23cm.
ISBN 0566004283

Legal issues of European integration. – Deventer : Kluwer, 1974-.
Law review of the Europa Instituut, University of Amsterdam.

Legal journals index. – Hebden Bridge, Yorkshire : Legal Information Resources, 1986.
ISBN 09504206

Legal Legends and Other True Stories. – White Lodge.
ISBN 1851900519 Hbk £12.95

Legal lexicon of taxation / Charles H. Thomas. – Abingdon, Oxon : Professional Books, 1987.
139p; 23cm.
ISBN 0862050367

Legal Liabilities of Practising Accountants. – London : Butterworths, 1984.
The unprecedented increase in professional liability for accountants and the new legal standards for auditing, accounting and taxation practice are discussed. Oriented to the private practitioner, this book gives practical approaches to minimizing the risk of professional liability.
ISBN 0406259607 Pbk £28.00

Legal Liability of Doctors and Hospitals. – 2nd ed. – Agincourt : Carswell, 1984.
ISBN 0459358200 Hbk £38.75

Legal links between Cyprus and the Balkans especially Macedonia during the Byzantine era / Criton G. Tornaritis. – Nicosia : s.n., 1982.
24 leaves.

Legal literature in small jurisdictions : a report of a conference held at Osgoode Hall Law School, York University, Downsview, Ontario on 3-5 November 1978 / edited by William Twining and Jenny Uglow for the Canadian Law Information Council, Canada and the Commonwealth Legal Education Association, London. – London : Commonwealth Secretariat, 1981.
188p; 30cm.
Bibliography: p.171-172. - Includes index.
ISBN 085092197X

Legal Maxims / Kersley. – Sweet & Maxwell, 1939 Reprint.
ISBN 0421160500 Hbk £28.00

Legal measures for the conservation of marine mammals. – Gland, Switzerland : International Union for Conservation of Nature and Natural Resources, 1982.
1 v. (loose-leaf); 23 cm.
Includes bibliographical references.
ISBN 2880320879

Legal mind : essays for Tony Honore / edited by Neil MacCormick and Peter Birks. – Oxford : Clarendon, 1986.
304p; 24cm.
Includes bibliography and index.
ISBN 0198761961 £35.00

Legal Mind - Essays For Tony Honore / Birks. – Oxford : Oxford University Press, 1986.
ISBN 0198761961 Hbk £35.00

Legal notices. – Maseru : Government Printer, 1966-.
Supplements to the Government gazette.

Legal opinions in international transactions : foreign lawyers' response to US opinion requests / report of the Subcommittee on Legal Opinions of Committee E of the Section on Business Law of the International Bar Association : Michael Gruson, Michael Kutschera. – London : Graham & Trotman and The Association, 1987.
120p; 23cm.
ISBN 1853330213 £35.00

Legal philosophies of Russian liberalism / Andrzej Walicki. – Oxford : Clarendon, 1987.
480p; 22cm.
Includes index.
ISBN 0198249306 £45.00

Legal Philosophy : Western, Eastern and Filipino. – Tacloban City : Divine Word University of Tacloban, 1984.
208p.
ISBN 9711060213 Hbk £7.00

Legal pluralism : proceedings of the Canberra Law Workshop VII / edited by Peter Sack and Elizabeth Minchin. – Canberra : Law Department, Research School of Social Sciences, Australian National University, 1986.
iii,280p.
Includes bibliographical references.
ISBN 0867848375

Legal Portraits : Lord Denning. – London : Butterworths.
ISBN 0406032505 Pbk £4.95

Legal Portraits : Lord Hailsham. – London : Butterworths.
ISBN 0406032513 Pbk £4.95

Legal practitioners' review. – Ibadan : Spectrum Books, 1986.

Legal problems arising from supranational institutions : the Andean Pact : a case study / by Jorge Uribe-Rolden. – London : The author, 1984.
55 leaves.
Includes bibliographical references.

Legal Problems Concerning Unmarried Couples : Proceedings of the 11th Collquy on European Law, Messina 1981. – Strasbourg : Council of Europe, 1982.
ISBN 9287101574 Hbk £6.00

Legal problems of credit and security / by R.M. Goode. – London : Sweet & Maxwell, 1982.
xviii,133p; 22cm.
Includes index.
ISBN 0421302704 Pbk £10.00

Legal problems of credit and security / by R.M. Goode. – 2nd ed. – London : Sweet & Maxwell, 1988.
xxxv,218p; 23cm.
Contains chapters on the nature and forms of consensual security and concepts of attachments and perfection. Section on treatment of negative pledges has been expanded. Analysis of the legal nature of subparticipation in loan assessments, and examination of twelve typical priority conflicts and their resolution, and an enlarged chapter on equitable, statutory and contractual set-off and set-off on insolvency.
ISBN 0421384301 Pbk £14.00

Legal problems of international banking / by F.R. Ryder. – London : Sweet & Maxwell, 1986.
70p; 23cm.
ISBN 0421367806 Pbk £16.00

Legal problems of international organizations / by Felice Morgenstern. – Cambridge : Grotius Publications, 1986.
xiv,147p.
Includes bibliographical references and index. At head of title: University of Cambridge Research Centre for International Law.
ISBN 0906496241

Legal Problems Relating to Shareholders' Agreements. – Vancouver : British Columbia Continuing Legal Education Society, 1982.
106p.
ISBN 0865040613 Hbk £12.50

Legal process : commentary and materials / Maher, Waller, Derham. – 5th ed. – Sydney : Law Book Co, 1988.
xxx, 593 p.; 26 cm.
First to 4th eds. published under title: Cases and materials on the legal process.
ISBN 0455207836 (pbk.)

Legal profession / New South Wales Law Reform Commission. – Sydney : The Commission, 1981.
229p; 25cm. – (Background paper 4).

Legal profession and quality of service : further report and proposals : report and materials of a National Workshop on Quality of Legal Services held in Toronto in October, 1980, as a sequel to the National Conference on Quality of Legal Services held in Ottawa in October, 1978 / editor and commentator, W.H. Hurlburt. – Edmonton, Alberta? : Federation of Law Societies of Canada, 1981.
417p.
Includes two parts in English and French.
ISBN 0969087101

Legal profession in England and Wales / Richard L. Abel. – Oxford, Oxfordshire, UK : Blackwell, 1988.
xxiii, 548p.
Includes index. Bibliography: p.507-537.
ISBN 0631141111

Legal profession in Ireland 1789-1922. – Dublin : Incorporated Law Society of Ireland, 1986.
xii,176p.
Bibliography: p.165-169. - Includes index.
ISBN 090202728X

Legal protection against sex discrimination : recommendation No. R(85)2 adopted by the Committee of Ministers of the Council of Europe on 5 February 1985 and explanatory memorandum. – Council of Europe. – Strasbourg : Council of Europe, 1985.
33p.
'Prepared by a committee of experts set up under the authority of the European Committee on Legal Co-operation (CDCJ)'. At head of cover title: Legal Affairs.
ISBN 9287103895

Legal protection for microbiological and genetic engineering inventions / Roman Saliwanchik. – London : Addison-Wesley, 1982.
xiii,256p; 25cm.
Includes index.
ISBN 0201109387 £33.30

Legal protection of computer programs and data / by Christopher J. Millard. – London : Sweet & Maxwell, 1985.
xxvi,239p; 23cm.
Includes index.
ISBN 0421334800 Pbk £24.00
ISBN 0459372300 Canada

Legal Protection of Computer Programs and Data. – Agincourt : Carswell, 1985.
250p.
This work provides a systematic investigation of general software copyright issues under American, United Kingdom, and Canadian law. The legal protection of software and data under copyright, trade secrets, confidentiality, contractual arrangements, and criminal law is analyzed in the book.
Hbk £31.00

Legal protection of computer software / edited by Lawrence Perry and Hugh Brett. – Oxford : ESC, 1981.
xiv,197p; 22cm.
Includes bibliographical references.
ISBN 0906214068 Pbk

Legal protection of persons suffering from mental disorder placed as involuntary patients : Recommendation No.R(83)2 adopted by the Committee of Ministers of the Council of Europe on 22 February 1983, and Explanatory memorandum. – Council of Europe. – Strasbourg : Council of Europe, 1983.
22p; 21cm.
'... prepared by a committee of experts on Legal Problems in the Medical Field set up under the authority of the European Committee on Legal Co-operation'. At head of title: Legal Affairs.
ISBN 9287102996

Legal protection of the collective interests of consumers by consumer agencies : Recommendation no. R(81)2 adopted by the Committee of Ministers of the Council of Europe on 23 January 1981 and explanatory memorandum. – Council of Europe. – Strasbourg : Council of Europe, 1981.
19p; 21cm.
'Prepared by a committee of experts set up under the authority of the European Committee on Legal Cooperation' - verso t.p.. At head of cover title: Council of Europe, Legal Affairs.

Legal Protection of the Collective Interests of Consumers by Governments by Consumer Agencies : Recommendation No. R 812/2 and Explanatory Memorandum. – Strasbourg : Council of Europe, 1981.
Hbk £1.25

Legal Regime for Deep Seabed Mining under the Law of the Sea Convention. – Frankfurt : Alfred Metzner, 1984.
ISBN 3787540180 Hbk £98.00

Legal Regime for Deep Seabed Mining under the Law of the Sea Convention. – Dordrecht : Kluwer, 1983.
250p.
ISBN 9065441166 Hbk £107.00

Legal Regime of Fisheries in the Caribbean Region / J.F. Pulvenis. – Berlin : Springer-Verlag, 1983.
x, 204p.
Pbk £43.00

Legal regime of foreign private investment in the Sudan and Saudi Arabia : a case study of developing countries / Fath el Rahman Abdalla El Sheikh. – Cambridge : Cambridge University Press in association with Khartoum University Press, 1984.
xxxix,462p; 23cm. – (Cambridge studies in international and comparative law).
Bibliography: p446-458. - Includes index.
ISBN 0521252865

Legal Regime of International Rivers and Lakes / Lucius Caflisch. – Dordrecht : Kluwer, 1981.
442p.
ISBN 9024725658 Hbk £170.00

Legal regime of the protection of the Mediterranean against pollution from land-based sources. – Dublin : Tycooly International, 1984.
256p.
ISBN 0907567827 Hbk £19.50
ISBN 0907567835 Pbk £11.50

Legal relevance of gender : some aspects of sex-based discrimination / edited by Sheila McLean, Noreen Burrows. – Basingstoke : Macmillan, 1988.
x,287p.
Includes bibliographical references and index.
ISBN 0333407717 Pbk £25.00
ISBN 0333407725 £8.95

Legal Remedies / Avtar Singh. – 5th rev. ed. – Lucknow : Eastern Book Company, 1986.
380p.
Pbk £40.00

Legal Reminders for Architects / Serjeantson. – London : Architectural Press.
ISBN 0851399118 Hbk

Legal requirements for arrest and enforced sale of vessels : a comparative study / Malcolm H. Pace. – S.l. : s.n., 1983.
xxvi,144 leaves.
Thesis (LL.D.) - University of Malta 1983. Bibliography: p.142-144.

Legal Research Foundation → Basis of judicial review in administrative law.
→ Bill of Rights for New Zealand : papers precsented by A. Sharp ... et al.
→ C. E. R. : the business and law essentials : papers presented at seminar, University of Auckland, 22-23 July 1983.
→ Existing and new forms of financing, University of Auckland, 27 May 1982 : papers presented at seminar.
→ Family law 1984 style.
→ Floating charges, crystallisation and after-acquired property.
→ Further aspects of maintenance law : some post 'Family law 1981' chapters.
→ Index to New Zealand legal writing.
—Intellectual property in New Zealand and Australia / papers presented by M.P. Crew ... et al. – Auckland : Legal Research Foundation, 1985.
227p.
ISBN 0908581378
→ Mental health : a case for reform.
—New Zealand business : entering the Australian market : Legal Research Foundation Inc. Seminar, 19 November 1985 / Barry J. McWilliams. – Auckland : Legal Research Foundation, 1985.
122p.
Papers presented by Barry J. McWilliams and others.
ISBN 0908581408
→ Outline of mining law : paper presented at Auckland Law Faculty Seminar Series 1982 at University of Auckland.
→ Practice and procedure in the Family Court : papers presented at the Family Law Seminar, University of Auckland, 26 May, 1984.
→ Professional responsibility.
→ Sexual violence : a case for law reform : papers presented at seminar, University of Auckland, 27 August 1982.

Legal Research Foundation Inc. → Judicial review of administrative action in the 1980's : problems and prospects : papers presented at a Conference held by the Legal Research Foundation Inc. at the University of Auckland on 20 and 21 February 1986.

Legal Research Handbook. – London : Butterworths, 1983.
ISBN 0409848298 Hbk £40.00

Legal research handbook / Douglass T. MacEllven. – 2nd ed. – Toronto : Butterworths, 1986.
xxix,411p.
Guide to all current sources of Canadian law. Includes additional chapters on legal writing and government and social science publications. Quebec material has been augmented. Includes a master research checklist, subject area checklists, and examination of management of law firm libraries, computer assisted research, and indices of research centres and legal publishers.
ISBN 0409847798 Hbk £60

Legal research in the United Kingdom 1905-84 : a classified list of legal theses and dissertations successfully completed for postgraduate degrees awarded by universities and polytechnics in the United Kingdom from 1905-1984 / Institute of Advanced Legal Studies. – London : The Institute, 1986.
xxx, ca. 300p.
Supersedes: List of legal research topics completed and approved since about 1935. - 2nd ed. - 1961; and, Supplement 1961-July 1966. Includes indexes. Supplemented by: List of current legal research topics.
ISBN 0901190292

Legal research techniques / by Nigel Smith. – Hebden Bridge : Legal Information Resources, 1987.
ii,40p.
ISBN 1870369017

Legal Restraints on the Use of Force 40 Years after the UN Charter. – Dordrecht : Kluwer, 1986.
546p.
ISBN 9024732476 Hbk £215.00

Legal right and social democracy : essays in legal and political philosophy / Neil MacCormick. – Oxford : Clarendon, 1982.
viii,272p; 23cm.
Includes index.
ISBN 0198253850 £17.50

Legal Right and Social Democracy-Essays. – Oxford : Oxford University Press, 1984.
ISBN 0198255020 Pbk £9.95

Legal Rights and Intellectual Disability : a Short Guide. – Redfern : Redfern Legal Centre Publishing, 1986.
96p.
Hbk £6.00

Legal rights and mental-health care / Stanley S. Herr, Stephen Arons, Richard E. Wallace. – Lexington, Mass. : Lexington Books, 1983.
xv,180p; 24cm.
Includes index.
ISBN 0669049107 £19.50

Legal rights in the Canadian Charter of Rights and Freedoms : a manual of issues and sources / David C. McDonald. – Toronto : Carswell, 1982.
xxv,275p.
Includes index.

Legal Rights of Citizens with Mental Retardation. – London : Eurospan.
ISBN 0819171107 Hbk £16.50

Legal Secretary Pitman 2000. – Pitman, 1986.
ISBN 0273022261 Pbk £4.95

Legal Secretary Today / Holden. – Maidenhead : McGraw-Hill, 1986.
ISBN 0070849749 Pbk £4.95

Legal secretary's handbook / Ann Newington and Hilary Willoughby. – 4th ed. – London : Longman Professional (UK), 1989.
Contains descriptions of the work of the various departments of a solicitor's practice and barrister's chambers. It includes an explanation of legal terms and gives examples of completed legal forms. Takes account of latest office technology, updates and useful addresses.
Legal secretaries, secretarial colleges, careers offices, practices, chambers
ISBN 0851215785 Sbd £18.95

Legal Secretary's Handbook. – Toronto : Butterworths, 1986.
288p.
Contains standard forms (not found in the Rules of Civil Procedure), prescribed Forms and proper usage, examinations for discovery and discovery of documents, pleadings, defences, counterclaims, crossclaims, third and subsequent party claims, amendments of pleadings, briefs, preparation of pleadings, discovery and trial briefs assembly of documents and sample Indexes.
ISBN 0409801720 Hbk £40.00

Legal service bulletin / assisted by the Fitzroy Legal Service. – Clayton, Vic. : Faculty of Law, Monash University, 1974.
Cumulative index: vols. 1-10 (1974-1985) published separately, 1986.
ISBN 08173516

Legal services for low income persons in the United States and Britain : trends for consideration in Australia / Edna R. Chamberlain. – Canberra : Commonwealth Legal Aid Commission, 1981.
30p.
Includes bibliographical references.

Legal services in rural areas : an evaluation : report / prepared for the Department of Justice, Ottawa, and the Faculty of Law, Queen's University by D. Laureen Snider. – Rev. ed. – Ottawa : Department of Justice, Evaluation and Statistics Section, 1981.
303p. – (An evaluation report).
Bibliography: p.257-266.

Legal services in rural Britain : access, accessibility and need / Mark Blacksell, Kim Economides and Charles Watkins. – Exeter : University of Exeter, 1984.
26p. – (Working paper).
Bibliography: p.22-26.

Legal Software Directory. – London : Longman Professional, 1985.
ISBN 0851210422 Pbk £16.50

Legal status of Berlin / by I.D. Hendry and M.C. Wood. – Cambridge : Grotius, 1987.
xxii,388p.
Describes the unique legal position of Berlin as it emerges from the actual practice and positions adopted by the four Occupying Powers. Deals with the original occupation rights of the four Powers, and their agreements and practices. Makes reference to Allied and German legislation, and includes chapters on the institutional framework and law applicable in Berlin, and the special Berlin area.
ISBN 0949009059

Legal Status of Singapore Women. – Singapore Association of Women Lawyers. – Singapore : Asiapac Books and Educational Aids.
ISBN 9971985128 Hbk £1.40

Legal status of the federal administration / Law Reform Commission of Canada. – Ottawa : The Commission, 1985.
106,111p. – (Working paper).
Includes bibliographical references. Added t.p. in French: Le statut juridique de l'administration federale. Pages numbered in opposite directions.

Legal Status of the Female in the Sri Lanka Law on Family Relations. – Colombo : Gunasena and Co..
Hbk £60.00

The legal status of the Muslims in Singapore. – Singapore : Malayan Law Journal, 1965.
95.
Intends to set out the legal position of the Muslims, including the Malays, in Singapore. Contains a historical introduction, a summary of the existing statute and the case law relating to the family law, the law of property and the law relating to the construction of wills and trust instruments as they affect the Muslims in Singapore, and the history of Muslim endowments.

Legal status of the police : a study paper prepared for the Law Reform Commission of Canada / by Philip C. Stenning. – Ottawa : Law Reform Commission of Canada, 1982.
169p; 25cm. – (Study paper).
ISBN 0662119967

Legal Structure of International Textile Trade. – Westport Publications.
ISBN 089930334X Hbk £36.95

Legal Structures for Voluntary Organisations / Bates. – London : Bedford Square Press, 1984.
ISBN 0719911168 Pbk £1.95

Legal Studies : The Journal of the Society of Public Teachers of Law. – London : Butterworths, 1986. Pbk £76.00
Back issues avail.

Legal Studies and Services →Tribunals practice and procedure.

Legal Studies for New South Wales Years 11 and 12. – Butterworths, 1989.
ca 432p.
ISBN 0409494682 Pbk £22.50

Legal Studies for South Australia. – Butterworths, 1988.
ca 288p.
ISBN 0409494712 Pbk £ 22.50

Legal System and Social Systems / Etal. – Oxford : Croom Helm, 1985.
ISBN 0709936125 Hbk £18.95

Legal system of Northern Ireland / by Brice Dickson. – Belfast : SLS Legal Publications (NI), 1984.
x,225p.
ISBN 0853892369

Legal System of Scotland. – London : HMSO, 1982.
54p.
ISBN 0114917477 Pbk £3.50

Legal system of Scotland : cases and materials / A.A. Paterson and T.St.J.N. Bates. – 2nd ed. – Edinburgh : Green, 1986.
xviii,395p.
Analyses the use of the principal sources of Scots law, in particular precedent and statutory interpretation. Considers the legal profession, the administration of civil and criminal justice and the operation of tribunals. Also deals with the Court of Justice of the European Communities and the European Commission and Court of Human Rights.
ISBN 0414007832

Legal systems & social systems / edited by Adam Padgorecki, Christopher J. Whelan & Dinesh Khosla. – London : Croom Helm, 1985.
xvii,262p; 23cm.
Includes bibliographies and index.
ISBN 070992075X £18.95

Legal systems, North and South : a study prepared for the New Ireland Forum / by C. K. Boyce. – Dublin : Stationery Office, 1984.
60p.

Legal Terminology : an Historical Guide to the Technical Language of Law. – Peterborough : Broadview Press Ltd., 1986.
192p.
ISBN 0921149026 Hbk £18.95

Legal theory : papers presented at the W.G. Hart Legal Workshop, 3rd-6th July 1984 at the Institute of Advanced Legal Studies, University of London / academic director: William Twining. – 1 v. – London : The Institute, 1984.
various pagings. – (W.G. Hart Legal Workshop).

Legal theory and common law / edited by William Twining. – Oxford : Blackwell, 1986.
300p.
ISBN 0631144773 £22.50

Legal theory and legal history : essays on the common law / A.W.B. Simpson. – London : Hambledon, 1987.
xiii,432p; 24cm.
Includes index.
ISBN 0907628834 £24.00

Legal Theory Meets Legal Practice. – Montreal : Academic Printing and Publishing, 1988.
400p.
ISBN 0920980228 Hbk £69.95
ISBN 0920980236 Pbk £34.95

Legal thesaurus / compiled by Nigel Smith and Christine Miskin. – Hebden Bridge : Legal Information Resources, 1987.
204p.
ISBN 1870369009

Legal Training Course on Trademarks. – Geneva : World Intellectual Property Organization, 1982.
ca 600p.
Hbk £50.00

Legal Wit and Whimsy : an Anthology of Legal Humour. – Agincourt : Carswell, 1988.
168p.
Hbk £22.00

Legal writing and research manual / John A. Yogis and Innis M. Christie. – 3rd ed. – Toronto : Butterworths, 1988.
xx, 199 p.; 23 cm.
Intends to help develop an understanding of, and some facility in, the techniques of legal research and writing. The distinction between primary and secondary materials is explained, Canadian and English sources are emphasised, but an outline of principle American materials is also provided.
ISBN 0409811548

Legal Writing for Understanding, Clarity and Precision. – Vancouver : British Columbia Continuing Legal Education Society, 1982.
84p.
ISBN 0865040672 Hbk £35.00

Legalists : Finnish legal science in the period of autonomy, 1809-1917 / by Hannu Tapani Klami. – Helsinki : Societas Scientiarum Fennica, 1981.
153 p., 4 leaves of plates; 24 cm.
Includes index. Bibliography: p. 141-150. Translation with revisions of: Oikeustaistelijat.
ISBN 9516531008 Pbk

Legality, ideology and the state / edited by David Sugarman. – London : Academic Press, 1983.
xiv,304p; 24cm.
Includes bibliographies and index.
ISBN 0126760802

Legality of non-forcible counter-measures in international law / Omer Yousif Elagab. – Oxford Oxfordshire : Clarendon Press, 1988.
Includes index. Bibliography: p.
ISBN 019825590X

Legality of space militarization / Bruce A. Hurwitz. – Amsterdam : North-Holland, 1986.
xii,252p; 25cm.
Bibliography: p243-252.
ISBN 0444700412 £48.83

Legally yours - law and the individual / Reed. – 2nd ed. – Maidenhead : McGraw-Hill, 1985.
ISBN 0070848777 Pbk £5.95

Legendre, Camille
French Canada in crisis : a new society in the making? / Camille Legendre. – Rev. ed. – London : Minority Rights Group, 1982.
20p. – (Report).
Previous ed.: 1980. Bibliography: p.17-18.

Legendre, P.
Ecrits Juridiques du Moyen Age Occidental. – London : Variorum.
ISBN 086078228X Hbk £32.00

Legislating for change? : review of the sex discrimination legislation : a consultative document / Equal Opportunities Commission. – London : Equal Opportunities Commission, 1986.
47p.

Legislating Foreign Policy / Steven J. Baker. – 1984 repr. – Delhi : Hindustan Publishing Corporation, 1986.
x, 230p.
Hbk

Legislation / by David R. Miers and Alan C. Page. – London : Sweet & Maxwell, 1982.
xviii,266p; 23cm.
Bibliography: p247-255. - Includes index.
ISBN 0421271108 Hbk £13.50
ISBN 0421271205 Pbk

Legislation and civil liberties in South Africa / A.S. Mathews. – S.l. : s.n., 1984.
p.10-15.

Legislation and its interpretation : the Acts Interpretation Act 1924 and related legislation : a discussion paper and questionnaire / Law Commission. – Wellington, N.Z. : The Commission, 1987.
xii,83p. – (Preliminary paper).

Legislation and public policy : public bills in the 1970-74 Parliament / by Ivor Burton and Gavin Drewry. – London : Macmillan, 1981.
xii,322p; 23cm.
Bibliography: p280-283. - Includes index.
ISBN 0333152042 £25.00

Legislation at Work : Safety and Health. – Department of Science and Technology. – 2nd ed. – Canberra : Australian Government Publishing Service, 1981.
41p. – (Occupational Safety & Health Working Environment: No. 4).
ISBN 0642052212 Hbk £1.90

Legislation Concerning Nursing/Midwifery Services and Education : Report on a WHO Working Group (Hamburg, 1979). – Geneva : World Health Organization, 1981.
47p.
ISBN 9289012110 Hbk £4.00

Legislation, legal rights and plain English / Law Reform Commission of Victoria. – Melbourne : The Commission, 1986.
iv,56p. – (Discussion paper).
Includes bibliographical references.

Legislation on coastal state requirements for foreign fishing / by Gerald Moore. – Rome : Food and Agriculture Organization of the United Nations, 1981.
viii, 411 p.; 28 cm. – (Legislative study / Food and Agriculture Organization of the United Nations).
ISBN 9251010382 Pbk

Legislation on Dangerous Substances : Classification and Labelling in the European Communities. – Luxembourg : Office for Official Publications of the European Communities, 1987.
xvi, 288p.
ISBN 928257279X Pbk £1,250.00

Legislation on foods for infants and small children. – Rome : Food and Agriculture Organization of the United Nations, 1983.
v,104p. – (Legislative study).
Includes bibliographical references.
ISBN 9251014876

Legislation on human infertility services and embryo research : a consultation paper / Department of Health and Social Security. – London : H.M.S.O., 1987.
15p.
ISBN 0101004621

Legislation on Productivity in Agriculture : a Comparative Outline. – Rome : FAO, Food and Agricultural Organization of the United Nations, 1985.
80p.
ISBN 9251021945 Hbk £6.00

Legislation on wildlife and protected areas in Africa / by Christian du Saussay for Legislation Branch, Legal Office, FAO. – Rome : Food and Agriculture Organization of the United Nations, 1984.
vii,158p. – (Legislative study).
Includes bibliographical references.
ISBN 9251011710

Legislative action to combat the world smoking epidemic / by Ruth Roemer : with a foreword by Sir George Godber. – Geneva : World Health Organization, 1982.
131p.
Bibliography: p.121-122.
ISBN 9241560746

Legislative Changes in the Construction Industry in Nova Scotia 1964 to 1975 : An Exercise in Industrial Democracy. – Halifax : Dalhousie University, Institute of Public Affairs.
v, 55p. – (Occasional Papers).
ISBN 088926810X Pbk £5.00

Legislative drafting / G.C. Thornton. – 3rd ed. – London : Butterworth, 1987.
396p; 24cm.
Previous ed.: 1979. Includes index.
ISBN 0406399824 £38.00

Legislative Draftsmen : Short List of Legislative Draftsmen Available for Short Ad Hoc Assignments. – London : Commonwealth Secretariat, 1982.
free

Legislative instruments. – Accra : Ghana Publishing Corporation, .
Issued with: Ghana gazette.

Legislative responses to terrorism / edited by Yonah Alexander, Allan S. Nanes. – Dordrecht Holland : M. Nijhoff, 1986.
xi, 327p.
ISBN 9024732131

Legitimate grievance : a report on the role of the ombudsman in the prison system / Geoffrey Wener. – London : Prison Reform Trust, 1983.
23p.
Bibliography: p20.
ISBN 0946209030

Legitimate pursuit. – Southampton : Ashford Press, 1988.
ISBN 1852531045 Hbk £12.95

Legomsky, Stephen H.
Immigration and the judiciary : law and politics in Britain and America / Stephen H. Legomsky. – Oxford : Clarendon, 1987.
xxxix,345p; 24cm.
Bibliography: p327-345.
ISBN 0198255616 £35.00

Lehane, J. R. F →Equity, doctrines, and remedies.

Lehmann, Geoffrey
Taxation Law in Australia / Cynthia Coleman. – Butterworths, 1989.
ca 960p.
ISBN 0409301388 Hbk £85.00
ISBN 0409494704 Pbk £75.00

Lehto, Leena →Finnish legal system.

Leibowitz, Arnold H
Defining status: a comprehensive analysis of United States/territorial relations. – Dordrecht : Nijhoff (Martinus), 1989.
752.
Analyses the possibility of Statehood for Guam and the Virgin Islands, and explores the bounds of the Commonwealth and Freely Associated States. These status alternatives are discussed against a backdrop of the political, economic, geographic, and cultural uniqueness of each territory.
ISBN 0792300696 Hbk £115

Leibowitz, David E. →Protection for semiconductor chip masks in the United States : analysis of the Semiconductor Chip Protection Act of 1984.

Leigh, Guy I. F. →EEC and intellectual property.

Leigh, L. H.
Companies Act 1981 : text and commentary / L.H. Leigh, H.C. Edey. – London : Butterworths, 1981.
v,329p.
ISBN 0406845301
—Control of commercial fraud / L.H. Leigh. – London : Heinemann, 1982.
xii,339p; 23cm. – (Cambridge studies in criminology).
Bibliography: p315-326p. - Includes index.
ISBN 0435825194 £16.50

→ Northey & Leigh's introduction to company law.

—Police powers in England and Wales / L.H. Leigh. – 2nd ed. – London : Butterworth, 1985.
330p; 22cm.
Previous ed.: 1975. Includes index.
ISBN 0406845417 Hbk £20.00 :
ISBN 0406845425 Pbk £14.95

—Strict and vicarious liability : a study in administrative criminal law / by L.H. Leigh. – London : Sweet & Maxwell, 1982.
xix,121p; 19cm.
Includes index.
ISBN 0421267607 Hbk £
ISBN 0421267704 Pbk £6.85

Leiser, Burton M. → Values in conflict : life, liberty, and the rule of law.

Leith, Philip → Jurisprudence of orthodoxy : Queen's University essays on H.L.A. Hart.
—Oxford Jurisprudence. – Oxford : Croom Helm, 1988.
ISBN 0709941560 Hbk £25.00

Lemar → Litigation Support and Financial Assessment of Damages.

Lemarchand, Rene → Burundi since the genocide.

Lending and Recovery : Benefits and Pitfalls of Consulting Engagements / Peter W. Aykroyd. – Agincourt : Carswell, 1985.
150p.
This work addresses the problems faced by Canadian corporations, financial institutions, insolvency consultants, and attorneys as they deal with questions of the solvency of a corporation to whom a loan has been made.
Hbk £40.50

Lending in booms and slumps / by L.S. Dyer : delivered under the auspices of King's College London. – London : King's College London, 1981.
35p; 25cm.
Pbk £2.00

Lending Packages for Small and Medium-Sized Companies. – Oxford : Croom Helm, 1983.
ISBN 070992254X Pbk £8.95

Lenkinski, Esther L.
Practical Guide to the Family Law Act 1986. – Agincourt : Carswell, 1988.
230p.
Hbk £37.50
—Practical Guide to the Family Law Act. – Agincourt : Carswell, 1988.
238p.
This is an in-depth guide to the law pursuant to the Family Law Act, 1986. Discussions include jurisdiction, property, matrimonial home, support obligations and domestic contracts. The complete text of the Act is included. Also included is the relevant caselaw.
Pbk £33.75

Lennon, et al
Agricultural law / McKay. – London : Longman Professional (UK), 1990.
Coverage includes agricultural holdings, milk quotas, product liability, finance and taxation, pollution, employment law, competition law, agrochemicals, recreation and diversification, contracts, housing and share farming.
Llf

Lenz, Carl Otto
Draft Treaty establishing the European Union : report on the Federal Republic of Germany / by Carl Otto Lenz. – Florence : European University Institute, 1985.
21p.

Leo Cussen Institute of Victoria → Advanced Family Law Seminar.
→ Company Law Lunchtime Series.

Leon, Jeffrey S.
Rules Review : Summaries of Cases Decided Under the Rules of Civic Procedure. – Butterworths, 1987.
288p.
Compendium of relevant cases decided under Ontario's new rules of practice (between January 1985 and December 1986). Follows the order of the rules, and consists of concise case digests. Cases are annotated, with commentary by the author.
ISBN 0409805912 Pbk £29.95

Leonard, Alice M.
Judging inequality : the effectiveness of the tribunal system in sex discrimination and equal pay cases / Alice M. Leonard. – London : Cobden Trust, 1987.
160p; 20cm.
Includes bibliography.
ISBN 0900137282 Pbk £7.95
—Pyrrhic victories : winning sex discrimination and equal pay cases in the industrial tribunals, 1980-84 / Alice M. Leonard. – London : H.M.S.O., 1987.
55p; 30cm. – (Research series).
ISBN 0117013285

Leonard, Bruce E.
Commercial Insolvency Reporter. – Toronto : Butterworths.
ISBN 0409806218 Hbk
—Commercial Insolvency Reporter. – London : Butterworths.
ISBN 0409492051 Hbk
—Guide to Commercial Insolvency in Canada. – Butterworths, 1988.
ca 388p.
Takes the reader through the relevant proceedings and applicable legislation, covering the commencement of bankruptcy proceedings, receiverships, liquidation of asset; to directors' responsibilities on insolvency and annulment of transactions.
ISBN 0409846740 Hbk

Leonard, M.
The 1988 Education Act : A Tactical Guide for Schools. – Oxford : Basil Blackwell.
ISBN 0631164553 Hbk £19.50
ISBN 0631164561 Pbk £6.95

Leone, U. → Phenomenology of kidnappings in Sardinia : towards an international perspective of a local crime problem.

Leonski the Brown-out Strangler. – Neutral Bay : Hale & Iremonger.
ISBN 0908094981 Hbk £24.95, 015
ISBN 090809499X Pbk £11.95, 015

Leopold, P. → Protest, Policing and the Law.

Lepofsky, M. David
Open justice: the constitutional right to attend and spek about criminal proceedings. – Scarborough, Ontario : Butterworths (Canada), 1985.
416.
Examines the extent to which Canadians are free to attend, criticize and report criminal court proceedings. Considers the impact of the Canadian Charter of Rights and Freedoms on the issues of public access to criminal courts, and assesses the practical aspects of the legal dilemma inherent in the free press/fair trial debate, against the background of the American experience.
ISBN 0409844730 Hbk

Lerrick, Alison
Saudi business and labor law : its interpretation and application / Alison Lerrick, Q. Javed Mian. – 2nd ed. – London : Grahamn & Trotman, 1987.
xlv,589p.
Previous edition: 1982. Includes bibliographical references and index.
ISBN 0860105733

Leser, Hans G. → German private and commercial law : an introduction.

Leslie, John
Equity - Practice and Procedure in New South Wales. – Woolloomooloo : International Business Communications, 1987.
Hbk £135.00

Leslie, William
Industrial tribunal practice in Scotland / by William Leslie. – Edinburgh : Green, 1981.
xxxxi,323p; 21cm.
Includes index.
ISBN 0414006801 Pbk

Lesotho law journal : a journal of law and development. – Lesotho : Faculty of Law, National University of Lesotho, 1985-.
Includes bibliographical references.

Lessnoff, Michael H.
Social contract / Michael Lessnoff. – London : Macmillan, 1986.
x,178p; 23cm.
Bibliography: p169-173. - Includes index.
ISBN 0333367901 Hbk £18.00
ISBN 033336791X Pbk £6.95

Lessons of history : an inaugural lecture delivered before the vice-chancellor and Fellows of the University of Oxford on Friday 6 March 1981 / by Michael Howard. – Oxford : Clarendon, 1981.
21p; 22cm.
ISBN 0199515328 Pbk £1.95

Lester, Anthony
Independent schools and the European Convention on Human Rights : a joint opinion / by Anthony Lester and David Pannick. – London : ISIS, 1982.
16p.
Published on behalf of The Association of Governing Bodies of Public Schools and The Association of Governing Bodies of Girls' Public Schools.

Lester, David
Joynson-Hicks on copyright / Paul Mitchell. – London : Sweet & Maxwell, 1989.
Covers works protected by Copyright Protection, qualifying for protection, first ownership, duration of copyright protection, restricted acts, secondary infringement, permitted acts, subsequent ownership, licensing and exploitation, remedies, moral rights, design rights, performance in rights, and Peter Pan.
ISBN 0421409606 Hbk

LeSueur Stewart, M
To see the world. – Dordrecht : Nijhoff (Martinus), 1989.
600. – (Utrecht studies in air and space law).
Analyses the principles governing the use of artificial earth satellites for international direct television broadcasting, adopted by the United Nations General Assembly in 1982. Proposes revisions to the principles. Includes Appendixes containing United Nations documentation on the subject.
ISBN 9024737443 Hbk £87.50

Letalik, Norman G. → Problems of development and ocean management in the eastern Caribbean : economic, legal, environmental and planning aspects : proceedings of an international seminar held in Kingstown, St. Vincent & the Grenadines, West Indies, May 11-13, 1981.

Lethbridge, H. J.
Hard graft in Hong Kong : scandal; corruption; the ICAC / H. J. Lethbridge. – Hong Kong : Oxford University Press, 1985.
viii,247p.
Bibliography: p232-243.
ISBN 0195838963

Let's Look at Law / Jennifer Bollen. – Butterworths, 1985.
78p.
ISBN 0409492647 Pbk £9.50

Lettall, Martyn
Mobile Homes : An Occupiers Guide. – London : Shelter, 1988.
ISBN 0901242837 Pbk £3.95

Letters of credit. – London : Euromoney, 1985.
xiv,174p.
ISBN 0903121794

Letters of credit : the law and current practice / by Lazar Sarna. – Toronto : Carswell Legal Publications, 1984.
xv, 204 p.; 24 cm.
Includes bibliographical references and indexes.
ISBN 0459359908 Hbk £27

Letters of credit : the law and current practice / by Lazar Sarna. – 2nd ed. – Toronto : Carswell, 1986.
xxii,254p.
Includes bibliographical references and index.
ISBN 045938810X

Letters of intent. – London : Butterworths, 1990.
310; 24cm.
Deals with the legal aspects of letters of intent and other pre-contractual documents. It addresses the problem of enforceability of such contracts to contract from the point of view of both common law and civil law jurisdictions as well as their effective use and drafting. Includes specimen documentation and forms.
Lawyers, businessmen and women
ISBN 0880632305 Hbk £50

Letters rogatory for the interception of telecommunications : Recommendation no.R (85) 10 adopted by the Committee of Ministers of the Council of Europe on 28 June 1985 and Explanatory memorandum. – Council of Europe. – Strasbourg : Council of Europe, 1986.
15p; 21cm. – (Legal affairs).
'... prepared by a select committee of experts under the authority of the European Committee on Crime Problems' - p.3.
ISBN 9287108390

Letting business premises. – 6th. – London : Longman Professional (UK), 1989.
– (Practitioner series).
Coverage includes the statutory renewal procedure; compensation for tenants' improvements; and the law governing the major lease. Covenants relating to rent, user, alterations and improvements, and assignments and subletting, lettings to partnerships, and special types of business premises.

Letting Business Premises. – 5th ed. – London : Longman Professional, 1985.
ISBN 0851209858 Hbk £28.00

Lettner, Margot → Ontario Business Corporations Act annotated.

Leung, Yew Kwong
Development Land and Development Charge in Singapore. – London : Butterworths, 1987.
ISBN 0409995371 Hbk £36.00
—Property Tax in Singapore. – Butterworths, 1985.
256p.
ISBN 040999510X Pbk £50.00

Levens, Bruce → Crisis intervention training for police.

Levenson → Legal Aid - How to use it.
→ Practitioner's Guide to the Police and Criminal Evidence Act '84.

Levenson, Howard
Price of justice : costs and defendants / Howard Levenson. – London : Cobden Trust, 1981.
88p.
ISBN 0900137177

Leveson →The Law of Collisions in Africa.

Leveson, G.
Company Directors : Law and Practice. – 2nd ed. – Durban : Professional Publisher, 1983.
ISBN 0409040711 Hbk

Levi, Michael
Commonwealth Developments in Health Law. – Legal Division, Commonwealth Secretariat. – London : Commonwealth Secretariat, 1984.
324p.
ISBN 0850922283 Hbk £6.00
ISBN 0850922070 Pbk £6.00
—Phantom capitalists : the organisation and control of long-firm fraud / by Michael Levi. – London : Heinemann, 1981.
346p; 23cm.
Bibliography: p335-341. - Includes index.
ISBN 0435825208 £16.50
—Regulating fraud : white-collar crime and the criminal process / Michael Levi. – London : Tavistock, 1987.
416p; 24cm.
Includes bibliography and index.
ISBN 0422611603 £35.00
—Regulatory Fraud : White Collar Crime and Criminal Process. – Tavistock.
ISBN 00422611700 Pbk £12.95

Levie, Howard S. →Law of non-international armed conflict : Protocol II to the 1949 Geneva conventions.

Levie, Hugo →Fighting Closures.

Levin, H. R. →South African Tax Journal.

Levin, J.
Divorce Handbook. – London : Allison & Busby, 1986.
ISBN 185031724X Pbk £4.95

Levin, Jennifer →Family law.

Levin, Jenny
Guide to supplementary benefit law / by Jenny Levin. – 3rd ed. – London : Legal Action Group, 1981.
136p.

Levine, Jane
Computers and the Law. – Melbourne : Oxford University Press, 1986.
204p.
Considers many areas, including the liability arising from computer error, computer crime, computers and intellectual property, and difficulties in marketing, acquiring and applying computers.
ISBN 0195546571 Hbk £25.00

Levine, Jane R. →New South Wales consumer credit legislation.
→ Victorian consumer credit legislation.

Levine, Julius Byron
Discovery : a comparison between English and American civil discovery law with reform proposals / Julius Byron Levine. – Oxford : Clarendon, 1982.
xl,208p; 23cm.
Bibliography: p154-160. - Includes index.
ISBN 0198253680 £20.00

Levine, S.
Business and Investment Almanac 1988. – New York : Dow Jones-Irwin, 1988.
ISBN 1556230478 Hbk £31.95

Levitt, A R →Taxation of Insurance Business.

Levitt, Howard A.
Law of Dismissal in Canada. – Aurora : Canada Law Book Co, 1985.
403p. – (Text Books-Civil).
Hbk £55.00

Levy →Adoption Of Children.
—Institute of Financial Management / Sarrat. – Prentice-Hall.
ISBN 0137097751 Pbk £16.95

Levy, Allan
Custody and Access. – 2nd ed. – London : Longman Professional.
ISBN 0851213162 Hbk £17.50
—Wardship Proceedings. – 2nd ed. – London : Oyez Longman, 1982.
– (Oyez Longman Practice Note Ser.: No. 21).
ISBN 0851206360 Hbk £7.95

Levy, Earl J.
Examination of witnesses in criminal cases / Earl J. Levy. – Toronto : Carswell, 1987.
xxxv,263p.
Includes index.
ISBN 0459308211

Levy, James
Tolley's taxation in Gibraltar 1981-82 / by James Levy and Simon Caplan : with an introduction by Sir Joshua Hassan. – 2nd ed. – Croydon : Tolley, 1982.
vii,152p.
Includes index.
ISBN 0854590447

Lew, Julian D M
Contemporary Problems in International Arbitration. – London : Centre for Commercial Law Studies, 1986.
ISBN 0951066412 Hbk £40.00
—Contemporary Problems in International Arbitration. – Dordrecht : Kluwer, 1987.
380p.
ISBN 0898389267 Pbk Gld125.00
→ International trade : law and practice.

Lewin, T.
Law of Trusts. – 17th ed. – London : Sweet & Maxwell, 1988.
ISBN 0421233907 Hbk

Lewis
Landlord and Tenant / Holland. – 4th ed. – Agincourt : Casdec.
ISBN 0907595464 Hbk £15.95
ISBN 0907595448 Pbk £8.95
→ Lawyers in Society, Volume 1 The Common Law World.

Lewis, A.
Law Relating to Banking. – London : Checkmate Gold.
ISBN 1853130397 Pbk £10.95

Lewis, A. D. E. →Studies in Justinian's Institutes in memory of J.A.C. Thomas.

Lewis, A. N.
Australian bankruptcy law / Lewis. – 8th ed. – North Ryde : Law Book Co., 1984.
xxiii,293p.
Includes bibliographical references and index.
ISBN 0455205205

Lewis and Lewis / John Juxon. – London : Collins, 1983.
320p,12p of plates; 23cm.
Bibliography: p310-312. - Includes index.
ISBN 0002164760 £10.95

Lewis, Carole →Contract and mercantile law : a source book, Vol. 1 : General principles of contract, agency and representation : edited by Ellison Kahn, Carole Lewis and Coenraad Visser.

Lewis, Catherine A.
Butterworths Ontario Family Law Quantum Service, 2 Vols. / Ellen E. Mole. – Butterworths.
Llf £150.00

Lewis, Charles J
Law and Ethics in the Medical Office incl. Bioethical Issues / Warden. – Second Revised Edition. – London : European Book Service.
ISBN 0803656173 Pbk £11.96
—Medical negligence : a plaintiff's guide / Charles J. Lewis. – London, England : F. Cass, 1988.
xxxiv, 379 p.; 24 cm.
'The law is stated as at 1 January 1988'–T.p. verso.
Includes index.
ISBN 0714633399 Hbk £20.00
ISBN 0714640611 Pbk £12.00
—State and diplomatic immunity. – 3rd. – London : Lloyds of London Press, 1989.
approx 240.
Explains the law affecting the immunity from judicial action of foreign governments, their embassies, staff, and their property. Includes a new chapter on the International Tin Council Litigation, and a discussion of the effects of the Diplomatic and Consular Premises Act 1987.
ISBN 1850442541 Hbk

Lewis, David →Aftermath of tribunal reinstatement and re-engagement.
→ Total environment control : the economics of cross-media pollution transfers.

Lewis, David E.
Canadian Oil and Gas, 9 Vols. / Andrew R. Thompson. – Butterworths.
Llf £265.00

Lewis E. A. L.
Legal ethics : a guide to professional conduct for South African attorneys / E.A.L. Lewis. – Cape Town : Juta, 1982.
xix,339p.
Bibliography: p.xiii-xi - Includes index.
ISBN 0702113026

Lewis, G.D.
Handy Hints on Legal Practice / E.J. Kyrou. – North Ryde : Law Book Co, 1985.
xiv, 196p.
ISBN 0455206058 Pbk £19.50

Lewis, Geoffrey
Lord Atkin / by Geoffrey Lewis. – London : Butterworths, 1983.
xi,248p,8p of plates; 25cm.
A biography of Lord Atkin, one of the greatest common lawyers and judges of the twentieth century in England.
ISBN 0406272107 Hbk £14.95

Lewis, I. M. →Nationalism and self determination in the Horn of Africa.

Lewis, J.
Victorian Bar. – Robert Hale, 1982.
ISBN 0709005334 Hbk £9.95

Lewis, J. R.
Striking a balance? : employment law after the 1980 Act / Roy Lewis and Bob Simpson. – Oxford : Martin Robertson, 1981.
ix,269p; 22cm.
Includes index.
ISBN 0855204427 Hbk £
ISBN 0855204435 Pbk £4.95

Lewis, Johnnie N.
Cases and materials on the criminal law of Liberia / by Johnnie N. Lewis. – 3. – S.l. : s.n., 1981.

Lewis, Norman →Noble lie : the British constitution and the rule of law.

Lewis, P.
Rights Guide. – Unwin Hyman.
ISBN 004440171X Pbk £3.50

Lewis, Paul
Twenty years of statutory redundancy payments in Great Britain / Paul Lewis. – Nottingham : The Universities of Leeds and Nottingham in association with the Institute of Personnel Management, 1985.
50p; 21cm.
ISBN 0900572639

Lewis, Philip →Gatley on libel and slander.
→ Sociology of the professions : lawyers, doctors and others.

Lewis, R.
Compensation for Industrial Disablement. – London : Butterworths, 1987.
ISBN 0862052149 Hbk £26.50
—Compensation for industrial injury : a guide to the revised scheme of benefits for work accidents and diseases / by Richard Lewis. – Abingdon : Professional Books, 1987.
359p; 25cm.
ISBN 0862052149

Lewis, Roy
Brought to justice / Roy Lewis. – Durham : Casdec, 1983.
83p.
ISBN 0907595111
→ Labour law and industrial relations : building on Kahn-Freund.
→ Labour law in Britain.
—Strike-free procedures : are they what they seem? / Roy Lewis. – Coventry : University of Warwick. School of Industrial and Business Studies. Industrial Relations Research Unit, 1988.
14 leaves.
Bibliography: p14.

Lewison, K.
Drafting Business Leases. – 2nd ed. – London : Longman Professional, 1986.
ISBN 0851210244 Hbk £28.95
—Lease or Licence. – London : Longman Professional, 1985.
ISBN 0851211240 Pbk £10.50

Lewison, Kim
Interpretation of contracts. – London : Sweet & Maxwell, 1989.
Covers the object of integration, implied terms, the canons of construction, ambiguity and uncertainty, mistakes and inconsistencies, preliminary parts of the deed, parcels and subject matter of the contract, exemption clauses, certificates, consents and similar clauses, stipulations as to time, penalties, terminations and forfeiture clauses.
ISBN 042136940X Hbk £45.00

Lews
Australian Bankruptcy Law / Dennis J Rose. – 8th ed. – London : Law Book Co, 1984.
ISBN 0455205213 Pbk £13.00

Lewsen, Phyllis
South African Constitution : Euphoria and Rejection. – Johannesburg : Witwatersrand University Press, 1982.
vi, 20p.
ISBN 0854947434 Pbk £3.00

Lewsley, Christopher →Encyclopedia of rating and local taxation : law and practice.

Lex Custumaria. – 2nd ed. Repr. of 1701 ed. – Abingdon : Professional Books.
Hbk £75.00

Lex mercatoria / Berthold Goldman. – Deventer : Kluwer Law and Taxation Publishers, 1983.
24p.
Includes bibliographical references.
ISBN 9065441948

Lexeconics : the Interaction of Law and Economics. – Dordrecht : Kluwer, 1981.
272p.
ISBN 0898380537 Hbk £75.00

LEXIS Educational User's Group
Bulletin / LEXIS Educational User's Group. – 4. – London : The Group, 1984.

Leys, W. C. S.
Commercial law in New Zealand / Leys and Northey. – 7th ed. – Wellington : Butterworths, 1982.
xlviii,852p.
Previous ed.: 1978. Includes index.
ISBN 0409600881

Liability for defective services / Derrick Owles & Hugh Cockerell. – London : Financial Times Business Information, 1985.
168p; 30cm.
ISBN 0903199858

Liability for Drilling- and Production-Source Oil Pollution in the Canadian Offshore. – Calgary : Canadian Institute of Resources Law.
84p.
ISBN 0919269206 Hbk £17.00

Liability in Negligence. – London : Sweet & Maxwell, 1984.
ISBN 0459365908 Hbk £24.00

Liability in negligence / by J.C. Smith. – Toronto : Carswell, 1984.
xxxiii, 273 p.; 24 cm.
Includes indexes.
ISBN 0459366009 Pbk

Liability Insurance Claims. – Witherby, 1983.
ISBN 0900886803 Hbk £28.00

Liability of an Industrialist. – London : Sweet & Maxwell, 1985.
– (Sweet and Maxwell's Law Files Ser.: No. 6).
ISBN 0421340304 Llf £29.50

Liability of banks under letters of credit / Matti Kurkela. – Helsinki : Union of the Finnish Lawyers Pub. Co., 1982.
85 p.; 22 cm.
Bibliography: p. 84-85.
ISBN 9516401503 mk70.00

Liability of contractors / edited by Humphrey Lloyd. – London : Centre for Commercial Law Studies, Queen Mary College, 1986.
xxvi,253p; 24cm.
Conference proceedings. Includes index.
ISBN 0582463688

Liability of the States and Regional and Local Authorities for Damage Caused by their Agents and Administrative Services. – Strasbourg : Council of Europe, 1981.
Hbk £4.50

Liability regime of the international air carrier : a commentary on the present Warsaw system / Rene H. Mankiewicz. – Deventer, The Netherlands : Kluwer, 1981.
xxvii,259p.
Includes index. Bibliography: pxv-xxii.
ISBN 9026811705

Lian, Koh Kheng
Penal Codes of Singapore and Malaysia, Vol 2 : Cases, Materials and Comments / Molly Cheang. – Singapore : Quins.
Hbk £63.00

Libel and Contempt : The Law and the Media. – Vancouver : British Columbia Continuing Legal Education Society, 1982.
414p.
ISBN 0865040834 Hbk £65.00

Liber amicorum for the Rt. Hon. Lord Wilberforce / edited by Maarten Bos and Ian Brownlie. – Oxford : Clarendon, 1987.
vi,251p; 24cm.
Includes index.
ISBN 0198255950 £30.00

Liber Placitandi : A Book of Special Pleadings Containing Precedents of Pleas in Abatement, Declaration, Barrs, etc., in the Now Most Common and Ordinary Actions, Also the Forms of Entries in Writs of Error etc. – 2nd ed. Repr. of 1674 ed. – Abingdon : Professional Books.
273p.
Hbk £125.00

Liberalism and the limits of justice / Michael J. Sandel. – Cambridge : Cambridge University Press, 1982.
ix,191p; 24cm.
Bibliography: p184-186. - Includes index.
ISBN 052124501X Hbk £17.50
ISBN 0521270774 Pbk £5.95

Liberation Deferred? : the ideas of the English-Canadian Suffragists. – Toronto : University of Toronto Press, 1983.
ISBN 0802024556 Hbk £25.00
ISBN 0802064663 Pbk £9.95

Liberman, Adam
Guidebook to Australian Trade Marks Law and Practice. – 2nd ed. – North Ryde : C.C.H. Australia, 1985.
364p.
ISBN 0869035657

Liberty and Justice. – Oxford : Croom Helm, 1986.
ISBN 070994523X Hbk £25.00

Liberty and Justice for All : Public Interest Law in the 1980's and Beyond. – Wildwood.
ISBN 0813306965 Hbk £23.50

Liberty of the citizen / Franklin Thomas, John Mortimer, Lord Hunt of Tanworth. – London : Granada, 1983.
93p.
ISBN 0246121157

Library and Information Services Council
Joint enterprise : roles and relationships of the public and private sectors in the provision of library and information services / report of Library and Information Services Council and British Library Research and Development Department Working Party. – London : H.M.S.O., 1987.
vii, 49p.
On cover: Office of Arts and Libraries.
ISBN 011430016X

Library and information services for the legal profession / C. Miskin. – London : British Library, 1981.
iv,60p; 30cm.
ISBN 0905984730 Pbk

Library Legislation in India. – Delhi : Reliance Publishing House, 1986.
xvi, 376p.
Hbk £225.00

Library of Congress
Accessions list : India : quinquennial serials cumulation : 1976 / Library of Congress. – 3 v. – New Delhi : Library of Congress Office, 1977.
ISBN 01457608
→ Dominican Republic : divorce law.

Licensed conveyancing : the new legislation / with annotations by Phillip H. Kenny. – London : Sweet & Maxwell, 1986.
vi,52p.
Text of the Administration of Justice Act 1985, Part II, with Appendix and notes.
ISBN 0421350504

Licensed dealers in securities : draft rules & regulations proposed to be made under the Prevention of Fraud (Investments) Act 1958. – London : H.M.S.O., 1982.
iii,60p; 30cm.
At head of title: Department of Trade.
ISBN 0115136509 Pbk £4.25

Licensed to live / Martin. – Oxford : Blackwell, 1985.
ISBN 0631141650 Pbk £17.50

Licensing Act, 1984. – 92nd ed. – London : Butterworths, 1984.
ISBN 0406335176 Hbk

Licensing Acts Nineteen Eighty-Seven. – 95th ed. – London : Butterworths, 1986.
ISBN 0406335206 Hbk

Licensing Acts Nineteen Eighty-Two / J. N. Martin. – 90th ed. – London : Butterworths, 1982.
ISBN 0406334528 Hbk £92.50

Licensing Entertainments in England and Wales. – London : Butterworths, 1985.
ISBN 0406200300 Pbk £24.00

Licensing Guide for Developing Countries : the Legal Aspects of the Negotiation and Preparation of Industrial Property Licenses and Technology Transfer Agreements Appropriate to the Needs of Developing Countries (1977). – Geneva : World Intellectual Property Organization, 1987.
184p.
Hbk £40.00

Licensing Power in India : a Government Action for Social Welfare. – New Delhi : S. Chand and Company.
Hbk £100.00

Licensing Practice and Procedure. – 3rd ed. – London : Fourmat.
ISBN 1851900594 Pbk £13.95

Licensing Practice and Procedure. – 2nd ed. – London : Fourmat, 1986.
ISBN 1851900098 Hbk £12.95

Licensing (Scotland) Act 1976 / Heather Baillie. – 2nd. – Edinburgh : Green (W.) & Son, 1989.
Annotated text of the Act, originally produced by J. Allen and C.D. Chapman (1977), as subsequently amended and taking into account case law since the publication of the original edition. Also includes an expanded introduction and details of individual licensing boards.
ISBN 041400826X Pbk £16.00

Lidgard, Hans Henrik → Survey of commercial agency.

Lidstone, D., et al
Municipal Officers. – Vancouver : British Columbia Continuing Legal Education Society, 1982.
100p.
ISBN 0865040702 Hbk £35.00

Lidstone, Ken W. → Guide to the Police and Criminal Evidence Act 1984.

Lie, Susan Grace → International commercial crime : second international commercial crime symposium.
→ Symposium on Commercial Crime, 15-19 December 1982, Jesus College, Cambridge.

Lieber, Francis
Manual of Political Ethics. – Repr. of 1838 ed. – Aalen Wuertt : Scientia.
Hbk £255.00

Lieberman, D.
Province of Legislation Determined : Legal Theory in 18th Century Britain. – Cambridge : Cambridge University Press.
ISBN 0521245923 Hbk £27.50

Lieberman, J.I.
Child Support in America Practical Advice on Negotiating & Collecting Fair Settlement. – Yale University Press.
ISBN 0300042108 Pbk £5.95

Liebowitz, S. J
Impact of reprography on the copyright system / S.J. Liebowitz. – Ottawa : Research and International Affairs Branch, Bureau of Corporate Affairs, Consumer and Corporate Affairs Canada, 1981.
82 p.; 28 cm.
Bibliography: p. 81-82.
ISBN 0662113969 Pbk

Liell, Peter
Council houses and the Housing Act 1980 / by Peter Liell. – London : Butterworths, 1981.
xxxi,457p.
Includes the text of the Act.
ISBN 0406270309

Life and works of Hugo Grotius (1583-1645) : address delivered to members of the South African Law Commission and other dignitaries on 26 July 1983 at the University of Pretoria to commemorate the 400th birthday of Hugo Grotius / by Ellison Kahn. – Pretoria : South African Law Commission, 1983.
iii,21p. – (Research series).

Life Assurance : Its Tax Implications Etc / Trimm. – Witherby, 1977.
ISBN 090088620X Hbk £7.50

Life Insurance Law in the Commonwealth Caribbean. – London : Butterworths, 1984.
xxiii,226; 23cm.
This book provides a comprehensive study of the English law of life insurance as it applies in Trinidad and Tobago.
ISBN 0406076308 Pbk £17.00

Life Insurance Laws of Canada / Genevieve Faribault. – Don Mills : Life Underwriters Association of Canada, 1985.
ISBN 0919361757 Hbk £15.95

Life-sentence prisoners. – Parliamentary All-Party Penal Affairs Group. – Chichester : Barry Rose, 1986.
44p.
ISBN 085992386X

Lift and Escalator Erection Repair and Maintenance Consolidated Agreement. – London : Engineering Employers Federation, 1985.
Hbk £0.50

Lifting the burden / presented to Parliament by the Minister without Portfolio : supported by the Secretary of State for the Home Department ... et al. – London : H.M.S.O., 1985.
40p.
ISBN 0101957106

Ligertwood, A.L.C.
Australian Evidence. – Butterworths, 1988.
443p.
ISBN 0409493562 Hbk £65.00
ISBN 0409493287 Pbk £42.50

Lightman, Gavin
Law of receivers of companies / by Gavin Lightman and Gabriel Moss : with a foreword by Sir John Vinelott. – London : Sweet & Maxwell, 1986.
xlix,358p; 24cm.
Guide to the law relating to administrative receiverships, covering all aspects of practice and procedure. Includes sections on administrators, title retention clauses, and the role of the receiver in the winding up of a company.
ISBN 0421300906 £38.00

Lights on human rights / by Sir James Fawcett. – Strasbourg : Council of Europe, 1987.
13p. – (H(87)1).
'Prepared at the request of the Committee of Experts for the Promotion of Education and Information in the Field of Human Rights of the Council of Europe'. - t.p..

Lightwood, J. M. → Fisher & Lightwood's law of mortgage.

Lilles, Heino → Canadian children's law : cases, notes and materials.
→ Young Offenders Act annotated.
→ Young Offenders Service, 2 vols.

Lillich, Richard B.
Human rights of aliens in contemporary international law / Richard Lillich. – Manchester : Manchester University Press, 1984.
xii,177p; 24cm.
Includes index.
ISBN 0719009146 £27.50
—International Claims : Adjudications by National Commission. – London : Eurospan.
ISBN 0813908345 Hbk £17.50
—International Claims : Contemporary European Practice / Weston. – London : Eurospan.
ISBN 0813909279 Hbk £21.95
—International Claims : Postwar British Practice. – London : Eurospan.
ISBN 0813908507 Hbk £17.50

—International Claims : Settlement by Lump Sum Agreement / Weston. – London : Eurospan.
ISBN 0813906423 Hbk £39.50

—International Claims : Their Preparation and Presentation / Christenson. – London : Eurospan.
ISBN 0813908353 Hbk £17.50

—International Law of State Responsibility for Injuries to Aliens. – London : Eurospan.
ISBN 0813909619 Hbk £30.95

—Iran - United States Claims Tribunal 1981-83. – London : Eurospan.
ISBN 0813910420 Hbk £21.95

—United States Ratification of the Human Rights Treaties : With or Without Reservations?. – London : Eurospan.
ISBN 0813908817 Hbk £12.95

—Valuation of the Nationalised Property in International Law. – London : Eurospan.
ISBN 081390465X Hbk £12.95

Lilly, J.
Collection of Modern Entries. – 4th ed. Repr. of 1771 ed. – Abingdon : Professional Books.
273p.
Hbk £45.00

Lim, Chin → Copyright, competition and Canadian culture : the impact of alternative Copyright Act import provisions on the book publishing and sound recording industries.

Lim, Joo-Jock → Armed separatism in Southeast Asia.

Lim-Lye, Irene Lin Heng
Landlord and Tenant. – London : Butterworths, 1988.
– (Singapore Law Series).
ISBN 0409995347 Pbk

—Singapore Law Series
Landlord and Tenant /. – Butterworths, 1988.
ca 200p.
Discusses leases, and the relationship between landlords and tenants, and contains chapters on leases of major landlords such as the Jurong Town Corporation and the Urban Renewal Authority, and rent control.
ISBN 0409995347 Pbk

Limitation Act 1950 : a discussion paper / Law Commision. – Wellington, N.Z. : The Commission, 1987.
v,92p. – (Preliminary paper).
Bibliography: pp.66-67. Includes text of the Act.

Limitation Act, 1953 (Act 253). – Kuala Lumpur : International Law Books Services.
Hbk £5.00

Limitation of Actions. – London : Butterworths.
ISBN 0406102309 Hbk £38.50

Limitation of Actions. – 2nd ed. – Toronto : Butterworths.
344p.
Hbk £55.00

Limitation of Liability. – London : Fairplay Publication, 1984.
ISBN 0905045637 Pbk £12.00

Limitation of liability for maritime claims / by Patrick Griggs and Richard Williams. – London : Lloyd's, 1986.
122p; 22cm.
ISBN 1850440832 £24.00

Limitation of shipowners' liability : the new law. – London : Sweet & Maxwell, 1986.
xxv,378p; 22cm.
Includes index.
ISBN 0421348909 £35.00

Limitation periods in personal injury claims / by Stephen Todd. – London : Sweet & Maxwell, 1982.
xxii,131p; 23cm.
Includes index.
ISBN 0421285907 £13.00

Limitations / Institute of Law Research and Reform. – Edmonton : The Institute, 1986.
vii,370p. – (Report for discussion).

Limitations Act, 1983, Bill 160 : An Act to Revise the Limitations Act. – Ontario : Ontario Government Publications Service, 1983.
18p.
Hbk £0.50

Limited liability and the corporation / edited by Tony Orhnial. – London : Croom Helm, 1982.
223p; 23cm.
Conference papers. Includes bibliographies.
ISBN 0709905157 £12.95

Limited Liability in Collision Cases / H. G. Rohreke. – London : LLoyd's of London Press, 1984.
Hbk £14.00

Limited Partnerships. – Toronto : DeBoo, 1983.
ISBN 0888201192 Hbk £135.00

Limited Partnerships and Their Use in Syndications. – Vancouver : British Columbia Continuing Legal Education Society, 1983.
205p.
ISBN 0865041318 Hbk £55.00

Limits of legal radicalism : reflections on teaching law at the University of Dar es Salaam / edited by Issa G. Shivji. – Dar es Salaam, Tanzania : Faculty of Law, University of Dar es Salaam, 1986.
135p.
'1961-1986, 25th anniversary volume, Faculty of Law, University of Dar es Salaam'. - T.p.. Includes bibliographical references.

Limits of the legal process : a study of landlords, law and crime / David Nelken. – London : Academic Press, 1983.
xiii,241p; 24cm.
Bibliography: p219-225. - Includes index.
ISBN 0125152809

Limqueco, Peter → Prevent the Crime of Silence : The Report of the Vietnam War Crimes Tribunal.

Lincoln
Stamp Law and Practice. – Allahabad : Universal Book Agency.
Hbk £225.00

Lindahl, Lars → Theory of legal science : proceedings of the Conference on Legal Theory and Philosophy of Science, Lund, Sweden, December 11-14, 1983.

Lindberg case. – Rutgers University Press, 1988.
ISBN 0813512336 Hbk £20.50

Lindell
Law of Partnership / Ernest H Scammell. – 15th ed. – London : Sweet & Maxwell, 1984.
ISBN 042129860X Hbk £92.00

Linden, A M
Canadian Tort Law. – 3rd ed. – London : Butterworths.
ISBN 0409845779 Hbk £68.00

—Canadian Tort Law. – 4th ed. – London : Butterworths.
ISBN 0409801917 Hbk £100.00

—Media, the Courts and the Charter / Philip Anisman. – Agincourt : Carswell, 1986.
567p.
This work is a collection of essays on the importance and societal function of the press and other media and the protection afforded to the media in Canada and the U.S. The importance of protecting the news media from governmental interference in Canada is discussed in the book.
Hbk £74.50

→ Remedies in Tort, 4 Vols.

Linden, Allen M. → Canadian Tort Law.

Lindencrona, Gustaf
Arbitration in taxation / Gustaf Lindencrona, Nils Mattsson. – Deventer, The Netherlands : Kluwer, 1981.
92 p.; 22 cm.
Includes bibliographical references.
ISBN 9065440003 Pbk

Linder, Marc
Supreme Labor Court in Nazi Germany : a jurisprudential analysis / Marc Linder. – Frankfurt a. M. : Klostermann, 1987.
xix,290p.
Includes bibliographical references.
ISBN 3465017579

Lindgren, K.E. → Business Law of Australia.

—Contract law in Australia / K.E. Lindgren, J.W. Carter, D.J. Harland. – Sydney : Butterworths, 1986.
lxxvii,817p.
Bibliography: p.791-793. - Includes index.
ISBN 0409490970 Hbk A$76.00
ISBN 0409491268 Pbk A$59

→ Introduction to Business Law.

—Time in the performance of contracts : especially for the sale of land / K.E. Lindgren. – 2nd ed. – Sydney : Butterworths, 1982.
xxv,201p.
Previous ed.: 1976. Includes bibliographical references and index.
ISBN 0409303909 Hbk £49

Lindley
Law of Partnership : Including Limited Partnership. – 15th ed. – London : Sweet & Maxwell, 1984.
ISBN 042129860X Hbk £82.00

Lindley, Nathaniel Lindley
Lindley on the law of partnership / Ernest H. Scamell, R. C. I'Anson Banks. – 15th ed. – London : Sweet and Maxwell, 1984.
clxxxiv,1214p; 26cm.
Previous ed.: 1979. Includes index.
ISBN 042129860X £70.00

Lindley on the law of partnership / Ernest H. Scamell, R. C. I'Anson Banks. – 15th ed. – London : Sweet and Maxwell, 1984.
clxxxiv,1214p; 26cm.
Previous ed.: 1979. Includes index.
ISBN 042129860X £70.00

Lindrup, Garth → Butterworths competition law handbook.

Lindsay, G.C.
Contract /. – North Ryde : Law Book Co, 1984.
x, 133p. – (Nutshells).
ISBN 0455203466

Lindsay, Kennedy
British Intelligence Services in Action. – 2nd ed. – Newtownabbey : Dunrod Press, 1981.
312p.
ISBN 0862021111 Hbk £19.75

Lindsay, Margie → European Banking Law : An Analysis of Community and Member State Legislation.
→ European Insurance Law : An Analysis of Community and Member State Legislation.

Lindsell, William Henry Barber → Clerk & Lindsell on torts.

Lingard, J. R.
Bank security documents / J.R. Lingard. – 2nd ed. – London : Butterworths, 1988.
xxxiii,402p; 26cm.
Previous ed.: 1985. Includes index.
ISBN 0406106258 £45.00

—Bank security documents / J.R. Lingard. – London : Butterworths, 1985.
xxvi,367p; 26cm.
Includes index.
ISBN 0406258198 £30.00

—Corporate rescues and insolvencies / J.R. Lingard. – London : Butterworths, 1986.
xxvi,222p; 26cm.
Includes index.
ISBN 0406100403 Pbk £27

Linguistic evidence : language, power, and strategy in the courtroom / William M. O'Barr. – New York : Academic Press, 1982.
xv,192p; 24cm.
Bibliography: p182-187. - Includes index.
ISBN 0125235208 £15.60

Linklater & Paines
Tolley's Estate Planning. – Linklater & Paines. – Tolley Publishing.
ISBN 0854592725 Hbk £17.95

Linn, Johannes F.
Cities in the developing world : policies for their equitable and efficient growth / Johannes F. Linn. – Oxford : Published for the World Bank by Oxford University Press, 1983.
xxi,230p; 24cm.
Bibliography: p213-223. - Includes index.
ISBN 0195203828 Hbk
ISBN 0195203836 Pbk

Linton, Ian
Promotion for the Professions : A Guide to Practice Development. – London : Kogan Page, 1985.
134p.
ISBN 0850389968 Hbk £12.95

Linton, R.B. → Practice on Motions and References.

Lionel Morphy - a Radical Judge : an Appraisal by Eleven Prominent Australians. – Carlton : McCulloch Publishing.
276p.
ISBN 0949646172 Hbk £29.95

Lipman → Electronic Pirates : DIY Crime of the Century.

Lippman
Islamic Criminal Law and Procedure : An Introduction / McConville. – Praeger.
ISBN 0275930092 Hbk £29.95

Lipscombe, G.
Economics and the Banks' Role in the Economy. – Pitman.
ISBN 0273028820 Pbk £6.95

Lipstein, K.
Principles of the conflict of laws, national and international / by K. Lipstein. – The Hague : Nijhoff, 1981.
xii,144p.
Revised edition of 'The general principles of private international law' published in vol.135 (1972-1) of the Recueil des Cours, The Hague Academy of International Law.
ISBN 9024725445 Hbk £75.00

Lipton, P.
Understanding Company Law / A. Herzberg. – 2nd ed. 1986. – North Ryde : Law Book Co.
xxxvi, 453p.
ISBN 0455206392 Hbk £42.00
ISBN 0455206406 Pbk £29.50

Liquidated damages and penalties / Law Reform Commission of Victoria. – Melbourne : The Commission, 1988.
i.20p. – (Discussion paper).
Includes bibliographical references.
ISBN 0724167293

Liquidation Manual. – 2nd ed. – Tolley Publishing, 1988.
ISBN 0854592229 Hbk £29.95

Liquidation manual / Paul Shewell, John Powell. – Croydon : Tolley, 1983.
xxi,368p.
Includes index. Cover title: Tolley's liquidation manual.
ISBN 0854590285

Liquidation of Insolvent Private Companies. – London : Butterworths, 1988.
ISBN 0406267006 Pbk

Liquor laws : a discussion paper. – Wellington : Law Reform Division, Department of Justice, 1985.
22p.
ISBN 0477072100

Liquor Laws Guide. – Butterworths, 1983.
176p.
ISBN 0409494011 Pbk £27.50

Liquor Laws in Victoria. – Butterworths, 1982.
ISBN 0409351024 Llf £105.00

Liquor Laws of New Zealand. – 4th ed. – Butterworths, 1983.
ISBN 0409600776 Hbk £106.15

Liquor licensing law / by David Field and Matthew Pink. – London : Sweet & Maxwell, 1983.
xxi,206p; 25cm.
Looks at how to obtain a justices licence, including the stages of deciding the relevant licence, the permitted hours in licensed premises, how to renew an existing licence, and its removal and transfer through to the conduct of licensed premises. Also contains a chapter on the nature of a registered club.
ISBN 0421299703 Pbk £11.50

List of barristers by chambers, with index. – 12th ed. – London : Holborn Law Society, 1983.
xlii,121p.

List of constitutional and Privy Council judgments affecting the Isle of Man from 1523 to 1986 and a complete year by year list of written Reasons for Judgment of Her Majesty's High Court of Justice of the Isle of Man and other Manx courts from 1884 to 1986 / compiled and with an introduction by Judy Thornley on the directions of H.M. Attorney General for the Isle of Man. – Douglas : Government Printer, 1987.
94p.
Cover title: A book of precedents.

List of current legal research topics : being topics forming the subject of research by students for degrees in universities and polytechnics in the United Kingdom / University of London, Institute of Advanced Legal Studies. – 34th ed. – London : The Institute, 1986.
iv,99p.
Supplements: Legal research in the United Kingdom 1905-1984. Includes indexes.

List of current legal research topics : being topics forming the subject of research by students for degrees in universities and polytechnics in the United Kingdom / University of London, Institute of Advanced Legal Studies. – 33rd ed. – London : The Institute, 1985.
51p.
Includes index. . Supplements: Legal research in the United Kingdom 1905-1984.

List of current legal research topics : being topics forming the subject of research by students for degrees in Universities and Polytechnics in the United Kingdom / Institute of Advanced Legal Studies. – 35th ed. – London : the Institute, 1987.
vii,111p.
Supplements: Legal research in the United Kingdom 1905-1984. Includes indexes.

List of current periodicals currently received in the Legal Advisers Library and the legal section, Cornwall House. – London : Foreign and Commonwealth Office, 1987.
5 leaves.

List of English law officers, King's counsel and holders of patents of precedence / compiled for the Selden Society by Sir John Sainty. – London : Selden Society, 1987.
xviii, 330p.

List of Ratifications of Conventions (as at 31 December 1985). – Geneva : International Labour Office, 1986.
102p.
ISBN 9221051730 Hbk £17.50

Listed buildings : the law and practice of historic buildings, ancient monuments and conservation areas / by Roger W. Suddards. – 2nd ed. – London : Sweet & Maxwell, 1988.
xxxi,307p.
Sets out and discusses the statutory basis for the protection and preservation of our 'built heritage'. Deals with listed buildings, conservation area control and the law relating to ancient monuments. Describes the effect of fixing canopies to listed buildings, and problems arising from cladding, rendering and cleaning of such buildings.
ISBN 0421381302 £40.00

Listed buildings and conservation areas. – London : Longman Professional (UK), 1989.
– (Practitioner series).
Explains how a building is listed, how far that listing extends, and considers the designation of conservation areas. Sets out the provisions relating to alteration and repair of listed buildings and the planning cotrols that apply, and sets out the financial considerations. Takes account of the General Development Order 1988.
ISBN 0851214088 Hbk £25.95

Lister, M.
European Community and the Developing World : The Role of the Lorne Convention. – Aldershot : Avebury.
ISBN 0566056097 Hbk £29.50

Lister, Ruth
Opportunity lost : a response to the Green Paper on the Reform of Personal Taxation from the Child Poverty Action Group / Ruth Lister and Fran Bennett. – London : Child Poverty Action Group, 1986.
34p.
—Welfare benefits / by Ruth Lister. – London : Sweet and Maxwell, 1981.
xxvi,284p; 22cm.
Bibliography: p251. - Includes index.
ISBN 0421249609 Pbk £8.00

Litigating Exploitation in India. – Bombay : Tripathi, 1986.
189p.
Hbk £75.00

Litigating in Spain: considerations for foreign practitioners including international judicial assistance, enforcement of foreign judgements, bankruptcy, arbitration and other civil proceedings in Spain. – Kluwer Law and Taxation, 1989.
579.
Informs investors, and potential investors how to protect their investments under Spanish law. Provides footnotes and other information relevant to precedents in Spanish courts. Contains a table of the Spanish Judicial Structure, and an appendix of all the International conventions ratified by Spain.
ISBN 9065443770 Hbk £52.75/Dfl 163

Litigating the Values of a Nation : The Canadian Charter of Rights and Freedoms / Robin M. Elliot. – Agincourt : Carswell, 1986.
448p.
This work is a collection of essays by leading Canadian Charter and American constitutional authorities on legal history, political science, legal philosophy, legal theory, and practical advice to litigators.
Hbk £65.75

Litigation : a journal of contentious business. – Chichester : Barry Rose, 1981.
With annual index.
ISBN 0859923193

Litigation : Evidence and Procedure. – 4th ed. – Butterworths, 1988.
1,108p.
ISBN 0409495077 Hbk £60.00

Litigation for the Law Society finals / by Craig Osborne. – London : Sweet & Maxwell, 1987.
xiii,434p; 24cm.
Includes index.
ISBN 0421369205 Pbk £15.95

Litigation in Complex Cases. – Vancouver : Continuing Legal Education Society of British Columbia, 1987.
188p.
ISBN 0865043574 Hbk £70.00

Litigation Opinions. – Vancouver : Continuing Legal Education Society of British Columbia, 1987.
94p.
ISBN 0865043175 Hbk £60.00

Litigation Practice And Service. – London : Longman Professional.
ISBN 085121083X Llf

Litigation strategy at the International Court
A case study of the Nicaragua v. United States dispute. – Dordrecht : Nijhoff (Martinus), 1989.
375. – (Legal aspects of international organization 9).
Examines the reasons States have for utilizing or resisting the utilization of the International Court as a means of pursuing and achieving foreign policy goals, and the methods they employ within the scope of the possibilities offered by the Courts Statute and Rule of procedure. This model is applied to the Nicaragua case.
ISBN 0792303326 Hbk £56

Litigation Support and Financial Assessment of Damages / Lemar. – London : Butterworths.
ISBN 0406504024 Hbk £55.00

Little →Election Law.

Little, A. J.
Planning controls and their enforcement / by A.J. Little. – 5th ed. – London : Shaw, 1983.
xlix,345p.
Previous ed. published as 'The enforcement of planning control' 1977. Includes index.
ISBN 0721904920

Littler, Craig R. →Industrial relations and the law in the 1980's : issues and future trends.

Litvak
Canadian Multinationals / Maule. – London : Butterworths.
ISBN 0409845256 Hbk £16.00

Livadas, Christopher
Winding up of insolvent companies in England and France / Christopher Livadas. – Deventer, Netherlands : Kluwer Law and Taxation Publishers, 1983.
xxxvi, 384 p.; 25 cm.
: Originally presented as the author's thesis (Ph.D.–City of London Polytechnic, 1981). Bibliography: p. 383-384.
ISBN 9065440879

Livens, L.
Share valuation handbook. – London : Fourmat, 1986.
ISBN 0906840988 Pbk £12.95

Livermore, J.
Exemption Clauses and Implied Obligations in Contracts. – North Ryde : Law Book Co, 1986.
xxxviii, 290p.
ISBN 0455206813 Pbk £45.00

Lives, liberties and the public good : new essays in political theory for Maurice Cranston / edited by George Feaver and Frederick Rosen. – Basingstoke : Macmillan in association with the London School of Economics and Political Science, 1987.
ix,272p; 23cm.
Bibliography: p259-266. - Includes index.
ISBN 0333392868 £27.50

Lives of the Lord Chancellors (1885-1940). – Oxford : Oxford University Press, 1987.
ISBN 0198213123 Hbk £45.00

Lives of the Lord Chancellors (1940-1970). – Oxford : Oxford University Press, 1987.
ISBN 0198200749 Hbk £25.00

Livesay, F.
Chartered Association of Certified Accountants Economics. – Pitman.
ISBN 0273028057 Pbk £11.95

Living and Retiring Abroad. – 2nd ed. – London : Kogan Page, 1988.
ISBN 1850914222 Pbk £6.95

Living down a criminal record : problems and proposals : a discussion paper / Law Reform Division, Department of Justice. – Wellington : The Department, 1985.
31p.
ISBN 0477072151

Living Together : A Guide to the Law on Marriage and Cohabitation in Scotland / Frances Wason. – Edinburgh : Scottish Association of Citizens Advice Bureau, 1984.
96p : Illus.
ISBN 0905831047 Hbk £1.95

Living together : young couples in de facto relationships : a report using Australian Family Formation Project Data / prepared for the Australian Institute of Family Studies. – Melbourne : Australian Institute of Family Stuides, 1986.
ii,50p. – (Working paper).
ISBN 0859244466

Living Will : Consent to Treatment at the End of Life. – London : Edward Arnold.
ISBN 0340491426 Pbk £3.95

Living with books / Joseph W. Scott. – London : University of London Library Resources Co-ordinating Committee, 1987.
8 p. – (Publication).
ISBN 0718708032

Living with terrorism : the problem of air piracy / Frank Brenchley. – London : Institute for the Study of Conflict, 1986.
iv,17p.

Il Sung, Kim
On the Land Law. – New Delhi : People's Publishing House, 1978.
ii, 20p.
Hbk £0.50

Llewellyn, David T.
Evolution of the British financial system / by D.T. Llewellyn. – London : Institute of Bankers, 1985.
59p.
Bibliography: p.59.
ISBN 0852971362
—Regulation and supervision of financial institutions / by D.T. Llewellyn. – London : Institute of Bankers, 1986.
77p.
Bibliography: p.75-77.
ISBN 0852971745

Lloyd
Building Law Reports
Index to Volumes 1-38 / Baatz. – London : Longman Professional.
ISBN 0582026229 Hbk £22.00
—Building Law Reports Vols 1-40 / Reese. – London : Longman Professional.
ISBN 0000999111 Hbk £880.00
—Building Law Reports Volume 42 / Baatz. – London : Longman Professional.
ISBN 00582019656 Hbk £22.00
—Lloyd's Introduction to Jurisprudence / M. D. A. Freedman. – 5th ed. – Agincourt : Carswell, 1985.
1257p.
This book is an anthology of selected extracts from the work of one hundred noted jurists throughout history. A discussion of different theories of jurisprudence from Plato to the present day is provided in the work.
Hbk £75.75
—Personal Injury : a Medico-Legal Guide to the Spine and Limbs / Ogilvie-Harris. – Aurora : Canada Law Book.
Hbk £33.00
—Practice of Law / Bowstock. – Methuen, 1988.
ISBN 0901715662 Pbk £6.50
ISBN 0901715670 Hbk £15.00

Lloyd-Bostock, Sally M. A. →Psychology in legal contexts : applications and limitations.

Lloyd, C.
Response to SNOP. – Cambridge : Institute of Criminology, 1986.
Hbk £5.00

Lloyd, Geoffrey J.
Personal Injury : A Medico-Legal Guide to the Spine and Limbs. – Aurora : Canada Law Book Co, 1986.
350p. – (Text Books-Civil).
This text is written specifically for lawyers and explains the medical aspects of a wide range of personal injuries in lay terms. Throughout, the text focuses on the functional and economic impact of particular injuries and considers the long-term life style effects of various disabilities.
Hbk £60.00

Lloyd, Humphrey → Liability of contractors.

Lloyd, Ian → Fifth report from the Energy Committee : session 1984-85 : government oil price policy and the spring supplementary estimate for 20 million in respect of the British National Oil Corporation including Government repsonse to Committee's fourth report of session 1984-85 ... together with minutes of proceedings relating to the report and minutes of evidence and appendices.
→ Fourth report from the Energy Committee : session 1984-85 : the winter supplementary estimate for 45 million in respect of the British National Oil Corporation together with minutes of proceedings relating to the report and minutes of evidence and appendices.

Lloyd-Jones → Employment Claims in the County Court.

Lloyd, M. G. → Land development and the infrastructure Lottery.

Lloyd, Michael Gordon
Legal databases in Europe : user attitudes and supplier strategies / Michael Lloyd. – Amsterdam : North-Holland, 1986.
xiii, 218 p.; 24 cm.
At head of title: Commission of the European Communities. 'Report no. EUR 10439 of the Commission of the European Communities'–T.p. verso. Bibliography: p.205.
ISBN 044470048X

Lloyd of Hampstead, Dennis Lloyd
Current Legal Problems : Lectures Delivered in the Faculty of Laws of University College London
Vol. 35 / Roger W Rideout. – London : Sweet & Maxwell, 1982.
ISBN 0420465405 Hbk £22.00
Vol. 36. – 1983.
ISBN 042046770X Hbk £22.00

—Idea of law / Dennis Lloyd. – Repr. with revisions. – Harmondsworth : Penguin, 1981.
365p; 20cm. – (Pelican books).
Originally published: 1964. Bibliography: p360. - Includes index.
ISBN 0140206884 Pbk £2.95

—Lloyd's Introduction to jurisprudence / M. D. A. Freeman. – 5th ed. – London : Sweet & Maxwell, 1985.
1300p.
Previous ed.: published as Introduction to jurisprudence. London : Stevens, 1979. Includes index.
ISBN 042047160X Hbk £30.00 :
ISBN 0420471707 Pbk £22.50

Lloyd's arbitration reports. – London : Lloyd's of London, 1988-.

Lloyds Bank Annual Review. – Pinter, 1988.
ISBN 0861879740 Hbk £20.00

Lloyd's Bank Tax Guide 1988-89 / Willman. – Penguin.
ISBN 0140113169 Pbk £4.95

Lloyd's Introduction to Jurisprudence / M. D. A. Freedman. – 5th ed. – Agincourt : Carswell, 1985.
1257p.
This book is an anthology of selected extracts from the work of one hundred noted jurists throughout history. A discussion of different theories of jurisprudence from Plato to the present day is provided in the work.
Hbk £75.75

Lloyd's Introduction to jurisprudence / M. D. A. Freeman. – 5th ed. – London : Sweet & Maxwell, 1985.
1300p.
Previous ed.: published as Introduction to jurisprudence. London : Stevens, 1979. Includes index.
ISBN 042047160X Hbk £30.00 :
ISBN 0420471707 Pbk £22.50

Lloyds Law Reports 1919-1987 158 Vols. – London : Lloyd's of London Press.
Hbk £6,075.00

Lloyd's law reports. – London : Lloyd's, 1919-.
First published as Lloyd's list law reports. Index in each vol. - Consolidated index (1919-1975), 1. 1981.

Lloyd's Law Reports : 1919-82, 146 Vols. – Abingdon : Professional Books, 1984.
Hbk

Lloyd's Law Reports : Bound Volumes, 1919-1987, 158 Vols. – London : LLoyd's of Londón Press.
Hbk £6075.00

Lloyd's Law Reports : Consolidated Index 1919-1975. – London : LLoyd's of London Press.
Hbk £35.00

Lloyd's Law Reports : Digests, 1919-1985, 16 Vols. – London : LLoyd's of London Press.
Hbk £785.00

Lloyd's Law Reports : Index. – London : Lloyd's of London Press.
ISBN 1850441715 Hbk £185.00

Lloyd's maritime and commercial law quarterly. – London : Lloyd's of London Press, 1974-.
Index in each vol. - Cumulative indexes, 1974-78, 1979-83.

Lloyd's Maritime Atlas. – 15th ed. – London : LLoyd's of London Press.
ISBN 1850440220 Hbk £30.00

Lloyd's Maritime Yearbook 1987-. – London : Lloyd's of London Press.
ISBN 1850441928 Hbk £65.00

Lloyd's nautical year book 1988. – London : Lloyd's of London Press, 1987.
488p.
ISBN 1850441340

Lloyds of London. – Rev ed. – Penguin.
ISBN 0140056467 Pbk £7.95
→ Modern liner contracts : an in depth study of current contracts of carriage in liner shipping.

Lloyd's of London Press → Charter-parties conference : a two-day conference.
→ Insurance in the Arab world : a Lloyd's List conference-London.
→ International reinsurance : the law and market practice : an RRG seminar.
→ Mareva injunctions : a one-day conference.
→ Marine claims (hull) for indemnity : the Eugenides Foundation, Athens, April 29/30, 1982.
→ Maritime law in bills of lading : a conference organised by Lloyd's of London Press : the Tower Hotel, London, 23rd June, 1982.
→ Time bars in maritime matters : a study.
→ War risks : the Tower Hotel, London, 24th June 1982.

Lloyd's Survey Handbook. – 4th ed. – London : LLoyd's of London Press.
ISBN 185044031X Hbk £27.50

Loan agreement documentation : sample annotated loan agreement for a syndicated Eurodollar transaction / by Anthony C. Gooch, Linda B. Klein. – London : Euromoney Publications, 1986.
iii,93p.
ISBN 1870031407

Lobbying government : understanding and influencing the corridors of power / Charles Miller. – Oxford : Basil Blackwell, 1987.
200p; 23cm.
Includes index.
ISBN 0631155252 £25.00

Local and Central Government. – 4th ed. – London : Hutchinson, 1984.
128p.
ISBN 0091588715 Pbk £3.95

Local and Personal Acts, Tables and Index. – London : HMSO, 1985.
ISBN 0118402714 Hbk £5.10

Local authority accounting in Europe : report / prepared by the Committee of Experts on Local and Regional Finance of the Steering Committee for Regional and Municipal Matters. – Strasbourg : Council of Europe, 1985.
120p.

Local Authority Accounts : Survey of Current Practise 1988. – London : CIPFA Computer Services.
ISBN 085299401X Hbk £10.00

Local authority enquiries : how can we eliminate delays? / a consultation paper from the Conveyancing Standing Committee. – London : The Committee, 1987.
20,7p.

Local Authority Licensing and Registration / Rosson. – London : Longman Professional, 1985.
ISBN 085120886X updat £125.00

Local Elections in Canada : the Law Governing Elections of Municipal Councils, School Boards and Other Local Authorities. – Butterworths, 1988.
864p.
ISBN 0409816051 Hbk £100.00

Local Government Act, 1976 (Act 171). – Kuala Lumpur : International Law Books Services.
Hbk £12.50

Local Government Act 1985. – London : Sweet & Maxwell, 1985.
ISBN 0421353503 Pbk £9.75

Local Government Administration. – 2nd ed. – London : Shaw & Sons, 1987.
ISBN 0721907121 Pbk £11.95

Local Government Audit Law. – London : HMSO, 1985.
ISBN 0117012599 Hbk £19.50

Local Government Finance Act 1982 / with annotations by Reginald Jones. – London : Sweet & Maxwell, 1982.
51p; 24cm.
ISBN 0421310006 Pbk £5.50

Local government finance in Canada / Harry M. Kitchen. – Toronto : Canadian Tax Foundation, 1984.
xvii,495p.
Includes bibliographical references and index.
ISBN 0888080204

Local Government Forms and Precedents : 1953-1956, 5 Vols. – Abingdon : Professional Books.
Hbk £60.00

Local government in Scotland / G Coutts. – 2nd. – Edinburgh : Green (W.) & Son, 1989.
Provides an introduction to the Scottish local government system including its historical context and possible future reforms. Updated to include the community charge and the changing relationship of local and central government.
ISBN 0414008898 Pbk

Local government in the modern states / by Martin Loughlin. – London : Sweet & Maxwell, 1986.
xxv,222p; 23cm.
Bibliography: p202-217. - Includes index.
ISBN 0421338601 Hbk £13.50
ISBN 0421338709 Pbk £12.50

Local government in the Third World : the experience of tropical Africa / edited by Philip Mawhood. – Chichester : Wiley, 1983.
xiii,261p; 24cm. – (A Wiley series on public administration in developing countries).
Includes bibliographies and index.
ISBN 0471105104

Local government law / Keith Davies. – London : Butterworths, 1983.
xxxvi,352p; 23cm.
Includes index.
ISBN 0406252661 Hbk £
ISBN 040625267X Pbk £17.95

Local Government Planning and Environment Service, New South Wales. – Butterworths.
Llf £370.00

Local Government, Planning and Land Act 1980 / with annotations by Victor Moore and Louise Catchpole. – London : Sweet & Maxwell, 1981.
294p; 25cm.
ISBN 0421288701 Pbk £10.00

Local Government, Planning and Land Act 1980. – London : Butterworths, 1981.
This book consists of an annotated guide to the complete Act. A table of cases and a guide to the definitions used in the Act is also included.
ISBN 0406584303 Hbk

Local Government Review : 1909-1914, 7 Vols. – Abingdon : Professional Books.
Hbk £95.00

Local Government Superannuation Scheme : An Explanation. – London : Shaw & Sons, 1982.
ISBN 0721903568 Pbk £0.48

Local government, the law and the constitution / Martin Loughlin. – s.l. : Local Government Legal Society Trust, 1983.
ii,143p.

Local land charges / by J.F. Garner. – 10th ed. – London : Shaw & Sons, 1987.
xxv,173p.
Previous ed.: 1982. Includes index.
ISBN 0721901255

Local land charges / by J.F. Garner. – 9th ed. – London : Shaw, 1982.
xxvii,171p; 22cm.
Previous ed.: 1977. Includes index.
ISBN 0721901247 Pbk

Local needs policies and development control strategies : an examination of the role of occupancy restrictions in development control / Martin Loughlin. – Bristol : University of Bristol, School for Advanced Urban Studies, 1984.
107p; 30cm. – (WP).
ISBN 0862921554

Local plans in British land use planning / by Patsy Healey. – Oxford : Pergamon, 1983.
xv,324p; 24cm.
Bibliography: p303-318. - Includes index.
ISBN 0080252427 £16.50

Local taxes in Europe : an analysis of how they function. – Amsterdam : International Bureau of Fiscal Documentation, 1985.
72p.
Conference proceedings.
ISBN 9070125269

Locke, M.
How to run committees and meetings. – London : Macmillan, 1982.
ISBN 0333207533 Hbk £33.00
ISBN 0333290356 Pbk £4.95

Locked up in care : a report on the use of secure accommodation for young people in care. – Children's Legal Centre. – London : Children's Legal Centre, 1982.
36p; 30cm.
Bibliography: p36. 'Locked up in care - new legislation' (sheet (2p)) as insert.
ISBN 0946109001 Pbk £3.00

Lockhart-Miriams, Andrew → Medical negligence.

Lockwood, Arthur → Bean and Lockwood's Rating valuation practice.

Locus standi : a commentary on the law of standing in Canada. – Toronto : Carswell, 1986.
xxiv,221p.
Includes index.
ISBN 0459388207

Lodge, Juliet → European Community : bibliographical excursions.

Loebecke → Auditing : An Integrated Approach.

Loeber, Dietrich Andre → Ruling Communist parties and their status under law.

Loewenberg
Comparing Legislations / Patterson. – London : Eurospan.
ISBN 081917050X Pbk £14.75

L'Office Et Aucthoritie de Justices de Peace. – Abingdon : Professional Books. – (Classical English Law Texts Ser.).
Hbk £44.00

Loftie
Inns of Court and Chancery / Railton. – Southampton : Ashford Press, 1985.
ISBN 090706910X Hbk £24.95

Logan, R G
Information sources in law. – London : Butterworths, 1986.
ISBN 0408114746 Hbk £38.00

Logic of the Law. – London : Eurospan.
ISBN 0802600182 Pbk £12.75

Lokapukta (Ombudsman in India) : a Socio-Legal Study / S.S. Singh. – New Delhi : Indian Institute of Public Administration, 1988.
Hbk £100.00

Lokhande, G.S.
Dr. Bhimrao Ramji Ambedkar : a Study in Social Democracy. – Kuala Lumpur : Intellectual Book Corner, 1982.
vii, 270p.
Hbk £80.00

Lomax
Enforcement in the Magistrates Courts : a Guide to Enforcing Money Payments / Reynolds. – London : Fourmat.
ISBN 1851900454 Pbk £12.95

Lomax & Reynolds
Arrears Proceedings and Related Matters in the Magistrates' Court. – Lomax & Reynolds. – Chichester : Barry Rose, 1985.
250p.
ISBN 0859922340 Hbk £19.50

Lomax, David F.
London markets after the Financial Services Act / David F. Lomax. – London : Butterworths, 1987.
225p; 24cm.
Includes bibliography and index.
ISBN 0406100748 £15.00
—Regulation after the Financial Services Act. – London : Butterworths, 1987.
ISBN 0406100748 Pbk

Lomer, Michael → Documentary evidence in Canada.

Lomnicka, Eva Z. → Encyclopedia of financial services law.

Lomnicki
Made Simple : Housing Tenancy and Planning Law. – London : MADE, 1981.
ISBN 0434984876 Pbk £2.95

Lon L. Fuller. – London : Edward Arnold, 1984.
192p.
ISBN 0713164093 Pbk £9.95

London Chamber of Commerce and Industry → Companies act 1980.

London County Courts Directory. – 11th ed. – London : HMSO, 1982.
ISBN 0113906323 Hbk £20.00

London Electricity Board : a report by the Director General of Fair Trading on an investigation under Section 3 of the Competition Act 1980 / Office of Fair Trading. – London : Office of Fair Trading, 1982.
78p; 30cm.

London Government Handbook / Travers. – London : Cassell.
ISBN 0304315745 Hbk £15.00

London, Malcolm
Insolvency. – London : Collins, 1986.
200p.
ISBN 0003832937 Hbk £17.50
→ Liquidation manual.

London markets after the Financial Services Act / David F. Lomax. – London : Butterworths, 1987.
225p; 24cm.
Includes bibliography and index.
ISBN 0406100748 £15.00

London money market / E.R. Shaw. – 3rd ed. – London : Heinemann, 1981.
xiv,267p; 22cm.
Previous ed.: 1975. Bibliography: p259-261. - Includes index.
ISBN 0434918334 Pbk £7.50

London School of Economics and Political Science → Woman's role in economic development.

London Underground Ltd. → Crime on the London Underground.

Long, Colin D
Telecommunications law and practice. – London : Sweet & Maxwell, 1988.
Examines satellite and cable television, the more technical aspects of licensing and the supply of apparatus and services. Discusses the Telecommunications Act 1984, system licensing, value added and data services licence, competition law, copyright, criminal and contractual liability, and contracting by telecommunications.
ISBN 0421377801 Hbk £29

Long, Olivier
Law and its limitations in the GATT multilateral trade system / Olivier Long. – Dordrecht : M. Nijhoff, 1985.
158p.
'An adaptation in English, brought up to date to the end of 1984, of a series of lectures delivered at the Hague Academy of International Law and published in French in its 'Collected courses' 1983, IV, volume 182'–Pref. Includes index. Bibliography.
ISBN 9024731895 Hbk £100.00

Long service leave / by Hugh Selby : with a foreword by F.V. Watson. – Sydney : Law Book Co., 1983.
xxviii,150p.
Includes index.
ISBN 0455204519

Long Suffering British Workers : Working Time in Europe. – London : Labour Research Department.
24p.
ISBN 0900508434 Hbk £0.60

Longman
Directory Of Local Authorities 1988/89. – London : Longman Professional.
ISBN 0851214320 Pbk £16.50
—Intelligence report : inheritance tax. – London : Longman Professional, 1986.
ISBN 085121245X Hbk £75.00
—Intelligence report : the film business. – London : Longman Professional, 1986.
ISBN 0851212387 Hbk £95.00
—Legal Software Directory. – London : Longman Professional, 1985.
ISBN 0851210422 Pbk £16.50

Longman Exam Guide : Business Law / Bailey. – London : Longman Professional, 1986.
ISBN 0582296781 Pbk £6.95

Longman Litigation Practice. – London : Longman Professional.
ISBN 085121083X Llf £150.00

Longstreth, B.
Modern Investment Management. – Oxford : Oxford University Press, 1986.
ISBN 0195041968 Hbk £29.50

Lontai, E.
Research Contracts : Civil-Law Means Promotion Scientific Technical Progress. – Dordrecht : Kluwer, 1977.
235p.
ISBN 9028603174 Hbk £59.00

Loomis, Terrence
Evaluation of the children's advocate scheme pilot in the Auckland Children and Young Persons Court / by Dr. Terrence Loomis : a study commissioned by the Department of Justice. – Auckland : Social Research and Development Trust, 1985.
88,26p.
'Carried out for the Department of Justice by the Social Research and Development Trust of Auckland'. - Abstract.

Loon, Hans van → Report on trusts and analogous institutions, Part 1 : 1ere partie.

Loose on liquidators : the role of a liquidator in a voluntary winding-up / Michael Crystal, John-Higham. – 2nd ed. – Bristol : Jordan, 1981.
xxviii,219p; 23cm.
Previous ed.: 1972. Includes index.
ISBN 085308064X £10.50

Loose, Peter
Loose on liquidators : the role of a liquidator in a voluntary winding-up / Michael Crystal, John-Higham. – 2nd ed. – Bristol : Jordan, 1981.
xxviii,219p; 23cm.
Previous ed.: 1972. Includes index.
ISBN 085308064X £10.50

Looseleaf service → Government Assistance for Canadian Business.

Loosemore, John
Employment Law Manual / Robert Parsons. – London : Sweet & Maxwell, 1988.
ISBN 0421370505 updat £85.00

Loots, P. C
Engineering and construction law : with illustrations and cases / P.C. Loots. – Cape Town : Juta, 1985.
xxxv, 431 p.; 26 cm.
'Being a commentary on the General conditions of contract for works of civil engineering construction (fifth edition) 1982.'. Includes indexes.
ISBN 0702115630

Lopez-Rey, Manuel
Guide to United Nations criminal policy / Manuel Lopez-Rey. – Aldershot : Gower, 1985.
xi,142p; 23cm.
Includes index.
ISBN 0566050706 £15.00

Lord
Modern Law Review. – London : Sweet & Maxwell.
Hbk £22.50

Lord Atkin. – London : Butterworths, 1984.
ISBN 0406272107 Hbk £18.50

Lord Chancellor's Department
Judicial Statistics Annual Report 1983. – Lord Chancellor's Department. – London : HMSO, 1984.
ISBN 0101937008 Hbk £9.10

Lord Chancellor's review of civil justice in England and Wales : personal injury litigation : a consumer response / National Consumer Council. – London : National Consumer Council, 1986.
38p.
At head to t.p.: Personal injury litigation.

Lord Denning : the judge and the law / edited by J.L. Jowell, J.P.W.B. McAuslan. – London : Sweet & Maxwell, 1984.
xxxv,486p; 26cm.
Bibliography: p477-478. - Includes index.
ISBN 0421281200 £25.00

Lord justice : a journal of the Law Students' Society, University of Ibadan. – Ibadan, Nigeria : Law Students' Society, University of Ibadan, 1987.

Lord, R.
Controlled Drugs Law and Practice. – London : Butterworths, 1984.
ISBN 0406016100 Pbk £20.95

Lord Reading : Rufus Isaacs, First Marquess of Reading, Lord Chief Justice and Viceroy of India, 1860-1935 / Denis Judd. – London : Weidenfeld and Nicolson, 1982.
x,316p.
Bibliography: p303-307.
ISBN 029778014X

Lordon
Foundations of Canadian Law / Bradford W Morse. – Toronto : Butterworths, 1987.
ISBN 0409811513 Hbk

Loree, Donald J. → Community policing in the 1980's : recent advances in police programs.

Lorenz, T.
Venture capital today. – Cambridge : Woodhead-Faulkner, 1985.
ISBN 085941275X Hbk £30.00

Los, M.W.
Communist Ideology Law and Crime. – London : Macmillan, 1988.
ISBN 0333421078 Hbk £35.00

Los, Maria
Welfare and justice / Maria Los. – Sheffield : Centre for Criminological and Socio-Legal Studies, 1982.
136p.
Bibliography: p.130-136.

Losing the fight against crime / Richard Kinsey, John Leo, Jock Young. – Oxford : Basil Blackwell, 1986.
viii,221p; 23cm.
Bibliography: p216-218. - Includes index.
ISBN 063113719X Hbk £22.50
ISBN 0631137211 Pbk £6.95

Loss, Louis
Trends in corporate governance and investor protection / by Louis Loss. – Lagos : Lagos University Press, 1981.
64p.
Includes bibliographies.
ISBN 9782264261

Loss of the 'City of Boston' : Inman v. Jenkins : an action for libel, tried at the Liverpool Assizes, before Mr. Justice Lush amd a special jury, on Tuesday and Wednesday, August 30th and 31st, 1870 / Benjamin George Jenkins. – Liverpool : Reported and printed by Lee and Nightingale, 1870.
85p.

Lost causes. – Secker & Warburg, 1982.
ISBN 0436105810 Hbk £8.50

Lotteries and Gaming - Voluntary Organisations and the Law. – NCVO. – London : Bedford Square Press, 1981.
ISBN 0719910706 Pbk £1.95

Lotz, J. → Policies with regard to grants to local authorities.

Loughlin, Martin
Local government in the modern states / by Martin Loughlin. – London : Sweet & Maxwell, 1986.
xxv,222p; 23cm.
Bibliography: p202-217. - Includes index.
ISBN 0421338601 Hbk £13.50
ISBN 0421338709 Pbk £12.50
—Local government, the law and the constitution / Martin Loughlin. – s.l. : Local Government Legal Society Trust, 1983.
ii,143p.
—Local needs policies and development control strategies : an examination of the role of occupancy restrictions in development control / Martin Loughlin. – Bristol : University of Bristol, School for Advanced Urban Studies, 1984.
107p; 30cm. – (WP).
ISBN 0862921554

Lousanoff, Oleg de
Facilitations of Proof in Medical Malpractice Cases : a Comparative Analysis of American and German Law. – Bern : Peter Lang, 1981.
approx 140p.
ISBN 3820470042 Pbk £31.00

Louw, K. V. →Golding: The law and practice of reinsurance.

Loval Government and Environmental Planning Law in New South Wales. – North Ryde : Law Book Co, 1981.
xvi, 174p.
ISBN 045520361X Pbk £28.50

Lovelass, P.
Law's Disposal of a Person's Estate Who Dies Without Will or Testament : The Disposal of Estates of Will, Form of Wills, and Directions for Executors etc. – 10th ed. Repr. of 1809 ed. – Abingdon : Professional Books.
492p.
Hbk £60.00

Lovelock, Douglas →Review of the National Association of Citizens Advice Bureaux.

Loveridge, J W →Textbook of commerce.

Low Pay and Poverty in the United Kingdom. – London : Policy Studies Institute, 1981.
Hbk £3.50

Low pay check : reforming the Truck Acts / Dominic Byrne. – London : Low Pay Unit, 1983.
24p.

Low Pay or No Pay? A Review of the Theory and Practice of Minimum-Wage Laws / S. R. Dennison. – London : Institute of Economic Affairs, 1984.
ISBN 0255361750 Pbk £2.50

Low Pay Unit
Who needs the wages councils?. – Low Pay Unit. – London : Low Pay Unit, 1983.
56p. – (Low pay unit publication).
Bibliography: p54.

Low, S.
Government of England. – Repr. of 1904 ed. – Abingdon : Professional Books.
220p.
Hbk £25.00

Low Wages, Family Circumstances and Minimum Wage Legislation. – London : Policy Studies Institute, 1985.
97p. – (Family Income Support Part 10).
Hbk £3.50

Lowder, Stella
Inside Third World cities / Stella Lowder. – London : Routledge, 1988.
xii,292p.
Originally published: London : Croom Helm, 1986.
Bibliography: pp.270-286. - Includes index.
ISBN 0415027756

Lowe →Ins and outs of immigration and nationality law.

Lowe, A. V.
Extraterritorial jurisdiction : an annotated collection of legal materials / by A.V. Lowe. – Cambridge : Grotius Publications, 1983.
xxiii,273p.
Bibliography: p.269-270. - Includes index.
ISBN 0906496357
→ Law of the sea.

Lowe, J. F.
Total environment control : the economics of cross-media pollution transfers / by Julian Lowe, David Lewis and Martin Atkins. – Oxford : Pergamon, 1982.
viii,126p; 23cm.
Includes index.
ISBN 0080262767 Pbk £10.95

Lowe, N. V. →Borrie and Lowe's Law of contempt.
→ Family law.
—Wards of court / N. V. Lowe and R. A. H. White. – 2nd ed. – London : Barry Rose, part of Kluwer Law Publishers, 1986.
xxviii,388p; 23cm.
→ White, Carr and Lowe: a guide to the Children Act 1989.

Lowe, Philip
Environmental groups in politics / Philip Lowe & Jane Goyder with additional contributions from Richard Bate, Sarah Buchanan and John McBride. – London : Allen & Unwin, 1983.
xii,208p; 24cm.
Bibliography: p186-197. - Includes index.
ISBN 0043290434 Hbk £
ISBN 0043290442 Pbk

Lowe, R.
Commercial law / by Robert Lowe. – 6th ed. – London : Sweet & Maxwell, 1983.
xlvi,578p; 23cm.
Previous ed.: 1976. Includes index.
ISBN 0421298707 Hbk £21.50
ISBN 0421298804 Pbk £14.50
—Consumer law and practice / by Robert Lowe and Geoffrey F. Woodroffe. – 2nd ed. – London : Sweet and Maxwell, 1985.
400p.
Includes the Supply of Goods and Services Act 1982, and explains the Consumer Credit Act 1974 regulations. Deals with the consumer and civil law, the consumer and the criminal law, fair trading, consumer credit, the EEC dimension, and selected codes of practice.
ISBN 0421334002 Hbk £17.75
ISBN 042133410X Pbk £14.00

Lowenfeld, A.F.
International monetary system. – 2nd ed. – Matthew Bender, 1984.
ISBN 0000999050 Hbk £26.50

Lowenfeld, A.T.
International private trade. – 2nd ed. – Matthew Bender, 1981.
ISBN 0000999048 Hbk £26.50

Low-income housing in the developing world : the role of sites and services and settlement upgrading / Geoffrey K. Payne. – Chichester : Wiley, 1984.
xii,271p; 25cm. – (A Wiley series on public administration in developing countries).
Includes bibliographies and index.
ISBN 0471902128 £29.95

Lowman, John →Transcarceration : essays in the sociology of social control.

Lowndes
Law Of General Average and York-Antwerp Rules (BSL) / Rudolf. – Sweet & Maxwell.
ISBN 0420429808 Hbk £75.00

Lowry, John
Fiduciary duties of directors : a review / John Lowry. – London : Thames Polytechnic School of Business Administration, 1984.

Lowry, Robert Lynd Erskine
Civil proceedings in a beleaguered society : a public lecture / delivered by Lord Lowry on ... 17th March 1987. – London : Inns of Court School of Law, 1987.
23p.

Luard, Evan
Economic relationships among states : a further study in international sociology / Evan Luard. – London : Macmillan, 1984.
xiii,328p.
ISBN 0333294777
—History of the United Nations Volume 2 : The Age of Decolonization 1955-65. – London : Macmillan.
ISBN 00333244249 Hbk £35.00
—Human rights and foreign policy / Evan Luard. – S.l. : s.n., 1986.
p.579-606.
Photocopy from: International affairs, vol. 56, no. 4 (Autumn 1980).
—War in international society : a study in international sociology / Evan Luard. – London : Tauris, 1986.
468p.
Includes bibliographical references and index.
ISBN 1850430128 £24.50

Luba, Jan
Defending possession proceedings / Jan Luba, Nic Madge, and Derek McConnell. – London : Legal Action Group, 1987.
xlvi,229p.
ISBN 090509915X Pbk £14
—Repairs : tenants' rights. – London : Legal Action Group, 1986.
ISBN 0905099133 Pbk £11.00
—Rights guide to non means tested benefits / Rowlands. – London : Central Books, 1988/89.
ISBN 0946744092 Pbk £4.50

Lubbe, G.F. →Law of Damages.

Lucan : Not Guilty. – London : Fontana.
ISBN 0006373666 Pbk £3.95

Lucas →Law Unit : Torts.

Lucas, Alastair R.
Canadian Electricity Exports : Legal and Regulatory Issues / J. Owen Saunders. – Calgary : Canadian Institute of Resources Law.
40p.
Hbk £9.50
→ Canadian Environmental Law, 7 Vols.
→ Environmental Law in the 1980s : a New Beginning.
→ Environmental Regulation : Its Impact on Major Oil and Gas Projects.
→ Handbook on the Conduct of Public Inquiries in Canada.

Lucey, T.
ACCA Study and Revision Manual : 1.2 Cost and Management Accounting 1. – London : BPP.
ISBN 0905435745 Pbk £9.95
—Cost and Management Accounting 2 : ACCA Study and Revision Manual Level 2.4. – London : BPP.
ISBN 1870941071 Pbk £9.95

Luciani, Giacomo
Oil companies and the Arab world / Giacomo Luciani. – London : Croom Helm, 1984.
197p; 23cm.
Includes index. Re translation of: Compagnie petrolifere e paesi arabi.
ISBN 0709916191 £15.95
ISBN 0312582765

Luckham, Robin →Law and social enquiry : case studies of research.
→ Political economy of law : a third world reader.

Ludlow, Bob →Unemployment Insurance.

Ludlow, Michael R.
Fair charges? : a review of controls over solicitors' costs / by M.R. Ludlow. – London : Waterlow Publishers, 1982.
x,64p.
ISBN 0900791802 Pbk £4.50

Luhmann, N.
Sociological theory of law. – Routledge, 1985.
ISBN 0710097476 Hbk £32.50

Luithi, Luingam
Nagaland File : A Question of Human Rights / Nandita Haksar. – New Delhi : Lancer International, 1984.
277p.
Hbk £115.00

Luke, George
It's All Quite Legal. – Butterworths, 1982.
48p.
ISBN 0409491500 Pbk £21.50

Lukes, Steven →Rationality and relativism.
→ Rules of sociological method and selected texts on sociology and its method.

Luluaki, John →Principles of family law in Papua New Guinea.

Lumb, R D
Australian Constitutionalism. – London : Butterworths, 1983.
ISBN 0409493104 Pbk £20.00
—Constitution of the Commonwealth of Australia / K.W. Ryan. – 4th ed. – Butterworths, 1986.
441p.
ISBN 0409491284 Hbk £59.00
ISBN 0409491292 Pbk £48.00
—Constitution of the Commonwealth of Australia annotated / by R.D. Lumb and K.W. Ryan. – 3rd ed. – Sydney : Butterworths, 1981.
xxiv, 426 p.; 25 cm.
Includes index. Bibliography: p. 405-410.
ISBN 0409300225 Pbk £42.00
—New bearings in the law of the sea : inaugural lecture delivered at the University of Queensland, 29 April 1981 / R.D. Lumb. – St. Lucia, Queensland : University of Queensland Press, 1982.
ISBN 0702216798 Pbk

Lundberg, T.
Starting in business. – Cambridge : Woodhead-Faulkner, 1985.
ISBN 0959412954 Pbk £6.95

Lundvik, Ulf
Ombudsmen in the provinces of Canada / by Ulf Lundvik. – Edmonton? : International Ombudsman Institute, 1981.
103p.
—Swedish Parliamentary Ombudsmen / Ulf Lundvik. – Stockholm : JO, 1982.
29p.
Bibliography: p.29.

Lunn, R.M.
Civil Procedure, South Australia. – Butterworths, 1987.
ISBN 0409492396 Llf £235.00

Luntz, Harold
Assessment of Damages for Personal Injury and Death. – 2nd ed. – London : Butterworths, 1983.
ISBN 0409491322 Hbk £48.00
—Torts : Cases and Commentary / D Hambly. – 2nd ed. – London : Butterworths.
ISBN 0409493506 Hbk £38.90

Lussier, Jean-Pierre →On Criminal Procedure.

Lust to kill : a feminist investigation of sexual murder / Deborah Cameron and Elizabeth Frazer. – Cambridge : Polity in association with Basil Blackwell, 1987.
xv,207p; 22cm.
Bibliography: p195-203. - Includes index.
ISBN 0745603351 Hbk £25.00
ISBN 074560336X Pbk £7.95

Lustgarten, Laurence
Governance of police / Laurence Lustgarten. – London : Sweet & Maxwell, 1986.
xv,197p; 23cm. – (Modern legal studies).
Bibliography: p183-190. - Includes index.
ISBN 0421319003 Hbk £17.00
ISBN 0421319100 Pbk £9.95

Lutter, Marcus →Forum Internationale.
—Law of Groups of Companies in Europe : a Challenge for Jurisprudence. – Dordrecht : Kluwer, 1984.
ISBN 9065441654 Pbk £25.00

Luxford, J. H.
Commercial law of New Zealand / by J.H. Luxford. – 2nd ed., rev. and enl. 6. – Wellington : Butterworths, 1961-.
loose-leaf.
Last supplement issued: Oct. 1974. - Kept up to date by Butterworths current law, No 1974-. Includes index.

Lyall, Francis
Air, noise, water and waste : a summary of the law in Scotland / by Francil Lyall. – Glasgow : Planning Exchange, 1982.
vii,195p; 21cm.
Includes index.
ISBN 0905011198 Pbk

Lybrand →Company Car Tax Guide 1988-89.
→ Form and Content of Company Accounts.

Lynch, T
Taxation of woodlands in the UK. – Edinburgh : Green (W.) & Son, 1989.
Traces the history and development of the special tax system for woodlands including changes in the income tax provision since April 1988. Covers transitional provision for income tax to 5 April 1993 with relevant statutory provisions and case law on the definition of what constitutes the management of commercial woodlands relative to income tax questions.
ISBN 0414008952 Hbk

Lynes, Tony
Penguin guide to supplementary benefits : supplementary benefits, the new regulations, the family income supplement and the appeals tribunal / Tony Lynes. – 4th ed. – Harmondsworth : Penguin, 1981.
319p; 18cm.
Previous ed.: 1975. Includes index. .
ISBN 0140464239 Pbk £2.50

Lyon, Christina M. →Cohabitation without marriage : an essay in law and social policy.
→ Journal of Social Welfare Law.
→ Law of residential homes and day-care establishments.

Lyon, Noel
Aboriginal Self-Government : Rights of Citizenship and Access to Governmental Services. – Kingston : Queen's University, Institute of Intergovernmental Relations, 70p.
ISBN 0889114226 Hbk £12.00

Lyon, Robert →Ordinances, laws and proclamations.

Lyon, T. →Tax Benefits and Family Finance.

Lyons, David
Ethics and the rule of law / David Lyons. – Cambridge : Cambridge University Press, 1984.
x,229p; 21m.
Bibliography: p220-226. - Includes index.
ISBN 0521257859 Hbk £17.50
ISBN 0521277124 Pbk £4.95

Lyons, Timothy J
Chapman's Inheritance Tax Supplement. – London : Longman Professional.
ISBN 00851214673 Hbk £20.00
—Insolvency : law and taxation / Timothy J. Lyons. – 1st ed. – London : Longman Professional (UK), 1988.
– (Law and Taxation).
Examines legal aspects and tax implications of both company and partnership insolvency. Chapters deal with the enforcement powers of the Inland Revenue and tax planning opportunities prior to and during an insolvency. Contains worked examples, precedents, forms and non-statutory material.
ISBN 0851214193 Hbk £35

Lysaght →Administration of Justice in Ireland.

Lyster, Simon
International wildlife law : an analysis of international treaties concerned with the conservation of wildlife / by Simon Lyster. – Cambridge : Grotius Publications, 1985.
xxiii,470p.
Covers the international conventions on whaling, wetlands, protection of cultural and natural heritage, international trade in endangered species, and Antarctic marine living resources.
ISBN 0906496225

Lytton
Prisons and Prisoners / Warton. – New Edition. – Virago.
ISBN 0860686825 Pbk £6.95

M.R.T.P. Act. Annotated Edition 1985. – Calcutta : R. Cambray and Company.
Hbk £140.00

Maas, Robert
Fringe benefits : a specially commissioned report / by Robert Maas. – 3rd ed. – London : Oyez Longman, 1984.
xvii,111 leaves; 30cm. – (Oyez Longman intelligence reports).
ISBN 0851209262 spiral

Maas, Robert W.
Development land tax / by Robert W. Maas. – 4th ed. – Croydon : Tolley, 1982.
xiii,244p; 23cm.
Previous ed.: 1981. Includes index.
ISBN 0854590560 Pbk £10.50
—Tax minimisation techniques : a specially commissioned report / by R.W. Maas. – London : Oyez Longman, 1984.
xi,102leaves; 30cm. – (Oyez Longman intelligence reports).
Previous ed.: 1982.
ISBN 0851209300 spiral £45.00
—Tolley's Property Taxes. – 2nd ed. – Tolley Publishing.
ISBN 0854593268 Hbk £19.95

Mabbett, Hugh →Chinese in Indonesia, the Philippines and Malaysia.

Mabbett, Ping-ching →Chinese in Indonesia, the Philippines and Malaysia.

MacAdam, Alastair
Statutes : Rules and Examples / Thomas M. Smith. – 2nd ed. – Butterworths, 1989.
ca 288p.
This book is designed to teach students how to read and understand statutes and how to apply them to specific sets of circumstances. It describes specific principles and illustrates them with extracts from appropriate cases.
ISBN 040949397X Pbk £39.00

Macalister-Smith, Peter
International humanitarian assistance : disaster relief actions in international law and organization / Peter Macalister-Smith. – Hague : M. Nijhoff Publishers, 1985.
260p.
ISBN 9024729939 Hbk £130.00

McAllister
World accounting / Orsini. – Matthew Bender, 1986.
ISBN 0000999081 Hbk £100.00

McAllister, A.
Introduction to the Scottish Law of Leases. – London : Butterworths, 1988.
ISBN 0406105898 Pbk

McAllister, Debra M
Mareva Injunctions. – 2nd ed. – Agincourt : Carswell, 1987.
This work presents the history and current legal status of the Canadian Mareva Injunction. Procedural issues involved in obtaining and enforcing this unique remedy are reviewed in the book.
ISBN 045939780 Hbk £16.75

McAllister, Richard →Draft Treaty establishing the European Union : report on the United Kingdom.

Mcardle, A.D.
International Ship Arrest : A Practical Guide. – London : Lloyd's of London Press.
ISBN 1850441901 Hbk £40.00

McAteer, Willie
Income tax / by Willie McAteer & George Reddin. – Dublin : Institute of Taxation in Ireland, 1981.
331p; 25cm.
Includes index.

Macaulay, Robert →Land use planning.
→ Land Use Planning : Practice Procedure and Policy.

McAuslan, J. P. W. B. →Law, legitimacy and the constitution : essays marking the centenary of Dicey's Law of the Constitution.
→ Lord Denning : the judge and the law.
—Representation, Democracy and Public Law. – London : Sweet & Maxwell, 1985.
– (Modern Legal Studies Ser.).
Hbk £19.50

McBarnet, Doreen J
Conviction : law, the State and the construction of justice / by Doreen J. McBarnet. – London : Macmillan, 1981.
vii,182p.
ISBN 0333255364

MacBean, Alasdair I.
International institutions in trade and finance / A.I. MacBean and P.N. Snowden. – London : Allen & Unwin, 1981.
xiv,255p; 23cm.
Bibliography: p249-252. - Includes index.
ISBN 0043820328 Hbk
ISBN 0043820336 Pbk

McBean, Jean
Marriage and Family Law in Alberta : the Rights of Husbands, Wives, Children, and Common-Law. – 3rd ed. – North Vancouver : International Self-Counsel Press, 1987.
203p.
ISBN 0889082456 Hbk £8.95

McBride, Tim
Police powers and the rights of suspects / by Tim McBride. – Auckland : Legal Research Foundation, 1982.
23,8,5p.
'Paper presented at Auckland Law Faculty seminar series 1982 at University of Auckland'.
ISBN 0908581246

McBrien, J. P. →Building society law : cases and materials.

McBryde, William
Bankruptcy. – Edinburgh : Green (W.) & Son, 1989.
Commentary on the law and practice of bankruptcy since the Bankruptcy (Scotland) Act 1985. Includes the text of the Act with subsequent amendments.
ISBN 0414008944 Hbk
—Law of contract in Scotland. – Edinburgh : Green (W.) & Son, 1987.
The most comprehensive analysis of the practical and theoretical aspects of contract law since Gloag on Contract in 1929. Practical guidance is also provided on drafting some of the commonly found contract clauses.
ISBN 041400793X Hbk
—Petition procedure in the Court of Session / Norman Dowrie. – 2nd. – Edinburgh : Green (W.) & Son, 1988.
Enlarged version of the first edition, substantially rewritten In the light of the considerable changes in Court of Session practice, particularly in the areas of family law, insolvency and judicial review. Provides a step by step approach to all the types of petition encountered in practice with descriptions of the miscellaneous procedures including appeals. New chapters deal with adoptions, children and applications under the Matrimonial Homes Act.
ISBN 0414008316 Pbk

McCabe, Sarah
Juvenile justice in the United Kingdom : comparisons and suggestions for change / Sarah McCabe and Phyllis Treitel. – London : New Approaches to Juvenile Crime, 1983.
81p.
Includes bibliographical references.
ISBN 0950929905

McCaffray, Charles
Index to Sheriff Court districts of Scotland. – Edinburgh : Green (W.) & Son, 1981.
Lists alphabetically each Scottish city, town, village and hamlet giving the appropriate sheriffdom and sheriff court for the place.
ISBN 0414006666 Pbk

McCall-Smith →Law and Medical Ethics.

MacCallum, Susan V. →Residential tenancy law and practice.

McCamus, John D
Freedom of Information : Canadian Perspectives. – London : Butterworths.
ISBN 0409857130 Hbk £60.00

McCarroll, Joseph
Marriage or Divorce : the Real Issue. – Dublin : Four Courts Press.
128p.
Hbk £8.95

McCarry, G.J.
Digest of Industrial and Labour Law Cases. – Woolloomooloo : International Business Communications, 1983.
430p.
Hbk £34.00
—Digest of Industrial Labour Law Cases. – 1st ed. – London : Legal Books, 1983.
ISBN 0949553013 Hbk £20.00
ISBN 0949553018 Pbk £15.00

McCarthy
Older Offenders : Perspectives, Criminology, Criminal Justice / Langworthy. – Praeger.
ISBN 0275927342 Hbk £36.95

McCarthy, W. E. J. →Future of labour law : two views.
→ Trade unions : selected readings.

McClean, J. D.
Hague Convention on International Access to Justice : Explanatory Documentation Prepared for Commonwealth Jurisdictions. – London : Commonwealth Secretariat, 1982.
ISBN 085092216X Hbk £4.00

McClean, John David
Hague Convention on the Taking of Evidence Abroad : explanatory documentation prepared for Commonwealth jurisdicitons / by David McClean and Campbell McLachlan : in association with the Commonwealth Secretariat. – Revised. – London : Commonwealth Secretariat (Legal Division), 1986.
30,16p.
Includes the text of the Convention.
ISBN 0850922879
—International conventions concerning applications for and awards of maintenance : explanatory documentation / prepared for Commonwealth Jurisdictions by David McClean in association with the Commonwealth Secretariat. – London : Commonwealth Secretariat, 1981.
v,83p.
ISBN 0850922003

—Recognition of family judgments in the Commonwealth / J.D. McClean. – London : Butterworths, 1983.
xxxvii,370p; 26cm.
Includes index.
ISBN 040640321X Hbk £42.00

McClenaghan, J.
Casebook on Compulsory Purchase and Compensation. – Oxford : Blackwell Scientific, 1988.
ISBN 0003834085 Hbk £35.00

McClintock, F. H.
Prosecution of the Mentally Disturbed / D. Chiswick. – Aberdeen : Aberdeen University Press, 1984.
192p.
ISBN 0080284817 Hbk £16.50

McClure, James
Cop World. – London : Macmillan, 1984.
352p.
ISBN 0333306880 Hbk £12.95

McCluskey, John Herbert McCluskey
Law, justice and democracy / Lord McCluskey. – London : Sweet & Maxwell, 1987.
116p; 21cm.
Includes index.
ISBN 0421378905 Hbk £9.95
ISBN 0563205490 Pbk £5.95

McColl, Miles
Family Law Journal / Elizabeth Walsh. – Bristol : Jordan & Sons Ltd, 1986.
Hbk £37.50

McComas, William Robert
Protection of trade secrets : a general guide / W.R. McComas, Mark R. Davison, David M. Gonski. – Sydney : Butterworths, 1981.
xiv,98p.
ISBN 0409300284 Hbk £48

McConnell
Senate, the Courts and the Constitution : a Debate / Tribe. – London : Eurospan.
ISBN 0944237223 Pbk £8.50

McConnell, Derek →Defending possession proceedings.

McConnell, John
U.S. Shipping Act of 1984 / by John McConnell. – London : Lloyd's of London, 1985.
345p; 25cm.
ISBN 1850440360 £38.00

McConville →Islamic Criminal Law and Procedure : An Introduction.

McConville, Michael
Courts, prosecution, and conviction / by Michael McConville and John Baldwin. – Oxford : Clarendon, 1981.
232p; 23cm.
Bibliography: p213-226. - Includes index.
ISBN 0198253559 £12.00

McConville, Sean
History of English prison administration Vol.1 : 1750-1877 / Sean McConville. – London : Routledge & Kegan Paul, 1981.
xvii,534p; 23cm.
Bibliography: p483-505. - Includes index.
ISBN 0710006942 £25.00

McCormack, G. →Ejectment for non-payment of rent.

McCormack, M.H.
Terrible Truth About Lawyers. – New Edition. – London : Fontana.
ISBN 0006372694 Pbk £3.95

MacCormick
Legal Mind - Essays For Tony Honore / Birks. – Oxford : Oxford University Press, 1986.
ISBN 0198761961 Hbk £35.00

MacCormick, Neil →Conditions of validity and cognition in modern legal thought.
—H.L.A. Hart / Neil MacCormick. – London : Edward Arnold, 1981.
184p; 22cm.
Includes index.
ISBN 071316333X Hbk £
ISBN 0713163348 Pbk £4.95
—Institutional theory of law : new approaches to legal positivism / Neil MacCormick and Ota Weinberger. – DordrechtHolland : Reidel, 1986.
xiv, 229p. – (Law and philosophy library).
ISBN 9027720797
→ Legal mind : essays for Tony Honore.
—Legal right and social democracy : essays in legal and political philosophy / Neil MacCormick. – Oxford : Clarendon, 1982.
viii,272p; 23cm.
Includes index.
ISBN 0198253850 £17.50
—Legal Right and Social Democracy-Essays. – Oxford : Oxford University Press, 1984.
ISBN 0198255020 Pbk £9.95

McCormick, Roger →Hybrid corporate securities : international legal aspects.

McCorquodale, J.
Aborigines and the Law. – Canberra City : Australian Institute of Aboriginal Studies, 1987.
ISBN 0855751738 Pbk £44.95

McCoubrey, H.
Effective Planning Appeals. – Oxford : Blackwell Scientific, 1988.
ISBN 0632021241 Hbk

McCoy, Gerard →Criminal Evidence in Hong Kong.
→ Law of Evidence in Criminal Trials in Hong Kong.

McCracken, S.A. →Financial Institutions Law.

McCredie, L.
Administration of the Estates of Deceased Persons in Victoria. – 2nd ed. – Sydney : Butterworths, 1988.
288p.
Hbk £54.00
—Wills, Probate and the Administration of the Estates of Deceased Persons in Victoria. – 2nd ed. – Butterworths, 1988.
272p.
ISBN 0409494747 Hbk £54.00
ISBN 0409338613 Pbk £35.00

McCrudden, Christopher →Regulation and public law.

McCune, D. Thomas
Asbatankvoy charter : a special report / by D. Thomas McCune. – London : Lloyd's of London Press, 1984.
ii,95 leaves.
Includes indexes.
ISBN 1850440336

McCutcheon, Barry D.
Capital transfer tax / by Barry D. McCutcheon. – 2nd ed. 2. – London : Sweet & Maxwell, 1984.
26cm.
Previous ed.: published as Understanding and planning for capital transfer tax. Maidenhead : McGraw-Hill, 1980.
ISBN 042131950X £80.00
—Inheritance tax. – 3rd ed. – London : Sweet & Maxwell, 1988.
ISBN 042139790X Pbk £110.00
—McCutcheon on Inheritance Tax. – 3rd ed. – Sweet & Maxwell.
ISBN 042139790X Hbk £75.00
—Tax Planning Through Inheritance Trusts. – London : Oyez Longman, 1983.
– (Oyez Longman Intelligence Report Ser.).
ISBN 0851208193 Hbk £45.00

McCutcheon, J P →Irish Legal System : Cases and Materials.
—Larceny Act, 1916. – Dublin : Round Hall Press, 1988.
ca 156p.
ISBN 0947686185 Hbk £17.50

McDaniel, Paul R →International aspects of tax expenditures : a comparative study.
—Introduction to United States international taxation / by Paul R. McDaniel, Hugh J. Ault. – 2nd rev. ed. – Deventer : Kluwer, 1981.
209p; 25cm.
Previous ed.: 1977. Includes index.
ISBN 9065440046

McDermott, Paul →Prisoners' rights : a study in Irish prison law.

McDonald, A J
Conveyancing manual. – 4th. – Edinburgh : Clark (T. & T.) Ltd.
Primarily a student manual written by a former Professor of Conveyancing at Dundee University. Covers, in six parts, preliminary matters, feus, resulting rights of superior and vassal, subordinate rites in the feu - securities and leases, transmission of the feu, and reform.
ISBN 0567291715 Pbk

McDonald, B. R.
Life Insurance Laws of Canada / Genevieve Faribault. – Don Mills : Life Underwriters Association of Canada, 1985.
ISBN 0919361757 Hbk £15.95

McDonald, D. C. →Certain R.C.M.P. activities and the question of governmental knowledge : third report.
→ Freedom and security under the law : second report.
—Legal rights in the Canadian Charter of Rights and Freedoms : a manual of issues and sources / David C. McDonald. – Toronto : Carswell, 1982.
xxv,275p.
Includes index.

Macdonald, Hugh R M
Guide to Family Law (Scotland) Act 1985. – London : CCH, 1986.
ISBN 0863250629 Pbk £9.00
—Guide to the Family Law (Scotland) Act 1985. – Bicester : CCH Editions Ltd, 1986.
vi,118p.
Includes the full text of the Act and of the new Rules of Court. Contains useful illustrations of how the principles will operate in practice. Covers obligations of aliment, actions for aliment, financial provisions on divorce, orders for financial provisions on divorce, nullity, agreements on aliment and financial provisions, and matrimonial property.
ISBN 0863250629 Pbk £9.00
ISBN 0863250807 Hbk

Macdonald, Ian A.
Immigration law and practice in the United Kingdom / Ian A. Macdonald. – 2nd ed. – London : Butterworths, 1987.
560p; 25cm.
Previous ed.: 1983. Includes index.
ISBN 0406283141 £50.55
—New nationality law / Ian A. Macdonald and Nicholas Blake. – London : Butterworths, 1982.
208p; 26cm.
This book provides a thorough discussion of the British Nationality Act of 1981. The three new categories of citizenship: British Citizenship, Citizenship of the British Dependent Territories, and British Overseas Citizenship are analyzed in detail.
ISBN 0406282803 Hbk £21.50

MacDonald, James C.
Canadian divorce law and practice / Lee K. Ferrier. – 2nd ed. – Toronto : Carswell, 1986.
Includes text of Divorce Act 1985.
ISBN 0459389505 Llf
—Law and Practice Under the Family Law Act of Ontario. – Revised Edit. – Agincourt : Carswell, 1986.
This looseleaf work provides analysis of the Family Law Act of Ontario for the practitioner, along with summaries of relevant case law. Problems in preparation and drafting of domestic documents are discussed in the work, as well as, income tax implications and the valuation of family property.
Llf £75.75

Macdonald, John →Administration of the courts : JUSTICE.

McDonald, Kevan
Onshore oil and gas pipelines : the problems / by Kevan MacDonald. – Dundee : University of Dundee, Centre for Petroleum and Mineral Studies, 1981.
xiii,102p. – (Occasional paper).

McDonald, M. →Writers and the Law.

McDonald, M.J. →You and the Law.

McDonald, Marc
Irish law of defamation / Marc McDonald : with a foreword by Thomas A. Finlay. – Dublin : Round Hall in association with Irish Academic Press, 1987.
xx,304p; 24cm.
Includes index.
ISBN 0947686150 £30.00

Macdonald, P.V.
Canada's Lawyers Take Stand & Relate Their Funniest Stories. – London : Lavis Marketing.
ISBN 0458808903 Pbk £5.50

Macdonald, Robert
Maori of New Zealand / by Robert Macdonald. – London : Minority Rights Group, 1985.
16p. – (Report).
Bibliography: p.16.
ISBN 0946690367

McDonald, Robert P.
International syndicated loans / by Robert P. McDonald. – London : Euromoney, 1982.
ix,264p.
Bibliography: p.261-262. - Includes index.
ISBN 0903121441

MacDonald, Ronald →International money : theory, evidence and institutions.

MacDonald, Ronald St. J. →On F.R. Scott : Essays on His Contributions to Law, Literature, and Politics.
—Structure and Process of International Law : Essays in Legal Philosophy, Doctrine and Theory / Douglas M. Johnston. – Dordrecht : Kluwer, 1986.
1,234p.
ISBN 9024732735 Pbk £175.00

McDonnell, Marie-Louise
Nigerian Commercial Law Reports : 1966 to date. – London : Sweet & Maxwell.
Hbk £90.00

McDonough, Brian G. →Maritime liens and claims.

McDonough, Darryl
Annotated Takeovers Code. – North Ryde : Law Book Co, 1987.
ca 250p.
Pbk £49.50

McDorman, Ted L. →Marine environment and the Caracas Convention on the Law of the Sea : a study of the Third United Nations Conference on the Law of the Sea and other Related Marine Environmental Activities.
—Maritime boundary delimitation : an annotated bibliography / Ted L. McDorman, Kenneth P. Beauchamp, Douglas M. Johnston. – Lexington, Mass. : Lexington Books, 1983.
xiii,207p; 24cm.
Includes index.
ISBN 0669061468

McDougal, Myres S.
Public Order of the Oceans : a Contemporary International Law of the Sea / William T. Burke. – Dordrecht : Kluwer, 1987.
1,300p.
ISBN 0898389011 Hbk £400.00

McDougall, A.
Institute of the Laws of Scotland in Civil Rights with Observations upon the Agreement or Diversity Between Them and the Laws of England, 3 Vols. – Repr. of 1753 ed. – Abingdon : Professional Books.
Hbk £75.00

MacDougall, D. J., et al
Family Law Review : 1981. – Vancouver : British Columbia Continuing Legal Education Society, 1981.
277p.
ISBN 0865040249 Hbk £50.00

McDougall, John N.
Fuels and the national policy / John N. McDougall. – Toronto : Butterworths, 1982.
vi,199p.
Bibliography: p188-194.

McDowall, David
Kurds / by David McDowall. – New ed. – London : Minority Rights Group, 1985.
32p. – (Report).
Previous ed.: by Martin Short and Anthony McDermott. 1981. Bibliography: p.24.
ISBN 094669026X
—Palestinians / by David McDowall. – New ed. – London : Minority Rights Group, 1987.
35p. – (Report).
Previous ed.: 1984. Includes bibliographical references.
ISBN 0946690421

MacEachern, Zandra →Subject Guide to Native Law Cases and Annotated Text of the Indian Act of Canada.

McEldowney, John F
Essays in Irish Legal History / Paul O'Higgins. – Dublin : Irish Academic Press, 1988.
ca 220p.
ISBN 0716523973 Hbk £27.50
→ Law, legitimacy and the constitution : essays marking the centenary of Dicey's Law of the Constitution.

MacEllven, Douglass T
Guide to purchasing law reports / Doug MacEllven, Guy Tanguay, Lorna K. Rees-Potter : edited by L.K. Rees-Potter. – Ottawa, Ont. : Canadian Law Information Council, 1985.
iv, 115 p.; 23 cm.
Includes index.
ISBN 0920358578
—Legal research handbook / Douglass T. MacEllven. – 2nd ed. – Toronto : Butterworths, 1986.
xxix,411p.
Guide to all current sources of Canadian law. Includes additional chapters on legal writing and government and social science publications. Quebec material has been augmented. Includes a master research checklist, subject area checklists, and examination of management of law firm libraries, computer assisted research, and indices of research centres and legal publishers.
ISBN 0409847798 Hbk £60
—Legal Research Handbook. – London : Butterworths, 1983.
ISBN 0409848298 Hbk £40.00

MacEwan, Grant
He Left Them Laughing When He Said Good-Bye : the Life and Times of Frontier Lawyer Paddy Nolan. – Saskatoon : Western Producer Prairie Books, 1987.
ISBN 0888332416 Pbk £12.95

McEwan, Jenny →Police powers and the individual.

McEwan, Robin Gilmour
Casebook on damages in Scotland / by Robin Gilmour McEwan and Ann Paton. – Edinburgh : Green, 1983.
xxiii,272p; 22cm.
Includes index.
ISBN 0414006984 Pbk
—McEwan and Paton on damages in Scotland / Ann Paton. – 2nd. – Edinburgh : Green (W.) & Son, 1989.
Chapters cover damages, provisional damages, interest, loss of earnings and employability, nervous shock, the unaware pursuer, nursing care, special aids, fatal cases, contributory negligence etc. and a review of awards. There is a full collection of recent Scottish decisions (including unreported) on solatium and loss of society, tables of multipliers, an inflation table, diagram of the skeleton. With relevant legislation and rules of court.
ISBN 0414008820 LOOSELEAF

MacEwen, Ann
National parks : conservation or cosmetics? / Ann and Malcolm MacEwen. – London : Allen & Unwin, 1982.
xxii,314p; 24cm.
Bibliography: p287-297. - Includes index.
ISBN 0047190035 Hbk £
ISBN 0047190043 Pbk £8.50

MacEwen, Malcolm →National parks : conservation or cosmetics?.

McFarlane, Bruce A.
Drug Offences in Canada. – 2nd ed. – Aurora : Canada Law Book Co, 1986.
800p. – (Text Books-Criminal).
This monograph is an important research tool for counsel involved in the prosecution or defense of substantive drug charges or drug conspiracies in Canada. The second edition is revised and reorganized to reflect the many judicial decisions delivered since the publication of the first edition, including a full review of the impact of the Canadian Charter of Rights and Freedoms.
Hbk £75.00

MacFarlane, Craig, et al
Land use planning / Robert Macaulay. – Scarborough, Ontario : Butterworths (Canada).
Survey of Ontario Municipal Board cases, precedents, pointers on the impact of the Charter of Rights, and relevant legislation, regulations, guidelines and interpretation bulletins. Covers planning authorities, provincial planning, official plans, zoning and development control, development levies and municipal finance, and the conduct of a planning application.
Llf
—Land Use Planning : Practice Procedure and Policy / Robert Macaulay. – Toronto : Butterworths.
Hbk

McFarlane, Gavin
Copyright through the cases. – London : Waterlow, 1986.
ISBN 0080392083 Pbk £15.00
—Customs & Excise Casebook. – London : Waterlow, 1987.
ISBN 0080392458 Hbk £50.00
—Layman's Dictionary of English Law. – London : Waterlow, 1984.
ISBN 0080391613 Hbk £12.95
—Practical introduction to copyright / Gavin McFarlane. – London : McGraw-Hill, 1982.
xiv,235p; 26cm.
Includes index.
ISBN 0070845697 £14.00

Macfarlane, L J
Theory and practice of human rights. – Smith (Maurice Temple), 1985.
ISBN 0851172563 Hbk £12.95

McFetridge, Donald G.
Canadian R & D incentives : their adequacy and impact / Donald G. McFetridge, Jacek P. Warda. – Toronto, Canada : Canadian Tax Foundation, 1983.
vii, 100 p.; 23 cm.
Includes index. Bibliography: p. 93-97.
ISBN 0888080131 Pbk £10.00

McGarvie, Richard Elgin →Report on criminal trials.

McGechan, R A →Law of Evidence.

McGee, Andrew →Insurance contract law.

Mcgee, R.W.
Accounting for Data Processing Costs. – Quorum Press.
ISBN 0899302149 Hbk £32.95

McGill Law Journal
Canadian Guide to Uniform Legal Citation. – McGill Law Journal. – 2nd ed. – Agincourt : Carswell, 1988.
288p.
Hbk £25.25

McGill, Stuart
Indigenous Resource Rights and Mining Companies in North America and Australia, February 1986 / G.J. Crough. – Kingston : Australian Government Publishing Service, 1986.
132p.
ISBN 0644046392 Hbk £7.60

McGill University
New Developments in Commercial Lending. – McGill University. – Toronto : DeBoo, 1981. – (Meredith Memorial Lecture Ser.).
ISBN 0888201095 Hbk £49.50

Macgillivray
Copyright Cases 1901-1949, 8 Vols. – London : Wildy & Sons.
Hbk £100.00

MacGillivray and Parkington on insurance law : relating to all risks other than marine / Michael Parkington. – 8th ed. – London : Sweet & Maxwell, 1988.
cxli,1014p.
Discusses legal aspects of the insurance contract and the insurance business. Includes a new chapter on Reinsurance, and looks at certain types of policy including those covering indemnity, personal accident, fire, motor vehicle and aviation, pecuniary loss and contractors' risk. Refers to North American decisions and to Scots law.
ISBN 0421354801 £90.00

MacGillivray, E. J.
MacGillivray and Parkington on insurance law : relating to all risks other than marine / Michael Parkington. – 8th ed. – London : Sweet & Maxwell, 1988.
cxli,1014p.
Discusses legal aspects of the insurance contract and the insurance business. Includes a new chapter on Reinsurance, and looks at certain types of policy including those covering indemnity, personal accident, fire, motor vehicle and aviation, pecuniary loss and contractors' risk. Refers to North American decisions and to Scots law.
ISBN 0421354801 £90.00

McGovern, Edmond
International trade regulation : GATT, the United States and the European Community / Edmond McGovern. – 2nd ed. – Exeter : Globefield, 1986.
xliv,629p; 25cm.
Previous ed. 1982. Bibliography: p599-619. - Includes index.
ISBN 0950846341 £36.00

McGowan, Michael →Ontario Supreme and District Court Practice 1989.

McGrath, E.H.
Industrial Disputes : a Guide to the Industrial Disputes Act, 1947, Revised Edition. – 3rd repr. 1985. – New Delhi : Prentice-Hall.
120p.
ISBN 0876923686 Hbk £25.00

MacGrath, Michael
Civil Liability Act. – Dublin : Round Hall Press, 1985.
150p.
ISBN 0947686037 Hbk £13.50

McGrath, Siobhan →Landlord and Tenant Act 1985.

McGregor, Harvey
McGregor on damages / by Harvey McGregor. – 15th ed. – London : Sweet & Maxwell, 1988.
xciii,1232p; 25cm.
Divided into three major sections; General Principles, Particular Contracts, and Torts and Procedures. In each section, the relevant points of law and practice are considered.
ISBN 0421370807 £100.00

McGregor, O. R.
Social history and law reform / by O.R. McGregor. – London : Stevens, 1981.
x,66p; 19cm.
Includes index.
ISBN 0420459200 Hbk £9.50
ISBN 0420459308 Pbk £4.25

McGudden, C.
Women employment and European law. – Oxford : Eclipse, 1988.
ISBN 1870771001 Hbk £25.00

McGuigan
Blueprint for Judicial Reform / Rader. – London : Eurospan.
ISBN 0942522087 Pbk £13.95
—Crime and Punishment in Modern America / Pascale. – London : Eurospan.
ISBN 0942522001 Pbk £13.75

McGuinness, Kevin Patrick
Construction lien remedies in Ontario / by Kevin Patrick McGuinness. – Toronto, Canada : Carswell Legal Publications, 1983.
xxxiii, 423 p.; 24 cm.
Includes index. Bibliography: p. 415-418.
ISBN 0459359606
—Law of guarantee : a treatise on guarantee, indemnity and the standby letter of credit / by Kevin Patrick McGuinness. – Toronto : Carswell, 1986.
lxv,456p.
This text on the Canadian law pertaining to various secondary obligations used to secure debt and other contract loss gives a detailed survey of the modern law as it has developed in the courts of both Canada and England.
ISBN 0459383906

McGuinness, W.
Law of Guarantee. – London : Sweet & Maxwell, 1986.
ISBN 0459383906 Hbk £45.00

McGurk, Peter
Guide to Housing Benefit / Nick Raynsford. – Rev. – London : CENT, 1986.
ISBN 0948857056 Pbk £4.95

McGurran, Mary K.
Alberta Corporate Income Tax : Alberta Annotated Legislation Series, 1 Vol. – Butterworths.
Llf £125.00

McHardy, Anne →Two Irelands : the problem of the double minority.

Machin, E. Anthony →Redgrave's health and safety in factories.

Machinery of Justice in England. – 8th ed. – Cambridge : Cambridge University Press, 1987.
ISBN 052129231X Pbk £19.50

McHugh, Paul
Maori land laws of New Zealand. – Saskatoon : University of Saskatchewan, Native Law Centre, 1983.
86p.
ISBN 088880122X Hbk £13.00

McIlroy, J.
Industrial tribunals. – Pluto Press, 1983.
ISBN 0861043685 Pbk £6.95

McInnes, Ron
Landlord-Tenant Rights in Ontario. – 6th ed. – North Vancouver : International Self-Counsel Press, 1986.
168p.
ISBN 0889083592 Hbk £7.95

Macintosh, Charles W
Nova Scotia Real Property Practice Manual. – London : Butterworths.
ISBN 0409855103 Hbk £100.00

Macintosh, J. C. → Law of agency in South Africa.

McIntyre → International space policy.

MacIntyre, Alasdair
Whose justice? Which rationality? / Alasdair MacIntyre. – London : Duckworth, 1988.
422p; 24cm.
Includes index.
ISBN 071562198X Hbk £35.00 :
ISBN 0715621998 Pbk £12.95

Mackaay, Ejan
Quebec Legal Documentation at the Beginning of the 80's : the Results of a Survey. – Ottawa : Canadian Law Information Council, 1981.
30p.
ISBN 0920358160 Pbk £10.00

McKague, Carla A. → Mental Health Law in Canada.

McKain, Bruce → Scots law for journalists.

McKay → Agricultural law.

MacKay, A. Wayne → Canadian Charter of Rights : law practice revolutionized.
→ Charterwatch : Reflections on Equality.
→ Courts and the Charter.
—Education law in Canada / A. Wayne MacKay. – Toronto : Emond-Montgomery, 1984.
xxiv,416p.
Bibliography: p.397-407. - Includes index.
ISBN 0920722121 Hbk £45.00
—Educational Law in Canada. – Aurora : Canada Law Book Co, 1984.
250p. – (Text Books-Civil).
Hbk £45.00
→ Recurring Issues in Canadian Federalism.
→ Rights, Freedoms and the Education System in Canada : Cases and Materials.

McKay, David H.
Planning and Politics in Western Europe. – London : Macmillan, 1982.
Illus.
ISBN 0333300815 Hbk £20.00

McKay, L.
Essays on Taxation / J. Prebble. – Wellington : Victoria University of Wellington, 1982.
ISBN 0705508307 Hbk £20.00

Mackay, Ronnie → Psychiatry and the criminal process.
—Role of psychiatric reports in the Crown Court trial processes. – Leicester : Leicester Polytechnic Law School, 1986.
21p. – (Leicester Polytechnic Law School monographs).
Includes bibliographical references.
ISBN 0948997303

McKean, Warwick
Equality and discrimination under international law / Warwick McKean. – Oxford : Clarendon, 1983.
ix,333p; 23cm.
Includes index.
ISBN 0198253117 Hbk £30.00
ISBN 0198255195 Pbk £12.50

McKechnie, G.
Energy Finance. – London : Euromoney, 1983.
ISBN 0903121476 Pbk £75.00

McKee, John → Industrial Tribunals in Northern Ireland.
→ Industrial tribunals in Northern Ireland : a practical guide.

McKelvey, K. Muir → Hosking's Pension schemes and retirement benefits.

Macken, J.J., et al
Law of Employment. – 2nd ed. – North Ryde : Law Book Co, 1984.
xix, 351p.
ISBN 0455205108 Pbk £30.00
ISBN 0455205094 Hbk £42.00
—Law Of Employment The. – 2nd ed. – London : Law Book Co.
ISBN 0455205094 Hbk £19.00

MacKenna, Brian → Justice in prison : a report.

McKennirey, John S.
Canadian law faculties : a report to the Consultative Group on Research and Education in Law based on the 1981 survey of Canadian law faculties and statistics of the Canadian deans of law / John S. McKennirey. – Ottawa : Consultative Group on Research and Education in Law, 1982.
149p.
—Canadian law professors : a report to the Consultative Group on Research and Education in Law based on the 1981 survey of full-time law professors in Canada / John S. McKennirey. – Ottawa : Consultative Group on Research and Education in Law, 1982.
viii,133p.
—Canadian law professors : a staff report on the survey of full-time law professors in Canada / submitted to the Consultative Group on Research and Education in Law by John S. McKennirey. – Ottawa : Social Sciences and Humanities Research Council of Canada, 1982.
vi,51,92 leaves.
—Sources of support for legal research : a report to the Consultative Group on Research and Education in Law based on a survey of foundations, law reform commissions, departments of justice, and attorneys and solicitors general in Canada / John S. McKennirey. – Ottawa : Consultative Group on Research and Education in Law, 1982.
iii,53p.

McKenzie
Practical approach to land law / Phillips. – London : Financial Training, 1986.
ISBN 1851850244 Pbk £14.95
—Utility Deposits Interest Act, 1983, Bill 126 : An Act to Require the Payment of Interest on Consumers' Utility Deposits. – Ontario : Ontario Government Publications Service, 1983.
1p.
Hbk £0.30

McKenzie, D. J.
Manual for the Simulation of the Family Court of Australia. – Canberra : Australian Government Publishing Service, 1981.
58p.
ISBN 064206749X Hbk £2.60

Mackenzie, G.
Institutions of the Laws of Scotland. – 5th ed. Repr. of 1723 ed. – Abingdon : Professional Books.
73p.
Hbk £110.00
—Laws and Customs of Scotland in Matters Criminal : Wherein is to be Seen How the Civil Law and Laws and Customs of Other Nations Do Not Agree With and Supply Ours. – Repr. of 1678 ed. – Abingdon : Professional Books.
74p.
Hbk £275.00
—Observations on the Acts of Parliament. – Repr. of 1686 ed. – Abingdon : Professional Books.
74p.
Hbk £95.00

McKenzie, Ian → Police interrogation: the effects of the Police and Criminal Evidence Act 1984.

Mackenzie, J.
Horse law. – Shaw & Sons, 1988.
ISBN 0721911307 Pbk

MacKenzie, John A. → International factoring.

Mackenzie, Mary Margaret
Plato on punishment / Mary Margaret Mackenzie. – Berkeley Calif. : University of California Press, 1981.
vii,278p; 25cm.
Bibliography: p251-259. - Includes index.
ISBN 0520041690 £17.25

McKenzie, P D → Law of Insolvency.

MacKenzie, R. M., et al
Municipal Law. – Vancouver : British Columbia Continuing Legal Education Society, 1981.
548p.
ISBN 0865040257 Hbk £21.00

Mackenzie Stuart, Alexander John Mackenzie Stuart
Control of power within the European Communities : being the presidential address of Lord Mackenzie Stuart, president of the Holdsworth Club of the Faculty of Law in the University of Birmingham, 1985-1986. – Birmingham : Holdsworth Club of the University of Birmingham, 1986.
18p. – (The Holdsworth Club).
ISBN 0704408953

McKeogh, J. P.
Intellectual Property. – Sydney : Butterworths, 1988.
144p. – (Student Companion Ser.).
This guide contains over 200 summaries of cases in the area of intellectual property. It is intended for use in conjunction with lecture notes, textbooks, and other working documents.
Pbk £9.95

McKeough, J.P.
Butterworths Student Companions
Intellectual Property /. – Butterworths, 1988.
111p.
ISBN 0409492892
→ Intellectual Property : Commentary and Materials.

Mackeurtan, Harold Graham
Mackeurtan's sale of goods in South Africa / by G. R. J. Hackwill. – 5th ed. – Cape Town : Juta, 1984.
xli,304p.
ISBN 0702114138

Mackeurtan's sale of goods in South Africa / by G. R. J. Hackwill. – 5th ed. – Cape Town : Juta, 1984.
xli,304p.
ISBN 0702114138

McKichan, D. J.
Drafting and Negotiating Commercial Leases in Scotland / A. H. Primrose. – London : Butterworths, 1985.
This work deals with the drafting, negotiating, and settling of commercial leases in Scotland. The book provides extensive references to English cases that may have a persuasive influence on judgements made in Scottish courts.
ISBN 0406359067 Hbk £27.00
→ Drafting and Negotiating Common Leases Scotland.

McKie, Alexander B.
Canada's Tax Treaties, 2 Vols. – Butterworths.
Llf £145.00
—Foreign Tax Credits and Foreign Affiliates. – Toronto : Butterworths, 1984.
176p.
Hbk £42.95

Mackie, Karl
Lawyers in business : and the law business / Karl J. Mackie. – Basingstoke : Macmillan, 1988.
viii,289p.
Includes bibliography and index.
ISBN 0333419081 £29.50

McKie, Robert
Housing and the Whitehall Bulldozer. – London : Institute of Economic Affairs.
Hbk £0.50

MacKinnon, Dan
Compendium of the Northern Regulatory Regime. – Don Mills : CCH Canadian Ltd, 1986.
176p.
ISBN 0887963676 Pbk £39.95

McKinnon, Sharon M.
Seventh Directive : consolidated accounts in the EEC / Sharon M. McKinnon : edited by Alan D.H. Newham. – Brentford : Kluwer, 1984.
392p.
Includes the official texts of Fourth and Seventh Directives.
ISBN 0903393700

Mackintosh, Simon → Revenue law in Scotland.

Macklem, Douglas N.
Construction and Mechanics' Liens in Canada / David I. Bristow. – 5th ed. – Agincourt : Carswell, 1985.
1,015p.
This work examines the Ontario Construction Lien Act of 1983 in detail and discusses the changes this new act makes to the law under the former Mechanics' Lien Act. The statute and case law of all Canadian provinces is presented in the text.
Hbk £77.50

MacKmin, David → Bean and Lockwood's Rating valuation practice.

McKnight, Allan
Forgotten treaties : a practical plan for world disarmament / Allan McKnight : with an introduction by Keith Suter. – Melbourne : Law Council of Australia, 1983.
xi,136p.
Includes bibliographical references and index. Part II is text of McKnight's Draft Disarmament Treaty.
ISBN 0959660879

McLachlan, Campbell Alan
Admission of Commonwealth lawyers : a technical survey for Commonwealth Law Ministers and the Commonwealth Lawyers' Association / Campbell Alan McLachlan. – London : Commonwealth Secretariat, 1985.
x, 168p.
→ Hague Convention on the Taking of Evidence Abroad : explanatory documentation prepared for Commonwealth jurisdicitons.

McLachlin, Beverley M.
British Columbia Court Forms, 3 Vols. / James P. Taylor. – Butterworths.
Llf £450.00
—British Columbia Court Forms, 3 vols / James Taylor. – Toronto : Butterworths.
Hbk
—British Columbia Court Forms / James Taylor. – London : Butterworths.
ISBN 0409994510 Hbk
—British Columbia Practice, 3 vols / James P Taylor. – 2nd ed. – Toronto : Butterworths.
Hbk

—Canadian Law of Architecture and Engineering / Wilfred J. Wallace. – Butterworths, 1987.
544p.
Coverage includes contract and tort, claims avoidance, liability insurance, copyright and patents, and remuneration. Collection of form contracts, municipal forms, and explanatory notes. Canadian statutes and cases provide the focus of the study, but the laws of other jurisdictions, notably England are included. Analyses the civil law of Quebec.
ISBN 0409804819 Hbk £100.00

McLaren →Falconbridge on Mortgages.

McLaren, Richard H.
Law and practice of commercial arbitration / by Richard H. McLaren and Earl Edward Palmer. – Toronto, Canada : Carswell, 1982.
xlii, 422 p.; 24 cm.
Includes bibliographical references and index.
ISBN 0459349902
—Personal Property Security : An Introductory Analysis / DeJong. - 4th ed. – Agincourt : Carswell, 1987.
454p.
Pbk £40.50
—Personal Property Security Act Cases, Vol. 4 : Supplement to Secured Transactions in Personal Property in Canada. – Agincourt : Carswell.
Hbk £192.50

McLarren, Philip H.
Employment in Alberta : a Guide to Conditions of Work and Employee Benefits, 1 Vol. – Butterworths.
Llf £85.00
—Employment in British Columbia : a Guide to Conditions of Work and Employee Benefits, 1 Vol. – Butterworths.
Llf £85.00

McLauchlan, David W. →Contractual Remedies Act 1979.

McLaughlin, Sue →Women and the law.

McLay, J. K. →Sexual violence : a case for law reform : papers presented at seminar, University of Auckland, 27 August 1982.

Maclean
House of Lords Appeals : 1821-1873, 28 Vols. 1835-1838, 3 Vols. /. – Abingdon : Professional Books.
Hbk
1838-1839, 1 Vol.. –
Hbk

Maclean, A. J. →Scots Criminal Law.

Maclean, Allan H., et al
Unemployment Insurance. – Vancouver : British Columbia Continuing Legal Education Society, 1983.
266p.
ISBN 0865041067 Hbk £55.00
—Unemployment Insurance / Bob Ludlow. – Vancouver : Vancouver People's Law School.
Illus.
Hbk

MacLean, Brian →Islington crime survey : crime, victimization and policing in inner-city London.

McLean, Ian
Criminal appeals : a practical guide to appeals to and from the Crown Court / by Ian McLean. – 2nd ed. – London : Barry Rose, 1986.
xxxv,249p.
Previous ed.: 1980. Includes bibliographical references and index. Includes examples of court forms.
ISBN 085992372X
—Crown Court pattern of sentencing : offenders aged 14 and over : being extracts from the Criminal statisties for England and Wales 1971-1978 / by Ian McLean. – Chichester : Barry Rose, 1981.
254p.
ISBN 085992209X
→ Industrial tribunal.
→ Industrial tribunal : a practical guide to employment law and tribunal procedure.
—Magistrates' Court : An Index of Common Penalties and Formalities in Cases Before Justices / Peter Morrish. – 7th ed. – Chichester : Barry Rose.
262p.
Hbk
—Magistrates' court : an index of common penalties and formalities in cases before justices (excluding the juvenile court) / by Ian McLean and Peter Morrish. – 6th ed. – Chichester : Rose, 1984.
205p; 22cm.
Previous ed.: 1980. Includes index.
ISBN 0859922170 £19.50
ISBN 085992369X
—Trade Union Representatives Handbook. – London : Industrial Society.
Hbk £1.95

McLean, Mary K
Thesaurus of provincial statutory terminology / compiled and edited by Mary K. McLean, with assistance from Lorna K. Rees-Potter. – 1st ed. – Ottawa : Canadian Law Information Council, 1986.
ix, 179 p.; 28 cm.
ISBN 0920358896 £40.00

Maclean, Mavis
Children and divorce : economic factors / by Mavis Maclean and John Eekelaar. – Oxford : SSRC Centre for Socio-Legal Studies, 1983.
vii,39p; 22cm.
ISBN 0862260698
→ Maintenance after divorce.

McLean, Scilla →Female circumcision, excision and infibulation : the facts and proposals for change.

McLean, Sheila A M →Legal issues in human reproduction.
→ Legal issues in medicine.
→ Legal relevance of gender : some aspects of sex-based discrimination.
—Medicine, morals and the law / Sheila McLean and Gerry Maher. – Aldershot : Gower, 1983.
ix,214p; 23cm.
Includes index.
ISBN 0566005336

McLellan, Bradley N. →Condominium : The Law and Administration in Ontario.
—Real Estate Law. – 3rd ed. – Toronto : Edmond-Montgomery, 1986.
1,475p.
ISBN 0920722199 Hbk £99.50

McLennan, Gregor →Crime and society : readings in history and theory.

McLennan, John Stopford
Aspects of the common-law powers and duties of company directors with special reference to (a) their authority to act on behalf of a company and (b) the scope and effect of certain legislative provisions / by John Stopford McLennan. – 1. – S.l. : s.n., 1984.
various pagings.
Offprints of 4 articles. Thesis (L.L.M.) - University of Witwatersrand 1984. Bibliography: p.i-ii. - Includes index.

McLeod, Angus
Butterworths Commercial Service. – Butterworths.
ISBN 0409681008 Llf
—Butterworths Current Law. – Butterworths.
Llf
—Butterworth's Current Law / Phillippa Oldham. – Wellington : Butterworths.
Hbk
→ Mazengarb's Industrial Law.

Macleod, J S
Taxation of Insurance Business / A R Levitt. – 2nd ed. – London : Butterworths.
ISBN 0406501017 Hbk £45.00

McLeod, James G.
Conflict of Laws. – Agincourt : Carswell, 1983.
967p.
This textbook for Canadian law students tracts the historical development of the principles of conflict of laws and critically analyzes the policies underlying the rules. The book explores relevant English, American, and Commonwealth laws, in addition to Canadian law.
ISBN 045936860X Hbk £82.50
—Family Dispute Resolution : Litigation and Its Alternatives. – Agincourt : Carswell, 1987.
118p.
Hbk £30.25
—Introduction to Family Law. – Toronto : Butterworths, 1983.
180p.
Pbk £21.95
—Introduction to Family Law. – Butterworths, 1983.
180p.
Outlines how the law operates in each common law province. Coverage includes marriage, rights and duties, marriage and property, termination of marriage, children, and reform in children's law.
ISBN 040984828X Pbk £21.95
—Reports of Family Law : 1824-1970, 5 Vols. – Agincourt : Carswell.
– (Reprint Ser.).
Hbk £252.00
→ Restitution.

MacLeod, Linda
Sentenced to separation : an exploration of the needs and problems of mothers who are offenders and their children / Linda MacLeod. – Ottawa : Ministry of the Solicitor General, 1986.
ii,66p,14p,8p. – (User report).

McLeod-Lindsay, A.
Ordinary Man : The Alexander McLeod-Lindsay Case. – Neutral Bay : Hale & Iremonger, 1984.
ISBN 0868060763 Hbk £24.95, 015
ISBN 08608060771 Pbk £10.95, 015

McLeod, Roderick M →Canadian charter of rights : prosecution and defence of criminal and other statutory offences.
—Criminal Code Driving Offences : Breathalyzer Law in Canada, 3 Vols. – Agincourt : Carswell, 1988.
This three volume set of looseleaf books provides a comprehensive treatment of the Criminal Code offenses. Offenses include criminal negligence, dangerous driving, failing to remain and driving while disqualified. The elements of each offense and caselaw analyzing such is discussed. Orders of prohibition and the Charter of Rights and Bill of Rights are discussed.
Hbk £189.00

MacLise, Kirstie
Domestic Contracts. – Agincourt : Carswell, 1987.
450p.
This looseleaf work is a practitioners guide to the drafting of cohabitation, marriage and separation agreements under the law of Ontario and British Columbia. Checklist, sample agreements, income tax considerations and related materials are included in the volume.
Hbk £71.50

McLoughlin, J.
Law and practice relating to pollution control in the member states of the European communities : a comparative survey / M. J. Forster. – 2nd ed. – London : Graham & Trotman for the Commission of the European Communities, 1982.
545p.
Previous ed: 1976.
ISBN 0860103153 £18.00
—Law and practice relating to pollution control in the United Kingdom / M. J. Forster. – 2nd ed. – London : Graham & Trotman for the Commission of the European Communities, 1982.
200p.
Previous ed: 1976. Includes index.
ISBN 0860103064 Hbk £18.00
ISBN 0860104400 Pbk £9.00
—Women and Insurance. – Pandora Press.
ISBN 004440378X Pbk £3.50

McLuskie, Robert
Great debate : New Zealand, Britain and the EEC : the shaping of attitudes / Robert ,McLuskie. – Wellington : Decision Research Centre, Victoria University of Wellington, 1986.
iv,175p.
Includes bibliographical references and index.
ISBN 0908772009

MacLynn, C.
Guide to Social Security Tribunals. – Belfast : Queen's University of Belfast, 1986.
200p.
Hbk

McMahon, Bryan M E
Casebook on the Irish Law of Torts / William Binchy. – London : Butterworths, 1983.
ISBN 0862050502 Hbk £35.00
ISBN 0862050561 Pbk £25.00
—EEC Law in Ireland. – London : Butterworths, 1988.
ISBN 0862052378 Hbk £35.00
—Irish Law of Torts / William Binchy. – London : Butterworths, 1982.
ISBN 0862050405 Hbk £36.00
—Judge or Jury? : the Jury Trial for Personal Injury Cases in Ireland. – Cork : Cork University Press, 1985.
35p.
ISBN 0902561383 Pbk £1.50

McMaster, R.
Trollope and the law. – London : Macmillan, 1986.
ISBN 0333400135 Hbk £25.00

Macmillan Dictionary of International Finance. – 2nd ed. – London : Macmillan, 1986.
ISBN 0333398343 Pbk £8.95

McMillan, John, et al
Australia's Constitution : Time for Change?. – North Sydney : Allen & Unwin, 1983.
432p.
ISBN 0868610399 Pbk £17.95

MacMillan, P. R.
Censorship and public morality / P. R. MacMillan. – Aldershot : Gower, 1983.
xxiii,547p; 24cm.
Bibliography: p521-530. - Includes index.
ISBN 0566003767 £22.95

MacMillan, S.
Law of Leases. – London : Estates Gazette, 1970.
ISBN 0900361174 Hbk £3.50

MacMinn, E. George
Parliamentary Practice in British Columbia. – Victoria : Government of British Columbia, 1981.
v, 1p.
ISBN 0771882467 Hbk £55.00

Mcmonnies, P.
Making Corporate Reports Valuable. – London : Kogan Page.
ISBN 1850914893 Pbk £10.95

McMorland, D W →Introduction to Land Law.

McMorris, Annie → HURIDOCS standard formats for the recording and exchange of information on human rights.

McMullen, J.
Rights at work. – 2nd ed. – Pluto Press, 1983.
ISBN 0861047303 Pbk £7.95

McMullen, John
Business transfers and employee rights / John McMullen. – London : Butterworths, 1987.
xxix,253p; 22cm.
Bibliography: p239-241. - Includes index.
ISBN 0406658544 Pbk £15.00
—Private company law. – 1st ed. – London : Longman Professional (UK), 1990.
– (Longman Practice Notes).
Overview of company law, covering the problems faced in the formation of a company, fees, the duties and responsibilities of those involved, and details of practice in relation to termination of a company. Contains checklists, addresses, a table of fees, and a table of company forms.
ISBN 0851215289 Pbk £9.95

McMurtry, R.
Architects Act, 1983, Bill 122 : An Act to Revise the Architects Act. – Ontario : Ontario Government Publications Service, 1983.
55p.
Hbk £0.70
—Famiy Law Reform Act, 1983, Bill 093 : An Act to Amend the Family Law Reform Act. – Ontario : Ontario Government Publications Service, 1983.
1p.
Hbk £0.30
—Limitations Act, 1983, Bill 160 : An Act to Revise the Limitations Act. – Ontario : Ontario Government Publications Service, 1983.
18p.
Hbk £0.50
—Professional Engineers Act, 1983, Bill 123 : An Act to Revise the Professional Engineers Act. – Ontario : Ontario Government Publications Service, 1983.
49p.
Hbk £0.70

McNae
Essential Law for Journalists. – 9th ed. – London : Butterworths, 1985.
ISBN 0406772819 Pbk £8.95

McNair
Law Of Treaties. – Reprint. – Oxford : Oxford University Press, 1961.
ISBN 0198251521 Hbk £70.00
→ Roman Law and Common Law.

McNair, D. Keith → Income taxation of partnerships and their partners.
—Meaning of cost in Canadian Income Tax / D. Keith McNair. – Toronto : Canadian Tax Foundation, 1982.
vi,277p.
Includes index.
ISBN 0888080123

→ Taxation of Corporations and Shareholders : Cases and Materials, Includes 1987-88 Supplements.

→ Unmarried couples : legal aspects of cohabitation.

McNair, John A. → Annotated Ontario Landlord and Tenant Statutes.

McNair, John H. → Annotated Employment Law Statutes of Ontario.

McNamara
Separation, Divorce and After. – St. Lucia : University of Queensland Press.
ISBN 0702219312 Pbk £12.95

McNamara, O F
Town planning in practice. – London : Butterworths, 1988.
ISBN 0406500754 Pbk

McNamara, Philip
Availability of Civil Remedies to Protect Persons and Property from Transfrontier Pollution Injury. – Hamburg : I.I.A., 1981.
ix, 163p.
Hbk £31.00

McNee, David
McNee's law / Sir David McNee. – London : Collins, 1983.
256p,8p of plates; 23cm.
Includes index.
ISBN 0002170078 £9.95

McNeil, John S.
Motor Carrier Cargo Claims. – Agincourt : Carswell, 1986.
222p.
Hbk £35.75

McNeil, Kent
Common law aboriginal title. – Oxford : Clarendon Press.
360.
Addresses the land rights question applied throughout the British Empire. Assesses the impact of English law in a colony acquired by settlememt where no form of aboriginal land ownership had previously existed. Conclusions reached suggest a doctrinal approach which could be used to resolve outstanding aboriginal land claims.
Academics, lawyers representing aboriginal peoples, students of human rights
ISBN 0198252234 Hbk £35
—Indian Hunting, Trapping and Fishing Rights in the Prairie Provinces of Canada. – Saskatoon : University of Saskatchewan, Native Law Centre, 1983.
64p.
ISBN 0888801254 Hbk £20.00
—Native Claims in Rupert's Land and the North-Western Territory : Canada's Constitutional Obligations. – Saskatoon : University of Saskatchewan, Native Law Centre, 1982.
41p.
ISBN 0888801181 Hbk £8.00
—Native Rights and the Boundaries of Rupert's land and the North-Western Territory. – Saskatoon : University of Saskatchewan, Native law Centre, 1982.
72p.
ISBN 0888801114 Hbk £12.00

McNeill → Imprisonent Today : Current Issues in the Prison Debate.

McNeill, Patricia → Canadian Market Place : a Consumer Rights Handbook.

McNeill, Peter G B
Adoption of children in Scotland. – 2nd. – Edinburgh : Green (W.) & Son, 1986.
Deals with adoptions in the sequence which occurs in practice and the relevant statute and case law. The appendices contain the Adoption (Scot.) Act 1978, the rules of court, and styles of writs, interlocutors and reports.
ISBN 0414007794 Pbk

McNeill, Sandra → Women against violence against women.

McNicol, Suzanne B.
Non Curial Privilege Against Self-Incrimination. – Clayton : Monash University Press, 1985.
ISBN 0867462841 Hbk £9.50

McNulty, Anthony → Right of peaceful assembly : its evolution and limits in a democratic society : a conference jointly organised by the British Institute of Human Rights and the United Kingdom Association for European Law in the Old Hall, Lincoln's Inn, on 30th April, 1982.

Macphail, I
Sheriff Court practice. – Edinburgh : Green (W.) & Son, 1988.
Explains modern statutory rules of proceedure and the principles and practices which regulate the conduct of civil litigation in the Sheriff Court. Covers drafting and amendment of written pleadings, interim orders, debates, proofs and appeals. Covers the practice and procedure in summary causes and the legislation conferring powers and duties on the Sheriff Court.
ISBN 0414008251 Hbk

Macpherson
Court of Session Cases : Series 1-5, 1821-1906, 63 Vols.
3rd Series, 1862-1873, 11 Vols. /. – Abingdon : Professional Books.
Hbk
—Scots Revised Reports : 1707-1873, 45 Vols. Court of Session Cases : 1863-1873, 11 Vols. /. – Abingdon : Professional Books.
Hbk

McPherson, Bruce Harvey
Law of company litigation : being the law relating to liquidation of limited liability companies / by B. H. McPherson. – 3rd ed. – Sydney : Law Book Co., 1987.
lxxxii,501p.
Previous ed.: 1980. Bibliography: pp.lxxix-lxxx. - Includes index.
ISBN 0455207410

Macpherson, C.
Rise and fall of economic justice. – Oxford : Oxford University Press, 1987.
ISBN 0192153609 Hbk £12.50
ISBN 0192851861 Pbk £4.95

MacPherson, P. → Acts and rules relating to insolvency.

Macqueen
House of Lords Appeals : 1821-1873, 28 Vols. 1851-1865, 4 Vols. /. – Abingdon : Professional Books.
Hbk

Macqueen, Hector L. → New perspectives in Scottish legal history.

McQuillan, Peter E. → Taxation of private corporations and their shareholders.

McQuoid-Mason, David J.
Outline of legal aid in South Africa / by David J. McQuoid-Mason. – Durban : Butterworths, 1982.
xxvii,310p.
Bibliography: pxiii-xvi.
ISBN 0409040894

McRae, Donald M.
Understanding the Canada-U.S. Free Trade Agreement / Debra P. Stegar. – Ottawa : Institute for Research on Public Policy, 1988.
ISBN 0886450799 Hbk

McRae, Hamish
Capital city : London as a financial centre / Hamish McRae and Frances Cairncross. – New and fully rev. ed. – London : Methuen, 1984.
264p; 23cm.
Previous ed.: 1973. Includes index.
ISBN 0413511200 Hbk £8.95
ISBN 041357900X Pbk £3.95

Macrory, Richard → Commercial nuclear power.
—Nuisance . – London : Longman Professional, 1982.
– (Practice Notes Series. No. 71).
ISBN 0851206247 Pbk £14.95
—Water law. – 2nd ed. – London : Longman Professional, 1985.
ISBN 0851209556 Pbk £19.95
—Water law : principles and practice / Richard Macrory. – London : Longman Professional, 1985.
xiii,167p; 22cm.
ISBN 0851209556

Mcshane → Criminological Theory.

McSweeney, L. B. → Information disclosure and the multinational corporation.

MacTavish, L. R.
Ontario Statute Annotations. – R.S.O. 1980 ed. – Aurora : Canada Law Book Co.
1000p. – (Statute Services).
Hbk £45.00
—Ontario Statute Annotations (R.S.O. 1980 Edition) 1930-80. – Aurora : Canada Law Book Co.
1000p.
Hbk £45.00
—Ontario Statute Annotations, R.S.O. 1980 Edition. – North Ryde : Law Book Co.
ca 1,000p.
Hbk £45.00
—Ontario Statute Citator (O.S.C.) R.S.O. 1980 Edition : 1980-Present. – Aurora : Canada Law Book Co.
Llf £126.00

McVeagh → Road traffic law.

McVeigh
High Court Manual. – Butterworths, 1989.
220p.
ISBN 0409787930 Hbk

McWhinney, Edward
Aerial piracy and international terrorism : the illegal diversion of aircraft and international law / Edward McWhinney. – 2nd rev. ed. – Dordrecht, the Netherlands : M. Nijhoff, 1987.
Re ed. of: Aerial piracy and international law / by Edward McWhinney and others. 1971. Includes index. Bibliography..
ISBN 0898389194
—Canada and the constitution, 1979-1982 : patriation and the charter of rights / Edward McWhinney. – Toronto : University of Toronto Press, 1982.
xii,227p.
Includes bibliographical references and index.
ISBN 0802065015 Pbk
—Conflict and compromise : international law and world order in a revolutionary age / Edward McWhinney. – Alphen aan den Rijn : Sijthoff and Noordhoff, 1981.
160p.
Bibliography: p156-158.
ISBN 0887940900
—Conflicts and compromise : International law and world order in a revolutionary age. – Dordrecht : Kluwer, 1981.
160p.
ISBN 9028626719 Hbk Gld40 /$17.50
—Constitution-making : principles, process, practice / Edward McWhinney. – Toronto : University of Toronto Press, 1981.
xiii,231p; 24cm.
Bibliography: p219-225. - Includes index.
ISBN 0802055532 £12.00
—International Court of Justice and the Western Tradition of International Law. – Dordrecht : Kluwer, 1987.
172p.
ISBN 9024735246 Hbk £125.00
—International Law and World Revolution. – Toronto : Canadian Broadcasting Corporation Enterprises.
116p.
Pbk £2.50
→ Nuclear Weapons and Contemporary International Law.

—Supreme courts and judicial law-making : constitutional tribunals and constitutional review / by Edward McWhinney. – Dordrecht : M. Nijhoff, 1985.
320p.
Includes index.
ISBN 9024732034 Hbk £165.00

McWilliams, Barry J. →Existing and new forms of financing, University of Auckland, 27 May 1982 : papers presented at seminar.
→ New Zealand business : entering the Australian market : Legal Research Foundation Inc. Seminar, 19 November 1985.

McWilliams, Peter K.
Canadian criminal evidence / by Peter K. McWilliams. – 2nd ed. – Aurora : Canada Law Book, 1984.
cxlii,1131p.
Previous ed.: 1974. Includes index.
ISBN 0888040180

Madan, Atam Prakash
Stridhana or Woman's Property in Indian Law : An Appraisal of its Concept and Contents. – Hoshiarpur : Vishveshvaranand Institute.
Hbk £2.65

Madarikan, C. O. →Criminal law and procedure of the southern states of Nigeria.

Made Simple : Housing Tenancy and Planning Law. – London : MADE, 1981.
ISBN 0434984876 Pbk £2.95

Madge, Nic →Defending possession proceedings.

Madge, Peter
Guide to the indemnity and insurance aspects of building contracts : based on the JCT Standard Forms of Building Contract / Peter Madge. – London : RIBA, 1985.
285p; 24cm.
ISBN 0900630914
—Indemnity and Insurance. – RIBA Publications, 1985.
ISBN 0900630914 Hbk £12.50

Madl, Ferenc
Law of Conflicts and Foreign Trade / L. Vekas. – Budapest : Akademiai Kiado.
xiv, 379p.
ISBN 9630542749 Hbk £38.00
—Law of international transactions / by Ferenc Madl : translated by J. Decsenyi. – Budapest : Akademiai Kiado, 1982.
206p.
Bibliography: p199-206. Translation of: Osszehasonlito nemzetkozi maganjog.
ISBN 9630529327

Madlener, Kurt →Philippines: human rights after martial law.

Magalona, Merlin M. →Survey of the Legal Profession in the Philippines : Focus on Region 4.

Magdelenat, Jean-Louis
Air cargo : regulation and claims / Jean-Louis Magdelenat. – Toronto : Butterworths, 1983.
xxvi,181p.
Bibliography: p.177-181. Summarizes the rules of liability. governing the carriage of goods by air. Surveys the economic and technical aspects of air cargo, systematically considering all their legal ratifications.
ISBN 0409847836 Hbk £55

Magee, J.
Company Accounts. – 3rd ed. – Plymouth : Macdonald & Evans, 1982.
ISBN 0712104704 Pbk £6.95

Magee, Philip P. →Irish criminal process.

Magistracy : interim report : first appointments as magistrates under the Local Courts Act, 1982 / New South Wales Law Reform Commission. – Sydney : The Commission, 1983.
xiii,87p. – (L.R.C. 38).

Magistrate : 1921-1975, 31 Vols. – Abingdon : Professional Books, 1984.
Hbk

Magistrate as Chairman / Geoffrey Norman. – London : Butterworths, 1987.
ISBN 0406104697 Pbk

Magistrate in the Crown Court / Robin David. – Chichester : Rose, 1982.
viii,48p; 21cm.
ISBN 0859922294 Pbk £4.25

Magistrates' Association
Suggestions for traffic offence penalties. – Magistrates' Association. – 8th ed. – London : The Association, 1983.
4p.

Magistrates' Association of the Republic of Trinidad and Tobago
Report of the proceedings and papers of the second Magistrates' Workshop / compiled and edited by Roland Crawford on behalf of the Magistrates' Association of the Republic of Trinidad and Tobago. – Port-of-Spain : The Association, 1982.
158p.
'Held on the 13th and 14th September, 1980, Chaguaramas Convention Centre'. At head of title: Republic of Trinidad and Tobago, the Magistrates' Association of the Republic of Trinidad and Tobago.

Magistrate's Companion : Guide for Magistrates in Announcing Sentence and Other Orders of the Court. – 3rd ed. – Chichester : Barry Rose, 1985.
88p.
ISBN 0859922332 Hbk £3.75

Magistrates' Court. – London : Longman Professional, 1988.
ISBN 0851214118 Pbk £9.95

Magistrates' Court : An Index of Common Penalties and Formalities in Cases Before Justices / Peter Morrish. – 7th ed. – Chichester : Barry Rose.
262p.
Hbk

Magistrates' court : an index of common penalties and formalities in cases before justices (excluding the juvenile court) / by Ian McLean and Peter Morrish. – 6th ed. – Chichester : Rose, 1984.
205p; 22cm.
Previous ed.: 1980. Includes index.
ISBN 0859922170 £19.50
ISBN 085992369X

Magistrates' Court Guide 1988. – London : Butterworths, 1988.
ISBN 0406108412 Pbk £15.95

Magistrates' Court Guide 1989. – London : Butterworths.
ISBN 0406108994 Pbk £16.95

Magistrates' Courts. – London : Longman Professional.
– (Longman Practice Notes).
ISBN 0851214118 Pbk £10.95

Magistrates' domestic courts : new perspectives / edited by Tony F. Marshall. – London : Home Office, 1984.
v,49p.
Conference papers.
ISBN 0862521696

Magistrates' Summary Jurisdiction : Guide to Sentencing Powers. – 6th ed. – Chichester : Barry Rose, 1983.
ISBN 0859923681 Hbk £4.50

Magnet, Joseph Eliot
Constitutional Law of Canada, 2 Vols. – 3rd ed. – Agincourt : Carswell, 1987.
ISBN 045930961 Hbk £61.60
ISBN 045930951X Pbk £36.00
—Constitutional law of Canada : Cases, notes and materials / by Joseph Eliot Magnet. – Toronto : Carswell, 1983.
xxii,1229p.
ISBN 0459356704

Magnus, George →International debt game.

Magrath →Police and the Criminal Evidence Act 1984.

Magrin, Edward P. →Utilising company tax losses and reliefs.

Maguire, Mike →Accountability and prisons : opening up a closed world.
—Burglary in a dwelling : the offence, the offender and the victim / Mike Maguire in collaboration with Trevor Bennett. – London : Heinemann, 1982.
ix,204p; 23cm. – (Heinemann library of criminology and penal reform).
Bibliography: p194-199. - Includes index.
ISBN 0435825674 £13.50
—Effects of crime and the work of victims support schemes / Mike Maguire and Claire Corbett. – Aldershot : Gower, 1987.
xiii,276p; 23cm.
Bibliography: p263-276.
ISBN 0566054124 £17.50

Mahaffy and Dodson : Road Traffic. – 3rd ed. – London : Butterworths.
Hbk

Mahajan, V.D.
Constitution of India. – New Delhi : S. Chand and Company, 1984.
Hbk £20.00
—Constitutional Law of India. – 6th ed. – Lucknow : Eastern Book Company, 1984.
600p.
Pbk £50.00

Maharashtra Cooperative Societies : Acts and Rules; as Amended by Acts no 10 and 20 of 1986, 2 Vols. – Indore : United Law Publishers, 1987.
Hbk £400.00

Maharashtra Cooperative Societies Act, 1960. – Bombay : Tripathi, 1981.
Hbk £85.00

Maharashtra Local Laws, 14 Vols. – Allahabad : Ashoka Law House, 1987.
Hbk £125.00 ea.

Maher, Chrissie →Small print : the language and layout of consumer contracts : Report to the National Consumer Council.

Maher, F. K. H.
Legal process : commentary and materials / Maher, Waller, Derham. – 5th ed. – Sydney : Law Book Co, 1988.
xxx, 593 p.; 26 cm.
First to 4th eds. published under title: Cases and materials on the legal process.
ISBN 0455207836 (pbk.)

Maher, Gerry
International private law : cases and statutes / G. Maher. – Edinburgh : Green, 1985.
xx,294p; 22cm. – (Concise College Texts).
Bibliography: p.xx. - Includes index.
ISBN 0414007611 Pbk £17.50
→ Medicine, morals and the law.

Maher, J. G. →Jessup's Forms and practice of the Lands Titles Office of South Australia.

Maher, L.W. →Consumer Protection Law in Australia.

Maher, Laurence W. →Consumer Protection Law in Australia.

Maheshwari, K.L.
Mercantile Law. – 11th ed. – Delhi : SBD Enterprises.
Hbk £35.00
—Problems in Mercantile Law. – Delhi : SBD Enterprises.
Hbk £15.00

Maheshwari, S.K.
Concepts and Problems in Mercantile Law. – New Delhi : Allied Publishers, 1984.
viii, 372p.
Hbk £30.00

Maheshwari, S.N.
Banking Law and Practice. – 5th ed. – New Delhi : Kalyani Publishers, 1988.
ISBN 8170960916 Hbk £60.00
—Elements of Banking Law. – New Delhi : Kalyani Publishers, 1987.
ISBN 8170960185 Hbk £25.00

Mahmood, M.
Colonization of Government Lands Act 1912 : Punjab. – Lahore : Pakistan Law Times.
Hbk £36.00
—Interpretation of Statutes. – 2nd ed. – Lahore : Pakistan Law Times, 1981.
Hbk £44.00
—Lands Law. – Lahore : Pakistan Law Times, 1981.
Hbk £36.00
—Law of Pre-Emption. – Lahore : Pakistan Law Times, 1981.
Hbk £36.00
—Law of Specific Reliefs : an Exhaustive Commentary on The Specific Relief Act 1887 : with Ammendments and Case Law Up-to-date. – Lahore : Pakistan Law Times.
Hbk £75.00
—Law Reforms Ordinance 1972. – Lahore : Pakistan Law Times.
Hbk £16.00

Mahmood, Tahir
Family Law and Social Change. – Bombay : Tripathi, 1975.
168p.
bd £30.00
—Hindu Law. – 2nd ed. – Allahabad : Law Book Company, 1986.
1,000p.
Hbk £200.00
—Hindu Marriage Act. – 2nd ed. – Allahabad : Law Book Company, 1986.
Hbk £100.00
—Hindu Minority and Guardianship : and Hindu Adoptions and Maintenance Act. – 2nd ed. – Allahad : Law Book Company, 1986.
200p.
Pbk £60.00

Mahmoudi, Said
Law of Deep Sea-Bed Mining : a Study of the Progressive Development of International Law Concerning the Management of the Polymetallic Nodules of the Deep Sea-Bed. – Stockholm : Almqvist & Wiksell, 1987.
356p.
ISBN 9122011560 Hbk £525.00

Mahoney →Women, the Law and the Economy.

Maidment, Susan
Child custody : what chance for fathers? / Susan Maidment. – London : National Council for One Parent Families, 1981.
23p.
Bibliography: p.21-23.
—Child Custody and Divorce. – Oxford : Croom Helm, 1984.
ISBN 0709917988 Pbk £8.95
—Child custody and divorce : the law in social context / Susan Maidment. – London : Croom Helm, 1984.
324p; 23cm.
Bibliography: p293-306. - Includes index.
ISBN 0709917376 £16.95

—Judicial Separation : A Research Study. – Oxford : Social Science Research Council, 1983.
102p.
ISBN 0862260574 Pbk £2.50

Maier, Irene →Protection of human rights in Europe : limits and effects : proceedings of the fifth International Colloquy about the European Convention on Human Rights.

Maingot
Parliamentary Privilege in Canada. – London : Butterworths.
ISBN 0409847860 Hbk £56.00

Maingot, Joseph
Parliamentary privilege in Canada / by Joseph Maingot. – Toronto : Butterworths, 1982.
xxx,290p.
Sets out the law relating to parliamentary procedures, giving an outline of the privilege procedure in the House of Commons. Traces the history, development and scope of parliamentary immunity, rights and privileges, including the privilege of freedom of speech. Also covers proceedings in Parliament, the Offical Secrets Act, and the criminal law.
ISBN 0409847860 Hbk £75

Mainprice, Hugh →Business tax handbook.
—VAT disputes and how to avoid them. – London : CCH, 1986.
ISBN 0863251005 Pbk £12.50

Maintenance after Divorce / Mavis Maclean. – Oxford : Oxford University Press, 1986.
ISBN 0198255292 Pbk £9.95
ISBN 0198255306 Hbk £22.50

Maintenance after divorce / John Eekelaar and Mavis Maclean. – Oxford : Clarendon, 1985.
x,171p; 22cm.
Bibliography: p161-168. - Includes index.
ISBN 0198255306 Pbk £19.50
ISBN 0198255292 £8.95

Maintenance agency for Australia / report of the National Maintenance Inquiry. – Canberra : Government Printer, 1984.
xx,381p. – (Parliamentary paper).
Includes bibliographical references. At head of t.p.: Parliament of the Commonwealth of Australia.
ISBN 0644031433 £13.00

Maintenance of commercial tenanted proerty / a consultative document by a working party of the Building Surveyors Division of the Royal Institution of Chartered Surveyors, January 1987. – London : The Institution, 1987.
9,12p.

Maintenance of Rights in Social Security. – Geneva : International Labour Office, 1983.
101p.
ISBN 9221031314 Hbk £17.50

Mair, George →Abstracts of race relations research.

Maitland, Frederic William
Constitutional History of England / Fisher. – Cambridge : Cambridge University Press, 1908.
ISBN 0521091373 Pbk £22.50
—Forms of Action at Common Law / Chaytor. – Cambridge : Cambridge University Press, 1936.
ISBN 0521091853 Pbk £7.95
→ Historical English Law before Edward I.
→ History of English law before the time of Edward I, Vol. 1.

Maitland-Walker, Julian
European Competition Law Review
Vol. 9. – Oxford : ESC Publishing Ltd, 1988.
Hbk £68.00
→ International anti-trust law, vol.2 : Recent developments in EEC and US anti-trust.

Major forms of crime / edited by Robert F. Meier. – Beverly Hills : Sage, 1984.
274p; 22cm. – (Sage criminal justice system annuals 21).
Includes bibliographies.
ISBN 0803920946 Hbk
ISBN 0803920954 Pbk £14.00

Major, G. A., et al
Mobile Homes for Legal Assistants. – Vancouver : British Columbia Continuing Legal Education Society, 1981.
142p.
ISBN 0865040400 Hbk £35.00

Major legal systems in the world today : an introduction to the comparative study of law / Rene David : translated and adapted by John E.C. Brierley. – 3rd ed. – London : Stevens, 1985.
xvi,624p; 22cm.
Previous ed.: 1978. Bibliography: p577-613. - Includes index. Translation of: Les grands systemes de droit contemporains.
ISBN 0420473408 Hbk £28
ISBN 0420473505 Pbk £23

Major, W.
Mastering basic English Law. – London : Macmillan, 1985.
ISBN 0333382897 Pbk £3.95

Major, W. T.
Building and Engineering Claims / A. Ranson. – London : Oyez Longman, 1980 Incl. July 1980 supplement.
ISBN 0851204252 Hbk £9.95
—Cases in Contract Law. – 3rd ed. Repr. of 1977 ed. – Plymouth : Macdonald & Evans, 1983.
256p. – (M and E Handbook Ser.).
ISBN 0712104801 Hbk £4.50

Majumder, A.B.
Laws Relating to Notices. – 5th ed. – Calcutta : Eastern Law House, 1982.
Hbk £90.00

Mak, Connie
Business and Tax Laws of the People's Republic of China / Fred Blaser. – North Ryde : C.C.H. Australia, 1986.
96p.
ISBN 0887963978 Pbk £14.95

Mak, W
Introduction to trade mark law in the Benelux / W. Mak, H. Molijn : translated by M.V. Snoxall, M.O. Snoxall. – Deventer, The Netherlands : Kluwer, 1982.
Includes index. Bibliography. Translation of: Merkenbescherming in de Benelux.
ISBN 9065440216

Makarczyk, Jerzy →Essays in international law in honour of Judge Manfred Lachs.

Makdisi, John
Law School Orientation : Cases and Materials. – Agincourt : Carswell, 1986.
341p.
This work for law students provides a series of introductory readings, cases, and materials for students beginning their studies at American law schools.
Pbk £18.75
—Workbook on Estates and Future Interests. – Agincourt : Carswell, 1987.
130p.
Discussions include a review of the common law in its present form as it relates to property law, a survey of the rules set in textual format, and a quick review of the subject matter from the advanced reader. This text has been written from use with a first year property text.
Pbk £12.50

Makec, John Wuol
Customary law of the Dinka people of Sudan : in comparison with aspects of western and Islamic laws / by John Wuol Makec. – London : Afroworld, 1988.
287p.
Includes bibliographical references and index.
ISBN 0948583037

Making a business of information : a survey of new opportunities. – London : H.M.S.O., 1983.
53p; 21cm.
Bibliography: p48. At head of title: Cabinet Office, Information Technology Advisory Panel.
ISBN 0116308249 Pbk £4.20

Making a Case. – Geneva : International Labour Office, 1981.
59p.
ISBN 9221022463 Hbk £5.00

Making a move? Your guide to conveyancing. – London : Sweet & Maxwell, 1988.
ISBN 0421399708 Pbk £18.75

Making a Will. – Community Legal Education Ontario. – 4th rev. ed. – Toronto : Community Legal Education Ontario, 1982.
30p.
ISBN 0889030561 Pbk £6.50

Making an Act of Parliament : Legislative Process. – House of Representatives Practice. – Canberra : Australian Government Publishing Service, 1981.
Hbk £1.40

Making and Applying Law in Finland. – Helsinki : Suomen valtio, 1983.
20p.
ISBN 9514670361 Hbk £15.00

Making and Revocation of Wills. – Victoria : Government of British Columbia, 1981.
Hbk £6.90

Making and revocation of wills / Scottish Law Commission. – Edinburgh : The Commission, 1986.
ii,84p. – (Consultative memorandum).

Making Commercial Contracts. – Oxford : Blackwell Scientific, 1988.
ISBN 0632018623 Hbk £19.95

Making Corporate Reports Valuable. – London : Kogan Page.
ISBN 1850914893 Pbk £10.95

Making crime a study of detective work / Richard V. Ericson. – Toronto : Butterworths, 1981.
xiii,257p.
Bibliography: p243-254.

Making European Policies Work. – Sage Publications.
ISBN 0803981384
Vol. 1. – 1988.
ISBN 0803981376 Hbk £25.00
Vol. 2. –
Hbk £25.00

Making good : prisons, punishment and beyond / Martin Wright : foreword by Barbara Wootton. – London : Burnett, 1982.
316p; 23cm.
Bibliography: p271-292. - Includes index.
ISBN 0091472202 Hbk £
ISBN 0091472210 Pbk £5.95

Making law bind : essays legal and philosophical / Tony Honore. – Oxford : Clarendon, 1987.
288p; 22cm.
Includes index.
ISBN 0198254670 Hbk £30.00

Making of India's Constitution. – Lucknow : Eastern Book Company, 1982.
vii, 121p.
Hbk £40.00

Making of labour law in Europe : a comparative study of nine countries up to 1945 / edited by Bob Hepple. – London : Mansell, 1986.
xiv,412p; 24cm.
Bibliography: p387-401. - Includes index.
ISBN 072011697X £39.95

Making of Resolution 242. – Dordrecht : Kluwer, 1985.
230p.
ISBN 9024730732 Hbk £130.00

Makkar, S.P. Singh
Law of Culpable Homicide, Murder and Punishment in India. – New Delhi : Deep and Deep Publications, 1988.
464p.
Hbk £250.00

Makuch, S.M.
Canadian Municipal and Planning Law. – Agincourt : Carswell, 1983.
358p.
This work examines the structure, organization, and authority of local government in Canada. Municipal finance, zoning, land use control and development control, municipal planning process, and other related issues are discussed in the book.
Hbk £46.25
—Municipal and Planning Law Text. – Agincourt : Carswell, 1983.
500p.
Hbk £46.25
—Spills Bill : Duties, Rights and Compensation. – Butterworths, 1986.
144p.
Collection of essays which intends to clear up the initial confusion surrounding the Environmental Protection Act. Covers common law liability, an overview of the bill, compensation and insurance, defence considerations, and factual situations; how the Bill will be and should be applied.
ISBN 0409805769 Hbk £44.95

Malan et al : Provisional Sentence on Bills of Exchange, Cheques and Promissory Notes. – Durban : Professional Publishers, 1986.
ISBN 040904086X Pbk £65.00

Malan, F. R.
Bills of exchange, cheques and promissory notes in South African law / by F.R. Malan : assisted by C. R. de Beer. – Durban : Butterworths, 1983.
xii,441p.
Bibliography: p.377-391. - Includes index.
ISBN 0409040738 Hbk £47.00
ISBN 0409040746 Pbk £34.70
—Collective securities depositories and the transfer of securities / by F.R. Malan. – Johannesburg : Rand Afrikaans University, 1983.
iv,257p.
Bibliography: p.240-252. - Includes index.
ISBN 0869702491
→ Index to the South African Law Reports : 1828-1946, 2 vols.
→ Index to the Southern African Law Reports 1828-1946, 4 Vols.
→ Index to the Southern African law reports 1828-1946, Vol. 1 : Transvaal.
—Malan et al : Provisional Sentence on Bills of Exchange, Cheques and Promissory Notes. – Durban : Professional Publishers, 1986.
ISBN 040904086X Pbk £65.00

Malan, Philip
Commercial Claimsmanship : With Special Reference to the FIDIC Form of Contract. – King's Ride : Institute of Building, 1983.
9p.
ISBN 0906600642 Hbk £2.00

Malaya Law Review. – National University of Singapore, Faculty of Law. – Singapore : University of Singapore.
ISBN 0542335X Hbk £45.00

Malaysian Customary Laws and Usage. – Singapore : Federal Publications.
Hbk £3.25

Malaysian Income Tax. – 4th ed. – Singapore : Quins, 1982.
lxi, 800p.
£135.00 with free Supplements

Malaysian Law. – Professional Law, 1988.
ISBN 09679958001 Hbk £35.00

Malaysian legal essays : a collection of essays in honour of Professor Emeritus Datuk Ahmad Ibrahim / edited by M.B. Hooker. – Kuala Lumpur : Malayan Law Journal, 1986.
xxxii,456p.
Collection of essays in honour of Professor Datuk Ahmad Ibrahim, covering aspects of Malaysian law, including family law, Islamic law, and legal history.
ISBN 9971700476

Malaysian legal source materials in London, Oxford and Cambridge / by Shaikha Zakaria : with a foreword by M.B. Hooker. – Kuala Lumpur : Perpustakaan Universiti Malaya, 1985.
x,66p.
Includes index.
ISBN 9679430057

Malaysian Taxation. – London : Butterworths, 1988.
ISBN 0409995622 Pbk

Male, J. M.
Landlord and Tenant. – 2nd ed. – Plymouth : Macdonald & Evans, 1985.
304p. – (M and E Handbook Ser.).
ISBN 0712128050 Hbk £6.50
—Landlord and Tenant. – 1st ed. – Plymouth : Macdonald & Evans, 1982.
304p. – (M and E Handbook Ser.).
ISBN 0712112510 Hbk £3.95

Malekian, Farhad
International criminal responsibility of states : a study on the evolution of state responsibility with particular emphasis on the concept of crime and criminal responsibility / by Farhad Malekian. – Stockholm : s.n., 1985.
xviii,234p.
Thesis (Doctor of Laws) - University of Stockholm, 1985. Bibliography: p.198-209. - Includes index.
ISBN 9171465022

Malhotra, M.
Criminal Jurisprudence and Law of Insanity. – New Delhi : Deep and Deep Publications, 1988.
172p.
Hbk £125.00

Malhotra, O.P.
Law of Industrial Disputes, 2 Vols. – 4th ed. in press. – Bombay : Tripathi.
Hbk £4238p

Malhotra, V.K.
Welfare State and Supreme Court in India. – New Delhi : Deep and Deep Publications, 1986.
140p.
Hbk £175.00

Malik
Art of Lawyer Advocacy : Cross Examination with Classes of Witnesses and Illustrative Cases. – Allahabad : Universal Book Agency, 1987.
Hbk £160.00
—Search and Seizure under Taxation Laws. – Allahabad : Law Publishers, 1982.
Hbk £22.50

Malik, B.
Commentaries on Urban Land (Ceiling and Regulation) Act, 1976. – 2nd ed. – Allahabad : Law Publishers, 1983.
Hbk £37.50
—Practical Hints on Cross-Examination. – 2nd ed. – Allahabad : Law Publishers, 1982.
Hbk £27.00

Malik, K.K. → Law Relating to Arms, Ammunition and Explosives.
—Supreme Court Rules, 1966. – Lucknow : Eastern Book Company, 1984.
119p.
Hbk £20.00

Malik, P.L.
Arms Act, 1959 with Rules, 1962 (Annotated). – 4th ed. – Lucknow : Eastern Book Company, 1984.
Hbk £20.00
→ Cases and Materials on Criminal Procedure Code.
—Commentaries on the Opium Act, 1878. – Lucknow : Eastern Book Company, 1984.
175p.
Hbk £30.00
→ Commentaries on Uttar Pradesh Kshettra Samitis and Zila Parishads Adhiniyam, Includes Supplement-1982.
—Criminal Court Handbook (Minor Acts), 4 Vols. – Lucknow : Eastern Book Company, 1985.
Hbk
—Criminal Court Handbook (Three Major Acts). – 17th ed. 1982 repr. – Lucknow : Eastern Book Company, 1985.
808p.
Hbk £90.00
—Customs Act, 1962. – 3rd ed. – Lucknow : Eastern Book Company, 1982.
649p.
Hbk £85.00
—Guide to Foreign Exchange Regulations. – Lucknow : Eastern Book Company, 1981.
336p.
Hbk £45.00
—Handbook of Labour and Industrial Law. – 3rd ed. – Lucknow : Eastern Book Company, 1986.
Hbk £80.00
—Industrial Law. – 14th ed. – Lucknow : Eastern Book Company, 1985.
1,774p.
Hbk £225.00
—Industries Development and Regulation. – 3rd ed. – Lucknow : Eastern Book Company, 1985.
337p.
Hbk
—Intermediate Education Act, 1921 : Together with Amending Acts, Regulations and Notifications. – Lucknow : Eastern Book Company, 1982.
173p.
Hbk £25.00
—Labour Laws in Uttar Pradesh / Kamlesh Chopra. – 3rd ed. – Lucknow : Eastern Book Company, 1985.
2,131p.
Hbk £330.00
—Law of Electricity in Uttar Pradesh. – 2nd ed. – Lucknow : Eastern Book Company, 1985.
—Law of Motor Vehicles in U.P. – 3rd ed. – Lucknow : Eastern Book Company, 1984.
820p.
Hbk £100.00
→ Law Relating to Drugs and Cosmetics in India.
—Law Relating to Forests in Uttar Pradesh. – 1981 repr. ed. – Lucknow : Eastern Book Company, 1984.
206p.
Hbk £25.00
—Minimum Wages Act : With Central and U.P. Rules and Notifications Fixing Minimum Wages in Various Industries and Establishments. – 5th ed. – Lucknow : Eastern Book Company, 1985.
Pbk £40.00
—U.P. Industrial Disputes Act, 1947 : With Rules and Notifications. – 2nd ed. – Lucknow : Eastern Book Company, 1986.
Hbk £30.00
—Uttar Pradesh Excise Act, 1910 : Together with Rules and Notifications. – 3rd ed. – Lucknow : Eastern Book Company.
Hbk
→ Uttar Pradesh Land Revenue Act, 1901.
—Uttar Pradesh Police Regulations. – 3rd ed. – Lucknow : Eastern Book Company, 1985.
Hbk
—Uttar Pradesh Sales Tax Act, 1948 : Together with Rules and Notifications as Amended up to U.P. Act No. 22 of 1984. – 6th ed. – Lucknow : Eastern Book Company, 1985.
220p.
Hbk £36.00

Malik, Surendra
Commentaries on Uttar Pradesh Municipalities Act, 1916. – Lucknow : Eastern Book Company, 1984.
366p.
Hbk £120.00
—Commentaries on Uttar Pradesh Nagar Mahapalika Act, 1959. – Lucknow : Eastern Book Company, 1985.
818p.
Hbk £115.00
—Commentaries on Uttar Pradesh Panchayat Raj Act, 1947. – Lucknow : Eastern Book Company, 1986.
346p.
Hbk £40.00
—Comparative Tables of Supreme Court Cases, 1950-85. – Lucknow : Eastern Book Company.
Hbk
—Complete Digest of Supreme Court Cases 1950 to Date, 16 Vols. – Lucknow : Eastern Book Company.
Hbk £85.00 ea.
—Complete Supreme Court Criminal Digest 1950 to Date, 6 Vols. in 7. – Lucknow : Eastern Book Company, 1983.
Hbk £90.00 ea.
→ Law Relating to Electricity in India.
—Supreme Court Labour and Services Digest, 1983-1986, 4 Vols. – Lucknow : Eastern Book Company, 1987.
Hbk £360.00
—Supreme Court on Essential Commodities Act, 1955. – Lucknow : Eastern Book Company, 1984.
161p.
Hbk £40.00
—Supreme Court on Law of Limitation 1950-79. – Lucknow : Eastern Book Company, 1981.
226p.
Hbk £25.00
—Supreme Court on Preventive Detention, 1950 to Date. – Lucknow : Eastern Book Company, 1985.
478p.
Hbk £90.00
→ Uttar Pradesh Local Acts in about 12 Volumes.

Malik, Sushma → Commentaries on Uttar Pradesh Cooperative Societies Act, 1965.

Malik, Vijay
Banking Regulation Act, 1949 : Together with the Banking Companies (Acquisition and Transfer of Undertakings) Act, 1980 and the Public Financial Institutions (Obligations as to Fidelity and Secrecy) Act, 1983. – Lucknow : Eastern Book Company, 1984.
163p.
Hbk £30.00
→ Cattle Trespass Act, 1871.
→ Commentaries on the Societies Registration Act, 1860.
—Criminal Manual. – Lucknow : Eastern Book Company, 1983.
550p.
Hbk £40.00
—Drugs and Cosmetics Act, 1940 : Together with Drugs and Cosmetics Rules, 1945 and Drugs (Price control) Order, 1979. – 2nd ed. – Lucknow : Eastern Book Company, 1984.
447p.
Hbk £65.00
—Explosives Act, 1884. – 4th ed. – Lucknow : Eastern Book Company.
288p.
Hbk £48.00
—Indian Explosives Act, 1884 and Explosive Rules, 1983 : Together with Explosive Substances Act, 1908, Gas Cylinders Rules, 1981 and Static Mobile Pressure Vessels (Unfired) Rules, 1981. – 3rd ed. – Lucknow : Eastern Book Company, 1984.
255p.
Hbk £40.00
—Law for Cinemas and Videos. – 4th ed. – Lucknow : Eastern Book Company, 1985.
Hbk £45.00
—U.P. Muslim Wakfs Acts. – Lucknow : Eastern Book Company, 1984.
91p.
Hbk £20.00
—Water (Prevention and Control of Pollution) Act, 1974. – 1982 repr. – Lucknow : Eastern Book Company, 1984.
147p.
Hbk £30.00

Mallal's Supreme Court Practice, Vol 1 / Min Tat Chang. – 2nd ed. – Singapore : Malayan Law Journal, 1983.
1,368p.
ISBN 9971700344 Hbk £500.00
Supplement Vol. 1. – 1986.
52p.
ISBN 9971700441 Pbk £15.00

Mallat, Chibli, et al
Islamic family law / Jane Connors. – London : Graham & Trotman, 1989.
350; 240mm.
Covers current research into areas of Islamic family law in the form of articles. Addresses historical issues such as the development of the law of succession in Islamic law, the colonial encounter and its impact on Islamic family law in India, as well as contemporary law of the family in Egypt, the sub-continent, Iran and Europe, and the law of minorities in their relation to the state.
ISBN 1853333018 Hbk £35
→ Islamic law and finance.

Mallick, M.R.
Employees' State Insurance Act. – 2nd ed. – Calcutta : Eastern Law House, 1984.
Hbk £142.00

Mallik, J.N.
Trade Union Law. – Calcutta : Sarkar & Sons, 1970.
xxiv, 247p.
Hbk £17.50

Malone, M.
Racial discrimination. – Ross Anderson, 1984.
ISBN 0863600042 Pbk £2.95
—Sex discrimination. – Ross Anderson, 1983.
ISBN 0863600050 Pbk £2.95

Malor, Jean → Australian Current Law.

Malpass, Peter
Housing Policy and Practice / Alan Murie. – London : Macmillan, 1982.
216p. – (Public Policy and Politics, General Ser.).
ISBN 0333328426 Hbk £15.00
ISBN 0333328434 Pbk £5.95

Malta → Revised edition of the laws of Malta, in force on 1st January, 1984.

Malton Memorial Recreation Association Act, 1983, Bill Pr030 : An Act to Revive the Malton Memorial Recreation Association. – Ontario : Ontario Government Publications Service, 1983.
2p.
Hbk £0.30

Malynes
Consuetodo Vel Lex Mercat. – 3rd ed. – Abingdon : Professional Books, 1986 Reprint.
ISBN 0862053250 Hbk £48.50

Mammoth Book of True Crime. – Robinson Publishers.
ISBN 0948164700 Pbk £4.95

Man for a New Country. – Victoria : Sono Nis Press.
334p.
ISBN 0888260687 Hbk £16.95

Man, law, and modern forms of life / edited by Eugenic Bulygin, Jean-Louis Gardies, and Ilkka Niiniluoto : introduction by Michael D. Bayles. – Dordrecht Netherlands : D. Reidel, 1985.
'Proceedings of the 11th IVR World Congress on Philosophy of Law and Social Philosophy ... held on August 14-20, 1983 in Helsinki'–Introd. Includes bibliographies and index.
ISBN 9027718695 Hbk £39.50

Man mismanagement / Alan Fox. – 2nd ed. – London : Business Books, 1985.
224p.
Previous ed.: London : Hutchinson, 1974. Includes bibliography and index.
ISBN 0091593808 Pbk £7.95

Man of Influence : Sir Siegmund Warburg. – Weidenfeld & Nicolson, 1986.
ISBN 0297789783 Hbk £16.95

Man of Law : a Model. – Saskatoon : Western Producer Prairie Books.
225p.
ISBN 0888330340 Pbk £12.95

Management Accounting 1988 : ICSA Study Text. – London : BPP.
ISBN 0862772133 Pbk £15.95

Management Accounting. – 2nd ed. – London : Addison-Wesley.
ISBN 0201157608 Hbk £17.95

Management and Cost Accounting. – London : VanNostrand Reinhold.
ISBN 0278000622 Pbk £15.95
Student Manual. –
ISBN 0278000630 Pbk £8.95
Teachers Manual. –
ISBN 0278000649 Pbk £18.95

Management and regulation of banks / John Cooper. – London : Macmillan, 1984.
xi,395p.
Bibliography: p383-386.
ISBN 0333342348

Management by Objectives in Local Government / R. E. H. Bullock. – Tonbridge : Ernest Benn.
255p.
Hbk £4.00

Management Contracting / A. C. Sidwell. – London : Collins, 1987.
250p.
ISBN 0003833143 Hbk £17.50

Management for Bankers. – London : Butterworths, 1988.
ISBN 0406503400 Pbk £13.50

Management Information Systems. – London : Kogan Page.
ISBN 1850914699 Hbk £18.95

Management of a student research project / Keith Howard & John A. Sharp. – Aldershot : Gower, 1983.
xiii,238p; 23cm.
Bibliography: p219-232. - Includes index.
ISBN 0566004623 Hbk £
ISBN 0566006138 Pbk

Management of collective bargaining : an international comparison / Keith Sisson. – Oxford : Basil Blackwell, 1987.
280p; 23cm.
Includes bibliography and index.
ISBN 0631134395 £25.00

Management of Correctional Institutions. – Jayewardene. – Toronto : Butterworths, 1981.
208p.
Analyses the aims and objectives of a correctional institution, the context in which it must operate, and the material and human resources available for it to operate, using the framework of extant sociological and physiological theory. Illustrates how from this analysis an efficient program of activity could be derived, using the framework of managerial theory.
ISBN 0409840513 Pbk £21.95

Management of Corrections in Asia and the Pacific. – Canberra : Australian Institute of Criminology.
Hbk £12.50

Management of Humanity's Resources : the Law of the Sea. Workshop 1981. – Dordrecht : Kluwer, 1982.
xvi, 434p.
ISBN 9024727626 Hbk £120.00

Management scrutiny : listing officers in the Crown Court / Lord Chancellor's Department. – London : The Department, 1984.
108p.
Includes bibliographical references.

Management Structure in Prison Department Establishments : A Cumulative Document. – London : Home Office, 1983.
iii, 26p.
Hbk

Management structures in local and regional government : report / prepared under the guidance of the Committee of Experts on Management in Local and Regional Government of the Steering Committee for Regional and Municipal Matters, by G. Kelly. – Strasbourg : Council of Europe, 1985.
54p.

Managerial Accounting / Jaedicke. – 7th ed. – London : Eurospan.
ISBN 0538019638 Pbk £11.75

Managerial Accounting. – 3rd ed. – New York : Dryden Press.
ISBN 0030119642 Hbk £23.95

Managerial Accounting : Method and Meaning / Chua. – London : VanNostrand Reinhold.
ISBN 00278000215 Pbk £14.95
Teachers Manual. –
ISBN 00278000223 Pbk £10.00

Managerial law. – Hull : Barmarick Publications, 1966-.
'Knight's Industrial Law Reports in their revised edition'. Supersedes: Knight's industrial law reports (1 vol. only). - Continues: Knight's industrial reports.

Manager's Guide to International Road Freighting. – London : Kogan Page, 1986.
320p.
ISBN 1850911495 Hbk £12.95

Manager's Guide to Patents, Trade Marks and Copyright. – London : Kogan Page, 1986.
150p.
ISBN 1850912033 Hbk £13.95
ISBN 1850912041 Pbk £6.95

Managing a foreign exchange department. – Cambridge : Woodhead-Faulkner, 1985.
ISBN 0859412768 Hbk £45.00

Managing Bank Assets and Liabilities. – London : Euromoney.
ISBN 1870031768 Hbk £75.00

Managing change in the USSR : the politico-legal role of the Soviet jurist / John N. Hazard. – Cambridge : Cambridge University Press, 1983.
ix,182p; 23cm.
'The Goodhart lectures 1982'. Bibliography: p175-177. - Includes index.
ISBN 0521253160 £17.50

Managing Construction Conflict. – London : Longman Scientific, 1988.
ISBN 0582003504 Pbk £18.00

Managing criminal justice : a collection of papers / edited by David Moxon, Home Office Research and Planning Unit. – London : H.M.S.O., 1985.
vi,216p.
Examines the individual's progress through the justice system from arrest to final disposal. Discusses current research on the subject.
ISBN 0113408110

Managing criminological research / by John Croft. – London : H.M.S.O., 1981.
iv,13p.
A Home Office Research Unit report.
ISBN 0113407092

Managing Financial Services Marketing. – Pitman.
ISBN 0273028499 Pbk £12.95

Managing Foreign Exchange Risk Exposure. – London : Law Book Co.
ISBN 0455206252 Pbk

Managing Global Money. – London : Macmillan.
ISBN 0333443772 Hbk £35.00

Managing Institutional Change : Role of Staffing Commissions in the Public Sector / White. – Policy Studies Institute.
ISBN 0853744254 Pbk £7.95

Managing Natural Resources in a Federal State. – Agincourt : Carswell, 1986.
354p.
This work contains a collection of articles on the development and control of northern and offshore oil and gas, development of resources within federal parks and aboriginal lands, revenue sharing, environmental management, and interjurisdictional cooperation.
Hbk £59.00

Managing Profitability and Lawyer Compensation. – Vancouver : British Columbia Continuing Legal Education Society, 1986.
70p.
ISBN 0865042470 Hbk £45.00

Managing Public Money. – University Press Of America, 1988.
ISBN 0819165050 Hbk £22.95
ISBN 0819165069 Pbk £11.50

Managing the long-term prison system : the report of the...Committee / A. J. Langdon. – London : H.M.S.O., 1984.
102p.
Presents the findings of the Control Review Committee for the prison system; including implications for physical security with particular reference to the dispersal system. Recommends central control of long-term allocations and specialised units for prisoners whose behaviour does not respond to the incentives of a better structured system.
ISBN 0113407971

Managing the Partnership Office. – London : Butterworths, 1978.
ISBN 0406221529 Pbk £8.50

Managing the water industry : the accounting, reporting and auditing dimension : a report to the Public Bodies Review Committee / from E. McL. Holmes. – Melbourne : Public Bodies Review Committee, 1982.
xi,237p.

Managing waste : the duty of care : the Government's response to the eleventh report of the Royal Commission on Environmental Pollution / Central Directorate of Environmental Protection, Department of the Environment. – London : H.M.S.O., 1986.
ISBN 0117518999

Managing Your Career in the Law. – London : Blackstone Press.
ISBN 1854310119 Hbk £8.00

Managing your finances. – London : Longman Professional, 1988.
ISBN 0851213723 Pbk £4.95

Managing Your Personal Taxes. – Ward Lock.
ISBN 0706366700 Pbk £4.99

Mance, Jonathan →Chalmers' Sale of Goods Act 1979 : including the Factors Acts 1889 & 1890.

Mancer
Introduction to Taxation in New Zealand. – Butterworths, 1988.
470p.
ISBN 0409788570 Pbk £45.00

Manchanda
Hindu Law of Partition under Income-Tax Law. – 2nd ed. repr. – Allahabad : Law Book Company, 1983.
Hbk £22.50

Manchester, A. H.
Sources of English legal history : law, history and society in England and Wales 1750-1950 / A.H. Manchester. – London : Butterworths, 1984.
xiv,443p; 26cm.
Includes bibliographies and index.
ISBN 0406516596 Hbk £39

Mancini
Town of Harrow Act, 1983, Bill Pr050 : An Act Respecting the Town of Harrow. – Ontario : Ontario Government Publications Service, 1983.
2p.
Hbk £0.30

Mandaraka-Sheppard, Alexandra
Dynamics of aggression in women's prisons in England / Alexandra Mandaraka-Sheppard. – Aldershot : Gower, 1986.
xiii,272p; 23cm.
Bibliography: p241-260. - Includes index.
ISBN 0566008637 £17.50

Manes Organized Advocacy : a Manual for the Litigation Practitioner / Valerie Edwards. – rev. ed. – Agincourt : Carswell, 1988.
ca 550p.
Llf

Manes, Ronald D.
Manes Organized Advocacy : a Manual for the Litigation Practitioner / Valerie Edwards. – rev. ed. – Agincourt : Carswell, 1988.
ca 550p.
Llf

Mangone, Gerard J.
Law for the world ocean / by Gerard J. Mangone. – London : Stevens, 1981.
ii,313p; 19cm.
Bibliography: p292-300. - Includes index.
ISBN 0421284803 £12.00

Manin, Philippe →European Communities in the international order.

Manitoba and Saskatchewan Taxation Service. – Toronto : DeBoo, 1984.
ISBN 0888201869 Hbk £175.00

Manitoba Decisions (1980-Present) Civil and Criminal Cases. – Aurora : Canada Law Book Co. – (Summary Services, Provincial Ser.).
Pbk £199.50

Manitoba Decisions Citator (1981-Present). – Aurora : Canada Law Book Co. – (Statute Services).
Pbk £99.50

Manitoba Decisions Civil and Criminal Cases. – Aurora : Canada Law Book Co.
Llf £199.50

Manitoba government publications for the month of ... : monthly checklist / compiled in the Legislative Library. – Winnipeg : Queen's Printer, 1975.
Continues: Publications of the Government of Manitoba.
ISBN 03181200

Manitoba Law Reform Commission
Report on administrative law
Part 1 : Procedures of provincial government agencies / Manitoba Law Reform Commission. – Winnipeg : Manitoba Law Reform Commission, 1984.
182p.
Includes bibliographical references.
—Report on an examination of 'the Dower Act' / Manitoba Law Reform Commission. – Winnipeg : Manitoba Law Reform Commission, 1984.
v,283p. – (Report).

Manitoba Law Reports : 1884-1962, 67 Vols. – Carswell Legal Publications. – Agincourt : Carswell, 1983.
Hbk

Manitoba regulations. – Winnipeg : Queen's Printer, 1975.

Manitoba statutes. – 30. – Winnipeg : Queen's Printer, 1970.
looseleaf.
'Based on Revised statutes of Manitoba, 1970' - A bibliography of Canadian law/ Reynold Boult (1977). Includes index (3).

Mankabady, Samir
International Maritime Organization
Vol.1 : International shipping rules / Samir Mankkabady. – 2nd ed. – London : Croom Helm, 1986.
xxi,450p; 23cm.
Previous ed.: published in 1 vol. 1984. Includes index.
ISBN 0709935919 £45.00
Vol.2 : Accidents at sea / Samir Mankabady. – 1987.
xxvii,452p; 23cm.
Previous ed.: published in 1 vol. 1984. Includes index.
ISBN 0709946406 Hbk £50.00
—Law of Collision at Sea. – Amsterdam : Elsevier Science Publishers, 1987.
xxxviii, 608p.
ISBN 0444703071 Hbk £250.00

Mankiewicz, Rene H
Liability regime of the international air carrier : a commentary on the present Warsaw system / Rene H. Mankiewicz. – Deventer, The Netherlands : Kluwer, 1981.
xxvii,259p.
Includes index. Bibliography: pxv-xxii.
ISBN 9026811705

Mann, Arnold
Medical Assessment of Injuries for Legal Purposes. – 4th ed. – Sydney : Butterworths, 1985.
372p.
ISBN 0409492981 Hbk
—Medical Negligence Litigation : Medical Assessment of Claims. – Butterworths, 1988.
ca 400p.
ISBN 0409494550 Hbk £59.00

Mann, Bruce
National Parole Board handbook for judges and crown attorneys / Bruce Mann. – Ottawa : Govt. of Canada, National Parole Board, 1983.
70, 72 p.; 23 cm.
English and French. Title on added t.p.: Un Manuel de la Commission nationale des liberations conditionnelles a l'intention des juges et avocats de la couronne. Includes bibliographical references.
ISBN 066252361X Pbk

Mann, F. A.
Foreign affairs in English courts / F.A. Mann. – Oxford : Clarendon, 1986.
300p; 22cm.
ISBN 0198255640 £30.00
—Legal aspect of money : with special reference to comparative private and public international law / by F.A. Mann. – 4th ed. – Oxford : Clarendon, 1982.
lvi,602p; 25cm.
Previous ed.: Oxford : Oxford University Press, 1971. Bibliography: pli - Includes index.
ISBN 0198253672 Hbk £45.00

Mann, J. Fraser
Computer technology and the law in Canada / J. Frazer Mann. – Toronto : Carswell, 1987.
xxviii,455p.
ISBN 0459398504

Mann, K.
Defending White-Collar Crime : A Portrait of Attorneys at Work. – Yale University Press.
ISBN 0300043686 Pbk £8.95

Mann, T.S.
Law and Practice of Life Insurance in India. – New Delhi : Deep and Deep Publications, 1987.
448p.
Hbk £275.00

Manners, A. J.
Family property in Scotland : an enquiry carried out on behalf of the Scottish Law Commission by the Social Survey Division of the Office of Population Censuses and Surveys in 1979 / A.J. Manners, I. Rauta. – London : H.M.S.O., 1981.
iv,45p.
ISBN 0116907797

Manning →Criminal Law.
—Protection of Privacy Act. – London : Butterworths.
ISBN 0409848859 Hbk £30.00

Manning, Douglas J. →Child and Family Services Act : a Guide to Part 3.

Manning, Janet →Practical guide to mental health law : the Mental Health Act 1983 and related legislation.

Manning, Morris →Criminal Law.
—Rights, freedoms and the courts : a practical analysis of the Constitution Act, 1982 / Morris Manning. – Toronto : Emond-Montgomery, 1983.
lxiv,760p.
Includes the text of the Act.
ISBN 0920722105

Mannix →Leading Cases on Australian Income Tax.

Mannix, E. F. →Australian income tax guide 1988.
—International transactions and Australian income tax : being a commentary on Division 13 of the Income Tax Assessment Act 1936 together with the text of the Legislation / by E. F. Mannix. – Sydney : Butterworths, 1982.
x,46p.
Includes index.
ISBN 0409493554
—Introduction to Capital Gains Tax. – Butterworths.
ISBN 0409493066 Pbk £7.95
—Leading Cases on Australian Income Tax / J.E. Mannix. – 5th ed. – Butterworths, 1985.
720p.
ISBN 0409493929 Hbk £61.00
—Professional negligence : being a discussion of the duties and responsibilities of auditors / by E.F. Mannix and J.E. Mannix. – 3rd ed. – Sydney : Butterworths, 1982.
viii,112p.
Previous ed.: 1976. Includes index.
ISBN 0409309338
—Tax and the Australian film industry : being a commentary on division 10BA of the Income Assessment Act 1936 together with text of the legislation / by E.F. Mannix. – Sydney : Butterworths, 1981.
xii,92p.
Includes index.
ISBN 040936018X
—Tax avoidance 1981 : the new law : being a commentary on part IVA of the Income Tax Assessment Act 1936 together with the text of the legislation / by E.F. Mannix. – Sydney : Butterworths, 1981.
ix,41p.
Includes index.
ISBN 0409357782

Mannix, J.E. →Leading Cases on Australian Income Tax.
→ Professional negligence : being a discussion of the duties and responsibilities of auditors.

Manohar, Murli
Art of Conveyancing and Pleading. – 1974 2nd repr. – Lucknow : Eastern Book Company, 1983.
290p.
Pbk £15.00

Manraj, A. Shakoor
Law on Speeding and Radar / Paul Douglas Haines. – Toronto : Macmillan of Canada, 1988.
120p.
ISBN 077159531X Pbk £6.95
—Law on Speeding and Radar / Paul Douglas Haines. – Butterworths, 1985.
136p.
States the law relating to speeding and examines all relevant authorities on speeding and the use of radar in speeding. Examines the identification of speeding as an absolute liability offence and presents a comprehensive picture of how the law has evolved.
ISBN 0409811793 Hbk £36.95

Mansfield, Graham
Director of Public Prosecutions : principles and practices for the Crown Prosecutor : an inquiry carried out at the Centre for Criminological Research, University of Oxford / Graham Mansfield and Jill Peay : foreword by Sir Thomas Hetherington. – London : Tavistock, 1986.
viii,246p; 23cm.
Bibliography: p237-241. - Includes index.
ISBN 0422600008 £16.00

Mansfield, J.L. →Financial Institutions Duties : Untangling the Web.

Mant →Principle and Practice of Medical Jurisprudence.

Manual for the Simulation of the Family Court of Australia. – Canberra : Australian Government Publishing Service, 1981.
58p.
ISBN 064206749X Hbk £2.60

Manual of Australian Constitutional Law. – 3rd ed. – North Ryde : Law Book Co, 1984.
ISBN 0455202893 Hbk £33.00

Manual of Banking and Public Financial Institutions : Laws with Allied Acts, 2 Vols. – Madhya Pradesh : Lawyers Home, 1986.
Hbk £175.00 ea

Manual of brief writing in the Court of Appeal and the Supreme Court of Nigeria / by Philip Nnaemeka-Agu. – Enugu, Nigeria : Fourth Dimension, 1986.
xviii,110p.
Bibliography: p. 109-110. - Includes index.

Manual of Civil Laws, 4 Vols. – Allahabad : Law Publishers, 1983.
Hbk £30.00

Manual of Commercial and Banking Laws, 4 Vols. – Allahabad : Law Publishers, 1983.
Hbk £30.00 ea

Manual of Criminal Laws, 4 Vols. – Allahabad : Law Publishers, 1983.
Hbk £30.00 ea

Manual of Employee Taxation. – London : Butterworths.
Service.
ISBN 0406413894 Llf £55.00

Manual of European Practice
Vol. 1 / A. Layton. – London : Sweet & Maxwell, 1986.
Explains English procedure and practice as they apply to cross-border litigation in the light of the 1982 Civil Jurisdiction and Judgements Act. Gives a comparative description of the legal systems of Belgium, Denmark, France, Germany, Ireland, Italy, Luxembourg, the Netherlands, England and Wales, Scotland and Northern Ireland.
ISBN 0421262907 Hbk
Vol. 2. –
ISBN 0421263008 Hbk

Manual of Financial Reporting and Accounting. – Touche Ross. – 2nd ed. – London : Butterworths, 1985.
This book describes the legal requirements and professional pronouncements relating to audit reports and financial statements. The work gives recommended accounting and consolidating principles, and contains many examples of different types of audit reports.
ISBN 0406500509 Pbk

Manual of housing law. – 4th. – London : Sweet & Maxwell, 1989.
Taking into account changes due to the Housing Act 1988, covers occupation status, security of tenure by Rent and Housing Acts, restricted security, lack of security, harassment and illegal eviction, break-up of relationships, homelessness and disrepair, multiple occupation and common lodging houses, and overcrowding.
ISBN 042140650X Pbk £14.95

Manual of instructions for legislative and legal writing / Elmer A. Driedger. – Ottawa : Canadian Government Publishing Centre, 1982.
6 v, vi, 568.; 25 cm.
Includes bibliographical references.
ISBN 0660111187 Pbk : set £25.00 (£30.00 other countries)

Manual of law librarianship : the use and organization of legal literature / edited by Elizabeth M. Moys. – 2nd ed. – Aldershot : Gower, for the British and Irish Association of Law Librarians, 1987.
xxxv,915p; 23cm.
Previous ed.: London : Deutsch, 1976. Bibliography: p802-891. - Includes index.
ISBN 056603512X £39.50

Manual of Mercantile Law. – 12th ed. – New Delhi : S. Chand and Company, 1983.
vii, 906p.
Hbk £35.00

Manual of Motor Vehicle Law, 2 Vols. – 3rd ed. – Agincourt : Carswell, 1982.
This looseleaf service is an annotated guide to the text of the Highway Traffic Act of Ontario, Canada. Cases and statutory references to the motor vehicle law of all provinces is included in the work.
Llf £138.75

Manual of Political Ethics. – Repr. of 1838 ed. – Aalen Wuertt : Scientia.
Hbk £255.00

Manual of Queensland succession law / by W. A. Lee. – 2nd ed. – Sydney : Law Book Company, 1985.
xlix,268p.
ISBN 0455205620

Manual of Road Accident Investigation
Vol. 2 /. – Pitman, 1981.
ISBN 0273016008 Hbk £6.50

Manual of Roman Law. – London : Butterworths, 1986.
ISBN 040905755X Pbk £14.00

Manual of the Law of Income Tax in Australia. – 6th ed. – North Ryde : Law Book Co, 1987.
xxvi, 360p.
ISBN 0455202974 Hbk £38.50
ISBN 0455202982 Pbk £26.50
Supplement 1987. –
ISBN 0455207313 Hbk £2.50

Manual of the law of real property / David J Hayton. – 6th ed. – London : Sweet & Maxwell, 1982.
ISBN 0420463305 Hbk £26.00
ISBN 0420463402 Pbk £16.50

Manual of the Victorian Residential Tenancies Act. – North Ryde : Law Book Co, 1982.
xx, 299p.
ISBN 045520540X Pbk £37.00

Manual on Legislative Drafting. – London : Commonwealth Secretariat, 1984.
free

Manuel des Corporations du Quebec. – Toronto : DeBoo, 1983.
ISBN 0888201478 Hbk £365.00

Manufacture of news : social problems, deviance and the mass media / Stanley Cohen and Jock Young (editors). – rev. ed. – London : Constable, 1981.
506p.
ISBN 0094637806

Manufacturers' Liability for Defective Goods. – Oxford : Blackwell Scientific, 1987.
ISBN 0003833623 Hbk £20.00

Manwaring-White, Sarah
Policing revolution : police technology, democracy and liberty in Britain / Sarah Manwaring-White. – Brighton : Harvester, 1983.
vii,231p; 23cm.
ISBN 0710805551 Hbk £18.95
ISBN 0710806159 Pbk

Manx law bulletin. – Douglas : Attorney General's Chambers, 1983-.
Covers legislation 'in a limited manner' and 'all written judgments from the High Courts'.

Manx law reports. – Oxford : Law Reports International, 1985-.

Maori Fishing Rights in New Zealand : an Economic Perspective. – Canterbury : Agricultural Economics Research Unit, 1986.
9p.
Hbk

Maori land laws of New Zealand. – Saskatoon : University of Saskatchewan, Native Law Centre, 1983.
86p.
ISBN 088880122X Hbk £13.00

Maori of New Zealand / by Robert Macdonald. – London : Minority Rights Group, 1985.
16p. – (Report).
Bibliography: p.16.
ISBN 0946690367

Maple, G. J. →Rayden and Jackson's law and practice in divorce and family matters.

Mapp, Wayne →Goods and Services Tax Act 1985 : the Application of the Act.

Mara-Brown, E.
Nigerian law of torts / E. Mara-Brown. – London : Sweet & Maxwell, 1987.
v,76p.
Includes index.
ISBN 0421361506

Marantelli, S. E.
Australian legal dictionary / by S.E. Marantelli. – 6th reprint. – Caulfield East, Victoria : Edward Arnold Australia, 1985.
242p.
ISBN 0713181184

Marasinghe, Lakshman
Food Famine and the Legal Order / Julio Menezes. – Colombo : Lake House Investments.
Pbk £10.00

Marasinghe, M.L.
Essays on Third World Perspectives in Jurisprudence / W.E. Conklin. – Singapore : Malayan Law Journal, 1984.
xvii, 442p.
Collection of jurisprudentially-orientated essays with particular reference to the problems and issues peculiar to the third world. Covers constitutional obligation in the third world, liberal conceptions and their applicability to the third world. and the jurisprudence of indigenous law.
ISBN 9971700352 Pbk £45.00

MARC : an introduction / Ellen Gredley. – London : Polytechnic of North London, School of Librarianship and Information Studies, 1983.
47p. – (Occasional publication).
Bibliography: p.45. - Includes index.
ISBN 0900639245

Mare Clausum : The Right and Dominion of the Sea. – Repr. of 1663 ed. – Abingdon : Professional Books.
515p.
Hbk £220.00

Maresceau, Marc
Political and legal framework of trade relations between the european community and eastern europe. – Dordrecht : Nijhoff (Martinus), 1989.
352.
Historical reflection on relations between the EEC and COMECON, and on analysis of the position of Western European countries in their relations with Eastern Europe, European enterprises in the EEC, export controls, financial cooperation and countertrade, and the position of Eastern European countries in the GATT.
ISBN 0792300467 Hbk £42

Mareva injunction and Anton Piller order : practice and precedents / by Richard N. Ough. – London : Butterworths, 1987.
xxii,175p; 22cm.
Includes index.
ISBN 0406102902 Pbk £28.95

Mareva Injunction and associated orders / by David G. Powles. – Abingdon : Professional Books, 1986.
xxiii,160p.
ISBN 0862050693 Hbk £35.00
ISBN 0862052033 Pbk £17.95

Mareva injunction and related orders / by Mark S.W. Hoyle. – London : Lloyd's of London Press, 1985.
viii,141p; 22cm.
ISBN 1850440441

Mareva injunction and related orders. – 2nd. – London : Lloyds of London Press, 1989.
Sets out the framework for applications in court for Mareva injunctions, Anton Pillar orders and similar and ancillary relief. The position in EEC countries is given, including the implications of the Civil Jurisdiction and Judgements Act 1982. The international section covers developments in Commonwealth and other jurisdictions.
ISBN 1850441618 Hbk

Mareva injunctions / edited by Marion Hetherington. – Sydney : Law Book Co., 1983.
xv,122p.
Includes index.
ISBN 0455204934

Mareva injunctions / by David Capper. – London : Sweet & Maxwell, 1988.
xxii,135p; 22cm.
Contains the definition and nature of a Mareva injunction, including matters which must be proved, the procedure for application, orders for the discovery of assets, the writ ne exeat regno, Bayer orders, and Anton Piller orders, and Mareva injunctions and the criminal law. Includes an appendix of precedents.
ISBN 0421389605 Pbk

Mareva Injunctions. – 2nd ed. – Agincourt : Carswell, 1987.
This work presents the history and current legal status of the Canadian Mareva Injunction. Procedural issues involved in obtaining and enforcing this unique remedy are reviewed in the book.
ISBN 045939780 Hbk £16.75

Mareva injunctions : a one-day conference / organised by Lloyds of London Press, the Tower Hotel, London, 22nd June 1982. – 1. – London : Lloyd's of London Press, 1982.
various pagings; 31cm.
ISBN 0907432433

Mareva injunctions : law and practice / Steven Gee and Geraldine Mary Andrews : foreword by Lord Denning. – London : Longman, 1987.
xxvii,143p; 25cm.
Includes index.
ISBN 0851209394 £30.00

Marfata, J.C.
Psychiatry and Law. – Bombay : Popular Prakashan.
Hbk £20.00

Margadant S., Guillermo Floris
Introduction to the history of Mexican law / Guillermo Floris Margadant S. – 1st English ed. – London : Oceana Publications, 1981.
Includes bibliographical references and index. Translation of: Introduccion a la historia del derecho mexicano, 4th ed.
ISBN 0379207443

Marginal seabed : United Kingdom legal practice / Geoffrey Marston. – Oxford : Clarendon Press, 1981.
xiii,316p; 22cm.
Bibliography: p299-302. - Includes index.
ISBN 0198253699 Hbk £22.50

Margrave-Jones, C →Agricultural law.

Marie, Jean-Bernard
Human rights or a way of life in a democracy / by Jean-Bernard Marie. – Strasbourg : Council of Europe, 1985.
114p.
Studies the extent to which respect for human rights depends on the public and the impact of those rights on daily life.
ISBN 9287103852 Pbk £3.80

Marin, Rene J.
Admissibility of Statements. – 6th ed. – Toronto : Balmuir Book Publishing Ltd..
xx, 231p.
ISBN 0919511236 Pbk £12.95
→ Report of the Commission of Inquiry Relating to the Security and Investigation Services Branch Within the Post Office Department.

Marine Affairs Bibliography : a Comprehensive Index to Marine Law and Policy Literature / Leslie A. Foster. – Dordrecht : Kluwer, 1987.
702p.
ISBN 902473570X Hbk £375.00

Marine Cargo Claims. – 3rd ed. – Montreal : International Shipping Publications, 1988.
1,448p.
Hbk £125.00

Marine claims handbook / by N.G. Hudson and J.C. Allen. – 4th ed. – London : Lloyds of London Press, 1984.
vi,102p.
ISBN 0907432913

Marine claims (hull) for indemnity : the Eugenides Foundation, Athens, April 29/30, 1982. – London : Lloyd's of London Press, 1982.
139leaves; 31cm.
Conference papers.
ISBN 0907432409

Marine encyclopaedic dictionary. – 2nd. – London : Lloyds of London Press, 1988.
Updated from the first edition, it contains definitions of technical shipping expressions, Latin usage in law and business. Abbreviations included carry varying meanings according to usage in different countries.
ISBN 1850441278 Hbk £37.50

Marine environment and the Caracas Convention on the Law of the Sea : a study of the Third United Nations Conference on the Law of the Sea and other Related Marine Environmental Activities / by Ted L. McDorman...et al. – Halifax, Nova Scotia : Dalhousie Ocean Studies Programme, 1981.
ix,127p.
ISBN 0770300790

Marine environment law in the United Nations Environment Programme : an emergent eco-regime / compiled by Peter H. Sand. – London : Tycooly, 1988.
xxvi,265p.
Contains the text of international treaties adopted under the United Nations Environment Programme.
ISBN 1851480242 Hbk £25.00

Marine insurance
vol. 1 : Principles & basic practice / by Robert H. Brown. – 5th ed. – London : Witherby & Co. Ltd, 1986.
xix,343p; 22cm.
ISBN 0948691190
Vol.2 : Cargo practice : incorporating Marine cargo claims by John J. Novitt / by Robert H. Brown. – 1985.
xiii,442,xxxviip; 23cm.
Previous ed.: 1979. Includes index. Contains text of the clauses.
ISBN 0900886838

Marine insurance / E.R. Hardy Ivamy. – 4th ed. – London : Butterworths, 1985.
lii,613p; 26cm. – (Butterworths insurance library).
Previous ed.: 1979. Includes index.
ISBN 0406253137

Marine Insurance Abbreviations. – London : Witherby, 1968.
ISBN 0900886005 Pbk £2.00

Marine insurance claims / by J. Kenneth Goodacre. – 2nd ed. – London : Witherby, 1981.
liv,1015p,12p of plates; 23cm. – (Monument series).
Previous ed.: 1974. Includes index.
ISBN 0900886536 £35.00

Marine Insurance Clauses / R. Swatton. – London : LLoyd's of London Press, 1985.
ISBN 1850440581 Hbk

Marine Insurance Law of Canada. – Butterworths, 1987.
304p.
Examines the Canadian judicial decisions in marine insurance, using as its basis the Marine Insurance Act, RSO 1980. Includes a table of statute concordance.
ISBN 0409805319 Hbk £48.00

Marine pilotage : legislative proposals / presented to Parliament by the Secretary of State for Transport... – London : H.M.S.O., 1986.
iii,12p.
ISBN 0101001525

Marine policy : the international journal for economics, planning and politics of ocean exploitation. – Guildford : IPC Science and Technology Press, 1977.
Subtitle varies: from 4, no. 3 subtitled: the international journal of ocean affairs.
ISBN 0308597X

Marine pollution / R.B. Clark. – Oxford : Clarendon, 1986.
xiii,215p; 24cm.
Bibliography: p208-209. - Includes index.
ISBN 019854183X Pbk £19.50
ISBN 0198541821 Pbk £9.50

Marine pollution in international and Middle Eastern law / by Sayed Hassan Amin : foreword by John P. Grant. – Glasgow : Royston, 1986.
138p; 22cm.
Bibliography: p119-135. - Includes index.
ISBN 0946706263 £30.00

Marine pollution in international law : material obligations and jurisdiction with special reference to the Third United Nations Conference on the Law of the Sea / by Kari Hakapaa. – Helsinki : Suomalainen Tiedeakatemia, 1981.
341 p.; 25 cm.
Errata slip and notice of public dissertation discussion inserted. Thesis (doctoral)–University of Helsinki, 1981. Includes indexes. Bibliography: p. 299-336.
ISBN 9514104021

Marine reinsurance / by Robert H. Brown and Peter B. Reed. – London : Witherby, 1981.
xi,343p; 23cm.
Includes index.
ISBN 0900886617 £21.00

Marine scientific research and the law of the sea / Alfred H.A. Soons. – Deventer, Netherlands : Kluwer Law and Taxation Publishers, 1982.
xix, 383 p.; 24 cm.
At head of title: T.M.C. Asser Instituut, The Hague. Includes index. Bibliography: p. 370-377.
ISBN 9065440658

Marison
System of law and courts governing New South Wales. – 2nd ed. – London : Butterworths, 1985.
ISBN 0409492531 Hbk £40.00

Marital Property Agreements. – Vancouver : Continuing Legal Education Society of British Columbia, 1988.
369p.
ISBN 086504970X Hbk £70.00

Marital violence : the community response / Margaret Borkowski, Mervyn Murch, Val Walker. – London : Tavistock, 1983.
x,230p; 23cm.
Bibliography: p216-222. - Includes index.
ISBN 0422781207 Hbk £
ISBN 0422781304 Pbk

Maritime affairs : a world handbook : a reference guide to maritime organizations, conventions and disputes and to the international politics of the sea / compiled and written by Henry W. Degenhard : editorial consultant, Brian Meredith : general editor, Alan J. Day. – Harlow : Longman, 1985.
viii,412p; 26cm. – (A Keesing's reference publication).
Bibliography: p385-390. - Includes index.
ISBN 0582902630 £50.00
ISBN 0810320517

Maritime boundaries and ocean resources / edited by Gerald Blake : International Geographical Union Study Group on the World Political Map. – London : Croom Helm, 1987.
284p; 23cm.
Bibliography: p257-271. - Includes index.
ISBN 0709939744 £27.50

Maritime Boundaries and Resource Development. – Calgary : Canadian Institute of Resources Law.
Hbk £15.00

Maritime boundary / S.P. Jagota. – Dordrecht : M. Nijhoff, 1985.
388p.
Bibliography.
ISBN 902473133X Hbk £175.00

Maritime boundary delimitation : an annotated bibliography / Ted L. McDorman, Kenneth P. Beauchamp, Douglas M. Johnston. – Lexington, Mass. : Lexington Books, 1983.
xiii,207p; 24cm.
Includes index.
ISBN 0669061468

Maritime Labour Conventions and Recommendations. – Geneva : International Labour Office, 1983.
viii, 224p.
ISBN 9221030962 Hbk £17.50

Maritime Law
Vol. 1: Arrest of Vessels. – Dordrecht : Kluwer, 1976.
108p.
ISBN 9026808941 Hbk £45.00
Vol. 2: Enforced Sales of Vessels. – 1977.
114p.
ISBN 9026809395 Hbk £57.00
Vol. 3: Mortgage on Vessels and Registration of Vessels, 2 pts.. – 1983.
324p.
ISBN 9065441298 Hbk £207.00

Maritime law / Christopher Hill. – 2nd ed. – London : Lloyds of London, 1985.
400p; 24cm.
Previous ed.: London : Pitman, 1981. Includes index.
ISBN 185044045X

Maritime Law : Third International Conference. – Vancouver : Continuing Legal Education Society of British Columbia, 1986.
566p.
ISBN 0865042721 Hbk £100.00

Maritime Law Association of Australia and New Zealand →MLAANZ journal.

Maritime Law Handbook / Hans Christian Albrecht. – Dordrecht : Kluwer, 1987.
350p.
Llf £185.00

Maritime law in bills of lading : a conference organised by Lloyd's of London Press : the Tower Hotel, London, 23rd June, 1982. – London : Lloyds of London Press, 1982.
96 leaves in various foliations; 31cm.
ISBN 0907432441

Maritime Law of Norway, Dated July 10th 1893. Laws, Statutes, etc. Norway. – Oslo : Fabritius og Sonners, 1896.
1148p.
ISBN 8207009187 Hbk £358.00

Maritime law of salvage / by Geoffrey Brice. – London : Stevens, 1983.
xxxvi,539p; 26cm.
Focuses on established principles and topics in which particular developments have been proposed, including the threat to the environment posed by the large laden tanker; the assessment of salvaged value; the liability of salvors for negligence and the limitation and exclusion of the liability. Appendices contain extracts from relevant statutes and statutory instruments.
ISBN 0420462406 Hbk £72.00

Maritime laws of the Arabian Gulf Cooperation Council States
Vol.1 / written and edited by Richard Price with chapters by Andreas Haberbeck. – London : Graham & Trotman, 1986.
267p; 25cm.
Includes index.
ISBN 086010821X £70.00
Vol.2 / Richard Price : with translations by James Whelan. – 1986.
ix,830p; 25cm.
ISBN 0860108309 Hbk £285.00

Maritime liens and claims / William Tetley with assistance from Brian G. McDonough. – London : Business Law Communications, 1985.
lxiv,686p.
Includes bibliographical references and index.
ISBN 0948406003

Maritime political boundaries of the world / J.R.V. Prescott. – London : Methuen, 1985.
xv,377p; 24cm.
Bibliography: 355-360. - Includes index.
ISBN 0416417507 £30.00

Maritime Provinces Reports : 1929-1968, 53 Vols. – Carswell Legal Publications. – Agincourt : Carswell, 1983.
Hbk

Maritime regulations of Saudi Arabia / Hussein M. El-Sayed. – London : Graham & Trotman, 1987.
250p; 24cm.
Includes bibliography and index.
ISBN 0860107361 £70.00

Maritime Safety and Environment Conventions. – London : Sweet & Maxwell, 1983.
– (British Shipping Laws).
Hbk £290.00

Maritime strategy for medium powers / J.R. Hill. – London : Croom Helm, 1985.
247p; 23cm.
ISBN 0709937199 £19.95

Marjoram, J. →Cost of Criminal Justice : A Preliminary International Survey.
—Crime in a New Community : The Case of Tuggeranong. – Canberra : Australian Institute of Criminology.
Hbk £1.50
→ Road Safety and Crime.

Mark, Michael →Chalmers' Sale of Goods Act 1979 : including the Factors Acts 1889 & 1890.

Markanday, Katju
Interpretation of Taxing Statutes. – Allahabad : Law Publishing House, 1984.
Hbk £90.00

Markandeya, Subodh →Customs Act, 1962.
→ Foreign Exchange Regulations Act, 1973.

Markesinis, B. S.
Comparative introduction to the German law of tort / B.S. Markesinis. – Oxford : Clarendon, 1986.
xxix,610p; 24cm.
Includes bibliographies and index. Spine title: The German law of torts.
ISBN 0198255314 £55.00
—German Law of Torts. – Oxford : Oxford University Press, 1986.
ISBN 0198255314 Hbk £55.00
—Outline of the law of agency / R J C Munday. – 2nd ed. – London : Butterworths, 1986.
ISBN 040662271X Hbk £15.00
ISBN 0406622728 Pbk £9.95
→ Tort law.
→ Tortious Liability for Unintentional Harm, Vol. 1.
→ Tortious liability for unintentional harm in the common law and the civil law.

Marketing Financial Services / T Watkins. – London : Butterworths, 1986.
ISBN 0402502706 Hbk £18.95

Marketing Legal services / edited by S.C. Silkin. – London : Waterlows, 1984.
86p; 21cm.
Conference papers.
ISBN 0080392156 Pbk £10.50

Marketing Your Service. – North Vancouver : International Self-Counsel Press, 1987.
ISBN 0889086540 Hbk £12.95

Markets and false hierarchies : some problems in transaction cost economics / Neil Kay. – San Domenico, Florence : European University Institute, 1987.
52p.
Bibliography: pp.50-52..

Markets, Morals and the Law. – Cambridge : Cambridge University Press.
ISBN 0521363055 Hbk £35.00
ISBN 0521368545 Pbk £12.95

Markham, H.
Legal Secretary Pitman 2000. – Pitman, 1986.
ISBN 0273022261 Pbk £4.95

Markovic, Mihailo
On the Legal Institutions of Socialist Democracy. – London : Spokesman Books, 1983.
50p.
Pbk individual 4.00

Marks, David →Nelson-Jones: Practical Tax Saving.

Marks, David G. M. →Rowlatt on the law of principal and surety.

Marks, Francis, et al
Guidebook to Insurance Law in Australia and New Zealand. – North Ryde : C.C.H. Australia, 1987.
341p.
ISBN 0869036378 Pbk £35.00
—Guidebook to Workers Compensation in Australia. – 5th ed. – North Ryde : C.C.H. Australia, 1986.
624p.
ISBN 086903846X Pbk £38.00
—Workers' Compensation Law and Practice in New South Wales. – North Ryde : C.C.H. Australia, 1983.
309p.
ISBN 0869033484 Hbk

Marks, Frank
Industrial Accidents : Employer Liability for Monetary Damages / Audrey Balla. – North Ryde : C.C.H. Australia, 1987.
180p.
ISBN 0869038664 Hbk

Markuson →Warren's forms of agreement.

Marre, Romola Mary →Time for change.

Marriage and Divorce. – Community Legal Education Ontario. – 3rd rev. ed. – Toronto : Community Legal Education Ontario, 1982.
47p.
ISBN 088903057X Pbk £6.50

Marriage and domestic violence in rural Papua New Guinea / results of a research project conducted by the Law Reform Commission of Papua New Guinea : by Susan Toft and Susanne Bonnell. – Waigani : Law Reform Commission of Papua New Guinea, 1985.
v,116p. – (Occasional paper).
Bibliography: p.111.
ISBN 9980550007

Marriage and Family Law in Alberta : the Rights of Husbands, Wives, Children, and Common-Law. – 3rd ed. – North Vancouver : International Self-Counsel Press, 1987.
203p.
ISBN 0889082456 Hbk £8.95

Marriage and Family Law in British Columbia : the Rights of Husbands, Wives, Children, and Common-Law. – 6th ed. – North Vancouver : International Self-Counsel Press, 1985.
160p.
ISBN 0889081697 Hbk £7.95

Marriage and Family Law in Ontario : the Rights of Husbands, Wives, Children, and Common-Law Spouses. – 4th ed. – North Vancouver : International Self-Counsel Press, 1986.
203p.
ISBN 0889083606 Hbk £6.95

Marriage and Family Law in Washington : the Rights of Husbands, Wives, Children and Cohabiting Couples. – 3rd ed. – North Vancouver : International Self-Counsel Press, 1988.
ISBN 0889087377 Hbk

Marriage, Divorce and Inheritance : Cambridge African Monographs No. 10. – London : African Studies Centre.
ISBN 0902993232 Pbk £5.50

Marriage in comparative conflict of laws : substantive conditions / Lennart Palsson. – The Hague : Martinus Nijhoff, 1981.
lxxvi,388p.
Continues Palsson, L. : Marriage and divorce in comparative conflict of laws, Leyden, 1974. Bibliography: pli-lx.
ISBN 9024725488 Hbk £200.00

Marriage in Papua New Guinea / results of a research project conducted by the Law Reform Commission and Administrative College of Papua New Guinea. – Waigani : The Commission, 1986.
xi,223p. – (Monograph).
ISBN 9980550031

Marriage laws of Nigeria : papers presented at a national workshop held at the Nigerian Institute of Advanced Legal Studies / edited by T. Akinola Aguda : assisted by Isabella Adi. – Lagos : The Nigerian Institute of Advanced Legal Studies, 1981.
170p.
ISBN 9782353000

Marriage, money, property, and the law : a guide to the legal and financial consequences of a marriage between Africans / by J.C. Bekker. – Durban, South Africa : Butterworths, 1983.
53 p.; 24 cm.
Bibliography: p. 53.
ISBN 0409012106 Pbk

Marriage or Divorce : the Real Issue. – Dublin : Four Courts Press.
128p.
Hbk £8.95

Marriages and customary unions of black persons / South African Law Commission. – Pretoria : The Commission, 1985.
xix,222p. – (Project).
Bibliography: p.vii-xi.
ISBN 062110180X

Marriott, Alfred S.
Practice in mortgage actions in Ontario : the practice in mortgage actions and in exercising power of sale / Marriott and Dunn. – 4th ed. – Toronto : Carswell, 1982.
xliii,511p.
Includes index.
ISBN 0459348809

Marriott and Dunn : Practice in Mortgage Actions in Ontario. – 4th ed. – Agincourt : Carswell, 1982.
575p.
This fourth edition text is a guide to what you need to know to decide upon and obtain remedies. Topics include the power of sales procedure and an analysis of all other types of remedies in mortgage actions in Ontario.
Hbk £71.50

Marrocco, Frank N.
Annotated Immigration Act of Canada 1988 / Henry M. Goslett. – Carswell, 1988.
482p.
Pbk £38.00

Mars, Gerald
Cheats at work : an anthropology of workplace crime / Gerald Mars. – London : Unwin Paperbacks, 1983.
xii,242p; 20cm.
Originally published: London : Allen and Unwin, 1982. Bibliography: p229-234. - Includes index.
ISBN 0043011667 Pbk £2.95

Marsden, R.G.
Collisions at Sea / R.G. Marsden. – 12th ed. – Stevens & Sons.
– (British Shipping Law).
ISBN 0420448608 Hbk £100.00

Marsh
Business Law / Soulsby. – 3rd ed. – Maidenhead : McGraw-Hill, 1985.
ISBN 0070848769 Pbk £7.95
—Outlines of English Law / Soulsby. – 3rd ed. – Maidenhead : McGraw-Hill, (1982).
ISBN 0070846553 Pbk £7.95
—Practice of Banking 2 / Wild. – 2nd ed. – Pitman.
ISBN 0273028189 Pbk £13.95
—Private Members' Bills / Read. – Cambridge : Cambridge University Press, 1988.
ISBN 0521330513 Hbk £22.50
—Terminology of business and company law / Bailey. – London : Kogan Page, 1987.
ISBN 0850914133 Pbk £8.95

Marsh, G. Barrie
Employer and employee : a complete and practical guide to the modern law of employment / by G. Barrie Marsh. – 2nd ed. – London : Shaw, 1981.
lix, 616p.
ISBN 0721907415

Marsh, Ian A. →Capital Taxes Encyclopaedia.

Marsh, J.R.
Managing Financial Services Marketing. – Pitman.
ISBN 0273028499 Pbk £12.95

Marsh, Malcolm →New fixed penalty system : and disqualification, endorsement and penalty points : including a detailed guide to part III of the Transport Act 1982 and associated provisions.

Marsh, Norman S
Public access to Government held information. – London : Sweet & Maxwell, 1987.
ISBN 0420476105 Pbk £35.00
→ Public access to government-held information : a comparative symposium.

Marsh, S. B. →Second Survey of Legal Education in the United Kingdom : Supplement No. 2.

Marshall, B.
Workable government? : Constitution after 200 years. – Norton (WH), 1988.
ISBN 0393024806 Hbk £14.95
ISBN 0393304310 Pbk £7.50

Marshall, Enid A.
General principles of Scots law / by Enid A. Marshall. – 4th ed. – Edinburgh : Green, 1982.
xxiv,584p; 22cm. – (Concise college texts).
Previous ed.: 1978. Includes bibliographies and index.
ISBN 041400681X Pbk
→ Law of arbitration.
—Rights in security over moveables, cautionary obligations and bankruptcy. – Edinburgh : Green (W.) & Son, 1983.
Offprint from Scots Mercantile law by the same author, bringing together cahpters relating to the law of insolvency.
ISBN 0414007131 Pbk
—Sale of goods, consumer credit and bills of exchange, cheques and promissory notes. – Edinburgh : Green (W.) & Son, 1983.
Offprint from the author's Scots Mercantile law of chapters covering sale of goods and consumer law.
ISBN 041400714X Pbk
—Scots mercantile law / Enid A. Marshall. – Edinburgh : Green (W.) & Son, 1983.
xxxviii,665p.
Covers the major areas of the commercial law of Scotland, with full references to statutory provisions and case law. Notes differences between English and Scottish mercantile law. Student textbook assuming no previous legal knowledge.
ISBN 0414007204 Pbk

Marshall, Geoffrey
Constitutional Convention. – Reprint. – Oxford : Oxford University Press, 1986.
ISBN 019876202X Pbk £8.95
—Constitutional conventions : the rules and forms of political accountability / Geoffrey Marshall. – Oxford : Clarendon, 1984.
xvi,247p; 23cm.
Bibliography: p233-239. - Includes index.
ISBN 019876183X £16.50
—Constitutional Theory. – Oxford : Oxford University Press, 1971.
ISBN 019876121X Pbk £8.50

Marshall, I. David
Medical Law Handbook. – North Vancouver : International Self-Counsel Press, 1985.
131p.
ISBN 0889086036 Hbk £6.95

Marshall, J. D.
Old Poor Law, 1795-1834 / prepared for the Economic History Society by J.D. Marshall. – 2nd ed. – Basingstoke : Macmillan, 1985.
57p; 22cm.
Previous ed.: 1968. Bibliography: p51-54. - Includes index.
ISBN 0333398807 Pbk £3.95

Marshall, Oshley Roy →Cases and commentary on the law of trusts.
→ Report of the constitutional commission 1986.

Marshall, T.R.
Public Opinion and the Supreme Court. – London : Allen & Unwin.
ISBN 0044970463 Hbk £30.00
ISBN 0044970471 Pbk £11.95

Marshall, Tony F.
Bringing people together : mediation and reparation projects in Great Britain / Tony F. Marshall and Martin E. Walpole. – London : Home Office, 1985.
iv,89p.
ISBN 0862522196
→ Magistrates' domestic courts : new perspectives.
—Reparation, conciliation and mediation : current projects and plans in England and Wales / Tony F. Marshall : incorporating a survey by the National Association of Victims Support Schemes. – London : Home Office, 1984.
vii,73p.
Bibliography: p.50-73.
ISBN 0862521734

Marston
Police powers and duties / Nottridge. – London : Fourmat, 1985.
ISBN 0906840821 Pbk £9.95

Marston, Geoffrey
Development of the law of the sea with special reference to the exclusive economic zone. – S.l. : s.n., 1982.
p.297-307.
—Marginal seabed : United Kingdom legal practice / Geoffrey Marston. – Oxford : Clarendon Press, 1981.
xiii,316p; 22cm.
Bibliography: p299-302. - Includes index.
ISBN 0198253699 Hbk £22.50

Marston, John
Public order : a guide to the 1986 Public Order Act / by John Marston. – London : Fourmat Publishing, 1987.
189p.
ISBN 1851900241

Martha, R S J
Jurisdiction to tax in international law: theory and practice of legislative fiscal jurisdiction. – Kluwer Law and Taxation, 1989.
238. – (Series on International Taxation 9).
Deals with the bases and the limits of the right of states under international lw to create tax obligations on persons within and outside their territory. Describes the practice of states on matters of taxation in terms of the doctrine of jurisdiction in international law. Examines topics such as the taxation of mining activities on the continental shelf.
ISBN 9065444165 Hbk £51/Dfl 160

Martin →Licensed to live.

Martin, Alan D →Regulatory framework for storage and disposal of radioactive waste in the member states of the European Community.

Martin, Andrew →More law reform NOW : a collection of essays on law reform.

Martin, D.
Revenue law. – London : Financial Training, 1987.
– (SWOT).
ISBN 090632291X Pbk £8.95

Martin, D.A.
New Asylum Seekers : Refugees Law in the 1980's. – Martinus Nijhoff.
ISBN 9024737303 Hbk £39.00

Martin, David →Burundi since the genocide.
—Specification 87. – London : Architectural Press, 1987.
1400p : Illus.
ISBN 0851396232 Pbk £65.00

Martin, Douglas F. →Child abuse : procedure and evidence in juvenile courts.
→ Towards a unified Family Court : the collection of maintenance and the enforcement of court orders for maintenance.

Martin, E.R.
Multiple Choice Questions on the Principles of Accounts. – 2nd ed. – London : Edward Arnold.
ISBN 0713177489 Pbk £3.95

Martin, Elizabeth A. →Concise dictionary of law.

Martin, F. M. →Children out of court.
→ Scottish juvenile justice system.

Martin, I.
Accounting for Foreign Exchange. – London : Butterworths, 1987.
ISBN 0406503206 Pbk £37.50

Martin, Ian →British Nationality.
→ Immigration law and practice.

Martin, J. C. →Martin's annual criminal code.
→ Martin's related criminal statutes 1987 : a selection of important statutes and regulations related to the practice of criminal law.
→ Martin's related statutes 1983 : a selection of important statutes and regulations related to the practice of criminal law.

Martin, J. N.
Licensing Acts Nineteen Eighty-Seven. – 95th ed. – London : Butterworths, 1986.
ISBN 0406335206 Hbk
→ Licensing Acts Nineteen Eighty-Two.

Martin, Jill E. →Modern equity.
—Security of tenure under the Rent Act / by Jill E. Martin. – London : Sweet & Maxwell, 1986.
xxi,163p; 22cm.
Includes index.
ISBN 0421363304 Hbk £14.00
ISBN 0421363401 Pbk £10.50

Martin, Marjorie →Welfare Rights and GAIN.

Martin, Robyn
Damages for personal injuries and fatal accidents in Hong Kong : a review of the law and a digest of the cases / Robyn Martin, Peter Rhodes. – London : Butterworths, 1982.
xxv,563p; 23cm.
Gives general principles of the assessment of damages in personal injuries, and in fatal accident cases, and how these have been applied in Hong Kong. Included in the appendices are multiplier tables, actuarial tables, a glossary of medical terms, and illustrations.
ISBN 0406357102 £45.00

Martin, Roderick →Ballots and trade union democracy.

Martin, Sheilah L →Equality and judicial neutrality.

Martineau, Yvon
Manuel des Corporations du Quebec. – Toronto : DeBoo, 1983.
ISBN 0888201478 Hbk £365.00

Martino, Antonio Anselmo →Automated analysis of legal texts : logic, informatics, law : edited versions of selected papers from the Second International Conference on 'Logic, Informatics, Law,'Florence, Italy, September 1985.
→ Edited versions of selected papers from the International Conference on 'Logic, Informatics, Law', Florence, Italy, April 1981, vol.2 : Deontic logic, computational linguistics, and legal information systems : Antonio A. Martino; editor.

Martino, V. di →Law Relating to Transport of Dangerous Wastes, Netherlands.
→ Law Relating to Transport of Dangerous Wastes, United Kingdom.

Martin's annual criminal code / with annotations by Edward L. Greenspan. – 1981. – Aurora, Ont. : Canada Law Book, 1981.
xcix, 948p.
Includes index.

Martin's annual criminal code / with annotations by Edward L. Greenspan. – 1984. – Ontario : Canada Law Book, 1984.
cxv,1067p.
Includes index.

Martin's annual criminal code / with annotations by Edward L. Greenspan. – 1988. – Aurora, Ont. : Canada Law Book, 1988.
cxxiv,1089p.
Includes index. Kept up to date by supplements.

Martin's annual criminal code / with annotations by Edward L. Greenspan. – 1982. – Aurora, Ont. : Canada Law Book, 1982.
cvii,986p.
Includes index.

Martin's annual criminal code / with annotations by Edward L. Greenspan. – 1985. – Ontario : Canada Law Book, 1985.
cxx,1117p.
Includes index.

Martin's annual criminal code / with annotations by Edward L. Greenspan. – 1983. – Aurora, Ont. : Canada Law Book, 1983.
cxii,1054p.
Includes index.

Martin's Annual Criminal Code. – Aurora : Canada Law Book.
Hbk £21.00

Martin's related criminal statutes 1985 : a selection of important statutes and regulations related to the practice of criminal law / with annotations by Edward L. Greenspan. – Aurora, Ont. : Canada Law Book, 1985.
xlii,414p.

Martin's related criminal statutes 1987 : a selection of important statutes and regulations related to the practice of criminal law / with annotations by Edward L. Greenspan. – Aurora, Ont. : Canada Law Book, 1987.
xlv,499p.

Martin's related statutes 1983 : a selection of important statutes and regulations related to the practice of criminal law / with annotations by Edward L. Greenspan. – 1983. – Aurora, Ont. : Canada Law Book, 1983.
xxxv,379p.

Martlew, Clive → Rating appeals and the 1985 revaluation : proceedings of a Planning Exchange conference.

Martyn, Nicholas C.
Housing disrepair / Nicholas C. Martyn and Edward Lloyd-Jones. – London : Longman Professional, 1985.
xxv,187p; 22cm. – (Longman professional practitioner series).
Includes index.
ISBN 0851209904 Pbk £13.50

Marx and justice : the radical critique of liberalism / Allen E. Buchanan. – London : Methuen, 1982.
xiv,206p; 25cm.
Bibliography: p197-199. - Includes index.
ISBN 0416334504 £12.95

Marxer
Companies and Taxes in Liechtenstein / Goup. – Vaduz, 1983.
99p.
Hbk £39.00

Marxism and Law. – Oxford : Oxford University Press, 1982.
ISBN 0192851446 Pbk £4.50

Marxism and law / Hugh Collins. – Oxford Oxfordshire : Clarendon Press, 1982.
viii,159p.
Bibliography: p150-155. .
ISBN 0198760930 Oxford University Press

Maryan Green, N. A.
International law / N.A. Maryan Green. – 3rd ed. – London : Pitman, 1987.
384p; 22cm.
Previous ed.: Plymouth : Macdonald and Evans, 1982. Includes bibliography and index.
ISBN 0273027328 £25.00
—International law : law of peace / N. A. Maryan Green. – 2nd ed. – Plymouth : Macdonald & Evans, 1982.
xxxiv,254p.
ISBN 0712109560

Mascarenhas, A.
Current Accounting Law and Practice 1986. – Quinta.
ISBN 0906157099 Pbk £26.50

Masodkar, B.A.
Company Law and Meetings. – Bombay : Tripathi.
Hbk
—Law of companies and meetings / B.A. Masodkar. – Bombay : Tripathi, 1984.
xxxii,263p.

Mason, H. H → Australian company law.
—Cases on Commercial Law. – 2nd ed. – North Ryde : Law Book Co, 1984.
ixi, 428p.
ISBN 0455204365 Pbk £29.50

Mason, J K
Forensic Medicine for Lawyers. – 2nd ed. – London : Butterworths, 1983.
ISBN 0407013709 Pbk £19.00
—Forensic medicine for lawyers / J.K. Mason with chapters by A.K.M. Macrae, J.S. Oliver, A.T. Proudfoot. – 2nd ed. – London : Butterworths, 1983.
xv,418p; 24cm.
Previous ed.: Bristol : J. Wright, 1978. Bibliography: p398-399. - Includes index.
ISBN 0407002448
—Human life and medical practice / J.K. Mason. – Edinburgh : Edinburgh University Press, 1988.
192p; 22cm.
Includes bibliography and index.
ISBN 0852245602 Hbk £15.00 :
ISBN 085224584X Pbk £7.50
—Law and medical ethics / J.K. Mason, R.A. McCall Smith. – 2nd ed. – London : Butterworths, 1987.
345p; 22cm.
Previous ed.: 1983. Includes index.
ISBN 0406501300 Hbk £18.95 :
ISBN 0406501319 Pbk £12.95

Mason, K.
Wills Probate and Administration Service, New South Wales / L.G. Handler. – Butterworths, 1985.
ISBN 0409491314 Hbk

Mason's Casebook on Australian Company Law. – 4th ed. – London : Butterworths, 1983.
ISBN 0409491810 Pbk £19.20

Mass, Robert W.
Tolley's Anti-Avoidance Provisions. – Croydon : Tolley, 1984.
344p.
ISBN 0854591516 Hbk £17.50

Massacre of the innocents - Infanticide. – Routledge, 1986.
ISBN 071020339X Hbk £16.95

Massey, Arnold Stewart → Court of Protection Practice, Supplement 1986.

Massey Hall and Roy Thomson Hall Act, 1983, Bill Pr044 : An Act Respecting The Corporation of Massey Hall and Roy Thomson Hall. – Ontario : Ontario Government Publications Service, 1983.
9p.
Hbk £0.50

Massey, I.P.
Administrative Law. – 2nd ed. – Lucknow : Eastern Book Company, 1985.
540p.
Hbk £60.00

Massey, W. G. S. → Taxation of Transactions in Intellectual Property.

Mastellone
Australian Wills Precedents (Italian Translation). – London : Butterworths.
ISBN 0409494410 Pbk £10.00

Mastering Banking. – London : Macmillan, 1985.
ISBN 0333369122 Pbk £3.25

Mastering basic English Law. – London : Macmillan, 1985.
ISBN 0333382897 Pbk £3.95

Mastering business law. – London : Macmillan, 1988.
ISBN 0333487982 Hbk £13.50
ISBN 0333487990 Pbk £4.50

Mastering Law Studies and Law Exam Techniques. – Sydney : Butterworths, 1986.
184p.
This book is designed to show students how to learn law and organize their study habits using exam-oriented techniques. Sample exam questions and answers are included. Other sections discuss study hints and how to read and brief a case.
Pbk £18.00

Mastrangelo, Eugene → 1987 annual on terrorism.

Matchett, Kathleen → Religious minorities in the Soviet Union : a report.

Materials on the law of the European Communities / edited by D.J. Gijlstra and E.L.M. Volker. – 1st ed. – Deventer, Netherlands : Kluwer Law and Taxation Publishers, 1983.
xxi, 530 p.; 25 cm.
'Europe Institute, University of Amsterdam.'.
ISBN 9065440690 Pbk fl 78.00

Maternal deprivation reassessed / Michael Rutter. – 2nd ed. – Harmondsworth : Penguin, 1981.
285p; 18cm. – (Penguin education).
Previous ed.: 1972. Bibliography: p219-272. - Includes index.
ISBN 0180805613 Pbk £1.95

Maternity rights. – London : Incomes Data Services, 1983.
44p. – (Handbook series).

Maternity Rights : The Experience of Employers. – London : Policy Studies Institute, 1981.
89p.
Hbk £5.00

Mates, David
Justice Delayed : Nazi War Criminals in Canada / Susan Charendoff. – Toronto : Summerhill Press.
220p.
ISBN 0920197426 Hbk £21.95

Mather, Gillian
Halsbury's Statutory Instruments, 23 Vols. – London : Butterworths.
This 23 volume work provides a complete reference to every statutory instrument in force and of general application in England and Wales. A separate volume of consolidated index is included in the work.
Hbk

Mather, Graham → Future of labour law : two views.
→ Striking out strikes : changing employment relations in the British labour market.

Mathers, J.
Motorist's Guide to the Law. – London : Fourmat, 1986.
ISBN 0906840953 Pbk £4.95

Matheson, D.
Legal Aid : the New Framework. – London : Butterworths.
ISBN 0406502951 Pbk £12.50

Matheson, Susan M. G.
Scottish Family Conciliation Service (Lothian) : report of an assessment of the first two years of the service, March 1984 - February 1986 / Susan M.G. Matheson, Hugh Gentleman. – Edinburgh : Scottish Office Central Research Unit, 1986.
6,53p.

Mathew, K.K.
Three Lectures. – Lucknow : Eastern Book Company, 1983.
75p.
Hbk £35.00

Mathews, Anthony S
Freedom, State Security and the Rule of Law. – London : Sweet & Maxwell, 1988.
ISBN 0421396407 Hbk £36.00
—Freedom, state security and the rule of law : dilemmas of the apartheid society / Anthony S. Mathews. – Cape Town : Juta, 1986.
xxv,312p.
Bibliography: p.xi-xi - Includes index.
ISBN 0702118125
—Legislation and civil liberties in South Africa / A.S. Mathews. – S.l. : s.n., 1984.
p.10-15.

Mathews, R.
EEC Antitrust Compliance. – London : European Business, 1986.
ISBN 094262055 Pbk £36.00

Mathias
Misuse of Drugs. – Butterworths, 1989.
251p.
ISBN 0409788163 Pbk £54.00

Mathieson, D.L.
Cross on Evidence : 4th New Zealand Edition 1989. – Butterworths.
700p.
ISBN 0409616540 Hbk £92.95

Mathijsen, P. S. R. F.
Guide to European Community law / by P.S.R.F. Mathijsen. – 4th ed. – London : Sweet & Maxwell, 1985.
xl,284p; 22cm.
Previous ed.: 1980. Includes bibliographies and index. Includes index.
ISBN 0421339306 Pbk £16.50
ISBN 0421339209 Hbk £22

Mathur, A.P.
Commentaries on Motor Vehicles Act, 2 Vols. – 8th ed. – Lucknow : Eastern Book Company, 1982.
2,000p.
Hbk £240.00
—Commentaries on Prevention of Corruption Act, 1947. – 3rd ed. – Lucknow : Eastern Book Company, 1981.
699p.
Hbk £80.00

Mathur, G.C. → Conveyancing, Precedents and Forms.
→ Law of Sales Tax in Uttar Pradesh, 2 Vols.

Matin, Douglas F. → Towards a unified family court : court orders concerning children : overlapping jurisdictions.

Matlow, P Theodore
Advocates' Quarterly (1977-Present). – Aurora : Canada Law Book Co.
Hbk £75.00
—Advocates' Quarterly (A.Q.) / Garry D. Watson. – Aurora : Canada Law Book Co.
Hbk £75.00

Matonovich, Rae → Probation : North American Literature Review (1971-1981).

Matrimonial Advocacy and Litigation. – London : Butterworths, 1988.
ISBN 0406103305 Pbk £19.95

Matrimonial Advocacy and Litigation. – London : Butterworths, 1987.
Pbk

Matrimonial and Domestic Injunctions / Purdie. – 2nd ed. – London : Butterworths, 1987.
ISBN 0406334412 Pbk £32.00

Matrimonial and domestic injunctions : practice and precedents / Mark Pelling, Robert Purdie : consulting editor Augustus Ullstein : foreword by Dame Margaret Booth. – London : Butterworths, 1982.
xxi,190p; 22cm.
Includes index.
ISBN 0406334404 Pbk

Matrimonial and Family Law Up to Date. – London : Law Society, 1985.
69p.
Hbk £6.30

Matrimonial and Family Proceedings Act 1984. – London : Longman Professional.
ISBN 0851212867 Pbk £19.95

Matrimonial and Family Proceedings Act 1984 : a practical guide / Richard M. Smith. – London : Oyez, 1984.
xviii,125p.
Includes index.
ISBN 0851208789

Matrimonial Causes (Amend No 2) Rules 1985. – London : Longman Professional, 1986.
ISBN 0851212069 Pbk £6.50

Matrimonial Consent Orders and Agreements. – London : Longman Professional, 1986.
ISBN 0851211127 Pbk £12.95

Matrimonial Conveyancing. – 3rd ed. – London : Longman Professional, 1988.
ISBN 0851212832 Pbk £22.00

Matrimonial Conveyancing : A Draftsman's Handbook. – London : Oyez Longman, 1981.
ISBN 0851206034 Hbk £9.95

Matrimonial Homes (Family Protection) (Scotland) Act 1981 / by D.I. Nichols and M.C. Meston. – 2nd ed. – Edinburgh : W. Green, 1986.
x,94p; 25cm.
Previous ed.: 1982. Includes index. Includes the text of the Matrimonial Homes (Family Protection) (Scotland) Act 1981.
ISBN 0414007786 Pbk £10.50

Matrimonial Proceedings. – 3rd ed. – London : Fourmat.
ISBN 1851900640 Hbk £12.95

Matrimonial Proceedings. – 2nd ed. – London : Fourmat, 1984.
180p.
ISBN 0906840783 Pbk £9.95

Matrimonial Proceedings / Marilyn Mornington. – London : Longman Professional.
– (Longman Practice Notes Series).
ISBN 0851214126 Pbk £10.95

Matrimonial proceedings before Magistrates / Horsman. – 4th ed. – London : Butterworths, 1981.
ISBN 040634602X Hbk £46.00

Matrimonial proceedings in magistrates courts / by Billy Strachan. – 2nd ed. – London : Sweet & Maxwell, 1987.
250p; 22cm.
Includes new material dealing with conciliation, and the effect of conduct on the amount of an order. Discusses grounds of an order for periodical payments, calculation and the amount of the order, orders for the custody of children, and for access to children, and the enforcement of orders.
ISBN 0421385006 Pbk £20.00

Matrimonial property / Scottish Law Commission. – Edinburgh : Scottish Law Commission, 1983.
207p. – (Consultative memorandum).

Matrimonial property / Law Reform Commission. – Canberra : Australian Government Publishing Service, 1987.
xxxiv,382p. – (Report).
Bibliography: p.367-372. - Includes index.

Matrimonial property : division of pension benefits upon marriage breakdown / Institute of Law Research and Reform. – Edmonton : The Institute, 1985.
ii,127,25,13p. – (Report for discussion).

Matrimonial property : division of pension benefits upon marriage breakdown / Institute of Law Research and Reform. – Edmonton : Institute of Law Research and Reform, 1986.
viii,115p. – (Report).

Matrimonial Property and Finance
2nd Supplement to 3rd ed. – London : Longman Professional.
ISBN 0851214029 Pbk £17.50

Matrimonial property law / Australian Law Reform Commission. – Sydney : Australian Law Reform Commission, 1985.
iv,105p. – (Discussion paper).

Matrimonial Suits and Property Proceedings : A Practitioner's Index of Practice and Procedure / Maurice Young. – 2nd ed. – Chichester : Barry Rose, 1986.
xliii, 222p.
ISBN 0859921328 Hbk £30.00

Matrimonial support failures : reasons, profiles and perceptions of individuals involved / by the Canadian Institute for Research and the Steering Committee : prepared for the Institute of Law Research and Reform. – 2. – Edmonton : Institute of Law Research and Reform, 1981.

Matte, Nicolas Mateesco
Aerospace law : telecommunications satellites / Nicolas Mateesco Matte. – Montreal : Butterworths, 1982.
xxi,354p.
Bibliography: p.347-349. Published in conjunction with the Institute and Centre of Air and Space law, McGill University, Montreal. Focuses on the legal issues raised by the rapid development of satellite systems, including the novel problem of 'signal poaching', and international political issues (including the opportunities afforded the Third World countries by the new technology). Covers INTELSTAT and the commercial use of satellites.
ISBN 0409848654

—Arms control and disarmament in outer space : lecture-seminars given at the Centre for Research of Air and Space Law
Vol 2. – Montreal : Centre for Research of Air and Space Law, McGill University, 1987.
282p.
Pbk £25.00

—International Air Transport : Law, Organization and Policies for the Future. – Montreal : Centre for Research of Air and Space Law.
172p.
Hbk £30.00

—Law of international telecommunications in Canada / Nicolas Mateesco Matte, Ram S. Jakhu. – Baden-Baden : Nomos, 1987.
131p.
Includes bibliographical references.
ISBN 3789013099

→ Space activities and emerging international law.

—Treatise on air-aeronautical law / Nicolas Mateesco Matte. – Montreal : Institute and Centre of Air and Space Law, McGill University, 1981.
832p; 24cm.
ISBN 0771700407

—Treatise on Air-Aeronautical Law. – 3rd ed. – Agincourt : Carswell, 1981.
848p.
This work for students of air law in Canada is a comprehensive study of the subject from the first days of flight to the present.
Hbk £63.00

Matter of justice : the legal system in ferment / Michael Zander. – London : Tauris, 1987.
250p; 22cm.
Includes bibliography and index.
ISBN 1850430403 £14.95

Matters of Justice. – Oxford : Croom Helm, 1986.
ISBN 0709914709 Hbk £22.50

Matthewman, Jim
Tolley's Social security and state benefits 1983/84 / by Jim Matthewman and Nigel A.D. Lambert. – Croydon : Tolley, 1984.
xii,496p; 23cm.
Includes index.
ISBN 0854591354 Pbk £10.95

—Tolley's social security and state benefits 1985 / by Jim Matthewman and Nigel A.D. Lambert. – Croydon : Tolley, 1985.
x,485p.
Includes index.
ISBN 0854591737

—Tolley's Social Security and State Benefits 1988-89 / Robinson. – Tolley Publishing.
ISBN 0854593608 Hbk £19.95

Matthews →Jervis on Coroners, Supplement 1.

Matthews, James M →Kime's international law handbook : brief facts about legal practice in most of the countries of the world.

Matthews, Janek
Development Land Tax Guide / Tony Johnson. – London : Butterworths, 1984.
ISBN 040626287X Pbk

Matthews, M H →Administrative law : cases and materials.
→ Tort : cases and materials.

Matthews, Paul
Jersey law of trusts / by Paul Matthews and Terry Sowden : foreword by Justice Hoffmann. – London : Key Haven, 1988.
102p; 30cm.
Includes index. English text with statutory material in French.
ISBN 1870070070 spiral

→ Jervis on the office and duties of coroners : with forms and precedents.

Matthews, Roger →Confronting crime.

Matthews, T. G. →Guidebook to Australian bankruptcy law.

Mattsson, Nils →Arbitration in taxation.

Maudsley and Burn: trusts and trustees - cases and materials / E H Burn. – 3rd ed. – London : Butterworths, 1984.
ISBN 0406623244 Hbk £35.00
ISBN 0406623252 Pbk £23.95

Maudsley and Burn's land law : cases and materials / R. H. Maudsley. – 5th ed. – London : Butterworths, 1986.
850p; 26cm.
Previous ed.: published as Land law / by R.H. Maudsley and E.H. Burns. 1980. Includes index.
ISBN 0406623082 Hbk £33.00 :
ISBN 0406623090 Pbk £22.50

Maudsley and Burn's Trusts and trustees : cases and materials / E. H. Burn, R. H. Maudsley. – 3rd ed. – London : Butterworths, 1984.
lxvii,828p; 26cm.
This work for students of the law of trusts in the United Kingdom draws its materials from a wide range of sources. The book provides many footnotes and references to non-case literature on the subject.
ISBN 0406623244 Hbk £31.00
ISBN 0406623252 Pbk £21.95

Maudsley and Burn's Trusts and trustees - cases and materials. – London : Butterworths, 1990.
904; 24cm.
Part one deals with trusts - their nature, requirements and constitutions, trusts and creditors, resulting trusts, constructive trusts and non-charitable purpose trusts; part two covers charities - charitable trusts, Cy-pres, and the administration of charities; part three is trusts and taxes - income tax, capital gains tax and capital transfer tax; and part four deals with trustees - general principles, duties and powers of trustees, variations of trusts, and breach of trust.
ISBN 040659211X Pbk £25.95

Maudsley, R. H. →Maudsley and Burn's land law : cases and materials.

—Maudsley and Burn's Trusts and trustees : cases and materials / E. H. Burn, R. H. Maudsley. – 3rd ed. – London : Butterworths, 1984.
lxvii,828p; 26cm.
This work for students of the law of trusts in the United Kingdom draws its materials from a wide range of sources. The book provides many footnotes and references to non-case literature on the subject.
ISBN 0406623244 Hbk £31.00
ISBN 0406623252 Pbk £21.95

→ Modern equity.

Maule →Canadian Multinationals.

Maurice, Spencer G
Family Provision on Death (LPPN33). – 6th ed. – London : Longman Professional, 1987.
ISBN 0851210694 Pbk £14.95

—Family Provision Practice. – 5th ed. – London : Oyez Longman, 1983.
– (Oyez Longman Practice Note Ser.: No. 33).
ISBN 0851207243 Hbk £8.95

→ Gale on easements.

→ Tudor on charities.

Mauritius law review / Revue de droit et de jurisprudence mauricienne. – Port Louis : s.n., 1977.

Mawby, R. I.
Crime victims : needs, services and the voluntary sector / R.I. Mawby, M.L. Gill. – London : Tavistock, 1987.
ix,261p; 22cm.
Bibliography: p241-254. - Includes index.
ISBN 0422614505 Pbk

—Probation officers' views of probation : a survey in West Yorkshire / R.I. Mawby. – Leeds : University of Leeds, Centre for Social Work and Applied Social Studies, 1981.
39p. – (Occasional paper).
Bibliography: p.35-39.

Mawhood, Philip →Local government in the Third World : the experience of tropical Africa.

Mawrey
Computers and the Law / Salmon. – Oxford : Blackwell Scientific, 1987.
ISBN 0632018496 Hbk

Max, Farraud
Framing of crime in the Constitution of the United States. – Bombay : Popular Prakashan, 1966.
212p.
Hbk £20.00

Max-Planck-Institut fur Auslandisches Offentliches Recht und Volkerrecht →Dispute settlement in public international law : texts and materials.
→ Encyclopedia of public international law.

Max-Planck-Institut fur Auslandisches und Internationales Strafrecht →Research in criminal justice : stock-taking of criminological research at the Max-Planck-Institute for Foreign and International Penal Law after a decade.

Max Weber / Anthony T. Kronman. – London : Edward Arnold, 1983.
214p; 22cm.
Includes bibliographies and index.
ISBN 0713163615 Pbk £9.95
ISBN 0713163623 Pbk £4.95

Maxfield, Michael J.
Fear of crime in England and Wales / by Michael J. Maxfield. – London : H.M.S.O., 1984.
v,46p; 25cm.
'A Home Office Research and Planning Unit report'.
ISBN 0113407726

Maxton, Julie
Nevill's Law of Trusts, Wills and Administration in New Zealand. – 8th ed. – Butterworths, 1985.
Guide to the law of trusts, wills and administration in New Zealand. Includes new chapters on unincorporated associations and construction of wills.
ISBN 040970170X Hbk A$76.45
ISBN 0409701858 Pbk A$50.05

Maxwell
Practice Queens Bench (Probate). – London : Butterworths.
ISBN 0862053331 Hbk £35.50

Maxwell and Brown's Check List of British and Colonial Reports and Periodicals. – 3rd ed. Repr. of 1937 ed. – Agincourt : Carswell.
Hbk £33.75

Maxwell, C.M. →Introduction to the Securities Industry Codes.

Maxwell, Peter →Report of the Review Body on Use of Judicial Time in the Superior Courts in Scotland.

Maxwell, T.G.
Summary Proceedings and Police Court Practice. – Butterworths, 1985.
Covers changes in procedure such as increases in jurisdiction of District Court Judges, the removal of a defendant's right to make an unsworn statement from the dock, the liberalization of procedures relating to the prosecution of young persons, the rights of an accused to remain present throughout the hearing, and the power of a Judge to clear a court.
ISBN 0409600474 Hbk £93.90

Maxwell, T. H.
Irish Reports Digests : 1894-1970, 6 Vols. Incl. Vol. 1. Irish Reports Digests : 1894-1918. – Abingdon : Professional Books.
Hbk £105.00
Vol. 1, 1894-1918. –
Hbk £105.00

May, Chris
Remands in the absence of the accused / Chris May. – London : Home Office, 1985.
vii,31p.
ISBN 0862522153

May, Joan
Zimbabwean women in colonial and customary law / by Joan May. – Gweru : Mambu Press, 1983.
vii,128p.
Bibliography: p.123-128. Cover title: Zimbabwean women in customary and colonial law.
ISBN 0869222406

May, Reinhard
Law and society east and west / dharma, li and nomos : by Reinhard May. – Wiesbaden : Franz Steiner, 1985.
251p,9p.
Revised version of the London Doctoral Theses 'An enquiry in comparative jurisprudene. Similarity and disparity between dharma, li, and nomos.'. Bibliography p.227-250. - Includes index.
ISBN 3515045376

May, Richard
Criminal evidence / by Richard May. – London : Sweet & Maxwell, 1986.
xlii,368p.
Covers aspects of the law of criminal evidence with emphasis on their practical application. Includes sections on burden and standard of proof, exclusionary rules and exceptions, and rules of evidence connected with the trial. Includes the Police and Criminal Evidence Act 1984.
ISBN 0421302909 Pbk £24
→ Phipson on evidence.

May, Thomas Erskine
Erskine May's treatise on the law, privileges, proceedings and usage of Parliament / Charles Gordon. – 20th ed. – London : Butterworths, 1983.
xlviii,1200p.
This book is a comprehensive work on the law, privileges, proceedings, and usage of the British Parliament. The book gives accurate and detailed information on the constituent parts of Parliament, its powers and jurisdiction, membership of either House, financial procedure, and the process of debate.
ISBN 0406291039 Hbk £55.00

Maycock, John
Lectures on English Commercial Law. – Dordrecht : Kluwer.
64p.
ISBN 9065441506 Pbk £30.00

Mayer, C. P. →Corporation tax : the impact of the 1984 budget.

Mayer, Claudette M.
Correspondent Banking. – London : Butterworths, 1987.
ISBN 0406007004 Pbk

Mayhall, Pamela D. →Police community relations and the administration of justice.
—Police community relations and the administration of justice / Pamela D. Mayhall. – 3rd ed. – New York : Wiley, 1984.
ix,438p; 25cm.
Previous ed.: published as: Community relations and the administration of justice. 1979. Includes bibliographies and index.
ISBN 0471060445 £27.95

Mayhew, Pat →British crime survey : first report.
→ Crime and public housing : proceedings of a workshop held in September 1980.
→ Taking account of crime : key findings from the second British crime survey.

Maynard
Year Books, 11 Vols. – Abingdon : Professional Books.
Hbk £390.00

Mayne
Hindu Law and Usage. – 12th ed. repr. 1986. – New Delhi : Bharat Law House.
Hbk £260.00

Mayson, Stephen W
Company Insolvency and Liquidation / French. – London : Blackstone Press, 1988.
ISBN 1854310143 Hbk
—Company Law 1988-89 / French. – 5th ed. – London : Blackstone Press.
ISBN 1854310186 Hbk £19.95
—Practical approach to company law / Stephen W. Mayson, Derek French and Christopher L. Ryan. – 4th ed. – London : Financial Training, 1987.
lxvii,618p.
ISBN 1851850686
—Practical approach to revenue law / Stephen S. Mayson and Susan Blake. – 8th ed. – London : Financial Training, 1987.
xlix,659p.
ISBN 1851850791
—Practical Approach to Revenue Law. – 9th ed. – London : Blackstone Press.
ISBN 1854310178 Pbk £20.95

Mazengarb's Industrial Law / Angus McLeod. – Butterworths.
Llf

M'Bai, Fafa E
Internal conflict of law problems in African legal systems / Fafa E M'Bai. – Banjul : Xam Xam, 198?.

Mbanefo, I
Nigerian Shipping Cases
Vol. 1. – Abingdon : Professional Books, 1987.
ISBN 0862052416 Hbk £75.00
—Nigerian Shipping Laws. – Abingdon : Professional Books, 1983.
ISBN 0862050464 Hbk £126.50

Mbanefo, Louis
Nigerian shipping laws / by Louis Nnamdi Mbanefo : foreword by Sir Darnley Alexander. – Abingdon : Professional Books, 1983.
xciv,1055p.
ISBN 0862050464

McCutcheon on Inheritance Tax. – 3rd ed. – Sweet & Maxwell.
ISBN 042139790X Hbk £75.00

McEwan and Paton on damages in Scotland / Ann Paton. – 2nd. – Edinburgh : Green (W.) & Son, 1989.
Chapters cover damages, provisional damages, interest, loss of earnings and employability, nervous shock, the unaware pursuer, nursing care, special aids, fatal cases, contributory negligence etc. and a review of awards. There is a full collection of recent Scottish decisions (including unreported) on solatium and loss of society, tables of multipliers, an inflation table, diagram of the skeleton. With relevant legislation and rules of court.
ISBN 0414008820 LOOSELEAF

McGeorge School of Law →Legal aspects of international business transactions : the Edinburgh Institute on International Business Transactions 1983 : a project of University of the Pacific McGeorge School of Law international programs.

McGill University →Arms control and disarmament in outer space : lecture-seminars given at the Centre for Research of Air and Space Law.
→ Earth-oriented space activities and their legal implications : proceedings of the symposium held on October 15-16, 1981, Centre for Research of Air & Space Law.
→ Space activities and implications : where from and where to at the threshold of the 80's : proceedings of the symposium held on October 16-17, 1980.

McGregor on damages / by Harvey McGregor. – 15th ed. – London : Sweet & Maxwell, 1988.
xciii,1232p; 25cm.
Divided into three major sections; General Principles, Particular Contracts, and Torts and Procedures. In each section, the relevant points of law and practice are considered.
ISBN 0421370807 £100.00

McNae's Essential Law for Journalists. – 9th ed. – London : Butterworths, 1985.
This book for working journalists offers information on the ways in which the law effects their professional activities. The work discusses the changes brought about by the Contempt of Court Act of 1981 and recent case in defamation.
ISBN 0406772819 Pbk £17.75

McNae's Essential Law for Journalists / Welsh. – 10th ed. – London : Butterworths.
ISBN 0406772827 Pbk £9.50

McNee's law / Sir David McNee. – London : Collins, 1983.
256p,8p of plates; 23cm.
Includes index.
ISBN 0002170078 £9.95

Mead, Malcolm
Unfair dismissal / Malcolm Mead. – London : Oyez, 1981.
xxxv,287p; 24cm.
Includes index.
Pbk £15.00
—Unfair dismissal handbook / Malcolm Mead. – 2nd ed. – London : Oyez Longman, 1983.
xxxvii,368p.
Previous ed.: published as 'Unfair dismissal', 1981. Includes index.
ISBN 0851206913
—Unfair dismissal handbook. – 3rd ed. – London : Longman Professional, 1988.
ISBN 0851212522 Pbk

Meadowcroft, C.
Homeowner's guide to the law. – London : Fourmat, 1987.
ISBN 1851900233 Pbk £6.95

Meadows, W. J.
Response of local authorities to central government incitement to reduce expenditure / by W. J. Meadows. – Strasbourg : Council of Europe, 1986.
33p.
Prepared under the guidance of the Committee of Experts on Local and Regional Finance of the Steering Committee for Regional and Municipal Matters.

Meagher, A J
Civil Procedure Simplified / Meagher. – London : Butterworths.
ISBN 0409848786 Hbk £36.00
—Parties to an action. – Scarborough, Ontario : Butterworths (Canada), 1988.
480.
Contains precedents, definitions of key terms, and a table of cases. Demonstrates how various types of 'persons' of groups become parties to a civil action and how they are described in the proceedings. Types of parties covered include infants, mentally incompetent persons, aliens, accused persons and convects, unincorporated associations, foreign sovereigns, states, administrators, and trade unions and employer organizations.
ISBN 0409809560 Hbk

Meagher, R.A. →Civil Procedure Simplified.

Meagher, R.P.
Ashburner's Principles of Equity 1933. – 2nd ed. – London : Legal Books, 1983.
ISBN 0949553077 Hbk £35.00
—Equity, doctrines, and remedies / R.P. Meagher, W.M.C. Gummow, J.R.F. Lehane : with a foreword from the first edition by Sir Frank Kitto. – 2nd ed. – Sydney : Butterworths, 1984.
xciii, 912 p.; 25 cm.
Includes bibliographical references and index.
ISBN 040949142X Hbk A$52.10
ISBN 0409491527 Pbk.A$39.30
→ Jacobs law of trusts in Australia.

Meaning and Truth in Juridical Decision. – Tampere : A-Tiete Oy.
ISBN 9419464271 Pbk £130.00

Meaning of cost in Canadian Income Tax / D. Keith McNair. – Toronto : Canadian Tax Foundation, 1982.
vi,277p.
Includes index.
ISBN 0888080123

Measures Against the Transfer and the Safekeeping of Funds of Criminal Origin : Recommendation No. R 80/10. – Strasbourg : Council of Europe, 1981.
Hbk £1.25

Measures against the transfer and the safekeeping of funds of criminal origin : recommendation no. R(80)10 adopted by the Committee of Ministers of the Council of Europe on 27 June 1980 and explanatory memorandum. – Council of Europe. – Strasbourg : Council of Europe, 1981.
12p.
'Prepared by a select committee of experts under the authority of the European Committee on Crime Problems' - verso t.p.. At head of cover title: Council of Europe, Legal Affairs.

Measures facilitating access to justice : recommendation no. R(81)7 adopted by the Committee of Ministers of the Council of Europe on 14 May 1981 and explanatory memorandum. – Council of Europe. – Strasbourg : Council of Europe, 1981.
26p.
Prepared under the authority of the European Committee on Legal Co-operation. At head of cover title: Council of Europe, Legal Affairs.

Measures for improving the level of voluntary compliance with tax obligations : technical papers and reports of the 18th General Assembly of the Inter-American Center of Tax Administrators (CIAT) Cartagena, Colombia, 21-25 May 1984. – Inter-American Center of Tax Administrators. – Amsterdam : International Bureau of Fiscal Documentation, 1985.
168 p.; 25 cm. – (Publications of the International Bureau of Fiscal Documentation).
Includes bibliographical references.
ISBN 9070125277 Pbk

Measures of police effectiveness and efficiency / Ian Sinclair, Clive Miller. – London : Home Office, 1984.
v,38p.
Bibliography: p.38.
ISBN 0862521599

Measures to be taken in cases of kidnapping followed by a ransom demand : Recommendation No.R(82)14 adopted by the Committee of Ministers of the Council of Europe on 24 September 1982 and Explanatory memorandum. – Council of Europe. – Strasbourg : Council of Europe, 1983.
13p; 21cm.
'... prepared by a select committee of experts under the authority of the European Committee on Crime Problems' - verso t.p.. At head of cover title: Legal Affairs.
ISBN 9287102309

Measures to prevent and reduce the excessive workload in the courts : recommendation no. R (86)12 adopted by the Committee of Ministers of the Council of Europe on 16 September 1986 and Explanatory memorandum. – Council of Europe. – Strasbourg : Council of Europe, 1987.
17p.
Prepared by a committee of experts on the working of the judicial system set up under the authority of the European Committee on Legal Co-operation. At head of cover title : Council of Europe Legal Affairs.
ISBN 9287110778

Mechanical and Electrical Services Price Book 1987. – Spon (E & FN).
ISBN 041914420X Hbk £32.00

Mechanics of constitutional change : the Sri Lankan style / by D.C. Jayasuriya. – Nawala, Sri Lanka : Asian Pathfinder Publishers, 1982.
130p.
Bibliography: p.103-125. - Includes index.

Mecklers Bibliographies on the History of Crime and Criminal
Great Britain and Ireland No.1. – London : Meckler.
ISBN 00887361579 Hbk £27.50
The United States No.2. –
ISBN 00887361587 Hbk £27.50

Medhurst, Kenneth
Basques and Catalans / by Professor Kenneth Medhurst. – Rev 3rd ed. – London : Minority Rights Group, 1987.
12p. – (Report).
Includes bibliographical references.
ISBN 0946690537

Media and the Image of Justice : Selected Papers from a Conference Held at the University of King's College, Halifax, N.S., September 10-12, 1980. – Ottawa : Canadian Law Information Council, 1981.
89p.
ISBN 0920358187 Pbk £10.00

Media Law / Nicol. – London : Longman Professional, 1984.
ISBN 0803997264 Pbk £8.50
ISBN 0851206506 Hbk £40.00

Media Law : Journalism v. the Law. – Melbourne : Law Institute of Victoria, 1986.
Hbk £25.00

Media law : the rights of journalists and broadcasters / Geoffrey Robertson, Andrew G.L. Nicol. – 1st ed. – London : Oyez, 1984.
xxxvi,403p.
Includes bibliographical references and index.
ISBN 0851206506

Media Law Handbook : a Guide for Canadian Journalists, Broadcasters, Photographers and Writers. – 2nd ed. – North Vancouver : International Self-Counsel Press, 1983.
146p.
ISBN 0889085749 Hbk £6.50

Media law in Australia / Mark Armstrong, Michael Blakeney, Ray Watterson. – Melbourne : Oxford University Press, 1983.
x,274p; 21cm.
Bibliography: p242-267. - Includes index.
ISBN 0195544447 Hbk
ISBN 0195544439 Pbk £13.00

Media Law Seminars 1985 : Centre for Commercial and Applied Legal Research. – Monash University, Faculty of Law. – Clayton : Monash University Press, 1985.
ISBN 0867463856 Hbk £40.00

Media law - the rights of journalists and broadcasters / Geoffrey Robertson and Andrew Nicol. – 2nd ed. – London : Longman Professional (UK), 1989.
An updated second edition which covers recent developments including the Copyright and Patents Act 1988. Also covered are the use of government powers over television, the Video Recordings Act, the Cable Act, recent decisions of the European Court of Human Rights, and European Court, and the right of the media to appeal against 'gag' orders.
ISBN 0851215522 Hbk £55

Media, the Courts and the Charter / Philip Anisman. – Agincourt : Carswell, 1986.
567p.
This work is a collection of essays on the importance and societal function of the press and other media and the protection afforded to the media in Canada and the U.S. The importance of protecting the news media from governmental interference in Canada is discussed in the book.
Hbk £74.50

Mediation and Criminal Justice : Victims, Offenders and Community / Galaway. – Sage Publications.
ISBN 0803980639 Hbk £27.50
ISBN 0803980647 Pbk £11.95

Mediation in Family Disputes. – Wildwood House.
ISBN 00704505851 Pbk £4.95

Mediation in New Zealand : the Attitudes of the Mediated / Susan Cathro. – Palmerston North : Dunmore Press Ltd..
126p.
ISBN 0864690541 Pbk £28.55

Medical Assessment of Injuries for Legal Purposes. – 4th ed. – Sydney : Butterworths, 1985.
372p.
ISBN 0409492981 Hbk

Medical Bill : draft report on the consolidation of the Medical Acts 1956 to 1978 and certain related provisions ... / the Law Commission and the Scottish Law Commission. – London : H.M.S.O., 1983.
11p; 25cm.
ISBN 0101883900

Medical evidence : the report of a Joint Committee of the British Medical Association, the Senate of the Inns of the Court and the Bar and the Law Society. – British Medical Association. – London : British Medical Association, 1981.
iiileaves,37p; 30cm.
spiral

Medical Jurisprudence / Raju. – 4th ed. 1981 repr. – Lucknow : Eastern Book Company, 1982.
681p.
Hbk £45.00

Medical Jurisprudence and Toxicology. – 5th ed. – Allahabad : Law Book Company, 1987.
800p.
Hbk £275.00

Medical Law and Ethics / Grubb. – London : Butterworths, 1988.
ISBN 0406500401 Hbk

Medical Law and Ethics Commentary and Materials. – London : Butterworths.
ISBN 0406500401 Hbk

Medical Law Handbook. – North Vancouver : International Self-Counsel Press, 1985.
131p.
ISBN 0889086036 Hbk £6.95

Medical Malpractice. – Vancouver : Continuing Legal Education Society of British Columbia, 1987.
181p.
ISBN 0865043035 Hbk £65.00

Medical negligence / edited by Michael J. Powers and Nigel H. Harris; consulting editor: Andrew Lockhart-Miriams. – London : Butterworths, 1990.
900; 24cm.
Deals with all aspects of medical negligence claims. The book explains the relevant rules of law, identifies the practical difficulties in bringing an action for damages in respect of negligent medical treatment, and shows how to prepare the medical evidence on liability, how to complete the medical report on quantum, and how to present the experts evidence at court.
ISBN 0406130019 Hbk £120

Medical negligence : a plaintiff's guide / Charles J. Lewis. – London, England : F. Cass, 1988.
xxxiv, 379 p.; 24 cm.
'The law is stated as at 1 January 1988'–T.p. verso. Includes index.
ISBN 0714633399 Hbk £20.00
ISBN 0714640611 Pbk £12.00

Medical Negligence Litigation : Medical Assessment of Claims. – Butterworths, 1988.
ca 400p.
ISBN 0409494550 Hbk £59.00

Medical Research Council → Improving the presentation of information to juries in fraud trials : a report of four research studies.

Medical research with children. – Oxford : Oxford University Press, 1986.
ISBN 0192615289 Hbk £12.50

Medical responsibility in Western Europe : research study of the European Science Foundation / edited by E. Deutsch and H.-L. Schreiber : with contributions by J. Blackie ... et al. – Berlin : Springer-Verlag, 1985.
ISBN 0387153659

Medical treatment for minors / the Law Reform Commission of Western Australia. – Perth : the Commission, 1988.
111p. – (Discussion paper).

Medical treatment for the dying / the Law Reform Commission of Western Australia. – Perth : the Commission, 1988.
66p. – (Discussion paper).

Medicine and law : an international journal. – Berlin : Springer, 1982.
Supersedes: International journal of medicine and law.
ISBN 07231393

Medicine and Surgery for Lawyers. – North Ryde : Law Book Co, 1986.
xxi, 675p.
ISBN 0455206759 Hbk £89.50

Medicine and the law / convocation address at the Second Convocation of the National Post-graduate Medical College of Nigeria on March 10, 1983, in Lagos, Nigeria : by R.O.A. Akinjide. – Lagos : s.n., 1983.
16p.

Medicine, Ethics and the Law. – London : Sweet & Maxwell, 1988.
ISBN 042048020X Pbk £18.00

Medicine for Lawyers 3 : the Whiplash Injury. – Vancouver : Continuing Legal Education Society of British Columbia, 1985.
83p.
ISBN 0865042128 Hbk £55.00

Medicine for Lawyers 4. – Vancouver : Continuing Legal Education Society of British Columbia, 1986.
156p.
ISBN 0865042756 Hbk £55.00

Medicine for Lawyers. – Vancouver : British Columbia Continuing Legal Education Society, 1982.
163p.
ISBN 0865040753 Hbk £50.00

Medicine for Lawyers : 11. – Vancouver : British Columbia Continuing Legal Education Society, 1984.
ISBN 086504161X Hbk £55.00

Medicine in contemporary society / edited by Peter Byrne. – London : King Edward's Hospital Fund for London, 1987.
156p; 23cm.
Includes index.
ISBN 0197246427 £16.95

Medicine, morals and the law / Sheila McLean and Gerry Maher. – Aldershot : Gower, 1983.
ix,214p; 23cm.
Includes index.
ISBN 0566005336

Medicine, Nursing, and the Law / Tingle et al. – London : Blackstone Press.
ISBN 1854310100 Hbk £15.00

Medicine, Patients and the Law. – Pelican, 1987.
ISBN 0140225579 Pbk £5.95

Medico-Legal Encyclopaedia. – London : Butterworths, 1987.
ISBN 0407003746 Hbk £55.00

Medicolegal Library
Vol. 1 Child Abuse / H. Zimrin. – Berlin : Springer-Verlag.
ca 224p.
ISBN 3540124713 Pbk £128.00
Vol. 3 Disability. – 1984.
ca 225p.
Pbk £138.00
Vol. 5 Psychiatry, Law and Ethics. – 1985.
ca 230p.
ISBN 3540157425 Pbk £178.00
Vol. 6 Drugs and Alcohol. – 1986.
ca 215p.
Pbk £152.00
Vol. 7 Hospital Law. – 1988.
ca 225p.
ISBN 3540186425 Pbk £148.00

Medium-term loan market / J.A. Donaldson and T.H. Donaldson. – London : Macmillan, 1982.
viii,229p.
Includes index.
ISBN 0333326067

Mednick, et al
Causes of Crime. – Cambridge : Cambridge University Press, 1987.
ISBN 0521304024 Hbk £35.00

Medvedev, Zhores
Secrecy of Correspondence is Guaranteed by Law. – London : Spokesman Books, 1983.
196p.
ISBN 085124128X Pbk £1.95

Medzikijan, Alis
International Buffer Stocks : Theory and Practice. – Bern : Peter Lang, 1983.
xxix, 342p.
ISBN 3261033185 Pbk £66.00

Meehan, Elizabeth M.
Women's rights at work : campaigns and policy in Britain and the United States / Elizabeth M. Meehan. – Basingstoke : Macmillan, 1985.
xvii,253p; 22cm.
Bibliography: p227-241. - Includes index.
ISBN 0333361253 Hbk £
ISBN 0333361261 Pbk £5.95

Meehan, Eugene
Creditor's Remedies in Alberta / Peter Vaartnou. – Agincourt : Carswell, 1987.
ca 620p.
Hbk £76.75

—Creditors' Remedies in Alberta / Peter Vaartnou. – Agincourt : Carswell, 1987.
620p.
This work focuses on collection practice in Alberta. Discussions are in-depth and include all the issues involved in the collection process, from making the decision to sue to drafting documents, realizing on security and enforcing judgments. Each chapter is arranged so that the procedures and possible problem areas are explained.
Hbk £81.50

—Law of Criminal Attempt. – Agincourt : Carswell, 1984.
330p.
This text examines the law of criminal attempt as set out in legislation and interpreted by the courts around the world, with an emphasis on Canadian law. The book includes numerous comparisons of differing legal responses to similar fact situations in attempt cases.
Hbk £54.75

Meekings, C.A.F.
Studies in 13th century justice and administration / C.A.F. Meekings. – London : Hambledon, 1981.
342p; 25cm. – (History series).
ISBN 0950688231

Meekison, J. Peter, et al
Origins and Meaning of Section 92A : the 1982 Constitutional Amendment on Resources. – Ottawa : Institute for Research on Public Policy, 1985.
xxii, 77p.
ISBN 0886450136 Hbk £10.00

Meeson, Nigel
Mortgages of Ships. – London : Lloyd's of London Press, 1988.
ISBN 1850441049 Hbk

—Practice and procedure of the Admiralty Court : forms and precedents / Nigel Meeson. – London : Lloyd's, 1986.
296p; 24cm.
Includes index.
ISBN 1850440875 £35.00

Meeting legal needs? : an evaluation of a scheme for personal injury victims / Hazel Genn. – Oxford : SSRC Centre for Socio-Legal Studies, 1982.
ix,69p; 22cm.
A report commissioned by the Greater Manchester Legal Services Committee.
ISBN 0862260442

Meeting of Commonwealth Law Ministers and Senior Officials : Harare, Zimbabwe, 26 July-1 August 1986 : memoranda. – London : Commonwealth Secretariat, 1986.
xxvi,592p.
Includes bibliographical references.
ISBN 0850923093

Meeting of Commonwealth law ministers, Colombo,Sri Lanka, 14-18 February 1983 : memoranda. – London : Commonwealth Secretariat, 1983.
xv,597p; 30cm.
ISBN 085092247X

Meeting of Experts on the Exploitation of the Child, November 12-13, 1984, Singapore and the Conference on Child Labour and Child Prostitution, February 21-23, 1986, Kuala Lumpur / convened by the LAWASIA Human Rights Standing Committee : editor, Patricia Hyndman. – Sydney : LAWASIA, 1986.
513p.
Includes bibliographical references.

Meeting of Law Officers of Small Commonwealth Jurisdictions : Port Vila, Vanuatu, 29 July to 2 August 1985. – London : Commonwealth Secretariat, 1985.
156p.
Includes bibliographical references.

Meeting of law officers of small Commonwealth jurisdictions, Douglas, Isle of Man, 4th to 8th July 1983. – Douglas : Isle of Man Government, 1984.
iii,235p; 30cm.
ISBN 0904869105

Meetings. – 3rd ed. – Plymouth : Macdonald & Evans, 1984.
ISBN 0712104496 Pbk £5.95

Meetings : Law and Practice / Rigby. – 4th ed. – Plymouth : Macdonald & Evans, 1987.
ISBN 0712113002 Pbk £6.50

Megarry, Robert
Law of real property / Sir Robert Megarry and H.W.R. Wade. – 5th ed. – London : Stevens, 1984.
cxxviii,123p; 24cm.
Previous ed.: 1975. Includes index.
ISBN 0420467106 Hbk £
ISBN 0420470301 Pbk £26

—Manual of the law of real property / David J Hayton. – 6th ed. – London : Sweet & Maxwell, 1982.
ISBN 0420463305 Hbk £26.00
ISBN 0420463402 Pbk £16.50

—Megarry's manual of the law of real property / David J. Hayton. – 6th ed. – London : Stevens, 1982.
lvii,615p; 24cm.
Previous ed.: 1975. Bibliography: pli-lii. - Includes index.
ISBN 0420463305 Hbk £19.50
ISBN 0420463402 Pbk £11.50

—Rent Acts. – 11th ed. 2 vols. – Stevens & Sons.
ISBN 0420448403 Hbk £125.00

Megarry's manual of the law of real property / David J. Hayton. – 6th ed. – London : Stevens, 1982.
lvii,615p; 24cm.
Previous ed.: 1975. Bibliography: pli-lii. - Includes index.
ISBN 0420463305 Hbk £19.50
ISBN 0420463402 Pbk £11.50

Meghalaya →Contingency Manual.

Meghe, D.R. →Panchayati Raj in India.

Megrah, Maurice →Law of bankers' commercial credits.
→ Law of Banking.
→ Paget's Law of banking.

Meherban, Ali
Principles of Natural Justice. – Lahore : Pakistan Law Times.
Hbk £6.00

Mehigan, Simon
Restraint of trade and business secrets : law and practice / Simon Mehigan and David Griffiths. – 1st ed. – London : Longman Professional (UK), 1987.
xxiv,247p; 24cm. – (Longman commercial series).
Coverage includes employment contracts, business sale, partnerships and joint ventures, breach of contract, commercial contracts including licensing, distribution agreements, trade associations, evaluation agreements and performing contracts. List of cases classified according to business type.
ISBN 0851211747 Hbk £42.00

Mehra
Handbook of Drug Laws : With Appropriate Technology for Drugs and Pharmaceuticals. – Allahabad : Universal Book Agency, 1985.
Hbk £300.00

Mehraj-ud-Din, Mir
Crime and Criminal Justice System in India. – New Delhi : Deep and Deep Publications, 1984.
338p.
Hbk £200.00

Mehrotra
Law of Defamation and Malicious Prosecution (Civil and Criminal). – 2nd ed. – Allahabad : Law Publishers, 1982.
Hbk £22.50

Mehrotra, K.C.
Law of Bails, Forfeiture of Bonds and Habeas Corpus / A.N. Saha. – 2nd ed. – Lucknow : Eastern Book Company, 1985.
391p.
Hbk £75.00

—Sessions Trial. – 5th ed. – Lucknow : Eastern Book Company, 1986.
468p.
Hbk £90.00

Mehta, Rama
Sociolegal Status of Women in India. – Delhi : Mittal Publications, 1987.
208p.
Hbk £140.00

Meier, Henri B.
Swiss capital markets / by Henri B. Meier. – 2nd ed. – London : Euromoney, 1985.
xi,128p.
Bibliography: p.125-126 - Includes index.
ISBN 0903121816

Meier, Robert F. →Major forms of crime.

Meinhardt, P.
Company law in Europe / P. Meinhardt. – 3rd ed. 1. – Farnborough, Hants. : Gower, 1981.
loose-leaf; 26cm.
Previous ed.: 1978. Includes bibliographies and index.
ISBN 0566022451 £40.00

—Company law in Great Britain / Peter Meinhardt with the assistance of Nigel Davis. – Aldershot : Gower, 1982.
178p in various pagings; 24cm.
Bibliography: 2p. - Includes index.
ISBN 056602389X

—Concise trade mark law and practice / Peter Meinhardt and Keith R. Havelock. – Aldershot : Gower, 1983.
xv,206p; 24cm.
Bibliography: p187-189. - Includes index.
ISBN 0566023695

Meins, Paul G →Coopers and Lybrand: tax and financial planning through pensions.

Meisel, Franklin →Auctions : law and practice.
→ Auctions Law and Practice.

Mellet, H. F →Our legal heritage.

Mellett →Accountancy : Study Text for Banking Students.
→ Introduction to Accountancy.

Mello, Bernard de →Vocabulary of Community Primary Law, 1985 Provisional Edition.

Mellows, Anthony R.
Law of succession / Anthony R. Mellows. – 4th ed. – London : Butterworths, 1983.
lv,619p; 26cm.
Previous ed.: 1977. Includes index.
ISBN 0406623775 Hbk £
ISBN 0406623783 Pbk £23.95
→ Modern law of trusts.

—Taxation for Executors and Trustees. – 6th ed. – London : Butterworths, 1984.
ISBN 0406623961 Hbk
ISBN 040662397X Pbk

—Taxation of land transactions. – 4th ed. – London : Butterworths, 1988.
ISBN 0406624100 Pbk

Melossi, Dario
Prison and the Factory / Massimo Pavarini. – London : Macmillan, 1981.
256p. – (Critical Criminology, General Ser.).
ISBN 0333266676 Hbk £18.00
ISBN 0333266684 Pbk £6.95

Melville, L.
Draftsman's Handbook. – London : Longman Professional, 1985.
ISBN 0851209505 Pbk £19.50

—Forms/Agreements Intellectual Property 2 vols. – London : Sweet & Maxwell, 1988.
ISBN 0421253002 Hbk

—Professional Practice for Building Works / Gordon. – London : Estates Gazette.
ISBN 0728200651 Hbk £19.50

Melvin, Michael
International money and finance / Michael Melvin. – New York : Harper & Row, 1985.
xiii,200p; 25cm.
Includes bibliographies and index.
ISBN 0060444177 £12.95

Memoirs of Edwin Waterhouse / Jones. – London : Batsford.
ISBN 0713455799 Hbk £15.00

Memoirs of the Life of Sir Samuel Romilly, 3 Vols. – Dublin : Irish Academic Press.
900p.
ISBN 0716517841 Hbk £48.00

Memoranda and draft : bills re : christian marriage, matrimonial causes, offences relating to property and lands (Banjul and Kombo St. Mary) / Law Reform Commission of the Gambia. – Banjul : The Commission?, 1985.
xv,112p.
Includes the text of draft legislation.

Memorandum and articles of association of Consumers' Association : incorporated 18 March 1957. – Consumers' Association. – London : Consumers' Association, 1981.
32p.
At foot of cover: The Companies Act 1948: company limited by guarantee and not having a share capital no. 580128.

Memorandum by the Joint Working Party on Intellectual Property : on proposals by the European Commission for a first Council directive to approximate the laws of the member states relating to trade marks and for a Council regulation on Community trade marks : Com (80) 635 Final/2 (published (1981) XXX Common Market Law Reports 357 & 365). – Joint Working Party on Intellectual Property. – London : Senate of the Inns of Court and the Bar, 1981.
13,4,3p; 30cm.
At head of title: The Senate of the Inns of Court and the Bar, The Law Society.

Memorandum of evidence to Farrand Committee on Conveyancing Procedure and Practice / Justice. – London : Justice, 1984.
17p.

Memorandum on guardianship : Law Commission working paper no. 91 / Justice. – London : Justice, 1986.
6 leaves.
A commentary on the Law Commission's working paper no. 91 entitled Family law: review of child law: guardianship.

Memorandum on Law Commission working paper no. 92: Formalities for contracts for sale of land and Law Commission working paper no. 93: Formalities for deeds and esrows / Justice. – London : Justice, .
9 leaves.

Memorandum on the White Paper on Criminal Justice / Justice. – London : Justice, 1986.
7 leaves.

Memorandum to the Lord Chancellor's Advisory Committee on Legal Aid / JUSTICE. – S.l. : JUSTICE, 1984.
9p; 30cm.

Menconi, Margo → Religious minorities in the Soviet Union : a report.

Mendeloff, J.M.
Dilemma of Toxic Substance Regulation. – London : MIT Press, 1988.
ISBN 0262132303 Hbk £31.50

Mendelsohn, E. W.
East Anglia and East Midlands probation hostels : a descriptive study / E.W. Mendelsohn. – Cambridge : Institute of Criminology, 1984.
95p. – (Occasional papers).
Includes bibliographical references.

Mendelsohn, M.
Guide to franchising / by Martin Mendelsohn. – 4th ed. – Oxford : Pergamon, 1985.
xvii,319p; 24cm.
Previous ed.: 1982. Includes index.
ISBN 0080312829 £25.00
→ International franchising - an overview.

—Law and Practice of Franchising / John Drysdale. – Pergamon, 1989.
ISBN 0080240356 Hbk

Mendelson, Maurice
Impact of European Community law on the implementation of the European Convention on Human Rights / by Maurice Mendelson. – Strasbourg : Council of Europe, 1984.
43p.
ISBN 928710350X

Mendes da Costa, Derek
Cambridge Lectures 1979. – Butterworths, 1981.
304p.
ISBN 0409849073 Hbk £46.95
—Property Law : Cases, Text and Materials / Richard J. Balfour. – Aurora : Canada Law Book Co, 1982.
1400p. – (Case books).
Property Law provides edited versions of the leading real property and personal property cases, statutory references to the Canadian Common Law jurisdictions and textual material and commentary. The historical perspective of the work is complemented by a description and analysis of many recent proposals for reform in this area.
Hbk £95.00

Menezes, Julio → Food Famine and the Legal Order.
→ Insurance law in Canada : a treatise on the principles of indemnity insurance as applied in the common law provinces of Canada.

Meng Qing-nan
Land-based marine pollution : international law development / by Meng Qing-nan. – London : Graham & Trotman, 1987.
xvi,254p.
Bibliography: p464-476. - Includes index.
ISBN 0860109097

Menon, K. Krishna
Law of Property-the Transfer of Property Act, 1882 : a Commentary. – Allahabad : Orient Law House.
ISBN 086125516X Hbk £35.00

Menon, P. K. → Commonwealth Caribbean legal essays.

Men's jobs? women's jobs? : practical guidance on why many jobs are done only by men or only by women, and how this pattern 'job segregation' can and should be changed. – London : HMSO, 1986.
vii,34p; 21cm.
At head of title: Equal Opportunities Commission.
ISBN 0117012998 Pbk £2.20

Mens Rea : Imputability Under the Law of England. – Repr. of 1914 ed. – Abingdon : Professional Books.
345p.
Hbk £75.00

Mental Disability and the Law in Canada. – Agincourt : Carswell, 1987.
518p.
This work contains a discussion of the common law and legislation of Canada's common law jurisdictions relating to the effect of mental disability on legal rights and liabilities. Topics include committees of estate and personal guardians, contracts, succession, tort liability, family law issues, the right to vote, discrimination and the Charter, litigation, admission to, and rights of patients in, mental health facilities.
Hbk £60.50

Mental Disorder and Criminal Law in Australia and New Zealand. – Butterworths, 1988.
ca 256p.
ISBN 0409494828 Hbk £55.00

Mental disorder and criminal responsibility / Stephen J. Hucker, Christopher D. Webster, Mark H. Ben-Aron. – Toronto : Butterworths, 1981.
xv,195p.
Examines Anglo-American concepts of criminal responsibility, mental disorder and criminal responsibility in Canadian law, the sense of justice and criminal responsibility, modern neurology and psychiatry and the problem of criminal responsibility, psychiatrists, lawyers and the adversial system, and the long term management of the mentally disordered offender.
ISBN 0409837342

Mental disorder and legal control / Philip Bean. – Cambridge : Cambridge University Press, 1986.
304p.
Includes bibliographical references and index.
ISBN 0521302099 £27.50

Mental disorder and the criminal trial process. – Scarborough, Ontario : Butterworths (Canada), 1978.
368.
Focuses on legal problems and procedures peculiar to the use of psychiatric expertise at the pre-trial and trial stages. Fitness to stand trial, 'psychiatric defences', and the consequences of a determination of abnormality are discussed.
ISBN 0409865605 Hbk

Mental element in crime : report on a reference under section 3(1)(e) of the Law Commissions Act 1965 / Scottish Law Commission. – Edinburgh : H.M.S.O., 1983.
v,48p.
Includes bibliographical references.
ISBN 0101904703

Mental health : a case for reform / papers presented by John Dawson ... et al. – Auckland : Legal Research Foundation, 1986.
161p.
Includes bibliographical references. At head of t.p.: Legal Research Foundation Inc., Seminar, 5 September 1986.
ISBN 0908581432
ISBN 0908581432

Mental Health : Tribunal Procedure. – London : Oyez Longman, 1984.
– (Oyez Longman Practice Note Ser.: No. 78).
ISBN 0851208444 Hbk

Mental Health Act 1983 : memorandum on Parts I to VI, VIII and X. – London : D.H.S.S., 1983.
iv,85p.

Mental Health Act 1983 : section 118 : draft code of practice. – London : Mental Health Division, Department of Health and Social Security, 1985.
236p.
Includes index.

Mental Health Act, 1983 : Summary of Procedural Requirements in Respect of Compulsory Admission to Hospital and Guardianship, Pt. II. – London : Shaw & Sons, 1983.
ISBN 0721901964 Hbk £0.80

Mental Health Act manual / edited by Richard M. Jones. – 2nd ed. – London : Sweet & Maxwell, 1988.
339p; 25cm.
Includes the Mental Health Act 1983, Mental Health Tribunal Rules 1983, Mental Health (Hospitals, Guardianship and Consent to Treatment) Regulations 1983, Court of Protection Rules 1984, and DHSS and Mental Health Act Commission Circulars.
ISBN 0421393300 Pbk £21.00

Mental health law / Brenda M. Hoggett. – 2nd ed. – London : Sweet & Maxwell, 1984.
xxiv,370p; 22cm.
Account of the basic legal rights of psychiatric patients before, during and after hospital confinement. Explains Mental Health Tribunals, and the Court of Protection. Also covers the Mental Health Act 1983.
ISBN 0421302208 Pbk £12.95

Mental health law : major issues / David B. Wexler. – New York : Plenum, 1981.
x,270p; 24cm.
Includes index.
ISBN 0306405385

Mental Health Law in Canada / Carla A. McKague. – Butterworths, 1987.
384p.
Assesses legal tools available to combat discrimination in employment, and against former psychiatric patients, analyses Lieutenant Governor Warrants, and offers procedural reforms to have them comply with Charter provisions, and includes recent human rights legislation and compares provincial human rights code provisions to those in the Charter.
ISBN 0409865095 Hbk £60.00

Mental Health Procedural Tables. – London : Shaw & Sons, 1983.
ISBN 0721901964 Pbk £0.80

Mental Health Services : Law and Practice. – London : Shaw & Sons, 1986.
ISBN 0721901972 updat £85.30

Mental Health Services - Law and Practice. – London : Shaw & Sons, 1986.
912p.
ISBN 0721901972 Hbk £85.00

Mental health, social policy and the law. – London : Macmillan, 1985.
ISBN 0333373014 Hbk £25.00

Mental Health-Tribunal Procedure. – London : Longman Professional, 1984.
ISBN 0851208444 Pbk £14.95

Mental illness and the law / Tony Whitehead. – Oxford : Basil Blackwell, 1982.
viii,181p; 23cm.
Includes index.
ISBN 0631127216 Hbk £
ISBN 0631126155 Pbk

Mental malfunction and criminal responsibility / Law Reform Commission of Victoria. – Melbourne : The Commission, 1988.
95p. – (Discussion paper).
Includes bibliographical references.
ISBN 0724167307

Mental retardation : law, policy and administration / by Susan C. Hayes and Robert Hayes : with a foreword by M. D. Kirby. – North Ryde : Law Book Co, 1982.
xxviii,428p.
Includes index.
ISBN 0455204691 Pbk
ISBN 0455204705

Mentally Disordered Offender. – Cambridge : Cambridge University Press.
ISBN 0521357144 Pbk £13.95

Menzies, Robert J. → Clinical assessment before trial : legal issues and mental disorder.

Meopham, Brian
FIDIC Conditions of Contract - Commercial Manual. – Waterlow, 1986.
ISBN 0080392342 Hbk £30.00
—GC/Works/1 Conditions of Contract. – London : Waterlow, 1985.
ISBN 0080392334 Hbk £20.00

Meos of India : Their Customs and Laws. – New Delhi : Deep and Deep Publications, 1983.
211p.
Hbk £90.00

Mercado, Leonardo N.
Legal Philosophy : Western, Eastern and Filipino. – Tacloban City : Divine Word University of Tacloban, 1984.
208p.
ISBN 9711060213 Hbk £7.00

Mercantile and General Reinsurance Company → Reinsurance.

Mercantile Law / K.C. Garg. – 4th ed. 1987 repr. – New Delhi : Kalyani Publishers.
ISBN 8170960517 Hbk £60.00

Mercantile Law. – 11th ed. – Delhi : SBD Enterprises.
Hbk £35.00

Mercantile Law. – 5th ed. Repr. of 1979 ed. – Plymouth : Macdonald & Evans, 1982.
320p. – (M and E Handbook Ser.).
ISBN 071211288X Hbk £3.50

Mercantile Law. – 4th ed. – Lucknow : Eastern Book Company, 1985.
1,172p.
Hbk £85.00

Mercantile law / Kenneth Smith, Denis Keenan. – 5th ed. – London : Pitman, 1982.
xiii,753p; 22cm.
Previous ed.: 1977. Includes index. 3rd ed. and earlier entitled: Essentials of mercantile law.
ISBN 0273017691 Pbk

Mercantile Law / Keenan. – 7th ed. – Pitman, 1988.
ISBN 027302843X Pbk £12.95

Mercantile Law : Including Company Law and Industrial Law / Saxena. – Delhi : SBN Enterprises.
Hbk £35.00

Mercantile Law and Mercantile Practice. – Rondebosch : University of Cape Town, 1985.
14p.
ISBN 0799210005 Pbk £0.30

Mercantile Law in New Zealand / H.R.C. Wild. – 8th ed. – Auckland : Whitcoulls, 1983.
347p.
ISBN 0723307059 Hbk £14.95

Mercenarism and international law / Chief R. O. A. Akinjide. – s.l. : s.n., 1986.
13p.
Lecture delivered at the International Law Seminar, Palais des nations, Geneva, on 27.5.1986.

Mercer, Peter P. → Introduction to business associations in Canada : cases, notes, and materials.

Merchandising intellectual property / John Adams : with an introduction by Iain C Baillie : and a chapter on taxation by K.V. Prichard Jones. – London : Butterworths, 1987.
xxxi,345p,2p of plates; 26cm.
Includes index.
ISBN 0406103402 £30.00

Merchant, Akbar G.
Comments on Company Law. – Karachi : Flecbon Corporation, 1987.
Hbk
—Comments on Finance Act, 1985 and Amendments in Mercantile Laws. – Karachi : Flecbon Corporation, 1987.
Hbk

Merchant Shipping Act 1970. – London : Lloyd's of London Press.
ISBN 1850441103 Pbk £17.50

Merchant shipping - legislative proposals / presented to Parliament by the Secretary of State for Transport .. – London : H.M.S.O., 1987.
ii,13p; 30cm.
ISBN 0101023928

Merchant Shipping (Linear Conferences) Act 1982 / annotated by E.R. Hardy Ivamy. – London : Lloyd's of London, 1987.
xx,92p; 22cm.
Includes index.
ISBN 1850441030 Pbk £16.50

Merchant Shipping (Safety Officials) Regulations 1982 : guidance notes for shipowners, crew employers, ship masters, safety officers, safety representatives and safety committees / issued by Marine Division, Department of Trade. – London : The Division, 1982.
78p.

Meredith, Colin
Overview and annotated bibliography of the needs of crime victims / Colin Meredith. – Ottawa : Ministry of the Solicitor General, 1984.
138p. – (User report).

Meredith, G. G.
Legal aid cost comparison : salaried and private lawyers / by G.G. Meredith. – Canberra : Australian Government Publishing Service, 1983.
viii,61p.
Bibliography: p.61. At head of title: Commonwealth Legal Aid Council, Attorney-General's Department.
ISBN 0644025441

Merger control in the EEC : a survey of European competition laws / prepared by the Brussels offices at Avenue de la Joyeuse Entree 1, Blijde Inkomstlaan 1 of : Advokaterne Bredgade 3 ... et al. – Deventer : Kluwer Law and Taxation Publishers, 1988.
xii,306p.
ISBN 9065443541

Mergers and acquisitions. – Oxford : Blackwell, 1986.
ISBN 0631147470 Hbk £35.00

Mergers and Acquisitions : Law and Practice. – London : Butterworths, 1988.
ISBN 0406103704 Hbk

Mergers and Acquisitions Handbook. – Maidenhead : McGraw-Hill.
ISBN 0070533504 Hbk £59.95

Mergers and joint ventures in Europe: the law and policy of the EEC. – London : Graham & Trotman, 1989.
220; 240mm.
Explores how articles 85 and 86 of the Treaty of Rome would operate in the context of mergers and production joint ventures, and to non EEC firms seeking to acquire firms in the EEC. Analyses the Draft Regulation for the Control of Mergers, and includes its text in the Annexes.
ISBN 185333314X Hbk £50

Mergers and takeovers : legal and financial issues : written proceedings of a seminar, 29 August 1985 / Victoria University of Wellington. Department of Accountancy. – Wellington : The University, 1985.
Various pagings.
Includes bibliographical references. Chairman: Whatarangi Winiata.

Mergers policy : a Department of Trade and Industry paper on the policy and procedures of merger control. – London : HMSO, 1988.
iii,40p.
ISBN 0115139990

Merkin, Robert
Competition law : antitrust policy in the U.K. and the EEC / by Robert Merkin and Karen Williams. – London : Sweet & Maxwell, 1984.
xliii,492p; 22cm.
Bibliography: p485-486. - Includes index.
ISBN 0421307307 Hbk £30.00
ISBN 0421307404 Pbk £22.50
→ Encyclopaedia of competition law.

—Guide to Consumer Protection Act. – Oxford : Croner Publications, 1987.
ISBN 1851850783 Pbk £11.95

—Richards Butler on latent damage / by Robert Merkin. – London : Lloyd's of London Press, 1987.
192p; 22cm.
ISBN 1850441286 £30.00

Merkin, Robert M.
Insurance contract law / Robert M. Merkin and Andrew McGee : editorial advisors, John S. Butler, Alison A. Green. – 2. – London : Kluwer, 1988.
looseleaf.
Includes index.
ISBN 1870080475
→ Reinsurance law.

Meron, Theodor
Human rights and humanitarian norms as customary law. – Oxford : OUP, 1989.
320.
Looks at the relationship between human rights/humanitarian norms and customary law, also between human rights/humanitarian norms and the law of state responsibility. Examines how contemporary human rights mesh with the general principles of international law and particularly with the principles governing the international responsibility of states.
International lawyers, international organizations, scholars and students of international law
ISBN 0198252390 Hbk £30.00
—Human rights in internal strife : their international protection / by Theodor Meron. – Cambridge : Grotius, 1987.
xiii,172p.
An examination of the problem of protecting human rights in internal strife and of developing adequate safeguards in areas beyond the scope of the Geneva Conventions.
ISBN 0949009040

—Human rights in International law. – rep 1986. – Oxford : Oxford University Press, 1984.
ISBN 0198255403 Pbk £17.50

→ Human rights in international law : legal and policy issues.

—Human rights law-making in the United Nations. – Oxford : Oxford University Press, 1986.
ISBN 0198255497 Hbk £35.00

—Human rights law-making in the United Nations : a critique of instruments and process / Theodor Meron. – Oxford : Clarendon, 1986.
350p; 22cm.
Includes index.
ISBN 0198255497 £35.00

Merren, H. Orren →C.I.F. and F.O.B. contracts.
→ CIF and FOB Contracts (BSL).

Merrills, J. G.
Anatomy of international law : a study of the role of international law in the contemporary world / by J.G. Merrills. – 2nd ed. – London : Sweet and Maxwell, 1981.
xv,146p; 19cm.
Previous ed.: 1976. Bibliography: p137-141. - Includes index.
ISBN 0421280107 Hbk £9.85
ISBN 0421280204 Pbk £6.00
—Current Bibliography of International Law. – London : Butterworths, 1978.
ISBN 0406623767 Hbk £33.00

—Development of Intern. Law by European Court Human Rights. – Manchester : Manchester University Press.
ISBN 0719026652 Hbk £29.95

—International dispute settlement / by J.G. Merrills. – London : Sweet & Maxwell, 1984.
xvi,211p; 19cm.
Includes index.
ISBN 0421303700 Hbk £
ISBN 0421303808 Pbk £6.95

Merritt, Adrian
Guidebook to Occupational Health and Safety Laws in Australia. – 2nd ed. – North Ryde : C.C.H. Australia, 1986.
600p.
ISBN 0869036939 Hbk £38.00

Merritt, Loretta
How to Study Law in Canada. – Butterworths, 1988.
72p.
Examines how to approach research problems and exam questions. Also includes brief outlines of major subject areas, and tactical tips on how to best structure your time and select the most appropriate courses for career development. Looks at extra-curricular activities, and contains a glossary of legal words and phrases.
ISBN 0409806056 Pbk £5.00

Merry, Malcolm
Hong Kong tenancy law : an introduction to the law of landlord and tenant / Malcolm Merry. – Singapore : Butterworths, 1985.
xix,343p.
Includes index. English and Chinese forms.
ISBN 0409995126 Pbk £24.00

Merwe, C.G. van der
Family, Things and Succession / H.J. Erasmus. – 2nd ed. – Durban : Professional Publishers, 1983.
xvii,615p.
ISBN 0409040525 Pbk £79.00

Merwe, S.W. van der
Practitioner's Guide to Legal Costs / H.V. Vorster. – Durban : Professional Publisher, 1983.
ISBN 0409059307 Pbk

Mesher, John →C.P.A.G.'s income support, the social fund and family credit : the legislation.
→ C.P.A.G.'s supplementary benefit and family income supplement : the legislation.

→ C.P.A.G's supplementary benefit and family income supplement : the legislation.

—C.P.A.G.'s supplementary benefit and family income supplement : the legislation / annotations by John Mesher. – 2nd ed. – London : Sweet & Maxwell, 1985.
400p.
Previous ed: published as CPAG's supplementary benefit legislation annotated. 1983. Includes index. Includes the text of the 1976 Supplementary Benefits Act, and the 1970 Family Income Supplements Act.
ISBN 0421342102 Pbk

—CPAG Incomeg Supp, The Social Fund & Family Cred : The Legis 88. – Sweet & Maxwell.
ISBN 0421402709 Pbk £19.50

—Supplementary Benefit and Family Income Supplement the Legislation
2nd Supplement to 4th ed. – Sweet & Maxwell.
ISBN 0421402504 Pbk £4.95

Meskin, Philip M, et al
Henochsberg on the Companies Act. – 4th ed. – Durban : Professional Publishers, 1985.
Hbk

Message →Asian Capital and Money Markets.

Messent, A. D. →CMR : contracts for the international carriage of goods by road.

Mestmacker, Ernst-Joachim →Law and economics of transborder telecommunications : a symposium.

Meston, M. C. →Matrimonial Homes (Family Protection) (Scotland) Act 1981.
—Succession (Scotland) Act 1964 / by Michael C. Meston. – 3rd ed. – Edinburgh : Green, 1982.
xv,136p; 24cm.
Includes text of the Act. Previous ed.: 1969. Includes index.
ISBN 0414007050 Pbk

Mestral, Armand L.C. de →Introduction to International Law.

Metcalf, David
Alternatives to unemployment : special employment measures in Britain / David Metcalf. – London : Policy Studies Institute, 1982.
66p. – (Policy Studies Institute).

Metcalf, N. P. →Road Traffic Reports : 1986.

Metcalfe, N. Percy
Criminal Appeal Reports. – London : Sweet & Maxwell.
Hbk £90.00

Methodology of international law / by Maarten Bos. – Amsterdam : North-Holland, 1984.
xxi,357p; 23cm.
'Published in collaboration with Interuniversitair Instituut voor Internationaal Recht T.M.C. Asser Instituut' - T.p. verso. Includes index.
ISBN 044486847X

Metropolitan Police
Public order review : civil disturbances 1981-1985 / Metropolitan Police Force. – London : Metropolitan Police, 1986.
iv,43p.

Metropolitan problem : papers from a conference held at Oxford, September 1984, organised by the Bar Council, the Law Society, and the Royal Institution of Chartered Surveyors / Gordon V. Hyde. – London : Sweet & Maxwell, 1985.
vi,102p; 25cm. – (Journal of planning and environmental law occasional papers).
ISBN 0421341505 Pbk £19.00

Mewett, Alan W.
Criminal Law / Morris Manning. – 2nd ed. – Butterworths, 1985.
816p.
Revised and expanded to take account of new developments in criminal law. Covers offences and defences, fundamental principles and problems in their application.
ISBN 0409849227 Hbk £95.00
—Criminal Law Quarterly (C.L.Q.) 1958-Present. – Aurora : Canada Law Book Co.
Hbk £74.00

—Introduction to the Criminal Process in Canada. – Agincourt : Carswell, 1988.
246p.
This is a comprehensive guide to Canadian criminal procedure. The various stages of the criminal process are outlined.
Hbk £40.50

Meyer, A., et al
Drafting Your Own Will. – Cape Town : Tafelberg Publishers, 1988.
80p.
Pbk £14.95

Meyer, Jan de
Belgium and the draft treaty establishing the European Union / by Jan de Meyer. – Florence : European University Institute, 1985.
38p.

Meyer, Michael A. →Conference on the application of international humanitarian law : March 12th, 1986, London SW1.

Meyer, Philippe
Child and the state : the intervention of the state in family life / Philippe Meyer : translated by Judith Ennew and Janet Lloyd. – Cambridge : Cambridge University Press, 1983.
128p; 23cm.
Translation of: L'enfant et la raison d'etat.
ISBN 052124871X Hbk £18.50
ISBN 2735100626 France : Pbk £5.95

Meyer, R.G., et al
Law for the Psychotherapist. – Norton.
ISBN 039370033X Hbk £25.00

Meyers, D. W.
Human Body and the Law. – Edinburgh : Edinburgh University Press.
215p.
ISBN 0852241739 Hbk £10.00

Meyers, Paul Richard
Criminal lawyers commonplace book. – 1 vol. – Scarborough, Ontario : Butterworths (Canada).
Deals with aspects of a criminal trial, such as cross-examination on criminal records, witnesses using notes, objectionable cross-examination techniques and evidence. Consists of legislation covering a range of issues and a series of digests of leading cases. Makes use of Western Canadian precedents, and those of the Supreme Court.
ISBN 0409994170 Llf

Mhajan, V.D.
British Constitution : Its Structure and Working. – New Delhi : S. Chand and Company, 1977.
386p.
Hbk £16.00

Mian, Q. Javed →Saudi business and labor law : its interpretation and application.

Micallef, J. A.
Towards a 21st century company philosophy : oration delivered in the Assembly Hall at the University of Malta Graduation Ceremony, 26th April 1984 / by J.A. Micallef. – Valletta : Malta University Press, 1984.
9p.

Michael, James
Politics of secrecy / James Michael. – Harmondsworth : Penguin, 1982.
240p; 20cm.
Bibliography: p225-229. - Includes index.
ISBN 0140220607 Pbk £2.50

Michaels, Amanda
Practical guide to trade marks / Amanda Michaels. – Oxford : ESC Publishing Ltd, 1982.
xxii,226p.
ISBN 0906214122 Hbk £21.50
ISBN 0906214092 Pbk £15.50

Michie, Michelle →Teaching, enacting and sticking up for human rights : an evaluation report on the Human Rights Commission's 'Teaching for Human Rights: Activities for Schools'.

Mickleburgh
Consumer Protection. – London : Butterworths.
ISBN 0903486466 Hbk £28.00
ISBN 0903486490 Pbk £11.95

Microeconomics of Money and Banking and other Essays. – Wheatsheaf Books.
ISBN 0745005101 Hbk £35.00

Micronesia : the problem of Palau / prepared by Roger Clark and Sue Rabitt Roff. – Rev ed. – London : Minority Rights Group, 1987.
22p. – (Report).
Includes bibliographical references.
ISBN 0946690146

Middle East and North Africa. – London : Europa Publications, 1964-.
Continues: Middle East.

Middle East legal systems / S.H. Amin. – Glasgow : Royston, 1985.
320p.
ISBN 0946706220 £29.95

Middle Temple
Middle Temple records / Ed. by Charles Henry Hopwood . – London : Published by order of the Masters of the bench, and sold by Butterworth & co, 1904.
4 v; 24 cm.
Added t.p.: Minutes of parliament of the Middle Temple. Tr. and ed. by Charles Trice Martin ... With an inquiry into the origin and early history of the Inn, by John Hutchinson, librarian .. Contents: 1. 1501-1603.– 2. 1603-1649.– 3. 1650-1703.– 4. Index of persons and places.

Middle Temple records / Ed. by Charles Henry Hopwood . – London : Published by order of the Masters of the bench, and sold by Butterworth & co, 1904.
4 v; 24 cm.
Added t.p.: Minutes of parliament of the Middle Temple. Tr. and ed. by Charles Trice Martin ... With an inquiry into the origin and early history of the Inn, by John Hutchinson, librarian .. Contents: 1. 1501-1603.– 2. 1603-1649.– 3. 1650-1703.– 4. Index of persons and places.

Middlesex Polytechnic
Law journals / Middlesex Polytechnic Library Services. – Hendon : The Polytechnic, 1982.
11p.,
'List of law related journals and law reports taken by Middlesex Polytechnic libraries'.

Middleton : the Beloved Judge. – Toronto : McClelland & Stewart, 1988.
240p.
ISBN 0771007957 Hbk £37.50

Midgal, et al
Law for Licensed Conveyancers. – London : Financial Training, 1988.
ISBN 1851850724 Pbk £7.95

Midgely, Harry
Butterworth's District Court Reports. – Wellington : Butterworths.
Hbk
—Butterworths District Court Reports. – Butterworths.
Hbk

Miers, David R →How to do things with rules : a primer of interpretation.
—Legislation / by David R. Miers and Alan C. Page. – London : Sweet & Maxwell, 1982.
xviii,266p; 23cm.
Bibliography: p247-255. - Includes index.
ISBN 0421271108 Hbk £13.50
ISBN 0421271205 Pbk

Mifsud, Frank M.
Customary Land Law in Africa : With Reference to Legislation Aimed at Adjusting Customary Tenures to the Needs of Development. – 2nd print 1985. – Rome : FAO, Food and Agricultural Organization of the United Nations, 1967.
96p.
ISBN 9251022267 Hbk £7.50

Migrant workers and civil liberties / by Alexis Pauly and Rene Diederich. – Florence : European University Institute, 1983.
102p.

Migrant workers in the Gulf / by Roger Owen. – London : Minority Rights Group, 1985.
23p. – (Report).
Bibliography: p.23.
ISBN 0946690332

Mikesell, Raymond F.
Foreign investment in mining projects : case studies of recent experiences / Raymond F. Mikesell : a project sponsored and administered by the FMME. – Cambridge, Mass. : Oelgeschlager, Gunn & Hain, 1983.
xv,297p; 24cm.
Bibliography: p281-285. - Includes index.
ISBN 0899461700

Mildred, R. H.
Expert witness / R. H. Mildred : with a foreword by the Right Honourable Lord Diplock. – London : Godwin, 1982.
x,131p; 24cm.
ISBN 0711456801

Miles, C.
VAT - Imports and exports. – London : CCH, 1987.
ISBN 0863251048 Pbk £15.00

Miles, C. W. N.
National Taxation : A Practical Handbook. – Reading : College of Estate Management.
94p.
Hbk £4.25

Miles, Christine
Cases for Students of Commercial Law. – North Ryde : C.C.H. Australia, 1987.
114p.
ISBN 0869039288 Hbk

Miles, John Charles →Cases Illustrating the Principles of the Laws of Torts.

Milgate
Cocaine Connection : Two Against the Drug Trade, A True Story / Milgate. – Sphere Books.
ISBN 0747402795 Pbk £3.50

Milgrim On Trade Secrets. – Matthew Bender, 1967.
ISBN 0000999076 Hbk £153.00

Milgrim, R.M.
Milgrim On Trade Secrets. – Matthew Bender, 1967.
ISBN 0000999076 Hbk £153.00

Milinsky, Aubrey →Genetics and the law III.

Military intervention in democratic societies / edited by Peter J. Rowe & Christopher J. Whelan. – London : Croom Helm, 1985.
312p; 23cm.
Includes bibliographies and index.
ISBN 0709922418 £18.95

Military Law in India : a Commentary / C.G. Goel. – New Delhi : Deep and Deep Publications, 1984.
450p.
Hbk £250.00

Milivojevic, Marko
The Debt Rescheduling Process / Marko Milivojevic. – London : Pinter, 1985.
200p.
Includes bibliography and index.
ISBN 0861875753 £18.50

Mill, John Stuart
Rationale of Judicial Evidence Specially Applied to English Practice, 5 Vols. / J. Bentham. – Repr. of 1827 ed. – Abingdon : Professional Books.
Hbk £145.00
—Utilitarianism / On liberty : John Stuart Mill : edited with an introduction by Mary Warnock. – 17th impression. – Glasgow : Fontana, 1985.
352p.
This selection originally published: 1962. Bibliography: p.343-4. - Includes index.

Millan, Victor →Falklands/Malvinas conflict : a spur to arms build-ups.

Millar, Ann →Investigating sexual assault.
→ Prosecuting sexual assault.

Millar, Ann R. →Debt recovery : a review of creditors' practices and policies.

Millar, John
Origin of the Distinction of Ranks. – Repr. of 1806 ed. – Aalen Wuertt : Scientia, 1986.
438p.
Hbk £105.00

Millar, Perry S.
Judicial administration in Canada / Perry S. Millar and Carl Baar. – Kingston : McGill-Queen's University Press, 1981.
xxiii,452p.
ISBN 0773503676

Millar, Robert →Policing the miners' strike.

Millar, T.
Current International Treaties. – Oxford : Croom Helm, 1984.
ISBN 0709917589 Hbk £30.00

Millard, Christopher J.
Legal Protection of Computer Programs and Data. – Agincourt : Carswell, 1985.
250p.
This work provides a systematic investigation of general software copyright issues under American, United Kingdom, and Canadian law. The legal protection of software and data under copyright, trade secrets, confidentiality, contractual arrangements, and criminal law is analyzed in the book.
Hbk £31.00
—Legal protection of computer programs and data / by Christopher J. Millard. – London : Sweet & Maxwell, 1985.
xxvi,239p; 23cm.
Includes index.
ISBN 0421334800 Pbk £24.00
ISBN 0459372300 Canada

Millard, Frances →Pressure politics in industrial societies : a comparative introduction.

Millard, I. R. →Morison's Company law in New Zealand.

Miller →Human rights.

Miller, Alice
Thou shalt not be aware : society's betrayal of the child / by Alice Miller : translated from the German by Hildegard and Hunter Hannum. – London : Pluto, 1985.
viii, 331p.
Originally published: Frankfurt am Main: Surkamp Verlag, 1981. Bibliography: p.327-331. Translation of: Du sollst nicht merken.
ISBN 0745300499

Miller, C. J. →Comparative product liability.
—Consumer and trading law : cases and materials / C.J. Miller, Brian W. Harvey. – London : Butterworths, 1985.
xiv,550p.
Includes index.
ISBN 0406012601 Hbk £ :
ISBN 040601261X Pbk
—Consumer and Trading Law - Cases and Materials / Brian W Harvey. – London : Butterworths, 1985.
ISBN 0406012601 Hbk £36.00
ISBN 040601261X Pbk £23.95
—Contempt of court / C.J. Miller. – 2nd ed. – Oxford : Clarendon Press, 1989.
lix,492p.
Previous ed.: 1976. Includes index. This new edition covers developments in the law of contempt and includes the Contempt of Court Act 1981.
ISBN 0198254784 Hbk £75

Miller, Charles
Lobbying government : understanding and influencing the corridors of power / Charles Miller. – Oxford : Basil Blackwell, 1987.
200p; 23cm.
Includes index.
ISBN 0631155252 £25.00

Miller, Christopher
Planning and pollution : an examination of the role of land use planning in the protection of environmental quality / Christopher Miller and Christopher Wood. – Oxford : Clarendon, 1983.
xi,232p; 23cm.
Includes index.
ISBN 0198232454

Miller, Clive →Measures of police effectiveness and efficiency.

Miller, Dallas K. →Rights of Indigenous Peoples in International Law : an Annotated Bibliography.

Miller, G.A. →Safety and Industry Laws, New South Wales, Vol. 1.

Miller, J.
Stock Exchange Press Dictionary of Financial Regulations. – Stock Exchange Press.
ISBN 0948209291 Hbk £29.95

Miller, J. G.
Family property and financial provision / by J.G. Miller. – 2nd ed. – London : Sweet & Maxwell, 1983.
xlvi,517p; 26cm.
Previous ed.: 1974. Includes index.
ISBN 0421282401 £36.00

Miller, Russell V
Annotated Trade Practices Act. – 8th ed. – North Ryde : Law Book Co, 1987.
xxxv, 413p.
ISBN 0455207399 Pbk £32.00
—Proprietary Company Practice Manual. – 2nd ed. – North Ryde : Law Book Co, 1983.
vii, 162p.
ISBN 0455204128 £21.00

Miller, W.
Dictionary of International Commerce. – London : Chapman & Hall, 1985.
ISBN 0412280108 Hbk £37.50

Millichamp, A.H.
ACCA Study and Revision Manual : 1.1 Accountancy. – London : BPP.
ISBN 1870941039 Pbk £9.95

Millin, Philip →Wille and Millin's Mercantile law of South Africa.

Millington, A.
Introduction to Property Valuation. – 2nd ed. – London : Estates Gazette, 1982.
ISBN 0728200589 Pbk £6.50

Mills →Building Society Law.
→ Guide to Export Finance.
—Spicer and Pegler's management buy-outs / Coyne. – Cambridge : Woodhead-Faulkner, 1987.
ISBN 0859413411 Hbk £30.00

Mills, C.P.
Industrial Disputes Law in Malaysia. – Singapore : Malayan Law Journal, 1984.
393p.
Reproduces the Industrial Relations Act with annotations from the decisions of the Industrial Court and the superior courts of Malaysia. Covers protection of rights of workmen and employers and their trade unions, collective bargaining and collective agreement, representation on dismissals, Industrial Relations Regulations 1967, and 1980.
ISBN 967962000X Hbk £90.00
—Workers Compensation, New South Wales. – Butterworths, 1987.
ISBN 0409492868 Hbk £210.00

Mills, J.
Essays on Law, Equality and Education. – London : Sweet & Maxwell, 1984.
ISBN 0710098804 Hbk £49.00
—On Liberty. – Penguin, 1974.
ISBN 0140432078 Pbk £2.50

Mills, J.E.A.
Ghana's Income Tax Law and the Investor. – Accra : Ghana Universities Press.
25p.
Hbk £2.50

Mills, Michael
Endowments and Deferred Giving sound recording : a Detailed Explanation of Legalities and Procedures. – Toronto : Association of Canadian Orchestras/Ontario Federation of Symphony Orchestras.
ISBN 1ac (60 min) £8.00

Millward, Neil
British workplace industrial relations 1980-1984 : the DE/PSI/ESRC/ACAS surveys / Neil Millward and Mark Stevens. – Aldershot : Gower, 1986.
xxi,341p; 22cm.
Includes index.
ISBN 0566053918 Hbk £22.50
ISBN 0566053969 Pbk £9.95
→ Workplace industrial relations in Britain : the DE/PSI/SSRC survey.

Milman, David →Annotated guide to the 1986 insolvency legislation: Insolvency Act 1986, Company Directors Disqualification Act 1986 and Insolvency Rules 1986 (as amended).
—Corporate Insolvency / Durrant. – London : Sweet & Maxwell, 1987.
ISBN 0421365005 Hbk £24.00
—Educational conflict and the law / David Milman. – London : Croom Helm, 1986.
160p; 23cm.
Includes index.
ISBN 0709935218 £16.95
—Modern partnership law / David Milman and Terence Flanagan. – London : Croom Helm, 1983.
xxix,178p; 23cm.
Includes index.
ISBN 0709910142 Hbk £15.95
ISBN 0709910150 Pbk
—Receivers and receiverships / David Milman and Jonathan Rushworth. – Bristol : Jordans, 1987.
xxi,82p; 21cm.
Includes index.
ISBN 0853081239 Pbk £8.50

Milne, Alan J M →Equality and discrimination : essays in freedom and justice : papers presented at the United Kingdom Association for Legal and Social Philosophy eleventh annual conference at University College London, 6th-8th April 1984.
—Human rights and human diversity : an essay in the philosophy of human rights / A.J.M. Milne. – London : Macmillan, 1986.
240p; 22cm.
Includes index.
ISBN 0333406184 £25.00

Milne, David
New Canadian Constitution. – Toronto : James Lorimer & Co.
240p.
ISBN 0888625448 Pbk £7.95
ISBN 0888625456 Hbk £19.95

Milner's Cases and Materials on Contracts. – 4th ed. – Aurora : Canada Law Book Co, 1985.
884p. – (Case Books).
This casebook examines the present common law of contracts with reference to the leading Canadian and English cases. Chapters include, among others: Remedies for Breach of Promise, The Kind of Promises Legally Enforced, Third Party Beneficiaries, Assignment and Agency, Third Parties and Mistakes in Dealings Between Others, and Written Documents.
ISBN 0920722172 Hbk £84.00

Milsom, S F C
Historical foundations of Common Law. – 2nd ed. – London : Butterworths, 1981.
496.
ISBN 0406625025 Hbk £22.50
ISBN 0406625034 Pbk £16.95
—Historical foundations of the common law / S.F.C. Milsom. – 2nd ed. – London : Butterworths, 1981.
xiii,475p; 22cm.
Previous ed.: 1969. Includes index. .
ISBN 0406625026 Hbk
ISBN 0406625034 Pbk
—Legal Framework of English Feudalism. – Cambridge : Cambridge University Press, 1976.
ISBN 0521209471 Hbk £30.00
—Nature of Blackstones achievement : Selden Society lecture delivered at Oxford on May 31st, 1980 in association with Pembroke College to commemorate Blackstones bicentenary / by S.F.C. Milsom. – London : Selden Society, 1981.
12p; 25cm.
The text of this lecture was set as part of the first issue of the Oxford Journal of Legal studies and is simultaneously published in the journal and in the Societys lecture series.

Milton, J. R. L. →South African criminal law and procedure, Vol.1 : General principles of criminal law : by E.M. Burchell and P.M.A. Hunt.

Milward, Jane M. →Emmet on title : Emmet's notes on perusing titles and on practical conveyancing.

Minan, John H →Law in the People's Republic of China: commentary, readings and materials.

Minattur, Joseph
Judicial reform : working paper : Conference on the Reform on sic the Indian Legal System. – New Delhi : Indian Law Institute, 1983.
53p.
Caption title: Judicial reforms.
—Publish and perish / Joseph Minattur. – New Delhi : VIVA, 1982.
80p.

Minchin, Elizabeth →Legal pluralism : proceedings of the Canberra Law Workshop VII.

Mind →Court of protection : a legal and policy analysis of the guardianship of the estate.
→ Practical guide to mental health law : the Mental Health Act 1983 and related legislation.

Mine, Yours Or Ours? A Study of Step-parent Adoption. – London : HMSO, 1983.
136p.
Discusses the effect of the changes in law on adoption recommended by the Houghton Committee and enacted in the 1975 Children's Act.
ISBN 0113208359 Pbk £3.95

Miner, Richard B.
Associated corporations / by Richard B. Miner. – Toronto : Carswell, 1983.
xvii,134p.
Includes index.
ISBN 0459354507
—Current Issues in Canadian Business Law. – Agincourt : Carswell, 1985.
600p.
This work is a collection of essays on a variety of business law topics written by Canadian practitioners. The essays cover topics ranging from corporate and commercial law to secured transactions and instruments of payment.
Hbk £75.75

Mines and Minerals Act, 1969, and the Mineral Tax Act, 1970 / E.J. Langevad. – Lusaka : Geological Survey of Zambia.
Hbk £1.25

Minimum Documentation under Rule 34.1 of the Regulations under the Patent Cooperation Treaty (PCT) : Non-Patent Literature, List of Perodicals. – Geneva : World Intellectual Property Organization.
Hbk £19.00

Minimum Standard Guidelines for Australian Prisons. – Canberra : Australian Institute of Criminology.
Hbk £2.00

Minimum Wages Act : With Central and U.P. Rules and Notifications Fixing Minimum Wages in Various Industries and Establishments. – 5th ed. – Lucknow : Eastern Book Company, 1985.
Pbk £40.00

Mining Act, 1983, Bill 129 : An Act to Revise the Mining Act. – Ontario : Ontario Government Publications Service, 1983.
90p.
Hbk £1.00

Mining and environmental law : proceedings of the seminar held at Washington D.C., 4-8 April 1982, ... organised by the Committee on Environmental Law, Section on Business Law, of the International Bar Association, in conjunction with the American Law Institute-American Bar Association Committee on Continuing Professional Education. – 2. – London : International Bar Association, 1982.
ISBN 0950587648

Mining and mineral laws of South Africa / by Blen Lloyd Stuart Franklin and Morris Kaplan. – Durban : Butterworths, 1982.
Bibliography: p.lxxvii-lxxviii. - Includes index.
ISBN 0409028983 Hbk R335

Mining Exploration Agreements. – Montreal : Canadian Institute of Mining and Metallurgy.
Hbk £40.00

Mining Labour Code. – 6th ed. – Karachi : Bureau of Labour Publications, 1987.
315p.
Pbk £39.00

Mining Law, 1983. – Vancouver : British Columbia Continuing Legal Education Society, 1983.
760p.
ISBN 0865041377 Hbk £85.00

Mining Law : 1986. – Vancouver : Continuing Legal Education Society of British Columbia, 1986.
330p.
ISBN 0865042861 Hbk £85.00

Mining ventures in developing countries
Part 2 : Analysis of project agreements : Erich Schanze...et al. : translated by Gary M. Friedman / Erich Schanze. – Deventer : Kluwer, 1981.
281p.
First published: Frankfurt am Main, Metzner; Deventer, Kluwer; 1977- , as 'Rohstofferschliessungsvorhaben in Entwicklungslandern'. Translated from German into English.
ISBN 9065440380

Ministry of Defence Police Review Committee
Report of the Ministry of Defence Police Review Committee : presented to Parliament by the Secretary of State for Defence ... – Ministry of Defence Police Review Committee. – London : H.M.S.O., 1986.
50p.
ISBN 0101985304

Ministry of the Attorney-General
Courts of Justice Act, Bill 100, 1983 : An Act to Revise and Consolidate the Law Respecting the Organization, Operation and Proceedings of Courts of Justice in Ontario. – Ministry of the Attorney-General. – Ontario : Ontario Government Publications Service, 1983.
91p.
Hbk £1.00

Minnis
Accounts' Liability in the 1980's / Nobles. – Oxford : Croom Helm, 1985.
ISBN 0709918305 Hbk £25.00

Minor Report on the Jurisdiction of Local Judges : Stays of Execution and Installment Orders. – Victoria : Government of British Columbia, 1984.
Hbk

Minor Report on the Land Act. – Victoria : Government of British Columbia, 1984.
Hbk

Minorities : community and identity : report of the Dahlem Workshop on Minorities - Community and Identity, Berlin 1982, Nov. 28 - Dec. 3 / C. Fried, editor : rapporteurs A.M.A. Dummett ... et al. – Berlin : Springer-Verlag, 1983.
x,417p.
Includes bibliographies and indexes.
ISBN 354012747X

Minorities and human rights law / Patrick Thornberry. – London : Minority Rights Group, 1987.
19p. – (Report).
Bibliography: p19.
ISBN 0946690480

Minorities in National and International Laws. – New Delhi : Deep and Deep Publications, 1985. 376p. Hbk £200.00

Minority Rights Group → Fiji.
→ Minorities and human rights law.
→ Outsider : newsletter of the Minority Rights Group.
→ Rights of mentally ill people.

Minors : the law and practice : the juvenile courts, the offences, the role of the local authorities / Kenneth W. Pain. – London : Fourmat Publishing, 1987. xvii,293p.
Concerns practice and procedure of juvenile courts, offences which can be committed by and against minors and the part played by local authorities in care proceedings.
ISBN 1851900306

Minty
Child Care and Adult Crime / Ashcraft. – Manchester : Manchester University Press, 1988.
ISBN 0719024692 Hbk £29.50

Mintz, Jack M. → Taxes on capital income in Canada : analysis and policy.

Minutes / Annual General Meeting, International Air Transport Association. – Montreal : IATA, 1981.
Continues: Reports and proceedings.

Minutes of evidence / Commission on the Constitution. – 6. – London : HMSO, 1970.
1: Wales - 2: Scotland - 3: Northern Ireland - 4: Scotland - 5: Wales - 6: The Channel Islands and the Isle of Man. Bound in one vol..

Minutes of evidence taken before the Company Law Committee / David Llewelyn Jenkins Jenkins. – London : H.M.S.O., 1960. 1607p.
Committee Chairman: Lord Jenkins. Bound with Report and Index.

Minutes of proceedings and evidence of the Special Committee on Pension Reform / Proces-verbaux et temoignages du Comite special sur la reforme des pensions. – Ottawa : The Special Committee, 1983. x,168p. – (House of Commons issue no 38).
'First session of the Thirty-second Parliament, 1980-81-82-83'. Cover title: Report of the Parliamentary Task Force on Pension Reform.

Miracle, Gordon E → European regulation of advertising : supranational regulation of advertising in the European economic community.

Mirfield, Peter
Confessions / by Peter Mirfield. – London : Sweet & Maxwell, 1985. 165p; 22cm.
Includes index.
ISBN 0421303905 Hbk £12.25 :
ISBN 0421304006 Pbk £8.25

Miscarriages of justice / Bob Woffinden. – London : Hodder & Stoughton, 1987. xiii,376p; 24cm.
Bibliography: p367. - Includes index.
ISBN 0340374209 £14.95

Miscellany two / by various authors : edited by David Sellar : with a preface by Lord Avonside. – Edinburgh : The Stair Society, 1984. ix,339p.
Includes indexes.
ISBN 0902292102

Misconduct of students : a legal and disciplinary study / Arun Bhattacharjee. – New Delhi : Deep & Deep, 1981. 440p.
Bibliography: p.425-427. - Includes index.

Mishra, Shashi
Fundamental Rights and the Supreme Court : Reasonableness of Restrictions. – New Delhi : Deep and Deep Publications, 1984. 232p. Hbk £125.00

Miskin, Christine → Directory of law libraries in the British Isles.
→ Legal thesaurus.
—Library and information services for the legal profession / C. Miskin. – London : British Library, 1981. iv,60p; 30cm.
ISBN 0905984730 Pbk

Misra, Anand Swarup
Law of Speaking Orders. – 3rd ed. – Lucknow : Eastern Book Company, 1985. Hbk
—Officer's Companion (in Administration and Law). – 3rd ed. – Lucknow : Eastern Book Company, 1985. Hbk
—Principles and Practices of Judicial Propriety : With Precedents and Case-Law. – Allahabad : Hind Publishing House, 1986. 359p. Hbk £120.00

Misra, V.B.
Evolution of the Constitutional History of India (1773-1947) : With Special Reference to the Role of the Indian Congress and the Minorities. – Delhi : Mittal Publications, 1987. 272p.
ISBN 8170990106 Hbk £160.00

Misrepresentation / by David K. Allen. – London : Sweet & Maxwell, 1988. xxii,178p; 22cm.
Includes index.
ISBN 0421347201 Hbk £16.00
ISBN 0421347309 Pbk £10.00

Mission to South Africa : the Commonwealth report / Malcolm Fraser, Olusegun Obasanjo. – Harmondsworth : Penguin Books for the Commonwealth Secretariat, 1986. 176p.
Co-chairmen: Malcolm Fraser and Olusegun Obasanjo.
ISBN 0140523847

Misuse of Drugs
2nd Supplement / Hamid Ghodse. – Waterlow. – (Criminal Law Library).
ISBN 0080331076 Pbk £10.00

Misuse of drugs. – London : Butterworths, 1986.
Summarises both English and Scots case law arranged in accordance with the sections of the 1971 Misuse of Drugs Act. With a glossary of controlled drugs and words and phrases likely to be encountered in practice. Published by Butterworths on behalf of the Law Society of Scotland.
ISBN 0406103909 Pbk

Misuse of drugs / Patrick Bucknell and Hamid Ghodse. – London : Waterlow, 1986. 512p; 23cm.
ISBN 0080392032 £30.00

Misuse of Drugs. – Butterworths, 1989. 251p.
ISBN 0409788163 Pbk £54.00

Mitchelhill, Alan
Bills of lading : law and practice / Alan Mitchelhill. – London : Chapman and Hall, 1982. x,127p; 31cm.
Includes index.
ISBN 0412239604 Hbk £
ISBN 041223940X Pbk

Mitchell, Barbara
Landlord and Tenant Law. – London : Collins, 1986. 256p.
ISBN 0003831183 Pbk £9.95

Mitchell, C.
Sterling commercial paper market. – Cambridge : Woodhead-Faulkner, 1988.
ISBN 0859414108 Hbk £40.00

Mitchell, C. Michael → Ontario Labour Relations Board Law and Practice.

Mitchell, Carlyle L.
Integration of marine space in national development strategies of small island states : the case of the Caribbean states of Grenada and St. Lucia / Carlyle L. Mitchell and Edgar Gold. – Halifax, N.S. : Dalhousie Ocean Studies Programme, 1982. x,346p.
Bibliography: p338-345.
→ Problems of development and ocean management in the eastern Caribbean : economic, legal, environmental and planning aspects : proceedings of an international seminar held in Kingstown, St. Vincent & the Grenadines, West Indies, May 11-13, 1981.

Mitchell, G. Duncan → Artificial family : a consideration of artificial insemination by donor.

Mitchell Hill, A.
Bills of Lading and Practice. – London : Sweet & Maxwell, 1982. Hbk £16.00

Mitchell, J
Constitutional law. – 2nd. – Edinburgh : Green (W.) & Son, 1968.
Deals with the relationships of the contral institutions of government, politics, ideas, and their relationships. Copious references to a wide range of legal and non-legal material related to constitutional law. Published under the auspices of the Scottish Universities Law Institute.
ISBN 041400504X Pbk
—Electronic Banking and the Consumer : the European Dimension. – Policy Studies Institute.
ISBN 0853744394 Pbk £4.95

Mitchell, J. D. B.
European Law and Institutions. – Edinburgh : Edinburgh University Press. 60p. Hbk £2.00
→ In memoriam J.D.B. Mitchell.

Mitchell, Jeffrey
Ontario Labour Relations Board Law and Practice : Citation Updater, 1 Vol. – Butterworths.
ISBN 0409847887 Llf £40.00

Mitchell, Paul → Joynson-Hicks on copyright.

Mitchell, Philip L.R.
Director's duties and insider dealing / Philip L.R. Mitchell. – London : Butterworths, 1982. xxiv,268p; 22cm.
Includes index.
ISBN 0406295808 Pbk £14.50

Mitchell, R. J. → Labour law : materials and commentary.

Mitchell, Stephen
Archbold : Pleading, Evidence, and Practice in Criminal Cases. – 41st ed. – London : Sweet & Maxwell, 1983.

Mitchell, V. A. → Compensation for criminal damage to property.
→ Compensation for criminal injuries.

Mitchelmore, Clem → Continuing legal education in the 1980's : papers and proceedings of the Conference on Continuing Legal Education in the 1980's, conducted by the Law Society of New South Wales and the Law Foundation of New South Wales at the College of Law, Sydney, 13-15 November 1980.

Mitchels, Barbara
Road Traffic. – London : Longman Professional.
ISBN 0851214134 Pbk

Mitchener, Donald G.
Valuation 85 : a Conceptual Outline / Fiona Abbott. – 1st ed. – North Ryde : C.C.H. Australia, 1984. 56p.
ISBN 0887962882 Pbk £5.00

Mitchnick, Mort G.
Union Security and the Charter : an Analysis of the Law. – Butterworths, 1987. 216p.
Analysis of the effects of sections 1 and 2(d) of the Charter, dealing with 'freedom of association', on union security. Makes reference to Canadian cases decided on this issue. Contains analysis based on the legal regimes in place in the United States, western Europe, Australia, and those reflected in international covenants.
ISBN 0409806536 Hbk £50.00

Mitra
Commentaries on Criminal Minor Acts, 6 Vols. – 2nd ed. – Allahabad : Law Publishers, 1982. Hbk £37.50
—Commentaries on the Limitation Act. – 4th ed. – Allahabad : Law Publishers, 1983. Hbk £45.00

Mitra, A.K.
Theory and Practice of Valuation. – 2nd ed. – Calcutta : Eastern Law House, 1986. Hbk £138.00

Mitra, B.C.
Law Relating to Bankers Letters of Credit. – Allahabad : Indian Press. 290p. Hbk £1.50
—Law Relating to Bills of Lading and Charterparties. – Allahabad : Indian Press. 253p. Hbk £1.50
—Law Relating to Marine Insurance. – Allahabad : Indian Press. 371p. Hbk £3.00

Mitra, Bijan Chandra
West Bengal Laws
Vol. 5 : Annotated Cooperative Societies Act to Establishments and Luxuries Tax Acts. – Calcutta : Hindustan Law Book Co., 1987. 467p. Hbk £125.00

Mitra, N.L.
Juvenile Delinquency and Indian Justice System. – New Delhi : Deep and Deep Publications, 1988. 516p. Hbk £375.00

Mitra's Civil Reference. – 2nd ed. – Calcutta : Eastern Law House. Hbk £86

Mittal, S.N.
Commercial Law. – Meerat : Pragati Prakashan, 1973. 380p. Hbk £9.00

Mitter, Dwarka Nath
Position of Women in Hindu Law. – 1913 repr. – New Delhi : Inter-India Publications, 1984. vi, ii, xxxii, xix, 707p.
ISBN 8121001641 Hbk £380.00

Mitter, V.
Law of Defamation and Malicious Prosecution. – 9th ed. – Allahabad : Law Publishers, 1987. 500p. Hbk £150,000
—Law of Identification and Discovery. – 6th ed. – Allahabad : Law Book Company, 1988. 500p. Hbk £150.00
—Police Diaries, Statements, Reports, Investigations. – 9th ed. 2 Vols. – Allahabad : Law Publishers, 1986. Hbk £170.00 ea

Mixed agreements / edited by David O'Keeffe and Henry G. Schermers. – Deventer : Kluwer, 1983.
x,248p.
At head of title: Europa Institute Leiden.
ISBN 9065441530

Mixed Marriages Act : a Historical and Theological Study. – Rondebosch : University of Cape Town, 1983.
viii, 108p.
ISBN 0799205206 Pbk £5.00

Miyatake →Japanese international taxation.

MLAANZ journal / the Maritime Law Association of Australia and New Zealand. – Sydney : The Association, 1983.
Supersedes the MLAANZ newsletter. Masthead title: Journal of the MLAANZ.
ISBN 08114293

M'Laurin, J.
Argument and Decisions in Remarkable Cases Before the High Court of Justiciary : 1670-1773. – Repr. of 1774 ed. – Abingdon : Professional Books.
76p.
Hbk £60.00

Mobbing and rioting / Scottish Law Commission. – Edinburgh : Scottish Law Commission, 1984.
102p. – (Consultative memorandum).

Mobbs, M.
Local Government Planning and Environment Service, New South Wales. – Butterworths.
Llf £370.00

Mobile Homes : An Occupiers Guide. – London : Shelter, 1988.
ISBN 0901242837 Pbk £3.95

Mobile homes and the law / by C.M. Brand. – London : Sweet & Maxwell, 1986.
xxiv,210p; 26cm.
Includes index.
ISBN 0421334703 £24.00

Mobile Homes for Legal Assistants. – Vancouver : British Columbia Continuing Legal Education Society, 1981.
142p.
ISBN 0865040400 Hbk £35.00

Mobile Offshore Units : Regulations Laid Down by Norwegian Official Control Institutions. – New complete. – Oslo : Fabritius og Sonners.
ISBN 8207009225 Hbk £1.452

Mocatta, Alan Abraham →Scrutton on charterparties and bills of lading.

Model agreement to enable members of the family forming part of the household of a member of a diplomatic mission or consular post to engage in a gainful occupation : recommendation no. R (87)2 adopted by the Committee of Ministers of the Council of Europe on 12 February 1987 and Explanatory memorandum. – Council of Europe. – Strasbourg : Council of Europe, 1987.
13p.
Prepared by the Committee of experts on public international law (CJ-DI) set up under the authority of the European Committee on Legal Co-operation. At head of cover title : Council of Europe, Legal Affairs.
ISBN 9287110859

Model Agreements for Visual Artists : a Guide to Contracts in the Visual Arts. – Ottawa : CARFAC, 1982.
Hbk £30.00

Model double taxation convention on estates and inheritances and on gifts / report of the OECD Committee on Fiscal Affairs. – Paris : Organisation for Economic Co-operation and Development, 1983.
147p.
ISBN 9264124039

Model financial statements. – Stoy Hayward & Co. – London : Butterworths, 1986.
ISBN 0406503907 Pbk £16.50

Model food legislation / National Health and Medical Research Council. – Canberra : Australian Govt. Pub. Service, 1983.
1 v. (loose-leaf); 28 cm.
Includes index.
ISBN 0644027282

Model handbook for interlending and copying / Graham P. Cornish. – Wetherby : Published jointly by IFLA Office for International Lending and Unesco, 1988.
79p; 30cm.
Bibliography: p72.
ISBN 0712320458 Pbk £5.00

Model Income Tax Treaties. – Dordrecht : Kluwer.
ISBN 9065441484 Pbk £30.00

Model of the building society sector / J. B. Wilcox. – London : Bank of England, 1985.
29p. – (Discussion papers).
Bibliography: p29.
ISBN 090331276X

Model Procedural Agreements. – London : Industrial Society.
Hbk £3.20

Model Provisions on the Protection of Computer Software : Text of the English Translation of the Stockholm Act (1967). – Geneva : World Intellectual Property Organization.
27p.
Hbk £20.00

Modelling the criminal justice system / Patricia M. Morgan. – London : Home Office, 1985.
v,64p.
Bibliography: p.64.
ISBN 0862522161

Models of organisation for the government of conurbations : report / prepared under the guidance of the Committee of Experts on Local and Regional Structures of the Steering Committee for Regional and Municipal Matters by Finn Bruun. – Strasbourg : Council of Europe, 1986.
24p; 30cm.

Modern Advanced Accounting / Larsen. – 4th ed. – Maidenhead : McGraw-Hill.
ISBN 0070365083 Hbk £29.50

Modern banking law / E.P. Ellinger. – Oxford : Clarendon, 1987.
400p; 24cm.
Includes index.
ISBN 0198761562 Hbk £35.00 :
ISBN 0198761570 Pbk £12.00

Modern bills of lading / Paul Todd. – London : Collins, 1986.
256p; 24cm.
Includes index.
ISBN 0003833224 £17.50

Modern Business Law / P. E. J. Brooks. – Durban : Butterworths.
Hbk

Modern Cases. – Repr. of 1730 ed. – Abingdon : Professional Books.
305p.
Orig. Title : Modern Cases in Law and Equity.
Hbk £60.00

Modern Cases of Negligence
First supplement. – 3rd ed. – London : Sweet & Maxwell, 1985.
ISBN 042132810X Hbk £12.50

Modern Commercial Knowledge. – 4th ed. Repr. of 1977 ed. – Plymouth : Macdonald & Evans, 1982.
320p. – (M and E Handbook Ser.).
ISBN 0712113991 Hbk £3.95

Modern Commonwealth / Sir William Dale. – London : Butterworths, 1983.
xxxi,345p; 26cm.
Bibiography: pxxvii-xxx. - Includes index. Second copy inscribed by the author.
ISBN 0406174040

Modern Company Law
Supplement 1988 /. – Sweet & Maxwell.
ISBN 04204477705 Pbk £6.50

Modern Constitution - Constitution Moderne. – Fribourg : Universitatsverlag.
256p.
ISBN 2827103923 Pbk £40.00

Modern Constitutions. – 2nd ed. 1966 repr. 1984. – New Delhi : Oxford University Press.
Pbk £25.00

Modern contract of guarantee / by James O'Donovan and John C. Phillips. – Sydney : Law Book Company, 1985.
xcv,675p.
ISBN 0455203490

Modern conveyancing / by Ruth Annand and Brian Cain. – London : Sweet & Maxwell, 1984.
xlii,514p; 24cm.
Includes index.
ISBN 0421320907 Hbk £
ISBN 0421321008 Pbk £15.95

Modern Conveyancing Precedents. – 2nd ed. – London : Butterworths, 1988.
ISBN 040633451X Hbk

Modern Development of City Government in the United Kingdom and the United States, 2 Vols. – Repr. of 1927 ed. – Aalen Wuertt : Scientia.
764p : Illus.
Hbk £190.00

Modern developments in the law of civic procedure / by D.B. Casson and I.H. Dennis. – London : Sweet & Maxwell, 1982.
xxv,112p; 22cm.
Includes index.
ISBN 0421290005 Pbk £4.95

Modern Director-Duties and Liabilities 1985 : Centre for Commercial Law and Applied Legal Research. – Monash University, Faculty of Law. – Clayton : Monash University Press.
ISBN 0867463848 Hbk £17.00

Modern Economic Analysis 2. – London : Butterworths, 1982.
The objective of this book is to provide an analysis of the economic policy of monetarism. The economics of industrial relations, health, housing, as well as, theories of the firm and central government intervention are discussed.
ISBN 0408107715 Pbk

Modern English land law / by Michael Harwood. – 2nd ed. – London : Sweet & Maxwell, 1982.
xliii,597p; 23cm.
Previous ed.: published as English land law. 1975. Includes index.
ISBN 0421278900 Hbk £
ISBN 0421279001 Pbk £12.95

Modern English legal system / by P.F. Smith and S.H. Bailey. – London : Sweet & Maxwell, 1984.
xxxix,783p; 24cm.
Includes index.
ISBN 0421271809 Hbk £30.00
ISBN 0421271906 Pbk £16.00

Modern equity / by Harold Greville Hanbury and Ronald Harling Maudsley. – 12th ed. – London : Stevens, 1985.
cxiv,920p; 26cm.
Previous ed.: 1981. Includes index.
ISBN 0420470506 Hbk £30.00
ISBN 0420470603 Pbk £19.75

Modern equity / by Harold Greville Hanbury. – 11th ed. – London : Stevens, 1981.
cvi,796p; 25cm.
Previous ed.: 1976. Includes index.
ISBN 0420461302 Hbk £27.50
ISBN 042046140X Pbk £16.50

Modern Equity / R H Maudsley. – 12th ed. – London : Sweet & Maxwell, 1985.
ISBN 0420470506 Hbk £32.00
ISBN 0420470603 Pbk £24.00

Modern Equity / Harling. – Stevens & Sons.
ISBN 0420481303 Hbk £36.00
ISBN 0420481400 Pbk £26.00

Modern Hindu Law. – Lucknow : Eastern Book Company, 1983.
992p.
Hbk £120.00

Modern insurance law / by John Birds. – 2nd ed. – London : Sweet & Maxwell, 1988.
xxxviii,335p.
Explanation of the fundamental principles of insurance law, including the meaning of insurance, the basic elements of the contract – parties, the insurable interest, formation, void and voidable contracts and premiums, agency and asigment and mechanisms for claiming under the policy. Discusses the Insurance Companies Act 1982, and the Financial Services Act 1986.
ISBN 0421371404 Pbk
ISBN 0421371501

Modern international law of outer space. – Pergamon, 1984.
ISBN 0080293670 Hbk £71.40

Modern Introduction to Law. – London : Edward Arnold, 1984.
544p.
ISBN 0713109041 Pbk £8.95

Modern Investment Management. – Oxford : Oxford University Press, 1986.
ISBN 0195041968 Hbk £29.50

Modern Japanese Law. – London : Butterworths, 1988.
ISBN 040666921X Hbk

Modern law of charities / George W. Keeton. – 3rd ed. – Cardiff : University College Cardiff Press, 1983.
lxxix,502p; 22cm.
Previous ed.: / by George W. Keeton and L.A. Sheridan. Belfast : Northern Ireland Legal Quarterly. 1971. Includes index.
ISBN 0906449545 £45.00

Modern law of copyright / Prescott. – 2nd ed. – London : Butterworths, 1988.
ISBN 0406616973 Hbk

Modern Law of Diplomacy : External Missions of States and International Organizations. – Dordrecht : Kluwer, 1988.
300p.
Hbk Gld135.00

Modern law of evidence. – London : Butterworths, 1985.
ISBN 0862051037 Hbk £22.50
ISBN 0862051045 Pbk £11.95

Modern Law of Highways. – London : Butterworths, 1981.
This book presents detailed coverage of the common law of highways and the Highways Act of 1980 for the practitioner in the United Kingdom. The full text of the Act, along with other relevant legislation, is included in the work along with extensive annotations.
ISBN 0406220808 Hbk

Modern Law of Insurance in India. – 2nd ed. in press. – Bombay : Tripathi.
364p.
bd £65.00

Modern Law of Negligence. – London : Butterworths.
ISBN 0406113009 Hbk £42.00

Modern law of pilotage / by F.D. Rose. – London : Sweet & Maxwell, 1984.
xxi,138p; 25cm.
Includes index.
ISBN 0421322705 Pbk £12.00

Modern law of real property / E H Burn. – 14th ed. – London : Butterworths, 1988.
ISBN 0406565481 Pbk
ISBN 0406565473 Hbk £38

Modern law of strikes / Duggan. – London : Financial Training, 1987.
ISBN 185185066X Pbk £12.95

Modern law of trusts / by David B. Parker and Anthony R. Mellows. – 5th ed. – London : Sweet & Maxwell, 1983.
xlviii,492p; 24cm.
Previous ed.: London : Sweet & Maxwell, 1979. Includes index.
ISBN 0421309709 Hbk £
ISBN 0421309806 Pbk £12.00

Modern Law Review. – London : Sweet & Maxwell.
Hbk £22.50
Bound Vol.. –
Hbk £10.50
Single copy. –
Hbk £5.50
Index Vols. 1-33. –
Hbk £21.00
Back Vols. avail..

Modern Law Review : 1937-date. – Abingdon : Professional Books, 1984.
Hbk

Modern liner contracts : an in depth study of current contracts of carriage in liner shipping. – London : Lloyd's of London Press, 1984.
90 leaves.
ISBN 1850440328

Modern Merchant Banking / Wheble. – 2nd ed. – Cambridge : Woodhead-Faulkner, 1983.
ISBN 0859412156 Pbk £9.95
ISBN 0859412164 Hbk £17.50

Modern methods of valuation / Davies. – 2nd ed. – London : Estates Gazette, 1981.
ISBN 072820049X Hbk £10.00

Modern Nigerian law of evidence / by Fidelis Nwadialo. – Benin City : Ethiope Publishing, 1981.
xlix,306p.
Includes bibliographical references and index.
ISBN 9781231068

Modern partnership law / David Milman and Terence Flanagan. – London : Croom Helm, 1983.
xxix,178p; 23cm.
Includes index.
ISBN 0709910142 Hbk £15.95
ISBN 0709910150 Pbk

Modern public records : selection and access : report of a committee appointed by the Lord Chancellor / Chairman Sir Duncan Wilson : presented to Parliament by the Lord High Chancellor. – London : H.M.S.O., 1981.
xiii,256p,1leaf of plates; 25cm.
ISBN 0101820402 Pbk £8.10

Modern public records : the government response to the report of the Wilson Committee / presented to Parliament by the Lord High Chancellor ... March 1982. – London : H.M.S.O., 1982.
ii,29p; 25cm.
Response to: Modern public records: selection and access (Cmnd.; 8204).
ISBN 0101853106

Modern Reports : From the 21st to the 29th of King Charles II in the King's Bench and Common Pleas, with the Great Case in Chancery, 22. Car 2 Between Fry and Porter. – Repr. of 1682 ed. – Abingdon : Professional Books.
304p.
Hbk £95.00

Modern Theories of Law 1933. – London : Wildy & Sons.
Hbk £8.25

Modern trends concerning the reduction of prosecutions / by Criton G. Tornaritis. – Nicosia : s.l., 1984.
13 leaves.

Modern wills precedents. – 2nd ed. – London : Butterworths, 1987.
ISBN 0406334617 Hbk £24.00

Modernization and law : theses and thoughts / Kalman Kulcsar. – Budapest : Institute of Sociology, Hungarian Academy of Sciences, 1987.
198p.
Bibliography: pp.181-198..
ISBN 9638301686

Modrall, James →Creation of the European Union and its relation to the EEC treaties.

Moens, Gabriel
Affirmative Action : the New Discrimination. – St. Leonards : Centre for Independent Studies.
116p.
ISBN 0949769274 Hbk £11.95

Moeran, Edward
Legal Aid Summary. – New ed. – London : Oyez Longman, 1983.
ISBN 0851205879 Hbk
—Practical conveyancing. – 10th ed. – London : Longman Professional, 1986.
ISBN 0851212239 Pbk £16.95
—Practical Legal Aid. – 3rd ed. – London : Oyez Longman, 1982.
– (Oyez Longman Practice Note Ser.: No. 62).
ISBN 0851205860 Hbk £11.95

Moffat
Trusts Law : Texts and Materials / Chesterman. – Weidenfeld & Nicolson.
– (Law in Context Series).
ISBN 0297794027 Hbk £35.00
ISBN 0297794035 Pbk £22.95

Moffitt, Athol →Australian Supplement to Borrie and Lowe's Law of Contempt.

Mogha's Law of Pleadings. – 14th ed. – Calcutta : Eastern Law House, 1987.
Hbk £180.00

Mohr, Konrad
Law Relating to Business Tenancies in Germany. – Plymouth : Macdonald & Evans, 1985.
72p.
ISBN 0712154701 Hbk £10.75

Moillin
Taxation of fringe benefits / Sargent. – London : CCH, 1988.
ISBN 0863251455 Pbk £8.50

Moinuddin, Hasan
Charter of the Islamic Conference and legal framework of economic co-operation among its member states : a study of the charter, the General Agreement for Economic, Technical and Commercial Co-operation and the Agreement for Promotion, Protection and Guarantee of Investments among Member States of the OIC / Hasan Moinuddin. – Oxford : Clarendon, 1986.
xx,322p; 22cm.
Bibliography: p297-313. - Includes index.
ISBN 0198255241 £30.00

Moiser, C H
Practice and procedure in Magistrates' Courts. – 2nd ed. – London : Fourmat, 1986.
ISBN 1851900136 Pbk £12.95

Moitra, A.C.
Law of Private Defence / B.L. Yadav. – 5th ed. – Allahabad : Universal Book Agency, 1987.
Hbk £175.00

Mok, Leo
International handbook on pensions law and similar employee benefits. – London : Graham & Trotman, 1989.
352.
On behalf of the International Association for Insurance Law, examines pension laws in over 17 countries. Topics include surplus reversion and the recapture of assets, predator proofing, the national and international nomad, human rights and sex equality in retirement pensions, share incentive, and stock option plans.
ISBN 0860109941 Hbk £85

Mole, Ellen E. →Butterworths Ontario Family Law Quantum Service, 2 Vols.
—Butterworth's Wrongful Dismissal Practice Manual, 2 vols. – Toronto : Butterworths.
Hbk
—Butterworths Wrongful Dismissal Practice Manual, 2 Vols. – Butterworths.
Llf £135.00

Mole, R. H.
BASIC Investment Appraisal. – London : Butterworths, 1985.
ISBN 0408015675 Pbk

Moles, Robert N.
Definition and rule in legal theory : a reassessment of H.L.A. Hart and the positivist tradition / Robert N. Moles. – Oxford : Basil Blackwell, 1987.
xii,285p; 24cm.
Bibliography: p275-278. - Includes index.
ISBN 063115342X £25.00

Molijn, H →Introduction to trade mark law in the Benelux.

Monahan, John
Predicting violent behavior : an assessment of clinical techniques / John Monahan : introduction by Stanley L. Brodsky : foreword by Saleem A. Shah. – Beverly Hills : Sage, 1981.
183p; 23cm. – (Sage library of social research 114).
Bibliography: p171-181.
ISBN 0803913133 Hbk
ISBN 0803913141 Pbk

Monahan, Patrick
Politics and the Constitution, The Charter, Federalism and the Supreme Court of Canada. – Agincourt : Carswell, 1987.
253p.
This work focuses on the constitutional issues presented to the Supreme Court of Canada over the last ten years. Discussions include a summary of the significance and implications of the initial Charter decisions. Charts and graphs are presented to illustrate the success rate of the Charter arguments.
Hbk £40.50

Monahan, Patrick J. →Rule of Law : Ideal or Ideology.

Monarchy to republic : Australian republican government / George Winterton. – Melbourne : Oxford University Press, 1986.
xi, 211 p.; 23 cm.
Includes index. Bibliography: p. 192-194.
ISBN 019554563X

Monash University, Faculty of Law
Advanced Family Law Seminar. – Monash University, Faculty of Law. – Clayton : Monash University Press, 1984.
ISBN 086746318X Hbk £15.00
—Company Law Lunchtime Series. – Monash University, Faculty of Law. – Clayton : Monash University Press, 1984.
ISBN 086746318X Hbk £15.00
—Corporate Securities and Creditors Rights on Insolvency 1984. – Monash University, Faculty of Law. – Clayton : Monash University Press, 1984.
ISBN 0867463414 Hbk £15.00
—Developments in Section 52 of the Trade Practices Act 1984-1985 : Centre for Commercial Law and Applied Legal Research. – Monash University, Faculty of Law. – Clayton : Monash University Press.
ISBN 086746397X Hbk £15.00
—Family Taxation Planning. – Monash University, Faculty of Law. – Clayton : Monash University Press, 1984.
ISBN 0867463422 Hbk £18.00
—Media Law Seminars 1985 : Centre for Commercial and Applied Legal Research. – Monash University, Faculty of Law. – Clayton : Monash University Press, 1985.
ISBN 0867463856 Hbk £40.00
—Modern Director-Duties and Liabilities 1985 : Centre for Commercial Law and Applied Legal Research. – Monash University, Faculty of Law. – Clayton : Monash University Press.
ISBN 0867463848 Hbk £17.00
—New Tax Penalties 1984. – Monash University, Faculty of Law. – Clayton : Monash University Press, 1984.
ISBN 0867463538 Hbk £21.00
—Practical uses of Section 52 of the Trade Practices Act. – Monash University, Faculty of Law. – Clayton : Monash University Press, 1984.
ISBN 086746352X Hbk £14.00
—Recent Developments in Banking Series : Off Shore Finance 1984. – Monash University, Faculty of Law. – Clayton : Monash University Press, 1984.
ISBN 0867463511 Hbk £16.00
—Securities Law Seminar Insider Training 1985 : Centre for Commercial Law and Applied Legal Research. – Monash University, Faculty of Law. – Clayton : Monash University Press.
ISBN 0867463856 Hbk £17.00
—Sport and the Law 1985 : Centre for Commercial Law and Applied Legal Research. – Monash University, Faculty of Law. – Clayton : Monash University Press.
Hbk £20.00
—Takeovers, Trading Trusts and More, 1984. – Monash University, Faculty of Law. – Clayton : Monash University Press, 1984.
ISBN 0867463546 Hbk £28.00

Mondy, W.
Crown Cases Reserved for Consideration and Decided by the Twelve Judges of England : 1824-1844, 2 Vols. – Repr. of 1844 ed. – Abingdon : Professional Books.
247p.
Hbk £40.00

Monetary limitations of liability in air law : legal, economic and socio-political aspects / Aleksander Tobolewski. – Montreal : De Daro, 1986.
vii,277p.
Bibliography: p.261-277.
ISBN 0969270305

Monetary policy : finding a place to stand / Gerald K. Bouey. – Toronto : Per Jacobsson Foundation, 1983.
v,28p.
Lecture delivered at the University of Toronto, 5 September 1982.

Monetary system and monetary policy in South Africa : final report of the Commission of Inquiry into the Monetary System and Monetary Policy in South Africa. – Pretoria : Government Printer, 1985.
1 vol. (various pagings).
Chairman: G. P. C. de Kock. Included in: South Africa. Parliament. House of Assembly. Votes and proceedings; (with printed annexures). Report no. RP70/1984.
ISBN 0621090336

Money advice services / Berthoud. – Policy Studies Institute, 1988.
ISBN 0853743789 Pbk £8.95

Money and Banking / Klise. – 9th ed. – London : Eurospan.
ISBN 0538082712 Hbk £29.95

Money and banking in the United Kingdom. – Routledge, 1988.
ISBN 0415004349 Hbk £45.00

Money and Message : the Law Governing Election Financing, Advertising, Broadcasting and Election Campaigning in Canada. – Butterworths, 1983.
672p.
ISBN 0409816305 Hbk £95.00

Money lenders : bankers in a dangerous world / Anthony Sampson. – Sevenoaks : Coronet, 1983.
377p; 18cm.
Originally published: London : Hodder and Stoughton, 1981. Includes index.
ISBN 0340287713 Pbk £2.50

Moneylenders Ordinance 1951 (F.M. Ord. No. 42 of 1951). – Kuala Lumpur : International Law Books Services.
Hbk £5.00

Mongolian legal system : contemporary legislation and documentation / edited by W.E. Butler : translations from Mongolian by A.J. Nathanson, translations from Russian by W.E. Butler. – The Hague : Nijhoff, 1982.
xxiii, 995 p.; 25 cm.
ISBN 9024726859 Hbk £450.00

Mongolian-English-Russian dictionary of legal terms and concepts / compiled and edited by W.E. Butler and A.J. Nathanson. – The Hague : M. Nijhoff, 1982.
ISBN 9024726778

Monies, George
Local government in Scotland / G Coutts. – 2nd. – Edinburgh : Green (W.) & Son, 1989.
Provides an introduction to the Scottish local government system including its historical context and possible future reforms. Updated to include the community charge and the changing relationship of local and central government.
ISBN 0414008898 Pbk

Monir
Law of Evidence. Short Edition in One Volume. – Allahabad : Universal Book Agency, 1984.
Hbk £175.00
—Principles and Digest of the Law of Evidence, 2 Vols. – 6th ed. – Allahabad : Universal Book Agency, 1986.
Hbk £550.00

Monitoring the Criminal Justice Act : youth custody service / NACRO. – London : NACRO, 1984.
6p.

Monk, Janet → Survey of defenders in debt actions in Scotland.

Monkcom, Stephen P → Law of Betting, Gaming and Lotteries.

Monopolies and Mergers Commission Reports. – London : HMSO, 1986.
ISBN 010198670X Hbk £9.80

Monopolies and Mergers Commission Reports. – London : HMSO, 1983.
ISBN 0101904606 Hbk £3.30

Monroe and Nock The law of stamp duties / R. S. Nock, J. G. Monroe. – 6th ed. – London : Sweet & Maxwell, 1986.
xli,371p; 25cm.
Previous ed.: published as The law of stamp duties. 1976. Includes index.
ISBN 0421310502 £47.50

Monroe, H. H.
Intolerable inquisition? : reflections on the law of tax / by Hubert Monroe. – London : Stevens published under the auspices of Hamlyn Trust, 1981.
xiii,84p; 19cm.
ISBN 0420461906 Hbk £11.25
ISBN 0420462007 4.60
→ Potter and Monroe's tax planning with precedents.

→ Tax Planning with Precedents.

Monroe, J. G.
Monroe and Nock The law of stamp duties / R. S. Nock, J. G. Monroe. – 6th ed. – London : Sweet & Maxwell, 1986.
xli,371p; 25cm.
Previous ed.: published as The law of stamp duties. 1976. Includes index.
ISBN 0421310502 £47.50
—Stamp Duties / R. S. Nock. – 6th ed. – London : Sweet & Maxwell, 1986.
Hbk £47.00

Montserrat → Montserrat consolidated index of statutes and subsidiary legislation to 1st January 1983.

Montserrat consolidated index of statutes and subsidiary legislation to 1st January 1983 / compiled at the Faculty of Law Library, University of the West Indies, Barbados. – Rev. ed. – Barbados : s.n., 1983.
iv,74p.
Previous ed.: 1st January 1980. One of a series in the West Indian Legislation Indexing Project (WILIP) compiled in cooperation with the British Development Division.

Moody, Susan R.
Operation of the judicial examination procedure : a study in two Scottish cities / Susan R. Moody. – Edinburgh : Scottish Office, 1986.
iv,87p.
—Prosecution in the public interest / Susan R. Moody and Jacqueline Tombs. – Edinburgh : Scottish Academic Press, 1982.
xii, 167p.
Examines the decision-making process of the Procurator Fiscal as to whether to prosecute, on what, and by what procedure to prosecute. Bibliography: p.160-163.
ISBN 0707303214 Hbk

Moore
Managerial Accounting / Jaedicke. – 7th ed. – London : Eurospan.
ISBN 0538019638 Pbk £11.75
—Practical Approach to Planning Law. – London : Financial Training.
ISBN 1851850708 Pbk £16.95
—Take-Over Guide / Stenning. – London : Longman Professional.
ISBN 0851213634 Pbk £12.95

Moore, Anthony P. → Residential tenancy law and practice.

Moore, D. A.
International Light, Shape and Sound Signals. – London : Stanford Maritime Ltd.
ISBN 0540072710 Pbk £6.95

Moore, David
Some Aspects of Capital Transfer Tax for Businesses and Farms. – Belfast : Queen's University of Belfast, 1986.
30p.
Pbk £2.95
—Some aspects of inheritance tax for businesses and farms / David Moore. – Belfast : SLS Legal Publications, 1986.
40p.
Includes bibliographical references.
—Some tax implications of marriage breakdown / David Moore. – Belfast : SLS Legal Publications, 1987.
35p.
Includes bibliographical references.

Moore, Evelyn Garth
Introduction to English Canon Law / Briden. – 2nd ed. – London : Dent (J M) & Sons, 1985.
ISBN 0264668545 Pbk £11.95

Moore, George
Guide to the children's hearings. – Edinburgh : Green (W.) & Son, 1989.
Explains the complex legal and administrative provisions and procedures of those involved: panel members, parents, reporters, social workers and the children themselves.
ISBN 0414009045 Pbk
—Practice of Social Inquiry. – Aberdeen : Aberdeen University Press, 1983.
176p.
ISBN 0080303692 Hbk £11.50
ISBN 0080303706 Pbk £7.25
—Social work and criminal law in Scotland / by George Moore and Chris Wood. – Aberdeen : Aberdeen University Press, 1981.
xii,208p; 26cm.
Provides information and guidance about those aspects of the judicial and penal systems and measures relating to child offenders which affect social workers. Chapters cover prosecution, social worker at court, social enquiry reports, non-custodial measures, probation, community service and unpaid work, and custodial measures. Includes bibliography and index.
ISBN 0080257313 Hbk

Moore, Gerald K.
Coastal state requirements for foreign fishing Vol.1 / by Gerald K. Moore. – Rev. ed. – Rome : Food and Agriculture Organization of the United Nations, 1983.
iv,242p. – (Legislative study).
Previous ed. published as: Legislation on coastal state requirements for foreign fishing.
ISBN 9251015031
—Legislation on coastal state requirements for foreign fishing / by Gerald Moore. – Rome : Food and Agriculture Organization of the United Nations, 1981.
viii, 411 p.; 28 cm. – (Legislative study / Food and Agriculture Organization of the United Nations).
ISBN 9251010382 Pbk

Moore, K.D.
Pardon : Justice Mercy and Public Interest. – Oxford : Oxford University Press.
ISBN 0195058712 Hbk £15.00

Moore, Matthew
Law and Procedure of Meetings. – London : Sweet & Maxwell, 1983.
– (Concise College Texts Ser.).
ISBN 0421253401 Pbk £7.50

Moore, Michael S.
Law and psychiatry : rethinking the relationship / Michael S. Moore. – Cambridge : Cambridge University Press, 1984.
xiv,527p; 24cm.
Bibliography: p495-513. - Includes index.
ISBN 0521255988 £35.00

Moore, R. Peter
Halsbury's Laws of England, 56 Vols. – 4th ed. – London : Butterworths.
Hbk

Moore, Rhonda → Criminal investigation : a selective literature review and bibliography.

Moore, S.F.
Lucan : Not Guilty. – London : Fontana.
ISBN 0006373666 Pbk £3.95

Moore, Sally
Law as Process : An Anthropological Approach. – London : Sweet & Maxwell, 1983.
ISBN 0710200218 Pbk £6.95

Moore, Terence G.
Juvenile court : a guide to law and practice / by Terence G. Moore and Tony P. Wilkinson. – Chichester : Barry Rose, 1984.
xiii,231p; 23cm.
Includes index.
ISBN 0859923355

Moore, Victor → 'Free two pence' Section 137 of the Local Government Act 1972 and Section 83 of the Local Governement (Scotland) Act 1973.
→ Local Government, Planning and Land Act 1980.

Moore, Vincent
Angelo Branca. – Vancouver : Douglas and McIntyre, 1981.
ISBN 0888943237 Hbk £16.95

Moores and Rowland's Orange Tax Guide 1988-89. – London : Butterworths.
ISBN 0406365024 Pbk £24.95

Moores & Rowland's orange tax guide. – London : Butterworths, 1987.
Continues in part: Moores & Rowland's tax guide.

Moores and Rowland's Yellow Tax Guide 1988-89. – London : Butterworths.
ISBN 0406366020 Pbk £24.95

Moores & Rowland's yellow tax guide. – London : Butterworths, 1987.
Continues in part: Moores & Rowland's tax guide.

Moores/Rowland's A-Z of Tax Planning / Garlick. – 2nd ed. – London : Longman Professional.
ISBN 0851213235 Pbk £18.95

Moor's Indian Appeals 1836-1872, 4 Vols. – Allahabad : Law Publishers.
Hbk £30.00 ea

Moorthy, V.K.
Petronas : Its Corporate and Legal Status. – Singapore : Malayan Law Journal, 1983.
137p.
Hbk £35.00

Morais, J. Victor
Tun Tan : Portrait of a Statesman. – Singapore : Quins, 1981.
Hbk (special ed.) £45.00

Moral foundation of rights / L.W. Sumner. – Oxford : Clarendon Press, 1987.
228p; 22cm.
Includes bibliography and index.
ISBN 0198247516 £22.50

Moral limits of the criminal law
Vol.1 : Harm to others / Joel Feinberg. – New York : Oxford University Press, 1984.
xiii,269p; 25cm.
Includes index.
ISBN 0195034090
Vol.2 : Offense to others / Joel Feinberg. – 1985.
xix,328p.
Includes bibliographical references and index.
ISBN 019503449X Hbk
Volume 3 : Harm to self. – 1989.
444.
Looks at the problems associated with the commonly proposed principle of 'legal paternalism'. Evaluates and rejects the principle that it can be right to impose coercion on a person for her own good, regardless of her wishes in the matter.
ISBN 0195059239 Pbk £9.95

Moral theory and capital punishment / Tom Sorell. – Oxford : Basil Blackwell in association with the Open University, 1987.
240p; 23cm.
Includes index.
ISBN 0631153217 Hbk £25.00 :
ISBN 0631153225 Pbk £5.95

Morality of freedom / Joseph Raz. – Oxford : Clarendon, 1986.
432p; 22cm.
ISBN 0198247729 £30.00

Morality Of Law. – Yale University Press, 1969.
ISBN 0300010702 Pbk £7.95

Moran, M.
Politics of banking. – 2nd ed. – London : Macmillan, 1986.
ISBN 0333424123 Pbk £8.95

Morawetz, Carl H. → Bankruptcy law of Canada.
—Canadian Bankruptcy Reports / David E. Baird. – Agincourt : Carswell.
Hbk £73.50

Morby, Grainne
Know how : to find out your rights / Grainne Morby. – London : Pluto, 1982.
188p; 20cm.
Includes index.
ISBN 0861043596 Pbk £3.95

Morcom, Christopher
Service marks : a guide to the new law : Trade Marks Act 1938 as amended by the Trade Marks (Amendment) Act 1984 and the Patents, Designs and Marks Act 1986 / Christopher Morcom. – Oxford : ESC Publishing, 1987.
vi,165p.
Includes texts from the Acts.
ISBN 0906214483

Mordey, R. → Planning control : philosophies, prospects and practice.

More law reform NOW : a collection of essays on law reform / and edited by Peter Archer and Andrew Martin. – Chichester : Barry Rose, 1983.
ix,304p.
Published in association with the Society of Labour Lawyers.
ISBN 0859923495

Moret, Edwina
Change in Eastern Europe. – Exeter : European Atlantic Movement, 1982.
Hbk £0.50

Morgage Debenture. – 3rd ed. – North Ryde : Law Book Co, 1985.
xii, 108p.
ISBN 0455206031 Pbk £21.50

Morgan, David Gwynn
Administrative Law / by David Gwynn Morgan and Gerard Hogan. – London : Sweet & Maxwell, 1986.
li,422p; 22cm.
Includes index.
ISBN 0421330600 Pbk £21.00
—Constitutional law of Ireland : the law of the executive, legislature, and judicature / David Gwynn Morgan. – Blackrock, County Dublin, Ireland : Round Hall Press in association with Irish Academic Press, 1985.
271 p.; 22 cm.
Includes index. Bibliography: p. 215-253.
ISBN 0950872598 Pbk

Morgan, J.
Law for Commercial Retailers. – London : Sweet & Maxwell.
ISBN 0421347902 Hbk

Morgan, Jane
Coming to Terms with Policing : Perspectives on Policy / Smith. – Routledge.
ISBN 0415009421 Hbk £14.95
—Conflict and order : the police and labour disputes in England and Wales, 1900-1939 / Jane Morgan. – Oxford : Clarendon, 1987.
325p,4p of plates; 22cm.
Includes bibliography and index.
ISBN 0198201281 £30.00

Morgan, Janet
Human Rights and World Peace
Vol. 2. – Enstone : Ditchley Foundation, 1981. – (Ditchley Conference Reports).
Hbk
—International Implications of New Telecommunications Technology
Vol. 4. – Enstone : Ditchley Foundation. – (Ditchley Conference Reports).
Hbk

Morgan, Leslie
Youth and the Law. – Vancouver : Vancouver People's Law School.
30p.
Hbk

Morgan, Patricia M.
Modelling the criminal justice system / Patricia M. Morgan. – London : Home Office, 1985.
v,64p.
Bibliography: p.64.
ISBN 0862522161

Morgan, Peter
Development Control / Susan Nott. – London : Butterworths, 1988.
ISBN 0406502501 Hbk £24.00
ISBN 040650551X Pbk
→ Planning law and practice in dwelling houses.

Morgan, Richard
Computer contracts / Graham Stedman. – 3rd ed. – London : Longman, 1987.
x,434p; 24cm. – (Longman commercial series).
Previous ed.: 1984. Includes index.
ISBN 085121259X £40.00

Morgan, Rod → Accountability and prisons : opening up a closed world.

Morgenstern, Felice
Deterrence and compensation : legal liability in occupational safety and health / Felice Morgenstern. – Geneva : International Labour Office, 1982.
iii,76p.
Bibliography: p73-74.
ISBN 9221030105
—International conflicts of labour law : a survey of the law applicable to the international employment relation / Felice Morgenstern. – Geneva : International Labour Office, 1986.
ix,129p; 25cm.
ISBN 922103593X
→ International labour law reports, Volume 7.
—Legal problems of international organizations / by Felice Morgenstern. – Cambridge : Grotius Publications, 1986.
xiv,147p.
Includes bibliographical references and index. At head of title: University of Cambridge Research Centre for International Law.
ISBN 0906496241

Morgren
American Cultural Pluralism and Law / Nanda. – Praeger.
ISBN 0275926958 Hbk £40.50
ISBN 0275926966 Pbk £15.75

Moriarty, Cecil C. H.
Moriarty's police law : an arrangement of law and regulations for the use of police officers / James Fryer, Walter Stansfield. – 24th ed. – London : Butterworths, 1981.
xviii,767p; 19cm.
Previous ed.: 1976. Includes index.
ISBN 0406846081 Pbk

Moriarty, Dick, et al
Sport Physical Activity and the Law. – Ottawa : Canadian Association for Health, Physical Education and Recreation.
Hbk £14.95

Moriarty's police law : an arrangement of law and regulations for the use of police officers / James Fryer, Walter Stansfield. – 24th ed. – London : Butterworths, 1981.
xviii,767p; 19cm.
Previous ed.: 1976. Includes index.
ISBN 0406846081 Pbk

Morison, C. B.
Morison's Company law in New Zealand / R. F. Pethig, I. R. Millard. – 4th ed. 2 vols. – Wellington N.Z. : Butterworths, 1981.
Volume 1 contains the Companies Act 1955 and other associated legislation, together with rules and regulations amended up to date. Volume 2 is a treatise on company law and the cases are discussed and cross-referenced to the statutes and regulations discussed in volume 1.
ISBN 0409646962 Llf
ISBN 0409646954 Llf

Morison, W. L.
Cases on torts / W.L. Morison ... et al. – 5th ed. – Sydney : Law Book Co., 1981.
xxxiv,1011p.
Includes bibliographical notes and index.
ISBN 0455202516 Pbk
ISBN 0455202524
—John Austin. – London : E. Arnold, 1982.
192p.
ISBN 0713163593 Hbk £11.00
ISBN 0713163607 Pbk £5.50
—System of Law and Courts Governing New South Wales. – 2nd ed. – Butterworths, 1985.
461p.
This book for the beginning law student contains a general examination of the NSW legal system. An institutional as opposed to a rule-oriented approach to law is adopted.
ISBN 0409492531 Hbk £65.00
ISBN 0409492639 Pbk £49.00

Morison's Company law in New Zealand / R. F. Pethig, I. R. Millard. – 4th ed. 2 vols. – Wellington N.Z. : Butterworths, 1981.
Volume 1 contains the Companies Act 1955 and other associated legislation, together with rules and regulations amended up to date. Volume 2 is a treatise on company law and the cases are discussed and cross-referenced to the statutes and regulations discussed in volume 1.
ISBN 0409646962 Llf
ISBN 0409646954 Llf

Morling, T. R. → Royal Commission of Inquiry into Chamberlain Convictions.

Mornington, Marilyn → Matrimonial Proceedings.

Morocco, Trial in Rabat Arising out of Disturbances on 20 and 21 June, 1981 : Trial in Rabat Arising Out of Disturbances on 20 and 21 June 1981. – Geneva : International Commission of Jurists.
25p.
Hbk £4.00

Morris, et al
European Community : The Practical Guide for Business and Government. – London : Macmillan, 1983.
ISBN 0333262050 Hbk £18.50
—Rule Against Perpetuities / Leach. – 1962 Reprint & Supplement. – Sweet & Maxwell.
ISBN 0421355506 Hbk £34.00

Morris, A. I.
Design : the modern law and practice / by A.I. Morris and Barry Quest. – London : Butterworth, 1987.
xxvii,377p,12p of plates; 25cm.
Bibliography: p369-370. - Includes index.
ISBN 0406103216 Hbk £52
ISBN 0406103208

Morris, Allison → Care and discretion : social workers' decisions with delinquents.
→ Providing criminal justice for children.
—Understanding juvenile justice / Allison Morris Henri Giller. – London : Croom Helm, 1987.
287p; 23cm.
ISBN 0709938322 Hbk £22.50
ISBN 070993890X Pbk £9.95
→ Women and crime : papers presented to the 13th Cropwood Round Table Conference, December 1980.
—Women, crime and criminal justice / Allison Morris. – Oxford : Basil Blackwell, 1987.
256p; 23cm.
Considers all aspects of women and crime including women as defendants and prisoners, as victims and as criminal justice professionals.
ISBN 0631154442 Hbk £25.00 :
ISBN 0631154450 Pbk £7.95

Morris, C. N. → North sea oil taxation : the development of the North Sea tax system.

Morris, Eric
Technique in litigation / Eric Morris. – 3rd ed. – Cape Town : Juta, 1985.
xxxiii, 373 p.; 26 cm.
Includes bibliographical references and index.
ISBN 0702115525 Pbk

Morris, Gillian
Strikes in essential services / Gillian S. Morris. – London : Mansell, 1986.
x,221p; 24cm.
Bibliography: p209-215. - Includes index.
ISBN 0720117917 Hbk £25.00
ISBN 0720118697 Pbk £15.00

Morris, Gordon
Directory of Courts in the United Kingdom : 1988/1989. – London : Shaw & Sons, 1988.
320p.
ISBN 072190985X Pbk £14.95

Morris, Gwen
Laying Down the Law : The Foundations of Legal Reasoning Research and Writing in Australia and New Zealand / C. Cook. – 2nd ed. – Sydney : Butterworths, 1988.
304p.
This workbook contains exercises which require students to find cases and statutes, analyze legal problems, interpret judicial decisions and legislation, and use basic research tools such as digests and encyclopedias. Additional material has been included to cover New Zealand.
Pbk £22.00
—Planning and Environment Law Service, Victoria. – Butterworths, 1984.
ISBN 040949321X Hbk £215.00

Morris, J. H. C.
Cases and materials on private international law / J.H.C. Morris, P.M. North. – London : Butterworths, 1984.
xxviii,757p; 26cm.
Includes index.
ISBN 0406252645 Hbk £36.00
ISBN 0406252653 Pbk £25.95
—Conflict of laws / by J.H.C. Morris. – 3rd ed. – London : Stevens, 1984.
xxxvii,544p; 25cm.
Previous ed.: 1980. Bibliography: pxxix. - Includes index.
ISBN 0420468900 Hbk £
ISBN 0420469001 Pbk
→ Dicey and Morris on the conflict of laws.

Morris, L.C.
Bibliography of Air and Space Law Materials : Incorporating a Select Index to Australian Air Law Materials. – 2nd ed. – Clayton : Monash Law Book Co-operative, 1985.
ISBN 0959549749 Hbk

Morris, M.A.
North-South Perspectives on Marine Policy Westview Special Studies in Ocean Science and Policy. – Westview Press.
ISBN 0813374286 Pbk

Morris, Mag
Importing for the small business. – London : Kogan Page, 1985.
ISBN 0850388694 Pbk £6.95

Morris, Pauline
Crime control and the police : a review of research / by Pauline Morris and Kevin Heal. – London : H.M.S.O., 1981.
v,67p.
Bibliography: p56-67. A Home Office Research Unit report.
ISBN 0113407076

Morris, R. J. B.
Solicitors and local authorities / by R.J.B. Morris. – Chichester : Rose, 1983.
ciii,349p; 23cm.
Includes index.
ISBN 0859923304

Morris, Simon
Financial services : regulating investment business / Simon Morris. – 1st ed. – London : Longman Professional (UK), 1989.
Examines the Financial Services Act 1986, and details its impact on areas of investment business, including the international aspect and the run up to 1992, and civil and criminal liability for operations outside the FSA.
ISBN 0851215572 Hbk £37.50

Morrish, Peter → Magistrates' Court : An Index of Common Penalties and Formalities in Cases Before Justices.
→ Magistrates' court : an index of common penalties and formalities in cases before justices (excluding the juvenile court).

Morrison, A.C.L. → Clarke Hall and Morrison on Children, 2 Vols.
→ Law in Relation to Children.
→ Law relating to children and young persons.

Morrison, Jane → Second Convention of Lome : EEC aid to the ACP countries (1981-1985).

Morrisson, Clovis C.
Dynamics of development in the European human rights convention system / Clovis C. Morrisson. – The Hague : Martinus Nijhoff, 1981.
xii,176p.
ISBN 9024725461 Hbk £100.00

Morritt, R. A.
Gilgate Holdings Limited, Raybourne Group Limited, Calomefern Limited, Desadean Properties Limited : investigation under Section 165(b) of the Companies Act 1948 / report by R.A. Morritt and P.L. Ainger. – London : Her Majesty's Stationery Office, 1981.
ca.780p; 30cm.
At head of title: Department of Trade.
ISBN 0115134859 Pbk £23.00

Morse, Bradford W. → Aboriginal peoples and the law : Indian, Metis and Inuit rights in Canada.
→ Foundations of Canadian Law.

Morse, Geoffrey → Charlesworth's company law.
→ Companies consolidation legislation 1985.
→ Companies consolidation legislation 1987.
—Companies Consolidation Legislation 1987. – Sweet & Maxwell.
ISBN 0421383607 Hbk £39.00
→ Financial Services Act 1986 : a guide to the new law.
—Introduction to partnership law / Geoffrey Morse. – London : Financial Training, 1986.
xiv,176p; 23cm.
Includes index.
ISBN 1851850252 Pbk £6.95
→ Sweet & Maxwell's tax statutes 1984/85.

Morse, Jeremy
Do we know where we're going? / Sir Jeremy Morse. – s.l. : Per Jacobsson Foundation, 1985.
v,31p.
Given at the Sejong Cultural Center, Seoul, Korea, Sunday, October 6, 1985.

Morse, W.J., et al
Management Accounting. – 2nd ed. – London : Addison-Wesley.
ISBN 0201157608 Hbk £17.95

Mortgagee sales and judgment debts / Law Reform Commission of Victoria. – Melbourne : The Commission, 1987.
iv,17p. – (Report no 8).
Includes bibliographical references.

Mortgagee sales and judgment debts / Law Reform Commission of Victoria. – Melbourne : The Commission, 1986.
iii,10p. – (Discussion paper of Victoria).
Includes bibliographical references.

Mortgages - 1985. – Vancouver : British Columbia Continuing Legal Education Society, 1985.
292p.
ISBN 0865042276 Hbk £60.00

Mortgages. – Vancouver : Continuing Legal Education Society of British Columbia, 1984.
163p.
ISBN 0865041431 Hbk £55.00

Mortgages : Advanced Topics. – Vancouver : Continuing Legal Education Society of British Columbia, 1987.
230p.
ISBN 0865043124 Hbk £70.00

Mortgages and Foreclosure : Know Your Rights. – 4th ed. – North Vancouver : International Self-Counsel Press, 1987.
105p.
ISBN 0889086567 Hbk £7.95

Mortgages and Securities / Thomas. – 3rd ed. – Sydney : Butterworths, 1986.
ISBN 0409491633 Hbk £55.00

Mortgages of land : the priority of further advances / Law Reform Commission of British Columbia. – Vancouver : The Commission, 1985.
iv,76p. – (Working paper).
Includes bibliographical references.

Mortgages of Ships. – London : Lloyd's of London Press, 1988.
ISBN 1850441049 Hbk

Mortgages of Ships : Marine Security in Canada. – Butterworths, 1986.
264p.
ISBN 0409988316 Hbk £95.00

Mortimer, Clifford → Williams, Mortimer and Sunnucks on executors, administrators and probate.

Mortimer, J.
Clinging to the wreckage. – Penguin, 1982.
ISBN 0297780107 Pbk £1.95

Mortimer, John
Famous Trials sound recording. – South Yarra : Louis Braille Productions Ltd..
ISBN 12ac £60.00
→ Liberty of the citizen.

Morton, F.L.
Law, Politics and the Judicial Process in Canada. – 4th repr. – Calgary : University of Calgary Press, 1987.
356p.
ISBN 0919813038 Pbk £16.95

Morton, James
Criminal Justice Acts 1987 and 1988 : A Commentary. – Waterlow.
– (Criminal Law Guides).
ISBN 0080330886 Pbk £14.95
—Defending Lawyer's Practical Guide. – 2nd ed. – London : Beattie (Derek), 1984.
ISBN 0907591035 Pbk £8.50
—Handling Criminal Cases. – London : Waterlow, 1986.
ISBN 0080391583 Pbk £9.95
→ Public defender : a report.

Morton, James C.
Presumption of innocence / by James C. Morton and Scott C. Hutchinson. – Toronto : Carswell, 1987.
154p.
Bibliography: pp.150-152. - Includes index.
ISBN 0459305816

Moser, Michael J
China Tax Guide / Zee. – Oxford : Oxford University Press, 1988.
ISBN 0195840593 Hbk £25.00
→ Foreign trade, investment, and the law in the People's Republic of China.

Moses, N.J.
Strata Titles / R. Tzannes. – North Ryde : Law Book Co, 1978.
v, 353p.
ISBN 0455194994 Hbk £64.00

Mosich
Modern Advanced Accounting / Larsen. – 4th ed. – Maidenhead : McGraw-Hill.
ISBN 0070365083 Hbk £29.50

Mosin, V. → Greek Charters of Serbian Rulers.

Mosler, H.
Judical Settlement of International Disputes : International Court of Justice; Other Courts and Tribunals : Arbitration and Conciliation : an International Symposium / R. Bernhardt. – Berlin : Springer-Verlag.
xii, 572p.
ISBN 3540067566 Hbk £94.00

Moss, Gabriel S. → Law of receivers of companies.
→ Rowlatt on the law of principal and surety.

Moss, S. → Some aspects of aid to the civil power in Australia.

Moss, S. G.
Canadian law reports and statutes held by the Faculty of Law Library, University of the West Indies, Cave Hill, Barbados / S.G. Moss : with the assistance of Waveney Webster. – Cave Hill, Barbados : University of the West Indies, Faculty of Law Library, 1986.
42p.

Mosteshar, Sa'id
Encyclopaedia of International Telecommunications Law. – London : Butterworths, 1987.
Pbk
—Satellite and Cable : International Protection / Stephen de B. Bate. – London : Oyez Longman, 1984.
– (Oyez Longman Intelligence Report Ser.).
ISBN 0851208614 Hbk
—Satellite and cable television : international protection : a specially commissioned report / by S. Alexander Mosteshar, and Stephen de B. Bate. – London : Longman Professional, 1986.
xiv,134p; 30cm. – (Longman professional intelligence reports).
Originally published: London : Oyez Longman, 1984.
Includes index.
ISBN 0851212042 spiral £95.00

Motha, Philip
Singapore Real Property Guide. – 2nd ed. – Singapore : Quins, 1983.
Pbk £54.00

Mothersole, B.
Citizen 16 : The Civil Law and You. – London : Macmillan, 1986.
ISBN 0333367944 Pbk £6.95

Motor Carrier Cargo Claims. – Agincourt : Carswell, 1986.
222p.
Hbk £35.75

Motor Claims Cases
Supplement only. – Wellington : Butterworths.
ISBN 0406118116 Pbk

Motor law
Vol. 1 / by W.E. Cooper : specialist contributor T.G. Schwar. – Cape Town : Juta, 1982.
cxxvi,740p.
Replaces: South African motor law / by W.E. Cooper and B.R. Bamford. Bibliography: p.x - Includes index.
ISBN 0702112534
Vol. 2 : Principles of liability for patrimonial loss / by W.E. Cooper. – 1987.
li,507p.
Replaces: South African motor law / by W.E. Cooper and B.R. Bamford. Bibliography: p.xi-xiii. - Includes index.
ISBN 0702119067 Hbk

Motor Transport Workers Act : with States Rules / Venkanna. – 3rd ed. – Allahabad : Law Book Company.
Hbk £200.00

Motor Vehicle Accident Claims - 1983. – Vancouver : British Columbia Continuing Legal Education Society, 1983.
547p.
ISBN 0865040141 Hbk £70.00

Motor Vehicle Accident Claims : 1983
Supplement only. – Vancouver : British Columbia Continuing Legal Education Society.
Hbk £25.00

Motor Vehicle Reports, 50 Vols. – Carswell Legal Publications. – Agincourt : Carswell, 1983.
Hbk £1260.00

Motor Vehicle Reports. – Butterworths.
Hbk

Motor Vehicle Reports. – Agincourt : Carswell, 1988.
This multi-volume set of books contains the key decisions in motor vehicle law from all Canadian jurisdictions. Discussions include alcoholic related offenses, civil actions relating to motor vehicles, and registration and licensing issues.
Hbk £75.00

Motor vehicle reports : annotated. – Toronto : Casrwell, 1988-.

Motor vehicle safety standards and product liability in the USA / by John Lambert. – London : Economist Intelligence Unit, 1982.
131p.

Motor Vehicles Act, 1939 : With All State Amendments, 2 Vols. – Allahabad : Ashoka Law House, 1987.
1,600p.
Hbk £320.00

Motor Vehicles Act, 2 Vols. – 5th ed. – Allahabad : Law Publishers, 1982.
Hbk £67.50

Motor Vehicles Act and Rules, Vols. 2 and 3. – Allahabad : Orient Law House.
Hbk £175.00

Motor Vehicles (Third Party Insurance) (Basic Protection Compensation) Act, (revised laws of Papua New Guinea, chapter no. 296) : a fourth review / Law Reform Commission of Papua New Guinea. – Waigani : Law Reform Commission of Papua New Guinea, 1983.
12p. – (LRC working paper).
Includes bibliographical references.

Motoring Law A-Z. – Ibadan : African Universities Press.
Hbk £2.95

Motoring Law in Northern Ireland. – Belfast : Queen's University of Belfast, 1986.
350p.
Hbk

Motoring Offences : Incl. the Rules on Drink/Drive and Penalty Points. – 2nd ed. – London : Law Society, 1985.
124p.
Hbk £7.50

Motorist and the law. – Penguin, 1987.
ISBN 0140068228 Pbk £4.95

Motorist and the Law. – 2nd ed. – London : Oyez Longman, 1982.
– (It's Your Law Ser.).
ISBN 0851204775 Hbk £3.95
ISBN 0851204783 Pbk

Motorist and the Law in Malaysia. – Singapore : Quins.
Hbk £54.00

Motorist and the Law in Singapore. – Singapore : Quins.
Hbk £54.00

Motorist's Guide to the Law. – London : Fourmat, 1986.
ISBN 0906840953 Pbk £4.95

Mott, G.
Accounting for Non-Accountants. – Revised Edition. – Pan Books.
ISBN 0330302809 Pbk £7.50

Mott, Joy
Adult prisons and prisoners in England and Wales 1970-1982 : a review of the findings of social research / Joy Mott. – London : H.M.S.O., 1985.
vi,68p.
Reviews social research results. Compares them with developments in the USA. Concludes that research in the UK has been inadequate, concentrating on prisoners and neglecting the prisons.
ISBN 0113408013

Mould, R. F.
Chernobyl : the real story / by Richard F. Mould. – Oxford : Pergamon, 1988.
90p; 25cm.
Includes index.
ISBN 0080357180 Hbk £12.90 :
ISBN 0080357199 Pbk £6.90

Moullin
Taxation of directors / Sargent. – London : CCH, 1986.
ISBN 0863251129 Pbk £5.00

Mountford, Toby →Practice development for accountants.

Mountjoy, Alan B.
Industrialization and developing countries / Alan B. Mountjoy. – 5th ed. – London : Hutchinson, 1982.
256p; 22cm. – (Hutchinson university library).
Previous ed.: 1975. Bibliography: p243-246. - Includes index.
ISBN 0091468019 Pbk £4.95

Mouty, A. →Workers' participation in the European Community : the fifth directive.

Movements and Markers in Criminal Law. – Auckland : Legal Research Foundation, 1984.
Hbk £16.50

Moverley-Smith, Stephen
Powers and liabilities of pension fund trustees. – Oxford : Blackwell Scientific, 1987.
ISBN 000383302X Hbk £20.00

Moverly Smith, Stephen
Powers and Liabilities of Pension Fund Trustees. – London : Collins, 1987.
200p.
ISBN 000383302X Hbk £17.50

Moving Up - Moving Out. – Vancouver : British Columbia Continuing Legal Education Society, 1985.
34p.
ISBN 0865042292 Hbk £30.00

Mowbray, A. →Australasian Legal Information Retrieval Handbook.
—Garner's Rights of Way. – 5th ed. – London : Longman Professional.
– (Longman Practitioner Series).
ISBN 0851215386 Hbk £18.00

Mowbray, J. →Law of Trusts.

Moxley, Ray
Architect's Guide to Fee Negotiations : An Architecture and Building Practice Guide Book. – London : Architectural Press, 1984.
160p.
ISBN 0946228051 Pbk £16.95

Moxon, David →Fine enforcement : an evaluation of the practices of individual courts.
—Juvenile sentencing : is there a tariff? / David Moxon, Peter Jones and Roger Tarling. – London : Home Office, 1985.
v,19p.
Bibliography: p.19.
ISBN 0862521874
→ Managing criminal justice : a collection of papers.
—Sentencing practice in the Crown Court / by David Moxon. – London : HMSO, 1988.
v,89p.
'A Home Office Research and Planning Unit report'.- T.p..
ISBN 0113409028

Moyer, Sharon
Pretrial diversion : an overview / by Sharon Moyer. – Ottawa : Solicitor General, Programs Branch, 1982.
12p.
ISBN 0662119177

Moyes, Adrian
Common ground : how changes in the Common Agricultural Policy affect the Third World / by Adrian Moyes. – Oxford : Oxfam, 1987.
98p; 21cm.
ISBN 0855980788 Pbk £1.50

Moyles, R.G.
British Law and Arctic Men : the Celebrated Murder Trials of Sinnisiak and Uluksuk, First Inuit Tried Under White Man's law. – Saskatoon : Western Producer Prairie Books.
125p.
ISBN 0888330251 Pbk £8.95

Moynihan, E.P.
Tolley's Payroll Handbook. – 2nd ed. – Tolley Publishing.
ISBN 0854593632 Hbk £21.00

Moys, Elizabeth M. →Manual of law librarianship : the use and organization of legal literature.

Mozley and Whiteley : Law Dictionary. – 10th ed. – London : Butterworths, 1988.
ca 500p.
Explains the precise meaning of words and phrases, giving where relevant an historical account of the term, and if further information is required, a reference to either statutory case law or other authority.
ISBN 0406625255 Hbk £15.00
ISBN 0406625263 Pbk £7.95

Mozolin →Contract Law in the USSR and the United States : History and General Concept.

Mridul, Narudhar
Public Interest Litigation : a Profile. – New Delhi : Bharat Law House, 1986.
200p.
Hbk £150.00

Mrs. Harris : the death of the Scarsdale diet doctor / Diana Trilling. – London : Abacus, 1983.
341p.
Originally published: New York : Harcourt Brace Jovanovich, 1981. Previously published: London : Hamilton, 1982.
ISBN 0349133948

Muecke, Robert →International environment law : multilateral treaties Droit international de l'environnement : traites multilateraux Internationales Umweltrecht : multilaterale Vertrage.

Mueller, Rudolf
German Antitrust Law / Hannes Schneider. – 2nd ed. – Plymouth : Macdonald & Evans, 1981.
296p.
ISBN 0712154817 Casebound £23.00
—German antitrust law : an introduction to the German antitrust law with German text and synoptic English translation of the Act against Restraints of Competition / Martin H. Heidenhain, Hannes Schneider. – 2nd rev. ed. – Frankfurt am Main : Fritz Knapp, 1981.
291p.
Previous ed., 1973, published as: The German law against restraints of competition. Added t.p. in German: Das Recht gegen Wettbewerbsbeschrankungen.
ISBN 3781928306

—GmbH-German Law Concerning Companies with Limited Liabilities. – 4th ed. – Plymouth : Macdonald & Evans, 1981.
176p.
ISBN 0712154809 Casebound £16.00

Muir Hunter on personal insolvency / Muir Hunter and John Briggs. – 1. – London : Stevens, 1987.
looseleaf.
Supersedes 19th ed. of Williams and Muir Hunter on bankruptcy. Includes index.

Muir Watt, J.
Agricultural Holdings Act. – Sweet & Maxwell, 1986.
ISBN 0421318007 Hbk £95.00

Mukerjee, T.P.
Commentary on the Customs Act with Rule and Notifications. – 3rd ed. – Allahabad : Law Publishers, 1982.
Hbk £51.00

Mukherjea's Hindu Law of Religious and Charitable Trusts. – 5th ed. – Calcutta : Eastern Law House, 1983.
Hbk £122.00

Mukherjee
International Law, 2 Vols. – Calcutta : Mukherjee & Co.
Hbk £43.00

Mukherjee, Devesh Chandra
Trade Marks Law in India with Up-to-date Act and Supreme Court Decision / S.C. Sarkar. – Calcutta : Sarkar & Sons.
xvi, 88p.
Hbk £7.00

Mukherjee, Satyanshu K.
Age and Crime. – Canberra : Australian Institute of Criminology.
Hbk £3.60

Mukherjee, Satyanshu Kumar
Crime trends in twentieth-century Australia / Satyanshu Kumar Mukherjee, assisted by Evelyn N. Jacobsen, John R. Walker, R. W. Fitzgerald. – Wooden : Australian Institute of Criminology, 1981.
xviii,199p.
Includes bibliographical references and index.
ISBN 086861386X
—Profile of Federal Prisoners. – Canberra : Australian Institute of Criminology.
Hbk £1.95

Muldoon, Paul R.
Cross-Border Litigation : Environmental Rights in the Great Lakes Ecosystem. – Agincourt : Carswell, 1986.
445p.
Hbk £56.25
—Cross-Border Litigation : Environmental Rights in the Great Lakes Ecosystem. – Agincourt : Carswell, 1986.
445p.
This book analyzes the pollution control legislation of the American states and Canadian provinces bordering the Great Lakes and discusses the procedural difficulties confronting potential individual litigants.
Hbk £65.75

Mulgan, Margaret A. →Dismissal and Redundancy Procedures.

Mulhern, John
Industrial tribunal / Ian McLean. – Chichester : Barry Rose, 1982.
ISBN 0859922243 Hbk £20.00
—Industrial tribunal : a practical guide to employment law and tribunal procedure / by John Mulhern and Ian McLean. – Chichester : Rose, 1982.
280p; 23cm.
Includes index.
ISBN 0859922243 £19.50

Mulholland, R D
Basic Law for Business. – Palmerston North : Dunmore Press Ltd., 1984.
117p.
ISBN 0864690258 Pbk £9.95
—Business Law Today. – Palmerston North : Dunmore Press Ltd..
368p.
ISBN 0864690398 Pbk £38.45
—Consumer law in New Zealand / R.D. Mulholland. – Palmerston North N.Z. : Dunmore Press, 1982.
163p.
Includes index.
ISBN 0908564821
—Introduction to the New Zealand Legal System. – 6th ed. – Butterworths, 1985.
ISBN 0409702285 Pbk £52.80

Mulla →Indian Contract and Specific Relief Acts.

Mulla, Dinshah Fardunji
Civil Procedure Code (Abridged). – Suppl. 1982 11th ed. – Bombay : Tripathi, 1982.
1070p.
Hbk £10.00
—Civil Procedure Code, Vol 1. – 14th ed. – Bombay : Tripathi, 1981.
1040p.
Hbk £150.00
—Hindu Law. – 15th ed. – Bombay : Tripathi. 1982.
£140.00
—India Stamp Act / Pratt. – 7th ed. – Bombay : Tripathi.
—Indian Registration Act. – 9th ed. in prep. – Bombay : Tripathi.
Hbk
—Principles of Hindu law, with a general introduction to Hindu law and with commentaries on the Hindu Marriage Act, 1955, the Hindu Succession Act, 1956, the Hindu Minority & Guardianship Act, 1956, the Hindu Adoptions & Maintenance Act, 1956 / Sunderlal Trikamlal Desai. – 15th ed. – Bombay : N.M. Tripathi Private, 1982.
lxxix, 1233 p.; 25 cm.
Title on spine: Hindu law. Includes index.
Rs140.00
—Principles of Mahomedan Law. – repr. 1983. – Bombay : Tripathi.
483p.
Pbk £45.00
—Transfer of Property Act, 1882. – 7th ed. in prep. – Bombay : Tripathi.
1100p.
Hbk £50.00

Mullan, David J.
Administrative Law Reports. – Agincourt : Carswell.
Hbk £74.75

Muller, Dave J. →Psychology and law : topics from an internatinal conference.

Muller, J.W.
Revival of Constitutionalism. – University of Nebraska Press.
ISBN 080323127X Hbk £23.95

Muller-Rappard, Ekkehart, et al
European inter-state co-operation in criminal matters/la cooperation inter-etatique europeenne en matiere penale / M.Cherif Bassiouni. – London : Graham & Trotman, 1988.
1500.
Contains the texts of the 18 European penal Conventions and Explanatory Reports, the lists of signatory states and status of ratifications, reservations and declarations by states, and resolutions and recommendations adopted by the Committee of Ministers of the Council of Europe on the application of these conventions.
ISBN 9024734657 £345

Mullin, Chris
Error of judgment. – Aurora : Cape, 1986.
ISBN 0701129786 Hbk £10.95
—Error of judgment : the Birmingham bombings / by Chris Mullin. – London : Chatto & Windus, 1986.
224p; 23cm.
ISBN 0701129786 £10.95
—Tibetans : two perspectives on Tibetan-Chinese relations / by Chris Mullin and Phuntsog Wangyal. – New ed. – London : Minority Rights Group, 1983.
27p. – (Report).
Previous ed.: 1981. Includes bibliographical references.
ISBN 0946690014

Multiculturalism and the Charter : A Legal Perspective. – Agincourt : Carswell, 1987.
200p.
This book consists of essays pertaining to s.27 of the Charter of Rights and Freedoms. Discussions include the possible impact of s.27 on other Charter provisions and the resulting effect on Canada's pluralistic society.
Hbk £40.50

Multidisciplinary partnerships and allied topics / The Law Society. – London : The Society, 1987.
11p.
Supplement to the Law Society's Gazette, (29 April 1987).

Multilateral Convention for the Avoidance of Double Taxation of Copyright Royalties : Original Text of the Convention Adopted by the Madrid Conference (1979). – rep. 1987. – Geneva : World Intellectual Property Organization.
41p.
Hbk £10.00

Multilateral Conventions and Agreements : Signatures and/or Conclusions by the European Communities. – Luxembourg : Office for Official Publications of the European Communities, 1987.
cxiv, 361p.
ISBN 9282567966 Pbk £1,200.00

Multilateral mediation : practical experiences and lessons. – Dordrecht : Nijhoff (Martinus), 1989.
384.
Analyses the successful mediation; the resolution of the dispute amongst members of the East African Community after its termination in 1977. By narrating his own involvement in a mediation exercise, the author intends to provide governments, practitioners and scholars of international law with a guide to the settlement process.
ISBN 9024737796 Hbk Gld175.00

Multilateral Treaties : Current Status and Index / Harris. – London : Butterworths, 1984.
ISBN 0406252785 Hbk £110.00
Third Supplement-1986. –
ISBN 0406252920 Pbk £20.00

Multilateral treaties : index and current status / compiled and annotated within the University of Nottingham Treaty Centre by M.J. Bowman and D.J. Harris. – London : Butterworths, 1984.
xii,516p; 26cm.
Includes index. Kept up to date by supplements.
ISBN 0406252777 Hbk £85.00

Multilateral treaties between Asian countries. – London : Butterworths, 1986.
ISBN 0409995185 Hbk £24.00

Multilateral Treaties Deposited with the Secretary-General : Status as at 31 December 1986. – Geneva : United Nations Publications.
ISBN 921332931 Hbk £60.00

Multilingual Glossary of Tax, Financial and Commercial Terms. – London : Oyez Longman, 1983.
ISBN 0851207618 Hbk £9.95

Multinational enterprise and economic analysis / Richard E. Caves. – Cambridge : Cambridge University Press, 1982.
xi,346p; 22cm. – (Cambridge surveys of economic literature).
Bibliography: p306-335. - Includes index.
ISBN 0521249902 Hbk £20.00
ISBN 0521271150 Pbk £7.50

Multinational enterprise between hammer and anvil / Georges van Hecke. – Deventer : Kluwer Law and Taxation Publishers, 1984.
16p.
Includes bibliographical references.
ISBN 9065441956

Multinational enterprise in historical perspective / edited by Alice Teichova, Maurice Levy-Leboyer and Helga Nussbaum. – Cambridge : Cambridge University Press, 1986.
viii,396p; 24cm.
Conference proceedings. Includes index.
ISBN 0521320402 France £30.00
ISBN 2735101517

Multinational Enterprises and Disclosure of Information : Clarification of the OECD Guidelines. – Paris : OECD, Organisation for Economic Co-operation and Development, 1988.
44p.
Hbk £31.00

Multinational Transfer Pricing. – London : Butterworths.
ISBN 0409871806 Hbk £23.00

Multinationals : company performance and global trends / John M. Stopford and John H. Dunning...et al. – London : Macmillan, 1983.
ix,147p.
Bibliographies.
ISBN 0333340930

Multinationals : theory and history / edited by Peter Hertner and Geoffrey Jones. – Aldershot : Gower, 1986.
vii,200p; 22cm.
Conference proceedings. Includes index.
ISBN 0566050781 £18.50

Multinationals and political control / John Robinson. – Aldershot : Gower, 1983.
xxi,507p; 23cm.
Includes index.
ISBN 0566003945

Multinationals beyond the market : intra-firm trade and the control of transfer pricing / edited by Robin Murray. – Brighton : Harvester, 1981.
335p; 24cm. – (Harvester studies in development).
Includes bibliographies and index.
ISBN 0855272031 £22.50

Multinationals in retreat : the Scottish experience / by Neil Hood and Stephen Young. – Edinburgh : Edinburgh University Press, 1982.
xi,193p; 24cm.
Includes index.
ISBN 0852244282 Pbk £10.00

Multiparty Business Disputes. – Paris : International Chamber of Commerce.
76p.
Hbk £16.50

Multiple Choice Questions on the Principles of Accounts. – 2nd ed. – London : Edward Arnold.
ISBN 0713177489 Pbk £3.95

Multi-State Cooperative Societies Act, 1984 : With Rules. – Indore : United Law Publishers, 1987.
Hbk £40.00

Mumby, F. A.
Mumbys publishing & bookselling in the twentieth century / Ian Norrie, F. A. Mumby. – 6th ed. – London : Bell & Hyman, 1982.
253p; 24cm.
Previous ed.: published as Publishing and bookselling. London : Cape, 1974. Bibliography: p229-232.
ISBN 0713513411 £12.95

Mumbys publishing & bookselling in the twentieth century / Ian Norrie, F. A. Mumby. – 6th ed. – London : Bell & Hyman, 1982.
253p; 24cm.
Previous ed.: published as Publishing and bookselling. London : Cape, 1974. Bibliography: p229-232.
ISBN 0713513411 £12.95

Munazzamah al-Dawliyah al-Arabiyah lil-Difa al-Ijtimai →Islamic criminal justice system.

Munch, Ingo von
International Law : the Essential Treaties. – Berlin : De Gruyter, 1985.
ca 832p.
ISBN 3110101122 Hbk £158.00

Munday, R. J. C. →Outline of the law of agency.

Mungall, Constance
Probate Guide for British Columbia : a Step-by-Step Guide to Probating an Estate. – 8th ed. – North Vancouver : International Self-Counsel Press, 1986.
96p.
ISBN 0889081794 Hbk £12.95

Mungham, Geoff →Essays in Law and Society.

Municipal Act Amendments. – Vancouver : British Columbia Continuing Legal Education Society, 1986.
ISBN 0865042586 Hbk £55.00

Municipal and planning law reports. – Toronto : Carswell, 1976-.
24cm.

Municipal and Planning Law Text. – Agincourt : Carswell, 1983.
500p.
Hbk £46.25

Municipal and School Tax Credit Assistance Lien Discharge Act, 1983, Bill 121 : An Act to Provide for the Discharge of Liens Registered Under the Municipal and School Tax Credit Assistance Act. – Ontario : Ontario Government Publications Service, 1983.
2p.
Hbk £0.30

Municipal councillors' handbook / Ian MacF. Rogers. – 4th ed. – Toronto : Carswell, 1982.
xi,135p.
Previous ed.: 1977. Bibliography: p.119. - Includes index.
ISBN 0459347306

Municipal Law 1985. – Vancouver : Continuing Legal Education Society of British Columbia, 1985.
350p.
ISBN 0865042306 Hbk £70.00

Municipal Law. – Vancouver : British Columbia Continuing Legal Education Society, 1981.
548p.
ISBN 0865040257 Hbk £21.00

Municipal Law : 11. – Vancouver : British Columbia Continuing Legal Education Society, 1983.
388p.
ISBN 0865041229 Hbk £65.00

Municipal Officers. – Vancouver : British Columbia Continuing Legal Education Society, 1982.
100p.
ISBN 0865040702 Hbk £35.00

Municipal Private Acts Repeal Act, 1983, Bill 120 : An Act to Repeal Certain Private Acts Related to Municipalities. – Ontario : Ontario Government Publications Service, 1983.
9p.
Hbk £0.50

Municipal Tax Sales Act, 1983, Bill 138 : An Act Respecting the Sale of Lands for Arrears of Municipal Taxes. – Ontario : Ontario Government Publications Service, 1983.
16p.
Hbk £0.50

Munkman, J.
Employer's Liability at Common Law. – 10th ed. – London : Butterworths, 1985.
ISBN 0406311072 Hbk £48.00

Munkman, John
Damages for personal injuries and death / John Munkman. – 7th ed. – London : Butterworths, 1985.
xxxiii,250p; 23cm.
Previous ed: 1980. Includes index.
ISBN 0406311137 Hbk £27.50
—Employer's liability at common law / by John Munkman. – 10th ed. – London : Butterworths, 1985.
lxxi,699p; 22cm.
Previous ed.: 1979. Includes index.
ISBN 0406311072

Munkman, John H.
Technique of advocacy / by John H. Munkman. – London : Sweet & Maxwell, 1986.
xiv,173p.
Originally published: London: Stevens, 1951. Includes bibliographical references.
ISBN 0421361700

Munro, Colin R.
Studies in constitutional law / Colin R. Munro. – London : Butterworths, 1987.
xviii,220p; 22cm.
Includes index.
ISBN 040626144X Hbk £11.00
ISBN 0406261458 Pbk £7.50

Munro, R. D →Environmental protection and sustainable development : legal principles and recommendations.

Murch, Mervyn →Grounds for divorce.
→ Marital violence : the community response.

Murder : mental element and punishment / Law Reform Commissioner, Victoria. – Melbourne : The Commission, 1984.
52p. – (Working paper no 8).
Includes bibliographical references.

Murder In Low Places. – Piatkus Books.
ISBN 0861887514 Hbk £10.95

Murder into manslaughter. – Oxford : Oxford University Press, 1984.
ISBN 0197121519 Hbk £10.00

Murder of Dele Giwa : The Right of a Private Prosecutor. – Lagos : Nigerian Law Publications.
ISBN 9782325236 Hbk £20.00

Murdie, Alastair →Sweet & Maxwell's Statutes for the Law Society finals.

Murdoch, H.
Dictionary of Irish Law. – Topaz.
ISBN 0951403206 Hbk £29.50
ISBN 0951403214 Pbk £19.50

Murdoch, John R
Estate Agents Act 1979. – 2nd ed. – London : Estates Gazette, 1982.
ISBN 0728200430 Pbk £7.60
→ Law for Estate Management Students.
—Law of estate agency and auctions / by J.R. Murdoch. – 2nd ed. – London : Estates Gazette, 1984.
xlii,576p.
Includes bibliographical references and index.

Murie, Alan
Housing inequality and deprivation / Alan Murie. – London : Heinemann Educational, 1983.
250p; 23cm.
Bibliography: p237-246. - Includes index.
ISBN 0435826263 £13.50
→ Housing Policy and Practice.

Murphy →Stage 3 Business Taxation.
→ Taxation 2.3.
—Understanding property law / Roberts. – London : Fontana, 1987.
ISBN 0006860737 Pbk £4.95

Murphy, B C →Overview of US export controls.

Murphy, Chris →Community policing in the 1980's : recent advances in police programs.

Murphy, Cornelius F
Search for world order : a study of thought and action / by Cornelius F. Murphy, Jr. – Dordrecht : M. Nijhoff, 1985.
xiii, 192 p.; 25 cm. – (Developments in international law).
Includes bibliographical references and index.
ISBN 9024731887

Murphy, D. F. → Leading cases and materials on the competition law of the E.E.C.

Murphy, D.J.M.
Guide to the Hong Kong Code on Takeovers and Mergers. – London : Longman Professional.
ISBN 0582999006 Hbk £95.00

Murphy, Daniel J. I.
Customers and thieves : an ethnography of shoplifting / Daniel J.I. Murphy. – Aldershot : Gower, 1986.
xi,266; 23cm.
Bibliography: p246-256. - Includes index.
ISBN 0566008823 £15.00

Murphy, J. David
Stare decisis in Commonwealth appellate courts / David J. Murphy and Robert Rueter. – Toronto : Butterworths, 1981.
xv,117p.
Includes index.
ISBN 0409853739

Murphy, John F.
United Nations and the control of international violence : a legal and political analysis / John F. Murphy. – Manchester : Manchester University Press, 1983.
xii,212p; 24cm.
Includes index.
ISBN 0719009421 £22.50
ISBN 0865980799

Murphy, Peter
Evidence : cases and argument / Peter Murphy and John Beaumont. – London : Financial Training, 1982.
xxv,469p; 23cm.
ISBN 0906322103
—Evidence & advocacy / Peter Murphy and David Barnard. – 2nd ed. – London : Published for Temple Lectures by Financial Training, 1986.
xi,227p; 22cm.
Previous ed.: 1984. Includes index.
ISBN 0906322960 Pbk £7.95
—Practical approach to evidence / Peter Murphy. – 2nd ed. – London : Financial Training, 1985.
xliv,477p; 24cm.
Previous ed.: 1980. Includes index.
ISBN 0906322693 Pbk £11.95

Murphy, S. M., et al
Problems and Procedures in Collections. – Vancouver : British Columbia Continuing Legal Education Society, 1983.
350p.
ISBN 0865040923

Murphy, W. T.
Family home / by W.T. Murphy and Hilary Clark. – London : Sweet & Maxwell, 1983.
229p; 19cm. – (Modern legal studies).
Includes index.
ISBN 0421287403 Hbk £
ISBN 0421287500 Pbk £6.95
→ Labour law and the community : perspectives for the 1980's.

Murray
Digests of Irish Reports and Irish Law Times Reports
1867-93 /. – Abingdon : Professional Books.
Hbk

Murray, A.
Sunday Telegraph 101 ways of investing. – Telegraph Publications, 1988.
ISBN 0863672027 Pbk £2.95

Murray, I.
Constitutions and Charitable Status Guide and Models for Voluntary Organisations in Scotland. – Scottish Council for Voluntary Organisations.
ISBN 1870904028 Hbk £10.00

Murray, Robin → Multinationals beyond the market : intra-firm trade and the control of transfer pricing.

Murray, Roger → Namibians.

Murray, T.
Laws and Acts of Parliament Made by King James I and Royal Successors : 1424-1621. – Repr. of 1682 ed. – Abingdon : Professional Books.
116p.
Hbk £250.00

Murray, Topsy → Protection of children : state intervention and family life.

Murtagh, Peter → Blind Justice.

Murthy, K.S.N.
Modern Law of Insurance in India. – 2nd ed. in press, – Bombay : Tripathi.
364p.
bd £65.00

Murthy, Mantha Rama
Law of Adverse Possession. – 2nd ed. – Allahabad : Law Publishers, 1983.
Hbk £27.00
—Law of Wills along with Model Forms. – 3rd ed. – Allahabad : Law Publishers, 1982.
Hbk £40.50

Murty, B.S
International law of diplomacy. – Dordrecht : Nijhoff (Martinus), 1989.
672. – (New Haven studies in international law and world public order 5).
A legal study from a policy-orientated perspective, which examines new patterns of diplomacy and their influence on the traditional ones. Looks at what world policies have so far regulated the use of the diplomatic process, and whether those policies are needlessly restrictive. Suggests what policies should guide the regulation in future.
ISBN 0792300831 Hbk £95

Murumba, Samuel K.
Commercial exploitation of personality / by Samuel K. Murumba. – North Ryde : Law Book Co, 1986.
xvii,184p.
Bibliography and index. Includes the text of a Draft Commonwealth Bill for an Unfair Publication Act.
ISBN 0455206929

Musgrave, Peggy B. → Public finance in theory and practice.

Musgrave, Richard A.
Public finance in theory and practice / Richard A. Musgrave, Peggy B. Musgrave. – 4th ed. – New York : McGraw-Hill, 1984.
xvi,824p; 25cm.
Previous ed: 1980. Includes bibliographies and index.
ISBN 007044126X £26.95

Music : the Business and the Law / G. Stevens. – North Ryde : Law Book Co, 1986.
xii, 247p.
ISBN 045520621X Pbk £24.00

Musicians and the law in Canada / by Paul Sanderson. – Toronto : Carswell, 1985.
xxxi, 258 p.; 24 cm.
This work examines the law of Canada impacting on musicians and their business affairs. Issues discussed include: copyright, music publishing, live performance, management and agency, merchandising, personal service contracts, income taxes, and other relevant topics. Includes index.
ISBN 0459372203

Muslim family law : a sourcebook / Keith Hodkinson. – London : Croom Helm, 1984.
401p; 22cm.
Bibliography: p367-377. - Includes index.
ISBN 0709912560 Pbk £14.95

Muslim Law. – 2nd ed. 1980 repr. – Lucknow : Eastern Book Company, 1985.
376p.
Hbk £20.00

Muslim Law and the Constitution. – Calcutta : Eastern Law House, 1985.
Hbk £68.00

Muslim marriages : formation and dissolution. – Banjul, The Gambia? : s.n., 1987.
17,xixp. – (Law reform project).
Contains a draft Muslim Marriages (Formation and Short Title Dissolution) Bill and a commentary.

Muspratt → Keep Account : Guide to Profitable Bookkeeping.

Mustill, Michael John
Law and practice of commercial arbitration in England / Sir Michael J. Mustill, Stewart C. Boyd. – London : Butterworths, 1985.
lxxiv,727p.
An extensive and detailed treatment of the subject of commercial arbitration is given in this work. The book covers appointment of arbitrators, the arbitration process, the award, and appeals in the United Kingdom.
ISBN 0406311218
→ Scrutton on charterparties and bills of lading.

Musto, D.F.
American Disease : Origins Of Narcotic Control. – 2nd ed. – Oxford : Oxford University Press, 1988.
ISBN 0195052110 Hbk £8.95

Mutch, Simon, R.E.
Insanity Defense : A Critical Assessment of Law and Policy in Post-Hinckley Era / Aaronson. – Praeger.
ISBN 0275927849 Hbk £38.65
ISBN 00275928306 Hbk £32.95
ISBN 0275928314 Pbk £12.50

Muwang'u, K. C. → Zambia industrial cases reports.

Mvunga, Mphanza P.
Land Law and Policy in Zambia. – Lusaka : University of Zambia, Publications Office, 1982.
112p.
Hbk £5.50

Myburgh, A.C.
Papers on Indigenous Law in Southern Africa. – Pretoria : VanSchaik.
ISBN 0627013988 Hbk £17.85

Myddleton, D.
On a cloth untrue : Inflation accounting. – Cambridge : Woodhead-Faulkner, 1984.
ISBN 0859412504 Hbk £19.95

Myers → Principles of corporate finance.

Myers, Edward R. → Legal education for Canadian youth : proceedings of a conference held at the College of Law, University of Saskatchewan, May 22-24, 1980.

Mynors, Charles
Listed buildings and conservation areas. – London : Longman Professional (UK), 1989. – (Practitioner series).
Explains how a building is listed, how far that listing extends, and considers the designation of conservation areas. Sets out the provisions relating to alteration and repair of listed buildings and the planning cotrols that apply, and sets out the financial considerations. Takes account of the General Development Order 1988.
ISBN 0851214088 Hbk £25.95
—Planning applications and appeals. – London : Architectural Press, 1987.
ISBN 085139504X Pbk £39.50

Myrants, G.
Protection Of Industrial Designs. – Maidenhead : McGraw-Hill, 1977.
ISBN 007084495X Hbk £6.95

Myres S. McDougal and Associates
Studies in World Public Order. – Myres S. McDougal and Associates. – Dordrecht : Kluwer, 1987.
1,080p.
ISBN 08938389003 Hbk £350.00

Myth of free trade : patterns of protectionism since 1945 / Harry Shutt. – Oxford : Blackwell, 1985.
193p.
Includes index.
ISBN 0631139974 £17.50

N.S.W. Strata Titles Act 1973. – North Ryde : C.C.H. Australia, 1987.
200p.
ISBN 0869038648 Hbk

N.V. Slavenburg's Bank v. Intercontinental Natural Resources Ltd. : (1980) 1 All E.R. 955 : memorandum / by the Society's Standing Committee on Company Law. – London : Law Society, 1981.
12p; 30cm.

Nabhi
Baggage Rules in India. – New Delhi : Nabhi Publications, 1984.
28p.
Hbk £30.00

Nabhi's All India Sales Tax Manual, 2 Vols. – New Delhi : Nabhi Publications, 1987.
1,830p.
Hbk £360.00

NACAB
Immigrants and the Welfare State. – NACAB. – London : CENT, 1983.
ISBN 0906072069 Pbk £4.80

NACRO
Black people and the criminal justice system : report of the NACRO Race Issues Advisory Committee / Clement Richards. – London : NACRO, 1986.
48p.
Includes bibliographical references. Chairman: Clement Richards. Accompanied by 'Summary of the report of the NACRO Race Issues Advisory Committee'.
ISBN 0850690404
—Community alternatives for juvenile offenders : development kit. – NACRO. – London : NACRO, 1983.
47p.
ISBN 0850690277
—Enforcement of the law relating to social security / report of a NACRO working party. – London : NACRO, 1986.
114p.
Chairman: Sir Norman Price.
ISBN 0850690412
—Homeless young offenders : an action programme : the Report of a NACRO Group. – NACRO. – London : NACRO, 1981.
69p.
Bibliography: p.67-69.
ISBN 0850690242
→ Prison system for the 80s and beyond.
—Submission to the Home Office on Intermittent custody, Cmnd 9281 / from the National Association for the Care and Resettlement of Offenders. – London : NACRO, 1984.
14p.

NACRO briefing. – London : NACRO, 1982-.

NACRO juvenile crime briefing. – London : NACRO, 1985-.

NACRO news digest. – London : NACRO, 1979-.

Nadin-Davis, R. Paul
Canadian Sentencing Digest : Quantam Service, 2 Vols. / Clarey B. Sproule. – Agincourt : Carswell, 1981.
This looseleaf service digest all Canadian cases an quantum of sentence from 1970 to the present. The work is organized by statute and section.
Llf £214.25
—Sentencing in Canada / by R. Paul Nadin-Davis. – Toronto : Carswell, 1982.
lxxii, 609 p.; 24 cm.
Includes bibliographical references and index.
ISBN 0459348507

Nadkarni, Meena
Canadian legal materials in microform / compiled by Meena Nadkarni. – Downsview, Ont. : York University Law Library in co-operation with the Canadian Association of Law Libraries, 1981.
Llf

Nadler, S.
Good Girls Gone Bad. – London : Futura, 1988.
ISBN 0356151603 Pbk £11.95

Naffin, Ngaire
Domestic violence and the law : a study of S.99 of the Justices Act (S.A.) / by Ngaire Naffin. – 1. – Adelaide : Women's Adviser's Office, Department of the Premier and Cabinet, 1985.
various pagings.

—Inquiry into the substantive law of rape / by Ngaire Naffin. – Adelaide : Women's Adviser's Office, Department of the Premier and Cabinet, 1984.
iii,80p.
Includes bibliographical references.

Nagaland File : A Question of Human Rights / Nandita Haksar. – New Delhi : Lancer International, 1984.
277p.
Hbk £115.00

Nagel, Stuart S.
Causation, prediction and legal analysis / Stuart S. Nagel. – New York : Quarum, 1986.
xxii,276p; 25cm.
Bibliography: p261-268. - Includes index.
ISBN 0899301800

Nagpal, R.C.
Modern Hindu Law. – Lucknow : Eastern Book Company, 1983.
992p.
Hbk £120.00

Nagy, T. →Taxation in European socialist countries.

Nahaylo, Bohdan
Ukrainians and Georgians / by Bohdan Nahaylo and C.J. Peters. – London : Minority Rights Group, 1981.
20p. – (Report).
Bibliography: p.20.

Nahlik, Stanislaw E.
Brief Outline of International Humanitarian Law. – Geneva : Comite International de la Croix-Rouge, 1984.
48p.
Hbk £3.00

Nair, P.M.K. →Law of Receivers.

Nairobi Treaty on the Protection of the Olympic Symbol (September 26, 1981), Nairobi Conference (1981). – Geneva : World Intellectual Property Organization.
31p.
Hbk £10.00

Nakagawa, Masanao →Antimonopoly legislation of Japan.

Nakatsu, Connie →Handbook to the Ontario Human Rights Code.

Names of states : an authority list of language forms for catalogue entries / compiled by the IFLA International Office of UBC. – London : The Office, 1981.
viii,49p; 30cm.
At head of title: International Federation of Library Associations and Institutions.
ISBN 0903043327 Pbk

Namibians / by Peter Fraenkel and Roger Murray : with additional material by Kaye Stearman. – New ed. – London : Minority Rights Group, 1985.
31p. – (Report).
Bibliography: p.31.
ISBN 0946690278

Nanavati
Estate Duty Act. – 4th ed. – Bombay : Tripathi.
Hbk

Nanda →American Cultural Pluralism and Law.

Nandan, Satya N. →Ocean management : a regional perspective : the prospects for Commonwealth maritime co-operation in Asia and the Pacific.

Nandi Customary Law. – 4th ed. – Nairobi : Kenya Literature Bureau, 1981.
Pbk £16.35

Nanes, Allan S →Legislative responses to terrorism.

Nanny for Your Child. – North Vancouver : International Self-Counsel Press, 1987.
Hbk £7.95

Napier
Pension Cost Accounting. – London : Butterworths, 1984.
ISBN 0406010544 Pbk

Napier, B. W.
Comparative dismissal law / B.W. Napier, J.-C. Javillier and P. Verge. – London : Croom Helm, 1982.
175p; 23cm.
ISBN 0709918089 £12.50

Napley, David
Technique of persuasion / David Napley : with a foreword by Melford Stevenson. – 3rd ed. – London : Sweet & Maxwell, 1983.
xvi,187p; 18cm.
Follows the same pattern as previous editions, but includes a new section on the strategy and tactics of advocacy. Also considers topics such as preparation for trial, the ethics of advocacy, and presentation in court.
ISBN 0421252804 Hbk £14.00
ISBN 0421252901 Pbk £5.85

Naqvi, Syed Nawab Haider
Individual Freedom, Social Welfare and Islamic Economic Order. – Islamabad : Pakistan Institute of Development Economics, 1982.
40p.
Pbk £5.00

Naradiya Dharmasastra : Judicial System in Ancient India. – Delhi : Ajanta Books International, 1981.
180p.
ISBN 8120200578 Hbk £70.00

Narang →Industrial Law.

Narang, D.B. →Delhi Sales Tax and Central Sales Tax Act.
→ Income Tax Law and Practice.

Narayanan, P.
Patent Law. – Calcutta : Eastern Law House, 1985.
950p.
Hbk £375.00

—Trade Mark Cases, 2 Vols. – Calcutta : Eastern Law House, 1985.
Hbk £775.00

—Trade mark cases and passing off cases. – 2 vols. – Sweet & Maxwell, 1986.
ISBN 0421344601 Hbk £110.00

—Trade Marks and Passing off. – 3rd ed. – Calcutta : Eastern Law House, 1981.
Hbk £300.00

Nash, G.
Criminal Law, Victoria. – Butterworths, 1981.
ISBN 0409352039 Llf £220.00

—Homicide : the law and the Proofs / G.K. Jaisimaha Rao. – North Ryde : Law Book 6, 1986.
ca xvi, 210p.
ISBN 0455206740 jb £45.00

—Homicide, the law and the proofs. – North Ryde : Law Book Co, 1986.
ISBN 0455206740 Hbk £22.75

Nasir, Jamal J.
Islamic law of personal status / Jamal J. Nasir. – London : Graham & Trotman, 1986.
xiv,328p; 25cm.
Bibliography: p314-319. - Includes index.
ISBN 0860108252 deluxe £45.00
ISBN 0860108260 £75.00

Natal and KwaZulu : constitutional and political options; proceedings of the workshop... / edited by Laurence Boulle and Lawrence Baxter. – Cape Town : Juta, 1981.
viii,211p.
Includes chapter in Afrikaans.

Natal University law and society review. – Durban : University of Natal, 1985.
Continues: Natal University law review.

Nath, B. →Cases and Materials on Code of Civil Procedure, Includes Supplement-1983 and 1985.

—Cases and Materials on Criminal Procedure Code / P.L. Malik. – 2nd ed. – Lucknow : Eastern Book Company, 1984.
1,199p.
Hbk £130.00

—Cases and Materials on Law of Evidence Includes Supplement-1984. – Lucknow : Eastern Book Company, 1983.
578p.
Hbk £80.00

Nathan, C. J. M
Eenvormige hofreels / deur C.J.M. Nathan, M. Barnett, A. Brink. – 3e uitg. / deur C.J.M. Nathan en M. Barnett. – Kaapstad : Juta, 1984.
lxii, 794 p.; 26 cm.
Title on added t.p.: Uniform rules of court. Afrikaans and English. Includes indexes.
ISBN 0702114154 R84.00

Nathan, Joseph Arnold →Cases and commentary on the law of trusts.

Nathan, R. K.
Practical approach to assessment of liability and damages in tort / by R.K. Nathan. – Singapore : Malayan Law Journal Pte., 1986.
xliv,312p.
Includes bibliographical references and index.
ISBN 9971700514

Nathanson, A. J →Mongolian-English-Russian dictionary of legal terms and concepts.

National and international boundaries. – Thessaloniki : Institute of Public International Law and International Relations of Thessaloniki, 1985.
xii,905p.
English, French or German.

National and Multinational Companies : Some Legal Issues. – Bombay : Tripathi, 1981.
546p.
Hbk £100.00

National Association of Probation Officers Directory 1988. – Wells (Owen).
ISBN 0904553183 Pbk £5.85

National Association of Victims Support Schemes →Reparation, conciliation and mediation : current projects and plans in England and Wales.

National Companies and Securities Commission
Annual report and financial statements / National Companies and Securities Commission. – Canberra : Australian Government Publishing Service, 1981.
Second and subsequent report years run 1st July to 30th June.

National Computing Centre
External auditor as privacy inspector : a study / by Deloitte Haskins & Sells and the National Computing Centre. – Manchester : The Centre, 1982.
38,7,5leaves; 30cm.
ISBN 085012381X Pbk £6.50

National Conference on Domestic Violence : proceedings, 11-15 November 1985 / edited by Suzanne E. Hatty. – Canberra, ACT : Australian Institute of Criminology, 1986.
2 v. (xix, 671 p.); 30 cm.
Includes bibliographies.
ISBN 0642102538 Pbk : v. 2

National Consumer Council
Air transport and the consumer : a need for change? : a report on air transport regulation in Europe. – National Consumer Council. – London : H.M.S.O., 1986.
xiii,251p.
Includes bibliographical references.
ISBN 0117012688

—Banking services and the consumer / a report by the National Consumer Council. – London : Methuen, 1983.
x,246p; 24cm.
ISBN 0416357601 Hbk £
ISBN 0416357709 Pbk

→ Consuming secrets : how official secrecy affects everyday life in Britain.

—Lord Chancellor's review of civil justice in England and Wales : personal injury litigation : a consumer response / National Consumer Council. – London : National Consumer Council, 1986.
38p.
At head to t.p.: Personal injury litigation.

—New tenancy agreements : a model for landlords and tenants based on the Housing Act 1980. – National Consumer Council. – London : The Council, 1981.
22p.
ISBN 0905653378

→ Plain English for lawyers : some guidelines on writing and designing legal documents.

→ Plain words for consumers : the language and layout of consumer contracts : the case for a plain language law.

→ Service please : services and the law : a consumer view.

→ Whose interest? : solicitors and their clients' accounts : a discussion paper.

National Council for Civil Liberties →Called to account : the case for police accountability in England and Wales.

→ Civil disorder and civil liberties : evidence to the Scarman inquiry.

→ Fair cop : reforming the police complaints procedure.

→ First rights : a guide to legal rights for young people.

—No way in Wapping : the effect of the policing of the News International dispute on Wapping residents / a report by the National Council for Civil Liberties. – London : National Council for Civil Liberties, 1986.
41p.
ISBN 0946088276

—Police and Criminal Evidence Bill 1982 : briefings / National Council for Civil Liberties. – 1. – London : The Council, 1983.
various pagings.
Contents: Clause 1: Stop and search of persons and vehicles - Clauses 9 and 10: Police powers to search private premises for evidence - Clauses 9 and 10: Opinion / by Ben Hytner - Part 3. Police powers of arrest - Part 4. Detention of suspects - Part 5. Questioning and treatment of persons by police - Part 6. Codes of practice - Clause 60: 'Confession' statements and the right to silence.

—Purging of the Civil Service. – National Council for Civil Liberties. – London : National Council for Civil Liberties, 1985.
20p.
ISBN 0946088179

—Stonehenge : a report into the civil liberties implications of the events relating to the convoys of summer 1985 and 1986. – National Council for Civil Liberties. – London : National Council for Civil Liberties, 1986.
43p.
ISBN 0946088284

→ Strip searching : an inquiry into the strip searching of women remand prisoners at Armagh Prison between 1982 and 1985.

→ We protest : the public order debate.

→ Women won't benefit : the impact of the Social Security Bill on women's rights.

National Council for One Parent Families → Child custody : what chance for fathers?.

National Crime Authority Bill 1983 : report / by the Senate Standing Committee on Constitutional and Legal Affairs. – Canberra : Australian Government Publishing Service, 1984.
xxv,154p. – (Parliamentary paper).
ISBN 0644033290

National Crime Prevention Institute → Understanding crime prevention.

National Crimes Commission? / M.J. Young, Special Minister of State, Gareth Evans, Attorney-General. – Canberra : Australian Government Publishing Service, 1983.
iv,41p.
Includes bibliographical references. Cover subtitle: a policy discussion paper.
ISBN 0644026928

National Deviancy Conference
Permissiveness and Control : The Fate of the Sixties Legislation. – National Deviancy Conference. – London : Macmillan.
224p. – (Critical Criminology Ser.).
ISBN 0333266803 Hbk £12.00
ISBN 0333266811 Pbk £4.95

National Finances. – Toronto : Canadian Tax Foundation, 1985-86.
Hbk £15.75
Issue from 1984-85. –
Hbk £14.75

National Foster Care Association → Review of the Children Act ten years on : its effect on foster care policy and practice.

National Guidelines for Control of Emission of Air Pollutants from New Stationary Sources. – Kingston : Australian Government Publishing Service, 1986.
19p.
ISBN 0644045361 Hbk £2.00

National Health and Medical Research Council
Model food legislation / National Health and Medical Research Council. – Canberra : Australian Govt. Pub. Service, 1983.
1 v. (loose-leaf); 28 cm.
Includes index.
ISBN 0644027282

National Housing Forum
Future for rented housing? : responses to the Government's proposals / National Housing Forum. – London : National Federation of Housing Associations, 1988.
iv,47p; 30cm.
ISBN 0862971306 Pbk

National Insurance and Family Allowances Acts, 4 Vols.
Vol. V. – London : HMSO.
ISBN 0117600016 Hbk £1.50
Vol. VI. –
ISBN 0117605166 Hbk £2.00
Vol. VIII. –
ISBN 011760643X Hbk £15.00

National Insurance contributions. – London : Butterworths, 1988.
ISBN 0406504601 Pbk

National Insurance (Industrial Injuries) Acts, 3 Vols.
Vol. I. – London : HMSO.
Hbk £1.75
Vol. II. –
Hbk £2.50
Vol. VI. –
ISBN 0117603821 Hbk £2.20

National Integration and Indian Constitution. – New Delhi : Deep and Deep Publications, 1986.
198p.
Hbk £150.00

National Land Code : a Commentary. – London : Sweet & Maxwell, 1982.
ISBN 0421306300 Hbk £95.00

National Land Code : a commentary / by Judith E. Sihombing : with a foreword by Tun Dr. Mohamed Suffian. – Kuala Lumpur, Singapore : Malayan Law Journal, 1981.
xxxix,905p.
Includes index.
ISBN 9971700174

National Land Code (Act 56 of 1965). – Kuala Lumpur : International Law Books Services.
Hbk £29.50

National laws and international commerce : the problem of extraterritoriality / Douglas E. Rosenthal and William M. Knighton. – London : Routledge & Kegan Paul, 1982.
xi,96p.
Bibliography: p94-96.
ISBN 0710093381

National legal control of illicit traffic in cultural property / by Lyndel V. Prott, P.J. O'Keefe. – Paris : UNESCO, 1983.
iv,144p.
Bibliography: p.144.

National Lending Library for Science and Technology → NLL review.

National Library of
Checklist of law reports and statutes in Canadian law libraries
4 : Canadian statutes and regulations : Statuts et reglements du Canada / National Library of Canada Resources Survey Division, Collections Development Branch : Bibliotheque nationale du Canada, Division de l'inventaire des ressources, Direction du developpement des collections. – Ottawa : The Library, 1981.
xii,249p.
Includes index. Text in English and French.
ISBN 0660504529

National Marriage Guidance Council → Change in marriage : a collection of papers presented at the National Guidance Council study days.

National parks : conservation or cosmetics? / Ann and Malcolm MacEwen. – London : Allen & Unwin, 1982.
xxii,314p; 24cm.
Bibliography: p287-297. - Includes index.
ISBN 0047190035 Hbk £
ISBN 0047190043 Pbk £8.50

National Parole Board handbook for judges and crown attorneys / Bruce Mann. – Ottawa : Govt. of Canada, National Parole Board, 1983.
70, 72 p.; 23 cm.
English and French. Title on added t.p.: Un Manuel de la Commission nationale des liberations conditionnelles a l'intention des juges et avocats de la couronne. Includes bibliographical references.
ISBN 066252361X Pbk

National Post-graduate Medical College of Nigeria → Medicine and the law.

National Preservation Office
Preservation, a survival kit / National Preservation Office. – 1 case. – S.l. : The Office, 1987.
various pagings.

National Society for the Prevention of Cruelty to Children → Trends in child abuse, 1977-82 : the fourth report on the children placed on N.S.P.C.C. Special Unit registers.

National survey of law libraries in Australia / by Beth Wilson : supervised by E.J. Glasson ; prepared for the Australian Law Librarians' Group. – Sydney : Australian Law Librarian's Group, 1984.
xv, 479 p.; 31 cm.
Includes bibliographical references.
ISBN 0959135901 £39.95

National Taxation : A Practical Handbook. – Reading : College of Estate Management.
94p.
Hbk £4.25

National Themes in Family Law / Diane Pask. – Agincourt : Carswell, 1988.
320p.
Hbk £45.50

National University of Singapore → Index to Singapore/Malaysia legal periodicals 1932-1984.

National University of Singapore, Faculty of Law
Malaya Law Review. – National University of Singapore, Faculty of Law. – Singapore : University of Singapore.
ISBN 0542335X Hbk £45.00

National welfare benefits / Read. – London : Central Books, 1988/89.
ISBN 0946744084 Pbk £5.50

National welfare benefits handbook. – London : Child Poverty Action Group, 1987.
288p; 21cm.
Includes index.
ISBN 0946744009 Pbk £4.50

National welfare benefits handbook / Lakhani. – 16th ed. – London : CENT, 1986.
ISBN 0906963957 Pbk £4.00

National Women's Advisory Council
Community of Property : Discussion Paper. – National Women's Advisory Council. – Canberra : Australian Government Publishing Service, 1982.
34p.
ISBN 0644021802 Hbk £2.00

Nationalisation of Guyana's bauxite : the case of Alcan / M. Shahabuddeen. – Georgetown : Ministry of Information, 1981.
xvii,306p.
Bibliography: p282-306.

Nationalised industries and public control : legal, constitutional and political issues / Tony Prosser. – Oxford : Blackwell, 1986.
220p; 23cm.
Examines constitutional form of nationalised industries and their relationship with government. Studies the role of public law in defining and limiting state activity as applied to nationalised industries.
ISBN 0631139982 £17.50

Nationalism and self determination in the Horn of Africa / edited by I. M. Lewis. – London : Ithaca Press, 1983.
ix,226p.
ISBN 0903729938

Nationality provisions of the Hong Kong Act 1985 : a draft Order-in-Council / presented to Parliament by the Secretary of State for the Home Department. – London : H.M.S.O., 1985.
19p.
ISBN 010196370X

Nationalization of foreign property : a study in North-South dialogue / Subhash C. Jain : foreword by B. Sen. – New Delhi : Deep & Deep, 1983.
298p.
Bibliography: p.268-298 - Includes index.

Native Claims in Rupert's Land and the North-Western Territory : Canada's Constitutional Obligations. – Saskatoon : University of Saskatchewan, Native Law Centre, 1982.
41p.
ISBN 0888801181 Hbk £8.00

Native criminal justice : research issues and data sources / Wanda Jamieson and Carol Laprairie. – Ottawa : Solicitor General Canada, 1987.
iii,84p. – (User report).
Bibliography: p.78-84. On cover: Programs Branch.

Native Law Bibliography. – Saskatoon : University of Saskatchewan, Native Law Centre, 1984.
100p.
ISBN 0888801416 Hbk £20.00

Native Rights and the Boundaries of Rupert's land and the North-Western Territory. – Saskatoon : University of Saskatchewan, Native law Centre, 1982.
72p.
ISBN 0888801114 Hbk £12.00

Natural Gas Clauses in Petroleum Arrangements. – Geneva : United Nations Publications.
ISBN 9211041988 Hbk £8.00

Natural Justice : Principles and Practical Application. – 2nd ed. – Butterworths, 1984.
205p.
ISBN 0409491233 Hbk £49.00

Natural Law and Consciousness. – West Perth : Gantheaume Press, 1987.
ISBN 0958861013 Hbk £8.95

Natural Law, Conciliarism and Consent in the Middle Ages. – Northampton : Variorum, 1984.
350p. – (Collected Studies Ser.: No. 189).
ISBN 0860781372 Hbk £26.00

Natural resources forum. – Dordrecht : Reidel for the United Nations, 1976.
Edited by: United Nations. Centre for Natural Resources, Energy and Transport. Vol. 7 onwards published by Graham & Trotman for the United Nations.
ISBN 01650203

Natural Resources Law In Australia 1987. – London : Law Book Co.
ISBN 0455207690 Pbk £28.00

Natural rights and natural law : the legacy of George Mason / edited by Robert P. Davidow. – 1. – Fairfax, Va. : George Mason University Press, 1987.
23cm.
Includes index.
ISBN 080260000X Hbk £17.95
ISBN 0802600018 Pbk £11.95

Nature and Scope of Police and Police Related Research. – Canberra : Australian Institute of Criminology.
Hbk £1.00

Nature of Blackstones achievement : Selden Society lecture delivered at Oxford on May 31st, 1980 in association with Pembroke College to commemorate Blackstones bicentenary / by S.F.C. Milsom. – London : Selden Society, 1981.
12p; 25cm.
The text of this lecture was set as part of the first issue of the Oxford Journal of Legal studies and is simultaneously published in the journal and in the Societys lecture series.

Nature of Management. – London : Butterworths, 1987.
ISBN 0406503400 Pbk

Nature of social laws. – Reprint. – Cambridge : Cambridge University Press, 1986.
ISBN 0521338298 Pbk £9.95

Naude, S. J.
Modern Business Law / P. E. J. Brooks. – Durban : Butterworths.
Hbk

Naval court-martial manual / Ministry of Defence. – 1. – London : H.M.S.O., 1969 - 1984. looseleaf. – (B.R.11).
Supersedes: Admiralty memorandum on naval court-martial procedure, 1958. Superseded by: Manual of naval law, 1981. Includes index.
ISBN 011770220X

NCVO
Lotteries and Gaming - Voluntary Organisations and the Law. – NCVO. – London : Bedford Square Press, 1981.
ISBN 0719910706 Pbk £1.95

Ndulo, Muna →Case book on criminal law.
→ Civil liberties cases in Zambia.

Neal, Alan C. →Law and the weaker party : an Anglo-Swedish comparative study, Vol. 1 : The Swedish experience, edited by Alan C. Neal.
→ Perspective on labour law.
—Swedish Statutes, 3 Vols.
Vol. 3 / Anders Victorin. – Abingdon : Professional Books, 1984.
– (Law and the Weaker Party : An Anglo-Swedish Comparative Study Ser.).
ISBN 0862050456 Hbk £21.00

Neal, David →On tap not on top : legal centres in Australia, 1972-1982.

Neale, A. D
International business and national jurisdiction / A.D. Neale and M.L. Stephens. – Oxford : Clarendon Press, 1988.
xix,216p.
Examines the relationship between issues in international and municipal law, specifically the relationship between historically exclusive spheres of sovereign interest, and legal and practical requirements of the modern international commercial environment. Concentrates on US antitrust law, but some EEC and English decisions are included.
ISBN 0198255322 Hbk £52.00

Neave, Marcia A. →Australian family property law.
→ Easements and restrictive covenants in Australia.
→ Property law : cases and materials.
—Sackville and Neave Property Law : Cases and Materials / C. Rossiter. – 4th ed. – Sydney : Butterworths, 1988.
992p.
The fourth edition of this casebook contains revised materials on the Trade Practices Act, leases, and mortgages.
Hbk £78.00
→ Wills and intestacy in Australia and New Zealand : being a revised and consolidated version of Hardingham, Neave and Ford's The Law of Wills and Hardingham's The Law of Intestate Succession in Australia and New Zealand.

Necatigil, Zaim M.
Cyprus question and the Turkish position in international law. – Oxford : OUP, 1989.
275.
Recounts the recent history o Cyprus and deals with the international law aspects of the developments since 1963. The 'doctrine of necessity', the Treaty of Guarantee and Turkish intervention of 1974, human rights and the constitutional proposals of the respective sides of future federation for Cyprus are discussed.
ISBN 0198252250 Hbk £27.50

Nederlandse wetboeken : zoals zij tot op 1 januari 1984 zijn gewijzigd en aangevuld / uitgegeven door J.A. Fruin : bewerkt door M.P.J.A. Cremers, J.H.F.J. Cremers, P.H.A.J. Cremers. – Zwolle : Tjeenk Willink, 1984.
2107p.
Includes index.
ISBN 9027121346

Nedjati, Zaim M.
Cyprus conflict : a lawyer's view / by Zaim M. Nedjatigil. – 2nd ed. – Nicosia : A-Z Publications, 1982.
xii,248p.
Previous ed.: 1981. Includes bibliographical references and index.

Need for and the feasibility of an appeals process in regard to municipal grants-in-lieu of taxes : a report prepared for the Minister of Public Works Canada / I.C. Pollack, R. Gaulin, G. Simpson. – Ottawa : Minister of Supply and Services Canada, 1983.
324 p. in various pagings; 28 cm.
English and French. Added t.p.: La necessite et la faisabilite d'une procedure d'appel dans le regime de subventions aux municipalites en compensation d'imp$ots.
ISBN 0662524039

Neff, Charlotte →Annotated Competition Act.

Negi, S.S.
Forest Law. – Delhi : Bishen Singh, 1983.
92p.
Hbk £4.00

Negligence and Damages for Personal Injuries : Some Recent Developments. – Belfast : Queen's University of Belfast, 1981.
34p.
Pbk £3.25

Negligence for 'A' Level. – 2nd ed. – London : Sweet & Maxwell, 1981.
ISBN 0421289805 Pbk £8.25

Negligence for 'A' Level. – 2nd ed. – London : Sweet & Maxwell, 1983.
ISBN 0421321709 Pbk £5.95

Negligence in surveying and building / Malcolm Ross. – London : Estates Gazette, 1986.
xxii,247p.
Bibliography: p.238-239. - Includes index.
ISBN 0728200953

Negligence Law in the 1990's. – Vancouver : Continuing Legal Education Society of British Columbia, 1985.
76p.
ISBN 0865041911 Hbk £50.00

Negotiable Instruments / Vanessa Stott. – Winchester : DP Publications.
ISBN 0905435583 Hbk £3.50

Negotiable Instruments / T. J. Scott. – Durban : Professional Publisher, 1984.
ISBN 0409040215 Pbk £30.00

Negotiable Instruments Act / Adiga. – 14th ed. – New Delhi : Bharat Law House, 1983.
Hbk £160.00

Negotiable Instruments Act. – 9th ed. – Allahabad : Law Book Company, 1988.
950p.
Hbk £275.00

Negotiable Instruments with Supplement. – 1980 repr. – Lucknow : Eastern Book Company, 1984.
329p.
Hbk £35.00

Negotiating a Database Contract. – Hawthorn : Australian Database Development Agency, 1987.
ISBN 0959096736 Hbk £5.00

Negotiating shorter working hours / Palmer. – London : Macmillan, 1985.
ISBN 0333388585 Hbk £29.50

Negotiating, Writing and Administering Contracts. – Ottawa : Canadian Library Association, 1981.
28p.
Pbk £2.75

Negotiation. – Vancouver : Continuing Legal Education Society of British Columbia, 1986.
140p.
ISBN 0865042489 Hbk £50.00

Negotiation and Drafting of Business Leases. – London : Law Society, 1984.
70p.
Hbk £5.80

Negotiorum Gestio in South African Law. – Durban : Butterworths, 1985.
ISBN 0409060704 Pbk

Neighbourhood watch : policing the people. – London : CENT, 1986.
ISBN 0951119508 Pbk £1.50

Neighbours and the Law. – Sweet & Maxwell.
ISBN 0421365706 Hbk £20.00

Neighbours in Law. – London : Sweet & Maxwell, 1985.
– (Sweet and Maxwell's Law Files Ser.: No. 4).
ISBN 042134010X Llf £29.50

Neill, Brian →Defamation.
→ Duncan and Neill on defamation.

Neill, Patrick
Administrative law : ladders and snakes : a public lecture / delivered by Sir Patrick Neill on ... 12th March 1985. – London : Inns of Court School of Law, 1985.
32p.
→ Regulatory arrangements at Lloyd's : report of the Committee of Inquiry.

Neilson, June
Reports of the European Communities 1952-1977 : an index to authors and chairmen / compiled by June Neilson. – London : Mansell, 1981.
xiv,561p; 23cm.
Includes index.
ISBN 0720115922 £27.50

Neither Roses Nor Thorns : an Autobiography by the Retired Judge of the Supreme Court of India. – Lucknow : Eastern Book Company, 1985.
208p.
Hbk

Nelken, David →Criminal law and criminal justice.
—Limits of the legal process : a study of landlords, law and crime / David Nelken. – London : Academic Press, 1983.
xiii,241p; 24cm.
Bibliography: p219-225. - Includes index.
ISBN 0125152809

Nelson
Indian Penal Code in 2 Vols. – 7th ed. – Allahabad : Law Book Company, 1981-83.
Hbk £280.00

Nelson, Christine Purden →Income tax enforcement, compliance, and administration : Corporate Management Tax Conference 1982.

Nelson-Jones
Employee ownership / Nuttall. – London : Fourmat, 1987.
ISBN 1851900330 Pbk £14.95
—Package holiday law and contracts / Stewart. – 2nd ed. – London : Fourmat, 1988.
ISBN 1851900411 Pbk £14.95
—Practical tax saving. – 4th ed. – London : Butterworths, 1984.
ISBN 0406536333 Pbk £22.00
—Tax and interest tables / Nuttall. – London : Fourmat, 1988.
ISBN 1851900470 Pbk £4.95

Nelson-Jones, Rodney
Product liability : the new law under the Consumer Protection Act 1987 / by Rodney Nelson-Jones and Peter Stewart. – London : Fourmat, 1987.
207p.
Contains the text of the Act.
ISBN 1851900497 Pbk £15.95

Nelson, Norma →Homelessness among women : report of an Ad Hoc Working Group, Women's National Commission.

Nelson-Jones: Practical Tax Saving / Nicholas Noble, David Marks. – 4th ed. – London : Butterworths, 1984.
ISBN 0406536333 Pbk

Nelson's Tables : Administration of Estates. – 7th ed. – London : Oyez Longman, 1983.
ISBN 0851207219 Hbk £2.95

Nelson's Tables : Company Procedure. – 8th ed. – London : Oyez Longman, 1983.
ISBN 0851207154 Hbk £6.95

Nelson's tables: company procedure / A M Peck, A Robertson. – 10th ed. – London : Longman Professional, 1987.
Contains explanatory notes regarding insolvency and references to relevant statutes and forms. Incorporates the new practice and procedure following on from the Insolvency Act 1986.
ISBN 0851202964 Pbk £14.50

Nerep, Erik
Extraterritorial control of competition under international law, with special regard to US antitrust law / Erik Nerep. – 2. – Stockholm : Norstedt, 1983.
xxvii,xvii,733p.
Thesis (doctoral) - University of Stockholm 1982?. Bibliography: p.665-716. - Includes index.
ISBN 9118373127

Nerhot, Patrick
Rationalism and the modern state / by Patrick Nerhot. – Florence : European University Institute, 1983.
73p.
At head of title: European University Institute, Florence, Law Department.

Nethercote, J. R.
Parliament and Bureaucracy. – Neutral Bay : Hale & Iremonger.
ISBN 0868060143 Hbk £24.95, 015
ISBN 0868060151 Pbk £12.95, 015

Netherlands Arbitration Act : Text and Annotations in English, French and German / Albert Jan van den Berg. – Dordrecht : Kluwer, 1987.
ISBN 9065442979 Pbk £67.50

Netherlands Committee for Human Rights →Human rights in Ghana : report of a mission.

Netherlands Institute for the Law of the Sea (NILOS)
International organizations and the law of the sea. – Netherlands Institute for the Law of the Sea (NILOS). – Dordrecht : Nijhoff (Martinus), 1989.
712. – (ILOS yearbook 3).
An annual publication. Reproduces the most important documents related to the law of the sea that are issued each year by international organisations.
ISBN 1853331627 Hbk £97
—International Organizations and the Law of the Sea : Documentary Yearbook 1985. – Netherlands Institute for the Law of the Sea (NILOS). – Dordrecht : Kluwer, 1987.
650p.
ISBN 9024734886 Hbk £275.00

Netherlands Securities Trading Act and Securities Trading Decree : with supplementary regulations and official commentary / a translation by H.C.S. Warendorf and R.L. Thomas : with the assistance of the Amsterdam Stock Exchange, and with an introduction by F.G.B. Graaf. – Deventer Netherlands : Kluwer Law and Taxation Publishers, 1986.
152p.
ISBN 9065442774 Pbk £50.00

Netherlands Yearbook of International Law
Vol. 11 /. – Dordrecht : Kluwer, 1981.
400p.
ISBN 9028627111 Hbk £80.00/$40.00
Vol. 12. – 1981.
ix, 438p.
ISBN 9028629610 Hbk Gld80.00/$40.00
Vol. 13. – 1982.
ca 515p.
ISBN 9024727766 Hbk Gld110.00/$40.00
Vol. 14. – 1984.
490p.
ISBN 9024729165 Hbk £110.00
Vol. 15 (1984). – 1985.
585p.
ISBN 9024731151 Hbk Gld110.00

Vol. 18 (1987). – 1988.
510p.
ISBN 9024736382 Hbk Gld135.00

Netherlands yearbook of international law. – T.M.C. Asser Institute. – Dordrecht : Nijhoff (Martinus), 1989.
600.
Articles on the practice of the Iran-United States Claims Tribunal. The documentation section surveys Dutch state practice for the parliamentary year 1987-1988; international agreements to which the Netherlands is a party, and Netherlands judicial decisions and municipal legislation involving questions of public international law, and Dutch literature in this field, and related matters.
ISBN 0792301048 Hbk £45

Nettheim, Garth →Understanding Law : Introduction to Australia's Legal System 1978.
—Victims of the law. – London : Allen & Unwin, 1982.
216p.
ISBN 0868613959 £17.95

Netto, Pascal →Sesquicentennial choronological tables of the written laws of the republic of Singapore 1834-1984.

Neuhaus, J E →Guide to the UNCITRAL model on international commercial arbitration: legislation, history and commentary.

Neumann, Franz →Social democracy and the rule of law.

Nevill, A. G.
Equity proceedings with precedents (New South Wales) / by A.G. Nevill and A.W. Ashe : consultant A.V. Ritchie : with a foreword by M.M. Helsham. – Sydney : Butterworths, 1981.
lii,379p.
Includes index.
ISBN 0409490393 Hbk A$77

Neville Russell
Tolley's Charities Manual. – 2nd ed. – Tolley Publishing.
ISBN 085459325X Hbk £25.00

Nevill's Law of Trusts, Wills and Administration in New Zealand. – 8th ed. – Butterworths, 1985.
Guide to the law of trusts, wills and administration in New Zealand. Includes new chapters on unincorporated associations and construction of wills.
ISBN 040970170X Hbk A$76.45
ISBN 0409701858 Pbk A$50.05

Nevill's Will Drafting Handbook. – 4th ed. – Butterworths, 1988.
149p.
ISBN 0409702226 Hbk £54.00

Nevitt, Peter K.
Project financing / by Peter K. Nevitt. – 4th ed. – London : Euromoney, 1983.
xiii,273p.
Includes index.
ISBN 0903121395

New Abridgment of the Law : 1736-1766, 5 Vols. – Abingdon : Professional Books.
Hbk £650.00

New agricultural structures policy. – Luxembourg : Office for Official Publications of the European Communities, 1985.
16p.

New Approach I.C.I. Conditions of Contract Vol. 1. – Oxford : Construction Press, 1975.
ISBN 0904406075 Hbk £27.00
Vol. 2. – 1976.
ISBN 0904406164 Hbk £27.00

New Approach to (Dom/1) Standard Form Building Contract 1983. – Oxford : Construction Press.
ISBN 0860957225 Hbk £42.50

New approach to JCT design/building contract. – Oxford : Construction Press, 1984.
ISBN 086095904X Hbk £38.00

New Approaches to Juvenile Crime →Juvenile justice in the United Kingdom : comparisons and suggestions for change.

New Asylum Seekers : Refugees Law in the 1980's. – Martinus Nijhoff.
ISBN 9024737303 Hbk £39.00

New bearings in the law of the sea : inaugural lecture delivered at the University of Queensland, 29 April 1981 / R.D. Lumb. – St. Lucia, Queensland : University of Queensland Press, 1982.
ISBN 0702216798 Pbk

New Brunswick →New Brunswick government publications : quarterly list.

New Brunswick Court Forms : Formulaire de procedure du Nouveau-Brunswick / Douglas G. Rouse. – Agincourt : Carswell, 1985.
800p.
This looseleaf volume presents in both French and English over two hundred eighty separate forms which document the steps of a civil action in the courts of New Brunswick, Canada.
Pbk £80.00

New Brunswick government publications : quarterly list / Publication du government du Nouveau-Brunswick. – Fredericton, N.B. : Legislative Library, 1986.
Annual cumulation entitled : New Brunswick government documents : a checklist of New Brunswick government documents received at the Legislative Library, Fredericton, N.B. during the calendar year ... (ISSN 0548-4006). Text in English and French.
ISBN 08301085

New Brunswick Reports : 1825-1930, 54 Vols. – Carswell Legal Publications. – Agincourt : Carswell, 1983.
Hbk

New Brunswick Statute Citator. – Agincourt : Carswell, 1987.
1250p.
This single volume looseleaf text contains the legislative history of all the Acts in the Revised Statutes of New Brunswick, 1973 and all of the Public General Statutes enacted subsequently. This is a helpful research tool. Cases interpreting portions of the statutes are digested.
Hbk £147.00

New Canada-U.S. Tax Treaty : Impact on Corporations and Individuals. – Don Mills : CCH Canadian Ltd, 1985.
ISBN 0887962904 Pbk £12.00

New Canada-U.S. Tax Treaty with Technical Explanation. – Don Mills : CCH Canadian Ltd, 1984.
ISBN 0887962890 Pbk £8.00

New Canadian Constitution. – Toronto : James Lorimer & Co.
240p.
ISBN 0888625448 Pbk £7.95
ISBN 0888625456 Hbk £19.95

New Cases Companion to Ryans Income Tax Manual. – 2nd ed. – North Ryde : Law Book Co, 1983.
xiii, 314p.
ISBN 0455204098 29.00

New Code of International Law. – Berrima : Peace Plans.

New Competition Law : Text and Commentary. – Don Mills : CCH Canadian Ltd, 1986.
136p.
ISBN 088796396X Pbk £14.95

New Constitution and the Charter of Rights : Fundamental Issues and Strategies / Eric Gertner. – Butterworths, 1983.
384p.
ISBN 0409832642 Hbk £55.00

New Constitution of the Philippines Explained (English and Pilipino). – Manila : National Book Store, 1983.
92p.
ISBN 9710816780 Pbk £1.00

New Court Guide. – London : Blackstone Press, 1988.
ISBN 185185049X Pbk £5.95

New criminologies in Canada : crime, state and control / edited by Thomas Fleming. – Toronto : Oxford University Press, 1985.
xii,343p.
ISBN 0195404890

New Developments in Commercial Lending. – McGill University. – Toronto : DeBoo, 1981. – (Meredith Memorial Lecture Ser.).
ISBN 0888201095 Hbk £49.50

New Developments in International Finance / Chew. – Oxford : Blackwell, 1988.
ISBN 063115115X Hbk £40.00
ISBN 0631152040 Pbk £15.00

New developments in the law of remedies. – Don Mills, Ont. : Richard de Boo, 1981.
574p.
Includes index.
ISBN 088820101X

New dimensions in international trade law : a Canadian perspective / edited by Jacob S. Ziegel and William C. Graham for the Faculty of Law, University of Toronto and The Canadian Bar Association - Ontario. – Toronto : Butterworths, 1982.
ix,211p.
Papers presented at a Conference held in Toronto, November 14, 1980. Includes bibliographical references.
ISBN 0409818828

New Directions in International Law : Essays in Honour of Wolfgang Abendroth. – Frankfurt : Campus Verlag, 1982.
592p.
ISBN 3593330229 Hbk £178.00

New directions in judicial review / edited by J.L. Jowell and D. Oliver. – London : Stevens, 1988.
xiii,96p.
Includes index.
ISBN 0420478000 £16.00

New directions in maritime law 1984 / editors David J. Sharpe and W. Wylie Spicer. – London : Carswell, 1984.
vi,254p.
Papers given at the New Directions in Maritime Law Conference, Halifax, N.S., May 1984. Includes bibliographical references.
ISBN 0459372106 Hbk £35

New directions in maritime law / W Wylie Spicer. – London : Sweet & Maxwell, 1985.
ISBN 0459372106 Hbk £35.00

New directions in the law of the sea : new series / compiled and edited by Kenneth R. Simmonds : with the collaboration of specialist consulting editors. – London : Oceana, 1983.
looseleaf.
ISBN 0379165503

New divorce law : a commentary on the Divorce Act, 1985 / Alastair Bissett-Johnson and David C. Day. – Toronto : Carswell, 1986.
xxiii, 291 p.; 24 cm.
Includes legislation. Includes bibliographical references and index.
ISBN 0459387405 Pbk

New Employment Law Legislation : A Guide to the Employment Acts 1980 and 1982. – London : Kogan Page, 1983.
192p.
ISBN 0850386144 Hbk £12.50

New Environment In International Accounting : Issues and Practices. – Quorum Press.
ISBN 089930267X Hbk £40.95

New family and the new property / Mary Ann Glendon. – Toronto : Butterworths, 1981.
xvii,269p; 23cm.
ISBN 0409834106

New financial instruments / by Ian Cooper ... et al. – London : Chartered Isntitute of Bankers, 1987.
x,89p.
Includes bibliographical references.
ISBN 0852971907

New fixed penalty system : and disqualification, endorsement and penalty points : including a detailed guide to part III of the Transport Act 1982 and associated provisions / by Adrain John Turner and Malcolm Marsh. – Chichester : Rose (Barry), 1986.
x,170p.
Includes index.

New form of incorporation for small firms : a consultative document. – London : H.M.S.O., 1981.
iii,44p; 25cm.
ISBN 010181710X Pbk £3.20

New forms of democracy / edited by David Held and Christopher Pollitt. – London : Sage in association with the Open University, 1987.
256p; 22cm.
Includes bibliography and index.
ISBN 0803980124 Pbk £20.00
ISBN 0803980132 £7.50

New foundations for insurance law / edited by F.D. Rose. – London : Stevens, 1987.
xvii,106p.
Collection of papers discussing the industry's revised scheme for self-regulation, the theory and practice of the fundamental obligation of utmost good faith, and the implication of that obligation for insurers, and the claims process with reference to the problems of causation and proof of loss in the context of marine insurance.
ISBN 0420477802

New GATT round of multilateral trade negotiations: legal and economic problems / Ernst-Ulrich Petersman, M Hilf. – Kluwer Law and Taxation, 1989.
– (Studies in Transitional Economic Law).
Reproduces contributions to an international conference in 1987 on the current 'Uruguay Round' of multilateral negotiations. Part 1 examines proposals for the strengthening of the internatinal framework of GATT systems, and for the implementation of GATT rules within the major trading countries.
ISBN 9065443657 Hbk £81/Dfl 250

New German Patent Law (1981) in English and German / translated by Hermann Kinkeldey and Wilfried Stockmair. – Weinheim : Verlag Chemie, 1981.
199 p.; 21 cm.
ISBN 3527259368

New Horizons Day Centre Incorporated Act, 1983, Bill Pr038 : An Act Respecting New Horizons Day Centre Incorporated. – Ontario : Ontario Government Publications Service, 1983.
3p.
Hbk £0.30

New horizons in international law / by T. O. Elias. – Alphen aan den Rijn : Sijthoff & Noordhoff, .
xxii,260p.
ISBN 9028600396

New Horizons of International Law and Developing Countries. – Bombay : Tripathi, 1983.
Hbk £90.00

New Impetus for Consumer Protection Policy. – Luxembourg : Office for Official Publications of the European Communities.
17p.
ISBN 9282566498 Pbk £100.00

New impetus for consumer protection policy / (communication from the Commission to the Council). – Luxembourg : Office for Official Publications of the European Communities, 1985.
23p.
At head of title: Commission of the European Communities.
ISBN 9282556689

New Institute clauses : a commentary on the new standard policy forms for marine risks issued by the London insurance market / by N.G. Hudson and J.C. Allen. – London : Lloyd's, 1986.
217p; 24cm.
ISBN 185044093X £47.50

New international economic order legal debate : background, status, and alternatives / Gabe Shawn Varges. – Frankfurt am Main : Peter Lang, 1983.
vi,138p.
Bibliography: p. 121-128.
ISBN 382047613X

New international status of civil defence : as an instrument for strengthening the protection of human rights / Bosko Jakovljevic. – The Hague : M. Nijhoff Publishers, 1982.
142p.
Includes bibliographical references and index.
ISBN 9024725674

New Ireland Forum →Legal systems, North and South : a study prepared for the New Ireland Forum.

New labour law : strikes, dismissals and the unfair labour practice in South African law / by M.S.M. Brassey ... et al. – Cape Town : Juta, 1987.
xxix,478p.
Includes bibliographical references.
ISBN 0702118281

New Law Journal. – London : Butterworths.
Pbk £119.00
Microfiche (1965-1977). –
ISBN 0406886032

New Law Journal : 1965-date. – Abingdon : Professional Books, 1984.
Hbk

New Law of Expropriation / Stephen F. Waque. – Toronto : DeBoo, 1984.
This text provides analyses of reform legislation in Alberta, Manitoba, New Brunswick, Nova Scotia and Canada. Provincial statutes contain section-by-section commentaries. The main topics discussed are compensation where no land is taken, ways to prove expropriation claims, and types of claims successfully made.
ISBN 0888201532 Hbk £135.00

New law of the sea : selected and edited papers of the Athens colloquium on the law of the sea, September 1982 / edited by Christos L. Rozakis and Constantine A. Stephanou. – Amsterdam : North-Holland, published in collaboration with the Pantios School of Political Science, Athens, 1983.
xiv,354p; 23cm.
Includes index.
ISBN 0444868046

New Law of the Sea for the Caribbean : an Examination of Marine Law and Policy Issues in the Lesser Antilles. – Berlin : Springer-Verlag, 1988.
ca 295p.
ISBN 3540968059 Pbk £69.00

New law-and-economics : a research review / C.G. Veljanovski. – Oxford : Centre for Socio-Legal Studies, 1982.
xi,169p.
Bibliography: p.144-169.
ISBN 0862260531

New Library of Irish Material Now on LEXIS. – London : Butterworths.
Pbk

New media : law & policy / edited by Mark Armstrong. – Kensington, NSW : Faculty of Law, University of New South Wales, 1981.
vii, 237 p.; 25 cm.
Includes bibliographical references.
ISBN 0858238950 Pbk

New nationality law / Ian A. Macdonald and Nicholas Blake. – London : Butterworths, 1982.
208p; 26cm.
This book provides a thorough discussion of the British Nationality Act of 1981. The three new categories of citizenship: British Citizenship, Citizenship of the British Dependent Territories, and British Overseas Citizenship are analyzed in detail.
ISBN 0406282803 Hbk £21.50

New Nature Brevium : With a Table of the Most Material Things Contained Therein, Composed by William Rastal, (also) the Authorities in Law Newly Translated by William Hughes. – Repr. of 1652 ed. – Abingdon : Professional Books.
269p.
Hbk £192.00

New Offences Against the Person : the Provisions of Bill C-127. – Butterworths, 1984.
288p.
Contains analysis of all relevant decisions, tables of included offences, assaults, abduction offences, evidentiary and procedural rules, hypothetical examples, sample verdict sheets simplifying the jury's task, sexual assaults and defences and exemptions.
ISBN 0409875759 Hbk £65.00

New, other activities and intiatives : (a) interregional linkages and co-operative arrangements : interregional linkages and co-operative arrangements among developing countries for their technological transformation / report by the UNCTAD secretariat. – s.l. : United Nations Conference on Trade and Developoment, 1984.
ii, 21p, 3 leaves. – (TD/B/C.6/118).
Item 6 (a) of the provisional agenda for the fifth session of the Committee on Transfer of Technology, Geneva, 22 October 1984.

New perspective in law and justice in Nigeria : the distinguished annual lecture delivered at the National Institute on 25th October, 1985 / by Timothy Akinola Aguda. – Kuru, Nigeria : National Institute for Policy and Strategic Studies, 1985.
16p. – (Distinguished lecture series).
Includes bibliographical references.

New perspectives and conceptions of international law : an Afro-European dialogue / edited by K. Ginther, W. Benedek. – Wien : Springer-Verlag, 1983.
ix,261p.
ISBN 3211817808

New perspectives in Scottish legal history / A K R Kiralfy, Hector L. Macqueen. – London : Cass, 1983.
100p.
ISBN 0714632511 £18.50

New politics of labour law / Lord Wedderburn of Charlton. – Durham : The University of Durham, Industrial Relations Group, 1983.
– (Occasional paper).

New position of East Africa's Asians : problems of a displaced minority / by Yash Tandon and Arnold Raphael. – 2nd rev. ed. – London : Minority Rights Group, 1984.
20p. – (Report).
Previous ed.: 1978. Bibliography: p.20.
ISBN 0946690200

New Protectionism : Non-Tariff Barriers and Their Effects for Canada. – Toronto : Lorimer & Co, 1981.
ISBN 0888624425 Hbk £16.95
ISBN 0888624417 Pbk £7.95

New reproductive techniques : a legal perspective / Douglas J. Cusine. – Aldershot, Hants. : Gower, 1988.
x,261p.
Bibliography: pp238-254. - Includes index.
ISBN 0566054108

New River : a legal history / Bernard Rudden. – Oxford : Clarendon, 1985.
xiii,335p,iileaves of plates; 23cm.
Bibliography: p321-329. - Includes index.
ISBN 0198254970 £20.00

New rules for victims of armed conflicts : commentary on the two 1977 protocols additional to the Geneva Conventions of 1949 / by Michael Bothe, Karl Josef Partsch, Waldemar A. Solf, with the collaboration of Martin Eaton. – The Hague : Martinus Nijhoff Publishers, 1982.
xxi,746p.
Bibliography: p. 707-716.
ISBN 9024725372

New select committees : a study of the 1979 reforms / edited by Gavin Drewry for the Study of Parliament Group. – Oxford : Clarendon, 1985.
x,340p; 25cm.
Includes bibliography and index.
ISBN 019822785X Hbk £17.50 :
ISBN 0198227841 Pbk

New Sentencing Options : Penalties and Sentences Act. – Melbourne : Law Institute of Victoria, 1986.
Hbk £15.00

New South Wales Construction Safety Act 1912 and Regulations. – 2nd ed. – North Ryde : C.C.H. Australia, 1985.
300p.
ISBN 0869034855 Hbk £24.00

New South Wales consumer credit legislation / with annotations by Jane R. Levine. – North Ryde, N.S.W. : CCH Australia, 1985.
xl,449p.
Includes index.
ISBN 0869038354

New South Wales Industrial Arbitration Act 1940 : including Regulations and Trade Union Legislation. – 4th ed. – North Ryde : C.C.H. Australia, 1986.
328p.
ISBN 0869035983 Hbk

New South Wales Law Reform Commission
Accident compensation
Working paper 1 : A transport accidents scheme for New South Wales / New South Wales Law Reform Commission. – Sydney : The Commission, 1983.
xix,231p. – (Working paper 22).
Includes bibliographical references.
Interim report : Worker's Compensation (Amendment) Bill 1982 and cognate billsl / New South Wales Law Reform Commission. – 1983.
viii,62p. – (L.R.C. 41).
Final report 1 : Report on a transport accidents scheme for New South Wales / New South Wales Law Reform Commission. – 1984.
– (L.R.C. 43).
Includes bibliographies and indexes. Accompanied by: Outline of report on a transport accidents scheme for New South Wales.

—Advertising and specialisation / New South Wales Law Reform Commission. – Sydney : The Commission, 1981.
xxxv,244p; 25cm. – (Discussion paper no 5).
Bibliography: p.228-244.

—Case study booklet / New South Wales. Law Reform Commission. – Sydney : Law Reform Commission of New South Wales, 1984.
x,66p.

—Community law reform program
1st report : Insurance contracts : non-disclosure and misrepresentation / New South Wales Law Reform Commission. – Sydney : The Commission, 1983.
61p. – (L.R.C. 34).
2nd report : Interest on certain debts / New South Wales Law Reform Commission. – 1983.
46p. – (L.R.C. 35).
3rd report : Service of civil process on Sunday / New South Wales Law Reform Commission. – 1983.
61p. – (L.R.C. 37).
4th report : Sound recording of proceedings of courts and commissions : the media, authors and parties / New South Wales Law Reform Commission. – 1984.
115p. – (L.R.C. 39).
Bibliography: p.113-115.
5th report : Passing of risk between vendor and purchaser of land / New South Wales Law Reform Commission. – 1984.
84p. – (L.R.C. 40).
Bibliography: p.83-84.
6th report : Conscientious objection to jury service / New South Wales Law Reform Commission. – 1984.
53p. – (L.R.C. 42).
7th report : Attachment of moneys deposited with building societies and credit unions / New South Wales Law Reform Commission. – 1985.
xiii,123p. – (L.R.C. 46).
Includes bibliographical references.
ISBN 0730514714 Hbk
8th report : Wills - execution and revocation / New South Wales Law Reform Commission. – 1986.
175p. – (L.R.C. 47).
Includes bibliographical references.
ISBN 0730514943 Hbk

—Criminal procedure : unsworn statements of accused persons : report / New South Wales Law Reform Commission. – Sydney : The Commission, 1985.
70p. – (L.R.C. 45).
Bibliography: p.65-66.
ISBN 0730514269 Hbk

—Criminal procedure report : the jury in a criminal trial / New South Wales Law Reform Commission. – Sydney : The Commission, 1986.
xxxi,203p. – (L.R.C. 48).
Includes bibliographical references.
ISBN 073051546X Hbk

—First report on the legal profession : general regulation and structure / New South Wales Law Reform Commission. – Sydney : The Commission, 1982.
242p. – (L.R.C.31).
Bibliography: p.227-229. - Includes index.

—Fourth report on the legal profession : solicitors' trust accounts / New South Wales Law Reform Commission. – Sydney : The Commission, 1984.
viii,228p. – (L.R.C. 44).
Bibliography: p.212-214. Includes indexes.

—Legal profession / New South Wales Law Reform Commission. – Sydney : The Commission, 1981.
229p; 25cm. – (Background paper 4).

—Magistracy : interim report : first appointments as magistrates under the Local Courts Act, 1982 / New South Wales Law Reform Commission. – Sydney : The Commission, 1983.
xiii,87p. – (L.R.C. 38).

—Registration and certification of births and deaths : discussion paper / New South Wales Law Reform Commission. – Sydney : Government Printer, 1987.
vii,33p. – (D.P. v 17.).
ISBN 0730546276 Hbk

—Report on de facto relationships / New South Wales Law Reform Commission. – Sydney : The Commission, 1983.
xx,423p. – (L.R.C. 36).
Bibliography: p.391-396. Includes index. Accompanied by: Outline of report on de facto relationships (19p).

—Report on incorporation of associations / New South Wales Law Reform Commission. – Sydney, 1982.
136p. – (L.R.C.).
Includes index.

—Second report on the legal profession : complaints, discipline and professional standards / New South Wales Law Reform Commission. – Sydney : The Commission, 1982.
121p. – (L.R.C.32).
Includes index.

—Solicitors' trust accounts and the Solicitors' Fidelity Fund / New South Wales Law Reform Commission. – Sydney : The Commission, 1981.
xxix,241p; 25cm. – (Discussion paper no 6).

—Structure of the profession
Part 1 / New South Wales Law Reform Commission. – Sydney : The Commission, 1981.
340p; 25cm. – (Discussion paper no 4 (1)).
Bibliography: p. 324-340.
Part 2 / New South Wales Law Reform Commission. – 1981.
p.344-644; 25cm. – (Discussion paper no 4 (2)).

—Third report on the legal profession : advertising and specialisation / New South Wales Law Reform Commission. – Sydney : The Commission, 1982.
155p. – (L.R.C. 33).

New South Wales Law Reports : 1971-date. – Abingdon : Professional Books, 1984.
Hbk

New South Wales Police Law Handbook. – Sydney : Butterworths, 1988.
176p.
This handbook contains sections devoted to interrogation, arrest, and search and seizure. Included are chapters on detention and questioning, powers of arrest, searches, and search warrants. The intended audience is law enforcement officers.
Pbk £22.00

New South Wales Real Property Legislation. – North Ryde : C.C.H. Australia, 1987.
360p.
ISBN 0869038885 Hbk

New South Wales Statutes Annotations, December 1987. – Butterworths, 1988.
1,159p.
ISBN 0409494585 Hbk £150.00

New South Wales Workers' Compensation Act 1926. – 3rd ed. – North Ryde : C.C.H. Australia, 1985.
424p.
ISBN 0869035983 Hbk £24.00

New Swedish family legislation : the Marriage Code : the Cohabitees (Joint Homes) Act : the Homosexual Cohabitees Act : the Inheritance Code, chapters 1-3 and 7. – Stockholm : Ministry of Justice, 1988.
37p.
'... translations of ... Swedish legislation published in the Swedish Code of Statutes (SFS)'. - p.1.

New Tables of the Written Laws of the Republic of Singapore. – Kent Ridge : Malaya Law Review, 1982.
ISBN 9971620332 Hbk £99.00

New Tax Penalties 1984. – Monash University, Faculty of Law. – Clayton : Monash University Press, 1984.
ISBN 0867463538 Hbk £21.00

New tenancy agreements : a model for landlords and tenants based on the Housing Act 1980. – National Consumer Council. – London : The Council, 1981.
22p.
ISBN 0905653378

New terrorism / edited by William Gutteridge for the Institute for the Study of Conflict. – London : Mansell, 1986.
192p; 24cm.
Includes index.
ISBN 0720118123 £20.00

New Towns Act 1981 : Report of the Cumbran Development Corporation. – London : HMSO, 1983.
Hbk £4.10

New trends in contemporary international law / T.O. Elias. – Hull : Hull University Press, 1985.
14p; 21cm. – (Josephine Onoh memorial lecture).
ISBN 0859584496

New trends in the development of international commercial arbitration and the role of arbitral and other institutions / general editor Pieter Sanders. – Deventer : Kluwer, 1983.
xii,393p.
Proceedings of a conference organised by the International Council for Commercial Arbitration.
ISBN 9065441204

New U.S. Residency Rules for Canadians : Tax Considerations. – North Ryde : C.C.H. Australia, 1986.
98p.
ISBN 0887963250 Pbk £12.00

New Victorian Supreme Court Rules. – Butterworths, 1986.
184p.
ISBN 0409491551 Pbk £18.00

New York Arbitration Convention of 1958 : towards a uniform judicial interpretation / door Albert Jan Van Den Berg. – The Hague : T.M.C. Asser Institute, 1981.
xv,480p.
Proefschrift: Erasmus Universiteit, Rotterdam. Bibliography: p440-450. With summary and conclusion in Dutch.
ISBN 9065440356

New York Convention on the Recognition and Enforcement of Foreign Arbitral Awards : explanatory documentation prepared for Commonwealth jurisdictions / by K.W. Patchett in association with the Commonwealth Secretariat. – London : Commonwealth Secretariat, 1981.
v,62p.
Includes the text of the Convention.
ISBN 0850922038

New Zealand →Working paper on contribution in civil cases.

New Zealand Banking Law. – Butterworths.
400p.
Pbk £119.00

New Zealand business : entering the Australian market : Legal Research Foundation Inc. Seminar, 19 November 1985 / Barry J. McWilliams. – Auckland : Legal Research Foundation, 1985.
122p.
Papers presented by Barry J. McWilliams and others.
ISBN 0908581408

New Zealand Commentary to Halsbury's Laws of England. – Wellington : Butterworths.
Hbk

New Zealand Companies and Securities Legislation. – C.C.H., 1987.
1,000p.
ISBN 086475082X Hbk £34.00

New Zealand Company Law Casebook. – Butterworths, 1984.
Collation of cases that deal with the law relating to companies, in particular the provisions of the Companies Act 1955. Takes into account the Companies Amendment Act 1983 (No 2). Includes leading cases.
ISBN 0409701777 Pbk £41.25

New Zealand company law cases. – Auckland : CCH (New Zealand), 1984-.
Originally published: in the publisher's loose-leaf reporting service, New Zealand company secretary's and company law service. Index in each vol.

New Zealand Contract and Commercial Legislation. – North Ryde : C.C.H. Australia, 1987.
900p.
ISBN 0864750722 Hbk

New Zealand Conveyancing and Property Reports. – Wellington : Butterworths, 1983.
ISBN 0409701416 Hbk

New Zealand Conveyancing Bulletin. – Wellington : Butterworths.
ISBN 0409781428 Pbk

New Zealand Council of Law Reporting
New Zealand Law Reports. – New Zealand Council of Law Reporting. – Wellington : Butterworths.
Hbk

New Zealand Current Taxation. – Wellington : Butterworths.
Hbk

New Zealand duties guide. – Auckland : Commerce Clearing House (New Zealand), 1985-.
Title history; New Zealand duties and sales tax guide (1983-1985). Includes index. Loose-leaf issues accompanied by a summary report.
Llf

New Zealand Duties Legislation. – North Ryde : C.C.H. Australia, 1987.
300p.
ISBN 0864750870 Hbk

New Zealand encyclopaedia of forms and precedents other than court forms / editor, E.C. Adams. – 15. – Wellington : Butterworths, 1963.
Superseded by: New Zealand forms and precedents, 1986.

New Zealand Family Law Legislation. – North Ryde : C.C.H. Australia, 1987.
1,600p.
ISBN 086475003X Hbk £30.00

New Zealand goods and services tax guide. – Auckland : Commerce Clearing House (New Zealand), 1985-.
Title history: New Zealand duties and sales tax guide (1983-1985);New Zealand sales, goods and services taxes guide (1983-1987). Includes index.
Llf

New Zealand Goods and Services Tax Legislation. – 2nd ed. – North Ryde : C.C.H. Australia, 1986.
100p.
ISBN 0864750579 Hbk

New Zealand Hire Purchase Law. – 3rd ed. – Butterworths, 1977.
ISBN 0409621811 Hbk £64.35

New Zealand in Vietnam : a Study of the Use of Force in International Law. – Palmerston North : Dunmore Press Ltd., 1987.
ISBN 0864690584 Pbk £16.45

New Zealand income tax law and practice / by Donald H. Simcock and John F.S. Rooke with CCH editorial staff. – 3. – Auckland : Commerce Clearing House (New Zealand), 1973.
looseleaf.
Loose-leaf issues accompanied by a summary report and a supplement.
ISBN 0869032003 v.3
ISBN 0869031966

New Zealand Insolvency Legislation. – North Ryde : C.C.H. Australia, 1987.
200p.
ISBN 086475082X Hbk

New Zealand Law Dictionary / M.S. Hinde. – 3rd rev. ed. – Butterworths, 1986.
ISBN 0409787620 Pbk £60.50

New Zealand Law Journal. – Wellington : Butterworths.
Hbk

New Zealand Law Register 1985. – Birkenhead : Reed Methuen, 1984.
ca 442p.
Hbk £26.00

New Zealand Law Reports. – New Zealand Council of Law Reporting. – Wellington : Butterworths.
Hbk

New Zealand Law Reports. – Butterworths.
Hbk £187.50

New Zealand Law Reports : 1883-date. – Abingdon : Professional Books, 1984.
Hbk

New Zealand Library Association →New Zealand royal commissions, commissions and committees of inquiry, 1864-1981 : a checklist.

New Zealand Master Tax Guide 1987. – North Ryde : C.C.H. Australia.
1,000p.
ISBN 0864750080 Hbk £34.00

New Zealand Recent Law. – Auckland : Legal Research Foundation, 1986.
Hbk £75.00
Back Issues. –
Hbk £6.00

New Zealand royal commissions, commissions and committees of inquiry, 1864-1981 : a checklist / compiled by Evelyn Robertson and Peter H. Hughes for the NZLA Professional Division. – Wellington : New Zealand Library Association, 1982.
30p.
ISBN 0908560109

New Zealand Statutes : Current Reprint. – Butterworths.
Hbk

New Zealand tax cases. – Auckland : Commerce Clearing House (New Zealand), 1975.
23cm.
Issued as bound volumes every two years, with the current issues forming part of the service to the loose-leaf publication: New Zealand income tax law and practice / by Donald H. Simcock and John F.S. Rooke. Looseleaf issues accompanied by a summary report.

New Zealand Town Planning Appeals. – Wellington : Butterworths.
Hbk

New Zealand University Law Review : 1963-date. – Abingdon : Professional Books, 1984.
Hbk

New Zealnd forms and precedents / editor in chief, the Hon. Mr. Justice Barker. – Wellington : Butterworths, 1986.
Supersedes: New Zealand encyclopaedia of forms and precedents, 1963-70. With index volume.
ISBN 0409702080 Llf

Newall : Law and Practice of Deeds Registration / R.F. Rorke. – 3rd ed. in prep. – Durban : Professional Publishers.
Hbk

Newbegin, John, et al
Mergers and Acquisitions : Law and Practice. – London : Butterworths, 1988.
ISBN 0406103704 Hbk

Newby, Howard
Green and pleasant land? : social change in rural England / Howard Newby : cartoons by Thelwell. – Updated ed. – London : Wildwood House, 1985.
324 p.
ISBN 0704505053

Newcombe
Standard Automobile Policy Annotated. – Toronto : Butterworths, 1986.
296p.
Hbk £45.00

Newcombe, H.B.
Handbook of Record Linkage Methods for Health and Statistical Studies, Admin. Business. – Oxford : Oxford University Press.
ISBN 019261732X Hbk £22.50

Newcombe, John
Insurance case law digest: property and casualty. – 2 vols. – Scarborough, Ontario : Butterworths (Canada).
Coverage of automobile and property insurance cases in Canada. Each part has a table of cases, and the case digests are arranged to reflect the organizational categories of the standard automobile and home insurance policies.
Loose leaf

—Standard Automobile Policy Annotated. – Butterworths, 1986.
288p.
Hbk £45.00

Newcomer's Guide to the U.S.A. – North Vancouver : International Self-Counsel Press, 1987.
ISBN 0889089205 Hbk £12.95

Newe Boke of Justice of the Peas. – Abingdon : Professional Books.
– (Classical English Law Texts Ser.).
Hbk £47.00

Newell
Buying Your Own House. – London : Longman Professional, 1988.
ISBN 0851213790 Pbk £4.95

Newell, David
New Employment Law Legislation : A Guide to the Employment Acts 1980 and 1982. – London : Kogan Page, 1983.
192p.
ISBN 0850386144 Hbk £12.50

—Understanding recruitment law / David Newell. – London : Waterlow, 1984.
xi,189p; 21cm. – (Waterlow's business library).
Includes index.
ISBN 0080391559 Pbk £9.75

Newfoundland and Dominion Status. – Agincourt : Carswell, 1987.
304p.
This work focuses on the pre-Confederation status of Newfoundland from a legal point of view. It is a comprehensive text providing archival sources in documenting the evolution of Newfoundland's external affairs competence between 1855 and 1934. It also provides a review in terms of Imperial constitutional law and international law. Up-to-date decisions of the Supreme Court of Canada and Newfoundland Court of Appeal are reviewed.
Hbk £38.00

Newfoundland Annual Bound Statutes 1971-1986. – Agincourt : Carswell.
Hbk £316.50

Newfoundland Law Reform Commission
Report on the limitation of actions / Newfoundland Law Reform Commission. – St. John's : The Commission, 1986.
vi,29p.

—Working paper on limitation of actions / Newfoundland Law Reform Commission. – St. John's : The Commission, 1985.
xi,481p.
Includes bibliographical references. With a supplement.

—Working paper on powers of attorney / Newfoundland Law Reform Commission. – St. John's : The Commission, 1987.
iv,64p.
Includes bibliographical references.

—Working paper on the Mechanics' Liens Act : certain substantive issues / Newfoundland Law Reform Commission. – St.John's : The Commission, 1987.
vi,294p.
Includes bibliographical references. Includes text of the Acts.

Newham, Alan D. H. →Seventh Directive : consolidated accounts in the EEC.

Newhouse →Workers' Compensation Practice Guide.

Newington, Ann
Legal secretary's handbook / Ann Newington and Hilary Willoughby. – 4th ed. – London : Longman Professional (UK), 1989.
Contains descriptions of the work of the various departments of a solicitor's practice and barrister's chambers. It includes an explanation of legal terms and gives examples of completed legal forms. Takes account of latest office technology, updates and useful addresses.
Legal secretaries, secretarial colleges, careers offices, practices, chambers
ISBN 0851215785 Sbd £18.95

Newman →Understanding company accounts.

Newman, Catherine
Bar finals guide / Catherine Newman. – 3rd ed. – London : Sweet & Maxwell, 1987.
300p; 23cm.
Previous ed.: 1984. Includes index.
ISBN 0421359102 Pbk £14.50

Newman, Frank →Academic freedom under Israeli military occupation : report of WUS/ICJ mission of enquiry into higher education in the West Bank and Gaza.

Newman, Graeme
Just and painful : a case for corporal punishment of criminals / Graeme Newman. – New York : Macmillan, 1983.
163p; 23cm.
Includes index.
ISBN 0029231302 £11.95

Newman, Joel →Tax On Maintenance Payments 1985/86.

Newman, K.
Law and Economic Organization. – Cambridge : Cambridge University Press, 1985.
ISBN 0512128966 Pbk £7.95

Newman, Phyllis E
Conveyancing Practice and Procedure / Vera Gittings. – 2nd ed. – London : Fourmat, 1985.
ISBN 0906840910 Pbk £9.95
→ Newman's Conveyancing Practice and Procedure.

Newman's Conveyancing Practice and Procedure / Phyllis E. Newman. – 2nd ed. – London : Fourmat, 1985.
135p.
ISBN 0906840910 Pbk £9.95

News from ISDS. – Paris : ISDS International Centre, 1984.
ISBN 02570009

Newsletter / Law Technology Centre & BILETA. – Warwick : LTC, School of Law, University of Warwick, 1987-.

Newsletter / British and Irish Association of Law Librarians. – British and Irish Association of Law Librarians. – London : The Association, 1983.

Newsletter / Commonwealth Legal Education Association. – Commonwealth Legal Education Association. – London : Commonwealth Legal Education Association, 1974.

Newsom, G. H.
Aculty jurisdiction of the Church of England. – Sweet & Maxwell, 1988.
xxix,262p.
Deals with the structure and workings of the court, and discusses reported case law since 1950. Analyses the problems faced by those who are entrusted with the care and development of historic buildings. Changes introduced by the Faculty Jurisdiction (Amendment) Rules 1987 are examined.
ISBN 0421387602 Pbk £12.20

—Church of England Faculty Jurisdiction. – Sweet & Maxwell, 1988.
ISBN 0421387602 Pbk £13.75

→ Preston and Newsom's restrictive covenants affecting freehold land.

Newsom, G. L. →Preston and Newsom's restrictive covenants affecting freehold land.

Newspaperman's guide to the law. – 4th ed. – Wellington : Butterworths (New Zealand), 1986.
ISBN 040903457 Hbk £33.00
ISBN 040905764 Pbk £23.00

Newth, John →Inheritance Tax 1988-89.
→ Tolley's inheritance tax 1987-88.
→ Tolley's inheritance tax 1988-89.

—Tolley's taxation in the Republic of Ireland 1987-88 / by John Newth and Glyn Saunders : from an original text by Eric L. Harvey. – Croydon : Tolley, 1987.
vii,293p.
Includes index.
ISBN 0854592946

Newton, Clive R.
General principles of law / by Clive R. Newton. – 3rd ed. – London : Sweet & Maxwell, 1983.
xix,373p; 22cm.
Previous ed.: 1977. Bibliography: p362-364. - Includes index.
ISBN 042128580X Pbk £7.95

Newton, J. E.
Factors Affecting Sentencing Decisions In Rape Cases. – Canberra : Australian Institute of Criminology.
Hbk £0.60

Newton, P.M.
Accounting : Questions and Answers. – London : Longman Professional.
ISBN 058202837X Pbk £3.50

Newton, Velma
Civil rights with special reference to the Commonwealth Caribbean : a select bibliography / Velma Newton. – Cave Hill, Barbados : Institute of Social and Economic Research (Eastern Caribbean), University of the West Indies, 1981.
110p. – (Occasional bibliography series).
Includes index.

—Commonwealth Caribbean legal literature : a bibliography of all primary sources to date and secondary sources for 1971-1985 / Velma Newton. – Cave Hill, Barbados : Faculty of Law Library, University of the West Indies, 1987.
492p.
Includes index.
ISBN 976800116X

NFU →Tax and the farmer.

Ngakane, M.R.
General Survey of Employment Protection Laws in Lesotho. – Maseru : National University of Lesotho, Institute of Labour Studies, 1983.
32p.
Hbk £3.50

Ngantcha, Francis
Right of innocent passage and the evolution of the international law of the sea. – London : Pinter, 1990.
250.
Debates the right of innocent passage in the light of the 1982 Law of the Sea Convention. Discusses the right of a coastal state to determine what is and is not innocent and to react accordingly.
ISBN 0861878515 Hbk £30

Ngwoke, Ikem Bu Chukwu B.
Religion and religious liberty in Nigerian law (from the colonial days to 1983) / Ikem Bu Chukwu B. Ngwoke. – Roma : Pontificia Universita Lateranense, 1984.
xvi,531p.
Bibliography: p.520-531.

Nhlapo, Ronald Thandabantu →Law and the other sex : the legal position of women in Swaziland.

Nibbs, C.
Accountancy In Banking. – Cambridge : Woodhead-Faulkner, 1983.
ISBN 0859411923 Hbk £19.95
ISBN 0859411931 Pbk £9.95

Niblett, Bryan →Data Protection Act 1984.

Nicaragua : the human rights record. – Amnesty International. – London : Amnesty International, 1986.
36p; 27cm.
ISBN 0862100941 Pbk

Nice, D.
Education and the law. – London : Longman Professional, 1986.
ISBN 090031320X Pbk £10.95

Nicholas
Duties and Responsibilities of Pension Plan Trustees / Williams. – London : CCH, 1984.
ISBN 0863250300 Pbk £11.50

Nicholas, Barry
French law of contract / Barry Nicholas. – London : Butterworths, 1982.
xxxviii,253p.
ISBN 040663095X Pbk £16.95
ISBN 0406630968 Hbk £23.00

—Introduction To Roman Law. – Oxford : Oxford University Press, 1962.
ISBN 0198760639 Pbk £7.95

Nicholas, D.
Commodities futures trading. – London : Mansell, 1985.
ISBN 0720117038 Pbk £18.00

Nicholls, Mark, et al
Legal Studies for South Australia. – Butterworths, 1988.
ca 288p.
ISBN 0409494712 Pbk £ 22.50

Nichols, D
Debtors (Scotland) Act 1987. – Edinburgh : Green (W.) & Son, 1987.
Annotated text of the Act from Scottish Current Law Statutes with two introductory chapters, including a diagram showing the principal effects of the Act on the debt recovery process.
ISBN 0414008227 Pbk

—Family Law (Scotland) Act 1985. – Edinburgh : Green (W.) & Son, 1986.
Full text of the Act with annotations reprinted from Scottish Current Law Statutes. The Act provides a new statement of the obligations of aliment and a new code for the settling of property and financial claims on a divorce.
ISBN 0414007840 Pbk

Nichols, David Ian
Living Together : A Guide to the Law on Marriage and Cohabitation in Scotland / Frances Wason. – Edinburgh : Scottish Association of Citizens Advice Bureau, 1984.
96p : Illus.
ISBN 0905831047 Hbk £1.95
—Matrimonial Homes (Family Protection) (Scotland) Act 1981 / by D.I. Nichols and M.C. Meston. – 2nd ed. – Edinburgh : W. Green, 1986.
x,94p; 25cm.
Previous ed.: 1982. Includes index. Includes the text of the Matrimonial Homes (Family Protection) (Scotland) Act 1981.
ISBN 0414007786 Pbk £10.50

Nichols, Lawrence T. → Beyond the courtroom : programs in community justice and conflict resolution.

Nichols, P.
Police Offences In Western Australia. – Sydney : Butterworths, 1981.
243p.
Hbk £0409322903

Nicholson
Medical research with children. – Oxford : Oxford University Press, 1986.
ISBN 0192615289 Hbk £12.50

Nicholson, C. G. B.
Law and practice of sentencing in Scotland / C.G.B. Nicholson. – Edinburgh : W. Green, 1981.
xxxi,274p; 22cm.
Includes index.
ISBN 0414006844 Pbk

Nickers : A Gentleman's Guide to Police Duty. – London : Police Review Publishing, 1982.
Illus.
ISBN 085164175X Pbk £2.50

Nicol, Andrew
Changing contempt of court / by Andrew Nicol and Heather Rogers. – London : National Council for Civil Liberties, 1981.
40p.
ISBN 0901108928
→ Media law : the rights of journalists and broadcasters.
→ Media law - the rights of journalists and broadcasters.

Niekirk, Paul H. → Family and child law statutes.
→ Penalties for road traffic offences : Schedule 4 to the Road Traffic Act 1972 as amended with editorial notes and additions.

Nield, Sarah
Annotation of the Hong Kong Conveyancing and Property Ordinance. – Butterworths, 1987.
ca 300p.
Deals with the 1984 Conveyancing and Property Ordinance, and annotates the 1988 Conveyancing and Property (Amendment) Ordinance. Discusses the background and the intended effects of the Ordinance, and gives a detailed analysis of each section. Sets out case authorities for the common law position.
ISBN 0409995401 Hbk £50.00
—Hong Kong conveyancing and property ordinance. – London : Butterworths, 1988.
ISBN 0409995401 Hbk £42.00

Nigeria → Supreme Court Rules 1985.

Nigeria : its petroleum geology, resources and potential / by Arthur Whiteman. – 2 v. – London : Graham & Trotman, 1982.
394p,5leaves of plates(folded).
In 2 vols. Bibliography: p.376-381.
ISBN 0860102645

Nigeria Court of Appeal reports. – Yaba : MIJ Publishers, 1985-.
v.

Nigeria Index to Federal Statutes in Force 1984. – Abingdon : Professional Books, 1985.
ISBN 0862050731 Hbk £19.25
ISBN 0862052009 Pbk £11.00

Nigeria journal of contemporary law. – Lagos : University of Lagos, 1970-.

Nigeria Law Reports : 1881-1955, 21 Vols. – London : Sweet & Maxwell.
ISBN 0421121602 Hbk £195.00

Nigeria lawyers' quarterly. – Lagos : s.n., 1964-.
2 issues only held: vol. 5, nos. 1-4, and vol. 7, nos. 1-4.
ISBN 00290025

Nigeria-Federal Statutes in Force 1982 : An Index of the Laws of Nigeria Which Are Still in Force As At the 31st December 1984. – Abingdon : Professional Books, 1984.
ISBN 0862050731 Hbk £24.00

Nigerian 1979 elections / edited by Oyeleye Oyediran. – London : Macmillan, 1981.
xi,182p.
ISBN 0333317858

Nigerian bulletin of contemporary law. – Benin City : Faculty of Law, University of Benin, 1985-.
Reports of cases in State and Federal courts of superior jurisdiction. Index in each vol..

Nigerian business law / by Gaius Ezejiofor and C.O. Okonkwo and C.U. Ilegbune. – London : Sweet & Maxwell, 1982.
lxvii,531p; 22cm.
Includes index.
ISBN 0421301201 Hbk £32.00
ISBN 042129230X Pbk £16.00

Nigerian business law / Cyprian Okonkwo, Peter Shears. – Ibadan : Spectrum, 1983.
207p; 24cm.
ISBN 0717511855 Pbk £4.85

Nigerian business law : a guide for students, managers and foreign investors / Efiong J. Etuk, E.K. Quansah. – Basingstoke : Macmillan, 1986.
208p; 22cm.
Includes index.
ISBN 0333435079 Pbk £5.95

Nigerian Commercial Law. – Onitsha : Africana-FEP.
Hbk

Nigerian commercial law and practice / by J. Olakunle Orojo. – 2. – London : Sweet & Maxwell, 1983.
22cm.
Includes index.
ISBN 0421291702 £85.00

Nigerian Commercial Law Reports : 1966 to date. – London : Sweet & Maxwell.
Hbk £90.00
Ea. Vol. until 1977. –
Hbk £45.00
Index 1966-1974. –
Hbk £20.50

Nigerian commercial laws : problems and perspectives / I.A. Ayua general editor. – Zaria : Department of Commercial Law, Ahmadu Bello University, 1984.
235p.
Includes bibliographical references.

Nigerian constitution today / by P.U. Umoh. – Uyo, Nigeria : Modern Business Press, 1985.
x,182p.
Includes bibliographical references and index.

Nigerian constitutional law / by Hari Chand. – 2nd ed. – Modinagar : Santosh Publishing House, 1982.
296p.
Includes index.

Nigerian Constitutional Law Reports
Vol. 1. – Lagos : Nigerian Law Publications, 1981.
ISBN 9782325000 Hbk £60.00
ISBN 9782325007 Hbk £20.00
Vol. 2. – 1981.
ISBN 9782325008 Hbk £20.00
Vol. 3. – 1982.
ISBN 9782325009 Hbk £70.00
Vol. 4. – 1983.
ISBN 9782325333 Hbk £60.00
Vol. 5. – 1984.
ISBN 9782325147 Hbk £60.00
Vol. 6. – 1985.
ISBN 9782325155 Hbk £60.00

Nigerian constitutional law reports. – Suru-Lere, Lagos : Nigerian Law Publications, 1981-.

Nigerian criminal cases index, 1880-1975 / by M.O. Olaitan. – Lagos : Libriservice Ltd., 1983.
vi,295p.
Includes index.
ISBN 978237203X

Nigerian Criminal Reports. – London : Sweet & Maxwell, 1981.
ISBN 090382647X Hbk £201.00
Vol. 1 1980. –
ISBN 0903826488 Hbk £36.00
Vol. 2 1980. –
ISBN 090382650X Hbk £36.00
Vol. 1 1981. –
ISBN 0903826542 Hbk £36.00
Vol. 2 1981. –
ISBN 0903826526 Hbk £29.00

Nigerian current law review. – Lagos : Nigerian Institute of Advanced Legal Studies, 1982-.

Nigerian Current Law Review. – London : Sweet & Maxwell, 1982.
ISBN 0421316004 Hbk £35.00

Nigerian Current Law Statutes Annotated 1958-1983. – Aba : Law & Educational Publishers.
ISBN 9782436011 Hbk

Nigerian current legal problems. – Lagos : Nigerian Institute of Advanced Legal Studies, 1985-.

Nigerian elections : a bibliography / by A.T. Agboola. – Lagos : University of Lagos Library, 1983.
ix,45p.
Includes index.

Nigerian electoral law / by D.I.O. Ewelukwa. – Lagos : Shelters International, 1983.
xii,252p.

Nigerian Grundnorm / delivered by Hon. Justice Kayode Eso on Thursday, 31st January 1985 at the University of Benin, Nigeria. – Lagos : Nigerian Law Publications, 1986.
92p.
Bibliography: p.89-90. - Includes index. Published under the auspices of Idigbe Memorial Lectures.

Nigerian income tax law and practice : incorporating income tax laws relating to personal income tax law, partnership tax law, companies income tax law, petroleum profits tax law, capital gains tax law, capital transfer tax law and guidelines to a tax system under the presidential system of government with accountancy and decided cases illustrations and a supplement (1985) / C.S. Ola. – London : Macmillan, 1985.
xxvi,566p; 22cm.
Includes index.
ISBN 0333400070 Pbk £8.95

Nigerian Institute of Advanced Legal Studies → Challenge of the Nigerian nation : an examination of its legal development, 1960-1985.
—Communique of the national seminar on effective law library services in Nigeria, June 5-7, 1984, held under the sponsorship of the Nigerian Institute of Advanced Legal Studies. – Nigerian Institute of Advanced Legal Studies. – Lagos : The Institute, 1984.
8p.
→ Constitutional relevance of the provision for the seat of government.
→ Financing the states : the constitutionality of sales tax laws.
→ Index to Nigerian legal periodicals, 1946-1981.
→ Judicial attitudes to freedom of speech and the press with particular reference to contempt of court.
→ Judiciary and the 1983 elections.
→ Legal implications of the creation of more states in Nigeria : being a paper presented at the National Conference on Creation of States in Nigeria.
→ Nigerian current law review.
→ Nigerian current legal problems.
→ Public Complaints Commission in a presidential system with particular reference to Nigeria.

Nigerian juridical review. – Nsukka, Nigeria : University of Nigeria Press, 1976.

Nigerian labour law / by Akintunde Emiola. – 2nd ed. – Ibadan : Ibadan University Press, 1982.
xxxviii,599p.
Previous ed.: 1979. Bibliography: p.599. - Includes index.
ISBN 9781211377

Nigerian Land Law. – 4th ed. – Sweet & Maxwell, 1971.
ISBN 0421160608 Pbk £19.00

Nigerian Land Use Act : policy and principles / by R.W. James. – Ife-Ife, Nigeria : University of Ife Press, 1987.
xxxi,195p.
Includes bibliographical references and index.
ISBN 9781360690

Nigerian law journal. – Lagos : African Universities Press, 1964-.

Nigerian law of contract / by I.E. Sagay. – London : Sweet & Maxwell, 1985.
450p.
Includes index.
ISBN 0421304200 Pbk £20.00

Nigerian Law of Contract (Nigerian Nutshells). – London : Sweet & Maxwell, 1987.
ISBN 0421361409 Pbk £3.95

Nigerian law of habeas corpus. – Lagos : Nigerian Law Publications, 1986.
lxvi,457p.
Contains cases on habeas corpus.
ISBN 9782325163

Nigerian Law of Libel and the Press. – Lagos : Nigerian Law Publications.
ISBN 9782325198 Hbk £90.00

Nigerian law of property / by Martin Chukwuka Okany. – Enugu, Nigeria : Fourth Dimension, 1986.
lxii,762p.
Bibliography: p.757-762. - Includes index.
ISBN 9781562153

Nigerian law of torts / E. Mara-Brown. – London : Sweet & Maxwell, 1987.
v,76p.
Includes index.
ISBN 0421361506

Nigerian Law Reports, Index-Digest 1881-1981, 2 Vols. – Aba : Law & Educational Publishers, 1984.
Hbk
1982-83 Supplement. –
ISBN 9782436038

Nigerian law times reports. – Benin City? : Patrac, 1986.
ISBN 07945892

Nigerian legal system : pluralism and conflict of laws in the Northern States / Ahmed Beita Yusuf. – New Delhi : National, 1982.
xiv,274p : 3 maps.
Bibliography: p.243-266. - Includes index.

Nigerian periodicals index. – Jos? : Committee of University Librarians of Nigerian Universities, 1986-.

Nigerian personal taxation : Law and practice with selected tax cases / S.A. Rabiu. – Ikeja, Nigeria : John West, 1986.
xiv,431p.
ISBN 978163040X

Nigerian petroleum law / G. Etikerentse. – London : Macmillan, 1985.
x,356p; 24cm.
Includes index.
ISBN 0333393570 Pbk £7.95

Nigerian petroleum law and practice / Martin M. Olisa. – Ibadan, Nigeria : Fountain Books, 1987.
x,261p.
Includes bibliographical references.
ISBN 978233118X

Nigerian Shipping Cases
Vol. 1. – Abingdon : Professional Books, 1987.
ISBN 0862052416 Hbk £75.00
Vol. 2. –
ISBN 0862052904 Hbk £75.00

Nigerian Shipping Laws. – Abingdon : Professional Books, 1983.
ISBN 0862050464 Hbk £126.50

Nigerian Society of International Law → Proceedings of the seventh, eighth and ninth annual conferences of the Nigerian Society of International Law, 1975-1978.

—Proceedings of the seventh, eighth and ninth annual conferences of the Nigerian Society of International Law, 1975-1978 / M. A. Ajomo. – Lagos : Nigerian Institute of International Affairs, 1982.
x,221p.
Includes bibliographical references. Edited by M.A. Ajomo.
ISBN 9782276111

→ T. O. Elias : citations, honours and awards.

Nigerian Supreme Court Law Reports 1956-1983 : Lawyers Edition 1956-1983, 16 Vols. – Aba : Law & Educational Publishers.
ISBN 9782436046 Hbk

Nigerian Tax Handbook. – Tolley Publishing, 1987.
ISBN 0854592318 Pbk £11.50

Nigerian Tax Law. – Abingdon : Professional Books, 1986.
350p.
ISBN 0862051169 Hbk

Nigerian weekly law reports. – Lagos : Nigerian Law Publications Ltd, 1985-.

Nigeria's presidential constitution : the second experiment in constitution democracy / Ben O. Nwabueze. – London : Longman, 1985.
xiv,488p; 21cm.
ISBN 0582644836 Hbk £15.00
ISBN 0582644747 Pbk £7.50

Nightingale
Joint ventures. – London : Longman Professional, 1988.
ISBN 0851213189 Hbk

Nihar, N.H.
Legal Decisions on Special Banking Laws. – Karachi : Royal Book, 1986.
235p.
Hbk £200.00

Nihon Kaiyo Kyokai → Exclusive economic zone : proceedings of the 7th International Ocean Symposium October 21-22, 1982, the Japan Shipping Club, Tokyo.
→ Frontier of the seas : the problems of delimitation : proceedings of the 5th International Ocean Symposium November 26-27, 1980, the Japan Shipping Club, Tokyo.
→ International cooperation in marine science and technology in the Pacific region : proceedings of the 6th International Ocean Symposium November 5-6, 1981, the Japan Shipping Club, Tokyo, Japan.

Niiniluoto, Ilkka → Man, law, and modern forms of life.

Nila, M.S.
Law of Suspension. – 2nd ed. – Lucknow : Eastern Book Company, 1985.
145p.
Hbk £30.00

Nimmer, M.B.
Nimmer On Copyright. – Matthew Bender, 1963.
ISBN 0000999072 Hbk £220.00

Nimmer On Copyright. – Matthew Bender, 1963.
ISBN 0000999072 Hbk £220.00

Niner, Pat → Housing association allocations : Achieving racial equality : a West Midlands case study : summary of a report by Pat Niner in association with Valerie Karn.

Nineteen Eighty-Eight Canadian Almanac and Directory. – Agincourt : Carswell, 1987.
1200p.
This is a reference book containing information on Canada. Lists include a directory of names, addresses, telephone numbers; contacts for all libraries, media, associations, foundations, clubs, business and government offices, agencies, and commissions; a directory of lawyers and law firms. Also included is information on the weather, climate, geographical data, population, transportation, astronomical data and forms of address.
Hbk £77.50

Nineteen Eighty-Five Tax Developments. – Toronto : Canadian Tax Foundation, 1985. – (Tax Memo: No. 70).
Hbk £9.00

Nineteen Eighty-Three Computers and Law Institute. – Vancouver : British Columbia Continuing Legal Education Society, 1983.
322p.
ISBN 0865041148 Hbk £50.00

Nineteen Seventy-Eight Protocol Relating to the International Convention for the Prevention of Pollution from Ships, 1973 : Regulations for the Prevention of Pollution by Oil-'86 Consolidated Version. – International Maritime Organization. – London : International Maritime Organization.
ISBN 9280111981 Hbk £7.00

Ninth report : lead in the environment / Royal Commission on Environmental Pollution : Chairman T.R.E. Southwood. – London : H.M.S.O., 1983.
x,183p; 25cm.
Includes index.
ISBN 0101885202 Pbk £9.20

Ninth report on top salaries / Review Body on Top Salaries : Chairman, Lord Plowden. – London : H.M.S.O., 1986.
v,31p. – (Report).
ISBN 0101978502

Ninth report to Parliament on subordinate legislation concerning Fishing (Abalone Licence Fee) Regulations 1987 (Statutory Rule no. 65/1987) / Legal and Constitutional Committee. – Melbourne : Government Printer, 1987.
vi,12p.
Includes Minority report.

Nishiyama, Yoshiki
Audit system for corporate enterprises in Japan : as compared with English company law / Yoshiki Nishiyama. – s.l. : s.n., 1987.
28p.
Offprint from: Kanazawa Law Review, vol. 30, no. 1 (1987).

Nitrate in water : a report of the Nitrate Coordination Group / Central Directorate of Environmental Protection, Department of the Environment. – London : H.M.S.O., 1986.
ISBN 0117518662

Nkala, Jericho
UN international law and Rhodesian industrial crisis. – Oxford : Oxford University Press, 1985.
ISBN 019825394X Hbk £30.00

—United Nations, international law, and the Rhodesian independence crisis / Jericho Nkala. – Oxford : Clarendon Press, 1985.
xii,288p.
Bibliography: p.275-283. - Includes index.

NLL review / National Lending Library for Science and Technology. – London : H.M.S.O., 1971.
Continued by: BLL review.

Nnaemeka-Agu, Philip
Manual of brief writing in the Court of Appeal and the Supreme Court of Nigeria / by Philip Nnaemeka-Agu. – Enugu, Nigeria : Fourth Dimension, 1986.
xviii,110p.
Bibliography: p. 109-110. - Includes index.

No just cause : the law of affinity in England and Wales : some suggestions for change / a report by a group appointed by the Archbishop of Canterbury. – London : CIO, 1984.
vi,151p; 21cm.
ISBN 0715136976 Pbk £5.50

No way in Wapping : the effect of the policing of the News International dispute on Wapping residents / a report by the National Council for Civil Liberties. – London : National Council for Civil Liberties, 1986.
41p.
ISBN 0946088276

Noakes, Patrick
Inheritance Tax 1988-89 / John Newth. – Belfast : Tolley Publishing.
ISBN 0854593497 Hbk £13.95

—Tolley's capital gains tax 1986-87 / Patrick Noakes and John Boulding. – 9th ed. – Croydon : Tolley Publishing, 1986.
viii,349p.
Includes index.
ISBN 0854592407

—Tolley's capital gains tax 1987-88 / Patrick Noakes and John Boulding. – 10th ed. – Croydon : Tolley, 1987.
viii,356p.
ISBN 0854592903

—Tolley's captial gains tax 1988-89 / Patrick Noakes and John Boulding. – Croydon : Tolley, 1988.
viii,376p.
Includes index.
ISBN 0854593489

→ Tolley's income tax 1986-87.

—Tolley's inheritance tax 1988-89 / by Patrick Noakes and John Newth. – Croydon : Tolley, 1988.
viii,245p.
Includes index.
ISBN 0854593497

→ Tolley's value added tax 1986-87.

→ Tolley's value added tax 1987-88.

Noam, Eli M. → Law of international telecommunications in the United States.

Nobel, Peter
Refugee Law in the Sudan. – Uppsala : Scandinavian Institute of African Studies, 1982.
56p.
ISBN 9171062092 Pbk £20.00

Nobes, C.
Interpreting US Financial Statements. – London : Butterworths.
ISBN 0406502412 Hbk £45.00

Noble, John P.
Women as Victims of Crimes. – Canberra : Australian Institute of Criminology.
free

Noble lie : the British constitution and the rule of law / Ian Harden and Norman Lewis : foreword by Sir Douglas Wass. – London : Hutchinson, 1986.
xiii,334p; 23cm.
Bibliography: p313-317. - Includes index.
ISBN 0091641306 £25.00

Noble, Nicholas → Company Reorganisations : Tax and Tax Planning.
→ Nelson-Jones: Practical Tax Saving.

Noble, Philip
Disability and compensation claims / Philip Noble, Bart Hellyer, Elizabeth Fanshawe. – London : Sweet & Maxwell, 1986.
68p; 22cm.
ISBN 042136890X Pbk £6.50

—Special damages for disability 1988 / by Philip Noble, Elizabeth Fanshawe, Bart Hellyer. – 2nd ed. – London : Sweet & Maxwell, 1988.
x,85p; 22cm.
Catalogues the expenses which a plaintiff in a personal injuries action can claim as part of his award. Each of the expenses, such as accommodation requirements and the cost of future care, are described in the context of the four disabilities of spinal injury, partial and total loss of sight, loss of a limb, and head injury. Each item is given an up-to-date value.
ISBN 0421393807 Pbk £7.50

Nobles → Accounts' Liability in the 1980's.

Nock, R. S. → Monroe and Nock The law of stamp duties.
→ Stamp Duties.

No-Fault Automobile Insurance in Canada. – Agincourt : Carswell, 1988.
250p.
Hbk £46.25

Noise Levels on Board Ships
English Edition. – International Maritime Organization. – London : International Maritime Organization, 1982.
Hbk £1.75
French Edition. –
Hbk £2.00

Nokes, Peter
Public relations and criminal justice policy / Peter Nokes. – Leeds : Centre for Social Work and Applied Social Studies, 1982.
43p. – (Occasional paper).
'Occasioned by the seminar on Alternatives to Imprisonment ... held October 1980 - October 1981 under the auspices of the Centre for Applied Social Studies'. Bibliography: p.42-43.

Nolledo, Jose N.
Revised Penal Code, Annotated. – Manila : National Book Store, 1984.
587p.
ISBN 9710812866 Pbk £6.00

—Supreme Court Decisions. – Manila : National Book Store.
Hbk

—Supreme Court Rulings. – Manila : National Book Store.
Pbk

Non Curial Privilege Against Self-Incrimination. – Clayton : Monash University Press, 1985.
ISBN 0867462841 Hbk £9.50

Non forcible counter measures in international law. – Oxford : Oxford University Press, 1988.
ISBN 019825590X Hbk

Non-appearance before the International Court Justice. – Cambridge : Cambridge University Press, 1985.
ISBN 0521265940 Hbk £27.50

Northern Territory judgments 1951-1976 : a selection of the judgments of the Supreme Court of the Northern Territory of Australia. – Canberra : Australian Government Publishing Service, 1982.
xviii,1079p.
Includes indexes which also cover Northern Territory Supreme Court judgments reported in Australian Law Reports, Australian Argus Law Reports and Federal Law Reports. Contains a selection of judgments not reported in Australian Law Reports, Australian Argus Law Reports and Federal Law Reports.
ISBN 0642050309

Northern Territory Supreme Court judgements : table of cases ... – s.l. : s.n., 1987.
Coverage begins in 1951.

Northey & Leigh's introduction to company law / L. H. Leigh, V. H. Joffe, D. Goldberg. – 4th ed. – London : Butterworths, 1987.
546p; 23cm.
Previous ed.: 1983. Includes index.
ISBN 0406631069 Hbk £27.50
ISBN 0406631077 Pbk £17.95

Northey, J. F.
Basis of judicial review in administrative law / by J.F. Northey. – Auckland : Legal Research Foundation, 1981.
31p.
Bibliography: p.30-31.
ISBN 0908581149
→ Commercial law in New Zealand.
—Index to New Zealand legal writing / J.F. Northey. – 2nd ed. – Auckland : Legal Research Foundation, 1982.
ix,260p.
Previous ed.: 1977.
ISBN 090858119X
—Introduction to company law in New Zealand / by J.F. Northey. – 9th ed. – Wellington : Butterworths, 1981.
xxxvi,452p.
Previous ed.: 1976. Includes index.
ISBN 0409600911
—Northey & Leigh's introduction to company law / L. H. Leigh, V. H. Joffe, D. Goldberg. – 4th ed. – London : Butterworths, 1987.
546p; 23cm.
Previous ed.: 1983. Includes index.
ISBN 0406631069 Hbk £27.50
ISBN 0406631077 Pbk £17.95

North-South Perspectives on Marine Policy Westview Special Studies in Ocean Science and Policy. – Westview Press.
ISBN 0813374286 Pbk

Northwest Territories Ordinances 1975-1986. – Agincourt : Carswell, 1987.
Pbk £153.25

Northwest Territories Reports. – Agincourt : Carswell, 1988.
This text is published under the authority of the Law Society of the Northwest Territories and contains in-depth coverage of cases reported in the Northwest Territories. It includes four parts per year plus a bound volume.
Hbk £82.50

Northwest Territories Revised Regulations Consolidated to 1980. – Agincourt : Carswell.
Hbk £75.75

Northwest Territories Supreme Court Reports : 1887-1898, 2 Vols. – Carswell Legal Publications. – Agincourt : Carswell, 1983.
Hbk

Norton, Alan
Government and administration of metropolitan areas in Western democracies : a survey of approaches to the administrative problems of major conurbations in Europe and Canade / Alan Norton. – Birmingham : Institute of Local Government Studies, University of Birmingham, 1983.
60 p.
ISBN 070440690X

Norton, J. J.
European Economic Community : Trade and Investment. – Matthew Bender, 1986.
ISBN 0000999064 Hbk £50.00

Norton, M
Accounting and Financial Management For Charities / Blume. – Turnaround Press, 1985.
ISBN 0907164188 Pbk £5.95
—Corporated donor's handbook. – Turnaround Press, 1987.
ISBN 0907164226 Pbk £12.50
—Covenants : A Practical Guide to the Tax Advantages of Giving. – 4th ed. – Turnaround Press.
ISBN 0907164390 Pbk
—Covenants : Practical Guide To Tax Advantages. – TUAR, 1982.
ISBN 0907164080 Pbk £3.95
—Guide to the benefits of charitable status. – TUAR, 1982.
ISBN 0907164099 Pbk £4.95
—Leaving Money to Charity. – TUAR, 1983.
ISBN 0907164129 Pbk £1.95
—Legacies - Practical Guide for Charities. – Turnaround Press, 1983.
ISBN 0907164110 Pbk £3.95
—Raising money from trusts. – TUAR, 1981.
ISBN 0907164048 Pbk £2.95

Norton, Philip
Constitution in flux / Philip Norton. – Oxford : Martin Robertson, 1982.
vii,312p; 22cm.
Bibliography: p295-300. - Includes index.
ISBN 0855205210 Hbk £
ISBN 0855205229 Pbk £8.50
→ Law and order and British politics.
→ Parliament in the 1980s.

Norway and Europe in the 1970's. – Oslo : University of Forlag.
289p.
Hbk £31.00

Norway's Security and European Foreign Policy in the 1980's. – Oslo : University of Forlag.
80p.
ISBN 8200057100 Pbk £81.00

Norwegian petroleum guide. – s.l. : Stokkand Forlag, 1984.
258p.
'... a translated edition of the Norwegian Petroleum Guide 1983 with four new articles ...' - Preface.
ISBN 8290496044

Norwegian social law / Asbjrn Kjnstad. – Oslo : Norwegian University Press, 1987.
303p; 23cm.
Presents Norwegian social law as an example of the Nordic model. Discusses social security legislation, its history and administration, financing of social security measures, disablement, and some health and welfare issues.
ISBN 8200059030 £30.00

Norwegian University Press →Continuity and development in law and society.

Norwest Holst Limited : investigation under section 165(b) of the Companies Act 1948 / report by John Davies and Thomas Garrard Harding. – London : H.M.S.O., 1981.
185p; 30cm.
At head of title: Department of Trade.
ISBN 0115134891 Pbk £12.50

Note on the law of Cyprus relating to offshore operations, shipping operations and shipping companies, foreign investments in Cyprus and transit trade / by Criton G. Tornaritis. – Nicosia : s.n., 1984.
52 leaves.

Note on the operation of the Hague Convention of 18 March 1970 on the taking of evidence abroad in civil or commercial matters / drawn up by the Permanent Bureau of the Hague Conference on Private International Law. – 1. – The Hague : The Bureau, 1985.
various pagings. – (Preliminary document).
Added title in French. English and French parallel texts.

Notes of Irish Legal Cases, 1969-1978, Vol. 3. – Cork : Cork University Press, 1982.
ISBN 0902561219 Hbk £12.50

Notes on Canadian federalism. – Ottawa : Minister of Supply and Services, 1984.
54p.
ISBN 0662130049

Notes on County Court Practice and Procedure / David Price. – 6th ed. – London : Oyez Longman, 1982.
– (Oyez Longman Practitioner Ser.).
ISBN 0851206301 Hbk £9.95

Notes on need for planning permission. – 3rd ed. – London : Longman Professional, 1984.
ISBN 0851207146 Pbk £16.95

Notes on Penal Code. – Zaria : Ahmadu Bello University Press.
Hbk £25.00

Notes on procedure by originating summons and in actions by mortgagees / by Master Hunter. – 2nd ed. – Belfast : SLS Legal Publications, 1985.
37p.
Cover title: Revised notes on procedure by originating summons and in actions by mortgagees.

Notes on the Mental Health Act 1983. – London : Shaw & Sons, 1983.
ISBN 0721902049 Pbk £1.95

Notes taken at the time. – London : Police Review, 1983.
ISBN 0851640552 Pbk £2.50

Nothing but the Truth. – 2nd ed. – London : Estates Gazette, 1975.
ISBN 0728200155 Hbk £3.50

Notices and Group Exemptions in EEC Competition Law. – Oxford : ESC Publishing Ltd.
ISBN 0906214041 Llf £45.00

Nott
Environmental planning and development law (NSW) / by A.J. Nott. – Sydney : Penman, 1982.
xlix,417p.
Includes index.
ISBN 0959431608

Nott, Susan →Development Control.

Nottridge →Police powers and duties.

Nova Scotia
Report to the House of Assembly of the Select Committee on Workers' Compensation. – Nova Scotia. – Halifax : Queen's Printer, 1981.
65p.
Includes bibliographical references.

Nova Scotia Annotated Rules of Practice. – Agincourt : Carswell.
This single volume looseleaf is arranged in eight sections and is published in cooperation with the Law Foundation of Nova Scotia. It consists of a Table of Contents, Judicature Act, Rules of Practice, Forms, Practice Memoranda, Index to Rules, and Index to Forms.
Pbk £71.50

Nova Scotia Annual Bound Statutes : 1967-1987. – Agincourt : Carswell.
Hbk £557.70

Nova Scotia civil procedure rules and related rules / made by the Judges of the Supreme Court of Nova Scotia on 2nd December 1971. To come into force on 1st March 1972. – 1. – Halifax, Nova Scotia : Queen's Printer, 1971.
looseleaf.
Includes index.

Nova Scotia Community Legal Needs Survey. – Ottawa : Canadian Law Information Council, 1984.
32p.
ISBN 0920358586 Pbk £7.50

Nova Scotia Real Property Practice Manual. – London : Butterworths.
ISBN 0409855103 Hbk £100.00

Nova Scotia Reports : 1834-1930, 60 Vols. – Carswell Legal Publications. – Agincourt : Carswell, 1983.
Hbk £1008.00

Nova Scotia Statute Citator. – Agincourt : Carswell, 1985.
610p.
This work focuses on the Revised Statutes of Nova Scotia 1967. It contains the amendments, repeals and consolidation of all public statutes of Nova Scotia since 1967. The statutes are annotated. Brief digests of the interpreting caselaw are included.
Pbk £80.00

Novgorod Kabala Books of 1614-1616. – Stockholm : Almqvist & Wiksell, 1982.
x, 200p.
ISBN 9122005528 Hbk £84.00

Novitt, John J. →Marine insurance, Vol.2 : Cargo practice : incorporating Marine cargo claims by John J. Novitt.

Nowlan, Kevin Ingram
Guide to planning legislation in the Republic of Ireland / by Kevin Ingram Nowlan. – Dublin : Incorporated Law Society of Ireland, 1988.
xxiii,375p; 26cm.
Includes index.
ISBN 0902027301

Noy, W.
Treatise of the Principle Grounds and Maximes of the Lawes of This Kingdome by W.N. A Dialogue and Treatise of the Laws of England and on Tenures, Estates, Heriditaments and Chattels / W. N. Bythewood. – 9th ed. Repr. of 1821 ed. – Abingdon : Professional Books.
243p.
ISBN 0862053269 Hbk £35.25

Noyce, John
Legal and Commercial Looseleaf Services Available in Australia and New Zealand. – Melbourne : , 1987.
Loose £99.00

Nozick, Robert S.
Annotated Competition Act / commentary prepared by Robert S. Nozick : annotations and index prepared by Charlotte Neff. – Toronto : Carswell, 1987.
xviii,290p.
ISBN 0459396609

Nuclear arms control : with effective international agreements / Julie Dahlitz : foreword by Rikhi Jaipal. – London : Allen & Unwin, 1983.
238p; 24cm.
Bibliography: p217-232. - Includes index.
ISBN 0043410235 Hbk £15.00
ISBN 0043410243 Pbk £4.95

Nuclear deterrence, morality and realism / John Finnis, Joseph M. Boyle, Jr., Germain Grisez. – Oxford : Clarendon, 1987.
xv,429p; 22cm.
Bibliography: p391-411. - Includes index.
ISBN 0198247923 Hbk £30.00
ISBN 0198247915 Pbk no price

Nuclear Law Bulletin. – Organisation for Economic Co-operation and Development. – London : HMSO.
Hbk £9.00

Nuclear Legislation. Analytical Study : Regulatory and Institutional Framework for Nuclear Activities. – Paris : OECD, Organisation for Economic Co-operation and Development.
Hbk
Vol. 1: Austria, Belgium, Canada, Denmark, France, Federal Republic of Germany, Greece, Iceland, Ireland, Italy, Japan, Luxembourg, the Netherlands. – 1983.
220p.
ISBN 9264125345 £25.00
Vol. 2: New Zealand, Norway, Portugal, Spain, Sweden, Switzerland, Turkey, United Kingdom, United States, International Conventions. – 1984.
228p.
ISBN 9264126023 £30.00

Nuclear non-proliferation and global security / edited by David B. Dewitt. – London : Croom Helm, 1987.
x,283p; 23cm.
Conference proceedings. Includes index.
ISBN 0709908962 £25.00

Nuclear war, nuclear proliferation and their consequences : proceedings of the Vth international colloquium organized by the Groupe de Bellerive, Geneva 27-29 June 1985 / edited by Sadruddin Aga Khan. – Oxford : Clarendon, 1986.
xii,483p; 25cm.
Includes index.
ISBN 0198255438 Hbk £25.00
ISBN 019825542X Pbk £12.50

Nuclear Weapons and Contemporary International Law / Edward McWhinney. – 2nd ed. – Martinus Nijhoff.
ISBN 9024736374 Hbk £86.50

Nuclear weapons, the peace movement and the law / edited by John Dewar ... et al. – Basingstoke : Macmillan, 1986.
xix,255p; 22cm.
Bibliography: p241-251. - Includes index.
ISBN 0333414101 Hbk £27.50
ISBN 033341411X Pbk £9.95

Nuffield Foundation →Town and country planning.

Nuffield, Joan
Parole decision-making in Canada : research towards decision guidelines / by Joan Nuffield. – Ottawa, Ont. : Communication Division, Solicitor General of Canada, 1982.
iv, 96 p.; 28 cm.
Bibliography: p. 91-96.
ISBN 0662121147 Pbk

Nugee, E. G. →Report of the Committee of Inquiry on the Management of Privately Owned Blocks of Flats.

Nuisance. – London : Longman Professional, 1982. – (Practice Notes Series. No. 71).
ISBN 0851206247 Pbk £14.95

Nurcombe, V.J.
Directory of Specialists in Official Publications. – 2nd ed. – Scoop Publications, 1988.
ISBN 0951201115 Pbk £6.00

Nuremberg and after : the continuing history of war crimes and crimes against humanity / by Geoffrey Best. – Reading : University of Reading, 1984.
29p.
ISBN 0704902141

Nurse's Legal Advisor Your Guide to Legally Safe Practice. – London ; Lippincott.
ISBN 0397547005 Pbk £6.95

Nurses, Midwives and Health Visitors Act 1979. – Welsh National Board for Nursing. – London : HMSO, 1983.
Hbk £2.20

Nursing law and ethics / edited by A. Carmi and S. Schneider : by M.B. Agostino ... et al. – Berlin : Springer-Verlag, 1985.
ISBN 0387152539

Nussbaum, Helga →Multinational enterprise in historical perspective.

Nuttal, T.
Role of local authorities in promoting the creation or operation of small or medium-sized firms within a general policy of endogenous development / report prepared under the guidance of the Committee of Experts on Social and Economic Activities of the Steering Committee for Regional and Municipal Matters by T. Nuttal. – Strasbourg : Council of Europe, 1986.
31p.
Bibliography: p.28-29.

Nuttall →Employee ownership.
→ Tax and interest tables.

Nwabueze, B. O.
Constitutional history of Nigeria / by B.O. Nwabueze. – London : C. Hurst, 1982.
xiii,272p; 23cm.
Includes index.
ISBN 0905838793 Hbk £12.50
—Constitutionalism in Emergent States. – London : Dent (J M) & Sons, 1973.
ISBN 0905838017 Pbk £7.50
—Federalism in Nigeria under the presidential constitution / by B.O. Nwabueze. – London : Sweet & Maxwell, 1983.
400p.
Includes index.
ISBN 0421316101 Hbk £
ISBN 0421315806 Pbk £16.00
—Judicialism in Commonwealth Africa. – London : Dent (J M) & Sons, 1977.
ISBN 0903983567 Hbk £15.00
—Nigeria's presidential constitution : the second experiment in constitution democracy / Ben O. Nwabueze. – London : Longman, 1985.
xiv,488p; 21cm.
ISBN 0582644836 Hbk £15.00
ISBN 0582644747 Pbk £7.50
—Presidential Constitution of Nigeria. – London : Dent (J M) & Sons, 1982.
ISBN 0905838602 Hbk £25.00
—Presidentialism in Commonwealth Africa. – London : Dent (J M) & Sons, 1974.
ISBN 090583805X Hbk £15.00

Nwadialo, Fidelis
Modern Nigerian law of evidence / by Fidelis Nwadialo. – Benin City : Ethiope Publishing, 1981.
xlix,306p.
Includes bibliographical references and index.
ISBN 9781231068

Nwamara, Timothy A.
Nigerian Current Law Statutes Annotated 1958-1983. – Aba : Law & Educational Publishers.
ISBN 9782436011 Hbk
—Nigerian Law Reports, Index-Digest 1881-1981, 2 Vols. – Aba : Law & Educational Publishers, 1984.
Hbk
—Nigerian Supreme Court Law Reports 1956-1983 : Lawyers Edition 1956-1983, 16 Vols. – Aba : Law & Educational Publishers.
ISBN 9782436046 Hbk

Nwogugu, E. I.
Quarter century of legal education in Nigeria : an appraisal / by E.I. Nwogugu. – Lagos : Nigerian Institute of Advanced Legal Studies, 1985.
28p. – (Occasional poaper).
Includes bibliographical references.

Nyberg, Cheryl
Subject compilations of state laws 1979-1983 : research guide and annotated bibliography / Cheryl Nyberg and Carol Boast. – Westport : Greenwood, 1984.
x,556p; 24cm.
Includes index.
ISBN 0313233357

Nye, David →Justice and predictability.

Nygh, J.
Conflict of Laws in Australia. – 4th ed. – Butterworths, 1984.
608p.
ISBN 0409491926 Hbk £79.00
ISBN 0409492027 Pbk £59.00

Nygh, P.
Guide to the Family Law Act. – 4th ed. – Sydney : Butterworths, 1986.
240p.
The fifth edition of this work has been revised to reflect the changes to the Act that have occurred since 1982. It discusses jurisdictional grounds for dissolution and settlement, proceedings relating to children, ancillary property proceedings, preparation for hearings, and other topics.
ISBN 0409491055 Hbk £45.00
ISBN 0409491063 Pbk £32.00

O. Hood Phillips' Constitutional and administrative law / Paul Jackson. – 7th ed. – London : Sweet & Maxwell, 1987.
lxxvi,808p; 26cm.
Previous ed.: 1978. Includes index.
ISBN 042135030X Hbk £21.00
ISBN 0421350407 Pbk £16.00

'O' level law / Paulene Collins. – Plymouth : Macdonald & Evans, 1984.
ISBN 0712115420 Pbk £4.75

'O' level law / Collins. – London : Pitman Publishing, 1984.
ISBN 0273025538 Pbk £4.95

Oakey, M.H.
Journey from the Gallows : Historical Evolution of the Penal Philosophies and Practices. – London : Eurospan.
ISBN 0819167231 Hbk £24.75

Oakley, A. J.
Constructive trusts / by A.J. Oakley. – 2nd ed. – London : Sweet & Maxwell, 1987.
200p; 22cm.
Previous ed.: 1978. Includes index.
ISBN 0421347406 Hbk £11.00 :
ISBN 0421347503 Pbk £7.85

Oakley, Francis
Natural Law, Conciliarism and Consent in the Middle Ages. – Northampton : Variorum, 1984.
350p. – (Collected Studies Ser.: No. 189).
ISBN 0860781372 Hbk £26.00

Oates, Kim →Child abuse : a community concern.
—Child abuse: a community concern. – North Ryde : Butterworths (Australia).
Gives an overview of the problem of child abuse with particular emphasis on the needs and future development of the battered child. Discusses the various types of children and families who suffer from abuse, considers the emotional stresses that face the professional working with child abuse, and describes research studies which have practical implications for predicting and preventing child abuse.
ISBN 0409303305 Hbk

Oaths Act / Shanglo. – 2nd ed. – Allahabad : Law Book Company, 1988.
60p.
Pbk £40.00

O'Barr, William M.
Linguistic evidence : language, power, and strategy in the courtroom / William M. O'Barr. – New York : Academic Press, 1982.
xv,192p; 24cm.
Bibliography: p182-187. - Includes index.
ISBN 0125235208 £15.60

Obasanjo, Olusegun →Mission to South Africa : the Commonwealth report.

Oberlander, H. Peter
Land, the central human settlement issue / H. Peter Oberlander. – Vancouver : University of British Columbia Press, 1985.
x, 103 p., 4 p. of plates; 24 cm.
Bibliography: p. 93-101.
ISBN 0774802359

Obi, N. O.
Law Library manual / by N.O. Obi. – Lagos : Law Library, Federal Ministry of Justice, 1984.
23p.
Includes a list of commonly used author and title abbreviations.

Obi-Okoye, A.
Development and Judicial Trial in Nigeria. – Onitsha : Africana-FEP.
Hbk
—Essays on Civil Proceedings, 4 Vols. – Enugu : Fourth Dimension Publishing, 1981.
ISBN 9781561637 Hbk

Objective Type Questions and Answers in Mercantile Law. – New Delhi : Kalyani Publishers.
Hbk £12.00

Objective Type Questions in Banking Law and Practice. – 6th rev. ed. – New Delhi : Sultan Chand and Sons, 1985.
iv, 124p.
Hbk £10.00

Obligations : report on civil liability in relation to animals / Scottish Law Commission. – Edinburgh : The Commission, 1985.
vi,72p.
Includes bibliographical references. Includes Draft Animals (Scotland) Bill.
ISBN 0102004862

Obligations : report on negligent misrepresentation / Scottish Law Commission. – Edinburgh : H.M.S.O., 1985.
v,13p.
Includes bibliographical references.
ISBN 0102143854

Obligations : report on rectification of contractual and other documents / Scottish Law Commission. – Edinburgh : H.M.S.O., 1983.
vi,35p.
Includes bibliographical references. Includes Draft Rectification of Documents (Scotland) Bill.
ISBN 0102036845

O'Brien, Arthur Henry
O'Briens encyclopedia of forms / Editor-in-chief: John D. Honsberger. – 11th ed. – Aurora, Ont. : Canada Law Book Inc., 1987.
looseleaf.
First edition by A.H. O'Brien entitled: The new conveyancer. Title of subsequent editions varies.
ISBN 088804044X Hbk

O'Brien, D. P.
Competition policy in Britain : the silent revolution / D.P. O'Brien. – Durham : Department of Economics, University of Durham, 1981.
20 leaves. – (Working paper).
Includes bibliographical references.

O'Brien, M.J.
Managing Your Personal Taxes. – Ward Lock.
ISBN 0706366700 Pbk £4.99

O'Brien, M. L., et al
Canadian Tax Treaties, 2 vols. – Toronto : Butterworths.
Hbk

O'Brien Quinn, J. A. →Gilbert Islands law reports.

O'Brien, Tim →Papers from the European Conference on Football Violence : held at the Tickled Trout Hotel, Salmesbury, Preston, Lancashire, 10-13 April 1987.

O'Briens encyclopedia of forms / Editor-in-chief: John D. Honsberger. – 11th ed. – Aurora, Ont. : Canada Law Book Inc., 1987.
looseleaf.
First edition by A.H. O'Brien entitled: The new conveyancer. Title of subsequent editions varies.
ISBN 088804044X Hbk

O'Brien's Encyclopedia of Forms : 1893-Present, 9 Vols.
Vols. 1-9. – Aurora : Canada Law Book Co. – (Divisions 1-5 Covering All Ser.).
Hbk £451.50
Binder. –
£18.00

O'Brien's Encyclopedia of Forms : Division Five-Wills and Trusts
Vol. 9. – Aurora : Canada Law Book Co. – (Abridgments and Encyclopedias).
Hbk £45.00
Supplement. –
Hbk £8.00

O'Brien's Encyclopedia of Forms : Division Four-Leases
Vol. 8. – Aurora : Canada Law Book Co. – (Abridgments and Encyclopedias).
Hbk £55.00

O'Brien's Encyclopedia of Forms : Division One-Commercial & General
Vols. 1-3. – Aurora : Canada Law Book Co. – (Abridgments and Encyclopedias).
Hbk £150.00
Supplement-1983. –
Hbk £39.50

O'Brien's Encyclopedia of Forms : Division Three-Conveyancing and Mortgages
Vol. 7. – Aurora : Canada Law Book Co. – (Abridgments and Encyclopedias).
Hbk £45.00
Supplement. –
Hbk £4.00

O'Brien's Encyclopedia of Forms : Division Two-Corporations
Vols. 4-6. – Aurora : Canada Law Book Co. – (Abridgments and Encyclopedias).
Hbk £150.00

Observance of human rights at the Villawood Immigration Detention Centre / Human Rights Commission. – Canberra : Government Publishing Service, 1983.
viii,37p. – (Report).
ISBN 0644027193 Pbk £2.30

Observations on the Acts of Parliament. – Repr. of 1686 ed. – Abingdon : Professional Books.
74p.
Hbk £95.00

Observations on the Criminal Justice Bill / the Justices' Clerks' Society. – Bristol b The Society, 1982.
21 leaves.

Observations on the Mental Health (Amendment) Bill / the Justices' Clerks' Society. – Bristol : The Society, 1982.
8p.

Observations on the Police and Criminal Evidence Bill / the Justices' Clerks' Society. – Bristol : The Society, 1983.
34p.

Obtaining reasons before applying for judicial scrutiny : Immigration Appeal Board / Law Reform Commission of Canada. – Ottawa : Law Reform Commission of Canada, 1982.
21,25p; 25cm. – (Report).
English and French text, in reverse.
ISBN 0662521064

Occupational Health and Safety Committees Manual. – North Ryde : C.C.H. Australia, 1987.
60p.
ISBN 086903460X Hbk

Occupational pension rights on divorce : a consultation paper / Lord Chancellor's Department. – London : The Department, 1985.
30p.
Includes bibliographical references.

Occupational Regulation and the Public Interest. – Turramura : Centre for Independent Studies.
ISBN 0949769134 Hbk £8.95

Occupational safety : an inquiry into the coordination of legislation on industrial safety, health, and welfare / by I.K. Walker. – Wellington, N.Z. : State Services Commission, 1981.
vi, 142 p.; 30 cm.
Bibliography: p. 140-142.
ISBN 0477015085 Pbk

Occupational safety and health : guide to regulations. – Ottawa : Minister of Supply and Services, 1984.
14,14p.
With French t.-p: Securite et hygiene au travail: guide des reglements. English and French text.
ISBN 0662529553

Occupiers' liability / The Law Reform Commission. – Sydney : The Commission, 1987.
13p. – (Discussion paper).
Bibliography: p.13.

Occupiers' liability / Law Reform Commission of Tasmania. – Hobart : Government Printer, 1988.
6p. – (Report).

Occupiers' liability / Law Reform Commission. – Canberra : Australian Government Publishing Service, 1988.
xi,54p. – (Report).
Bibliography: pp. 53-54. Includes draft legislation.
ISBN 0644068965

Occupiers' liability and access to the countryside / memorandum by the Council's Law Reform Committee. – London : Law Society, 1982.
7p.

Occupiers' Liability in Canada. – Agincourt : Carswell, 1981.
328p.
The book analyzes the common law rules of occupiers liability and comments on legislation in Ontario, Alberta and British Columbia.
Hbk £54.75

Occupiers' Liability in Singapore and Malaysia. – Butterworths, 1986.
320p.
Covers the duty of reasonable care arising in particular circumstances, out of a special status, and out of current operations or activities, classes of entrant, duty to invitees, to licensees and to trespassers, defences, public and private premises, multiple defendants, and duties towards children.
ISBN 0409995134 Hbk £90.00

Occupiers' rights and constructive notice : the text of a lecture delivered to the Belfast Solicitors' Association on 2 December 1982 / by Hebert Wallace. – Belfast : SLS Legal Publications, 1982.
35p.
Includes bibliographical references.

Ocean and Coastal Law / Johnson. – Prentice-Hall, 1983.
ISBN 0136292046 Hbk £35.05

Ocean Boundary Making / Saunders. – Oxford : Croom Helm, 1988.
ISBN 0709914954 Hbk £35.00

Ocean management : a regional perspective : the prospects for Commonwealth maritime co-operation in Asia and the Pacific / report by a Commonwealth Group of Experts. – London : Commonwealth Secretariat, 1984.
Chairman: Satya N. Nandan.
ISBN 0850922615

Ockelton, Mark
Trusts for accountants. – London : Butterworths, 1987.
ISBN 0406500908 Pbk £10.95

O'Connell, D. P. →International law of the sea, Vol.1 : by D.P. O'Connell : edited by I.A. Shearer.

O'Connor
Irish Justice Pease. – London : Butterworths.
ISBN 0862053463 Hbk £52.75

O'Connor, D O
Criminal Defences / P.A. Fairall. – 2nd ed. – Butterworths, 1988.
288p.
ISBN 0409492760 Hbk £49.00

O'Connor, Paul
Key Issues in Irish Family Law. – Dublin : Round Hall Press, 1988.
ca 192p.
ISBN 0947686312 Hbk £22.50

O'Connor, Paul A
Key Issues in Irish Family Law. – Round Hall Press.
ISBN 0947686312 Pbk £22.50

O'Connor, R.
Irish Notary. – London : Butterworths, 1987.
ISBN 0862052386 Hbk £35.00

Oda, Hiroshi →Japanese banking, securities and anti-monopoly law.
—Modern Japanese Law. – London : Butterworths, 1988.
ISBN 040666921X Hbk

Oda, Shigeru
International Law of Ocean Development, 2 Vols.
Vol. 1. – Leiden : Sijthoff, 1975-1982.
Bibliography: 1, p.515-519; 2, 629-631.
ISBN 9028601228 Llf £10.00
—International law of the ocean development : basic documents / by Shigeru Oda. – 2nd ed. 2. – Leiden : Sijthoff, 1977.
looseleaf.

→ Practice of Japan in international law, 1961-1970.

Odeh, Rosaline →Who is who in the judiciary.

Odell, Peter R.
Oil and world power / Peter R. Odell. – 7th ed. – Harmondsworth : Penguin, 1983.
287p; 20cm.
Previous ed.: 1981. Includes index.
ISBN 0140222847 Pbk £2.95

Odgers' principles of pleading and practice in civil actions in the High Court of Justice / D. B. Casson, I. H. Dennis. – 22nd ed. – London : Stevens, 1981.
lix,565p; 22cm.
Previous ed.: 1975. Includes index.
ISBN 0420457100 Pbk £13.50

Odgers, William Blake
Odgers' principles of pleading and practice in civil actions in the High Court of Justice / D. B. Casson, I. H. Dennis. – 22nd ed. – London : Stevens, 1981.
lix,565p; 22cm.
Previous ed.: 1975. Includes index.
ISBN 0420457100 Pbk £13.50

Odi, Hiroshi
Modern Japanese Law. – London : Butterworths, 1987.
ISBN 040666921X Hbk

O'Donnell, G.C.
Short Note on Anti-Copyright. – Wollstone Craft : Leksand Press.
82p.
ISBN 095897800X Hbk £8.00

O'Donovan, James
Company receivers and managers / by James O'Donovan. – Sydney : Law Book Copany, 1981.
lxxxiii,545p.
Includes index.
ISBN 0455200823
—Modern contract of guarantee / by James O'Donovan and John C. Phillips. – Sydney : Law Book Company, 1985.
xcv,675p.
ISBN 0455203490
—Winding up and receivership under the Companies Act 1981 / by James O'Donovan. – Sydney : Law Book Co., 1982.
xix,48p.
ISBN 0455204438

O'Donovan, Joan E.
George Grant and the Twilight of Justice. – Toronto : University of Toronto Press, 1984.
208p.
ISBN 0802056377 Hbk £30.00
ISBN 0802065384 Pbk £12.50

O'Donovan, Katherine
Equality and sex discrimination law / Katherine O'Donovan and Erika Szyszczak. – Oxford : Blackwell, 1988.
xiv,254p.
Includes bibliographical references and index.
ISBN 0631147713 Hbk £29.50
ISBN 0631155988 Pbk £10.95
—Sexual divisions in law / Katherine O'Donovan. – London : Weidenfeld and Nicolson, 1985.
xii,242p; 23cm.
Bibliography: p226-233. - Includes index.
ISBN 0297786644 Hbk £16.95
ISBN 0297786652 Pbk £8.95

Odour Nuisances and Their Control. – London : Shaw & Sons, 1984.
ISBN 0721910009 Pbk £9.00

O'Dowd, Anthony →Encyclopedia of insurance law.

Oduba, F A
Nigeria Index to Federal Statutes in Force 1984. – Abingdon : Professional Books, 1985.
ISBN 0862050731 Hbk £19.25
ISBN 0862052009 Pbk £11.00
—Nigeria-Federal Statutes in Force 1982 : An Index of the Laws of Nigeria Which Are Still in Force As At the 31st December 1984. – Abingdon : Professional Books, 1984.
ISBN 0862050731 Hbk £24.00

OECD guidelines for multinational enterprises and labour relations, 1982-1984 : experience and review / by R. Blanpain : foreword by M. Eyskens. – Deventer : Kluwer Law and Taxation Publishers, 1985.
Includes index.
ISBN 9065442073

OECD Nuclear Energy Agency →Chernobyl and the safety of nuclear reactors in OECD countries : report.

Oellers-Frahm, Karin
Dispute settlement in public international law : texts and materials / compiled by Karin Oellers-Frahm und Norbert Wuhler. – Berlin : Springer Verlag, 1984.
At head of title: Max-Planck-Institut fur Auslandisches Offentliches Recht und Volkerrecht. English and German text. Includes index. Bibliography: p.
ISBN 0387131906

Oerton, R. T.
Lament for the Law Commission / R.T. Oerton. – Chichester : Countrywise Press, 1987.
v,117p.

Of manners gentle : enforcement strategies of Australian business regulatory agencies / Peter Grabosky, John Braithwaite. – Melbourne : Oxford University Press, 1986.
viii,260p.
Includes index.
ISBN 0195546911

Of order and disorder : the relevance of international law : an inaugural lecture delivered at the University of Lagos on Wednesday, 15th February, 1984 / by M.A. Ajomo. – Lagos : Lagos University Press, 1984.
35p. – (Inaugural lecture series).
Includes bibliographical references.
ISBN 9782264490

Offence to others. – Oxford : Oxford University Press, 1985.
ISBN 019503449X Hbk £25.00

Offences against public order / the Law Commission. – London : H.M.S.O., 1982.
viii,194p. – (Working paper).
ISBN 0117301620

Offences against public order : including the Public Order Act 1986 / by A.T.H. Smith. – London : Sweet and Maxwell, 1987.
xlvii,326p; 25cm.
Analysis of the Public Order Act 1986, explaining provisions and their practical applications. Also deals with features of existing law not affected by the act, such as obstructing the highway, obstructing a police officer in the execution of his duty, and the possession of offensive weapons.
ISBN 0421365803 Pbk £10.00

Offences against religion and public worship / the Law Commission. – London : H.M.S.O., 1981.
vi,166p; 21cm. – (Working paper).
ISBN 0117301590 Pbk £5.70

Offences committed under the influence of liquor or drugs / South African Law Commission. – Pretoria : The Commission, 1986.
vii,132p. – (Report).
Bibliography: p.123-132.
ISBN 0621102075

Offences committed under the influence of liquor or drugs / South African Law Commission. – Pretoria : The Commission, 1984.
vi,118 leaves. – (Project).
Bibliography: p.113-118.

Offences Relating to Motor Vehicles, England and Wales 1980 : Supplementary Tables. – London : Home Office, 1981.
ISBN 0862520231 Pbk £4.00

Offences Under the Penal Code of Ceylon. – Colombo : Lake House Investments.
Pbk £10.00

Offenders suffering from psychopathic disorder / joint DHSS-Home Office consultation document. – London : Department of Health and Social Security, 1986.
13p.

Offensive literature : decensorship in Britain, 1960-1982 / John Sutherland. – London : Junction Books, 1982.
207p; 22cm.
ISBN 0862450640

Offer, Avner
Property and politics 1870-1914 : landownership, law, ideology and urban development in England / Avner Offer. – Cambridge : Cambridge University Press, 1981.
xviii,445p; 24cm.
Bibliography: p407-428. - Includes index.
ISBN 0521224144 £27.50

Office and Duty of Executors : Treatise of Wills and Executors Directed to Testators in the Choice of Their Executors and Contrivance of Their Wills. – Repr. of 1774 ed. – Abingdon : Professional Books.
494p.
Hbk £40.00

Office Auccthoritie. – 2nd ed. – Professional Books, 1986 Reprint.
ISBN 086205317X Hbk £30.00

Office of Fair Trading
British Airports Authority : arrangements for the provision of chauffer-driven hire car services at Gatwick Airport : a report / by the Director General of Fair Trading. – London : H.M.S.O., 1984.
50p; 30cm.

—Scottish and Universal Newspapers Limited : a report by the Director General of Fair Trading on an investigation under section 3 of the Competition Act, 1980 / Office of Fair Trading. – London : H.M.S.O., 1983.
45p; 30cm.

—World's Fair Limited and Marcus Publishing PLC : refusal to publish advertisements which contain certain price information : a report by the Director General of Fair Trading on two investigations under section 3 of the Competition Act 1980 / Office of Fair Trading. – London : Office of Fair Trading, 1987.
30p.

Office of sheriff / by Gordon Turriff and Elizabeth Edinger. – Victoria : Queen's Printer, 1983.
246p.
'A study prepared for the Law Reform Commission of British Columbia with financial assistance from the Law Foundation of British Columbia' - title page.
ISBN 0771883927

Office of Speaker in the Parliaments of the Commonwealth / Philip Laundy. – London : Quiller Press, 1984.
xiii,274p.
Bibliography: p261-269.
ISBN 0907621317

Office of the Legislative Assembly (Ontario)
Education Act : Elementary and Secondary Schools and Schools for Trainable Retarded Pupils. – Office of the Legislative Assembly (Ontario). – Ontario : Ontario Government Publications Service, 1983.
15p.
Hbk £0.75

—Education Act : Supervised Alternative Learning for Excused Pupils. – Office of the Legislative Assembly (Ontario). – Ontario : Ontario Government Publications Service, 1983.
3p.
Hbk £0.50

—Education Act : Supervisory Officers. – Office of the Legislative Assembly (Ontario). – Ontario : Ontario Government Publications Service, 1983.
6p.
Hbk £0.50

—Game and Fish Act : Revised Statutes of Ontario, 1980. – Office of the Legislative Assembly (Ontario). – Ontario : Ontario Government Publications Service, 1983.
38p.
Hbk £1.75

—Labour Relations Act : Rules of Procedure, Regulations and Practice Notes. – Office of the Legislative Assembly (Ontario). – Ontario : Ontario Government Publications Service, 1983.
177p.
Hbk £4.50

—Ontario Water Resources Act : Revised Regulations of Ontario, 1980. – Office of the Legislative Assembly (Ontario). – Ontario : Ontario Government Publications Service, 1983.
199p.
Pbk £4.50

—Provincial Land Tax Act : Revised Statutes of Ontario, 1980. – Office of the Legislative Assembly (Ontario). – Ontario : Ontario Government Publications Service, 1983.
42p.
Hbk £2.00

Officer's Companion (in Administration and Law). – 3rd ed. – Lucknow : Eastern Book Company, 1985.
Hbk

Official Catchword Index to the Fourth Edition (1984) of the International Patent Classification. – World Intellectual Property Organization. – Cologne : Carl Heymanns Verlag.
335p.
ISBN 3452200299 Pbk £125.00

Official Chinese Customs Guide 1985/86. – London : Longman Professional, 1985.
ISBN 08512010848 Hbk £35.00

Official Handbook of the European Parliament-1984. – Kirchberg : Commission of the European Communities, 1985.
333p.
Hbk

Official Information Bill / by Ian Eagles. – Auckland : Legal Research Foundation Inc., 1982.
31p.
'Paper presented at Auckland Law Faculty Seminar Series 1982 at University of Auckland'.

Official Journal of the European Communities. – London : HMSO.
– (Ser. L: Legislation, Ser. C: Information and Notices, and Series S: Supplement).
Hbk £121.25
Ser. S: Supplement. –
Hbk £54.25

Official journal of the European Patent Office / Amtsblatt des Europaischen Patentamts. – Munchen : European Patent Office, 1981-.

Official publications in Britain / David Butcher. – London : Bingley, 1983.
161p; 23cm.
Includes index.
ISBN 0851573517

Official publications of Western Europe
Vol.1 : Denmark, Finland, France, Ireland, Italy, Luxembourg, Netherlands, Spain and Turkey : edited by Eve Johansson / Eve Johansson. – London : Mansell, 1984.
xvi,313p; 24cm.
Includes bibliographies and index.
ISBN 0720116236 £28.00
Vol.2 : Austria, Belgium, Federal Republic of Germany, Greece, Norway, Portugal, Sweden, Switzerland and United Kingdom / edited by Eve Johansson. – 1988.
x,278p.
Includes bibliographies and index.
ISBN 0720116627 Hbk £38.50

Official record of debates of the Australian Constitutional Convention at Parliament House, Adelaide, 26 to 29 April 1983. – Adelaide : Government Printer, 1983.
299p.
Includes index. Cover title: Proceedings of the Australian Constitutional Convention.

Official records of the International Conference on the Limitation of Liability for Maritime Claims, 1976. – London : International Maritime Organization, 1983.
vii,527p.
ISBN 9280111566

Official referees' business / by Edgar Fay : Foreword by Sir John Stephenson. – 2nd ed. – London : Sweet & Maxwell, 1988.
xviii,170p; 25cm.
Looks at the developments in the Official Referees' Courts since 1983. Chapters cover the trying of cases outside London, the use of expert witnesses, and Scott Schedules. Contains a new chapter on the position of the Users' Committee, and how to make use of it, and one on construction litigation procedures.
ISBN 0421396903 £29.00

Official Referees' Users' Committee
Report of the Official Referees' Users' Committee ... – Official Referees' Users' Committee. – London : The Committee, 1983.
1st report covers 1983 to 1986.

Official Secrets : the Use and Abuse of the Act. – New edition. – Oxford : Coronet Books.
ISBN 0340426500 Pbk £3.95

Official Secrets Act, 1972 (Act 88). – Kuala Lumpur : International Law Books Services.
Hbk £4.00

Official Tax Forms Manual. – 2nd ed. – London : Oyez Longman, 1982.
ISBN 0851206433 Hbk £12.50
Third edition. –
ISBN 0851207537 Hbk

Officium Clerici Pacis : A Book of Indictments, Information, Appeals, and Inquisitions. – 3rd ed. Repr. of 1726 ed. – Abingdon : Professional Books.
232p.
Hbk £65.00

Officium Vicecomitum (1623). – Reprint. – Abingdon : Professional Books, 1986.
ISBN 0862053455 Hbk £35.00

Offner, Jerome A.
Law and politics in Aztec Texcoco. – Cambridge : Cambridge University Press, 1984.
354.
Analyses the Aztec legal system. Discusses land tenure, inheritance, kinship relations, business trade and local and imperial administration.
ISBN 0521234751 Hbk £35.00

Off-Road Vehicles Act, 1983, Bill 061 : An Act to Regulate Off-Road Vehicles. – Ontario : Ontario Government Publications Service, 1983.
11p.
Hbk £0.50

Offshore Banking Committee
Report of the Committee established by the Premier of New South Wales to report on the steps necessary to establish offshore banking activity in Australia with particular reference to Sydney. – Offshore Banking Committee. – Sydney : The Committee, 1984.
28p.

Offshore Survival. – London : Deloitte Haskins & Sells.
– (Trouble with the Taxman Series).
ISBN 0863491324 Pbk £9.95

Offshore tax planning / Vlarke. – London : Butterworths, 1986.
ISBN 0406502102 Hbk £32.00

Ofori-Amankwah, E. H.
Criminal law in the northern states of Nigeria / by E.H. Ofori-Amankwah. – Zaria, Nigeria : Gaskiya Coroporation, 1986.
xix,505p.
Includes bibliographical references.
ISBN 9781940808

Ogbobine, R. A. I.
Oshimili and Aniocha : their people and land tenure / by R.A.I. Ogbobine. – S.l. : s.n., 1981.
viii,192p.

Ogilvie-Harris →Personal Injury : a Medico-Legal Guide to the Spine and Limbs.

Ogilvie, Margaret H
Banking : the Law in Canada. – Agincourt : Carswell, 1985.
This book describes the corporate structure of banks in Canada including the role of directors and officers and the rights of shareholders. The Bank Act and the Bills of Exchange Act are set out in the appendices to the work.
ISBN 045937290 Pbk £30.80

—Historical Introduction to Legal Studies. – Agincourt : Carswell, 1982.
411p.
This textbook for Canadian law students examines the historical development of the Canadian Constitution and the legal institution of Canada from their Anglo-Saxon origins to the present.
Hbk £40.50

Ogley, Roderick
Internationalizing the seabed / Roderick Ogley. – Aldershot : Gower, 1984.
vii,256,9p; 23cm.
Bibliography: p248-256. - Includes index.
ISBN 0566006294 £17.95

Ogobobine, R. A. I.
Outline of customary court procedure Part 1 / by R.A.I. Ogbobine. – Benin City, Nigeria : Ruf-Bine, 1985.
vi,46p.
ISBN 9783004514

Ogus, A. I. →Law of social security.
→ Policing pollution : a study of regulation and enforcement.
—Readings in economics of law and regulation / Cento G Veljanovski. – Oxford : Oxford University Press, 1984.
ISBN 0198761430 Pbk £12.95
→ Readings in the economics of law and regulation.

O'Hagan, Timothy
End of Law? / Timothy O'Hagan. – Oxford : Blackwell, 1985.
vii,183p; 23cm.
ISBN 0631145354 Pbk £7.50

O'Hair, J. S
Australian company law / John O'Hair, John (Sean) Kearns. – 4th ed. – Sydney : McGraw-Hill Book Co., 1985.
xvii, 469 p.; 25 cm.
Re ed. of: Australian company law / Harvey Mason. 3rd ed. 1981. Includes bibliographical references and indexes.
ISBN 0074520334 Pbk

O'Hare, John
Civil litigation / John O'Hare, Robert N. Hill. – 4th ed. – London : Longman, 1986.
xxvi,507p; 24cm.
Previous ed.: Oyez Longman, 1985. Includes index.
ISBN 0851212220 Pbk £15.95

OHiggins, Paul
Bibliography of Irish trials and other legal proceedings / Paul OHiggins. – Abingdon, Oxon. : Professional Books, 1986.
xxvii,504p.
Includes indexes.
ISBN 0862050804
→ Employment law.
→ Essays in Irish Legal History.
—Social security law in Britain and Ireland : a bibliography / Paul O'Higgins and Martin Partington with the assistance of Sally Hughes. – London : Mansell, 1986.
424p; 24cm.
Includes index.
ISBN 0720117941 £36.00

Oil and gas in Canada : a new environment for development / Colin and Pamela Karasek. – London : Financial Times Business Information, 1985.
ix,206p.
Bibliography: p.201-206.
ISBN 0903199939

Oil & gas law and taxation review : a monthly review covering court decisions, legislation and international news. – Oxford : ESC, 1982-.

Oil and world power / Peter R. Odell. – 7th ed. – Harmondsworth : Penguin, 1983.
287p; 20cm.
Previous ed.: 1981. Includes index.
ISBN 0140222847 Pbk £2.95

Oil companies and the Arab world / Giacomo Luciani. – London : Croom Helm, 1984.
197p; 23cm.
Includes index. Re translation of: Compagnie petrolifere e paesi arabi.
ISBN 0709916191 £15.95
ISBN 0312582765

Oil companies in the international system / Louis Turner. – 3rd ed. – London : Allen & Unwin for the Royal Institute of International Affairs, 1983.
279p; 22cm.
Previous ed.: 1980. Bibliography: p253-268. - Includes index.
ISBN 0043820409 Pbk

Oil pollution from ships : international, United Kingdom and United States law and practice / Richard L. Jarashow. – 2nd ed. – London : Stevens, 1985.
l,619p; 26cm.
Deals with the international law and practice relating to oil pollution from ships, and includes new chapters dealing with United States law and selected aspects of United Kingdom law. There are also chapters on salvage in oil pollution cases and rights and obligations in customary international law. The Civil Jurisdiction and Judgements Act 1982, and Law of the Sea Convention 1982 are included.
ISBN 042047000X £95.00

Oil pollution of the sea : the government response to the eighth report of the Royal Commission on Environmental Pollution. – London : H.M.S.O., 1983.
ISBN 0117516856

Oil supplies industry : a comparative study of legislative restrictions and their impact. – London : Financial Times Business Information, 1986.
ix,242p.
Bibliography: p.238-242..
ISBN 0903199920

Oil Taxation Acts 1975-1983. – London : HMSO, 1984.
– (Taxes Act Ser.).
ISBN 0116413506 Pbk £11.95

Oil Taxation Acts. – London : HMSO, 1985.
ISBN 0116413514 Pbk £12.50

Oily-Water Separating and Monitoring Equipment. – International Maritime Organization. – English Edition. – London : International Maritime Organization, 1982.
Hbk £2.25

Ojo, Abiola
Constitutional law and military rule in Nigeria / Abiola Ojo. – Ibadan, Nigeria : Evans Brothers, 1987.
vii,316p.
ISBN 9781675691

Okany, Martin Chukwuka
Nigerian law of property / by Martin Chukwuka Okany. – Enugu, Nigeria : Fourth Dimension, 1986.
lxii,762p.
Bibliography: p.757-762. - Includes index.
ISBN 9781562153
—Role of customary courts in Nigeria / by Martin C. Okany. – Enugu : Fourth Dimension Publishing Co., 1984.
264p.
Includes bibliographical references and index.
ISBN 9781562145

O'Keefe
Introduction to New Zealand Law / J T Farrand. – 4th ed. – London : Butterworths, 1981.
ISBN 0409655376 Pbk £34.00
—Law Relating to Trade Descriptions / Smith. – London : Butterworths, 1971.
Service.
ISBN 0406326347 Llf £110.00

O'Keefe, G. C. →Commercial law in New Zealand.

O'Keefe, Patrick J
Creation and Preservation : Law and the Cultural Heritage / Lyndel V Prott. – Abingdon : Professional Books, 1985.
– (Volume II).
ISBN 0862050774 Hbk £33.50
ISBN 0862050820 Pbk £22.00
—Existing legislative protection of the cultural and natural heritage of the Pacific region / Patrick O'Keefe, Lyndel V. Prott. – s.l. : UNESCO, 1982.
v,140p.
→ Law and the cultural heritage, Vol. 1 : Discovery and excavation.
→ National legal control of illicit traffic in cultural property.

O'Keeffe, David →Essays in European law and integration : to mark the silver jubilee of the Europa Institute, Leiden, 1957-1982.
→ Mixed agreements.

Okeke, C. Nwachukwu
Theory and practice of international law in Nigeria / by C. Nwachukwu Okeke. – Enugu, Nigeria : Fourth Dimension Publishers, 1986.
xx, 316p.
Bibliography: p.293-309. - Includes index.
ISBN 9781562420

Oke's Magisterial Formulist, 2 Vols. / Stuart Baker. – 20th ed. – London : Butterworths, 1986.
This looseleaf service provides immediate access to all the prescribed forms relating to proceeding in British magistrates' courts. A comprehensive range of precedents for all statutory offenses and many regulatory offenses within the jurisdiction of the courts is included.
ISBN 040632400X £125.00

Okochi, Akio →Overseas business activities : proceedings of the Fuji Conference.

Okonkwo, C O
Introduction To Nigerian Law. – Sweet & Maxwell.
ISBN 0421239409 Hbk £17.50
ISBN 0421239506 Pbk
→ Nigerian business law.
—Nigerian business law / Cyprian Okonkwo, Peter Shears. – Ibadan : Spectrum, 1983.
207p; 24cm.
ISBN 0717511855 Pbk £4.85
—Penal Code of Northern Nigeria. – London : Sweet & Maxwell.
ISBN 0421318201 Hbk

Okunniga, A. A. O.
Transplants and mongrels and the law : the Nigerian experiment : an inaugural lecture delivered at the University of Ife on 17th May, 1983 / by A.A.O. Okunniga. – Ile-Ife, Nigeria : University of Ife Press, 1984.
32p. – (Inaugural lecture series).
Includes bibliographical references.

Ola, Christopher S
Income tax law for corporate and unincorporated bodies in Nigeria / C.S. Ola. – 2nd ed. – Ibadan : Heinemann Educational Books (Nigeria) Ltd, 1981.
xx,556p.
Previous ed. published 1974 under title: Income-tax law and practice in Nigeria.
ISBN 9781292911
—Nigerian income tax law and practice : incorporating income tax laws relating to personal income tax law, partnership tax law, companies income tax law, petroleum profits tax law, capital gains tax law, capital transfer tax law and guidelines to a tax system under the presidential system of government with accountancy and decided cases illustrations and a supplement (1985) / C.S. Ola. – London : Macmillan, 1985.
xxvi,566p; 22cm.
Includes index.
ISBN 0333400070 Pbk £8.95

Olaitan, M. O.
Basic resourses on Nigerian law / by M.O. Olaitan and Oluremi Jegede. – Lagos : Libriservice, 1983.
iii,64p.
ISBN 9782372048
—Nigerian criminal cases index, 1880-1975 / by M.O. Olaitan. – Lagos : Libriservice Ltd., 1983.
vi,295p.
Includes index.
ISBN 978237203X

Old Attorney General. – Halifax : Nimbus.
ISBN 0920852076 Hbk £3.95

Old Poor Law, 1795-1834 / prepared for the Economic History Society by J.D. Marshall. – 2nd ed. – Basingstoke : Macmillan, 1985.
57p; 22cm.
Previous ed.: 1968. Bibliography: p51-54. - Includes index.
ISBN 0333398807 Pbk £3.95

Old Tenures and Old Natura Brevium. – Reprint. – Abingdon : Professional Books, 1986.
ISBN 0862053293 Hbk £27.00

Older Offenders : Perspectives, Criminology, Criminal Justice / Langworthy. – Praeger.
ISBN 0275927342 Hbk £36.95

Oldfield, M.
Understanding pension schemes. – 3rd ed. – London : Fourmat, 1987.
ISBN 185190025X Pbk £10.95

Oldham, Phillippa →Butterworth's Current Law.

Olesnicky, M.
Hong Kong company legislation. – London : Butterworths, 1988.
ISBN 0409995525 Llf

Olisa, Martin M.
Nigerian petroleum law and practice / Martin M. Olisa. – Ibadan, Nigeria : Fountain Books, 1987.
x,261p.
Includes bibliographical references.
ISBN 978233118X

Oliver, Dawn →Changing constitution.
—Cohabitation : the legal implications / Dawn Oliver. – Bicester : CCH Editions, 1987.
xvi,140p; 23cm.
Includes index.
ISBN 0863251080 Pbk
→ Judicial review.
→ New directions in judicial review.
→ Some legal issues arising out of the miners' strike 1984/5.

Oliver, M C
Cases in Company Law. – 4th ed. – Plymouth : Macdonald & Evans, 1984.
ISBN 0712104844 Pbk £7.50
—Company Law. – 10th ed. – Plymouth : Macdonald & Evans, 1987.
ISBN 0712106987 Hbk £6.50
—Private company in Germany : a translation and commentary / M.C. Oliver, M.A. Barrister. – 2nd ed. – Deventer, Netherlands : Kluwer Law and Taxation Publishers, 1986.
92p.
Includes English and German text of Gesetz betreffend die Gesellschaften mit beschrankter Haftung.
ISBN 9065442448 Pbk £72.00

Oliver, Peter
Free movement of goods in the EEC. – London : European Law Centre, 1982.
285p.
Supplement 1984.
ISBN 0907451055 £34.00
—Free Movement of Goods in the EEC Under Articles 30 to 36 of the Rome Treaty. – London : European Law Centre.
ISBN 0907451209 Hbk £75.00

Oliver, Peter J.
Spicer and Pegler's the business of partnerships / by Peter J. Oliver and Nigel T. Davey. – London : Sweet & Maxwell, 1986.
xii,193p; 22cm.
Includes index.
ISBN 0421353309 Pbk £16.75

Oliver, Peter Raymond →Report of the Review Body on the Chancery Division of the High Court.

Ollennu, Nii Amaa
Ollennu's principles of customary land law in Ghana / Gordon R. Woodman. – 2nd ed. – Birmingham : CAL Press, 1985.
xxviii,184p.
Includes bibliographical references and index.
ISBN 0951053000

Ollennu's principles of customary land law in Ghana / Gordon R. Woodman. – 2nd ed. – Birmingham : CAL Press, 1985.
xxviii,184p.
Includes bibliographical references and index.
ISBN 0951053000

Olliff
Working Abroad : You and Tax / Greaves. – London : Deloitte Haskins & Sells.
ISBN 0863491278 Pbk £5.95

Ollivant, Simon
Court of the official in pre-Reformation Scotland : based on the surviving records of the officials of St. Andrews and Edinburgh / by Simon Ollivant. – Edinburgh : The Stair Society, 1982.
x,224p. – (Publications).
Bibliography: p201-206.
ISBN 0902292099

Olmesdahl, M. C. J. →Criminal justice in South Africa : selected aspects of discretion.

Olmstead, Cecil J. →Extra-territorial application of laws and responses thereto.

O'Loghlen, M. →Accident compensation Victoria.

Oluyede, P.A.
Public Complaints Commission in a presidential system with particular reference to Nigeria / by P.A. Oluyede. – Lagos : Nigerian Institute of Advanced Legal Studies, 1983.
19p.
Seminar paper presented at the Institute on Thursday May 19th, 1983. Includes bibliographical references.

O'Malley and Hardcastle's Election Cases : 1869-1929, 7 Vols. – Abingdon : Professional Books.
Hbk £110.00

O'Malley, J
Magistrates' Court. – London : Longman Professional, 1988.
ISBN 0851214118 Pbk £9.95
—Magistrates' Courts. – London : Longman Professional.
– (Longman Practice Notes).
ISBN 0851214118 Pbk £10.95

O'Malley, Liam
Business law / by Liam O'Malley. – London : Sweet & Maxwell, 1982.
xxxii,222p.
ISBN 0421285001
—Business Law (ILT). – London : Sweet & Maxwell, 1982.
ISBN 0421285001 Pbk £14.50

O'Malley, Pat
Law, Capitalism and Democracy : a Sociology of Australian Legal Order. – North Sydney : Allen & Unwin, 1983.
180p.
ISBN 0868613819 Pbk £16.95

O'Malley, S.
Manual of European Practice
Vol. 1 / A. Layton. – London : Sweet & Maxwell, 1986.
Explains English procedure and practice as they apply to cross-border litigation in the light of the 1982 Civil Jurisdiction and Judgements Act. Gives a comparative description of the legal systems of Belgium, Denmark, France, Germany, Ireland, Italy, Luxembourg, the Netherlands, England and Wales, Scotland and Northern Ireland.
ISBN 0421262907 Hbk

Omar : The Islamic Law of Succession and its Application in South Africa. – Durban : Professional Publishers, 1988.
ISBN 0409045969 Pbk £35.00

Omar, M.S.
Omar : The Islamic Law of Succession and its Application in South Africa. – Durban : Professional Publishers, 1988.
ISBN 0409045969 Pbk £35.00

Ombudsman : an autobiography / by Pat Cook. – London : BKT, 1981.
155p; 22cm.
ISBN 0904677192 £6.95

Ombudsman journal. – Edmonton, Alta. : International Ombudsman Institute, Faculty of Law, University of Alberta, 1981-.

Ombudsman seminar, held at the Oude Libertas Centre, Stellenbosch, South Africa, on 30th and 31st March 1982. – Edmonton : International Ombudsman Institute, 1982.
161p.
Organised by the International Bar Association Ombudsman Forum, in association with the International Ombudsman Institute and the Association of Law Societies of the Republic of South Africa.

Ombudsmen and the constitution / Allan Blake in association with Lancashire Polytechnic. – 2 videocassettes. – London : Sweet & Maxwell, 1985.
– (Sweet & Maxwell's lawfilms).
Contents: Ombudsmania - The Local Ombudsman investigates.

Ombudsmen in the Commonwealth : a survey. – Rev. – London : Commonwealth Secretariat, 1983.
ii leaves,28p.
Previous edition: 1980. Bibliography: p.24-28.
ISBN 0850922488

Ombudsmen in the provinces of Canada / by Ulf Lundvik. – Edmonton? : International Ombudsman Institute, 1981.
103p.

Omissions, negligence and endangering / Law Reform Commission of Canada. – Ottawa : The Commission, 1985.
42,48p. – (Working paper).
Includes bibliographical references. Added t.p. in French: L'omission, la negligence et la mise en danger. Pages numbered in opposite directions. Text in English and French.
ISBN 0662540824

Omotola, J. A.
Cases on the Land Uses Act / J.A. Omotola. – Lagos : Lagos University Press, 1983.
170p.
ISBN 9782264407
→ Essays in honour of Judge T.O. Elias.
→ Land Use Act : report of a National Workshop held at the University of Lagos, May 25 - May 28, 1981.
→ Law and development.

On a cloth untrue : Inflation accounting. – Cambridge : Woodhead-Faulkner, 1984.
ISBN 0859412504 Hbk £19.95

On a Singular Book of Cervidius Scaevola. – Berlin : Duncker and Humblot, 1987.
103p.
ISBN 3428062922 Hbk £54.00

On Being a Tenant Farmer : A Guide to the Tenant and Landlord System. – London : Farming Press.
ISBN 0852361815 Hbk £8.95

On Buying a Job : The Regulation of Taxicabs in Canberra. – Turramura : Centre for Independent Studies.
20p.
ISBN 0959648550 Hbk £2.00

On costs. – Service to Lawyers, 1986.
ISBN 0950417661 updat £69.50

On Criminal Procedure / Jean-Pierre Lussier. – Agincourt : Carswell, 1982.
481p.
Hbk £42.00

On Discrimination. – Vancouver : Fraser Institute, 1985.
– (Focus Ser.).
ISBN 0889750807 Hbk £5.00

On F.R. Scott : Essays on His Contributions to Law, Literature, and Politics / Ronald St. J. MacDonald. – Montreal : McGill-Queen's University Press.
226p.
ISBN 0773503978 Hbk £25.00
ISBN 0773503986 Pbk £8.95

On industrial relations : interprofessional relationships in health care and the role of criminal law in industrial relations / R. Dyson and A.N. Khan. – Leeds : Centre for Social Work and Applied Social Studies, University of Leeds, 1982.
27p. – (Occasional papers).

On International Construction and Project Export Contracts. – Helsinki : Lakimiesliiton kustannus, 1982.
168p.
Hbk £102.00

On law and policy in the European Court of Justice : a comparative study in judicial policymaking / by Hjalte Rasmussen. – Dordrecht : M. Nijhoff, 1986.
xxv, 555 p.; 25 cm.
Summary in Danish. Thesis (doctoral)–University of Copenhagen, 1985. Includes bibliographies and indexes.
ISBN 9024732174 Hbk £295.00

On Liberty. – Penguin, 1974.
ISBN 0140432078 Pbk £2.50

On solicitors. – 8th ed. – London : Butterworths, 1988.
ISBN 04061617120 Hbk

On tap not on top : legal centres in Australia, 1972-1982 / edited by David Neal. – S.l. : Legal Service Bulletin, 1984.
64p.
ISBN 0959472738

On the Income Tax Law. – Allahabad : Orient Law House, 1983-1984.
Hbk £300.00

On the Issue of the Continental Shelf : Two Legal Opinions / R. Walter. – Berlin : Springer-Verlag, 1986.
ca 100p.
Pbk £35.00

On the Land Law. – New Delhi : People's Publishing House, 1978.
ii, 20p.
Hbk £0.50

On the law of ultra vires / Satya Ranjan Das. – 2nd ed. – Calcutta : Cambray, 1981.
xvi,340p.
Previous ed.: published as 'The law of ultra vires in British India', 1923. Includes index.

On the Legal Institutions of Socialist Democracy. – London : Spokesman Books, 1983.
50p.
Pbk individual 4.00

On the road to unification of the law of sales / John Honnold. – Deventer : Kluwer Law and Taxation Publishers, 1983.
31p.
ISBN 9065441662

On the Utility of Legal Theory / Mark van Hoecke. – Tampere : A-Tiete Oy.
ISBN 9519464352 Pbk £140.00

One Europe: one world : a first exploration of Europe's potential contribution to world order / a report by Christopher Layton in conjunction with a gorup sponsored by the Federal Trust for Education and Research, the Wyndham Place Trust and the One World Trust. – London : Journal of World Trade Law, 1986.
70p.
Special supplement no. 4 to the Journal of World Trade Law, vol. 20 (1986).

One L : What They Really Teach You at Harvard Law School. – Sceptre.
ISBN 0340431008 Pbk £2.95

One man's judgement : an autobiography / Lord Wheatley. – London : Butterworths, 1987.
ix,230p,8p of plates; 24cm.
Includes index.
ISBN 0406100195 Hbk £17.50

O'Neill
Financial Accounting / Holmes. – London : Letts.
ISBN 085097853X Pbk £7.95

O'Neill, N. K. F.
Criminal jurisdiction of magistrates in Papua New Guinea / by N.K.F. O'Neill and R.N. Desailly : with a foreword by Buri Kidu. – 1. – Sydney : New South Wales Institute of Technology, 1982.
loose-leaf.
Includes index.
ISBN 0909684375

Ongoing Revolution in American Banking. – Stockholm : American Enterp Institute.
– (AEI Studies No. 472).
ISBN 0844736546 Hbk £14.75

Onkelinx, Ivo →EEC Customs Law.

Online bibliographic databases : a directory and sourcebook / Marjorie J. Brown. – 3rd ed. – London : Aslib, 1983.
xiv,383p; 24cm.
Previous ed.: 1981. Bibliography: p315-331. - Includes index.
ISBN 0851421679 North America £
ISBN 0810305305

Online public access to library files : conference proceedings / edited by Janet Kinsella. – Oxford : Elsevier International Bulletins, 1985.
200p; ?cm.
Includes bibliographies and index.
ISBN 0946395187 Pbk £14.50

Only the Good News : on the Law of the Press in India. – New Delhi, 1987.
514p.
Hbk Manohar Publications

Onshore oil and gas pipelines : the problems / by Kevan MacDonald. – Dundee : University of Dundee, Centre for Petroleum and Mineral Studies, 1981.
xiii,102p. – (Occasional paper).

Ontario annotated family law service. – Student edition. – Scarborough, Ontario : Butterworths (Canada), 1988.
Covers leading cases relating to a particular section, annotated, all Ontario and Federal statutes pertaining to federal law, together with regulations made under the statutes, and a legislative history following each amended section, giving the citation of the amendment.
ISBN 0409887021 Llf

Ontario Annual Bound Statutes 1981-1987. – Agincourt : Carswell.
Hbk £167.50

Ontario Annual Practice. – Aurora : Canada Law Book Co.
– (Text Books-Civil).
Hbk £1-10 copies 42.00 ea.

Ontario Annual Practice (O.A.P) / W. A. Derry Miller. – Aurora : Canada Law Book Co.
This 1987-88 edition of Ontario Annual Practice provides a revised publication up-to-date on the Rules of Practice as well as all significant cases on the Rules of the past 30 years.
Hbk For 1-10 Copies 42.00 each

Ontario Business Corporations Act annotated / Margot Lettner. – Scarborough, Ontario : Butterworths (Canada), 1990.
352.
ISBN 1234124312 Pbk £36

Ontario Business Corporations Act with Regulations. – 10th ed. – Don Mills : CCH Canadian Ltd, 1987.
244p.
ISBN 0887964117 Pbk £10.95

Ontario Civil Procedure, 3 Vols.
Vols. 1-3. – Agincourt : Carswell.
This two volume set provides complete textual analysis on practice and procedure topics arising under the Ontario, Canada Rules of Civil Procedure and Courts of Justice Act. Annotated cases relevant to the Ontario Rules and comparisons to rules in other provinces are included in the work.
Pbk £189.00

Ontario Corporation and Income Tax Legislation : with Related Taxes. – 25th ed. – North Ryde : C.C.H. Australia, 1988.
254p.
ISBN 0887964745 Pbk £13.95

Ontario Corporation Manual. – Toronto : DeBoo.
ISBN 088820132X Llf £325.00

Ontario Decisions Criminal Conviction and Sentence Cases. – Aurora : Canada Law Book Co.
– (Summary Services, Provincial Ser.).
Pbk £199.50

Ontario Economic Council →Canadian financial institutions : changing the regulatory environment.

Ontario Employment Law Handbook : an Employer's Guide. – rev. ed. – Butterworths, 1986.
96p.
Pbk £21.95

Ontario employment law handbook: an employer's guide. – Scarborough, Ontario : Butterworths (Canada), 1986.
96.
Examines the changes in Ontario's employment law since the fist edition in 1982. Covers the hours of work and minimum wages, overtime pay and public holidays, health and safety regulations, unemployment insurance, lockouts and strikes, and negotiations and arbitration.
ISBN 0409804860 Pbk

Ontario Estate Administration : A Guide for Legal Secretaries and Law Clerks. – Toronto : Butterworths, 1987.
162p.
Pbk £35.00

Ontario estate administration: a guide for legal secretaries and law clerks. – Scarborough, Ontario : Butterworths (Canada), 1987.
162.
Contains details on opening the file, application for probate, application for Letters of Administration, estate administration, estate accounting, executors fees, passing of accounts and income tax compliance.
ISBN 0409806510 Pbk

Ontario Estate Practice / J.R. Wilson. – 2nd ed. – Don Mills : CCH Canadian Ltd, 1986.
604p.
ISBN 0887962998 Pbk £39.95

Ontario Family Law Act. – Aurora : Canada Law Book Co.
– (Text Books-Civil).
This manual is a working guide to the Ontario Family Law Act of 1986. Divided into four main parts, this manual includes the full text of each section of the Act, insightful author commentary, convenient cross-referencing and case law with unreported decisions.
Hbk £89.00

Ontario Family Law Reform Act Manual (O.F.L.R.) 1979-Present. – Aurora : Canada Law Book Co.
Llf £89.00
Bdrs. and Contents. –
£47.00

Ontario Family Law Reports / Jeffery Wilson. – Butterworths.
ISBN 0409809136 Llf £135.00

Ontario Health and Safety Guide : A Dictionary of Legal Compliance. – Toronto : DeBoo, 1984.
This guidebook provides comprehensive discussion of the legal provisions affecting workplace health and safety in Ontario, Canada. The book is organized to provide quick reference in the design and review of workplace policies and procedures.
ISBN 0888201834 Hbk £85.00

Ontario Labour Relations Board
Annual report / Ontario Labour Relations Board. – Ontario Labour Relations Board. – Toronto : The Board, 1981.
Report year ends 31 Mar..
ISBN 071184 9X

—Ontario Labour Relations Board Reports : A Monthly Series of Decisions from the Ontario Labour Relations Board. – Ontario Labour Relations Board. – Ontario : Ontario Government Publications Service, 1983.
215p.
Hbk £5.25

Ontario Labour Relations Board Law and Practice / C. Michael Mitchell. – Butterworths, 1985.
ca 736p.
Deals with labour relations issues dealt with by the Ontario Labour Relations Board. Issues and proceedings covered include certification and termination of bargaining rights, unfair labour practices, sale of a business and related employer provisions, jurisdictional disputes, occupational health and safety, all construction matters and judicial review.
ISBN 0409865400 Hbk £115.00

Ontario Labour Relations Board Law and Practice : Citation Updater, 1 Vol. – Butterworths.
ISBN 0409847887 Llf £40.00

Ontario Labour Relations Board Reports : A Monthly Series of Decisions from the Ontario Labour Relations Board. – Ontario Labour Relations Board. – Ontario : Ontario Government Publications Service, 1983.
215p.
Hbk £5.25

Ontario Land Titles Procedural Guide. – Don Mills : CCH Canadian Ltd, 1986.
196p.
ISBN 0887962823 Pbk £8.00

Ontario Law Reports (1901-1930), 66 Vols. – Aurora : Canada Law Book Co.
– (Law Reports).
Hbk £2178.00
Back Vols.. –
Hbk £33.00 ea.

Ontario Law Reports : Tables of Cases (For Vols. 1-66). – Aurora : Canada Law Book Co.
247p. – (Law Reports).
Hbk £15.00

Ontario Law Reports : Years 1901-1930. – North Ryde : Law Book Co.
Hbk £2,310.00

Ontario Law Reports (O.L.R.) 1901-1931, 66 Vols. – Law Society of Upper. – Aurora : Canada Law Book Co.
– (Predecessor to the Ontario Reports (O.R.)).
Hbk £2178.00
Back Vols.. –
Hbk £33.00 each
Table of Cases 1901-1908. –
Hbk £15.00

Ontario Legislative Digest Service : Carswell. – Agincourt : Carswell, 1988.
Llf £298.25

Ontario Limitation Periods : A Handbook of Limitation Periods and Other Statutory Time Limits. – Toronto : Butterworths.
Hbk

Ontario Municipal Board Reports (O.M.B.R.) 1972-Present. – Aurora : Canada Law Book Co.
1000p.
Hbk £80.00
Back Vols.. –
Hbk £53.00 each

Ontario Provincial Court Civil Division Practice : 1987. – Agincourt : Carswell, 1987.
309p.
This work sets out the complete text of the rules of the civil Division courts, previously known as the 'Small Claims Court'. The book includes commentary and annotations to the rules of practice, along with relevant forms and fee schedules.
Hbk £41.75

Ontario Regulations : 1981, 2 Vols. – Agincourt : Carswell.
Hbk £42.00

Ontario Regulations : 1982, 2 Vols. – Agincourt : Carswell, 1982.
Hbk £42.00

Ontario Regulations : 1983, 2 Vols. – Agincourt : Carswell, 1983.
Hbk £42.00

Ontario Regulations Service 1987. – Agincourt : Carswell, 1987.
Hbk £222.75

Ontario Regulations Service 1988, 2 Vols. – Agincourt : Carswell, 1988.
Hbk £248.00

Ontario Reports
Inc. Bound Vol. 34. – Toronto : Butterworths.
ISBN 0409880027 15.00
Bound Vol. 35. –
ISBN 0409880043 15.00
Bound Vol. 36. –
ISBN 15.00
Bound Vol. 37. –
ISBN 0409880086 15.00
Bound Vol. 38. –
ISBN 0409880116 15.00
Bound Vol. 39. –
ISBN 0409880159 15.00
Bound Vol. 40. –
ISBN 0409880183 15.00
Consolidated Index, 2nd series, 2 Vol. set. –
ISBN 95.00
Supplement 1985 to Index. –
ISBN 35.00

Ontario Reports New Series (1963-1973), 26 Vols. – Aurora : Canada Law Book Co.
– (Law Reports).
Hbk £936.00
Back Vols.. –
Hbk £36.00 ea.

Ontario Reports (O.R.) 1931-62, 32 Vols. – Aurora : Canada Law Book Co.
– (Old Ser.).
Hbk £1152.00
Back Vols.. –
Hbk £36.00 ea.

Ontario Reports (O.R.) 1963-73, 26 Vols. – Aurora : Canada Law Book Co.
– (New Ser.).
Hbk £936.00
Back Vols.. –
Hbk £36.00 ea.

Ontario Reports (O.R.) 1974-Present. – Aurora : Canada Law Book Co.
– (Second Ser.).
Hbk Back Vols. 36.00 each
Current subscriptions-outside Canada. –
Hbk £73.00
Current Subscription. –
Hbk £68.00

Ontario Reports Old Series (1931-1962), 32 Vols. – Aurora : Canada Law Book Co.
– (Law Reports).
Hbk £1152.00
Back Vols.. –
Hbk £36.00 ea.

Ontario Reports, Second Consolidated Index, 2 Vols.
Index. – Butterworths, 1984.
1296p.
Hbk £95.00
Index and Supplement. –
ISBN 0409844330 Hbk £140.00
Supplement-1988. – 1988.
544p.
ISBN 0409808970 Pbk £70.00

Ontario Reports Second Series (1974-Present). – Aurora : Canada Law Book Co.
– (Law Reports).
Hbk £68.00
Back Vols.. –
Hbk £36.00 ea.

Ontario Revised Statutes : 1980, Vols. 1-11. – Agincourt : Carswell.
Hbk £149.75

Ontario Revised Statutes : Sectional Tables of Concordance 1980-1970, 1970-1980. – Agincourt : Carswell, 1983.
576p.
Hbk £61.00

Ontario Securities Legislation. – 14th ed. – North Ryde : C.C.H. Australia, 1988.
508p.
ISBN 0887964486 Pbk £15.95

Ontario Statute Annotations. – R.S.O. 1980 ed. – Aurora : Canada Law Book Co.
1000p. – (Statute Services).
Hbk £45.00

Ontario Statute Annotations (R.S.O. 1980 Edition) 1930-80. – Aurora : Canada Law Book Co.
1000p.
Hbk £45.00

Ontario Statute Annotations, R.S.O. 1980 Edition. – North Ryde : Law Book Co.
ca 1,000p.
Hbk £45.00

Ontario statute citator. – R.S.O. 1980 ed. 2. – Agincourt, Ont. : Canada Law Book, 1981.
loose-leaf.

Ontario statute citator. – R.S.O. 1970 ed. 2. – Agincourt, Ont. : Canada Law Book, 1975.
loose-leaf.

Ontario Statute Citator Current Bills Service. – Law Book Publisher. – Aurora : Canada Law Book Co.
Llf £85.00

Ontario Statute Citator (O.S.C.) R.S.O. 1980 Edition : 1980-Present. – Aurora : Canada Law Book Co.
Llf £126.00
Binders and Contents. –
£67.00

Ontario Supreme and District Court Practice 1989 / Michael McGowan. – Agincourt : Carswell, 1988.
1,192p.
Hbk £40.50

Ontario Taxation Service. – Toronto : DeBoo.
ISBN 0888201400 Hbk £195.00

Ontario Water Resources Act : Revised Regulations of Ontario, 1980. – Office of the Legislative Assembly (Ontario). – Ontario : Ontario Government Publications Service, 1983.
199p.
Pbk £4.50

Ontario Weekly Notes, 13 Vols.
Series 1950-1962. – Carswell Legal Publications. – Agincourt : Carswell.
Hbk £302.50
Series 1933-1962. –
Pbk £109.25

Ontario Weekly Reporter : 1902-1916, 27 Vols. – Agincourt : Carswell.
Hbk

Onwuchekwa, Y. C.
Broadsheet on the law of contract / by Y.C. Onwuchekwa. – Lagos : s.n., 1984.
42p.

Onwuka, Ralph I. →Future of regionalism in Africa.

Oosterhoff, A. H. →Anger and Honsberger: law of real property.
—Text, Commentary and Cases on Trusts / E.E. Gillese. – 3rd ed. – Agincourt : Carswell, 1987.
1,046p.
ISBN 0459397400 Pbk £22.00

Oosthuizen, A. J.
Law of property / A.J. Oosthuizen. – Cape Town : Juta, 1981.
xiii,105p.
Bibliography: p.
ISBN 0702111937
—Law of succession / A.J. Oosthuizen. – Cape Town : Juta, 1982.
xiv,96p.
Bibliography: p. Includes the text of the Wills Act 7 of 1953.
ISBN 0702112879

Oosthuizen, G. C. →Professional secrecy in South Africa : a symposium.

Opaek, Kazimierz →Social justice and individual responsibility in the welfare state.

Opas, Philip
Law Has Long Ears. – Fitzroy : Wildgrass Books, 1986.
256p.
Hbk £24.96

OPEC official resolutions and press releases 1960-1983. – Organization of the Petroleum Exporting Countries. – 2nd ed. – Oxford : Published and distributed on behalf of OPEC, Vienna by Pergamon, 1984.
x,216p; 30cm.
Previous ed.: published as OPEC official resolutions and press releases 1960-1980. 1980. Includes index. Latest supplement held: 1984-1985.
ISBN 0080311229 Pbk £31.25

Open and Shut : Enhancing the Right to Know and the Right to Privacy. – Ottawa : Canadian Government Publishing Centre, 1987.
130p.
Pbk £16.50

Open Criminal Justice. – London : Gabbay (E & J).
ISBN 0950144886 Pbk £3.00

Open government : freedom of information and local government : a study conducted for the Local Government Legal Society Trust and the Society of Town Clerks' Education and Research Trust / Patrick Birkinshaw. – London : Local Government Legal Society Trust in association with the Society of Town Clerks' Education and Research Trust, 1985.
84p.
ISBN 0951110101

Open justice: the constitutional right to attend and spek about criminal proceedings. – Scarborough, Ontario : Butterworths (Canada), 1985.
416.
Examines the extent to which Canadians are free to attend, criticize and report criminal court proceedings. Considers the impact of the Canadian Charter of Rights and Freedoms on the issues of public access to criminal courts, and assesses the practical aspects of the legal dilemma inherent in the free press/fair trial debate, against the background of the American experience.
ISBN 0409844730 Hbk

Open University →New forms of democracy.
→ States and societies.

Opening the Door a Crack Includes : Cracks in the Federal Information Foundation. – Ottawa : Ken Rubin, 1984.
Hbk £30.00

Operation and Administration of the Freedom of Information Legislation. – Kingston : Australian Government Publishing Service.
340p.
Hbk £29.95

Operation and management of protection and indemnity clubs / Stuart D. Capewell. – London : Insurance Institute of London, 1983.
81 leaves.
Bibliography: 1.61-64.

Operation of the Drug Treaties : Australia 1978-1980. – Department of Health. – Canberra : Australian Government Publishing Service, 1981.
19p.
ISBN 0642068070 Hbk £1.60

Operation of the judicial examination procedure : a study in two Scottish cities / Susan R. Moody. – Edinburgh : Scottish Office, 1986.
iv,87p.

Operation of the unsecured creditors' remedies system in Alberta / Institute of Law Research and Reform. – Edmonton : The Institute, 1986.
vii,188p. – (Research paper).
Includes bibliographical references.

Opinion on the proposal for a tenth Council directive based on Article 54(3)(g) of the Treaty concerning cross-border mergers of public limited companies / (COM(84)727 final) : European Communities. Economic and Social Committee. – Luxembourg : Office for Official Publications of the European Communities, 1985.
9 leaves. – (CES(85) 780).
ISBN 9277085061

Opinions of Attorneys General of the Commonwealth of Australia. – Attorney-General's Department. – Canberra : Australian Government Publishing Service, 1981.
723p.
ISBN 0642066043 Hbk £49.50

Opinions, Recommendations, Resolutions and Orders Adopted by the Assembly. – Council of Europe, Parliamentary Assembly. – Strasbourg : Council of Europe.
Hbk £1.90

Oppenheim, C.
Tax on all the people : poll tax. – Oxford : Bookspeed, 1988.
ISBN 0946744068 Pbk £1.95

Oppermann, Thomas
Reforming the International Economic Order : German Legal Comments / Ernst-Ulrich Petersmann. – Berlin : Duncker and Humblot, 1987.
264p.
ISBN 3428062191 Hbk £98.00

Opportunities for progress in systems, organisation and technology in prison administrations, especially with regard to automation and computer technology / by Luigi Daga. – Stasbourg : Council of Europe, 1986.
29p. – (CDAP (85) 5 rev).
A paper presented to the seventh conference of Directors of Prison Administrations. Bibliography: p.27-28.

Opportunity lost : a response to the Green Paper on the Reform of Personal Taxation from the Child Poverty Action Group / Ruth Lister and Fran Bennett. – London : Child Poverty Action Group, 1986.
34p.

Options. – London : Euromoney, 1987.
ISBN 1870031563 Pbk £75.00

Options. – Cambridge : Woodhead-Faulkner, 1988.
ISBN 0859414418 Hbk £35.00

Opton, Frank G
Decedents' estates, wills, and trusts in the U.S.A. / by Frank G. Opton. – Deventer, The Netherlands : Kluwer Law and Taxation Publishers, 1986.
Includes index.
ISBN 9065442715 Hbk
—Doing business in the United States / Frank G. Opton, Herbert Feiler. – Deventer, Netherlands : Kluwer Law and Taxation Publishers, 1984.
Includes index and bibliography.
ISBN 9065441700

Oputa, C. A.
Law and the twin pillars of justice / by C.A. Oputa. – Owerri Nigeria : Government Printer, 1981.
146p.
Collection of law lectures and papers presented by the author at various seminars and symposia.

Orange Tax Handbook 1986-1987. – Butterworths. – London : Butterworths.
ISBN 0406508321 Pbk £17.00

Orbit of space law / Damodar Wadegaonkar : foreword by Y.V. Chandrachud. – London : Stevens, 1984.
xii,172p.
Includes index.
ISBN 0420470107 Hbk £16.00

Order and conflict in contemporary capitalism / edited by John H. Goldthorpe : sponsored by the Joint Committee on Western Europe of the American Council of Learned Societies and the Social Science Research Council. – Oxford : Clarendon, 1984.
352p.
Conference papers.
ISBN 0198780087 Hbk £22.50
ISBN 0198780079 Pbk £8.50

Order of Christian Unity →Reconciliation and conciliation in the context of divorce.

Order of Serjeants at Law : a chronicle of creations, with related texts and a historical introduction / by J.H. Baker. – London : Selden Society, 1984.
xxvi,610p,xvip of plates.
Includes index.

Order of the Coif / By Alexander Pulling. – London : W. Clowes and sons, 1884.
xxvi, 288 p; 27 cm.
'The subject of this work has been foreshadowed in the article under the same title in the Edinburgh review' for October, 1878.'–Pref.

Ordering of justice : a study of accused persons as dependants in the criminal process / Richard V. Ericson, Patricia M. Baranek. – Toronto : Published in association with the Centre of Criminology, University of Toronto by University of Toronto Press, 1982.
xvi, 268 p.; 25 cm.
Includes index. Bibliography: p. 253-261.
ISBN 0802064639 Pbk

Orders of Knighthood, Awards and the Holy See : The Authoritative, Juridical and Practical Compendium. – 3rd ed. – Gerrards Cross : Van Duren, 1985.
336p : Illus.
ISBN 0905715268 Hbk £29.50

Ordinance of British Columbia. – British Columbia. – 63 leaflets. – Victoria? : s.n., 1864.
Continues British Columbia proclamations, 1858-1863. Continued by ordinances of the combined colonies of British Columbia and Vancouver Island, 1867-1870. This library has 1864 only. Bound with British Columbia proclamations, 1858-1863. Numbering begins anew each year.

Ordinances. – Australian Capital Territory. – Canberra : Commonwealth Government Printer, 1911.
Extracted from: Commonwealth of Australia Gazette. This library has 1939-1959 in this form. Ordinances 1960 onwards are included in the bound volumes of 'Laws of the Australian Capital Territory made during the year ...'.

Ordinances and acts : Belize. – Belmopan : Government Printer, 1973-.
Supplement to the Government gazette. Continues: Ordinances of British Honduras.

Ordinances and regulations of the Province of the Orange Free State / compiled by W.E. Verschuur : saamgestel deur W.E. Verschuur. – Johannesburg : Lex-Patria, 1971.
looseleaf.
Previous ed.: Ordinances of the Province of the Orange Free State 1911-1965. Includes index. Contains enactments since 1911 which are still in force. Added t.p. in Afrikaans. Spine title: Consolidated ordinances and regulations Orange Free State. Parallel text in English and Afrikaans.

Ordinances, laws and proclamations / compiled and edited by Charles Fitzwilliam Cadiz and Robert Lyon. – Pietermaritzburg : Vause, Slatter & Co., 1879.
'By authority'. Includes index. Contents: vol. 1. 1845-70 - vol. 2. 1870-79.

Ordinary Man : The Alexander McLeod-Lindsay Case. – Neutral Bay : Hale & Iremonger, 1984.
ISBN 0868060763 Hbk £24.95, 015
ISBN 08608060771 Pbk £10.95, 015

Ordinary People : Homeless in the Housing Crisis. – Shelter. – London : Shelter, 1982.
ISBN 0901242659 Pbk £2.50

O'Reilly, Michael F.
Carroll's tax planning in Ireland / by Michael F. O'Reilly : consultant author Brian A. Carroll. – London : Sweet & Maxwell, 1986.
xxi,467p; 25cm.
Includes index.
ISBN 0421367504 £40.00

Organisation and Management : ACCA Study Text 2.5B. – London : BPP.
ISBN 0862772451 Pbk £14.95

Organisation and Management of a Solicitor's Practice. – Woolloomooloo : International Business Communications, 1984.
ISBN 094907201X Llf £175.00

Organisation for Economic Co-operation and Development →Biotechnology and patent protection : an international review.
→ Compensation for pollution damage.
→ Competition policy and joint ventures.
→ Computer-related crime : analysis of legal policy.
→ Export credit financing systems in OECD member countries.
→ Food policy.
→ International tax avoidance and evasion : four related studies.
→ International trade in service : securities.
→ Internationalisation of banking : the policy issues.
→ Personal income tax systems under changing economic conditions.
→ Prudential supervision in banking.
→ Taxes on immovable property : report by the Committee on Fiscal Affairs and the ad hoc Group on Urban Problems.
→ Transborder data flows : proceedings of an OECD conference held December 1983.

→ Transfer pricing and multinational enterprises : three taxation issues : reports of the OECD Committee on Fiscal Affairs, 1984.

Organisation for Economic Co-operation and Development
Empirical analysis of changes in personal income taxes / a report by the Committee on Fiscal Affairs. – Paris : Organisation for Economic Co-operation and Development, 1986.
38p.
ISBN 926412778X

—Generalised system of preferences : review of the first decade: report by the secretary-general. – Organisation for Economic Co-operation and Development. – Paris : Organisation for Economic Co-operation and Development, 1983.
98p.

—Information computer communication policy 8 : An exploration of legal issues in information and communication technologies / Organisation for Economic Co-operation and Development. – Paris : O.E.C.D., 1983.
136p; 24cm.
Discusses the development of computer and communications technologies with relation to the existing legal regulations.
ISBN 9264125272 Pbk £7.00

—Model double taxation convention on estates and inheritances and on gifts / report of the OECD Committee on Fiscal Affairs. – Paris : Organisation for Economic Co-operation and Development, 1983.
147p.
ISBN 9264124039

—Nuclear Law Bulletin. – Organisation for Economic Co-operation and Development. – London : HMSO.
Hbk £9.00

—Tax expenditures : a review of the issues and country practices / report by the Committee on Fiscal Affairs. – Paris : Organisation for Economic Co-operation and Development, 1984.
88p.
Examines how governments account for tax expenditures which favour particular types of taxpayers.
ISBN 9264125892 Hbk £30.00

—Taxes on immovable property : report by the Committee on Fiscal Affairs and the ad hoc Group on Urban Problems. – Organisation for Economic Co-operation and Development. – Paris : O.E.C.D., 1983.
201p.
ISBN 9264124756

—Telecommunications : pressures and policies for change. – Organisation for Economic Co-operation and Development. – Paris : Organisation for Economic Co-operation and Development, 1983.
142p.
ISBN 9264124284

Organisation in its environment / I. A. Todd. – 2nd ed. – London : Sweet & Maxwell, 1984.
xill,624p; 22cm.
'The Organisation in its environment is a new edition, in one volume of ... Organisation series.' - Preface. Includes index.
ISBN 042132290X Pbk £9.50

Organisation of an independent prosecution service / observations on the Discussion Paper circulated on behalf of the Home Office Working Party on Prosecution Arrangements. – s.l. : the Society, 1983.
19p.

Organisation of an independent prosecution service : a discussion paper / Working Party on Prosecution Arrangements. – London : Home Office, 1982.
11 leaves.

Organisation of Solicitors Practice. – London : Longman Professional.
ISBN 0851204805 Pbk £85.00

Organising Knowledge : an introduction to information retrieval / Jennifer E. Rowley. – Aldershot : Gower, 1987.
xviii,454p; 23cm.
Includes bibliographies and index. Previous control number ISBN 0566034867.
ISBN 056603574X Hbk £25.00
ISBN 0566034867 Pbk £12.95

Organization of American States →
Inter-American system : treaties, conventions & other documents : a compilation.
—Inter-American Yearbook on Human Rights. – Organization of American States. – Dordrecht : Kluwer, 1987.
1,276p.
ISBN 0898389232 Hbk £450.00

Organization of the Petroleum Exporting Countries
OPEC official resolutions and press releases 1960-1983. – Organization of the Petroleum Exporting Countries. – 2nd ed. – Oxford : Published and distributed on behalf of OPEC, Vienna by Pergamon, 1984.
x,216p; 30cm.
Previous ed.: published as OPEC official resolutions and press releases 1960-1980. 1980. Includes index. Latest supplement held: 1984-1985.
ISBN 0080311229 Pbk £31.25

Organizational police deviance : its structure and control / Clifford D. Shearing. – Toronto : Butterworths, 1981.
ix,208p.
Includes bibliographical references.
ISBN 0409848808

Organizing a Law Office : Law Office Management Series. – Agincourt : Carswell, 1988.
160p.
This is a guidebook to correct law office management. The author presents flow charts, sample precedents, effective accounting procedures and, in general, a cost efficient operation.
Hbk £33.75

Organotin in antifouling paints : environmental considerations / prepared by the Central Directorate of Environmental Protection, the Department of the Environment. – London : H.M.S.O., 1986.
ISBN 0117519030

Orhnial, Tony → Limited liability and the corporation.

Origin and Development of International Humanitarian Law. – Geneva : Comite International de la Croix-Rouge, 1982.
40p.
Hbk £1.00

Origin and Development of Legal and Political System in India, 3 Vols. – 2nd ed. – New Delhi : Deep and Deep Publications, 1982.
ca 700p.
Hbk £165.00

Origin and development of the law of the sea : history of international law revisited / R.P. Anand. – The Hague : Nijhoff, 1983.
xvi,249p; 25cm.
Includes index.
ISBN 9024726174 Hbk £115.00

Origin of rights / by Roger E. Salhany. – Toronto : Carswell, 1986.
viii, 175 p.; 24 cm.
Includes index. Bibliography: p. 163-171.
ISBN 045938760X Pbk

Origin of the Distinction of Ranks. – Repr. of 1806 ed. – Aalen Wuertt : Scientia, 1986.
438p.
Hbk £105.00

Original Americans : U.S. Indians / by James Wilson. – New ed. – London : Minority Rights Group, 1986.
24p. – (Report).
Previous edition: 1980. Bibliography: p.24.
ISBN 0946690391

Origins and consequences of default : an examination of the impact of diligence (summary) / by Michael Adler and Edward Wozniak. – Edinburgh : Central Research Unit, 1981.
viii,71p; 30cm.
spiral

Origins and Meaning of Section 92A : the 1982 Constitutional Amendment on Resources. – Ottawa : Institute for Research on Public Policy, 1985.
xxii, 77p.
ISBN 0886450136 Hbk £10.00

Origins Of Muhammadan Jurisprudence. – Oxford : Oxford University Press, 1950.
ISBN 0198253575 Pbk £6.50

Origins of Rights. – Agincourt : Carswell, 1986.
186p.
This work traces the historical and legal development of such fundamental freedoms as freedom of religion; freedom of the press; freedom from arbitrary detention and search and seizure; freedom from self incrimination; and the right to counsel.
Hbk £25.25

Origins of the conflict of laws / Ronald Graveson. – Tubingen : Mohr, 1981.
p.93-107; 23cm.
Reprinted from: Festschrift fur Konrad Zweigert zum 70. Geburtstag/herausgegeben von Herbert Bernstein, Ulrich Drobnig, Hein Kotz. - Tubingen: Mohr, 1981.

Origins of the vigilante state : the London Metropolitan Police Special Branch before the First World War / Bernard Porter. – London : Weidenfeld and Nicolson, 1987.
xvi,256p,8p of plates; 24cm.
Bibliography: p239-243. - Includes index.
ISBN 0297790676 £15.95

Origins of trade union power / by Henry Phelps Brown. – Oxford : Clarendon, 1983.
vi,320p; 25cm.
Includes index.
ISBN 0198771150 £15.00

Orion Royal Bank Limited
International capital markets 1984 / prepared by Orion Royal Bank Limited. – London : Euromoney, 1984.
vi,207p.
ISBN 0903121638

O'Riordan, D.P.
Supreme Court Fees and Fixed Costs. – 13th ed. – London : Fourmat.
ISBN 1851900551 Pbk £3.50

Orkin, M.M.
Law of Costs. – 2nd ed. – Aurora : Canada Law Book, 1987.
Llf £49.50

Ormandy, David
Environmental health standards in housing / David Ormandy & Roger Burridge. – London : Sweet & Maxwell, 1988.
xlv,373p.
Covers the initial inspection of a house, the assessment of conditions (including particular problems of dampness), the application of the various standards, the drafting of the notices and the steps involved in the enforcement of statutory standards.
ISBN 0421365501 £25.00

Ormerod and Burns : Raising Venture Capital in the UK. – London : Butterworths, 1987.
ISBN 0406103100 Hbk £27.50

Ormerod, John
Ormerod and Burns : Raising Venture Capital in the UK. – London : Butterworths, 1987.
ISBN 0406103100 Hbk £27.50

Ormrod, Roger → Divorce matters.

Orojo, J. Olakunle
Company law and practice in Nigeria / by J. Olakunle Orojo. – 2nd ed. 2. – London : Sweet & Maxwell, 1984.
23cm.
Previous ed.: published in 1 1976. Includes index.
ISBN 0421312106 £85.00
—Introduction to Nigerian Company Law. – London : Sweet & Maxwell.
ISBN 0421312203 Hbk
ISBN 0421312300 Pbk
—Nigerian commercial law and practice / by J. Olakunle Orojo. – 2. – London : Sweet & Maxwell, 1983.
22cm.
Includes index.
ISBN 0421291702 £85.00

Orr, William K. → Private Placements in Canada.

Orsini → World accounting.

O'Ryan, F. J.
Australian Company Practice / J. C. Cooke. – 2nd ed. – Wellington : Butterworths, 1982.
Pbk

O'Ryan, Stephen → Australian family law.
→ Guide to the De Facto Relationships Act-New South Wales.

Osborn, P. G.
Osborn's Concise law dictionary / Roger Bird. – 7th ed. – London : Sweet & Maxwell, 1983.
vii,390p; 23cm.
Includes definitions of legal words and phrases, Roman law terms, and a list of Law Reports with their abbreviations. Many developments in the law since the sixth edition are included.
ISBN 0421296704 Hbk £7.50
ISBN 0421296801 Pbk £4.50

Osborne, Coulter A → Report of Inquiry into Motor Vehicle Accident Compensation in Ontario.
→ Report of Inquiry into Motor Vehicle Accident Compensation in Ontario : summary of findings and recommendations.

Osborne, Craig → Introduction to legal practice, Vol.2 : edited by Craig Osborne.
—Litigation for the Law Society finals / by Craig Osborne. – London : Sweet & Maxwell, 1987.
xiii,434p; 24cm.
Includes index.
ISBN 0421369205 Pbk £15.95

Osborn's Concise law dictionary / Roger Bird. – 7th ed. – London : Sweet & Maxwell, 1983.
vii,390p; 23cm.
Includes definitions of legal words and phrases, Roman law terms, and a list of Law Reports with their abbreviations. Many developments in the law since the sixth edition are included.
ISBN 0421296704 Hbk £7.50
ISBN 0421296801 Pbk £4.50

Osgoode Society → Essays in the history of Canadian law.

O'Shea, B. → Questions on the Law and Practice of Company Accounting.

Oshimili and Aniocha : their people and land tenure / by R.A.I. Ogbobine. – S.l. : s.n., 1981.
viii,192p.

Osieke, Ebere
Constitutional law and practice in the International Labour Organisation / by E. Osieke. – The Hague : M. Hijhoff, 1984.
xxi, 266p.
Bibliography: p.243-258.
ISBN 9024729858 Hbk £160.00

Ostreng
Soviet Union in Artic waters : security implications for the northern flank of NATO / by Willy Ostreng : translated by Eric Hansen from the original Norwegian text. – Honolulu : Law of the Sea Institute, 1987.
ix,77p. – (Occasional paper).
Includes bibliographical references. Translation of: Soviet i nordlige farvann, published by Gylendal Norsk, Oslo, 1982.
ISBN 0911189157

O'Sullivan, John
Law for Nurses. – 3rd ed. – North Ryde : Law Book Co, 1983.
xi, 282p.
ISBN 0455204950 Pbk £28.50

O'Sullivan, Philip
Sourcebook on planning law in Ireland / Katherine Shepherd. – Abingdon : Professional Books, 1984.
xxxviii,568p.
ISBN 0862050901 Hbk £31
Supplement 1987. – 1984.
ISBN 0862050901 Hbk £31.00
Supplement. – 1987.
ISBN 086205219X Hbk £11

Oswin, Maureen
Holes in the Welfare Net. – London : Bedford Square Press.
ISBN 0719909392 Hbk £6.95
ISBN 0719909406 Pbk £3.95

Other price of Britain's oil : safety and control in the North Sea / W.G. Carson. – Oxford : Robertson, 1981.
xi,320p; 24cm.
Includes index.
ISBN 0855203927 Hbk £15.00
ISBN 0855203935 Pbk £5.95

Otley, D.
Case Studies In Management Accounting. – Deddington : Allan (Philip).
ISBN 0860035522 Hbk £45.00

Ott, David H.
Public international law in the modern world / David H. Ott. – London : Pitman, 1987.
480p; 18cm.
Includes bibliography and index.
ISBN 0712107568 Pbk £13.95
ISBN 0273028154

Ottawa Civic Hospital Act, 1983, Bill Pr043 : An Act Respecting the Ottawa Civic Hospital. – Ontario : Ontario Government Publications Service, 1983.
7p.
Hbk £0.30

Ouellet, Andrea
Professional Liability in Conveyancing in New Brunswick. – Agincourt : Carswell, 1986.
127p.
This book addresses the lawyer's liability in conveyancing in New Brunswick, Canada. The role of the real estate practitioner is reviewed and the legal grounds for liability are analyzed in the work.
Hbk £35.50

Ough, Richard N.
Mareva injunction and Anton Piller order : practice and precedents / by Richard N. Ough. – London : Butterworths, 1987.
xxii,175p; 22cm.
Includes index.
ISBN 0406102902 Pbk £28.95

Oughton, R. D. → Fisher & Lightwood's law of mortgage.
→ Tyler's family provision.

Ould, J.
Controlling Subsidiary Companies. – Cambridge : Woodhead-Faulkner, 1986.
ISBN 0859413284 Hbk £40.00

Our common future / World Commission on Environment and Development. – Oxford : Oxford University Press, 1987.
320p; 21cm.
ISBN 019282080X Pbk £5.95

Our Courts on Trial. – Delhi : B.R. Publishing Corporation, 1987.
174p.
ISBN 8170184487 Hbk £75.00

Our legal heritage / co-editors, H.F. Mellet, Susan Scott, Paul van Warmelo. – Durban : Butterworths, 1982.
12,204p.
'A project of De rebus–the South African attorneys' journal, under the auspices of the Association of Law Societies of the Republic of South Africa.'. Includes index. Bibliography: p194.
ISBN 0409040843 Pbk R29

Our Legal System. – 2nd ed. – North Ryde : Law Book Co, 1983.
ISBN 0455202680 Pbk £10.50

Our unions, our democracy : LRD's response to the Tory green paper. – Labour Research Department. – London : LRD Publications, 1983.
24p.

Outer space : new challenges to law and policy / J.E.S. Fawcett. – Oxford : Clarendon, 1984.
vi,169p; 22cm.
Bibliography: p161. - Includes index.
ISBN 0198253982 £16.00

Outer space and legal liability / by Morris D. Forkosch. – The Hague : Nijhoff, 1982.
xvi,290p.
Includes index. Bibliography: p267-270.
ISBN 9024725828 Hbk £100.00/$43.50

Outer Space and Military Supremacy : Jurisdiction in International Law. – New Delhi : Deep and Deep Publications, 1985.
180p.
Hbk £100.00

Outline of Austrian constitutional law. – Kluwer Law and Taxation, 1989.
72.
A brief introduction to the law of Austria. Covers leading statutesand commentaries, basic principles of the constitution, neutrality, and legislation of the Federation.
ISBN 9065444041 Pbk £16.25/Dfl 50

Outline of Companies and Securities Law. – Butterworths, 1987.
221p.
ISBN 040949285X Pbk £19.95

Outline of customary court procedure
Part 1 / by R.A.I. Ogbobine. – Benin City, Nigeria : Ruf-Bine, 1985.
vi,46p.
ISBN 9783004514

Outline of English civil procedure / by Sir Jack Jacob. – s.l. : Jack Jacob, 1984.
44p in various pagings.
'Prepared for lectures for delivery at the Faculty of Law of the Universities of Florence, Sienna, Milan, Pavia, Rome and Macerata, April 1984.'.

Outline of Equity and Trusts. – Butterworths, 1988.
xlii, 365p.
This introductory text covers such areas as the nature of equity, equity assignments, fiduciary obligations, marshalling, contribution, subrogation, discretionary trusts, charitable trusts, and the rights of beneficiaries.
ISBN 0409493767 Hbk £45.00
ISBN 0409493546 Pbk £35.00

Outline of Income Tax Statutory Amendments : 1971-1985. – Cape Town : Legal & Financial Publishing, 1983.
Hbk £8.75

Outline of Labour Legislation and Practices in India. – New Delhi : Indian Investment Centre.
48p.
Hbk £7.00

Outline of legal aid in South Africa / by David J. McQuoid-Mason. – Durban : Butterworths, 1982.
xxvii,310p.
Bibliography: pxiii-xvi.
ISBN 0409040894

Outline of mining law : paper presented at Auckland Law Faculty Seminar Series 1982 at University of Auckland / by Kenneth Palmer. – Auckland : Legal Research Foundation Inc., 1982.
29p.
ISBN 0908581254

Outline of planning law. – 9th. – London : Sweet & Maxwell, 1987.
Examines the Acts and statutory instruments regulating planning law, including the nine new acts introduced since the 1982 edition. Contains discussion of the impact of the abolition of the Metropolitan County Councils, and planning gain, use and misuse of planning conditions, conservation areas, and National Parks.
ISBN 042125459X Pbk £22.50

Outline of the Income Tax Statutory Amendments 1971/1985. – Cape Town.
Hbk Legal and Financial Publishing Co

Outline of the law of agency / R J C Munday. – 2nd ed. – London : Butterworths, 1986.
ISBN 040662271X Hbk £15.00
ISBN 0406622728 Pbk £9.95

Outline of the law of contract / G.H. Treitel. – 3rd ed. – London : Butterworths, 1984.
xxxiii,366p; 22cm.
Previous ed.: 1979. Includes index.
ISBN 0406668485 Pbk

Outline of the law of evidence / Wilkins. – 6th ed. – London : Butterworths, 1986.
ISBN 0406570809 Hbk £19.00
ISBN 0406570817 Pbk £12.95

Outlines of Criminal Procedure. – 2nd ed. – Lucknow : Eastern Book Company, 1984.
692p.
Hbk £75.00

Outlines of English Law / Soulsby. – 3rd ed. – Maidenhead : McGraw-Hill, (1982).
ISBN 0070846553 Pbk £7.95

Outlines of Indian Legal History. – 4th ed. – Bombay : Tripathi, 1981.
xxiii, 640p.
Hbk £60.00

Outlines of Labour Law. – Bombay : Tripathi, 1974.
Hbk £25.00

Outrage : the abuse of diplomatic immunity / Chuck Ashman and Pamela Trescott. – London : W.H. Allen, 1986.
224p; 24cm.
ISBN 0491037139 £10.95

Outsider : newsletter of the Minority Rights Group. – London : The Group, 1984.
Continues: Newsletter.

Overcrowding : Part IV Housing Act 1957. – Shelter. – London : Shelter, 1984.
ISBN 0862650097 Hbk £1.75

Over-ruled on Welfare / Arthur Seldon. – London : Institute of Economic Affairs.
Pbk £3.00

Overseas business activities : proceedings of the Fuji Conference / the International Conference on Business History 9 : edited by Akio Okochi, Tadakatsu Inoue. – Tokyo : University of Tokyo Press, 1984.
xiii, 296 p.; 24 cm.
Includes bibliographies and index.
ISBN 4130470191 Y5000

Overseas Development Institute → Adjustment and financing in the developing world : the role of the International Monetary Fund.
→ IMF and stabilisation : developing country experiences.
→ Quest for economic stabilisation : the IMF and the Third World.

Overview and annotated bibliography of the needs of crime victims / Colin Meredith. – Ottawa : Ministry of the Solicitor General, 1984.
138p. – (User report).

Overview of US export controls / B C Murphy. – Kluwer Law and Taxation, 1989.
160.
A general overview of the US laws controlling the export of goods and technology from the US. Covers individual validated licenses, special licenses, technical data, Nuclear Short Supply Controls, restrictive trade practices and boycotts, and common exporting terms and acronyms.
ISBN 9065443967 Pbk £28/Dfl 85

Ovey, Elizabeth → Building Societies Act 1986.

Owen, David → Review of the Children Act ten years on : its effect on foster care policy and practice.

Owen, David R. → Court appointed experts in maritime cases : a comparative law study.

Owen, Denis
What's in a name / Denis Owen : illustrated by Andrew Martin. – London : BBC, 1985.
143p; 20cm.
Bibliography: p137-138. - Includes index.
ISBN 0563203358 Pbk £3.95

Owen, Dynes
The Times Guide to 1992 : A Complete Handbook to Europe Without Frontiers. – Times.
ISBN 0723003165 Pbk £5.95

Owen, Eric C. H.
County court litigation / by Eric Owen. – London : Sweet and Maxwell, 1988.
lv,405p; 26cm.
An exposition of practice and procedure in county courts, cross-referenced with the Green and White Books. Suggests ways of handling procedure, and includes a section on preparation for trial and giving evidence. Looks at circumstances such as the financial position of a client on legal aid, and at changes resulting from the Civil Jurisdiction and Judgements Acts.
ISBN 0421354704 £38.00

Owen, Morfydd E. → Lawyers and laymen.

Owen, Roger
Migrant workers in the Gulf / by Roger Owen. – London : Minority Rights Group, 1985.
23p. – (Report).
Bibliography: p.23.
ISBN 0946690332

Owles, Derrick
Avoiding liability for defective products : a guide to the law on disclaimer of liability clauses in contracts for the sale of goods / Derrick Owles. – London : Product Liability International, 1987.
ix,52p.
ISBN 1850441200 Pbk £14.50
—Husband and wife business partnership: what the law says / Margot Owles. – London : Graham & Trotman, 1989.
116; 215mm.
Deals with the legal aspects of a business partnership between husband and wife, and examines the nature and formation of a partnership, the partners, liabilities, how to avoid major pitfalls, the present income tax procedure with reference to the separate taxation of spouses due to be implemented in 1990, and how to provide for the future in retirement.
ISBN 1853330574 Hbk £14.95
ISBN 1853333131 Pbk £7.50
—Liability for defective services / Derrick Owles & Hugh Cockerell. – London : Financial Times Business Information, 1985.
168p; 30cm.
ISBN 0903199858
—Unsafe Product, The / Derrick Owles. – London : Kogan Page.
ISBN 1850916888 Hbk £16.95

—US business tax : law and practice after the Tax Reform Act / Derrick & Margot Owles. – London : Financial Times Business Information, 1987.
xviii,146p; 30cm.
Includes index.
ISBN 0902101994 spiral

Owles, Margot → Husband and wife business partnership: what the law says.
→ US business tax : law and practice after the Tax Reform Act.

Oxby, Clare → Ethnic minorities and complaints against the police.

Oxfam → Common ground : how changes in the Common Agricultural Policy affect the Third World.

Oxford book of legal anecdotes / Michael Gilbert. – Oxford : OUP, 1989.
xvi,333p; 23cm.
Anthology of over 350 anecdotes about legal goings-on in Britain, the United States, and Australia.
Anyone practising, or interested in, law
ISBN 0192141120 Pbk £12.50

Oxford essays in jurisprudence : third series / edited by John Eekelaar and John Bell. – Oxford : Clarendon, 1987.
267p; 22cm.
Includes index.
ISBN 0198255071 £27.50

Oxford Jurisprudence. – Oxford : Croom Helm, 1988.
ISBN 0709941560 Hbk £25.00

Oxford Lawyer, 1958-1965, 3 Vols. – London : Wildy & Sons.
Hbk £53.00

Oxford University Statutes, Decrees and Regulations 1987 1988. – Oxford : Oxford University Press.
ISBN 0199201633 Pbk £16.00

Oxfordshire County Record Office
Oxfordshire Election of 1754. – Oxfordshire County Record Office. – Oxford : Oxfordshire County Record Office.
– (Archive Teaching Unit).
Hbk £1.41

Oxfordshire Election of 1754. – Oxfordshire County Record Office. – Oxford : Oxfordshire County Record Office.
– (Archive Teaching Unit).
Hbk £1.41

Oxley-Oxland, J.
Commercial Law / A. Freilich. – Butterworths, 1986.
94p. – (Butterworth's Student Companion Ser.).
ISBN 0409490873 Pbk £9.95
—Commercial Law II /. – Butterworths, 1986.
90p. – (Butterworth's Student Companion Ser.).
ISBN 0409490954 Pbk £9.95
—Federal constitutional law /. – North Ryde : Law Book Co, 1984.
x, 86p. – (Nutshells).
ISBN 0455203482
—New South Wales Police Law Handbook. – Sydney : Butterworths, 1988.
176p.
This handbook contains sections devoted to interrogation, arrest, and search and seizure. Included are chapters on detention and questioning, powers of arrest, searches, and search warrants. The intended audience is law enforcement officers.
Pbk £22.00
—Principles of Criminal Law in New South Wales. – Butterworths, 1984.
219p.
The cases contained in this introductory text are analyzed by their history, facts, problems, and the basic principles of law involved. Diagrams and tables are included in some chapters.
ISBN 0409491357 Pbk £38.00
—Understanding Land Law / R.T.J. Stein. – North Ryde : Law Book Co, 1985.
xx, 171p.
ISBN 0455203032 Hbk £25.00
ISBN 0455203040 Pbk £14.00

Oxner, Sandra, et al
Law in Colonial Society : The Nova Scotia Experience. – Agincourt : Carswell, 1984.
300p.
ISBN 0459364200 Hbk £36.50

Oyediran, Oyeleye → Nigerian 1979 elections.

Oyewo, A. Toriola
Cases and materials on the principles of natural justice in Nigeria / by A. Toriola Oyewo. – Ibadan, Nigeria : Jator Publishing, 1987.
xi,153p.
Includes bibliographical references and index.
ISBN 9782660000
—Principles of administrative and local government law in Nigeria / by A. Toriola Oyewo. – Ibadan, Nigeria : Jator Publishing, 1987.
xxiii,276p.
Bibliography: p.xix-xxiii. - Includes index.
ISBN 9782660019

Oyez Longman Directory of Local Authorities 1983. – London : Oyez Longman, 1983.
Hbk £10.45

P & I Clubs: law and practice. – London : Lloyds of London Press, 1989.
Discusses the constitution, workings and practice of shipowners' mutual protection and in indemnity associations. Covers the historical development and legal structure of clubs. Issues including the Court of Appeal ruling in the cases of the FANTI and PADRE ISLAND are contained, as is the clubs' method for their own reinsurance.
ISBN 1850442304 Hbk

P.C.T. Applicant's Guide : General Information for Users of the Patent Cooperation Treaty Vol. 1 /. – Geneva : World Intellectual Property Organization.
£95.00

Pace, Malcolm H.
Legal requirements for arrest and enforced sale of vessels : a comparative study / Malcolm H. Pace. – S.l. : s.n., 1983.
xxvi,144 leaves.
Thesis (LL.D.) - University of Malta 1983. Bibliography: p.142-144.

Pace, P J
Family Law. – 3rd ed. – Plymouth : Macdonald & Evans, 1986.
– (M and E Handbook Ser.).
ISBN 0712107584 Pbk £6.50

PACEA 1984 : Guide for Duty Solicitors. – London : Fourmat, 1986.
ISBN 1851900195 Pbk £4.95

Pacific constitutions : proceedings of the Canberra Law Workshop VI / edited by Peter Sack. – Canberra : Law Department, Research School of Social Sciences, Australian National University, 1982.
xi,374p.
Bibliography: p.361-374.
ISBN 0867841648

Pacific Courts and Justice. 20 Pacific Writers. – 4th ed. – Suva : University of the South Pacific, Institute of Pacific Studies, 1984.
150p.
Hbk £4.00

Pacific Courts and Legal Systems. – rev. ed. – Suva : University of the South Pacific, Institute of Pacific Studies, 1987.
270p.
Hbk £13.00

Paciocco, David M.
Charter principles and proof in criminal cases / David M. Paciocco. – Toronto : Carswell, 1987.
xlviii,616p.
Includes index.
ISBN 0459308114

Pacione, Michael → Problems and planning in Third World cities.

Package holiday law and contracts / Stewart. – 2nd ed. – London : Fourmat, 1988.
ISBN 1851900411 Pbk £14.95

Packer, B.
Touche Ross : Tax Practice Manual. – 3rd ed. – London : Butterworths.
ISBN 0406402221 Pbk £22.95
—Touche Ross Tax Guide for the Family 1988-89 / Sandy. – London : Macmillan.
ISBN 033346835X Pbk £4.95
—Touche Ross Tax Guide to Pay and Perks 1988-89 / Sandy. – London : Macmillan.
ISBN 0333468376 Pbk £4.95
—Touche Ross VAT : a business by business guide. – London : Butterworths, 1988.
ISBN 0406501440 Pbk £23.95

Packman, M. J. → UK Companies Operating Overseas : Tax and Financial Strategies.

Paddison → Reform of Local Government Finafnce in Britain.

Padmanabha Rau, K. V.
Federal Constitution of Malaysia : a commentary / by K.V. Padmanabha Rau : assisted by Hamid Ibrahim. – Kuala Lumpur : Malaysian Current Law Journal Sdn. Bhd., 1986.
xlvi,605p.
Includes bibliographical references and index.

Paenson, Isaac
English-French-Spanish-Russian Manual of the Terminology of Public International Law (Law of Peace) and International Organizations. – Brussels : Emile Bruylant, 1983.
xlviii, 846p.
ISBN 2802702831 Hbk £6,360.00

Pagan, Jill C.
Taxation aspects of currency fluctuations / Jill C. Pagan. – London : Butterworths, 1983.
xi,162p.
Describes the United Kingdom tax law and the attitude of the Inland Revenue on the subject of currency fluctuations. Foreign exchange management, accounting treatment, and taxation are analyzed in the book.
ISBN 0406406308 Hbk £22.00

Pagare, Dinkar
Tax Laws. – New Delhi : Sultan Chand and Sons.
Hbk £65.00

Page
Financial Services Act 1986 / Ferguson. – London : Sweet & Maxwell, 1987.
ISBN 0421366907 Pbk £13.50

Page, Alan C. → Financial Services Act 1986.
→ Legislation.

Page, N.S. → Webster and Page : South African Law of Trade Marks.

Paget-Brown, Ian
Paget-Brown's commercial law of the Cayman Islands. – Grand Cayman : distributed by Graffix, 1982.
235p.

Paget, John
Law of Banking / Maurice Megrah. – 10th ed. – London : Butterworths, 1988.
ISBN 040633353X Hbk
—Paget's Law of banking / Maurice Megrah, F. R. Ryder, Antonio Bueno. – 9th ed. – London : Butterworths, 1982.
lxxv,678p; 26cm.
One of the major texts in the field of United Kingdom banking law. The book is fully updated to reflect major changes in legislation affecting banking.
ISBN 0406333521 Hbk £54.00

Paget-Brown's commercial law of the Cayman Islands. – Grand Cayman : distributed by Graffix, 1982.
235p.

Paget's Law of banking / Maurice Megrah, F. R. Ryder, Antonio Bueno. – 9th ed. – London : Butterworths, 1982.
lxxv,678p; 26cm.
One of the major texts in the field of United Kingdom banking law. The book is fully updated to reflect major changes in legislation affecting banking.
ISBN 0406333521 Hbk £54.00

Pahl, Jan → Private violence and public policy : the needs of battered women and the response of the public services.

Pain, Kenneth W.
Emergency Applications to Magistrates / Whale. – London : Fourmat, 1986.
ISBN 1851900012 Pbk £12.95
—Licensing Practice and Procedure. – 2nd ed. – London : Fourmat, 1986.
ISBN 1851900098 Hbk £12.95
—Licensing Practice and Procedure. – 3rd ed. – London : Fourmat.
ISBN 1851900594 Pbk £13.95
—Minors : the law and practice : the juvenile courts, the offences, the role of the local authorities / Kenneth W. Pain. – London : Fourmat Publishing, 1987.
xvii,293p.
Concerns practice and procedure of juvenile courts, offences which can be committed by and against minors and the part played by local authorities in care proceedings.
ISBN 1851900306
—Practice and procedure in juvenile courts / by Kenneth W. Pain. – London : Fourmat, 1982.
xiii,149p; 22cm.
Includes index.
ISBN 090684049X Pbk £7.95

Painter
Employment Law / Holmes. – London : Financial Training, 1988.
– (SWOT).
ISBN 1851850848 Pbk £7.50

Painter, A. A. → Butterworths law of food and drugs.

Painter, Anthony Arthur
Guide to Consumer Protection Law. – Chichester : Barry Rose.
173p.
ISBN 0859921247 Hbk £5.25

Painter, D.
Commercial Law : Case Studies in a Business Context. – London : Macmillan.
ISBN 0333434668 Hbk £29.50
—Company Law : Case Studies in a Business Context. – London : Macmillan.
ISBN 033343465X Pbk £29.95

Paisley, Sylvia E.
Guide to EEC law in Northern Ireland / by Sylvia E. Paisley. – Belfast : SLS Legal Publications (NI), Queen's University, Belfast, 1986.
xxii,247p; 21cm.
Bibliography: p237. - Includes index.
ISBN 0853892628 Pbk

Paizes, A. → Parol evidence with particular reference to contract.

Pak, C.Y.
Korean Straits. – Martinus Nijhoff.
ISBN 9024737249 Hbk £42.00

Pakistan : human rights violations and the decline of the rule of law / an Amnesty International report. – London : Amnesty International, 1982.
57p; 30cm.
ISBN 0862100410

Pakistan : the trial and treatment of political prisoners convicted by special military courts / Amnesty Internatiinal. – London : Amnesty International, 1985.
56p.

Pakistan Labour Statutes PLS : Acts, Ordinances, Rules, Regulations, 21 Vols. – Karachi : Bureau of Labour Publications, 1983-87.
Hbk £19.00 ea

Pal, Chandra
State Autonomy in Indian Federation. – New Delhi : Deep and Deep Publications, 1984.
318p.
Hbk £150.00

Palestine yearbook of international law. – Al-Shaybani Society of International Law. – Nicosia : Al Shaybani Society of International Law, 1984-.

Palestinians / by David McDowall. – New ed. – London : Minority Rights Group, 1987.
35p. – (Report).
Previous ed.: 1984. Includes bibliographical references.
ISBN 0946690421

Palfreman, D. →Cases in Banking Law.

Palfreman, David
Elements of Banking / Ford. – 2nd ed. – Pitman.
ISBN 0273029525 Pbk £9.95
—Law of Banking
Supplement 1987. – 3rd ed. – Plymouth : Macdonald & Evans, 1986.
ISBN 0712106820 Pbk £6.50

Paliwala, Abdul H
Appeals by the Prosecution Against Sentences and Acquittals : A Survey of the Situation in Some Commonwealth Countries / Jill Cottrell. – London : Commonwealth Secretariat, 1984.
ISBN 0850922259 Hbk £2.00
→ Introduction to the law in Papua New Guinea.
→ Law and social change in Papua New Guinea.

Palkhivala, N.A. →Law and Practice of Income Tax, 2 Vols.

Pallis, Christopher
ABC of brain stem death / Christopher Pallis. – London : British Medical Journal, 1983.
33p; 29cm.
Articles published in the British Medical Journal.
ISBN 0727900994

Palmer →Negotiating shorter working hours.

Palmer, Camilla
Rights without remedies : the European Convention of Human Rights and UK immigration law / Camilla Palmer. – London : Runnymede Trust, 1981.
29,5p.
Bibliography p.5. - Includes index.
—Sex and race discrimination in employment / Kate Poulton. – London : Sweet & Maxwell, 1987.
ISBN 0905099176 Pbk £14.00

Palmer, Earl E
Canadian Company Law : Cases, Notes and Materials / Bruce Welling. – 3rd ed. – Butterworths, 1986.
640p.
Examines and discusses the main areas of company law in a sequential manner, making use of Canadian, American and Australian authorities. Covers new statutory developments, the corporate constitution, corporate entity, company liability, management, capital structure, and distributions.
ISBN 0409805106 Pbk £70.00
—Collective Agreement Arbitration in Canada. – Butterworths.
Hbk £130.00
→ Law and practice of commercial arbitration.

Palmer, Francis Beaufort
Company Cases 1987. – Stevens & Sons.
ISBN 0420480803 Hbk £28.00
→ Issues and offers of company securities : the new regimes.
—Palmer's company law
Vol. 1 : The treatise / under the general editorship of Clive M. Schmitthoff. – 24th ed. – London : Stevens, 1987.
cci,1857p.
Previous ed.: 1982. Includes index. Kept up to date by 'Reporter and Supplement' binder.
ISBN 0420479104
Vol.1 : The treatise. – 1982.
various pagings; 26cm.
Previous ed.: 1976. Includes index. Kept up to date by 'Reporter and Supplement' binder.
ISBN 0420457607 set £
ISBN 0420446605

Palmer, Kenneth A.
New Zealand Recent Law. – Auckland : Legal Research Foundation, 1986.
Hbk £75.00
—Outline of mining law : paper presented at Auckland Law Faculty Seminar Series 1982 at University of Auckland / by Kenneth Palmer. – Auckland : Legal Research Foundation Inc., 1982.
29p.
ISBN 0908581254
—Planning and development law in New Zealand / by Kenneth A. Palmer : with a foreword by Sir Robin Cooke. – 2nd ed. 2. – Sydney : Law Book Co., 1984.
lviii,1023p.
ISBN 0455203725

Palmer's company cases. – London : Stevens, 1985.
Cumulative index.

Palmer's Company Law 4 vols.
Service 1988. – Sweet & Maxwell.
ISBN 0420446605 Hbk £260.00

Palmer's company law
Vol. 1 : The treatise / under the general editorship of Clive M. Schmitthoff. – 24th ed. – London : Stevens, 1987.
cci,1857p.
Previous ed.: 1982. Includes index. Kept up to date by 'Reporter and Supplement' binder.
ISBN 0420479104
Vol.1 : The treatise. – 1982.
various pagings; 26cm.
Previous ed.: 1976. Includes index. Kept up to date by 'Reporter and Supplement' binder.
ISBN 0420457607 set £
ISBN 0420446605

Palsson, Lennart
Marriage in comparative conflict of laws : substantive conditions / Lennart Palsson. – The Hague : Martinus Nijhoff, 1981.
lxxvi,388p.
Continues Palsson, L. : Marriage and divorce in comparative conflict of laws, Leyden, 1974. Bibliography: pli-lx.
ISBN 9024725488 Hbk £200.00

Panagiotou, S.
Justice, Law and Method in Plato and Aristotle. – London : Biblios.
ISBN 092098018X Hbk £27.95
ISBN 0920980201 Pbk £14.50

Panama / by Enrique de Alba. – London : Lloyds of London Press, 1987.
204p; 22cm.
ISBN 1850441413 £25.50

Panchayati Raj in India / D.R. Meghe. – New Delhi : Deep and Deep Publications, 1984.
286p.
Hbk £150.00

Pandect of Commercial Law and Jurisprudence. – Manila : National Book Store, 1984.
515p.
ISBN 9710805185 Hbk £34.00

Pandey, Shri Nivas
Wealth Taxation in India. – Allahabad : Vohra, 1987.
195p.
ISBN 8185072094 Hbk £150.00

Panel of Inquiry into the Circumstances Surrounding the Death of Jasmine Beckford
Child in trust : the report of the Panel of Inquiry into the Circumstances Surrounding the Death of Jasmine Beckford / presented to Brent Borough Council and to Brent Health Authority by the Members of the Panel of Inquiry ... Louis Blom-Cooper (in the chair). – London : London Borough of Brent, 1985.
304,cxlp; 21cm.
Bibliography: pcxxxix-cxl.
ISBN 0951106805

Panel on Take-overs and Mergers →City code on take-overs and the rules governing substantial acquisitions of shares.

Panel on Take-Overs and Mergers
Statements. – Panel on Take-Overs and Mergers. – London : The Panel, 1968.

Panel services for offenders : comparative studies of England and Poland 1984/85 / edited by Thelma Wilson. – Aldershot : Avebury, 1987.
ix,103p; 22cm.
Bibliography: p96-103.
ISBN 0566054205 £19.50

Panet, A. de Lotbiniere
Canadian Customs and Excise Reports / Grant A. Jameson. – Butterworths.
Llf £150.00

Panhuys, H. F. van →International law in the Netherlands.

Pani, Narendar
Reforms to Pre-Empt Change : Land Legislation in Karnataka. – New Delhi : Concept Publishing Company, 1983.
x, 122p.
Hbk £70.00

Pannett →'A' Level Law.

Pannett, A.
Principles of Hotel and Catering Law. – 2nd ed. – London : Cassell.
ISBN 0304322164 Pbk £9.95

Pannick, David
Judges / David Pannick. – Oxford : Oxford University Press, 1987.
224p; 22cm.
Includes index.
ISBN 0192159569 £10.95
—Judges . – Oxford : Oxford University Press.
ISBN 0192822365 Pbk £4.95
—Judicial review of the death penalty / David Pannick. – London : Duckworth, 1982.
245p; 23cm.
Includes index.
ISBN 0715615947 £18.00
—Sex discrimination law. – Oxford : Oxford University Press, 1985.
ISBN 0198254814 Hbk £30.00

Panou, Stavros →Conditions of validity and cognition in modern legal thought.

Panteios Anotate Schole Politikon Epistemon → New law of the sea : selected and edited papers of the Athens colloquium on the law of the sea, September 1982.

Papaconstantinou, H.
Free Trade & Competition in the European Economic Community : Law, Poicy and Practice. – Routledge.
ISBN 0415001102 Hbk £27.50

Papacy and England : 12th-14th Centuries. – Northampton : Variorum, 1982.
346p : Illus.. – – (Collected Studies Ser.: CS 154).
ISBN 0860780996 Hbk £24.00

Papadakis, N →International law of the sea and marine affairs, a bibliography, Supplement to the 1980 edition.

Papadopoulos, Hellen
Butterworth's Company Reports. – Wellington : Butterworths.
Hbk
—Butterworths Company Reports. – Butterworths. – (Report Series).
Hbk £434.50
→ Butterworth's Family Law Bulletin.
→ Butterworth's Family Law Reports.
—Butterworths Taxation Library, 3 Vols. – Butterworths.
ISBN 0409661287 Llf £770.00
—Tax Reports (New Zealand), 10 Vols. – Wellington : Butterworths, 1986.
Pbk

Papal government and England during the pontificate of Honorius III. – Cambridge : Cambridge University Press.
Studies thirteenth-century administrative revolution of the papacy. Gives details of registers and the registrative system. Discusses development of canon law in relation to England.
ISBN 0521259118 Hbk £32.50

Paper Chasing : Resources for Legal Studies. – North Ryde : C.C.H. Australia, 1986.
308p.
ISBN 086903670X Hbk

Papers. – Canberra : Australian Government Publishing Service, 1986.
xiv,402p. – (Occasional paper).
Includes bibliographical references.
ISBN 0644055901 £19.95

Papers : Hungarian-Finnish Penal Law Seminary on Petty Offences / editor, Lenke Feher. – Budapest : Geza Kilenyi, 1984.
199 leaves.

Papers and comments delivered at the ninth annual Workshop on Commercial and Consumer Law, Toronto, November 2-3, 1979 / edited by Jacob S. Ziegel. – Toronto : Butterworths, 1981.
xi,279p.
Includes bibliographical references. At head of cover title: Canadian Association of Law Teachers, Faculty of Law, University of Toronto and the Osgoode Hall Law School of York University.
ISBN 0409879614

Papers and comments delivered at the tenth annual Workshop on Commercial and Consumer Law, Toronto, October 17-18, 1980 / edited by Jacob S. Ziegel. – Toronto : Butterworths, 1982.
x,218p.
Includes bibliographical references. At head of title: Canadian Association of Law Teachers, Faculty of Law, University of Toronto, and the Osgoode Hall Law School of York University..
ISBN 0409879622

Papers from the European Conference on Football Violence : held at the Tickled Trout Hotel, Salmesbury, Preston, Lancashire, 10-13 April 1987 / edited by Tim O'Brien. – Preston? : Lancashire Polytechnic, 1987.
81p.
Bibliographies.
ISBN 090669406X

Papers of Daniel Webster
Vol.1 : The New Hampshire practice : Alfred S. Konefsky and Andrew J. King / Alfred S. Konefsky, Andrew J. King. – Hanover, N.H. : Published for Dartmouth College by the University Press of New England, 1982.
xxxix,571p; 25cm.
Includes index.
ISBN 0874512328

Papers on Indigenous Law in Southern Africa. – Pretoria : VanSchaik.
ISBN 0627013988 Hbk £17.85

Papers presented at the 22nd Australian Legal Convention, Brisbane, 1983. – Brisbane : Queensland Law Society for the Law Council of Australia, 1984.
444p.
Includes bibliographical references.
ISBN 0949677353

Papp
International space policy / McIntyre. – Quorum Press, 1988.
ISBN 0899302157 Hbk £39.25

Papua New Guinea, in the Supreme Court of Justice ... In the matter of a reference under section 18 of the Constitution, and in the matter of Ralph Rakhinand Premdas against the Independent State of Papua New Guinea, and others. Re Rooney: being a transcript of the proceedings 27th August - 5th and 11th September 1979. – Port Moresby : Council of Law Reporting for Papua New Guinea, 1981.
vi,390p; 34cm.
Cover title: The Rooney case.

Papua New Guinea law reports : cases determined in the Supreme Court of the Territory of Papua and New Guinea, the Supreme Court of Papua New Guinea and in the High Court of Australia. – Sydney : Law Book Co., 1963-.

Parac, Z. →Credit and Guarantee Financing, Transfer of Technology.

Parallel imports. – Oxford : Blackwell Scientific, 1987.
ISBN 0003833666 Hbk £20.00

Parameswaran, K.
Power of Taxation Under the Constitution. – Lucknow : Eastern Book Company, 1987.
Hbk £90.00

Pardon : Justice Mercy and Public Interest. – Oxford : Oxford University Press.
ISBN 0195058712 Hbk £15.00

Parental responsibilities : recommendation no.R (84)4 adopted by the Committee of Ministers of the Council of Europe on 28 February 1984, and Explanatory memorandum. – Council of Europe. – Strasbourg : Council of Europe, 1984.
19p; 21cm.
'... prepared by the Committee of Experts on Family Law set up under the authority of the European Committee on Legal Co-operation' - preface..
ISBN 9287103291

Parental supervision and juvenile delinquency / by David Riley and Margaret Shaw. – London : H.M.S.O., 1985.
v,85p; 25cm.
Bibliography: p81-85. A Home Office Research and Planning Unit report.
ISBN 0113407998

Parent-Child Law in Singapore. – London : Butterworths, 1984.
ISBN 0406181217 Pbk £25.00

Parenthood in the balance : an assessment of benefits and leave around the time of childbirth / Equal Opportunities Commission. – Manchester : Equal Opportunities Commission, 1982.
28,ivp; 21cm.
ISBN 0905829603 Pbk

Parents and children: the law of parental responsibility. – 3rd. – London : Sweet & Maxwell, 1987.
Places legal problems in their social context, and discusses the nature of parental rights and duties, the consequences of marriage breakdown, and the legal response to child abuse. Covers the Family Law Reform Act, the legal implications of surrogacy arrangements, the sterilisation of a mentally handicapped ward of court, the custodianship provision of the Children Act 1975, and the Law Commission's review of the private law relating to children.
ISBN 042136050X Pbk £17

Parfitt, Tudor
Jews of Africa and Asia : contemporary anti-semitism and other pressures / Tudor Parfitt. – London : Minority Rights Group, 1987.
15p. – (Report).
Bibliography: p.15.
ISBN 0946690561

Paris Convention for the Protection of Industrial Property : Official English Text of the Stockholm Act (1967). – rep. 1987. – Geneva : World Intellectual Property Organization.
43p.
Hbk £10.00

Paris Convention for the Protection of Industrial Property from 1883 to 1983. – Geneva : World Intellectual Property Organization, 1983.
229p.
Hbk £100.00

Parish Councillor's Guide. – London : Shaw & Sons, 1988.
246p.
ISBN 0721905137 Pbk £6.50

Park
Treatise On Law Of Dower. – Professional Books.
ISBN 086205298X Hbk £49.75

Park, A.
Sources of Nigerian Law, The. – Sweet & Maxwell, 1972.
ISBN 0421172703 Pbk £10.00

Park, Kyung Jae
Intellectual property laws of Korea / by Kyung Jae Park. – Seoul : Lee & Ko, 1986.
xx,372p.

Park, William →International commercial litigation.

Parker →Companies Acts.
—Modern Conveyancing Precedents. – 2nd ed. – London : Butterworths, 1988.
ISBN 040633451X Hbk
—Modern wills precedents. – 2nd ed. – London : Butterworths, 1987.
ISBN 0406334617 Hbk £24.00

Parker, A.C.
Constitution of the Five Nations : or the Iroquois Book of the Great Law. – 1916 repr. – Oshweken : Iroqrafts.
158p.
ISBN 0919645003 Hbk £6.95

Parker, C.G.A.
Hazell's Guide to the Judiciary and the Courts 1989 With Holborn Law Society List of Barristers by Chambers. – Hazell.
ISBN 0901718483 Pbk £17.00

Parker, Catherine M.
Inventory of current legal research in Canada / l'inventaire des activites de recherche juridique courantes au Canada : compilers, Catherine M. Parker, Laurie A. Davidson. – Ottawa : Canadian Law Information Council, 1986.
vi,169p.
Includes index.
ISBN 0920358888

Parker, David B.
Modern law of trusts / by David B. Parker and Anthony R. Mellows. – 5th ed. – London : Sweet & Maxwell, 1983.
xlviii,492p; 24cm.
Previous ed.: London : Sweet & Maxwell, 1979. Includes index.
ISBN 0421309709 Hbk £
ISBN 0421309806 Pbk £12.00
→ Tudor on charities.

Parker, G. Brian →Buckley on the Companies Acts.

Parker, Howard
Instead of the Dole : Enquiry into Integration of Tax and Benefit Systems. – Routledge.
ISBN 0415009618 Hbk £35.00
—Receiving juvenile justice : adolescents and state care and control / Howard Parker, Maggie Casburn, David Turnbull. – Oxford : Basil Blackwell, 1981.
259p; 23cm.
Criticises official discretion, deviation and diversity in the selection and sentencing process.
ISBN 0631127275 Hbk £12.00
ISBN 0631127453 Pbk £5.50

Parker, R.
Understanding company financial statements. – 2nd ed. – Pelican, 1982.
ISBN 0140091025 Pbk £4.95

Parker, Stephen
Cohabitees / Stephen Parker. – Chichester : Barry Rose, 1981.
xxii,230p.
Bibliography: p224-225.
ISBN 0859922103

Parker's Conduct of Parliamentary Elections. – Tonbridge : Ernest Benn, 1983.
610p. – (Knight's Looseleaf Library).
ISBN 0853143137 Llf £47.50

Parkington, Michael →MacGillivray and Parkington on insurance law : relating to all risks other than marine.

Parkinson : Financial Instruments for the Corporate Treasurer. – London : Butterworths, 1987.
ISBN 0406103550 Pbk

Parkinson, Andrew
Financial Instruments for Corporate Treasurer. – London : Butterworths, 1988.
ISBN 0406103550 Pbk
—Parkinson : Financial Instruments for the Corporate Treasurer. – London : Butterworths, 1987.
ISBN 0406103550 Pbk

Parkinson, Lisa
Conciliation in separation and divorce : finding common ground / Lisa Parkinson. – London : Croom-Helm, 1986.
192p; 23cm.
Includes bibliography and index.
ISBN 0709940475 Hbk £17.95
ISBN 070994053X Pbk £8.95
→ Services for Conciliation in Divorce.

Parks, A.
Law of Tug, Tow and Pilotage. – 2nd ed. – London : Chapman & Hall, 1982.
ISBN 0412250209 Hbk £60.00

Parks, Alex L.
Law and practice of marine insurance and average / by Alex L. Parks. – 2 v. – London : Stevens, 1988.
Concentrates on United States marine insurance law, and practice, and includes relevant case citations, extending to those not directly concerned with marine insurance, but of fundamental importance in understanding the liabilities which underwriters insure, such as collision wreck removal, personal injury and cargo damage.
ISBN 0420476504 £140.00

Parliament and administrative agencies : a study paper prepared for the Law Reform Commission of Canada / by Frans F. Slatter. – Ottawa : Law Reform Commission of Canada, 1982.
6,154p; 25cm. – (Study paper).
ISBN 0662116259

Parliament and Bureaucracy. – Neutral Bay : Hale & Iremonger.
ISBN 0868060143 Hbk £24.95, 015
ISBN 0868060151 Pbk £12.95, 015

Parliament and information : the Westminster scene / Dermot Englefield. – London : Library Association, 1981.
vii,132p; 24cm.
Includes index.
ISBN 0853655707 Hbk
ISBN 0853659931 Pbk

Parliament and the executive. – London : Royal Institute of Public Administration, 1982.
66p; 21cm.
ISBN 0900628278 Pbk £3.50

Parliament Government in Britain. – Carleton : Pitman Pty Ltd, 1984.
ISBN 0273016156 Hbk £38.95, 015

Parliament House book. – 1st looseleaf ed. 2. – Edinburgh : Green, 1982-.
Previous ed.: 156th, 1981.
ISBN 0414006887 Loose leaf

Parliament in the 1980s / edited by Philip Norton. – Oxford : Blackwell, 1985.
240p.
Includes bibliography and index.
ISBN 0631140565 Hbk £17.50 :
ISBN 0631140573 Pbk £5.95

Parliament of England 1559-1581. – Cambridge : Cambridge University Press, 1986.
411.
Study of functions of parliament, political and legislative. Finds that legislative capacity was far more important. Discusses the interests involved in promoting bills and problems associated with making them law.
ISBN 0521328357 Hbk £32.50

Parliament, the executive, and the governor-general : a constitutional analysis / George Winterton. – Carlton, Vic. : Melbourne University Press, 1983.
viii, 376 p.; 23 cm.
Includes index. Bibliography: p. 329-346.
ISBN 0522842429

Parliamentary All-Party Penal Affairs Group
Life-sentence prisoners. – Parliamentary All-Party Penal Affairs Group. – Chichester : Barry Rose, 1986.
44p.
ISBN 085992386X
—Prevention of crime among young people / Parliamentary All-Party Penal Affairs Group. – Chichester : Rose, 1983.
112p; 21cm.
ISBN 0859923533 Pbk £7.00
—Statutory restrictions on the use of custody for young offenders : a consultative paper. – Parliamentary All-Party Penal Affairs Group. – London : Parliamentary All-Party Penal Affairs Group, 1985.
8,3 leaves.

Parliamentary Assembly : procedure and practice / Kenneth Bradshaw, John Sweetman. – 8th ed. – Strasbourg : Council of Europe, 1983.
370p.
Includes index.
ISBN 9287102325

Parliamentary challenge to the community law making process : the Exeter Lecture in European Community Law, delivered in the University on 4 March 1983 / by Alan R. Tyrrell. – Exeter : University of Exeter, 1983.
11p.

Parliamentary Debates on Establishing the Australian Broadcasting Control Board, 1948. – North Ryde : Australian Film and Television School.
166p.
ISBN 0642924651 Hbk £12.00

Parliamentary Practice in British Columbia. – Victoria : Government of British Columbia, 1981.
v, 1p.
ISBN 0771882467 Hbk £55.00

Parliamentary Privilege in Canada. – London : Butterworths.
ISBN 0409847860 Hbk £56.00

Parliamentary Privileges in India. – New Delhi : Deep and Deep Publications, 1986.
268p.
Hbk £175.00

Parliamentary Surveys of the Duchy of Cornwall Pt. 1. – Exeter : Devon & Cornwall Record Society, 1982.
Hbk £8.00
Pt. 2. – 1984.
ISBN 0901853275 Hbk £8.00

Parliamentary yearbook 1988. – London : Blake's, 1988.
448p.
ISBN 0905846605

Parliaments of the world : a comparative reference compendium. – 2nd ed. 2. – Aldershot : Gower, 1986.
1422p; 25cm.
Previous ed.: published in 1 vol. London : Macmillan, 1976. Includes index.
ISBN 0566052288 v.2 £65.00

Parmar, H. A. →Aviation Law for Pilots.

Parnell, Alan
Building Legislation and Historic Buildings. – London : Architectural Press, 1987.
ISBN 0851397905 Pbk £14.95

Parol evidence with particular reference to contract / by D. T. Zeffertt and A. Paizes. – Johannesburg : Centre for Banking Law, Rand Afrikaans University, 1986.
108p.
Includes bibliographical references.

Parole decision-making in Canada : research towards decision guidelines / by Joan Nuffield. – Ottawa, Ont. : Communication Division, Solicitor General of Canada, 1982.
iv, 96 p.; 28 cm.
Bibliography: p. 91-96.
ISBN 0662121147 Pbk

Parole system in England and Wales : report of the Review Committee / presented to Parliament by the Secretary of State for the Home Department by Command of Her Majesty , November 1988. – London : HMSO, 1988.
v,148p.
Chairman: Lord Carlisle of Bucklow.
ISBN 0101053223

Parr →Research and development in Canada: a practical guide to financing, protecting and exploiting new technology.

Parr, Gael
Seminar for Librarians in the Criminal Justice System. – Canberra : Australian Institute of Criminology.
Hbk £2.50

Parrington, Sheila →Taxation of Land Development.
→ Whillans's Tax Tables.

Parris, John
Arbitration : Principles and Practice. – Oxford : Blackwell Scientific, 1983.
ISBN 000383171X Hbk £19.95
—Arbitration : principles and practice / John Parris. – London : Granada, 1983.
xi,242p; 25cm.
Includes index.
ISBN 0246118997
—Commercial Contracts. – London : Collins, 1987.
208p.
ISBN 0003832341 Hbk £17.50
—Construction Law Digest, 3 Vols. – London : Collins.
Pbk £185.00
—Construction Law Digest. – Oxford : Blackwell Scientific.
ISBN 0002639351 Hbk £225.00
—Contract strategies for construction professionals. – Oxford : Blackwell Scientific, 1987.
ISBN 0003833259 Hbk £19.95
—Default by Sub-Contractors and Suppliers. – Oxford : Blackwell Scientific, 1985.
ISBN 0003830470 Hbk £19.95
—Effective retention of title clauses / John Parris. – London : Collins, Profession & Technical, 1986.
256p; 24cm.
Includes index.
ISBN 0003830748 £17.50
—Law for Civil Engineers. – London : Collins, 1987.
280p.
ISBN 0003832570 Hbk £19.50
—Making Commercial Contracts. – Oxford : Blackwell Scientific, 1988.
ISBN 0632018623 Hbk £19.95
—Retention of title on the sale of goods / John Parris. – London : Granada, 1982.
186p; 24cm.
Includes index.
ISBN 0246116129
—Standard form of building contract : JCT 80 / John Parris. – 2nd ed. – London : Collins, 1985.
xii,256p; 24cm.
Previous ed.: London : Granada, 1982. Includes index.
ISBN 0003830276 £17.50
—Standard form of building contract JCT 1980. – 2nd ed. – Oxford : Blackwell Scientific, 1985.
ISBN 0003830276 Hbk £19.95

Parrish →Essential Law for Landowners and Farmers.

Parry
Valuation and Conversion Tables. – London : Estates Gazette, 1978.
ISBN 0728200641 Hbk £10.00

Parry and Clark: the law of succession. – 9th. – London : Sweet & Maxwell.
Includes the Family Law Reform Act 1987, and the Inheritance Tax Act of 1984. Also covers the Non-Contentious Probate Rules, and the Insolvency Act 1986. New cases are referred to throughout the text, in particular where they illustrate the exercise of the courts' power to order financial provision for the family of the deceased.
ISBN 0421359803 Hbk £34
ISBN 0421359900 Pbk £24.00

Parry, Anthony
EEC Law / James Dinnage. – 2nd ed. – London : Sweet & Maxwell, 1981.
lvi,531p; 25cm.
Previous ed.: 1973. Includes index.
ISBN 0421260904 Hbk £25.00
ISBN 0421261005 Pbk £16.00

Parry, Audrey →Law and international resource conflicts.

Parry, Clive →Law Officers' opinions to the Foreign Office 1793-1860 : a reproduction of the manuscript series with index and commentaries.

Parry, David Hughes
Sanctity of contracts in English law / by Sir David Hughes Parry. – London : Sweet & Maxwell, 1986.
viii,77p. – (Legal reprint series).
Reprint originally published: London, Stevens, 1959. Includes bibliographical references. 'Published under the auspices of the Hamlyn Trust'.
ISBN 0421376007

Parry, Deborah L. →Law of consumer protection and fair trading.

Parry, Jacques →Fraud.

Parry, Martin L. →Children act 1975.
—Cohabitation / by Martin L. Parry : with a foreword by H.K. Bevan. – London : Sweet and Maxwell, 1981.
xxv,162p; 22cm.
Includes bibliographies and index.
ISBN 0421267305 Pbk £5.75
—Law relating to cohabitation / by Martin L. Parry. – 2nd ed. – London : Sweet & Maxwell, 1988.
xxxiii,263p.
Changes effected by the Family Law Reform Act 1987 and the Social Security Act 1986 are included. Discusses home ownership, home occupation, money, tax, children, violence, death, and contracts, and contains an appendix of precedents.
ISBN 0421371102 £20.00

Parry, Robert M.
Employment Standards Handbook. – Aurora : Canada Law Book Co, 1986.
– (Text Book-Civil).
Llf £95.00

Parsons, Guy T. E.
Tolley's employees' rights in receiverships and liquidations / Guy T.E. Parsons, William F. Ratford. – 2nd ed. – Croyden : Tolley, 1984.
xiv,210p; 30cm.
Previous ed.: 1979. Bibliography: p201. - Includes index.
ISBN 0854591443 £25.00

Parsons, R.W.
Income Taxation in Australia : Principles of Income, Deductibility and Tax Accounting. – North Ryde : Law Book Co, 1985.
lxxiii, 901p.
ISBN 0455206007 Hbk £82.00
ISBN 0455206015 Pbk £65.00

Parsons, Robert →Employment Law Manual.

Parsons, Robert B
Canadian Mining Taxation. – London : Butterworths.
ISBN 0409859445 Hbk £24.00
—Canadian mining taxation / Robert B. Parsons. – Toronto : Butterworths, 1982.
x,253p.
ISBN 0409859745

Part 2: List of Goods and Services in Class Order. – Geneva : World Intellectual Property Organization.
Pbk £80.00
Records of the Nairobi Diplomatic Conference for the Adoption of a Treaty on the Protection of the Olympic Symbol (September 24 to 26, 1981). –
194p.
Hbk £30.00

Part, Anthony
Taxation of North Sea Oil. – London : Institute for Fiscal Studies, 1981.
24p.
Hbk £5.00

Part II of the Landlord and Tenant Act 1954 / the Law Commission. – London : HMSO, 1988.
viii,144p. – (Working paper).
Includes sections from the Act.
ISBN 0117301930

Parthasarathy, M.S.
Banking Law : Leading Indian Cases. – 2nd ed. in prep. – Bombay : Tripathi.
Hbk

Partial Revision of the Indigenous and Tribal Populations Convention, 1957 (No. 107). – Geneva : International Labour Office, 1988.
iv, 127p.
ISBN 9221060225 Hbk £20.00

Parties to an action. – Scarborough, Ontario : Butterworths (Canada), 1988.
480.
Contains precedents, definitions of key terms, and a table of cases. Demonstrates how various types of 'persons' of groups become parties to a civil action and how they are described in the proceedings. Types of parties covered include infants, mentally incompetent persons, aliens, accused persons and convects, unincorporated associations, foreign sovereigns, states, administrators, and trade unions and employer organizations.
ISBN 0409809560 Hbk

Parties to an Offence. – Agincourt : Carswell, 1982.
226p.
This book deals with issues of complicity and constructive complicity in a wide range of criminal offenses under Canadian law. Aiders and abettors; parties to a common unlawful purpose; inciters; procurers; accessories after the fact; and other crimes involving more than one party are covered in the work.
Hbk £40.50

Partington, J. →Teachers and the Law.

Partington, Martin →Housing Law, Supplement 2 (1986).
→ Quiet enjoyment : remedies for harassment and illegal eviction.
→ Social security law in Britain and Ireland : a bibliography.
—Socio-legal studies and social welfare / Martin Partington : a report for the Government and Law Committee of the Economic and Social Research Council. – London : Economic and Social Research Council, 1986.
78p.
Bibliography: p59-78.
ISBN 0862261872

Partisans and mediators : the resolution of divorce disputes / Gwynn Davis. – Oxford : Clarendon Press, 1988.
x,219p.
Bibliography: pp.211-215. - Includes index. Concerns divorcing couples who seek help in negotiating over money or children, and the partisans or mediators who assist. Concludes that the prospect of a genuine non-coercive agreement is being undermined by such considerations as cost, and the limitations of the 'due process'.
ISBN 0198256124 Hbk £25

Partition Act. – 4th ed. – Allahabad : Law Publishers, 1983.
178p.
Hbk £15.00

Partition in Ireland, India and Palestine : theory and practice / T.G. Fraser. – London : Macmillan, 1984.
xiii,225p; 23cm.
Bibliography: p210-213. - Includes index.
ISBN 0333322800 £22.50

Partlett, David F.
Professional negligence / by David F. Partlett. – Sydney : Law Book Co., 1985.
xxxvii, 425 p.; 25 cm.
Includes bibliographical references and indexes.
ISBN 0455205949

Partnership / Henning and Delport. – Durban : Professional Publisher, 1984.
ISBN 0409040223 Hbk £33.00

Partnership. – London : Butterworths.
ISBN 0409843156 Hbk £30.00

Partnership Act, 1961 (Act 135) and Specific Relief Act, 1950 (Act 137). – Kuala Lumpur : International Law Books Services.
Hbk £9.00

Partnership Law. – 11th ed. – Plymouth : Macdonald & Evans.
ISBN 0712116745 Pbk £3.50

Partnership taxation / Nigel T. Davey. – 3rd ed. – London : Butterworth, 1987.
372p; 25cm.
Previous ed.: London : HFL, 1978. Includes index.
ISBN 0406678200 Pbk £25.00

Partnership taxation : basis of assessment : a consultative document. – London : Inland Revenue, 1984.
19p.

Parton, Nigel
Politics of child abuse / Nigel Parton. – Basingstoke : Macmillan, 1985.
xii,245p; 22cm.
ISBN 0333363167 Pbk
ISBN 0333363175

Partsch, Karl Josef →New rules for victims of armed conflicts : commentary on the two 1977 protocols additional to the Geneva Conventions of 1949.

Part-time employment and sex discrimination legislation in Great Britain : a study of the demand for part-time labour and of sex discrimination in selected organizations and establishments / by Olive Robinson and John Wallace. – London : H.M.S.O., 1984.
53p. – (Research paper).

Party statutes of the Communist world / edited by William B. Simons and Stephen White. – The Hague : M. Nijhoff, 1984.
viii,545p.
Prepared for the International Conference on Ruling Parties and their Status under Law, Kiel, Germany, June 1984. Bibliographies.
ISBN 9024729750

Parvez
Basic Human Rights. – Dhaka : Islamic Foundation Bangladesh.
Hbk £0.50

Pascale →Crime and Punishment in Modern America.

Pasic, Najdan →Workers' management in Yugoslavia : recent developments and trends.

Pask, Diane →National Themes in Family Law.
—Women, the Law and the Economy / Mahoney. – Toronto : Butterworths, 1985.
414p.
ISBN 0409988650 Pbk £31.95

Pasquino, Gianfranco
Institutions and the decision-making process in the draft treaty / by Gianfranco Pasquino and Luciano Bardi. – Florence : European University Institute, 1985.
66p.

Passamaneck, S. M.
Insurance in Rabbinic Law. – Edinburgh : Edinburgh University Press.
230p.
ISBN 0852242581 Hbk £10.00

Passing down the family business: solving the tax problems. – 4th. – London : Longman Professional (UK), 1988.
– (Longman Intelligence Report).
Information and advice on reducing the tax burden and maximising the prosperity of the business when transferring control to another member of the family. Outlines tax planning strategies, and how to use tax reliefs to their full advantage.
ISBN 0851212719 Hbk £95.00

Passing Down the Family Farm / Robert Venables. – London : Oyez Longman, 1983.
– (Oyez Longman Intelligence Report Ser.).
ISBN 0851207367 Hbk £45.00

Passing off. – London : Longman Professional, 1988.
ISBN 0851213928 Pbk

Passing off : law and practice / John Drysdale, Michael Silverleaf. – London : Butterworths, 1986.
xxxiv,224p; 26cm.
Includes index.
ISBN 0406253404 £25.00

Passing off trade deception trade marks / Charles Joseph Bannon. – Sydney : Butterworths, 1985.
xxv,172p.
ISBN 0409492442 A$59

Passingham, Bernard
Law and Practice in Matrimonial Causes / Caroline Harmer. – 4th ed. – London : Butterworths, 1985.
This text is an introduction to matrimonial law and a guide to developments in the area for students of the subject in England. All forms and model pleadings reflect the Matrimonial and Family Proceedings Act of 1984 and the Matrimonial Homes Act of 1983.
ISBN 0406637075 Pbk £21.95
ISBN 0406637083 Hbk £38.00

Past or future crimes : deservedness and dangerousness in the sentencing of criminals / Andrew von Hirsch. – Manchester : Manchester University Press, 1986.
xii,220p; 24cm.
Originally published: New Brunswick, N.J. : Rutgers University Press, 1985. Bibliography: p201-212. - Includes index.
ISBN 0719017122 £21.00
ISBN 0813511151

Pastoral Discipline and the Church Courts : The Hexham Court, 1680-1730. – York : St. Anthony's Press, 1982.
– (Borthwick Papers Ser.).
Pbk £3.00

Patchett, K. W.
New York Convention on the Recognition and Enforcement of Foreign Arbitral Awards : explanatory documentation prepared for Commonwealth jurisdictions / by K.W. Patchett in association with the Commonwealth Secretariat. – London : Commonwealth Secretariat, 1981.
v,62p.
Includes the text of the Convention.
ISBN 0850922038
—Recognition of commercial judgments and awards in the Commonwealth / K.W. Patchett. – London : Butterworths, 1984.
xlv,326p; 26cm.
Bibliography: pxxix. - Includes index.
ISBN 0406403201

Patel, V.B.
Commentary on the Industrial Disputes Act, Vols 1 and 2. – 3rd ed. – Allahabad : Orient Law House, 1984.
Hbk £325.00

Patent and Trademark Law of the People's Republic of China (1985). – Geneva : World Intellectual Property Organization, 1984.
66p.
Hbk £15.00

Patent claim : drafting and interpretation. – London : Longman Professional, 1983.
ISBN 0851206859 Hbk £58.00

Patent claim drafting and interpretation / general editor John A. Kemp. – London : Oyez Longman, 1983.
xi,251p; 23cm.
Includes index.
ISBN 0851206859

Patent co-operation treaty : a new era : papers prepared for presentation at a seminar held at the Brewery Conference Centre...November 11, 1985 / edited by James Lahore. – London : Centre for Commercial Law Studies, Queen Mary College, University of London, 1986.
vi, 46p.
ISBN 0951066420

Patent Co-operation Treaty (PCT) : Original Text of the Treaty and Regulations as in Force on Jan 1, 1981. – Geneva : World Intellectual Property Organization.
166p.
Hbk £15.00

Patent Information and Documentation Handbook. – Geneva : World Intellectual Property Organization.
1,600p.
Hbk £150.00

Patent Law. – Calcutta : Eastern Law House, 1985.
950p.
Hbk £375.00

Patent licensing and EEC competition rules : Regulation 2349/84 / Valentine Korah. – Oxford : ESC Publishing, 1985.
xiv,126p. – (European competition law monographs).
Includes bibliographies.
ISBN 090621436X

Patent licensing in Europe / by B.I. Cawthra. – 2nd ed. – London : Butterworths, 1986.
xxi,249p; 22cm.
Previous ed.: 1978. Bibliography: p236-240. - Includes index.
ISBN 0406148414 Hbk £47.00

Patent Licensing Transactions. – Matthew Bender, 1968.
ISBN 0000999079 Hbk £112.00

Patent system and inventive activity. – Manchester : Manchester University Press, 1984.
ISBN 0719009979 Hbk £21.00

Patent Trade Marks & Designs Office
Guide for Applicants for Patents. – Patent Trade Marks & Designs Office. – Canberra : Australian Government Publishing Service, 1981.
45p.
ISBN 0642060371 Hbk £2.30

Patentability of computer software : an international guide to the protection of computer-related inventions / by H.W.A.M. Hanneman. – Deventer : Kluwer Law and Taxation Publishers, 1985.
257p; 23cm.
ISBN 9065442251

Patenting Manual. – 2nd. – Waterloo, 1983.
381p.
ISBN 094341802X Hbk £48.50

Patents. – Matthew Bender, 1978.
ISBN 0000999073 Hbk £344.00

Patents : a Basic Guide to Patenting in Biotechnology. – Cambridge : Cambridge University Press.
– (Cambridge Studies in Biotechnology No. 6).
ISBN 052132954X Pbk £20.00

Patents Act, 1983 (Act 291). – Kuala Lumpur : International Law Books Services.
Hbk £9.00

Patents for inventions : and the protection of industrial designs / by T.A. Blanco White. – 5th ed. – London : Stevens, 1983.
xxxv,304p; 26cm.
Previous ed.: 1974. Includes index.
ISBN 0420463100 Hbk £44.00

Patents in chemistry and biotechnology. – 2nd ed. – Oxford : Oxford University Press, 1987.
ISBN 0198552211 Pbk £12.50

Patents in perspective : a collection of essays / edited by Jeremy Phillips. – Oxford : ESC Publishing Ltd, 1985.
xii,121p.
ISBN 0906214378

Patents of Inventions. – 3rd ed. – Agincourt : Carswell, 1981.
This textbook includes the text of the Patent Act of Canada and rules, as well as, an exhaustive summation of case law and statutes pertaining to patent law.
ISBN 045934500 Hbk £25.30

Patents, trade marks, copyright and industrial designs / Robin Jacob. – 3rd ed. – London : Sweet & Maxwell, 1986.
xiv,182p; 22cm.
Previous ed.: 1978. Includes index.
ISBN 0421349603 Hbk £13.50
ISBN 0421349700 Pbk £8.95

Paterson
House of Lords Appeals : 1821-1873, 28 Vols. 1866-1873, 2 Vols. /. – Abingdon : Professional Books.
Hbk
—Licensing Act, 1984. – 92nd ed. – London : Butterworths, 1984.
ISBN 0406335176 Hbk
—Licensing Acts Nineteen Eighty-Two / J. N. Martin. – 90th ed. – London : Butterworths, 1982.
ISBN 0406334528 Hbk £92.50
—UNCITRAL Arbitration Model in Canada / Thompson. – Agincourt : Carswell, 1987.
262p.
This work outlines the process of adopting and implementing the UNCITRAL Model Law. Canadian legislation and the UNCITRAL Model Law and Rules are provided. Discussions include that of arbitration as a universally accepted method of resolving international commercial disputes and the adoption in British Columbia of the model law on international commercial arbitration.
Hbk £41.25

Paterson, A. A.
Legal system of Scotland : cases and materials / A.A. Paterson and T.St.J.N. Bates. – 2nd ed. – Edinburgh : Green, 1986.
xviii,395p.
Analyses the use of the principal sources of Scots law, in particular precedent and statutory interpretation. Considers the legal profession, the administration of civil and criminal justice and the operation of tribunals. Also deals with the Court of Justice of the European Communities and the European Commission and Court of Human Rights.
ISBN 0414007832

Paterson, Alan
Appellate decision making in the common law world / Alan Paterson : Aleksander Peczenik. – Arnhem : Gouda Quint, 1985.
52p.
Papers presented at the first Symposium on Legal Decision Making of the Institute of Legal Decision Making, Erasmus University.
ISBN 9060003772
—Law lords / Alan Paterson. – London : Macmillan, 1982.
x,288p; 23cm.
ISBN 0333238869

Paterson, Ian
Private company share sale manual. – 1st ed. – London : Longman Professional (UK), 1988.
– (Longman Commercial Series).
Transaction-based manual, providing a guide through the various stages of a company sale in chronological order. Gives practical suggestions to the vendor and purchaser on procedure. Examines taxation aspects, and contains checklists, case and statute references.
ISBN 0851213146 Hbk £42.00

Paterson, M.
Pensions : agenda for change. – Cambridge : Woodhead-Faulkner, 1987.
ISBN 0859413802 Hbk £32.50

Paterson, W. E.
Australian Company Law, 4 Vols. / H. H. Ednie. – Wellington : Butterworths, 1982.
Pbk
—Australian Company Law Reports (ACLR) / H. H. Ednie. – Wellington : Butterworths.
Hbk

Paterson's Licensing Acts 1989. – 97th ed. – London : Butterworths.
ISBN 0406335222 Hbk £70.00

Patfield →Changing law.

Patients' Rights : A guide for NHS Patients and Doctors. – London : HMSO, 1983.
60p.
ISBN 0117010448 Pbk £1.50

Paton, Ann →Casebook on damages in Scotland.
→ McEwan and Paton on damages in Scotland.

Patrick, Fitzgerald
Crime, Justice, and Codification : Essays in Commemoration of Jacques Fortin. – Agincourt : Carswell, 1986.
196p.
This book contains eleven essays dealing with the theory, philosophy, reform and codification of criminal law. Rationality and legitimacy of criminal law the goals of reform are addressed in the essays.
Hbk £40.50

Pattabhiraman, V.
Handbook of Tax on Salaries : Incorporating the Finance Act. – New Delhi : Tata McGraw-Hill Publishing Co, 1988.
354p.
ISBN 0074518291 Pbk £5.00

Pattendon, Rosemary
Judge, discretion, and the criminal trial / by Rosemary Pattendon. – Oxford : Clarendon, 1982.
xv,299p; 23cm.
Includes index.
ISBN 0198253737 £20.00
—Judicial discretion and criminal litigation. – 2nd. – Oxford : Clarendon Press, 1989.
350; 23.5.
Examines the discretions exercised by criminal trial courts both at Crown Court and Magistrates level, and discretion in the criminal appellate process. Intends to provide a theoretical framework within which to discuss and assess the discretions. Concentrates on the law and practice in England and Wales, but also refers to statutes and decision in Australia, New Zealand and Canada.
ISBN 0198255675 Pbk £14.95

Patterns of authority : an analysis of Canadian citation patterns / by Lorna K. Rees-Potter. – Ontario : Canadian Law Information Council, 1982.
vii,61p. – (Working paper).
ISBN 092035825X

Patterson →Comparing Legislations.

Patterson, Mark T.
Divorce Guide for Washington : Step-By-Step Guide for Obtaining Your Own Divorce. – 5th ed. – North Vancouver : International Self-Counsel Press, 1988.
ISBN 0889087385 Hbk

Patterson, W.M.
Family Protection and Testamentary Promises in New Zealand. – Butterworths, 1985.
Discusses the principles behind the statutory provisions, and the cases in support of the Law of Family Protection and the Law of Testamentary Promises. Considers the amendments to the text if the statutory provisions dealing with Family Protection, particularly those which have given rights to new classes of claimants such as grandchildren.
ISBN 0409701432 Hbk £36.00

Patton, Bruce →Getting to YES : negotiating agreement without giving in.

Patwari, A.B.M.M.I.
Fundamental Rights and Personal Liberty in India, Pakistan and Bangladesh. – New Delhi : Deep and Deep Publications, 1988.
480p.
Hbk £325.00

Paul, et al
Equal Opportunities. – Oxford : Blackwell Scientific, 1988.
ISBN 0631159754 Pbk £8.95
—Human rights / Miller. – Oxford : Blackwell, 1984.
ISBN 0631136991 Pbk £6.95
→ Law of Meetings.
—Philosophy and Law. – Oxford : Blackwell, 1987.
ISBN 0631125271 Pbk £8.50
→ Philosophy of Law.

Paul, Jeffrey →Reading Nozick : essays on Anarchy, state and utopia.

Paul, Patrick B. →Handbook of Hong Kong tax statutes : profits tax, salaries tax, property tax, interest tax, estate duty, stamp duty, Board of Review decisions.

Paul, T.F.
Law and Administration of Incorporated Societies. – 2nd ed. – Butterworths, 1986.
276p.
Covers the nature of societies, the procedure of incorporation, branches, the registrar and assistant registrar, rules, members and membership, the secretary and other officers, secretarial and administrative duties, accounts taxation, dissolution and winding up, conduct of meetings, conventions and conferences, public relations, and the law of defamation.
ISBN 0409787442 Pbk £49.50

Pauly, Alexis
Migrant workers and civil liberties / by Alexis Pauly and Rene Diederich. – Florence : European University Institute, 1983.
102p.

Pauw, Willem →Some cases heard in the Hooge Raad.
—Some cases heard in the Hooge Raad / reported by Willem Pauw : translated and edited by R. Feenstra, P. van Warmelo, D.T. Zeffertt. – Pretoria : Government Printer on behalf of the South African Law Commission, 1985.
viii,117p. – (Research series).
Includes index. Translation of: Observationes tumultuariae novae.
ISBN 0621097152

Pavarini, Massimo →Prison and the Factory.

Pavithran, A.K
Civil Procedure Code / S. Venkataraman. – Allahabad : Orient Law House.
ISBN 0861256700 Hbk £25.00
—Criminal Procedure Code / S. Venkataraman. – Allahabad : Orient Law House.
ISBN 086131154X Hbk £35.00

Pavlich, Dennis J
Condominium Law in Alberta. – Toronto : Butterworths, 1986.
ISBN 0409980293 Hbk
—Condominium Law in British Columbia. – Butterworths, 1983.
434p.
Discusses the major participants in a condominium scheme, including the owner, the owner-developer, the lawyer, the Strata counsel, and the Strata corporation.
ISBN 0409988383 Hbk £75.00

Pavlopoulos, B. →Law and practice relating to pollution control in Greece.

Pawlikowski, Thomas
Intra-Group Arrangements under Articles 85 and 86 of the Treaty Establishing the European Economic Community : with a Comparative Survey. – Bern : Peter Lang, 1984.
xii, 173p.
ISBN 3820451668 Pbk £41.00

Pawlowski, Hans-Martin
Law and social conflict / by Hans-Martin Pawlowski. – Florence : European University Institute, 1983.
19p.
At head of title page: European University Institute, Florence, Department of Political and Social Sciences.

Pawlowski, Mark →Casebook on Rent Review and Lease Renewal.

Pawson, Jennie →Crime and society : readings in history and theory.

Paxman, John M.
Laws and policies affecting adolescent health / by John M. Paxman and Ruth Jane Zuckerman. – Geneva : World Health Organization, 1987.
x,300p.
Includes bibliographical references.
ISBN 9241560959

Paxton, John
Dictionary of the European Communities / John Paxton. – 2nd ed. – London : Macmillan, 1984.
282p; 23cm.
Previous ed.: published as A dictionary of the European Economic Community. 1977. Bibliography: p279-282.
ISBN 0333334388 Hbk £25.00
ISBN 0333370376 Pbk

PAYE Audits. – London : Butterworths, 1988.
ISBN 0406263000 Pbk

Paying for politics / the report of the Commission upon the financing of political parties. – London : Hansard Society, 1981.
49 p.

Paying for Welfare. – Oxford : Blackwell, 1985.
ISBN 0631139729 Pbk £7.95

Paylee, M.V.
Constitutional History of India. – New Delhi : S. Chand and Company.
Hbk £20.00

Payment by the State of advances on child maintenance : Recommendation No.R (82) 2 adopted by the Committee of Ministers of the Council of Europe on 4 February 1982 and explanatory memorandum. – Council of Europe. – Strasbourg : Council of Europe, 1982.
15p; 21cm.
'Prepared by a committee of experts set up under the authority of the European Committee on Legal Co-operation'. At head of cover title : Council of Europe, Legal Affairs.
ISBN 9287101736

Payment obligations in commercial and financial transactions / by R.M. Goode. – London : Sweet & Maxwell, 1983.
xxiii,151p; 22cm.
Includes index.
ISBN 0421318104 Pbk £11.00

Payment of Bonus Act, 1965. – 5th ed. – Lucknow : Eastern Book Company, 1982.
588p.
Hbk £80.00

Payment of Gratuity Act. – 3rd ed. – Calcutta : Eastern Law House, 1983.
Hbk £65.00

Payment of Wages Act (Act 4 of 1936) : with Central State Rules. – 3rd ed. – Allahabad : Law Book Company, 1987.
915p.
Hbk £275.00

Payment of witnesses in civil proceedings / the Law Reform Commission of Western Australia. – Perth : Law Reform Commission of Western Australia, 1988.
iii,11 leaves. – (Discussion paper).

Payment Systems and Productivity / Thorpe. – London : Macmillan, 1986.
ISBN 333394828 Hbk £29.50

Payments on termination of employment. – 2nd ed. – London : Longman Professional, 1984.
ISBN 0851206662 Pbk £9.95

Payne and Ivamy's Carriage of goods by sea / E. R. Hardy Ivamy. – 12th ed. – London : Butterworths, 1985.
xlix,366p; 22cm.
This textbook is a straightforward discussion of the field of carriage of goods by sea under the laws of the United Kingdom for students of the subject.
ISBN 0406640602 Hbk £18.00
ISBN 0406640610 Pbk £14.95

Payne, Geoffrey K.
Low-income housing in the developing world : the role of sites and services and settlement upgrading / Geoffrey K. Payne. – Chichester : Wiley, 1984.
xii,271p; 25cm. – (A Wiley series on public administration in developing countries).
Includes bibliographies and index.
ISBN 0471902128 £29.95

Payne, Julien D, et al
Payne's Digest on Divorce in Canada (1968-1980). – Toronto : DeBoo, 1982.
ISBN 0888201176 Hbk £100.00
—Spousal Property Rights Under the Ontario Family Law Act. – Butterworths, 1987.
80p.
Contains commentary on present and prospective interpretation of the Act, insights into the prospective operation of Parts I, II, and IV of the Act, up-to-date reported and unreported judgements incorporated in the commentary, applicable provincial rules and forms, and an analysis of issues including business valuation, professional licences and pensions.
ISBN 0409809365 Hbk £55.00

Payne, William
Carriage of Goods by Sea / E R Hardy Ivamy. – 12th ed. – London : Butterworths, 1985.
ISBN 0406640602 Hbk £18.00
ISBN 0406640610 Pbk £15.95
—Payne and Ivamy's Carriage of goods by sea / E. R. Hardy Ivamy. – 12th ed. – London : Butterworths, 1985.
xlix,366p; 22cm.
This textbook is a straightforward discussion of the field of carriage of goods by sea under the laws of the United Kingdom for students of the subject.
ISBN 0406640602 Hbk £18.00
ISBN 0406640610 Pbk £14.95

Payne's Digest on Divorce in Canada (1968-1980). – Toronto : DeBoo, 1982.
ISBN 0888201176 Hbk £100.00

Payumo, Pablo R.
Philippine International Radio Laws and Regulations. – Manila : National Book Store, 1984.
512p.
ISBN 9710804995 Pbk £5.00

Peace and security : the United Nations and national interests : report of the nineteenth United Nations of the Next Decade Conference convened June 17-22 1984 in Cape Cod, Mass., USA / sponsored by the Stanley Foundation. – Muscatine, Iowa : Stanley Foundation, 1984.
40p; 22cm.

Peace Palace
Protection du droit a la vie a la lumiere des regles du droit international : bibliographie selective / preparee par la Bibliotheque du Palais de la Paix, La Haye : selective bibliography : prepared by the Library of the Peace Palace, The Hague. – The Hague : Centre for Studies and Research of the Hague Academy of International Law, 1983.
17 leaves.
—Statut juridique international des minorites : bibliographie selective / preparee par la Bibliotheque du Palais de la Paix, La Haye : selective biliography : prepared by the Library of the Peace Palace, the Hague. – The Hague : Center for Studies and Research of the Hague Academy of International Law, 1984.
29 leaves.

Peacock, Alan →Report of the Committee on Financing the BBC.

Peak, Steve
Troops in strikes : military intervention in industrial disputes / Steve Peak. – London : Cobden Trust, 1984.
177p.
Bibliography: p172-174.
ISBN 0900137223

Peake, T.
Cases Determined at Nisi Prius in the Court of King's Bench from Easter Term : 30 Geo 3 to Michaelmas Term, 35 Geo 3. – Repr. of 1795 ed. – Abingdon : Professional Books.
335p.
Hbk £35.00

Pearce, D. C.
Commonwealth administrative law / D.C. Pearce. – Sydney : Butterworths, 1986.
xxix,282p.
Includes index.
ISBN 0409490881 Hbk A$45.00
ISBN 0409490881 Pbk A$32.00
—Statutory Interpretation in Australia. – 3rd ed. – Butterworths, 1988.
288p.
ISBN 0409495255 Hbk £49.00
ISBN 0409308102 Pbk £42.00

Pearce, Joan
Common agricultural policy, prospects for change / Joan Pearce. – London : Published for Royal Institute of International Affairs by Routledge & K. Paul, 1981.
122p.
Includes bibliographical references.
ISBN 0710090692

Pearce, Nasreen
Adoption practice and procedure / by Nasreen Pearce. – London : Fourmat, 1984.
xii,133p; 22cm.
Includes index.
ISBN 0906840791 Pbk
—Custodianship : the law and practice / by Nasreen Pearce. – London : Fourmat, 1986.
xi,77p.
ISBN 1851900152 Pbk £7.95
—Wardship : the law and practice / by Nasreen Pearce. – London : Fourmat, 1986.
xvii,126p.
ISBN 090684097X

Pearce, Robert A.
Land law / by Robert A. Pearce. – London : Sweet & Maxwell, 1985.
200p; 22cm.
Includes index.
ISBN 0421312009 Pbk £17.25

Pearcy, Jeff
How to account for foreign currencies / Jeff Pearcy. – London : Macmillan, 1984.
x,264p; 22cm.
ISBN 0333365461 £30.00

Peardon
Planning your pension. – London : Longman Professional, 1988.
ISBN 0851213715 Pbk £4.95

Pearl, D. →Aging world : dilemmas and challenges for law and social policy.

Pearl, David →Family, law and society : cases and materials.
—Family law and the immigrant communities / David Pearl. – Bristol : Family law, 1986.
xxi,104p; 21cm. – (Guide and practice series).
ISBN 0853081026
—Interpersonal Conflict of Laws in India, Pakistan and Bangladesh. – Bombay : Tripathi, 1981.
350p.
bd £50.00
—Interpersonal conflict of laws in India, Pakistan and Bangladesh / David Pearl. – London : Stevens, 1981.
xxviii,176p; 25cm.
Bibliography: p.165-69. Includes index.
ISBN 0420457704
—Social welfare law / David Pearl and Kevin Gray. – London : Croom Helm, 1981.
308p; 23cm.
Bibliography: p265. - Includes index.
ISBN 085664644X Hbk £14.95
ISBN 0709920040 Pbk £8.95
→ Textbook on Muslim personal law.
—Textbook on Muslim personal law / David Pearl. – 2nd ed. – London : Croom Helm, 1987.
284p; 23cm.
ISBN 0709940890 Pbk £14.95

Pearson, Charles
Emergency Protection in the Footwear Industry. – London : Trade Policy Research Centre, 1983.
99p. – (Thames Essays Ser.: No. 36).
ISBN 0900842652 Hbk £3.00

Pearson, Geoffrey
Hooligan : a history of respectable fears / Geoffrey Pearson. – London : Macmillan, 1983.
xi,283p.
Bibliography: p244-275.
ISBN 0333233999

Pearson, Hilary E
Computer Contracts. – Dordrecht : Kluwer, 1984.
ISBN 9065441980 Pbk £125.00
—Computer contracts : an international guide to agreements and software protection / Hilary E. Pearson. – London : Financial Training, 1984.
ISBN 0906322480

Pearson, John E.
Oke's Magisterial Formulist, 2 Vols. / Stuart Baker. – 20th ed. – London : Butterworths, 1986.
This looseleaf service provides immediate access to all the prescribed forms relating to proceeding in British magistrates' courts. A comprehensive range of precedents for all statutory offenses and many regulatory offenses within the jurisdiction of the courts is included.
ISBN 040632400X £125.00

Pearson, L.
Company Law. – Sydney : Butterworths, 1986.
117p. – (Butterworth's Student Companion Ser.).
ISBN 0409490962 Pbk £9.95

Pease and Chitty's Law of Markets and Fairs / Robert Anthony. – 3rd ed. – Tonbridge : Ernest Benn, 1984.
414p. – (Knights Looseleaf Library).
ISBN 0853143188 Hbk £45.00

Pease, C.
Law of markets and fairs. – Croydon : Tolley, 1984.
ISBN 0853143188 Hbk £45.00

Pease, Ken
Community service order : a first decade of promise / a review undertaken by Ken Pease on behalf of the Howard League for Penal Reform. – London : Howard League for Penal Reform, 1981.
ix,76p; 21cm.
Bibliography: p66-70.
Pbk £1.75
→ Crime and punishment : interpreting the data.
→ Psychology of judicial sentencing.

Peaslee, Amos Jenkins
Constitutions of Nations, 4 Vols. – Dordrecht : Kluwer.
Hbk £275.00 ea.
—Constitutions of nations
Vol. 2 : Asia, Australia and Oceania / by Amos J. Peaslee. – Rev. 4th ed. – Dordecht : M. Nijhoff, 1985.
1824p.
ISBN 902472905X Hbk £60.00

Peat Marwick McLintock
Acquisitions in the United States of America. – Peat Marwick McLintock. – London : Butterworths.
ISBN 0406502552 Hbk £45.00

Peay, Jill →Director of Public Prosecutions : principles and practices for the Crown Prosecutor : an inquiry carried out at the Centre for Criminological Research, University of Oxford.
—Tribunals on trial: a study of decision-making under the Mental Health Review Tribunals. Based on empirical enquiry into the operation of the Tribunal system, assesses the process of decision-making from the initial application by a patiTribunals on trial: a study of decision-making under the Mental Health Act 1983. – Oxford : Clarendon Press, 1989.
240; 21.5.
Insight into the decision-making processes of the Mental Health Review Tribunals. Based on empirical enquiry into the operation of the Tribunal system, assesses the process of decision-making from the initial application by a patient, through descriptions of tribunal hearings, to an examination of their deliberations. Examines individual cases in detail.
ISBN 0198252498 Hbk £25.00

PEBCO : a Black Mass Movement / K. Ensor. – Johannesburg : South African Institute of Race Relations, 1982.
58p.
Hbk £2.00

Pecchioli, R. M.
Internationalisation of banking : the policy issues / by R.M. Pecchioli. – Paris : O.E.C.D., 1983.
221p.
Includes bibliographical references.
ISBN 9264124888
—Prudential supervision in banking / by R. M. Pecchioli. – Paris : Organisation for Economic Co-operation and Development, 1987.
298p.
Bibliography: p279-298.
ISBN 9264129162

Pechman, Joseph A.
Rich, the poor and the taxes they pay / by Joseph A. Pechman. – Brighton : Wheatsheaf, 1986.
xvi,317p; 25cm.
Includes index.
ISBN 0745000983 £28.50
—Tax Policy : New Directions and Possibilities. – London : Eurospan.
ISBN 0944237096 Pbk £8.50

Peck, A M →Nelson's tables: company procedure.

Peck, D. E. →County Court Practice 1986.

Peczenik, Aleksander →Appellate decision making in the common law world.
—Essays in Legal Theory. – Copenhagen : Samfundsvidenskaberne.
Hbk £19.10
→ Theory of legal science : proceedings of the Conference on Legal Theory and Philosophy of Science, Lund, Sweden, December 11-14, 1983.

Peden, Helen
Sources of funding for research and publication / Helen Peden and Philip Hills. – Leicester : Primary Communications Research Centre, University of Leicester, 1983.
46p; 20x21cm.
Bibliography: p46. - Includes index.
ISBN 0906083249 Pbk

Peden, J. R
Law of unjust contracts : including the Contracts Review Act 1980 (NSW) with detailed annotations, procedure, and pleadings / by John R. Peden. – Sydney : Butterworths, 1981.
xix, 187 p.; 22 cm.
Includes bibliographical references and index.
ISBN 0409309311 Hbk £28.00
—Teaching Materials and Cases on Commercial Transactions. – 2nd ed. – Butterworths, 1983.
559p.
ISBN 0409493643 Hbk £51.00

Peden, Murray D.
Hearken to the Evidence. – Stittsville : Canada's Wings, 1983.
254p.
ISBN 0920002242 Hbk £18.95

Pedlar, D.
Divorce Guide for Manitoba. – North Vancouver : International Self-Counsel Press, 1987.
ISBN 0889085110 Hbk £11.95

Peel, M.
How to make meetings work. – London : Kogan Page, 1988.
ISBN 0850915077 Pbk

Peel, N.A. →Criminal Procedure in Practice : a Manual for the Defence of Cases in Provincial Court.

Peele, Gillian
Rule of law in Britain today / Gillian Peele. – London : Constitutional Reform Centre in cooperation with the Hughenden Foundation, 1987.
18p.
ISBN 0948419075

Peerage law / by R.P. Gadd. – Bristol : ISCA Publishing Ltd., 1985.
viii,178p.
Bibliography: p.163-164. - Includes index.
ISBN 0948343001

Pegg, Leonard
Family law in Hong Kong / Leanard Pegg. – 2nd ed. – Singapore : Butterworths (Asia), 1986.
vii,256.
Explains the current law relating to the family in Hong Kong. Deals with the transition from customary to enacted law, and notes the problems that have arisen, and could arise in the future. Covers marriage and concubinage, matrimonial causes, financial obligations to the family, and adoption.
ISBN 040999524X Hbk £80

Pegrum, Roger
Bush Capital : How Australia Chose Its Federal City. – Neutral Bay : Hale & Iremonger.
ISBN 0868060666 Hbk £24.95, 015

Peiris, G.L.
Essays on Administrative Law. – Colombo : Lake House Investments.
Pbk £7.15
—Fundamental Rights, Vol. 1 : General Principles of Criminal Liability in Ceylon. – Colombo : Lake House Investments.
Pbk £8.80
—Law of Evidence in Sri Lanka. – Colombo : Lake House Investments.
Hbk £6.60
—Law of Property in Sri Lanka, Vol 1. – Colombo : Lake House Investments.
Pbk £15.50
—Offences Under the Penal Code of Ceylon. – Colombo : Lake House Investments.
Pbk £10.00
—Servitude and Partition. – Colombo : Lake House Investments.
Hbk £5.50
—Some Aspects of the Law of Unjust Enrichment. – Colombo : Lake House Investments.
Hbk £4.70

Pellew, Jill
Home Office 1848-1914 : from clerks to bureaucrats / Jill Pellew. – London : Heinemann, 1982.
xi,271p; 22cm.
Bibliography: p225-233. - Includes index.
ISBN 0435326856 £12.50

Pellicciotti, J.M.
Handbook on Basic Trial Evidence. – 2nd ed. – University Press of America.
ISBN 00819167150 Hbk £23.50
ISBN 00819167169 Pbk £13.50

Pelling, Henry
History of British trade unionism / by Henry Pelling. – 4th ed. – London : Macmillan, 1987.
336p; 22cm.
Previous ed.: 1976. Includes bibliography and index.
ISBN 0333442857 £27.50

Pelling, Mark
Matrimonial and Domestic Injunctions / Purdie. – 2nd ed. – London : Butterworths, 1987.
ISBN 0406334412 Pbk £32.00
—Matrimonial and domestic injunctions : practice and precedents / Mark Pelling, Robert Purdie : consulting editor Augustus Ullstein : foreword by Dame Margaret Booth. – London : Butterworths, 1982.
xxi,190p; 22cm.
Includes index.
ISBN 0406334404 Pbk

Pellonpaa, Matti
Expulsion in international law : a study in international aliens law and human rights with special reference to Finland / by Matti Pellonpaa. – Helsinki : Suomalainen Tiedeakatemia, 1984.
xiii, 508 p.; 25 cm.
Includes index. Bibliography: p. 489-506.
ISBN 9514104730

Peltason, J.W.
Understanding the Constitution. – 11th ed. – Holt.
ISBN 0030229332 Pbk £7.95

Peltzer, Martin → German Banking Law : A Synoptical Translation of the Banking with an Introduction in English Gesetz Uber das Kreditwesen : Deutsch-Englische Textausgabe Des Gesetzes Uber das Kreditwesen Mit Einer Englischen Einleitung.
—German Labour Management Relations Act / Rolf Boer. – 3rd ed. Repr. of 1976 ed. – Plymouth : Macdonald & Evans, 1983.
384p.
ISBN 0712154736 Hbk £32.50
—German Law Pertaining to Companies with Limited Liability : A Synoptic Translation Including Comprehensive Introductory Comments on the Laws Affecting the German GmbH / Jermyn Brooks. – Cologne : Otto Schmidt, 1986.
ISBN 3504325321 Hbk
→ U.S. Business Law : A Bilingual Guide for the German Businessman and Investor U.S. - Amerikanisches Wirtschaftsrecht : E. Zweisprach., Grundriss Fur D. Deutschen Geschaftsmann und Investor.

Penal Code (F.M.S. Cap. 45). – Kuala Lumpur : International Law Books Services.
Hbk £15.00

Penal Code of Northern Nigeria. – London : Sweet & Maxwell.
ISBN 0421318201 Hbk

Penal Codes of Singapore and Malaysia, Vol 2 : Cases, Materials and Comments / Molly Cheang. – Singapore : Quins.
Hbk £63.00

Penal Law of India : Being an Analytical, Critical and Expository Commentary on the Indian Penal Code, 4 Vols. – Allahabad : Law Publishers, 1983.
Hbk £45.00

Penal Law of Islam. – Lahore : Kazi Publications.
Hbk £55.00

Penal protection of works of art. – Siracusa : International Institute of Higher Studies in Criminal Sciences, 1983.
447p.
Includes bibliographical references. English, French or Italian.

Penalties for road traffic offences : Schedule 4 to the Road Traffic Act 1972 as amended with editorial notes and additions / compiled by Paul H. Niekirk. – London : Oyez Longman, 1983.
46p; 21cm.
ISBN 0851207413 Pbk £4.25

Pendlebury, N → Business Law.
→ Business Law : Instructional Manual.
→ Public Sector Accounting.

Pendleton, Michael D. → Chinese intellectual property and technology transfer Law.
—Intellectual property law in the People's Republic of China : a guide to patents, trade marks and technology transfer / Michael D.Pendleton. – Singapore : Butterworths, 1986.
xvii,138p.
ISBN 0409995193 Pbk £17.00
—Law of Intellectual and Industrial Property in Hong Kong. – London : Butterworths, 1984.
ISBN 0406181179 Pbk £50.00
—Law of intellectual and industrial property in Hong Kong : a guide to trade marks, copyright, patents, registered designs and other protected commercial information / Michael D. Pendleton. – London : Butterworth, 1984.
xxxix,556p.
Deals with Hong Kong's intellectual property law, including both civil and criminal remedies. Discusses passing off, registered trademarks, trade descriptions, legislation, copyright, patents, registered designs, and trade secrets.
ISBN '0406181179

Pengelley, Nicholas → Criminal Law Advocacy.

Pengilley, Warren
Federal deceptive practices and misleading advertising law : judgements, materials and policy / Warren Pengilley and Alan A. Ransom. – Sydney : Legal Books Pty., 1987.
lxiii,1184p.
Bibliography: pp.1021-1022. - Includes index.
ISBN 0949553344
→ Restrictive trade practices : judgments, materials and policy.
—Trade associations, fairness and competition / by Warren Pengilley. – Sydney : Law Book Company, 1981.
xxvii,247p.
Includes index. Includes text of Trade Practices Act 1974.
ISBN 0455200866

Penguin guide to supplementary benefits : supplementary benefits, the new regulations, the family income supplement and the appeals tribunal / Tony Lynes. – 4th ed. – Harmondsworth : Penguin, 1981.
319p; 18cm.
Previous ed.: 1975. Includes index. .
ISBN 0140464239 Pbk £2.50

Penguin guide to the law. – 2nd ed. – Penguin, 1986.
ISBN 0140511466 Pbk £9.95

Penlington, Peter
High Court Forms / A.A.P Willy. – Butterworths, 1985.
Contains 167 forms for use with the new High Court Rules. Of those, 114 are completely new. All the forms, including the Schedule forms, are annotated. The book is cross-referenced with Sim and Cain's Practice and Procedure.
ISBN 0409600792 Hbk £89.10

Penlington, V.
Law in Hong Kong. – 2nd ed. – London : Federal, 1986.
ISBN 9623020015 Pbk £15.00

Penn, G. A.
Banking Law
Vol.1 : The law relating to domestic banking / by G.A. Penn, A.M. Shea and A. Arora. – London : Sweet & Maxwell, 1987.
xlix,537p; 24cm.
In five sections covering bank regulation, the banker-customer relationship, negotiable instruments, guarantees and securities and insolvency. Covers the Insolvency Act 1986, the Financial Services Act 1986, and the Banking Act 1987.
ISBN 042139000X Hbk £
ISBN 0421360607 Pbk £18.95
Vol.2 : The law and practice of international banking / by G.A. Penn, A.M. Shea and A. Arora. – 1987.
500p.
Discusses the legal effect of specimen clauses, agreements and other documentation used in international banking transactions. Takes a practical approach to the principles and emerging issues in the area of international financial markets.
ISBN 0421390107 Hbk £
ISBN 0421390107 Pbk £25.00
—Banking Supervision. – London : Butterworths.
ISBN 0406136033 Hbk £30.00

Penn, Graham → Boyle & Birds' Company law.

Penney, Malcolm
Indexation of Capital Gains : Computations and Examples / Paul Elliott. – London : Butterworths, 1983.
This work is designed to assist United Kingdom tax practitioners with the new rules for indexing of capital gains. Worked examples are provided throughout the work to explain the subject matter.
ISBN 0406256101 Pbk

Pennington
High Court Forms / E. H. J. Wily. – Wellington : Butterworths.
Hbk

Pennington, Donald C. → Psychology of sentencing : approaches to consistency and disparity.

Pennington, Robert R
Bank finance for companies / by R. Pennington. – London : Sweet & Maxwell, 1987.
150p; 22cm.
Discusses bank finance for specific purposes by way of letters of credit, bank guarantees and performance bonds, the issue of settling sterling commercial paper by companies, the legal implications of factoring, the provision of third party guarantees and securities for loans to companies within a group, and legal remedies available to banks to recover advances of all kinds made to them.
ISBN 0421384905 £15.00
—Companies Acts 1980 and 1981 : a practitioners' manual / by Robert R. Pennington. – London : Lloyds of London Press, 1983.
lxii,313p; 25cm.
Includes index.
ISBN 0907432573
—Company law / Robert R. Pennington. – 5th ed. – London : Butterworths, 1985.
cvi,1077p; 26cm.
Previous ed.: 1979. Includes index.
ISBN 0406336830 Hbk £26.00
ISBN 0406336857 Pbk £20.00
—Company law in the European Communities / Frank Wooldridge. – 3rd ed. – London : Oyez Longman, 1982.
viii,200p.
Previous ed., 1970, entitled: Companies in the Common Market.
ISBN 0851206387
—Company liquidations : the substantive law / Robert Pennington. – Bristol : Jordans, 1987.
xxvi,150p; 21cm.
Includes index.
ISBN 0853081220 Pbk £8.50
—Directors' personal liability. – 1st. – Oxford : Blackwell Scientific.
270. – (Blackwell Law Library).
Examines the erosion by recent legislation of the principle that neither directors nor shareholders of limited companies are personally liable for their company debts and torts. Advice on potential liabilities is offered in the light of the Companies Act 1985 and the Insolvency Act 1986.
Company directors, Accountants, Solicitors
ISBN 0632026197 Pbk £19.50
—Directors' personal liability / Robert R. Pennington. – London : Collins Professional and Technical, 1987.
256p; 24cm.
Includes index.
ISBN 0003832945 £20.00
—Italian Agency Agreements. – London : Longman Professional, 1977.
– (ECLL).
ISBN 0851203019 Pbk £26.00
—Law of the investment markets. – Oxford : Blackwell Scientific, 1990.
672. – (Blackwell Law Library).
A detailed guide to the complex rules and procedures prescribed by the Financial Services Act 1986; covers the history, structure, and regulation of investment markets. Further chapters cover finacial, accounting and reporting rules, the marketing of unlisted securities, unit trusts, investment schemes and overseas aspects of investments.
Investment practitioners, Lawyers, Investors, Financial advisors
ISBN 0632023724 Hbk £85
—Stock exchange listing : the new requirements / Robert R. Pennington. – London : Butterworths, 1985.
ix,199p; 26cm.
Includes the text of The Stock Exchange (Listing) Regulations 1984.
ISBN 0406337004

Penny
Indexation of Capital Gains : Examples etc (83) / Paul Elliott. – London : Butterworths.
ISBN 0406256101 Pbk £9.00

Pension Cost Accounting. – London : Butterworths, 1984.
ISBN 0406010544 Pbk

Pension fund investment. – Cambridge : Woodhead-Faulkner, 1987.
ISBN 0859414000 Hbk £35.00

Pension fund reform. – London : Longman Professional, 1986.
ISBN 0851211828 Pbk £10.95

Pension Plan Financial Statements. – Toronto : Butterworths, 1986.
96p.
ISBN 0409801798 Pbk

Pension Plans 2. – Vancouver : Continuing Legal Education Society of British Columbia, 1987.
223p.
ISBN 0865043132 Hbk £70.00

Pension Plans. – Vancouver : Continuing Legal Education Society of British Columbia, 1986.
492p.
ISBN 0865042519 Hbk £70.00

Pension scheme accounts : a discussion paper by the Accounting Standards Committee : memorandum / by the Society's Standing Committee on Company Law. – London : Law Society, 1982.
4p.

Pension Scheme Model Annual Report. – Tolley Publishing.
ISBN 0854593241 Hbk £7.00

Pension Scheme Trustee / Spill. – 2nd ed. – Taxbriefs.
ISBN 00907342124 Hbk £17.00

Pension Schemes. – London : Butterworths, 1982.
ISBN 0406406502 Hbk

Pensions : a practical guide. – 3rd ed. – London : Longman Professional, 1987.
ISBN 0851211879 Pbk £25.00

Pensions : agenda for change. – Cambridge : Woodhead-Faulkner, 1987.
ISBN 0859413802 Hbk £32.50

Pensions and Insurance Administration : ICSA Study Text. – Institute of Chartered Secretaries and Administrators. – London : BPP.
ISBN 0862772168 Pbk £14.95

Pensions guide. – Allied Hambro. – London : Longman Professional, 1984.
ISBN 0851209750 Hbk £11.95

Pensions Revolution : An Employers Guide. – London : Kogan Page.
ISBN 1850917639 Hbk £12.95
ISBN 1850917647 Pbk £6.95

Pentney, William F.
Aboriginal Rights Provisions in the Constitution Act, 1982. – Saskatoon : University of Saskatchewan, Native Law Centre, 1987.
276p.
ISBN 0888801920 Hbk £50.00
—Canadian Human Rights Yearbook / Daniel Proulx. – Agincourt : Carswell, 1987.
308p.
Hbk £48.75
→ Human Rights and Freedoms in Canada : Cases, Notes and Materials.

Pentony, Patrick
Conciliation under the Racial Discrimination Act 1975 : a study in theory and practice / by Patrick Pentony. – Canberra : Australian Government Publishing Service, 1986.
xi,206p. – (Occasional paper).
Bibliography: p203-205.
ISBN 064405672X

Penwill, D.J.
Kamba Customary Law. – 3rd ed. – Nairobi : Kenya Literature Bureau, 1983.
Pbk £24.50

People against the press : an enquiry into the Press Council / Geoffrey Robertson. – London : Quartet, 1983.
182p; 23cm.
Includes index.
ISBN 0704323842 £7.95

People and employment / Baruch. – London : Butterworths, 1981.
ISBN 0408106921 Pbk £8.50

People's justice : a major poll of public attitudes on crime and punishment / Stephen Shaw. – London : Prison Reform Trust, 1982.
29p; 30cm.
Cover title.
ISBN 0946209006 Pbk £1.00

Peoples' law : a journal of contemporary Nigerian and African laws, justice and legality. – Lagos, Nigeria : Pan-Afrika Peoples' Law Center and Akademy, 1987.

People's law and state law : the Bellagio papers / Antony Allott and Gordon R. Woodman (eds.). – Dordrecht : Foris Publications, 1985.
354p.
Papers presented at the first conference of the Commission on Folk Law and Legal Pluralism at Bellagio, Como, Italy from 21st to 25th September 1981.
ISBN 9067651001

People's Republic of China : Modernisation and Legal Development. – London : Oyez Longman, 1983.
ISBN 0851208045 Hbk £22.50

People's Republic of China Laws for Chinas Traders, Investors. – 2nd ed. – Taylor & Francis.
ISBN 0800280024 Hbk £64.00

Peppiatt, D.A.
Practice on Motions and References / R.B. Linton. – Butterworths, 1988.
128p.
Guidance on how to present motions and effectively argue before the Masters. Section on practical tips on advocacy before the Masters, a section on motions before the Master in Matrimonial actions, guidance on proper notices of hearing, discussion of jurisdiction on references, sets out powers of the referee and referee's reports, and a chapter on contested motions.
ISBN 0409806293 Hbk

Percom Limited → How to comply with the Data Protection Act : policies, practice and procedures.

Percy, David → Contracts : Cases and Commentaries.

Percy, David R.
Framework of Water Rights Legislation in Canada. – Calgary : Canadian Institute of Resources Law.
103p.
ISBN 0919269214 Hbk £20.00

Pereboom, Z. → Land Use Law : B.C. Handbook.

Perell, Paul M.
Remedies and the Sale of Land. – Butterworths, 1988.
352p.
Chapters develop the theme of finding ways to enforce, or conversely, to escape the agreement of sale. Examines over 100 ways to get out of or enforce contracts for the sale of land, analyses the operation of the standard sale contract, discusses the classic remedies of damages, and describes possible claims against third parties.
ISBN 0409805343 Hbk £55.00

Peremptory Challenges in Civil Jury Trials. – Victoria : Government of British Columbia, 1983.
Hbk £1.30

Peremptory challenges in civil jury trials / Law Reform Commission of British Columbia. – Vancouver : The Commission, 1982.
ii,31p. – (Working paper).
Includes bibliographical references.

Peremptory Norma (Jus Cogens) in International Law : Historical Development, Criteria, Present Status. – Helsinki : Lakimiesliiton Kustannus, 1988.
781p.
ISBN 9516403948 Hbk £519.00

Performance. – 2nd ed. – London : Offord Publications Ltd, 1985.
600p.
ISBN 0903931362 Hbk £18.00
ISBN 0903931591 Pbk £14.95

Performance bonds and contract guarantees : with special reference to the risk of unfair calling and injunction procedures : proceedings of the seminar held in Paris in January, 1982 / International Bar Association Section on Business Law (London), Institute of International Business Law and Practice (Paris). – London : International Bar Association, 1983.
ii,126p.
The papers contained in this volume are reproduced from transcripts of the speeches delivered at the Seminar rather than written articles.

Performance under protest / Law Reform Commission of British Columbia. – Vancouver : The Commission, 1984.
ii,35p. – (Working paper).
Includes bibliographical references.

Performers' Protection. – Milsons Point : Australian Copyright Council.
Hbk £14.00

Performing Artist and the Law. – North Ryde : Law Book Co, 1985.
xvi, 204p.
ISBN 0455206244 Pbk £26.50

Periods of limitation : with practical notes / J.F. Josling. – 6th ed. – London : Longman Professional, 1986.
144p; 22cm. – (Longman professional practice notes).
Previous ed.: London : Oyez, 1981.
ISBN 0851211453 Pbk £12.95

Perkins, Clifford S
PAYE Audits. – London : Butterworths, 1988.
ISBN 0406263000 Pbk
—Sweet & Maxwell's tax computations and tables 1984/85 / by Clifford S. Perkins : computations on double taxation relief contributed by Richard Briffett. – 2nd ed. – London : Sweet & Maxwell, 1984.
395p; 25cm.
ISBN 042133200X

Perks from shares. – 2nd ed. – London : Kogan Page, 1985.
ISBN 0850389461 Hbk £8.95
ISBN 085038947X Pbk £4.95

Perl, Raphael → Falkland Islands dispute in international law and politics : a documentary sourcebook.

Permanent incapacity : invalid pension in Australia / Alan Jordan. – Canberra : Department of Social Security, 1984.
264p. – (Research paper).
ISBN 0642515565

Permanent sovereignty over natural resources in international law / Kamal Hossain, Subrata Roy Chowdhury. – London : Pinter, 1984.
250p.
ISBN 0861873025 £16.50

Permissiveness and Control : The Fate of the Sixties Legislation. – National Deviancy Conference. – London : Macmillan.
224p. – (Critical Criminology Ser.).
ISBN 0333266803 Hbk £12.00
ISBN 0333266811 Pbk £4.95

Perone, Gian Carlo
Law of collective agreements in the countries of the European Community / report submitted by Gian Carlo Perone : with the assistance of Antonio Vallebona. – Luxembourg : Office for Official Publications of the European Communities, 1985.
47p.
Describes the tasks given to the Commission of the European Communities in the social sector, particularly under Articles 117 and 118 of the Treaty of Rome.
ISBN 9282550125 Pbk £3.30

Perpetuities Act 1984 / P.J. Butt. – North Ryde : Law Book Co, 1986.
xx, 188p.
ISBN 0455206082 Hbk £25.00

Perrier, David C. → From Crime to Punishment.

Perrins
Practical Book-Keeping. – London : Butterworths, 1977.
ISBN 0372300049 Pbk £5.50

Perrins, Bryn
Trade union law / Bryn Perrins. – London : Butterworths, 1985.
350p.
Includes index.
ISBN 0406258309 Hbk £26.50
ISBN 0406258317 Pbk £17.95

Perritt, Henry H
Labour injunctions. – Chichester : Wiley (John), 1990.
104; 25.
ISBN 0471515868 Pbk £44.35

Perrott, David L. → Current issues in international business law.

Perry, Erskine
Cases Illustrative of Oriental Life and the Application of English Law to India-Decided in H.M. Supreme Court at Bombay. – 1853 repr. – New Delhi : Asian Educational Services, 1988.
620p.
Hbk £195.00

Perry, F. E. → Banking Points From Case and Statute Law.
—Dictionary of banking / F.E. Perry. – 3rd ed. – London : Pitman, 1988.
356p; 19cm.
Previous ed.: Plymouth : Macdonald and Evans, 1983.
ISBN 0712107657 Pbk £9.95
ISBN 0273029614 correct
—Dictionary of banking / F.E. Perry. – 2nd ed. – Plymouth : Macdonald and Evans, 1983.
385p; 23cm. – (M & E professional dictionaries).
Previous ed: 1979.
ISBN 0712104321 Hbk £12.50
ISBN 0712104372 Pbk
—Dictionary of Banking. – 3rd ed. – Pitman.
ISBN 0273029614 Pbk £9.95
—Elements of Banking. – 5th ed. – Routledge.
ISBN 0415034752 Hbk £6.95
—Law and practice relating to banking / F.E. Perry. – 4th ed. – London : Methuen, 1983.
x,566p; 20cm.
Previous ed.: 1981. Includes index.
ISBN 041635680X Pbk £7.50

Perry, J.
Elements of Banking. – 5th ed. – London : Sweet & Maxwell, 1986.
ISBN 0416383009 Pbk £5.95

Perry, J. Harvey
Background of current fiscal problems / J. Harvey Perry. – Toronto : Canadian Tax Foundation, 1982.
v,159p.
Includes index.
ISBN 0888080107
—Taxation in Canada / J. Harvey Perry. – 4th ed. – Toronto : Canadian Tax Foundation, 1984.
xii,248p.
Bibliography: p.234-240. - Includes index.

Perry, John G.
Contract Strategies for Construction Projects. – London : Collins, 1987.
240p : Illus.
ISBN 0003832716 Hbk £17.50

Perry, Lawrence → Legal Protection of Computer Software.

Persistent petty offenders / by Suzan Fairhead. – London : H.M.S.O., 1981.
vi,74p.
Bibliography: p74. A Home Office Research Unit report.
ISBN 0113407068

Personal and Corporate Liabilities. – Product Liability Briefing.
ISBN 1870317351 Pbk £6.50

Personal and Family Law. – Manila : National Book Store, 1984.
602p.
ISBN 9710805282 Hbk £35.00

Personal Equity Plans. – Cambridge : Woodhead-Faulkner, 1987.
ISBN 0859414191 Pbk £4.95

Personal Equity Plans. – Telegraph Publications, 1988.
ISBN 0863672299 Pbk £5.95

Personal Financial Planning Manual 1986-87 / John Rayer. – London : Butterworths, 1986.
This manual is a guide to the compilation of personal financial packages for United Kingdom investors. Investments, family finances, life insurance, pensions, and capital transfer tax are covered in the book.
ISBN 040600563X Hbk

Personal Financial Planning Manual. – 4th ed. – London : Butterworths.
ISBN 0406005656 Pbk £18.95

Personal income tax systems under changing economic conditions / report by the Committee on Fiscal Affairs of OECD. – Paris : Organisation for Economic Co-operation and Development, 1986.
381p.
ISBN 9264127895

Personal Income Taxation in India. – Allahabad : Chugh Publications, 1987.
296p.
ISBN 8185076197 Hbk £175.00

Personal information: privacy and the law. – Oxford : Clarendon Press, 1989.
320.
Argues that at the core of the privacy problem is a concern for the use and misuse of personal information. Identifies four main areas of privacy, and suggests that by finding the centre of the problem, it may more easily be solved.
ISBN 0198256116 Hbk £30

Personal Injury. – Vancouver : Continuing Legal Education Society of British Columbia, 1988.
115p.
ISBN 0865049904 Hbk £70.00

Personal Injury. – London : Longman Professional. – (Longman Practice Notes).
ISBN 0851214487 Pbk £10.95

Personal Injury : a Medico-Legal Guide to the Spine and Limbs / Ogilvie-Harris. – Aurora : Canada Law Book.
Hbk £33.00

Personal Injury : A Medico-Legal Guide to the Spine and Limbs. – Aurora : Canada Law Book Co, 1986.
350p. – (Text Books-Civil).
This text is written specifically for lawyers and explains the medical aspects of a wide range of personal injuries in lay terms. Throughout, the text focuses on the functional and economic impact of particular injuries and considers the long-term life style effects of various disabilities.
Hbk £60.00

Personal injury damage assessments in Alberta. – 1 vol. – Scarborough, Ontario : Butterworths (Canada).
Catalogue of Alberta judicial awards in motor vehicle accident cases since 1969 arranged under 14 categories of injury. Group one relates to the damage assessment arising in death, group two to cases of gravest injury and subsequent groups are classified by specific part of the body or other specific nature of the injuries.
Loose leaf

Personal injury damage assessments in British Columbia. – 2 vols. – Scarborough, Ontario : Butterworths (Canada).
Catalogue of British Columbia judicial awards in motor vehicle accident cases since 1969 arranged under 15 categories of injury. Group one relates to the damage assessment arising in death, group two to cases of gravest injury and subsequent groups are classified by specific part of the body or other specific nature of the injuries.
Loose leaf

Personal injury damages in Canada / by Kenneth D. Cooper- Stephenson and Iwan B. Saunders. – Toronto : Carswell, 1981.
lii,762p; 26cm.
Includes index.
ISBN 0459333305

Personal Injury File. – London : Butterworths.
Pbk

Personal injury litigation. – 5th ed. – London : Longman Professional, 1986.
ISBN 0851212034 Pbk £26.00

Personal Injury Litigation : Practice and Precedents / Margaret R De Haas. – London : Butterworths, 1985.
This work for personal injury practitioners in the United Kingdom covers a wide range of procedural and practical points. The book includes chapters on deduction of collateral benefits, the Motor Insurers' Bureau, medical examination of plaintiffs, and limitation of damages.
ISBN 0406016607 Llf £105.00

Personal Injury Practice. – Vancouver : Continuing Legal Education Society of British Columbia, 1986.
260p.
ISBN 0865042799 Hbk £65.00

Personal insolvency. – London : Sweet & Maxwell, 1986.
ISBN 0420475605 Hbk £220.00

Personal insolvency : a practical guide / Ian S. Grier, Richard E. Floyd. – London : Sweet & Maxwell, 1987.
xxiii,224p; 26cm.
Deals with the law and procedure relating to personal insolvency, through the full range of bankruptcy from the pre-petition stage to the closing procedures. Covers changes introduced by the Insolvency Act 1986, and includes forms of available voluntary arrangements, falling short of bankruptcy, and aspects of criminal bankruptcy.
ISBN 0421360100 £19.50

Personal Laws in India. – Allahabad : Orient Law House, 1984.
Hbk £50.00

Personal liability under a mortgage or agreement for sale / Law Reform Commission of British Columbia. – Vancouver : The Commission, 1985.
ii,52p. – (Working paper).
Includes bibliographical references.

Personal Property Security : An Introductory Analysis / DeJong. – 4th ed. – Agincourt : Carswell, 1987.
454p.
Pbk £40.50

Personal Property Security Act Cases, Vol. 4 : Supplement to Secured Transactions in Personal Property in Canada. – Agincourt : Carswell.
Hbk £192.50

Personal Tax Losses. – London : Butterworths, 1984.
This practical book shows tax advisers how to maximize tax relief for clients through use of tax losses under the tax laws of the United Kingdom. The work presents a variety of realistic tax planning options in tax loss situations.
ISBN 0406263604 Pbk £16.50

Personal Tax Planning. – Vancouver : British Columbia Continuing Legal Education Society, 1984.
ISBN 0865041466 Hbk £50.00

Personal violence / by Roy Walmsley. – London : H.M.S.O., 1986.
vi, 79p; 25cm.
A Home Office Research and Planning Unit report.
ISBN 0113408277

Persons with Special Needs : Law and the Handicapped. – Montreal : McGill Campus Legal Aid Clinic, 1981.
100p.
Hbk £7.00

Perspective on labour law / Ole Hasselbalch, Alan C. Neal, Anders Victorin. – Stockholm : Almqvist & Wiksell, 1982.
128p.
ISBN 0421307102

Perspective on Legal Aid. – London : Pinter Publishers Ltd.
Hbk

Perspectives for the Common Agricultural Policy / communication of the Commission to the Council and the Parliament. – Luxembourg : Office for Official Publications of the European Communities, 1985.
viii,62p. – (Document).
Includes a statistical annex.
ISBN 9277070285

Perspectives in Criminal Law : Essays in Honour of John LL.J. Edwards / Edward L. Greenspan. – Aurora : Canada Law Book Co, 1984.
384p. – (Text Books-Criminal).
This collection of fifteen essays brings together some of the best legal minds in Canada and elsewhere to explore the key and perplexing issues in the fields of criminal law and criminology. This book also commemorates the founding of the University of Toronto's Centre of Criminology 21 years ago.
Hbk £53.00

Perspectives on Soviet law for the 1980s / edited by F.J.M. Feldbrugge and William B. Simons. – The Hague : M. Nijhoff, 1982.
Selected papers from the Second World Congress for Soviet and East European Studies, held in Garmisch-Patenkirchen, Germany, Sept. 30-Oct. 4, 1980, organized by Deutsche Gesellschaft fur Osteuropakunde and the International Committee for Soviet and East European Studies. Includes bibliographical references and index.
ISBN 9024725615 Hbk £75.00

Perspectives on the harmonization of law in Canada / Ronald C.C. Cuming research coordinator. – Toronto : University of Toronto Press in cooperation with the Royal Commission on the Economic Union and Development Prospects for Canada and the Canadian Government Publishing Centre, 1985.
xviii,178p. – (Collected research studies).
Bibliography: p.176-177.
ISBN 0802073026

Peru : Amnesty International briefing. – Amnesty International. – London : Amnesty International, 1985.
15p.
List of the 'disappeared' of Peru (November 1984) in pocket.
ISBN 0862100801

Peru : 'disappearances', torture and summary executions by government forces after the prison revolts of June 1986 / Amnesty International. – London : Amnesty International, 1987.
ii,71p.
ISBN 0862101166

Pesando, James E.
Issues regarding the reform of Canada's private pensions system / James E. Pesando. – Canada : Policy Research, Analysis and Liaison Directorate, Consumer and Corporate Affairs, 1983.
ISBN 0662121643

Pescatore, P.
Court of Justice of the European Communities : References for Preliminary Rulings Under Article 177 of the E.E.C. Treaty and Cooperation between the Court and National Courts. – Luxembourg : Office for Official Publications of the European Communities, 1986.
47p.
Pbk

Pescod : Takeover Bids. – London : Butterworths, 1987.
ISBN 0406103690 Hbk

Pescod, Michael
Pescod : Takeover Bids. – London : Butterworths, 1987.
ISBN 0406103690 Hbk
—Takeover bids. – London : Butterworths, 1988.

Company executives
ISBN 0406103690 Hbk

Pesek, B.P.
Microeconomics of Money and Banking and other Essays. – Wheatsheaf Books.
ISBN 0745005101 Hbk £35.00

Pesticide Labelling Legislation. – Rome : FAO, Food and Agricultural Organization of the United Nations, 1988.
159p.
ISBN 925102619X Hbk £10.50

Pesticides : Recommendations on the Safe Use of Pesticides in Ships
English Edition. – International Maritime Organization. – Rev. ed. – London : International Maritime Organization, 1981.
Hbk £1.25
French Edition. –
Hbk £1.50

Pesticides in Canada : an examination of federal law and policy / a study paper prepared for the Law Reform Commission of Canada by J.F. Castrilli, Toby Vigod. – Ottawa : The Commission, 1987.
131p. – (Study paper).
Added t.p. in French: Les pesticides au Canada. Pages numbered in opposite directions. Text in English and French.
ISBN 0662554132

Peter, Wolfgang
Arbitration and renegotiation of international investment agreements : a study with particular reference to means of conflict avoidance under natural resources investment agreements / Wolfgang Peter. – Dordrecht : M. Nijhoff, 1986.
xxiii, 297p.
Includes index. Bibliography: p.267-284.
ISBN 9024733146

Peteri, Zoltan →General reports to the 10th International Congress of Comparative Law.
—Legal Development and Comparative Law 1986 : Selected Essays for the 12th Congres International de Droit Compare / Lamm. – Budapest : Akademiai Kiado, 1986.
330p.
ISBN 9630544342 Hbk £29.00

Peters, C. J. →Ukrainians and Georgians.

Peters, E.
Torture. – Oxford : Blackwell, 1985.
ISBN 0631137238 Pbk £5.95

Petersdorff, C.
Practical Precedents in Pleading. – Repr. of 1835 ed. – Abingdon : Professional Books.
278p.
Hbk £45.00

Petersman, Ernst-Ulrich →New GATT round of multilateral trade negotiations: legal and economic problems.

Petersmann, Ernst-Ulrich →Reforming the International Economic Order : German Legal Comments.

Peterson
Sensenbrenner Hospital Employees Compensation Act, 1983, Bill 110 : An Act Respecting the Compensation of Certain Employees at Sensenbrenner Hospital in Kapuskasing. – Ontario : Ontario Government Publications Service, 1983.
2p.
Hbk £0.30
—Virginia Statute for Religious Freedom : Its Evolution and Consequences in American History Conf. Proc. / Vaughan. – Cambridge : Cambridge University Press.
ISBN 0521343291 Hbk £35.00

Peterson, Nicolas →Aboriginal land rights : a handbook.
—Aborigines, Land and Land Rights / M. Langton. – Canberra City : Australian Institute of Aboriginal Studies, 1983.
476p.
ISBN 0855751436 Hbk £14.90

Pethig, R. F. →Morison's Company law in New Zealand.

Petition procedure in the Court of Session / Norman Dowrie. – 2nd. – Edinburgh : Green (W.) & Son, 1988.
Enlarged version of the first edition, substantially rewritten In the light of the considerable changes in Court of Session practice, particularly in the areas of family law, insolvency and judicial review. Provides a step by step approach to all the types of petition encountered in practice with descriptions of the miscellaneous procedures including appeals. New chapters deal with adoptions, children and applications under the Matrimonial Homes Act.
ISBN 0414008316 Pbk

Petitioning the United Nations : a study in human rights / Ton J.M. Zuijdwijk. – Aldershot : Gower, 1982.
xv,397p; 23cm.
Bibliography: p383-389. - Includes index.
ISBN 0566004631 £
ISBN 0312603819

Petroleum concession agreements of the United Arab Emirates, 1939-1981 (Abu Dhabi)
Vol.1 : 1939-1971 / compiled by Mana Saeed al-Otaiba. – 2. – London : Croom Helm, 1982.
26cm.
In slip-case.
ISBN 0709919158
Vol.2 : 1972-1981 / Mana Saeed Al-Otaiba. – 1982.
385p.

Petroleum Development : Law and Policy, a Comparative Study. – London : Commonwealth Secretariat.
Hbk £15.00

Petroleum development and New Zealand law : essays prepared for the Faculty of Law, Victoria University of Wellington. – Wellington, N.Z. : Victoria University Press, 1984.
118p.
Reprinted in Victoria University of Wellington Law Review, vol. 14, no.1. Includes bibliographical references.
ISBN 0864730144

Petroleum income tax in Malaysia. – Singapore : Malayan Law Journal, 1982.
xv,240.
Covers oil exploration and PETRONAS, taxation of petroleum companies, and administration and appeals. Appendices reproduce the Petroleum (Income Tax) Act 1967 and all subsequent Amendments up to 1977, the Petroleum Mining Act 1966, and a map showing the location of oil and gas fields in Malaysia.
Hbk

Petroleum Law 1985. – London : Applied Science.
ISBN 0853343314 Hbk £25.00

Petroleum licensing : a comparative study / Peter Cameron. – London : Financial Times Business Information, 1984.
x,195p.
Bibliography: pp.191-194.
ISBN 0903199785

Petroleum Operations on the Canadian Continental Margin : the Legal Issues in a Modern Perspective. – Calgary : Canadian Institute of Resources Law.
113p.
Hbk £10.00

Petroleum revenue tax : valuation and pricing / Inland Revenue. – London : Inland Revenue Press Office, 1986.
3p. – (Press release).

Petroleum Tax Analysis : North Sea : A Comparative Study of the Oil Exploitation Taxation System of the United Kingdom, Norway, Denmark and the Netherlands / David Rose. – London : Financial Times Ltd, 1983.
Hbk £130.00

Petroleum Taxation Law. – Glenside : Australian Mineral Foundation, 1985.
Hbk £40.00

Petronas : Its Corporate and Legal Status. – Singapore : Malayan Law Journal, 1983.
137p.
Hbk £35.00

Petter Refrigeration Limited : a report by the Director General of Fair Trading on an investigation under section 3 of the Competition Act 1980. – London : Office of Fair Trading, 1981.
56p.

Pettet, B. G. → Company law in change.
—Company law in change. – London : Sweet & Maxwell, 1987.
ISBN 0420477500 Pbk £17.00

Pettit, D.M.
Will Draftsman's Handbook. – 5th ed. – London : Longman Professional.
ISBN 0851212743 Hbk £20.75

Pettit, Philip H.
Equity and the law of trusts / Philip H. Pettit. – 5th ed. – London : Butterworths, 1984.
lvii,649p; 26cm.
Previous ed.: 1979. Includes index.
ISBN 0406641676 Hbk £25.00
ISBN 0406641684 Pbk £21.95
—Private sector tenancies / Philip H. Pettit. – 2nd ed. – London : Butterworths, 1981.
li,327p; 26cm.
Previous ed.: published as Landlord and tenant under the Rent Act 1979. 1978. Includes index.
ISBN 0406337225
—Private sector tenancies. – 2nd ed. – London : Butterworths, 1981.
ISBN 0406337225 Hbk £20.00

Pettitt, D. M.
Will Draftsman's Handbook. – 3rd ed. – London : Oyez Longman, 1983.
ISBN 0851208037 Hbk £13.50

Pettyfoggers and vipers of the Commonwealth : the 'lower branch' of the legal profession in early modern England / C.W. Brooks. – Cambridge : Cambridge University Press, 1986.
410p; 23cm. – (Cambridge studies in English legal history).
Researches professional and social history of attorneys, solicitors, clerical officials and court holders in early modern society. Examines the nature of legal services provided for the public, considers how the legal system responded to the increase in litigation of the late sixteenth century.
ISBN 0521305748 £30.00

Petzold, Herbert
European Convention on Human Rights : Cases and Materials. – 4th ed. – Cologne : Carl Heymanns Verlag, 1981.
440p.
Pbk £40.00

Pezier, J.
Options. – Cambridge : Woodhead-Faulkner, 1988.
ISBN 0859414418 Hbk £35.00

Phantom capitalists : the organisation and control of long-firm fraud / by Michael Levi. – London : Heinemann, 1981.
346p; 23cm.
Bibliography: p335-341. - Includes index.
ISBN 0435825208 £16.50

Phegan, C. S. → Cases on torts.
→ Product liability in Australia.

Phelps
Solicitors and VAT / Gizzi. – London : Butterworths, 1986.
ISBN 0406503605 Pbk £8.75

Phenomenology of kidnappings in Sardinia : towards an international perspective of a local crime problem / by I.F. Caramazza, U. Leone. – Rome : Fratelli Palombi, 1984.
211p. – (Publication).
Bibliography: p.182-208.
ISBN 8876218270

Phil → Injunctions and specific performance.

Philip, Allan → Arrest of ships 6 : Denmark, Greece, Hong Kong, Kuwait, Qatar.
→ Danish law : a general survey.

Philippine Agrarian Reform and The New Taxation / A.O. Yoingco. – Quezon City : Katha Publishing Co., 1983.
Hbk £3.50

Philippine International Radio Laws and Regulations. – Manila : National Book Store, 1984.
512p.
ISBN 9710804995 Pbk £5.00

Philippines: human rights after martial law / report of a mission by Virginia Leary, A.A. Ellis, Kurt Madlener. – Geneva : International Commission of Jurist, 1984.
123p.
Includes bibliographical references.
ISBN 9290370238

Philips, C. H. → Investigation and prosecution of criminal offences in England and Wales : the law and procedure.
→ Report.

Phillips
Legal Reminders for Architects / Serjeantson. – London : Architectural Press.
ISBN 0851399118 Hbk
→ Practical approach to land law.

Phillips, Allan D. M. → Swiss company law.

Phillips, Andrew
Charitable status : a practical handbook / Andrew Phillips with Keith Smith. – 2nd ed. – London : Inter-Action, 1982.
83p; 22cm. – (Inter-action guides).
Previous ed.: 1980. Bibliography: p74-76. - Includes index.
ISBN 0904571394 Pbk £3.95
—Charitable Status - A Practical Handbook / Kenneth Smith. – 2nd ed. – TUAR, 1982.
ISBN 0904571394 Pbk £4.50

—First Book of English Law / Hood. – 8th ed. – London : Sweet & Maxwell, 1988.
ISBN 0421393602 Hbk £16.00
ISBN 042139370X Pbk £11.50

Phillips, Douglas W.
Child and Family Services Act : a Guide to Part 3 / Douglas J. Manning. – Butterworths, 1986.
208p.
Contains commentary following each section of the act, analysing both similarities and differences in the Child Welfare Act, major changes and modifications and intent in the new Act, selections of summaries of major cases decided under the old Act, and analyses key terms and categories, with reference to other relevant sections.
ISBN 0409805246 Hbk £55.00

Phillips, Erin → Women and Work : Inequality in the Labour Market.

Phillips, Gerald E.
Labour relations and the collective bargaining cycle / Gerald E. Phillips. – 2nd ed. – Toronto : Butterworths, 1981.
xiii,333p.
Previous ed.: published as 'The practice of labour relations and collective bargaining in Canada', 1977. Includes bibliographies and index.

Phillips, I. M. → Prideaux's Forms and precedents in conveyancing.

Phillips, J. H.
Forensic science and the expert witness / by J.H. Phillips, J.K. Bowen : with a foreword by Sir Daryl Dawson. – North Ryde, N.S.W. : Law Book Company, 1985.
ix,114p; 22cm.
Introductory guide to forensic science. Contains chapters on forensic science and crime; crime science examiners; continuity of exhibits; photographic evidence; forensic chemistry; forensic biology; firearms and toolmarks; fingerprints; and document examination.
ISBN 0455205914 Pbk £12

Phillips, Jennifer
Economic importance of copyright / Jennifer Phillips. – London : Common Law Institute of Intellectual Property, 1985.
38p.

Phillips, Jeremy
Butterworths intellectual property law handbook. – London : Butterworths, 1989.
624; 248.
Includes patents, copyright, semiconductor typographies, registered designs, unregistered design right, trademarks, plant varieties protection, intellectual property and competition, professional status, and practice.
ISBN 0406504717 Pbk £19.95
—Charles Dickens and The Poor Man's Tale of a Patent. – Oxford : ESC Publishing Ltd, 1984.
53p.
ISBN 0906214300 Hbk £5.50
→ Employees' inventions : a comparative study.
—Employees' inventions in the United Kingdom : law and practice / by Jeremy Phillips and Michael J. Hoolahan. – Oxford : ESC, 1982.
xviii,164p; 22cm.
ISBN 0906214114 Pbk £9.50
ISBN 0906214106
—Introduction to intellectual property law / Jeremy Phillips. – London : Butterworths, 1986.
230p; 22cm.
Includes index.
ISBN 0406258325 Hbk £18.00
ISBN 0406258333 Pbk £12.50
→ Inventors' information guide.
→ Patents in perspective : a collection of essays.
→ Whale on copyright.

Phillips, John
Advocacy with Honour. – Allahabad : Law Book Company, 1985.
xi, 100p.
ISBN 0455206511 Pbk £14.00

Phillips, John C. → Modern contract of guarantee.

Phillips, L.
Individual Income Taxes 1989 : Federal Taxation. – Prentice-Hall.
ISBN 0137032668 Hbk £48.15

Phillips, O. Hood
O. Hood Phillips' Constitutional and administrative law / Paul Jackson. – 7th ed. – London : Sweet & Maxwell, 1987.
lxxvi,808p; 26cm.
Previous ed.: 1978. Includes index.
ISBN 042135030X Hbk £21.00
ISBN 0421350407 Pbk £16.00

Phillips, P.
Advocacy With Honour. – North Ryde : Law Book Co, 1985.
ISBN 0455206511 Pbk £7.50
—Inside the new gilt-edged market. – 2nd ed. – Cambridge : Woodhead-Faulkner, 1987.
ISBN 0859413462 Hbk £25.00

Phillips, Paul Arthur
Women and Work : Inequality in the Labour Market / Erin Phillips. – Toronto : Lorimer & Co, 1983.
– (Canadian Issues Ser.).
ISBN 0888626088 Hbk £15.95
ISBN 088862607X Pbk £6.95

Phillips, Roderick
Divorce in New Zealand : a social history / Roderick Phillips. – Auckland : Oxford University Press, 1981.
154p.
Bibliography: p.149-152. - Includes index.
ISBN 019558077X

Philosophical Perspectives in Jurisprudence. – Helsinki : Suomen filosofinen ydhistus ry, 1983.
288p.
ISBN 9519505490 Hbk £106.00

Philosophy and Law. – Oxford : Blackwell, 1987.
ISBN 0631125271 Pbk £8.50

Philosophy and the criminal law : Association for Legal and Social Philosophy Tenth Annual Conference at the University of Manchester, 8-10th April 1983 / edited by Antony Duff and Nigel Simmonds. – Wiesbaden West Germany : Franz Steiner, 1984.
120p.
Bibliography: p.117-120.
ISBN 3515041699

Philosophy of law / by Z. O. Aje. – s.l. : s.n., 1986.
ix,160p.
Includes bibliographical references.

Philosophy of Law / Paul. – Oxford : Blackwell Scientific, 1987.
ISBN 0631152571 Pbk £8.95

Philosophy of law : an exposition of the fundamental principles of jurisprudence as the science of right / translated from the German by W. Hastie. – Edinburgh : Clark, 1887.
xxxvi, 265p.
Translation of Metaphysische Anfangsgrunde der Rechtslehre, pr.1 of the author's Die Metaphysik der Sitten.

Philosophy Of Law, The. – Oxford : Oxford University Press, 1977.
ISBN 0198750226 Pbk £3.50

Philpott, Frederick
Sale of Goods Litigation / Richard Spearman. – London : Longman Professional (UK), 1983.
ISBN 0851206905 Pbk £19.95

Phipson on Evidence
Nineteen Eighty-Seven Supplement. – London : Sweet & Maxwell.
Pbk

Phipson on evidence / Richard May, M.N Howard. – 13th. – London : Sweet & Maxwell, 1982 & 1987.
– (Common Law Library).
Includes changes in the chapters which deal with problems that regularly arise in modern civil and criminal legislation, and new material in the chapters on confessions and the course of the trial. Extra sections have been added to the chapters on public policy and privilege.
ISBN 0421269901 Hbk £108
ISBN 042137070X SUPPLEMENT £9

Phipson, Sidney L.
Elliott and Phipson manual of the law of evidence / D. W. Elliott, Sidney L. Phipson. – 12th ed. – London : Sweet & Maxwell, 1987.
380p; 24cm.
Previous ed.: published as Phipson and Elliott manual of the law of evidence. 1980. Includes index.
ISBN 0421338105 Hbk £20.00
ISBN 0421338202 Pbk £15.00

—Law of Evidence. – 13th ed. – London : Sweet & Maxwell, 1982.
– (Common Law Library : No. 10).
Hbk £89.00

Physical Planning and Crime in Canberra. – Canberra : Australian Institute of Criminology.
Hbk £1.50

Picard, E.
Legal Liability of Doctors and Hospitals. – 2nd ed. – Agincourt : Carswell, 1984.
ISBN 0459358200 Hbk £38.75

Picarda, Hubert →Bradford disaster appeal : the administration of an appeal fund.

—Law Relating to Receivers and Managers. – London : Butterworths, 1984.
ISBN 0406337608 Hbk £66.00

Piche
Township of Mattice-Val Cote Act, 1983, Bill Pr039 : An Act to Continue the Corporation of the Union of Townships of Elber and Devitt Under the Name of The Corporation of the Township of Mattice-Val Cote. – Ontario : Ontario Government Publications Service, 1983.
1p.
Hbk £0.30

Pichler, Marie Helen
Copyright Problems of Satellite and Cable Television in Europe. – Dordrecht : Kluwer, 1987.
208p.
ISBN 0860109526 Hbk Gld125.00

Pick, Albert
Standard Catalog of World Paper Money. – Munich : Ernst Battenberg, 1983.
959p.
Hbk £85.00

Pickerill, R. J.
Capital allowances in law and practice / R. J. Pickerill. – 2nd ed. – London : Institute of Chartered Accountants, 1981.
xix,307p. – (Chartac taxation guides).
ISBN 0852913079

Picketing : industrial disputes, tactics and the law / by Peggy Kahn...et al. – London : Routledge & Kegan Paul, 1983.
xv,223p.
Bibliography: p219-220.
ISBN 0710095341

Pickles, J.
Straight from the Bench. – Oxford : Coronet Books.
ISBN 0340422718 Pbk £2.95

Pickover, D. →Concise Criminal Law.

→ Criminal Law-Offences Against Person.

→ Police and Criminal Evidence Act 1984 : Guide.

Pictet, Jean
Development and Principles of International Humanitarian Law. – Geneva : Comite International de la Croix-Rouge, 1983.
99p.
Hbk £20.00

—Development and principles of international humanitarian law : course given in July 1982 at the University of Strasbourg as part of the courses organized by the International Institute of Human Rights / by Jean Pictet. – Dordrecht Netherlands : M. Nijhoff, 1985.
108p.
Bibliography. Translation of: Developpement et principes du droit international humanitaire.
ISBN 9024731992 Pbk £49.50

→ Etudes et essais sur le droit international humanitaire et sur les principes de la Croix-Rouge en l'honneur de Jean Pictet : Studies and essays on international humanitarian law and Red Cross principles in honour of Jean Pictet.

Pierce, David G, et al
Current Issues in International Financial Law. – Kent Ridge : Malaya Law Review.

→ Current issues of international financial law.

Piergiovanni, Vito
Courts and the Development of Commercial Law. – Berlin : Duncker and Humblot, 1987.
203p.
ISBN 3428061764 Pbk £78.00

Piesch, Walter
Suitability of concentration measures for EEC competition policy / Walter Piesch, Ingo Schmidt. – Luxembourg : Office for Official Publications of the European Communities, 1983.
101 p.; 25 cm.
ISBN 9282531783 Pbk £5.50 (U.S.)

Piesse, E. L.
Elements of drafting / by E.L. Piesse. – 6th ed. – Sydney : Law Book Co., 1981.
xv,154p; 19cm.
Bibliography: p.ix-x. - Includes index.
ISBN 0455202559

Pifer, Alan
South Africa in the American mind / Alan Pifer. – Braamfontein : South African Institute of International Affairs, 1981.
17p. – (Commemoration Day Lecture).
ISBN 0909239932

Pigeon, Louis-Philippe
Drafting and Interpreting Legislation. – 3rd ed. – Agincourt : Carswell, 1988.
110p.
Hbk £33.25

Pigott, N.
Common Recoveries : Their Nature and Use. – 2nd ed. Repr. of 1770 ed. – Abingdon : Professional Books.
490p.
Hbk £75.00

Pikale, G.S. →Non-Residents : Taxation and Investment in India.

Pikale, S.V.
Non-Residents : Taxation and Investment in India / G.S. Pikale. – Bombay : Jaico Publishing House.
Hbk £160.00

Pike →Human rights.

Pike, A.
Engineering Tenders, Sales and Contracts. – Spon, 1982.
ISBN 0419125302 Hbk £42.00

Pike, Andrew
Engineering Tenders Sales and Contracts. – London : Sweet & Maxwell, 1982.
ISBN 0419125302 Hbk £45.00

—I.Mech.E/I.E.E. conditions of contract : a commentary on five I.Mech.E./I.E.E. model forms of general conditions of contract and on the BEAMA contract price adjustment clauses and formulae / by Andrew Pike. – London : Sweet & maxwell, 1984.
xix,333p; 26cm.
Includes index.
ISBN 0421299908 £38.00

Pike, M.
Principles of policing. – London : Macmillan Press Ltd, 1985.
ISBN 0333382447 Hbk £22.50
ISBN 0333382455 Pbk £7.95

Pilkington →Canadian Business Corporations.

Pillai, P.S.A.
Criminal Law. – 6th ed. – Bombay : Tripathi, 1982.
xxxii, 892p.
Pbk £60.00

—Jurisprudence and Legal Theory. – 3rd ed. – Lucknow : Eastern Book Company, 1986.
358p.
Hbk £25.00

—Law of Evidence. – 2nd ed. – Bombay : Tripathi, 1984.
£50.00

—Principles of the Law of Tort. – 8th ed. – Lucknow : Eastern Book Company, 1986.
Hbk

Pillai, Philip N
Companies and Securities H/B Singapore and Malaysia. – London : Butterworths, 1984.
ISBN 040999507X Pbk £19.00

—Companies and Securities Handbook Singapore and Malaysia
1984 with 1985 Supplement / by Philip N. Pillai. – Butterworths, 1984.
xxv,1401p.
Provides company and securities legislation in Singapore and Malaysia. Coverage includes the text of the Companies Acts and Companies Regulations for Singapore and Malaysia, as well as the Securities Industry legislation for the two legislations. Also contains the Practice Notes and Guidelines issues by the Registrars of Companies in both jurisdictions.
ISBN 0409181209 Pbk £195.00

—Company Law and Securities Regulation in Malaysia. – London : Butterworths, 1987.
ISBN 0409995517 Pbk £28.00

—Company Law and Securities Regulation in Singapore. – Butterworths, 1987.
ca 170p.
Examines corporate and securities regulation, with reference to Singapore legislation, regulations, non-statutory guidelines, case law and administrative practice.
ISBN 0409995495 Pbk £55.00

—Sourcebook of Singapore and Malaysian company law. – 2nd ed. – London : Butterworths, 1986.
ISBN 0409995118 Hbk £115.00

—State enterprise in Singapore : legal importation and development / Philip Nalliah Pillai. – Singapore : Singapore University Press, National University of Singapore, 1983.
xxiv, 223 p.; 23 cm.
Originally presented as the author's thesis (doctoral–Harvard). Includes bibliographical references and index.
ISBN 9971690764 Pbk

Pillai, T.K. Narayana
Law of Evidence. – Allahabad : Orient Law House.
ISBN 0861254104 Hbk £30.00

Pilloud, Claude →Commentary on the additional protocols of 8 June 1977 to the Geneva Conventions of 12 August 1949.

Pilotage Act 1987. – London : Lloyd's of London Press, 1987.
ISBN 1850441391 Pbk £18.75

Pinder, John
Economic and social powers of the European Union and the member states : subordinate or coordinate relationship? / by John Pinder. – Florence : European University Institute, 1985.
47p.

Pinder, Richard
Encountering diversity : observations on the social work assessment of black children / Richard Pinder. – Leeds : Centre for Social Work and Applied Social Studies, 1982.
32p. – (Occasional paper).
Bibliography: p.31-32.

Pineus, Kaj
General average : the practical problems / Kaj Pineus. – Stockholm, Sweden : Almqvist & Wiksell International, 1985.
58 p.; 21 cm.
Includes bibliographical references.
ISBN 9122007326 Pbk kr150

—Limited Liability in Collision Cases / H. G. Rohreke. – London : LLoyd's of London Press, 1984.
Hbk £14.00

—Ship's value / by Kaj Pineus. – 2nd ed. – London : Lloyd's of London, 1986.
135p; 22cm.
Previous ed.: Gothenburg : Gothenburg Maritime Law Association, 1975. Includes bibliography and index.
ISBN 185044062X £35.00

—Time barred actions / H G Rohreke. – London : Lloyd's of London Press, 1984.
ISBN 0907432425 Hbk £34.00

—Time bars in maritime matters : a study / by Kaj Pineus. – London : Lloyd's of London Press, 1982.
168p.
ISBN 0907432425

Pink, G.
Remuneration planning manual. – London : Butterworths, 1986.
ISBN 040650430X Pbk £19.95

Pink, J N
Paterson's Licensing Acts 1989. – 97th ed. – London : Butterworths.
ISBN 0406335222 Hbk £70.00

Pink, Joel E.
From Crime to Punishment / David C. Perrier. – Agincourt : Carswell, 1988.
ca 330p.
Hbk

Pink, Matthew →Liquor licensing law.

Pinner, H. L.
Pinner's World unfair competition law : an encyclopedia / Heinz David. – 2d ed. – Alphen aan de Rijn, Netherlands : Sijthoff & Noordhoff, 1978.
v.; 26 cm.
Loose-leaf for updating. Includes bibliographical references.
ISBN 9028605576 v. 1

Pinner's World unfair competition law : an encyclopedia / Heinz David. – 2d ed. – Alphen aan de Rijn, Netherlands : Sijthoff & Noordhoff, 1978.
v.; 26 cm.
Loose-leaf for updating. Includes bibliographical references.
ISBN 9028605576 v. 1

Pinson, Barry
Pinson on revenue law : comprising income tax; capital gains tax; development land tax; corporation tax; inheritance tax; value added tax; stamp duties; tax planning / Roger Thomas. – 17th ed. – London : Sweet & Maxwell, 1986.
lxxx,780p; 25cm.
Previous ed.: 1985. Includes index. Kept up to date by supplements.
ISBN 0421370009 £55.00
—Revenue law : comprising income tax, surtax, capital gains tax, corporation tax, estate duty tax, stamp duties, tax and estate planning / by Barry Pinson. – 5th ed. – London : Sweet & Maxwell, 1971.
lxvi,641p.
Previous ed.: 1970. Includes index.
ISBN 0421163607 Pbk
ISBN 0421163704

Pinson on revenue law : comprising income tax; capital gains tax; development land tax; corporation tax; inheritance tax; value added tax; stamp duties; tax planning / Roger Thomas. – 17th ed. – London : Sweet & Maxwell, 1986.
lxxx,780p; 25cm.
Previous ed.: 1985. Includes index. Kept up to date by supplements.
ISBN 0421370009 £55.00

Pipes, mains, cables and sewers. – 5th. – London : Longman Professional (UK), 1989.
– (Practitioner series).
Guide to the basic principles of the law governing the laying of conduits by private agreement and statutory authority for electricity, telecommunicatins, water, gas, oil and effluent. Takes account of the privatisation of British Telecom, British Gas and British Petroleum, the building of the Channel Tunnel, and the abolition of the Metropolitan Councils. Includes about 60 new cases.
Hbk £17.95

Piquet, Howard S.
U.S. Trade Expansion Act of 1962 : How Will It Affect Canadian-U.S. Trade?. – Toronto : C.D. Howe Institute, 1963.
ISBN 0888060998 Hbk £5.00

Piracy and counterfeiting of industrial property and copyright : papers given at the inaugural conference of the Common Law Institute of Intellectual Property Ltd in London on 28th and 29th January 1983 / edited by W.R. Cornish. – London : Common Law Institute of Intellectual Property, 1983.
143p.
ISBN 0903067277

Piracy of phonograms : a study requested by the Commission of the European Communities / Gillian Davies. – 2nd ed. – Oxford : ESC Publishing for the Commission of the European Communities Cultural Sector, 1986.
ix,151p.
ISBN 0906214424

Piragoff, Donald K.
Similar fact evidence : probative value and prejudice / by Donald K. Piragoff. – Toronto : Carswell, 1981.
xxiii,309p.
Includes bibliographical references and index.
ISBN 0459337807

Pitch, Harvin D.
Damages for Breach of Contract / Elizabeth Carmen. – Agincourt : Carswell, 1985.
260p.
This book reviews the principles underlying the law of contracts relating to damages for the Canadian Practitioner. The trends of Canadian cases and how the courts are treating breach of contract issues are discussed in depth.
ISBN 0459373307 Hbk £24.20

Pithani
Supreme Court Criminal Digest. – Allahabad : Orient Law House, 1973-1982.
Hbk £120.00
—Supreme Court Referencer, 5 Vols. – Allahabad : Orient Law House.
Hbk £600.00

Pithisaria, Chaturvedi
Estate Duty Law. – 2nd ed. – Nagpur : Wadhura & Co, 1983.
Hbk £220.00

Pithisaria, S.M. →Income Tax Law, Vol. 1: 1981.

Pitt, Peter
Building Control In Inner London : The London Building Acts and Bylaws and Their Interpretation / J. Dufton. – London : Architectural Press, 1983.
224p.
ISBN 0851397697 Pbk £16.50
—Guide to Building Control by Local Acts 1987. – London : Architectural Press, 1987.
128p : Illus.
ISBN 0851398413 Pbk £19.50
—Guide to Building Control in Inner London 1986. – London : Architectural Press, 1987.
ISBN 0851398421 Pbk £19.50

Pitts, John
Politics of juvenile crime / John Pitts. – London : Sage, 1988.
192p; 22cm. – (Sage contemporary criminology).
Includes bibliography and index.
ISBN 0803981325 Hbk £22.50 :
ISBN 0803981333 Pbk £7.95

Pivot of the system : a briefing paper on immigration appeals. – London : The Runnymede Trust, 1981.
32fol.

Pizzey, A.
Regulatory Framework of Accounting 2.8 : ACCA Study and Revision Manual. – London : BPP.
ISBN 1870941217 Pbk £9.95

Pizzorusso, A.
Law in the Making : a Comparative Survey. – Berlin : Springer-Verlag, 1987.
ca 410p.
ISBN 3540184457 Hbk £198.00

Placita Coronae : Pleas of the Crown in Matters Criminal and Civil. – Repr. of 1723 ed. – Abingdon : Professional Books.
366p.
Hbk £210.00

Plain English and the law : a report / Law Reform Commission of Victoria. – Melbourne : The Commission, 1987.
xvi,109p. – (Report no 9).
Includes bibliographical references and index.
Accompanied by appendices 1-8 (3).

Plain English Campaign →Small print : the language and layout of consumer contracts : Report to the National Consumer Council.

Plain English for lawyers : some guidelines on writing and designing legal documents. – London : National Consumer Council, 1984.
26p; 30cm.
ISBN 0905653726

Plain Language and the Law. – Ottawa : Canadian Law Information Council.
Hbk £7.50

Plain words for consumers : the language and layout of consumer contracts : the case for a plain language law / Liz Dunbar. – London : National Consumer Council, 1984.
78p.
'Written by Richard Thomas with considerable help from Liz Dunbar'.
ISBN 090565370X

Plan, Roland
External debt rescheduling / Roland Plan. – Vienna : Manzsche Verlags-und Universitatsbuchhandlung, 1985.
x,276p. – (Law, economics, international trade).
Bibliography: p254-266.
ISBN 3214065572

Planetary Citizens →Disarmament : the human factor : proceedings of a colloquium on the societal context for disarmament.

Planned practice development. – London : Longman Professional, 1984.
ISBN 0851208673 Pbk £13.95

Planning : appeals, call-in and major public inquiries : the Government's response to the fifth report from the Environment Committee, session 1985-86 / presented to Parliament by the Secretary of State for the Environment supported by the Secretary of State for Scotland...et al. – London : H.M.S.O., 1986.
44p.
ISBN 010100432X

Planning and Compensation Reports : 1950-1981, 42 Vols. – Abingdon : Professional Books.
Hbk £650.00

Planning and development law / by Edward M. Walsh. – 2nd ed. – Dublin : Incorporated Law Society of Ireland, 1984.
xxi,209p.
Previous ed.: 1979. Includes index.
ISBN 0902027247

Planning and development law in New Zealand / by Kenneth A. Palmer : with a foreword by Sir Robin Cooke. – 2nd ed. 2. – Sydney : Law Book Co., 1984.
lviii,1023p.
ISBN 0455203725

Planning and Environment Law Service, Victoria. – Butterworths, 1984.
ISBN 040949321X Hbk £215.00

Planning and implementing the Family Court project, Jamaica / Gloria Cumper. – Kingston, Jamaica : Institute of Social and Economic Research, University of the West Indies, 1981.
i,75p. – (Working paper).

Planning and Politics in Western Europe. – London : Macmillan, 1982.
Illus.
ISBN 0333300815 Hbk £20.00

Planning and pollution : an examination of the role of land use planning in the protection of environmental quality / Christopher Miller and Christopher Wood. – Oxford : Clarendon, 1983.
xi,232p; 23cm.
Includes index.
ISBN 0198232454

Planning appeal decisions. – London : Sweet & Maxwell, 1985-.

Planning Application Fees. – London : Oyez Longman, 1981.
ISBN 085120600X Hbk £2.95

Planning applications. – Oxford : Blackwell Scientific, 1987.
ISBN 0632018941 Pbk £19.95

Planning applications and appeals. – London : Architectural Press, 1987.
ISBN 085139504X Pbk £39.50

Planning by agreement in Scotland / Eric Young. – Edinburgh : Green (W.) & Son, 1989.
Provides a guide to the law and practice of planning by agreement with an examination of the complexities that can arrive from section 50 of the Town and Country Planning (Scotland) Act 1972, the mechanics of such agreements and descriptions of the purposes for which they have been employed. Covers other statutory agreements governing land use, particularly the countryside. Concludes with a review of the arguments for and against the pursuit of 'planning gain'.
ISBN 0414008553 Pbk

Planning control : philosophies, prospects and practice / edited by M.L. Harrison and R. Mordey. – London : Croom Helm, 1986.
234p; 23cm. – (Croom Helm series in geography and environment).
Bibliography: p227-232. - Includes index.
ISBN 0709937903 £25.00

Planning controls and their enforcement / by A.J. Little. – 5th ed. – London : Shaw, 1983.
xlix,345p.
Previous ed. published as 'The enforcement of planning control' 1977. Includes index.
ISBN 0721904920

Planning Crime Prevention. – Canberra : Australian Institute of Criminology.
Hbk £18.95

Planning decisions digest / Michael Purdue and Vincent Fraser. – London : Sweet & Maxwell, 1986.
300p; 24cm.
Covers judicial decisions back to 1948, and selected ministerial decisions since 1974. Brief summaries of each decision are included, and referenced. Material is arranged under subject headings following the structure of the Town and Country Planning Act 1971.
ISBN 0421325704 Pbk £19.00

Planning Exchange →Rating appeals and the 1985 revaluation : proceedings of a Planning Exchange conference.
—Scottish Planning Appeal Decisions : Monthly. – Planning Exchange. – Glasgow : Planning Exchange.
ISBN 01438972 Pbk £70.00

Planning for growth and decline : papers from a conference held at Oxford, September 1986, organised by the Bar Council, the Law Society and the Royal Institution of Chartered Surveyors. – London : Sweet & Maxwell, 1987.
vi,70p; 25cm.
Conference proceedings.
ISBN 0421382600 Pbk £20.00

Planning for leisure in the countryside : papers from a conference held at Oxford September 1982 / organised by the Bar Council, the Law Society and the Royal Institution of Chartered Surveyors. – London : Sweet & Maxwell, 1984.
vi,107p; 25cm.
Conference papers.
ISBN 0421326700 Pbk £18.00

Planning for Stamp Duty Reserve Tax / Ball. – London : Butterworths, 1987.
ISBN 0406051033 Hbk £26.00

Planning for Stamp Duty Reserve Tax. – London : Butterworths, 1987.
Hbk

Planning inquiries / Gordon V. Hyde. – London : Sweet & Maxwell, 1983.
75p.
Conference papers.
ISBN 0421318600 Pbk £12.00

Planning Inspectorate
Chief Planning Inspector's report to the Secretary of State for the Environment, the Secretary of State for Transport and the Secretary of State for Wales / the Planning Inspectorate. – London : H.M.S.O., 1982.

Planning law. – London : Longman Professional (UK), 1988.
– (Longman practice notes).
Sets out procedure from initial stages to the final decision of the planning authority. Contains information on how to challenge a planning application, sample forms and precedents, and details time limits and fees.
ISBN 0851214452 Pbk £9.95

Planning law and practice in dwelling houses / Peter Morgan. – London : Sweet & Maxwell, 1987.
ISBN 0421366206 Hbk

Planning law and procedure. – London : Butterworths, 1988.
ISBN 0406103836 Hbk

Planning law and procedure / A.E. Telling. – 7th ed. – London : Butterworth, 1986.
xxxii,351p; 23cm.
Previous ed.: 1982. Includes index.
ISBN 0406665214 Hbk £22.00
ISBN 0406665222 Pbk £14.50

Planning law casebook. – London : Laureate-Thomson Press, 1984.
ISBN 0907392091 Pbk £19.50

Planning law for conveyancers / Clive Brand and D.W. Williams. – 3rd ed. – London : Longman Professional (UK), 1989.
– (Longman Practitioner Series).
Gives practical advice on how to solve such problems as planning authorities car parking standards, and conversion of roof space. Contains new chapters on planning policy guidance, housing action trust areas, and minerals policy, and covers the Town and Country Planning Regulations of 1988 and 1989, and the General Development Order 1988.
Conveyancing solicitors and licensed conveyancers, chartered surveyors, local authority planning departments, students
ISBN 0851216226 Pbk £22.50

Planning law handbook. – Butterworths. – London : Butterworths, 1987.
ISBN 0406505802 Pbk £22.50

Planning law handbook / by Malcolm Grant. – London : Sweet & Maxwell, 1981.
xxx,488p; 25cm.
ISBN 0421285702 Pbk £12.50

Planning Law in Practice. – London : Butterworths, 1985.
ISBN 0406260508 Hbk £22.50

Planning Office's Advice and Undertakings : Estoppel and Personal Bar in Public Law / Colin T. Reid. – Glasgow : Planning Exchange, 1982.
70p. – (Scottish Planning Law and Practice Occasional Paper Ser.: No. 3).
Pbk £6.00

Planning Procedure Tables. – 4th ed. – London : Oyez Longman, 1981.
ISBN 0851205585 Hbk £9.25

Planning use classes. – Oxford : Blackwell Scientific, 1987.
ISBN 063202125X Pbk £14.95

Planning your pension. – London : Longman Professional, 1988.
ISBN 0851213715 Pbk £4.95

Plant protection legislation / by Luis M. Bombin. – Rome : Food and Agriculture Organization of the United Nations, 1984.
165p. – (Legislative study).
ISBN 9251014604

Plant, Raymond
Equality, markets and the state / Raymond Plant. – London : Fabian Society, 1984.
28p.
ISBN 0716304945

Plastic and Electronic Money. – Cambridge : Woodhead-Faulkner, 1985.
ISBN 0859412903 Hbk £40.00

Plateau law reports : containing selected cases decided in the High Court of Plateau State and in the other superior courts in Nigeria including the Supreme Court and the Federal Court of Appeal, and also of certain tribunals. – Enugu : Fourth Dimension Publishing, 1981.

Plato on punishment / Mary Margaret Mackenzie. – Berkeley Calif. : University of California Press, 1981.
vii,278p; 25cm.
Bibliography: p251-259. - Includes index.
ISBN 0520041690 £17.25

Platt, Tony
Crime and Social Justice / Paul Takagi. – London : Macmillan, 1981.
232p. – (Critical Criminology Ser.).
ISBN 0333282604 Hbk £18.00
ISBN 0333282612 Pbk £6.95

Platzoder, Renate →Seerecht : Testausgabe Law of the sea.

Plaut, W. Gunther
Refugee determination in Canada : proposals for a new system : a report to the Honourable Flora MacDonald, Minister of Employment and Immigration / by W. Gunther Plaut. – Ottawa : Minister of Supply and Services Canada, 1985.
221,286p.
With French t.p.: Reconnaissance au Canada du statut de refugie. Pages numbered in opposite directions. English and French text.
ISBN 0662538234

Player, Elaine →Race relations in prisons.
→ Women in the penal system.

Pleader's Guide. – 5th ed. Repr. of 1808 ed. – Abingdon : Professional Books.
262p.
Hbk £75.00

Pleading and Precedents in India. – 2nd ed. – Allahabad : Law Publishers, 1983.
Hbk £37.50

Pleading Before the Court of Justice of the European Communities : The Law Society's European Group. – London : Law Society.
free

Pleading, Evidence and Practice. – 43rd ed. – London : Sweet & Maxwell, 1988.
ISBN 0421363606 Hbk £49.00
ISBN 0421054808 Hbk £60.00

Pleading, Evidence, and Practice in Criminal Cases 2 vols. – 43rd ed. – Sweet & Maxwell.
ISBN 0421375108 Hbk £110.00

Pleading Precedents. – 3rd ed. – North Ryde : Law Book Co, 1984.
xvii, 285p.
ISBN 0455202923 Hbk £43.00

Pleadings and Practice. 2 Vols. – 7th ed. – Allahabad : Law Book Company, 1984.
Hbk £300.00

Pleas of the Crown 1678. – Reprint. – Abingdon : Professional Books, 1986.
ISBN 0862053218 Hbk £24.75

Pleas of the Crown : Summary. – Abingdon : Professional Books.
– (Classical English Law Texts Ser.).
Hbk £35.00

Please Your Worship : Lighter Side of a Magistrate's Court. – Bombay : Tripathi, 1965.
196p.
Hbk £10.00

Plees del Coron. – 1st ed. – Abingdon : Professional Books, 1986 Reprint.
ISBN 0862053285 Hbk £24.75

PLEI Directory 1985. – Ottawa : Canadian Law Information Council, 1985.
75p.
ISBN 0920358802 Pbk £4.50

Plender, Richard →Basic documents on international migration law.
—International migration law / Richard Plender. – Rev. 2nd ed. – Dordrecht, Netherlands : M. Nijhoff, 1987.
xxvii,587p.
Includes index.
ISBN 9024736048
—Problems raised by certain aspects of the present situation of refugees from the standpoint of the European Convention on Human Rights / by Richard Plender. – Strasbourg : Council of Europe, Directorate of Human Rights, 1984.
38p.
ISBN 9287103550

Plodding. – Police Review, 1986.
ISBN 0851640257 Pbk £1.95

Ploman, Edward W. →International law governing communications and information : a collection of basic documents.
—Space, earth and communication / Edward W. Ploman. – London : Pinter, 1984.
xi,237p; 22cm.
Bibliography: p225-229. - Includes index.
ISBN 0861873610 Hbk £26.00

Plotting and Planning. – Canberra : Australian Institute of Criminology.
Hbk £5.00

Plowden, Edwin Noel Plowden →Ninth report on top salaries.

Plowden, F. P.
Principles and Law of Tithing. – Repr. of 1806 ed. – Abingdon : Professional Books.
282p.
Hbk £40.00

Plucknett, T. F. T.
Studies in English legal history / T.F.T. Plucknett. – London : Hambledon, 1983.
352p in various pagings; 24cm.
Includes index. Includes text in Latin.
ISBN 0907628117 £24.00

Plumb, Angela →Probate Manual.

Plummer, F.
Rating valuation and practice guide. – London : Longman Professional, 1987.
ISBN 0851213200 Pbk £15.95

Pocket Criminal Code of Canada. – Agincourt : Carswell, 1988.
760p.
This work contains the Criminal Code of Canada including the Young Offenders Act as amended, Canada Evidence Act, Canadian Bill of Rights ss.1 5, Competition Act, Criminal Records Act, Extradition Act, Food and Drugs Act, Interpretation Act, Identification of Criminals Act ss.1 3, Narcotic Control Act and Constitution Act.
Hbk £11.00

Pockson, Jonathan R. H. H.
Accountant's professional negligence : developments in legal liability / Jonathan R.H.H. Pockson. – London : Macmillan, 1982.
xxi,212p; 23cm.
Bibliography: p192-208. - Includes index.
ISBN 0333278453 £25.00

Pocock, J. G. A.
Ancient constitution and the feudal law : a study of English historical thought in the seventeenth century / J.G.A. Pocock. – Reissue with a retrospect i.e. 2nd ed. – Cambridge : Cambridge University Press, 1987.
xv,402p; 24cm.
Second edition to a work examining seventeenth-century English ideas of constitutionalism as a set of beliefs based on the common law. The Retrospect considers how arguments in the original book may be improved in the light of recent work.
ISBN 0521303524 Hbk £27.50
ISBN 052131643X Pbk £8.95
—Virtue, commerce, and history : essays on political thought and history, chiefly in the eighteenth century / J.G.A. Pocock. – Cambridge : Cambridge University Press, 1985.
x,321p; 24cm.
Includes index.
ISBN 0521257018 Hbk £25.00
ISBN 0521276608 Pbk

Podgorecki, Adam
Legal System and Social Systems / Etal. – Oxford : Croom Helm, 1985.
ISBN 0709936125 Hbk £18.95
→ Legal systems & social systems.
→ Sociological approaches to law.

Poh, Chu Chai
Law of Negotiable Instruments. – Singapore : Malayan Law Journal, 1984.
139p.
Discusses what constitutes a valid negotiable instrument, problems arising in cases of forgery and material alterations, concepts of holder and holder in due course, and provisions relating to cheques under the Singapore provisions that are in line with the English Cheques Act 1957.
ISBN 9971700417 Pbk £28.00

Pointing, John →Alternatives to custody.

Pointon, Leo D.
Revenue law in Singapore and Malaysia / cases and commentary : Leo D. Pointon. – Singapore : Butterworths, 1986.
xxvii,281p.
Includes the interpretation of statutes and cases, administration, income, exempt income, deductions, capital allowances, personal reliefs, partnerships, and estate duty.
ISBN 0409995266 Hbk £78

Points of Order. – 4th ed. – London : Shaw & Sons, 1987.
ISBN 0721904025 Pbk £4.95

Points to prove. – 2nd ed. – Police Review, 1987.
ISBN 085164032X Pbk £5.25

Poirier, Donald
Educational Rights of Exceptional Children in Canada. – Agincourt : Carswell, 1988.
144p.
Hbk £25.00

Pok, Soy Yoong
Singapore Taxation / Damian C.F. Hong. – Butterworths, 1985.
636p.
ISBN 0409995053 Pbk £90.00

Polak, M.V. →Private International Law in the Netherlands.

Polarised Law. – Sweet & Maxwell, 1914 Reprint.
ISBN 0421355204 Hbk £21.00

Polay, E.
Iniuria Types in Roman Law. – Budapest : Akademiai Kiado, 1986.
226p.
ISBN 9630544598 Hbk £24.00

Polden, Patrick
Guide to the records of the Lord Chancellor's Department / Patrick Polden. – London : HMSO, 1988.
xxx,376p.
Guide to Lord Chancellor's records on judges, courts and the legal profession and on the making of law on property, divorce, transport and lunacy.
ISBN 0113800150

Police : autonomy and consent / Michael Brogden. – London : Academic Press, 1982.
xv,265p; 24cm.
Bibliography: p251-259. - Includes index.
ISBN 0121351807 £21.00

Police : Organisation and Command. – Plymouth : Macdonald & Evans, 1984.
400p : Illus.. – – (Police Studies Ser.).
ISBN 0712116710 Hbk £7.50

Police : powers, procedures and proprieties / edited by John Benyon and Colin Bourn : with a foreword by Lord Scarman. – Oxford : Pergamon, 1986.
xxiv,334p; 24cm.
Bibliography: p299-312. - Includes index.
ISBN 0080326978 Hbk £17.00
ISBN 008032696X Pbk £6.90

Police Act, 1967 (Act No. 41 of 1967). – Kuala Lumpur : International Law Books Services.
Hbk £7.00

Police action on motoring offences / David Riley. – London : Home Office, 1983.
iv,17p.
Bibliography: p.10.
ISBN 0862521130

Police Acts 1964 and 1976 : complaints against the police which are withdrawn / Ken Russell. – Leicester : Leicester Polytechnic, 1986.
33p. – (Leicester Polytechnic School of Law Monographs).
Includes bibliographical references.
ISBN 0900937408

Police Acts. With 1985 supplement. – 5th ed. – Allahabad : Law Book Company, 1983.
Hbk £170.00

Police and complaints / Eric Edwards. – London : G.L.C., 1983.
12p. – (Research documents guide).
ISBN 0716813661

Police and Criminal Evidence Act 1984 / with annotations by M.D.A. Freeman. – London : Sweet & Maxwell, 1985.
x,185,44,8p; 24cm.
ISBN 0421329009

Police and Criminal Evidence Act 1984 / by Michael Zander : foreword by Leon Brittan. – London : Sweet & Maxwell, 1985.
xxi,315p; 25cm.
Includes index.
ISBN 0421326905 Pbk £12.50

Police and Criminal Evidence Act 1984 : Guide / D Pickover. – Police Review, 1986.
ISBN 0851640214 Pbk £4.95

Police and Criminal Evidence Act 1984 (s.66) : codes of practice. – London : H.M.S.O., 1985.
97p.
Provisions supersede some existing rules including the Judges' Rules. Codes cover police powers of stop and search; searching of premises and seizure of property; detention, treatment and questioning by police and identification procedures.
ISBN 011340624X

Police and Criminal Evidence Bill 1982 : briefings / National Council for Civil Liberties. – 1. – London : The Council, 1983.
various pagings.
Contents: Clause 1: Stop and search of persons and vehicles - Clauses 9 and 10: Police powers to search private premises for evidence - Clauses 9 and 10: Opinion / by Ben Hytner - Part 3. Police powers of arrest - Part 4. Detention of suspects - Part 5. Questioning and treatment of persons by police - Part 6. Codes of practice - Clause 60: 'Confession' statements and the right to silence.

Police and criminal evidence bill : briefing guide. – London : Home Office, 1983.
67p.
ISBN 0862521211

Police and Criminal Evidence Bill : draft code of practice for the exercise of powers of stop and search. – London : Home Office, 1984.
9p.
ISBN 0862521556

Police and Law Enforcement
Vol. 4. – London : Eurospan, 1988.
ISBN 0404112080 Hbk £47.25

Police and people in London
vol.1 : A survey of Londoners : David J. Smith / David J. Smith. – London : Policy Studies Institute, 1983.
350p. – (PSI).
ISBN 0853742235
vol.2 : A group of young black people : Stephen Small. – 1983.
169p. – (PSI).
ISBN 0853742243
vol.3 : A survey of police officers : David J. Smith. – 1983.
197p. – (PSI).
ISBN 0853742251
vol.4 : The police in action : David J. Smith, Jeremy Gray. – 1983.
354p. – (PSI).
ISBN 085374226X

Police and public order in Europe / edited by John Roach and Jurgen Thomaneck. – London : Croom Helm, 1985.
293p; 23cm.
Includes bibliographies and index.
ISBN 0709922426 £18.95

Police and the community / Eric Edwards. – London : G.L.C., 1983.
20p. – (Research documents guide).
ISBN 0716813688

Police and the Criminal Evidence Act 1984 / Magrath. – London : Longman Professional, 1985.
ISBN 0851207669 Pbk £19.95

Police and the law / Charles Wegg-Prosser. – 3rd ed. – London : Longman Professional, 1986.
xiv,287p; 20cm. – (It's your law series).
Previous ed.: London : Oyez, 1979. Bibliography: p273-279. - Includes index.
ISBN 0851207588 Pbk £6.95

Police and the law in Nigeria / S.G. Ehindero. – Lagos : Times Press, 1986.
xxv,158p.
Bibliography: p.155. - Includes index.
ISBN 9783023608

Police community relations and the administration of justice / Pamela D. Mayhall. – 3rd ed. – New York : Wiley, 1984.
ix,438p; 25cm.
Previous ed.: published as: Community relations and the administration of justice. 1979. Includes bibliographies and index.
ISBN 0471060445 £27.95

Police complaints and discipline procedures / presented to Parliament by the Secretary of State for the Home Department... – London : H.M.S.O., 1983.
ii,23p.
ISBN 0101907206

Police Complaints Authority
Annual report of the Police Complaints Authority. – Police Complaints Authority. – London : H.M.S.O., 1986-.
Continues: Report of the Police Complaints Board.

Police Complaints Board
Police Complaints Board Triennial Review Report 1983. – Police Complaints Board. – London : HMSO.
ISBN 010188530X Hbk £3.35
—Triennial review report ... / Police Complaints Board. – 3. – London : HMSO, 1980-.

Police Complaints Board Final Report 1977-1985. – London : HMSO.
ISBN 0101958404 Hbk £3.50

Police Complaints Board Triennial Review Report 1983. – Police Complaints Board. – London : HMSO.
ISBN 010188530X Hbk £3.35

Police complaints procedure : a survey of complainants' views / by David Brown. – London : H.M.S.O., 1987.
v,91p; 25cm.
Survey of complainants' views, carried out shortly before the Police and Criminal Evidence Act 1984. Explores tensions involved in the complaints procedure and assesses its effectiveness.
ISBN 0113408536

Police Diaries, Statements, Reports, Investigations. – 9th ed. 2 Vols. – Allahabad : Law Publishers, 1986.
Hbk £170.00 ea

Police, Government and Accountability / Qual. – Oxford : Oxford University Press, 1987.
ISBN 0333432266 Pbk £8.95

Police guidelines - pretrial eyewitness identification procedures : a study paper / prepared for the Law Reform Commission of Canada by Neil Brooks. – Ottawa : the Commission, 1983.
260p; 25cm. – (Criminal law series).
ISBN 0662127315

Police Handbook. – Allahabad : Law Publishers, 1982.
Hbk £45.00

Police In Society. – London : Sinclair Browne.
ISBN 0863000185 Pbk £4.95

Police Institutions and Issues : American and Australian Perspectives. – Canberra : Australian Institute of Criminology.
Hbk £5.00

Police interrogation. – Police Review, 1987.
ISBN 0851640311 Pbk £5.95

Police interrogation: the effects of the Police and Criminal Evidence Act 1984 / Ian McKenzie. – London : Policy Studies Institute, 1989.
250; 21.
A comparison of research data from 1979 with new research data from 1986 in one police station in Brighton.
ISBN 0947692118 Hbk £18.95

Police Investigations and Prosecutions. – 5th ed. 1986 repr. 1987. – Allahabad : Law Book Company, 1987.
900p.
Hbk £200.00

Police law / Card. – 2nd ed. – London : Butterworths, 1988.
ISBN 0406840008 Pbk £15.95

Police law primer. – 3rd ed. – London : Butterworths, 1987.
ISBN 0406846529 Pbk £8.95

Police Manual of Arrest, Seizure and Interrogation. – 4th ed. – Agincourt : Carswell, 1988.
182p.
This work is an updated handbook relected recent Canadian Criminal Code revisions and recent case law affecting police powers of arrest, seizure, and interrogation.
Hbk £29.50

Police misconduct : legal remedies / John Harrison. – London : Legal Action Group, 1987.
xxix,218p.
Guide to the remedies and procedures available in this area. Covers police complaints, civil actions against the police, the European Convention on Human Rights, police discipline, judicial review, wrongful convictions, criminal proceedings, and legal aid. Appendices include levels of damages and useful names and addresses.
ISBN 0905099168

Police of Britain. – London : Macmillan.
ISBN 0029307600 Hbk £19.95

Police Offences In Western Australia. – Sydney : Butterworths, 1981.
243p.
Hbk £0409322903

Police Officer in Court : A Guide to Presenting Evidence. – London : Police Review Publishing, 1983.
ISBN 0851640060 Pbk

Police Officers' Manual : 1988. – 11th ed. – Agincourt : Carswell.
Hbk

Police powers and accountability. – Oxford : Croom Helm, 1986.
ISBN 0709916604 Hbk £16.95

Police powers and duties / Nottridge. – London : Fourmat, 1985.
ISBN 0906840821 Pbk £9.95

Police Powers and Individual Rights. – Montreal : McGill Campus Legal Aid Clinic, 1986.
117p.
Hbk £6.00

Police powers and politics / Richard Kinsey. – London : Quartet, 1982.
1v.
ISBN 0704323338 Hbk £9.95
ISBN 0704334127 Pbk £3.95

Police powers and the individual / St. John A. Robilliard and Jenny McEwan. – Oxford : Basil Blackwell, 1986.
viii,260p; 23cm.
Compares actual police practice with their legal powers. Discusses constraints on and remedies for police misbehaviour.
ISBN 0631139958 Hbk £27.50 :
ISBN 0631139966 Pbk £9.95

Police powers and the rights of suspects / by Tim McBride. – Auckland : Legal Research Foundation, 1982.
23,8,5p.
'Paper presented at Auckland Law Faculty seminar series 1982 at University of Auckland'.
ISBN 0908581246

Police powers in England and Wales / L.H. Leigh. – 2nd ed. – London : Butterworth, 1985.
330p; 22cm.
Previous ed.: 1975. Includes index.
ISBN 0406845417 Hbk £20.00 :
ISBN 0406845425 Pbk £14.95

Police powers - search and seizure in criminal law enforcement / Law Reform Commission of Canada. – Ottawa : The Commission, 1983.
356,403p; 25cm. – (Working paper).
Added t.p. in French: Les pouvoirs de la police : les fouilles, les perquisitions et les saisies en droit penal. Pages numbered in opposite directions. In English and French.
ISBN 066252277X

Police probationer training in race relations / Peter Southgate. – London : Home Office, 1982.
iv,38p.
Bibliography: p.31.
ISBN 0862520630

Police Promotion Handbooks. – London : Butterworths.
Pbk

Police, Race and Ethnicity : A Guide For Law Enforcement Officers / Chris Toole. – Toronto : Butterworths, 1986.
256p.
Guidelines for 'on the street' level of policing and providing police officers with administrative considerations. Also considers the structure and practice of relevant criminal law and the function of the Ontario Human Rights Commission in enforcing the Ontario Human Rights Code. The mechanism of the Ontario Human Rights Commission.
ISBN 0409805017 Pbk £18.25

Police response to calls from the public / Paul Ekblom and Kevin Heal. – London : Home Office, 1982.
v,95p; 30cm.
Bibliography: p85-88.
ISBN 0862520657 Pbk

Police Source Book. – Canberra : Australian Institute of Criminology.
Hbk £8.00

Police, the law and the people / Nick Blake. – New ed. – London : Haldane Society of Socialist Lawyers, 1982.
55p.
Includes bibliographical references.
ISBN 0907412025

Police Training in Australia. – Canberra : Australian Institute of Criminology.
free

Police training manual / Houghton. – 5th ed. – Maidenhead : McGraw-Hill, 1986.
ISBN 0070847975 Pbk £12.95

Police - where now? : a public lecture / delivered by John C. Alderson on ... 18th March 1982. – London : Inns of Court School of Law, 1982.
12p; 23cm.

Policeman's lot. – Police Review, 1983.
ISBN 0851649939 Pbk £1.95

Police-public encounters / by Peter Southgate with the assistance of Paul Ekblom. – London : H.M.S.O., 1986.
vi,143p; 25cm.
Report from the Research and Planning Unit. Describes a study of everyday contact between the public and uniformed police in London, Birmingham and Bristol. Examines problems during such encounters.
ISBN 011340834X

Policewoman and Equality (1988). – London : Macmillan, 1988.
ISBN 0333424417 Pbk £8.95

Policies Against Low Pay : An International Perspective. – London : Policy Studies Institute, 1984.
208p. – (PSI Research Papers).
Hbk £6.50

Policies for the Police Service / Association of Metropolitan Authorities. – London : The Association, 1982.
8p.

Policies in the Developed Countries. – London : British-North American Research Association, 1983.
Hbk £8.00

Policies with regard to grants to local authorities / report prepared by the Committee of Experts on Local and Regional Finance of the Steering Committee for Regional and Municipal Matters and drafted by J. Lotz, Chairman. – Strasbourg : Council of Europe, 1986.
35p.

Policing a Democracy. – Canberra : Australian Institute of Criminology.
free

Policing and Private Security. – Canberra : Australian Institute of Criminology.
Hbk £4.00

Policing and Social Policy : Proceedings of the Cranfield-Wolfson Colloquium. – London : Police Review Publishing, 1984.
Hbk £8.75

Policing by coercion. – Pluto Press, 1983.
ISBN 071681336X Pbk £1.50

Policing by multi-racial consent : the Handsworth experience / John Brown. – London : Bedford Square Press, 1982.
xv,174p.
Bibliography: p173-174.

Policing immigration : Britain's internal controls / Paul Gordon. – London : Pluto, 1985.
v,160p.
Includes index.
ISBN 0861046234 Pbk £4.95

Policing industrial disputes: 1893 to 1985 / Roger Geary. – Cambridge : Cambridge University Press, 1985.
vii,171p; 24cm.
Includes index.
ISBN 052130315X £19.50

Policing liberal society / Steve Uglow. – Oxford : Oxford University Press, 1988.
viii, 165 p.; 23 cm. – (An OPUS book).
Examines the role of the police force in late twentieth-century Britain; how it has changed, and prospects for the future. Questions whether the police are crime-fighters, social workers, guardians of the law, or maintainers of public order. Suggests that the constitutional role of the police should be re-examined.
ISBN 0192192221 Hbk £19.50

Policing Minorities in Europe : Proceedings foom the Cranfield-Wolfson Colloquium. – London : Police Review Publishing, 1984.
ISBN 0851640087 Pbk

Policing pollution : a study of regulation and enforcement / Genevra Richardson with Anthony Ogus and Paul Burrows. – Oxford : Clarendon Press, 1982.
ix,204p; 23cm.
Includes index.
ISBN 0198275102 Hbk £15.00
ISBN 0198275129 Pbk

Policing revolution : police technology, democracy and liberty in Britain / Sarah Manwaring-White. – Brighton : Harvester, 1983.
vii,231p; 23cm.
ISBN 0710805551 Hbk £18.95
ISBN 0710806159 Pbk

Policing the miners' strike / edited by Bob Fine and Robert Millar. – London : Lawrence and Wishart, 1985.
xii,243p.
ISBN 0853156336

Policing today / edited by Kevin Heal, Roger Tarling and John Burrows, Home Office Research and Planning Unit. – London : H.M.S.O., 1985.
v,176p.
12 studies from the Home Office Research and Planning Unit. Discusses management, efficiency and economy, and police/public relations.
ISBN 0113408005

Policy arguments in judicial decisions / by John Bell. – Oxford : Clarendon, 1983.
xiv,283p; 23cm.
Bibliography: p271-276. - Includes index.
ISBN 0198253974

Policy formation in the European Communities : a bibliographic guide to Community documentation 1958-1978 / Michael Hopkins. – London : Mansell, 1981.
xx,339p; 24cm.
Includes index.
ISBN 0720115973 £24.50

Policy implementation, compliance and administrative law / Law Reform Commission of Canada. – Ottawa : Law Reform Commission of Canada, 1986.
105,115p; 25cm. – (Working paper).
Cover title: Administrative law - policy implementation, compliance and administrative law. Added t.p. in French: Droit, objectifs publics et observation des normes. Pages numbered in opposite directions. Text in English and French.
ISBN 0662540832

Policy process in the modern capitalist state / Christopher Ham and Michael Hill. – Brighton : Wheatsheaf Books Ltd, 1984.
xiii,210p.
Bibliography: p190-204.
ISBN 0710801904

Policy Studies Institute → Industrial relations in West Germany : a case study of the car industry.
→ Police and people in London.
→ Workplace industrial relations and technical change.

Policy-making in the European Community / edited by Helen Wallace, William Wallace and Carol Webb. – 2nd ed. – Chichester : Wiley, 1983.
xv,451p; 24cm.
Previous ed.: 1977. Includes index.
ISBN 0471901490 Hbk
ISBN 0471901504 Pbk

Polish Contributions to the Theory and Philosophy of Law. – Amsterdam : Editions Rodopi, 1987.
212p.
ISBN 9062037992 Hbk £170.00

Political and legal framework of trade relations between the european community and eastern europe. – Dordrecht : Nijhoff (Martinus), 1989.
352.
Historical reflection on relations between the EEC and COMECON, and on analysis of the position of Western European countries in their relations with Eastern Europe, European enterprises in the EEC, export controls, financial cooperation and countertrade, and the position of Eastern European countries in the GATT.
ISBN 0792300467 Hbk £42

Political aspects of the Westland affair / editor, Dawn Oliver. – London : Faculty of Laws, University College London, 1986.
51p; 30cm. – (Working papers (University College London, Faculty of Laws)).

Political economy of environmental hazards : a study paper prepared for the Law Reform Commission of Canada / by T.F. Schrecker. – Ottawa : Law Reform Commission of Canada, 1984.
vi,112p.
ISBN 066213236X

Political economy of international money : in search of a new order / edited by Loukas Tsoukalis. – London : Royal Institute of International Affairs, 1985.
313p; 22cm.
Includes index.
ISBN 0803997108 Hbk £
ISBN 0803997116 Pbk £9.50

Political economy of law : a third world reader / edited by Yash Ghai, Robin Luckham, Francis Snyder. – Delhi : Oxford University Press, 1987.
xvi,821p.
A view of Indian legal systems as they operate nationally and internationally. Law is analysed in terms of its relationships to economy, the state, political conflict, class, and international relations.
ISBN 0195619919 Hbk £32.50

Political economy of nationalism / Dudley Seers. – Oxford : Oxford University Press, 1983.
218p; 22cm.
Bibliography: p198-203. - Includes index.
ISBN 019828456X Hbk £
ISBN 019828473X Pbk £6.95

Political economy of underdevelopment / S.B.D. de Silva. – London : Routledge & Kegan Paul in association with the Institute of Southeast Asian Studies, Singapore, 1983.
viii,645p; 22cm.
Includes index.
ISBN 0710202733 Pbk £12.50

Political justice : outline of a philosophical theory / by Otfried Hoffe. – Florence : European University Institute, 1985.
20p.

Political killings by governments. – Amnesty International. – London : Amnesty International, 1983.
131p; 22cm.
Includes index.
ISBN 0862100518 Pbk

Political policing in Wales / John Davies, Lord Gifford, Tony Richards. – Cardiff : Welsh Campaign for Civil & Political Liberties, 1984.
111p; 19cm.
ISBN 0947740007 Pbk £1.50

Political Rights : the Legal Framework of Elections in Canada. – London : Butterworths.
ISBN 0409816019 Hbk £64.00

Political rights for European citizens / Guido van den Berghe. – Aldershot : Gower, 1982.
xii,245p; 23cm.
Bibliography: p218-235. - Includes index.
ISBN 0566005247

Political role of law courts in modern democracies / edited by Jerold L. Waltman and Kenneth M. Holland. – Basingstoke : Macmillan, 1988.
viii,237p; 23cm.
Includes index.
ISBN 0333394054 £25.00

Political terrorism : theory, tactics, and counter-measures / Grant Wardlaw. – Cambridge : Cambridge University Press, 1982.
xiii,218p; 24cm.
Bibliography: p204-212. - Includes index.
ISBN 0521250323 Hbk £
ISBN 0521271479 Pbk

Political Value Patterns and Parties in Sweden / Ulla Bergryd. – Stockholm : Almqvist & Wiksell.
ISBN 9122004130 Hbk £165.00

Political Violence and Civil Disobedience in Western Europe. – London : Institute for the Study of Conflict, 1982.
– (Conflict Studies Ser.: No. 145).
Hbk £5.50

Political Violence and the Law in Ireland / Walker. – Manchester : Manchester University Press.
ISBN 00719029104 Hbk £25.00

Politics and power
4 : Law, politics and justice. – London : Routledge and Kegan Paul, 1981.
328p; 24cm.
ISBN 0710009844

Politics and process in the specialised agencies of the United Nations / Houshang Ameri. – Aldershot : Gower, 1982.
xiii,284p; 23cm.
Bibliography: p265-273. - Includes index.
ISBN 0566005387

Politics and the Constitution, The Charter, Federalism and the Supreme Court of Canada. – Agincourt : Carswell, 1987.
253p.
This work focuses on the constitutional issues presented to the Supreme Court of Canada over the last ten years. Discussions include a summary of the significance and implications of the initial Charter decisions. Charts and graphs are presented to illustrate the success rate of the Charter arguments.
Hbk £40.50

Politics and the Law in Late 19th Century Germany. – Oxford : Clarendon Press.
ISBN 0198227485 Hbk £35.00

Politics of banking. – 2nd ed. – London : Macmillan, 1986.
ISBN 0333424123 Pbk £8.95

Politics of child abuse / Nigel Parton. – Basingstoke : Macmillan, 1985.
xii,245p; 22cm.
ISBN 0333363167 Pbk
ISBN 0333363175

Politics of clean air / Eric Ashby and Mary Anderson. – Oxford : Clarendon, 1981.
viii,178p; 24cm.
Includes index.
ISBN 0198583303 £15.00

Politics of industrial relations / Colin Crouch. – 2nd ed. – London : Fontana, 1982.
255p.
Bibliography: p223-239.

Politics of informal justice / edited by Richard L. Abel. – 2. – 1981.
– (Studies on law and social control).
Includes bibliographies. Contents: 1. The American experience - 2. Comparative studies.
ISBN 0120415011 v. 1

Politics of international economic relations / Joan Edelman Spero. – 3rd. ed. – London : Allen & Unwin, 1985.
viii,447p.
Bibliography: p405-431.
ISBN 0043820441

Politics of juvenile crime / John Pitts. – London : Sage, 1988.
192p; 22cm. – (Sage contemporary criminology).
Includes bibliography and index.
ISBN 0803981325 Hbk £22.50 :
ISBN 0803981333 Pbk £7.95

Politics of Latin American development / Gary W. Wynia. – 2nd ed. – Cambridge : Cambridge University Press, 1984.
xv,318p,2p of plates; 24cm.
Previous ed.: 1978. Includes bibliographies and index.
ISBN 0521261201 Hbk £25.00
ISBN 0521278422 Pbk

Politics of mental health legislation / Clive Unsworth. – Oxford : Clarendon, 1987.
384p; 22cm.
Includes bibliography and index.
ISBN 0198255128 £30.00

Politics of secrecy / James Michael. – Harmondsworth : Penguin, 1982.
240p; 20cm.
Bibliography: p225-229. - Includes index.
ISBN 0140220607 Pbk £2.50

Politics of the Imagination : a Life of F.R. Scott. – Toronto : McClelland & Stewart.
ISBN 0771028253 Hbk £39.95

Politics of the judiciary / J. A. G. Griffith. – 3rd ed. – London : Fontana, 1985.
255p.
ISBN 0006860206

Pollack, I. C → Need for and the feasibility of an appeals process in regard to municipal grants-in-lieu of taxes : a report prepared for the Minister of Public Works Canada.

Pollard : Regulation of US Banking. – London : Butterworths, 1987.
ISBN 040610350X Pbk

Pollard, Alfred
Banking Law in the USA. – London : Butterworths, 1987.
ISBN 040610350X Hbk £80.00
—Pollard : Regulation of US Banking. – London : Butterworths, 1987.
ISBN 040610350X Pbk

Pollard, D. E.
Law and policy of producers' associations / D.E. Pollard. – Oxford : Clarendon, 1984.
xii,372p; 23cm.
Includes index.
ISBN 0198254806 Hbk £40.00

Pollard, David
Social Welfare Law. – London : Longman Professional.
ISBN 0851204694 Llf £125.00

Pollock
Eastern Pentecostal Bible College Act, 1983, Bill Pr034 : An Act Respecting Eastern Pentecostal Bible College. – Ontario : Ontario Government Publications Service, 1983.
8p.
Hbk £0.30
—Indian Contract and Specific Relief Acts / Mulla. – 10th ed. in press. – Bombay : Tripathi.
bd

Pollock, Frederick
Historical English Law before Edward I / Frederic William Maitland. – 2nd ed. – Cambridge : Cambridge University Press, 1988.
ISBN 0521095166 Pbk £30.00
—History of English law before the time of Edward I
Vol. 1 / by Sir Frederick Pollock and Frederic William Maitland. – 2nd edition. – Cambridge : Cambridge University Press, 1988.
xxxviii,688p.
ISBN 0521095166 Hbk
Vol. 2 / by Sir Frederick Pollock and Frederic William Maitland. – 1988.
xiv,691p.

Pollution by Dumping. The Law of the Sea. – Geneva : United Nations Publications.
77p.
Pbk £11.50

Pollution of international watercourses : search for substantive rules and principles of law / by J.G. Lammers. – The Hague : M. Nijhoff, 1984.
xxvi, 724 p.; 25 cm.
Includes indexes. Bibliography: p. 663-703.
ISBN 9024729556 Hbk £275.00

Pollution of outer space, in particular of the geostationary orbit / W. de Graaff. – Dordrecht : Nijhoff (Martinus), 1989.
188. – (Utrecht studies in air and space law).
Survey of the status of the pollution of outer space, dealing with both the scientific and legal aspects. Shows that the emerging international regulations are few, scanty, and in urgent need of elaboration.
ISBN 9024737508 Hbk £39

Polska Akademia Nauk → Essays in international law in honour of Judge Manfred Lachs.

Polygamous marriages : capacity to contract a polygamous marriage and the concept of the potentially polygamous marriage / The Law Commission and The Scottish Law Commission. – London : H.M.S.O., 1982.
vii,126p; 21cm. – (Consultative memorandum).
ISBN 0117301639

Polygraph test : lies, truth and science / editor, Anthony Gale. – London : Sage, 1988.
256p; 22cm.
Includes bibliography and index.
ISBN 0803981228 £19.95

Polytechnic of North London → Land law lecture notes.

Polyviou, Polyvios G.
Search & seizure : constitutional and common law / Polyvios G. Polyviou. – London : Duckworth, 1982.
viii,391p; 26cm.
Includes index.
ISBN 0715615920 £35.00

Pombo, F.
Doing Business in Spain. – Matthew Bender, 1987.
ISBN 0000999037 Hbk £50.00

Pomerance, Michla
Self-determination in law and practice : the new doctrine in the United Nations / by Michla Pomerance. – The Hague : M. Nijhoff, 1982.
xi,154p.
Includes index. Bibliography: p130-138.
ISBN 9024725941

Pond, Chris
Case for a national minimum wage / Chris Pond and Steve Winyard. – London : Low Pay Unit, 1983.
64p. – (Pamphlet).
Bibliography: p61-63.

Ponting, Clive
Right to know : the inside story of the Belgrano affair / Clive Ponting. – London : Sphere Books, 1985.
214p.
ISBN 0722169442
—Secrecy in Britain. – Oxford : Blackwell (Basil), 1990.
96; 20.
ISBN 0631169121 Pbk £3.75

Pool, Derek → Exporting goods from the United Kingdom : export co-operatives and contract warehousing.

Poole, K. P.
Education law : an outline of the law relating to the public system of education in England and Wales / K.P. Poole. – London : Sweet & Maxwell, 1988.
lviii,355p; 26cm.
Sets out the framework of the education system, and gives an account of the law on central and local administration. Deals with schools from nursery onwards, up to further education establishments. Considers issues such as awards, and grants, the Manpower Services Commission, adult education and freedom of speech. Includes the Education (no 2) Act 1986, and the Teachers Pay and Conditions Act 1987.
ISBN 0421328304 £30.00

Poole, Michael
Industrial relations. – Routledge, 1986.
ISBN 0710097964 Hbk £16.95
—Theories of trade unionism : a sociology of industrial relations / Michael Poole. – London : Routledge and Kegan Paul, 1981.
xi,265p; 23cm.
Bibliography: p221-242. - Includes index.
ISBN 0710006950 £12.50

Poolman : Equity, the Court and Labour Relations. – Durban : Professional Publisher, 1988.
ISBN 0409048976 Pbk

Poolman, Theodorus
Poolman : Equity, the Court and Labour Relations. – Durban : Professional Publisher, 1988.
ISBN 0409048976 Pbk
—Principles of unfair labour practice / Theodorus Poolman. – Cape Town : Juta, 1985.
xxx,243p.
Bibliography: p.xi-xxi. - Includes index.
ISBN 0702115657

Poor law : the mass arrest of homeless claimants in Oxford / by Ros Franey : illustrated by Jim Stanes and Nina Carroll. – London : CHAR, 1983.
93p; 21cm. – (Poverty pamphlet).
ISBN 0906951046 Pbk £1.95

Pope, A. W.
Arboreal Emblem Act, 1983, Bill 143 : Arboreal Emblem Act, 1983. – Ontario : Ontario Government Publications Service, 1983.
1p.
Hbk £0.30
—Mining Act, 1983, Bill 129 : An Act to Revise the Mining Act. – Ontario : Ontario Government Publications Service, 1983.
90p.
Hbk £1.00

Popplewell, Oliver Bury → Final report.
→ Interim report.

Popular Law Series. – Bombay : Popular Prakashan.
Hbk
Constitutional Law. –
£3.50
Evidence Act and Limitation. –
£2.50
General Mercantile Law. –
£1.75
Hindu Law. –
£5.00
Indian Contract Act. –
£2.50
Negotiable Instruments Act. –
£2.25
Private International Law.
Roman Law. –
£2.25

Population and Law in India. – New Delhi : S. Chand and Company.
Hbk £30.00

Population, pension costs and pensioners' incomes : a background paper for the Inquiry into Provision for Retirement. – London : H.M.S.O., 1984.
29p.
At head of title page: Department of Health and Social Security.
ISBN 0113210035

Pornography and politics : the Williams Committee in retrospect / A. W. B. Simpson. – London : Waterlow Publishers, 1983.
143p.
ISBN 0080391567

Pornography and prostitution : issues paper : this is a discussion paper / prepared by the Special Committee on Pornography and Prostitutiôn appointed by the Minister of Justice for Canada. – Ottawa, Canada : Dept. of Justice, Communications and Public Affairs, 1983.
ii, 78, 100 p.; 28 cm.
English and French. Title on added t.p.: Pornographie et prostitution.
ISBN 0662527682 Pbk

Pornography and prostitution in Canada : report of the Special Committee on Pornography and Prostitution : summary. – Ottawa : Department of Justice, 1985.
65,71p.
With French t.p.: La pornographie et la prostitution au Canada. Pages numbered in opposite directions. English and French text.
ISBN 066253686X

Pornography and prostitution in Canada : report of the Special Committee on Pornography and Prostitution. – 2 v. – Ottawa : Canadian Government Publishing Centre, 1985.
ISBN 0660118092

Porter → State Supreme Courts in State and Nation.

Porter, Bernard
Origins of the vigilante state : the London Metropolitan Police Special Branch before the First World War / Bernard Porter. – London : Weidenfeld and Nicolson, 1987.
xvi,256p,8p of plates; 24cm.
Bibliography: p239-243. - Includes index.
ISBN 0297790676 £15.95

Porter, Brian
Protected Persons and Their Property in N.S.W. / Mark Robinson. – North Ryde : Law Book Co, 1987.
xiv, 176p.
ISBN 0455207194 Pbk £27.50

Porter, D.
Financial Management For Solicitors. – 3rd ed. – London : Longman Professional, 1985.
ISBN 0851209998 Pbk £15.95

Porter, Julian
Canadian Libel Practice / David Potts. – London : Butterworths.
ISBN 0409860891 Hbk £56.00

Porter, L.
Law and treatment of drug- and alcohol-dependent persons : a comparative study of existing legislation / by L. Porter, A. E. Arif, W. J. Curran. – Geneva : World Health Organization, 1986.
216p.
Bibliography: p209-216.
ISBN 9241560932

Pose, Kevin S → Legal process : commentary and materials.

Position of Women in Hindu Law. – 1913 repr. – New Delhi : Inter-India Publications, 1984.
vi, ii, xxxii, xix, 707p.
ISBN 8121001641 Hbk £380.00

Positive covenants affecting land / report of the Property Law and Equity Reform Committee. – Wellington : The Committee, 1985.
85p.

Positive discrimination, social justice and social policy : moral scrutiny of a policy practice / John Edwards : foreword by Lord Scarman. – London : Tavistock, 1986.
x,243p; 22cm.
Bibliography: p222-235. - Includes index.
ISBN 0422614009 Hbk £19.95
ISBN 0422789909 Pbk £8.95

Possemiers, M.
Dictionary of Shipping Spanish/English. – London : Lloyd's of London Press, 1988.
ISBN 1850444537 Pbk

Post, Alexandra Merle
Deepsea mining and the law of the sea / Alexandra Merle Post. – The Hague : M. Nijhoff Publishers, 1983.
xxiii,358p.
Bibliography: p329-358.
ISBN 902473049X

Postal Security and Mail Opening : a Review of the Law. – Toronto : University of Toronto, Centre of Criminology, 1981.
vi, 233p.
ISBN 0919584527 Pbk £8.00

Post-death Rearrangements of Wills and Intestacies. – 3rd ed. – London : Longman Professional.
– (Longham Practical Tax Series).
ISBN 0851214223 Hbk £9.95

Postema, Gerald J
Bentham and the common law tradition. – Oxford : Clarendon Press, 1989.
506. – (Clarendon Law Series).
Offers a philosphical interpretation of the historical debate between Bentham and classical common law theory, which has shaped contemporary conceptions of the nature, tasks and limits of law and adjudication.
ISBN 0198256515 Pbk £15
ISBN 0198255055 Hbk £40

Posthumous Works : Consisting of a Reading on the Statute of Inrolments, Arguments in the Case of General Stanwix, and Cases and Opinions / T. M. Shadwell. – 2nd ed. Repr. of 1797 ed. – Abingdon : Professional Books.
338p.
Hbk £25.00

Post-seizure procedures / Law Reform Commission of Canada. – Ottawa : the Commission, 1985.
77,84p. – (Working paper).
Includes bibliographical references. Added t.p. in French: Les procedures posterieures a la saisie. Cover title: Criminal law: post-seizure procedures. Pages numbered in opposite directions. Text in English and French.
ISBN 0662534603

Potas, Ivan
Legal Basis of Probation. – Canberra : Australian Institute of Criminology.
Hbk £0.60
—Sentencing Drug Offenders in New South Wales. – Canberra : Australian Institute of Criminology.
Hbk £4.50

—Sentencing Sex Offenders in New South Wales : An Interim Report. – Canberra : Australian Institute of Criminology.
Hbk £1.00

—Sentencing the Federal Drug Offender / John Walker. – Canberra : Australian Institute of Criminology.
Hbk £4.50

Pothier, Robert-Joseph
Treatise on the quasi-contract called promutuum and on the condictio indebiti / by Robert-Joseph Pothier : translated by W.J. Hosten and C. van Soelen : and editied by W.J. Hosten. – Pretoria : Government Printer on behalf of the South African Law Commission, 1987.
v,40p. – (Research series).
ISBN 0621107220

Potter
Historical Introduction To English Law / A K R Kiralfy. – 4th ed. – Sweet & Maxwell, 1969.
ISBN 0421136308 Pbk £11.50
—Quest for Justice. – Repr. of 1951 ed. – London : Sweet & Maxwell, 1986.
ISBN 0421355107 Hbk £15.00

—Quest of Justice. – Sweet & Maxwell, 1951 Reprint.
ISBN 0421355107 Hbk £16.00

Potter and Monroe's tax planning with precedents / H. H. Monroe, Andrew R Thornhill, K. Prosser, G. Goodfellow. – 10th ed. – London : Sweet & Maxwell, 1987.
xviii,500p; 26cm.
Previous ed.: 1982. Includes index. Kept up to date by supplements.
ISBN 0421334207 £50.00

Potter and Monroe's Tax Planning with Precedents / K Prosser. – 11th ed. – Sweet & Maxwell.
ISBN 00421396008 Hbk

Potter, D. C.
Potter and Monroe's tax planning with precedents / H. H. Monroe, Andrew R Thornhill, K. Prosser, G. Goodfellow. – 10th ed. – London : Sweet & Maxwell, 1987.
xviii,500p; 26cm.
Previous ed.: 1982. Includes index. Kept up to date by supplements.
ISBN 0421334207 £50.00
—Tax Planning with Precedents / H. H. Monroe. – London : Sweet & Maxwell, 1987.
Hbk

Potter, Robert B.
Urbanisation and planning in the 3rd World : spatial perceptions and public participation / Robert B. Potter. – London : Croom Helm, 1985.
284p; 23cm. – (Croom Helm series in geography and environment).
Bibliography: p254-275. - Includes index.
ISBN 0709920555 £19.95

Potts → Financial Services Law.

Potts, David → Canadian Libel Practice.

Poullet, Y → Advanced topics of law and information technology.
→ Freedom of data flows and EEC law.

Poulose, T.T.
Succession in International Law. – Allahabad : Orient Law House.
ISBN 0861252756 Hbk £65.00

Poulter, Sebastian
English Law and Ethnic Minority Customs. – London : Butterworths, 1986.
xxviii,300p; 25cm.
ISBN 040618008 Pbk £27.95
→ Law and population growth in Lesotho.

Poulton, Kate → Sex and race discrimination in employment.

Pound, R.
Introduction To Philosophy Of Law. – Rev Ed. – Yale University Press, 1954.
ISBN 0300001886 Pbk £7.95

Pounds, N. J. G.
Parliamentary Surveys of the Duchy of Cornwall Pt. 1. – Exeter : Devon & Cornwall Record Society, 1982.
Hbk £8.00

Povall, M. → Equal pay and opportunities : a study of the implementation and effects of the Equal Pay and Sex Discrimination Acts in 26 organizations.

Poverty and the Poor Law in the North Riding of Yorkshire : Circa 1780-1837. – York : St. Anthony's Press, 1982.
– (Borthwick Papers Ser.).
Pbk £3.00

Powder Keg or Damp Squib? : Black Opinion and the Group Areas Act. – Johannesburg : South African Institute of Race Relations, 1987.
Hbk £4.00

Powell
How to conduct arbitrations / Smith. – London : Architectural Press, 1988.
ISBN 0851392164 Hbk
—Police and the Criminal Evidence Act 1984 / Magrath. – London : Longman Professional, 1985.
ISBN 0851207669 Pbk £19.95
→ Understanding tort law.

Powell, John → Liquidation manual.
—Liquidation manual / John Powell, Malcolm London. – 2nd ed. – Croydon : Tolley, 1988.
xxii,318p.
Guide to conduct of UK company liquidations including creditors' voluntary liquidations. Explains liquidator's role and responsibilities to creditors, employees and members.
ISBN 0854592229

Powell, John L.
Issues and offers of company securities : the new regimes / by John L. Powell : with a foreword by Clive M. Schmitthoff. – London : Sweet & Maxwell, 1988.
xxvii,154p; 26cm.
Based on: Palmer's company law. 24th ed., ch.23 and 27. Includes index.
ISBN 042139630X £25.00
→ Professional negligence.

Powell-Smith, Vincent
BPF-ACA Form of Building Agreement 1984. – London : Architectural Press, 1984.
16p : Illus. – – (ACA Contract Documents).
ISBN 0851397565 Pbk £4.95
—Building contract casebook / Vincent Powell-Smith and Michael Furmston. – Rev ed. – Oxford : BSP Professional Books, 1987.
x,422p.
Previous ed.: 1984. Includes index.
ISBN 0632021098
—Building Contract Claims / John Sims. – London : Collins, 1983.
320p.
ISBN 0003830942 Hbk £20.00
—Building Contract Claims / John Sims. – 2nd ed. – Oxford : BSP Professional.
ISBN 0632020792 Hbk £25.00
—Building contract claims / Vincent Powell-Smith and John Sims. – London : Granada, 1983.
319p; 25cm.
Includes index.
ISBN 0246119683

—Building Contract Dictionary : An Architectural Press Legal Guide / David Chappell. – London : Architectural Press, 1985.
464p : Illus.
ISBN 0851397581 Hbk £35.00

—Building Contracts Compared and Tabulated. – London : Architectural Press, 1987.
ISBN 0851397891 Pbk £39.50

—Building Contracts Tabulated and Compared : An Architectural Press Legal Guide / David Chappell. – London : Architectural Press, 1987.
320p : Illus.
ISBN 0851397891 Pbk £39.50

→ Building Regulations : Explained and Illustrated.

—Building Regulations Explained and Illustrated / Billington. – 7th ed. – Oxford : Blackwell Scientific, 1986.
ISBN 0003832260 Pbk £14.00

—Building Sub-Contract Documentation / John Sims. – Oxford : Blackwell Scientific, 1988.
ISBN 0003831558 Hbk £17.00

—Civil Engineering Claims / J Stephenson. – Oxford : Blackwell Scientific, 1987.
ISBN 0003830594 Hbk £25.00

→ Construction Law Reports 10 vols, Vol. 1.

→ Construction Law Reports.

—Contract Documentation for Contractors / John Sims. – Oxford : Blackwell Scientific, 1985.
ISBN 0003830187 Hbk £17.95

—Design and Build Contracts / Stephen J. Pymont. – London : Collins, 1986.
250p.
ISBN 0003830500 Hbk £17.50

—Determination and Suspension of Construction Contracts / John Sims. – Oxford : Blackwell Scientific, 1985.
ISBN 0003831566 Hbk £19.95

—Engineering Contract Casebook / Michael P Furmston. – Oxford : Blackwell Scientific, 1988.
ISBN 0003832627 Hbk £30.00

—Essential Law for Horseowners. – Oxford : Blackwell Scientific, 1987.
ISBN 0003832864 Pbk £9.95

→ JCT Intermediate Form of Contract : An Architectural Press Legal Guide.

→ JCT Minor Works Form of Contract : An Architectural Press Legal Guide.

—Quantification of Building Claims / John Sims. – London : Collins, 1987.
260p.
ISBN 0003832651 Hbk £20.00

Powell, Wayne
Divorce Guide for British Columbia : Step-by-Step Guide to Obtaining Your Own Divorce. – 10th ed. – North Vancouver : International Self-Counsel Press, 1986.
88p.
ISBN 0889081816 Hbk £10.95

Power and policy in quest of the law : essays in honor of Eugene Victor Rostow / edited by Myres S. McDougal, W. Michael Reisman. – The Hague : M. Nijhoff Publishers, 1984.
640p.
Bibliography: p441-447. Includes index.
ISBN 9024729114 Hbk £235.00

Power, B.J.
Accounting Law and Practice for Limited Companies : Format and Disclosure Requirements Under the Irish Companies Acts, 1963 to 1986, and Accounting Standards. – Dublin : Gill and Macmillan, 1987.
ISBN 0717115186 Hbk £30.00

Power, crime, and mystification / Steven Box. – London : Tavistock, 1983.
xi,257p; 23cm. – (Tavistock studies in sociology).
Bibliography: p224-246. - Includes index.
ISBN 0422764000 Hbk £
ISBN 0422764108 Pbk

Power, D. J.
Criminal law and psychiatry / by D.J. Power : co-author D.H.D. Selwood. – S.l. : Barry Rose, 1987.
xviii,265p.
ISBN 1870080254

Power, J.M.
Will Making and the Administration of Estates : a Short Guide. – Butterworths, 1984.
223p.
This book aims at assisting the practitioner in the drafting of a will which accurately effects and carries out the wishes of the testator and then the efficient administration of the estate after death.
ISBN 0409492329 Hbk £36.00

Power, Jonathan
Against oblivion : Amnesty International's fight for human rights / Jonathan Power. – London : Fontana, 1981.
254p; 18cm.
Includes index.
ISBN 0006364268 Pbk £1.95

—Western Europe's migrant workers / by Jonathan Power in collaboration with Anna Hardman. – 2nd rev. ed. – London : Minority Rights Group, 1984.
35p. – (Report).
Bibliography: p.34.
ISBN 0946690197

Power of a Testator to Dispose of the Property of Another : a Study of the South African Law of Massing and Election, with a Comparative Look at English, Dutch and German Law. – Pijnacker : Dutch Efficiency Bureau.
ISBN 9062310273 Hbk £30.80

Power of Taxation Under the Constitution. – Lucknow : Eastern Book Company, 1987.
Hbk £90.00

Power of the Court of Appeal Criminal Division to order a retrial / prepared by the Criminal Law Team of the Law Commission ... – London : The Commission, 1986.
23,4p.
Includes bibliographical references.

Power of the Law. – Toronto : Canadian Broadcasting Corporation Enterprises.
72p.
Pbk £2.50

Power, prejudice and pride. – Southampton : Ashford Press, 1987.
ISBN 0950764612 Hbk £8.95

Power, property and corporatism : the political sociology of planning / James Simmie. – London : Macmillan Press, 1981.
ix,351p.
Bibliography: p.321-345.
ISBN 0333243455

Power to Dispose of the Assets of the Universal Matrimonial Community of Property. – Pijnacker : Dutch Efficiency Bureau.
ISBN 9062310060 Hbk £43.60

Power to punish : contemporary penality and social analysis / edited by David Garland and Peter Young. – London : Heinemann Educational, 1983.
x,238p; 23cm.
Bibliography: p217-230. - Includes index.
ISBN 0435823256 Hbk £14.50
ISBN 0391029010 : Pbk

Power, W. Kent → Family law in Canada.

Powers and duties of trustees : presented to parliament ... October 1982 / Law Reform Committee. – London : H.M.S.O., 1982.
iv,71p; 25cm. – (Report).
ISBN 0101873301 Hbk £5.25

Powers and liabilities of pension fund trustees. – Oxford : Blackwell Scientific, 1987.
ISBN 000383302X Hbk £20.00

Powers, Michael J.
Medical negligence / edited by Michael J. Powers and Nigel H. Harris; consulting editor: Andrew Lockhart-Miriams. – London : Butterworths, 1990.
900; 24cm.
Deals with all aspects of medical negligence claims. The book explains the relevant rules of law, identifies the practical difficulties in bringing an action for damages in respect of negligent medical treatment, and shows how to prepare the medical evidence on liability, how to complete the medical report on quantum, and how to present the experts evidence at court.
ISBN 0406130019 Hbk £120

→ Thurston's coronership : the law and practice on coroners.

Powers of Attorney. – 7th ed. – London : Longman Professional.
– (Practitioner Series).
ISBN 0851213901 Hbk £24.25

Powers of Attorney Ordinance, 1949 (No. 64/1949) and Wills Ordinance, 1959 (No. 38/1959). – Kuala Lumpur : International Law Books Services.
Hbk £7.50

Powers of Investigation in Revenue, Companies and Trade Practices Law / R.H. Woellner. – Butterworths, 1983.
486p.
ISBN 0409493813 Pbk £65.00

Powers-of-Attorney Act. – 2nd ed. – Allahabad : Law Book Company, 1988.
94p.
Pbk £40.00

Powles, David G.
Mareva Injunction and associated orders / by David G. Powles. – Abingdon : Professional Books, 1986.
xxiii,160p.
ISBN 0862050693 Hbk £35.00
ISBN 0862052033 Pbk £17.95

Powles, Guy → Relationship between legal aid agencies and social agencies : research report for the Commonwealth Legal Aid Council.

Pozdynakov, V.S.
U.S.S.R. Contract Law. – Helsinki : Lakimiesliiton Kustannus, 1982.
219p.
Hbk £113.00

Praaning, Rio D → Future of European defence : proceedings of the Second International Round Table Conference of the Netherlands Atlantic Commission on May 24 and 25, 1985.

Prabhu, Mohan
Annotated Customs Act. – Carswell, 1988.
192p.
Hbk £50.50

Prabhu, Mohan A.
Customs and Excise. – Agincourt : Carswell, 1983.
182p.
This textbook provides a thorough examination of the law with respect to Canadian customs and excise. The work covers the Customs Act, the Anti-Dumping Act, Customs Tariff, the Excise Tax Act, and the Excise Act.
Hbk £33.75

Practical Accounts
Book 1 / Bright. – London : Macmillan.
– (New Edition).
ISBN 0333481410 Pbk £4.95
Book 2. –
ISBN 0333481445 Pbk £4.95

Practical Application of Evidence : Materials Prepared for a Continuing Legal Education Seminar Held in Vancouver, B.C., February 19, 1983 / Thomas J. Chamber. – Vancouver : British Columbia Continuing Legal Education Society, 1983.
ISBN 0865041024 Hbk

Practical approach to assessment of liability and damages in tort / by R.K. Nathan. – Singapore : Malayan Law Journal Pte., 1986.
xliv,312p.
Includes bibliographical references and index.
ISBN 9971700514

Practical approach to company law / Stephen W. Mayson, Derek French and Christopher L. Ryan. – 4th ed. – London : Financial Training, 1987.
lxvii,618p.
ISBN 1851850686

Practical approach to contract and consumer law / Sewell. – London : Financial Training, 1984.
ISBN 0906322456 Pbk £12.95

Practical Approach to Criminal Procedure. – 3rd ed. – London : Blackstone Press.
ISBN 0906322774 Hbk £14.95

Practical approach to EEC Law. – London : Financial Training, 1988.
ISBN 1851850988 Pbk £14.95

Practical approach to employment law / John Bowers. – 2nd ed. – London : Financial Training, 1986.
liv,385p.
ISBN 1851850279

Practical approach to evidence / Peter Murphy. – 2nd ed. – London : Financial Training, 1985.
xliv,477p; 24cm.
Previous ed.: 1980. Includes index.
ISBN 0906322693 Pbk £11.95

Practical Approach to Family Law. – 2nd ed. – London : Blackstone Press, 1988.
ISBN 1851850097 Pbk £16.95

Practical approach to land law / Phillips. – London : Financial Training, 1986.
ISBN 1851850244 Pbk £14.95

Practical Approach to Planning Law. – London : Financial Training.
ISBN 1851850708 Pbk £16.95

Practical Approach to Revenue Law. – 9th ed. – London : Blackstone Press.
ISBN 1854310178 Pbk £20.95

Practical approach to revenue law / Stephen S. Mayson and Susan Blake. – 8th ed. – London : Financial Training, 1987.
xlix,659p.
ISBN 1851850791

Practical approach to sentencing / Christopher J. Emmins. – London : Financial Training, 1985.
xxvii,350p; 23cm.
ISBN 0906322669 Pbk
ISBN 0906322715

Practical Aspects of Capital Gains Tax : Exemptions and Reliefs Explained. – Bicester : CCH.
ISBN 0863251935 Pbk £25.50

Practical auditing. – Spicer and Pegler. – 17th ed. – London : Butterworths, 1985.
ISBN 0406678014 Pbk £13.50

Practical Book-Keeping. – London : Butterworths, 1977.
ISBN 0372300049 Pbk £5.50

Practical business law. – London : Pitman Publishing, 1983.
ISBN 0712104631 Pbk £8.50

Practical Business Law. – 2nd ed. – Londonh : Macmillan.
ISBN 0333481461 Pbk £5.95

Practical Business Law. – London : Pan Books Ltd, 1984.
ISBN 033026835X Hbk £2.95

Practical commercial precedents / Jeffrey Green. – 4 vols. – London : Longman Professional, 1986.
Contains precedent documents to cover organization of a business, sale of shares and businesses, pensions, computer contracts, sale of goods, leasing and hire, and merchandising and sponsprship. Each precedent has introduction and commentary, which examines tax and stamp duty implications, and offers alternative clauses.
ISBN 0851209386 Llf £395

Practical Company Law. – London : Pan Books Ltd, 1984.
ISBN 0330282034 Hbk £2.95

Practical conveyancing. – 10th ed. – London : Longman Professional, 1986.
ISBN 0851212239 Pbk £16.95

Practical conveyancing precedents. – London : Longman Professional, 1985.
ISBN 0851207707 updat £95.00

Practical Cost and Management Accounting. – London : Macmillan.
– (New Edition Breakthrough Series).
ISBN 0333481399 Pbk £5.95

Practical CTT planning / John E. Redman, Nigel Eastaway, Ralph P. Ray. – 2nd ed. – London : Butterworths, 1982.
xix,347p; 22cm. – (Butterworths tax management series).
Previous ed.: published as Practical capital transfer tax planning, 1977. Includes index.
ISBN 0406536155 Pbk

Practical food law / Gresty. – London : Sweet & Maxwell, 1988.
ISBN 0421251608 Llf £95.00

Practical food law manual. – 1. – London : Sweet & Maxwell, 1988-.
Includes index.
ISBN 0421351608 Llf

Practical Guide to Accepting Insurance Risks. – Woolloomooloo : International Business Communications, 1986.
ISBN 0949553255 Hbk £13.50

Practical guide to contracts of affreightment and hybrid contracts / by Lars Gorton and Rolf Ihre. – London : Lloyd's, 1985.
ix,87p; 25cm.
Includes index.
ISBN 1850440603 £45.00

Practical guide to creative accounting. – London : Kogan Page, 1988.
ISBN 1850913013 Hbk £16.95
ISBN 185091611X Pbk £6.95

Practical Guide to Financial Futures Trading. – London : Butterworths.
ISBN 0406200106 Hbk £35.00

Practical guide to intellectual property. – London : Butterworths, 1988.
ISBN 040610140X Pbk

Practical guide to labour arbitration procedure. – Aurora : Canada Law Book, 1987.
Hbk £16.50

Practical Guide to Law Office Automation : 1988 / Kenneth A. Grant. – Agincourt : Carswell, 1988.
274p.
This 1988 edition provides information towards the selection and implementation of a law office automation system. Guidelines also include a comprehensive directory of software in Canada for lawyers and a glossary of common terms and definitions. The book also outlines the benefits of automation and the process of selecting and implementing a computer system.
Hbk £40.50

Practical guide to mental health law : the Mental Health Act 1983 and related legislation / Larry Gostin : foreword by Lady Bingley : edited by Janet Manning. – Rev ed. – London : MIND, 1983.
xvi,102p; 21cm.
Bibliography: p77-78.
ISBN 0900557591 Pbk

Practical Guide to Obtaining Permanent Residence in Australia. – 3rd ed. – Woolloomooloo : International Business Communications, 1987.
ISBN 0949553387 Hbk £14.50

Practical guide to patent law / Brian C. Reid. – Oxford : ESC Publishing Limited, 1984.
xxii,438p.
ISBN 0906214165

Practical Guide to the Family Law Act 1986. – Agincourt : Carswell, 1988.
230p.
Hbk £37.50

Practical Guide to the Family Law Act. – Agincourt : Carswell, 1988.
238p.
This is an in-depth guide to the law pursuant to the Family Law Act, 1986. Discussions include jurisdiction, property, matrimonial home, support obligations and domestic contracts. The complete text of the Act is included. Also included is the relevant caselaw.
Pbk £33.75

Practical Guide to the Use of the European Communities' Scheme of Generalized Tariff Preferences. – Kirchberg : Commission of the European Communities, 1984.
353p.
Hbk

Practical guide to trade marks / Amanda Michaels. – Oxford : ESC Publishing Ltd, 1982.
xxii,226p.
ISBN 0906214122 Hbk £21.50
ISBN 0906214092 Pbk £15.50

Practical handbook on the operation of the Hague Convention of 15 November 1965 on the service abroad of judicial and extrajudicial documents in civil or commercial matters. – Antwerpen : Maarten Kluwer's Internationale Uitgeversonderneming, 1983.
vii,150p.
Bibliography: p148-150.
ISBN 906215073X

Practical Hints on Cross-Examination. – 2nd ed. – Allahabad : Law Publishers, 1982.
Hbk £27.00

Practical inheritance tax. – London : Butterworths, 1988.
ISBN 040600710 Pbk

Practical introduction to copyright / Gavin McFarlane. – London : McGraw-Hill, 1982.
xiv,235p; 26cm.
Includes index.
ISBN 0070845697 £14.00

Practical introduction to trade marks. – London : Waterlow, 1984.
ISBN 0080391702 Hbk £14.95

Practical Law for Arts Administrators. – London : Offord Publications Ltd, 1983.
400p.
ISBN 0903931583 Hbk £8.95

Practical lease precedents. – London : Longman Professional, 1988.
ISBN 0851211542 Llf £95.00

Practical Legal Aid. – 3rd ed. – London : Oyez Longman, 1982.
– (Oyez Longman Practice Note Ser.: No. 62).
ISBN 0851205860 Hbk £11.95

Practical partnership
Supplement / Camp. – London : Longman Professional, 1982.
ISBN 0851210392 Pbk £13.95

Practical Partnership / P. Camp. – London : Oyez Longman, 1982.
ISBN 0851206638 Hbk £6.95

Practical partnership for solicitors / C. Harmer and P. Camp. – 2nd ed. – London : Longman Professional (UK), 1990.
Examines drafting a partnership agreement, taxation, finance, accounts, and matters of professional conduct. Covers the Practice Rules, Publicity Code 1988 and the Introductions and Referrals Code 1988. Includes material on practising abroad, the Overseas Practice Rules 1987, and the effect of the European element and 1992 on the profession. Also deals with Solicitors Incorporated Practice Rules 1988.
ISBN 0851215513 Hbk £29.50

Practical Precedents in Pleading. – Repr. of 1835 ed. – Abingdon : Professional Books.
278p.
Hbk £45.00

Practical Share Valuation. – 2nd ed. – London : Butterworths, 1987.
ISBN 0406190151 Hbk

Practical Share Valuation / Harry Booth. – London : Butterworths, 1983.
This book provides a practical guide to valuation questions for purposes of tax assessment for practitioners in the United Kingdom. Share valuation, whether that of a private or a public company, often requires negotiation with the Inland Revenue and this manual explores the many issues raised by such negotiations.
ISBN 0406190143 Hbk

Practical skills of the solicitor. – 2nd ed. – London : Longman Professional, 1985.
– (Practice Today Series).
ISBN 0851209947 Pbk £12.50

Practical Skills of the Solicitor. – London : Oyez Longman, 1981.
ISBN 0851206107 Hbk £6.95

Practical Social Work / Lane. – London : Macmillan.
ISBN 0333420764 Hbk £20.00

Practical tax planning and precedents. – London : Longman Professional, 1987.
ISBN 0851213103 Llf £110.00

Practical tax saving. – 4th ed. – London : Butterworths, 1984.
ISBN 0406536333 Pbk £22.00

Practical timeshare and group ownership. – London : Butterworths, 1987.
ISBN 0406103283 Pbk £26.95

Practical timesharing : UK and overseas. – London : Butterworths, 1988.
ISBN 0406100500 Pbk

Practical trust administration. – 2nd ed. – London : Europa Publications, 1984.
ISBN 0905118944 Hbk £17.50

Practical trust precedents. – London : Longman Professional, 1986.
ISBN 0851211836 updat £95.00

Practical uses of Section 52 of the Trade Practices Act. – Monash University, Faculty of Law. – Clayton : Monash University Press, 1984.
ISBN 086746352X Hbk £14.00

Practice and Advocacy in the Supreme Court of Canada. – Vancouver : British Columbia Continuing Legal Education Society, 1983.
463p.
ISBN 0865041180 Hbk £65.00

Practice and law of banking / P. J. M. Fidler. – 11th ed. – Pitman, 1982.
ISBN 0712119787 Pbk £11.95

Practice and procedure in industrial tribunals. – London : Legal Action Group, 1986.
ISBN 0905099141 Pbk £7.50

Practice and procedure in juvenile courts / by Kenneth W. Pain. – London : Fourmat, 1982.
xiii,149p; 22cm.
Includes index.
ISBN 090684049X Pbk £7.95

Practice and procedure in Magistrates' Courts. – 2nd ed. – London : Fourmat, 1986.
ISBN 1851900136 Pbk £12.95

Practice and procedure in Sheriff Court. – London : Fourmat, 1988.
ISBN 1851900373 Pbk £12.95

Practice and procedure in the Family Court : papers presented at the Family Law Seminar, University of Auckland, 26 May, 1984 / by B.D. Inglis. – Auckland : Legal Research Foundation, 1984.
22p.
At head of title: Legal Research Foundation Inc. Family Law Seminar.
ISBN 0908581351

Practice and Procedure in the Federal Court of Canada. – Vancouver : Continuing Legal Education Society of British Columbia, 1984.
493p.
ISBN 0865041784 Hbk £75.00

Practice and Procedure in the Supreme Court of British Columbia. – Vancouver : British Columbia Continuing Legal Education Society, 1982.
167p.
ISBN 0865040559 Hbk £17.50

Practice and procedure of the Admiralty Court : forms and precedents / Nigel Meeson. – London : Lloyd's, 1986.
296p; 24cm.
Includes index.
ISBN 1850440875 £35.00

Practice and procedure of the Commercial Court / by Anthony D. Colman. – 2nd ed. – London : Lloyd's of London, 1986.
230p; 24cm.
Previous ed.: 1983. Includes index.
ISBN 1850440611

Practice and Procedure of the High Court and Court of Appeal in New Zealand. – 12th ed. – Butterworths.
ISBN 0409667617 Llf £264.00

Practice and procedure of the High Court and the Federal Court of Australia / editor, B.J. Camilleri. – Sydney : Butterworths, 1978.
looseleaf.
ISBN 0409373508

Practice and Procedure Under the Access to Information and Privacy Acts. – Toronto : Butterworths, 1986.
128p.
ISBN 0409811645 Hbk

Practice Before the Registrar 1984. – Vancouver : Continuing Legal Education Society of British Columbia, 1984.
203p.
ISBN 0865041725 Hbk £55.00

Practice Before the Registrar in British Columbia. – Vancouver : British Columbia Continuing Legal Education Society, 1982.
199p.
ISBN 0865040427 Hbk £40.00

Practice development for accountants / Toby Mountford. – London : Butterworths, 1984.
ISBN 0406260400 Pbk £15.00

Practice development for professional firms / Aubrey Wilson. – London : McGraw-Hill, 1984.
xvi,232p; 26cm.
Bibliography: p221-223. - Includes index.
ISBN 0070847614 £15.95

Practice in Mortgage Actions in Alberta / Marguerite Trussler. – Agincourt : Carswell, 1985.
630p.
This work reviews the law and practice in Alberta including relevant case law from other provinces in Canada relating to mortgage law.
Hbk £80.00

Practice in mortgage actions in Ontario : the practice in mortgage actions and in exercising power of sale / Marriott and Dunn. – 4th ed. – Toronto : Carswell, 1982.
xliii,511p.
Includes index.
ISBN 0459348809

Practice in the High Court of Chancery, 2 Vols. – 8th ed. Repr. of 1914 ed. – Abingdon : Professional Books.
Hbk £95.00

Practice of banking/1. – Pitman, 1984.
ISBN 0712116796 Pbk £9.95

Practice of Banking 2 / Wild. – 2nd ed. – Pitman.
ISBN 0273028189 Pbk £13.95

Practice of banking / Kelly. – 3rd ed. – Plymouth : Macdonald & Evans, 1981.
ISBN 0712117555 Pbk £5.95

Practice of Japan in international law, 1961-1970 / edited by Shigeru Oda and Hisashi Owada, with the assistance of Kazuya Hirobe. – Tokyo : University of Tokyo Press, 1982.
xxxii, 471 p.; 24 cm.
Includes bibliographical references and index.
ISBN 0860083012 Y10000

Practice of Law / Bowstock. – Methuen, 1988.
ISBN 0901715662 Pbk £6.50
ISBN 0901715670 Hbk £15.00

Practice of Social Inquiry. – Aberdeen : Aberdeen University Press, 1983.
176p.
ISBN 0080303692 Hbk £11.50
ISBN 0080303706 Pbk £7.25

Practice of the Court of King's Bench and Common Pleas in Personal Actions and Ejectments, 2 Vols. – 6th ed. Repr. of 1824 ed. – Abingdon : Professional Books.
279p.
Hbk £85.00

Practice of the Ecclesiastical Courts. – Repr. of 1847 ed. – Abingdon : Professional Books.
77p.
Hbk £20.00

Practice of the solicitor profession in Scotland : a discussion paper / Scottish Home and Health Department. – Edinburgh : The Department, 1987.
13p.

Practice of the Superior Courts of Common Law. – Repr. of 1850 ed. – Abingdon : Professional Books.
Hbk £20.00

Practice on Motions and References / R.B. Linton. – Butterworths, 1988.
128p.
Guidance on how to present motions and effectively argue before the Masters. Section on practical tips on advocacy before the Masters, a section on motions before the Master in Matrimonial actions, guidance on proper notices of hearing, discussion of jurisdiction on references, sets out powers of the referee and referee's reports, and a chapter on contested motions.
ISBN 0409806293 Hbk

Practice, Procedure and Sentencing in the Magistrates' Courts. – Chichester : Barry Rose, 1986.
543p.
ISBN 0859923606 Hbk £65.00

Practice Queens Bench (Probate). – London : Butterworths.
ISBN 0862053331 Hbk £35.50

Practice relating to the appointment of Queen's Counsel and senior counsel in some Commonwealth jurisdictions. – Rev. ed. – London : Commonwealth Secretariat, 1981.
33p.
Previous ed.: 1973.

Practice today. – London : Julian Harris, 1985-.
Supplement to: Solicitors' journal. Added t.p. title: The management magazine for solicitors.

Practitioner's Guide to Child Care Law / Vaughan Bevan. – Bristol : Jordan & Sons Ltd, 1986.
– (Family Law Practitioner's Ser.).
ISBN 085308100X Pbk

Practitioner's Guide to Legal Costs / H.V. Vorster. – Durban : Professional Publisher, 1983.
ISBN 0409059307 Pbk

Practitioner's Guide to the Alienation of Land Act / S. H. Treisman. – 2nd ed. – Durban : Butterworths, 1984.
– (Eng. & Afrikaans).
ISBN 040906078X Hbk
ISBN 0409060798 Pbk

Practitioner's Guide to the Police and Criminal Evidence Act '84 / Levenson. – London : Legal Action Group.
ISBN 0905099079 Pbk £13.00

Pragmatism and theory in English law. – London : Sweet & Maxwell, 1987.
ISBN 0420475907 Hbk £14.50
ISBN 0420476008 Pbk £8.50

Prais, S. J.
Evolution of giant firms in Britain : a study of the growth of concentration in manufacturing industry in Britain 1909-70 / by S.J. Prais. – 2nd impression. – Cambridge : Cambridge University Press, 1981.
xxii,321p; 23cm. – (NIESR students' edition).
Originally published: 1976. Bibliography: p302-315. - Includes index.
ISBN 052128273X Pbk £7.50

Prakash, Gyan →Law Relating to the Sugar Industries in Uttar Pradesh, with Case-Law and Comments as Amended Up-to-Date.

Prakash, Jai
Essential Commodities Act ... – 7th ed. – Allahabad : Law Book Company, 1988.
1,000p.
Hbk £300.00

Prasad
Motor Vehicles Act and Rules, Vols. 2 and 3. – Allahabad : Orient Law House.
Hbk £175.00

Prasad, Anirudh
Centre-State Relations in India : Constitutional Provisions, Judicial Review, Recent Trends. – New Delhi : Deep and Deep Publications, 1985.
826p.
Hbk £400.00

Prasad, H.
Supreme Court Labour Digest, 1950-82. 2 Vols. / V.K. Kharbanda. – 2nd ed. – Allahabad : Law Publishing House, 1984.
Hbk £200.00

Prasad, M.S.
Study in Law of Evidence. – Lucknow : Eastern Book Company, 1982.
292p.
Pbk £15.00

Prasad, Sarjoo
Commentaries on Essential Commodities Act. – 4th ed. – Allahabad : Law Publishers, 1982.
Hbk £45.00

Prashker, Stanley →Reparation and mediation : a bibliography.

Pratt →India Stamp Act.

Praveen
Problems in Mercantile Law. – 7th rev. ed. – New Delhi : Sultan Chand and Sons, 1984.
iv, 238p.
Pbk £15.00

—Suggested Answers in Mercantile Law (Q.A.). – 2nd ed. – New Delhi : Sultan Chand and Sons, 1985.
v, 317p.
Pbk £18.00

Prebble, J. →Essays on Taxation.

Prebble, John
Advance rulings on tax liability / by John Prebble. – Wellington, N.Z. : Victoria University Press, 1986.
191p.
Bibliograpy: p.156-157. - Includes index. Published for the Institute of Policy Studies.
ISBN 0864730586

—Taxation of Companies and Corporate Investors. – Wellington : Butterworths, 1984.
ISBN 0409701424 Pbk

—Taxation of international income. – London : Butterworths, 1988.
ISBN 0409788015 Pbk

—Taxation of property transactions. – London : Butterworths, 1986.
ISBN 040978740X Pbk £30.00

Precedence in England and Wales / G.D. Squibb. – Oxford : Clarendon Press, 1981.
xviii,139p; 23cm.
Bibliography: p126-130. - Includes index.
ISBN 0198253893 £12.50

Precedent and law : dynamics of common law growth / Julius Stone. – Sydney : Butterworths, 1985.
xx,289p.
Account of the sources from which categories of illusory reference in precedent law spring, of the refinements and elaborations of the operations and of the social and political problems which the operation creates. The author's concepts and arguments are applied to the realities of contemporary judicial process.
ISBN 040949304X A$59

Precedent In Conveyancing. – Sweet & Maxwell.
ISBN 042134590X Hbk £150.00

Precedent In English Law. – 3rd ed. – Oxford : Oxford University Press, 1977.
ISBN 0198760736 Pbk £7.95

Precedent in law / edited by Laurence Goldstein. – Oxford : Clarendon Press, 1987.
xvi,279p; 23cm.
Bibliography: p249-273. - Includes index.
ISBN 0198255268 £27.50

Precedent in Nigerian courts / by P.U. Umoh. – Enugu : Fourth Dimension Publishers, 1984.
xxviii,334p.
Bibliography: p.xxv-xxvi. Based on University of London Ph.D. thesis no. 526.
ISBN 9781561696

Precedents for the Conveyancer, 2 Vols.
Service only. – London : Sweet & Maxwell.
Hbk £52.00

Precedents For The Conveyancer
Service 1988. – Sweet & Maxwell.
ISBN 042125520X updat £160.00

Precedents in matrimonial causes and ancillary matters / by Roger Bird and C.F. Turner. – 2nd ed. – London : Sweet & Maxwell, 1988.
looseleaf.
Previous ed.: 1985. Includes index.
ISBN 0421385200 £50.00

Precedents in practice / by Tony Graham : illustrated by George Haddon : with a foreword by H. G. Ogden. – Sydney : Law Book Co., 1983.
xiii,263p.
Includes index.
ISBN 0455204926

Precedents on objects of incorporation / by Philip Begho. – s.l. : s.n., 1986.
92p.

Pre-contract deposits : a practice recommendation by the Conveyancing Standing Committee. – London : Conveyancing Standing Committee, 1987.
ii,5,3p.

Pre-Contract Practice for Architects and Quantity Surveyors. – AQUA Group. – 7th ed. – London : Collins, 1986.
100p : Illus.
ISBN 0003832546 Hbk £8.95

Predicting violent behavior : an assessment of clinical techniques / John Monahan : introduction by Stanley L. Brodsky : foreword by Saleem A. Shah. – Beverly Hills : Sage, 1981.
183p; 23cm. – (Sage library of social research 114).
Bibliography: p171-181.
ISBN 0803913133 Hbk
ISBN 0803913141 Pbk

Preferences on insolvency : working paper 1 / South African Law Commission. – Pretoria : Government Printer, 1982.
ix,119p.
On title page: Project 37.
ISBN 0621078387

Preliminary enquiries : house purchase : a practice recommendation / the Conveyancing Standing Committee of the Law Commission. – London : Longman, 1987.
16p; 26x11cm.
ISBN 0851213219 Pbk £5.50

Preliminary Inquiry. – Vancouver : British Columbia Continuing Legal Education Society, 1983.
82p.
ISBN 0865041199 Hbk £50.00

Preliminary report to Parliament on delays in courts / Legal and Constitutional Committee. – Melbourne : Parliament of Victoria, 1984.
xxvii,395p.
Bibliography: p.391-395.

Preliminary to the preparation of a third report on aspects of insurance law. – Wellington : Contracts and Commercial Law Reform Committee, 1984.
i,9 leaves. – (Discussion paper).

Prem, D.R.
Cross-Examination Arguments and Instructive Trials. – 5th ed. 1984. – Allahabad : Orient Law House, 1984.
Hbk £135.00

Prem, Daulat Kam
Criminal Practice (1864-1986). – 16 vols. – Allahabad : Ashoka Law House, 1987.
Hbk £150.00 ea.
Vol. 6 : P-R. – 1987.
836p.
Hbk £150.00

—Criminal Practice, 6 Vols. – 7th ed. – Allahabad : Orient Law House.
Hbk £130.00 ea

Prentice, Daniel D. →Reform of the ultra vires rule : a consultative document.

Preparation of legislation. – London : Sweet & Maxwell, 1981.
ISBN 0421291907 Pbk £8.50

Preparatory Committee for the Russell Hearings on Lebanon and the Occupied Territories
Israel and Palestine. – Preparatory Committee for the Russell Hearings on Lebanon and the Occupied Territories. – London : Spokesman Books, 1984.
– (End Papers: No. 9).
ISBN 0851244041 Hbk £3.95

Preparing and Presenting a Civil Case. – Vancouver : British Columbia Continuing Legal Education Society, 1984.
103p.
ISBN 0865041687 Hbk £55.00

Preparing Information on the Law : Guidelines for Writing, Editing and Design / Gayla Reid. – Ottawa : Canadian Law Information Council, 1985.
84p.
ISBN 0920358810 Pbk £10.00

Prerogative writs and orders under Nigerian law and constitution / by S.I.O. Aguolu. – Enugu : Star Printing and Publishing Company, 1981.
xxii,167p.
Includes index.

Prescott →Modern law of copyright.

Prescott, J.R.V.
Australia's Maritime Boundaries. – Deakin : Australian Institute of International Affairs, 1985.
Hbk £10.00

—Maritime political boundaries of the world / J.R.V. Prescott. – London : Methuen, 1985.
xv,377p; 24cm.
Bibliography: 355-360. - Includes index.
ISBN 0416417507 £30.00

Prescription and Limitation of Actions. – Durban : Professional Publishers, 1984.
ISBN 0409040134 Hbk

Prescription and limitation of actions (latent damage) / Scottish Law Commission. – Edinburgh : The Commission, 1987.
v,162p. – (Consultative memorandum).
Includes bibliographical references.

Prescription and the limitation of actions : report on personal injuries actions and private international law questions / Scottish Law Commission. – Edinburgh : H.M.S.O., 1983.
v,61p.
ISBN 0102153833

Prescriptive title for a co-owner in possession / report of the Property Law and Equity Reform Committee. – Wellington : Government Printer, 1986.
17p.

Present and the future of the profession : (the Elzaburu survey) / compiled by Alberto de Elizaburu. – Special ed. – Edinburgh : F.I.C.P.I., 1982.
266p.
A survey presented to the F.I.C.P.I. (International Federation of Industrial Property Attorneys) World Congress, Edinburgh, October 1981.

Present Constitutional Issues and Views. – Delhi : Metropolitan Book Co, 1987.
378p.
ISBN 8120002598 Hbk £200.00

Presentation and settlement of contractors' claims / Geoffrey Trickey. – London : Spon, 1983.
xiv,358p; 24cm.
Includes index.
ISBN 0419114300

Presenting financial proposals to banks. – London : Butterworths, 1986.
ISBN 0406100705 Pbk £15.00

Preservation, a survival kit / National Preservation Office. – 1 case. – S.l. : The Office, 1987.
various pagings.

Preserving freedom under the law : being the presidential address of the Rt. Hon. Lord Bridge of Harwich, President of the Holdsworth Club of the Faculty of Law in the University of Birmingham, 1981-82. – Birmingham : Holdsworth Club, 1982.
14p. – (Holdsworth Club Presidential Address 1982).
ISBN 0704406179

President in the Indian Constitution. – New Delhi : Deep and Deep Publications, 1985.
180p.
Hbk £100.00

Presidential constitution of Nigeria / B.O. Nwabueze. – London : Hurst in association with Nwamife, 1982.
xvii,558p; 23cm.
Includes index.
ISBN 0905838602 Pbk : Nigeria £19.50
ISBN 9781240458

Presidentialism in Commonwealth Africa. – London : Dent (J M) & Sons, 1974.
ISBN 090583805X Hbk £15.00

Presley, J.R.
Directory of Islamic Banking and Financial Institutions. – Oxford : Croom Helm, 1988.
ISBN 0709913478 Hbk £50.00

Press and Apartheid : Repression and Propaganda in South Africa / C. Anthony Giffard. – London : Macmillan, 1984.
336p.
ISBN 0333384350 Hbk £33.00

Press and Media Access to the Criminal Court. – Quorum Press.
ISBN 0899303285 Hbk £32.95

Press Law (CCT). – Sweet & Maxwell, 1978.
ISBN 0421234504 Pbk £7.75

Press Laws of the World. – New Delhi : Allied Publishers.
Hbk

Pressure groups and government in Great Britain / Geoffrey Alderman. – Harlow : Longman, 1984.
vii,164p; 20cm.
Bibliography: p151-157. - Includes index.
ISBN 0582296269 Pbk £3.75

Pressure politics in industrial societies : a comparative introduction / Alan R. Ball and Frances Millard. – Basingstoke : Macmillan Education, 1986.
xi,308; 23cm.
Bibliography: p290-302. - Includes index.
ISBN 0333347579 Hbk £25.00
ISBN 0333347587 Pbk £6.95

Prest, A. R.
Public finance in developing countries / A. R. Prest. – 3rd ed. – London : Weidenfeld and Nicolson, 1985.
xiii,236p.
Bibliography: p226-228.
ISBN 0297785788
—Public finance in theory and practice / A.R. Prest, N.A. Barr. – 7th ed. – London : Weidenfeld and Nicolson, 1985.
xvi, 553p.
Includes bibliographical references.

Prest, Wilfrid R.
Rise of the barristers : a social history of the English bar, 1590-1640 / Wilfrid R. Prest. – Oxford : Clarendon, 1986.
xii,440p; 22cm.
Includes index.
ISBN 0198217641 Hbk £35.00

Prest, Wilfrid Robertson →Lawyers in early modern Europe and America.

Preston, A. D.
Understanding Business Taxation. – London : Waterlow, 1984.
192p.
ISBN 0080391362 Pbk £7.95

Preston and Newsom's restrictive covenants affecting freehold land / G. H. Newsom, G. L. Newsom. – 7th ed. – London : Sweet & Maxwell, 1982.
xl,387p; 23cm.
Previous ed.: 1976. Includes index.
ISBN 0421284900 £30.00

Preston, C. H. S.
Preston and Newsom's restrictive covenants affecting freehold land / G. H. Newsom, G. L. Newsom. – 7th ed. – London : Sweet & Maxwell, 1982.
xl,387p; 23cm.
Previous ed.: 1976. Includes index.
ISBN 0421284900 £30.00

Preston, Christopher A. L. →VAT Guide and Casebook.

Preston, R.
Succinct View of the Rule of Shelley's Case. – Repr. of 1794 ed. – Abingdon : Professional Books.
486p.
Hbk £40.00

Presumption of innocence / by James C. Morton and Scott C. Hutchinson. – Toronto : Carswell, 1987.
154p.
Bibliography: pp.150-152. - Includes index.
ISBN 0459305816

Presumptions of Survivorship. – Victoria : Government of British Columbia, 1982.
Hbk £1.60

Preter, Cristina de
Vocabulary of Community Primary Law 1985 Provisional Edition / Bernard de Mello. – Luxembourg : Office for Official Publications of the European Communities, 1985.
427p.
ISBN 9282554392 Pbk £1,200.00

Pretrial diversion : an overview / by Sharon Moyer. – Ottawa : Solicitor General, Programs Branch, 1982.
12p.
ISBN 0662119177

Pre-trial justice : a study of case settlement in magistrates' courts / John Baldwin. – Oxford : Blackwell, 1985.
vi,190p.
Observational research into case settlement in Magistrates' Courts.
ISBN 0631140646 £19.50

Prevent the Crime of Silence : The Report of the Vietnam War Crimes Tribunal / Peter Limqueco. – London : Spokesman Books, 1983.
384p.
ISBN 0713901802 Hbk £10.00

Preventing rent arrears / Sue Duncan, Keith Kirby. – London : H.M.S.O., 1983.
144p; 21cm.
At head of title: Department of the Environment.
ISBN 0117517100 Pbk £4.00

Prevention, 4 Vols.
Vol. 1. – International Maritime Organization Staff. – rev. ed. – London : International Maritime Organization, 1983.
– (Manual on Oil Pollution Ser.).
Hbk £3.75

Prevention and prosecution of computer and high-tech crime / William E Kaplan. – Matthew Bender, 1988.
ISBN 0000999061 Hbk £50.00

Prevention and settlement of industrial conflict in the Community member states. – Luxembourg : Office for Official Publications of the European Communities, 1984.
162,16p.
At head of title page: Commission of the European Communities.
ISBN 9282550095

Prevention of Blackmarketing and Maintenance of Supplies of Essential Commodities Act, 1980 / Alka Argawal. – Allahabad : Law Book Company, 1987.
116p.
ISBN 8185029415 Hbk £40.00

Prevention of Corruption Act, 1961 (Act 57) and Emergency (Essential Powers Ordinance 22/1970). – Kuala Lumpur : International Law Books Services.
Hbk £7.50

Prevention of crime among young people / Parliamentary All-Party Penal Affairs Group. – Chichester : Rose, 1983.
112p; 21cm.
ISBN 0859923533 Pbk £7.00

Prevention of Food Adulteration Act Includes Supplement-1986 / H.D. Trivedi. – 8th ed. – Lucknow : Eastern Book Company, 1983.
838p.
Hbk £115.00

Prevention of Food Adulteration Act with Central and State Rules and Foreign Law on the Subject. – 1983. – Allahabad : Law Book Company.
xxii, 548p.
Hbk £250.00

Prevention of Food Adulteration and the Law. – New Delhi : Deep and Deep Publications, 1985.
278p.
Hbk £150.00

Prevention of Terrorism Act : the case for repeal / Catherine Scorer and Patricia Hewitt. – London : National Council for Civil Liberties, 1981.
68p; 20cm.
ISBN 0901108944 Pbk £1.75

Prevention of terrorism in British Law. – Manchester : Manchester University Press, 1986-1988.
ISBN 0719022037 Pbk £9.95

Preventive Detention under Indian Constitution. – New Delhi : Deep and Deep Publications, 1986.
324p.
Hbk £250.00

Previte, J. E. →Gatley on libel and slander.

Prewo, Wilfried
Evolution of Ocean Property Rights. – London : Trade Policy Research Centre.
Hbk

Price Control Act, 1946 (Act 121) and Control of Supplies Act, 1961 (Act 122). – Kuala Lumpur : International Law Books Services.
Hbk £7.50

Price, David
Appeals / by David Price. – London : Fourmat, 1982.
xii,439p; 22cm.
Includes index.
ISBN 0906840422 Pbk £12.95
→ County court practice handbook.
→ Notes on County Court Practice and Procedure.

Price, E.
Computers and the Law in South Africa. – Durban : Professional Publisher, 1983.
ISBN 0409049344 Pbk

Price, Frances
Practice in Mortgage Actions in Alberta / Marguerite Trussler. – Agincourt : Carswell, 1985.
630p.
This work reviews the law and practice in Alberta including relevant case law from other provinces in Canada relating to mortgage law.
Hbk £80.00

Price, G.
Law of Maritime Liens. – Reprint of 1940 edition. – Abingdon : Professional Books.
Hbk

Price, John A M
Currency and Interest Rate Swaps / Schuyler K Henderson. – 2nd ed. – London : Butterworths, 1988.
ISBN 0406073619 Hbk £40.00

Price, Leolin →Bradford disaster appeal : the administration of an appeal fund.

Price, Norman →Enforcement of the law relating to social security.

Price of justice : costs and defendants / Howard Levenson. – London : Cobden Trust, 1981.
88p.
ISBN 0900137177

Price, Richard
Maritime laws of the Arabian Gulf Cooperation Council States
Vol.1 / written and edited by Richard Price with chapters by Andreas Haberbeck. – London : Graham & Trotman, 1986.
267p; 25cm.
Includes index.
ISBN 086010821X £70.00
Vol.2 / Richard Price : with translations by James Whelan. – 1986.
ix,830p; 25cm.
ISBN 0860108309 Hbk £285.00

Price, Terry
Mastering business law. – London : Macmillan, 1988.
ISBN 0333487982 Hbk £13.50
ISBN 0333487990 Pbk £4.50
—Practical Business Law. – 2nd ed. – Londonh : Macmillan.
ISBN 0333481461 Pbk £5.95
—Practical Business Law. – London : Pan Books Ltd, 1984.
ISBN 033026835X Hbk £2.95

Price, Victoria Curzon
Industrial policies in the European Community / Victoria Curzon Price. – London : Macmillan for the Trade Policy Research Centre, 1981.
xvi,141p.
Bibliography: p132-135.
ISBN 0333319117

Price Waterhouse
Guide to V.A.T. in Europe. – Price Waterhouse. – London : Graham & Trotman, 1989.
144; 216mm.
A guide to VAT systems in operation in Western Europe, including the EC member states. Emphasis is placed on registration requirements, and there is an explanation of how to reclaim input tax incurred in each state under the EC 8th and 13th VAT directive procedure. The law is as stated in 1988.
ISBN 1853333069 Hbk £25

Prichard, A. M.
Squatting / by A.M. Prichard. – London : Sweet & Maxwell, 1981.
xvi,177p; 19cm.
Includes index.
ISBN 0421267402 Hbk £9.50
ISBN 042126750X Pbk £5.75

Prichard Jones, K. V. →Hiring and Leasing : Practice and Precedents.

Prichard, Robert
Crown Corporations in Canada : The Calculus of Instrument Choice. – Toronto : Butterworths, 1983.
496p.
Considers the nature of the Crown corporation and how it becomes 'the instrument of choice' over other forms of government intervention. Covers the politics of public enterprise, the uncharted universe of federal public corporations, an overview of the origins, growth, size and functions of provincial crown corporations, and World War II crown corporations.
ISBN 0409859540 Hbk £60.00

Pricing and capacity determination in international air transport : a legal analysis / by P.P.C. Haanappel. – 2nd ed. – Deventer, Netherlands : Kluwer Law and Taxation Publishers, 1984.
xv, 210 p.; 25 cm.
Re ed. of: Ratemaking in international air transport. 1978. Includes index. Bibliography: p. 201-204.
ISBN 9065441549 Pbk

Pricing and Related Policies of Publicly Owned Electrical Utilities. – Halifax : Dalhousie University, Institute of Public Affairs.
ISBN 0889260265 Hbk

Priddle, L. G.
Guidebook to Australian bankruptcy law / L.G. Priddle and T.G. Matthews. – North Ryde, N.S.W. : CCH Australia, 1982.
vii,255p.
Includes index.
ISBN 0869033727

Prideaux, Frederick
Precedent In Conveyancing. – Sweet & Maxwell.
ISBN 042134590X Hbk £150.00
—Prideaux's Forms and precedents in conveyancing / T. K. Wigan, I. M. Phillips. – 25th ed. 3. – London : Sweet & Maxwell in co-operation with Ashford Press, 1985.
24cm.
Previous ed.: London : Stevens & Sons : Solicitors' Law Stationery Society, 1948. Includes index. Editors: T.K. Wigan et al.
ISBN 042134590X £170.00

Prideaux's Forms and precedents in conveyancing / T. K. Wigan, I. M. Phillips. – 25th ed. 3. – London : Sweet & Maxwell in co-operation with Ashford Press, 1985.
24cm.
Previous ed.: London : Stevens & Sons : Solicitors' Law Stationery Society, 1948. Includes index. Editors: T.K. Wigan et al.
ISBN 042134590X £170.00

Pridham
Managing your finances. – London : Longman Professional, 1988.
ISBN 0851213723 Pbk £4.95

Priest, J. A.
Custody law in practice in the divorce and domestic courts / by J.A. Priest and J.C. Whybrow. – London : H.M.S.O., 1986.
vii,113p; 21.
Supplement to: Working paper no. 96, entitled Family law: review of child law: custody.
ISBN 0117301817

Priest, Jacqueline
In Place of a Parent. – Bristol : Jordan & Sons Ltd, 1986.
– (Family Law Practitioner's Ser.).
ISBN 0853081018 Pbk

Priestley, Diana M.
Law Libraries in Canada / Joan N Fraser. – Agincourt : Carswell, 1988.
This work presents a series of articles written about Canadian law library services and delivery of legal information in Canada. Topics include the types of primary legal materials and law libraries found in Canada, development of law collections, library automation and the impact of bilingualism. Information as to Canadian universities, courthouses, legislative law libraries, government publishing agencies, and more, are also included.
Hbk £46.25

Primary Sector Taxation. – Butterworths, 1987.
Pbk

Primorac, Igor
Is retributivism analytic? / Igor Primorac. – s.l. : s.n., 1981.
9 leaves.
Photo-copy of an article in Philosophy, vol. 56 (1981), p.203-211. Includes bibliographical references.

Primrose, A. H. →Drafting and Negotiating Commercial Leases in Scotland.

Prince Edward Island Annual Bound Statutes, 1975-1980, 1982, 1985-1987. – Agincourt : Carswell.
Hbk £207.00

Principal Actions of ECMT in the Field of Road Safety. – European Conference of Ministers of Transport. – Paris : European Conference of Ministers of Transport, 1986.
443p.
Hbk

Principal instruments of the Warsaw system. – 2nd ed. – Montreal : I.A.T.A., 1981.
102p.
Prepared by the I.A.T.A. Legal Department.

Principality of Liechtenstein : a documentary handbook / edited by Walter Kranz : translated from the German by J.A.Nicholls. – 5th rev ed. – Vaduz : Press and Information Office of the Government of the Principality of Liechtenstein, 1981.

Principals of Law of Transfer. – 6th ed. 1980 repr. – Bombay : Tripathi, 1982.
Hbk £50.00

Principle and Practice of Medical Jurisprudence / Mant. – 13th ed. – Edinburgh : Churchill Livingstone, 1984.
ISBN 0443014817 Hbk £35.00

Principle and Practice of Rating Valuation. – 4th ed. – London : Estates Gazette, 1984.
ISBN 0728200694 Pbk £22.00

Principles and Digest of the Law of Evidence, 2 Vols. – 6th ed. – Allahabad : Universal Book Agency, 1986.
Hbk £550.00

Principles and Law of Tithing. – Repr. of 1806 ed. – Abingdon : Professional Books.
282p.
Hbk £40.00

Principles and Practice of Company Law in India. – 2nd ed. – New Delhi : Prentice-Hall, 1983.
928p.
ISBN 0876823333 Hbk £54.00

Principles and practice of discovery : with an appendix of forms including suggested forms for stating objections to discovery / by Edward Bray. – London : Reeves and Turner, 1885.
xlix, 704 p.; 22 cm.
Slips inserted containing new material. Includes index.

Principles and practice of interruption insurance. – London : Witherby & Co, 1982.
ISBN 0900886560 Hbk £35.00

Principles and Practices of Judicial Propriety : With Precedents and Case-Law. – Allahabad : Hind Publishing House, 1986.
359p.
Hbk £120.00

Principles and Precedents of Pleadings. – 2nd ed. – Lucknow : Eastern Book Company, 1983.
1,174p.
Hbk £75.00

Principles for occupational regulation / Law Reform Commission of Victoria. – Melbourne : The Commission, 1988.
iv,35p. – (Report no 17).
At head of cover title: Regulation Review Unit.
ISBN 0724167234 Hbk

Principles of administrative and local government law in Nigeria / by A. Toriola Oyewo. – Ibadan, Nigeria : Jator Publishing, 1987.
xxiii,276p.
Bibliography: p.xix-xxiii. - Includes index.
ISBN 9782660019

Principles of Administrative Law / S.N. Jain. – 4th ed. – Bombay : Tripathi, 1986.
1138p.
Hbk £200.00

Principles of administrative law / by David Philip Jones and Anne S. de Villars. – Toronto : Carswell, 1985.
xlv,489p.
ISBN 0459377604

Principles of administrative law / D.C.M. Yardley. – 2nd ed. – London : Butterworths, 1986.
275p; 22cm.
A collection of essays, with particular emphasis on issues of control of power and the maintenance of a fair balance between competing interests of the individual and governmental entities in the United Kingdom, make up this book. Privatization of corporations, rent assessment, and the changing role of the Ombudsman are addressed.
ISBN 040668992X Hbk £14.50
ISBN 0406689938 Pbk £8.95

Principles of Australian administrative law. – 6th ed. – North Ryde : Law Book Co, 1985.
ISBN 0455205752 Hbk £40.00

Principles of Business Law / Howard. – Prentice-Hall.
ISBN 0137052790 Hbk £47.10

Principles of business law / Andrew Emefiene. – Akoka, Lagos : Management Science Centre, 1985.
i,194p.
ISBN 9782404098

Principles of Business Law and the Legal Environment. – London : Allyn & Bacon.
ISBN 0205115683 Pbk £35.65

Principles of By-Law Writing. – Vancouver : University of British Columbia, Centre for Continuing Education.
Hbk £5.00

Principles of Company Law. – 4th ed. – London : Butterworths, 1986.
ISBN 0409490679 Hbk £42.00
ISBN 0409490687 Pbk £26.00

Principles of company law / by H.A.J. Ford. – 3rd ed. – Sydney : Butterworths, 1982.
lxix,650p.
Previous ed.: 1978. Includes index.
ISBN 040930932X

Principles of Company Law / S.S. Gulshan. – 7th ed. – New Delhi : S. Chand and Company.
608p.
Hbk £35.00

Principles of corporate finance / Myers. – 2nd ed. – Maidenhead : McGraw-Hill, 1986.
ISBN 007007383X Pbk £14.50

Principles of corporation tax in the Republic of Ireland / by A. Graham Williams. – 1. – Dublin : Incorporated Law Society of Ireland, 1981.
loose-leaf; 27cm.
Includes index.
ISBN 0902027166

Principles of criminal evidence. – Oxford : Clarendon Press, 1878.
352; 21.5. – (Clarendon Law Series).
Examines the role played by the lay judgements of jurors. Discusses judicial practices which have evolved to satisfy the desire to discover the truth, the need to protect the innocent from conviction, and the need to maintain standards in the criminal process. A central feature of the law of criminal evidence is the attempt to balance these three principles.
Students and teachers of criminal law, evidence and legal philosophy
ISBN 0198761031 Hbk £30
ISBN 0198762348 Pbk £11.95

Principles of Criminal Law. – Agincourt : Carswell, 1986.
380p.
This work for law students in Canada discusses the fundamental criminal law concepts of mens rea and acutus rea, strict and absolute liability, justification and excuse, diminished metal capacity, and secondary liability under Canadian law.
Hbk £48.75

Principles of Criminal Law : With Model Questions and Suggested Readings. – 1979 repr. – Lucknow : Eastern Book Company, 1985.
186p.
Pbk £12.00

Principles of Criminal Law in New South Wales. – Butterworths, 1984.
219p.
The cases contained in this introductory text are analyzed by their history, facts, problems, and the basic principles of law involved. Diagrams and tables are included in some chapters.
ISBN 0409491357 Pbk £38.00

Principles of English Law Including Mercantile Law. – Nairobi : Heinemann Educational Books (East Africa), 1982.
276p.
Hbk £75.00

Principles of Equitable Remedies. – 3rd ed. – North Ryde : Law Book Co, 1984.
lix, 668p.
ISBN 0455203997 Hbk £73.00

Principles of equitable remedies : specific performance, injunctions, rectification and equitable damages / by I.C.F. Spry. – 3rd ed. – London : Sweet & Maxwell, 1984.
lix,668p; 25cm.
Sets out the principles by reference to which injunctions and orders for specific performance are granted and analyses equitable doctrines such as laches and part performance. Covers the changes in the law relating to Mareva injunctions and Anton Piller orders. Also includes a new chapter on rectification.
ISBN 0421332409 Canada £
ISBN 0459368001

Principles of equity / by M. I. Jegede. – Benin City, Nigeria : Ethiope Publishing Corporation, 1981.
xxv,262p. – (Ethiope law series).
Includes bibiographical references and index.

Principles of Evidence. – 3rd ed. – North Ryde : Law Book Co, 1985.
322p.
ISBN 0455206139 Pbk £27.50
ISBN 0455206147 Hbk £41.50

Principles of family law / by S.M. Cretney. – 4th ed. – London : Sweet & Maxwell, 1984.
lxxx,1018p; 25cm.
Covers marriage, the termination of marriage, protection, children and family law, family financial obligations and property rights and the courts. Includes changes effected by the Matrimonial and Family Proceedings Act 1984, and the section on the law governing children in care has been expanded.
ISBN 042128840X Hbk
ISBN 0421288507 Pbk £19.50

Principles of family law in Papua New Guinea / by Owen Jessep and John Luluaki. – Waigani : University of Papua New Guinea Press, 1985.
205p.
Bibliography: pp.194-197. - Includes index.
ISBN 9980840137

Principles of Hindu law, with a general introduction to Hindu law and with commentaries on the Hindu Marriage Act, 1955, the Hindu Succession Act, 1956, the Hindu Minority & Guardianship Act, 1956, the Hindu Adoptions & Maintenance Act, 1956 / Sunderlal Trikamlal Desai. – 15th ed. – Bombay : N.M. Tripathi Private, 1982.
lxxix, 1233 p.; 25 cm.
Title on spine: Hindu law. Includes index.
Rs140.00

Principles of Hotel and Catering Law. – 2nd ed. – London : Cassell.
ISBN 0304322164 Pbk £9.95

Principles of Income Taxation / Green. – Sydney : Butterworths, 1985.
256p.
ISBN 040949058X Hbk

Principles of international development law : progressive development of the principles of international law relating to the new international economic order / Milan Bulajic. – Dordrecht, Netherlands : Martinus Nijhoff Publishers, 1986.
403p.
Bibliography: p.359-366.
ISBN 9024733049

Principles of international double taxation relief / by David R. Davies. – London : Sweet & Maxwell, 1985.
xix,321p; 26cm.
Includes index.
ISBN 0421317507 Hbk £45.00

Principles of Irish law / Brian Doolan. – 2nd ed. – Dublin : Gill and Macmillan, 1986.
xix,395p.
Previous ed.: 1981. Includes index.
ISBN 0717114384 Pbk £12.50

Principles of law : a normative analysis / Michael D. Bayles. – Dordrecht : D. Reidel, 1987.
xxi, 398p.
Includes index. Bibliography: p.372-380.
ISBN 902772413X Pbk

Principles of Law : for Company Secretaries Exam. – 4th ed. – New Delhi : Sultan Chand and Sons, 1986.
xiii, 776p.
Pbk £35.00

Principles of Law of Conviction. – Allahabad : Law Book Company, 1988.
Hbk £50.00

Principles of local government law / by C.A. Cross. – 6th ed. – London : Sweet & Maxwell, 1981.
ISBN 0421248602 Hbk
ISBN 042124870X Pbk

Principles of Mahomedan Law. – repr. 1983. – Bombay : Tripathi.
483p.
Pbk £45.00

Principles of marine insurance / Alexander. – 7th ed. – Stone & Cox, 1986.
ISBN 0854431128 Pbk £15.00

Principles of Mercantile Law. – New Delhi : S. Chand and Company, 1983.
Hbk £27.50

Principles of Modern Company Law
2nd Cumulative Supplement to 4th ed. – Stevens & Sons.
ISBN 0420477705 Pbk £5.95

Principles of Natural Justice. – Lahore : Pakistan Law Times.
Hbk £6.00

Principles of petroleum legislation : the case of a developing country / by Anis Al-Qasem. – London : Graham & Trotman, 1985.
xiv,245p.
ISBN 0860105601

Principles of policing. – London : Macmillan Press Ltd, 1985.
ISBN 0333382447 Hbk £22.50
ISBN 0333382455 Pbk £7.95

Principles of Sales Tax Laws, 2 Vols. / P. Kothary. – 5th ed. – Nagpur : Wadhura & Co, 1987.
£630.00

Principles of Scottish Law. – 4th ed. – Oxford : Clarendon Press.
ISBN 0198762178 Hbk £40.00

Principles of Scottish private law. – Oxford : Oxford University Press, 1983.
ISBN 019876735X Hbk £30.00
Vol. 1: Introductory international private law, law of persons / by David M. Walker. – 1988.
584; 24cm.
Previous ed.: 1982. Includes index.
ISBN 0198762151 £40.00
Vol.2. Bk.4: Obligations / by David M. Walker. – 1988.
816; 24cm.
Previous ed.: 1982. Includes index. Volume 1 contains an outline of the sources, scope and literature of Scottish private law and discusses fundamental legal concepts and basic doctrines. Volume 2 gives a statement of the principles and rules of the private law of Scotland and specifically examines the law of obligations.
ISBN 019876216X Hbk £40.00
Vol.3 Bk.5: Law of property / by David M. Walker. – 1988.
cxi,595p.
Previous ed: 1983. Includes index.
ISBN 0198762178 £40.00
Vol.4 Bk.6 - Bk.10 / by David M. Walker. – 1983.
lxix,421p; 24cm.
Previous ed.: 1975. Includes index. Contents: bk.VI. Law of trusts - bk.VII. Law of succession - bk.VIII. Law of civil remedies - bk.IX. Law of diligence - bk.X. Law of insolvency.
ISBN 019876135X Hbk £25.00.

Principles of Statutory Interpretation. – 3rd ed. repr. 1984. – New Delhi : Bharat Law House.
lxxx, 664p.
Hbk £125.00

Principles of the conflict of laws, national and international / by K. Lipstein. – The Hague : Nijhoff, 1981.
xii,144p.
Revised edition of 'The general principles of private international law' published in vol.135 (1972-1) of the Recueil des Cours, The Hague Academy of International Law.
ISBN 9024725445 Hbk £75.00

Principles of the Law of Crimes / O.P. Srivastava. – Lucknow : Eastern Book Company, 1982.
505p.
Hbk £75.00

Principles of the Law of Partnership / Anne Webb. – 4th ed. – Butterworths, 1987.
ISBN 0409787892 Pbk

Principles of the Law of Scotland, 2 Vols. – Repr. of 1754 ed. – Abingdon : Professional Books.
Hbk £160.00

Principles of the Law of Tort. – 8th ed. – Lucknow : Eastern Book Company, 1986.
Hbk

Principles of the Law of Treaties. – London : Pinter, 1989.
250.
Translated from the French and updated in the light of the 1986 Convention on the Law of Treaties between States and International Organizations.
ISBN 0861879546 Hbk £30

Principles of the law of trusts / by H.A.J. Ford and W.A. Lee. – Sydney : Law Book Co., 1983.
cxvii,1055p.
Includes bibliographical references and index.
ISBN 045520375X

Principles of the law of workers' compensation, particularly in Victoria / by E. F. Hill and J. B. Bingeman. – Sydney : Law Book Company Limited, 1981.
xxiv,276p.
ISBN 0455200882

Principles of unfair labour practice / Theodorus Poolman. – Cape Town : Juta, 1985.
xxx,243p.
Bibliography: p.xi-xxi. - Includes index.
ISBN 0702115657

Prins, Herschel A.
Criminal behaviour : an introduction to criminology and the penal system / Herschel Prins. – 2nd ed. – London : Tavistock, 1982.
x,309p; 21cm.
Previous ed.: London : Pitman, 1973. Includes bibliographies and index.
ISBN 0422776807 Hbk £
ISBN 0422776904 Pbk
—Dangerous behaviour, the law, and mental disorder / Herschel Prins. – London : Tavistock, 1986.
xiii,258p; 20cm. – (Social science paperback).
Includes bibliographies and index.
ISBN 0422792209 Pbk £6.95

Printing Presses and Publications Act, 1984 (Act 301). – Kuala Lumpur : International Law Books Services.
Hbk £6.00

Prior Consultation in International Law : a Study of State Practice. – London : Eurospan.
ISBN 0813909716 Hbk £30.95

Prior, Peter J. →Report of the Committee on the Prison Disciplinary System.

Prior-Willard, Prior-Willard, C
Farming Futures. – Cambridge : Woodhead-Faulkner, 1984.
ISBN 0859412830 Hbk £12.50

Priorities. – Vancouver : British Columbia Continuing Legal Education Society, 1984.
119p.
ISBN 0865041814 Hbk £55.00

Priorities / Law Reform Commission of Victoria. – Melbourne : The Commission, 1988.
iv,19p. – (Discussion paper).
ISBN 0724167129

Prison and the Factory / Massimo Pavarini. – London : Macmillan, 1981.
256p. – (Critical Criminology, General Ser.).
ISBN 0333266676 Hbk £18.00
ISBN 0333266684 Pbk £6.95

Prison disciplinary system in England and Wales : presented to Parliament by the Secretary of State for the Home Department. – London : H.M.S.O., 1986.
34p; 25cm.
ISBN 0101992009

Prison information bulletin. – Strasbourg : Council of Europe, 1983.

Prison Reform Trust
The bail lottery. – Prison Reform Trust. – London : Prison Reform Trust, 1986.
5 leaves.
→ People's justice : a major poll of public attitudes on crime and punishment.

Prison regimes / study prepared by the Select Committee of Experts on Prison Regimes and Prison Leave. – Strasbourg : Council of Europe, 1986.
33p. – (CDPC (84) 8 rev. addendum VI).

Prison struggle : changing Australia's penal system / George Zdenkowski and David Brown. – Ringwood, Vic., Australia : Penguin Books, 1982.
xxi, 440 p., 8 p. of plates; 21 cm.
Includes bibliographical references and index.
ISBN 014022324X Pbk £14.95

Prison system for the 80s and beyond / NACRO. – London : Nacro, 1983.
vi,73p.
By Andrew Ashworth et al..
ISBN 0850690293

Prisoners' rights : a study in Irish prison law / by Raymond Byrne, Gerard W. Hogan, Paul McDermott. – Dublin : Co-op Books, 1981.
xvi,145p.
ISBN 0905441400

Prisoners' rights : a study of human rights and Commonwealth prisoners / by Gordon Hawkins. – Canberra : Australian Government Publishing Service, 1986.
vii,102p. – (Occasional paper).
Bibliography: p.95-102.
ISBN 0644054603

Prisons and Prisoners / Warton. – New Edition. – Virago.
ISBN 0860686825 Pbk £6.95

Prisons and punishment in Scotland : from the Middle Ages to the present / Joy Cameron. – Edinburgh : Canongate, 1983.
x,274p,16p of plates; 23cm.
Bibliography: p237-239. - Includes index.
ISBN 0862410312 £12.95

Prisons and the process of justice / Andrew Rutherford. – Oxford : Oxford University Press, 1986.
xii,217p; 20cm. – (Oxford paperbacks).
Originally published: London : Heinemann, 1984.
Bibliography: p193-205. - Includes index.
ISBN 0192819321 Pbk £3.95

Pritchard, J.
County Court Costs. – 7th ed. – London : Longman Professional, 1985.
– (LPPN24).
ISBN 0851209599 Pbk £11.95
—Motorist and the law. – Penguin, 1987.
ISBN 0140068228 Pbk £4.95
—Personal injury litigation. – 5th ed. – London : Longman Professional, 1986.
ISBN 0851212034 Pbk £26.00

Pritchard, John
Legal 500 : the major law firms in England, Wales and Scotland / John Pritchard. – London : Legalease, 1988.
352p.
—Reminders on County Court Costs 1983. – London : Oyez Longman, 1983.
ISBN 0851207502 Hbk £3.75
—Which firm of solicitors?. – 2nd ed. – London : Legalease, 1988.
ISBN 1870854101 Hbk £6.90
—Young Solicitors Handbook. – 2nd ed. – London : Legalease.
ISBN 1870854152 Pbk £6.95

Pritchard, W.E.
Capital Gains Tax. – 7th ed. – Pitman, 1985.
ISBN 0582083397 Pbk £7.95
—Corporation Tax. – 9th ed. – London : Pitman Publishing, 1986.
ISBN 0712106944 Pbk £7.95
—Income Tax 1986/87. – Pitman.
ISBN 0712109749 Pbk £7.95
—Income Tax. – 17th ed. – Pitman.
ISBN 0273029460 Pbk £8.95
—Stage 3 Business Taxation / Murphy. – 2nd ed. – Pitman.
ISBN 027303418 Pbk £12.95
—Taxation 2.3 / Murphy. – Pitman.
– (ACCA Series).
ISBN 0273028634 Pbk £12.95
—Taxation . – 7th ed. – London : Pitman Publishing, 1986.
ISBN 0712120378 Pbk £7.95

Privacy / Law Reform Commission. – 3 v. – Canberra : Australian Government Publishing Service, 1983.
– (Report).

Privacy : Proposals
Vol. 2. – Law Reform Commission. – Canberra : Australian Government Publishing Service, 1983.
xvi, 443p. – (ALRC Report Ser.: No. 22).
ISBN 0644012501 Hbk £10.40

Privacy : Summary of Report. – Law Reform Commission. – Canberra : Australian Government Publishing Service, 1983.
v, 50p. – (ALRC Report Ser.).
ISBN 0644012544 Hbk £2.90

Privacy and data protection : an international bibliography / edited with an introduction by David H. Flaherty with the assistance of Terence J. Donohue and Peter J. Harte. – London : Mansell, 1984.
304p.
Includes index.
ISBN 0720117194 £23.50

Privacy Committee, New South Wales
Acquired immune deficiency syndrome (A.I.D.S.) : guidelines for the testing of antibodies to the HTLV - III (A.I.D.S.) virus / Privacy Committee. – Sydney : The Committee, 1986.
5 leaves.

Private antitrust legislation. – London : MIT Press, 1988.
ISBN 026223131X Hbk £35.95

Private company in Germany : a translation and commentary / M.C. Oliver, M.A. Barrister. – 2nd ed. – Deventer, Netherlands : Kluwer Law and Taxation Publishers, 1986.
92p.
Includes English and German text of Gesetz betreffend die Gesellschaften mit beschrankter Haftung.
ISBN 9065442448 Pbk £72.00

Private company law. – 1st ed. – London : Longman Professional (UK), 1990.
– (Longman Practice Notes).
Overview of company law, covering the problems faced in the formation of a company, fees, the duties and responsibilities of those involved, and details of practice in relation to termination of a company. Contains checklists, addresses, a table of fees, and a table of company forms.
ISBN 0851215289 Pbk £9.95

Private company share sale manual. – 1st ed. – London : Longman Professional (UK), 1988.
– (Longman Commercial Series).
Transaction-based manual, providing a guide through the various stages of a company sale in chronological order. Gives practical suggestions to the vendor and purchaser on procedure. Examines taxation aspects, and contains checklists, case and statute references.
ISBN 0851213146 Hbk £42.00

Private copying of sound and audio-visual recordings. – Oxford : ESC, 1984.
180p.
ISBN 0906214262 £22.00

Private international law / North. – 11th ed. – London : Butterworths, 1987.
ISBN 0406565708 Hbk £38.00
ISBN 0406565716 Pbk £26.95

Private international law : cases and materials / edited by Mark S.W. Hoyle. – London : Laureate, 1982.
xx,441p; 25cm.
Includes index.
ISBN 0907392040 Hbk £
ISBN 0907392059 Pbk £18.45

Private international law : choice of law in tort and delict. – London : H.M.S.O., 1984.
xiv,293p. – (Consultative memorandum).
Includes bibliographical references. Prepared by a Joint Working Party of the Law Commission and the Scottish Law Commission.
ISBN 011730168X

Private international law : choice of law rules in marriage / the Law Commission and the Scottish Law Commission. – London : H.M.S.O., 1987.
37p. – (1987/88 HC3).
ISBN 0102003882

Private international law : Council of Europe Conventions on Foreign Money Liabilities(1967) and on the Place of Payment of Money Liabilities (1972) : report on a reference under section 3 (1)(e) of the Law Commissions Act 1965 / the Law Commission and the Scottish Law Commission. – London : H.M.S.O., 1981.
iv,53p; 25cm.
Includes the text of the Conventions.
ISBN 0101831803

Private international law : foreign money liabilities / the Law Commission. – London : H.M.S.O., 1981.
ix,195p; 22cm. – (Working paper).
ISBN 0117301604

Private International Law : Indian and English. – New Delhi : Deep and Deep Publications, 1988.
700p.
Hbk £475.00

Private international law : polygamous marriages : capacity to contract a polygamous marriage and related issues / the Law Commission and Scottish Law Commission. – London : H.M.S.O., 1985.
v,65p.
ISBN 0101959508

Private international law : recognition of foreign nullity decrees and related matters : presented to Parliament ... September 1984 / the Law Commission and the Scottish Law Commission. – London : H.M.S.O., 1984.
v,134p; 25cm.
ISBN 0101934106

Private international law : the law of domicile / the Law Commission and the Scottish Law Commission. – London : H.M.S.O., 1985.
vi,92p. – (Consultative memorandum).
ISBN 0117301698

Private international law : the modern Roman-Dutch law including the jurisdiction of the Supreme Court / C.F. Forsyth assisted by T.W. Bennett. – Cape Town : Juta, 1981.
xxxviii,384p.
Bibliography: p.xiii-xvi. - Includes index.
ISBN 0702112305

Private international law : the Soviet approach / by M.M. Boguslavskii : translated by David Winter and William B. Simons. – Dordrecht : Nijhoff, 1988.
272p.
Includes index and bibliography.
ISBN 9024736293 Hbk £165.00

Private international law - foreign money liabilities : report on a reference under section 3(1)(e) of the Law Commissions Act 1965 / The Law Commission. – London : H.M.S.O., 1983.
vii,94p; 25cm.
ISBN 0101906404

Private international law in Finland : an outline / by Hannu Tapani Klami. – Turku : Turun yliopiston offsetpaino, 1986.
67 p.; 21 cm. – (Turun yliopiston oikeustieteellisen tiedekunnan julkaisuja. Yksityisoikeuden sarja A).
Bibliography: p. 64-65. Includes index.
ISBN 9516427871

Private international law in the European Community / Stone. – London : Butterworths, 1987.
ISBN 0862050812 Hbk £28.00

Private International Law in the Netherlands / M.V. Polak. – Dordrecht : Kluwer, 1987.
350p.
ISBN 9065442863 Hbk £150.00

Private international law - the law of domicile / The Law Commission and the Scottish Law Commission. – London : H.M.S.O., 1987.
vi,57p; 30cm.
ISBN 0101020023

Private international litigation / general editor, Sir Jack Jacob : contributors, Michael Carpenter ... et al. – London : Longman, 1988.
lxxvii,494p; 25cm.
Includes index.
ISBN 0851208274 £60.00

Private justice / Stuart Henry. – London : Routledge & Kegan Paul, 1983.
ix,245p.
Includes index. Bibliography: p229-235.
ISBN 0710097034 Pbk

Private Members' Bills / Read. – Cambridge : Cambridge University Press, 1988.
ISBN 0521330513 Hbk £22.50

Private Placements in Canada / William K. Orr. – Agincourt : Carswell, 1985.
224p.
This book discusses essential statutory concepts, private placement exemptions, offering memoranda, rules governing secondary trading, stock exchange requirements, and other issues pertaining to private placements under Canadian securities law.
Hbk £49.00

Private prosecutions / Law Reform Commission of Canada. – Ottawa : Law Reform Commission of Canada, 1986.
51,59p; 25cm. – (Working paper).
Cover title: Criminal law - private prosecutions. Added t.p. in French: Les poursuites privees. Pages numbered in opposite directions. Text in English and French.
ISBN 0662544595

Private prosecutions. – London : Shaw & Sons, 1988.
ISBN 0712910904 Pbk £9.95

Private rented sector : the government's legislative proposals. – London? : Dept. of the Environment, Welsh Office, 1987.
10p.
At foot of last page: Department of the Environment, Welsh Office.

Private sector tenancies / Philip H. Pettit. – 2nd ed. – London : Butterworths, 1981.
li,327p; 26cm.
Previous ed.: published as Landlord and tenant under the Rent Act 1979. 1978. Includes index.
ISBN 0406337225

Private Supply of Public Services : Evaluation Real Estate Exctions, Linkage, and Alternative Land Policies. – New York University Press.
ISBN 0814705898 Hbk £23.50

Private tenants handbook. – London : Allison & Busby, 1985.
ISBN 0850316200 Pbk £3.95

Private violence and public policy : the needs of battered women and the response of the public services / edited by Jan Pahl. – London : Routledge & Kegan Paul, 1985.
vi,214p; 22cm.
Bibliography: p196-207. - Includes index.
ISBN 0710099924 Pbk £6.95

Privatisation and regulation. – Oxford : Oxford University Press, 1986.
ISBN 019877253X Pbk £9.95
ISBN 0198772548 Hbk £25.00

Privatisation of the Water Authorities in England and Wales / presented to Parliament by the Secretary of State for the Environment ... et al. ... – London : H.M.S.O., 1986.
iv,27p.
ISBN 0101973403

Privatising London's Airports / D. Thompson. – London : Institute for Fiscal Studies.
– (Report Ser.).
Hbk £10.00

Privilege against self-incrimination and reform of the practice of police interrogation / by C.B. Cato. – Auckland : Legal Research Foundation, 1985.
65,11p.
At head of title: Legal Research Foundation Inc. Seminar.
ISBN 0908581394

Privity of contract / a report by the Contracts and Commercial Law Reform Committee. – New Zealand : The Committee, 1981.
iii,79p.

Privy Council, Federal Court and Supreme Court : Hindu Law Digest 1837-1986. – 4th ed. – Allahabad : Law Book Company, 1987.
535p.
ISBN 8185029385 Hbk £120.00

Privy Council judgments : opinions of the Judicial Committee of the Privy Council in appeals from West Africa,1841 to 1973 / by Olisa Chukura. – Ibadan : Gillford, 1981.
xxxii,1063p.
Includes index.

Probability Theory and Circumstantial Evidence. – Oslo : Norwegian University Press, 1983.
38p.
ISBN 8200067467 Hbk £23.00

Probate. – 11th ed. – London : Fourmat, 1987.
– (LCFS 3).
ISBN 1851900314 Pbk £2.45

Probate and Administration Act, 1959 (Act 97). – Kuala Lumpur : International Law Books Services.
Hbk £7.50

Probate and Administration Practice in New Zealand / J.B.K. Curran. – 4th ed. – Butterworths, 1986.
Includes material from various statutes, regulations, the new High Court Rules, Court decisions, and textbooks. Covers the developments in probate and administration law in New Zealand. Cross-referenced to Garrow and Alston's Law of Wills and Administration 5th edition 1984.
ISBN 0409621412 Hbk £51.00

Probate Guide for Alberta : a Step-by-Step Guide to Probating an Estate. – 2nd ed. – North Vancouver : International Self-Counsel Press, 1983.
76p.
ISBN 088908226X Hbk £10.95

Probate Guide for British Columbia : a Step-by-Step Guide to Probating an Estate. – 8th ed. – North Vancouver : International Self-Counsel Press, 1986.
96p.
ISBN 0889081794 Hbk £12.95

Probate Guide for Ontario : a Step-by-Step Guide to Probating an Estate. – 4th ed. – North Vancouver : International Self-Counsel Press, 1986.
86p.
ISBN 088908355X Hbk £11.95

Probate Handbook. – 8th ed. – London : Longman Professional.
– (Practitioner Series (3 volumes Supplements)).
ISBN 0851214703 Hbk £38.50

Probate Manual / Angela Plumb. – 23rd ed. – Waterlow.
ISBN 0080331092 Hbk £29.95

Probate Practice
Nineteen Eighty-Six supplement only. – Wellington : Butterworths.
This work is a comprehensive treatment of the subject of probate for United Kingdom practitioners in the field. The book provides an up to date reference for contentious and non-contentious probate matters.
ISBN 0406403228 Pbk

Probate Practice / Cootes. – 27th ed. – London : Butterworths.
ISBN 0406403406 Hbk £135.00

Probate Practice : MacDonell, Sheard and Hull / Maurice C Cullity. – 3rd ed. – Agincourt : Carswell, 1981.
774p.
This is a comprehensive volume for estate law practitioners in Ontario, Canada. The text covers valid wills, the recognition of holographic wills, survivorship, ancillary letters probate, conflict of laws relating to wills and estates, and numerous other probate topics.
Hbk £80.00

Probate practice and procedure / A P Rogers. – 3rd ed. – London : Fourmat, 1988.
ISBN 1851900403 Pbk £19.95

Probate Practice Manual, 1984. – Vancouver : British Columbia Continuing Legal Education Society, 1984.
369p.
ISBN 0865041601 Hbk £70.00

Probate Procedure Notes. – Waterlow.
– (Procedure Notes Series).
ISBN 0080368980 Pbk £9.95

Probation : Current Positions and New Directions. – Canberra : Australian Institute of Criminology.
Hbk £3.60

Probation : North American Literature Review (1971-1981) / Rae Matonovich. – Regina : Prairie Justice Research, 1982.
ISBN 0773100512 Hbk £22.00

Probation and Parole : Interstate Supervision and Enforcement / Mary W. Daunton-Fear. – Canberra : Australian Institute of Criminology.
Hbk £1.40

Probation and the community : a practice and policy reader / edited by John Harding. – London : Tavistock, 1987.
vii,248p; 22cm.
Includes bibliographies and index.
ISBN 0422795801 Hbk £16.95
ISBN 0422795909 Pbk £7.95

Probation journal. – London : National Association of Probation Officers, 1974-.
Continues: Probation.

Probation Law : Social Work Law File Social Work Monographs. – Norwich : University of East Anglia.
ISBN 0946751528 Pbk £4.95

Probation of Offenders Act and Rules : Central and States. – 6th ed. – Allahabad : Law Book Company, 1988.
Hbk £200.00

Probation Officer's Manual
Nineteen Eighty-Three supplement only. – London : Butterworths.
This work is a guide to the legal and administrative framework within which the probation officer works in the United Kingdom. The book covers all aspects of probation work from rules, duties, and procedures to the details of penal and training centres and rehabilitation programs.
ISBN 0406256063 Pbk

Probation officer's manual. – 4th ed. – London : Butterworths, 1987.
ISBN 040625608X Pbk £14.95

Probation officers' views of probation : a survey in West Yorkshire / R.I. Mawby. – Leeds : University of Leeds, Centre for Social Work and Applied Social Studies, 1981.
39p. – (Occasional paper).
Bibliography: p.35-39.

Probation service in England and Wales : statement of national objectives and priorities. – London : Home Office, 1984.
6p.

Problem of old convictions / the Law Reform Commission of Western Australia. – Perth : Law Reform Commission of Western Australia, 1984.
97,vip. – (Discussion paper).

Problem of the trial of complex commercial crimes : a proposal for reform. – Hong Kong : Attorney General's Chambers, 1984.
93p.

Problems and planning in Third World cities / edited by Michael Pacione. – London : Croom Helm, 1981.
290p; 23cm.
Includes bibliographies and index.
ISBN 0709901925 £12.95

Problems and Procedures in Collections. – Vancouver : British Columbia Continuing Legal Education Society, 1983.
350p.
ISBN 0865040923

Problems encountered by local and regional authorites as a result of their new tasks in respect of environmental protection / report prepared under the guidance of the Committee of Experts on Social and Economic Activities of the Steering Committee for Regional and Municpal Matters by G. Tendron. – Strasbourg : Council of Europe, 1986.
29p.
Bibliography: p.28-29.

Problems for the Business Client in the Marketing of Goods : Licensing and the Infringement of Rights. – London : Law Society, 1986.
17p.
Hbk £1.95

Problems in Mercantile Law. – New Delhi : Kalyani Publishers.
Hbk £12.00

Problems in Mercantile Law. – Delhi : SBD Enterprises.
Hbk £15.00

Problems in Mercantile Law. – 7th rev. ed. – New Delhi : Sultan Chand and Sons, 1984.
iv, 238p.
Pbk £15.00

Problems of a Master of the Rolls : being the presidential address of Sir John Donaldson, president of the Holdsworth Club of a the Faculty of Law in the University of Birmingham, 1985-1986. – Birmingham : University of Birmingham. Holdsworth Club, 1985.
14p. – (The Holdsworth Club).
ISBN 0704407744

Problems of development and ocean management in the eastern Caribbean : economic, legal, environmental and planning aspects : proceedings of an international seminar held in Kingstown, St. Vincent & the Grenadines, West Indies, May 11-13, 1981 / edited by Edgar Gold, Norman G. Letalik, Carlyle L. Mitchell. – 2nd printing. – Halifax, N.S. : Dalhousie Ocean Studies Programme, 1982.
xviii,184p.
'Held under the auspices of the West Indies (Associated States) Council of Ministers and sponsored by the Dalhousie Ocean Studies Programme in cooperation with the Foundation Reshaping the International Order (RIO)

Problems of International Justice. – Wildwood.
ISBN 0813303923 Hbk £31.00

Problems of jury trials in small jurisdictions / John Spry. – London : Commonwealth Secretariat, 1985.
19p.
Includes bibliographical references.

Problems of public housing. – Policy Studies Institute, 1988.
ISBN 0853743509 Pbk £6.95

Problems of regional and local authorities involved in planning policies : report / prepared under the guidance of the Committee of Experts on Social and Economic Activities of the Steering Committee for Regional and Municipal Matters by Jacques Robert. – Strasbourg : Council of Europe, 1985.
36p.

Problems raised by certain aspects of the present situation of refugees from the standpoint of the European Convention on Human Rights / by Richard Plender. – Strasbourg : Council of Europe, Directorate of Human Rights, 1984.
38p.
ISBN 9287103550

Procedure in Industrial Tribunals. – London : Engineering Employers Federation, 1985.
Hbk

Procedure in the International Court : a commentary on the 1978 Rules of the International Court of Justice / Shabtai Rosenne. – The Hague : M. Nijhoff, 1983.
xvii, 305p.
Includes bibliographical references and index.
ISBN 9024730457 Hbk £130.00

Procedure of the UN Security Council / Sydney D. Bailey. – 2nd ed. – Oxford : Clarendon press, 1988.
xii,499p.
Bibliography: pp.449-452. - Includes index. A revised and updated edition, taking in new developments, including a new chapter on voting and veto. All aspects of the Security Council's prcedure are covered.
ISBN 0198275668 Hbk £45/$60

Procedures for meetings and organizations / M. Kaye Kerr and Hubert W. King. – Agincourt, Ont. : Carswell Legal Publications, 1984.
xv, 313 p.; 24 cm.
Includes index. Bibliography: p. 276.
ISBN 0459361503

Procedures for the Control of Ships. – International Maritime Organization. – English Edition. – London : International Maritime Organization, 1982.
Hbk £2.00

Proceedings and papers of the 7th Commonwealth Law Conference, Hong Kong, 18-23 September 1983. – Hong Kong : The Conference, 1984.
xvii,539p.

Proceedings and resolutions of the ... provincial meeting of the members of the Society / the Law Society. – 25 v. – London : The Law Society, 1903.
Continues: Proceedings and resolutions / Incorporated Law Society. Continued by: Annual conference of the Law Society, 1st(1948). Bound with the annual reports of the Council of the Law Society. Typewritten index to proceedings for 1887-1928 bound with our 1924-1928 volume.

Proceedings of a seminar on commercial arbitration held in Ottawa, 19 June 1985 / edited by Paul J. Davidson. – Ottawa : Canadian Arbitration, Conciliation and Amicable Composition Centre, 1986.
xxi,154p.
At head of t.p.: Canadian Arbitration, Conciliation and Amicable Composition Centre, and Canadian National Section, Inter-American Commercial Arbitration Commission.

Proceedings of Forum London : a seminar organised by the International Bar Association, Section on Business Law, in conjunction with the Solicitors' European Group of the Law Society of England and Wales, 23-26 September 1981, London. – London : International Bar Association, 1982.
iv,166p.
ISBN 0950587656

Proceedings of Seminar : Protection of Sellers in Transnational Sales - Beyond Letters of Credit, at the Cafe Royal, London, 2- 3 June 1982. – 1. – London : International Bar Association, Section on Business Law, 1982.
various pagings.

Proceedings of the 7th, 8th and 9th Annual Conferences of the Nigerian Society of International Law. – Lagos : Nigerian Institute of International Affairs, 1983.
227p.
Hbk £5.00

Proceedings of the Administrative Law Conference : held at the University of British Columbia Faculty of Law on 18-19 October 1979. – Vancouver : U.B.C. Law Review, 1981.
391p; 23cm.

Proceedings of the Conference of Institutions Responsible for Teaching the Subject 'Computers and Law', Rome, 9-11 October 1985 : reports presented at the Conference. – Strasbourg : Council of Europe, 1987.
357p; 29cm.
At head of cover title: Legal affairs.
ISBN 9287110603

Proceedings of the Conference on International Law : critical choices for Canada, 1985-2000 / Droit international. – Kingston Ont. : Queens Law Journal, 1986.
xxxiv,563p.
Includes bibliographical references. Cover title: International law: critical choices for Canada, 1985-2000.
ISBN 0889114706

Proceedings of the Court of Justice of the European Communities. – Kirchberg : Commission of the European Communities.
10p.
Hbk

Proceedings of the First Euro Arab Arbitration Conference / actes de 1er Colloque Euro-Arab sur l'arbitrage : under the high patronage of Habib Bourguiba. – London : Lloyd's of London Press, 1987.
ix,370p; 25cm.
At head of title: Euro-Arab Chambers of Commerce.
ISBN 1850441251 Pbk £60.00

Proceedings of the Regional Energy Law Seminar, Oslo, Norway, 8-9 May 1984 / the Section on Energy and Natural Resources Law of the International Bar Association in conjunction with the Scandinavian Institute of Maritime Law, University of Oslo. – London : International Bar Association, 1984.
Various pagings.
Includes bibliographical references.

Proceedings of the Round Table with European Ombudsmen : Madrid, 5-6 June 1985 / organised by the Secretariat General of the Council of Europe in co-operation with the Spanish Defensor del Pueblo. – Strasbourg : Directorate of Human Rights, Council of Europe, 1987.
141p.
ISBN 928711000X

Proceedings of the Seminar on Middle East Law, with reference to Bahrein, Egypt, Iran, Kuwait, Oman, Qatar, Saudi Arabia, U.A.E., 1-4 July 1981, Hamburg, Germany. – London : International Bar Association, 1981.
170p.
ISBN 0950587664

Proceedings of the seminar on planning law for industry : March 29th-April 2nd 1981, Churchill College, Cambridge, England / organised by the Committee on Environmental Law (Committee F), Section on Business Law, International Bar Association : edited with discussion summaries by John Salter and Patricia Thomas. – 2. – London : International Bar Association in cooperation with Sweet and Maxwell, 1981.
21cm.
ISBN 0950587621 Pbk

Proceedings of the seventh, eighth and ninth annual conferences of the Nigerian Society of International Law, 1975-1978 / M. A. Ajomo. – Lagos : Nigerian Institute of International Affairs, 1982.
x,221p.
Includes bibliographical references. Edited by M.A. Ajomo.
ISBN 9782276111

Process of Law in Australia : Intercultural Perspectives. – Butterworths, 1988.
454p.
ISBN 0409494488 Pbk £39.00

Proclamations / by James Douglas, governor and commander-in-chief of Her Majesty's colony of British Columbia and its dependencies. – 72 leaflets. – Victoria : s.n., 1858.
Continued by British Columbia ordinances, 1864-1866. Proclamations nos. 1-3, 1858 issued by James Douglas as governor of Vancouver Island and its dependencies. Bound together with British Columbia ordinances, 1864. Numbering begins anew each year.

Prodhan
Accounting Research Database / Al-Najjar. – Routledge.
ISBN 0415000947 Hbk £35.00

Producers, importers and own-branders. – Product Liability Briefing, 1988.
ISBN 1870317254 Pbk £6.50

Product differentiation in terms of packaging presentation, advertising, trade marks, etc. : an assessment of the legal situation regarding pharmaceuticals and certain other consumer goods / Jules Stuyck. – Antwerp : Kluwer, 1983.
xv,118p.
Bibliography: p.111-118.
ISBN 9065440844

Product liability / the Law Reform Commission. – Sydney : The Commission, 1988.
xii,86p. – (Discussion paper).
Bibliography: p.85-86.

Product liability : the new law under the Consumer Protection Act 1987 / by Rodney Nelson-Jones and Peter Stewart. – London : Fourmat, 1987.
207p.
Contains the text of the Act.
ISBN 1851900497 Pbk £15.95

Product Liability and Safety Encyclopaedia. – London : Butterworths.
Service.
ISBN 0000999091 Hbk £110.00

Product Liability Briefing : Executive Guide Vols. 1-12. – Deddington : Pandora Press, 1987.
ISBN 187031705X Pbk £71.80

Product liability casebook. – London : Lloyd's of London Press, 1984.
ISBN 1850440158 Pbk £32.50

Product liability in Australia / S.W. Cavanagh and C.S. Phegan. – Sydney : Butterworths, 1983.
xxxvi, 267 p.; 25 cm.
Includes bibliographical references and index.
ISBN 0409491012 Hbk £30.00

Product Liability Manual. – Bern : European Office for Quality Control.
Hbk £50.00

Product Quality, Standardization and the Law : 4th European Seminar on Product Liability. – Bern : European Office for Quality Control, 1981.
Hbk £20.00

Product Safety : Measures to Protect Children. – Paris : OECD, Organisation for Economic Co-operation and Development, 1984.
86p.
ISBN 9264125884 Hbk £9.00

Product Safety : Risk Management and Cost-Benefit Analysis. – Paris : OECD, Organisation for Economic Co-operation and Development, 1983.
106p.
ISBN 9264125108 Hbk £10.00

Products Liability : 1982. – Vancouver : British Columbia Continuing Legal Education Society, 1982.
114p.
ISBN 0865040494 Hbk £45.00

Products Liability : Conference Papers. – Woolloomooloo : International Business Communications, 1986.
ISBN 0949072052 Hbk £55.00

Products Liability : III. – Vancouver : British Columbia Continuing Legal Education Society, 1984.
ISBN 0865041512 Hbk £45.00

Products liability and personal injury compensation in Canada : towards integration and rationalization
Vol. 1 / E.P. Belobaba. – Canada : Policy Research, Analysis and Liaison Directorate, Consumer and Corporate Affairs, 1983.
168p.
Bibliography: p.144-168.
ISBN 0662124154

Professional Accounting Practice Management. – Quorum Press.
ISBN 0899302904 Hbk £36.90

Professional competence and the law / editor, Leon E. Trakman : assistant editor, Douglas Watters : sponsored by Dalhousie Law School, the Law Foundation of Nova Scotia, the CLE Society of Nova Scotia, the Canadian Bar Association. – Halifax, Nova Scotia : Dalhousie University Faculty of Law, 1981.
iv,245p. – (Dalhousie Continuing Legal Education Ser.: No. 21).
Includes bibliographical references.
ISBN 0770301274 Hbk £20.00

Professional Conduct for Solicitors. – London : Butterworths.
ISBN 0406504113 Pbk £8.95

Professional conduct of solicitors / Law Society. – 1. – London : The Society, 1986.
loose-leaf; 23cm.

Professional Conduct of the Jurist. – Durban : Professional Publishers, 1983.
ISBN 0409025054 Pbk

Professional Direction →Solicitor's guide to advertising & publicity.

Professional Driver's Guide : A Reference Handbook. – 8th rev. ed. – New Malden : Croner Publications, 1986.
ISBN 0900319453 Hbk £6.00

Professional Engineers Act, 1983, Bill 123 : An Act to Revise the Professional Engineers Act. – Ontario : Ontario Government Publications Service, 1983.
49p.
Hbk £0.70

Professional Ethics of the Bar. – 2nd ed. – Allahabad : Law Book Company, 1987.
370p.
Hbk £120.00

Professional Guide to Fund Raising, Corporate Giving People Giving to People. – London : Eurospan.
ISBN 0899302513 Hbk £29.95

Professional indemnity claims. – London : Architectural Press, 1984.
ISBN 0851397484 Hbk £14.50

Professional Liability : An Architectural Press Legal Guide. – 2nd ed. – London : Architectural Press, 1986.
208p : Illus.
ISBN 0851399525 Hbk £19.95

Professional liability and construction / Leo Barros D'Sa. – 1. – Ascot : Chartered Institute of Building, 1987.
30cm. – (Occasional paper).
ISBN 090660088X Pbk

Professional Liability in Conveyancing in New Brunswick. – Agincourt : Carswell, 1986.
127p.
This book addresses the lawyer's liability in conveyancing in New Brunswick, Canada. The role of the real estate practitioner is reviewed and the legal grounds for liability are analyzed in the work.
Hbk £35.50

Professional liability insurance : a one-day conference organised by Lloyd's of London Press Ltd., the London Press Centre, October 3, 1980. – London : Lloyds of London Press, 1981.
58 leaves in various pagings; 31cm.
ISBN 090409393X Hbk £20.00

Professional negligence / K M Stanton. – 2nd ed. – London : Butterworths, 1988.
ISBN 0406179115 Hbk

Professional negligence / by Rupert M. Jackson and John L. Powell. – 2nd ed. – London : Sweet & Maxwell, 1987.
xlvii,472p; 25cm.
Considers the reported cases on professional negligence, with particular emphasis on recent developments. Uses cases reported in established law reports, but also those appearing in individual professional journals. Commonwealth cases are also included.
ISBN 0421341602 £36.00

Professional negligence / by David F. Partlett. – Sydney : Law Book Co., 1985.
xxxvii, 425 p.; 25 cm.
Includes bibliographical references and indexes.
ISBN 0455205949

Professional negligence / by Ashley Underwood and Stephen Holt. – London : Fourmat, 1981.
xv,96p; 23cm.
ISBN 0906840368

Professional negligence : a journal of liability, ethics and discipline. – London : Cass, 1985-.

Professional negligence : being a discussion of the duties and responsibilities of auditors / by E.F. Mannix and J.E. Mannix. – 3rd ed. – Sydney : Butterworths, 1982.
viii,112p.
Previous ed.: 1976. Includes index.
ISBN 0409309338

Professional negligence today : the text of two lectures delivered to the Belfast Solicitors' Association on 9 and 23 May 1985 / by D.S. Greer and Ethne E. Harkness. – Belfast : SLS Legal Publications, 1985.
61p.
Includes bibiographical references.

Professional partnerships: law and taxation. – 2nd. – London : Longman Professional (UK), 1990.
Considers partnerships from the time of creation through changes in the partnerships by admission, retirement and merger, to the ultimate dissolution. Covers the Insolvency Act 1986, and changes brought about by the Finance Act 1989. New chapter on mergers and demergers.
ISBN 0851215734 Pbk £35.00

Professional Practice for Building Works / Gordon. – London : Estates Gazette.
ISBN 0728200651 Hbk £19.50

Professional responsibility
Part 1 : papers presented by Paul Finn ... et al / Paul D Finn. – Auckland : Legal Research Foundation, 1987.
254p.
Includes bibliographical references. At head of t.p.: Legal Research Foundation Inc. seminar. 'University of Auckland, 28/29 May, 1987'. - Cover.
Part 2 : paper presented by Mr. Justice Rogers : and commentaries on papers published in part one presented by John C. Hagen ... et al. – 1987.
p.255-382.
At head of t.p.: Legal Research Foundation Inc. seminar. 'University of Auckland, 28/29 May, 1987'. - Cover.

Professional secrecy in South Africa : a symposium / edited by G. C. Oosthuizen, H. A. Shapiro, S. A. Strauss. – Cape Town : Oxford University Press, 1983.
178p.
ISBN 0195703200

Professions and services in the European Economic Community / by D. Lasok. – Deventer, The Netherlands : Kluwer Law and Taxation Publishers, 1986.
ISBN 9065442537 Hbk

Professions in the European Community : towards freedom of movement and mutual recognition of qualifications / J.-P. de Crayencour. – Luxembourg : Office for Official Publications of the European Communities, 1981.
137p.
ISBN 9282527913

Professor Gower's review of investor protection : views of the Council for the Securities Industry. – Council for the Securities Industry. – London : The Council, 1982.
9p.

Profile of Federal Prisoners. – Canberra : Australian Institute of Criminology.
Hbk £1.95

Profile of published legal research : a report to the Consultative Group on Research and Education in Law based on a survey of Canadian legal publications / Alice Janisch. – Ottawa : Consultative Group on Research and Education in Law, 1982.
39p.

Profiles of progress : contributions to criminal justice in Canada. – OTTAWA : Minister of Supply and Services, 1984.
32p.
ISBN 0662134133

Profits of crime and their recovery / report of a committee chaired by Sir Derek Hodgson. – London : Heinemann, 1984.
viii,165p; 23cm.
Includes index.
ISBN 0435826506

Profit-sharing and share incentive. – London : Fitzwilliam, 1988.
ISBN 187055504X Hbk £25.00

Progress in Crime Prevention In Papua New Guinea. – Canberra : Australian Institute of Criminology.
free

Progress in natural resource economics : essays in resource analysis by members of the Programme in Natural Resource Economics (PNRE) at the University of British Columbia / edited by Anthony Scott with the assistance of John Helliwell, Tracy Lewis and Philip Neher. – Oxford : Clarendon, 1984.
vii,440p; 24cm.
ISBN 0198284608 £20.00

Progress of scrutiny / House of Lords Select Committee on the European Communities. – London : H.M.S.O., 1981.
First three reports entitled: Report on the progress of scrutiny.

Progress report on the Constitution Act 1975 : the role of Upper Houses of Parliament (interim report) / Statute Law Revision Committee. – Melbourne : Government Printer, 1982.
iv,4p. – (D v no 1/1982).

Progress through partnership : 1980/1981 / Canadian Law Information Council. – Ottawa : CLIC, 1981-.
36p.
Annual reports for 1978/1979 and 1979/1980 published as one volume entitled: Yesterday, today and tomorrow : 1978-1980 / Canadian Law Information Council. Continued by: Annual report / Canadian Law Information Council, 1981/1982 onwards. Includes annual report of CLIC for 1980/1981.

Progression of Judges : a History of the Supreme Court of British Columbia. – Vancouver : University of British Columbia Press, 1988.
197p.
ISBN 0774802936 Hbk £31.95

Prohibiting restrictions on trade within the EEC : the theory and application of Articles 30-36 of the EEC Treaty / by Laurence W. Gormley. – Amsterdam : North-Holland, 1985.
xxv,458p.
Bibliography: p.429-443. - Includes index. At head of title: T.M.C. Asser Instituut - The Hague.
ISBN 0444868488

Prohibitions or Restrictions on the Use of Certain Conventional Weapons. – Geneva : Comite International de la Croix-Rouge, 1981.
33p.
Hbk £2.00

Project financing / by Peter K. Nevitt. – 4th ed. – London : Euromoney, 1983.
xiii,273p.
Includes index.
ISBN 0903121395

Promises, morals, and law / by P.S. Atiyah. – Oxford : Clarendon Press, 1981.
218p; 23cm.
Includes index.
ISBN 019825377X £14.00

Promotion for the Professions : A Guide to Practice Development. – London : Kogan Page, 1985.
134p.
ISBN 0850389968 Hbk £12.95

Proof in Criminal Cases in New Zealand. – North Ryde : Law Book Co, 1984.
xxxii, 407p.
ISBN 0455205221 Hbk £49.00
ISBN 0455205930 Pbk £32.00

Proof of fact in criminal trials. – Edinburgh : Green (W.) & Son, 1984.
Based on extensive court experience and psychological study, it is a systematic and comprehensive analysis of the fact-finding process in criminal trials examining lying and its detection, examination of witnesses, how real issues of fact emerge and the principles on which evidence is assessed and verdicts reached.
ISBN 0414007399 Pbk

Proof Of Guilt, The (Hamlyn 3). – 3rd ed. – Belfast : Sweet & Maxwell, 1963.
ISBN 0420383204 Pbk £9.25

Propeosed EC unfair contract terms directive / Department of Trade and Industry. Consumer Affairs Division 3A. – London : The Department, 1987.
45p.
Contents include: Futher draft articles for discussion on unfair terms of contract / European Commission. Also includes examples of relevant European national legislation.

Propert Law and Equity Reform Committee, New Zealand
Prescriptive title for a co-owner in possession / report of the Property Law and Equity Reform Committee. – Wellington : Government Printer, 1986.
17p.

Property / Andrew Reeve. – London : Macmillan, 1986.
208p; 22cm.
Includes bibliography.
ISBN 0333367960 Hbk £20.00 :
ISBN 0333367979 Pbk £6.95

Property and construction tax handbook. – Spon (E & FN), 1986.
ISBN 0419140506 Hbk £17.50

Property and Finance in Family Law / R. Bailey. – Canberra : Australian National University, Research School of Social Sciences, 1981.
ISBN 0909596662 Pbk £9.00

Property and marriage : an integrated approach : property, tax, pensions and benefits in the family / Judith Freeman...et al. – London : Institute for Fiscal Studies, 1988.
viii,170p. – (Report series).
Bibliography: p156-161.
ISBN 0902992686

Property and political theory / Alan Ryan. – Oxford : Blackwell, 1984.
198p; 24cm.
Includes index.
ISBN 0631136916 £15.00

Property and politics 1870-1914 : landownership, law, ideology and urban development in England / Avner Offer. – Cambridge : Cambridge University Press, 1981.
xviii,445p; 24cm.
Bibliography: p407-428. - Includes index.
ISBN 0521224144 £27.50

Property companies : accounting, audit and tax. – London : Butterworths, 1988.
ISBN 0406005249 Pbk

Property development / Austin-Crowe. – 2nd ed. – Spon (E & FN), 1983.
ISBN 0419128204 Pbk £9.50

Property Development Library, 4 Vols. – London : Sweet & Maxwell, 1984.
Hbk £135.00
Vol. 1. –
Hbk £42.50
Vol. 2. –
Hbk £37.50

Property Development Library
Vol. 1, 5 titles. – Reading : College of Estate Management, 1983.
– (College of Estate Management Handbooks Ser.).
Hbk £25.00
Vol. 2, 4 titles. –
Hbk £36.50

Property distribution on divorce / Margaret R De Haas. – 2nd ed. – London : Longman Professional, 1985.
ISBN 0851210015 Pbk £14.95

Property Division on Marriage Breakdown. – North Ryde : C.C.H. Australia, 1984.
660p.
ISBN 0869035797 Hbk £50.00

Property, divorce and retirement pension rights / by K.J. Gray : by C.C. Turpin. – Deventer : Kluwer, 1986.
vii,269p.
Includes bibliographical references.
ISBN 9065442510

Property Guide. – Unwin Hyman.
– (Saga Guides).
ISBN 0044401728 Pbk £3.50

Property Handbook / Fowler. – Sphere Books.
ISBN 074740108X Pbk £10.99

Property Law : Cases and Materials / Marcia A. Neave. – 4th ed. – Butterworths, 1988.
1,008p.
ISBN 0409492876 Hbk £79.00
ISBN 0409492884 Pbk £65.00

Property law : cases and materials / by Ronald Sackville and M.A. Neave. – 3rd ed. – Sydney : Butterworths, 1981.
lxxi,936p.
Includes index.
ISBN 0409300411 Pbk
ISBN 040930042X

Property Law : Cases, Text and Materials / Richard J. Balfour. – Aurora : Canada Law Book Co, 1982.
1400p. – (Case books).
Property Law provides edited versions of the leading real property and personal property cases, statutory references to the Canadian Common Law jurisdictions and textual material and commentary. The historical perspective of the work is complemented by a description and analysis of many recent proposals for reform in this area.
Hbk £95.00

Property law : fourth report on land registration / the Law Commission. – London : HMSO, 1988.
iii,147p. – (H.C. 1987-88).
ISBN 0102680884

Property law : liability for chancel repairs / the Law Commission. – London : HMSO, 1985.
v,48p.
ISBN 0102039860

Property law : rights of reverter : report on a reference under section 3 (1) (e) of the Law Commissions Act 1965 / the Law Commission. – London : H.M.S.O., 1981.
vi,52p; 25cm.
ISBN 0101841000

Property law : second report on land registration : inspection of the register / the Law Commission. – London : H.M.S.O., 1985.
iii,43p.
ISBN 0102551855

Property law : the implications of William & Glyn's Bank Ltd. v. Boland : report on a reference under section 3(1)(e) of the Law Commission Act 1965 / the Law Commission. – London : H.M.S.O., 1982.
v,56p.
ISBN 0101863608

Property law : third report on land registration, A. overriding interests, B. rectification and indemnity, C. minor interests / the Law Commission. – London : H.M.S.O., 1987.
v,107p.
ISBN 0102269874

Property Law and Equity Reform Committee
Final report on legislation relating to landlord and tenant / report of the Property Law and Equity Reform Committee. – Wellington : The Committee, 1986.
3,105p.
—Interim report on legislation relating to landlord and tenant / report of the Property Law and Equity Reform Committee. – Wellington : The Committee, 1983.
29p.
—Law relating to water courses : interim report / Property Law and Equity Reform Committee. – Wellington : The Committee, 1983.
15,9,2,8p.
—Positive covenants affecting land / report of the Property Law and Equity Reform Committee. – Wellington : The Committee, 1985.
85p.
—Report on residential tenancies / Property Law and Equity Reform Committee. – Wellington : The Committee, 1985.
66p.

Property law handbook. – London : Butterworths, 1984.
ISBN 0406258171 Pbk £17.50

Property Offences / M.S. Weinberg. – 2nd ed. – North Ryde : Law Book Co, 1986.
xl, 445p.
ISBN 0455206325 Hbk £65.00
ISBN 0455206333 Pbk £45.00

Property, Planning and Compensation Reports. – London : Sweet & Maxwell.
Hbk £80.00
Bound Vol.. –
Hbk £29.00
Single copy. –
Hbk £18.50
Back Vols. avail..

Property Purchase Tax Act. – Vancouver : Continuing Legal Education Society of British Columbia, 1987.
135p.
ISBN 086504323X Hbk £65.00

Property Rights and Compensation : Compulsory Acquisition and Other Losses. – Butterworths, 1983.
192p.
Includes alternative bases for assessing economic losses, compulsory acquisition of business, compensation for goodwill and licences, economic value and property, reservation values and compulsory acquisitions, compensation claims and the taking of public property.
ISBN 0409843059 Hbk £45.00

Property rights and sovereign rights : the case of North Sea oil / Peter D. Cameron. – London : Academic Press, 1983.
x,210p; 24cm.
Bibliography: p194-202. - Includes index.
ISBN 0121570606

Property Statutes. – 5th ed. – Sweet & Maxwell.
ISBN 0421352701 Pbk £13.95

Property Tax in Singapore. – Singapore : Butterworths, 1985.
This book acts as a guide to the working of the property tax system in Singapore. The author discusses the chargeability of properties, the property tax surcharge and exemptions, concessions and refunds available, and the rights and obligations of the property owner. Relevant legislation is reproduced in full in the appendices.
ISBN 040999510X Pbk £19.00

Property tax planning manual. – London : Butterworths, 1987.
ISBN 0406137390 Pbk £18.95

Property taxes. – Croydon : Tolley, 1986.
ISBN 0854592237 Pbk £15.95

Property Valuation Handbook. – Reading : College of Estate Management.
ISBN 090213289X Hbk £38.00

Property valuation in South Africa. – Cape Town : Juta, 1984.
x,181p.
ISBN 0702114855

Prophet, John
Councillor. – 10th ed. – London : Shaw & Sons, 1987.
ISBN 0721908519 Pbk £4.95
—Fair rents : a practical guide to the law relating to the rents of residential tenancies including the work of rent officers, rent assessment committees and rent tribunals / by John Prophet. – 3rd ed. – London : Shaw and Sons, 1985.
xxxi,243p.
ISBN 0721907024 Pbk £7.50
—Parish Councillor's Guide. – 15th ed. – London : Shaw & Sons, 1988.
ISBN 0721905137 Pbk

Proposal for a commission of inquiry into the effect of domestic intelligence activities on criminal trials in the United States of America. – Amnesty International. – London : Amnesty International, 1981.
iii,141p; 30cm.
Cover title.
ISBN 0862100380 Pbk

Proposal for a Council regulation on the European Co-operation Grouping (COM (78) 139 Final) : memorandum / by the Society's Standing Committee on Company Law. – London : Law Society, 1981.
4p; 30cm.

Proposal for an eleventh Council directive : based on article 54(3)(g) of the treaty concerning disclosure requirements in respect of branches opened in a member state by certain types of companies governed by the law of another state / Council of the European Communities. – London : Department of Trade and Industry, 1987.
17,7p.
Includes a 'Background note' from the Deparment of Trade and Industry.

Proposals for a compulsory mental health care act : report to the Minister of Justice / Law Reform Commission of Saskatchewan. – Saskatoon : The Commission, 1985.
40p.
Includes bibliographical references.

Proposals for a Frustrated Contracts Act : report to the Minister of Justice / Law Reform Commission of Saskatchewan. – Saskatoon : The Commission, 1988.
31p.

Proposals for a guardianship act : Report to the Attorney General
Part 1 : personal guardianship / Law Reform Commission of Saskatchewan. – Saskatoon : Law Reform Commission of Saskatchewan, 1983.
19p.

Proposals for a Human Artificial Insemination Act / Law Reform Commission of Saskatchewan. – Saskatoon : The Commission, 1987.
12p.

Proposals for a new Alberta Arbitration Act / Institute of Law Research and Reform, Edmonton, Alberta. – Edmonton : The Institute, 1988.
iv,166p. – (Report).
Includes draft legislation and the text of the Convention on the Recognition and Enforcement of Foreign Arbitral Awards.
ISBN 0888648669

Proposals for a new Alberta Incorporated Associations Act / Institute of Law Research and Reform, Edmonton, Alberta. – Edmonton : The Institute, 1987.
i,223p. – (Report).

Proposals for a new coroners act : report to the Minister of Justice / Law Reform Commission of Saskatchewan. – Saskatoon : The Commission, 1984.
62p.
Includes bibliographical references.

Proposals for a survival of actions act : report to the Minister of Justice / Law Reform Commission of Saskatchewan. – Saskatoon : The Commission, 1985.
19p.
Includes bibliographical references.

Proposals for an Equality of Status of Married Persons Act : report to the Attorney General / Law Reform Commission of Saskatchewan. – Saskatoon : The Commission, 1982.
17p.

Proposals for defences to provincial offences : report to the Minister of Justice / Law Reform Commission of Saskatchewan. – Saskatoon : The Commission, 1986.
18p.
Includes bibliographical references.

Proposals for restoring civil remedies lost upon forfeiture under the Automobile Accident Insurance Act : report to the Minister of Justice / Law Reform Commission of Saskatchewan. – Saskatoon : The Commission, 1984.
11p.
Includes bibliographical references.

Proposals for revision of the Immigration Rules / Home Office. – London : H.M.S.O., 1982.
vii,40p.
ISBN 0101868308

Proposals on custody, parental guardianship, and the civil rights of minors : report to the Attorney General / from the Law Reform Commission of Saskatchewan. – Saskatoon : Law Reform Commission of Saskatchewan, 1981.
iv,40p.

Proposals relating to ademption by equitable conversion / Law Reform Commission of Saskatchewan. – Saskatoon : The Commission, 1984.
12p.
Includes bibliographical references.

Proposals relating to joint obligations : report to the Minister of Justice / Law Reform Commission of Saskatchewan. – Saskatoon : The Commission, 1985.
13p.

Proposals relating to matrimonial property legislation / Law Reform Commission of Saskatchewan. – Saskatoon : The Commission, 1985.
22p.

Proposals relating to the change of name of children of divorced parents : report to the Minister of Justice / Law Reform Commission of Saskatchewan. – Saskatoon : The Commission, 1985.
8p.

Proposals relating to the rules against perpetuities and accumulations : report to the Minister if Justice / Law Reform Commission of Saskatchewan. – Saskatoon : The Commission, 1987.
29p.

Proposals under the Securities Act 1978 for regulations relating to contributory mortgages / Securities Commission. – Wellington : The Commission, 1981.
50,48p.

Proposed A.C.T. Mental Health Ordinance 1981 / Human Rights Commission. – Canberra : Australian Government Publishing Service, 1982.
vii,44p. – (Report).
ISBN 0644022477

Proposed amendments to the Indian Act concerning conditionally surrendered land and band taxation powers. – Ottawa : Department of Indian Affairs and Northern Development, 1987.
iii,11,12,iiip.
French title on added t.p.: Modifications proposees a la Loi sur les Indiens concernant les terres cedees sous condition et les pouvoirs d'imposition des bandes indiennes. Pages numbered in opposite directions. Text in English and French.
ISBN 0662552555

Proposed Crown Prosecution Service : The Distribution of Functions Between the Headquarters and Local Offices of the Service. – London : HMSO, 1984.
ISBN 0101941102 Hbk £1.30

Proposed recommendations for securities regulations
2nd draft / Securities Commission. – Wellington : The Commission, 1981.
xiii,89,2p.

Proprietary Company Practice Manual. – 2nd ed. – North Ryde : Law Book Co, 1983.
vii, 162p.
ISBN 0455204128 £21.00

Proprietary rights and insolvency in sales transactions / by R.M. Goode. – London : Sweet & Maxwell, 1985.
xv,137p; 22cm.
Includes index.
ISBN 0421351403 Pbk £13.00

Prosecuting sexual assault / G. Chambers, A. Millar. – Edinburgh : H.M.S.O., 1986.
ix,144p.
Research by the Central Research Unit of the Scottish Office. Reports on police investigation of sexual assault cases and on prosecution and trial methods.
ISBN 0114933715

Prosecuting Solicitors' Society of England and Wales
Organisation of an independent prosecution service / observations on the Discussion Paper circulated on behalf of the Home Office Working Party on Prosecution Arrangements. – s.l. : the Society, 1983.
19p.

Prosecution in the public interest / Susan R. Moody and Jacqueline Tombs. – Edinburgh : Scottish Academic Press, 1982.
xii, 167p.
Examines the decision-making process of the Procurator Fiscal as to whether to prosecute, on what, and by what procedure to prosecute. Bibliography: p.160-163.
ISBN 0707303214 Hbk

Prosecution of the Mentally Disturbed / D. Chiswick. – Aberdeen : Aberdeen University Press, 1984.
192p.
ISBN 0080284817 Hbk £16.50

Prosecution policy of the Commonwealth : guidelines for the making of decisions in the prosecution process and the considerations upon which these decisions are made / Attorney-General's Department. – Canberra : Australian Government Publishing Service, 1983.
20p.
Originally published: 1982.
ISBN 0644022779

Prosecution without Trial. – Butterworths, 1989.
ca 336p.
ISBN 040949478X Hbk £55.00

Prospect of Gray's Inn. – 2nd ed. – London : GRAY, 1985.
ISBN 0420473300 Hbk £10.00

Prospects for a new Law of the Sea : papers read at a seminar conducted by the International Law Association in Sydney on 19 June 1982 / edited by Ivan Shearer. – Sydney, N.S.W. : International Law Association (Australian Branch), 1983.
v, 97, 93 p.; 30 cm.
ISBN 0949685011 Pbk £7.00 (£6.00 to members)

Prospects for the European Community in 1982 : the Exeter Lecture in European Community law, delivered in the University on 19 February 1982 / by Douglas Hurd. – Exeter : University of Exeter, Centre for European Legal Studies, 1982.
12p.

Prosser, K. → Potter and Monroe's tax planning with precedents.

Prosser, Tony
Nationalised industries and public control : legal, constitutional and political issues / Tony Prosser. – Oxford : Blackwell, 1986.
220p; 23cm.
Examines constitutional form of nationalised industries and their relationship with government. Studies the role of public law in defining and limiting state activity as applied to nationalised industries.
ISBN 0631139982 £17.50
—Test cases for the poor : legal techniques in the politics of social welfare / Tony Prosser. – London : Child Poverty Action Group, 1983.
v,102p.
ISBN 090396371X
→ Waiving the Rules : The Constitution Under Thatcherism.

Protected Persons and Their Property in N.S.W. / Mark Robinson. – North Ryde : Law Book Co, 1987.
xiv, 176p.
ISBN 0455207194 Pbk £27.50

Protecting consumers and the public at large. – Product Liability Briefing, 1988.
ISBN 1870317157 Pbk £6.50

Protecting human rights in the Americas : selected problems / Thomas Buergenthal, Robert Norris, Dinah Shelton. – 2nd rev ed. – Kehl, W. Germany : Engel, 1986.
xviii,389p.
Previous ed.: 1982. Bibliography: pp.315-322. - Includes index. Includes the texts of the Charter of the Organization of American States, the American Convention on Human Rights and other basic documents.
ISBN 3883570559

Protecting intellectual property in Asia - Pacific : a specially commissioned report / edited by John A. Connors. – London : Oyez Longman, 1984.
108 leaves; 30cm. – (Oyez Longman intelligence reports).
Bibliography: leaf 108.
ISBN 0851208851 Pbk

Protecting privacy in two-way electronic services / by David H. Flaherty : foreword by Ronald L. Plasser. – London : Mansell, 1985.
viii,172p; 24cm.
Bibliography: p165-166. - Includes index.
ISBN 0720117445 £23.50

Protecting the Protectors. – Canberra : Australian Institute of Criminology.
Hbk £12.50

Protecting Workers' Rights. – Redfern : Redfern Legal Centre Publishing, 1987.
170p.
Hbk £10.00

Protection against the expropriation risk in investing abroad. – Matthew Bender, 1988.
ISBN 0000999071 Hbk £50.00

Protection du droit a la vie a la lumiere des regles du droit international : bibliographie selective / preparee par la Bibliotheque du Palais de la Paix, La Haye : selective bibliography : prepared by the Library of the Peace Palace, The Hague. – The Hague : Centre for Studies and Research of the Hague Academy of International Law, 1983.
17 leaves.

Protection for semiconductor chip masks in the United States : analysis of the Semiconductor Chip Protection Act of 1984 / David Ladd, David E. Leibowitz and Bruce G. Joseph. – Weinheim : VCH, 1986.
vi,99p.
ISBN 0895734842

Protection of a purchaser of securities / South African Law Commission. – Pretoria : The Commission, 1987.
xiv,116p. – (Project 62).
Bibliography: pp.ix-xi. Includes draft legislation.
ISBN 0797014608

Protection of a purchaser of securities / South African Law Commission. – Pretoria : The Commission, 1987.
ii,47p. – (Project).

Protection of children : state intervention and family life / Robert Dingwall, John Eekelaar, Topsy Murray. – Oxford : Basil Blackwell, 1983.
x,286p; 24cm.
Bibliography: p267-282. - Includes index.
ISBN 0631131051 £22.50

Protection of children's interests in custody disputes / Institute of Law Research and Reform. – Edmonton : The Institute, 1984.
ii,42p. – (Report no 43).

Protection of Civil Rights Act. – 2nd ed. – Allahabad : Law Book Company, 1986.
Hbk £75.00

Protection of foreign investments: a private law study of safeguarding devices in internatiohal crisis situations. – Kluwer Law and Taxation, 1989.
500.
Deals primarily with the situation in the USA, but also summarises the discussions and ideas developed from twenty years of practical studies. Includes chapters on the Canadian Trading with the Enemy Act, the treatment of Private Enemy Property in the USA, proof of ownershihp and documentation.
ISBN 9065443827 Hbk £54/Dfl 165

Protection of human rights in Europe / Council of Europe. – New ed. – Strasbourg : Council of Europe, 1983.
16p.

Protection of human rights in Europe : limits and effects : proceedings of the fifth International Colloquy about the European Convention on Human Rights / edited by Irene Maier. – Heidelberg : C.F. Muller Juristischer Verlag, 1982.
xviii, 378 p.; 24 cm.
Includes bibliographical references and index.
ISBN 3811411829

Protection Of Industrial Designs. – Maidenhead : McGraw-Hill, 1977.
ISBN 007084495X Hbk £6.95

Protection of liberty / I.N. Stevens & D.C.M. Yardley. – Oxford : Basil Blackwell, 1982.
x,188p; 24cm.
Examines the extent to which incursions are made on our civil liberties.
ISBN 0631129448 Hbk £15.00
ISBN 0631131760 Pbk £5.95

Protection of military information : government response to the report of the Study Group on Censorship / Ministry of Defence. – London : H.M.S.O., 1985.
10p.
ISBN 0101949901

Protection of military information : report of the Study Group on Censorship ... : presented to Parliament by the Secretary of State for Defence ... December 1983. – Study Group on Censorship. – London : H.M.S.O., 1983.
vii,91p; 25cm.
Bibliography: p60-63. - Includes index.
ISBN 0101911203 Pbk £6.40

Protection of Moral Rights. – Milsons Point : Australian Copyright Council.
Hbk £4.00

Protection of Movable Cultural Property : Compendium of Legislative Texts
Vol. 1 /. – Paris : UNESCO.
Hbk £65.00
Vol. 2. –
ISBN 9231018914 Hbk £80.00

Protection of movable cultural property : compendium of legislative texts / Hanna Saba, Nabil G Salame. – Paris : Unesco, 1984.
v. 1, 2; 24 cm.
Prepared by Hanna Saba, with assistance of Nabil G. Salame. Translation of: Protection du patrimoine culturel mobilier.
ISBN 9231016385 Pbk : v. 1

Protection of Offences. – London : Sweet & Maxwell, 1986.
ISBN 0421349107 Pbk

Protection of officials of foreign states according to international law / Franciszek Przetacznik. – The Hague : Nijhoff, 1983.
xix,390p; 25cm.
Bibliography: p313-344. - Includes index.
ISBN 9024727219 Hbk £160.00

Protection of people at work. – Product Liability Briefing, 1988.
ISBN 1870317203 Pbk £6.50

Protection of personal data used for scientific research and statistics : recommendation no.R (83)10 adopted by the Committee of Ministers of the Council of Europe on 23 September 1983, and Explanatory memorandum. – Council of Europe. – Strasbourg : Council of Europe, 1984.
23p; 21cm.
'Prepared by the Committee of Experts on Data Protection set up under the authority of the European Committee on Legal Co-operation'. At head of cover title: Legal Affairs.
ISBN 9287103178

Protection of personal data used for the purposes of direct marketing : recommendation no. R(85) 20 adopted by the Committee of Ministers of the Council of Europe on 25 October 1985 and Explanatory memorandum. – Council of Europe. – Strasbourg : Council of Europe, 1986.
19p.
Prepared by the committee of experts on data protection set up under the authority of the European Committee on Legal Co-operation. At head of cover title: Council of Europe, Legal Affairs.
ISBN 9287108765

Protection of persons satisfying the criteria in the Geneva Convention who are not formally recognised as refugees : recommendation no.R (84)1 adopted by the Committee of Ministers of the Council of Europe on 25 January 1984, and Explanatory memorandum. – Council of Europe. – Strasbourg : Council of Europe, 1984.
10p; 21cm.
'... prepared by the ad hoc Committee of Experts on Legal Aspects of Territorial Asylum and Refugees' - preface.
ISBN 9287103275

Protection of Privacy Act. – London : Butterworths.
ISBN 0409848859 Hbk £30.00

Protection of privacy, automatic data processing and progress in statistical documentation. – Luxembourg : Office for Official Publications of the European Communities, 1986.
348p. – (Series C).
Eurostat News special edition. 'The papers reproduced in this volume were first presented at an international seminar held under the auspices of the Statistical Office of the European Communities (EUROSTAT) at Luxembourg in December 1984'. - Preface.

Protection of the individual with reagard sic to the acts of the tax and customs administrations : proceedings of the colloquy organised by the Council of Europe in co-operation with the International Centre of Sociological and Penitentiary Research and Studies in Messina 25-27 March 1986. – Strasbourg : Council of Europe, 1986.
39p.
ISBN 9287108749

Protection of the underwater heritage. – Paris : Unesco, 1981.
200p.
Includes bibliographies.
ISBN 9231018639

Protection of trade secrets / Institute of Law Research and Reform. – Edmonton : The Institute, 1984.
159p. – (Report for discussion).
Includes bibliographical references.

Protection of trade secrets : a general guide / W.R. McComas, Mark R. Davison, David M. Gonski. – Sydney : Butterworths, 1981.
xiv,98p.
ISBN 0409300284 Hbk £48

Protection of users of computerised legal information services : Recommendation no.R (83) 3 adopted by the Committee of Ministers of the Council of Europe on 22 February 1983 and Explanatory memorandum. – Council of Europe. – Strasbourg : Council of Europe, 1983.
23p; 21cm.
'... prepared by the Committee of Experts on Legal Data Processing un der the authority of the European Committee on Legal Co- operation'. At head of cover: Council of Europe, Legal Affairs.
ISBN 9287102791

Protection of Women under the Law : an Annotated Bibliography / Badar Anwar. – New Delhi : Deep and Deep Publications, 1982.
200p.
Hbk £75.00

Protectionism and the European Community : import relief measures taken by the European Economic Community and the member states, and the legal remedies available to private parties / J.H.J. Bourgeois ... et al. – Antwerp : Kluwer, 1983.
xii,199p.
By members of a working group on the law of international relations established by the Europa Institute of the University of Amsterdam. - Edited by E.L.M. Volker.
ISBN 9065441271

Protectionism and the European Community : Import Relief Measures Taken by the European Economic Community and the Member States, and the Legal Remedies Available to Private Parties. – 1983 2nd rev. update ed. – Dordrecht : Kluwer, 1987.
252p.
ISBN 9065443134 Pbk £94.00

Protectionism and the future of international shipping : the nature, development, and role of flag discriminations and preferences, cargo reservations and cabotage restrictions, state intervention and maritime subsidies / Dr. Ademuni-Odeke. – Dordrecht : M. Nijhoff, 1984.
xxviii,446p.
Includes bibliographies and index.
ISBN 9024729181 Hbk £235.00

Protective legislation for women in the member states of the European Community / communication by the Commission. – Luxembourg : Office for Official Publications of the European Communities, 1987.
29p. – (COM(87) 105 final).
Includes bibliographical references.
ISBN 9277228741

Protest, Policing and the Law / P. Leopold. – London : Institute for the Study of Conflict, 1985.
– (Conflict Studies Ser.: No. 175).
Hbk £5.50

Protocol additional to the Geneva conventions for the protection of victims of international armed conflicts and the United Nations Convention on the Law of the Sea : repercussions on the law of naval warfare : report to the Committee for the Protection of Human Life in Armed Conflict of the International Society for Military Law and Law of War / by Elmar Rauch. – Berlin : Duncker & Humblot, 1984.
165p; 24cm.
ISBN 3428057031

Protocol No. 6 to the Convention for the Protection of Human Rights and Fundamental Freedoms Concerning the Abolition of the Death Penalty. – Strasbourg : Council of Europe, 1983.
ISBN 928710235X

Prott, Lyndel V →Creation and Preservation : Law and the Cultural Heritage.
→ Existing legislative protection of the cultural and natural heritage of the Pacific region.
—Law and the cultural heritage
Vol. 1 : Discovery and excavation / by Lyndel V. Prott and P.J. O'Keefe : foreword by Henry Cleere. – Abingdon : Professional Books, 1983.
xxvii,434p.
Bibliography: p.371-386. - Includes index. Cover title: Law and the cultural heritage/ by P.J. O'Keefe and Lyndel V. Prott.
ISBN 086205060X
ISBN 0862050650
—National legal control of illicit traffic in cultural property / by Lyndel V. Prott, P.J. O'Keefe. – Paris : UNESCO, 1983.
iv,144p.
Bibliography: p.144.

Proulx, Daniel →Canadian Human Rights Yearbook.

Prouse, Robert J. →Canadian Private Security Manual.

Providing civil justice for children / Hugh Geach and Elizabeth Szwed. – London : Edward Arnold, 1983.
250p; 22cm.
Includes bibliographies and index.
ISBN 071316400X Pbk £9.95

Providing criminal justice for children / edited by Allison Morris and Henri Giller. – London : Edward Arnold rc 1983, 1983.
164p; 22cm.
Includes index.
ISBN 0713163976 Pbk £7.95

Province of Legislation Determined : Legal Theory in 18th Century Britain. – Cambridge : Cambridge University Press.
ISBN 0521245923 Hbk £27.50

Province of Natal consolidated ordinances and regulations / compiled by H.L. Van Graan : saamgestel deur H.L. Van Graan. – Johannesburg : Lex-Patria, 1964.
looseleaf.
Includes index. Contains enactments since 1911 which are still in force. Added t.p. in Afrikaans. Spine title: Consolidated ordinances and regulations Natal. Parallel text in English and Afrikaans.

Province of Transvaal ordinances and regulations : including pre-union legislation in force in that province together with a reference to decided cases / compiled and anotated by C.W.B. Hart : insluitende voor-unie-wetgewing van krag in daardie provinsie tesame met 'n verwysing na gewysde sake : saamgestel en geannoteer deur C.W.B. Hart. – Johannesburg : Lex Patris, 1961.
looseleaf.
Previous ed.: Consolidated ordinances of the Transvaal 1902 to 1947 / compiled by S.A. Lombard. Includes index. Added t.p. in Afrikaans. Spine title: Consolidated ordinances and regulations Transvaal. Parallel text in English and Afrikaans.

Provincial and Municipal Finances. – Toronto : Canadian Tax Foundation, 1985.
Hbk £14.75

Provincial Court Criminal Hearings 1985. – Vancouver : Continuing Legal Education Society of British Columbia, 1985.
112p.
ISBN 0865042349 Hbk £55.00

Provincial Insolvency Act. – 5th ed. – Allahabad : Law Book Company, 1988.
xiv, 958p.
Hbk £275.00

Provincial Land Tax Act : Revised Statutes of Ontario, 1980. – Office of the Legislative Assembly (Ontario). – Ontario : Ontario Government Publications Service, 1983.
42p.
Hbk £2.00

Proving Discrimination in Canada. – Agincourt : Carswell, 1987.
281p.
This book deals with the factual requirements of the three theories of proving discrimination in Canada and available defenses. Canadian law is analyzed in comparison to the American and British experience.
Hbk £38.00

Provisional damages. – London : LEST, 1986.
ISBN 0907822835 Pbk £17.50

Provocation and diminished responsibility as defences to murder / Law Reform Commissioner, Victoria. – Melbourne : The Commission, 1982.
48p. – (Report no 12).
Includes bibliographical references.

Prowse, Janet A.
Working Manual of Criminal Law, 1 Vol. – Agincourt : Carswell.
This work for Canadian practitioners in the field of criminal law covers defences, evidence, offenses, procedure, and sentencing. The book is designed to facilitate the preparation of a case for trial as prosecutor or defense counsel.
Pbk £71.50

Prudential supervision in banking / by R. M. Pecchioli. – Paris : Organisation for Economic Co-operation and Development, 1987.
298p.
Bibliography: p279-298.
ISBN 9264129162

Prying Eyes : a Review and Indictment of the 1982 Canadian Privacy Act. – Ottawa : Ken Rubin, 1983.
Hbk £18.00

Pryke, Richard
Competition among international airlines / by Richard Pryke. – Aldershot : Gower for the Trade Policy Research Centre, 1987.
100p; 22cm.
Includes bibliography.
ISBN 0566053330 Pbk £9.00

Pryles, Michael Charles
Australian citizenship law / by Michael Pryles. – Sydney : Law Book Co., 1981.
xxv,271p.
Includes index.
ISBN 0455203598
→ Australian private international law.
—Dispute Resolutions in Australia-Japan Transactions / K. Iwasaki. – North Ryde : Law Book Co, 1983.
xxix, 185p.
ISBN 0455202648 Hbk £91.00
→ International and interstate conflict of laws.

Przetacznik, Franciszek
Protection of officials of foreign states according to international law / Franciszek Przetacznik. – The Hague : Nijhoff, 1983.
xix,390p; 25cm.
Bibliography: p313-344. - Includes index.
ISBN 9024727219 Hbk £160.00

Psychiatric Issues in Criminal Law. – Vancouver : British Columbia Continuing Legal Education Society, 1982.
ISBN 0865040826 Hbk £45.00

Psychiatry and Law. – Bombay : Popular Prakashan.
Hbk £20.00

Psychiatry and the criminal process / edited by Ronnie Mackay and Ken Russell. – Leicester : Leicester Polytechnic Law School, 1986.
48p. – (Leicester Polytechnic Law School monographs).
Includes bibliographical references.
ISBN 0948997281

Psychiatry behind bars : a legal perspective / by Marc E. Schiffer. – Toronto : Butterworths, 1982.
xxiv,509p.
Covers the psychiatric interrogation of accused persons, the myth of confidentiality, forms of treatment, psychiatric treatment and offenders' rights, and the psychiatrist as jailer.
ISBN 0409865613

Psychiatry, Human Rights and the Law / Bluglass. – Cambridge : Cambridge University Press, 1985.
ISBN 0521261945 Hbk £30.00

Psychiatry, law, and ethics / edited by A. Carmi : with contributions by G. Ammon ... et al. – Berlin : Springer-Verlag, 1984.
ISBN 0387157425

Psycholinguistic Principles Applicable to the Formulation of Jury Instructions : an Annotated Bibliography. – Ottawa : Canadian Law Information Council, 1985.
60p.
ISBN 0920358853 Pbk £5.00

Psychological survival : the experience of long-term imprisonment / Stanley Cohen and Laurie Taylor. – 2nd ed. – Harmondsworth : Penguin, 1981.
239p; 19cm. – (Pelican books).
Previous ed.: 1972. Bibliography: p230-239.
ISBN 014021657X Pbk £2.25

Psychologist in Criminal Justice : An Australian Perspective. – Canberra : Australian Institute of Criminology.
free

Psychology and law : topics from an internatinal conference / edited by Dave J. Muller, Derek E. Blackman and Antony Chapman. – Chichester : Wiley, 1984.
xxii,472p; 24cm.
Conference papers. Includes bibliographies and index.
ISBN 0471903361 £29.75

Psychology in legal contexts : applications and limitations / edited by Sally M.A. Lloyd-Bostock. – London : Macmillan, 1981.
xix,246p. – (Oxford socio-legal studies).

Psychology of judicial sentencing / Catherine Fitzmaurice and Ken Pease. – Manchester : Manchester University Press, 1986.
vii,174p; 22cm.
Bibliography: p159-171. - Includes index.
ISBN 0719018196 £19.95

Psychology of juvenile crime / Amy Lamson. – New York : Human Sciences, 1983.
123p; 22cm.
Includes index.
ISBN 0898850606

Psychology of sentencing : approaches to consistency and disparity / edited by Donald C. Pennington and Sally Lloyd-Bostock. – Oxford : Centre for Social-Legal Studies, 1987.
xvi,240p; 24cm.
Includes bibliographies and index.
ISBN 0948774002 Pbk

Public access to environmental information : report of an interdepartmental Working Party on public access to information held by pollution control authorities. – London : H.M.S.O., 1986.
ISBN 0117518654

Public access to Government held information. – London : Sweet & Maxwell, 1987.
ISBN 0420476105 Pbk £35.00

Public access to government-held information : a comparative symposium / general editor, Norman S. Marsh ... et al. – London : Stevens, 1987.
xxi, 342 p.; 22 cm.
Includes bibliographical references and index.
ISBN 0420476105 Pbk

Public Acts of New Zealand : 1908-date. – Abingdon : Professional Books, 1984.
Hbk

Public administration : a select bibliography. – 6th rev. ed. – London : Overseas Development Administration, 1986.
iv,25,7p.
Previous ed.: 1985.

Public administration in Canada : selected readings / edited by A.M. Willms, W.D.K. Kernaghan. – 4th ed. – Toronto : Methuen, 1982.
viii,354p.
Includes bibliographies.
ISBN 0458952508

Public administration in Japan / edited by IIAS Tokyo Round Table organizing committee. – Tokyo : Institute of Administrative Management, 1982.
299p.
Proceedings of a conference.

Public Advocate Act, 1983, Bill 125 : An Act to Provide for a Public Advocate in Ontario. – Ontario : Ontario Government Publications Service, 1983.
3p.
Hbk £0.30

Public Affairs and The Successor Generation. – Exeter : European Atlantic Movement, 1982.
Pbk £0.50

Public and media access to the criminal process / Law Reform Commission of Canada. – Ottawa : The Commission, 1987.
106,120p. – (Working paper).
Includes bibliographical references. Added t.p. in French: L'acces du public et des medias au processus penal. Pages numbered in opposite directions. Text in English and French.
ISBN 0662551168

Public and private in social life / edited by S.I. Benn and G.F. Gaus. – London : Croom Helm, 1983.
viii,412p; 23cm.
Includes indexes.
ISBN 0709906684 £19.95
ISBN 0312653573

Public Complaints Commission in a presidential system with particular reference to Nigeria / by P.A. Oluyede. – Lagos : Nigerian Institute of Advanced Legal Studies, 1983.
19p.
Seminar paper presented at the Institute on Thursday May 19th, 1983. Includes bibliographical references.

Public defender : a report / by JUSTICE : chairman of committee James Morton. – London : JUSTICE, 1987.
51p.
ISBN 0907247091

Public Demands Recovery Act. – 2nd ed. – Calcutta : Eastern Law House, 1959.
115p.
Hbk £5.50

Public disórder : a review of research and a study in one inner city area / by Simon Field and Peter Southgate. – London : H.M.S.O., 1982.
v, 73p.
Bibliographies. Contents: Urban disorders in Britain and America: a review of research/Simon Field - The disturbances of July 1981 in Handsworth, Birmingham: a survey of the views and experiences of male residents/Peter Southgate. A Home Office Research and Planning Unit report.
ISBN 011340767X

Public Employment Law : The Role of the Contract of Employment in Australia and Britain. – Sydney : Butterworths, 1987.
208p.
This book describes the statutory and institutional framework of public employment law in Australia and Britain. Also discussed are the distinctions between Crown servants and other public employees, discipline, dismissal, tenure of employment, and remedies.
Pbk £29.00

Public Enterprise and Fundamental Rights. – Bombay : Tripathi.

Public enterprise in Portugal and Spain : analysis from the point of view of competition policy. – Luxembourg : Office for Official Publications of the European Communities, 1988.
213p.
At head of title: Commission of the European Communities.
ISBN 9282579107

Public finance in developing countries / A. R. Prest. – 3rd ed. – London : Weidenfeld and Nicolson, 1985.
xiii,236p.
Bibliography: p226-228.
ISBN 0297785788

Public finance in theory and practice / Richard A. Musgrave, Peggy B. Musgrave. – 4th ed. – New York : McGraw-Hill, 1984.
xvi,824p; 25cm.
Previous ed: 1980. Includes bibliographies and index.
ISBN 007044126X £26.95

Public finance in theory and practice / A.R. Prest, N.A. Barr. – 7th ed. – London : Weidenfeld and Nicolson, 1985.
xvi, 553p.
Includes bibliographical references.

Public General Acts and General Synod Measures. – London : H.M.S.O., 1973.
Continues: The Public General Acts and the Church Assembly Measures.

Public General Acts and Measure 1983, 3 Vols. – London : HMSO.
ISBN 011840234X Hbk £127.00
Tables and Index 1983. –
ISBN 0118402358 Pbk £20.00

Public General Acts of ... Northern Ireland ... – Belfast : HMSO, 1921.
Legislation enacted as Orders in Council from 1972. Looseleaf from 1982.

Public General Statutes : 1831-1979. – Abingdon : Professional Books.
Hbk £1250.00

Public Health (Control of Disease) Bill : report on the consolidation of certain enactments relating to the control of disease / The Law Commission. – London : H.M.S.O., 1984.
6p; 25cm.
ISBN 0101912803

Public interest law / edited by Jeremy Cooper and Rajeev Dhavan. – Oxford : Basil Blackwell, 1986.
xviii,482p.
Discusses the conflict between rights and duties of individuals and public interest in the legal system.
ISBN 0631142991 £25.00

Public Interest Litigation : a Profile. – New Delhi : Bharat Law House, 1986.
200p.
Hbk £150.00

Public international law in the modern world / David H. Ott. – London : Pitman, 1987.
480p; 18cm.
Includes bibliography and index.
ISBN 0712107568 Pbk £13.95
ISBN 0273028154

Public Law / A. Bradley. – London : Sweet & Maxwell.
Hbk £36.00
Bound Vol.. –
Hbk £16.95
Single copy. –
Hbk £13.50
Back Vols. avail..

Public Law. – 1st ed. – Plymouth : Macdonald & Evans, 1984.
260p.
ISBN 0712117598 Pbk £7.50

Public law and politics / edited by Carol Harlow. – London : Sweet & Maxwell, 1986.
250p; 24cm.
Includes index.
ISBN 0421333901 £24.00

Public Law and the Retail Sector Oxford Reports on Retailing / Hughes. – London : Longman Professional.
ISBN 0582037352 Pbk £40.00

Public legal services : a comparative study of policy, politics and practice / by Jeremy Cooper. – London : Sweet & Maxwell, 1983.
ix,320p; 22cm.
Bibliography: p305-313. - Includes index.
ISBN 0421303506 Pbk £9.50

Public legal services in three countries : a study of the relationship between policy and practice / Jeremy Cooper. – Florence : European University Institute, Department of Law, 1981.
436p.
Thesis (Doctoral) - European University Institute,1981. Includes bibliographical references.

Public lending right : reports of an ALAI symposium and additional materials / edited by H. Cohen Jehoram. – Deventer (Netherlands) : Kluwer Law and Taxation Publishers, 1983.
vi, 198p.
Reports of the 1977 ALAI Antwerp symposium, organised by the Belgian Copyright Association, and additional contributions from Australia - New Zealand, Iceland, Norway, the USA and the UK.
ISBN 9065441344

Public liability : Recommendation no.R(84) 15 adopted by the Committee of Ministers of the Council of Europe on 18 September 1984, and explanatory memorandum. – Council of Europe. – Strasbourg : Council of Europe, 1985.
19p; 21cm.
'... prepared by the committee of experts on administrative law set up under the authority of the European Committee on Legal Co-operation. On cover: Council of Europe, Legal Affairs.
ISBN 9287103798

Public liberty and the police role / Philip Knights. – S.l. : University of Wales. Institute of Science and Technology, 1985.
23p.
Bibliography: p22-23.

Public Opinion and the Supreme Court. – London : Allen & Unwin.
ISBN 0044970463 Hbk £30.00
ISBN 0044970471 Pbk £11.95

Public order : a guide to the 1986 Public Order Act / by John Marston. – London : Fourmat Publishing, 1987.
189p.
ISBN 1851900241

Public Order Act : Elizabeth II, 1986. Chapter 64 / Peter Thornton. – London : Financial Training Publications, 1987.
xxi, 226p.
Bibliography: p.219-220. Includes the text of the Public Order Act 1986.
ISBN 1851850406

Public order and the law / by Andrew Hiller : with a foreword by Judge Gibney. – Sydney : Law Book Co., 1983.
xx,230p.
Bibliography: p.xix-xx. - Includes index.
ISBN 0455202761
ISBN 0455204101 Pbk £26.00

Public Order of the Oceans : a Contemporary International Law of the Sea / William T. Burke. – Dordrecht : Kluwer, 1987.
1,300p.
ISBN 0898389011 Hbk £400.00

Public order review : civil disturbances 1981-1985 / Metropolitan Police Force. – London : Metropolitan Police, 1986.
iv,43p.

Public order - the new law / Richard Card. – London : Butterworths, 1987.
170p; 25cm.
Includes index.
ISBN 0406504407 Pbk £12.50

Public prosecutor : the memoirs of Sir Norman Skelhorn, Director of Public Prosecutions, 1964-1977 / Sir Norman Skelhorn. – London : Harrap, 1981.
8,207p.
ISBN 0245537635

Public Records : 21st Annual Report of the Keeper of Public Records on the Work of the Public Record Office and the 21st Report of the Advisory Council on Public Records, 1979. – London : HMSO, 1981.
ISBN 0100280196 Hbk £3.20

Public relations and criminal justice policy / Peter Nokes. – Leeds : Centre for Social Work and Applied Social Studies, 1982.
43p. – (Occasional paper).
'Occasioned by the seminar on Alternatives to Imprisonment ... held October 1980 - October 1981 under the auspices of the Centre for Applied Social Studies'. Bibliography: p.42-43.

Public rights and private interests / J. A. G. Griffith. – Trivandrum : Academy of Legal Publications, 1981.
12196,iv.

Public Rights and the Private Press. – Toronto : Butterworths, 1981.
224p.
Examines the various points at which the law intersects with journalism, and looks into the complications arising from the increased tendency of the mass media to acquire a monopolistic status in society. Concludes with a speculative enquiry into what the future of media law will be like.
ISBN 0409812951 Hbk £19.95

Public secrets : a study in the development of government secrecy / K. G. Robertson. – London : Macmillan, 1982.
x,216p.
Bibliography: p198-209.

Public Sector Accounting / N Pendlebury. – 2nd ed. – Pitman.
ISBN 0273029304 Pbk £12.95

Public sector housing law / D.J. Hughes. – 2nd ed. – London : Butterworths, 1987.
xxxix,329p.
Previous ed.: 1981. Includes bibliographies and index.
ISBN 0406600627 Pbk £16.95

Public sector housing law in Scotland. – 3rd. – Edinburgh : Green (W.) & Son, 1989.
Describes the functions with regard to housing responsibilities of local authorities, the Scottish Office, Scottish Homes and housing associations. Chapter on public sector secure tenancies, assured tenancies for housing associations, the right to buy, homelessness and the improvement of sub-standard housing.
ISBN 041400891X Pbk

Public Sector Prices and Compensation Review Act, 1983, Bill 111 : An Act to Provide for the Review of Prices and Compensation in the Public Sector and for the Elderly Transition to the Resumption of Full Collective Bargaining. – Ontario : Ontario Government Publications Service, 1983.
18p.
Hbk £0.50

Public servant and the law / by Akintunde Emiola. – Ile-Ife : University of Ife Press, 1985.
xxii,225p.
Includes bibliographical references and index.
ISBN 9781360658

Public torts and contracts / by Mark Aronson and Harry Whitmore. – Sydney : Law Book Co., 1982.
xviii, 296 p.; 25 cm.
Includes bibliographical references and indexes.
ISBN 0455204411 Pbk

Public Trusts and Taxation. – Lucknow : Eastern Book Company, 1987.
418p.
Hbk £125.00

Publication Department of Grampian Police
Road Traffic Law. – Publication Department of Grampian Police. – Aberdeen : Aberdeen University Press.
1532p.
ISBN 090001511X Hbk

Publications, documentation and means for their dissemination in the Commission of the European Communities / M. Hopkins. – London : British Library, 1981.
iv,28p; 30cm.
ISBN 0905984692 Pbk

Publish and perish / Joseph Minattur. – New Delhi : VIVA, 1982.
80p.

Publishers Association → Book trade year book.
—Comments to Her Majesty's Government on the consultative document Cmnd. 8302 : reform of the law relating to copyright, designs and performers' protection / the Publishers Association. – London : The Association, 1982.
69p.

Publishing agreements : a book of precedents / edited by Charles Clark. – 2nd ed. – London : Allen & Unwin, 1984.
xvi,230p; 23cm.
Previous ed.: 1980. Includes index.
ISBN 004655016X £15.00

Pufendorf, S.
Law of Nature and Nations / B. Kennett. – Repr. of 1703 ed. – Abingdon : Professional Books.
597p.
Hbk £450.00

Pugh, D. S.
Writers on organizations / D. S. Pugh, D. J. Hickson and C. R. Hinings. – 3rd ed. – Harmondsworth : Penguin, 1983.
234p; 20cm. – (Penguin education).
Previous ed.: 1971. Includes bibliographies and indexes.
ISBN 0140802665 Pbk £2.50

Pugh, John
Administration of Foreign Estates. – Sweet & Maxwell, 1988.
ISBN 0421346507 Hbk £34.00
→ Adminstration of foreign estates.

Pugh, Leslie M.
Matrimonial proceedings before Magistrates / Horsman. – 4th ed. – London : Butterworths, 1981.
ISBN 040634602X Hbk £46.00
—Pugh's matrimonial proceedings before magistrates / J. Basil Horsman. – 4th ed. – London : Butterworths, 1981.
xli, 820p.
ISBN 040634602X

Pugh-Smith, John
Neighbours and the law / by John Pugh-Smith. – London : Sweet & Maxwell, 1988.
lii,218p.
Discusses the impact of planning permissions, building regulations, and actions in tort, on the way we live as neighbours. Statute case law is cross-referenced, and guidance on litigation procedure and the collection of relevant precedents is also included.
ISBN 0421365706 £20.00
—Planning law and practice in dwelling houses / Peter Morgan. – London : Sweet & Maxwell, 1987.
ISBN 0421366206 Hbk

Pugh's matrimonial proceedings before magistrates / J. Basil Horsman. – 4th ed. – London : Butterworths, 1981.
xli, 820p.
ISBN 040634602X

Pugwash → Chemical industry and the projected chemical weapons convention : proceedings of a SIPRI/Pugwash conference.

Puigblanch, Antonio
Inquisition Unmasked, 2 Vols. – Repr. of 1816 ed. – Aalen Wuertt : Scientia.
lxxxviii, 362p.
Hbk £230.00

Pulea, Mere
Family Law and Population in the Pacific Islands. – Suva : University of the South Pacific, Institute of Pacific Studies.
Pbk £5.00

Pullen, J. R. → Civil justice project : preliminary study.
—Court surveys and studies 1978-1984, concerning the civil caseloads of the Supreme Court, the County Court and the Magistrates' Courts of Victoria / J.R. Pullen, N.F. Young, S.J. Geddes. – Melbourne : Civil Justice Committee, 1985.
xvi,403p.
At head of title: Civil Justice Committee.

Pullen, M.
Do Your Own Book-Keeping. – London : Kogan Page.
ISBN 1850917116 Hbk £12.95
ISBN 1850917108 Pbk £5.95

Pulling, Alexander
Order of the Coif / By Alexander Pulling. – London : W. Clowes and sons, 1884.
xxvi, 288 p; 27 cm.
'The subject of this work has been foreshadowed in the article under the same title in the Edinburgh review' for October, 1878.'–Pref.

Pulling, Francis Herbert → Dunlop Holdings Limited : investigation under Section 172 of the Companies Act 1948 : interim report.

Pullinger, Hugh
Criminal justice system model : the flow model / Hugh Pullinger. – London : Home Office, 1985.
vi,56p.
Bibliography: p.56.
ISBN 0862522234

Pulton
De Pace Regis Et Regni. – Abingdon : Professional Books.
– (Classical English Law Texts Ser.).
Hbk £37.50

Pulvenis, J.F. → Legal Regime of Fisheries in the Caribbean Region.

Punch, Maurice
Conduct Unbecoming : The Social Construction of Police Deviance and Control. – London : Tavistock Publications, 1985.
300p.
ISBN 0422792101 Pbk £7.95

Punishment : a philosophical and criminological inquiry / Philip Bean. – Oxford : Robertson, 1981.
viii,215p; 23cm.
Bibliography: p202-210. - Includes index.
ISBN 0855203919 £12.50

Punishment : an introduction to principles / M.A. Rabie, S.A. Strauss. – 3rd ed. – Johannesburg : Lex Patria, 1981.
365p.
Previous ed.: 1979. First published 1977 as: Theories of punishment. Bibliographies: p.333-348. - Includes index.
ISBN 0628018495

Punishment : the supposed justifications / Ted Honderich. – Rev.ed. – Harmondsworth : Pelican Books, 1984.
248p.
Revised edition issued in Peregrine Books 1976.
ISBN 0140213120

Punishment and Responsibility. – Oxford : Oxford University Press, 1968.
ISBN 0198251815 Pbk £6.50

Punishment and welfare : a history of penal strategies / David Garland. – Aldershot : Gower, 1985.
x,297p; 23cm.
Bibliography: p280-290. - Includes index. Previous control number ISBN 0-435-82327-2.
ISBN 0566008556 £21.45

Punishment practice by prison Boards of Visitors / Susan Iles ... et al. – London : Home Office, 1984.
iv,41p.
Bibliography: p.40.
ISBN 086252167X

Purchase by a Company of its Own Shares. – Deloitte, Haskins and Sells. – London : Butterworths, 1983.
ISBN 0406252688 Pbk £16.25

Purdie → Matrimonial and Domestic Injunctions.

Purdie, Robert → Matrimonial and domestic injunctions : practice and precedents.

Purdue, et al
Planning law and procedure. – London : Butterworths, 1988.
ISBN 0406103836 Hbk

Purdue, Michael
Planning decisions digest / Michael Purdue and Vincent Fraser. – London : Sweet & Maxwell, 1986.
300p; 24cm.
Covers judicial decisions back to 1948, and selected ministerial decisions since 1974. Brief summaries of each decision are included, and referenced. Material is arranged under subject headings following the structure of the Town and Country Planning Act 1971.
ISBN 0421325704 Pbk £19.00

Purging of the Civil Service. – National Council for Civil Liberties. – London : National Council for Civil Liberties, 1985.
20p.
ISBN 0946088179

Puri, K.K.
Industrial design law in Australia and New Zealand. – Sydney : Butterworths, 1986.
256p.
Chapters include the role of design in modern society, recent changes in design law, design basics, application for registration, the registrar of design, the owner, the scope of legal protection for designs, design duration and fees, specific features of the New Zealand law of industrial designs, and design legislation in Australia and New Zealand.
ISBN 0409490482 Hbk £55.00

Purich, Don
Canadian Farm Law. – Saskatoon : Western Producer Prairie Books, 1982.
145p.
ISBN 0888330871 Pbk £8.95

Purnell, Howard → Criminal law in New South Wales, Vol. 1 : by Ray Watson and Howard Purnell.

Purposes of Government Expenditure. – London : Policy Studies Institute, 1984.
38p.
Hbk £1.30

Pursuit of nationalized property / M. Sornarajah. – Dordrecht : M. Nijhoff, 1985.
248p.
Bibliography.
ISBN 9024731305 Hbk £120.00

Purves, Gavin
Counsel. – London : Sweet & Maxwell.
Hbk £5.00

Purvis, Hoyt
Legislating Foreign Policy / Steven J. Baker. – 1984 repr. – Delhi : Hindustan Publishing Corporation, 1986.
x, 230p.
Hbk

Puthenparampil, J. Philip → Cultural Relations in the Global Community : Problems and Prospects.

Putnam, Thomas D.
Law of guarentees / Thomas Putnam and Julienne Walker. – 2nd ed. – London : Longman Professional (UK), 1989.
– (Commercial Series).
Discusses the law relating to contracts where one party agrees to be answerable for the debts or obligations of another to a third party. Deals with guarentees in loans, consumer credit, hire purchase, landlord and tenant (to guarentee payment of rent), building contracts, and commercial contracts. Contains specimen pleadings.
ISBN 0851215395 Hbk £40
—Suretyship . – London : Longman Professional. – (LPPN70).
ISBN 0851206123 Pbk £17.95

Puttick, Keith
Challenging delegated legislation / Keith Puttick. – London : Waterlow, 1988.
xxxiv,315p; 30cm. – (Waterlow practitioner's library).
Includes index.
ISBN 0080330711 £19.95
—Wages and the law. – London : Shaw & Sons, 1988.
ISBN 0721911102 Pbk

Putting the Charter to Work : Designing a Constitutional Labour Code. – Montreal : McGill-Queen's University Press, 1987.
ca 240p.
ISBN 0773506004 Hbk £30.00
ISBN 0773506012 Pbk £14.95

Puu, Tonu
Effects of Monetary and Fiscal Policy : A Contribution to Pure Theory. – Stockholm : Almqvist & Wiksell.
74p.
Hbk £2850.00

Puxon, Grattan
Roma : Europe's gypsies / by Grattan Puxon. – Rev updated ed. – London : Minority Rights Group, 1987.
15p. – (Report).
Bibliography: p.13.
ISBN 0946690456

Pye, Nigel
Property Companies : Accounting, Audit and Tax / Graham Walker. – London : Butterworths, 1986.
A guide to accounting for the property company in an environment of fluctuating interest and inflation rates. This book covers all relevant areas of United Kingdom accounting practice for property companies.
ISBN 0406005249 Pbk

Pyle, David J.
Economics of Crime and Law Enforcement. – London : Macmillan, 1983.
228p.
ISBN 0333282000 Hbk £33.00

Pylee, M.V.
Constitutional Government of India. – New Delhi : S. Chand and Company.
Hbk £120.00

Pymont, Stephen J. → Design and Build Contracts.

Pyrrhic victories : winning sex discrimination and equal pay cases in the industrial tribunals, 1980-84 / Alice M. Leonard. – London : H.M.S.O., 1987.
55p; 30cm. – (Research series).
ISBN 0117013285

Quaestiones juris privati / by Cornelius van Bijnkershoek : translated by R.A. Whitaker. – 2. – Pretoria : Government Printer on behalf of the South African Law Commission, 1987.
– (Research series).
Includes bibliographical references.

Quah
Police, Government and Accountability / Qual. – Oxford : Oxford University Press, 1987.
ISBN 0333432266 Pbk £8.95

Quakers and the English Legal System 1660-68. – Witney : Academic & University Publishing Group.
ISBN 0812281012 Hbk £33.20

Qual → Police, Government and Accountability.

Quangos : The Australian Experience / C. A. Saunders. – Neutral Bay : Hale & Iremonger, 1984.
ISBN 0868060860 Hbk £24.95
ISBN 0868060879 Pbk £11.95

Quansah, E. K. → Nigerian business law : a guide for students, managers and foreign investors.

Quantification of building claims / John Sims. – Oxford : Blackwell Scientific, 1988.
ISBN 0003832651 Hbk £20.00

Quantitative Analysis : ACCA Study Text 2.6. – Oxford : BPP.
ISBN 0862772478 Pbk £15.95

Quantum of damages in personal injury and fatal accident claims
Vol. 1 : Law and practice - fatal accident awards / Kemp & Kemp. – Special ed. by David A. McI. Kemp assissted by Derrick Turriff ... et al. 1. – London : Sweet & Maxwell, 1986.
various pagings.
Includes index.
ISBN 0421366001
Vol.2 : law and practice - personal injury reports / Kemp & Kemp. – 1975-.
Volume 1 collects the law and practice applicable to personal injury and to fatal injury claims. Appendices set out the Fatal Accident Acts and other texts. Volume 2 deals with case reports classified according to injury, and the damages awarded.
ISBN 0421216808 Llf

Quarter century of legal education in Nigeria : an appraisal / by E.I. Nwogugu. – Lagos : Nigerian Institute of Advanced Legal Studies, 1985.
28p. – (Occasional poaper).
Includes bibliographical references.

Quarterly law reports of Nigeria. – Ibadan : University Press, 1986.
Includes practice notes.

Quasi-legislation : recent developments in secondary legislation / by Gabriele Ganz. – 2nd ed. – London : Sweet & Maxwell, 1987.
xiv,114p; 23cm.
New ed. - Previous ed.: published as Administrative procedures. 1974. Includes index.
ISBN 0421370203 Hbk £18.50
ISBN 0421298502 Pbk £10.95

Quayle, V. J.
Food Hygiene I: Market Stalls and Delivery Vehicles. – London : Shaw & Sons, 1981.
– (Shaway Guide : No. 5).
ISBN 072190873X Pbk £2.50
—Food Hygiene II: Food Premises. – London : Shaw & Sons, 1981.
– (Shaway Guide: No. 6).
ISBN 0721908748 Pbk £2.50

Quebec Corporation Manual. – Toronto : DeBoo.
ISBN 0888201338 Llf £140.00

Quebec Guide to Immigration. – Montreal : McGill Campus Legal Aid Clinic, 1981.
77p.
Hbk £6.00

Quebec Law Reports : 1874-1971, 17 Vols. – Agincourt : Carswell, 1983.
Hbk

Quebec Legal Documentation at the Beginning of the 80's : the Results of a Survey. – Ottawa : Canadian Law Information Council, 1981.
30p.
ISBN 0920358160 Pbk £10.00

Quebec Taxation Service. – Toronto : DeBoo.
ISBN 0888201419 Llf £195.00

Queen Mary College → Contemporary problems in international arbitration.
→ International commercial crime : second international commercial crime symposium.
→ Inventors' information guide.
→ Symposium on Commercial Crime, 15-19 December 1982, Jesus College, Cambridge.

Queen's Regulations for the Royal Navy. – Consolidated ed., incorporating changes 1-61. 2 v. – London : H.M.S.O., 1984.
looseleaf. – (B.R. 31).
Includes index.
ISBN 011772386X

Queen's University → Legal services in rural areas : an evaluation : report.

Queensberry leases : petitions, answers, speeches and other documents of the Court of Session regarding leases on the entailed estates of the late William, Duke of Queensberry. – 6 v. – Edinburgh : s.n., 1813.
Various printers. Ms. contents lists and marginalia. Spine title. Includes Latin text.

Queensland Law Reform Commission
Working paper on legislation to review the role of juries in criminal trials / Queensland Law Reform Commission. – Brisbane : The Commission, 1984.
viii,146p. – (Q.L.R.C.W.P. 28).

Queensland Real Property Legislation. – North Ryde : C.C.H. Australia, 1986.
200p.
ISBN 0869038966 Hbk

Queensland State Reports : 1860-date. – Abingdon : Professional Books, 1984.
Hbk

Queensland statutes reprint : 1982. – Brisbane : Lawyers Bookshop, 1982.
looseleaf.
Previous ed.: 1962. Title from spine.

Queensland Supreme Court Practice. – Butterworths, 1984.
ISBN 0409493015 Hbk £235.00

Quemner, T.
Dictionnaire Juridique Fr/Eng Eng/Fr. – 2nd ed. – London : Edition de Navarre, 1984.
ISBN 2713300045 Pbk £31.00

Quest, Barry → Design : the modern law and practice.

Quest for economic stabilisation : the IMF and the Third World / directed and edited by Tony Killick : contributors Graham Bird ... et al. – London : Heinemann Educational in association with the Overseas Development Institute, 1984.
ix,340p; 23cm.
Bibliography: p321-331. - Includes index.
ISBN 043584427X Hbk £16.50
ISBN 0435844288 Pbk

Quest for Justice. – Repr. of 1951 ed. – London : Sweet & Maxwell, 1986.
ISBN 0421355107 Hbk £15.00

Quest for Justice : Aboriginal Peoples and Aboriginal Rights. – Toronto : University of Toronto Press, 1985.
ISBN 0802025722 Hbk £45.00
ISBN 0802065899 Pbk £17.50

Quest for Reform : The Royal Commission on Taxation Twenty Years Later. – Agincourt : Carswell, 1987.
475p.
This work analyzes the history of tax reform in Canada up to and including up-to-date proposals. The author outlines the process and substance of tax reform while comparing it to the Carter Report.
Hbk £58.50

Quest for security : employees, tenants, wives / by Tony Honore. – London : Stevens, 1982.
xiv,128p; 19cm.
Includes index.
ISBN 0420464107 Hbk £12.00
ISBN 0420464204 Pbk £5.80

Quest for Tax Reform : Royal Commission on Taxation 20 Years Later. – Agincourt : Carswell, 1988.
475p.
Hbk £58.50

Quest of Justice. – Sweet & Maxwell, 1951 Reprint.
ISBN 0421355107 Hbk £16.00

Question of a Reference to International Obligations in the United Nations Code of Conduct on Transnational Corporations : a Different View. – Geneva : United Nations Publications.
ISBN 9211041864 Hbk £4.00

Question of life : the Warnock report on human fertilisation and embryology / chairwoman Mary Warnock. – Oxford : Blackwell, 1985.
xvii,110p; 20cm.
The Warnock Report on Human Fertilization and Embryology. Discusses medical, legal and moral aspects of the subject.
ISBN 0631142576 Pbk £4.95

Questioning suspects / Law Reform Commission of Canada. – Ottawa : the Commission, 1984.
104,112p; 25cm. – (Working paper).
Cover title: Criminal law - questioning suspects. Added t.p. in French : L'interrogatoire des suspects. Pages numbered in opposite directions. In English and French.
ISBN 0662529162

Questioning suspects / Law Reform Commission of Canada. – Ottawa : The Commission, 1984.
25,28p. – (Report).
Added t.p. in French: L'interrogatoire des suspects. Pages numbered in opposite directions. Text in English and French.
ISBN 0662533208

Questions and Answers Company Law. – Nairobi : Heinemann Educational Books (East Africa).
196p.
Hbk £55.00

Questions and Answers for Professional Accountancy Students. – Bristol : SCCA Publishing.
ISBN 0950391352 Pbk

Questions and answers on English law. – London : Financial Training, 1983.
ISBN 0906322391 Pbk £5.95

Questions and answers on practical banking. – Cambridge : Woodhead-Faulkner, 1984.
ISBN 085941258X Pbk £8.95

Questions in Commercial Law. – 2nd ed. – North Ryde : C.C.H. Australia, 1986.
147p.
ISBN 0869037587 Hbk

Questions of international law
vol.2 : edited by Gyorgy Haraszti / Gyorgy Haraszti. – Alphen a/d Rijn : Sijthoff and Noordhoff, 1981.
244p.
ISBN 9028608303

Questions on the Law and Practice of Company Accounting / B. O'Shea. – 4th ed. – Sydney : Butterworths, 1987.
206p.
ISBN 040949206X Pbk

Quick Reference Index to NWLR
Parts 1-67. – Lagos : Nigerian Law Publications.
ISBN 09782325334 Hbk £25.00

Quiet enjoyment : remedies for harassment and illegal eviction / by Andrew Arden and Martin Partington. Edited by S. Carrott and C. Hunter. – 3rd. – London : Legal Action Group, 1990.
127.
Includes index.
ISBN 0905099265 Pbk £11

Quiet Revolution. – United Nations. – London : HMSO, 1984.
61p. – (The United Nations Convention on the Law of the Sea).
Describes the processes by which the negotiation of the Convention on the Law of the Sea took place.
ISBN 0119081733 Pbk £4.75

Quinn, John
International Legal Environment. – Toronto : University of Toronto Press, 1986.
288p.
ISBN 0802072984 Hbk £18.95

Quinn, John J. →Tariff Board : a study prepared for the Law Reform Commission of Canada.

Quinn, Peter D. →Real Estate Practice in Ontario.

Quinn, Sean E.
Criminal law in Ireland / Sean E. Quinn. – Bray, Co. Wicklow : Magh Itha, 1988.
xxvii,227p.
Includes index.
ISBN 1871509009 Pbk £20.00
ISBN 1871509017 £10.00

Quintessence of justice : University of Maiduguri, 6th convocation lecture delivered on Thursday, January 31st, 1985 / by Timothy Akinola Aguda. – Maiduguri, Nigeria : University of Maiduguri, 1985.
34p. – (Convocation lecture).
ISBN 9782323462

Quiroga, Cecilia Medina
Battle of Human Rights : Gross, Systematic Violations and the Inter-American System. – Dordrecht : Kluwer, 1988.
390p.
ISBN 9024736870 Hbk £170.00

Quotable lawyer / Frost. – London : Facts On File, 1986.
ISBN 0816011842 Hbk £17.95

R & D and the EEC competition rules : Regulation 418/85 / Valentine Korah. – Oxford : ESC Publishing, 1986.
xxi,114p. – (European competition law monographs).
Bibliography: p.xxi.
ISBN 0906214459

Raad, K. van
Model Income Tax Treaties. – Dordrecht : Kluwer.
ISBN 9065441484 Pbk £30.00
—Nondiscrimination in International Tax Law. – Dordrecht : Kluwer, 1986.
304p.
ISBN 9065442669 Hbk Gld135.00

Raap, Bonne K →Dutch business law : legal, accounting, and tax aspects of business in the Netherlands.

Raay, J. L. Janssen van →Workers' participation in the European Community : the fifth directive.

Rabie, Andre
Bibliography of South African criminal law : general principles / by Andre Rabie. – Cape Town : Juta, 1987.
viii,91p.
ISBN 0702118524

Rabie, M. A.
Punishment : an introduction to principles / M.A. Rabie, S.A. Strauss. – 3rd ed. – Johannesburg : Lex Patria, 1981.
365p.
Previous ed.: 1979. First published 1977 as: Theories of punishment. Bibliographies: p.333-348. - Includes index.
ISBN 0628018495

Rabiu, S. A.
Nigerian personal taxation : Law and practice with selected tax cases / S.A. Rabiu. – Ikeja, Nigeria : John West, 1986.
xiv,431p.
ISBN 978163040X

Raboy, David G →Value-added tax : orthodoxy and new thinking.

Race and council housing in Hackney / report of a formal investigation conducted by the Commission for Racial Equality into the allocation of housing in the London Borough of Hackney. – London : The Commission, 1984.
145p; 30cm.
ISBN 0907920411 Pbk

Race and the law in South Africa : a volume of essays by members of the School of Law, Howard College, University of Natal, Durban, to commemorate the sixtieth anniversary of the Durban School / edited by A. J. Rycroft ... et al. – Cape Town : Juta, 1987.
xx,258p.
Includes bibliographical references and index.
ISBN 0702119105

Race and the police / Eric Edwards. – London : G.L.C., 1983.
21p. – (Research documents guide).
ISBN 071681367X

Race Problems in ESCAP. – Canberra : Australian Institute of Criminology.
free

Race Relations Act 1976 : time for a change? / Commission for Racial Equality. – London : C.R.E., 1983.
43p; 30cm.
ISBN 0907920306

Race relations in prisons / Elaine Player. – Oxford : Clarendon Press, 1989.
200.
Based on a detailed research project undertaken at the request of the Home Office. Examines three institutions and their staff and inmates, and relates their experiences in detail. Demonstrates difficulties arising from trying to isolate race problems, and identifies problems in trying to enforce policies to eradicate discriminating behaviour.
ISBN 0198256175 Hbk £20

Racek, Vaclav →Human Rights and Disarmament.

Racial discrimination. – Ross Anderson, 1984.
ISBN 0863600042 Pbk £2.95

Racial Discrimination / Redman. – Shaw & Sons, 1977.
ISBN 0721907709 Pbk £7.50

Racism and equal opportunity policy in the 1980's / Solomos. – Cambridge : Cambridge University Press, 1987.
ISBN 0521330130 Hbk £25.00

Racism awareness training for the police : report of a pilot study for the Home Office / Peter Southgate. – London : Home Office, 1984.
v,17p.
Bibliography: p.17.
ISBN 0862521726

Radcliffe, Francis Reynolds Yonge
Cases Illustrating the Principles of the Laws of Torts / John Charles Miles. – Repr. of 1904 ed. – Aalen Wuertt : Scientia.
xx, 628p.
Hbk £150.00

Radcliffe, Geoffrey Reynolds Yonge
Student's Property Statutes. – Repr. of 1927 ed. – Aalen Wuertt : Scientia.
xv, 244p.
Hbk £70.00

Rader →Blueprint for Judicial Reform.

Radevic, Milorad M →Workers' management in Yugoslavia : recent developments and trends.

Radevsky, Tony
Service of documents. – 2nd. – London : Longman Professional (UK), 1989.
– (Practitioner series).
Contains a section dealing with service out of the jurisdiction. Second edition revised to take account of new rules governing county court summonses. Includes assessment of the impact of the Judgement Act 1982 (in force 1987), and all new forms and tables are covered.
ISBN 0851216099 Hbk £24.95

Radhaswamy, M.
Textbook of Banking : Law Practice and Theory of Banking / S.V. Vasudevan. – 3rd ed. – New Delhi : S. Chand and Company, 1984.
xv, 834p.
Hbk £42.00

Radio : choices and opportunities : a consultative document ... – London : H.M.S.O., 1987.
iv,44p.
ISBN 0101009224

Radio Documentary Handbook. – North Vancouver : International Self-Counsel Press, 1987.
ISBN 0889086532 Hbk £8.95

Radomski, Harry B. →Annotated Insurance Act of Ontario.

Radzinowicz, Leon
Cambridge Institute of Criminology : its background and scope : a report / by Sir Leon Radzinowicz : for the Home Office. – London : H.M.S.O., 1988.
viii,190p.
Describes the formation of the Institute, early problems, the scope and content of courses offered and how the work of the Institute has evolved over the years.
ISBN 0113408846
—History of English criminal law and its administration from 1750
Vol.5 : The emergence of penal policy : by Sir Leon Radzinowicz, Roger Hood / Roger Hood. – London : Stevens, 1986.
xv,1101p; 26cm.
Bibliography: p781-1039. - Includes index.
ISBN 0420462805 £75.00
—Illusions about crime & justice / Leon Radzinowicz. – London : Encounter, 1981.
p.31-39.
Extracted from: Encounter, Feb./March 1981.

Rae
Women's Economic Equality Act, 1983, Bill 108 : An Act to Provide for Affirmative Action and Equal Pay for Work of Equal Value. – Ontario : Ontario Government Publications Service, 1983.
11p.
Hbk £0.50

Rae, Maggie
First rights : a guide to legal rights for young people / Maggie Rae, Patricia Hewitt and Barry Hugill : illustrated by Corinne Pearlman. – 3rd ed. – London : National Council for Civil Liberties, 1985.
128p; 20cm.
Previous ed.: 1981. Includes bibliography and index.
ISBN 0946088152 Pbk £1.95

Raffe, David
Fourteen to Eighteen : The Changing Pattern of Schooling in Scotland. – Aberdeen : Aberdeen University Press, 1983.
192p.
ISBN 0080303749 Pbk £8.75

Raghavachariar, N.R.
Hindu law. – 8th ed. – Nagpur : Wadhura & Co, 1987.
Hbk £330.00

Raghavan, V.V.
Law of Crimes. – 3rd ed 1984. – Allahabad : Orient Law House, 1984.
Hbk £200.00

Rahim, Macbul
Study on the legislative framework, agreements and financial impositions affecting the mining industry in Pacific Commonwealth countries / by Macbul Rahim and Ruckia Hamisi. – 1. – London : Commonwealth Secretariat, 1981.
various pagings.
Cover title: The legislative framework, agreements and financial impositions affecting the mining industry in Pacific Commonwealth countries.
—Study on the legislative framework, agreements and financial impositions affecting the mining industry in African Commonwealth countries / prepared for the Commonwealth Fund for Technical Co-operation by Macbul Rahim and Juliet Broad under the supervision of Roland Brown and Mike Faber. – 1. – London : Commonwealth Secretariat, 1981.
various pagings.
Cover title: The legislative framework, agreements and financial impositions affecting the mining industry in African Commonwealth countries.

Rahman, Altafur
Guide to International Law Periodicals. – Ibadan : University Press.
Hbk

Rahman, Obaidur
Law of industrial relations in Pakistan : commentary on the Industrial Relations Ordinance 1969 / Obaidur Rahman. – Karachi : Asia Law House, 1984.
v,43p.
Bibliography: p.44.

Rail Unions in Britain and West Germany : A Study of their Structure and Policies / Wolfgang Steeck. – London : Policy Studies Institute, 1982.
109p.
Hbk £3.50

Railton →Inns of Court and Chancery.

Railway and Canal Traffic Cases : 1835-1950, 36 Vols. – Abingdon : Professional Books.
Hbk £750.00

Railway Property (Unlawful Possession) Act 1966. – Lucknow : Eastern Book Company, 1983.
471p.
Pbk £45.00

Railway Property (Unlawful Possession) Act. – Allahabad : Orient Law House, 1984.
Hbk £60.00

Raising money from trusts. – TUAR, 1981.
ISBN 0907164048 Pbk £2.95

Raistick, Donald
Statutes in Force : Index. – London : Sweet & Maxwell.
ISBN 0421317809 Hbk

Raistrick, Donald
Index to Legal Citations and Abbreviations. – London : Butterworths, 1981.
ISBN 0862050375 Hbk £30.25
—Index to statutes in force. – London : Sweet & Maxwell, 1988.
ISBN 0421317809 Hbk
—Law Commission Digest. – London : Butterworths.
ISBN 0903486512 Hbk £37.75
—Law Commission Reports, 13 Vols.
Nos. 1-120. – Repr. – Abingdon : Professional Books.
Hbk £680.00
—Lawyers' law books : a practical index to legal literature / by Donald Raistrick. – 2nd ed. – Milton, Oxon. : Professional Books, 1985.
xxxv,604p. – (Professional Books law reference library).
ISBN 0862050723 Hbk £32.50

Rajagopalachari, C.
Law of Partnership with Central and All State Rules, 2 Vols. – 2nd ed. – Allahabad : Law Publishers, 1983.
Hbk £66.00 set

Rajak, Harry
Company Liquidations. – London : CCH.
ISBN 0863251447 Hbk £48.00
ISBN 0863250831 Pbk £36.00
→ Sweet & Maxwell's companies statutes for students.

Rajan, Mannaraswamighala Sreeranga
Expanding jurisdiction of the United Nations / M.S. Rajan. – Bombay : Tripathi, 1981.
xii,252p.
ISBN 0379207273 £30.00

Rajput, R.S.
Panchayati Raj in India / D.R. Meghe. – New Delhi : Deep and Deep Publications, 1984.
286p.
Hbk £150.00

Raju → Medical Jurisprudence.

Raju, V.B.
Indian Penal Code, 1860, 2 Vols. – 4th ed. – Lucknow : Eastern Book Company.
Hbk £220.00

Rakesh
Criminal Major Acts (Pocket Ed.) / Surya Rao,. – Allahabad : Law Book Company, 1987.
Hbk £45.00
—Law of Kidnapping and Sexual Offences / Singh. – Allahabad : Law Book Company, 1988.
500p.
Hbk £180.00

Rakusen, Michael L.
Costs in Matrimonial Causes. – London : Butterworths, 1984.
This book gives practitioners a practical discussion of the control of costs in matrimonial causes in the United Kingdom. This work provides guidance to the lawyer seeking to avoid costs out of proportion to the settlement in the case.
ISBN 0406255202 Pbk
—Distribution of matrimonial assets on divorce / Michael L. Rakusen, D. Peter Hunt. – 2nd ed. – London : Butterworths, 1982.
xxii,375p.
Latest supplement held: 1986.
ISBN 0406351015 Hbk £46.00
ISBN 0406351023 Pbk £12.00

Ralph, Lady
Magistrate as Chairman / Geoffrey Norman. – London : Butterworths, 1987.
ISBN 0406104697 Pbk

Ralph, N.
Case for advice centres / N. Ralph. – Sheffield : Sheffield Advice Centres Group, 1985.
34p.

Ralphs
Magistrate as Chairman / Norman. – London : Butterworths, 1987.
ISBN 0406104697 Pbk £8.95

Ramachandran, V.G.
Administrative Law : Origin, Development Process, Power, Procedure, Justice and Tribunals. – 2nd ed. – Lucknow : Eastern Book Company, 1984.
1,100p.
Hbk £200.00
—Contempt of Court / V.R. Gopalan. – 5th ed. – Lucknow : Eastern Book Company, 1983.
1,146p.
Hbk £140.00
—Fundamental Rights and Constitutional Remedies. – 2nd ed. – Lucknow : Eastern Book Company, 1982.
2,452p.
Hbk £150.00
—Law of Agency. – Lucknow : Eastern Book Company, 1985.
784p.
Hbk £175.00
—Law of Contract in India, 3 Vols. – 2nd ed. – Lucknow : Eastern Book Company, 1983-1985.
Hbk £150.00 ea.
—Law of Land Acquisition and Compensation, 2 Vols. – 7th ed. – Lucknow : Eastern Book Company, 1986.
2,144p.
Hbk £400.00
—Law of Limitation, 3 Vols. – Lucknow : Eastern Book Company, 1984.
Hbk £450.00
—Law of Writs. – 3rd ed. – Lucknow : Eastern Book Company, 1983.
1,070p.
Hbk £155.00

Ramage, James → Housing Associations Act 1985.

Ramage, R.W.
Companies Acts : Table A 1856-1985. – 2nd ed. – London : Butterworths, 1985.
ISBN 0406351244 Hbk £25.00
→ Kelly's Draftsman.

Ramaiya, A.
Guide to Monopolies and Restrictive Trade Practices Act. – 2nd ed. – Nagpur : Wadhura & Co, 1982.
Hbk £145.00
—Sale of Goods Act. – 3rd ed. – Allahabad : Law Book Company, 1985.
Hbk £200.00

Ramakrishna
Law of Bails. – 5th ed. – Allahabad : Law Book Company, 1986.
750p.
Hbk £180.00

Ramcharan, B. G.
Concept and present status of the international protection of human rights : forty years after the universal declaration. – Dordrecht : Nijhoff (Martinus), 1989.
624. – (International Studies in Human Rights 13).
In commemoration of the fortieth anniversary of the Universal Declaration of Human Rights. Explores how the United Nations has been able to establish and operate instruments and procedures of protection, to place a shield around groups in jeopardy. Deals with the concept of protection in existing law and practice, and practice notes from the author's files are appended to the chapters.
ISBN 9024737591 Hbk Gld295.00
—Humanitarian good offices in international law : the good offices of the United Nations Secretary General in the field of human rights : the 1981 Reid Lectures delivered at Acadia University, Wolfville, Nova Scotia, Canada / B.G. Ramcharan. – The Hague : Nijhoff, 1983.
xii,220p; 25cm.
Bibliography: p217-218. - Includes index.
ISBN 9024728053 Hbk £95.00
→ International law and fact - finding in the field of human rights.
→ Right to life in international law.

Ramm, Thilo → International labour law reports, Volume 7.

Ramsay, I.
Consumer Protection : Text and Materials. – Weidenfeld & Nicolson.
ISBN 0297794981 Hbk £25.00
ISBN 029779499X Pbk £16.95

Ramsay, Iain
Debtors and Creditors. – London : Butterworths, 1986.
ISBN 0862051010 Hbk £26.95

Ramsay, Malcolm
City-centre crime : the scope for situational prevention / Malcolm Ramsay. – London : Home Office, 1982.
v,50p.
Bibliography: p.42.
ISBN 0862520665
—Effectiveness of the Forensic Science Service / by Malcolm Ramsay. – London : H.M.S.O., 1987.
v,93p; 25cm.
Examines the extent to which the work of the FSS assists the police and courts in solving crimes.
ISBN 0113408420

Ramsey, A.
Perks from shares. – 2nd ed. – London : Kogan Page, 1985.
ISBN 0850389461 Hbk £8.95
ISBN 085038947X Pbk £4.95

Rana, I.S.
Law of Obscenity : a Comparative Study. – Delhi : Mittal Publications, 1988.
Hbk £300.00

Randall, F.
British Government and Politics. – 3rd ed. – Plymouth : Macdonald & Evans, 1984.
ISBN 0712124071 Pbk £3.95
—British Government and Politics. – 3rd ed. – Plymouth : Macdonald & Evans, 1984.
xi, 288p. – (M and E Handbook Ser.).
ISBN 0712102922 Hbk £3.95

Randall, G.
Housing rights guide. – 2nd ed. – Turnaround Press, 1987.
ISBN 0948854145 Pbk £4.95

Randell, G. H.
South African Attorneys handbook / Randell and Bax. – 3rd ed. – Durban : Butterworths, 1983.
xxv,345p.
Bibliography: p.xx - Includes index. Addendum (Appendix 9) as loose insert.
ISBN 0409050113

Rani, Bilimoria
Female Criminality. – Lucknow : Eastern Book Company, 1985.
Hbk

Ranken, M. B. F. → Greenwich Forum IX : Britain and the sea : future dependence - future opportunities : conference papers delivered 14-16 September, 1983.

Rankin, Harry
Rankin's Law : Recollections of a Radical. – Vancouver : November House.
Hbk £7.95

Ranking, Devey F
Business Law for Accountants / Ernest E Spicer. – 15th ed. – London : Butterworths.
ISBN 0406678308 Pbk £15.95
—Company Law / Ernest E Spicer. – 13th ed. – London : Butterworths, 1987.
ISBN 0406678901 Pbk £14.95
—Executorship Law and Accounts / Ernest E Spicer. – 23rd ed. – London : Butterworths, 1987.
ISBN 0406679010 Hbk £45.00
—Ranking, Spicer and Pegler's Mercantile Law / Ernest E. Spicer. – 15th ed. – London : Butterworths.
ISBN 0406361401 Hbk

Ranking, Spicer and Pegler's Mercantile Law / Ernest E. Spicer. – 15th ed. – London : Butterworths.
ISBN 0406361401 Hbk

Rankin's Law : Recollections of a Radical. – Vancouver : November House.
Hbk £7.95

Ransom, Alan A. → Federal deceptive practices and misleading advertising law : judgements, materials and policy.
—Restrictive trade practices : judgments, materials and policy / Alan A. Ransom and Warren Pengilley. – Sydney : Legal Books Pty, 1985.
xlix,1193p.
Includes index.
ISBN 0949553158

Ranson, A. → Building and Engineering Claims.

Rantanlal
Indian Penal Code / Dhirajlal. – 26th ed. – Nagpur : Wadhura & Co, 1987.
Hbk £220.00

Rao, A.S. Ramanchandra
Administrative Tribunals Act, 1985, as Amended by the Adminstrative Tribunals (Amendment Act) 1986. – Bombay : Tripathi, 1987.
436p.
Hbk £120.00

Rao, C.A. Krishna
Personal Income Taxation in India. – Allahabad : Chugh Publications, 1987.
296p.
ISBN 8185076197 Hbk £175.00

Rao, C. Hameshwara
Law of Damages and Compensation, 3 Vols. – 5th ed. – Allahabad : Law Publishers, 1983.
Hbk £30.00

Rao, K. Venkoba
Law of Agency. – 2nd ed. – Allahabad : Law Book Company, 1986.
918p.
Hbk £200.00

Rao, Subba
Jurisprudence and Legal Theory. – 9th ed. 1975 repr. – Lucknow : Eastern Book Company, 1985.
Pbk £18.00

Rao,, Surya → Criminal Major Acts (Pocket Ed.).

Rao, V.N. Srinivasa
Administrative Law. – Allahabad : Orient Law House.
ISBN 0861310357 Pbk £35.00

Rao, Y.H.
Circumstantial and Presumptive Evidence. – Nagpur : Wadhura & Co.
455p.
£25.00
—Law of Pre-Trial Statements, Depositions and Police Diaries / Y.R. Rao. – 2nd ed. – Nagpur : Wadhura & Co, 1987.
763p.
Hbk £220.00

Rao, Y.R. → Law of Pre-Trial Statements, Depositions and Police Diaries.

Rape / the Law Reform Commission. – Dublin : The Commission, 1987.
ix,101p. – (Consultation paper).

Rape : allied offences / the Law Reform Commission. – Dublin : The Commission, 1988.
vii,38p. – (LRC).

Rape : the ultimate violation. – Pluto Press, 1986.
ISBN 0745300928 Pbk £4.95

Rape and allied offences : procedure and evidence / Law Reform Commission of Victoria. – Melbourne : The Commission, 1987.
iii,31p. – (Discussion paper).
Calatogued from cover. Includes bibliographical references.
ISBN 072414319X

Rape and allied offences : procedure and evidence / Law Reform Commission of Victoria. – Melbourne : The Commission, 1988.
v,62p. – (Report no 13).
ISBN 0724166351 Hbk

Rape and allied offences : substantive aspects / Law Reform Commission of Victoria. – Melbourne : The Commission, 1986.
iv,55p. – (Discussion paper).
Includes bibliographical references.

Rape and allied offences : victims with impaired mental functioning / Law Reform Commission of Victoria. – Melbourne : The Commission, 1987.
39p. – (Discussion paper).
Includes bibliographical references.
ISBN 0724167064

Rape and alllied offences : substantive aspects / Law Reform Commission of Victoria. – Melbourne : The Commission, 1987.
viii,40p. – (Report no 7).
Includes bibliographical references.

Rape and the legal process / by Jennifer Temkin. – London : Sweet & Maxwell, 1987.
220p; 23cm.
Includes index.
ISBN 0421338407 Hbk £16.00
ISBN 0421338504 Pbk £10.00

Rape controversy / Melissa Benn, Anna Coote, Tess Gill. – 3rd rev. and updated ed. – London : NCCL Rights for Women Unit, 1986.
32p; 20cm.
Re ed. - Previous ed. i.e. 2nd ed.: 1983. Bibliography: p32.
ISBN 0946088233 Pbk £1.50

Rape Law Reform. – Canberra : Australian Institute of Criminology.
Hbk £4.00

Rape law reform in South Australia : a study of the background to the reforms of 1975 and 1976 and of their subsequent impact / P.A. Sallmann and Duncan Chappell. – Adelaide : Adelaide Law Review Association, 1982.
x,110p.
ISBN 0908448023

Rape on trial / Zsuzsanna Adler. – London : Routledge & Kegan Paul, 1987.
viii,195p; 23cm.
Bibliography: p188-192. - Includes index.
ISBN 0710208049 £15.00

Rape study : a study directed by Mel Smith and Warren Young and undertaken by the Department of Justice and the Institute of Criminology / Mel Smith, Warren Young. – Wellington, N.Z : Dept. of Justice and Institute of Criminology at Victoria University of Wellington, 1983.
2 v.; 30 cm.
Includes bibliographical references. Contents: 1. A discussion of law and practice / by Warren Young – 2. Research reports.

Raphael, Arnold → New position of East Africa's Asians : problems of a displaced minority.

Rare books for law libraries / by Thomas H. Reynolds. – London : Glanville, 1983.
141p.

Rashid, Khalid
Muslim Law. – 2nd ed. 1980 repr. – Lucknow : Eastern Book Company, 1985.
376p.
Hbk £20.00

Rashid, Syed Khalid
Islamic Law in Nigeria. – Lagos : Islamic Publications Bureau, 1988.
ISBN 9782470376 Hbk £25.00

Rashkis, Morton W.
Income Tax and Family Law Handbook, 1 Vol. / Mary Lou Benotto. – Butterworths.
ISBN 0409806471 Llf £100.00
—Income tax and family law handbook / Mary Lou Benotto. – 1 vol. – Scarborough, Ontario : Butterworths (Canada).
Includes coverage of alimony and maintenance, attribution, child care expenses, child tax credit, common law spouses, dependants, family allowances, legal costs, pension benefits, principle residence, property division, registered retirement savings plan, and tax liability.
ISBN 0409806471 Loose leaf

Rasmussen, Hjalte
On law and policy in the European Court of Justice : a comparative study in judicial policymaking / by Hjalte Rasmussen. – Dordrecht : M. Nijhoff, 1986.
xxv, 555 p.; 25 cm.
Summary in Danish. Thesis (doctoral)–University of Copenhagen, 1985. Includes bibliographies and indexes.
ISBN 9024732174 Hbk £295.00

Rastafarians / E. E. Cashmore. – London : Minority Rights Group, 1984.
11p. – (Report).
Bibliography: p11.

Ratanlal
Code of Criminal Procedure / Dhirajlal. – 13th ed. – Nagpur : Wadhura & Co, 1987.
Hbk £220.00
—Law of Crimes, 2 Vols. / Dhirajlal. – 23rd ed. – New Delhi : Bharat Law House, 1987.
Hbk £280.00 ea.
—Law of Evidence / Dhirajlal. – 17th ed. – Nagpur : Wadhura & Co, 1987.
Hbk £180.00
—Law of Torts / Dhirajlal. – 21st ed. – Nagpur : Wadhura & Co, 1987.
£250.00

Ratcliffe, John
Introduction to town and country planning / John Ratcliffe. – 2nd ed. – London : Hutchinson, 1981.
506p; 22cm.
Previous ed.: 1974. Bibliography: p483-487. - Includes index.
ISBN 0091440203 Hbk £15.00
ISBN 0091440211 Pbk £6.95

Rate capping and the law. – 2nd ed. – London : Sweet & Maxwell, 1986.
ISBN 0902052063 Pbk £9.25

Rate Regulation : Legislative and Legal Aspects. – Hamilton : Society of Management Accountants of Canada.
Hbk £5.00

Rates : proposals for rate limitation and reform of the rating system / presented to Parliament by the Secretary of State for the Environment and the Secretary of State for Wales ... – London : H.M.S.O., 1983.
24p.
ISBN 0101900805

Ratford, William F. → Guide to the Insolvency Act 1985.
—Insolvency - Understanding the new law. – London : Financial Training, 1987.
ISBN 1851850627 Pbk £9.95
→ Tolley's employees' rights in receiverships and liquidations.

Rath, S.N.
Prevention of Food Adulteration and the Law. – New Delhi : Deep and Deep Publications, 1985.
278p.
Hbk £150.00

Rathfelder, M.
How to claim state benefits. – 2nd ed. – Northcote House, 1988.
ISBN 0746305311 Pbk £5.95

Rating and income tax. – 53 v. – London : Solicitors' Law Stationery Society, 1924.
Continued by: Rating and valuation reporter.

Rating and valuation reporter. – London : Solicitor's Law Stationery Department, 1961-.
Continues: Rating and income tax reporter. Published: London: Rating Publishers, 1965-.
ISBN 00486817

Rating appeals and the 1985 revaluation : proceedings of a Planning Exchange conference / edited by Clive Martlew. – Glasgow : Planning Exchange, 1985.
29 leaves. – (Occasional paper).

Rating Relief for Charitable Organisations : Shaway Guide No. 8. – London : Shaw & Sons, 1982.
ISBN 0721908764 Pbk £2.50

Rating valuation and practice guide. – London : Longman Professional, 1987.
ISBN 0851213200 Pbk £15.95

Ratio Juris : an international journal of jurisprudence and philosophy of law. – Oxford : Blackwell, 1988-.

Rational as reasonable : a treatise on legal justification / Aulis Aarnio. – Dordrecht : D. Reidel, 1986.
xix, 276p.
Includes index. Bibliography: p 261-271.
ISBN 9027722765 Hbk

Rationale of Judicial Evidence Specially Applied to English Practice, 5 Vols. / J. Bentham. – Repr. of 1827 ed. – Abingdon : Professional Books.
Hbk £145.00

Rationalising Rustic Regulation. – Turramura : Centre for Independent Studies.
96p.
ISBN 0949769029 Hbk £5.50

Rationalism and the modern state / by Patrick Nerhot. – Florence : European University Institute, 1983.
73p.
At head of title: European University Institute, Florence, Law Department.

Rationality and relativism / edited by Martin Hollis and Steven Lukes. – Oxford : Basil Blackwell, 1982.
viii,312p; 23cm.
Bibliography: p306-310. - Includes index.
ISBN 0631127739 Hbk £
ISBN 0631131264 Pbk

Rationality and ritual : the Windscale inquiry and nuclear decisions in Britain / Brian Wynne. – Faringdon : British Society for the History of Science, 1982.
x,222p. – (Monographs).
Bibliography: p178.
ISBN 0906450020

Rauch, Elmar
Protocol additional to the Geneva conventions for the protection of victims of international armed conflicts and the United Nations Convention on the Law of the Sea : repercussions on the law of naval warfare : report to the Committee for the Protection of Human Life in Armed Conflict of the International Society for Military Law and Law of War / by Elmar Rauch. – Berlin : Duncker & Humblot, 1984.
165p; 24cm.
ISBN 3428057031

Rauta, I. → Family property in Scotland : an enquiry carried out on behalf of the Scottish Law Commission by the Social Survey Division of the Office of Population Censuses and Surveys in 1979.

Rawlings, H. F.
Law and the electoral process / by H.F. Rawlings. – London : Sweet & Maxwell, 1988.
xix,252p; 23cm.
Bibliography: p243-248. - Includes index.
ISBN 0421376406 Pbk £13.50

Rawlings, Richard → Law and administration.

Rawlinson, Peter Anthony Grayson Rawlinson → Report of the Committee on the Constitution of the Senate.

Rawson, Donald W. → Trade Union Law in Australia : the Legal Status of Australian Trade Unions.
—Unions and Arbitration '81 - Papers and Discussion of the Armidale Industrial Law and Relations Seminar / D. Smith. – Sydney : Butterworths, 1981.
152p.
ISBN 040930929X Pbk

Ray, Basudev
M.R.T.P. Act. Annotated Edition 1985. – Calcutta : R. Cambray and Company.
Hbk £140.00

Ray, Edward E.
Partnership taxation / Nigel T. Davey. – 3rd ed. – London : Butterworth, 1987.
372p; 25cm.
Previous ed.: London : HFL, 1978. Includes index.
ISBN 0406678200 Pbk £25.00

Ray, Ralph P.
—Practical CTT planning / John E. Redman, Nigel Eastaway, Ralph P. Ray. – 2nd ed. – London : Butterworths, 1982.
xix,347p; 22cm. – (Butterworths tax management series).
Previous ed.: published as Practical capital transfer tax planning, 1977. Includes index.
ISBN 0406536155 Pbk
—Practical inheritance tax. – London : Butterworths, 1988.
ISBN 040600710 Pbk

Raybould → Teacher's Guide to Special Needs : A Positive Response to the 1981 Education Act.

Raybould, David
Comparative law of monopolies. – London : Graham & Trotman, 1989.
590.
ISBN 1853332763 Llf £172
Supplement service. – 1989.
120.
Examines the laws on restrictive agreements, monopolies and mergers in the jurisdictions of the US, the UK, the Federal Republic of Germany and the European Community. Standards applied in each jurisdiction are analysed and the similarities and differences are explored in detail.
ISBN 1853332682 £54

Rayden and Jackson's law and practice in divorce and family matters / Joseph Jackson, Margaret Booth, G. J. Maple, A. K. Biggs. – 15th ed. 2 vols. – London : Butterworths, 1988.
26cm.
This work in two volumes offers a complete encyclopedia for practitioners in the field of divorce in the United Kingdom. Relevant statutes, statutory instruments, Practice Directions, and material relating to tax and legal aid are included. Cumulative supplements are provided. Kept up to date by a looseleaf service.
ISBN 0406351317 Llf £285.00

Rayden, William
Rayden and Jackson's law and practice in divorce and family matters / Joseph Jackson, Margaret Booth, G. J. Maple, A. K. Biggs. – 15th ed. 2 vols. – London : Butterworths, 1988.
26cm.
This work in two volumes offers a complete encyclopedia for practitioners in the field of divorce in the United Kingdom. Relevant statutes, statutory instruments, Practice Directions, and material relating to tax and legal aid are included. Cumulative supplements are provided. Kept up to date by a looseleaf service.
ISBN 0406351317 Llf £285.00

Rayer, John → Personal Financial Planning Manual 1986-87.

Raymond, Brian
Introduction to criminal and civil litigation / Brian Raymond. – London : Oyez, 1981.
170p; 24cm.
ISBN 0851205569 Pbk

Rayner, M.
Asset Valuation. – London : Macmillan, 1988.
ISBN 033336515 Pbk £5.95

Rayner, W. B. → Anger and Honsberger: law of real property.

Raynmer
Falconbridge on Mortgages / McLaren. – 4th ed. – Aurora : Canada Law Book, 1977.
Hbk £27.50

Raynor, P.
Social work, justice and control. – Oxford : Blackwell, 1985.
ISBN 0631137327 Pbk £8.50

Raynsford, Nick →Guide to Housing Benefit.
—Guide to housing benefit / by Nick Raynsford, Peter McGurk. – Rev. ed. – London : SHAC, 1987.
xvi,137p.
Includes index.
ISBN 0948857161

Raz, Joseph
Morality of freedom / Joseph Raz. – Oxford : Clarendon, 1986.
432p; 22cm.
ISBN 0198247729 £30.00

RCMP and the Management of National Security / Andre Beliveau. – Montreal : Institute for Research on Public Policy.
xiii, 79p.
ISBN 0920380182 Hbk

Reaction : the New Combines Investigation Act. – Vancouver : Fraser Institute, 1986.
240p.
ISBN 0889750831 Pbk £14.95

Reactions to crime : the public, the police, courts, and prisons / edited by David P. Farrington and John Gunn. – Chichester : Wiley, 1985.
ix,189p; 24cm.
Includes bibliographies and index.
ISBN 047190497X £23.00

Read →National welfare benefits.
→ Private Members' Bills.

Readability and Legal Writing : a Bibliography. – Ottawa : Canadian Law Information Council, 1985.
15p.
ISBN 0920358756 Pbk £2.00

Reade, James Derek →Land registry practice in Northern Ireland.

Reader, M.
Tax Investigation Handbook. – London : Butterworths, 1981.
ISBN 0406254109 Pbk £25.00
—Taxation of Renumeration Packages. – London : Longman Professional.
ISBN 085121374X Pbk £95.00

Reader's Digest Legal Question and Answer Book. – Reader's Digest Association (Canada), 1989.
ISBN 0888501595 Hbk £35.00

Reading →International employment tax handbook.

Reading Narrative : Form, Ethics, Ideology. – London : Eurospan.
ISBN 0814204589 Hbk £26.50

Reading Nozick : essays on Anarchy, state and utopia / edited with an introduction by Jeffrey Paul. – Oxford : Basil Blackwell, 1982.
xi,418p; 22cm.
Originally published: Totowa : Rowman & Littlefield, 1981. Bibliography: p412-416.
ISBN 0631129774 Hbk £
ISBN 0631129782 Pbk

Reading the law : a critical introduction to legal method and techniques / Peter Goodrich. – Oxford : Basil Blackwell, 1986.
ix,229p; 23cm.
Introduction to the study of law. Illustrates how lawyers and students read legal texts.
ISBN 0631146296 Hbk £27.50
ISBN 0631146318 Pbk £9.95

Readings in economics of law and regulation / Cento G Veljanovski. – Oxford : Oxford University Press, 1984.
ISBN 0198761430 Pbk £12.95

Readings in Ohio Civil Procedure. – Agincourt : Carswell, 1987.
1216p.
This text analyzes and discusses common problems often not focused on in texts on this subject. The information is presented in a series of articles of varying length.
Hbk £85.00

Readings in the Economics of Contract Law. – Cambridge : Cambridge University Press.
ISBN 0521341205 Hbk £25.00

Readings in the economics of law and regulation / edited by A.I. Ogus and C.G. Veljanovski. – Oxford : Clarendon, 1984.
x,361p; 24cm.
Includes index.
ISBN 0198761422 Hbk £17.50
ISBN 0198761430 Pbk £10.95

Ready, Nigel P. →Greek Code of Private Maritime Law.

Real Estate : Advanced Update for Legal Assistants. – Vancouver : Continuing Legal Education Society of British Columbia, 1988.
272p.
ISBN 0865043906 Hbk £75.00

Real Estate Agency in Victoria / A.H. Goldberg. – 2nd ed. – Butterworths, 1975.
386p.
ISBN 0409420700 Hbk £74.00

Real estate agency law / William F. Foster. – Toronto : Carswell, 1984.
xliii,272p.
Includes bibliographical references and index.
ISBN 0459370502

Real Estate Agency Law in Queensland. – North Ryde : Law Book Co, 1985.
xxiv, 273p.
ISBN 0455202915 Pbk £32.50

Real Estate and Landlord and Tenant. – 2nd ed. – Agincourt : Carswell, 1986.
853p. – (Bar Admission Course Materials).
This work for the law student is a practical guide to the handling of most real estate transactions under Canadian law. The Planning Act of 1983 and the Land Registration Reform Act of 1984 are reviewed in the text.
ISBN 045939500 Hbk £39.60

Real Estate Development. – Vancouver : Continuing Legal Education Society of British Columbia, 1988.
242p.
ISBN 0865049769 Hbk £75.00

Real Estate Finance. – London : Butterworths.
ISBN 0406115001 Hbk £50.00

Real Estate in South Africa. – 2nd ed. – Cape Town : Legal and Financial Publishing Co.
Hbk £29.50

Real Estate Law. – 3rd ed. – Toronto : Edmond-Montgomery, 1986.
1,475p.
ISBN 0920722199 Hbk £99.50

Real Estate Law / R. C. B. Risk. – 3rd ed. – Aurora : Canada Law Book Co, 1986.
1300p. – (Text Books-Civil).
The third edition of this text has undergone significant changes to make it an even more useful and relevant sourcebook for Canadian Real Estate practitioners. This new edition includes up-to-date forms and materials used in routine real estate transactions reflecting the changes brought about by the Land Registration Reform Act.
Hbk £99.50

Real estate law locator 1988. – New York : Bowker, 1988.
ISBN 0835223515 Hbk £30.00

Real Estate Litigation 1987. – Vancouver : Continuing Legal Education Society of British Columbia, 1987.
132p.
ISBN 086504306X Hbk £65.00

Real Estate Practice in Ontario / Peter D. Quinn. – 3rd ed. – Toronto : Butterworths, 1982.
304p.
Explains judicial decisions and statutory changes since the second edition. Covers the Foreign Investment Review Act, Ontario New Home Warranties Act, Road Access Act, and the Family Law Reform Act, along with a reorganised chapter on the Planning Act. New chapters on real estate agents, and mortgage default proceeding.
ISBN 0409830046 Hbk £55.00

Real Property 1986. – Vancouver : Continuing Legal Education Society of British Columbia, 1986.
642p.
ISBN 0865042624 Hbk £75.00

Real Property : II. – Vancouver : British Columbia Continuing Legal Education Society, 1984.
494p.
ISBN 0865041105 Hbk £65.00

Real property and real people : principles of land law / K.J. Gray, P.D. Symes. – London : Butterworths, 1981.
xxxi,655p; 26cm.
Includes index.
ISBN 0406591105 Hbk
ISBN 0406591113 Pbk

Real Property Assessment 1988. – Vancouver : Continuing Legal Education Society of British Columbia, 1988.
126p.
ISBN 0865043825 Hbk £70.00

Real Property Assessment. – Vancouver : British Columbia Continuing Legal Education Society, 1982.
200p.
ISBN 0865040729 Hbk £45.00

Real Property Assessment : II. – Vancouver : British Columbia Continuing Legal Education Society, 1983.
69p.
ISBN 0865041210 Hbk £45.00

Real Property Assessment and Taxation. – Vancouver : Continuing Legal Education Society of British Columbia, 1985.
165p.
ISBN 086504192X Hbk £60.00

Real property financing in Singapore. – Singapore : Malayan Law Journal, 1988.
390.
Examines the law and practice of the security and documentation involved in real property financial transactions in Singapore. Covers the security and financing devices adopted by financiers to protect their interest, a list of financing institutions, both public and private, and the various financing schemes available. Provides a number of forms and precedents of loans documents.
ISBN 997170062X Hbk

Real Property Gains Tax Act 1976 (Act 169). – Kuala Lumpur : International Law Books Services.
Hbk £9.00

Real Property Gains Tax in Malaysia. – 2nd ed. – Singapore : Quins, 1982.
£36.00

Real Property in Germany / D. Weber. – 2nd ed. – Plymouth : Macdonald & Evans, 1983.
200p.
ISBN 0712154760 Hbk £18.00

Real property reports. – Agincourt, Ont. : Carswell, 1977-.
24cm.

Real Property Reports : With Consolidated and Cumulative Index
Vol. 1-47. – Agincourt : Carswell.
Hbk £1382.00

Real Property Statutes. – Professional Books.
ISBN 0862053382 Hbk £37.75

Realism in Law-Making : Essays on International Law in Honour of Willem Riphagen / Hugo Siblesz. – Dordrecht : Kluwer, 1986.
316p.
ISBN 9024733995 Hbk £165.00

Realization and Insolvency. – Vancouver : Continuing Legal Education Society of British Columbia, 1986.
229p.
ISBN 0865042691 Hbk £55.00

Ream, Betty
Guide to Employment Practices. – London : Industrial Society.
– (Managers Ser.).
Hbk £2.50

Rear →Chinese Labour Under British Rule.

Reardon, T.
Planning Your Pension. – London : Longman Professional.
ISBN 0851213715 Pbk £4.95

Reason and reality / Stig Jrgensen. – Aarhus : Aarhus University Press, 1986.
159p.
Includes bibliographical references.
ISBN 8772880023

Reason in Law : Proceedings of the Conference Held in Bologna, 12-15 December 1984
Vol. 1. – Milan : Giuffre, 1987.
viii, 384p.
Hbk £36,000.00
Vol. 3. – 1988.
viii, 440p.
Hbk £40,000.00

Reasonable arm of the law? : the law enforcement procedures of environmental health officers / Bridget M. Hutter. – Oxford : Clarendon Press, 1988.
Includes index. Bibliography.
ISBN 0198255942

Reay Tolfree, W.
Understanding personal and business finance. – 2nd ed. – Cambridge : Woodhead-Faulkner, 1986.
ISBN 0859413624 Pbk £5.25

Rebel advocate : a biography of Gerald Gardiner / by Muriel Box. – London : Gollancz, 1983.
242p,8p of plates; 24cm.
Bibliography: p236. - Includes index.
ISBN 0575032693 £10.95

Receivers. – Vancouver : Continuing Legal Education Society of British Columbia, 1985.
97p.
ISBN 0865042225 Hbk £55.00

Receivers and receiverships / David Milman and Jonathan Rushworth. – Bristol : Jordans, 1987.
xxi,82p; 21cm.
Includes index.
ISBN 0853081239 Pbk £8.50

Receivership manual / Martin Iredale, Christopher Hughes. – 3rd ed. – Croydon : Tolley, 1987.
xiv,178p.
Guide to receivership including recent Insolvency Acts and company law changes.
ISBN 0854592202 Hbk £21.95

Receiverships. – Agincourt : Carswell, 1985.
ISBN 0459374303 Hbk £38.75

Receiverships : Carswell's Canadian Legal Classic Series. – Agincourt : Carswell, 1985.
588p.
This work explains all aspects of the receivership process in Canada from the use of consultants in the decision to appoint a receiver through to the discharge. A table of cases and extensive precedents are included in the book.
Hbk £80.00

Receiving juvenile justice : adolescents and state care and control / Howard Parker, Maggie Casburn, David Turnbull. – Oxford : Basil Blackwell, 1981.
259p; 23cm.
Criticises official discretion, deviation and diversity in the selection and sentencing process.
ISBN 0631127275 Hbk £12.00
ISBN 0631127453 Pbk £5.50

Receiving stolen property / the Law Reform Commission. – Dublin : The Commission, 1987.
x,130p. – (LRC).

Recent and Prospective Changes in Company Law / Charles M. Allen-Jones. – London : Law Society, 1982.
– (Oxford Weekend Courses).
Hbk £2.00

Recent and Prospective Developments in Civil and Criminal Litigation. – London : Law Society, 1985.
32p. – (Nineteen Eighty-Five Crash Course Transcripts).
Hbk £2.05

Recent developments in administrative law / edited by Neil R. Finkelstein, Brian MacLeod Rogers. – Toronto : Carswell, 1987.
xl,354p.
' ... a collection of essays which were originally presented at programs sponsored by the Law Society of Upper Canada on 'Administrative law: recent developments and emerging trends' in Toronto and Ottawa in November 1986'. - Preface.
ISBN 0459304615

Recent Developments in Banking Series : Off Shore Finance 1984. – Monash University, Faculty of Law. – Clayton : Monash University Press, 1984.
ISBN 0867463511 Hbk £16.00

Recent Developments in Business and Litigation. – Vancouver : Continuing Legal Education Society of British Columbia, 1987.
278p.
ISBN 0865043493 Hbk £80.00
Competition and Merger. –
ac £25.00

Recent developments in EEC competition law : seminar documentation : Monday 8th December 1986, Cavendish Conference Centre, London W1 / Valentine Korah. – 1. – London : Legal Studies & Services, 1986.
various pagings.
Includes bibliographical references. Chairman: Valentine Korah.

Recent Developments in the Law Relating to Damages With Particular Reference to Professional Claims / Alexander Layton. – London : Law Society, 1981.
– (Oxford Weekend Courses).
Hbk £2.00

Recent extra-marital child legislation annotated : being also a cumulative supplement to the fourth edition of Spiro's Law of parent and child / Erwin Spiro. – Cape Town : Juta, 1988.
ix,20p.
Includes index.
ISBN 0702120510

Recent International Developments to Counter Tax Avoidance and Evasion. – International Fiscal Association. – Toronto : DeBoo, 1982.
– (IFA Seminars Ser.).
ISBN 0888201168 Hbk £35.00

Recent multilateral debt restructurings with official and bank creditors / by a Staff team headed by E. Brau...et al. – Washington, D.C. : International Monetary Fund, 1983.
vii,43p. – (Occasional paper).

Recent personal injury awards made in the Supreme Court of Judicature of Jamaica / compiled by Ursula Khan. – s.l. : s.n., 1981.
xxvii,200p.

Recent tax problems / edited by Jacqueline Dyson. – London : Stevens, 1985.
xiv,108p; 22cm.
Includes index.
ISBN 0420474102 Pbk £15.00

Recent trends in human rights / Lawasia Human Rights Standing Committee. – Sydney : Law Association for Asia and the Western Pacific, 1982.
viii,112p.

Recession, crime and punishment / Steven Box. – London : Macmillan Education, 1987.
240p; 25cm.
Includes index.
ISBN 0333438523 Hbk £20.00 :
ISBN 0333438531 Pbk £6.95

Reciprocal enforcement : a practical guide to magistrates' courts' jurisdiction & procedure in international domestic proceedings / Desmond A.G. James : with a foreword by Dewi E. Davies. – Chichester : Rose, 1984.
133p; 22cm.
Includes index.
ISBN 0859923320 £17.75

Recognition and the United Nationsby John Dugard. – Cambridge : Grotius, 1987.
xiv,192p.
An analysis of the impact on the law of recognition of recent developments in the practice of the United Nations on the admission of new members, and of the practical relevance of the modern concepts of peremptory norms of international law and jus cogens.
ISBN 0949009008

Recognition of commercial judgments and awards in the Commonwealth / K.W. Patchett. – London : Butterworths, 1984.
xlv,326p; 26cm.
Bibliography: pxxix. - Includes index.
ISBN 0406403201

Recognition of family judgments in the Commonwealth / J.D. McClean. – London : Butterworths, 1983.
xxxvii,370p; 26cm.
Includes index.
ISBN 040640321X Hbk £42.00

Recommendations for changes to the Human Rights Code of British Columbia / Human Rights Commission of British Columbia. – Victoria, B.C. : The Commission, 1981.
22p.

Recommendations from the Arusha Conference on African Refugee Problem : Recommendations de la Conference D'Arusha sur le Probleme des Refugies. – Stockholm : Almqvist & Wiksell, 1981.
46p.
ISBN 9171061843 Hbk £25.00

Recommendations of the Committee of Ministers being of particular interest to prison administrations. – Council of Europe. – Strasbourg : Council of Europe, 1981.
various pagings; 30cm.
Introduction by Directorate of Legal Affairs (Division of Crime Problems). At head of title: Legal Affairs.

Recommended Holdings for Law Libraries : The Law Librarian. – London : Sweet & Maxwell, 1983.
ISBN 0421317205 Pbk £2.50

Reconciliation and conciliation in the context of divorce / by a committee of the Order of Christian Unity. – 2nd ed. – London : Order of Christian Unity, 1983.
48p.
Includes bibliographies.

Reconstructing reality in the courtroom / W. Lance Bennett and Martha S. Feldman. – London : Tavistock Publications, 1981.
x, 203p.

Reconstructing the past : the role of psychologists in criminal trials / edited by Arne Trankell. – Deventer, The Netherlands : Kluwer, 1982.
398p.
'This book contains papers and panels from the first international conference on Witness Psychology...Stockholm...September 1981'.
ISBN 9065441123

Reconstructions, Hive-Downs and Management Buyouts. – London : Law Society, 1984.
28p.
Hbk £1.95

Recording and rental of audio and video copyright material : a consultative document / presented to Parliament by the Secretary of State for Trade and Industry. – London : H.M.S.O., 1985.
iii,14p.
ISBN 0101944500

Records of the Diplomatic Conference for the Conclusion of a Treaty on the International Recording of Scientific Discoveries. – Geneva : World Intellectual Property Organization.
216p.
Hbk £30.00

Records of the general eyre / David Crook. – London : H.M.S.O., 1982.
x, 271p.
ISBN 0114401233

Records of the Luxembourg Conference on the Community patent, 1975. – Luxembourg : Office for Official Publications of the European Communities, 1982.
334p.
ISBN 9282400891

Recourse to tax havens : use and abuse : proceedings of a seminar held in Paris during the 34th Congress of the International Fiscal Association... / organised by the International Fiscal Association. – Deventer : Kluwer on behalf of the IFA, 1981.
147p; 21cm. – (IFA congress seminar series).
Bibliography: p.141-148.
ISBN 9065440054

Recovery of money. – 7th. – London : Longman Professional (UK), 1989.
– (Practitioner series).
Guide to the law practice and procedure of debt collection from contract to enforcement. Coverage includes contract drafting and formation, preservation of assets pending proceedings, a consideration of the foreign element, mortgage repossession, computer support and office procedure. Takes account of Consumer Credit Act, Insolvency Act and Rules 1986, and Civil Jurisdiction and Judgements Act.
ISBN 0851215165 Hbk £26.50

Recovery of possession of heritable property / Scottish Law Commission. – Edinburgh : The Commission, 1984.
iii,122p. – (Consultative memorandum no 59).
Includes bibliographical references.

Recreation and the Law. – London : Sweet & Maxwell, 1984.
Hbk £15.50

Recreation and the law. – Spon (E & FN), 1984.
ISBN 0419121900 Hbk £18.50
ISBN 0419122001 Pbk £8.95

Recruiting volunteers / Hilary Jackson. – London : Home Office, 1985.
iv,50p.
Bibliography: p.49-50.
ISBN 0862521769

Recueil des cours
Volume 208 (1988-1). – Academie de Droit International de la Haye. – Dordrecht : Nijhoff (Martinus), 1988.
406.
Includes chapters on the concept and claims of geographically disadvantaged states at the third UN Law of the Sea Conference, geographically disadvantaged states of the Exclusive Economic Zone, and these states and the exploitation of the mineral resources of the sea-bed and ocean floor.
ISBN 0792300580 Hbk £57.50

Recurring Issues in Canadian Federalism / A. Wayne Mackay. – Toronto : University of Toronto Press, 1986.
232p.
ISBN 0802073042 Hbk £14.95

Redclift, Michael
Development and the environmental crisis : red or green alternatives? / Michael Redclift. – London : Methuen, 1984.
149p; 23cm.
Bibliography: p131-146. - Includes index.
ISBN 0416321305 Hbk £
ISBN 0416321402 Pbk
—Sustainable development : exploring the contradictions / Michael Redclift. – London : Methuen, 1987.
viii,200p; 22cm.
Includes index.
ISBN 0416902405 Hbk £20.00 :
ISBN 0416902502 Pbk £7.95

Reddin, George → Income tax.

Redefining the Supreme Courts' Role : A Theory of Managing the Federal Judicial Process / Sexton. – Yale University Press.
ISBN 0300037341 Pbk £8.95

Redfern, Alan
Law and practice of international commercial arbitration / by Alan Redfern, Martin Hunter : foreword by Sir Robert Jennings. – London : Sweet & Maxwell, 1986.
xliii,462p; 24cm.
Reviews the process of international commercial arbitration, from the drafting of the arbitration agreement to the enforcement of the arbitral tribunal's award. Describes the role of the main international arbitral institutions, and comments on institutional and international rules of arbitration.
ISBN 0421324902 £64.00

Redfern, Michael → Australian Tenancy Practice and Precedents.

Redgment, John
Introduction to the legal system of Zimbabwe / by John Redgment. – 2nd ed., rev. and enl. – Salisbury Rhodesia : Book Centre, 1981.
107p.
Bibliography: p.106-107.

Redgrave, Alexander
Health and safety in factories / Ian Fife. – 2nd ed. – London : Butterworths, 1982.
ISBN 0406353077 Hbk £52.00
—Redgrave's health and safety in factories / Ian Fife, E. Anthony Machin. – 2nd ed. – London : Butterworths, 1982.
lix,1932p; 18cm.
Previous ed.: i.e. new ed. 1976. Includes index. Includes the text of relevant legislation. Kept up to date by supplements.
ISBN 0406353077

Redgrave's health and safety in factories / Ian Fife, E. Anthony Machin. – 2nd ed. – London : Butterworths, 1982.
lix,1932p; 18cm.
Previous ed.: i.e. new ed. 1976. Includes index. Includes the text of relevant legislation. Kept up to date by supplements.
ISBN 0406353077

Redman → Racial Discrimination.

Redman, John E. → Practical CTT planning.

Redman, Joseph Haworth → Hill and Redman's law of landlord and tenant.
→ Landlord and Tenant, 2 Vols.
→ Landlord and Tenants.

Redmond
Introduction to Business Law / Dawson. – Plymouth : Macdonald & Evans.
ISBN 0071211173 Pbk £6.95

Redmond, Mary
Dismissal law in the Republic of Ireland / by Mary Redmond. – Dublin : Incorporated Law Society of Ireland, 1982.
xliii, 296 p.; 22 cm.
Includes indexes. Bibliography: p. 274-284.
ISBN 0902027220 Pbk
—Labour law and industrial relations in Ireland / Mary Redmond. – Dublin : Bridgefoot Press, 1984.
188p.
Includes index. Cover title: Redmonds guide to Irish labour law.

Redmond, Peter William Dawson
Bankruptcy Law. – 8th ed. – Plymouth : Macdonald & Evans, 1981.
ISBN 0712102647 Pbk £3.95
—General Principles of English Law. – 5th ed. – Plymouth : Macdonald & Evans, 1988.
ISBN 0712107479 Pbk £6.95
—Mercantile Law. – 5th ed. Repr. of 1979 ed. – Plymouth : Macdonald & Evans, 1982.
320p. – (M and E Handbook Ser.).
ISBN 071211288X Hbk £3.50
—Partnership Law / Ernest Miles Taylor. – 11th ed. Repr. of 1977 ed. – Plymouth : Macdonald & Evans, 1981.
160p. – (M and E Handbook Ser.).
ISBN 0712116745 Hbk £3.95

Reducing Labor Turnover in Financial Institutions / Creery. – Quorum Press.
ISBN 0899302963 Hbk £32.95

Reducing the prison population : an exploratory study in Hampshire / David Smith ... et al. – London : Home Office, 1984.
v,65p. – (Research and Planning Unit Paper).
Bibliography: p.56-58.
ISBN 0862521246

Reducing Your Personal Tax Bill 1988-1989. – London : Deloitte Haskins & Sells.
ISBN 0863491340 Pbk £4.95

Redundancy law and practice / Colin Bourn. – London : Butterworths, 1983.
xxv,320p; 22cm.
Includes index.
ISBN 0406258147 Pbk

Reed →Legal Environment of Business.
→ Legally yours - law and the individual.

Reed, Peter B. →Marine reinsurance.

Reeday, T.
Law Relating to Banking. – 5th ed. – London : Butterworths, 1985.
ISBN 0406647682 Hbk £19.50
ISBN 0406647690 Pbk £16.50
—Legal Decisions Affecting Bankers Vols. 1-11 / P E Smart. – Professional Books.
ISBN 0862052459 Hbk £395.00

Reekie, Peter D.
Family law and practice / Peter D. Reekie and Richard Tuddenham. – London : Sweet & Maxwell, 1988.
xxxv,415p; 22cm.
Sections cover divorce and other decrees; financial provision (including property adjustment); children; and family violence. Also contains a chapter on legal aid and legal advice and assistance, and discusses the courts and conciliation.
ISBN 0421360003 Pbk £13.50

Re-enacted statutes of Manitoba 1987 : being a consolidation and revision of certain acts in the Continuing Consolidation of the Statutes of Manitoba ... / Lois readoptees du Manitoba de 1987. – Winnipeg : Queen's Printer for the Province of Manitoba, 1987.
looseleaf.
Parallel text in English and French.

Rees, A. S.
Policing and Private Security. – Canberra : Australian Institute of Criminology.
Hbk £4.00

Rees, John
John Stuart Mill's On liberty / John C. Rees : constructed from published and unpublished sources by G.L. Williams. – Oxford : Clarendon, 1985.
xi,210p; 22cm.
Bibliography: p204-207. - Includes index.
ISBN 0198247664 £19.50

Rees, Judith →International oil industry : an interdisciplinary perspective.

Rees-Potter, Lorna K. →Applications of computer technology to law (1979-1982) : a selected bibliography.
—Communicating Court Information : Towards a Canadian Records Handling System. – Ottawa : Canadian Law Information Council, 1984.
103p.
ISBN 0920358640 Pbk £15.00
—Patterns of authority : an analysis of Canadian citation patterns / by Lorna K. Rees-Potter. – Ontario : Canadian Law Information Council, 1982.
vii,61p. – (Working paper).
ISBN 092035825X

Rees, W.
Valuation : principles into practice. – 2nd ed. – London : Estates Gazette, 1984.
ISBN 0728201070 Pbk £22.00

Reese →Building Law Reports Vols 1-40.

Re-establishment of Free Trade Unionism : a bill to repeal the Employment, Employment and Training, Trade Union and Wages Acts 1980 to 1988, to re-enact previous legislation repealed by those Acts, and for purposes connected therewith / presented by Tony Benn ... et al. – London : HMSO, 1988.
2p. – (H.C. Bill 1987-88).
ISBN 0103199888

Reeve, Andrew
Property / Andrew Reeve. – London : Macmillan, 1986.
208p; 22cm.
Includes bibliography.
ISBN 0333367960 Hbk £20.00 :
ISBN 0333367979 Pbk £6.95

Reeves' history of the English law, from the time of the Romans to the end of the reign of Elizabeth / W. F. Finlason. – New ed. 3 v. – London : Reeves & Turner, 1869.
Includes index. .

Reeves, John
Reeves' history of the English law, from the time of the Romans to the end of the reign of Elizabeth / W. F. Finlason. – New ed. 3 v. – London : Reeves & Turner, 1869.
Includes index. .

Reeves, Peter
Are two legal professions necessary? / Peter Reeves. – London : Waterlow, 1986.
xiii,175p; 21cm.
Bibliography: p145-171. - Includes index.
ISBN 0080392180 Pbk £11.95

Reference book of marine insurance clauses. – 58th ed. – London : Witherby & Co, 1986.
ISBN 0948691182 Pbk £18.00

Reference Guide to Mining Legislation in Canada. – 2nd ed. – Calgary : Canadian Institute of Resources Law, 1988.
120p.
ISBN 0919269257 Hbk £30.00

Reference on admiralty jurisdiction
Research paper no. 1 : Australian admiralty act : the ambit of admiralty jurisdiction / Australian Law Reform Commission. – Sydney : The Commission, 1984.
xvii,296p.
Bibliography: p.291-296.
Research paper no. 2 : Admiralty jurisdiction in Australia : the courts exercising original and appellate jurisdiction / Australian Law Reform Commission. – 1984.
v,77p.
Bibliography: p.75-77.
Research paper no.3 : Draft legislation : admiralty procedure and rules / Australian Law Reform Commission. – 1985.
iv,136p.
Includes bibliographical references.
Research paper no. 5 : Prize law, jurisdiction and procedure / Australian Law Reform Commission. – 1984.
iii,70 leaves.
Bibliography: p.68-70.

Reference on contempt of courts, tribunals and commissions
Research paper no.1 : Contempt in relation to commissions and tribunals / Australian Law Reform Commission. – Sydney : The Commission, 1986.
vii,114p.
Bibliography: p.112-114.
Research paper no. 2 : Improper behaviour in court / Australian Law Reform Commission. – 1984.
viii,119p.
Includes bibliographical references.
Research paper 3 : Improper pressure on parties to court proceedings / Australian Law Reform Commission. – 1986.
iv,49p.
Includes bibliographical references.
Research paper no.4 : Prejudicial publicity and the courts / Australian Law Reform Commission. – 1986.
v,134p.
Bibliography: p.130-134.
Research paper no. 6A : Contempt and family law / Australian Law Reform Commission. – 1985.
various pagings.

Reference on service and execution of process
Research paper no. 2 : Commencing process / Australian Law Reform Commission. – Sydney : The Commission, 1984.
v,175p.
Bibliography: p.175.
Research paper no. 3 : Tribunals / Australian Law Reform Commission. – 1984.
vii,87p.
Bibliography: p.86-87.
Research paper no. 4 : Enforcement of judgments / Australian Law Reform Commission. – 1984.
iv,89p.
Bibliography: p.89.
Research paper no. 5 : Service of other process / Australian Law Reform Commision. – 1984.
iv,64p.
Bibliography: p.64.
Reserach paper no. 7 : Discussion of reference : Draft Interstate Procedure Bill and regulations / Australian Law Reform Commission. – 1986.
iii,80p.
Includes text of draft bill.

Reference on service and execution of warrants and writs of attachment
Research paper no. 6 : Interstate execution of warrants and writs of attachment / Australian Law Reform Commission. – Sydney : The Commission, 1984.
v,109,6p.
Bibliography: p.109.

Referendum : The End of an Era. – Cardiff : University of Wales, 1981.
14p.
ISBN 0708308082 Pbk £0.95

Reflections of a Country Magistrate. – Saracen.
ISBN 0951394606 Hbk £10.00

Reflections on International Arbitration and Litigation in the International Court of Justice. – Dordrecht : Kluwer, 1988.
24p.
ISBN 9065443517 Hbk £30.50

Reflections on the Royal Commission on Legal Services : a public lecture / delivered by Lord Benson. – London : Inns of Court School of Law, 1981.
10p; 23cm.

Reform and punishment : essays on criminal sentencing / Michael Tonry and Franklin E. Zimring, editors. – Chicago : University of Chicago Press, 1983.
viii,210p; 24cm.
Includes bibliographies and index.
ISBN 0226808165

Reform Issues : Audiovisual Copying. – Milsons Point : Australian Copyright Council.
Hbk £6.50

Reform of civil procedural law and other procedure / Sir Jack I.H. Jacob. – London : Sweet & Maxwell, 1982.
xii,359p; 26cm.
ISBN 0421301104 £18.50

Reform of Local Government Finafnce in Britain / Paddison. – Deddington : Routledge.
ISBN 0415005302 Pbk £27.50

Reform of mental health legislation / Department of Health and Social Security ... et al. – London : H.M.S.O., 1981.
26p; 25cm.
ISBN 0101840500 Pbk £2.65

Reform of Muslim Personal Law. – New Delhi : Deep and Deep Publications, 1988.
172p.
Hbk £125.00

Reform of personal taxation : presented to Parliament by the Chancellor of the Exchequer by Command of her Majesty March 1986. – London : H.M.S.O., 1986.
82p; 30cm.
Green paper. Proposals for reform of personal taxation. Introduction of new personal tax allowances to all persons to replace married man's allowance. Closer integration between tax and benefits system.
ISBN 0101975600 Pbk £8.00

Reform of revenue law : memorandum / by the Law Society. – London : Law Society, 1983.
38p.

Reform of social security
v.1 / presented to Parliament by the Secretary of State for Social Services. – London : HMSO, 1985.
48p.
ISBN 0101951701
v.2 : Programme for change / presented to Parliament by the Secretary of State for Social Services. – 1985.
iii,62p.
ISBN 0101951809 Hbk
v.3 : Background papers / presented to Parliament by the Secretary of State for Social Services. – 1985.
138p.
ISBN 0101951906 Hbk
Technical annex. – 1985.
51p.
Technical annex to White Paper Cmnd 9691. Contents: 1. Illustrations of individuals' future pensions expectations. 2. Illustrative effects of reforming the structure of income-related benefits.
ISBN 0113210183 Hbk

Reform of social security / A.W.Dilnot, J.A.Kay and C.N. Morris. – Oxford : Clarendon, 1984.
viii,166; 23cm.
Bibliography: p158-160. - Includes index.
ISBN 0198772262 Pbk £10.00
ISBN 0198772254 £3.95

Reform of social security : programme for action / presented to Parliament by the Secretary of State for Social Services. – London : H.M.S.O, 1985.
53p.
Includes bibliographical references.
ISBN 0101969104

Reform of the Criminal Law. – Agincourt : Carswell.
130p.
This work contains papers that had been delivered at the July 1987 conference on criminal law reform held in London, England. Discussions include white collar crime, sentencing reform and the defenses.
Hbk

Reform of the law of sexual offences / J.C. Smith : with comments by Antony Grey. – Leeds : University of Leeds, Centre for Social Work and Applied Social Studies, 1981.
ii,17p. – (Occasional paper).

Reform of the law relating to copyright, designs and performers' protection : a consultative document / presented to Parliament by the Secretary of State for Trade... – London : H.M.S.O., 1981.
25cm.
ISBN 0101830203

Reform of the ultra vires rule : a consultative document / Department of Trade and Industry. – London : H.M.S.O., 1986.
4,81p.
'Report by Dr. D.D. Prentice' - Introduction.

Reform the law : essays on the renewal of the Australian legal system / Michael Kirby. – Melbourne, Oxford : Oxford University Press, 1983.
xii,284p; 21cm.
ISBN 0195543955 Pbk £12.99
ISBN 0195543955 Hbk £27.50

Reforming the International Economic Order : German Legal Comments / Ernst-Ulrich Petersmann. – Berlin : Duncker and Humblot, 1987.
264p.
ISBN 3428062191 Hbk £98.00

Reforms of local and regional authorities in Europe : theory, practice and critical appraisal : colloquy organised by the Council of Europe, Linz, 5-6 November 1981. – Strasbourg : Council of Europe, 1983.
220p.
Bibliography: p.181-182.
ISBN 9287101914

Reforms to Pre-Empt Change : Land Legislation in Karnataka. – New Delhi : Concept Publishing Company, 1983.
x, 122p.
Hbk £70.00

Refreshing Pauses : Coca-Cola and Human Rights in Guatemala. – Praeger.
ISBN 0275927644 Hbk £29.50

Refugee determination in Canada : proposals for a new system : a report to the Honourable Flora MacDonald, Minister of Employment and Immigration / by W. Gunther Plaut. – Ottawa : Minister of Supply and Services Canada, 1985.
221,286p.
With French t.p.: Reconnaissance au Canada du statut de refugie. Pages numbered in opposite directions. English and French text.
ISBN 0662538234

Refugee dilemma / by Frances D'Souza and Jeff Crisp : additional research by Stevanne Hill : with a foreword by Prince Sadruddin Aga Khan. – New ed. – London : Minority Rights Group, 1985.
20p. – (Report).
Previous ed.: 1981. Bibliography: p.19.
ISBN 0946690235

Refugee in international law / Guy S. Goodwin-Gill. – Oxford Oxfordshire : Clarendon Press, 1983.
xxvii,318p.
Includes index. Bibliography: p306-311.
ISBN 0198253729

Refugee Law in the Sudan. – Uppsala : Scandinavian Institute of African Studies, 1982.
56p.
ISBN 9171062092 Pbk £20.00

Regalado, Florenz D.
Remedial Law Compendium. – Manila : National Book Store.
Hbk

Rege, M.P.
Concepts of Justice and Equality in the Indian Tradition. – Allahabad : Orient Law House, 1985.
28p.
ISBN 0861316029 Hbk £15.00

Regina Native Legal Counsel Project : a Legal Service for Native Organizations, Groups, and Societies in the City of Regina. – rev. ed. – Regina : Prairie Justice Research, 1983.
ISBN 0773100482 Hbk £10.00

Regional and local affairs : news. – Strasbourg : Council of Europe, 1982-.
Supersedes: Information bulletin: municipal and regional matters.

Regional compendium of fisheries legislation (Indian Ocean Region) / prepared by Legislation Branch, FAO Legal Office, with the assistance of the International Centre for Ocean Development. – Provisional ed. 2. – Rome : Food and Agriculture Organization of the United Nations, 1986.
– (Legislative study).

Regional compendium of fisheries legislation West Africa (CECAF region) / prepared under the direction of the Legislation Branch, Legal Office Compendium regional de la legislation sur la peche l'Afrique occidentale (region du COPACE) / prepare sous la direction du Service de legislation, Bureau juridique. – Rome : Food and Agriculture Organization of the United Nations, 1983.
v, 525 p.; 30 cm. – (Legislative study).
At head of title: Norway Funds-in-trust, FI: GCP/INT/400/NOR. English and French. Includes bibliographical references.
ISBN 9250013078 Pbk

Regional compendium of fisheries legislation (Western Pacific region) / prepared by Legislation Branch, Legal office, FAO, in cooperation with the South Pacific Forum Fisheries Agency. – 2 v. – Rome : F.A.O., 1984. – (Legislative study).
ISBN 925102202X

Regional development agencies and peripheral regions : report / prepared under the guidance of the Committee of Experts on Social and Economic Activities of the Steering Committee for Regional and Municipal Matters by Jacques Robert. – Strasbourg : Council of Europe, 1985.
23p.

Regional Developments in Corrections. – Canberra : Australian Institute of Criminology.
Hbk £12.50

Regional Forum on the Judiciary and the Intellectual Property system / organized jointly by the World Intellectual Property Organization (WIPO) and the judges of the Superior Courts of Pakistan in association with the Law Association for Asia and the Western Pacific (LAWASIA) and with the assistance of the United Nations Development Programme, Islamabad, Pakistan, October 5 to 9, 1986. – Geneva : WIPO, 1987.
303p.
At head of t.p.: World Intellectual Property Organization; Supreme Court of Pakistan.

Regional government in England / edited by Brian W. Hogwood, Michael Keating. – Oxford : Clarendon Press, 1982.
x,277p; 23cm.
Includes index.
ISBN 0198274343 £18.50

Regional Levies Handbook. – Durban : Professional Publisher.
Hbk £12.50

Regional Seminar on Licensing and Other Technology Transfer Arrangements. – Geneva : World Intellectual Property Organization, 1987.
263p.
Hbk £30.00

Regional Symposium on Intellectual Property Law Teaching and Research in Asia and the Pacific. – Geneva : World Intellectual Property Organization, 1987.
ca 300p.
Hbk £35.00

Register Notule Communium 14 of the Diocese of Barcelona (1345-1348) A Calendar with Selected Documents / Julio Silano. – Toronto : Pontifical Institute of Mediaeval Studies, 1983.
x, 365p. – (Subsidia Mediaevalia: No. 13).
ISBN 0888443625 Hbk £30.00

Register of Current Community Legal Instruments, 2 Vols. – London : HMSO.
ISBN 9282536580 Hbk £30.50

Register of Fixed Assets. – Cape Town : Legal & Financial Publishing, 1983.
– (Merlen Ser. of Registers).
Hbk £3.52

Register of Graduate Employment and Training with Legal Prof. 1988. – London : Central Services Unit for University & Polytechnic Careers Advisory Services.
ISBN 0951070045 Pbk £5.75

Register of laws of the Arabian Gulf. – London : Graham & Trotman, 1989.
520.
ISBN 1853332534 Llf £545
Supplements. – 1989.
260.
A database of all laws and regulations originating in each country of the Arabian Gulf from the commencement of legislative promulgation to the present day. Drawn from original Arabic sources.
ISBN 1853331686 Llf £489

Register of policing research. No. 2. – London : Police Foundation, 1989.
220; 21.
Covers topics in a register of 200 police research projects - includes police management, organisation, policy making, operations, relations with voluntary and statutory agencies, and the history of policing and crime prevention.
ISBN 0947692126 Pbk £9.95

Register of research / Scottish Office. Central Research Unit. – Edinburgh : Scottish Office, 1985.
ii,31p.

Registered Homes Act 1984 / with annotations by Richard M. Jones. – London : Sweet & Maxwell, 1984.
58p; 24cm.
ISBN 0421333707 Pbk £4.00

Registered Homes Bill : report on the consolidation of certain enactments relating to residential care homes and nursing homes and registered homes tribunals / The Law Commission. – London : H.M.S.O., 1983.
3p; 25cm.
ISBN 0101911505

Registered land / by David J. Hayton. – 3rd ed. – London : Sweet & Maxwell, 1981.
xxiii,222p; 20cm.
Previous ed.: 1977. Includes index.
ISBN 042128160X Hbk £10.00
ISBN 0421281707 Pbk £6.50

Registered land practice notes. – Law Society. – 2nd ed. – London : Longman Professional, 1986.
ISBN 0851212573 Pbk £5.95

Registration Act : with State Amendments, Rules and Table of Fees. – 3rd ed. – Allahabad : Law Book Company, 1988.
ca 900p.
Hbk £250.00

Registration and certification of births and deaths : discussion paper / New South Wales Law Reform Commission. – Sydney : Government Printer, 1987.
vii,33p. – (D.P. v 17.).
ISBN 0730546276 Hbk

Registration, Certification and Maintenance of Aircraft-A Guide : Notes on the Legislation Governing Airworthiness of Civil Aircraft Registered in the United Kingdom. – Civil Aviation Authority. – 5d ed. Ed. by Great Britain. – London : Civil Aviation Authority, 1981.
vi, 46p : Illus.
ISBN 0860391272 Hbk £1.00

Registration of Adoptions Act, 1952 (Act 253) and Adoptions Act, 1952 (Act 257). – Kuala Lumpur : International Law Books Services.
Hbk £5.00

Registration of Businesses Act, 1956 (Act 197). – Kuala Lumpur : International Law Books Services.
Hbk £4.00

Registration of Criminals and Undesirable Persons Act, 1969 (Act 7). – Kuala Lumpur : International Law Books Services.
Hbk £4.00

Registration of Engineers Act, 1967 (Act 138) and Rules, 1972. – Kuala Lumpur : International Law Books Services.
Hbk £7.00

Registration of Title to Land. – Agincourt : Carswell, 1987.
950p.
This work is a comparitive analysis of the Canadian Torrens Acts with the representative body of Australian, New Zealand, and Tasmanian Acts. The book examines the application of the Torrens system in the context of transfer, leases, mortgages, lis pendens, restrictive covenants, and other dealings in all the jurisdictions.
ISBN 045935440 Hbk £48.40

Regulae Iuris: From Juristic Rules to Legal Maxims / J. Shand. – Edinburgh : Edinburgh University Press.
216p.
ISBN 0852241437 Hbk £8.50

Regulating custodial interviews. – Police Foundation, 1988.
ISBN 0947692088 Pbk £6.95

Regulating fraud : white-collar crime and the criminal process / Michael Levi. – London : Tavistock, 1987.
416p; 24cm.
Includes bibliography and index.
ISBN 0422611603 £35.00

Regulating Scotland / Jeremy Rowan-Robinson. – T & T Clark.
ISBN 00567291502 Pbk £14.95

Regulating the airlines : administrative justice and agency discretion / Robert Baldwin. – Oxford : Clarendon, 1985.
xvi,317p. – (Oxford socio-legal studies).
Includes index.
ISBN 0198275153 Hbk £22.50
ISBN 0198275161 Pbk £9.95

Regulating the city / by Malcolm A. Clarke. – Open University Press, 1986.
ISBN 0335153828 Pbk £7.95

Regulating the media (MLS). – London : Sweet & Maxwell, 1988.
ISBN 0421374500 Hbk
ISBN 0421374608 Pbk

Regulation after the Financial Services Act. – London : Butterworths, 1987.
ISBN 0406100748 Pbk

Regulation and its reform / Stephen Breyer. – Cambridge, Mass. : Harvard University Press, 1982.
xii,472p; 25cm.
Bibliography: p382-385. - Includes index.
ISBN 0674753755

Regulation and public law / Robert Baldwin, Christopher McCrudden with contributions by Paul Craig ... et al. – London : Weidenfeld and Nicolson, 1987.
xx,399p; 22cm.
Bibliography: p332-347. - Includes index.
ISBN 0297787802 Hbk
ISBN 0297787810 Pbk £14.95

Regulation and supervision of financial institutions / by D.T. Llewellyn. – London : Institute of Bankers, 1986.
77p.
Bibliography: p.75-77.
ISBN 0852971745

Regulation by Municipal Licensing. – Toronto : University of Toronto Press, 1984.
ISBN 0802033903 Pbk £6.50

Regulation, Investor/Depositor Protection and the Campbell Report / W.P. Hoogan. – Newcastle : University of Newcastle, 1982.
64p.
ISBN 0725904445 Pbk £2.50

Regulation of auditors : implementation of the EC Eighth Company Law Directive : a consultative document / Department of Trade and Industry. – London : Department of Trade and Industry, 1987.
77,11 leaves.
Includes the text of the Directive.

Regulation of authorised unit trust schemes : a consultative document on the proposed regulations for unit trust schemes authorised under the Financial Services Bill / Department of Trade and Industry. – London : HMSO, 1986.
viii.74p.
ISBN 0115138498

Regulation of banks in the member states of the EEC / edited by Jane Welch for the British Bankers Association. – 2nd ed. – The Hague : Nijhoff, 1981.
viii,277p; 25cm.
Previous ed.: 1978. Includes index.
ISBN 9024725739

Regulation of Building Standards Queensland / D.K. Woodhead. – Butterworths, 1988.
ISBN 0409300942 Llf

Regulation of Expert's Fees in the European Community. – 3rd rev. exp. ed. – Dusseldorf : VDI-Verlag, 1986.
70p.
ISBN 3184007405 Pbk £28.00

Regulation of insurance in the United Kingdom and Ireland / editor: T. Henry Ellis : associate editor: James A. Wiltshire : life assurance contributor: Peter G. Ward. – London : Kluwer, 1983.
looseleaf.
Includes index.
ISBN 0903393638

Regulation of international banking / Richard Dale. – Cambridge : Woodhead-Faulkner, 1984.
vii,208p.
ISBN 085941261X

Regulation of international economic relations through law / by Palitha Tikiri Bandara Kohona. – Dodrecht : M. Nijhoff Publishers, 1985.
Based on author's thesis (Ph. D.)–Cambridge University.
ISBN 9024731046

Regulation of investment business / The Securities and Investments Board. – 2 (loose-leaf). – London : The Board, 1986.
34cm.
Accompanied by: Further ammendments proposed to the February drafts of rules ... xix,125p.

Regulation of nationality in international law / Ruth Donner. – Helsinki : The Finnish Society of Sciences and Letters, 1983.
287p.
Bibliography: p273-284.
ISBN 9516531172

Regulation of pharmaceuticals in developing countries : legal issues and approaches / by D.C. Jayasuriya. – Geneva : World Health Organization, 1985.
118p.
Includes bibliographical references.
ISBN 9241560894

Regulation of quality. – Scarborough, Ontario : Butterworths (Canada), 1983.
368.
Considers the subjects' ethical, political and legal framework, looking at the rationale for government regulation of quality, regulating quality in product markets, regulating enviromental quality, the administration of the Hazardous Products Acts, regulating occupational health and safety, markets for insurance, regulating the quality of psychotherapeutic services and the control of diesel exhaust pollution.
ISBN 040982495X Hbk

Regulation of Toxic and Oxidant Air Pollution in North America. – North Ryde : C.C.H. Australia, 1986.
272p.
ISBN 088796351X Pbk £27.95

Regulations, Crown Corporations, and Adminstrative Tribunals / Andree Lajoie. – Toronto : University of Toronto Press, 1986.
224p.
ISBN 0802072933 Hbk £16.95

Regulations for the Prevention of Pollution by Oil. – International Maritime Organization. – London : International Maritime Organization, 1982.
Hbk £5.50

Regulations of the International Stock Exchange, 31st May 1988. – International Stock Exchange of the United Kingdom and Republic of Ireland. – London : International Stock Exchange, 1988.
ca. 175p.
Supersedes The Sock Exchange regulations.

Regulatory arrangements at Lloyd's : report of the Committee of Inquiry / chairman: Sir Patrick Neill : presented to Parliament by the Secretary of State for Trade and Industry... – London : H.M.S.O., 1987.
ix,117p.
ISBN 010100592X

Regulatory framework for storage and disposal of radioactive waste in the member states of the European Community / G.D. Burholt and A. Martin. – London, UK : Published by Graham & Trotman for the Commission of the European Communities, 1988.
ix, 121 p.; 25 cm.
Includes bibliographies.
ISBN 1853331090

Regulatory Framework of Accounting 2.8 : ACCA Study and Revision Manual. – London : BPP.
ISBN 1870941217 Pbk £9.95

Regulatory Framework of Accounting / Suresh Tanna. – Plymouth : Macdonald & Evans, 1985.
320p. – (M and E Professional Studies Ser.).
Hbk £13.95

Regulatory Framework of Accounting : ACCA Study Text 2.8. – London : BPP.
– (ACCA Practice and Revision Kit Series).
ISBN 0862772494 Hbk £15.95
ISBN 0862772761 Pbk £6.95

Regulatory Framework of Accounting : Level 2.8. – Witney : A.T.C. Publications.
ISBN 0747700001 Pbk £12.95

Regulatory Fraud : White Collar Crime and Criminal Process. – Tavistock.
ISBN 00422611700 Pbk £12.95

Regulatory Reform in Canada / Fred Thompson. – Ottawa : Institute for Research on Public Policy, 1982.
vi, 139p.
ISBN 0920380719 Hbk £7.95

Regulatory reform in international air transport : address by H.A. Wassenbergh on the occasion of the introduction of the International Institute of Air and Space Law of the State University at Leyden 17 March 1986. – Deventer : Kluwer Law and Taxation Publishers, 1986.
10p; 25cm.
ISBN 9065442618 Pbk

Rehabilitation of Offenders : a Guide to the Law. – London : Fourmat.
ISBN 1851900578 Pbk £9.95

Rehbinder, Eckard →Integration through law : Europe and the American federal experience : a series, Vol. 2 : Environmental protection policy : by Eckard Rehbinder and Richard Stewart : associate editor Patrick del Duca.

Reid, Brian C.
Cases on Patents : A New Anthology. – Waterlow.
– (Waterlow Practitioners Library).
ISBN 0080330878 Pbk £30.00
—Confidentiality and the law / Brian C. Reid. – London : Waterlow, 1986.
xvi,208p; 24cm.
Includes index.
ISBN 0080392369 £20.00
—Practical guide to patent law / Brian C. Reid. – Oxford : ESC Publishing Limited, 1984.
xxii,438p.
ISBN 0906214165
—Practical introduction to trade marks / Brian C. Reid. – London : Waterlow, 1984.
viii,184p; 22cm.
Includes index.
ISBN 0080391702 Pbk £14.50
ISBN 0080391621 £7.50

Reid, Colin T. →Planning Office's Advice and Undertakings : Estoppel and Personal Bar in Public Law.

Reid, D.H.S.
Child Abuse and the K C Factor. – Napier Press.
ISBN 1871479002 Pbk £12.00

Reid, G. S. →Constitutional Challenge : Essays on the Australian Constitution, Constitutionalism and Parliamentary Practice.

Reid, Gayla →Preparing Information on the Law : Guidelines for Writing, Editing and Design.

Reid, Len S.
Human Rights First : the Child. – Dandenong : Society of Those Who Have Less, 1982.
Hbk £2.00

Reid, M.
All-Change in the City : The Revolution in Britain's Financial Sector. – London : Macmillan.
ISBN 0333362349 Hbk £17.95

Reid, Margaret I.
Secondary banking crisis, 1973-75 : its causes and course / Margaret Reid. – London : Macmillan, 1982.
ix,219p.

Reid, Robert F.
Advocacy : views from the bench / Robert F. Reid and Richard E. Holland. – Aurora, Ont. : Canada Law Book, 1984.
xii,164p.
Includes index.
ISBN 0888040245
—Handbook of administrative tribunals / Sara Blake. – Scarborough, Ontario : Butterworths (Canada), 1988.
256.
Examination of how tribunals should conduct themselves in order to minimize the risks of judicial review. Cover compliance with prescribed rules, Ontario and Alberta Codes of Procedure, specific procedural rules, parties, notice, disclosure of the case to be met, adjournments, effective participation, the in-camers hearing, evidence, witnesses and the right to make submissions.
ISBN 0409806650 Hbk

Reid, Robert J. →Income Tax Administration, Avoidance and Evasion.
—Tax Aspects of Incorporation. – Toronto : Butterworths, 1983.
128p.
Pbk £19.95

Reijnen, Gijsbertha Cornelia Maria, et al
Pollution of outer space, in particular of the geostationary orbit / W. de Graaff. – Dordrecht : Nijhoff (Martinus), 1989.
188. – (Utrecht studies in air and space law).
Survey of the status of the pollution of outer space, dealing with both the scientific and legal aspects. Shows that the emerging international regulations are few, scanty, and in urgent need of elaboration.
ISBN 9024737508 Hbk £39
—Utilization of outer space and international law / Gijsbertha C.M. Reijnen. – Amsterdam : Elsevier Scientific, 1981.
xvi,179p; 25cm.
Bibliography: p169-171. - Includes index.
ISBN 0444419659

Reiner, Robert →Durkheim and modern sociology.

Reinsurance / R.L. Carter. – 2nd ed. – Brentford : Kluwer in association with the Mercantile and General Reinsurance Company plc, 1983.
xv,630p; 24cm.
Previous ed.: 1979. Bibliography: p613-622. - Includes index.
ISBN 0903393654 £65.00

Reinsurance in practice. – 2nd ed. – London : Witherby & Co, 1986.
ISBN 0900886986 Hbk £30.00

Reinsurance law / John S. Butler and Robert M. Merkin. – 2. – London : Kluwer, 1986.
looseleaf.
ISBN 1870080076

Reisner, Ralph →Sovereign lending : managing legal risk.

Reiter, Barry J. →Contracts : Cases, Notes and Materials.
→ Contracts : Cases, Text, and Materials.
—Real Estate Law / R. C. B. Risk. – 3rd ed. – Aurora : Canada Law Book Co, 1986.
1300p. – (Text Books-Civil).
The third edition of this text has undergone significant changes to make it an even more useful and relevant sourcebook for Canadian Real Estate practitioners. This new edition includes up-to-date forms and materials used in routine real estate transactions reflecting the changes brought about by the Land Registration Reform Act.
Hbk £99.50

Relation Of Custom To Law, The. – Sweet & Maxwell, 1919 Reprint.
ISBN 0421375701 Hbk £14.75

Relationship between legal aid agencies and social agencies : research report for the Commonwealth Legal Aid Council / by Peter Hanks, Kate Lavender, Guy Powles. – Canberra : Australian Government Publishing Service, 1983.
51p.
Bibliography: p.48.
ISBN 0644024674

Relationships between the supervisors, auditors and managements of banks / consultative paper by the Bank of England. – London : The Bank, 1985.
13,5 leaves.

Release of Manual of Central Acts and Important Rules : Criminal, Taxation and Labour, 15 Vols. – Allahabad : Law Publishers, 1986.
£120.00 ea

Relevance of the judiciary in the polity : in historical perspective / by A.G. Karibi-Whyte. – Lagos : Nigerian Institute of Advanced Legal Studies, 1987.
100p.
ISBN 9782353051

Relevant circumstances and maritime delimitation. – Oxford : OUP, 1988.
288.
Examines delimitation as a process. The conceptual basis of seabed jurisdiction and the historical development of delimitation criteria are discussed. Also contains an extended study of the features and factors considered relevant to continental shelf and EEC delimitation.
ISBN 0198252404 Hbk £27.50

Relf, David G.
VAT Guide and Casebook / Christopher A. L. Preston. – London : Oyez Longman, 1983.
ISBN 0851206611 Llf £50.00

Relief from Taxes Granted to Imports Made by Private Persons. – Commission of the European Communities. – Kirchberg : Commission of the European Communities, 1984.
71p.
ISBN 9282512991

Relief of poverty, 1834-1914 / prepared for the Economic History Society by Michael E. Rose. – 2nd ed. – Basingstoke : Macmillan, 1986.
92p; 22cm.
Previous ed.: 1972. Includes bibliography and index.
ISBN 0333424158 Pbk £3.95

Religion and religious liberty in Nigerian law (from the colonial days to 1983) / Ikem Bu Chukwu B. Ngwoke. – Roma : Pontificia Universita Lateranense, 1984.
xvi,531p.
Bibliography: p.520-531.

Religion and the law : religious liberty in Modern English law / St John A. Robilliard. – Manchester : Manchester University Press, 1984.
xii,223p; 23cm.
Includes index.
ISBN 0719009561 £22.50

Religion, law, and the growth of constitutional thought 1150-1650 / Brian Tierney. – Cambridge : Cambridge University Press, 1982.
xi,114p; 23cm.
Bibliography: p109-114.
ISBN 0521234956 £12.50

Religion-State Relationship and Constitutional Rights in India. – New Delhi : Deep and Deep Publications, 1987.
468p.
ISBN 8171000096 Hbk £325.00

Religious minorities in the Soviet Union : a report / prepared for the Minority Rights Group by Michael Bourdeaux and two associates, Kathleen Matchett and Cornelia Gerstenmaier. – Rev. 4th ed. – London : Minority Rights Group, 1984.
24p. – (Report).
Bibliography: p.23.
ISBN 0946690154

Remand in Victoria : A Review of the Nature and Size of Facilities Needed. – Canberra : Australian Institute of Criminology.
Hbk £4.50

Remands in custody : evidence on House of Commons Home Affairs Committee / Justice. – London : Justice, 1984.
3 leaves.

Remands in the absence of the accused / Chris May. – London : Home Office, 1985.
vii,31p.
ISBN 0862522153

Remarkable Decisions in the Court of Session : 1716-52, 2 Vols. – 2nd ed. Repr. of 1799 ed. – Abingdon : Professional Books.
57p.
Hbk £225.00

Remedial Law Compendium. – Manila : National Book Store.
Hbk
Vol. 1. – 1984.
424p.
ISBN 9710800477 £25.00
Vol. 2. –
ISBN 9710805258 £30.00

Remedies 1986. – Vancouver : Continuing Legal Education Society of British Columbia, 1986.
313p.
ISBN 0865040389 Hbk £65.00

Remedies / by Bruce Kercher and Michael Noone. – Sydney : Law Book Co., 1983.
xxxvi,408p.
Includes index.
ISBN 0455204454 Hbk £62

Remedies and the Sale of Land. – Butterworths, 1988.
352p.
Chapters develop the theme of finding ways to enforce, or conversely, to escape the agreement of sale. Examines over 100 ways to get out of or enforce contracts for the sale of land, analyses the operation of the standard sale contract, discusses the classic remedies of damages, and describes possible claims against third parties.
ISBN 0409805343 Hbk £55.00

Remedies for breach of contract : a comparative account / G.H. Treitel. – Oxford : Clarendon Press, 1988.
xliii,422p.
Includes index. Discusses remedies for a breach of contract from a comparative perspective. Contrasts civil and common law solutions, and differences between English and American common law, and French and German civil law. The aim is to identify types of solutions and consider how far differences in theoretical approaches are reflected in practical results.
ISBN 0198255004 Hbk £45/$60

Remedies for breach of contract in Islamic and Iranian law. – Glasgow : Royston, 1984.
250p.
ISBN 0946706212 £45.95

Remedies for police misconduct (LAG). – London : Sweet & Maxwell, 1987.
ISBN 0905099168 Pbk £12.00

Remedies for torts and breach of contract / A.S. Burrows. – London : Butterworths, 1987.
lviii,435p; 22cm.
Includes index.
ISBN 0406501505 Hbk £18.00
ISBN 0406501513 Pbk £12.95

Remedies for Trademark Infringement. – Agincourt : Carswell, 1988.
192p.
This book provides a comprehensive discussion of the remedies available for trademark infringement. Topics include the ramifications of injunctive relief, ancillary relief, and monetary remedies. The text also discusses how these various remedies interact with each other.
Hbk £43.75

Remedies for victims of crime / Tucker. – London : Legal Action Group, 1984.
ISBN 0905099060 Pbk £5.00

Remedies in contract and tort / Donald Harris. – London : Weidenfeld & Nicolson, 1988.
xxxvii,411p.
Includes index.
ISBN 0297793551

Remedies in Tort, 4 Vols. / A M Linden. – Agincourt : Carswell, 1987.
This multi-volume set of looseleaf books provides an in-depth coverage of the area of torts. There are 23 chapters. Discussions include related proceedings, elements the plaintiff must establish to succeed in an action, available defenses, remedies, necessary and proper parties to an action, and practice issues pertaining to tort law. Special features include a legal research guide and sample statements of claims.
Hbk £159.75

Remedies of unsecured creditors / Institute of Law Research and Reform. – Edmonton : The Institute, 1986.
xiv,370p. – (Report for discussion).
Includes bibliographical references.

Remedies under the contract, CS No 3 / Cain. – London : Sweet & Maxwell, 1988.
ISBN 0421381108 Hbk £22.00

Reminders on County Court Costs 1983. – London : Oyez Longman, 1983.
ISBN 0851207502 Hbk £3.75

Reminiscences and Reflections of a Chief Justice. – Delhi : B.R. Publishing Corporation, 1985.
ix, 234p.
ISBN 8170182530 Hbk £150.00

Removal of certain restrictions in respect of land / South African Law Commission. – Pretoria : The Commission, 1984.
iv,9p. – (Report).
ISBN 0621102008

Remuneration planning manual. – London : Butterworths, 1986.
ISBN 040650430X Pbk £19.95

Renas, Stephen M. → Anglo-American privacy law : an economic analysis.

Rendall, James A. → Cases of the Canadian Law of Insurance.
→ Cases on the Canadian law of insurance.

Rendel, Margherita → Women, power and political systems.

Rendell, Robert S. → International financial law.

Renfree, Harold Edward
Executive power of the Commonwealth of Australia / by H.E. Renfree. – Sydney : Legal books, 1984.
xxxvii,599p.
Includes index.
ISBN 0949553093
—Federal judicial system of Australia / by Harold Edward Renfree. – Sydney : Legal Books Pty Ltd., 1984.
xxxiii,802p.
Includes bibliographical references and index.
ISBN 0949553085

Renner, Karl
Institutions of Private Law and Their Social Functions. – London : Sweet & Maxwell.
ISBN 0710083025 Hbk £16.95

Rennie, M.-T. Michele
Computer contracts handbook : precedents of contracts for the sale, purchase, support, distribution and licence of computers and computer software / by M.-T. Michele Rennie : consultant editor, Elizabeth Jarvie. – London : Sweet & Maxwell, 1985.
xi,136p; 30cm.
Includes precedents for software licence, software and support agreements, software distributions agreements, escrow agreements, sales agreements, and distribution agreement. Where appropriate, includes two agreements for each subject, one drafted when acting for the supplier, and one when acting for the purchaser.
ISBN 0421332301 Pbk £17.50
—Further computer contracts. – London : Sweet & Maxwell, 1989.
Includes precedents for shrink-wrap software license, software development agreements, agreements for the supply of a customised computer system, escrow agreement, agreements for provisions of On-Line service and data protection, and software authors agreements.
ISBN 0421403306 Pbk £25.00

Renouf, John P.
Canada Tax Cases Index and Citator : Consolidated from 1972. – Toronto : DeBoo, 1983.
ISBN 0888201486 Hbk £95.00

Rensburg, A.D.J. van → Law of Delict.

Renshall, Michael → Butterworths company law guide.

Renshaw, Geoffrey → Employment, trade, and north-south co-operation.

Rent Act : Including Ownership of Old Buildings. – Bombay : Universal Book Corporation.
Hbk £125.00

Rent Act Nineteen Seventy-Seven Revised. – London : Oyez Longman, 1981.
ISBN 0851206131 Hbk £7.50

Rent Acts. – 11th ed. 2 vols. – Stevens & Sons.
ISBN 0420448403 Hbk £125.00

Rent Acts. – 10th ed. 3. – London : Stevens, 1967.

Rent acts and regulations amended and annotated / Andrew Arden, J. T. Farrand. – 2nd ed. – London : Sweet & Maxwell, 1981.
xl,435p; 26cm.
ISBN 0421282207 £16.50

Rent arrears and the courts : a report by the Lay Advocacy Service / by Les Burrows. – Bristol : Lay Advocacy Service, 1986.
63p.
ISBN 0951115006

Rent Control : Cost and Consequences. – Turramura : Centre for Independent Studies.
256p.
ISBN 0959648577 Hbk £9.95

Rent control and leasehold enfranchisement. – 9th. – London : Longman Professional (UK), 1989.
– (Practitioner series).
Guide to rent restriction rules governing the varius types of residential tenancies and the qualifications and procedure for enfranchisement. New edition revised to take account of the Landlord and Tenant Acts 1985, and 1987, and the Housing Act 1988, including details of assured tenancies.
ISBN 0851213871 Hbk £32.50

Rent Control Legislation in Malaysia. – Butterworths, 1986.
292p.
Covers tenancy and licence, premises, parties, rent, rent tribunals, recovery of possession of premises, subtenancies, penal provisions, the repeal provisions, redevelopment, decontrol, and notice to quit.
ISBN 0409995231 Hbk £41.00

Rent reviews. – Oxford : Blackwell Scientific, 1987.
ISBN 000383106X Hbk £19.50

Rent reviews and variable rents / J E Adams. – 3rd. – London : Longman Professional (UK), 1989.
– (Practitioner series).
Examines rent review clauses and other methods. Analysis of some 100 cases decided since 1984, and model forms published by the Law Society, the Royal institute of Chartered Surveyors, and the ISVA.
ISBN 0851213863 Hbk £37.50

Rent (Scotland) Act 1984 / J Hope. – Edinburgh : Green (W.) & Son, 1986.
Annotated text of the Act reprinted from Scottish Current Law Statutes, along with the rent regulations passed under the earlier legislation, supplemented with a table of cases and index.
ISBN 0414007522 Pbk

Renton, D.
Preparation of Legislation. – London : Sweet & Maxwell, 1981.
ISBN 0421291907 Pbk £7.25

Renton, R. W.
Criminal Procedure According to the Law of Scotland / R. H. Brown. – 5th ed. – Edinburgh : W Green, 1983.
ISBN 0414007158 Hbk £110.00

Rentzmann, W.
Alternative measures to imprisonment / by W. Rentzmann and J.P. Robert. – Strasbourg : Council of Europe, 1986.
35p. – (CDAP (85) 6).
A paper presented to the seventh Conference of Directors of Prison Administrations.

Renvoize, Jean
Incest : a family pattern / Jean Renvoize. – London : Routledge & Kegan Paul, 1982.
viii,224p; 23cm.
Bibliography : p217-220. - Includes index.
ISBN 0710090730 £7.95

Repairs : tenants' rights. – London : Legal Action Group, 1986.
ISBN 0905099133 Pbk £11.00

Reparation : a discussion document. – London : Home Office, 1986.
7 leaves.
Photocopy.

Reparation and mediation : a bibliography / prepared by Stanley Prashker and Nigel Brearley for Forum for Initiatives in Reparation and Mediation (FIRM). – s.l. : Forum for Initiatives in Reparation and Mediation, 1986.
52p.

Reparation, conciliation and mediation : current projects and plans in England and Wales / Tony F. Marshall : incorporating a survey by the National Association of Victims Support Schemes. – London : Home Office, 1984.
vii,73p.
Bibliography: p.50-73.
ISBN 0862521734

Repertory of Practice of United Nations Organs, Supplement No 5, Vol. 5 : Articles 92-111 of the Charter. – Geneva : United Nations Publications.
ISBN 9211332834 Hbk £19.00

Report
17th : Prostitution : off-street activities / Criminal Law Revision Committee. – London : H.M.S.O., 1985.
31 p.
ISBN 0101968809
Vol.1 : Chapters 1-15 / Committee on Enforcement Powers of the Revenue Departments : chairman, Lord Keith of Kinkel. – 1983.
xiv,334p; 25cm.
Vol.2 : Chapters 16-28 and notes / Committee on Enforcement Powers of the Revenue Departments : chairman, Lord Keith of Kinkel. – 1983.
336-804p; 25cm.
Vol.3 : Chapters 29-33 and notes : Development land tax, petroleum revenue tax, capital transfer tax and stamp duties / Committee on Enforcement Powers of the Revenue Departments : chairman, Lord Keith of Kinkel. – 1984.
iv,251p; 25cm.

Report. – International Civil Aviation Organization. – s.l. : International Civil Aviation Organaization, 984.
19p. – (LC/SC-ICA-Report 1984 10 03).
'The Sub-Committee met at Montreal and held eleven meetings between 25 September and 3 October 1984' - Introduction.

Report / P. D. Robinson. – London : H.M.S.O., 1983.
lv. (various pagings).
Chairman: P. D. Robinson.
ISBN 011390634X

Report / the Royal Commission on Criminal Procedure : chairman: Sir Cyril Philips. – London : H.M.S.O., 1981.
xiii,240p; 25cm.
Includes index.
ISBN 0101809204 Pbk £10.00

Report / Judicial Studies Board. – London : H.M.S.O., 1983-.

Report / International Civil Aviation Organization Legal Committee. – Montreal : I.C.A.O., 1983-.
Continues: Report and minutes.

Report. – Canberra : Australian Government Publishing Service, 1986.
88p.
ISBN 0644046961

Report / Royal Commission of Inquiry into Drug Trafficking, the Government of the Commonwealth of Australia and the Governments of the States of New South Wales, Victoria and Queensland. – Canberra : Australian Government Publishing Service, 1983.
xv,908p.
Includes bibliographical references and index.
ISBN 0644024747

Report / Canadian Federal-Provincial Task Force on Justice for Victims of Crime. – Ottawa : Canadian Government Publishing Centre, 1983.
viii,202p.
ISBN 0660114135

Report / Department of Constitutional Development and Planning. – 3. – Pretoria : Government Printer, 1983.
Text in Afrikaans and English.

Report / Lord Justice Watkins's Working Party on the Criminal Trial. – London : Lord Chancellor's Department, 1982.
23p.

Report / adopted by the Committee of Experts. – Geneva : World Intellectual Property Organization, 1986.
10p. – (BIOT/CE/II/3).
'Convened ... as part of the 1986/87 program of the International (Paris) Union for the Protection of Industrial Property' - Introduction.

Report : adopted by the Committee of Experts. – World Intellectual Property Organization. – Geneva : World Intellectual Property Organization, 1985.
22,10p. – (IPIC/CE/I/7).
The Committee met in Geneva from November 26 to 29, 1985. Draft treaty entitled: Draft Treaty on the Protection of Intellectual Property in Respect of Integrated Circuits.

Report : the modernisation of charity law in Northern Ireland. – Belfast : H.M.S.O., 1985.
39,ca. 200p.
ISBN 0337203415

Report : The Shops Act : Late-night and Sunday Opening. – Committee of Inquiry into Proposals to Amend the Shops Act. – London : HMSO, 1984.
ISBN 0101937601 Hbk £9.15

Report : young persons : effects of age in civil law / the Law Reform Commission of Hong Kong. – Hong Kong : The Commission, 1986.
various pagings. – (Topic 11).

Report and accounts ... / Air Travel Trust. – London : Published on behalf of the Air Travel Trust by Civil Aviation Authority, 1987.

Report and minutes / International Civil Aviation Organization Legal Committee. – Montreal : I.C.A.O., 1983.
v,202p.
Continues: Minutes and documents. - Continued by: Report.

Report and recommendations for reform on fifteen conveyancing matters / Law Refrom Commission of Tasmania. – Hobart : Government Printer, 1984.
20p. – (Report).

Report and recommendations of an Amnesty International mission to the government of the Republic of Iraq, 22-28 January 1983, including the government's response and Amnesty International comments. – Amnesty International. – s.l. : Amnesty International, 1983.
74p.
ISBN 0862100615

Report and recommendations of Commission on Judges' Salaries and Benefits / Submitted to the Minister of Justice of Canada. – Ottawa : Department of Justice, 1983.
16,16p.
With French t.-p.: Rapport et recommandations de la Commission sur le Traitement et les Avantages des Juges. French and English text.
ISBN 0662527208

Report and recommendations on rape and sexual offences / Law Reform Commission of Tasmania. – Hobart : Government Printer, 1982.
44p. – (Report).

Report and recommendations on the law and procedure relating to the sale of land by instalments / Law Reform Commission of Tasmania. – Hobart : Government Printer, 1983.
25p. – (Report).

Report and recommendations on the use of tranquillizer guns / Law Reform Commission of Tasmania. – Hobart : Government Printer, 1982.
16p. – (Report).

Report and recommendations relating to consumer claims and small debts / Law Reform Commission of Tasmania. – Hobart : Government Printer, 1982.
55p. – (Report).

Report and recommendations relating to exclusion clauses and implied obligations in contracts for the supply of goods and services / Law Reform Commission of Tasmania. – Hobart : Government Printer, 1983.
23p. – (Report).

Report and recommendations upon perpetuities and accumulations / Law Reform Commission of Tasmania. – Hobart : Government Printer, 1983.
25p. – (Report).

Report by Expert Group on Effects of Cannabis Use. – London : Home Office, 1982.
ISBN 0862520312 Pbk £3.10

Report by the Committee for Privileges on parliamentary privilege and the mental health legislation, together with the minutes of evidence. – London : H.M.S.O., 1984.
xi,26p. – (254).
ISBN 010425484X

Report by the Minister for the Arts on library and information matters during ... / presented to Parliament by the Secretary of State for Education and Science. – London : H.M.S.O., 1981-.
v.

Report ... dealing with disparate subjects in the inherited imperial law / Law Reform Committee of South Australia. – Adelaide : Government Printer, 1984.
56p. – (68th report).

Report ... dealing with the inherited imperial law / Law Reform Committee of South Australia. – Adelaide : Government Printer, 1984.
28p. – (79th report).

Report ... dealing with the inherited imperial law between 1751 and 1780 / Law Reform Committee of South Australia. – Adelaide : Government Printer, 1984.
46p. – (85th report).

Report ... dealing with the inherited imperial law between 1781 and 1800 / Law Reform Committee of South Australia. – Adelaide : Government Printer, 1984.
41p. – (86th report).

Report ... dealing with the inherited imperial law between 1801 and 1820 / Law Reform Committee of South Australia. – Adelaide : Government Printer, 1984.
41p. – (89th report).

Report ... dealing with the inherited imperial law between 1821 and 1836 / Law Reform Committee of South Australia. – Adelaide : Government Printer, 1985.
32p. – (91st report).

Report from Amnesty International to the government of the Syrian Arab Republic. – Amnesty International. – s.l. : Amnesty International, 1983.
ii,65p.
ISBN 0862100585

Report of a working party on computer facilities for teaching in universities. – Computer Board for Universities and Research Councils. – London : The Board, 1983.
25,3,11p.
Includes bibliography.

Report of Advisory Committee on Youth and Law in our Multicultural Society / E. Te R. Tauroa. – Wellington : The Committee, 1983.
284p.

Report of an Amnesty International mission to Sri Lanka, 31 January-9 February 1982. – Amnesty International. – London : Amnesty International, 1983.
2,iii,72p; 30cm.
ISBN 0862100542 Pbk

Report of an Amnesty International mission to the Republic of the Philippines 11-28 November 1981. – Amnesty International. – London : Amnesty International Publications, 1982.
ii,127p.
Includes bibliographical references.
ISBN 086210050X

Report of an Amnesty International mission to the Socialist Republic of Viet Nam, 10-21 December 1979 : including memoranda exchanged between the government and Amnesty International. – Amnesty International. – London : Amnesty International, 1981.
ii,42p.
ISBN 086210033X

Report of Commission of Inquiry into the North Creek Development Project 1986-87 / submitted to the Governor, Turks and Caicos Islands, by the Commissioner, Mr. Louis Blom-Cooper : presented to parliament by the Secretary of State for Foreign and Commonwealth Affairs by command of Her Majesty, July 1987. – London : H.M.S.O., 1987.
x,148p.
ISBN 0101019521

Report of formal investigation into the fire aboard and abandonment of the Canadian tanker Hudson Transport in the St. Lawrence River on December 25, 1981 / Commissioner James K. Hugessen : assessors, J. Augustin Dionne, John J. DeLuca. – Ottawa : Canadian Government Publishing Centre, Supply and Services Canada, 1982.
iii,140p. – (Report of formal investigation).
Bound with French ed.: Rapport de l'investigation formelle sur l'incendie a bord du petrolier canadien Hudson Transport et son abandon dans le fleuve Saint-Laurent le 25 decembre 1981. At head of title: Canada Shipping Act. - Cover title: Hudson Transport.
ISBN 0660519720

Report of Her Majesty's Chief Inspector of Prisons. – London : H.M.S.O., 1982-.

Report of Her Majesty's Chief Inspector of Prisons for Scotland ... – Edinburgh : H.M.S.O., 1982-.

Report of Inquiry into Motor Vehicle Accident Compensation in Ontario / Coulter A. Osborne, commissioner. – Toronto : Ontario Ministry of the Attorney General, 1988.
2 v.; 25 cm.
Title from cover. Co-published by: Ministry of Financial Institutions. Bibliography: p. 667-712 (2.). Contents: 1. Report – 2. Research studies and 1 appendices.
ISBN 0772938466 (v.2)

Report of Inquiry into Motor Vehicle Accident Compensation in Ontario : summary of findings and recommendations / Coulter A. Osborne, Commissioner. – Toronto : Ontario Ministry of the Attorney General, 1988.
68, 79 p.; 25 cm.
Title from cover. Co-published by: Ministry of Financial Institutions. Text in English and French with French text on inverted pages. Title on added t.p.: Rapport de l'enquete sur l'indemnisation des victimes d'accidents d'automobiles en Ontario.
ISBN 0772938474

Report of Police Complaints Board 1984. – London : HMSO.
ISBN 0102359857 Hbk £7.50

Report of Providing and Funding Legal Aid Conference. – Canberra : Commonwealth Legal Aid Commission, 1981.
46,8p; 25cm.
ISBN 0642895538

Report of the Air Travel Trust Committee ... – London : Published on behalf of the Air Travel Trust Committee by Civil Aviation Authority, 1987.

Report of the Belize Constitutional Conference, London, April 1981. – London : H.M.S.O., 1981.
29p; 25cm.
ISBN 0101824505 unbound £2.40

Report of the Commission of Inquiry Relating to the Security and Investigation Services Branch Within the Post Office Department / Rene J Marin. – Hull, Quebec : Canadian Government Publishing Centre, 1981.
iv,338p.
Commissioner: Rene J. Marin.
ISBN 0660108585

Report of the Commission to Review the Police Act & Regulations / Nathan Green. – Halifax : Queen's Printer, 1981.
96,26,36p.
Commissioner: Nathan Green.

Report of the Commissioner of Police of the Metropolis for the Year 1985. – London : HMSO, 1986.
ISBN 0101979002 Hbk £11.30

Report of the Committee established by the Premier of New South Wales to report on the steps necessary to establish offshore banking activity in Australia with particular reference to Sydney. – Offshore Banking Committee. – Sydney : The Committee, 1984.
28p.

Report of the Committee of Inquiry into Human Fertilisation and Embryology / Chairman: Mary Warnock. – London : H.M.S.O., 1984.
At head of title: Department of Health and Social Security.
ISBN 0101931409

Report of the Committee of Inquiry on the Management of Privately Owned Blocks of Flats / E. G. Nugee. – 2 v. – London : The Committee, 1985.
Chairman: E.G. Nugee.

Report of the Committee of Review, Landlord and Tenant (Consolidatioin) Ordinance. – Hong Kong : Government Printer, 1981.
vii,269p.

Report of the Committee on Enforcement Powers of the Revenue Departments, 3 Vols.
Vols. 1 and 2. – London : HMSO, 1983.
ISBN 0101882203 Hbk £24.50
Vol. 3, 1984. –
ISBN 0101912005 Hbk £9.95

Report of the Committee on Financing the BBC / chairman, Alan Peacock. – London : H.M.S.O., 1986.
xx,219p; 30cm.
A report to the Secretary of State for the Home Department.
ISBN 0101982402

Report of the Committee on Professional Legal Education in Northern Ireland. – Belfast : HMSO, 1985.
ix,48p; 25cm.
ISBN 0337041504 Pbk £4.20

Report of the Committee on the Constitution of the Senate / Chairman: Rt. Hon. Lord Rawlinson of Ewell. – London : Senate of the Inns of Court and the Bar, 1986.
71p.

Report of the Committee on the Prison Disciplinary System / Chairman, Peter J. Prior. – 2 v. – London : H.M.S.O., 1985.
Contents: 1. Report - 2. Appendices.
ISBN 0101964102

Report of the committee set up to consider the system of banking supervision / presented to Parliament by the Chancellor of the Exchequer. – London : H.M.S.O., 1985.
iii,26p.
Chairman: Robert Leigh-Pemberton.
ISBN 0101955006 Pbk £3.50

Report of the constitutional commission 1986 / presented to parliament by the Secretary of State for Foreign and Commonwealth Affairs by Command of Her Majesty April 1987. – London : H.M.S.O., 1987.
iv,43p.
Chairman: Roy Marshall. At head of t.p.: Turks and Caicos Islands.
ISBN 0101011121

Report of the Data Protection Registrar ... – London : HMSO, 1985-.

Report of the Federal/Provincial Task Force on Uniform Rules of Evidence / prepared for the Uniform Law Conference of Canada. – Toronto, Canada : Carswell, 1982.
xxxiv, 615 p.; 26 cm.
Includes bibliographical references, legislation, and indexes.
ISBN 0459349309

Report of the Inquiry into cable expansion and broadcasting policy / chairman, Lord Hunt of Tanworth : Home Office. – London : H.M.S.O., 1982.
vi,45p; 25cm.
ISBN 0101867905 Pbk £4.40

Report of the inquiry into child abuse in Cleveland 1987 / presented to Parliament by the Secretary of State for Social Services by Command of Her Majesty, July 1988. – London : HMSO, 1988.
320p.
'Presented to the Secretary of State for Social Services by the Right Honourable Lord Justice Butler-Sloss DBE'. - p.i.
ISBN 0101041225

Report of the inquiry into child abuse in Cleveland 1987 : short version extracted from the complete text / presented to Parliament by the Secretary of State for Social Services by Command of Her Majesty, July 1988. – London : HMSO, 1988.
21p.
Chairman: ELizabeth Butler-Sloss.
ISBN 0101041322

Report of the Inquiry into Disclosure of Electoral Expenditure / Clarrie W. Harders. – Canberra : Australian Government Publishing Service, 1981.
101p.
Sole member of the Inquiry: Sir Clarrie W. Harders.
ISBN 0642066396

Report of the Inter-Departmental Working Party on Road Traffic Law. – London : H.M.S.O., 1981.
vii,66p; 25cm.
ISBN 0115505490 Pbk £4.20

Report of the Law Reform Commission on a bill to consolidate, amend and reform the Supreme Court Acts and ancillary acts regulating civil proceedings in the Supreme Court. – Brisbane? : the Commission?, 1982.
159p. – (Q.L.R.C.).

Report of the Matrimonial Causes Procedure Committee : presented to the Lord Chancellor July 1985 / Margaret Booth. – London : H.M.S.O., 1985.
ix,134p.
Chairman: the Hon. Mrs Justice Booth.
ISBN 0113800045

Report of the Ministry of Defence Police Review Committee : presented to Parliament by the Secretary of State for Defence ... – Ministry of Defence Police Review Committee. – London : H.M.S.O., 1986.
50p.
ISBN 0101985304

Report of the Nineteen Eighty-One Meeting of Pacific Islands Officers : Port Vila, Vanuatu, 20-22 July 1981. – London : Commonwealth Secretariat, 1982.
free

Report of the Official Referees' Users' Committee ... – Official Referees' Users' Committee. – London : The Committee, 1983.
1st report covers 1983 to 1986.

Report of the Penal Policy Review Committee, 1981 / M. E. Casey. – Wellington : Government Printer, 1982.
232p.
Chairman: M. E. Casey.

Report of the Police Complaints Board. – 8 v. – London : H.M.S.O., 1978-85.
Continued by: Annual report of the Police Complaints Authority.

Report of the practitioner members of the Commercial Court Committee approved and adopted by the Commercial Court Committee. – London : Lord Chancellor's Department, 1986.
50p.

Report of the proceedings and papers of the second Magistrates' Workshop / compiled and edited by Roland Crawford on behalf of the Magistrates' Association of the Republic of Trinidad and Tobago. – Port-of-Spain : The Association, 1982.
158p.
'Held on the 13th and 14th September, 1980, Chaguaramas Convention Centre'. At head of title: Republic of Trinidad and Tobago, the Magistrates' Association of the Republic of Trinidad and Tobago.

Report of the Review Body on the Chancery Division of the High Court / presented to Parliament by the Lord High Chancellor. – London : H.M.S.O., 1981.
v,115p; 25cm.
Chairman: Lord Justice Oliver.
ISBN 010182050X

Report of the Review Body on Use of Judicial Time in the Superior Courts in Scotland / Chairman: The Honourable Lord Maxwell. – Edinburgh : Scottish Courts Administration, 1986.
vi,164p.

Report of the review of the Australian Institute of Aboriginal Studies / by R.J. Walsh. – Canberra : Australian Government Publishing Service, 1982.
89p.
ISBN 0644022698

Report of the Royal Commission on Family and Children's Law
1st-13th, Summary of recommendations / Thomas R. Berger. – 20 v. – Vancouver : Queen's Printer, 1974.
Includes bibliographies. Chairman: Thomas R. Berger.

Report of the Royal Commission to inquire into certain matters related to drug trafficking / D. G. Stewart. – Wellington : Government Printer, 1983.
110p.
Commissioner: the Hon. Mr. Justice D.G. Stewart.

Report of the Saint Christopher and Nevis Constitutional Conference : London, December 1982. – London : H.M.S.O., 1983.
31p; 25cm.
ISBN 0101879601 unbound £2.95

Report of the Securities Commission for the year ended 31 March ... – Wellington : Government Printer, 1980-.

Report of the Security Commission, May 1981. – London : H.M.S.O., 1981.
9p; 25cm.
ISBN 0101823509 unbound £1.40

Report of the Select Committee on Insurance Laws and Practices. – Suva : Parliament of Fiji, 1984.
115p. – (Parliamentary paper).

Report of the Select Committee on the Advocate-General Bill
South Africa. – Pretoria : Government Printer. Parliament.

Report of the seventh Commonwealth Magistrates' Conference : Nicosia, Cyprus 8th to 14th September 1985. – London : Commonwealth Magistrates' Association, 1985.
294p.

Report of the Social Security Advisory Committee ... – London : HMSO, 1981-.

Report of the Sri Lanka Law's Delays and Legal Culture Committee / appointed by Hon. Dr. Nissanka Wijeyeratne, Minister of Justice. – Colombo : Ministry of Justice, 1985.
v,69p.
Chairman: R.S. Wanasundera.

Report of the Task Force on Child Care. – Ottawa, Ont. : Status of Women Canada, 1986.
xxvi, 395 p.; 23 cm.
Bibliography: p. 345-365.
ISBN 0660120380 Pbk £9.95 (£11.95 other countries)

Report of the Task Force on Tax Reform / P.M. McCaw (Chairman). – Wellington : Govt. Printer, 1982.
xiii,274p.

Report of the Working Group on Current Problems in the International Protection of Refugees and Displaced Persons in Asia, International Institute of Humanitarian Law, San Remo (Italy), 19-22 January 1981. – Working Group on Current Problems in the International Protection of Refugees and Displaced Persons in Asia. – Geneva : under the auspices of the Office of the United Nations High Commissioner for Refugees, 1981.
17p.

Report of the Working Group on Juvenile Crime. – 1. – Hong Kong : Government Printer, 1981.
various pagings.

Report of the Working Party on Company Residence, Tax Havens, and Upstream Loans / Edmund Dell. – London : Institute for Fiscal Studies, 1982.
35p; 22cm.
ISBN 0902992309 Pbk

Report on administrative law
Part 1 : Procedures of provincial government agencies / Manitoba Law Reform Commission. – Winnipeg : Manitoba Law Reform Commission, 1984.
182p.
Includes bibliographical references.
Part 2 : Judicial review of administrative action / Manitoba Law Reform Commission. – 1987.
vi,243p. – (Report).
Includes bibliographical references.
ISBN 0771108338

Report on allegations of ill-treatment of prisoners at Archambault Institution, Quebec, Canada, including a memorandum to the Government of Canada following a mission from 10 to 15 April 1983 / Amnesty International. – London : Amnesty International, 1983.
ii,44p.
ISBN 0862100623

Report on alteration of ground levels / the Law Reform Commission of Western Australia. – Perth : The Commission, 1986.
94p. – (Project).
Includes bibliographical references.

Report on amendment of the law of contract / Ontario Law Reform Commission. – Toronto : Ministry of the Attorney General, 1987.
xiii,305p.

Report on an examination of 'the Dower Act' / Manitoba Law Reform Commission. – Winnipeg : Manitoba Law Reform Commission, 1984.
v,283p. – (Report).

Report on arbitration / Law Reform Commission of British Columbia. – Vancouver : The Commission, 1982.
149p.
ISBN 0771883110

Report on arrest / Law Reform Commission of Canada. – Ottawa : the Commission, 1986.
65,71p. – (Report).
Pages numbered in opposite directions. Text in English and French.
ISBN 0662544757

Report on bail / Criminal Law Reform Committee. – Wellington : Government Printer?, 1982.
113p.

Report on bankruptcy and related aspects of insolvency and liquidation / Scottish Law Commission. – Edinburgh : H.M.S.O., 1982.
xv,597p; 25cm. – (HC).
ISBN 0102176825 Pbk £14.90

Report on breach of promise of marriage. – Law Reform Commission of British Columbia. – Victoria : Queen's Printer, 1983.
36p.
ISBN 0771883811

Report on breach of promise to marry / Manitoba Law Reform Commission. – Winnipeg : The Commission, 1984.
33p. – (Report).
Includes bibliographical references. Breach of promise; Manitoba.

Report on bulk sales legislation / Law Reform Commission of British Columbia. – Victoria : Queen's Printer, 1983.
45p.
Includes bibliographical references.
ISBN 0771883943

Report on business records and computer output / Evidence Law Reform Committee. – Wellington, N.Z. : The Committee, 1987.
58p.
Includes bibliographical references. Includes extract from Evidence Amendment Act (No. 2) 1980.

Report on cable systems. – Information Technology Advisory Panel. – London : H.M.S.O., 1982.
54p; 20cm.
At head of title: Cabinet Office. Information Technology Advisory Panel.
ISBN 0116308214 Pbk £3.60

Report on cable television and defamation. – Victoria : Queen's Printer, 1981.
23p.
ISBN 0771882572

Report on certificates of lis pendens / Law Reform Commission. – Winnipeg : Queen's Printer, 1983.
28p. – (Report).

Report on civil liability : contribution / Scottish Law Commission. – Edinburgh : The Commission, 1988.
vi,75p.
Includes draft of a Bill.
ISBN 0102007896

Report on civil liability for animals / the Law Reform Commission. – Dublin : The Commission, 1982.
v,26p. – (LRC).

Report on class actions / Ontario Law Reform Commission. – 3. – Toronto : Ministry of the Attorney General, 1982.
880p.
ISBN 0774370890

Report on compensation for non-pecuniary loss / Law Reform Commission of British Columbia. – Vancouver : Law Reform Commission of British Columbia, 1984.
40p.
ISBN 0771884567

Report on competence and compellability of spouses as witnesses / the Law Reform Commission. – Dublin : The Commission, 1985.
v,86p. – (LRC).
Includes general scheme of a bill to reform the law relating to the evidence of spouses in criminal cases.

Report on competence and compellability of spouses in criminal proceedings / the Law Reform Commission of Hong Kong. – Hong Kong : The Commission, 1988.
viii,181p. – (Topic).
Bibliography:pp. 180-181.

Report on computer crime / Scottish Law Commission. – Edinburgh : H.M.S.O., 1987.
v,38p.
Includes bibliographical references. Includes Draft Computer Crime (Scotland) Bill.
ISBN 0101017421

Report on computer misuse / Law Reform Commission of Tasmania. – Hobart : Government Printer, 1986.
37p. – (Report v no 47).

Report on confessions. – Wellington : Evidence Law Reform Committee, 1987.
58p.
Bibliographical references: p.51-55.

Report on contempt of court / the Law Reform Commission of Hong Kong. – Hong Kong : The Commission, 1986.
v,102p. – (Topic).
Includes bibliographical references.

Report on contracts and the disposition of property by minors / Law Reform Commission of Tasmania. – Hobart : Acting Government Printer, 1987.
14p. – (Report).
Includes text of the Infants' Relief Act 1875.

Report on co-ownership of land / Law Reform Commmission of British Columbia. – Vancouver : The Commission, 1988.
Includes bibliographical references. Includes draft legislation and text of the Partition of Property Act.
ISBN 0771887256

Report on coroners / the Law Reform Commission of Hong Kong. – Hong Kong : The Commission, 1987.
viii,176p. – (Topic).
Includes bibliographical references.

Report on corroboration / Evidence Law Reform Committee, New Zealand. – Wellington : The Committee, 1984.
59p.
Includes bibliographical references.

Report on covenants in restraint of trade. – Law Reform Commission of British Columbia. – Victoria : Queen's Printer, 1984.
76p.
Includes bibliographical references.
ISBN 077188429X

Report on criminal trials / Peter A. Sallmann. – Canberra : Australian Institute of Judicial Administration, 1985.
xiii,217p.
Report of a joint committee of the Victorian Bar Council and the Australian Institute of Judicial Administration. Includes bibliographical references. At head of cover: Shorter Trials Committee. Chairman: Hon. Mr. Justice McGarvie.
ISBN 095900291X

Report on de facto relationships / New South Wales Law Reform Commission. – Sydney : The Commission, 1983.
xx,423p. – (L.R.C. 36).
Bibliography: p.391-396. Includes index. Accompanied by: Outline of report on de facto relationships (19p).

Report on debt collection : (1) the law relating to sheriffs / the Law Reform Commission. – Dublin : The Commission, 1988.
viii,62p. – (LRC).

Report on deeds and seals / Law Reform Commission of British Columbia. – Vancouver : The Commission, 1988.
ii,47p.
Includes bibliographical references.
ISBN 0771886799

Report on defective premises / the Law Reform Commission. – Dublin : The Commission, 1982.
v,49p. – (LRC).

Report on diligence and debtor protection / Scottish Law Commission. – 2 v. – Edinburgh : H.M.S.O., 1985.
Vol. 2: Appendices.
ISBN 0102005869

Report on disclosure by the prosecution / Law Reform Commission of Canada. – Ottawa : the Commission, 1984.
38,36p. – (Report).
Pages numbered in opposite directions. Text in English and French.
ISBN 0662530942

Report on discovery in criminal cases / Criminal Law Reform Committee. – Wellington : Government Printer?, 1986.
59p.

Report on disposition of seized property : post-seizure procedures / Law Reform Commission of Canada. – Ottawa : The Commission, 1986.
76,83p. – (Report).
Includes bibliographical references. Added t.p. in French : La facon de disposer des choses saisies. Pages numbered in opposite directions. Text in English and French.
ISBN 0662540816

Report on distress for rent. – Victoria : Queen's Printer, 1982.
72p.
ISBN 0771882947

Report on divorce a mensa et thoro and related matters / the Law Reform Commission. – Dublin : The Commission, 1983.
vii,90p. – (LRC).
Includes bibliographical references.

Report on domicile and habitual residence as connecting factors in the conflict of laws / the Law Reform Commission. – Dublin : The Commission, 1983.
v,26p. – (LRC).

Report on fines / Law Reform Commission of Tasmania. – Hobart : Government Printer, 1985.
12p. – (Report v no 41).

Report on foreign money liabilities / Law Reform Commission of British Columbia. – Vancouver : The Commission, 1983.
64p.
Includes bibliographical references.
ISBN 0771883919

Report on fraudulent conveyances and preferences : Law Reform Commission of British Columbia. – Law Reform Commission of British Columbia. – Vancouver : The Commission, 1988.
vii,180p.
Includes bibliographical references. Includes draft legislation.
ISBN 0771886314

Report on human artificial reproduction and related matters / Ontario Law Reform Commission. – 2 v. – Toronto : Ministry of the Attorney General, 1985.
ISBN 0772900019

Report on illegal transactions. – Law Reform Commission of British Columbia. – Victoria : Queen's Printer, 1983.
115p.
ISBN 077188401X

Report on illegitimacy / the Law Reform Commission. – Dublin : The Commission, 1982.
vii,182p. – (LRC).

Report on incorporation of associations / New South Wales Law Reform Commission. – Sydney, 1982.
136p. – (L.R.C.).
Includes index.

Report on independent administrative agencies : a framework for decision making. – Law Reform Commission of. – Ottawa : Law Reform Commission of Canada, 1985.
101,11p. – (Working paper).
Bibliography: p.87-94. Added t.p. in French: Rapport sur organismes administratifs autonomes. Pages numbered in opposite directions. Text in English and French.
ISBN 0662537483

Report on interest on pre- and post-judgment debts / Law Reform Commission of Tasmania. – Hobart : Government Printer, 1985.
17p. – (Report v no 44).

Report on international interference with domestic relations / Law Reform Commission of British Columbia. – Victoria : Queen's Printer, 1983.
27p.
Includes bibliographical references.
ISBN 0771883986

Report on interpretation of wills. – Law Reform Commission of British Columbia. – Victoria : Queen's Printer, 1982.
58p.
ISBN 0771883455

Report on interspousal immunity in tort / Law Reform Commission of British Columbia. – Victoria : Queen's Printer, 983.
21p.

Report on intestate succession / Manitoba Law Reform Commission. – Winnipeg : The Commission, 1985.
iii,66p. – (Report).
Includes bibliographical references.

Report on intoxication as a defence to a criminal charge / Criminal Law Reform Committee. – Sydney : Law Reform Commission of New South Wales, 1984.
55p.
Includes bibliographical references.

Report on investigative tests - alcohol, drugs and driving offences / Law Reform Commission of Canada. – Ottawa : Law Reform Commission of Canada, 1983.
33,34p; 25cm. – (Report).
English and French texts back to back. French title: L'alcool, la drogue et la conduit des vehicules.
ISBN 0662527259

Report on investment provisions under 'The Trustee Act' / Law Reform Commission. – Winnipeg : Queen's Printer, 1982.
i,38p. – (Report).

Report on judicial review of administrative decisions : procedural aspects and the right to reasons / Law Reform Commission of Western Australia. – Perth : The Commission, 1986.
77p. – (Project).
Includes bibliographical references.

Report on jurisdiction in proceedings for nullity of marriage, recognition of foreign nullity decrees, and the Hague Convention on the Celebration and Recognition of the Validity of Marriage (1978) / the Law Reform Commission. – Dublin : The Commission, 1985.
v,63p. – (LRC).
Bibliography: pp.51-2. Includes text of the Convention.

Report on laws on insurance / the Law Reform Commission of Hong Kong. – Hong Kong : The Commission, 1986.
vi,172p. – (Topic 9).
Bibliography: p.97-102. Summary in Chinese.

Report on liability for stock straying on to the highway / Law Reform Commission of Western Australia. – Perth : Law Reform Commission of Western Australia, 1981.
51p. – (Project).

Report on limitation and notice of actions : latent disease and injury / Law Reform Commission of Western Australia. – Perth : The Commission, 1982.
125p. – (Project).

Report on local courts / Law Reform Commission of Tasmania. – Hobart : Government Printer, 1985.
29p. – (Report v no 45).

Report on malicious damage / the Law Reform Commission. – Dublin : The Commission, 1988.
viii,56p. – (LRC).

Report on medical privilege / Manitoba Law Reform Commission. – Winnipeg : The Commission, 1983.
52p. – (Report).
Includes bibliographical references.

Report on minors' contracts / the Law Reform Commission. – Dublin : The Commission, 1985.
v,167p. – (LRC).
Bibliography: p.163.

Report on minors' contracts / the Law Reform Commission of Western Australia. – Perth : Law Reform Commission of Western Australia, 1988.
117p. – (Project).

Report on mortgages of land : the priority of further advances / Law Reform Commission of British Columbia. – Vancouver : The Commission, 1986.
60p.
Includes bibliographical references.
ISBN 0771885067

Report on nullity of marriage / the Law Reform Commission. – Dublin : The Commission, 1984.
ix,193p. – (LRC).
Bibliography: p.193.

Report on obsolete remedies against estate property : Estate Administration Act, Part 9 / Law Reform Commission of British Columbia. – Vancouver : The Commission, 1987.
22p.
Includes bibliographical references.
ISBN 0771885695

Report on obtaining forensic evidence : investigative procedures in respect of the person / Law Reform Commission of Canada. – Ottawa : The Commission, 1985.
45,48p; 25cm. – (Report).
Added t.p. in French: Rapport sur les techniques d'investigation policiere et les droits de la personne. Cover title: Obtaining forensic evidence. Pages numbered in opposite directions. In English and French.
ISBN 0662537351

Report on offences under the Dublin Police Acts and related offences / the Law Reform Commission. – Dublin, 1985.
v,90p. – (LRC).

Report on our criminal procedure. – Law Reform Commission of. – Ottawa : Law Reform Commission of Canada, 1988.
56,60p. – (Report).
Includes t.p. in French. Pages numbered in opposite directions. Text in English and French.
ISBN 0662557360

Report on pecuniary interests of municipal councillors / Statute Law Revision Committee. – Melbourne : Government Printer, 1981.
ii,27p. – (D v no 14/1980-81.).

Report on peremptory challenges in civil jury trials. – Law Reform Commission of British Columbia. – Victoria : Queen's Printer, 1983.
22p.
ISBN 0771883773

Report on performance under protest / Law Reform Commission of British Columbia. – Vancouver : The Commission, 1985.
21p.
Includes bibliographical references.
ISBN 077188477X

Report on periodic payment of damages for personal injury and death / Manitoba Law Reform Commission. – Winnipeg : The Commission, 1987.
iv,128p. – (Report).
Includes bibliographical references.
ISBN 0771108346

Report on personal liability under a mortgage or agreement for sale. – Law Reform Commission of British Columbia. – Victoria : Queen's Printer, 1986.
37p.
Date on front cover: 1985. Includes bibliographical references.
ISBN 0771884982

Report on political activity, public comment and disclosure by crown employees / Ontario Law Reform Commission. – Toronto : Ministry of the Attorney General, 1986.
xi,381p.
Includes bibliographical references.
ISBN 0772917728

Report on powers of attorney / Law Reform Commission of Tasmania. – Hobart : Government Printer, 1984.
21p. – (Report v no 39).

Report on powers of entry / Ontario Law Reform Commission. – Toronto : Ministry of the Attorney General, 1983.
v,87p.
Includes text of draft bill.
ISBN 0774381051

Report on prejudgment compensation on money awards : alternatives to interest / Law Reform Commission. – Winnipeg : Queen's Printer, 1982.
iv,108p. – (Report).

Report on pre-judgment interest / Law Reform Commission of Western Australia. – Perth : Law Reform Commission of Western Australia, 1981.
38p. – (Project v no 70 part 1).

Report on presumptions of survivorship. – Law Reform Commission of British Columbia. – Victoria : Queen's Printer, 1982.
29p.
ISBN 0771883382

Report on private international law aspects of capacity to marry and choice of law in proceedings for nullity of marriage / the Law Reform Commission. – Dublin : The Commission, 1985.
v,161p. – (LRC).
Bibliography: pp.156-8.

Report on private rights of access to neighbouring land / Law Reform Commission of Tasmania. – Hobart : Government Printer, 1985.
23p. – (Report v no 42).

Report on recodifying criminal law / Law Reform Commission of Canada. – Rev. and enl. ed. – Ottawa : The Commission, 1987.
213,233p; 25cm. – (Report).
Includes text of draft legislation. 'Revised and enlarged edition of Report 30' - t.p.. Added t.p. in French: Rapport pour une nouvelle codification du droit penal. Cover title: Recodifying criminal law. Pages numbered in opposite directions. Pages numbered in opposite directions. In English and French.
ISBN 0662547578

Report on recodifying criminal law / Law Reform Commission of Canada. – Ottawa : the Commission, 1986.
– (Report).
Pages numbered in opposite directions. Text in English and French.
ISBN 0662547322

Report on recognition of foreign divorces and legal separations / the Law Reform Commission. – Dublin : The Commission, 1985.
v,38p. – (LRC).

Report on recognition of interstate and foreign grants of probate and administration / the Law Reform Commission of Western Australia. – Perth : The Commission, 1984.
128p. – (Project).
Includes bibliographical references.

Report on reform in the law of wills / Law Reform Commission of Tasmania. – Hobart : Government Printer, 1983.
17p. – (Report v no 35).

Report on requirements of writing / Scottish Law Commission. – Edinburgh : HMSO, 1988.
vii,197p.
Includes bibliographical references. Includes draft legislation.
ISBN 010255188X

Report on residential tenancies / Property Law and Equity Reform Committee. – Wellington : The Committee, 1985.
66p.

Report on restitution of conjugal rights, jactitation of marriage and related matters / the Law Reform Commission. – Dublin : The Commission, 1983.
v,31p. – (LRC).
Includes bibliographical references.

Report on review of administrative decisions : part 1, appeals / the Law Reform Commission of Western Australia. – Perth : The Commission, 1982.
114p. – (Project).

Report on review of civil jury awards / Law Reform Commission of British Columbia. – Vancouver : The Commission, 1984.
60p.
Includes bibliographical references.
ISBN 0771884478

Report on search and seizure / Law Reform Commission of Canada. – Ottawa : The Commission, 1984.
78,86p; 25cm. – (Report).
Added t.p. in French: Rapport sur les fouilles, les perquisitions et les saises. Cover title: Searches and seizures. Pages numbered in opposite directions. Text in English and French.
ISBN 0662532872

Report on secondary education / by an ad-hoc working group of the Women's National Commission. – London : Women's National Commission, 1983.

Report on section 5 of the Damages (Scotland) Act 1976 / Scottish Law Commission. – Edinburgh : H.M.S.O., 1981.
iii,8p; 25cm. – (HC).
ISBN 0102272816 Pbk £1.80

Report on section 83 of 'The Queen's Bench Act' : the conclusiveness of foreign judgments in Manitoba / Manitoba Law Reform Commission. – Winnipeg : The Commission, 1986.
i,22p. – (Report).
Includes bibliographical references.

Report on section 9(7), (8) and (9) of the Worker's Compensation Act 1927 / Law Reform Commission of Tasmania. – Hobart? : Goverment Printer?, 1985.
17p. – (Report).

Report on sections 33 and 34 of 'The Wills Act' / Manitoba Law Reform Commission. – Winnipeg : The Commission, 1986.
ii,34p. – (Report).
Includes bibliographical references.

Report on settlement offers / Law Reform Commission of British Columbia. – Vancouver : Law Reform Commission of British Columbia, 1984.
47p.
ISBN 0771884494

Report on small projects / Manitoba Law Reform Commission. – Winnipeg : The Commission, 1985.
iv,48p. – (Report).
Includes bibliographical references.
ISBN 0771101074

Report on some aspects of medical treatment and criminal law / Law Reform Commission of Canada. – Ottawa : The Commission, 1986.
19,19p. – (Report).
Pages numbered in opposite directions. Text in English and French.
ISBN 0662543793

Report on spousal agreements / Law Reform Commission of British Columbia. – Victoria : Queens Printer, 1986.
37p.
Includes bibliographical references.
ISBN 0771885326

Report on Statute Law Revision Bill 1984 / Legal and Constitutional Committee. – Melbourne : Government Printer, 1984.
xiii,52p.
Bibliography: p.52.

Report on statutory succession rights / Law Reform Commission of British Columbia. – Vancouver : The Commission, 1983.
209p.
Date on title page 1983.
ISBN 0771884087

Report on succession rights on intestacy / Law Reform Commission of Tasmania. – Hobart : Government Printer, 1985.
21p. – (Report v no 43).

Report on suretyship and guarantee / Law Reform Commission of Tasmania. – Hobart : Government Printer, 1987.
30p. – (Report v no 50).

Report on the action per quod servitium amisit / Law Reform Commission of British Columbia. – Victoria : Queens Printer, 1986.
20p.
Includes bilbiographical references.
ISBN 0771885490

Report on the administration of assets of the solvent estates of deceased persons in the payment of debts and legacies / Law Reform Commission of Western Australia. – Perth : Law Reform Commission of Western Australia, 1988.
50p. – (Project).

Report on the adoption of the UNCITRAL model law of arbitration / the Law Reform Commission of Hong Kong. – Hong Kong : The Commisssion, 1987.
v,121p. – (Topic).
Includes bibliographical references.

Report on the age of consent in relation to sexual offences / Policy Advisory Committee on Sexual Offences : presented to Parliament by the Secretary of State for the Home Department. – London : H.M.S.O., 1981.
v,32p; 25cm.
ISBN 0101821603 unbound £2.70

Report on the Boundary Fences Act 1908 / Law Reform Commission of Tasmania. – Hobart : Government Printer, 1984.
19p. – (Report v no 37).

Report on the burden of proof in criminal proceedings and statutory offences / Law Reform Commission of Tasmania. – Hobart : Government Printer, 1987.
26p. – (Report v no 49).

Report on the buyer's lien : a new consumer remedy / Law Reform Commission of British Columbia. – Vancouver : The Commission, 1987.
iv,62p.
Includes bibliographical references.
ISBN 0771885954

Report on the consolidation of the Housing Acts : Housing Bill, Housing Associations Bill, Landlord and Tenant Bill / the Law Commission and the Scottish Law Commission. – London : H.M.S.O., 1985.
49p.
ISBN 0101951507

Report on the control of exemption clauses / the Law Reform Commission of Hong Kong. – Hong Kong : The Commission, 1986.
vi,98p. – (Topic).
Includes bibliographical references.

Report on the Court Order Interest Act / Law Reform Commission of British Columbia. – Vancouver : The Commission, 1987.
139p.
Includes bibliographical references.
ISBN 077188561X

Report on the Crown as creditor : priorities and privileges. – Law Reform Commission of British Columbia. – Victoria : Queen's Printer, 1982.
99p.
ISBN 0771883404

Report on the enforcement of judgment debts and related matters / Ontario Law Reform Commission. – 5 v. – Toronto : Ministry of the Attorney General, 1981.
Includes bibliographical references.
ISBN 0774360593 v.3

Report on the Expert Group Meeting of Law Teachers to Develop Curriculum Materials on Violence against Women : London, 11-15 May 1987. – London : Commonwealth Secretariat, 1987.
19p.

Report ... on the further consideration of the Contracts Review Bill 1978 / Law Reform Committee of South Australia. – Adelaide : Government Printer, 1986.
73p. – (74th report).
Bibliography: p.51-52.

Report on the Hague Convention on the Civil Aspects of International Child Abduction and some related matters / the Law Reform Commission. – Dublin : The Commission, 1985.
v,76p. – (LRC).
Includes text of Convention.

Report on the Hague Convention on the Taking of Evidence Abroad in Civil or Commercial Matters / the Law Reform Commission. – Dublin : The Commission, 1985.
v,75p. – (LRC).
Includes text of the Convention.

Report on 'The Human Tissue Act' / Manitoba Law Reform Commission. – Winnipeg : The Commission, 1986.
iv,145p. – (Report).
Bibliography: p. 134-145.

Report ... on the inherited imperial statute law with regard to proceedings in summary jurisdiction. – Law Reform Committee of South Australia. – Adelaide : Government Printer, 1981.
16p. – (58th report).

Report on the jurisdiction, procedures and administration of local courts / Law Reform Commission of Western Australia. – Perth : Law Reform Commission of Western Australia, 1988.
262p. – (Project).
Cover title: Report on local courts.

Report on the jury. – Law Reform Commission of. – Ottowa : Minister of Supply and Services, 982.
86p,91p. – (Report).
Added t.p. in French: Rapport sur le jury. Pages numbered in opposite directions. Text in English and French.
ISBN 0662518667

Report on the Land (Settled Estate) Act / Law Reform Commission of British Columbia. – Vancouver : The Commission, 1988.
41p.
Includes text of the Land (Settled Estate) Act and Trust Variation Act.
ISBN 0771887248

Report on the law of domicile / Law Reform Commission. – Winnipeg : Queen's Printer, 1982.
i,46p. – (Report).

Report on the law of mortgages / Ontario Law Reform Commission. – Toronto : Ministry of the Attorney General, 1987.
xiii,401p.
Includes text of draft bill.
ISBN 0772923205

Report on the law of trusts / Ontario Law Reform Commission. – 2. – Toronto : Ministry of the Attorney General, 1984.
ISBN 0774389141

Report on the law relating to the age of majority, the age for marriage and some connected subjects / the Law Reform Commission. – Dublin : The Commission, 1983.
v,75p. – (LRC).

Report on the legal capacity and responsibility of minors and pupils / Scottish Law Commission. – Edinburgh : HMSO, 1987.
vi,93p.
Includes draft legislation.
ISBN 0102151881

Report on the liability in tort of mentally disabled persons / the Law Reform Commission. – Dublin : The Commission, 1985.
v,78p. – (LRC).
Bibliography: p.75.

Report on the liability in tort of minors and the liability of parents for damage caused by minors / the Law Reform Commission. – Dublin : The Commission, 1985.
iv,123p. – (LRC).
Bibliography: pp.118-120.

Report on the liability of highway authorities for non-feasance / Law Reform Commission of Western Australia. – Perth : Law Reform Commission of Western Australia, 1981.
116p. – (Project v no 62).

Report on the limitation of actions / Newfoundland Law Reform Commission. – St. John's : The Commission, 1986.
vi,29p.

Report on 'The Married Women's Property Act' and related matters / Manitoba Law Reform Commission. – Winnipeg : The Commission, 1985.
i,76p. – (Report).
Includes bibliographical references.
ISBN 0771101163

Report on the Minister's Advisory Committee on the Personal Property Security Act. – Toronto : Ministry of Consumer and Commercial Relations, 1984.
iii,106p.

Report on the Pawnbrokers Act 1860-1984 / the Law Reform Commission of Western Australia. – Perth : The Commission, 1985.
82p. – (Project).

Report on the problem of old convictions / the Law Reform Commission of Western Australia. – Perth : Law Reform Commission of Western Australia, 1986.
267p. – (Project).

Report on the review of the law of admiralty / South African Law Commission. – S.l. : s.n., 1984.
47p. – (Report).
Photocopy.

Report on the rule against hearsay in civil cases / the Law Reform Commission. – Dublin : The Commission, 1988.
vii,34p. – (LRC).

Report on the rule in Hollington v. Hewthorn / Law Reform Commission of Tasmania. – Hobart : Government Printer, 1982.
7p. – (Report v no 29).

Report on the rules against accumulations and perpetuities / Law Reform Commission. – Winnipeg : Queen's Printer, 1982.
i,105p. – (Report).

Report on the Scottish term and quarter days / presented to Parliament by the Lord Advocate by Command of Her Majesty, October 1987. – Edinburgh : HMSO, 1987.
vi,29p.
ISBN 0101020821

Report on the Statute Law Revision Bill / Legal and Constitutional Committee. – Melbourne : Parliament of Victoria, 1983.
iii,12p.

Report on the Statute Law Revision (Repeals) Bill / Legal and Constitutional Committee. – Melbourne : Parliament of Victoria, 1982.
iii,3p.

Report on the statute of limitations : claims in respect of latent personal injuries / c the Law Reform Commission. – Dublin : The Commission, 1987.
65p. – (LRC).
Cover title: Personal injuries.

Report on the Strata Titles Act / the Law Reform Commission of Western Australia. – Perth : Law Reform Commission of Western Australia, 1982.
387p. – (Project).

Report on the structure of the courts
Part 1 : Amalgamation of the Court of Queen's Bench and the County Courts of Manitoba / Law Reform Commission. – Winnipeg : Queen's Printer, 1982.
iii,38,6p. – (Report).
Part II : the adjudication of smaller claims / Law Reform Commission. – 1983.
iii,56p. – (Report).

Report on 'The Survivorship Act' / Law Reform Commission. – Winnipeg : Queen's Printer, 1982.
ii,44p. – (Report).

Report on 'The Testators Family Maintenance Act' / Manitoba Law Reform Commission. – Winnipeg : The Commission, 1985.
iii,125p. – (Report).
Includes bibliographical references.
ISBN 0771101201

Report on the Uniform Sale of Goods Act / Manitoba Law Reform Commission. – Winnipeg : The Commission, 1983.
70p. – (Report).
Includes text of Act.

Report on the variation of private trusts / Law Reform Commission of Tasmania. – Hobart : Acting Government Printer, 1987.
28p. – (Report).
Includes text of Model Bill.

Report on trustees' powers of investment / Law Reform Commission of Western Australia. – Perth : Government Printer, 1984.
141p. – (Project v no 34 part 5).
Includes bibliographical references.

Report on trusts and analogous institutions
Part 1 : 1ere partie / Rapport sur les trusts et institutions analogues : Adair Dyer, Hans van Loon. – Provisional ed. – La Haye : Bureau Permanent de la Conference de la Haye de droit international prive, 1982.
127p.
At head of title: Conference de La Haye de droit international prive Hague Conference on Private International Law. English and French tables of contents as inserts. Parallel English and French text.

Report on vagrancy and related offences / the Law Reform Commission. – Dublin : The Commission, 1985.
v,129p. – (LRC).
Includes bibliographical references.

Report on variations of charitable trusts / Law Reform Commission of Tasmania. – Hobart? : Government Printer?, 1984.
23p. – (Report).

Report on wills : substantial compliance / Law Reform Commission of Western Australia. – Perth : The Commission, 1985.
60p. – (Project).
Includes bibliographical references.

Report on witnesses before legislative committees / Ontario Law Reform Commission. – Toronto : Ministry of the Attorney-General, 1981.
vii,129p.
ISBN 0774367296

Report on writs of assistance and telewarrants / Law Reform Commission of Canada. – Ottawa : The Commission, 1983.
110,124p; 25cm. – (Report).
Cover-title: Writs of assistance and telewarrants. Added t.p. in French: Rapport sur le mandat de main-forte et le telemandat. Pages numbered in opposite directions. In English and French.
ISBN 0662525159

Report ... relating to a general rule of standing in environmental matters / Law Reform Committee of South Australia. – Adelaide : Government Printer, 1987.
141,5,4p. – (97th report).
Bibliography: p.1-2. Includes text of draft bill..

Report ... relating to administrative appeals / Law Reform Committee of South Australia. – Adelaide : Government Printer, 1984.
67p. – (82nd report).
Bibliography: p.65-68.

Report ... relating to civil actions for perjury committed in criminal proceedings and to the tort of malicious prosecution / Law Reform Committee of South Australia. – Adelaide : Government Printer, 1984.
13p. – (83rd report).
Bibliography: p.14.

Report ... relating to claims for injuries from toxic substances and radiation effects / Law Reform Committee of South Australia. – Adelaide : Government Printer, 1985.
96p. – (87th report).

Report ... relating to group defamation. – Law Reform Committee of South Australia. – Adelaide : Government Printer, 1982.
13p. – (69th report).

Report ... relating to locus standi : prisoners' rights. – Law Reform Committee of South Australia. – Adelaide : Government Printer, 1982.
6p. – (70th report).

Report ... relating to maintenance, champerty, embracery and barratry, malicious prosecution and abuse of process / Law Reform Committee of South Australia. – Adelaide : Government Printer, 1987.
86,3p. – (101st report).
Includes text of the Abolition of Obsolete Offences Act (1969).

Report ... relating to owners or occupiers of land and trespassers on that land / Law Reform Committee of South Australia. – Adelaide : Government Printer, 1985.
13p. – (48th report).

Report ... relating to powers of attorney. – Law Reform Committee of South Australia. – Adelaide : Government Printer, 1981.
17p. – (47th report).

Report ... relating to prescription and limitation of actions / Law Reform Committee of South Australia. – Adelaide : Government Printer, 1987.
59,14p. – (76th report).

Report ... relating to problems of proof of survivorship as between two or more persons dying at about the same time in one accident / Law Reform Committee of South Australia. – Adelaide : Government Printer, 1985.
37p. – (88th report).
Bibliography: p.29.

Report ... relating to proceedings by and against the crown / Law Reform Committee of South Australia. – 1. – Adelaide : Government Printer, 1987.
Various pagings. – (104th report).

Report...relating to qui tam and penal actions and common informers / Law Reform Committee of South Australia. – Adelaide : Government Printer, 1985.
16p. – (94th report).

Report ... relating to reform of the law of delivery of deeds / Law Reform Committee of South Australia. – Adelaide : Government Printer, 1987.
42p. – (77th report).
Includes Bill for an act to amend the Law of Property Act, 1936.

Report ... relating to the amendment of the law of escheat. – Law Reform Committee of South Australia. – Adelaide : Government Printer, 1983.
7p. – (64th report).

Report ... relating to the demise of the Crown / Law Reform Committee of South Australia. – Adelaide : Government Printer, 1984.
13p. – (81st report).

Report relating to the doctrine of frustration in the law of contract / Law Reform Committee of South Australia. – Adelaide : Government Printer, 1983.
40p. – (71st report).

Report ... relating to the effect of mistake upon contracts / Law Reform Committee of South Australia. – Adelaide : Government Printer, 1987.
112p. – (106th report).
Bibliography: p.109-112.

Report ... relating to the fatal accidents provisions of the Wrongs Act 1936. – Law Reform Committee of South Australia. – Adelaide : Government Printer, 1981.
9p. – (56th report).

Report ... relating to the inherited imperial law / Law Reform Committee of South Australia. – Adelaide : Government Printer, 1984.
38p. – (80th report).

Report ... relating to the inherited imperial law and constitutional statutes / Law Reform Committee of South Australia. – Adelaide : Government Printer, 1985.
9p. – (96th report).

Report ... relating to the inherited imperial law and to statutes previously covered by the Colonial Laws Validity Act 1865. – Law Reform Committee of South Australia. – Adelaide : Government Printer, 1986.
22p. – (102nd report).

Report ... relating to the inherited imperial law on gaming and wagering in South Australia. – Law Reform Committee of South Australia. – Adelaide : Government Printer, 1982.
9p. – (68th report).

Report ... relating to the inherited imperial law regarding the Crown. – Law Reform Committee of South Australia. – Adelaide : Government Printer, 1981.
15p. – (65th report).

Report ... relating to the inherited imperial observance of Lord's Day Acts / Law Reform Committee of South Australia. – Adelaide : Government Printer, 1987.
40p. – (92nd report).
Bibliography: p.40.

Report ... relating to the irrecoverability of benefits obtained by reason of mistake of law / Law Reform Committee of South Australia. – Adelaide : Government Printer, 1984.
40p. – (84th report).

Report ... relating to the law governing locus standi : non-party interventions and amici curiae in relation to proceedings in civil jurisdiction. – Law Reform Committee of South Australia. – Adelaide : Government Printer, 1982.
9p. – (67th report).

Report ... relating to the law of detinue, conversion and trespass to goods / Law Reform Committee of South Australia. – Adelaide : Government Printer, 1987.
100p. – (95th report).
Bibliography: p.99-100.

Report ... relating to the reform of the law of distress. – Law Reform Committee of South Australia. – Adelaide : Government Printer, 1983.
8p. – (66th report).

Report relating to the reform of the law of set-off / Law Reform Committee of South Australia. – Adelaide : Government Printer, 1983.
11p. – (75th report).
Includes draft Act.

Report ... relating to the reform of the law on wills and intestacies / Law Reform Committee of South Australia. – Adelaide : Government Printer, 1983.
7p. – (72nd report).

Report ... relating to the reform of the law regarding entire contracts and the rule usually known as the rule in Cutter v. Powell / Law Reform Committee of South Australia. – Adelaide : Government Printer, 1986.
29p. – (90th report).

Report ... relating to the review and reappraisal of the twenty-fifth report of this committe sic on the subject of misfeasance and non-feasance / Law Reform Committee of South Australia. – Adelaide : Government Printer, 1986.
48p. – (51st report).
Bibliography: p.39-40.

Report relating to the use of or reference to the records of proceedings of the House in the courts : together with minutes of proceedings of the Committee / the Parliament of the Commonwealth of Australia, House of Representatives, Committee of Privileges. – Canberra : Commonwealth Government Printer, 1981.
vii,108p. – (Parliamentary paper).
ISBN 0642057206

Report to Parliament on a proposal for a Statute Law (Miscellaneous Provisions) Bill / Legal and Constitutional Committee. – Melbourne : Parliament of Victoria, 1985.
xii,189p.

Report to Parliament on a proposal for a Statute Law (Miscellaneous Provisions) Bill / Legal and Constitutional Committee. – Melbourne : Government Printer, 1985.
xii,189p.

Report to Parliament on overseas court delays and remedies / Legal and Constitutional Committee. – Melbourne : Parliament of Victoria, 1984.
xxiii,310p.
Bibliography: p.299-310.

Report to Parliament on the Australian Constitutional Convention : an assessment of the 1985 Brisbane plenary session; the Convention generally and its future / Legal and Constitutional Committee. – Melbourne : Parliament of Victoria, 1986.
ix,49p.
Cover title: Second report on the Australian Constitutional Convention.

Report to Parliament on the Australian Constitutional Convention : issues before the 1985 plenary session / Legal and Constitutional Committee. – Melbourne : Parliament of Victoria, 1985.
xix,187p.
Bibliography: p.185-187. Cover title: First report on the Australian Constitutional Convention.

Report to Parliament on the burden of proof in criminal cases / Legal and Constitutional Committee. – Melbourne : Government Printer, 1985.
xvi,101p.
Bibliography: p.100-101.

Report to Parliament on the desirability or otherwise of legislation defining and protecting Human rights / Legal and Constitutional Committee. – Melbourne : Government Printer, 1987.
xxiii,225p.

Report to Parliament on the proposals contained in the Interpretation Bill 1982 / Legal and Constitutional Committee. – Melbourne : Parliament of Victoria, 1983.
xxvii,235p.
Bibliography: p.228-235.

Report to Parliament on the Subordinate Legislation (Deregulation) Bill 1983 / Legal and Constitutional Committee. – Melbourne : Parliament of Victoria, 1984.
lxiv,474p.
Bibliography: p.450-474.

Report to Parliament upon support services for victims of crime / Legal and Constitutional Committee. – Melbourne : Government Printer, 1987.
xxxii,125p.

Report to the Attorney-General concerning the administration of civil justice in Victoria
Volume 1 / John Young. – Melbourne : Government Printer, 1984.
xxxiv,382p.
Chairman: Sir John Young.
ISBN 0908417152
Volume 2 : Appendices. – 1984.
1 vol. (various pagings).
Chairman: Sir John Young.
ISBN 0908417160 Hbk

Report to the House of Assembly of the Select Committee on Workers' Compensation. – Nova Scotia. – Halifax : Queen's Printer, 1981.
65p.
Includes bibliographical references.

Report to the Secretary of State on the framework of legislation to replace the Cruelty to Animals Act 1876 / Advisory Committee on Animal Experiments. – London : Home Office, 1981.
40p.

Reported decisions of the Commissioner under the Social Security and Child Benefit Acts / Department of Health and Social Security. – London : H.M.S.O., 1980-.
Continues: Reported decisions of the Commissioner under the Social Security, National Insurance and Family Allowances Acts.

Reported decisons of the Commissioner under the Social Security Act (1975) / Department of Health and Social Security. – London : H.M.S.O., 1982-.
Continues: Reported decisions of the Commissioner under the Social Security and National Insurance (Industrial Injuries) Acts.

Reports
4th : non-departmental public bodies : observations by the government. – London : H.M.S.O., 1985.
8 p.
ISBN 0101956304
16th : Prostitution in the street. – 1984.
ISBN 0101932901 Pbk £4.00

Reports and Pleas of Assizes at York : 1631-50. – Repr. of 1651 ed. – Abingdon : Professional Books.
335p.
Hbk £120.00

Reports Court of Chancery : 1737-83. – Repr. of 1790 ed. – Abingdon : Professional Books.
344p.
Hbk £75.00

Reports King's Bench : 1737-1738. – Repr. of 1754 ed. – Abingdon : Professional Books.
292p.
Hbk £55.00

Reports of Cases in King's Bench. – Repr. of 1766 ed. – Abingdon : Professional Books.
298p.
Hbk £55.00

Reports of Cases in the Court of King's Bench : With Some Special Cases in the Courts of Chancery, Common Pleas and Exchequer, Alphabetically Digested Under Proper Heads for the 1st of William and Mary to the 10th of Anne (1689-1712, 3 Vols. – Repr. of 1724 ed. – Abingdon : Professional Books.
308p.
Hbk £90.00

Reports of Family Law, 50
Vols. 1-50 incl. consolidated index, 4 Vols. – Carswell Legal Publications. – Agincourt : Carswell.
– (Second Ser.).
Hbk £1260.00
Back Vols.. –
Hbk £33.75 ea.

Reports of Family Law
Individual Vols. /. – Agincourt : Carswell.
Hbk £33.75 ea.

Reports of family law. – Toronto : Carswell, 1971.
Consolidated indexes published for first and second series.

Reports of Family Law : 1824-1970, 5 Vols. – Agincourt : Carswell.
– (Reprint Ser.).
Hbk £252.00

Reports of Family Law Consolidated Index, 4 Vols. Vol. 3 /. – Agincourt : Carswell, 1984.
Pbk £80.00
Vol. 4. – 1986.
Pbk £65.75

Reports of Income Tax Cases (1886-1937), Vols. – Allahabad : Law Publishers.
£24.00 ea

Reports of International Arbitral Awards. – United Nations. – London : HMSO, 1982.
532p.
Reports on awards in three arbitration cases; the delimitation of the continental shelf between UK and France, the air service agreement between USA and France, and the taxation liability of EURATOM.
ISBN 0119074761 Hbk £24.75

Reports of Judgments, Advisory Opinions and Orders
ICJ No 521: Yearbook No 40, 1985-1986. – International Court of Justice. – Geneva : United Nations Publications.
Hbk £12.00
ICJ No 523: Case Concerning Border and Transborder Armed Actions (Nicaragua/Costa Rica), Order of 21 October 1986. –
Hbk £1.00
ICJ No 525: Case Concerning the Frontier Dispute (Burkina Faso/Republic of Mali), Judgment of 22 December 1986. –
Hbk £12.00
ICJ No 526: Case Concerning Elettronica Sicula S.p.A. (ELSI) (U.S.A./Italy), Order of 2 March 1987, Constitution of Chamber. –
Hbk £1.00
ICJ No 528: Bibliography No 39, 1985. –
Hbk £2.00
ICJ No 529: Case Concerning the Land, Island and Maritime Frontier Dispute (El Salvador/Honduras), Order of 8 May 1987, Constitution of Chamber. –
Hbk £1.00
ICJ No 530: Index 1986. –
Hbk £2.00
ICJ No 531: Case Concerning the Land, Island and Maritime Frontier Dispute (El Salvador/Honduras), Order of 27 May 1987. –
Hbk £1.00
ICJ No 532: Application for Review of Judgment No 333 of the United Nations Administrative Tribunal, Advisory Opinion of 27 May 1987. –
Hbk £16.00
ICJ No 533: Case Concerning the Land, Island and Maritime Frontier Dispute (El Salvador/Honduras), Order of 29 May 1987. –
Hbk £1.00
Reports of Judgments, Advisory Opinions and Orders. – 1986.
Hbk £68.00
Reports of Judgments Advisory Opinions and Orders. – 1986.
Hbk £6.00

Reports of Patent Cases 1884-1986 103 vols. – Professional Books.
ISBN 0862052785 Hbk £5,550.00

Reports of Patent Cases : 1884-date, 98 Vols. (subject to contractual arrangements with Patent Office). – Abingdon : Professional Books.
Hbk

Reports of Tax Cases : 1875-1982, 53 Vols. – Abingdon : Professional Books, 1984.
Hbk

Reports of the European Communities 1952-1977 : an index to authors and chairmen / compiled by June Neilson. – London : Mansell, 1981.
xiv,561p; 23cm.
Includes index.
ISBN 0720115922 £27.50

Reports Tax Cases 1875-1987 58 vols. – Professional Books.
ISBN 0862052823 Hbk £1,550.00

Representation and Urban Community. – London : Macmillan, 1981.
200p.
ISBN 0333288785 Hbk £20.00

Representation, Democracy and Public Law. – London : Sweet & Maxwell, 1985.
– (Modern Legal Studies Ser.).
Hbk £19.50

Reproducing order : a study of police patrol work / Richard V. Ericson. – Toronto : Published in association with the Centre of Criminology, University of Toronto, by University of Toronto Press, 1982.
xii,243p; 24cm. – (Canadian studies in criminology).
Bibliography: p225-236. - Includes index.
ISBN 0802055699 Hbk
ISBN 0802064752 Pbk £9.90

Reproduction revolution / Wells. – Oxford : Oxford University Press, 1984.
ISBN 0192177362 Hbk £15.00
ISBN 0192860445 Pbk £3.95

Reproductive technology. – Oxford : Blackwell, 1987.
ISBN 0745602096 Pbk £7.95

Reprographic copying of books and journals : a guide for librarians, teachers and all users of copyright works. – British Copyright Council. – London : British Copyright Council, 1985.
10p.
ISBN 0901737046

Re-promulgation of ordinances : a fraud on the constitution of India / D. C. Wadhwa. – Pune : Gokhale Institute of Politics and Economics, 1983.
xxxi,259p.
ISBN 0861314328 Hbk £95.00

Republic of Korea : violations of human rights : an Amnesty International report. – London : Amnesty International Publications, 1981.
43p; 30cm.
ISBN 0862100313 unbound

Res Judicata and Collateral Estoppel Tools for Plaintiffs and Defendants. – Westport Publications.
ISBN 0899302777 Hbk £32.95

Rescuing nationals abroad through military coercion and intervention on grounds of humanity / Natalino Ronzitti. – Dordrecht Netherlands : M. Nijhoff Publishers, 1985.
236p.
Includes index. Bibliography.
ISBN 9024731356 Hbk £125.00

Research and development in Canada: a practical guide to financing, protecting and exploiting new technology / Bereskin, Parr. – Scarborough, Ontario : Butterworths (Canada), 1987.
288.
Gives details on how to manage proprietary information, legally protect new technology, cash in on the many federal and provincial government research and development assistance programmes, pursue private venture captial funding, benefit from tax incentivs available to Canadian research and development, license technology, and how publicly funded institutions can profit from the exploitation of technology.
ISBN 0409805670 Hbk

Research Contracts : Civil-Law Means Promotion Scientific Technical Progress. – Dordrecht : Kluwer, 1977.
235p.
ISBN 9028603174 Hbk £59.00

Research Guide to Criminology Material. – Canberra : Australian Institute of Criminology.
Hbk £1.00

Research in criminal justice : stock-taking of criminological research at the Max-Planck-Institute for Foreign and International Penal Law after a decade / edited by the Criminological Research Unit. – Freiburg : Max-Planck-Institute for Foreign and International Penal Law, 1982.
xiii, 508 p.; 21 cm. – (Kriminologische Forschungsberichte aus dem Max-Planck-Institut fur Auslandisches und Internationales Strafrecht, Freiburg).
Includes bibliographies and index.
ISBN 3922498019 Pbk

Research on the range and quality of broadcasting services : a report for the Committee on Financing the BBC / West Yorkshire Media in Politics Group, Centre for Television Research, The University of Leeds. – London : H.M.S.O., 1986.
180p.
Based on two internal papers, prepared for the Home Office. Provides information on the level of violent crime in England and Wales, the form it takes and the measures being taken to combat it.
ISBN 0113408331

Research opportunities in Commonwealth developing countries : universities, non-university research institutions : a register prepared by the Association of Commonwealth Universities in association with the Commonwealth Secretariat. – Association of Commonwealth Universities. – New ed. – London : The Association, 1984.
235p.
Previous ed. published as: Research strengths of universities in the developing countries of the Commonwealth. London, 1978. Includes index.

Research paper on actions of ejection and removing / by A.G.M. Duncan. – Edinburgh : Law Commission, 1984.
xv,204p.
'Published by the Scottish Law Commission in connection with Consultative Memorandum No. 59'. Includes bibliographical references.

Research paper on computer misuse / by W.G. Briscoe. – Hobart? : Government Printer?, .
167p. – (Research paper).

Research paper on fines / by C.A. Warner. – Hobart? : Government Printer?, 1984.
vi,115,6p. – (Research paper).
Includes bibliographical references.

Research paper on occupiers' liability law / Max Atkinson. – Hobart : Government Printer?, 1984.
iv,75p.

Research paper on the variation of private trusts / by E.L.G. Tyler. – Hobart? : Government Printer?, 1985.
54p.

Research Study on Supplementary Benefit Appeal Tribunals : Review of Main Findings; Conclusions; Recommendations. – London : HMSO.
55p.
ISBN 011760335X Hbk

Reserach on white collar crime : exploring the issues / S.E. Varette ... et al. – Ottawa : Ministry of the Solicitor General, 1985.
84,36p. – (User report).
Biliography: 4 pages.

Reservation of title : draft Council of Europe Convention (CDCJ(82)15) / memorandum by a Working Party of the Senate of the Inns of Court and the Bar and the Law Society. – London? : the Working Party?, 1983.
4p.
Bound with 'Draft proposal for a Council Directive on the legal consequences of agreements creating simple reservation of title (III/872/79-EN)'.

Reservation of title clauses / Brice Dickson. – Belfast : SLS Legal Publications, 1987.
ii,96p.
Bibliography: pp.93-94..

Reservations and Interpretative Declarations to Multilateral Treaties. – Amsterdam : Elsevier Science Publishers, 1988.
xxviii, 514p.
ISBN 0444703985 Hbk £250.00

Reservoirs Act 1975 : A Legal Commentary. – Property Lawyer.
ISBN 00951354701 Pbk £5.75

Resettling refugees : the lessons of research / by Simon Field. – London : H.M.S.O., 1985.
vi,60p; 25cm.
Bibliographical references: p55-60. A Home Office Research and Planning Unit report.
ISBN 0113408153 Hbk

Residence, domicile and UK taxation. – London : Butterworths, 1986.
ISBN 0406580103 Pbk £32.00

Resident landlords and owner-occupiers: law and practice. – London : Longman Professional (UK), 1987.
– (Practitioner series).
Details the issues raised by the relationship between resident landlords, owner-occupiers, and their tenants. Analyses the nature of tenancies, and gives advice on the correct formalities and procedures to be followed, including the right of the landlord to possession.
ISBN 085121293X Hbk £14.50

Residential burglary : the limits of prevention / by Stuart Winchester and Hilary Jackson. – London : H.M.S.O., 1982.
v,42p; 25cm.
Bibliography: p40-42. 'A Home Office Research and Planning Unit report'.
ISBN 0113407696

Residential Complex Sales Representation Act, 1983, Bill 113 : An Act to Regulate Conveyances of Dwelling Units in Residential Complexes. – Ontario : Ontario Government Publications Service, 1983.
3p.
Hbk £0.30

Residential estate conveyancing : practice and precedents / John Cawthorn. – London : Butterworths, 1983.
xviii,501p; 26cm.
Includes index.
ISBN 0406148201

Residential leases : draftsman's handbook. – London : Longman Professional, 1985.
ISBN 085120774X Pbk £19.95

Residential possession proceedings / R Davidson. – 3rd. – London : Longman Professional (UK), 1990.
– (Practitioner series).
Contains legal and procedural instructions as to how to effect or prevent the recovery of possession of residential premises. Explains the relevant law, procedure to adopt, evidence required, and orders the court may make. Over 100 specimen forms.

Residential tenancies. – London : Butterworths, 1988.
ISBN 0409787507 Pbk £34.00

Residential tenancies. – London : Longman Professional (UK), 1988.
– (Longman practice notes).
Contains information on the law and procedure of private residential tenancies. Covers precedents for use in court proceedings, and procedures such as obtaining possession of premises, applying for a fair rent, granting tenancies or bringing an action for arrears of rent.
ISBN 0851214479 Pbk £9.95

Residential Tenancies. – 4th ed. – Agincourt : Carswell, 1983.
366p.
This textbook is a comprehensive treatment of the Canadian law of landlord and tenant in the residential tenancy. Numerous reported and unreported decisions from courts across Canada are summarized in the work.
Hbk £40.50

Residential Tenancies Handbook. – Butterworths.
ISBN 0409787507 Hbk £47.30

Residential Tenancies Handbook - Victoria. – Butterworths, 1982.
224p.
ISBN 0409309168 Pbk £39.00

Residential tenancy law and practice / by Adrian J. Bradbrook, Susan V. MacCallum, Anthony P. Moore : with a foreword by the Honourable Mr. Justice King. – Sydney : Law Book Co., 1983.
lx,940p.
Bibliography: p.891-898. - Includes index. Includes texts of Residential Tenancies Act 1980 of Victorian jurisdiction and Residential Tenancies Act 1978-81 of South Australian jurisdiction.
ISBN 0455204977

Resolution of disputes under the Official Information Act 1982 / by K. J. Keith. – Wellington : Information Authority, 1984.
12p. – (Occasional paper).

Resolution of family conflict : comparative legal perspectives / edited by John M. Eekelaar, Sanford N. Katz. – Toronto : Butterworths, 1984.
xviii,610p.
Includes bibliographical references.
ISBN 0409839841 Hbk £32.00

Resolutions and Other Decisions of the Assembly : 11th Session 1979 (Res. 410-462)
Chinese /. – London : International Maritime Organization.
Hbk £10.00
English. –
ISBN 9280111027 Hbk £10.00
French. –
ISBN 928012093X Hbk £10.00
Russian. –
ISBN 928014040X Hbk £10.00

Resolutions and Other Decisions of the Assembly : 12th Session 1981 (Res. 463-512)
English. – International Maritime Organization. – London : International Maritime Organization, 1982.
ISBN 9280111477 Hbk £12.00
French. –
ISBN 9280121189 Hbk £12.00
Russian. –
ISBN 9280140426 Hbk £12.00
Spanish. –
ISBN 9280130854 Hbk £12.00
Chinese. –
Hbk £12.00

Resolutions and Other Decisions of the Assembly : 13th Session 1983 (Res. 513-557)
Chinese /. – London : International Maritime Organization.
ISBN 9280160036 Hbk £14.00
English. –
ISBN 9280111752 Hbk £12.00
French. –
ISBN 9280121405 Hbk £14.00
Russian. –
Hbk £14.00

Resolutions of the United Nations Security Council. – Dordrecht : Nijhoff (Martinus), 1989.
179. – (Legal aspects of international organisation 8).
Presents a picture of the legal questions concerning Security Council resolutions and their place in the international legal order. Makes a comparison of Charter provisions with the Security Council's practice. The last chapter of the book examines the question of whether a Security Council resolution is binding.
ISBN 902473567X Hbk Gld120.00

Resolving family conflict in the 1980s : a unified family court / Justices' Clerks' Society. – Bristol : The Society, 1982.
88p.

Resolving Transnational Disputes Through Intern. Arbitration. – London : Eurospan.
ISBN 0813910234 Hbk £26.50

Resource recovery : a report for the Royal Commission on Environmental Pollution / prepared by Environmental Resources Limited. – 1. – London : HMSO, 1986.
various pagings.
ISBN 0117301329

Response by the Law Society of Scotland to Consultative Paper on Conveyancing by Employed Solicitors in Scotland. – Law Society of Scotland. – Edinburgh : The Society, 1984.
20p.

Response of local authorities to central government incitement to reduce expenditure / by W. J. Meadows. – Strasbourg : Council of Europe, 1986.
33p.
Prepared under the guidance of the Committee of Experts on Local and Regional Finance of the Steering Committee for Regional and Municipal Matters.

Response to 'Small claims in the County Court' / JUSTICE. – London : JUSTICE, 1987.
20p.

Response to SNOP. – Cambridge : Institute of Criminology, 1986.
Hbk £5.00

Responses to crime / Lord Windlesham. – Oxford : Clarendon, 1987.
xviii,357p; 24cm.
Includes index.
ISBN 0198255837 £17.95

Responsibility in health care / edited by George J. Agich. – Dordrecht, Holland : D. Reidel, 1982.
xxiii, 285p.
Outgrowth of the Eleventh Trans-disciplinary Symposium on Philosophy and Medicine held in Springfield, Ill., on March 16-18, 1981. Includes bibliographies and index.
ISBN 9027714177

Rest Assured : a Guide to Wills, Estates and Funerals. – Redfern : Redfern Legal Centre Publishing, 1988.
96p.
Hbk £9.95

Restitution / by G.H.L. Fridman, and James G. McLeod. – Toronto, Canada : Carswell Co., 1982.
lxviii, 649 p.; 26 cm.
Includes bibliographical references and index.

Restitution / P. Birks. – London : Sweet & Maxwell, 1986.
ISBN 0420472908 Hbk

Restitution imposed on property offenders in New Zealand courts : a study of orders and compliance / Burt Galaway, Walton Walker. – Wellington : Department of Justice, 1985.
v,27p. – (Study series).
Bibliography: p.26.

Restraint of trade and business secrets : law and practice / Simon Mehigan and David Griffiths. – 1st ed. – London : Longman Professional (UK), 1987.
xxiv,247p; 24cm. – (Longman commercial series).
Coverage includes employment contracts, business sale, partnerships and joint ventures, breach of contract, commercial contracts including licensing, distribution agreements, trade associations, evaluation agreements and performing contracts. List of cases classified according to business type.
ISBN 0851211747 Hbk £42.00

Restrictions on the kind of organisation through which members of professions may offer their services / a report by the Director General of Fair Trading. – London : Office of Fair Trading, 1986.
86p,36p.

Restrictive Practices. – Shelter. – London : Shelter, 1984.
ISBN 0901242691 Hbk £1.50

Restrictive trade practices : judgments, materials and policy / Alan A. Ransom and Warren Pengilley. – Sydney : Legal Books Pty, 1985.
xlix,1193p.
Includes index.
ISBN 0949553158

Restructuring labour in the enterprise : law and practice in France, F.R. of Germany, Italy, Sweden and the United Kingdom / edited by R. Blanpain. – Deventer, The Netherlands : Kluwer, .
v,145p.
Includes bibliographical references. At head of cover: Institute for Labour Relations, Catholic University of Leuven.
ISBN 9065442839

Restructuring the International Economic Order : the Role of Law and Lawyers. – Dordrecht : Kluwer, 1987.
280p.
ISBN 9065442758 Hbk £125.00

Resurrection of the Pauper-Labour Argument. – London : Trade Policy Research Centre, 1981.
82p.
Hbk £2.00

Retail Banking / Lavis. – Oxford : Blackwell.
ISBN 0631149325 Hbk £29.50

Retail financial services : development and future. – London : Butterworths, 1988.
ISBN 0406259437 Pbk

Retail sales tax in Canada / A.J. Robinson. – Toronto : Canadian Tax Foundation, 1986.
165p. – (Canadian Tax Papers: No. 77).
Bibliography: p.152-161. - Includes index.
ISBN 0888080255 Hbk £12.50

Retailers, dealers, wholesalers and distributors. – Product Liability Briefing, 1988.
ISBN 1870317300 Pbk £6.50

Retention of title on the sale of goods / John Parris. – London : Granada, 1982.
186p; 24cm.
Includes index.
ISBN 0246116129

Rethinking the sources of international law / by G. J. H. van Hoof. – Deventer : Kluwer, 1983.
xiv,322p; 25cm.
Dutch summary, p.313-321.
ISBN 9065440852 Pbk £121.00

Retired, unemployed or at risk : changes in the Australian labour market for older workers. – Canberra : Australian Government Publishing Service, 1983.
ix,150p. – (Research report).
Bibliography: p144-150.
ISBN 0644028580 £6.50

Retirement Planning for Solicitors and Other Self-Employed Persons : 1984 Crash Course Lecture. – London : Law Society, 1984.
20p.
Hbk £1.95

Retirement planning guide. – Allied Dunbar. – 2nd ed. – London : Longman Professional (UK), 1988.
ISBN 0851212115 £13.50

Retirement Policy : The Next Fifty Years. – London : Policy Studies Institute, 1982.
212p. – (Joint Studies in Public Policy).
Hbk £15.00

Retirement relief - New CGT Rules. – London : CCH, 1986.
ISBN 0863250815 Pbk £7.50

Retirement relief; the capital gains tax rules explained. – 2nd. – Bicester : CCH Editions Ltd, 1988.
Examines the changes introduced by the 1987 and 1988 Finance Acts. Includes two new chapters on two-tier relief and the Inland Revenue concession on date of disposal. Also covers how retirement relief works, the date of disposal, unincorporated businesses, partners, directors, trustees, full-time employees, furnished holiday lettings, husband and wife, interactions with tax, and a legislation finding list.
ISBN 0863251668 Hbk £15.50

Retirement Villages : Conference Papers. – Woolloomooloo : International Business Communications, 1986.
ISBN 0949072095 Hbk £75.00

Retrenchment, Lay-Off and Closure Based on Latest Amendments and Up-to-date Case-Laws. – Allahabad : Law Publishing House, 1982.
ca 400p.
Hbk £60.00

Rettie
Court of Session Cases : Series 1-5, 1821-1906, 63 Vols.
4th Series, 1873-1898, 25 Vols. /. – Abingdon : Professional Books.
Hbk

Return to an order of the Honourable House of Commons dated 16 July 1987 for report of an inquiry by Her Majesty's Chief Inspector of Prisons for England and Wales into the disturbances in prison service establishments in England between 29 April-2 May 1986. – London : H.M.S.O., 1987.
viii,127p; 30cm.
Spine title: Report of an inquiry by Her Majesty's Chief Inspector of Prisons for England and Wales into the disturbances in prison service establishments in England between 29 April-2 May 1986.
ISBN 0117013366 Pbk £10.00

Reukema, Barbara
Discriminatory Refusal of Carriage in North America. – Dordrecht : Kluwer, 1982.
310p.
ISBN 9065440496 Hbk £165.00

Reuss-Ianni, Elizabeth
Two cultures of policing : street cops and management cops / Elizabeth Reuss-Ianni. – New Brunswick, N.J. : Transaction Books, 1983.
145p; 24cm.
Bibliography: p137-142. - Includes index.
ISBN 0878554696

Reuter
Young Solicitors' Guide, The / Simkin. – London : Reuter Simkin.
ISBN 0951110705 Pbk £2.25

Reuter, Paul
Principles of the Law of Treaties. – London : Pinter, 1989.
250.
Translated from the French and updated in the light of the 1986 Convention on the Law of Treaties between States and International Organizations.
ISBN 0861879546 Hbk £30

Revenue budget process of the Government of Canada : description, appraisal and proposals / Douglas G. Hartle. – Toronto : Canadian Tax Foundation, 1982.
xii,76p.
Includes index.
ISBN 0888080093

Revenue investigations manual / B E V Sabine. – London : Butterworths, 1987.
ISBN 0406500703 Pbk £19.50

Revenue law. – London : Financial Training, 1987. – (SWOT).
ISBN 090632291X Pbk £8.95

Revenue law : comprising income tax, surtax, capital gains tax, corporation tax, estate duty tax, stamp duties, tax and estate planning / by Barry Pinson. – 5th ed. – London : Sweet & Maxwell, 1971.
lxvi,641p.
Previous ed.: 1970. Includes index.
ISBN 0421163607 Pbk
ISBN 0421163704

Revenue law : principles and practice / Chris Whitehouse, Elizabeth Stuart-Buttle. – 6th ed. – London : Butterworths, 1988.
xxxi,690p.
Previous ed.: 1987.
ISBN 0406502692 Pbk £23.50

Revenue law in Scotland / Simon Mackintosh. – London : Butterworths, 1986.
Starts with an introduction to the Scottish legal system and a discussion of applying UK revenue law in Scotland. Chapters on taxation of persons, property, charities and partnership with longer chapters on trusts and succession. Styles for discretionary and accumulation and maintenance trusts provided.
ISBN 040650170X Pbk £18.50

Revenue law in Singapore and Malaysia / cases and commentary : Leo D. Pointon. – Singapore : Butterworths, 1986.
xxvii,281p.
Includes the interpretation of statutes and cases, administration, income, exempt income, deductions, capital allowances, personal reliefs, partnerships, and estate duty.
ISBN 0409995266 Hbk £78

Review and Analysis of Canadian PLEI Research. – Ottawa : Canadian Law Information Council, 1983.
104p.
ISBN 0920358527 Pbk £7.50

Review Body on Use of Judicial Time in the Superior courts in Scotland
Report of the Review Body on Use of Judicial Time in the Superior Courts in Scotland / Chairman: The Honourable Lord Maxwell. – Edinburgh : Scottish Courts Administration, 1986.
vi,164p.

Review of administrative action / by Mark Aronson and Nicola Franklin : with a chapter on freedom of information legislation by Peter Bayne. – Sydney : Law Book Co., 1987.
lxvii,720p.
Includes bibliographical references and index.
ISBN 0455207216

Review of appeals under the Immigration Act 1971 : a discussion document / Home Office. – Croydon : Home Office, 1981.
16p.

Review of Australian Criminological Research, 1983. – Canberra : Australian Institute of Criminology.
Hbk £3.75

Review of Australian Law and Practice Relating to the Conventions Adopted by the International Labour Conference. – Department of Industrial Relations. – Canberra : Australian Government Publishing Service, 1981.
ISBN 0642052166 Llf £14.20

Review of child care law : publication of interim discussion papers by the inter-Departmental working party / Department of Health and Social Security. – 1. – London : The Department, 1986.
various pagings.
ISBN 1851970401

Review of child care law : report to ministers of an interdepartmental working party : published by the government as a consultative document / Rupert Hughes. – London : H.M.S.O., 1985.
v,179p.
Chairman: Rupert Hughes. At head of title-page: Department of Health and Social Security.
ISBN 0113210426

Review of Civil Jury Awards. – Victoria : Government of British Columbia, 1984.
Hbk £7.75

Review of civil jury awards / Law Reform Commission of British Columbia. – Vancouver : The Commission, 1983.
iii,104p. – (Working paper).
Includes bibliographical references.

Review of Crimes Act 1914 and other crimes legislation of the Commonwealth / Human Rights Commission. – Canberra : Australian Government Publishing Service, 1983.
viii,44p. – (Report).
Includes extracts from legislation.
ISBN 0644027207

Review of criminal procedure / the Law Society. – London : Law Society, 1981.
24p.

Review of Ghana law. – Accra : General Legal Council, 1969-.
Index in each vol.

Review of government legal services / report by Sir Robert Andrew. – London : HMSO, 1989.
102p.
At head of title: Cabinet Office.
ISBN 0114300348

Review of Import Control and Customs Bylaw Decision. – Administrative Review Council. – Canberra : Australian Government Publishing Service, 1982.
22p.
ISBN 0642070679 Hbk £1.20

Review of International Business Law
Vol. 1. – Agincourt : Carswell, 1987.
This work focuses on international trade, securities and banking law, international commercial arbitration and dispute settlement, foreign investment, transactional resource issues, and international taxation issues. There are articles, updates on current issues, case comments and book reviews.
Hbk £59.00

Review of investor protection : a discussion document / by L.C.B. Gower. – London : H.M.S.O., 1982.
iii,142p.
'Commissioned by the Secretary of State for Trade' - introd..
ISBN 0115135405

Review of investor protection : report Part 2 / L. C. B. Gower. – London : H.M.S.O., 1985.
vii,64p.
Part 1 published as Command Paper 9125 in Parliamentary Papers 1983-84.
ISBN 0115138234

Review of investor protection : report : part 1 / by L.C.B. Gower : presented to Parliament by the Secretary of State for Trade and Industry ... – London : H.M.S.O., 1984.
x,212p.
Includes bibliographical references.
ISBN 0101912501

Review of legislation on false and misleading price information : report of the inter-departmental working party / Department of Trade and Industry. – London : The Department, 1984.
67p.

Review of pensions decisions under repatriation legislation : report to the Attorney-General / Administrative Review Council. – Canberra : Australian Government Publishing Service, 1983.
vi,60p. – (Parliamentary paper).
ISBN 0644028920

Review of preferent claims in insolvency / South African Law Commission. – Pretoria : The Commission, 1984.
viii,75p. – (Report).
Bibliography: p.vii-viii.

Review of public order law / presented to Parliament by the Secretary of State for the Home Department and the Secretary of State for Scotland. – London : H.M.S.O., 1985.
iii,53p; 25cm.
ISBN 0101951000

Review of Road Freight Regulation in Britain. – Bureau of Transport Economics. – Canberra : Australian Government Publishing Service, 1981.
78p. – (BTE Occasional Paper: No. 43).
ISBN 0642067953 Hbk £3.80

Review of the Children Act ten years on : its effect on foster care policy and practice / David Owen ... et al. : with an introduction by Alan Holden. – London : National Foster Care Association, 1986.
44p; 21cm.
ISBN 0946015252 Pbk £2.95

Review of the Commonwealth Superannuation Scheme : a report to the Minister for Finance / by E.S. Knight & Co. – Canberra : Australian Government Publishing Service, 1983.
28p.
ISBN 0644027363

Review of the Justices Act 1902-1982 : constitution, powers and procedure of Courts of Petty Sessions / the Law Reform Commission of Western Australia. – Perth : Law Reform Commission of Western Australia, 1984.
ii,253p. – (Discussion paper).
Cover title: Courts of Petty Sessions: constitution, powers and procedure.

Review of the law and practice of extradition in the United Kingdom / Report of an interdepartmental working party. – London : Criminal Justice Department, Home Office, 1982.
vii,128p.

Review of the law of evidence / South African Law Commission. – Pretoria : The Commission, 1986.
vii,88 leaves. – (Project).
Bibliography: p.81-88.

Review of the law of evidence / South African Law Commission. – Pretoria : The Commission, 1986.
xi,60p. – (Report).
Bibliography: pp.vi-ix. Includes draft legislation.
ISBN 0621113484

Review of the law of prize. – South African Law Commission. – Pretoria : The Commission, 1984.
iv,17p. – (Project).

Review of the law of succession / South African Law Commission. – Pretoria : The Commission, 1986.
ix,34 leaves. – (Project).
Bibliogrpahy: p.iv-viii.

Review of the law of succession : alteration and revocation of wills / South African Law Commission. – Pretoria : The Commission, 1987.
vii,86 leaves. – (Project).
Bibliography: leaves vi-viii.

Review of the law of succession : disqualification from inheriting, substitution, succession rights of adopted children / South African Law Commission. – Pretoria : The Commission, 1987.
ix,99p. – (Project).
Photocopy of original. Includes bibliographical references.
ISBN 0797014020

Review of the law of succession : formalitites of a will / South African Law Commission. – Pretoria : South African Law Commission, 1986.
xiii,139 leaves. – (Project).
Bibliography: p.viii-xiii.

Review of the law of succession : intestate succession / South African Law Commission. – Pretoria : The Commission, 1985.
vii,37p. – (Report).
Bibliography: p.vi-vii.
ISBN 0621096113

Review of the law of succession : the introduction of a legitimate portion or the granting of a right to maintenance to the surviving spouse / South African Law Commission. – Pretoria : The Commission, 1987.
x,46p. – (Report).
Bibliography: pp.v-ix. Includes draft legislation.
ISBN 0621113603

Review of the law of trusts / South African Law Commission. – Pretoria : The Commission, 1987.
viii,135p. – (Report).
Bibliography: p. vii-viii. Includes text of bill.

Review of the National Association of Citizens Advice Bureaux / chairman, Sir Douglas Lovelock : presented to Parliament by the Secretary of State for Trade and Industry ... February 1984. – London : H.M.S.O., 1984.
iii,91p; 25cm.
ISBN 0101913907

Review of the operation of the Northern Ireland (Emergency Provisions) Act 1978 / by Sir George Baker : presented to Parliament by the Secretary of State for Northern Ireland. – London : H.M.S.O., 1984.
171p.
ISBN 0101922205

Review of the operation of the Prevention of Terrorism (Temporary Provisions) Act 1976 / by Earl Jellicoe. – London : H.M.S.O., 1983.
v,144p; 25cm.
At head of title: Home Office.
ISBN 0101880308 Pbk £8.30

Review of the Operation of the Prevention of Terrorism (Temporary Provisions) Act 1984 / by the Viscount Colville of Culross : presented to Parliament by the Secretary of State for the Home Department ... – London : HMSO, 1987.
v,70p.
ISBN 0101026420

Review of the Pawnbrokers Act, 1860 : proposals paper / the Law Reform Commission of Western Australia. – Perth : The Commission, 1985.
46 leaves. – (Project).

Review of the Price Marking (Bargain Offers) Orders 1979 : a report / by the Director General of Fair Trading. – London : Office of Fair Trading, 1981.
57p.

Reville's Divorce Act Annotated
Binder and Contents. – Aurora : Canada Law Book Co.
The third edition of Reville's Divorce Act Annotated is an immediate guide to the interpretation of any section of the new Divorce Act. Over 1500 cases from the previous Act, with ongoing relevance, are considered in terms of the new Act. The new edition is provided in looseleaf format permitting quarterly updates.
£45.00

Revised edition of the laws of Malta, in force on 1st January, 1984 / prepared under the authority of the Statute Law Revision Act, 1980 by the Law Commission. – Valletta : Information Division, 1986.
English version of L-edizzjoni riveduta tal-ligijiet ta Malta.

Revised framework for insolvency law / presented to Parliament by the Secretary of State for Trade and Industry ... – London : H.M.S.O., 1984.
53p.
ISBN 0101917503

Revised Notes on Procedure by Originating Summons and In Actions By Mortgages. – Belfast : Queen's University of Belfast.
35p.
Pbk £3.25

Revised Penal Code. – Quezon City, 1983.
366p.
Pbk Univeristy of the Philippines, Law Center

Revised Penal Code, Annotated. – Manila : National Book Store, 1984.
587p.
ISBN 9710812866 Pbk £6.00

Revised regulations of Ontario, 1980 : a revision and consolidation of regulations published under the authority of the Regulations Revision Act, 1979. – 8. – Toronto : Queen's Printer, 1981.
Accompanied by: Supplement (2).

Revised regulations of the Northwest Territories 1980 : a consolidation and revision of the regulations of the Northwest Territories prepared by the Registrar of Regulations and representing the laws as at 31st December, 1980. – Yellowknife : Territorial Printer, Northwest Territories, 1981.
xii,1679p.

Revised rules of court (adopted on 24 November 1982) / European Court of Human Rights : Cour Europeenne des Droits de l'Homme. – Strasbourg : Council of Europe, 1983.
90p.

Revised statutes of Alberta 1980. – Alberta. – 8. – Edmonton : Queen's Printer, 1981.

Revised Statutes of Canada 1985. – Ottawa : Canadian Government Publishing Centre.
Hbk £675.00
Individual Statutes. –
Hbk

Revised Statutes of Canada 1985. – Agincourt : Carswell.
Hbk

Revised Statutes of Canada, 1985. – Law Book Publisher. – Aurora : Canada Law Book Co.
Llf £550.00

Revised statutes of Canada, 1985 : prepared under the authority of the Statute Revision Act / Lois revisees du Canada, 1985. – 13. – Ottawa : Queen's Printer, 1985.
looseleaf.
. Spine titles: Statutes of Canada Lois du Canada. Updated to 1988 by special supplements and by looseleaf insertions thereafter. Parallel text in English and French.

Revised statutes of Ontario, 1980 : being a revision and consolidation of the Public General Acts of the legislature of Ontario, published under the authority of the Statutes Revision Act, 1979. – 9. – Toronto : Queen's Printer, 1981.

Revised statutes of the Yukon, 1986 : a revision and consolidation fo the statutes of the legislature of the Yukon Territory : proclaimed and published under authority of the Revised Statutes Act. – 2. – Whitehorse : Cawley, Queen's Printer, 1986.
Includes index.

Revision of the Convention Concerning Statistics of Wages and Hours of Work, 1983 (No. 63). – Geneva : International Labour Office, 1985.
Hbk

Revision of the Convention Concerning Statistics of Wages and Hours of Work. – Geneva : International Labour Office, 1984.
Hbk

Revision of the licensed dealers' rules / Council for the Securities Industry. – London : The Council, 1982.
8p. – (Press statement).
Caption title.

Revision of the licensed dealers' rules : memorandum / by the Department of Trade. – London : Department of Trade, Companies Division, 1982.
16 leaves.

Revision of the Plantations Conventions (No. 110) and Recommendation (No. 110), 1958 : Report 7. Sixty-Eighth Session of the International Labour Conference, 1982
Part 1: Preliminary Report and Questionnaire. – Geneva : International Labour Office.
30p.
ISBN 9221027996 Hbk £12.50
Part 2: Replies of Governments. –
31p.
ISBN 9221028003 Hbk £12.50

Revision of the Repatriation of Seamen Convention, 1926 (No. 23) and of the Repatriation (Ship Masters and Apprentices) Recommendation, 1926 (No. 27). – Geneva : International Labour Office, 1987.
ISBN 9221057925 Hbk £15.00

Revival of Constitutionalism. – University of Nebraska Press.
ISBN 080323127X Hbk £23.95

Revival of the Discretionary Trust : 1983 / Andrew R. Thornhill. – London : Law Society, 1983.
– (Oxford Weekend Courses).
Hbk £3.50

Reynaud, A.
Human rights in prisons / by A. Reynaud. – Strasbourg : Council of Europe, Directorate of Human Rights, 1986.
218p.
Describes human rights problems prison establishments may encounter. Outlines the relevant international human rights law, in particular the European Convention on Human Rights and its case law.
ISBN 9287108811

Reynolds → Acquisitions & Mergers : Accounting, Financial & Strategic Issues.
→ Enforcement in the Magistrates Courts : a Guide to Enforcing Money Payments.

Reynolds, F. M. B. → Bowstead on agency.

Reynolds, Kirk → Handbook of rent review.

Reynolds, Michael P.
Expert witness and his evidence / Michael P. Reynolds and Philip S.D. King. – London : BSP Professional, 1988.
x,160p; 24cm.
Includes index.
ISBN 0632018542 £17.95

Reynolds, Thomas H.
Rare books for law libraries / by Thomas H. Reynolds. – London : Glanville, 1983.
141p.

Rhodes, Dusty → Women against violence against women.

Rhodes, F. W.
Williams' and Rhodes' Canadian Law of Landlord and Tenant, 2 Vols. – 5th ed. – Agincourt : Carswell, 1983.
1400p.
This two volume looseleaf text is a comprehensive guide to commercial and residential tenancies in every province of Canada. Topics covered include: rent control, the creation of the landlord and tenant relationship, recovery of rent, and related issues.
Llf £143.00

Rhodes, Gerald
Inspectorates in British government : law enforcement and standards of efficiency / Gerald Rhodes. – London : Allen & Unwin for the Royal Institute of Public Administration, 1981.
xiii,281p; 23cm.
Includes index.
ISBN 0043510566 £15.00

Rhodes, Peter → Damages for personal injuries and fatal accidents in Hong Kong : a review of the law and a digest of the cases.

Rhodes, Robson
Personal Financial Planning Manual 1986-87 / John Rayer. – London : Butterworths, 1986.
This manual is a guide to the compilation of personal financial packages for United Kingdom investors. Investments, family finances, life insurance, pensions, and capital transfer tax are covered in the book.
ISBN 040600563X Hbk
—Personal Financial Planning Manual. – 4th ed. – London : Butterworths.
ISBN 0406005656 Pbk £18.95

Rhyne, E.H.
Small Business Banks and Small Business Administration Loan Subsidising the Weak or Bridging a Credit Gap. – London : Eurospan.
ISBN 0899302564 Hbk £32.95

Rice, Paul R.
Evidence : common law and federal rules of evidence / Paul R. Rice. – New York : Matthew Bender, 1987.
xlvi,1212p.
Bibliography : pp.LR1-5. - Includes index. With a separate 'Teacher's guide'.

Rice, Susan
Criminal justice system model : magistrates' courts sub-model / Susan Rice. – London : Home Office, 1984.
vi,66p.
Bibliography: p.59.
ISBN 0862521254

Rich
Sociology of Criminal Law. – London : Butterworths.
ISBN 0409862207 Hbk £14.00

Rich, the poor and the taxes they pay / by Joseph A. Pechman. – Brighton : Wheatsheaf, 1986.
xvi,317p; 25cm.
Includes index.
ISBN 0745000983 £28.50

Richard, Hugues G., et al
Canadian Trademarks Act Annotated. – Toronto : DeBoo, 1984.
This volume covers the practice, procedure, and legislation of Canadian trade mark law. Practice notes from the Trade Marks Journal, references to the Trade Marks Examination Manual, and a list of 'confusing' and 'non-confusing' trademarks are included in the work.
ISBN 0888201583 Hbk £135.00

Richard, Ivor
Future of Community social legislation / Ivor Richard. – Exeter : University of Exeter, 1984.
11p.

Richard, John D.
Canada-U.S. Free Trade Agreement : Commentary and Related Documents / Richard G. Dearden. – North Ryde : C.C.H. Australia.
138p.
ISBN 0887964583 Pbk £14.95
—Canada-U.S. Free Trade Agreement : Final Text and Analysis / Richard G. Dearden. – North Ryde : C.C.H. Australia.
420p.
ISBN 0887964621 Pbk £22.95

Richard N, Parr → Humphreys' Notes on district registry practice and procedure.

Richards → Hong Kong stamp duties.
—Planning for Stamp Duty Reserve Tax / Ball. – London : Butterworths, 1987.
ISBN 0406051033 Hbk £26.00

Richards Butler on latent damage / by Robert Merkin. – London : Lloyd's of London Press, 1987.
192p; 22cm.
ISBN 1850441286 £30.00

Richards, Clement → Black people and the criminal justice system : report of the NACRO Race Issues Advisory Committee.

Richards, Denbigh
Crime Prevention : Planning and Participation in Geelong. – Canberra : Australian Institute of Criminology.
free

Richards, G. R.
Planning for Stamp Duty Reserve Tax. – London : Butterworths, 1987.
Hbk

Richards, Martin → Divorce matters.

Richardson → Government & Pressure Groups in Britain.
→ Law of Estate and Gift Duties in New Zealand.

Richardson, Ann
Family Income Support Part 4 : Widow Benefits. – London : Policy Studies Institute, 1984.
119p.
Hbk £3.85

Richardson, Dudley
Guide to negotiable instruments and the Bills of Exchange Acts / Dudley Richardson. – 7th ed. – London : Butterworths, 1983.
viii,220p; 22cm.
A student and reference introduction to the law of negotiable instruments in the United Kingdom. The impact of cheque cards and credit cards on the negotiable instrument is discussed in detail.
ISBN 0406648247 Pbk £22.40

Richardson, F. Dwight → Tremeear's 1971-1986 criminal annotations.

Richardson, Genevra
Policing pollution : a study of regulation and enforcement / Genevra Richardson with Anthony Ogus and Paul Burrows. – Oxford : Clarendon Press, 1982.
ix,204p; 23cm.
Includes index.
ISBN 0198275102 Hbk £15.00
ISBN 0198275129 Pbk

Richardson, Henry Gerald
English Parliament in the Middle Ages / H.G. Richardson and G.O. Sayles. – London : The Hambledon Press, 1981.
560p in various pagings; 25cm.
Includes bibliographical references and index.
ISBN 0950688215

Richardson, J.
Protection of Offences. – London : Sweet & Maxwell, 1986.
ISBN 0421349107 Pbk

Richardson, J.W.
Guide to the Hague and Hague-Visby rules. – 2nd. – London : Lloyds of London Press, 1989.
Revised and updated since the 1985 edition. Includes the York-Antwerp Rules related to General Average, and details of the Hague-Visby SDR Convention and the Limitation Convention. Also includes the latest position in the 'Gold Clause Agreement', and a list of signatories to both sets of rules.
ISBN 1850442436 Pbk

Richardson, S.S.
Notes on Penal Code. – Zaria : Ahmadu Bello University Press.
Hbk £25.00

Riches → Business Law.

Richman, John → Stone's Justices' Manual.

Richmond, D.
Introduction to Valuation. – 2nd ed. – London : Macmillan, 1985.
ISBN 0333384377 Pbk £5.95

Rickard, John
H.B. Higgins. – North Sydney : Allen & Unwin, 1984.
248p.
ISBN 0868616818 Hbk £29.95

Ricketson, Sam
Berne Convention for the Protection of Literary and Artistic Works : 1886-1986 / Sam Ricketson. – London : Centre for Commercial Law Studies, Queen Mary College, 1987.
lxii,1030p.
Bibliography: pp.981-1006. - Includes index. Includes the text of the Convention with revisions.

Ricketson, Staniforth
Law of intellectual property / by Staniforth Ricketson. – North Ryde : Law Book Co., 1985.
clxxv,1201p.
Bibliography: p.cxxxix-clxx - Includes index.
ISBN 0455204179

Ricketts, Alistair
Russian serials / ... prepared by Alistair Ricketts ... in cyrillic script, with a transliterated version and an English translation. – Oxford : Bodleian Law Library, 1986.
12 leaves.

Ricquier, W.J.M.
Breaches of Trust in Singapore and Malaysia / Meng Heong Stanley Yeo. – Butterworths, 1984.
98p.
ISBN 0406181152 Pbk £13.00
→ Current problems of international trade financing.

—Land Law. – Singapore : University of Singapore, 1985.
– (Singapore Law Series).
The text discusses the structure of Singapore land law and considers the various basic land law concepts. Topics covered include: types of land transfer and registration, consideration of commercial interests in land, and land planning and the planning acts.
ISBN 0409995010 Hbk £25.00

Riddall, J. G.
Introduction to land law / J.G. Riddall. – 3rd ed. – London : Butterworth, 1983.
xxxii,487p; 26cm.
Previous ed.: 1979. Includes index.
ISBN 0406648344 Hbk £
ISBN 0406648395 Pbk unpriced
—Introduction to land law / J.G. Riddall. – 4th ed. – London : Butterworths, 1988.
547p; 25cm.
Previous ed.: 1983. Includes index.
ISBN 0406648441 Hbk £24.00 :
ISBN 040664845X Pbk £16.00

—Introduction to Land Law. – 4th ed. – London : Butterworths, 1988.
ISBN 0406648395 Pbk £14.95
ISBN 0406648441 Hbk £30.00

—Law of industrial relations / by J.G. Riddall. – London : Butterworths, 1981.
xxiv,319p; 25cm.
Includes index. Supplement for 1982 covers the Employment Act 1982.
ISBN 0406648107 Pbk

—Law of trusts / J.G. Riddall. – 3rd ed. – London : Butterworths, 1987.
420p; 24cm.
Previous ed.: 1982. Includes index.
ISBN 0406648425 Hbk £27.00
ISBN 0406648433 Pbk £17.95

—Law of trusts / J.G. Riddall. – 2nd ed. – London : Butterworths, 1982.
xxxi, 371p.
This textbook for United Kingdom students of trusts deals with the creation of trusts; the appointment, powers, and duties of trustees; and beneficiaries. Hypothetical examples, tables, and diagrams are included in the book.
ISBN 0406648379

Riddell-Dixon, Elizabeth
Canada and the International Seabed Domestic Interests and External Constraints. – Montreal : McGill-Queen's University Press.
ISBN 0773506942 Hbk £34.95

Riddle, I.
Shipbuilding credit. – Cardiff : University of Wales Press, 1983.
ISBN 07080308430 Pbk £12.00

Rideout, Roger W →Current Legal Problems : Lectures Delivered in the Faculty of Laws of University College London, Vol. 36.
—Rideout's Principles of labour law / Jacqueline C. Dyson. – 4th ed. – London : Sweet & Maxwell, 1983.
lxxvi,658p; 25cm.
Previous ed.: 1979. Includes index.
ISBN 0421296100 Hbk £20.00
ISBN 0421296208 Pbk

Rideout's Principles of labour law / Jacqueline C. Dyson. – 4th ed. – London : Sweet & Maxwell, 1983.
lxxvi,658p; 25cm.
Previous ed.: 1979. Includes index.
ISBN 0421296100 Hbk £20.00
ISBN 0421296208 Pbk

Rider, Barry Alexander K.
Combating international commercial crime / by B. Rider. – Barking : International Maritime Bureau, 1984.
36p.
—Guide to the Financial Services Act 1986 / Barry A.K. Rider, David A. Chaikin, Charles Abrams. – Bicester : CCH Editions, 1987.
xxii,472p; 23cm.
Examines Investor protection, the Act and the City revolution, the regulatory structure, the need for authorisation, obtaining authorisation, the conduct of investment business, insider dealing, public issues, marketing of investments, and collective investment schemes.
ISBN 0863250785 Pbk £15.00

—Insider trading / Barry A. K. Rider. – Bristol : Jordan and Sons, 1983.
xix, 338p.
ISBN 0853080755

Ridgway, B.H.
Some Developments in the Law of Contract. – Armidale : University of New England, Publications Office.
49p.
ISBN 0858342146 Pbk £3.00

Ridley
Safety at Work. – 2nd ed. – London : Butterworths.
ISBN 0408008407 Hbk £45.00

Ridley, Jasper
Law of the carriage of goods by land, sea and air / by Jasper Ridley. – 6th ed. – London : Shaw, 1982.
xlviii,328p; 22cm.
Previous ed.: 1978. Includes index.
ISBN 0721906222 Pbk £9.50
—Statesman and the fanatic : Thomas Wolsey and Thomas More / Jasper Ridley. – London : Constable, 1982.
338p,16p of plates; 24cm.
Bibliography: p294-299. - Includes index.
ISBN 009463470X £12.50

Riekert, Julian
Basic employment law / Julian Riekert. – Cape Town : Juta, 1987.
xvii,120p.
ISBN 0702118427

Rigby →Meetings : Law and Practice.

Rigby, P.
Contentious Costs. – London : Longman Professional.
– (Longman Practice Notes).
ISBN 0851214509 Pbk £10.95

Right of appeal : a practical digest of charter-party disputes and the right of appeal under the Arbitration Act 1979 / W.E. Astle. – London : Fairplay, 1983.
153p; 24cm.
ISBN 0905045513 Pbk

Right of innocent passage and the evolution of the international law of the sea. – London : Pinter, 1990.
250.
Debates the right of innocent passage in the light of the 1982 Law of the Sea Convention. Discusses the right of a coastal state to determine what is and is not innocent and to react accordingly.
ISBN 0861878515 Hbk £30

Right of peaceful assembly : its evolution and limits in a democratic society : a conference jointly organised by the British Institute of Human Rights and the United Kingdom Association for European Law in the Old Hall, Lincoln's Inn, on 30th April, 1982 / report prepared by Anthony McNulty. – London : British Institute of Human Rights, 1982.
ii,94p.
ISBN 0950835706

Right of peaceful assembly in the A.C.T. – Canberra : Australian Government Publishing Service, 1985.
233p. – (Occasional paper).
Bibliography: p194-205.
ISBN 0644038934

Right of the accused to defence in the USSR / Yuri Stetsovsky : translated from the Russian by H. Campell Creighton. – Moscow : Progress Publishers, 1982.
283 p.; 21 cm.
Includes bibliographical references and index.

Right to a Home. – Labour Housing Group. – London : Spokesman Books, 1984.
165p.
ISBN 0851243991 Hbk £15.00
ISBN 0851244009 Pbk £4.95

Right to buy : legislative proposals. – London : Department of the Environment, 1987.
3p.

'Right to Buy' Handbook. – Butterworths Editorial Staff. – London : Butterworths, 1984.
This book sets out the text of the Housing and Building Control Act of 1984 concerning the 'right to buy' provisions of the United Kingdom Housing Act of 1980. Detailed annotations to the Act are provided.
ISBN 0406548250 Hbk

Right to buy in rural areas : an investigation of section 19 of the Housing Act 1980 / Neil Hawke. – Leicester : Leicester Polytechnic. School of Law, 1985.
33p. – (Research monographs).

Right to Communicate : a New Human Right / L.S. Harms. – Dublin : Boole Press Ltd., 1983.
xxvi, 229p.
ISBN 0906783186 Hbk £45.00
ISBN 0906783194 Pbk £30.00

Right to dismiss. – Oxford : Blackwell Scientific, 1987.
ISBN 0632018933 Hbk £17.95

Right to Food : Guide through Applicable International Law. – Dordrecht : Kluwer, 1986.
388p.
ISBN 9024733650 Hbk £165.00

Right to Freedom of Movement (1968, Bangalore). – Geneva : International Commission of Jurists.
Hbk £8.00

Right to know / Floyd Abrams, Michael Kirby, Lord Scarman. – London : Granada, 1985.
79p.
Includes bibliographical references.
ISBN 0586066810

Right to know : the inside story of the Belgrano affair / Clive Ponting. – London : Sphere Books, 1985.
214p.
ISBN 0722169442

Right to leave and return in international law and practice / by Hurst Hannum. – Dordrecht : Nijhoff, 1987.
xiii, 189p. – (International studies in human rights).
Includes index.
ISBN 9024734452

Right to liberty and the rights of persons deprived of their liberty as guaranteed by Article 5 of the European Convention on Human Rights. – Strasbourg : Council of Europe, 1981.
22p; 30cm.
'Prepared by the Council of Europe Directorate of Human Rights'.

Right to Life and Personal Liberty in India. – New Delhi : Deep and Deep Publications, 1987.
296p.
Hbk £175.00

Right to life in international law / edited by B.G. Ramcharan. – Dordrecht : Martinus Nijhoff, 1985.
xii,371p; 25cm. – (International studies in human rights).
ISBN 9024730740 Hbk £175.00

Right to private property / Jeremy Waldron. – Oxford : Clarendon Press, 1988.
viii,470p.
Bibliography: pp.446-463. - Includes index..
ISBN 0198249594

Right to Property. – Jodhpur : Scientific Publishers, 1985.
x, 308p.
ISBN 8185046220 Hbk £125.00

Right to respect for private and family life, home and correspondence as guaranteed by Article 8 of the European Convention on Human Rights / by Andrew Drzemczewski. – Strasbourg : Council of Europe, Directorate of Human Rights, 1984.
29p.
ISBN 9287103526

Right to Strike?. – London : Institute of Economic Affairs, 1986.
ISBN 0255361904 Pbk £2.50

Right to strike in Britain/ the English floating charge / K D Ewing, R M Goode. – Kluwer Law and Taxation, 1989.
72. – (Lectures on the common law).
Covers the position under the common law, protection of the trade unions from the common law, legislation and the individual striker, the foundation of security, the priority of security interests, and the second creditors rights over the assets given in security.
ISBN 9065444114 Pbk £15/Dfl 48

Right to strike in Community law : the incorporation of fundamental rights in the legal order of the European Communities / by Lammy Betten. – Amsterdam : North-Holland, 1985.
xviii, 319p.
At head of title: T.M.C. Asser Instituut, The Hague. Includes index. Bibliography: p.291-306.
ISBN 0444878459

Right to Travel Under the Constitution. – Lucknow : Eastern Book Company, 1986.
272p.
Hbk £50.00

Right Way to Prove a Will. – Ibadan : African Universities Press.
Hbk £2.95

Righting the Balance : Canada's New Equality Rights. – Agincourt : Carswell, 1986.
450p.
Hbk £39.50

Rights / by Alan R. White. – Oxford : Clarendon, 1984.
viii,186p; 23cm.
Bibliography: p177-184. - Includes index.
ISBN 0198247168 £12.50

Rights and duties of directors. – Touche Ross. – London : Butterworths, 1987.
ISBN 0406504709 Pbk £18.50

Rights and Statutes of the Individual in International Law. – New Delhi : Deep and Deep Publications, 1984.
200p.
Hbk £110.00

Rights and wrongs in medicine : King's College studies 1985-6 / edited by Peter Byrne. – London : King Edward's Hospital Fund for London, 1986.
ISBN 0197246370

Rights and wrongs of children / M.D.A. Freeman. – London : Pinter, 1983.
295p; 24cm.
Includes index.
ISBN 0903804204 Hbk £
ISBN 0861872266 Pbk £6.95

Rights at work. – 2nd ed. – Pluto Press, 1983.
ISBN 0861047303 Pbk £7.95

Rights, freedoms and the courts : a practical analysis of the Constitution Act, 1982 / Morris Manning. – Toronto : Emond-Montgomery, 1983.
lxiv,760p.
Includes the text of the Act.
ISBN 0920722105

Rights, Freedoms and the Education System in Canada : Cases and Materials / A. Wayne McKay. – Toronto : Edmond-Montgomery, 1988.
ca 750p.
ISBN 0920722237 Hbk £68.00

Rights Guide. – Unwin Hyman.
ISBN 004440171X Pbk £3.50

Rights guide to non means tested benefits / Rowlands. – London : Central Books, 1988/89.
ISBN 0946744092 Pbk £4.50

Rights in Residence. – Redfern : Redfern Legal Centre, 1988.
140p.
Hbk £10.00

Rights in security over moveables, cautionary obligations and bankruptcy. – Edinburgh : Green (W.) & Son, 1983.
Offprint from Scots Mercantile law by the same author, bringing together cahpters relating to the law of insolvency.
ISBN 0414007131 Pbk

Rights, institutions and impact of international law according to the German Basic Law : the contribution of the Federal Republic of Germany to the Second World Congress of the International Association of Constitutional law / edited by Christian Starck. – Baden-Baden : Nomos, 1987.
264p.
Includes bibliographical references and index.
ISBN 3789013749

Rights, killing, and suffering : moral vegetarianism and applied ethics / R.G. Frey. – Oxford : Blackwell, 1983.
xi,256p; 24cm.
Includes index.
ISBN 0631126848 £17.50

Rights of access to neighbouring land / the Law Commission. – London : H.M.S.O., 1985.
v,85p.
ISBN 0101969201

Rights of access to neighbouring land : Law Commission Working paper no. 78 : memorandum / by the Council's Law Reform Committee. – London : Law Society, 1981.
9p; 30cm.

Rights of Accused under Indian Constitution. – New Delhi : Deep and Deep Publications, 1984.
380p.
Hbk £200.00

Rights of children / edited by Bob Franklin. – Oxford : Blackwell, 1986.
x,237p; 24cm.
Includes index.
ISBN 063114711X Hbk £22.50
ISBN 0631147128 Pbk £7.95

Rights of Indigenous Peoples in International Law : an Annotated Bibliography / Ruth Thompson. – Saskatoon : University of Saskatchewan, Native Law Centre, 1986.
33p.
ISBN 0888801769 £9.00
Supplement 1986. –
Hbk

Rights of Indigenous Peoples in International Law : an Annotated Bibliography / Dallas K. Miller. – Saskatoon : University of Saskatchewan, Native Law Centre, 1985.
97p.
ISBN 0888801637 Hbk £35.00

Rights of Indigenous Peoples in International Law : Selected Essays on Self-Determination. – Saskatoon : University of Saskatchewan, Native Law Centre, 1987.
68p.
ISBN 0888801858 Hbk £15.00

Rights of Indigenous Peoples in International Law : Workshop Report. – Saskatoon : University of Saskatchewan, Native Law Centre, 1986.
66p.
ISBN 0888801696 Hbk £15.00

Rights of mentally ill people / Chris Heginbotham. – London : Minority Rights Group, 1987.
12p. – (Report).
ISBN 0946690499

Rights of Minority Shareholders. – Bombay : Tripathi, 1983 in prep.
£85.00

Rights of peoples / edited by James Crawford. – Oxford : Clarendon Press, 1988.
x,236p.
Bibliography: pp.213-232. - Includes index. Includes the texts of selected treaties, resolutions and other documents. The essays in this volume discuss the claims made for a third generation of peoples rights, including the rights of communities under colonial rule, the claims of the Aborigines in Australia, and economic rights such as the right to development, and the right to permanent sovereignty over natural resources.
ISBN 0198256248 Hbk £25

Rights of Prisoners After Sentence. – Sweet & Maxwell.
ISBN 0421322306 Pbk £20.00

Rights of Refugees. – Bombay : Tripathi.
Hbk £35.00

Rights of review under the Migration Act 1958 and related legislation : interim report on the constitution for the Administrative Appeals Tribunal : report to the Attorney-General / Administrative Review Council. – Canberra : Australian Government Publishing Service, 1983.
v,6p. – (Report).
ISBN 0644028432

Rights of Salaried Authors and Inventors. – Geneva : International Labour Office, 1987.
ISBN 9221059103 Hbk

Rights of shareholders. – 1st. – Oxford : Blackwell Scientific, 1990.
275. – (Blackwell Law Library).
Discusses the exercise of power and control over companies and explains the principles and structure of shareholders rights. Reference is made to European Community proposals for the harmonisation of company law. Considers in some detail self-regulatory codes such as the Stock Exchange 'Yellow Book' and the City Code on Take-Overs and Mergers.
Practitioners, Financial advisers
ISBN 0632012489 Hbk £35

Rights of Spouses Relating to the Occupation of the Family Home and the Use of the Household Contents. – Strasbourg : Council of Europe, 1982.
ISBN 928710042X

Rights of the child / Austin Asche. – Melbourne : Institute of Family Studies, 1982.
18p. – (Discussion paper).
Includes bibliographical references. Paper delivered as the first Vernon Collins Memorial Lecture in Melbourne, 14 October, 1981.
ISBN 0642888000

Rights of way : a guide to law and practice / by Paul Clayden and John Trevelyan. – Henley-on-Thames : Open Spaces Society, 1983.
viii,359p; 21cm.
Includes index.
ISBN 0946574006 Pbk £4.00
ISBN 0900613491 Ramblers' Association

Rights of way and access to the countryside / J.F. Garner. – 4th ed. – London : Oyez Longman, 1982.
xi,122p. – (Oyez Longman practice notes).
Title supersedes: Freeman's rights of way. Includes index.
ISBN 085120466X

Rights of way guide to law and practice / by Paul Clayden and John Trevelyan. – Open Spaces Society, 1983.
ISBN 0946574006 Hbk £4.00

Rights of working women in the European Community / by Eve C. Landau. – Luxembourg : Office for Official Publications of the European Communities, 1985.
244p.
At head of title: Commission of the European Communities.
ISBN 9282553418 Hbk £3.00

Rights to oceanic resources / Louis DeVorsey, Jr. – Dordrecht : Nijhoff (Martinus), 1989.
224. – (Publications on ocean development 13).
Collection of presentations from a multi-disciplinary group of experts involved in the resolution of maritime jurisdictional disputes, at state, national, and international levels. Papers discuss equitable resource management, develop an international analytical methodology, and identify the possible impact of dispute resolution on the principles used as state level.
ISBN 079230019X Hbk £39

Rights without remedies : the European Convention of Human Rights and UK immigration law / Camilla Palmer. – London : Runnymede Trust, 1981.
29,5p.
Bibliography p.5. - Includes index.

Rijkens, Rein
European regulation of advertising : supranational regulation of advertising in the European economic community / by Rein Rijkens, Gordon E. Miracle. – Amsterdam : North-Holland, 1986.
xxxiv, 375 p.; 25 cm.
Includes index. Bibliography: p. 337-358.
ISBN 0444879722

Rijksuniversiteit te Leiden →Essays in European law and integration : to mark the silver jubilee of the Europa Institute, Leiden, 1957-1982.
→ International air transport in the eighties : including the proceedings of the first Netherlands Colloquium on International Air Transport, 'The Changing Scene', Wassenaar, August 25-29, 1980.
→ Judicial protection in the European Communities.
→ Mixed agreements.

Riley, D.
Parental supervision and juvenile delinquency / by David Riley and Margaret Shaw. – London : H.M.S.O., 1985.
v,85p; 25cm.
Bibliography: p81-85. A Home Office Research and Planning Unit report.
ISBN 0113407998
—Police action on motoring offences / David Riley. – London : Home Office, 1983.
iv,17p.
Bibliography: p.10.
ISBN 0862521130

Riley, David
Triable-either-way cases : Crown Court or Magistrates' Court? / by David Riley and Julie Vennard. – London : H.M.S.O., 1988.
52 p.
Discusses whether the balance of either-way business could be redistributed in favour of the Magistrates' Court by encouraging them to accept jurisdiction more often in such cases.
ISBN 0113408900

Riley, Denis
Business Interruption and Consequent Loss Insurance / Cloughton. – 6th ed. – London : Sweet & Maxwell, 1985.
ISBN 0421319208 Hbk £50.00

Riley, John R.
Safety at Work. – 2nd ed. – London : Butterworths, 1986.
This textbook provides a comprehensive discussion of safety management, law, occupational health and hygiene, and other issues of work safety. Recent changes in safety legislation in the United Kingdom are reflected in the text.
ISBN 0408008407 Pbk

Riley on business interruption and consequential loss insurances and claims / by David Cloughton. – 6th ed. – London : Sweet & Maxwell, 1985.
480p.
Examination of business interruption consequential loss insurances and claims with emphasis on practice and procedure. Covers loss of profits, wages, and book debts, and perils and contingencies such as labour disturbances, strikes, riots, and the special conditions applicable in Northern Ireland and South Africa.
ISBN 0421319208 £46.00

Riley, Tom →Freedom of information trends in the information age.

Rimmer, Brenda M.
Guide to official industrial property literature : the Netherlands, Belgium, Luxembourg, Benelux / Brenda M. Rimmer. – London : British Library, Science Reference Library, 1981.
28p; 25cm.
Includes index.
ISBN 090291460X Pbk

Rinaldi, Fiori
Drug offences in Australia
Vol. 1 : Sentencing / by Fiori Rinaldi. – Sydney : Law Book Co., 1986.
xxv,247p.
Includes index.
ISBN 045520649X

Rines, S. Melvin →Supranationals.

Ring, Tony
Tax warranties and indemnities / John Clark. – London : Butterworths, 1983.
ISBN 0406395403 Hbk £18.00

Ringhofer, K.
On the Issue of the Continental Shelf : Two Legal Opinions / R. Walter. – Berlin : Springer-Verlag, 1986.
ca 100p.
Pbk £35.00

Ringrose, H. G.
Law and practice of employment / by H.G. Ringrose. – 2nd ed. – Cape Town : Juta, 1983.
xi,275p.
Previous ed.: 1976. Includes index.
ISBN 0702114057

Rintoul, Margaret E
Ontario Estate Administration : A Guide for Legal Secretaries and Law Clerks. – Toronto : Butterworths, 1987.
162p.
Pbk £35.00
—Ontario estate administration: a guide for legal secretaries and law clerks. – Scarborough, Ontario : Butterworths (Canada), 1987.
162.
Contains details on opening the file, application for probate, application for Letters of Administration, estate administration, estate accounting, executors fees, passing of accounts and income tax compliance.
ISBN 0409806510 Pbk
—Solicitor's Guide to Estate Practice in Ontario. – Butterworths, 1986.
280p.
Practical guide covering retainer, application for Probate and Letters of Administration, asset administration, interpretation of wills finding beneficiaries, estate litigation, distribution of estate, preparation and passing off of accounts, and tax returns.
ISBN 0409810266 Hbk £50.00

Rise and fall of economic justice. – Oxford : Oxford University Press, 1987.
ISBN 0192153609 Hbk £12.50
ISBN 0192851861 Pbk £4.95

Rise of the barristers : a social history of the English bar, 1590-1640 / Wilfrid R. Prest. – Oxford : Clarendon, 1986.
xii,440p; 22cm.
Includes index.
ISBN 0198217641 Hbk £35.00

Rise of the corporate economy / Leslie Hannah. – 2nd ed. – London : Methuen, 1983.
xii,266p; 23cm.
Previous ed.: 1976. Includes index.
ISBN 0416348505 Hbk £
ISBN 0416348602 Pbk

Risk as a ground for liability in delict / South African Law Commission. – Pretoria : The Commission, 1986.
x,41p. – (Report).
Includes bibliographical references.
ISBN 0621102024

Risk management / Comer. – Maidenhead : McGraw-Hill, 1986.
ISBN 0070849269 Hbk £19.95

Risk, R. C. B. → Real Estate Law.

Risley, John Shuckburgh → Clergyman's handbook, and churchwarden's guide : being a manual of the laws affecting the relative rights, position, and duties of the clergy and their parishioners ..., with appendices containing important statutes, including the Benefices Act, 1898.

Ritchie, K. J. M.
Official Tax Forms Manual. – 2nd ed. – London : Oyez Longman, 1982.
ISBN 0851206433 Hbk £12.50

Ritchie, N → Big Bang.
—What goes on in the City?. – 4th ed. – Cambridge : Woodhead-Faulkner, 1986.
ISBN 0859413217 Hbk £7.95
ISBN 0859413225 Pbk £4.25

Ritsumeikan law review. – International ed. – Kyoto, Japan : Ritsumeikan University, 1986-.
International ed. of: Ritsumeikan law review. Includes articles in German, French and Japanese.

Rittaler, Jan B → Critical evaluation of the Chicago School of Antitrust Analysis.

Rivalry in Retail Financial Services / Jowett. – London : Macmillan.
ISBN 0333445309 Hbk £29.50

Rivard, Glen
Telephone Legal Information Services : Review and Current Issues. – Ottawa : Canadian Law Information Council, 1982.
37p.
ISBN 0920358993 Pbk £5.00

River State Law Reporting Committee
River State Law Reports Vol. 1 (1980). – River State Law Reporting Committee. – Enugu : Fourth Dimension Publishing, 1982.
304p.
ISBN 9781561866 Hbk £20.00

River State Law Reports Vol. 1 (1980). – River State Law Reporting Committee. – Enugu : Fourth Dimension Publishing, 1982.
304p.
ISBN 9781561866 Hbk £20.00

Rizvi → Book Keeping and Accounting Examinations Explained.

Roach, J. Ashley → Index of International Humanitarian Law.

Roach, John → Police and public order in Europe.

Road Safety and Crime / J. Marjoram. – Canberra : Australian Institute of Criminology.
Hbk £2.00

Road to Hillsborough : the shaping of the Anglo-Irish agreement / by Anthony Kenny. – Oxford : Pergamon, 1986.
xi,141p; 21cm.
ISBN 0080347754 Pbk £12.95
ISBN 0080342485 £6.50

Road traffic / Patrick Halnan. – Chichester : Rose for the Magistrates' Association, 1981.
50p; 21cm.
ISBN 0859922073 Pbk £2.50

Road traffic. – London : Longman Professional (UK), 1988.
– (Longman practice notes).
Contains a table of principle offences, notes on common offences, a chapter on evidence, flow charts, checklists, tables showing the rates of elimination of alcohol for the purposes of back-calculation.
ISBN 0851214134 Pbk £9.95

Road Traffic Bill : Road Traffic Offenders Bill : Road Traffic (Consequential Provisions) Bill : report on the consolidation of certain enactments relating to road traffic / the Law Commission and the Scottish Law Commission. – London : H.M.S.O., 1988.
7p.
ISBN 0101039026

Road Traffic (Jersey) Law, 1956 (as amended up to 3rd February, 1981). – 1. – Jersey : States Greffe, 1981.
loose-leaf.
Subsequently amended up to 25th October, 1983. Cover title.

Road Traffic Law. – Publication Department of Grampian Police. – Aberdeen : Aberdeen University Press.
1532p.
ISBN 090001511X Hbk

Road traffic law / McVeagh. – London : Butterworths, 1981.
ISBN 0409798185 Llf £127.00

Road traffic law in Scotland. – London : Butterworths, 1989.
Concentrates of those areas of law which arise most frquently in practice. Covers reckless and careless driving, road side breath tests, defences to drink driving cases, construction and use regulations, public service vehicles and carriage of goods by road. Includes relevant EEC legislation and schedules with penalties and the DVLC codes.
ISBN 0406112258 Pbk

Road Traffic Law Review
Consultation document / Road Traffic Law Review. – London : The Review, 1985.
96,15p.
Chairman: P.M. North.
—Consultation paper : removal, impounding and wheelclamping of vehicles / Road Traffic Law Review. – London : Road Traffic Law Review, 1986.
12,12p.
Chairman: P.M. North.

Road traffic law review : memorandum to the Department of the Environment / Justice. – London : Justice, 1986.
7 leaves.

Road traffic offenders and crime policy / by Laszlo Viski. – Budapest : Akademiai Kiado, 1982.
205p.
Bibliographies: p.175-201. - Includes index. Translation of: Kozlekedesi buntetojog. - Tr. by: J. Decsenyi.
ISBN 963052841X

Road Traffic Ordinance, 1958 (No. 49 of 1958). – Kuala Lumpur : International Law Books Services.
Hbk £15.00

Road traffic regulation bill : report on the consolidation of the Road Traffic Regulation Act 1967 and certain related enactments / The Law Commission and The Scottish Law Commission. – London : H.M.S.O., 1984.
17p; 25cm.
ISBN 0101916205

Road Traffic Reports : 1986 / N. P. Metcalf. – London : Mason Publications Ltd, 1987.
416p. – (Road Traffic Reports Ser.).
ISBN 0859373398 Hbk £20.00

Road transport law. – 26th ed. – London : Butterworths, 1988.
ISBN 0406106738 Pbk £19.95

Road Vehicle Regulations : Information Paper 1. – Kingston : Australian Government Publishing Service, 1987.
xi, 209p.
Pbk £19.95

Robb, James C.
Employee-Employer Rights in Alberta : a Guide to Alberta Labour Law / Tim Christian. – 2nd ed. – North Vancouver : International Self-Counsel Press, 1984.
95p.
ISBN 0889082324 Hbk £6.95

Robbie, et al
Lending Packages for Small and Medium-Sized Companies. – Oxford : Croom Helm, 1983.
ISBN 070992254X Pbk £8.95

Robbins, A. J. → Civil justice project : preliminary study.

Robe, Jean-Philippe → Approach to the analysis of joint ventures.

Robert, J.P. → Alternative measures to imprisonment.

Robert, Jacques
Problems of regional and local authorities involved in planning policies : report / prepared under the guidance of the Committee of Experts on Social and Economic Activities of the Steering Committee for Regional and Municipal Matters, by Jacques Robert. – Strasbourg : Council of Europe, 1985.
36p.
—Regional development agencies and peripheral regions : report / prepared under the guidance of the Committee of Experts on Social and Economic Activities of the Steering Committee for Regional and Municipal Matters by Jacques Robert. – Strasbourg : Council of Europe, 1985.
23p.

Robert, Paterson K., et al
Canadian Regulation of International Trade and Investment. – Agincourt : Carswell, 1986.
470p.
This work describes and analyzes international conventions and domestic legislation that regulate Canadian world trade. International barriers to foreign investment and the new domestic laws that embody the flexible Canadian approach to the issues are discussed in the book.
Hbk £67.25

Roberts
Anticombines and Antitrust : the Competition Law of Canada. – London : Butterworths.
ISBN 0409862800 Hbk £84.00
→ Understanding property law.

Roberts, Adam
Academic freedom under Israeli military occupation : report of WUS/ICJ mission of enquiry into higher education in the West Bank and Gaza / Adam Roberts, Boel Joergensen, Frank Newman. – London : World University Service (UK), 1984.
87p.
Bibliography: p.84-87.
ISBN 0906405203
—Documents on the Laws of War / Richard Guelff. – Geneva : Comite International de la Croix-Rouge, 1982.
498p.
Pbk £25.00

→ United Nations, divided world : the UN's roles in international relations.

Roberts, Alfred Adrian
Index to the opinions of Roman-Dutch lawyers and the decisions of the courts of the Netherlands which have been digested in the Algemeen Beredeneerd Register of Nassau La Leck (1741-1795) / by the late Alfred Adrian Roberts : edited byt S.I.E. van Tonder. – 8. – Pretoria : Government Printer on behalf of the South African Law Commission, 1985.
– (Research series).

Roberts, B.
Whence They Came : Deportation from Canada 1900-35. – Witney : Academic & University Publishing Group.
ISBN 0776601636 Pbk £19.95

Roberts, David
Practical Application of Evidence : Materials Prepared for a Continuing Legal Education Seminar Held in Vancouver, B.C., February 19, 1983 / Thomas J. Chamber. – Vancouver : British Columbia Continuing Legal Education Society, 1983.
ISBN 0865041024 Hbk

Roberts, Frank
East-West Tensions World Wide. – Exeter : European Atlantic Movement, 1982.
Hbk £0.50

Roberts, Gwyneth
Essential Law for Social Workers. – 2nd ed. – London : Oyez Longman, 1981.
ISBN 0851205143 Hbk £9.95

Roberts, H. V. → Law relating to supplementary benefits and family income supplements : the statutes, regulations and orders as now in force.

Roberts, M.
Mediation in Family Disputes. – Wildwood House.
ISBN 00704505851 Pbk £4.95

Roberts, Simon → Rules and processes : the cultural logic of dispute in an African context.

Roberts, Stephen A.
Cost management for library and information services / Stephen A. Roberts. – London : Butterworths, 1985.
181 p.
ISBN 0408013761

Robertson, A → Nelson's tables: company procedure.

Robertson, Arthur Henry
Human Rights in Europe : Being an Account of the European Convention for the Protection of Human Rights and Fundamental Freedoms Signed in Rome on 4 November 1950 of the Protocol Thereto and of the Machinery Created Thereby : The European Commission of Human Rights and the European Court of Human Rights. – Amsterdam : University Press.
Hbk
—Human rights in the world : an introduction to the study of the international protection of human rights / by A.H. Robertson. – 2nd ed. – Manchester : Manchester University Press, 1982.
viii,243p; 23cm.
Previous ed.: 1972. Includes index.
ISBN 0719008638 £17.50

Robertson, Bill → Introduction of P & I.

Robertson, Dilys
Ontario Health and Safety Guide : A Dictionary of Legal Compliance. – Toronto : DeBoo, 1984.
This guidebook provides comprehensive discussion of the legal provisions affecting workplace health and safety in Ontario, Canada. The book is organized to provide quick reference in the design and review of workplace policies and procedures.
ISBN 0888201834 Hbk £85.00

Robertson, Evelyn
New Zealand royal commissions, commissions and committees of inquiry, 1864-1981 : a checklist / compiled by Evelyn Robertson and Peter H. Hughes for the NZLA Professional Division. – Wellington : New Zealand Library Association, 1982.
30p.
ISBN 0908560109

Robertson, Geoffrey
Courts and the Media. – London : Butterworths.
ISBN 0409862851 Hbk £46.00
—Media Law / Nicol. – London : Longman Professional, 1984.
ISBN 0803997264 Pbk £8.50
ISBN 0851206506 Hbk £40.00
—Media law : the rights of journalists and broadcasters / Geoffrey Robertson, Andrew G.L. Nicol. – 1st ed. – London : Oyez, 1984.
xxxvi,403p.
Includes bibliographical references and index.
ISBN 0851206506
—Media law - the rights of journalists and broadcasters / Geoffrey Robertson and Andrew Nicol. – 2nd ed. – London : Longman Professional (UK), 1989.
An updated second edition which covers recent developments including the Copyright and Patents Act 1988. Also covered are the use of government powers over television, the Video Recordings Act, the Cable Act, recent decisions of the European Court of Human Rights, and European Court, and the right of the media to appeal against 'gag' orders.
ISBN 0851215522 Hbk £55
—People against the press : an enquiry into the Press Council / Geoffrey Robertson. – London : Quartet, 1983.
182p; 23cm.
Includes index.
ISBN 0704323842 £7.95

Robertson, George Stuart
Law of Copyright. – Repr. of 1912 ed. – Aalen Wuertt : Scientia.
xxxii, 351p.
Hbk £115.00

Robertson, Gerald B.
Mental Disability and the Law in Canada. – Agincourt : Carswell, 1987.
518p.
This work contains a discussion of the common law and legislation of Canada's common law jurisdictions relating to the effect of mental disability on legal rights and liabilities. Topics include committees of estate and personal guardians, contracts, succession, tort liability, family law issues, the right to vote, discrimination and the Charter, litigation, admission to, and rights of patients in, mental health facilities.
Hbk £60.50

Robertson, Graham →Sentenced to hospital : offenders in Broadmoor.

Robertson, K. G.
Public secrets : a study in the development of government secrecy / K. G. Robertson. – London : Macmillan, 1982.
x,216p.
Bibliography: p198-209.

Robertson, Stuart
Courts and the Media. – Butterworths, 1981.
400p.
ISBN 0409862851 Hbk £59.95
—Media Law Handbook : a Guide for Canadian Journalists, Broadcasters, Photographers and Writers. – 2nd ed. – North Vancouver : International Self-Counsel Press, 1983.
146p.
ISBN 0889085749 Hbk £6.50

Robilliard, St. John A.
Police powers and the individual / St. John A. Robilliard and Jenny McEwan. – Oxford : Basil Blackwell, 1986.
viii,260p; 23cm.
Compares actual police practice with their legal powers. Discusses constraints on and remedies for police misbehaviour.
ISBN 0631139958 Hbk £27.50 :
ISBN 0631139966 Pbk £9.95
—Religion and the law : religious liberty in Modern English law / St John A. Robilliard. – Manchester : Manchester University Press, 1984.
xii,223p; 23cm.
Includes index.
ISBN 0719009561 £22.50

Robinson
Alex Manoogian Cultural Centre Act, 1983, Bill Pr056 : An Act Respecting the Alex Manoogian Cultural Centre. – Ontario : Ontario Government Publications Service, 1983.
3p.
Hbk £0.30
—Debt Management and Collection. – London : Butterworths, 1988.
ISBN 040635880X Pbk
—House of Lords Appeals : 1821-1873, 28 Vols. 1840-1841, 2 Vols. /. – Abingdon : Professional Books.
Hbk
—Institute of Management Consultants of Ontario Act, 1983, Bill Pr026 : An Act Respecting the Institute of Management Consultants of Ontario. – Ontario : Ontario Government Publications Service, 1983.
4p.
Hbk £0.30
→ Tolley's Social Security and State Benefits 1988-89.

Robinson, A. J.
Retail sales tax in Canada / A.J. Robinson. – Toronto : Canadian Tax Foundation, 1986.
165p. – (Canadian Tax Papers: No. 77).
Bibliography: p.152-161. - Includes index.
ISBN 0888080255 Hbk £12.50

Robinson, Bill →Tax reform : options for the third term.

Robinson, Christopher
Allied Hambro Investment Guide 1984. – London : Oyez Longman, 1984.
ISBN 085120838X Hbk £10.95

Robinson, Derek
Deeds of Covenant. – 3rd ed. – London : Longman Professional, 1987.
ISBN 0851212182 Pbk £9.50

Robinson, J. Michael →International securities : Law and practice.

Robinson, John
Catching Criminals : Some More Basic Skills. – London : Police Review Publishing, 1983.
ISBN 0851640044 Pbk £2.50
—Multinationals and political control / John Robinson. – Aldershot : Gower, 1983.
xxi,507p; 23cm.
Includes index.
ISBN 0566003945

Robinson, K.
Law of Town and Country Planning. – 3rd ed. – Butterworths, 1981.
ISBN 0409600377 Hbk £103.95

Robinson, L.
Strata Title Units in New South Wales - A Guide to the Strata Titles Act. – 3rd ed. – Sydney : Butterworths, 1985.
200p.
ISBN 0409493147 Hbk

Robinson, Mark →Protected Persons and Their Property in N.S.W.

Robinson, Mark A.
Accident compensation in Australia : no-fault schemes / by Mark A. Robinson. – Sydney : Legal Books Pty., 1987.
xiv,94p.
Bibliography: pp.86-89. - Includes index.
ISBN 094955331X

Robinson, Nigel M.
Construction Law in Singapore and Malaysia / Anthony P. Lavers. – Butterworths, 1988.
Explains the main principles governing the law of construction and refers to and treats in detail the local forms of building contracts amd statutory provisions in Singapore and Malaysia. The digest section contains summaries and extracts of cases referred to in the text.
ISBN 0409995614 Hbk £90.00

Robinson, O F, et al
Introduction to European legal history. – London : Butterworths, 1985.
ISBN 086205107X Hbk £35.00
ISBN 0862051088 Pbk £16.95

Robinson, Olive
Part-time employment and sex discrimination legislation in Great Britain : a study of the demand for part-time labour and of sex discrimination in selected organizations and establishments / by Olive Robinson and John Wallace. – London : H.M.S.O., 1984.
53p. – (Research paper).

Robinson, P. D. →Report.

Robinson, Ray
Housing Economics and Public Policy. – London : Macmillan.
176p. – (Studies in Planning Ser.).
ISBN 0333211073 Pbk £4.95

Robinson, S
Drafting: its applications to conveyancing and commercial documents. – North Ryde : Butterworths (Australia), 1973.
Guide to the drafting of legal and commercial documents. Explains the underlying princples of drafting and demonstrates the link between those principles and the rule of law. Discusses the language of law, and generality of expression, and sets out the most salient features of parliamentary drafting practice relevant to document drafting.
ISBN 0409438251 Hbk

Robinson, Scott S.
Law of Interdict. – London : Butterworths, 1987.
ISBN 040610445X Pbk

Robinson, Stanley
Australian Encyclopaedia of Forms and Precedents : 1987 Cumulative Supplement. – Butterworths, 1987.
905p.
Pbk £67.50

Robinson, T.
Common Law of Kent. – 3rd ed. Repr. of 1822 ed. – Abingdon : Professional Books.
303p.
Hbk £30.00

Robinson, T. H.
Establishing the validity of contractual claims. – King's Ride : Institute of Building, 1983.
28p.
ISBN 0901822191 Hbk £3.85

Robinson's County Court Costs. – 6th ed. – London : Oyez Longman, 1982.
– (Oyez Longman Practice Note Ser.: No. 24).
ISBN 0851206409 Hbk £7.95

Robson, A.P.
Essential Accounting for Managers. – 5th ed. – London : Cassell, 1988.
ISBN 0304314714 Pbk £6.95

Robson, Peter →Developments in homelessness and the law 1983-1985.
→ Homelessness and the law.
—Housing (Scotland) Act 1988. – Edinburgh : Green (W.) & Son, 1988.
The annotated Act reprinted from Scottish Current Law Statutes with an introduction and the text of the regulations made under the Act which introduced new categories of tenancies in the private sector with corresponding effects on security of tenure. Rights of succession were also curtailed.
ISBN 0414008960 Pbk
→ Justice, Lord Denning and the constitution.

Roche versus Adams / Stanley Adams. – London : Cape, 1984.
xii,236p,8p of plates; 23cm.
Includes index.
ISBN 022402180X £8.95

Rock, M.
Mergers and Acquisitions Handbook. – Maidenhead : McGraw-Hill.
ISBN 0070533504 Hbk £59.95

Rock, Paul →Understanding deviance : a guide to the sociology of crime and rule-breaking.
—View from the shadows : the Ministry of the Solicitor General of Canada and the making of the justice for victims of crime initiative / Paul Rock. – Oxford : Clarendon, 1986.
xix,396p; 22cm. – (Oxford socio-legal studies).
An empirical study of the evolution of the Canadian Solicitor General's Justice for Victims of Crime Initiative. Focuses on the complexity of policies for victims, and also the more general problems of the policy-making process in a federal government.
ISBN 0198255233 Hbk £35

Rock, Paul Elliott →History of British criminology.

Roddering, Richard J.
Green Bans : The Birth of Australian Environmental Politics. – Neutral Bay : Hale & Iremonger.
ISBN 090809423X Hbk £17.95, 015

Rodgers, C.
Housing : the New Law. – London : Butterworths.
ISBN 0406503214 Pbk £16.50

Rodgers, C. P.
Agricultural tenancies : law and practice / by C.P. Rodgers : consulting editor C.V. Margrave-Jones. – London : Butterworth, 1985.
xxxvii,447p; 25cm.
Includes index. Chapter 13 by C.V. Margrave-Jones.
ISBN 0406258406 Pbk £20.00

Rodgers-Magnet, Sanda →Issues in Tort Law.

Rodley, Nigel S.
Treatment of prisoners under international law / Nigel S. Rodley. – Paris : Unesco, 1987.
xxii,374; 25cm.
Includes index.
ISBN 0198255519 Hbk £40.00
ISBN 0198255632 Pbk £15.00

Rodrigues, Gary P.
Police Officers' Manual : 1988. – 11th ed. – Agincourt : Carswell.
Hbk

Rodwell, P.
Lawyer's Guide to Software. – Pinter, 1985.
ISBN 0861874978 Hbk £15.00

Roebuck, Derek
Background of the Common Law. – Oxford : Oxford University Press.
ISBN 0195849353 Pbk £4.95
—Background of the common law : a historical sketch / Derek Roebuck. – Waigani : University of Papua New Guinea Press, 1983.
135p.
Includes index.
—Context of contract in Papua New Guinea / Derek Roebuck, Dhirendra K. Srivastava, John Nonggorr. – Waigani : University of Papua New Guinea Press, 1984.
268p.
Bibliography: p.256-262. - Includes index.
ISBN 9980840005

Roemer, Ruth
Legislative action to combat the world smoking epidemic / by Ruth Roemer : with a foreword by Sir George Godber. – Geneva : World Health Organization, 1982.
131p.
Bibliography: p.121-122.
ISBN 9241560746

Roermund, G. van →Theory of legal science : proceedings of the Conference on Legal Theory and Philosophy of Science, Lund, Sweden, December 11-14, 1983.

Roesch, R., et al
Fitness Interview Test : a Method for Examining Fitness to Stand Trial. – Toronto : University of Toronto, Centre of Criminology, 1984.
£4.50

Rogers
Research and development in Canada: a practical guide to financing, protecting and exploiting new technology / Bereskin, Parr. – Scarborough, Ontario : Butterworths (Canada), 1987.
288.
Gives details on how to manage proprietary information, legally protect new technology, cash in on the many federal and provincial government research and development assistance programmes, pursue private venture captial funding, benefit from tax incentivs available to Canadian research and development, license technology, and how publicly funded institutions can profit from the exploitation of technology.
ISBN 0409805670 Hbk

Rogers, A P → Probate practice and procedure.

Rogers, Andrew John → Professional responsibility, Part 2 : paper presented by Mr. Justice Rogers : and commentaries on papers published in part one presented by John C. Hagen ... et al.

Rogers, Brian MacLeod → Charter Issues in Civil Cases.
→ Recent developments in administrative law.

Rogers, C, et al
Agricultural law / C Margrave-Jones. – London : Longman Professional (UK), 1989.
Covers the Agricultural Holdings Act of 1984 and 1986 tenancies, tied accomodation, security of tenure and its removal, and succession to holdings. Sets out cases for possession and compulsory purchase and the relevant compensatory proceedings. Also deals with taxation, public control of land use, resolving agricultural disputes, and European Agricultural law.
ISBN 0851214290 Hbk £27.50

Rogers, Heather → Changing contempt of court.

Rogers, Ian MacFee
Canadian Law of Planning and Zoning, 1 Vol. – Agincourt : Carswell.
318p.
This looseleaf service covers every aspect of land use in Canada including: master plans, non-conforming uses, building construction permits, enforcement, appeals, and remedies. The work contains the text of planning legislation from all provinces.
Llf £113.50
—Law of Canadian municipal corporations / by Ian MacF. Rogers. – 2d ed. – Toronto : Carswell, 1971.
2 v. (loose-leaf); 25 cm.
ISBN 0459307606
—Municipal councillors' handbook / Ian MacF. Rogers. – 4th ed. – Toronto : Carswell, 1982.
xi,135p.
Previous ed.: 1977. Bibliography: p.119. - Includes index.
ISBN 0459347306

Rogers, Margaret
Decade of women and the law in the Commonwealth / prepared by Margaret Rogers for the Hubert Humphrey Institute of Public Affairs in association with the Commonwealth Secretariat. – London : Legal Division, Commonwealth Secretariat, 1985.
xvii,342p.
ISBN 0850922720

Rogers, T.M.
Investor Prot., Corp. Disclosure and Insider Dealing in HK. – London : Butterworths, 1988.
ISBN 0409995460 Hbk

Rogers, W. V. H. → Winfield and Jolowicz on tort.

Rogerson, Carol J. → Competing Constitutional Visions : the Meech Lake Accord.

Rohreke, H. G. → Limited Liability in Collision Cases.
→ Time barred actions.

Rohwer, C. → Legal aspects of international business transactions : the Edinburgh Institute on International Business Transactions 1983 : a project of University of the Pacific McGeorge School of Law international programs.

Roitman Investments Limited Act, 1983, Bill Pr009 : An Act to Revive Roitman Investments Limited. – Ontario : Ontario Government Publications Service, 1983.
2p.
Hbk £0.30

Rojot, Jacques → Labour law and industrial relations in France.

Role of an auditor in detecting fraud and other irregularities : a study / prepared on behalf of The Chartered Association of Certified Accountants. – London : Certified Accountant Publications, 1986.
46p.
'Prepared for publication by Christine Johnston, Technical Officer of the Chartered Association of Certified Accountants in conjunction with the Association's Working Party on Fraud and the Auditor's Responsibility, chaired by the Hon. Sir Irvine Goulding, and the School of Financial Studies, University of Glasgow' - Note.
ISBN 1850110212

Role of criminal law in consumer protection / European Committee on Crime Problems. – Strasbourg : Council of Europe, 1983.
24p; 21cm.
Report and recommendations of the European Committee on Crime Problems on the role of criminal law in protecting consumers from exploitation by suppliers.
ISBN 928710218X Pbk £1.25

Role of customary courts in Nigeria / by Martin C. Okany. – Enugu : Fourth Dimension Publishing Co., 1984.
264p.
Includes bibliographical references and index.
ISBN 9781562145

Role of district tribunals in the administration of criminal justice in the Gambia : a critical appraisal / by K. Gyeke-Dako. – Banjul : Government Printer, 1984.
20 leaves.

Role of Government Industrial Property Authorities and the Legal Profession in Administering Industrial Property Rights in Asia and the Pacific. – Geneva : World Intellectual Property Organization, 1983.
314p.
Hbk £35.00

Role of Industrial Property in the Protection of Consumers. – Geneva : World Intellectual Property Organization, 1983.
69p.
Hbk £25.00

Role of Law in Central-Local Relations. – Oxford : Social Science Research Council, 1981.
105p.
ISBN 0862260248 Pbk £2.50

Role of law in society : East and West, national and international / by Bin Cheng. – S.l. : s.n., 1981.
p.15-18.
Reprinted from: Chinese University bulletin, Winter 1978. Cover title with subtitle: 'Address on behalf of the honorary graduates at the twentieth Congregation of the Chinese University of Hong Kong on Thursday, 30th November 1978'.

Role of local authorities in promoting the creation or operation of small or medium-sized firms within a general policy of endogenous development / report prepared under the guidance of the Committee of Experts on Social and Economic Activities of the Steering Committee for Regional and Municipal Matters by T. Nuttal. – Strasbourg : Council of Europe, 1986.
31p.
Bibliography: p.28-29.

Role of Parliament in relation to the national companies scheme / report by Senate Standing Committee on Constitutional and Legal Affairs. – Canberra : Australian Government Publishing Service, 1987.
vii,106p. – (Parliamentary paper).
ISBN 0644051175

Role of patent information in the transfer of technology : proceedings of the International Conference held at Varna, Bulgaria, May 27-30, 1980 / organised by the World International i.e. Intellectual Property Organization : edited by F.A. Sviridov. – McLean, Va. : Pergamon International Information, 1981.
viii,265p; 23cm.
ISBN 0080275559 Pbk £6.00

Role of psychiatric reports in the Crown Court trial processes. – Leicester : Leicester Polytechnic Law School, 1986.
21p. – (Leicester Polytechnic Law School monographs).
Includes bibliographical references.
ISBN 0948997303

Role of Psychologists in the Criminal Justice System. – Canberra : Australian Institute of Criminology.
Hbk £4.00

Role of subscription agents / by Alan Singleton : with a supplementary report on U.K. libraries, trade with agents by Alan Cooper. – Leicester : Primary Communications Research Centre, University of Leicester, 1981.
68p; 21cm. – (Occasional papers).
ISBN 0906083176 Pbk

Role of Supreme Court in Indian Constitution. – New Delhi : Deep and Deep Publications, 1987.
208p.
Hbk £150.00

Role of tariff quotas in commercial policy / by Michael Rom : with an introduction by Gerard Curzon. – London : Macmillan for the Trade Policy Research Centre, 1978.
272p.
ISBN 0333176383 £12.00

Role of the court interpreter / by Omkar Nath Channan : with a foreword by the Lord Hailsham of St Marylebone. – London : Shaw, 1982.
44p; 22cm.
ISBN 0721909205 Pbk

Role of the judge in contemporary society. – Rome : Fratelli Palombi for UNSDRI and the International Association of Judges, 1984.
80p. – (Publication).

Role of the judiciary in plural societies / edited by Neelan Tiruchelvam and Radhika Coomaraswamy. – London : Pinter, 1987.
xxi,193p; 23cm.
Includes index.
ISBN 0861876644 £22.50

Role of the jury in criminal trials / Law Reform Commission of Victoria. – Melbourne : The Commission, 1985.
xxvi,220p. – (Background paper).
Bibliography: pp.185-220.. With appendices in separate vol..

Role of the Lawyer in the European Communities. – Edinburgh : Edinburgh University Press.
106p.
Hbk £4.00

Role of the Prosecutor. – London : LSEPS, 1987.
ISBN 0566057239 Hbk £22.50

Role of the United Kingdom in the amendment of the Canadian Constitution : background paper / Jean Chretien, Minister of Justice of Canada. – Ottawa : Government of Canada, 1981.
54p; 23cm.

Roles of Labour Law in Developing Countries : Record of Proceedings of, and Documents Submitted to, a Round Table (Geneva, 10-14 September and Selva di Fasano, Italy, 17-19 September 1974). – Geneva : International Labour Office, 1975.
iii, 266p.
ISBN 9221012875 Hbk £27.50

Rolfe, R → Guarantees For New Homes.

Roll of the Shropshire eyre of 1256 / edited for the Selden Society by Alan Harding. – London : Selden Society, 1981.
lxxiv,403p.

Roll-over relief for business assets : the Capital Gains Tax Rules explained / Kevin S. Slevin. – Bicester : CCH Editions, 1987.
v,66p; 23cm.
Includes index.
ISBN 0863251196

Rolls, R.J. → Conduct of an Action.
—Williston and Rolls : Court Forms, 2 Vols. Vol. 1: 1987. – 2nd ed. – Butterworths.
ISBN 0409801836 Llf £150.00

Rolph, C H
As I was saying. – Police Review, 1985.
ISBN 0851640168 Pbk £6.95
—Further particulars. – Oxford : OUP, 1987.
240. – (Oxford letters and memoirs).
Second volume of C.H. Rolph's memoirs, taking up the story from 'London Particulars' at the end of the First World War. He describes his 25 years with the City Police, rising to the rank of Chief Inspector, his work as a freelance journalist for the New Statesman and at the BBC.
Legal historians, criminologists
ISBN 0192117904 Hbk £12.50
ISBN 0192821431 Pbk £4.95

Rolt, Sidney
Tax Planning Strategies for Companies in South East Asia. – London : Oyez Longman, 1984. – (Oyez Longman Intelligence Report Ser.).
ISBN 0851208126 Hbk

Rom, Michael
Role of tariff quotas in commercial policy / by Michael Rom : with an introduction by Gerard Curzon. – London : Macmillan for the Trade Policy Research Centre, 1978.
272p.
ISBN 0333176383 £12.00

Roma : Europe's gypsies / by Grattan Puxon. – Rev updated ed. – London : Minority Rights Group, 1987.
15p. – (Report).
Bibliography: p.13.
ISBN 0946690456

Romain, Alfred
Dictionary Legal/Commercial Terms : German/English, 2 Vols. / Rutter. – London : Butterworths, 1984.
ISBN 0406038104 Hbk £98.00

Roman Constitutional History. – Rotterdam : A.A. Balkema, 1948.
195p.
Hbk £50.00

Roman Dutch law in Sri Lanka / by Marleen H.J. van den Horst. – Amsterdam : Free University Press, 1985.
154 p.; 24 cm.
Re translation of: Het Rooms Hollandse recht in Sri Lanka. : Originally presented as the author's thesis (M.A.–Free University, Amsterdam) in 1984. Includes index. Bibliography: p. 138-144.
ISBN 9062562361 Pbk

Roman Law. – Plymouth : Macdonald & Evans, 1966.
ISBN 0712118535 Pbk £4.95

Roman Law and Common Law / McNair. – 2nd ed. – Cambridge : Cambridge University Press, 1965.
ISBN 0521043611 Hbk £31.00

Roman law of trusts / David Johnston. – Oxford : Clarendon Press, 1988.
xiii,306p.
Discusses the Roman equivalent of a trust, a fideicommissum, which affected the strategies of succession open to testators. Provides an illustration of the emperor's involvement in building private law. Relates Roman law to social history and uses the development of the trust as a case study in legal evolution.
ISBN 0198252161 Hbk £37.50

Roman Private Law. – 4th rev. ed. – Pretoria : University of South Africa, 1984.
455p.
ISBN 0869813161 Pbk £18.50

Roman, provincial and Islamic law : the origins of the Islamic patronate / Patricia Crone. – Cambridge : Cambridge University Press, 1987.
178p; 23cm. – (Cambridge studies in Islamic civilization).
Examines cultural origins of Islamic Law. Studies hypothesis that a substantial source was Roman law with reference to patronate. Concludes Roman law contributed only through being part of the law of Near Eastern provinces.
ISBN 0521322537 £25.00

Romanow, Roy
Canada Notwithstanding : The Making of a Constitution 1976-1982 / John D Whyte. – Agincourt : Carswell, 1984.
300p.
Hbk £40.50

Romero, Ana Teresa
International regulation of data services: the debate over the trade and development issues. – London : Pinter, 1990.
250.
Bibliography and index included.
ISBN 0861878531 Hbk £30

Romero, Flerida Ruth P.
First Asian Congress of Labour Law and Social Security. – Quezon City : University of the Philippines, Law Center, 1982.
608p.
Pbk £60.00

Romero, Louis J.
Sale of Goods. – Agincourt : Carswell, 1986.
200p.
This textbook sets out the basic principles of the law of sale of goods in Canada's four western provinces in legislation and case law. Each paragraph of the text is accompanied by extensive footnotes which summarize relevant case law from Canada, England, and the Commonwealth.
Pbk £25.25

Romilly, Samuel
Memoirs of the Life of Sir Samuel Romilly, 3 Vols. – Dublin : Irish Academic Press.
900p.
ISBN 0716517841 Hbk £48.00

Ronald Dworkin and contemporary jurisprudence / edited and with a preface by Marshall Cohen. – London : Duckworth (Gerald), 1984.
ISBN 0715618172 Pbk £9.95

Ronald Dworkin and contemporary jurisprudence / edited and with a preface by Marshall Cohen. – London : Duckworth, 1984.
xii,304p; 24cm.
Originally published: Totowa, N.J. : Rowman and Allanheld, 1983. Bibliography: p301-302.
ISBN 071561813X

Ronzitti, Natalino
Law of Naval Warfare : A Collection of Agreements and Documents with Commentaries. – Martinus Nijhoff.
ISBN 9024736528 Hbk £117.00
—Rescuing nationals abroad through military coercion and intervention on grounds of humanity / Natalino Ronzitti. – Dordrecht Netherlands : M. Nijhoff Publishers, 1985.
236p.
Includes index. Bibliography.
ISBN 9024731356 Hbk £125.00

Rood, M.G.
Fifty Years of Labour Law and Social Security. – Dordrecht : Kluwer, 1986.
166p.
ISBN 9031203653 Pbk £90.00

Rooij, M. van
Private International Law in the Netherlands / M.V. Polak. – Dordrecht : Kluwer, 1987.
350p.
ISBN 9065442863 Hbk £150.00

Rooke, John F. S. →New Zealand income tax law and practice.

Rooney, Kevin
Guide to the Mental Health (NI) Order 1986. – Belfast : Queen's University of Belfast, 1986.
150p.
Pbk

Rooney, Nahau
Papua New Guinea, in the Supreme Court of Justice ... In the matter of a reference under section 18 of the Constitution, and in the matter of Ralph Rakhinand Premdas against the Independent State of Papua New Guinea, and others. Re Rooney: being a transcript of the proceedings 27th August - 5th and 11th September 1979. – Port Moresby : Council of Law Reporting for Papua New Guinea, 1981.
vi,390p; 34cm.
Cover title: The Rooney case.

Rooy, F.P. de
Documentary Credits. – Dordrecht : Kluwer, 1984.
ISBN 9065440755 Pbk £125.00

Roper, Robert B →English Encyclopedia of Forms and Precedents.
→ Ruoff & Roper on the law and practice of registered conveyancing.

Rorke, R.F. →Newall : Law and Practice of Deeds Registration.

Roscoe
Digest of the Law of Evidence on the Trial of Civil Actions (Nisi Prius) 5th ed. – Repr. of 1839 ed. – Abingdon : Professional Books.
306p.
Hbk £35.00

Rose, David →Petroleum Tax Analysis : North Sea : A Comparative Study of the Oil Exploitation Taxation System of the United Kingdom, Norway, Denmark and the Netherlands.

Rose, Dennis J →Australian Bankruptcy Law.

Rose, F.
Civil Liability Statutes. – London : Blackstone Press, 1987.
ISBN 1815850538 Pbk £8.95
—Restitution / P. Birks. – London : Sweet & Maxwell, 1986.
ISBN 0420472908 Hbk

Rose, F. D. →International commercial and maritime arbitration.
—International commercial and maritime arbitration. – Sweet & Maxwell, 1988.
ISBN 0421392207 Pbk £18.00
→ Kennedy's law of salvage.
—Modern law of pilotage / by F.D. Rose. – London : Sweet & Maxwell, 1984.
xxi,138p; 25cm.
Includes index.
ISBN 0421322705 Pbk £12.00
→ New foundations for insurance law.
—New foundations for insurance law. – London : Sweet & Maxwell, 1987.
ISBN 0420477802 Pbk £18.50

Rose, Gillian
Dialectic of nihilism : post-structuralism and law / Gillian Rose. – Oxford : Blackwell, 1984.
232p; 24cm.
Critique of post-structuralist theory related to law.
ISBN 0631131914 Hbk £22.00
ISBN 0631137084 Pbk

Rose, Gordon V.
Parties to an Offence. – Agincourt : Carswell, 1982.
226p.
This book deals with issues of complicity and constructive complicity in a wide range of criminal offenses under Canadian law. Aiders and abettors; parties to a common unlawful purpose; inciters; procurers; accessories after the fact; and other crimes involving more than one party are covered in the work.
Hbk £40.50

Rose, L.
Massacre of the innocents - Infanticide. – Routledge, 1986.
ISBN 071020339X Hbk £16.95

Rose, Michael E.
Relief of poverty, 1834-1914 / prepared for the Economic History Society by Michael E. Rose. – 2nd ed. – Basingstoke : Macmillan, 1986.
92p; 22cm.
Previous ed.: 1972. Includes bibliography and index.
ISBN 0333424158 Pbk £3.95

Rosen, Avra, et al
Articling Handbook. – Butterworths, 1988.
ca 200p.
Guidance on how to deal with the everyday aspects of working in a law office. Advice on how to conduct interviews, handle incorporations, draft pleadings, conduct real estate searches and closings, prepare for examinations for discovery and for trial, and to attend on motions.
ISBN 0409804800 sb

Rosen, Frederick →Constitutional code, Vol.1 : edited by F. Rosen and J.H. Burns.
—Jeremy Bentham and representative democracy : a study of the Constitutional code / Frederick Rosen. – Oxford : Clarendon Press, 1983.
vi,255p; 23cm.
Bibliography: p243-248. - Includes index.
ISBN 019822656X £19.50

Rosenberg, Marc →Criminal Procedure.
—Weekly Criminal Bulletin (W.C.B.) 1987-Present / Chris N. Buhr. – Aurora : Canada Law Book Co.
Llf Parts and Bound Vol. 123.00

Rosenfeld, W.P. →Foreign Investment Review Law in Canada.

Rosenfield →Immigration Law and Procedure.

Rosenne, Shabtai
Breach of treaty / by Shabtai Rosenne. – Cambridge : Grotius Publications, 1981.
xii,142p; 24cm.
At head of title: University of Cambridge Research Centre for International Law.
ISBN 0906496365
—Law and practice of the International Court / Shabtai Rosenne. – Dordrecht : Martinus Nijhoff, 1985.
xxv, 811p.
Reprint. Originally published: Leyden : A.W. Sijthoff, 1965. Includes index.
ISBN 9024729866 Hbk £350.00
—Procedure in the International Court : a commentary on the 1978 Rules of the International Court of Justice / Shabtai Rosenne. – The Hague : M. Nijhoff, 1983.
xvii, 305p.
Includes bibliographical references and index.
ISBN 9024730457 Hbk £130.00
—Reflections on International Arbitration and Litigation in the International Court of Justice. – Dordrecht : Kluwer, 1988.
24p.
ISBN 9065443517 Hbk £30.50

Rosenthal, Douglas E
National laws and international commerce : the problem of extraterritoriality / Douglas E. Rosenthal and William M. Knighton. – London : Routledge & Kegan Paul, 1982.
xi,96p.
Bibliography: p94-96.
ISBN 0710093381

Roskams, Julian →Lawyer's Remembrancer 1988.

Roskamus →Lawyers Remembrancer 1989.

Roskill, Eustace Wentworth Roskill →Fraud Trials Committee report.
—Half-a-century of commercial law, 1930-1980 / being the presidential address of Lord Roskill ... – Birmingham : Holdsworth Club of the University of Birmingham, 1981.
17p; 21cm. – (Presidential addresses/Holdsworth Club).
ISBN 0704406187
→ Improving the presentation of information to juries in fraud trials : a report of four research studies.

Ross, D.
International treasury management. – Cambridge : Woodhead-Faulkner, 1987.
ISBN 0859413632 Hbk £45.00

Ross, David J. →Existing and new forms of financing, University of Auckland, 27 May 1982 : papers presented at seminar.

Ross, Donald C
BAC Business Law / Woods. – Agincourt : Carswell, 1986.
ISBN 045939520 Hbk £36.50
—Business Law / Judith M. Woods. – Agincourt : Carswell, 1986.
616p. – (Bar Admission Course Materials Ser.).
Hbk £71.50

Ross, George →Unions, change and crisis : French and Italian union strategy and the political economy, 1945-1980.

Ross, Harry J →Capital Gains Tax On Businesses.

Ross, M.
Drafting and Negotiating Commercial Leases. – 2nd ed. – London : Butterworths, 1984.
ISBN 0406359075 Hbk £29.00
—Drafting and Negotiating Common Leases Scotland / D J McKichan. – London : Butterworths, 1985.
ISBN 0406359067 Hbk £41.50

Ross, Malcolm Geoffrey
Negligence in surveying and building / Malcolm Ross. – London : Estates Gazette, 1986.
xxii,247p.
Bibliography: p.238-239. - Includes index.
ISBN 0728200953

Ross Martyn, John G.
Family provision : law and practice / by John G. Ross Martyn. – 2nd ed. – London : Sweet & Maxwell, 1985.
xviii,187p; 22cm.
Previous ed.: published as The modern law of family provision. 1978. Includes index.
ISBN 0421342803 £14.50

Ross, Robert R.
Cognitive model of crime and delinquency prevention and rehabilitation, 2 Vols.
Vol. 1 : assessment procedures / Elizabeth A. Fabiano. – Ontario : Ontario Government Publications Service, 1983.
89p.
ISBN 0774386681 Hbk free
—Cognitive Model of Crime and Delinquency Prevention and Rehabilitation : Intervention Techniques, 2 Vols.
Vol. 2 : intervention techniques / Elizabeth A. Fabiano. – Ontario : Ontario Government Publications Service, 1983.
89p.
ISBN 0774386673 Hbk free
—Correctional Officer. – Toronto : Butterworths, 1981.
342p.
ISBN 0409863203 Pbk £36.95

Ross, S.A.
Corporate Finance. – Mosby, 1988.
ISBN 0801642116 Hbk £31.00

Rossi, Hugh
Landlord and Tenant Act 1987. – London : Shaw & Sons, 1987.
ISBN 072191070X Pbk £10.95

Rossiter, C. → Sackville and Neave Property Law : Cases and Materials.

Rossiter, C.J.
Vendor and Purchaser : Commentary and Materials. – North Ryde : Law book Co, 1985.
xxviii, 436p.
ISBN 0455206066 Hbk £57.50
ISBN 0455206074 Pbk £38.50

Rosson → Local Authority Licensing and Registration.

Rostow, Eugene V → Power and policy in quest of the law : essays in honor of Eugene Victor Rostow.

Roth
Psychiatry, Human Rights and the Law / Bluglass. – Cambridge : Cambridge University Press, 1985.
ISBN 0521261945 Hbk £30.00

Rothenberg
Understanding company accounts / Newman. – Telegraph Publications, 1988.
ISBN 0863671918 Pbk £6.95

Rothman, Melvin L. → Justice beyond Orwell.

Rothman, Mitchell P → Economic analysis of a performers' right.
→ Framework for evaluating Canada's Trade Marks Act.

Rothwell
Rivalry in Retail Financial Services / Jowett. – London : Macmillan.
ISBN 0333445309 Hbk £29.50

Rothwell, Roy
Industrial Innovation and Public Policy : Preparing for the 1980's and the 1990's / Walter Zegveld. – London : Pinter Publishers Ltd, 1981.
251p.
ISBN 0903804921 Hbk £17.50
ISBN 0861872509 Pbk £7.75

Rough justice / Martin Young & Peter Hill. – London : British Broadcasting Corporation, 1983.
176p,4p of plates; 20cm. – (Ariel books).
ISBN 0563201290 Pbk £1.95

Roulston, Barbara → Guide to Appearing Before the Surface Rights Board of Alberta.

Roundell, Francis
Company law in a nutshell / Francis Roundell. – 3rd ed. – London : Sweet & Maxwell, 1985.
vii,88p. – (New nutshells).
Includes index.
ISBN 0421348402

Rouse → UK Tax Offshore Oil and Gas.

Rouse, Douglas G. → New Brunswick Court Forms : Formulaire de procedure du Nouveau-Brunswick.

Rout, B.C.
Democratic Constitution of India. – New Delhi : S. Chand and Company, 1983.
Hbk £14.00

Rout, R.K.
Library Legislation in India. – Delhi : Reliance Publishing House, 1986.
xvi, 376p.
Hbk £225.00

Rovere, Richard H.
Howe & Hummel / Richard H. Rovere. – London : Arlington, 1986.
xvii,169p; 22cm.
Originally published: New York : Farrar, Straus and Giroux, 1985.
ISBN 0851406890 £9.95

Rovet, Ernest
Employee-Employer Rights : a Complete Guide for the Ontario Work Force. – 6th ed. – North Vancouver : International Self-Counsel Press, 1988.
113p.
ISBN 0889083681 Hbk

Row, Sanjiva
Advocates Act and Legal Practitioners Act. – 5th ed. – Allahabad : Law Book Company, 1987.
600p.
Hbk £160.00
—Code of Civil Procedure in 3 Vols. – 5th ed. – Allahabad : Law Book Company, 1982-84.
Hbk £450.00
—Code of Criminal Procedure. – 3rd ed. – Allahabad : Law Book Company, 1988.
1,900p.
Hbk £350.00
—Commentaries on Registration Act. – 7th ed. – Allahabad : Law Publishers, 1982.
Hbk £45.00
—Commentaries on the Law of Easements and Licences with Model Forms. – 2nd ed. – Allahabad : Law Publishers, 1982.
Hbk £27.00 ea
—Contract Act and Law Relating to Tenders etc., 3 Vols. – 9th ed. – Allahabad : Law Publishers, 1983.
Hbk £45.00
—Indian Stamp Act : With State Amendments. – 6th ed. – Allahabad : Law Book Ccompany, 1986.
800p.
Hbk £180.00
—Indian Succession Act. – 5th ed. – Allahabad : Law Book Company, 1985.
Hbk £220.00
—Law of Injunctions, 2 Vols. – 6th ed. – Allahabad : Law Book Company, 1985.
2,200p.
Hbk £400.00
—Law of Land Acquisition and Compensation, 2 Vols. – 7th ed. – Allahabad : Law Book Company, 1984.
With 1987 supplement.
Hbk £360.00
—Negotiable Instruments Act. – 9th ed. – Allahabad : Law Book Company, 1988.
950p.
Hbk £275.00
—Provincial Insolvency Act. – 5th ed. – Allahabad : Law Book Company, 1988.
xiv, 958p.
Hbk £275.00
—Transfer of Property Act, 2 Vols. – 5th ed. – Allahabad : Law Book Company, 1988.
3,000p.
Hbk £600.00

Rowan-Robinson, Jeremy
Land development and the infrastructure Lottery / J. Rowan-Robinson, M.G. Lloyd. – Edinburgh : T. & T. Clark, 1988.
xvi,160p; 22cm.
Includes index. Examines the relationship between local authorities and the private sector in the provision of supporting services and 'infrastructure' for private development. Looks at the discretionary powers of local authorities, at the legislation conferring this discretion and at how this is exercised.
ISBN 0567291499 Pbk £12.50
—Planning by agreement in Scotland / Eric Young. – Edinburgh : Green (W.) & Son, 1989.
Provides a guide to the law and practice of planning by agreement with an examination of the complexities that can arrive from section 50 of the Town and Country Planning (Scotland) Act 1972, the mechanics of such agreements and descriptions of the purposes for which they have been employed. Covers other statutory agreements governing land use, particularly the countryside. Concludes with a review of the arguments for and against the pursuit of 'planning gain'.
ISBN 0414008553 Pbk
→ Regulating Scotland.
→ Scottish planning law and procedure.

Rowan, Steven
Ulrich Zasius : a jurist in the German Renaissance, 1461-1535 / Steven Rowan. – Frankfurt a. M. : Klostermann, 1987.
xiii,286p.
Includes bibliographies and index.
ISBN 3465017722

Rowat, Donald C.
Critique of the Japanese study group's report on the ombudsman / by Donald C. Rowat. – Edmonton : International Ombudsman Institute, 1983.
16 leaves. – (Occasional paper).
—Spread of the ombudsman plan in western Europe / by Donald C. Rowat. – Edmonton : International Ombudsman Institute, 1983.
30p. – (Occasional paper).
'An excerpt from the chapter on developed countries in Professor Rowat's book, The Ombudsman Plan (Toronto, McClelland and Stewart, 1973), as revised for publication in Japanese by Waseaa University Press, Tokyo, in 1983'.

Rowe, Jane → Social work decisions in child care : recent research findings and their implications.

Rowe, Michael
Electronic trade payments / by Michael Rowe. – London : International Business Communications, 1987.
256p; 25cm. – (The IBC financial technology series).
Includes bibliography and index.
ISBN 1852710152 Pbk £65.00
—Letters of credit. – London : Euromoney, 1985.
xiv,174p.
ISBN 0903121794

Rowe, P.
Defence - the legal implications. – Pergamon, 1987.
ISBN 0080335969 Hbk £29.95

Rowe, Peter J
Evidence and Procedure in Magistrates Courts / Knapp. – 2nd ed. – London : Longman Professional, 1985.
ISBN 0851208681 Pbk £19.95
—Evidence and Procedure in Magistrates' Courts / Stephen Knapp. – London : Oyez Longman, 1982.
– (Oyez Longman Practitioner Ser.).
ISBN 0851202926 Hbk £12.95
→ Military intervention in democratic societies.

Rowell
Practical food law / Gresty. – London : Sweet & Maxwell, 1988.
ISBN 0421251608 Llf £95.00

Rowell, M. S.
Law of supplementary benefits / M. S. Rowell, A. M. Wilton. – London : Butterworths, 1982.
xxxi,239p; 22cm.
ISBN 0406649103

Rowell, Roland
Counterfeiting and forgery : a practical guide to the law / Roland Rowell. – London : Butterworths, 1986.
220p; 22cm.
Includes index.
ISBN 0406101108 Pbk £32

Rowes, P.
Taxation. – London : DP Publications.
ISBN 0905435915 Pbk £8.50

Rowland → Non-means-tested social security benefits.
—Rowland's Tax Guide. – London : Butterworths, 1983.
ISBN 0406359172 Pbk £63.00
—Rowland's Tax Guide : 1981-82. – 2nd ed. – London : Butterworths, 1981.
ISBN 0406359164 Pbk £50.00

Rowland, Charles J
Hutley's Australian Wills Precedents / Gary Tamsitt. – 4th ed. – 1989.
ca 240p.
This text, intended for both student and practitioners, includes materials on wills and trusts and examples of complete wills. The fourth edition changes the form of the precedents to the legislative drafting style.
ISBN 0409494887 Hbk £49.00

Rowland, J.
Rape : the ultimate violation. – Pluto Press, 1986.
ISBN 0745300928 Pbk £4.95

Rowland, Mark
Industrial injuries benefits scheme / Mark Rowland. – London : Legal Action Group, 1983.
xxvii,122p.
Includes index.
ISBN 0905099052

Rowland, Peter M. B.
Arbitration law and practice / Peter M.B. Rowland. – London : Institute of Chartered Accountants, 1988.
xxvii,185p.
ISBN 0852918887

Rowlands → Rights guide to non means tested benefits.

Rowland's Tax Guide, 1984-1985 / David Trill. – London : Butterworths, 1984.
ISBN 0406359199 Pbk

Rowland's Tax Guide. – London : Butterworths, 1983.
ISBN 0406359172 Pbk £63.00

Rowland's Tax Guide : 1981-82. – 2nd ed. – London : Butterworths, 1981.
ISBN 0406359164 Pbk £50.00

Rowlatt on the law of principal and surety / David G. M. Marks, Gabriel S. Moss, Sidney Arthur Taylor Rowlatt. – 4th ed. – London : Sweet & Maxwell, 1982.
liv,289p; 26cm.
Covers the construction and effect of guarantees, rights of a surety, loss of securities, bankruptcy, winding up, negotiable instruments, building contracts, and consumer credit. Draws on Commonwealth and United States authorities where appropriate.
ISBN 0421262400 £24.00

Rowlatt, Sidney Arthur Taylor
Rowlatt on the law of principal and surety / David G. M. Marks, Gabriel S. Moss, Sidney Arthur Taylor Rowlatt. – 4th ed. – London : Sweet & Maxwell, 1982.
liv,289p; 26cm.
Covers the construction and effect of guarantees, rights of a surety, loss of securities, bankruptcy, winding up, negotiable instruments, building contracts, and consumer credit. Draws on Commonwealth and United States authorities where appropriate.
ISBN 0421262400 £24.00

Rowley, J. E.
Organising Knowledge : an introduction to information retrieval / Jennifer E. Rowley. – Aldershot : Gower, 1987.
xviii,454p; 23cm.
Includes bibliographies and index. Previous control number ISBN 0566034867.
ISBN 056603574X Hbk £25.00
ISBN 0566034867 Pbk £12.95

Roy
Ottawa Civic Hospital Act, 1983, Bill Pr043 : An Act Respecting the Ottawa Civic Hospital. – Ontario : Ontario Government Publications Service, 1983.
7p.
Hbk £0.30

Roy, Bernadette Kelly
Rights of Indigenous Peoples in International Law : an Annotated Bibliography / Ruth Thompson. – Saskatoon : University of Saskatchewan, Native Law Centre, 1986.
33p.
ISBN 0888801769 £9.00

Roy, Sripati
Customs and Customary Law in British India. – Delhi : Mittal Publications, 1986.
Hbk £395.00

Royal Aeronautical Society → International Aviation Law Seminar : the Mount Irvine Bay Hotel, Tobago, West Indies March 16, 17, 18, 19, 1981.

Royal Baccarat Scandal / Grayson. – Souvenir Press.
ISBN 0285628526 Hbk £12.95
ISBN 0285628372 Pbk £6.95

Royal Commission of Inquiry into Chamberlain Convictions / report of the Commissisoner T.R. Morling. – Canberra : Government Printer, 1987.
379p. – (Parliamentary paper).
At head of cover title: Parliament of the Commonwealth of Australia.
ISBN 0724512985

Royal Commission on Criminal Procedure
Investigation and prosecution of criminal offences in England and Wales : the law and procedure / the Royal Commission on Criminal Procedure : Chairman: Sir Cyril Philips. – London : H.M.S.O., 1981.
vii,229p; 25cm.
ISBN 0101809212 Pbk £7.50
—Royal Commission on Legal Services in Scotland 1980, 2 Vols.
Vol: 1: Report. – Royal Commission on Criminal Procedure. – London : HMSO.
ISBN 0101784600 Hbk £8.50

Royal Commission on Criminal Procedure : memorandum by the Council of the Law Society on the Royal Commission's Report. – Law Society. – London : Law Society, 1981.
38p; 30cm.

Royal Commission on Environmental Pollution
Eighth report : oil pollution of the sea / Royal Commission on Environmental Pollution : chairman: Sir Hans Kornberg. – London : HMSO, 1981.
ISBN 0101835809
—Tenth report : tackling pollution : experience and prospects / Royal Commission on Environmental Pollution : Chairman: Sir Richard Southwood. – London : H.M.S.O., 1984.
ISBN 0101914903

Royal Commission on Legal Services in Scotland 1980, 2 Vols.
Vol. 1: Report. – Royal Commission on Criminal Procedure. – London : HMSO.
ISBN 0101784600 Hbk £8.50
Vol. 2: Appendices. –
ISBN 0101784619 Hbk £12.50

Royal Commission on Legal Services in Scotland → Scottish Consumer Council's response to the Hughes report : the report of the Royal Commission on Legal Services in Scotland (Volume one : Cmnd 7846).

Royal Commission on Newspapers / Tom Kent. – Hull, Quebec : Canadian Government Publishing Centre, 1981.
xiii,296p; 25cm.
Includes index. Chairman: Tom Kent.
ISBN 0660109549

Royal Commission on the Economic Union and Development Prospects for → Consumer protection, environmental law, and corporate power.
→ Family law and social welfare legislation in Canada.

Royal commissions and boards of inquiry : some legal and procedural aspects / by Leonard Arthur Hallett. – Sydney : Law Book Company, 1982.
xxxvi,368p.
Bibliography: pxxxi-xxxvi.
ISBN 0455204721

Royal Courts of Justice, 1983. – London : Wildy & Sons.
Illus.
Hbk £1.95

Royal Institute of International Affairs → Law and international resource conflicts.
→ Oil companies in the international system.
→ Political economy of international money : in search of a new order.
→ South Africa in crisis.

Royal Institute of Public Administration → Home Office : perspectives on policy and administration : bicentenary lectures 1982.
→ Parliament and the executive.

Royal Institution of Chartered Surveyors → Challenging decision : papers from a conference held at Oxford, September 1985.
→ Contemporary planning policies : papers from a conference entitled Making the Planning System Work held at Oxford, September 1983.
→ Current problems in property law.
→ Handbook of rent review.
→ Keeping pace with change.
—Maintenance of commercial tenanted proerty / a consultative document by a working party of the Building Surveyors Division of the Royal Institution of Chartered Surveyors, January 1987. – London : The Institution, 1987.
9,12p.
→ Metropolitan problem : papers from a conference held at Oxford, September 1984, organised by the Bar Council, the Law Society, and the Royal Institution of Chartered Surveyors.
→ Planning for growth and decline : papers from a conference held at Oxford, September 1986, organised by the Bar Council, the Law Society and the Royal Institution of Chartered Surveyors.
→ Planning for leisure in the countryside : papers from a conference held at Oxford September 1982.

Royal prerogative / by H.V. Evatt : commentary by Leslie Zines : foreword by Sir Ninian Stephen. – Sydney : Law Book Co. Ltd, 1987.
xviii, 34, 282 p.; 25 cm.
Includes bibliographical references and index.
ISBN 0455207569

Royall, David
Law Teacher : Journal of the Association of Law Teachers / John Tilotson. – London : Sweet & Maxwell, 1986.
Hbk £22.00

Rozakis, Christos L. → New law of the sea : selected and edited papers of the Athens colloquium on the law of the sea, September 1982.

Rozenberg, Joshua
Case for the crown : the inside story of the Director of Public Prosecutions / Joshua Rozenberg : foreword by Sir Michael Havers. – Wellingborough : Equation, 1987.
206p,24p of plates; 24cm.
Bibliography: p201-202. - Includes index.
ISBN 0722515332 £12.95
ISBN 1853360112

Rozovsky, Fay A. → Canadian Law of Consent to Treatment.

—Canadian Law of Patient Records / Rozovsky. – London : Butterworths.
ISBN 0409862886 Hbk £24.00

Rozovsky, Lorne E
Canadian Dental Law. – London : Butterworths.
ISBN 0409863351 Hbk £28.00
—Canadian Law of Consent to Treatment / Fay A. Rozovsky. – Butterworths, 1988.
ca 288p.
Deals with specific medico-legal consent problems such as consent relating to the treatment of children, prisoners and the mentally handicapped. Details circumstances in which consent may be waived, examines the essential elements of consent litigation, discusses how to prevent consent litigation and includes a special section on documenting consent.
ISBN 0409806307 Hbk £70.00
—Canadian Law of Patient Records / Fay A. Rozovsky. – Butterworths, 1984.
168p.
Examines the legal problems arising from patient records and how to avoid such problems. Contains incident reports as a tool for preventing possible serious injury to patients, the identification, evaluation elimination, reduction and prevention of risks, and practical advice on drafting administrative rules and guidelines on minimizing legal risks.
ISBN 0409862886 Hbk £40.00

Rubenstein, Michael
Equal pay for work of equal value. – London : Macmillan, 1984.
ISBN 0333375572 Hbk £22.50
—Unfair dismissal : a guide to relevant case law / by Michael Rubenstein and Yvonne Frost. – S.l. : s.n., 1983.
63p; 30cm.
—Unfair dismissal : a guide to relevant case law / by Michael Rubenstein and Yvonne Frost. – 4th edition. – London : Industrial Relations Service, 1986.
iv, 84p.
—Wage Discrimination : The Sex Discrimination Issue of the 1980's. – London : Pinter Publishers Ltd, 1984.
200p.
ISBN 0861872487 Hbk £15.00

Rubin, G. R. → Law, economy and society, 1750-1914 : essays in the history of English law.
—War, law and labour : the Munitions Acts, state regulation and the unions, 1915-1921 / Gerry R. Rubin. – Oxford : Clarendon Press, 1987.
288p; 22cm.
Includes index.
ISBN 0198255381 Hbk £27.50

Rubin, Ken
Access to Cabinet Confidence. – Ottawa : Ken Rubin, 1986.
ISBN 092062112 Hbk £35.00
—Opening the Door a Crack Includes : Cracks in the Federal Information Foundation. – Ottawa : Ken Rubin, 1984.
Hbk £30.00
—Prying Eyes : a Review and Indictment of the 1982 Canadian Privacy Act. – Ottawa : Ken Rubin, 1983.
Hbk £18.00
—Suggested Changes in Canada's 1982 Access to Information Act. – Ottawa : Ken Rubin, 1986.
ISBN 0920621139 Hbk £30.00
—Suggested Changes to Canada's 1982 Privacy Act. – Ottawa : Ken Rubin, 1986.
ISBN 0920621198 £25.00
—Testing the Spirit of Canada's Access to Information Act, 2 Vols. – Ottawa : Ken Rubin, 1984.
Hbk £30.00

Ruby, Clayton C., et al
Canadian Rights Reporter. – Butterworths.
Hbk £95.00
—Sentencing . – 3rd ed. – Butterworths, 1987.
712p.
Coverage of general principles of sentencing, finding an appropriate sentence, procedure, criminal record, psychiatric aspect of sentencing, factors affecting sentence, matters that are not taken into consideration on sentencing, parole and the role of prerogative mercy, suspended sentence and probation, corporate crime, and imprisonment.
ISBN 0409864226 Hbk £95.00

Rudden, Bernard
Basic Community cases / Bernard Rudden. – Oxford : Clarendon, 1987.
360p; 24cm.
Includes index.
ISBN 0198762127 Hbk £28.00
ISBN 0198762119 Pbk £11.50
→ Basic Community laws.
→ Law of property.
—New River : a legal history / Bernard Rudden. – Oxford : Clarendon, 1985.
xiii,335p,iileaves of plates; 23cm.
Bibliography: p321-329. - Includes index.
ISBN 0198254970 £20.00

Rude, George
Criminal and victim : crime and society in early nineteenth-century England / George Rude. – Oxford : Clarendon, 1985.
ix,160p; 22cm.
Includes bibliography and index.
ISBN 0198226462 £17.50

Rudolf → Law Of General Average and York-Antwerp Rules (BSL).

Rudolph, Harold
Security, terrorism, and torture : detainees' rights in South Africa and Israel : a comparative study / by Harold Rudolph. – Cape Town : Juta, 1984.
xviii, 270 p.; 22 cm.
Includes indexes. Bibliography: p. 253-259.
ISBN 0702115088 Pbk R38.00

Rueter, Robert → Stare decisis in Commonwealth appellate courts.

Ruff, Anne R
Commercial and Industrial Law. – 3rd ed. – Plymouth : Macdonald & Evans, 1984.
ISBN 0712101950 Pbk £6.50

Ruffolo, U. →Law and practice relating to pollution control in Italy.

Rule Against Perpetuities / Leach. – 1962 Reprint & Supplement. – Sweet & Maxwell.
ISBN 0421355506 Hbk £34.00

Rule in White and Carter (Councils) Limited v. McGregor / a report by the Contracts and Commercial Law Reform Committee. – Wellington : Government Printer, 1983.
15p.

Rule of Law : Foundation of Constitutional Democracy. – Carlton : Melbourne University Press, 1988.
504p.
ISBN 0522843476 Hbk £62.95

Rule of Law : Ideal or Ideology / Patrick J. Monahan. – Agincourt : Carswell, 1987.
224p.
This work contains a series of essays responding to recent attacks on the concept of 'Rule of Law'. These essays evaluate the present predicament of the 'Rule of Law' and offer prognosis for the future prospects of the ideal in modern society.
Hbk £40.50

Rule of Law : Ideal or Ideology / Patrick J Monahan. – Agincourt : Carswell, 1987.
ISBN 0459395408 Hbk £20.50

Rule of Law in a Free Society (1959, Delhi). – Geneva : International Commission of Jurists.
Hbk £9.00

Rule of law in Britain today / Gillian Peele. – London : Constitutional Reform Centre in cooperation with the Hughenden Foundation, 1987.
18p.
ISBN 0948419075

Rule of law in the areas administered by Israel / Israel National Section of the International Commission of Jurists. – Tel Aviv : Israel National Section of the International Commission of Jurists, 1981.
xiv,114p.
Includes bibliographical references.

Rule of Law within the European Communities. – Brussels : Editions de l'Universite de Bruxelles.
34p.
ISBN 2800402644 Hbk £50.00

Rules / The Securities Association. – 3rd ed. 1. – London : The Association, 1988.
looseleaf.
Popular title: TSA rule book.

Rules and processes : the cultural logic of dispute in an African context / John L. Comaroff, Simon Roberts. – Chicago : University of Chicago, 1981.
ix,293p; 23cm.
Bibliography: p277-288. - Includes index.
ISBN 0226114244 £19.25

Rules and regulations / The Securities and Investments Board. – 3. – London : The Board, 1987.
looseleaf.
Accompanied by: Overview, consultative papers and documents, etc..

Rules for the ICC court of arbitration / International Chamber of Commerce. – 1980 ed. – Paris : International Chamber of Commerce, 1981.
32p.
Previous ed.: 1975. The Rules of the ICC Court of Arbitration were first published in April 1975 as Publication 291. The text of the Rules remains unchanged in the present edition but a new section called 'the Internal Rules of the Court' has been added to it. 'The schedule of costs' has also been revised..

Rules Governing Medicaments in the European Community. – Luxembourg : Office for Official Publications of the European Communities, 1985.
115p.
ISBN 9282545318 Pbk £300.00

Rules governing substantial acquisition of shares : restrictions of market raids / Council for the Securities Industry. – Rev. ed. – London : The Council, 1982.
15p. – (CSI).

Rules of Civil Procedure : A Guide for Legal Secretaries and Law Clerks. – Toronto : Butterworths, 1985.
196p.
Summarizes and explains the various sections of the Courts of Justice Act and the new Rules. Contains special chapters on divorce, family law, and mortgage action proceedings.
ISBN 0409810304 Pbk £24.95

Rules of Court. – Vancouver : British Columbia Continuing Legal Education Society, 1983.
93p.
ISBN 0865041075 Hbk £45.00

Rules of Court : a Study of Rule-Making Powers and Procedures. – North Ryde : Law Book Co, 1985.
xxix, 271p.
ISBN 0455206309 Hbk £49.50

Rules of procedure / European Parliament. – Strasbourg : European Parliament, 1981.
108p.

Rules of procedure of the Council of 24 July 1979 as amended on 20 July 1987. – Council of the European Communities. – Luxembourg : Office for Official Publications of the European Communities, 1987.
9p.
ISBN 9282404803

Rules of sociological method and selected texts on sociology and its method / Emile Durkheim : edited with an introduction by Steven Lukes : translated by W. D. Halls. – London : Macmillan, 1982.
vi,264p.
ISBN 0333280717

Rules of the High Court, 1980. – Kuala Lumpur : International Law Books Services.
Hbk £22.50

Rules of the ICC Court of Arbitration. – Paris : International Chamber of Commerce.
32p.
Hbk £4.50

Rules of the International Stock Exchange, 31st May 1988. – International Stock Exchange of the United Kingdom and Republic of Ireland. – London : International Stock Exchange, 1988.
ca. 100p.
Supersedes the Stock Exchange rules.

Rules of the Supreme Court 1980 (P.U.(A) 33/80). – Kuala Lumpur : International Law Books Services.
Hbk £7.50

Rules Review : Summaries of Cases Decided Under the Rules of Civic Procedure. – Butterworths, 1987.
288p.
Compendium of relevant cases decided under Ontario's new rules of practice (between January 1985 and December 1986). Follows the order of the rules, and consists of concise case digests. Cases are annotated, with commentary by the author.
ISBN 0409805912 Pbk £29.95

Rules to Keep the Rascals Out. – Vancouver : November House.
ISBN 0920156045 Hbk £1.95

Ruling Communist parties and their status under law / edited by D.A. Loeber (editor in chief) ... et al. – The Hague : M. Nijhoff, 1986.
Includes bibliographies and index.
ISBN 9024732093

Ruling performance / Seldon. – Oxford : Blackwell Scientific, 1987.
ISBN 0631156453 Hbk £25.00

Rumbelow, D.
Houndsditch Murders and the Siege of Sidney Street. – Allan (WH).
ISBN 0491031785 Hbk £12.95

Rumble, Wilfrid E.
Thought of John Austin : jurisprudence, colonial reform and the British constitution / Wilfrid E. Rumble. – London : Athlone, 1985.
278p.
Includes bibliography and index.
ISBN 0485112922 £20.00

Runnymede Trust →Pivot of the system : a briefing paper on immigration appeals.
→ Rights without remedies : the European Convention of Human Rights and UK immigration law.

Ruoff & Roper on the law and practice of registered conveyancing / Robert B. Roper. – 5th ed. – London : Sweet & Maxwell, 1986.
lxxiv,1233p; 26cm.
Previous ed.: 1979. Includes index.
ISBN 0420469109 £82.00

Ruoff, Theodore B. F.
Concise land registration practice / Christopher West. – 3rd ed. – London : Sweet & Maxwell, 1982.
xvii,313p; 23cm.
Previous ed.: / by Theodore B.F. Ruoff. 1967. Includes index.
ISBN 0421287705 £19.50

—Land registration forms / Christopher West. – 3rd ed. – London : Sweet & Maxwell, 1983.
xv,261p; 23cm.
Previous ed.: 1973. Includes index.
ISBN 0421287608 £19.50

—Legal Legends and Other True Stories. – White Lodge.
ISBN 1851900519 Hbk £12.95

—Ruoff & Roper on the law and practice of registered conveyancing / Robert B. Roper. – 5th ed. – London : Sweet & Maxwell, 1986.
lxxiv,1233p; 26cm.
Previous ed.: 1979. Includes index.
ISBN 0420469109 £82.00

—Solicitor and the automated office / Theodore Ruoff. – London : Sweet & Maxwell, 1984.
x,136p; 22cm.
Includes index.
ISBN 0421331100 £8.50

—Solicitor and The Silicon Chip. – London : Oyez Longman, 1981.
ISBN 0851205690 Hbk £6.95

Rural development and human rights in South East Asia : report of a seminar in Penang, December 1981 / organized by the International Commission of Jurists and Consumers' Association of Penang. – Geneva : International Commission of Jurists, 1982.
254p.
ISBN 9290370173

Rural Poverty in the United Kingdom. – London : Policy Studies Institute, 1981.
Hbk £4.95

Rushbrooke, Peter
Working with FIDIC : A Practical Approach to its Use in the Middle East. – King's Ride : Institute of Building, 1983.
25p.
ISBN 0906600154 Hbk £6.30

Rushworth, Jonathan →Receivers and receiverships.

Russ
Legal Secretary Today / Holden. – Maidenhead : McGraw-Hill, 1986.
ISBN 0070849749 Pbk £4.95

Russel, Alexander David →First Step in Islamic Law in West Africa.

Russell
British Columbia Annotated Industrial Relations Act, 2 Vols. / A B P DuMoulin. – Butterworths.
Llf £160.00
→ British Columbia annotated Industrial Relations Act.

—Canadian Criminal Justice History. – University of Toronto, 1988.
ISBN 0802057209 Hbk £45.00

Russell, Bertrand
Justice in Wartime. – London : Spokesman Books, 1983.
232p.
ISBN 0851240895 Hbk £6.00

Russell-Clarke, A.
Copyright In Industrial Designs. – 5th ed. – Sweet & Maxwell, 1974.
ISBN 0421176008 Hbk £40.00

Russell, Francis
Russell on Crime. – 12th ed. – London : Sweet & Maxwell, 1986.
– (Sweet and Maxwell Library Reprints).
ISBN 0421355603 Hbk £100.00

Russell, Ken
Complaints against the police : a sociological view / Ken Russell. – 3rd rev ed. – Glenfield, Leicester : Milltak, 1985.
iv,132p.
Bibliography: p.125-130. - Includes index.
ISBN 0950490660

—Police Acts 1964 and 1976 : complaints against the police which are withdrawn / Ken Russell. – Leicester : Leicester Polytechnic, 1986.
33p. – (Leicester Polytechnic School of Law Monographs).
Includes bibliographical references.
ISBN 0900937408
→ Psychiatry and the criminal process.

Russell, M.
Banking Law in New Zealand. – North Ryde : 43.00, 1986.
xxxiii, 287p.
ISBN 0455206570 Hbk £27.50
ISBN 0455206589 Pbk

Russell, Mark W →Company Law and Securities Regulation in New Zealand.

Russell on Crime. – 12th ed. – London : Sweet & Maxwell, 1986.
– (Sweet and Maxwell Library Reprints).
ISBN 0421355603 Hbk £100.00

Russell, Peter H. →Leading constitutional decisions : cases on the British North America Act.

Russell Tribunal, III
Censorship, Legal Defence and Domestic Intelligence Service in W. Germany. – Russell Tribunal, III. – London : Spokesman Books, 1983.
50p.
Pbk individual 4.00

Russian serials / ... prepared by Alistair Ricketts ... in cyrillic script, with a transliterated version and an English translation. – Oxford : Bodleian Law Library, 1986.
12 leaves.

Rustomji
Law and Tax for the Layman. – Bombay : India Book House.
Pbk £25.00

Rutherford, Andrew
Growing out of crime / Andrew Rutherford. – Harmondsworth : Penguin Books, 1986.
188p.
Bibliography: p176-182.
ISBN 0140223835
—Prisons and the process of justice / Andrew Rutherford. – Oxford : Oxford University Press, 1986.
xii,217p; 20cm. – (Oxford paperbacks).
Originally published: London : Heinemann, 1984. Bibliography: p193-205. - Includes index.
ISBN 0192819321 Pbk £3.95

Rutherford, Brian A
Cases In Company Financial Reporting / Wearing. – Paul Chapman, 1988.
ISBN 1853960047 Pbk £5.95
—Financial Reporting in the Public Sector. – London : Butterworths, 1983.
ISBN 0406361401 Pbk £13.50

Rutherford, L. A.
Introduction to law / by L.A. Rutherford, I.A. Todd and M.G. Woodley. – 2nd ed. – London : Sweet & Maxwell published in association with the Institute of Legal Executives, 1987.
400p; 26cm.
Previous ed.: 1982. Includes index.
ISBN 0421367601 Pbk £17.50
—Introduction to law / by L.A. Rutherford, I.A. Todd, M.G. Woodley. – London : Sweet and Maxwell published in association with the Institute of Legal Executives, 1982.
xxiii,379p; 25cm.
Includes index.
ISBN 0421293802 Pbk £14.50

Rutter → Dictionary Legal/Commercial Terms : German/English, 2 Vols.
—Occupiers' Liability in Singapore and Malaysia. – London : Butterworths, 1986.
ISBN 0409995134 Hbk £43.00

Rutter, Michael
Applicable law in Singapore and Malaysia:a guide to reception, precedent and sources of law in the republic of Singapore and the federation of Malaysia. – Singapore : Malayan Law Journal, 1990.
600.
Account of the applicable law in Singapore and Malaysia, and a summary of legislation and case law. Appendices contain a digest of selected cases, politico-legal landmarks reception in other countries, comparative charts of the English and Singapore legal system, and a chart on precedent in Singapore.
Hbk
—Juvenile delinquency : trends and perspectives / Michael Rutter and Henri Giller. – Harmondsworth : Penguin, 1983.
432p; 20cm. – (Penguin education).
Bibliography: p363-415. - Includes index. Also published: New York, Guilford Press, 1984.
ISBN 0140804625 Pbk £5.95

—Maternal deprivation reassessed / Michael Rutter. – 2nd ed. – Harmondsworth : Penguin, 1981.
285p; 18cm. – (Penguin education).
Previous ed.: 1972. Bibliography: p219-272. - Includes index.
ISBN 0180805613 Pbk £1.95

Rutter, Michael F.
Damages for Personal Injuries and Death in Singapore and Malaysia. – Singapore : Malayan Law Journal, 1988.
ca 1,000p.
Presents the main principles governing the assessment of damages for personal injury and death in Singapore and Malaysia, with reference to pertinent cases and statutory provisions.
ISBN 9971700603 Hbk £265.00
—Occupiers' Liability in Singapore and Malaysia. – Butterworths, 1986.
320p.
Covers the duty of reasonable care arising in particular circumstances, out of a special status, and out of current operations or activities, classes of entrant, duty to invitees, to licensees and to trespassers, defences, public and private premises, multiple defendants, and duties towards children.
ISBN 0409995134 Hbk £90.00

Rutterford, Janette
Handbook of UK Corporate Finance. – London : Butterworths, 1987.
Pbk

Ryan → Criminal Law.
→ Textbook on Criminology.

Ryan, Alan
Property and political theory / Alan Ryan. – Oxford : Blackwell, 1984.
198p; 24cm.
Includes index.
ISBN 0631136916 £15.00

Ryan, Christopher
Company Directors. – London : CCH, 1987.
ISBN 0863250947 Pbk £25.00
—Company directors : liabilities, rights and duties / Christopher L. Ryan. – 2nd ed. – Bicester : CCH Editions, 1986.
xvi,407p; 23cm.
Covers the relevant provisions of the Business Names Act 1985, the Companies Act 1985, the Company Securities (Insider Dealing) Act 1985, the Insolvency Act 1986, the Company Directors Disqualification Act 1986, the Financial Services Act 1986, and other relevant statutes.
ISBN 0863250947 Pbk
→ Practical approach to company law.

Ryan, E. F.
Irish Reports Digests : 1894-1970, 6 Vols. Vol. 6, 1959-1970 /. – Abingdon : Professional Books.
Hbk £46.00

Ryan, Edward F.
Irish criminal process / Edward F. Ryan and Philip P. Magee. – Dublin : Mercier Press, 1983.
lxxi,595p.
Includes index.
ISBN 0853427003
—Notes of Irish Legal Cases, 1969-1978, Vol. 3. – Cork : Cork University Press, 1982.
ISBN 0902561219 Hbk £12.50

Ryan, F. J. O.
Control of the acquisition of shares : the new national take-overs code / F.J.O. Ryan. – Sydney : Butterworths, 1981.
ix, 134 p.; 24 cm.
Includes indexes.
ISBN 040930025X Pbk

Ryan, K.
International law in Australia. – 2nd ed. – North Ryde : Law Book Co, 1984.
ISBN 0455202699 Pbk £25.00
ISBN 0455205183 Hbk £35.00

Ryan, K.W. → Constitution of the Commonwealth of Australia.
→ Constitution of the Commonwealth of Australia annotated.
—International Law in Australia. – 2nd ed. – Deakin : Australian Institute of International Affairs, 1985.
Hbk £59.50
—Manual of the Law of Income Tax in Australia. – 6th ed. – North Ryde : Law Book Co, 1987.
xxvi, 360p.
ISBN 0455202974 Hbk £38.50
ISBN 0455202982 Pbk £26.50
—Queensland Supreme Court Practice. – Butterworths, 1984.
ISBN 0409493015 Hbk £235.00

Ryan, Leonard J.
Canada Statute Annotations (1941-1971) R.S.C. – 1970 Ed. – Aurora : Canada Law Book Co.
523p. – (Statute Services).
Hbk £50.00
→ Tremeear's 1971-1986 criminal annotations.
→ Tremeear's criminal annotations 1964-1970.

Ryan, M.
Executorship and Administration. – London : Fourmat, 1986.
ISBN 1851900039 Pbk £12.95

Rycroft, A. J. → Race and the law in South Africa : a volume of essays by members of the School of Law, Howard College, University of Natal, Durban, to commemorate the sixtieth anniversary of the Durban School.

Ryde on Rating
Supplement-1986. – Wellington : Butterworths.
This text covers the basis of liability, rateable property, exemptions and reliefs, the measure of liability, the valuation list, and the rate of its recovery on land in the United Kingdom. All the important case decisions of the Superior Court and Lands Tribunal are included along with statutes, rules, orders and instruments.
ISBN 0406363153 Pbk

Ryder, F. R. → Paget's Law of banking.

Ryder, Frank R. → Banks abroad : establishment - operations - supervision.
—Legal problems of international banking / by F.R. Ryder. – London : Sweet & Maxwell, 1986.
70p; 23cm.
ISBN 0421367806 Pbk £16.00

Ryland, R. H.
Irish Reports Digests : 1894-1970, 6 Vols. Vol. 2, 1919-1928 /. – Blue. – Abingdon : Professional Books.
Hbk £46.00
Vol. 3, 1929-1938. –
Hbk £56.00

S.C. Sen's Mergers, Amalgamations, and Take-Overs : the Law, the Procedure, and the Valuation of Shares. – 2nd ed. – Calcutta : Eastern Law House, 1981.
310p.
Hbk £90.00

Saba, Hanna → Protection of movable cultural property : compendium of legislative texts.

Saban, Hairani
Real property financing in Singapore. – Singapore : Malayan Law Journal, 1988.
390.
Examines the law and practice of the security and documentation involved in real property financial transactions in Singapore. Covers the security and financing devices adopted by financiers to protect their interest, a list of financing institutions, both public and private, and the various financing schemes available. Provides a number of forms and precedents of loans documents.
ISBN 997170062X Hbk
—Ship financing in Singapore. – Singapore : Malayan Law Journal, 1983.
xxi,305.
An examination of ship financing in Singapore on two levels; the individual in the commercial world, and the national on the international scene.
ISBN 9971700301 Hbk

Sabine, B.E.V.
Economist Publications Pocket Guide Business Taxes. – London : Edward Arnold.
ISBN 0340499138 Hbk £15.00
→ Revenue investigations manual.
—Tax appeals handbook. – London : Butterworths, 1983.
ISBN 0406535221 Pbk £13.00
—Time Limits for Tax Claims, Elections and Reliefs. – London : Butterworths, 1984.
ISBN 0406535108 Pbk

Sabine, M.
Corporate Finance. – London : Butterworths, 1987.
ISBN 0406259569 Hbk £42.00

Sachdeva, G.S.
International Transportation : Law of Carriage by Air. – New Delhi : Deep and Deep Publications, 1987.
328p.
ISBN 8171000010 Hbk £110.00

Sachdeva, Updesh Singh
Hindu Undivided Family : Law, Judiciary and Bankers. – Delhi : UDH Publishers, 1986.
Hbk £100.00

Sachs, Albie
Justice in South Africa. – Ibadan : Heinemann Educational Books (Nigeria).
Hbk £5.53

Sack, Jeffrey
Ontario Labour Relations Board Law and Practice / C. Michael Mitchell. – Butterworths, 1985.
ca 736p.
Deals with labour relations issues dealt with by the Ontario Labour Relations Board. Issues and proceedings covered include certification and termination of bargaining rights, unfair labour practices, sale of a business and related employer provisions, jurisdictional disputes, occupational health and safety, all construction matters and judicial review.
ISBN 0409865400 Hbk £115.00

Sack, Peter → Legal pluralism : proceedings of the Canberra Law Workshop VII.

Sack, Peter G. → Pacific constitutions : proceedings of the Canberra Law Workshop VI.

Sackville and Neave Property Law : Cases and Materials / C. Rossiter. – 4th ed. – Sydney : Butterworths, 1988.
992p.
The fourth edition of this casebook contains revised materials on the Trade Practices Act, leases, and mortgages.
Hbk £78.00

Sackville, Ronald
Property Law : Cases and Materials / Marcia A. Neave. – 4th ed. – Butterworths, 1988.
1,008p.
ISBN 0409492876 Hbk £79.00
ISBN 0409492884 Pbk £65.00
—Property law : cases and materials / by Ronald Sackville and M.A. Neave. – 3rd ed. – Sydney : Butterworths, 1981.
lxxi,936p.
Includes index.
ISBN 0409300411 Pbk
ISBN 040930042X

Sadikali, Moiz
Butterworth's Orange Tax Handbook 1986-87. – London : Butterworths, 1986.
This annual handbook contains the up to date text of all United Kingdom enactments relating to capital transfer tax, national insurance contributions, stamp duty, and value added tax. The material is arranged chronologically.
ISBN 0406508321 Pbk £35.75
—Butterworth's Yellow Tax Handbook 1986-87. – London : Butterworths, 1986.
This work provides the text of all legislation in the United Kingdom relating to income tax, capital gains tax, and corporation tax for tax practitioners. The book is extensively cross-referenced and indexed.
ISBN 0406510032 Pbk £42.00

Sadler
Relation Of Custom To Law, The. – Sweet & Maxwell, 1919 Reprint.
ISBN 0421375701 Hbk £14.75

Sadurski, Wojciech
Giving desert its due : social justice and legal theory / Wojciech Sadurski. – Dordrecht : D. Reidel, 1985.
xii, 329p.
Includes index. Bibliography: p 309-318.
ISBN 9027719411 Hbk £47.00

Saetevik, Sunneva
Environmental cooperation between the North Sea states : success or failure? / Sunneva Saetevik. – London : Belhaven Press, 1988.
xiv,173p.
Revision of thesis (cand. polit.): University of Oslo, 1986. Bibliography: p.161-165..
ISBN 1852930489 £22.50

Safarian, A. E.
Governments and multinationals : policies in the developed countries / A. E. Safarian. – London : British North American Research Organisation, 1983.
x,118p.
Bibliography: p105-110.
ISBN 089068071X
—Policies in the Developed Countries. – London : British-North American Research Association, 1983.
Hbk £8.00

Safe place of work. – London : Butterworths, 1983.
ISBN 0406013044 Hbk £9.50

Safe port of berth reachable on arrival : charterers' and shipowners' responsibilities and liabilities / W.E. Astle. – London : Fairplay, 1986.
x,109p.
Cover title: The safe port.
ISBN 0905045912

Safeguarding the Worker : Job Hazards and the Role of the Law. – North Ryde : Law Book Co, 1984.
xxiv, 426p.
ISBN 0455205043 Pbk £25.00

Safety and health in the construction of fixed offshore installations in the petroleum industry. – International Labour Office. – Geneva : International Labour Office, 1981.
135 p.; 18 cm.
Includes index.
ISBN 922102900X Pbk £20.00

Safety and Industry Laws, New South Wales Vol. 1 / G.A. Miller. – Butterworths.
ISBN 0409412503 Hbk
Vol. 2. –
ISBN 0409412511 Hbk

Safety at Work. – 2nd ed. – London : Butterworths.
ISBN 0408008407 Hbk £45.00

Safety at Work : the Limits of Self-Regulation. – Cambridge : Cambridge University Press.
ISBN 0521354978 Hbk £35.00

Safety of Consumer Products. Policy and Legislation in OECD Member Countries. – Paris : OECD, Organisation for Economic Co-operation and Development, 1981.
90p.
ISBN 9264121307 Hbk £3.20

Safety of goods / presented to Parliament by the Secretary of State for Trade and Industry. – London : H.M.S.O., 1985.
10p.
ISBN 0101930208

Safety Recommendations on the Use of Ports by Nuclear Merchant Ships French Edition /. – London : International Maritime Organization.
Hbk £1.50

Sagay, Itsejuwa E.
Casebook on Nigerian Family Law and Succession. – Abingdon : Professional Books, 1986.
800p.
ISBN 0862051150 Hbk £42.00
—Casebook on Nigerian Law of Contract. – Professional Books, 1983.
ISBN 0862050472 Hbk £37.50
ISBN 0862050533 Pbk £22.00
—Casebook on the Nigerian law of contract / by I.E. Sagay. – Abingdon, Oxon. : Professional Books, 1983.
xxvi,518p.
Includes index.
ISBN 0862050472
—International law and struggle for the freedom and welfare of man in Africa / by Itsejuwa E. Sagay. – Ile-Ife : University of Ife Press, 1983.
41p. – (Inaugural lecture series).
'An inaugural lecture delivered at the University of Ife on 3rd June, 1982'.
—Legal Aspects of the Namibian Dispute. – Ile-Ife : Obafemi Awolowo University Press.
xxli, 402p.
Hbk £10.00
—Nigerian law of contract / by I.E. Sagay. – London : Sweet & Maxwell, 1985.
450p.
Includes index.
ISBN 0421304200 Pbk £20.00

Sage companion. – Paradigm, 1988.
ISBN 0948825669 Pbk £5.95

Saha, A.N.
Civil Courts Practice and Procedure. – Delhi : Vinod Prakashan, 1986.
Hbk £240,00
—Code of Civil Procedure. – 3rd ed. – Calcutta : Eastern Law House, 1986.
Hbk £320.00
—Criminal Reference. – 3rd ed. – Calcutta : Eastern Law House, 1986.
£160.00
—Exhaustive and Critical Commentary on the Customs Act, 1962, Vol. 1 : With Notifications. – Delhi : Vinod Prakashan, 1987.
1,121p.
Hbk £250.00
→ Law of Bails, Forfeiture of Bonds and Habeas Corpus.
—Law of Evidence. – Calcutta : Eastern Law House, 1987.
Hbk £158.00
—Mitra's Civil Reference. – 2nd ed. – Calcutta : Eastern Law House.
Hbk £86

Saharay, H.K.
Administrative Law and Tribunal. – Calcutta : Eastern Law House, 1987.
Hbk £120.00
—Cases and Materials on the Constitution of India. – Bombay : Tripathi, 1987.
882p.
Hbk £160.00
→ Ghosh on Principles and Forms of Pleading.
—Industrial and Labour Laws of India, Second Edition. – New Delhi : Prentice-Hall, 1986.
704p.
ISBN 0876924259 Hbk £95.00
—Principles and Practice of Company Law in India. – 2nd ed. – New Delhi : Prentice-Hall, 1983.
928p.
ISBN 0876823333 Hbk £54.00

Saint Christopher and Nevis consolidated index of statutes and subsidiary legislation to 1st January 1984 / compiled at the Faculty of Law Library, University of the West Indies, Barbados. – Barbados? : s.n., 1984.
iv,78p.
Previous ed.: 1st January 1980. One of a series in the West Indian Legislation Indexing Project (WILIP) compiled in cooperation with the British Development Division.

Saint Christopher, Nevis and Anguilla
Laws of Saint Christopher, Nevis and Anguilla : printed by authority. – Saint Christopher, Nevis and Anguilla. – St. Michael, Barbados : Coles Printer, appointed Government Printer, 1982.
Continued in part by: Laws of Anguilla, 1971-. Includes ordinances and statutory rules and orders.

St. Clair, John
Judicial review in Scotland / John St. Clair, Neil F. Davidson. – Edinburgh : W. Green, 1986.
xxi,94p; 22cm.
Includes index.
ISBN 0414007743 £8.00
—Law of corporate insolvency in Scotland / by John B. St. Clair and J.E. Drummond Young. – Edinburgh : W. Green & Son Ltd., 1988.
xxix,381p; 25cm.
Includes index. A comprehensive guide to the law of corporate insolvency in the light of the reforming legislation of 1986. Deals with winding-up, receivership, administration and related problems such as trust and retention of title.
ISBN 0414008170 Pbk

St John Bate
Automated Office / Burgess. – Oxford : Blackwell Scientific, 1985.
ISBN 000383008X Pbk £7.95

St John-Brooks, Caroline
Who controls training? : the rise of the Manpower Services Commission / Caroline St John-Brooks. – London : Fabian Society, 1985.
20p; 22cm.
ISBN 0716305062 unbound £1.50

Saint Lucia consolidated index and subsidiary legislation to 1st January 1984 / compiled at the Faculty of Law Library, University of the West Indies, Barbados. – Barbados? : s.n., 1984.
v,108p.
Previous ed.: 1st January 1983. One of a series in the West Indian Legislation Indexing Project (WILIP) compiled in cooperation with the British Development Division.

Saint Lucia consolidated index of statutes and subsidiary legislation to 1st January 1983 / compiled at the Faculty of Law Library, University of the West Indies, Barbados. – Cave Hill : Faculty of Law Library, University of the West Indies, 1983.
vi,112p.
One of a series in the West Indian Legislation Indexing Project (WILIP) compiled in cooperation with the British Development Division.

Saint Piran Limited : investigation under Section 165(b) and Section 172 of the Companies Act 1948 : final report / by G.M. Godfrey and A.J. Hardcastle. – London : H.M.S.O., 1981.
228p; 30cm.
At head of title: Department of Trade.
ISBN 0115134735 Pbk £14.00

Saint Vincent and the Grenadines consolidated index of statutes and subsidiary legislation to 1st January 1986 / compiled at the Faculty of Law Library, University of the West Indies, Barbados in co-operation with the Ministry of Legal affairs, Kingston, St. Vincent. – Holmes Beach, Fla. : Gaunt, 1986.
ix,103p.
Previous ed.: 1st January 1985. 'One of a series in the West Indian Legislation Indexing Project (WILIP) compiled in co-operation with the British Development Division'.

Saintonge-Poitevin, Lise
Codes civils - The Civil Codes / by Lise Saintonge-Poitevin. – Reedition a jour au 1er dec. 1982. 1. – Montreal : Wilson & Lafleur, 1982-.
Previous ed.: 1978. Includes indexes.
ISBN 2891270177 Llf

Sainty, John
List of English law officers, King's counsel and holders of patents of precedence / compiled for the Selden Society by Sir John Sainty. – London : Selden Society, 1987.
xviii, 330p.

Saksena, N.S.
Law and Order in India. – New Delhi : Abhinav Publications, 1987.
359p.
ISBN 8170172160 Hbk £190.00

Salazar-Carillo →Foreign Investment Debt and Economy.

Sale and Management of Flats : Practice and Precedents. – London : Butterworths, 1985.
This book provides a practical guide to the subject of leasehold conveyancing in the United Kingdom. Particular attention is given to the establishment and maijntenance of subsequent management of the property from the tenant's and developer's point of view.
ISBN 0406526702 Hbk £38.00

Sale and purchase of real property in Malaysia. – London : Butterworths, 1984.
ISBN 0406181187 Hbk £45.00

Sale and supply of goods / The Law Commission, The Scottish Law Commission. – London : H.M.S.O., 1983.
viii,134p; 21cm. – (Consultative memorandum).
ISBN 0117301655

Sale and supply of goods. – Oxford : Blackwell Scientific, 1987.
ISBN 0003832430 Hbk £20.00

Sale and supply of goods : report on a reference under section 3(1)(e) of the Law Commissions Act 1965 / The Law Commission and the Scottish Law Commission. – London : H.M.S.O., 1987.
vi,125p.
ISBN 0101013728

Sale of flats / by Edward F. George and Arthur George. – 5th ed. – London : Sweet & Maxwell, 1984.
xxvii,447p; 23cm.
Expanded section on the treatment of remedies. Covers the 1980 Housing Act, and schedule 19 to the 1980 Act on services and service charges is examined in detail. New chapter on leases demanded by secure tenants from local authorities. Contains precedents, including articles of association of a management company.
ISBN 0421305509 £25.00

Sale of goods / P.S. Atiyah. – 7th ed. – London : Pitman, 1985.
xxxvi,448p; 22cm.
Previous ed.: 1980. Includes index.
ISBN 0273022067 Pbk £9.95

Sale of Goods. – Butterworths, 1988.
1,024p.
Incorporates detailed references to modern Canadian consumer and personal property security legislation, and recent legislative and case law developments in the area, and includes material on equitable proprietary principles and on relief against forfeiture.
ISBN 0409816264 Hbk £125.00

Sale of Goods. – Agincourt : Carswell, 1986.
200p.
This textbook sets out the basic principles of the law of sale of goods in Canada's four western provinces in legislation and case law. Each paragraph of the text is accompanied by extensive footnotes which summarize relevant case law from Canada, England, and the Commonwealth.
Pbk £25.25

Sale of goods : second report / New South Wales Law Reform Commission. – Sydney : Government Printer, 1987.
xvii,60p. – (L.R.C.).
Includes bibliographical references. Includes text of draft bill.
ISBN 0730530698

Sale of Goods Act. – 3rd ed. – Allahabad : Universal Book Agency, 1987.
Hbk £160.00

Sale of Goods Act. – 3rd ed. – Allahabad : Law Book Company, 1985.
Hbk £200.00

Sale of goods and consumer credit / A.P. Dobson. – 3rd ed. – London : Sweet & Maxwell, 1984.
xxvii,369p; 22cm.
Previous ed.: 1979. Includes index.
ISBN 0421292105 Hbk £14.50
ISBN 0421292202 Pbk £9.50

Sale of Goods and Consumer Law /. – North Ryde : Law Book Co, 1986.
x, 102p. – (Nutshells).
ISBN 0455206783

Sale of Goods and Hire-Purchase. – 3rd ed. – Lucknow : Eastern Book Company, 1985.
189p.
Pbk £20.00

Sale of Goods and Partnership. – 4th ed. – Allahabad : Orient Law House, 1984.
Hbk £100.00

Sale of goods and supply of services : a guide to the legislation / Vincent Grogan, Thelma King and Edward J. Donelan. – Dublin : Incorporated Law Society of Ireland, 1983.
xxii,133p.
Includes index.
ISBN 0902027239

Sale of goods, consumer credit and bills of exchange, cheques and promissory notes. – Edinburgh : Green (W.) & Son, 1983.
Offprint from the author's Scots Mercantile law of chapters covering sale of goods and consumer law.
ISBN 041400714X Pbk

Sale of Goods, Hire Purchase and Moneylending in Malaysia. – Singapore : Quins.
xliv, 391p.
Hbk £81.00

Sale of Goods in Canada. – 3rd ed. – Agincourt : Carswell, 1986.
603p.
This treatise given on the law of sale of goods in Canada has been updated to discuss the recommendations of the Ontario Law Reform Commission's Report on the Sale of Goods, provisions of the International Convention on the Sale of Goods, consumer protection legislation, and related materials on sale of goods.
Hbk £80.00

Sale of Goods Litigation / Richard Spearman. – London : Longman Professional (UK), 1983.
ISBN 0851206905 Pbk £19.95

Sale of land / Law Reform Commission of Victoria. – Melbourne : The Commission, 1988.
iv,40p. – (Discussion paper).
Includes bibliographical references.
ISBN 0724166947

Sale of land : commentary and cases / Skapinker. – London : Legal Books, 1986.
ISBN 0949553220 Hbk £20.00

Sale of Real Property and Law of Agency in NSW. – 4th ed. – Sydney : Butterworths, 1983.
176p.
This book is a working guide for those involved in conveyancing transactions. The fourth edition has been revised and updated to include new materials on the contract of sale of land, strata titles, agents' commissions, registration of titles, valuation of land, and other topics.
ISBN 0409494119 Pbk £26.00

Sale of Real Property and Law of Agency in Queensland / W.B. Hutchinson. – Butterworths, 1986.
160p.
This is a working guide for students and those involved with conveyancing transactions. Included are materials on contracts for sale of land, strata titles, registration of titles, agents, commissions, unjust contracts, valuations of land, land subdivisions, and local authority requirements for land development.
ISBN 0409491179 Pbk £26.00

Saleh, Nabil A.
Unlawful gain and legitimate profit in Islamic law : riba, gharar and Islamic banking / Nabil A. Saleh. – Cambridge : Cambridge University Press, 1986.
xii,130p; 24cm. – (Cambridge studies in Islamic civilization).
Examines ban on taking interest and rejection of aleatory contracts in Islamic law. Considers consequent conflict with world banking system. Studies these rules in the four Sunni schools of law and the Ibadi.
ISBN 0521322987 £19.50

Saleh, Samir
Commercial arbitration in the Arab Middle East : a study in Shara and statute law / Samir Saleh. – London : Published under the patronage of the International Chamber of Commerce by Graham & Trotman, 1984.
380p.
Bibliography: p445-455. - Includes index.
ISBN 0860104532 £55.00

Sales and consumer law in Australia and New Zealand / by K.C.T. Sutton. – Being 3rd ed. of The law of sale of goods in Australia and New Zealand. – Sydney : Law Book Co., 1983.
lxx,658p.
Includes bibliographical references and index.
ISBN 0455204675

Sales and sales financing in Canada : cases and materials / by M.G. Bridge, F.H. Buckley, with the assistance of L.R. Ganong. – Toronto : Carswell, 1981.
xlix,694p.
Includes bibliographical references.
ISBN 0459337505

Sales, G.
How to deal with your bank manager. – London : Kogan Page, 1988.
ISBN 1850915962 Hbk £12.95
ISBN 1850915970 Pbk £5.95

Sales, Harry → Encyclopedia of rating and local taxation : law and practice.

Sales promotion law. – Oxford : Blackwell Scientific, 1987.
ISBN 0003833941 Hbk £25.00

Sales Tax Act. – Durban : Professional Publishers.
Hbk £45.00

Sales Tax Register. – Cape Town : Legal & Financial Publishing, 1983.
– (Merlen Ser. of Registers).
Hbk £3.52

Sales Tax Strategy. – Durban : Butterworths.
Hbk

Salhany, Roger E.
Canadian criminal procedure. – 4th ed. – Aurora, Ont. : Canada Law Book, 1984.
cv,610p.
Includes index. Latest supplement held: 2nd, 1986.
ISBN 0888040202
—Cross-Examination : the Art of the Advocate. – Butterworths, 1988.
152p.
Shows how to conduct an effective cross-examination of a witness in criminal and civil trials. Sets out how to properly examine various types of witness, attacking the method used by the expert witness, contradicting the witness by prior testimony, attacking identification evidence, and how to cross-examine on criminal record.
ISBN 0409809691 Hbk £39.95
—Origin of rights / by Roger E. Salhany. – Toronto : Carswell, 1986.
viii, 175 p.; 24 cm.
Includes index. Bibliography: p. 163-171.
ISBN 045938760X Pbk
—Origins of Rights. – Agincourt : Carswell, 1986.
186p.
This work traces the historical and legal development of such fundamental freedoms as freedom of religion; freedom of the press; freedom from arbitrary detention and search and seizure; freedom from self incrimination; and the right to counsel.
Hbk £25.25
—Police Manual of Arrest, Seizure and Interrogation. – 4th ed. – Agincourt : Carswell, 1988.
182p.
This work is an updated handbook relected recent Canadian Criminal Code revisions and recent case law affecting police powers of arrest, seizure, and interrogation.
Hbk £29.50

Salim, Rafiah
Cases and materials on evidence in Malaysia and Singapore. – Singapore : Malayan Law Journal, 1990.
500.
Deals with the cases and statutory provisions on the law of evidence in Malaysia and Singapore, based on the Malaysian Evidence Act 1950 (revised 1971), and the Singapore Evidence Act 1976 (revised 1985). Examines the general position of the law, in each chapter, and then sets out the important judgements of cases in Singapore and Malaysia.
Hbk

Salinger, F. R.
Tolley's factoring : a guide to factoring practice and law / by F.R. Salinger. – Croydon : Tolley, 1984.
xvii,253p; 23cm.
Includes index.
ISBN 0854591648 Pbk £17.50

Saliwanchik, Roman
Legal protection for microbiological and genetic engineering inventions / Roman Saliwanchik. – London : Addison-Wesley, 1982.
xiii,256p; 25cm.
Includes index.
ISBN 0201109387 £33.30

Salkeld, Marilyn → Helping the Victim : Your Guide to Claiming Compensation.

Salkeld, W.
Reports of Cases in the Court of King's Bench : With Some Special Cases in the Courts of Chancery, Common Pleas and Exchequer, Alphabetically Digested Under Proper Heads for the 1st of William and Mary to the 10th of Anne (1689-1712, 3 Vols. – Repr. of 1724 ed. – Abingdon : Professional Books.
308p.
Hbk £90.00

Sallmann, Peter A
Australian and New Zealand Journal of Criminology / John Willis. – Wellington : Butterworths.
Hbk
—Criminal justice in Australia / Peter Sallmann and John Willis. – Melbourne : Oxford University Press, 1984.
240p.
Bibliography: p227-235.
ISBN 0195544595
—Rape law reform in South Australia : a study of the background to the reforms of 1975 and 1976 and of their subsequent impact / P.A. Sallmann and Duncan Chappell. – Adelaide : Adelaide Law Review Association, 1982.
x,110p.
ISBN 0908448023
—Report on criminal trials / Peter A. Sallmann. – Canberra : Australian Institute of Judicial Administration, 1985.
xiii,217p.
Report of a joint committee of the Victorian Bar Council and the Australian Institute of Judicial Administration. Includes bibliographical references. At head of cover: Shorter Trials Committee. Chairman: Hon. Mr. Justice McGarvie.
ISBN 095900291X

Salmon → Computers and the Law.

Salmon and Freshwater Fisheries Act 1975 / William Howarth. – London : Financial Training, 1987.
xxiv,311p; 23cm.
Bibliography: p302-304. - Includes index. Includes text of the Salmon and Freshwater Fisheries Act 1975. Originally published: London : H.M.S.O., 1975.
ISBN 1851850309 £17.95

Salmon, P.
Compulsory Acquisition of Land in New Zealand. – London : Butterworths, 1984.
ISBN 0409601225 Hbk £25.40

Salmond and Heuston on the law of torts / R. F. V. Heuston, R. A. Buckley, John Salmond. – 19th ed. – London : Sweet & Maxwell, 1987.
700p; 25cm.
Previous ed.: 1981. Includes index.
ISBN 0421343001 Hbk £30.00 :
ISBN 0421343109 Pbk £24.00

Salmond, John
Salmond and Heuston on the law of torts / R. F. V. Heuston, R. A. Buckley, John Salmond. – 19th ed. – London : Sweet & Maxwell, 1987.
700p; 25cm.
Previous ed.: 1981. Includes index.
ISBN 0421343001 Hbk £30.00 :
ISBN 0421343109 Pbk £24.00

Salter, D. A. → Humphreys' matrimonial causes.
—Matrimonial Consent Orders and Agreements. – London : Longman Professional, 1986.
ISBN 0851211127 Pbk £12.95

Salter, John → Proceedings of the seminar on planning law for industry : March 29th-April 2nd 1981, Churchill College, Cambridge, England.
—U.K. onshore oil and gas law : a practical guide to the legal regime relating to United Kingdom onshore oil and gas operations / by J.R. Salter : preface by Terence Daintith and Geoffrey Willoughby. – London : Sweet & Maxwell, 1986.
xxvi,505p; 25cm.
A compendium of the relevant statute law and all the secondary legislation made pursuant to it. Includes forms and precedents for every stage of legal proceedings and a section on government memoranda, departmental guidance notes, and other policy documents.
ISBN 0421347805 £55.00

Salzwedel, Jurgen
Law and practice relating to pollution control in the Federal Republic of Germany / Heinhard Steiger. – 2nd ed. – London : Graham & Trotman for the Commission of the European Communities, 1982.
xxvii,308p; 23cm.
Previous ed.: 1976 / by Heinhard Steiger and Otto Kimminich. Bibliography: p301-302. Includes index.
ISBN 0860103080 £21.00

Sami of Lapland / by Mervyn Jones. – London : Minority Rights Group, 1981.
15p. – (Report).
Bibliography: p.15.

Sammon, William J.
Advocacy in Child Welfare Cases. – Agincourt : Carswell, 1985.
258p.
This book discusses the representation of the parties to child welfare cases under the Child Welfare Act and the Child and Family Services Act of Canada.
Hbk £35.75

Sampath Iyengar's Law of Income Tax, 4 Vols. – 7th ed. – New Delhi : Bharat Law House, 1981-83.
Hbk £175.00 ea.

Sampford, C. J. G. → Law, rights and the welfare state.

Sampson, Anthony
Money lenders : bankers in a dangerous world / Anthony Sampson. – Sevenoaks : Coronet, 1983.
377p; 18cm.
Originally published: London : Hodder and Stoughton, 1981. Includes index.
ISBN 0340287713 Pbk £2.50

Sampson, D. H. →South African Attorneys handbook.

Samuel, G. H. →Cases in Tort.

Samuel Walker Griffith. – St. Lucia : University of Queensland Press, 1984.
448p.
ISBN 0702216887 Hbk £45.00

Samwell, Stanley David
Corporate receiverships : a practical approach / by Stanley Samwell. – London : Institute of Chartered Accountants in England and Wales, 1981.
xv,190p; 22cm.
Includes index.
ISBN 0852912870 Pbk £11.95

San of the Kalahari / by David Stephen. – London : Minority Rights Group, 1982.
16p. – (Report).
Includes bibliographical references.

Sanajaoba, N.
Socio-Legal Problems and Developing Society. – New Delhi : Deep and Deep Publications, 1986.
331p.
Hbk £225.00

Sanctity of contract : wisdom or folly? : an inaugural lecture given in the University of Fort Hare on the 24th May 1984 / by Peter L. Volpe. – Alice, South Africa : Fort Hare University Press, 1984.
14p.
ISBN 094997465X

Sanctity Of Contracts In English Law. – Sweet & Maxwell, 1959 Reprint.
ISBN 0421376007 Hbk £14.75

Sanctuary, G.
Before You See A Solicitor (It's Your Law). – 2nd ed. – London : Longman Professional, 1983.
ISBN 0851207790 Pbk £6.95

Sand, Peter H →Marine environment law in the United Nations Environment Programme : an emergent eco-regime.

Sandalow, Terrance →Courts and free markets : perspectives from the United States and Europe, Vol.1.

Sandel, Michael J.
Liberalism and the limits of justice / Michael J. Sandel. – Cambridge : Cambridge University Press, 1982.
ix,191p; 24cm.
Bibliography: p184-186. - Includes index.
ISBN 052124501X Hbk £17.50
ISBN 0521270774 Pbk £5.95

Sanden, V.D.
Community Order and National Economic Policies : Disciplines Communautaires et Politiques Economiques Nationales. – Dordrecht : Kluwer.
538p.
ISBN 9065442014 Pbk £125.00

Sanders, A. J. G. M. →Southern Africa in need of law reform : proceedings of the Southern African Law Reform Conference, Sun City, Bophuthatswana, 11-14 August 1980.

Sanders, N.
Computer-Aided Management. – Cambridge : Woodhead-Faulkner, 1986.
ISBN 085941308X Hbk £19.95

Sanders, Pieter →Arbitration in settlement of international commercial disputes involving the Far East: arbitration in combined transportation.
→ Art of arbitration : essays on international arbitration : liber amicorum Pieter Sanders, 12 September 1912-1982.
→ Comparative arbitration practice and public policy in arbitration.
→ International handbook on commercial arbitration.
—Netherlands Arbitration Act : Text and Annotations in English, French and German / Albert Jan van den Berg. – Dordrecht : Kluwer, 1987.
ISBN 9065442979 Pbk £67.50
→ New trends in the development of international commercial arbitration and the role of arbitral and other institutions.
→ UNCITRAL's project for a model law on international commercial arbitration.

Sanderson →Economics of Foreign Exchange.

Sanderson, John P.
Labour Arbitrations and All That. – 2nd ed. – Aurora : Canada Law Book Co, 1985.
146p. – (Text Books-Civil).
Pbk £17.50

Sanderson, Paul
Model Agreements for Visual Artists : a Guide to Contracts in the Visual Arts. – Ottawa : CARFAC, 1982.
Hbk £30.00
—Musicians and the law in Canada / by Paul Sanderson. – Toronto : Carswell, 1985.
xxxi, 258 p.; 24 cm.
This work examines the law of Canada impacting on musicians and their business affairs. Issues discussed include: copyright, music publishing, live performance, management and agency, merchandising, personal service contracts, income taxes, and other relevant topics. Includes index.
ISBN 0459372203

Sandevarn, Arne →Shipbroking and chartering practice.

Sandhi, R.
Divided Families. – Turnaround Press, 1987.
ISBN 0902397575 Pbk £2.95

Sandoz, Yves →Commentary on the additional protocols of 8 June 1977 to the Geneva Conventions of 12 August 1949.
→ Implementation of international humanitarian law.
—Prohibitions or Restrictions on the Use of Certain Conventional Weapons. – Geneva : Comite International de la Croix-Rouge, 1981.
33p.
Hbk £2.00

Sandrey, R.A.
Maori Fishing Rights in New Zealand : an Economic Perspective. – Canterbury : Agricultural Economics Research Unit, 1986.
9p.
Hbk

Sands, Philippe Joseph
Chernobyl : law and communication : transboundary nuclear air pollution : the legal materials / Philippe Sands. – Cambridge : Grotius, 1988.
xxxiii,312p.
Reproduces texts including multilateral and bilateral treaties, non-binding acts of international organisations and private associations of scholars, and national legislation. Covers the development of the law up to and including the 1986 IAEA Conventions on Early Notification and assistance, and the 1987 Resolution of the Institut de Droit International on Transboundary Air Pollution.
ISBN 0949009229 £38.00

Sandy →Touche Ross Tax Guide for the Family 1988-89.
→ Touche Ross Tax Guide to Pay and Perks 1988-89.

Sandys-Winsch, G.
Gun Law. – 5th ed. – Shaw & Sons, 1988.
ISBN 0721903630 Pbk £6.00
—Your dog and the law. – London : Shaw & Sons, 1984.
ISBN 0721910106 Pbk £2.25

Sandys-Winsch, Godfrey
Animal law / by Godfrey Sandys-Winsch. – 2nd ed. – London : Shaw & Sons, 1984.
xxxiv,260p.
Includes index.
ISBN 0721908012
—Garden law / by Godfrey Sandys-Winsch. – London : Shaw & Sons, 1982.
xiii,245p; 22cm.
Includes index.
ISBN 0721909302 Pbk
—Your Dog and the Law. – London : Shaw & Sons, 1984.
ISBN 0721910106 Pbk £2.25

Sangal, P.S.
National and Multinational Companies : Some Legal Issues. – Bombay : Tripathi, 1981.
546p.
Hbk £100.00

Sanger, Clyde →Stitches in time : the Commonwealth in world politics.
—To Settle the Oceans : the Law of the Sea in Practice. – Toronto : University of Toronto Press, 1986.
256p.
ISBN 0802057071 Hbk £30.00
ISBN 0802066356 Pbk £14.95

Sanilevici, Renee
Bibliography of Israeli law in European languages / Renee Sanilevici. – Jerusalem : Harry Sacher Institute for Legislative Research, 1985.
221p.
Supersedes: A bibliography of Israel law in English and other European languages / compiled by Judith Romney Wegner. 1972; and, A bibliography of Israel law ... 1972-1979 / compiled by Judith Deborah Wilkenfeld. 1979. Includes index.

Sann
Carriage Of Goods By Sea / Katzman. – 7th ed. – Matthew Bender, 1973.
ISBN 0000999054 Hbk £112.00
→ Treaties and Related International Documents.

Santikam, Mingsam
Technology transfer : a case study / Mingsam Santikam. – Singapore : Singapore University Press, 1981.
xiv,270p.
Bibliography: p257-264.

Santoro, Carlo Masotti →World directory of criminological institutes.

Santos, Gonzalo T.
Casebook on Taxation, Fourth Edition. – Quezon City : University of the Philippines, Law Center, 1981.
239p.
Pbk £20.00

Sappideen, C. →Cases on torts.

Sappideen, C.M.
Perpetuities Act 1984 / P.J. Butt. – North Ryde : Law Book Co, 1986.
xx, 188p.
ISBN 0455206082 Hbk £25.00

Sapronov, W.
Telecommunications and the Law. – Freeman (WH).
ISBN 0716781557 Hbk £39.95

Saran, G. →Commentaries on Contract Labour Act, 1970 : Regulation and Abolition.
→ Commentaries on Workmen's Compensation Act, 1923.
→ Contract Labour : Regulation and Abolition Act, 1970.

Sarathi, V.P.
Elements of the Law of Evidence. – 3rd ed. – Lucknow : Eastern Book Company, 1984.
411p.
Pbk £15.00
—Interpretation of Statues. – 3rd ed. – Lucknow : Eastern Book Company, 1986.
704p.
Hbk £180.00
→ Trade and Merchandise Marks Act, 1958.

Sarcevic, Petar
Essays on international commercial arbitration. – London : Graham & Trotman, 1989.
256.
Focuses on Model Law as prepared by the United Nations Commission on International Trade Law, accepted by the General Assembly in 1985. Also discusses ICSID arbitration and the New York Convention of 1958.
ISBN 0860107051 Hbk £46.50

Sargant, Tom
Criminal trials : the search for truth / Tom Sargant, Peter Hill. – London : Fabian Society, 1986.
33p.
ISBN 0716313480

Sargent
City of Owen Sound Act, 1983, Bill Pr053 : An Act Respecting the City of Owen Sound. – Ontario : Ontario Government Publications Service, 1983.
2p.
Hbk £0.30
→ Taxation of directors.
→ Taxation of fringe benefits.

Sarin
Encyclopedia of Petroleum Laws. – Allahabad : Universal Book Agency, 1982/83.
Hbk £250.00

Sarin, Ranjit Lal
Crimes : Commentary on the Narcotic Drugs and Psychotrophic Substances Act, 1985, and the Narcotic Drugs and Psychotrophic Substances Rules, 1985 with State Rules and Notifications. – Delhi : Vinod Prakashan, 1987.
615p.
Hbk £150.00

Sarkar, A.K.
Summary of Salmond's Jurisprudence. – 3rd ed. – Bombay : Tripathi, 1981.
204p.
Hbk £15.00

Sarkar, S.C. →Trade Marks Law in India with Up-to-date Act and Supreme Court Decision.

Sarna, Lazar
Authors and Publishers : Agreements and Legal Aspects of Publishing. – 2nd ed. – Butterworths, 1987.
232p.
Examines the obligations of parties to publishing agreements. Covers all aspects of the law and business practice relating to author-publisher contracts and includes a clause-by-clause analysis of the fundamental provisions of agreements currently used. Revised to include the new copyright legislation and software agreements.
ISBN 0409806285 Hbk £50.00
—Law of Declaratory Judgments. – Agincourt : Carswell, 1978.
ISBN 045932200 Hbk £22.00
—Letters of credit : the law and current practice / by Lazar Sarna. – 2nd ed. – Toronto : Carswell, 1986.
xxii,254p.
Includes bibliographical references and index.
ISBN 045938810X

—Letters of credit : the law and current practice / by Lazar Sarna. – Toronto : Carswell Legal Publications, 1984.
xv, 204 p.; 24 cm.
Includes bibliographical references and indexes.
ISBN 0459359908 Hbk £27

Sarrat →Institute of Financial Management.

Sarre, David A. G. →Charlesworth's Mercantile law.

Sartre, Jean Paul
War Crimes in Vietnam / Vladimir Dedijer. – London : Spokesman Books.
40p.
Pbk individual 4.00

Saskatchewan Annual Bound Statutes, 1977-1982, 1984-1988. – Agincourt : Carswell.
Hbk £329.50

Saskatchewan Decisions : Civil and Criminal Cases (1980-Present). – Aurora : Canada Law Book Co.
– (Summary Services, Provincial Ser.).
Hbk £199.50

Saskatchewan Decisions Citator (1979-1983). – Aurora : Canada Law Book Co, 1983.
– (Statute Services).
Pbk £99.50

Saskatchewan Decisions Citator. – Aurora : Canada Law Book Co.
Llf £99.50

Saskatchewan Law Reports : 1908-1931, 25 Vols. – Agincourt : Carswell, 1983.
1200p.
Hbk £588.00

Sassoon, David M.
C.I.F. and F.O.B. contracts / H. Orren Merren. – 3rd ed. – London : Stevens, 1984.
xlv,528p; 26cm.
Previous ed.: 1975. Includes index.
ISBN 0420465308 £60.00

—CIF and FOB Contracts (BSL) / H Orren Merren. – 3rd ed. – London : Sweet & Maxwell, 1984.
ISBN 0420465308 Hbk £80.00

—Judicial Enforcement of International Debt Obligations / Bradlow. – London : Eurospan.
ISBN 0935328483 Hbk £38.75

Sastri →Law of Easements, Includes Supplement-1986.

Sastri, Golap-Chandra Sarkar
Child Marriage Restraint Act. – 4th ed. – Allahabad : Law Book Company, 1988.
70p.
Pbk £40.00

—Hindu Law of Inheritance : As in the Viramitrodaya of Mitramisa. – Delhi : Gian Publishing House, 1986.
xv, 286p.
ISBN 8121200164 Hbk £180.00

—Law of Succession Certificate. – 6th ed. – Allahabad : Law Book Company, 1987.
Hbk £75.00

—Privy Council, Federal Court and Supreme Court : Hindu Law Digest 1837-1986. – 4th ed. – Allahabad : Law Book Company, 1987.
535p.
ISBN 8185029385 Hbk £120.00

—Vivadaratnakara of Candesvara Thakkura : Law of Partition and Inheritance / Digambar Chattopadhyaya. – Delhi : Gian Publishing House, 1986.
ii, liii, 94, 61, xvp.
ISBN 8121200121 Hbk £140.00

Sastri, L.S.
Societies Registration Act. – 7th ed. – Allahabad : Law Book Company, 1983.
460p.
Hbk £130.00

Sastri's Law of Succession Certificate. – 6th ed. – Allahabad : Law Publishers, 1987.
Hbk £75.00

Satellite and Cable : International Protection / Stephen de B. Bate. – London : Oyez Longman, 1984.
– (Oyez Longman Intelligence Report Ser.).
ISBN 0851208614 Hbk

Satellite and cable television : international protection : a specially commissioned report / by S. Alexander Mosteshar, and Stephen de B. Bate. – London : Longman Professional, 1986.
xiv,134p; 30cm. – (Longman professional intelligence reports).
Originally published: London : Oyez Longman, 1984. Includes index.
ISBN 0851212042 spiral £95.00

Sathe, S.P.
Administrative Law. – Bombay : Tripathi, 1984.
Hbk £50.00

Sathi, R.B.
Payment of Wages Act (Act 4 of 1936) : with Central State Rules. – 3rd ed. – Allahabad : Law Book Company, 1987.
915p.
Hbk £275.00

Sathirathai, S. →Third World Attitudes Toward International Law : an Introduction.

Satterfield, Mary T. →Law for social workers : a Canadian guide.

Saudi business and labor law : its interpretation and application / Alison Lerrick, Q. Javed Mian. – 2nd ed. – London : Grahamn & Trotman, 1987.
xlv,589p.
Previous edition: 1982. Includes bibliographical references and index.
ISBN 0860105733

Saunders →Ocean Boundary Making.

Saunders, C. A. →Quangos : The Australian Experience.

Saunders, Glyn
Tax Planning for Businesses in Europe. – 2nd ed. – London : Butterworths, 1984.
ISBN 0406535515 Hbk
→ Tolley's capital gains tax 1981-82.

—Tolley's corporation tax 1981-82 / by Glyn Saunders and David Harrington. – Croydon : Tolley, 1981.
viii,292p.
Includes index. Up to date to 1 August 1981.
ISBN 0854590358

—Tolley's corporation tax 1986-87 / by Glyn Saunders and John Boulding. – 22nd ed. – Croydon : Tolley, 1986.
ix,356p.
ISBN 0854592393

—Tolley's corporation tax 1987-88 / by Glynn Saunders and John Boulding. – Croydon : Tolley Publishing, 1987.
ix,357p.
ISBN 085459289X

—Tolley's corporation tax 1988-89 / by Glyn Saunders and John Boulding. – Croydon : Tolley, 1988.
x,345p.
Includes index.
ISBN 0854593470

→ Tolley's income tax 1986-87.

→ Tolley's income tax 1988-89.

→ Tolleys tax planning 1985.

→ Tolley's tax planning 1986.

→ Tolley's tax planning 1987.

→ Tolley's tax planning 1988.

—Tolley's taxation in the Republic of Ireland 1981-82 / by Glyn Saunders and Eric L. Harvey. – Croydon : Tolley, 1981.
x,193p.
Includes index.
ISBN 0854590439

→ Tolley's taxation in the Republic of Ireland 1987-88.

Saunders, Iwan B. →Personal injury damages in Canada.

Saunders, J. Owen →Canadian Electricity Exports : Legal and Regulatory Issues.

—Interjurisdictional Issues in Canadian Water Management. – Calgary : Canadian Institute of Resources Law.
127p.
ISBN 0919269273 Hbk £22.00

—Managing Natural Resources in a Federal State. – Agincourt : Carswell, 1986.
354p.
This work contains a collection of articles on the development and control of northern and offshore oil and gas, development of resources within federal parks and aboriginal lands, revenue sharing, environmental management, and interjurisdictional cooperation.
Hbk £59.00

—Trading Canada's Natural Resources : (Essays from the Third Banff Conference on Natural Law) Canadian Institute of Resources Law. – Agincourt : Carswell, 1987.
374p.
This work contains a collection of essays outlining the issues associated with the resource sector trade in Canada. It provides a discussion of Canadian and international trade in natural resources. Other discussions include trade distortions brought about by government protectionism, the impact of domestic regulatory schemes, and the ways in which private sector players can best structure their own legal relations in order to adapt to the changing nature of resources trade.
Hbk £63.00

Saunders, John B.
Words and Phrases Legally Defined. – 3rd ed. – Butterworths, 1988-89.

Saunders, M. Roy
International Tax Systems and Planning Techniques. – London : Oyez Longman, 1984.
ISBN 085120760X Llf £75.00

Saunders, N.
Personal Injury. – London : Longman Professional.
– (Longman Practice Notes).
ISBN 0851214487 Pbk £10.95

Sauvain, Stephen
Highway law / by Stephen J. Sauvain. – London : Sweet and Maxwell, 1989.
lxxiv,404p.
Sets out the common law and statutes in their operative context, with the text numbered in paragraphs. Covers civil liability of highway authorities, inquiries, compensation with particular emphasis on areas such as stopping up, and diversion of highways.
ISBN 0421311908 Hbk £36.00
→ Highways Act 1980.

Sauveplanne, Jean Georges
Studies in Comparative Law
Vol. 1: Security Over Corporeal Movables. – Dordrecht : Kluwer, 1974.
320p.
ISBN 9028600744 Hbk £92.00
→ Unification : and comparative law in theory and practice : et le droit compare dans la theorie et la pratique.

Savage enquiry : who controls childbirth? / Wendy Savage. – London : Virago, 1986.
xvii,189p,8p of plates; 20cm.
ISBN 0860688593 Pbk £2.95

Savage, Harvey S.
Justice for Some : a Discussion Book on Law for People with Mental Handicap. – Downsview : Roeher Institute, 1983.
95p.
£10.00

Savage, N.
Sold! : With or Without an Estate Agent. – Tadworth : Elliot Right Way.
– (Paperfronts Series).
ISBN 0716007894 Pbk £1.50

Savage, Nigel
Business Law / Bradgate. – London : Butterworths, 1987.
ISBN 040601843X Pbk £16.95

—Guide to the Data Protection Act : its implications for business / Nigel Savage & Chris Edwards. – London : Financial Training, 1984.
ISBN 0906322537

Savage, Wendy
Savage enquiry : who controls childbirth? / Wendy Savage. – London : Virago, 1986.
xvii,189p,8p of plates; 20cm.
ISBN 0860688593 Pbk £2.95

Savaiko, B.
Trading in soft commodity futures. – Cambridge : Woodhead-Faulkner, 1985.
ISBN 0859412393 Hbk £25.00

Savary, Julien
French multinationals / Julien Savary : foreword by Francois Morin. – London : Pinter, 1984.
220p.
Translation of: Les multinationales francaises.
ISBN 0861873637 £16.50

Saville, John →Strict settlement : a guide for historians.

Savings and Fiscal Privilege. – 2nd ed. – London : Institute for Fiscal Studies.
– (Report Ser.).
Hbk £6.00

Sawiak, Grant V.
Toronto Stock Exchange : a Procedural Guide for Companies and Their Professional Advisers. – Butterworths, 1986.
576p.
ISBN 0409805998 Hbk £95.00

Sawyer, G.
Australian Constitution : Australia's Most Important Document. – Kingston : Australian Government Publishing Service, 1988.
Pbk £19.95

—Australian Constitutional Cases. – 4th ed. – North Ryde : Law Book Co, 1982.
xxxv, 774p.
ISBN 0455204608 Pbk £52.50
ISBN 0455204594 Hbk £73.00

Sawyer, Glenn Ivan →Law and Medicine in Canada.

Sawyerr, Akilagpa →Law and social change in Papua New Guinea.

Saxby
Encyclopaedia of Information Technology Law. – London : Sweet & Maxwell, 1988.
ISBN 0421372109 Hbk

Saxe, Stewart D.
Ontario Employment Law Handbook : an Employer's Guide. – rev. ed. – Butterworths, 1986.
96p.
Pbk £21.95

—Ontario employment law handbook: an employer's guide. – Scarborough, Ontario : Butterworths (Canada), 1986.
96.
Examines the changes in Ontario's employment law since the fist edition in 1982. Covers the hours of work and minimum wages, overtime pay and public holidays, health and safety regulations, unemployment insurance, lockouts and strikes, and negotiations and arbitration.
ISBN 0409804860 Pbk

Saxena → Banking Law.
→ Business Law : Including Banking Law; For B. Com Students.
→ Company Law.
→ Industrial and Commercial Law : For I.C.W.A. Students.
→ Industrial Law : For B Com. and I.C.W.A. Students.
—Law of Arms and Explosives : with Act Rules and Notifications. – 4th ed. – Allahabad : Law Publishers, 1982.
Hbk £30.00
→ Mercantile Law : Including Company Law and Industrial Law.

Saxena, R.D.
Commentaries on Notaries Act, 1985 : Act No. 53, 1952 / J.P. Bhatnagar. – Allahabad : Ashoka Law House, 1987.
240p.
Hbk £90.00
—Law Relating to Notaries Act / Bhatnagar. – Allahabad : Ashoka Law House, 1987.
300p.
Hbk £80.00

Saxena, R.P.
Commentaries on Uttar Pradesh Kshettra Samitis and Zila Parishads Adhiniyam / P.L. Malik. – 2nd ed. – Lucknow : Eastern Book Company, 1978.
843p.
Hbk £75.00

Saxton, Barrie J. → Understanding Criminal Offenses.

Say → Stoy Hayward Business Tax Guides 1988-89.

Sayer, P.
Credit Cards and the Law. – London : Fourmat, 1988.
ISBN 1851900462 Hbk £14.95

Sayers, Jane E.
Law and Records in Medieval England Studies on the Medieval Papacy. – London : Varorium.
ISBN 00860782263 Hbk £34.00
—Papal government and England during the pontificate of Honorius III. – Cambridge : Cambridge University Press.
Studies thirteenth-century administrative revolution of the papacy. Gives details of registers and the registrative system. Discusses development of canon law in relation to England.
ISBN 0521259118 Hbk £32.50

Sayles, G. O. → English Parliament in the Middle Ages.
—Scripta diversa / G.O. Sayles. – London : Hambledon, 1982.
xi,371p; 24cm.
Includes index. Includes text in Latin.
ISBN 0907628125 £22.00

SBD Enterprises, Jain, S.C.
Guardians and Wards Act, 1980 : Bare Act with Commentary. – Delhi.
Hbk £5.00

Scace, Arthur R.
Income Tax Law in Canada / Douglas S. Ewens. – Agincourt : Carswell, 1983.
640p. – (Bar Admission Course Materials Ser.).
This treatise for law students follows the same general structure as the Income Tax Act of Canada to review the Canadian tax system. Personal and corporate taxation, tax deferral plans, assessment, appeals, and administration are covered in the work.
Hbk £60.50

Scaffardi, S.
Fire Under the Carpet. – London : CENT, 1986.
ISBN 0853156549 Pbk £4.95

Scaglion, Richard → Customary law in Papua New Guinea : a Melanesian view.
→ Homicide compensation in Papua New Guinea : problems and prospects.

Scales of Justice : Seven Famous Criminal Cases Recreated. – Toronto : Canadian Broadcasting Corporation Enterprises, 1984.
256p.
ISBN 0887941206 Pbk £10.95
ISBN 0887941249 Hbk £16.95

Scamell, Ernest H. → Butterworths property law handbook.
→ Lindley on the law of partnership.

Scammell
Law of Agricultural Holdings / H. A. C. Densham. – 7th ed. – London : Butterworths, 1987.
A thorough treatment of the United Kingdom law of agricultural holdings is included in this text. The work presents a commentary on the law, statutes and statutory instruments, and useful forms and precedents.
ISBN 0406368139 Hbk

Scammell, Ernest H → Law of Partnership.

Scandinavian Institute of Maritime Law → Proceedings of the Regional Energy Law Seminar, Oslo, Norway, 8-9 May 1984.

Scandinavian Studies in Law, 30 Vols. / Folke Schmidt. – Stockholm : Almqvist & Wiksell.
Hbk £188.00 ea.
Vol. 31 (1987). – 1988.
238p.
ISBN 9185142417 Hbk £188.00

Scanlan
Criminal Law / Ryan. – London : Financial Training, 1986.
– (SWOT).
ISBN 0906322987 Pbk £6.95
→ Guide to the Criminal Justice Act 1988.

Scannell, Yvonne
Law and practice relating to pollution control in Ireland / prepared by Yvonne Scannell for Environmental Resources Limited. – 2nd ed. – London : Graham & Trotman for the Commission of the European Communities, 1982.
xxix,215p; 22cm.
Previous ed. : 1976. Includes index.
ISBN 0860103137 £18.00

Scapegoat Famous Courts Martial. – Severn House.
ISBN 0727821032 Pbk £12.95

Scarff, Elisabeth
Evaluation of the Canadian gun control legislation : final report / by Elisabeth Scarff. – Ottawa : Ministry of the Solicitor General, 1983.
xxiv,217p.
Includes English and French parallel texts of the Criminal Law Amendment Act 1977. 'A research report prepared under contract with the Research Division of the Programs Branch, Ministry of the Solicitor General of Canada' - t.p. verso.
ISBN 0660114046 Hbk
Executive summary / by Elisabeth Scarff. – 1983.
14,17p.
With French t.p.: L'Evaluation des mesures legislatives canadiennes relatives au controle des armes a feu: rapport final: resume. English and French text.
ISBN 0662526015 Hbk

Scarman and after : essays reflecting on Lord Scarman's report, the riots and their aftermath / edited by John Benyon : with an epilogue by Lord Scarman. – Oxford : Pergamon, 1984.
xiv,292p; 24cm.
Conference papers. Bibliography: p263-274. - Includes index.
ISBN 0080302173 Hbk £
ISBN 0080302181 Pbk £7.50

Scarman, Leslie George Scarman
Brixton disorders 10-12 April 1981 : report of an enquiry / by Lord Scarman. – London : H.M.S.O., 1981.
viii,168p; 25cm.
Report of inquiry by Lord Scarman. Discusses causes of the riots and lessons for the future about riot control and prevention.
ISBN 0101842708 Pbk £8.00
→ Changing policing : a conference based on the Scarman Report, 1 May 1982 : proceedings.
—English Law-The New Dimension (Hamlyn 26). – Sweet & Maxwell, 1975.
ISBN 0420227008 Pbk £6.95
—Law reforms in a democratic society / the Rt. Hon. Lord Scarman. – New Delhi : National Publishing House, 1985.
114p.
Includes index.
→ Right to know.
—Scarman Report : the Brixton disorders, 10-12 April 1981 : report of an inquiry / by Lord Scarman. – Reprint, with preface. – Harmondsworth : Penguin, 1986.
xx,255p. – (Pelican books).
Previous ed.: 1982.
ISBN 014022744X

Scarman Report : the Brixton disorders, 10-12 April 1981 : report of an inquiry / by Lord Scarman. – Reprint, with preface. – Harmondsworth : Penguin, 1986.
xx,255p. – (Pelican books).
Previous ed.: 1982.
ISBN 014022744X

Schacht, J.
Introduction To Islamic Law. – Oxford : Oxford University Press, 1964.
ISBN 0198251610 Hbk £9.50
—Origins Of Muhammadan Jurisprudence. – Oxford : Oxford University Press, 1950.
ISBN 0198253575 Pbk £6.50

Schadee, H.
Transport : International Transport Treaties / M.H. Claringbould. – Dordrecht : Kluwer.
Hbk £285.00

Schafer, I.D.
Family Law Service. – Durban : Professional Publisher.
ISBN 0409015547 £245.00 with binder
ISBN 0409015539 £25.00 binder only

Schain, Martin A. → Socialism, The State, and Public Policy in France.

Schanze, Erich → Mining ventures in developing countries, Part 2 : Analysis of project agreements : Erich Schanze...et al. : translated by Gary M. Friedman.

Schaps, David
Economic Rights of Women in Ancient Greece. – Edinburgh : Edinburgh University Press.
180p.
ISBN 0852244231 Pbk £7.50

Schaub, Stefan → German competition law : (legislation and commentary).

Schauer, Frederick
Free speech : a philosophical enquiry / Frederick Schauer. – Cambridge : Cambridge University Press, 1982.
xiv,.237p; 24cm.
Bibliography: p222-229. - Includes index.
ISBN 0521243408 Hbk £20.00
ISBN 0521286174 Pbk £6.50

Scheme for the transfer of convicted offenders within the Commonwealth : explanatory documentation prepared for Commonwealth jurisidictions / by A.M.F. Webb. – London : Commonwealth Secretariat, 1987.
iii,92p.

Schermers, Henry G, et al
Article 177 EEC : Experiences and Problems. – Amsterdam : Elsevier Science Publishers, 1987.
xxxiv, 442p.
ISBN 0444700862 Hbk £200.00
→ Essays in European law and integration : to mark the silver jubilee of the Europa Institute, Leiden, 1957-1982.
—International institutional law / Henry G. Schermers. – 3. – Leiden : Sijthoff, 1972.
Volumes 1 and 2 superseded by later edition in one volume. Includes bibliography and index.
ISBN 9028603948 v.3
—Judicial protection in the European Communities / Denis Waelbroeck. – 4th ed. – Deventer : Kluwer Law and Taxation Publishers, 1987.
xviii,510p; 25cm.
Previous ed.: 1983. Includes index. At head of title: Europa Instituut, University of Leiden.
ISBN 9065443274 Pbk
—Judicial protection in the European Communities / Henry G. Schermers. – 3rd ed. – Deventer, 1983.
xvi,495p.
ISBN 9065440518
→ Mixed agreements.
—Non-Contractual Liabilities of the European Communities. – Martinus Nijhoff.
ISBN 9024737958 Hbk £42.50

Schick, Anne → Law and economics.

Schiels, I.
Tramp ship agency practice. – London : Lloyd's of London Press, 1987.
ISBN 1850441480 Hbk £23.50

Schiff, Stanley A.
Evidence in the litigation process / by Stanley A. Schiff. – 2nd ed. 2. – Toronto : Carswell, 1983.
xxxiv,1211p.
Previous ed.: 1978. Includes bibliographical references and index.
ISBN 045935650X

Schiffer, Marc E
Mental disorder and the criminal trial process. – Scarborough, Ontario : Butterworths (Canada), 1978.
368.
Focuses on legal problems and procedures peculiar to the use of psychiatric expertise at the pre-trial and trial stages. Fitness to stand trial, 'psychiatric defences', and the consequences of a determination of abnormality are discussed.
ISBN 0409865605 Hbk
—Psychiatry behind bars : a legal perspective / by Marc E. Schiffer. – Toronto : Butterworths, 1982.
xxiv,509p.
Covers the psychiatric interrogation of accused persons, the myth of confidentiality, forms of treatment, psychiatric treatment and offenders' rights, and the psychiatrist as jailer.
ISBN 0409865613

Schiller, A. Arthur → Studies in Roman law in memory of A. Arthur Schiller.

Schiller, J. E.
Selected texts and cases on the Roman law of things : with an excursus on the Roman law of slavery / J.E. Schiller. – Cape Town : Juta, 1982.
xiii,127p; 25cm.
ISBN 0702112941

Schina, Despina
State aids under the EEC treaty articles 92 to 94 / Despina Schina. – Oxford : ESC Publishing, 1987.
xviii, 221p.
Bibliography: p.179-185. - Includes index.
ISBN 0906214440

Schindler, Dietrich → Laws of armed conflicts : a collection of conventions, resolutions and other documents.

Schioppa, Antonio Padoa
Trial Jury in England, France, Germany 1700-1900. – Berlin : Duncker and Humblot, 1987.
305p.
ISBN 3428061780 Hbk £124.00

Schlberg, Stein
Computers and Penal Legislation. – Oslo : Norwegian University Press, 1983.
166p.
ISBN 8200065707 Hbk £84.00

Schlechtriem, Peter
Uniform sales law : the UN Convention on Contracts for the International Sale of Goods / Peter Schlectriem. – Wien : Manz, 1986.
120p.
Bibliography: pp.11-16. - Includes index. Translation of: Einheitliches UN-Kaufrecht. - Tubingen: Mohr, 1981.
ISBN 3214065580

Schmeiser, Douglas A.
Canadian criminal law : cases and comments / by Douglas A. Schmeiser. – 5th ed. – Toronto : Butterworths, 1985.
848.
Previous ed.: published as 'Criminal law', 1977. Incorporates recent Supreme Court decisions on such topics as criminal and transferres intent, mistake of law, necessity, insanity, drunkeness, autrfois convict and autrefois acquit, issue estoppel, Crown liability, police powers, excessive force and attempt. Contains a detailed index.
ISBN 0409865389 Pbk

Schmidhauser, John R. → Comparative judicial systems : challenging frontiers in conceptual and empirical analysis.

Schmidt, Folke → Scandinavian Studies in Law, 30 Vols.

Schmidt, Ingo L
Critical evaluation of the Chicago School of Antitrust Analysis / Jan B Rittaler. – Dordrecht : Kluwer, 1989.
145. – (Studies in industrial organization).
Examines the implications of the Chicago approach to antitrust theory with its implicit and explicit premises and discusses its policy recommendations. Includes chapters on antitrust theory and public policy, and the evaluation of anticompetition behaviour.
ISBN 9024737923 Hbk £36
→ Suitability of concentration measures for EEC competition policy.

Schmitthoff, Clive M. → Charlesworth's Mercantile law.
—Commercial law in a changing economic climate / Clive M. Schmitthoff. – 2nd ed. – London : Sweet & Maxwell, 1981.
xii,78p; 22cm.
Previous ed.: 1977. Includes index. .
ISBN 0421268301 Pbk £5.25
→ Companies act 1980.
—Export Finance. – London : Sweet & Maxwell.
ISBN 0421333103 Pbk
—Export Trade, Law and Practice. – 8th ed. – London : Sweet & Maxwell, 1986.
ISBN 0420466509 Pbk £29.00
—Extrajudicial dispute settlement / Clive M. Schmitthoff. – Deventer : Kluwer Law and Taxation, 1985.
18p.
Includes bibliographical references.
ISBN 9065442340
—Journal of Business Law. – London : Sweet & Maxwell.
Hbk £41.00
→ Palmer's company law, Vol. 1 : The treatise.
—Schmitthoff's Export trade : the law and practice of international trade / John N Adams, Clive M Schmitthoff. – 8th ed. – London : Stevens, 1986.
lix,689p; 26cm. .
Includes new chapters on GATT, and product liability, which covers the EEC Directive on Product Liability, and Part I of the Consumer Protection Act 1987. Discusses the Vienna Convention, and the effects on export trade law of the establishment of the Single Market in 1992.
ISBN 0420466401 Hbk £32.00
ISBN 0420466509 Pbk £25.00
→ Transnational law of international commercial transactions.

Schmitthoff's Export trade : the law and practice of international trade / John N Adams, Clive M Schmitthoff. – 8th ed. – London : Stevens, 1986.
lix,689p; 26cm.
Includes new chapters on GATT, and product liability, which covers the EEC Directive on Product Liability, and Part I of the Consumer Protection Act 1987. Discusses the Vienna Convention, and the effects on export trade law of the establishment of the Single Market in 1992.
ISBN 0420466401 Hbk £32.00
ISBN 0420466509 Pbk £25.00

Schneider, Carl E. → Law and politics of abortion.

Schneider, Hannes → German Antitrust Law.
→ German antitrust law : an introduction to the German antitrust law with German text and synoptic English translation of the Act against Restraints of Competition.
—German Banking System / H. Hellwig. – 2nd ed. – Plymouth : Macdonald & Evans, 1984.
252p.
ISBN 0712154795 Pbk £22.50

Schneider, Richard D.
Social Work : Annotated Ontario Mental Health Statutes. – Agincourt : Carswell, 1988.
358p.
Hbk £46.25

Schneider, S. → Medicolegal Library, Vol. 6 Drugs and Alcohol.
→ Nursing law and ethics.

Schnurr, Brian A.
Estate Litigation. – Agincourt : Carswell, 1987.
400p.
This is an in-depth guide to various types of proceedings which can arise when dealing with an estate. Discussions include committeeship proceedings, proceedings related to mental incapability, and the role of the Official Guardian in estate matters related to children. Also included is a comprehensive discussion of the entire process of estate litigation.
Hbk £46.25
—Estate Planning and Administration. – Agincourt : Carswell, 1987.
406p. – (Bar Admission Course Material Ser.).
This text discusses will planning and drafting, administration of an estate and how to advise the executor on applications for probate or distribution of the estate.
ISBN 045938050 Hbk £30.00

Schoeman, J → Law of Property.

Schofield
Arabian Boundaries : Primary Documents 1853-1957, 25 Vols. / Blake. – London : Archive Editions.
On behalf International Boundaries Research.
ISBN 1852071303 Hbk £4,995.00
—Election Law / Little. – London : Shaw & Sons, 1984.
ISBN 0721903444 Hbk £85.00

Schofield, John
Laytime and demurrage / by John Schofield. – London : Lloyds of London, 1985.
393p; 24cm.
Include index.
ISBN 1850440573

Schofield, P.
First Principles Preparatory to Constitutional Code. – Oxford : Clarendon Press.
ISBN 0198227477 Hbk £40.00

Schofield, Peter → Law for Estate Management Students.

Scholefield, Paul
Intellectual Property and Technology Transfer in the People's Republic of China. – Hong Kong : Hong Kong University Press, 1988.
ISBN 9622092020 Hbk

School Law. – Vancouver : Continuing Legal Education Society of British Columbia, 1987.
160p.
ISBN 0865043558 Hbk £70.00

Schools and students : legal aspects of administration / W.H. Giles. – Toronto : Carswell, 1988.
xxix, 206 p.; 24 cm.
Includes index.
ISBN 0459312014

Schools, disruptive behaviour and delinquency : a review of research / by John Graham. – London : H.M.S.O., 1988.
v,69p.
Reviews research on effects of schooling on young people. Concludes that schools can by promoting pro-social and stable patterns of behaviour, help protect children from embarking on criminal careers.
ISBN 0113408870

Schopflin, George
Censorship and Political Communication Examples from Eastern Europe. – London : Pinter Publishers Ltd.
180p.
ISBN 0861872614 Hbk £19.00

Schrecker, T. F.
Political economy of environmental hazards : a study paper prepared for the Law Reform Commission of Canada / by T.F. Schrecker. – Ottawa : Law Reform Commission of Canada, 1984.
vi,112p.
ISBN 066213236X

Schreiber, Hans-Ludwig → Medical responsibility in Western Europe : research study of the European Science Foundation.

Schreiner, Oliver Deneys → Fiat iustitia : essays in memory of Oliver Deneys Schreiner.

Schreuer, Christoph H
Decisions of international institutions before domestic courts / Christoph Schreuer. – London : Oceana, 1981.
xiii,407p; 25cm.
Revised and updated version of 1977 German original.
ISBN 0379207095
—State immunity : some recent developments / by Christoph H. Schreuer. – Cambridge : Grotius, 1988.
xxiii,200p.
Examines the principle international and national aspects of suits against States and State-owned corporations in foreign courts.
ISBN 0949009148

Schrijver → UN Under Attack.

Schroth, Hans-Jurgen
Economic Offences in EEC Law : With Special Reference to English and German Law. – Kehl am Rhein : Norbert Paul Engel, 1983.
228p.
ISBN 3883570273 Hbk £48.00

Schuck, Peter H.
Suing government : citizen remedies for official wrongs / Peter H. Schuck. – New Haven : Yale University Press, 1983.
xxi,262p; 22cm.
Includes index.
ISBN 0300029578 Hbk

Schuit, Steven R
Dutch business law : legal, accounting, and tax aspects of business in the Netherlands / by Steven R. Schuit and Jan M. van der Beek and Bonne K. Raap, and Michael W. den Boogert ... et al. – 2nd ed. – Deventer, Netherlands : Kluwer Law and Taxation Publishers, 1983.
xl, 552 p.; 25 cm.
Includes index.
ISBN 9065441220

Schulenburg, Johann-Mattias → Law and economics and the economics of legal regulation.

Schultsz, Jan C → Art of arbitration : essays on international arbitration : liber amicorum Pieter Sanders, 12 September 1912-1982.

Schuster-Herr, Raquel → Advocacy and Mental Handicap.

Schwampe, Dieter
Charterers' liability insurance / by Dieter Schwampe : translated from the German by Burravoe Ltd. – London : Lloyd's of London Press, 1988.
xx,156p; 24cm.
Bibliography: pp.145-151. - Includes index. Translated from the German.
ISBN 1850441847 £45.00

Schwank, Friedrich → Banks abroad : establishment - operations - supervision.

Schwartz, B.
Unpublished Opinions of the Burger Court. – Oxford : Oxford University Press.
ISBN 00195053176 Hbk £26.00

Schwartz, Bryan
Fathoming Meech Lake. – Winnipeg : University of Manitoba, Legal Research Institute, 1987.
Hbk £18.00

Schwartz, Bryan P.
First Principles : Constitutional Reform with Respect to the Aboriginal Peoples of Canada 1982-1984. – Kingston : Queen's University, Institute of Intergovernmental Relations.
292p.
ISBN 0889114323 Hbk £20.00

Schwartz, Walter
Tamils of Sri Lanka / by Walter Schwarz. – 3rd rev ed. – London : Minority Rights Group, 1986.
15p. – (Report).
Previous edition: 1983.
ISBN 0946690375

Schwarz-Liebermann von Wahlendorf, H. A.
Forms of action at international law : the spirit of English law and international law / H.A. Schwarz-Liebermann von Wahlendorf. – Birmingham : Institute of Judicial Administration, University of Birmingham, 1981.
iii,55p.
ISBN 2903642001

Schwarz, P.J.
Twice Condemned : Slaves & Criminal Laws : Virginia 1705-1865. – Louisiana : Louisiana State University Press.
ISBN 0807114014 Hbk £35.65

Schwarzenberger, Georg → Contemporary problems of international law : essays in honour of Georg Schwarzenberger on his eightieth birthday.
—Focus on Beirut / by Georg Schwarzenberger. – Leeds : University of Leeds, 1983.
11p.
Bibliography: p.10-11.
—International Law as Applied by International Courts and Tribunals
Vol. 4. – London : Sweet & Maxwell, 1985.
ISBN 0420446109 Hbk £85.00

Vol.4 : International judicial law / by Georg Schwarzenberger. – 1986.
lxx,899p.
Bibliography: p823-888. - Includes index.
ISBN 0420446109 £90.00

Schwebel, Stephen M.
International arbitration : three salient problems / by Stephen M. Schwebel. – Cambridge : Grotius Publications, 1987.
xviii,303p.
At head of title: University of Cambridge. Research Centre for International Law.
ISBN 0949009024
—Legal effect of resolutions and codes of conduct of the United Nations. – Deventer : Kluwer, 1986.
16p.
Includes bibliographical references.
ISBN 9065442421

Schwendinger, Herman
Adolescent subcultures and delinquency / Herman Schwendinger and Julia Siegel Schwendinger. – Research ed. – New York : Praeger, 1985.
xvi,524p; 25cm.
Bibliography: p497-511. - Includes index.
ISBN 0030009391 Hbk £76.95
ISBN 0030009421 Pbk

Schwendinger, Julia R. →Adolescent subcultures and delinquency.

Science Council of
Workshop on information technologies and personal privacy in Canada / Science Council of Canada. – Ottawa : The Council, 1985.
62p.
Includes bibliographical references.
ISBN 0662140354

Science du Droit Dans le Midi de la France au Moyen Age. – Northampton : Variorum, 1984.
360p : Illus.. – – (Collected Studies Ser.: 196).
ISBN 0860781445 Hbk £28.00

Science of a legislator : the natural jurisprudence of David Hume and Adam Smith / Knud Haakonssen. – Cambridge : Cambridge University Press, 1981.
vii,240p; 24cm.
Bibliography: p227-229. - Includes index.
ISBN 0521238919 £17.50

Science of peace / by J.G. Starke. – 2nd ed. – Sydney : Law Books, 1986.
xvi,193p.
Previous ed. published by A.W. Sijthoff, 1968.
Bibliography: p.180-183. Includes index.
ISBN 0949553298

Science Reference and Information Service → Guide to government department and other libraries 1988.

Scientific Identification of Disputed Documents, Fingerprints and Ballistics. – 3rd ed. 1980 repr. – Lucknow : Eastern Book Company, 1984.
155p.
Hbk £35.00

Scmidt, M
Common heritage or common burden: the US position on the development of a regime for deep seabed mining in the law of the sea convention. – Oxford : Clarendon Press, 1989.
288; 23.5.
Assesses the US role in the negotiations on the UN Convention on the LAW of the Sea, particularly with regard to the ocean floor. Examines the US view of the lawfulness of deep seabed mining under international law. Suggests that despite significant compromises negotiated between the US and developing countries at the Conference up to 1980, the emerging seabed regime was not as widely endorsed by US officials as is assumed.
ISBN 0198252277 Hbk £30.00

SCOLMA directory of libraries and special collections on Africa in the United Kingdom and Western Europe / edited by Harry Hannam. – 4th rev. and expanded ed. – Munchen : Saur, 1983.
183p.
Previous ed: London: Crosby Lockwood Staples, 1973.

SCONUL statistical database part 2 : library operations ... – London : Standing Conference of National & University Libraries, 1986.
ISBN 0951936X

Scope for reforming stamp duties : an Inland Revenue consultative document / Board of Inland Revenue. – London : The Board, 1983.
63p.

Scorer, Catherine
Amending the equality laws / Catherine Scorer and Ann Sedley. – London : NCCL Rights for Women Unit, 1983.
38p; 21cm.
ISBN 0946088047 Pbk £0.95
—Prevention of Terrorism Act : the case for repeal / Catherine Scorer and Patricia Hewitt. – London : National Council for Civil Liberties, 1981.
68p; 20cm.
ISBN 0901108944 Pbk £1.75

Scotland →Laws of Scotland : Stair memorial encyclopaedia.

Scots conveyancing miscellany: essays in honour of Professor J.M. Halliday. – Edinburgh : Green (W.) & Son, 1987.
Collection of essays in the fields of conveyancing and related subjects - enforcement of title conditions, floating charges, fair rents, completion of title, land obligations, securities, etc.
ISBN 0414008030 Hbk

Scots Conveyancing Statutes 1983 : Reprinted from the Parliament House Book. – Edinburgh : W Green, 1983.
ISBN 0414007247 Hbk £5.50

Scots Conveyancing Statutes 1984. – Edinburgh : W Green.
ISBN 0414007484 Hbk £9.75

Scots Court Statutes 1983 : Reprinted from the Parliament House Book. – Edinburgh : W Green, 1983.
ISBN 0414007212 Hbk £21.50

Scots Courts Statutes Civil 1985. – Edinburgh : W Green.
– (Reprint from Parliament House Book).
ISBN 0414007719 Hbk £19.50

Scots Courts Statutes Criminal 1985. – Edinburgh : W Green.
– (Reprint from Parliament House Book).
ISBN 0414007727 Hbk £8.50

Scots criminal law / A J MacLean. – 1st. – London : Butterworths, 1988.
ISBN 0406252696 Hbk

Scots law for journalists / Bruce McKain. – 5th. – Edinburgh : Green (W.) & Son, 1988.
The standard text book on media law in Scotland, revised to include new judicial interpretation of the journalistic privilege in quoting from documents not read out in court, the publishing of leaked information, the effects of the Data Protection Act, public right of access to local authority meetings and the way divorces under the reformed procedures may be safely reported. With coverage of the European Courts of Justice and Human Rights, and the new procedure for judicial review.
ISBN 0414008146 Pbk

Scots law terms and expressions / John Angus Beaton. – Edinburgh : Green, 1982.
116p.
ISBN 0414006917

Scots mercantile law / Enid A. Marshall. – Edinburgh : Green (W.) & Son, 1983.
xxxviii,665p.
Covers the major areas of the commercial law of Scotland, with full references to statutory provisions and case law. Notes differences between English and Scottish mercantile law. Student textbook assuming no previous legal knowledge.
ISBN 0414007204 Pbk

Scots Mercantile Law Statutes 1984. – Edinburgh : W Green.
– (Reprint from Parliament House Book).
ISBN 0414007689 Hbk £18.00

Scots Revised Reports : 1707-1873, 45 Vols. Incl. Court of Session Cases : 1821-1838, 6 Vols. – Abingdon : Professional Books.
Hbk

Scots Statutes 1983 : Family Law; Succession, Trusts, Liferents and Judicial Factors. – Edinburgh : W Green, 1983.
ISBN 0414007255 Hbk £6.50

Scots Statutes 1984 : Family Law; Succession, Trusts, Liferents and Judicial Factors. – Edinburgh : W Green.
ISBN 041400745X Hbk £14.75

Scots Statutes 1985 : Family Law - Succession, Trusts, Liferent andJudicial Factors. – Edinburgh : W Green.
– (Reprint from the Parliament House Book).
ISBN 0414007662 Hbk £10.00

Scott →Securitisation.

Scott, Anthony →Progress in natural resource economics : essays in resource analysis by members of the Programme in Natural Resource Economics (PNRE) at the University of British Columbia.

Scott, D M M →A-Level English Law.
—English Law for GCSE / Marianne Giles. – 5th ed. – London : Butterworths, 1987.
ISBN 0406653070 Pbk £5.50

Scott, G.L.
Chinese Treaties. – Dordrecht : Kluwer, 1975.
328p.
ISBN 9028602259 Hbk £78.00

Scott, I. R.
Civil justice project : preliminary study / I. R. Scott, J. R. Pullen, A. J. Robbins. – Melbourne : Government Printer, 1984.
xviii,423p.
Cover title: Preliminary study concerning the administration of civil justice in Victoria.
ISBN 0908417179
→ Jubilee lectures celebrating the foundation of the Faculty of Law, University of Birmingham.

Scott, Joseph W.
Living with books / Joseph W. Scott. – London : University of London Library Resources Co-ordinating Committee, 1987.
8 p. – (Publication).
ISBN 0718708032

Scott, Leslie Frederic
Case of the Requisition / Alfred Hildesley. – Aalen Wuertt : Scientia.
xxiv, 307p.
Hbk £85.00

Scott, Michael
Law of public leisure services / by Michael Scott : foreword by Charles Cross. – London : Sweet & Maxwell, 1985.
lvii,352p; 26cm.
Draws together the spectrum of legal rights and duties arising out of the public leisure services, from the taking on of staff, to licensing activities and safety procedures. Includes sections on employment law, duties in tort, commons, open spaces, National Parks, and libraries and museums.
ISBN 0421326808 £25.00

Scott Robinson, S.
Law of Interdict. – London : Butterworths, 1987.
ISBN 040610445X Pbk £17.00

Scott, Russell
Body as property / Russell Scott. – London : Allen Lane, 1981.
x,274p; 24cm.
Includes index.
ISBN 0713913215 £7.95

Scott, Stuart C.
Commercial Transport for New Zealanders. – Wellington : Butterworths.
ISBN 0409627119 Pbk

Scott, Susan →Our legal heritage.
→ Wille's law of mortgage and pledge in South Africa.

Scott, T.J. →Law of South Africa.
→ Negotiable Instruments.
→ Wille's law of mortgage and pledge in South Africa.

Scottish and Universal Newspapers Limited : a report by the Director General of Fair Trading on an investigation under section 3 of the Competition Act, 1980 / Office of Fair Trading. – London : H.M.S.O., 1983.
45p; 30cm.

Scottish Cases and Materials in Commercial Law / A. Forte. – London : Butterworths, 1987.
ISBN 0406108706 Pbk

Scottish civil law reports. – Edinburgh : Law Society of Scotland, 1987-.
Includes index.

Scottish community charge / Neil Walker. – Edinburgh : Green (W.) & Son, 1989.
Provides full commentary on every section of the Abolition of Domestic Rates Etc. (Scot) Act 1987 and an analysis of subsequent developments with the full set of regulations.
ISBN 0414008634 Pbk

Scottish Consumer Council →Class actions in the Scottish courts : a new way for consumers to obtain redress?.
—Scottish Consumer Council's response to the Hughes report : the report of the Royal Commission on Legal Services in Scotland (Volume one : Cmnd 7846). – Scottish Consumer Council. – Glasgow : The Council, 1981.
28p; 30cm.
ISBN 0907067026 Pbk £1.00
→ Waiting for justice : an SCC survey of facilities in Scotland's Sheriff Courts : results and recommendations by Sheila Gilmore.

Scottish Consumer Council's response to the Hughes report : the report of the Royal Commission on Legal Services in Scotland (Volume one : Cmnd 7846). – Scottish Consumer Council. – Glasgow : The Council, 1981.
28p; 30cm.
ISBN 0907067026 Pbk £1.00

Scottish Courts Administration
Diligence and debtor protection : consultation paper. – Scottish Courts Administration. – Edinburgh : Scottish Courts Administration on behalf of the Lord Advocate, 1985.
15 leaves.
Consultation paper on Scottish Law Commission's report on diligence and debtor protection (Scot. Law Com. no. 95.
→ Hague Convention on the civil aspects of international child abduction : consultative document.
—Small claims procedure in the Sheriff court : detailed proposals : consultation paper. – Scottish Courts Administration. – Edinburgh : Scottish Courts Administration, 1987.
94p in various pagings.
Includes example of forms. Issued on behalf of the Lord Advocate and the Sheriff Court Rules Council.

Scottish criminal case reports. – Edinburgh : Law Society of Scotland, 1981-.

Scottish Criminal Law : Police Duties and Procedure. – Grampian Police. – Aberdeen : Aberdeen University Press.
1590p.
ISBN 0900015454 Hbk

Scottish current law case citator. – Edinburgh : W. Green, 1977-.
Kept up to date by annual Scottish current law citator. Contains both Scottish and English law.

Scottish current law statute citator. – Edinburgh : W. Green, 1972-.
Kept up to date by annual Scottish current law citator. Contains both Scottish and English law.

Scottish current law statutes. – Edinburgh : Green, 1961-.
Contains both English and Scottish law. Not published: 1963-1972.

Scottish current law year book : being a complete statement of all the law.. from every source. – Edinburgh : W. Green, 1948.
Cumulation of monthly Scottish current law. Master volumes for 1956, 1961, 1966 and 1971. Contains both Scottish and English law.
ISBN 03087166

Scottish Family Conciliation Service (Lothian) : report of an assessment of the first two years of the service, March 1984 - February 1986 / Susan M.G. Matheson, Hugh Gentleman. – Edinburgh : Scottish Office Central Research Unit, 1986.
6,53p.

Scottish jurists / by David M. Walker. – Edinburgh : W. Green, 1985.
xv,492p.
ISBN 0414007573

Scottish juvenile justice system / edited by F.M. Martin and Kathleen Murray. – Edinburgh : Scottish Academic Press, 1982.
xii, 200p.
Replaces earlier edition: 'Children's hearings', Edinburgh: Scottish Academic Press, 1976. Bibliography: p.198-200.
ISBN 070730296X

Scottish land law. – Edinburgh : Green (W.) & Son, 1989.
A fresh treatment of Scottish land law, filling the gap since the last edition of Rankine's 'Landownership' (1909), with particular attention to the very large body of legislation affecting the use of land in the intervening 80 years. The increasing impact of European law, particularly affecting the enviroment, is also noted. With full cross references to Halliday's 'Conveyancing Law and Practice'. Published under the auspices of the Scottish Universities Law Institute.
ISBN 0414008812 Hbk

Scottish Law Commission

Adjudications for debt and related matters / Scottish Law Commission. – 2. – Edinburgh : The Commission, 1988.
– (Discussion paper).

→ Amendment of the Companies Acts 1948-1983 : report under section 116 of the Companies Act 1981.

—Annual report / Scottish Law Commission. – Edinburgh : H.M.S.O., 1966-.
Numbered in series Scot Law Com.

—Attempted homicide / Scottish Law Commission. – Edinburgh : Scottish Law Commission, 1984.
52p. – (Consultative memorandum).

—Breach of confidence : report on a reference under section 3(1)(e) of the Law Commissions Act 1965 / Scottish Law Commission. – Edinburgh : Scottish Law Commission, 1984.
vi,73p.
ISBN 0101938500

—Child abduction / Scottish Law Commission. – Edinburgh : The Commission, 1985.
116p. – (Consultative memorandum).

—Child abduction : report on a reference under section 3(1)(e) of the Law Commissions Act 1965 ... / Scottish Law Commission. – Edinburgh : H.M.S.O., 1987.
vi,50p.
ISBN 010100642X

→ Chronological table of local legislation.

—Civil liability : contribution / Scottish Law Commission. – Edinburgh : Scottish Law Commission, 1986.
iv,230p. – (Consultative memorandum).

—Civil liability in relation to animals / Scottish Law Commission. – Edinburgh : Scottish Law Commission, 1982.
xiii,180p. – (Consultative memorandum).

—Computer crime / Scottish Law Commission. – Edinburgh : The Commission, 1986.
146p. – (Consultative memorandum).
Includes bibliographical references.

—Constitution and proof of voluntary obligations and the authentication of writings / Scottish Law Commission. – Edinburgh : The Commission, 1985.
v,203p. – (Consultative memorandum).

—Contract law : exchange of standard term forms in contract formation : law reform proposals / Scottish Law Commission. – 2 v. – Edinburgh : The Commission, 1982.
– (Consultation paper).

—Court of Session Bill : report on the consolidation of certain enactments, and the repeal of other enactments, relating to the Court of Session / presented to Parliament by the Lord Advocate by Command of Her Majesty : Scottish Law Commission. – Edinburgh : HMSO, 1988.
36p.
ISBN 0101031521

—Criminal evidence : affidavit evidence, hearsay and related matters in criminal proceedings / Scottish Law Commission. – Edinburgh : The Commission, 1988.
iv,145p. – (Discussion paper).
Includes excerpts from the Criminal Justice Act 1967 and the Police and Criminal Evidence Act 1984.

—Criminal law : art and part guilt of statutory offences / Scottish Law Commission. – Edinburgh : H.M.S.O., 1985.
v,21p.
ISBN 0101955103

→ Dentists Bill : report on the consolidation of the Dentists Acts 1957 to 1983.

—Equalisation of diligences / Scottish Law Commission. – Edinburgh : The Commission, 1988.
vii,146p. – (Discussion paper).

—Evidence : blood group tests, DNA tests and related matters / Scottish Law Commission. – Edinburgh : The Commission, 1988.
i,45p. – (Discussion paper).

—Evidence : report on corroboration, hearsay and related matters in civil proceedings / Scottish Law Commission. – Edinburgh : H.M.S.O., 1986.
vi,63p.
Includes bibliographical references.
ISBN 010237886X

—Evidence : report on evidence in cases of rape and other sexual offences / Scottish Law Commission. – Edinburgh : H.M.S.O., 1983.
vi,33p.
Includes bibliographical references. Includes Draft Evidence in Sexual Offences (Scotland) Bill.
ISBN 0102028842

—Evidence of children and other potentially vulnerable witnesses / Scottish Law Commission. – Edinburgh : The Commission, 1988.
iv,160p. – (Discussion paper).

—Family law : illegitimacy / Scottish Law Commission. – Edinburgh : The Commission, 1982.
170p. – (Consultative memorandum).

—Family law : report on financial provision after foreign divorce / Scottish Law Commission. – Edinburgh : H.M.S.O., 1982.
47p.
ISBN 0102515824

—Family law : report on illegitimacy / Scottish Law Commission. – Edinburgh : H.M.S.O., 1984.
vii,134p.
Includes bibliographical references.
ISBN 0102186847

—Family law : report on matrimonial property / Scottish Law Commission. – Edinburgh : H.M.S.O., 1984.
v,35p.
Includes draft Bill.
ISBN 0102467846

—Family law : report on outdated rules in the law of husband and wife / Scottish Law Commission. – Edinburgh : H.M.S.O., 1983.
vi,53p.
ISBN 0102330832

→ Family law, custody of children - jurisdiction and enforcement within the United Kingdom : report on a reference under section 3(1)(e) of the Law Commissions Act 1965.

—Family law, report on aliment and financial provision / Scottish Law Commission. – Edinburgh : H.M.S.O., 1981.
x,239p; 25cm. – (H.C.).
ISBN 0102002827 Pbk £8.40

→ Family property in Scotland : an enquiry carried out on behalf of the Scottish Law Commission by the Social Survey Division of the Office of Population Censuses and Surveys in 1979.

—Floating charges and receivers / Scottish Law Commission. – Edinburgh : The Commission, 1986.
iv,151p. – (Consultative memorandum).
Includes bibliographical references. Catalogued from cover.

—Fourth programme of consolidation and statute law revision / Scottish Law Commission. – Edinburgh : H.M.S.O., 1982.
10p.
ISBN 0102516820

→ Further amendments of the Companies Acts 1948-1983 : report under section 116 of the Companies Act 1981.

—Ground for divorce : should the law be changed? / Scottish Law Commission. – Edinburgh : The Commission, 1988.
23p. – (Discussion paper).

—Housing (Scotland) Bill : report on the consolidation of certain enactments relating to housing in Scotland ... / Scottish Law Commission. – Edinburgh : H.M.S.O., 1987.
11p.
ISBN 0101010427

—Inheritance : who should have a claim to a persons property on death? : is the present law fair? / Scottish Law Commission. – Edinburgh : The Commission, 1986.
35p.

—Intestate succession and legal rights / Scottish Law Commission. – Edinburgh : The Commission, 1986.
v,241p. – (Consultative memorandum).
Includes bibliographical references. Catalogued from cover.

—Irritancies in leases / Scottish Law Commission. – Edinburgh : Scottish Law Commission, 1981.
42p. – (Memorandum).

—Irritancies in leases : report on a reference under section 3(1)(e) of the Law Commissions Act 1965 / Scottish Law Commission. – Edinburgh : H.M.S.O., 1983.
vi,41p.
ISBN 0101876009

—Law of incest in Scotland : report of a reference under Section 3(1)(e) of the Law Commissions Act 1965 / Scottish Law Commission. – Edinburgh : H.M.S.O., 1981.
vii,74p; 25cm.
ISBN 0101842201 Pbk £4.80

—Legal capacity and responsibility of minors and pupils / Scottish Law Commission. – Edinburgh : The Commission, 1985.
280p. – (Consultative memorandum).
Includes bibliographical references.

—Making and revocation of wills / Scottish Law Commission. – Edinburgh : The Commission, 1986.
ii,84p. – (Consultative memorandum).

—Matrimonial property / Scottish Law Commission. – Edinburgh : Scottish Law Commission, 1983.
207p. – (Consultative memorandum).

→ Medical Bill : draft report on the consolidation of the Medical Acts 1956 to 1978 and certain related provisions.

—Mental element in crime : report on a reference under section 3(1)(e) of the Law Commissions Act 1965 / Scottish Law Commission. – Edinburgh : H.M.S.O., 1983.
v,48p.
Includes bibliographical references.
ISBN 0101904703

—Mobbing and rioting / Scottish Law Commission. – Edinburgh : Scottish Law Commission, 1984.
102p. – (Consultative memorandum).

—Obligations : report on civil liability in relation to animals / Scottish Law Commission. – Edinburgh : The Commission, 1985.
vi,72p.
Includes bibliographical references. Includes Draft Animals (Scotland) Bill.
ISBN 0102004862

—Obligations : report on negligent misrepresentation / Scottish Law Commission. – Edinburgh : H.M.S.O., 1985.
v,13p.
Includes bibliographical references.
ISBN 0102143854

—Obligations : report on rectification of contractual and other documents / Scottish Law Commission. – Edinburgh : H.M.S.O., 1983.
vi,35p.
Includes bibliographical references. Includes Draft Rectification of Documents (Scotland) Bill.
ISBN 0102036845

→ Polygamous marriages : capacity to contract a polygamous marriage and the concept of the potentially polygamous marriage.

—Prescription and limitation of actions (latent damage) / Scottish Law Commission. – Edinburgh : The Commission, 1987.
v,162p. – (Consultative memorandum).
Includes bibliographical references.

—Prescription and the limitation of actions : report on personal injuries actions and private international law questions / Scottish Law Commission. – Edinburgh : H.M.S.O., 1983.
v,61p.
ISBN 0102153833

→ Private international law : choice of law in tort and delict.

→ Private international law : choice of law rules in marriage.

→ Private international law : Council of Europe Conventions on Foreign Money Liabilities(1967) and on the Place of Payment of Money Liabilities (1972) : report on a reference under section 3(1)(e) of the Law Commissions Act 1965.

→ Private international law : polygamous marriages : capacity to contract a polygamous marriage and related issues.

→ Private international law : recognition of foreign nullity decrees and related matters : presented to Parliament ... September 1984.

→ Private international law : the law of domicile.

→ Private international law - the law of domicile.

—Recovery of possession of heritable property / Scottish Law Commission. – Edinburgh : The Commission, 1984.
iii,122p. – (Consultative memorandum no 59).
Includes bibliographical references.

—Report on bankruptcy and related aspects of insolvency and liquidation / Scottish Law Commission. – Edinburgh : H.M.S.O., 1982.
xv,597p; 25cm. – (HC).
ISBN 0102176825 Pbk £14.90

—Report on civil liability : contribution / Scottish Law Commission. – Edinburgh : The Commission, 1988.
vi,75p.
Includes draft of a Bill.
ISBN 0102007896

—Report on computer crime / Scottish Law Commission. – Edinburgh : H.M.S.O., 1987.
v,38p.
Includes bibliographical references. Includes Draft Computer Crime (Scotland) Bill.
ISBN 0101017421

—Report on diligence and debtor protection / Scottish Law Commission. – 2 v. – Edinburgh : H.M.S.O., 1985.
Vol. 2: Appendices.
ISBN 0102005869

—Report on requirements of writing / Scottish Law Commission. – Edinburgh : HMSO, 1988.
vii,197p.
Includes bibliographical references. Includes draft legislation.
ISBN 010255188X

—Report on section 5 of the Damages (Scotland) Act 1976 / Scottish Law Commission. – Edinburgh : H.M.S.O., 1981.
iii,8p; 25cm. – (HC).
ISBN 0102272816 Pbk £1.80

→ Report on the consolidation of the Housing Acts : Housing Bill, Housing Associations Bill, Landlord and Tenant Bill.

—Report on the legal capacity and responsibility of minors and pupils / Scottish Law Commission. – Edinburgh : HMSO, 1987.
vi,93p.
Includes draft legislation.
ISBN 0102151881

—Report on the Scottish term and quarter days / presented to Parliament by the Lord Advocate by Command of Her Majesty, October 1987. – Edinburgh : HMSO, 1987.
vi,29p.
ISBN 0101020821

→ Research paper on actions of ejection and removing.

→ Road traffic regulation bill : report on the consolidation of the Road Traffic Regulation Act 1967 and certain related enactments.

→ Sale and supply of goods.

→ Sale and supply of goods : report on a reference under section 3(1)(e) of the Law Commissions Act 1965.

—Some miscellaneous topics in the law of succession / Scottish Law Commission. – Edinburgh : The Commission, 1986.
155p. – (Consultative memorandum).

—Some obsolete and discriminatory rules in the law of husband and wife / Scottish Law Commission. – Edinburgh : The Commission, 1982.
61p. – (Consultative memorandum).

→ Statute law revision.

→ Trustee savings banks bill : report on the consolidation of the Trustee Savings Banks Acts 1969 to 1978.

Scottish law directory. – Edinburgh : Clark (T. & T.) Ltd.
Known as the 'White Book', the directory contains official lists of certified practitioners and professional lists of the Faculty of Advocates, Chartered Accountants and Chartered Surveyors as well as branches of Building Societies, Insurance Companies, Banks, Property and Estate Agents, Messengers-at-Arms, Sheriff Officers, and licensing boards. Other sections deal with Scottish courts, central and local government, fees, Stamp Duties, Scottish Legal Societies, the Rutland Exchange and Fax Users.
Hbk

Scottish law of evidence / A.B. Wilkinson. – London : Butterworths, 1986.
200p; 22cm.
Includes index.
ISBN 0406261105 Pbk £25.00

Scottish Law Reporter : 1865-1924, 61 Vols. – Abingdon : Professional Books, 1984.
Hbk

Scottish legal system : an introduction to the study of Scots law / by David M. Walker. – 5th ed., rev. – Edinburgh : Green, 1981.
xlv,543p; 23cm.
Previous ed.: 1976. Includes bibliographies and index.
ISBN 0414006836

Scottish Mutual guide to the Financial Services Act. – Rosters Ltd, 1988.
ISBN 0948032162 Hbk £12.95

Scottish Planning Appeal Decisions : Monthly. – Planning Exchange. – Glasgow : Planning Exchange.
ISBN 01438972 Pbk £70.00

Scottish planning law and procedure / by Eric Young and Jeremy Rowan-Robinson : with a contribution by C.M.G. Himsworth. – Glasgow : William Hodge, 1985.
xliv,564p.
Supersedes Eric Youngs The law of planning in Scotland. Includes index. Provides a guide through the legislative and regulatory system of Scottish planning law and procedure and sets the subject matter in the context of administrative law. Considerable attention is given to control of development.
ISBN 0852791224

Scottish Planning Law Practice. – Glasgow : Planning Exchange, 1983.
36p.
ISBN 01448196 Pbk £7.50
Back issues 1-6, June 1982. – Pbk £2.00 ea.
Back issues 7, October 1982-present. – Pbk £3.00 ea.

Scottish Poor Law 1745-1845. – Edinburgh : Scottish Academic Press Ltd, 1981.
186p.
ISBN 0707302897 Hbk £8.75

Scottish Universities Law Institute → Conveyancing law and practice in Scotland.
→ Law of delict in Scotland.
→ Law of husband and wife in Scotland.

Scott's English Law for GCSE. – 5th ed. – London : Butterworths, 1987.
ISBN 0406653070 Pbk £10.50

Scovazzi, Tullio → International Law for Antarctica.

Scraton, P.
Law, Order and the Authoritarian State. – Open University Press.
ISBN 0353155111 Hbk £25.00

Scripta diversa / G.O. Sayles. – London : Hambledon, 1982.
xi,371p; 24cm.
Includes index. Includes text in Latin.
ISBN 0907628125 £22.00

Scrivener
Family Day Care Services Act, 1983, Bill Pr019 : An Act Respecting Family Day Care Services. – Ontario : Ontario Government Publications Service, 1983.
1p.
Hbk £0.30

—Frontier College Act, 1983, Bill Pr002 : An Act Respecting Frontier College. – Ontario : Ontario Government Publications Service, 1983.
2p.
Hbk £0.30

—Massey Hall and Roy Thomson Hall Act, 1983, Bill Pr044 : An Act Respecting The Corporation of Massey Hall and Roy Thomson Hall. – Ontario : Ontario Government Publications Service, 1983.
9p.
Hbk £0.50

—Roitman Investments Limited Act, 1983, Bill Pr009 : An Act to Revive Roitman Investments Limited. – Ontario : Ontario Government Publications Service, 1983.
2p.
Hbk £0.30

Scruton, Roger
Dictionary of Political Thought. – London : Macmillan, 1982.
512p.
ISBN 0333334396 Hbk £12.00

—Sexual desire : a philosophical investigation / Roger Scruton. – London : Weidenfeld and Nicolson, 1986.
x,428p; 24cm.
Includes index.
ISBN 029778479X Hbk £18.95
ISBN 0297788779 Pbk £8.95

Scrutton on charterparties and bills of lading / Alan Abraham Mocatta, Michael John Mustill, Stewart C. Boyd. – 19th ed. – London : Sweet & Maxwell, 1984.
cv,593p; 25cm.
Section on time charters has been substantially revised and rewritten to take account of developments. Four House of Lords decisions on the problem of withdrawal for non-payment of hire are discussed, and there is an analysis of the related problem of deductions from hire.
ISBN 0421297107 £50.00

Scrutton, Thomas Edward
Scrutton on charterparties and bills of lading / Alan Abraham Mocatta, Michael John Mustill, Stewart C. Boyd. – 19th ed. – London : Sweet & Maxwell, 1984.
cv,593p; 25cm.
Section on time charters has been substantially revised and rewritten to take account of developments. Four House of Lords decisions on the problem of withdrawal for non-payment of hire are discussed, and there is an analysis of the related problem of deductions from hire.
ISBN 0421297107 £50.00

Scull, Andrew T.
Decarceration : community treatment and the deviant : a radical view / Andrew Scull. – 2nd ed. – Cambridge : Polity Press, 1984.
202p.
1st ed.: Englewood Cliffs, N.J.: Prentice-Hall, 1977. Bibliography: p191-198.
→ Social control and the state : historical and comparative essays.

Scully → Drainage Cases : Ontario 1898-1903, 2 Vols.

Scutt, Jocelynne A.
Lionel Morphy - a Radical Judge : an Appraisal by Eleven Prominent Australians. – Carlton : McCulloch Publishing.
276p.
ISBN 0949646172 Hbk £29.95

—Rape Law Reform. – Canberra : Australian Institute of Criminology.
Hbk £4.00

—Violence in the Family. – Canberra : Australian Institute of Criminology.
Hbk £3.00

Sea lawyer grade for yachtsmen. – 2nd ed. – Oxford : Collins, 1986.
ISBN 0229117627 Pbk £6.95

Sea-bed energy and mineral resources and the law of the sea
Vol.1 : The areas within national jurisdiction : by E.D. Brown. – London : Graham & Trotman, 1984.
350p in various pagings; 25cm.
Includes index.
ISBN 0860104605 Hbk £39.00
ISBN 0860106152 unbound £35.00
Vol.2 : The areas beyond the limits of national jurisdiction / by E.D. Brown. – 1986.
400p; 24cm.
Includes index.
ISBN 0860106233 Hbk £45.00 :
ISBN 0860106217 Llf-leaf £45.00
Vol.3 : Selected documents, tables, bibliography / by E.D. Brown. – 1986.
520p; 24cm.
Includes bibliography.
ISBN 0860106241 Hbk £55.00 :
ISBN 0860106225 Llf-leaf £55.00

Seabrooke, Stephen
Evidence in a nutshell / Stephen Seabrooke. – London : Sweet & Maxwell, 1981.
vii,84p; 18cm. – (New nutshells).
Includes index.
ISBN 042127820X Pbk £1.75

Seago, Peter → 'A' level law : cases and materials.

—Criminal law / by Peter Seago. – 2nd ed. – London : Sweet & Maxwell, 1985.
xx,326p; 22cm.
Previous ed.: 1981. Bibliography: p317-318. - Includes index.
ISBN 0421338903 Pbk £9.50

Sealy, L. S., et al
Annotated guide to the 1986 insolvency legislation: Insolvency Act 1986, Company Directors Disqualification Act 1986 and Insolvency Rules 1986 (as amended) / David Milman. – 2nd. – Bicester : CCH Editions Ltd, 1988.
viii,994p; 23cm.
Reproduces the Act in full text, together with commentary and notes to each provision, explaining its meaning, effort and implications. Includes lists of statutory definitions, a table of destinations, reference to the rules and regulations, and a comprehensive index.
ISBN 0863251617 Hbk £26.00

→ Cambridge-Tilbury Law Lectures, Vol. 4.

—Cases and materials in company law / L.S. Sealy. – 3rd ed. – London : Butterworths, 1985.
xxvii,609p.
Previous ed.: 1978. Includes index.
ISBN 0406370125 Pbk £24.00 :
ISBN 0406370133 £15.95

—Company law and commercial reality / by L.S. Sealy. – London : Sweet & Maxwell, 1984.
xii,91p; 22cm.
Includes index.
ISBN 0421333502 Pbk £12.00

—Disqualification and personal liability of directors : a guide to the changes made by the insolvency legislation of 1985 and 1986 / by L.S. Sealy. – 2nd ed. – Bicester : CCH, 1987.
iv,53p.
Explains the rules regarding directors' disqualification, the imposition of personal liability on company directors and others (including wrongful trading), and the rules on the restriction of use of certain company names by directors and shadow directors.
ISBN 0863251307

—Insolvency : Disqualification and personal liability of directors. – London : CCH, 1986.
ISBN 0863250920 Pbk £6.00

Search & seizure : constitutional and common law / Polyvios G. Polyviou. – London : Duckworth, 1982.
viii,391p; 26cm.
Includes index.
ISBN 0715615920 £35.00

Search and Seizure under Taxation Laws. – Allahabad : Law Publishers, 1982.
Hbk £22.50

Search for world order : a study of thought and action / by Cornelius F. Murphy, Jr. – Dordrecht : M. Nijhoff, 1985.
xiii, 192 p.; 25 cm. – (Developments in international law).
Includes bibliographical references and index.
ISBN 9024731887

Searches and Enquiries : A Conveyancer's Guide. – London : Butterworths, 1985.
This book gives a step by step guide to the process of searches and enquiries made by conveyancers in the United Kingdom. The work includes an analysis of common searches and a reference guide to unusual searches.
ISBN 040625513X Pbk

Searching for Safety. – Oxford : Clio Distribution.
ISBN 0887387144 Hbk £11.25

Searle, G.
Corruption in British Politics 1895-1930. – Oxford : Oxford University Press, 1987.
ISBN 0198229151 Hbk £19.50

Seccombe, Monica → Access to justice and the welfare state.
→ Integration through law : Europe and the American Federal experience : a series, Vol. 5 : The legal integration of energy markets : by Terence Daintith and Stephen F. Williams.

Second ACP-EEC Convention : signed at Lome on 31 October 1979 and related documents / ACP-EEC Council of Ministers, Brussels. – 1981 ed. – Luxembourg : Office for Official Publications of the European Communities, 1981.
549p; 21cm.
ISBN 9282400719

Second Commonwealth Conference on Delegated Legislation. – 3 v. – Ottawa? : Queen's Printer, 1983.
Contents: 1. Report of the conference - 2. Documents of the conference - 3. Transcript of proceedings.

Second Convention of Lome : EEC aid to the ACP countries (1981-1985) / by Catherine Goybet : with the collaboration of Jane Morrison. – Brussels : Bureau d'Informations Europeennes, 1982.
317 leaves.

Second enlargement of the EEC : the integration of unequal partners / edited by Dudley Seers and Constantine Vaitsos : with the assistance of Marja-Liisa Kiljunen. – London : Macmillan, 1982.
xx,275p; 23cm.
ISBN 0333291891

Second interim report of the Commission of Inquiry into the Structure and Functioning of the Courts. – Pretoria : Govt. Printer, 1981.
5, 5 p.; 30 cm.
Title on added t.p.: Tweede tussentydse verslag van die Kommissie van Ondersoek na die Struktuur en Funksionering van die Howe. English and Dutch.
ISBN 0621065781 Hbk R3.60

Second International Maritime Law Seminar : Carriage of Goods by Sea, Maritime Liens, Marine Insurance. – Vancouver : Continuing Legal Education Society of British Columbia, 1981.
395p.
ISBN 0865040273 Hbk £100.00

Second Part of the Institutes of the Lawes of England : Containing the Exposition of Many Ancient and Other Statutes. – Repr. of 1642 ed. – Abingdon : Professional Books.
546p.
Hbk £1600.00

Second report : Commission of Inquiry into the Appearance of Advocates in the Supreme Court of South Africa / F.S. Smuts. – Pretoria : Printed by and obtainable from the Government Printer, 1985.
70 p.; 30 cm.
Afrikaans and English. Report of F.A. Smuts, the Chairman, and only member of the Commission of Inquiry into the Appearance of Advocates in the Supreme Court of South Africa.
ISBN 0621097195 Pbk R4.00 (R5.00 other countries)

Second Report : Conveyancing Simplifications. – Conveyancing Committee. – London : HMSO, 1985.
ISBN 0113800029 Hbk £8.60

Second report from the Social Services Committee, session 1983- 84 : children in care
Vol.1 : Report together with the proceedings of the Committee. – London : H.M.S.O., 1984.
clxxii p.; 25cm. – (H.C.).
ISBN 0102880840
Vol.2 : Minutes of evidence (24 November 1982-9 February 1983). – 1984.
ix,1-410p; 25cm. – (H.C.).
ISBN 0102881847 Hbk
Vol.3 : Minutes of evidence (16 February-4 May 1983 and an appendix. – 1984.
ix,411-740p; 25cm. – (H.C.).
ISBN 0102882843 Hbk

Second report on the legal profession : complaints, discipline and professional standards / New South Wales Law Reform Commission. – Sydney : The Commission, 1982.
121p. – (L.R.C.32).
Includes index.

Second report on trustee's powers of investment : miscellaneous powers. – Wellington? : the Committee?, 1984.
10,14,2,4p.

Second report to Parliament on subordinate legislation / Legal and Constitutional Committee. – Melbourne : Government Printer, 1986.
vii,5p.

Second report to Parliament on the operation of section 32 of the Interpretation of Legislation Act 1984 ... / Legal and Constitutional Committee. – Melbourne : Government Printer, 1986.
v,3p.

Second Survey of Legal Education in the United Kingdom : Supplement No. 2 / S. B. Marsh. – London : Institute of Advanced Legal Studies, 1981.
ISBN 090119025X Hbk £2.00

Secondary banking crisis, 1973-75 : its causes and course / Margaret Reid. – London : Macmillan, 1982.
ix,219p.

Secondary liability : participation in crime and inchoate offences / Law Reform Commission of Canada. – Ottawa : The Commission, 1985.
53,61p. – (Working paper).
Includes bibliographical references. Added t.p. in French: La responsabilite secondaire: complicite et infractions inchoatives. Cover title: Criminal law - secondary liability. Pages numbered in opposite directions. English and French text.
ISBN 0662537491

Second-best bed : a diversion on wills / Fenton Bresler : illustrations by Michael Heath. – London : Weidenfeld and Nicolson, 1983.
158p; 23cm.
ISBN 0297782134 £7.50

Secrecy in Britain. – Oxford : Blackwell (Basil), 1990.
96; 20.
ISBN 0631169121 Pbk £3.75

Secrecy of Correspondence is Guaranteed by Law. – London : Spokesman Books, 1983.
196p.
ISBN 085124128X Pbk £1.95

Secrets : on the ethics of concealment and revelation / Sissela Bok. – Oxford : Oxford University Press, 1984.
xviii,332p; 23cm.
Originally published: New York : Pantheon, 1983. Includes index.
ISBN 0192177338 Pbk £12.95

Secrets file : the case for freedom of information in Britain today / Des Wilson. – London : Heinemann Educational Books, 1984.
viii,(2),166p.
Bibliography: p59.
ISBN 0435839403

Sectional Titles Protocol Register. – Cape Town : Legal & Financial Publishing, 1983.
– (Merlen P.A.Y.E. Registers Ser.).
Hbk £21.81

Sectional titles, share blocks and time-sharing / by C.G. van der Merwe and D.W. Butler. – Durban : Butterworths, 1985.
xiii,573p.
Bibliography: p. xv-xxi. - Includes indexes.
ISBN 0409059293 Hbk R105

Secure provision. – Tavistock, 1985.
ISBN 0422784303 Pbk £7.95

Secure Provision for Mental Patients. – London : Sweet & Maxwell, 1985.
ISBN 0422784206 Hbk £16.95
ISBN 0422784303 Pbk £7.95

Secured Financing : Conference Papers. – Woolloomooloo : International Business Communications, 1987.
ISBN 0949072133 Hbk £95.00

Securities Act (B.C.) and Regulations. – Vancouver : Continuing Legal Education Society of British Columbia, 1987.
473p.
ISBN 0865042497 Hbk £85.00

Securities Act (B.C.) and Regulations : 1988 Update. – Vancouver : Continuing Legal Education Society of British Columbia, 1988.
213p.
ISBN 0865049947 Hbk £75.00

Securities and commodities enforcement : criminal prosecutions and civil injunctions / Howard M. Friedman. – Lexington, Mass. : Lexington Books, 1981.
xiii,238p; 24cm.
Includes index.
ISBN 066903617X £21.50

Securities and Investments Board / a report by the Director General of Fair Trading to the Secretary of State for Trade and Industry. – London : Office of Fair Trading, 1987.
77p.

Securities and Investments Board
Conduct of business rules : a new approach / Securities and Investments Board. – 1. – London : The Board, 1988.
various pagings.
—Regulation of investment business / The Securities and Investments Board. – 2 (loose-leaf). – London : The Board, 1986.
34cm.
Accompanied by: Further ammendments proposed to the February drafts of rules ... xix,125p.
—Rules and regulations / The Securities and Investments Board. – 3. – London : The Board, 1987.
looseleaf.
Accompanied by: Overview, consultative papers and documents, etc..
→ Securities and Investments Board.

Securities Association
Bulletin / the Securities Association. – London : The Association, 1988.
Alternative title: TSA bulletin.
—Rules / The Securities Association. – 3rd ed. 1. – London : The Association, 1988.
looseleaf.
Popular title: TSA rule book.

Securities Industry Act, 1983 (Act 280) and Regulations, 1976. – Kuala Lumpur : International Law Books Services.
Hbk £12.50

Securities Law and Practice, 4 Vols. – 2nd ed. – Agincourt : Carswell, 1984.
1570p.
This multi-volume work is a comprehensive guide to securities law in Canada. The Securities Act of Ontario, regulations, blanket rulings, policy statements, and practice notes of the Ontario Securities Commission are included in the work.
Llf £294.00

Securities Law in New Zealand / R. Clarke. – Butterworths, 1983.
Sets out the Securities Act 1978 with its amendments, the Regulations, and the Exemption Notices issues by the Commission, with useful comments and background information.
ISBN 0409600490 Pbk £54.45

Securities Law Seminar Insider Training 1985 : Centre for Commercial Law and Applied Legal Research. – Monash University, Faculty of Law. – Clayton : Monash University Press.
ISBN 0867463856 Hbk £17.00

Securities market in Japan 1986. – Japan Securities Research Institute. – 7th ed. – Tokyo : Japan Securities Research Institute, 1986.
xiii,215p.
Previous edition: 1985.
ISBN 4890328068

Securities Practice and Procedure. – Vancouver : British Columbia Continuing Legal Education Society, 1983.
481p.
ISBN 0865041393 Hbk £65.00

Securities Practice for Legal Assistants. – Vancouver : Continuing Legal Education Society of British Columbia, 1987.
278p.
ISBN 0865043426 Hbk £75.00

Securities regulation in the UK. – London : IFR Publishing, 1987.
268p.
Includes schedules 1 & 5 of the Financial Services Act, 1986.
ISBN 0946559368

Securities regulation of take-over bids in Canada / by John T. D. Courtright. – Calgary, Alta. : Carswell Legal Publications, Western Division, 1985.
xxii, 122 p.; 24 cm.
Includes index.
ISBN 0459373404 Pbk

Securitisation / Scott. – Cambridge : Woodhead-Faulkner, 1988.
ISBN 0859414167 Hbk £40.00

Securitisation in international finance. – London : Butterworths, 1988.
ISBN 0406100616 Pbk

Security and Privacy : Symposium Proceedings 1988. – London : Electronica Books.
ISBN 0818608501 Hbk £48.00

Security and society : reflections on law, order and politics / R.N. Berki. – London : Dent, 1986.
256p.
Includes bibliography and index.
ISBN 0460046551 Hbk £15.00 :
ISBN 0460024698 Pbk £6.95

Security computer based information systems. – London : Macmillan, 1985.
ISBN 0333364376 Pbk £7.95

Security Council adopts resolution demanding cessation of hostilities and withdrawal of Argentine forces from the Falkland Islands : Council also calls for diplomatic solution of the situation. – London : United Nations Information Centre, 1982.
9 leaves. – (BR/82/10).
'Background information for media only'.

Security of tenure under the Rent Act / by Jill E. Martin. – London : Sweet & Maxwell, 1986.
xxi,163p; 22cm.
Includes index.
ISBN 0421363304 Hbk £14.00
ISBN 0421363401 Pbk £10.50

Security on movable property and receivables in Europe : the principal forms of security in the European Community (except Greece) and Switzerland / edited by Michael G. Dickson ... et al. – Oxford : ESC Publishing, 1988.
227p.
ISBN 0906214491

Security over property other than land : consultation document / by A.L. Diamond. – London : Department of Trade and Industry, 1986.
67p.

Security, terrorism, and torture : detainees' rights in South Africa and Israel : a comparative study / by Harold Rudolph. – Cape Town : Juta, 1984.
xviii, 270 p.; 22 cm.
Includes indexes. Bibliography: p. 253-259.
ISBN 0702115088 Pbk R38.00

Seddon, N. C. → Cheshire and Fifoot's Law of Contract : Fifth Australian Edition.

Sedition Act, 1948 (Act 15). – Kuala Lumpur : International Law Books Services.
Hbk £3.00

Sedley, Ann → Amending the equality laws.

Seear, Beatrice Nancy
Women in the penal system / by Baroness Seear and Elaine Player : report prepared for the Howard League for Penal Reform. – London : Howard League for Penal Reform, 1986.
20p.

Seerecht : Testausgabe Law of the sea / Renate Platzoder, Wolfgang Graf Vitzthum. – 1. Aufl. – Baden-Baden : Nomos, 1984.
500 p.; 18 cm.
Contains conventions adopted by the United Nations conferences on the law of the sea, and related legislation of various countries. English and German.
ISBN 3789009318

Seers, Dudley
Political economy of nationalism / Dudley Seers. – Oxford : Oxford University Press, 1983.
218p; 22cm.
Bibliography: p198-203. - Includes index.
ISBN 019828456X Hbk £
ISBN 019828473X Pbk £6.95
→ Second enlargement of the EEC : the integration of unequal partners.

Seervai, H M
Constitutional Law of India
Vol. 1. – 3rd ed. – London : Sweet & Maxwell, 1983.
ISBN 0421316608 Hbk £54.00
—Constitutional law of India : a critical commentary
Vol.1 / by H.M. Seervai. – 3rd ed. – Bombay : Tripathi, 1983.
xlvii,1071,262p; 26cm.
Previous ed.: 1975. Includes index. Includes text of the Constitution of India.
ISBN 0421316608 £45.00

Vol.2 / by H.M. Seervai. – 1984.
various pagings; 25cm.
Previous ed.: in 3 1975-1979. Includes index.
ISBN 0421339705 £70.00

Segal, Gary L.
Immigrating to Canada : Who is Allowed? What is Required? How to Do It. – 6th ed. – North Vancouver : International Self-Counsel Press, 1986.
179p.
ISBN 0889086133 Hbk £14.95

Segal, Murray D.
Manual of Motor Vehicle Law, 2 Vols. – 3rd ed. – Agincourt : Carswell, 1982.
This looseleaf service is an annotated guide to the text of the Highway Traffic Act of Ontario, Canada. Cases and statutory references to the motor vehicle law of all provinces is included in the work.
Llf £138.75
—Motor Vehicle Reports. – Agincourt : Carswell, 1988.
This multi-volume set of books contains the key decisions in motor vehicle law from all Canadian jurisdictions. Discussions include alcoholic related offenses, civil actions relating to motor vehicles, and registration and licensing issues.
Hbk £75.00

Seglin, J.L.
Bank Administration Manual. – 3rd ed. – Merehurst.
ISBN 01556231458 Hbk £53.95

Seglow, Peter
Rail Unions in Britain and West Germany : A Study of their Structure and Policies / Wolfgang Steeck. – London : Policy Studies Institute, 1982.
109p.
Hbk £3.50
—Trade Unions and Change in the British Car Industry / Patricia Wallace. – London : Policy Studies Institute, 1984.
72p. – (PSI Research Papers).
Hbk £3.50

Seidentopf
Making European Policies Work
Vol. 1 / Ziller. – Sage Publications, 1988.
ISBN 0803981376 Hbk £25.00

Seidl-Hohenveldern, Ignaz
Corporations in and under international law / by Ignaz Seidl-Hohenveldern. – Cambridge : Grotius, 1987.
xviii,138p.
Covers the nationality of corporations and the effect upon them of nationalisation measures, as well as the special responsibilities of state-owned corporations. The second part of the book examines problems connected with the legal personality of international organizations.
ISBN 0949009091
—International economic law. – Dordrecht : Nijhoff (Martinus), 1989.
274.
Updated and extended version of the General Course held by the author at the Hague Academy of International Law in 1986. References to literature have been increased, and a detailed keyword index and an index of cases cited are included. Contains chapters on various aspects on international law.
ISBN 9024737990 Hbk £47

Seighart, P.
International law of human rights. – Oxford : Oxford University Press, 1984.
ISBN 0198760973 Pbk £21.00

Seigle, Larry
Workers' Rights Versus the Secret Police. – Sydney : Pathfinder Press.
46p.
Hbk £1.00

Seingry, G.F.
Yearbook European Communities and other European Organisations 1988. – London : Cedar Tree House.
ISBN 2802900781 Hbk £38.50

Sekhar → Controlling Corporate Sickness : Lessons from Experiences for Managers and Bankers.

Selby
Human rights / Pike. – Bradford : Mary Glasgow, 1988.
ISBN 01852341688 Hbk £16.95

Selby, Hugh
Long service leave / by Hugh Selby : with a foreword by F.V. Watson. – Sydney : Law Book Co., 1983.
xxviii,150p.
Includes index.
ISBN 0455204519

Selby, Ralph
Leasing in Canada : A Business Guide. – Toronto : Butterworths, 1986.
ISBN 0409805041 Pbk £35.00

Selden, J.
Mare Clausum : The Right and Dominion of the Sea. – Repr. of 1663 ed. – Abingdon : Professional Books.
515p.
Hbk £220.00

Selden Society
Vols. 1-99. – Professional Books.
ISBN 0862052807 Hbk £3,295.00

Selden Society
Centenary guide to the publications of the Selden Society. – Selden Society. – London : The Society, 1987.
242 p. – (Publications).
Supersedes: General guide to the Society's publications (1960).
→ Roll of the Shropshire eyre of 1256.
→ Select cases on defamation to 1600.

Seldon → Ruling performance.

Seldon, Arthur → Over-ruled on Welfare.

Select cases from the ecclesiastical courts of the Province of Canterbury, c.1200-1301 / edited for the Selden Society by Norma Adams and Charles Donahue Jr. – London : Selden Society, 1981.
xxx,119,756p.
Text in Latin and English.

Select Cases of Newfoundland : 1817-1828. – Repr. of 1938 ed. – Agincourt : Carswell.
600p. – (Carswell's Classic Reprints).
This work is a reprint of a rare 1893 collection of early decisions of the courts of province of Newfoundland, Canada.
Hbk £71.50

Select cases of trespass from the King's Courts, 1307-1399
Vol.1 : edited for the Selden Society by Morris S. Arnold / Morris S. Arnold. – London : Selden Society, 1985.
lxxxv,179,179p; 26cm.
Opposite pages of main sequence bear duplicate numbering. Parallel Latin text and English translation.
Vol. 2 : edited for the Selden Society by Morris S. Arnold. – 1987.
504 p. – (Publications).

Select cases on defamation to 1600 / edited for the Selden Society by R.H. Helmholz. – London : Selden Society, 1985.
cxi,118p.
Includes bibliographical references and index.

Select Cases on the Family Law Act 1976-1985. – North Ryde : C.C.H. Australia, 1986.
1,006p.
Hbk £32.00
Supplement-1987. –
48p.
ISBN 0869039652

Select Committee on the European Communities Report No. 17, 1982. – London : HMSO.
ISBN 0104204826 Hbk £10.00
Report No. 18, 1984. –
Hbk £9.15

Select Committee on the European Communities. – London : HMSO.
ISBN 0104239867 Hbk £6.50

Select Constitutions. – New Delhi : S. Chand and Company, 1983.
Hbk £80.00

Select Legal Papers. – limited ed. – Woolloomooloo : International Business Communications, 1983.
ISBN 0949553050 Hbk £34.95

Selected articles from Chinese yearbook of international law / edited by Chinese Society of International Law. – Beijing : China Translation & Publishing Corporation, 1983.
vi,308p.

Selected Basic Agreements and Joint Declarations on Labour-Management Relations. – Geneva : International Labour Office, 1983.
iv, 299p.
ISBN 9221034607 Hbk £25.00

Selected essays on Nigerian constitutional laws / D.O. Aihe. – Benin City : Idodo Umeh Publishers Ltd., 1985.
xxviii,264p.
Bibliography: p.255-257. - Includes index.
ISBN 9782340448

Selected Essays on the Law of the Sea. – Metro Manila : Development Academy of the Philippines, 1982.
vii, 26p.
ISBN 9711520028 Pbk £2.50

Selected income tax aspects of the purchase and sale of a business : Corporate Management Tax Confetence 1984. – Toronto : Canadian Tax Foundation, 1984.
xii,347p.
Bibliography: p.75-82.
ISBN 0888080220

Selected International Labour Conventions and Recommendations
Vol. 1. – Geneva : International Labour Office, 1984.
xv, 216p.
ISBN 9221038386 Pbk £14.00
Vol. 2. – 1985.
iv, 205p.
ISBN 9221038955 Pbk £14.00
ISBN 9221038963 Hbk £17.50

Selected Judgments of the Federal Supreme Court of Nigeria : 1956-60, 3 Vols. – Abingdon : Professional Books, 1984.
ISBN 0862050480 Hbk £104.00

Selected Judgments of the High Court of Oyo State : 1976-1980. – Abingdon : Professional Books, 1984.
Hbk

Selected judgments of the Ogun State High Court. – Abeokuta : High Court of Justice, 1978-.

Selected Legal Essays. – Colombo : Lake House Investments.
Hbk £6.60

Selected Multilateral Treaties in the Field of the Environment. – Geneva : United Nations Publications.
525p.
Pbk £38.00

Selected problems of construction law : international approach / Terence M. Burke ... et al. : published i.e. edited by Peter Gauch and Justin Sweet. – Fribourg : University Press, 1983.
287p.
Includes bibliographical references. 'The papers collected are revised versions of working papers prepared for and presented at the First International Construction Law Conference, Fribourg, 1982'.
ISBN 3727802863
ISBN 0-421-31650-0 Hbk £25.00

Selected Proceedings of the International Seminar Inventiveness for Development Purposes. – Geneva : World Intellectual Property Organization, 1985.
185p.
Hbk £30.00

Selected texts and cases on the Roman law of things : with an excursus on the Roman law of slavery / J.E. Schiller. – Cape Town : Juta, 1982.
xiii,127p; 25cm.
ISBN 0702112941

Selected trends in Canadian criminal justice / Research and Statistics Group. – Ottawa : Minister of Supply and Services, 1984.
vi,84p.
ISBN 0660117126

Selected Writing on Soviet Law and Marxism. – Sharpe.
ISBN 0873324730 Hbk £51.50

Selection from the Proceedings of the Royal Institute of Philosophy Conference on the Philosophy of Law (September 1979). – Dordrecht : Kluwer, 1982.
184p.
Pbk £43.50

Selections from the Laws of England, 2 Vols. – Repr. of 1806 ed. – Abingdon : Professional Books.
Hbk £35.00

Selective safeguard measures in multilateral trade relations : issues of protectionism in GATT, European Community, and United States law / M.C.E.J. Bronckers. – Deventer, Netherlands : Kluwer Law and Taxation Publishers, 1985.
306p.
Includes index and bibliography.
ISBN 9065442227 Hbk £150.00

Self-administered pensions for directors. – London : Fitzwilliam, 1988.
ISBN 1870555031 Hbk £25.00

Self-determination in law and practice : the new doctrine in the United Nations / by Michla Pomerance. – The Hague : M. Nijhoff, 1982.
xi,154p.
Includes index. Bibliography: p130-138.
ISBN 9024725941

Self-Help Groups for Drug Addicts' Families / Gay. – Policy Studies Institute.
ISBN 0853744076 Pbk £4.95

Sellar, Lindsay →Councils, committees & boards : a handbook of advisory, consultative, executive & similar bodies in British public life.

Selling for a future : proposals for a British policy on refugees / British Refugee Council. – London : The Council, 1987.
25p.

Selling the state : privatisation in Britain / Cento Veljanovski. – London : Weidenfeld and Nicolson, 1987.
xiv, 239p.
Bibliography: p.213-217.
ISBN 0297790803

Sells →Tolley's Accounting Problems of the Companies Acts : Practical Guidance on Recent Legislation.
→ Tolley's Double Taxation Relief.

Selman, P.H.
Countryside Planning in Practice. – Stirling University Press, 1988.
ISBN 0948812028 Hbk £22.50

Selmer, Knut S.
Lawdata Papers. – Oslo : Norwegian University Press, 1982.
48p.
ISBN 8200059650 Hbk £26.00

Selwood, D. H. D. →Criminal law and psychiatry.

Selwyn, Norman M.
Dictionary of employment law / by Norman Selwyn. – London : Butterworths, 1985.
165p; 22cm. – (Butterworths professional dictionary series).
ISBN 0406207909 Hbk £
ISBN 0406207917 Pbk
—Law of employment / N.M. Selwyn. – 6th ed. – London : Butterworths, 1988.
xlv,582p.
Previous ed.: 1985. Includes index. Cover title: Selwyn's law of employment.
ISBN 0406653461 £14.95
—Law of Employment. – 5th ed. – London : Butterworths, 1985.
ISBN 0406653445 Pbk £15.95
—Law of Employment. – 6th ed. – London : Butterworths.
ISBN 0406653461 Pbk £16.95
—Law of Health and Safety at Work. – London : Butterworths, 1982.
ISBN 0406667500 Pbk £10.95

Seminar for Librarians in the Criminal Justice System. – Canberra : Australian Institute of Criminology.
Hbk £2.50

Seminar on a legal profession act for Papua New Guinea : Port Moresby, 4th & 5th of May 1982 / Law Reform Commission and Legal Training Institute. – 1. – Waigani : Law Reform Commission of Papua New Guinea, 1982.
various pagings. – (LRC Working Paper).

Seminar on Computerization in Industrial Property Administration for Asian Countries. – Geneva : World Intellectual Property Organization, 1987.
222p.
Hbk £30.00

Semiotics and legal theory / Bernard S. Jackson. – London : Routledge and Kegan Paul, 1985.
xii,373p; 22cm.
Bibliography: p.349-373.
ISBN 0710097190

Semiotics, law and social science / edited by Domenico Carzo and Bernard S. Jackson. – Roma : Gangemi, 1985.
227p.
'Based largely upon papers prepared for a colloquium on legal semiotics organised by Professor Roque Carrion-Wam in March 1985'. Includes bibliographies. At head of title: Congress volume for Aix Colloquium.

Sen, A.C.
Mukherjea's Hindu Law of Religious and Charitable Trusts. – 5th ed. – Calcutta : Eastern Law House, 1983.
Hbk £122.00

Sen, A.K.
Justice for the Common Man / M.C. Setalvad. – Lucknow : Eastern Book Company, 1964.
97p.
Hbk £7.50

Sen, B.
Diplomat's Handbook of International Law and Practice. – 3rd ed. – Martinus Nijhoff.
ISBN 9024736471 Hbk £65.00

Sen, Prasanta Kumar
From Punishment To Prevention. – Repr. of 1932 ed. – Aalen Wuertt : Scientia.
xv, 152p.
Hbk £43.00

Sen, Samarendra Chandra
S.C. Sen's Mergers, Amalgamations, and Take-Overs : the Law, the Procedure, and the Valuation of Shares. – 2nd ed. – Calcutta : Eastern Law House, 1981.
310p.
Hbk £90.00

Sen, T.K.
Corporate Income Tax and Profit Rates. – New Delhi : Deep and Deep Publications, 1984.
268p.
Hbk £150.00

Sena, Giuseppe →Italian patent law.

Senate of the Inns of Court and the Bar
Code of conduct for the Bar of England and Wales : effective from 1st January 1981 / Senate of the Inns of Court and the Bar. – 2nd ed. Incorporating all amendments up to 31st December 1982. – London : The Senate, 1983.
76p.
Previous ed.: 1981. Includes index.
—Code of conduct for the Bar of England and Wales : effective from 1st January 1981. – Senate of the Inns of Court and the Bar. – 3rd ed. (incorporating all amendments up to 31st December 1984). – London : The Senate, 1985.
74p.
Includes index.
→ Counsel : the journal of the Bar of England and Wales.
—Lawyers and the courts : the response of the Bar to a discussion paper issed bu the Law Society's Contentious Business Committee. – Senate of the Inns of Court and the Bar. – London : Senate of the Inns of Court and the Bar, 1986.
14p.
Includes bibliographical references. At head of p.3: Seanate of the Inns of Court and the Bar.
—Report of the Committee on the Constitution of the Senate / Chairman: Rt. Hon. Lord Rawlinson of Ewell. – London : Senate of the Inns of Court and the Bar, 1986.
71p.

Senate Select Committee
Allegations Concerning a Judge : Report to the Senate. – Senate Select Committee. – Canberra : Australian Government Publishing Service, 1984.
Hbk £6.80

Senate, the Courts and the Constitution : a Debate / Tribe. – London : Eurospan.
ISBN 0944237223 Pbk £8.50

Sengupta, Surajit
Business Law in India. – New Delhi : Oxford University Press.
Hbk £65.00

Senior Citizens and the Law : Towards a Greater Quality of Life. – Montreal : McGill Campus Legal Aid Clinic, 1985.
92p.
Hbk £7.00

Sensenbrenner Hospital Employees Compensation Act, 1983, Bill 110 : An Act Respecting the Compensation of Certain Employees at Sensenbrenner Hospital in Kapuskasing. – Ontario : Ontario Government Publications Service, 1983.
2p.
Hbk £0.30

Sentence of the court : a handbook for courts on the treatment of offenders / Home Office. – 4th ed. – London : H.M.S.O., 1986.
109p; 21cm.
ISBN 0113408072

Sentenced to hospital : offenders in Broadmoor / by Susanne Dell, Graham Robertson. – Oxford : Oxford University Press, 1988.
x, 170 p.; 25 cm.
Based on interviews with staff and patients at Broadmoor, it describes how men come to be sent to Broadmoor, and their subsequent treatment, including procedures and decision-making related to discharge. Recommends controversial changes in the law and in detention policy.
ISBN 019712156X Hbk £22.50

Sentenced to separation : an exploration of the needs and problems of mothers who are offenders and their children / Linda MacLeod. – Ottawa : Ministry of the Solicitor General, 1986.
ii,66p,14p,8p. – (User report).

Sentencing / edited by Hyman Gross, Andrew von Hirsch. – New York : Oxford University Press, 1981.
ix,397p; 25cm.
ISBN 0195027639 Pbk £12.75
ISBN 0195027647 £6.50

Sentencing / Law Reform Commission. – Canberra : Australian Government Publishing Service, 1988.
lv,203p. – (Report).
Bibliography: p.197-203. Includes draft legislation.
ISBN 0644069104

Sentencing. – 3rd ed. – Butterworths, 1987.
712p.
Coverage of general principles of sentencing, finding an appropriate sentence, procedure, criminal record, psychiatric aspect of sentencing, factors affecting sentence, matters that are not taken into consideration on sentencing, parole and the role of prerogative mercy, suspended sentence and probation, corporate crime, and imprisonment.
ISBN 0409864226 Hbk £95.00

Sentencing / Eric Stockdale and Keith Devlin. – London : Waterlow, 1987.
xxviii,297p; 24cm.
Bibliography: p285-291. - Includes index.
ISBN 0080392482 £30.00

Sentencing : penalties / the Law Reform Commission. – Sydney : The Commission, 1987.
234p. – (Discussion paper).
Bibliography: p.223-234..

Sentencing : prisons / The Law Reform Commission. – Sydney : The Commission, 1987.
vii,64p. – (Discussion paper).
Bibliography: pp.63-64.

Sentencing : procedure / The Law Reform Commission. – Sydney : The Commission, 1987.
xii,114p. – (Discussion paper).
Bibliography: pp.111-114.

Sentencing : state and federal law in Victoria / Richard G. Fox, Arie Freiberg. – Melbourne : Oxford University Press, 1985.
lxxv,615p.
ISBN 0195546563 Hbk £50.00

Sentencing : Theory, Law and Practice. – London : Butterworths, 1985.
Pbk

Sentencing : theory, law and practice / Nigel Walker. – London : Butterworth, 1985.
xlix,510p; 26cm.
Bibliography: pxxxiii-xl - Includes index.
ISBN 0406252637 Hbk £33
ISBN 0406252815 Pbk £21.95

Sentencing and penal policy / Andrew Ashworth. – London : Weidenfeld and Nicolson, 1983.
xx,500p; 22cm.
Bibliography: p487-495. - Includes index.
ISBN 0297782363 Hbk

Sentencing and Post-Conviction Representation. – Vancouver : Continuing Legal Education Society of British Columbia, 1986.
236p.
ISBN 0865042853 Hbk £60.00

Sentencing and the penal system : text and materials / by Christopher Harding and Laurence Koffman. – London : Sweet & Maxwell, 1988.
xxvii,401p; 25cm.
Bibliography: p385-396. - Includes index.
ISBN 0421357703 Pbk £13.50

Sentencing approach / Clifford E.M. Chatterton. – Chichester : Rose, 1984.
43p; 22cm.
ISBN 0859923576 Pbk £7.50

Sentencing by Computer : an Experiment. – Norwegian University Press, 1982.
246p.
ISBN 8200064360 Hbk £133.00

Sentencing by English magistrates as a human process / by Andreas Kapardis. – Nicosia : Asselia, 1985.
xi,288p.
Bibliography: p.270-286. - Includes index.
ISBN 9963750079

Sentencing Drug Offenders in New South Wales. – Canberra : Australian Institute of Criminology.
Hbk £4.50

Sentencing in Canada / by R. Paul Nadin-Davis. – Toronto : Carswell, 1982.
lxxii, 609 p.; 24 cm.
Includes bibliographical references and index.
ISBN 0459348507

Sentencing in environmental cases : a study paper / prepared for the Law Reform Commission of Canada by John Swaigan and Gail Bunt. – Ottawa : The Commission, 1985.
81p. – (Study paper).
ISBN 0662138295

Sentencing in New Zealand. – Butterworths.
Hbk £99.00

Sentencing law and practice / by C.K. Boyle and M.J. Allen. – London : Sweet & Maxwell, 1985.
xxxvi,338p.
Includes index.
ISBN 0421344008 Pbk £15.00

Sentencing law and practice in Northern Ireland / by C.K. Boyle and M.J. Allen. – Belfast : SLS Legal, 1983.
xxxix,256p; 23cm.
Includes index.
ISBN 0853892245

Sentencing practice in the Crown Court / by David Moxon. – London : HMSO, 1988.
v,89p.
'A Home Office Research and Planning Unit report'.- T.p..
ISBN 0113409028

Sentencing reform : a Canadian approach / report of the Canadian Sentencing Commission. – Ottawa : Minister of Supply and Services, 1986.
xl,592p.
Bibliography: pp.575-592. Chairman: J. R. Omer Archambault.
ISBN 0660122456

Sentencing reform : a Canadian approach : summary / report of the Canadian Sentencing Commission. – Ottawa : Minister of Supply and Services, 1987.
34,37p.
French title on added t.p.: Reformer la sentence. Pages numbered in opposite directions. Text in English and French.
ISBN 0662550757

Sentencing reform : guidance or guidelines? / edited by Martin Wasik and Ken Pease. – Manchester : Manchester University Press, 1987.
viii,208p; 23cm.
Includes bibliographies and index.
ISBN 0719018900 £27.50

Sentencing Sex Offenders in New South Wales : An Interim Report. – Canberra : Australian Institute of Criminology.
Hbk £1.00

Sentencing the Federal Drug Offender / John Walker. – Canberra : Australian Institute of Criminology.
Hbk £4.50

Sentencing young people : what went wrong with the Criminal Justice Act 1982 / Elizabeth Burney. – Aldershot : Gower, 1985.
120p; 22cm.
ISBN 0566051273 £14.50

Separation and Divorce in Northern Ireland. – Belfast : Queen's University of Belfast, 1986.
125p.
Pbk

Separation, Divorce and After. – St. Lucia : University of Queensland Press.
ISBN 0702219312 Pbk £12.95

Seres, J.
Pensions : a practical guide. – 3rd ed. – London : Longman Professional, 1987.
ISBN 0851211879 Pbk £25.00

Sergeant and Sims on stamp duties and capital duty and stamp duty reserve tax / B. J. Sims, J. F. W. Hinson, E. M. E. Sims, R. D. Fulton. – 9th ed. – London : Butterworths, 1988.
lviii,739p.
Previous ed.: 1982. Includes index. Kept up to date by supplements.
ISBN 0406370435 £110.00

Sergeant, E. G.
Sergeant and Sims on stamp duties and capital duty and stamp duty reserve tax / B. J. Sims, J. F. W. Hinson, E. M. E. Sims, R. D. Fulton. – 9th ed. – London : Butterworths, 1988.
lviii,739p.
Previous ed.: 1982. Includes index. Kept up to date by supplements.
ISBN 0406370435 £110.00

Serial murder / Deburger. – Sage Publications, 1988.
ISBN 0803928408 Hbk £25.95
ISBN 0803928416 Pbk £12.00

Serisier, Ian
Australian Family Law Forms and Precedents / Alexander Duff. – Woolloomooloo : International Business Communications, 1987.
ISBN 0949553247 Hbk £225.00

Serjeantson → Legal Reminders for Architects.

Service Agreements. – 5th ed. – London : Longman Professional (UK), 1986.
– (Practitioner Series).
Guidance on drafting service agreements. Looks at different types of agreement showing benefits designed to protect compant interests and to offer security to the employee.
ISBN 0851212212 Pbk £22.50

Service and execution of process / Law Reform Commission. – Canberra : Australian Government Publishing Service, 1987.
lix,539p. – (Report).
Bibliography: pp.527-531. - Includes index. Includes draft legislation.
ISBN 0644013796

Service marks : a guide to the new law : Trade Marks Act 1938 as amended by the Trade Marks (Amendment) Act 1984 and the Patents, Designs and Marks Act 1986 / Christopher Morcom. – Oxford : ESC Publishing, 1987.
vi,165p.
Includes texts from the Acts.
ISBN 0906214483

Service of documents. – 2nd. – London : Longman Professional (UK), 1989.
– (Practitioner series).
Contains a section dealing with service out of the jurisdiction. Second edition revised to take account of new rules governing county court summonses. Includes assessment of the impact of the Judgement Act 1982 (in force 1987), and all new forms and tables are covered.
ISBN 0851216099 Hbk £24.95

Service please : services and the law : a consumer view / prepared for the National Consumer Council by Barbara Lantin and Geoffrey Woodroffe. – London : National Consumer Council, 1981.
35p; 30cm.
ISBN 0905653386 Pbk

Services charges-Law and practice / Shapiro. – Stewart (Henry), 1986.
ISBN 0946700311 Pbk £17.50

Services for Conciliation in Divorce / Lisa Parkinson. – Aberdeen : Aberdeen University Press, 1984.
ISBN 008030379X Hbk

Services of Process Abroad : Hague Convention. – London : Butterworths.
Hbk

Services to victims and witnesses of crime in Canada / by Geoff Norquay, Richard Weiler. – Ottawa : Communication Division, Solicitor General Canada, 1981.
163 p.; 28 cm.
'A research report prepared by the Canadian Council on Social Development under contract with the Research Division, Ministry of the Solicitor General of Canada'–Verso t.p.
ISBN 0662117735 Pbk

Servicing the Legal System
Annual report / Servicing the Legal System, Queen's University of Belfast. – Servicing the Legal System. – Belfast : Servicing the Legal System, 1981-.
Servicing the Legal System was originally established as a committee of the Faculty of law, Queen's University of Belfast. Report year ends 31 July.

Servitude and Partition. – Colombo : Lake House Investments.
Hbk £5.50

Servitudes To International Law. – Sweet & Maxwell, 1958 Reprint.
ISBN 0421375302 Hbk £29.50

Sesay, Amadu → Future of regionalism in Africa.

Sesquicentennial choronological tables of the written laws of the republic of Singapore 1834-1984 / Elizabeth Srinivasagam, Pascal Netto. – Singapore : Malayan Law Journal, 1987.
cxii,350.
Examines the legislative history of the Straits settlements and Singapore. Lists all the Indian acts from 22 November 1814 to 1 April 1867, and all other local legislation from 1867 to 1984. Each act is indicated as to its applicability to the present. Account of the various legislatures for Singapore over the last 150 years.
ISBN 9971700530 Hbk

Session cases. – 3-4 parts. – Edinburgh : Clark (T. & T.) Ltd.
The official law reports in Scotland. Publication commenced in 1821. Prepared and edited by members of the Scottish Bar, the judgements are checked and revised by the judges. Where appropriate, exerpts from the written pleadings and arguments of counsel are included. The reports cover actions in the supreme civil and criminal courts (Justiciary cases) in Scotland, as well as civil cases appealed to the House of Lords. Each annual volume contains an index and case tables.

Session Cases : New Series, 1907-date. – Abingdon : Professional Books, 1984.
Hbk

Sessional information digest / House of Commons. – London : H.M.S.O., 1983.
Compiled in the Public Information Office, Department of the Library, House of Commons.

Sessions Trial. – 5th ed. – Lucknow : Eastern Book Company, 1986.
468p.
Hbk £90.00

Setalvad, M.C.
Indian Constitution. – Madras : Ramaswami Aiyar Foundation.
Hbk £5.00
→ Justice for the Common Man.

Seth → Comments on Prevention of Food Adulteration Act with Central and All State Rules.

Seth, D.D.
Commentaries on the Industrial Disputes Act 1947. – 3rd ed. – Allahabad : Law Publishing House, 1983.
ca 1,000p.
Hbk £150.00

Seth, H.N. → Law of Court Fees and Suits Valuation in India.

Seth, Ram
Pricing and Related Policies of Publicly Owned Electrical Utilities. – Halifax : Dalhousie University, Institute of Public Affairs.
ISBN 0889260265 Hbk

Sethi, K.L.
Maharashtra Cooperative Societies : Acts and Rules; as Amended by Acts no 10 and 20 of 1986, 2 Vols. – Indore : United Law Publishers, 1987.
Hbk £400.00
—Multi-State Cooperative Societies Act, 1984 : With Rules. – Indore : United Law Publishers, 1987.
Hbk £40.00

Sethi, R B
Banking Regulation Act, 1949. – Allahabad : Law Publishers, 1983.
227p.
Hbk £18.00
—Banking Regulation Act along with Rules and Various Allied Laws. – 4th ed. – Allahabad : Law Publishers, 1983.
Hbk £18.00
—Cattle Trespass Act along with Prevention of Cruelty of Animals Act. – 2nd ed. – Allahabad : Law Publishers, 1983.
Hbk £10.50
—Commentaries on Central Excise Act. – 3rd ed. – Allahabad : Law Publishers, 1982.
Hbk £45.00
—Commentaries on Hire-Purchase Act, 1972 with Model Forms. – 2nd ed. – Allahabad : Law Publishers, 1983.
Hbk £22.50
—Commentaries on Probation of Offenders Act. – 4th ed. – Allahabad : Law Publishers, 1983.
Hbk £33.00
—Factories Act. – 2nd ed. – Allahabad : Law Book Company, 1967.
500p.
With 1986 supplement.
Hbk £100.00
—Hindu Succession Act / Gopalakrishnan. – 5th ed. – Allahabad : Law Book Company, 1981.
Hbk £45.00
—Law of Employees State Insurance / Dwivedi. – 2nd ed. – Allahabad : Law Book Company.
700p.
With 1987 supplement.
Hbk £150.00
—Law of Foreigners and Citizenship ... – 3rd ed. – Allahabad : Law Publishers, 1983.
£33.00
—Police Acts. With 1985 supplement. – 5th ed. – Allahabad : Law Book Company, 1983.
Hbk £170.00
—Prevention of Food Adulteration Act with Central and State Rules and Foreign Law on the Subject. – 1983. – Allahabad : Law Book Company.
xxii, 548p.
Hbk £250.00

Sethna, Jehangir M.J.
Indian Company Law, 2 Vols. – 10th ed. – Nagpur : Wadjura & Co, 1987.
1,360p.
Hbk £525.00

Sethu, R.R.
Rent Control Legislation in Malaysia. – Butterworths, 1986.
292p.
Covers tenancy and licence, premises, parties, rent, rent tribunals, recovery of possession of premises, subtenancies, penal provisions, the repeal provisions, redevelopment, decontrol, and notice to quit.
ISBN 0409995231 Hbk £41.00

Set-off / Law Reform Commission of British Columbia. – Vancouver : The Commission, 1987.
iv,81p. – (Working paper).
Includes bibliographical references.

Set-off / S. Rory Derham. – Oxford : Clarendon, 1987.
320p; 22cm.
Includes bibliography and index.
ISBN 019825556X £40

Seton : Forms of Judgements and Orders in the High Court of Appeal, 3 Vols. – London : Sweet & Maxwell, 1985.
– (Sweet and Maxwell Library Reprints).
ISBN 0421346000 Hbk £150.00

Setting environmental standards : guidelines for decision-making / edited by H.W. de Koning. – Geneva : World Health Organization, 1987.
vii,98p; 24cm.
Bibliography: p71-76.
ISBN 9241542144 Pbk

Settlement of disputes in early medieval Europe / edited by Wendy Davies and Paul Fouracre. – Cambridge : Cambridge University Press, 1986.
549p.
Collection of original essays on settlement of disputes in early middle ages. Case material from the evidence of charters used. Discusses examples from fifth century Gaul, later Merovingian Francia, ninth century Brittany and Anglo Saxon England.
ISBN 0521307880 £30.00

Settlement of Disputes on the New Natural Resources : Workshop 1982. – Dordrecht : Kluwer, 1983.
502p.
ISBN 9024729017 Hbk £120.00

Settlement of international water law disputes in international drainage basins / by B.R. Chauhan. – Berlin : Schmidt, 1981.
480p; 21cm.
ISBN 3503019294

Settlement offers / Law Reform Commission of British Columbia. – Vancouver : The Commission, 1984.
iii,92p. – (Working paper).
Includes bibliographical references.

Settlement Offers. – Victoria : Government of British Columbia, 1984.
Hbk £7.00

Seventh annual conference of Canadian legislative ombudsmen, Saskatoon, Saskatchewan, August 30 - September 3, 1981 : the ombudsman in the eighties : new challenges. – Edmonton : International Ombudsman Institute, 1981.
143p.
Includes appendices in French.

Seventh Directive : consolidated accounts in the EEC / Sharon M. McKinnon : edited by Alan D.H. Newham. – Brentford : Kluwer, 1984.
392p.
Includes the official texts of Fourth and Seventh Directives.
ISBN 0903393700

Seventh report from the Social Services Committee, session 1984-85 : the government's green paper 'Reform of social security', together with the proceedings of the Committee, the minutes of evidence and appendices. – London : H.M.S.O., 1985.
liv,100p. – (H.C.).

Seventh report to Parliament on subordinate legislation concerning Teaching Service ... Regulations 1986 ... / Legal and Constitutional Committee. – Melbourne : Government Printer, 1986.
v,5p.

Sevilla, Victor J →Disorderly Conduct : Real Life Comedy from the Courtrooms.
—Justices of the Supreme Court. – Quezon : New Day.
Hbk

Seward, Desmond
Italy's Knights of St. George : The Historical Development and Juridical Position of the Sacred and Military Constantinian Order of St. George. – Gerrards Cross : Van Duren.
ISBN 0905715284 Hbk £12.00

Sewell →Practical approach to contract and consumer law.

Sewell, John
Public Affairs and The Successor Generation. – Exeter : European Atlantic Movement, 1982.
Pbk £0.50

Sex and ethnic monitoring, discrimination and equal pay : new codes and regulations / by Greville Janner. – New Malden : Croner Publications, 1984.
vi,120p.
Includes index.
ISBN 0900319321

Sex and race discrimination in employment / Kate Poulton. – London : Sweet & Maxwell, 1987.
ISBN 0905099176 Pbk £14.00

Sex and the law / by Fenton Bresler. – London : Century, 1988.
192p; 22cm.
Includes bibliography and index.
ISBN 0091736838 £12.95

Sex discrimination. – Ross Anderson, 1983.
ISBN 0863600050 Pbk £2.95

Sex discrimination : some recent titles and periodical articles / Department of Employment Library. – London : The Library, 1983.
8p. – (Library checklist).

Sex Discrimination Act 1986 / Department of Employment. – London : The Department, 1986.
2 leaves. – (Press notice).
Bound with two other press notices.

Sex Discrimination Act 1986 : summary of provisions / Department of Employment. – London : The Department, 1986.
7 leaves. – (Press notice).
Bound with two other press notices.

Sex discrimination and retirement / Department of Employment. – London : The Department, 1986.
2,4 leaves. – (Press notice).

Sex discrimination law. – Oxford : Oxford University Press, 1985.
ISBN 0198254814 Hbk £30.00

Sex discrimination legislation in Australia / Constance Larmour. – Canberra : Legislative Research Service, Department of the Parliamentary Library, 1985.
29p. – (Basic paper).

Sexton →Redefining the Supreme Courts' Role : A Theory of Managing the Federal Judicial Process.

Sexual Abuse Allegations in Custody Litigation. – Vancouver : Continuing Legal Education Society of British Columbia, 1987.
484p.
Hbk £85.00

Sexual Assault. – Agincourt : Carswell, 1984.
200p.
This book is a critical analysis of the Canadian Criminal Code provisions governing the offense of sexual assault. Statutory rape and incest, offenses against children, and many other issues are discussed in the work.
ISBN 045936720 Hbk £18.70

Sexual crimes and confrontations : a study of victims and offenders / D.J. West. – Aldershot : Gower, 1987.
x,319p; 22cm.
Bibliography: p285-306. - Includes index.
ISBN 0566053802 £18.50

Sexual desire : a philosophical investigation / Roger Scruton. – London : Weidenfeld and Nicolson, 1986.
x,428p; 24cm.
Includes index.
ISBN 029778479X Hbk £18.95
ISBN 0297788779 Pbk £8.95

Sexual divisions in law / Katherine O'Donovan. – London : Weidenfeld and Nicolson, 1985.
xii,242p; 23cm.
Bibliography: p226-233. - Includes index.
ISBN 0297786644 Hbk £16.95
ISBN 0297786652 Pbk £8.95

Sexual Harassment in the Workplace. – London : Butterworths.
ISBN 0409805351 Hbk £32.00

Sexual Offences : Bill C-127. – Vancouver : British Columbia Continuing Legal Education Society, 1983.
155p.
ISBN 0865041032 Hbk £45.00

Sexual offences : fifteenth report / Criminal Law Revision Committee. – London : H.M.S.O., 1984.
ix,105p; 25cm.
ISBN 0101921306 Pbk £6.40

Sexual offences against children / Law Reform Commission of Victoria. – Melbourne : The Commission, 1988.
iv,80p. – (Discussion paper).
Includes bibliographical references.
ISBN 0724167218

Sexual offences against children : report of the committee on Sexual Offences Against Children and Youths appointed by the Minister of Justice and Attorney General of Canada, the Minister of National Health and Welfare. – 2. – Ottawa : Supply and Services Canada, 1984.
Includes bibliographical references.
ISBN 0660116391

Sexual offences against children in Canada : summary of the report of the Committee on Sexual Offences Against Children and Youths appointed by the Minister of Justice and Attorney General of Canada, the Minister of National Health and Welfare, Government of Canada 1984. – Ottawa : Supply and Services Canada, 1984.
viii,80p.
ISBN 0660116987

Sexual offences against people with impaired mental functioning / Law Reform Commission of Victoria. – Melbourne : The Commission, 1988.
ii,52p. – (Report no 15).
ISBN 0724167153 Hbk

Sexual Offences, Bill C-127. – Vancouver : Continuing Legal Education Society of British Columbia, 1983.
155p.
ISBN 0865041032 Hbk £55.00

Sexual violence : a case for law reform : papers presented at seminar, University of Auckland, 27 August 1982 / by Margaret A. Wilson, J.K. McLay, Lannes Johnson. – Auckland : Legal Research Foundation Inc., 1982.
40p.
ISBN 0908581262

Seychelles digest / by M.J. Gerard Lalouette. – 1. – Oxford : African Law Reports, 1982.
Covers cases from 1936 onwards.
Loose leaf

Seychelles Government
Civil Code. – Seychelles Government. – Mahe : Seychelles National Printing Co.
Hbk £40.00
—Code of Civil Procedure. – Seychelles Government. – Mahe : Seychelles National Printing Co.
Hbk £20.00
—Control of Rent and Tenancy Agreement. – Seychelles Government. – Mahe : Seychelles National Printing Co.
Hbk £4.00
—Immigration Decree 1979. – Seychelles Government. – Mahe : Seychelles National Printing Co.
Hbk £8.00
—Law Report. – Seychelles Government. – Mahe : Seychelles National Printing Co.
Pbk £20.00
—Subsidiary Legislation 1977. – Seychelles Government. – Mahe.
Hbk £100.00

Seychelles law reports. – Seychelles : Government Printer, .

Seymour
Stoy Hayward Business Tax Guides 1988-89 / Say. – London : Kogan Page.
ISBN 1850916440 Hbk £12.95

Seymour, John
Juvenile justice in South Australia / by John Seymour. – Sydney : Law Book Company in association with the Australian Institute of Criminology, 1983.
xix,146p.
Includes bibliographical references and index.
ISBN 0455204853

Seymour, S. M.
Seymour's Customary law in Southern Africa / J. C. Bekker, J. J. J. Coertze. – 4th ed. – Cape Town : Juta, 1982.
lxi,446p.
ISBN 070211233X Pbk
ISBN 0702112933

Seymour's Customary law in Southern Africa / J. C. Bekker, J. J. J. Coertze. – 4th ed. – Cape Town : Juta, 1982.
lxi,446p.
ISBN 070211233X Pbk
ISBN 0702112933

Sgayias, David
Federal Court Practice : 1988. – Agincourt : Carswell, 1987.
800p.
This is a comprehensive guide to the Federal Court Act, Federal Court Rules, Forms, Tariffs and related statutes. Also included is a guide to difficult jurisdictional issues such as the choice between Federal and provincial courts for commencing proceedings and locus standi.
Hbk £46.25

Shackle
Sikhs / by Christopher Shackle. – Rev. ed. – London : Minority Rights Group, 1986.
19p. – (Report).
Bibliography: p.18.
ISBN 0946690413

Shackleton, Frank
Shackleton on the law and practice of meetings / I. Shearman. – 7th ed. – London : Sweet & Maxwell, 1983.
xxix,368p; 23cm.
Previous ed.: 1977. Includes index.
ISBN 0421296305 £17.00

Shackleton on the law and practice of meetings / I. Shearman. – 7th ed. – London : Sweet & Maxwell, 1983.
xxix,368p; 23cm.
Previous ed.: 1977. Includes index.
ISBN 0421296305 £17.00

Shadbolt, et al
International construction contracts. – London : Butterworths, 1988.
ISBN 0406009007 Hbk

Shadwell, T. M. →Posthumous Works : Consisting of a Reading on the Statute of Inrolments, Arguments in the Case of General Stanwix, and Cases and Opinions.

Shaffer, Ed
United States and the control of world oil / Ed Shaffer. – London : Croom Helm, 1983.
246p; 23cm.
Bibliography: p232-236. - Includes index.
ISBN 070992366X £15.95

Shafi, M.
Charge-Sheet, Enquiry and Punishment. – Karachi : Bureau of Labour Publications, 1983.
36p.
Pbk £3.00
—Complete Set of Labour Laws. – 12th ed. – Karachi : Bureau of Labour Publications, 1986.
407p.
Pbk £30.00
—Employees Cost of Living Relief Act. – 8th ed. – Karachi : Bureau of Labour Publications, 1987.
Pbk £2.40
—Gratuity : Law and Practice. – 4th ed. – Karachi : Bureau of Labour Publications, 1987.
Pbk £2.40
—Hours of Work and Over Time. – 3rd ed. – Karachi : Bureau of Labour Publications, 1987.
Pbk £2.40
—Labour Code of Pakistan. – 12th ed. – Karachi : Bureau of Labour Publications, 1987.
1,439p.
Hbk £102.00
—Labour Law Cases : 1981-1988. – Karachi : Bureau of Labour Publications.
400p.
Hbk £36.00
—Labour Law Cases LLC (Pakistan) : Decisions of Supreme Court, High Courts and Labour Courts on Labour Laws, 21 Vols. – Karachi : Bureau of Labour Publications, 1947-1980.
Hbk £597.00
—Law of Factories. – 5th ed. – Karachi : Bureau of Labour Publications, 1987.
60p.
Pbk £4.50
—Law of Industrial Relations. – 8th ed. – Karachi : Bureau of Labour Publications, 1987.
102p.
Pbk £6.00
—Law of Social Security. – Karachi : Bureau of Labour Publications, 1986.
40p.
Pbk £3.00
—Law of Workers' Children Education. – Karachi : Bureau of Labour Publications, 1986.
54p.
Pbk £4.50
—Law of Workers' Participation in Companies Profits. – Karachi : Bureau of Labour Publications, 1986.
Pbk £3.00
—Law of Workmen's Compensation. – 2nd ed. – Karachi : Bureau of Labour Publications, 1986.
48p.
Pbk £23.00
—Leave and Holidays. – 3rd ed. – Karachi : Bureau of Labour Publications, 1987.
Pbk £3.00
—Mining Labour Code. – 6th ed. – Karachi : Bureau of Labour Publications, 1987.
315p.
Pbk £39.00
—Pakistan Labour Statutes PLS : Acts, Ordinances, Rules, Regulations, 21 Vols. – Karachi : Bureau of Labour Publications, 1983-87.
Hbk £19.00 ea
—Workers Welfare Fund Ordinance. – Karachi : Bureau of Labour Publications, 1986.
Pbk £2.00

Shagari opens conference of Nigeria judges : spotlight on Mr. President's one day visit to Kwara State. – Ilorin : Department of Information, 1982.
38p.

Shah Bano Controversy. – Allahabad : Orient Law House, 1987.
253p.
Hbk £165.00

Shah, J.C., et al
Guide to the Companies Act. – 11th rev. ed. – Nagpur : Wadhura & Co, 1988.
Hbk £440.00

Shah, S.M.
Lectures on Company Law. – 18th ed. 1981 repr. – Bombay : Tripathi, 1983.
Hbk £65.00
—Principals of Law of Transfer. – 6th ed. 1980 repr. – Bombay : Tripathi, 1982.
Hbk £50.00

Shahabuddeen, M.
Conquest of Grenada : sovereignty in the periphery / M. Shahabuddeen. – Georgetown : University of Guyana, 1986.
xiv,266p.
Includes bibliographical references. Includes the text of the Treaty Establishing the Orgainisation of Eastern Caribbean States.
—From plantocracy to nationalisation : a profile of sugar in Guyana / M. Shahabuddeen. – Georgetown? : University of Guyana, 1983.
xiii,440p.
Bibliography: p411-440.
—Law reform in Guyana / address delivered by Attorney General to Guyana Bar Association on 21st September 1981. – S.l. : s.n., 1981.
43p.
At head of title: 'Extracts printed in the Guyana Bar Association journal'.. Includes bibliographical references.
—Nationalisation of Guyana's bauxite : the case of Alcan / M. Shahabuddeen. – Georgetown : Ministry of Information, 1981.
xvii,306p.
Bibliography: p282-306.

Shaikh, N.M.
Islamic Jurisprudence. – Islamabad : Islamic Research Institute.
ca 500p.
Hbk

Shaikha Zakaria
Malaysian legal source materials in London, Oxford and Cambridge / by Shaikha Zakaria : with a foreword by M.B. Hooker. – Kuala Lumpur : Perpustakaan Universiti Malaya, 1985.
x,66p.
Includes index.
ISBN 9679430057

Shamsh, Shamsuddin
Meos of India : Their Customs and Laws. – New Delhi : Deep and Deep Publications, 1983.
211p.
Hbk £90.00

Shanahan, D. R.
Australian trade mark law and practice / by D.R. Shanahan. – Sydney : The Law Book Company Ltd, 1982.
lv,522p.
ISBN 0455201196 Hbk £35.00

Shanbhogue, K.V.
Company Law Procedures. – 3rd ed. – New Delhi : Bharat Law House, 1984.
Hbk £200.00
—Company Resolutions. – 3rd ed. repr. 1986. – New Delhi : Bharat Law House.
Hbk £150.00
—Filing of Forms, Returns and Applications Under Company Law. – 2nd ed. – New Delhi : Bharat Law House, 1986.
Hbk £220.00

Shand, J. →Regulae Iuris: From Juristic Rules to Legal Maxims.

Shanghai Advanced Patent Course. – Geneva : World Intellectual Property Organization, 1985.
ca 400p.
Hbk £40.00

Shanglo
Art of Attracting Clients. – Allahabad : Law Book Company, 1988.
64p.
Pbk £50.00
—Art of Becoming a Successful Criminal Lawyer. – 3rd ed. – Allahabad : Law Book Company, 1988.
Hbk £40.00
—Art of Handling Hostile Courts. – Allahabad : Law Book Company, 1988.
70p.
Pbk £45.00
—Law of Dying Declaration. – Allahabad : Law Book Company, 1988.
60p.
Pbk £40.00
—Lawyers' Etiquette. – 2nd ed. – Allahabad : Law Book Company, 1988.
Hbk £50.00
→ Oaths Act.
—Principles of Law of Conviction. – Allahabad : Law Book Company, 1988.
Hbk £50.00

Shani, B. M.
Criminal procedure in the Northern states of Nigeria / by B.M. Shani. – 2nd ed. – s.l. : s.n., 1985.
xxviii,536p.
Includes bibliographical references.

Shannon, David
Franchising in Australia : a legal guide / by David Shannon. – Sydney : Law Book Co., 1982.
xxii,275p.
Includes index.
ISBN 045520456X

Shape of Britain's Tariff. – London : Institute of Economic Affairs.
Pbk £0.50

Shapiro →Forensic Medicine.
→ Services charges-Law and practice.

Shapiro, Ian
Evolution of rights in liberal theory / Ian Shapiro. – Cambridge : Cambridge University Press, 1986.
x,326p; 24cm.
Bibliography: p307-320. - Includes index.
ISBN 0521320437 Hbk £27.50
ISBN 0521338530 Pbk £8.95

Shapiro, M.
Who Guards the Guardians? Judicial Control of Administration. – University of Georgia Press.
ISBN 082030963X Hbk £17.50

Shapland, Joanna
Between conviction and sentence : the process of mitigation / Joanna Shapland. – London : Routledge & Kegan Paul, 1981.
vi,167p.
Bibliography: p.165.
ISBN 0710009453
—Victims in the criminal justice system / Joanna Shapland, Jon Willmore, Peter Duff. – Aldershot : Gower, 1985.
vi,203p; 23cm.
Bibliography: p195-201. - Includes index.
ISBN 0566008947 Hbk £20.45
ISBN 0566008777 Pbk £8.95

Share Capital : Company Law and Taxation / David Bellringer. – London : Butterworths, 1984.
ISBN 0406258163 Hbk

Share (Land Based Company) Transfer Tax Act, 1984 (Act 310). – Kuala Lumpur : International Law Books Services.
Hbk £7.50

Share options and incentives for directors and employees. – Tolley Publishing, 1986.
ISBN 085459180X Pbk £7.95

Share Schemes for Directors and Employees. – 2nd ed. – London : Butterworths.
ISBN 0406503346 Pbk £40.00

Share Valuation Cases / Harry Booth. – London : Butterworths, 1985.
This work is a compendium of extracts from judgements in cases which deal with principles of share valuation in the United Kingdom. The case extracts are presented in alphabetical order.
ISBN 0406009805 Hbk

Share valuation handbook. – London : Fourmat, 1986.
ISBN 0906840988 Pbk £12.95

Shared liability / Law Reform Commission of British Columbia. – Vancouver : The Commission, 1985.
iv,62p. – (Working paper).
Includes bibliographical references.

Shareholders' agreements / Graham Stedman, Janet Jones. – London : Longman, 1986.
xvii,396p; 24cm. – (Longman commercial series).
Includes index.
ISBN 0851210252 £42.50

Shariahi : Islamic Law. – Ta-Ha Publishers, 1984.
ISBN 0907461387 Pbk £6.50

Sharkey
Commercial Arbitration / John B Dorter. – North Ryde : Law Book Co, 1986.
ISBN 0455205841 Hbk £29.75

Sharkey, John J.A. →Building and Construction Contracts in Australia : Law and Practice.

Sharma
Excise Laws on Medical Preparations. – Allahabad : Orient Law House, 1983.
Hbk £130.00
—Guide to Jurisprudence. – New Delhi : B. Jain Publishers.
Hbk £3.00
—Veterinary Jurisprudence. – 3rd ed. – New Delhi : Oxford University Press.
Hbk £50.00

Sharma, B.R.
Socio-Economic Justice under Indian Constitution. – New Delhi : Deep and Deep Publications, 1984.
460p.
Hbk £200.00

Sharma, G.K.
Study and Practice of Military Law. – New Delhi : Deep and Deep Publications, 1988.
496p.
ISBN 8171000126 Hbk £250.00

Sharma, S.D.
Administration of Justice in Ancient India. – New Delhi : Harnam Publications, 1988.
296p.
Hbk £240.00

Sharma, S.R.
Constitutional History of India. – Allahabad : Orient Law House.
ISBN 0861250419 Hbk £35.00
ISBN 0861257227 Pbk £25.00

Sharp, A. →Bill of Rights for New Zealand : papers precsented by A. Sharp ... et al.

Sharp, John A. →Management of a student research project.

Sharpe, A. →Computer Contracts : Principles and Practice 1987.

Sharpe, David J. →New directions in maritime law 1984.
—New directions in maritime law / W Wylie Spicer. – London : Sweet & Maxwell, 1985.
ISBN 0459372106 Hbk £35.00

Sharpe, Diana
Performing Artist and the Law. – North Ryde : Law Book Co, 1985.
xvi, 204p.
ISBN 0455206244 Pbk £26.50

Sharpe, Gilbert S
Health Law in Canada. – Toronto : Butterworths. Hbk
—Law and Medicine in Canada / Glenn Ivan Sawyer. – 2nd ed. – Butterworths, 1987.
704p.
Analysis of recent case law and a review of statutory developments. Covers consent, the confidentiality of health records, artificial reproduction, biomedical research involving human subjects. Separate chapters discuss in more detail experimentation, organ transplants, determination of death, and a completely new chapter on abortion.
ISBN 0409865907 Hbk £85.00

Sharpe, Ian G.
Regulation, Investor/Depositor Protection and the Campbell Report / W.P. Hoogan. – Newcastle : University of Newcastle, 1982.
64p.
ISBN 0725904445 Pbk £2.50

Sharpe, J.A.
Crime in seventeenth century England. – Cambridge : Cambridge University Press.
Studes court records in Essex. Analyses social processes involved in prosecution.
ISBN 0521250749 Hbk £32.50

Sharpe, Neil F
Conveyancing requisitions. – Scarborough, Ontario : Butterworths (Canada).
232.
Aspects of a real estate transaction are covered, from drafting an agreement of purchase and sale to reviewing the abstract of title, to submission of and response to requisitions and all the requirements of closing.
ISBN 0409866270 Hbk

Sharpe, R
Law of habeas corpus. – Oxford : Clarendon Press, 1989.
300; 21.5.
Updated to include references to current developments in the law of habeas corpus. Examines the nature of the judicial reivew exercised on habeas corpus, and explores the past, present, and potential uses of the writ. Also contains discussions on the law in Commonwealth countries.
ISBN 0198254040 Hbk £30.00

Sharpe, Robert J.
Charter Litigation. – Butterworths, 1987.
480p.
Examines the procedural, evidential and remedial issues arising in Charter litigation. Considers remedial issues and the use of social science data and other extrinsic evidence. Examines the relevance of American and European sources. Covers intervention and Amicus Curiae, the Charter and social change, proof of facts, legislative history, the relevance of American constitutional law, and damages as a Charter remedy.
ISBN 0409805270 Hbk £85.00
—Injunctions and specific performance / by Robert J. Sharpe. – Toronto : Canada Law Book Ltd., 1983.
lxxiv,450p.
ISBN 0888040172
—Injunctions and specific performance / Phil. – Aurora : Canada Law Book, 1983.
Hbk £35.75
—Interprovincial product liability litigation / Robert J. Sharpe. – Toronto : Butterworths, 1982.
xxi,145p.
Includes bibliographical references and index.
ISBN 0409866423

Sharpe, W.
Investments. – 3rd ed. – Prentice-Hall, 1985.
ISBN 0135047137 Pbk £18.50

Sharrock, Robert
Business transactions law / Robert Sharrock Andrew Borrowdale. – Cape Twon : Juta, 1986.
xiv,385p.
Includes index.
ISBN 070211684X

Shatt Al-Arab Boundary Question : A Legal Reappraisal. – Oxford : Oxford University Press.
ISBN 0198255918 Hbk £25.00

Shatt-al-Arab Boundary question : a legal reappraisal / Kaiyan Homi Kaikobad. – Oxford : Clarendon, 1988.
160p; 24cm. – (Oxford monographs in international law).
Includes bibliography and index.
ISBN 0198255918 £20.00

Shatt-Al-Arab questions. – Oxford : Oxford University Press, 1988.
ISBN 0198255918 Hbk

Shatter, Alan Joseph
Shatter's Family law in the Republic of Ireland / Alan Joseph Shatter. – 3rd ed. – Dublin : Wolfhound, 1986.
608p; 25cm.
Previous ed.: published as Family law in the Republic of Ireland. 1981. Includes index.
ISBN 0863270808 Hbk £45.00
ISBN 0863270816 Pbk £30.00

Shatter's Family law in the Republic of Ireland / Alan Joseph Shatter. – 3rd ed. – Dublin : Wolfhound, 1986.
608p; 25cm.
Previous ed.: published as Family law in the Republic of Ireland. 1981. Includes index.
ISBN 0863270808 Hbk £45.00
ISBN 0863270816 Pbk £30.00

Shavaksha, K.S.
Indian Trade and Merchandise Marks Act. – 3rd ed. in prep. – Bombay : Tripathi.
Hbk

Shaw
Banking Law / Howcroft. – Oxford : Blackwell, 1985.
ISBN 0631143025 Pbk £9.50
—Court of Session Cases : Series 1-5, 1821-1906, 63 Vols.
Incl. 1st Series, 1821-1838, 16 Vols. – Abingdon : Professional Books.
Hbk
—House of Lords Appeals : 1821-1873, 28 Vols.
Incl. 1821-1824, 2 Vols. – Abingdon : Professional Books.
Hbk
1825-1835, 7 Vols.. –
Hbk
—Local Government Administration. – 2nd ed. – London : Shaw & Sons, 1987.
ISBN 0721907121 Pbk £11.95
—Mental Health Procedural Tables. – London : Shaw & Sons, 1983.
ISBN 0721901964 Pbk £0.80
—Scots Revised Reports : 1707-1873, 45 Vols.
Incl. Court of Session Cases : 1821-1838, 6 Vols. – Abingdon : Professional Books.
Hbk
—Tax and the farmer / NFU. – London : Shaw & Sons, 1988.
ISBN 0721911609 Pbk

Shaw, Antony →Standard for justice : a critical commentary on the proposed Bill of Rights for New Zealand.

Shaw, D. J.
Admiralty jurisdiction and practice in South Africa / by D. J. Shaw. – Cape Town : Juta, 1987.
xxvii,264p.
Bibliography: p. xi. - Includes index.
ISBN 0702118168

Shaw, E. R.
London money market / E.R. Shaw. – 3rd ed. – London : Heinemann, 1981.
xiv,267p; 22cm.
Previous ed.: 1975. Bibliography: p259-261. - Includes index.
ISBN 0434918334 Pbk £7.50

Shaw, Malcolm
Title to territory in Africa : international legal issues / Malcolm Shaw. – Oxford : Clarendon, 1985.
xii,428p; 22cm.
Includes bibliography and index.
ISBN 0198253796 £35.00

Shaw, Malcolm N.
International Law / by Malcolm N. Shaw. – 2nd ed. – Cambridge : Grotius, 1986.
39,627p; 23cm.
A revised and updated edition. An introduction to international law, setting the subject in the context of world political events. Also examines the importance of the political, cultural and economic influences that affect international law. Student text, also for private practitioners, governmental and civil servants.
ISBN 0906496373 Pbk £10.95

Shaw, Margaret →Parental supervision and juvenile delinquency.

Shaw, P., et al
Digest of Cases Decided in the Supreme Courts of Scotland From 1800-1852. – Repr. of 1867 ed. – Abingdon : Professional Books.
104p.
Hbk £95.00

Shaw, Roger
Who uses social inquiry reports? : a study of the use of social inquiry reports outside the courts and their influence upon decisions / Roger Shaw. – Cambridge : Institute of Criminology, 1981.
53p. – (Institute of Criminology occasional papers).
Includes bibliographical references.

Shaw, S.
Airline Marketing and Management. – 2nd ed. – Pitman, 1985.
ISBN 0273022407 Hbk £17.95

Shaw, Stephen
People's justice : a major poll of public attitudes on crime and punishment / Stephen Shaw. – London : Prison Reform Trust, 1982.
29p; 30cm.
Cover title.
ISBN 0946209006 Pbk £1.00

Shaway Guides Series 8 vols.
Vol. 1. – Shaw & Sons.
ISBN 0721908705 Pbk £2.50
Vol. 2. –
ISBN 0721908713 Pbk £2.50
Vol. 3. –
ISBN 0721908721 Pbk £2.50
Vol. 4. –
ISBN 0721908756 Pbk £2.50
Vol. 5. –
ISBN 072190873X Pbk £2.50
Vol. 6. –
ISBN 0721908748 Pbk £2.50
Vol. 7. –
ISBN 0721908764 Pbk £2.50
Vol. 8. –
ISBN 0721908772 Pbk £2.50

Shawcross
Air Law / Beaumont. – 4th ed. – London : Butterworths, 1983.
Service to Date.
ISBN 0406373191 Hbk £280.00

Shea, A. M. →Banking Law, Vol.1 : The law relating to domestic banking.

Sheard, Terence
Canadian forms of wills / Rodney Hull, Michael M. K. Fitzpatrick. – 4th ed. – Toronto : Carswell, 1982.
lxix,333p.
Previous ed.: 1970. Bibliography: p.293. - Includes index.
ISBN 0459347004

Shearer, I. A. →International law of the sea, Vol.2 : by D.P. O'Connell : edited by I.A. Shearer.
→ Prospects for a new Law of the Sea : papers read at a seminar conducted by the International Law Association in Sydney on 19 June 1982.

Shearing, Clifford D. →Organizational police deviance : its structure and control.

Shearman, I. →Shackleton on the law and practice of meetings.

Shears, Peter
Law for GCSE / Collins. – London : Pitman Publishing, 1987.
ISBN 0273028367 Pbk £5.95
→ Nigerian business law.
—O level law / Paulene Collins. – Plymouth : Macdonald & Evans, 1984.
ISBN 0712115420 Pbk £4.75
—O level law / Collins. – London : Pitman Publishing, 1984.
ISBN 0273025538 Pbk £4.95

Sheffield Advice Centres Group →Case for advice centres.

Sheffield Newspapers Limited : a report by the Director General of Fair Trading on an investigation under section 3 of the Competition Act 1980. – London : Office of Fair Trading, 1981.
72p; 30cm.

Shehadeh, Raja →Civilian administration in the occupied West Bank : analysis of Israeli Military Government Order no. 947.

Sheils, W. J. →Confiscation and Restoration : The Archbishopric Estates and the Civil War.
—Ecclesiastical Cause papers at York : files transmitted on appeal 1500-1883 / W.J. Sheils. – York : University of York, Borthwick Institute of Historical Research, 1983.
xiv,135p; 25cm.
Includes index.
Pbk

Shekhar, K.C.
Banking Theory and Practice. – 4th ed. – London : Vikas.
ISBN 0706936841 Pbk £10.95

Sheldon
Practice and law of banking / P. J. M. Fidler. – 11th ed. – Pitman, 1982.
ISBN 0712119787 Pbk £11.95

Sheldon and Fidler's practice and law of banking / P. J. M. Fidler, M. I. Freeman, Herbert Percival Sheldon. – 11th ed. – Plymouth : Macdonald and Evans, 1982.
liv,792p; 22cm.
Previous ed.: published as Sheldon's practice and law of banking. 1972. Bibliography: p769-770. - Includes index.
ISBN 0712119906 Pbk £8.95

Sheldon, Herbert Percival
Sheldon and Fidler's practice and law of banking / P. J. M. Fidler, M. I. Freeman, Herbert Percival Sheldon. – 11th ed. – Plymouth : Macdonald and Evans, 1982.
liv,792p; 22cm.
Previous ed.: published as Sheldon's practice and law of banking. 1972. Bibliography: p769-770. - Includes index.
ISBN 0712119906 Pbk £8.95

Sheleff, L S
Ultimate penalties. – London : Eurospan, 1988.
ISBN 0814204368 Hbk £23.25

Shell, D.
House of Lords. – Allan (Philip), 1988.
ISBN 086003402X Hbk £34.50
ISBN 0860037029 Pbk £14.95

Shelter
Build Homes, Build Hope : 1981 Campaign Report. – Shelter. – London : Shelter, 1981.
ISBN 0901242608 Pbk Individuals 2.25
—Ferndale : A Caring Repair Service for Elderly Home Owners. – Shelter. – London : Shelter, 1982.
ISBN 0901242632 Pbk £2.50
—Homes Wasted. – Shelter. – London : Shelter, 1982.
ISBN 0901242640 Hbk £2.50
—Housing Act Nineteen Eighty : The Tenant's Charter. – Shelter. – London : Shelter, 1981.
ISBN 0901242578 Pbk £1.75
—Housing and Campaigning. – Shelter. – London : Shelter, 1983.
ISBN 0901242667 Pbk £3.00/Members 1.25
—Ordinary People : Homeless in the Housing Crisis. – Shelter. – London : Shelter, 1982.
ISBN 0901242659 Pbk £2.50
—Overcrowding : Part IV Housing Act 1957. – Shelter. – London : Shelter, 1984.
ISBN 0862650097 Hbk £1.75
—Restrictive Practices. – Shelter. – London : Shelter, 1984.
ISBN 0901242691 Hbk £1.50
—Unfitness . – Shelter. – 2nd ed. – London : Shelter, 1984.
ISBN 0862650038 Hbk £1.95

Shelton, Dinah →Protecting human rights in the Americas : selected problems.

Shenfield, Arthur
Right to Strike?. – London : Institute of Economic Affairs, 1986.
ISBN 0255361904 Pbk £2.50

Shepherd, A.
Pension fund investment. – Cambridge : Woodhead-Faulkner, 1987.
ISBN 0859414000 Hbk £35.00
—Tax and Financial Planning Through Pensions / Abramson. – London : Butterworths.
ISBN 0406503478 Pbk £26.50

Shepherd, J C
Law of Fiduciaries. – London : Sweet & Maxwell, 1982.
ISBN 0459343009 Hbk £35.00

Shepherd, John W.
Identification evidence : a psychological evaluation / John W. Shepherd, Hadyn D. Ellis and Graham M. Davies : foreword by Lord Devlin. – Aberdeen : Aberdeen University Press, 1982.
xii,155p; 26cm.
Bibliography: p140-149. - Includes index.
ISBN 0080284418 £12.50

Shepherd, Katherine →Sourcebook on planning law in Ireland.

Sheppard, W.
England's Balme : Proposals By Way of Grievance and Remedy Presented to His Highness and the Parliament Towards the Regulation of the Law and Better Administration of Justice. – Repr. of 1657 ed. – Abingdon : Professional Books.
251p.
Hbk £150.00
—Faithful Councellor or Marrow of the Law in English. – 2nd ed. Repr. of 1653 ed. – Abingdon : Professional Books.
278p.
Hbk £175.00
—Touch-Stone of Common Assurances : Treatise Opening the Learning of Common Assurances or Conveyances of the Kingdome. – 2nd ed. Repr. of 1648 ed. – Abingdon : Professional Books.
487p.
Hbk £250.00

Sheridan, L, et al
Constitution of Malaysia / Harry Groves. – 4th. – Singapore : Malayan Law Journal, 1987.
649.
Discusses citizenship, relations between the federation and the states, financial provisions, elections, the judiciary, public services, special and emergency powers, additional protection for Sabah and Sarawak, and temporary and transitional provisions.
ISBN 9971700557 Hbk

Sheridan, L A →Digest English Law Trust.
→ Equity.
—Law of trusts / George W. Keeton. – 11th ed. – Chichester : Rose, 1983.
lxiv,578p; 26cm.
Previous ed.: 1974. Includes index.
ISBN 085992369X £45.00
—Modern law of charities / George W. Keeton. – 3rd ed. – Cardiff : University College Cardiff Press, 1983.
lxxix,502p; 22cm.
Previous ed.: / by George W. Keeton and L.A. Sheridan. Belfast : Northern Ireland Legal Quarterly. 1971. Includes index.
ISBN 0906449545 £45.00

Sheriff Court practice. – Edinburgh : Green (W.) & Son, 1988.
Explains modern statutory rules of proceedure and the principles and practices which regulate the conduct of civil litigation in the Sheriff Court. Covers drafting and amendment of written pleadings, interim orders, debates, proofs and appeals. Covers the practice and procedure in summary causes and the legislation conferring powers and duties on the Sheriff Court.
ISBN 0414008251 Hbk

Sheriff Court Rules 1984. – Edinburgh : W Green. – (Reprint from the Parliament House Book).
ISBN 0414007352 Hbk £2.50

Sheriff court rules. – 3rd. – Edinburgh : Green (W.) & Son, 1989.
Reprinted from the Parliament House Book, providing updated and amended Ordinary and Summary Cause Rules. Includes Small Claims Rules.
ISBN 0414008839 Pbk

Sherman, S.L.
Customs Valuation : a Commentary on GATT Customs Valuation Code / H. Glashoff. – Dordrecht : Kluwer, 1988.
400p.
ISBN 9065443215 Hbk £153.00

Sherr, Avrom
Client interviewing for lawyers : an analysis and guide / by Avrom Sherr. – London : Sweet & Maxwell, 1986.
190p; 22cm.
Includes bibliography and index.
ISBN 0421361603 Pbk £7.95
—Freedom, Public Order and the Law. – Oxford : Basil Blackwell.
ISBN 063115809X Hbk £29.50
ISBN 0631158111 Pbk £10.95

Sherrin, C. H.
Law and practice of intestate succession / by C.H. Sherrin, R.C. Bonehill. – London : Sweet & Maxwell, 1987.
xliii,515p; 25cm.
Areas such as social security benefits, private pension entitlements, bank accounts, small estates and the tax position and law relating to marital homes are covered. Reference has been made within the text to the usually more modern Commonwealth codes, where a contrast can elucidate the English law.
ISBN 0421326301 £39.00
→ Williams' law relating to wills.
—Williams on wills / R F D Barlow, R A Wallington. – 6th ed. 2 vols. – London : Butterworths, 1987.
ISBN 0406421978 Hbk £175.00

Shetreet, Shimon →Judicial independence : the contemporary debate.

Shewell, Paul
Liquidation manual / Paul Shewell, John Powell. – Croydon : Tolley, 1983.
xxi,368p.
Includes index. Cover title: Tolley's liquidation manual.
ISBN 0854590285

Shindler
Law of Trusts / Hodkinson. – London : CCH, 1984.
ISBN 086325019X Pbk £20.00

Ship financing in Singapore. – Singapore : Malayan Law Journal, 1983.
xxi,305.
An examination of ship financing in Singapore on two levels; the individual in the commercial world, and the national on the international scene.
ISBN 9971700301 Hbk

Ship Owners (BSL) / Raoul Colinvaux. – Sweet & Maxwell, 1967.
ISBN 0420416609 Hbk £75.00

Ship sale and purchase : law and technique / by Iain S. Goldrein. – London : Lloyd's of London, 1985.
345p; 25cm.
Includes index.
ISBN 1850440522

Shipbrokers' Manual
Vol 1 / Institute of Shipbrokers. – London : Lloyd's of London Press.
ISBN 090743259X Hbk £17.50

Shipbroking and chartering practice / by Lars Gorton, Rolf Ihre, Arne Sandevarn. – 2nd ed. – London : Lloyd's of London Press, 1984.
xv,298p; 26cm.
Bibliography: p.247. - Includes index.
ISBN 0907432638

Shipbuilding contracts / edited by Malcolm A. Clarke. – London : Lloyd's, 1982.
xx,228p.
Includes index. At head of title: Comite Maritime International.
ISBN 0907432255

Shipbuilding credit. – Cardiff : University of Wales Press, 1983.
ISBN 07080308430 Pbk £12.00

Shipping and contracting / Lars Gorton. – Lund : Juridiska Foreningen i Lund, 1983.
85p.
Includes bibliographical references and index.
ISBN 9154415012

Shipping conferences. – London : Lloyd's of London, 1983.
viii,255p.
Bibliography: p.253-255. Bibliography: p253-255. Includes text of the Convention on a Code of conduct for liner conferences (1974).
ISBN 9065440895 Hbk £116.00

Shipping, energy, and environment : Southeast Asian perspectives for the eighties : proceedings of a Workshop held in Honolulu, Hawaii, 10-12 December 1980 / edited by Mark J. Valencia ... et al. – Halifax, N.S. : Dalhousie Ocean Studies Programme, 1982.
xi,333p.
Held at the Environment and Policy Institute of the East-West Center at the University of Hawaii.
ISBN 0770302769

Shipping Finance : Loans, Ship Mortgages and Other Securities. – Abingdon : Professional Books, 1984.
ISBN 0862050618 Hbk £63.00
ISBN 0862050669 Pbk

Shipping Law (CCT). – Sweet & Maxwell, 1978.
ISBN 042121130X Pbk £8.00

Shipping practice : with consideration of the relevant law / C. S. J. Butterfield. – 11th ed. – London : Pitman, 1981.
xi,173p; 22cm.
Previous ed.: 1978. Includes index.
ISBN 0273016164 Pbk £9.95

Ship's value / by Kaj Pineus. – 2nd ed. – London : Lloyd's of London, 1986.
135p; 22cm.
Previous ed.: Gothenburg : Gothenburg Maritime Law Association, 1975. Includes bibliography and index.
ISBN 185044062X £35.00

Shirazi, Habib →Shirazi: Islamic banking.

Shirazi: Islamic banking / Habib Shirazi. – London : Butterworths, 1990.
170; 248.
Covers the basis of the credit system, regulations and basic criteria, Qardalhasanah grant, Modharabah, civil partnership, equity partnership, direct investment, instalment sales, hire purchase, forward deals, Jo'aalah, Mozara'ah, Mosa'qaat, debt purchase and guarantees.
ISBN 0406100357 Hbk £75.00

Shivji, Issa Gulamhussein
Law, state and the working class in Tanzania : c.1920-1964 / Issa G. Shivji. – London : Currey, 1986.
xix,268p; 24cm.
Bibliography: p253-260. - Includes index.
ISBN 0852553021 Hbk £25.00
ISBN 043508013X £9.95
—Law, State and Working Class in Tanzania. – London : Dent (J M) & Sons, 1986.
ISBN 085255303X Pbk £9.95
→ Limits of legal radicalism : reflections on teaching law at the University of Dar es Salaam.

Shock, John W
Capital Allowances. – London : Oyez Longman, 1980. Includes December 1982 supplement.
ISBN 0851204864 Hbk £25.00
—Capital allowances / by John W. Shock. – 2nd ed. – London : Sweet & Maxwell, 1984.
xxxiii,371p; 25cm.
Previous ed.: London : Oyez, 1981. Includes index.
ISBN 0421328207 Pbk £16.95

Shooter →Zulu Law.

Shooting in the Dark : Riot Police in Britain. – London : Faber.
ISBN 057115090X Hbk £12.95

Shoplifting, and thefts by shop staff : a review / by the Home Office Standing Committee on Crime Prevention 1983. – London : H.M.S.O., 1983.
23p.
ISBN 0113407890

Shopping Centre Leases, 2 Vols.
Vols. 1 and 2. – Aurora : Canada Law Book Co.
1438p.
Hbk £92.50
Vol. 1. –
Hbk £45.00
Vol. 2. –
This is the first Canadian book written specifically for lawyers and their clients interested in Shopping Centres, with particular emphasis on landlord/tenant problems. The text contains 38 separate articles on the subject written by 34 acknowledged experts in the field.
Hbk £56.50

Shorlin, P.
Bills of Exchange and other Negotiable Instruments. – Cambridge : Woodhead-Faulkner.
ISBN 0859414523 Hbk £25.00

Short constitutional history of England / by H. St. Clair Feilden. – 2nd ed., rev. and enl. – Oxford : Blackwell, 1887.
xii,338p.
Includes bibliographical references and index.

Short guide to divorce in the Sheriff Court. – 2nd. – Edinburgh : Green (W.) & Son, 1987.
A practical handbook detailing the more important rules and procedure with specimen craves, style divorce writs and the relevant Ordinary Cause forms.
ISBN 0414007816 Pbk

Short guide to Landlord and Tenant Act 1987 / Whippman. – Temple Lectures, 1987.
ISBN 1870800052 Pbk £8.00

Short history of legal thinking in the West / Stig Stromholm. – Stockholm, Sweden : Norstedts, 1985.
317 p.; 23 cm.
Includes index.
ISBN 9118571425

Short Note on Anti-Copyright. – Wollstone Craft : Leksand Press.
82p.
ISBN 095897800X Hbk £8.00

Shorter Constitution of India, Ninth Edition. – New Delhi : Prentice-Hall, 1984.
1,104p.
ISBN 0876923341 Hbk £150.00

Shorter forms of building contract. – 2nd ed. – Oxford : Blackwell Scientific, 1988.
ISBN 0003834123 Pbk £17.95
ISBN 0632018437 Hbk £19.95

Shorter Trials Committee →Report on criminal trials.

Shorter working time through national industry agreements / by Michael White. – London : Department of Employment, 1982.
– (Research paper).

Shott, Arnold
Australian Supplement to Borrie and Lowe's Law of Contempt / Athol Moffitt. – Butterworths, 1988.
ca 128p.
ISBN 0409494593 Pbk £29.00

Shrager
Quotable lawyer / Frost. – London : Facts On File, 1986.
ISBN 0816011842 Hbk £17.95

Shrand, David
1986-87 Income Tax Legislation and Recent Estate Duty Amendments : Together with Income Tax and Estate Duty Tables. – Cape Town : Legal and Financial Publishing Co, 1987.
Hbk £8.50

—Auditor's Manual / Keeton. – Cape Town : Legal & Financial Publishing, 1983.
ISBN 0869940198 Hbk £5.00

—Company Forms Chart. – Cape Town : Legal & Financial Publishing, 1983.
– (Merlen P.A.Y.E. Registers Ser.).
Hbk £1.79

—Company Law and Company Taxation in South Africa / Keeton. – Cape Town : Legal & Financial Publishing, 1983.
ISBN 0869940171 Hbk £32.50

—Company Share Register. – Cape Town : Legal & Financial Publishing, 1983.
– (Merlen Ser. of Registers).
Hbk £3.52

—Every Man His Own Income Tax Consultant. – Cape Town : Legal & Financial Publishing.
Hbk £17.50

—Fifty-Six Schedule. – Cape Town : Legal & Financial Publishing, 1983.
– (Merlen P.A.Y.E. Registers Ser.).
Hbk £7.07

—Guide to General Sales Tax. – Cape Town : Legal & Financial Publishing, 1983.
ISBN 0869940333 Hbk £10.50

—How to Re-Organise Your Affairs so as to Pay the Least Amount of Tax. – Cape Town : Legal & Financial Publishing, 1983.
ISBN 0869940139 Hbk £13.50

—Income Tax Statutory Amendments and Recent Amendments to the Estate Duty Act Including Estate Planning Aspects, 1985-1986. – Cape Town : Legal & Financial Publishing.
Hbk £8.50

—Judges I Have Known. – Cape Town : Legal & Financial Publishing, 1983.
Hbk £8.04

—Law and Finance for the Farmer / Davis. – Cape Town : Legal and Financial Publishing Co.
Hbk £17.47

—Outline of Income Tax Statutory Amendments : 1971-1985. – Cape Town : Legal & Financial Publishing, 1983.
Hbk £8.75

—Outline of the Income Tax Statutory Amendments 1971/1985. – Cape Town.
Hbk Legal and Financial Publishing Co

—Real Estate in South Africa. – 2nd ed. – Cape Town : Legal and Financial Publishing Co.
Hbk £29.50

—Register of Fixed Assets. – Cape Town : Legal & Financial Publishing, 1983.
– (Merlen Ser. of Registers).
Hbk £3.52

—Sales Tax Register. – Cape Town : Legal & Financial Publishing, 1983.
– (Merlen Ser. of Registers).
Hbk £3.52

—Sectional Titles Protocol Register. – Cape Town : Legal & Financial Publishing, 1983.
– (Merlen P.A.Y.E. Registers Ser.).
Hbk £21.81

—Shrand on Sectional Titles Act. – Cape Town : Legal and Financial Publishing Co.
Hbk £22.50
ISBN supplement 5.50

—Studies in Income Tax. – 2nd ed. – Cape Town : Legal and Financial Publishing Co.
Hbk £14.40

—Supplement to the Administration of Deceased Estates in South Africa, Trusts in South Africa, The Making of a Will Plus The Matrimonial Property Act Including Estate Duty Aspects. – Cape Town : Legal & Financial Publishing, 1985.
Hbk £11.50

—Taxation of Co-operative Societies in South Africa. – Cape Town : Legal & Financial Publishing, 1983.
ISBN 0869940317 Hbk £13.50

—Today and Yesterday. – Cape Town : Legal and Financial Publishing Co.
Hbk £9.50

—Trusts in South Africa with Up-to-Date Addendum. – Cape Town : Legal and Financial Publishing Co.
Hbk £33.50

—Twelve Schedule. – Cape Town : Legal & Financial Publishing, 1983.
– (Merlen P.A.Y.E. Registers).
Hbk £2.95

—Twenty-four Schedule. – Cape Town : Legal & Financial Publishing, 1983.
– (Merlen P.A.Y.E. Registers Ser.).
Hbk £4.04

—What Every Attorney Should Know About Income Tax. – Cape Town : Legal & Financial Publishing, 1983.
– (Merlen Ser. of Income Tax Publications).
Hbk £12.64

—What Every Company Secretary Should Know About Income Tax. – Cape Town : Legal & Financial Publishing, 1983.
– (Merlen Ser. of Income Tax Publications).
Hbk £12.64

—What Every Dental Surgeon Should Know About Income Tax. – Cape Town : Legal & Financial Publishing, 1983.
– (Merlen Ser. of Income Tax Publications).
ISBN 0869940341 Hbk £12.64

—What Every Executor-Trustee Should Know About Income Tax. – Cape Town : Legal & Financial Publishing, 1983.
– (Merlen Ser. of Income Tax Publications).
ISBN 0869940201 Hbk £12.64

—What Every Farmer Should Know About Income Tax. – Cape Town : Legal & Financial Publishing, 1983.
– (Merlen Ser. of Income Tax Publications).
Hbk £12.64

—What Every Hotelier Should Know About Income Tax. – Cape Town : Legal & Financial Publishing, 1983.
– (Merlen Ser. of Income Tax Publications).
ISBN 0869940074 Hbk £12.64

—What Every Insurance Company or Broker Should Know About Income Tax. – Cape Town : Legal & Financial Publishing, 1983.
– (Merlen Series of Income Tax Publications).
ISBN 0869940228 Hbk £12.64

—What Every Medical Practitioner Should Know About Income Tax. – Cape Town : Legal & Financial Publishing, 1983.
– (Merlen Ser. of Income Tax Publications).
Hbk £12.64

—What Every Merchant-Trader Should Know About Income Tax. – Cape Town : Legal & Financial Publishing, 1983.
– (Merlen Ser. of Income Tax Publications).
ISBN 0869940112 Hbk £12.64

—What Every Ophthalmic Surgeon Should Know About Income Tax. – Cape Town : Legal & Financial Publishing, 1983.
– (Merlen Ser. of Income Tax Publications).
ISBN 086994021X Hbk £12.64

—What Every Pharmacist Should Know About Income Tax. – Cape Town : Legal & Financial Publishing, 1983.
– (Merlen Ser. of Income Tax Publications).
ISBN 086994035X Hbk £12.64

—What Every Professional Person Should Know About Income Tax. – Cape Town : Legal & Financial Publishing, 1983.
– (Merlen Ser. of Income Tax Publications).
ISBN 0869940082 Hbk £12.64

—What Every Property Owner Should Know About Income Tax. – Cape Town : Legal & Financial Publishing, 1983.
– (Merlen Ser. of Income Tax Publications).
Hbk £10.82

—What Every Real Estate Agent Should Know About Income Tax. – Cape Town : Legal & Financial Publishing, 1983.
– (Merlen Ser. of Income Tax Publications).
ISBN 0869940066 Hbk £12.64

—What Every Salaried Person Should Know About Income Tax. – Cape Town : Legal & Financial Publishing, 1983.
– (Merlen Ser. of Income Tax Publications).
ISBN 0869940104 Hbk £12.64

—What Every Taxpayer Should Know About Income Tax. – 9th ed. – Cape Town : Legal & Financial Publishing, 1983.
– (Merlen Ser. of Income Tax Publications).
Hbk £12.64

Shrand on Sectional Titles Act. – Cape Town : Legal and Financial Publishing Co.
Hbk £22.50
ISBN supplement 5.50

Shrubsall, V.
Contracts of Employment. – Oxford : BSP Professional.
ISBN 0632021454 Pbk £17.95

Shtein, B.J.L.
Introduction to Business Law / K.E. Lindgren. – 4th ed. – North Ryde : Law Book Co, 1984.
xv, 285p.
ISBN 0455202117 Pbk £7.50

Shukla, B.C.
Uttar Pradesh Agricultural Credit Act, 1973. – 4th ed. repr. – Lucknow : Eastern Book Company, 1985.
Hbk £30.00

Shukla, K.S.
Lokapukta (Ombudsman in India) : a Socio-Legal Study / S.S. Singh. – New Delhi : Indian Institute of Public Administration, 1988.
Hbk £100.00

Shukla, M C
Banking Law / Saxena. – Delhi : SBD Enterprises.
Hbk £10.00

—Business Law : Including Banking Law; For B. Com Students / Saxena. – Delhi : SBD Enterprises.
Hbk £25.00

—Company Law / Saxena. – Delhi : SBD Enterprises.
Hbk £13.50

—Industrial and Commercial Law : For I.C.W.A. Students / Saxena. – Delhi : SBD Enterprises.
Hbk £35.00

—Industrial Law : For B Com. and I.C.W.A. Students / Saxena. – Delhi : SBD Enterprises.
Hbk £35.00

—Manual of Mercantile Law. – 12th ed. – New Delhi : S. Chand and Company, 1983.
vii, 906p.
Hbk £35.00

—Mercantile Law : Including Company Law and Industrial Law / Saxena. – Delhi : SBN Enterprises.
Hbk £35.00

—Principles of Company Law / S.S. Gulshan. – 7th ed. – New Delhi : S. Chand and Company.
608p.
Hbk £35.00

Shukla, R.D.
Law Relating to Execution of Decrees : Along with Executability of the Orders of Tribunals. – Allahabad : Hind Publishing House, 1986.
Hbk £100.00

Shukla, V.M.
Legal Remedies / Avtar Singh. – 5th rev. ed. – Lucknow : Eastern Book Company, 1986.
380p.
Pbk £40.00

—Principles and Precedents of Pleadings. – 2nd ed. – Lucknow : Eastern Book Company, 1983.
1,174p.
Hbk £75.00

Shukla, V.N.
Constitution of India / D.K. Singh. – 7th ed. – Lucknow : Eastern Book Company, 1982.
871p.
Hbk £90.00

Shuklendra, Acharya
Guide to the Deeds. – 4th rev. ed. – Allahabad : Modern Law Publications, 1986.
Hbk £330.00

—Supreme Court on Direct Taxes 1950 to 1986. – Allahabad : Modern Law Publications, 1986.
Hbk £220.00

—Supreme Court on Direct Taxes. – New Delhi : Bharat Law House, 1986.
Hbk £220.00

Shuklendra, Charya
Central Excise : Law, Practice and Procedure, 2 Vols. – Allahabad : Modern Law Publications, 1987.
Hbk £550.00

Shumiatcher, Morris
Man of Law : a Model. – Saskatoon : Western Producer Prairie Books.
225p.
ISBN 0888330340 Pbk £12.95

Shurman, Laurence
Practical Skills of the Solicitor. – London : Oyez Longman, 1981.
ISBN 0851206107 Hbk £6.95
—Practical skills of the solicitor. – 2nd ed. – London : Longman Professional, 1985. – (Practice Today Series).
ISBN 0851209947 Pbk £12.50

Shuter
Zulu Law / Shooter. – Pietermaritzburg : Shuter & Shooter, 1984.
Hbk

Shuter, J.
Copyright Licensing. – Bradford : MCB University Press. – (Library Management Series).
ISBN 086176353X Hbk £27.95

Shutt, Harry
Myth of free trade : patterns of protectionism since 1945 / Harry Shutt. – Oxford : Blackwell, 1985.
193p.
Includes index.
ISBN 0631139974 £17.50

Shuttleworth, C. W.
Check-Lists for Solicitors. – 4th ed. – London : Oyez Longman, 1983.
Hbk £9.95

Shweikart, L.
Banking In The American South From The Age Of Jackson. – Louisiana : Louisiana State University Press, 1988.
ISBN 0807114030 Hbk £33.25

Shymko
City of Toronto Act, 1983, Bill Pr036 : An Act Respecting the City of Toronto. – Ontario : Ontario Government Publications Service, 1983.
1p.
Hbk £0.30

Sia, Suat Hwa
Business Firms and Companies. – Singapore : Times Books International.
128p.
ISBN 9971650916 Pbk £7.50

Siblesz, Hugo →Realism in Law-Making : Essays on International Law in Honour of Willem Riphagen.

Sick Pay : A Negotiators Guide. – London : Labour Research Department, 1985.
Hbk £1.50

Siddayao, Corazon Morales →Criteria for energy pricing policy : a collection of papers commissioned for the Energy Pricing Policy Workshop organized under the Regional Energy Development Programme (RAS/84/001), Bangkok, 8-11 May 1984.

Siddiqi, M.S.
Company Law in Pakistan : Companies Act 1913. – Lahore : Pakistan Law Times.
900p.
Hbk £120.00

Siddiqi, Muhammad Iqbal
Family Laws of Islam. – Lahore : Kazi Publications.
Hbk £85.00
—Penal Law of Islam. – Lahore : Kazi Publications.
Hbk £55.00

Siddiqi, Qamar S. →Sovereign borrowers : guidelines on legal negotiations with commercial lenders.

Siddique, Ahmed
Criminology : Problems and Perspectives. – 2nd ed. – Lucknow : Eastern Book Company, 1983.
483p.
Hbk £50.00

Sidwell, A. C. →Management Contracting.

Siebel, Kingsley →Legal Costs, New South Wales.

Sieghart, Paul
Human Rights in the United Kingdom. – Pinter.
ISBN 0861877454 Hbk £22.50
ISBN 0861877500 Pbk £6.95
—Lawful rights of mankind : an introduction to the international legal code of human rights / Paul Sieghart. – Oxford : Oxford University Press, 1985.
xiii,252p; 23cm.
Bibliography: p247-248. - Includes index.
ISBN 019219190X £9.95
—Sri Lanka : a mounting tragedy of errors: report of a mission to Sri Lanka in January 1984 on behalf of the International Commission of Jurists and its British Section, Justice / Paul Sieghart. – London : International Commission oof Jurists and Justice, 1984.
95p.
Bibliography: p93-94.
ISBN 0907247040
→ World of science and the rule of law : a study of the observance and violations of the human rights of scientists in the participating states of the Helsinki Accord.

Siekmann, Robert C. R →Basic documents on United Nations and related peace-keeping forces.

Siemers, J. P
European integration : select international bibliography of theses and dissertations Europaische Integration : Internationales Auswahlverzeichnis von Dissertationen und Diplomarbeiten Integration europeenne : bibliographie internationale selective de theses et memoires, 1957-1980 / J.P. Siemers, E.H. Siemers-Hidma : preface, Ralf Dahrendorf. – 2nd rev. and enl. ed. – The Hague : Martinus Nijhoff, 1981.
xx, 412 p.; 24 cm.
English, French, German, and Italian. Includes indexes.
ISBN 9024725429

Sieper, E.
Rationalising Rustic Regulation. – Turramura : Centre for Independent Studies.
96p.
ISBN 0949769029 Hbk £5.50

Sigeman, Tore →International labour law reports, Volume 7.

Sigurdson, J. S., et al
Rules of Court. – Vancouver : British Columbia Continuing Legal Education Society, 1983.
93p.
ISBN 0865041075 Hbk £45.00

Sihombing, Judith E.
National Land Code : a Commentary. – London : Sweet & Maxwell, 1982.
ISBN 0421306300 Hbk £95.00
—National Land Code : a commentary / by Judith E. Sihombing : with a foreword by Tun Dr. Mohamed Suffian. – Kuala Lumpur, Singapore : Malayan Law Journal, 1981.
xxxix,905p.
Includes index.
ISBN 9971700174

Sijthoff, A.W. →International Labour Law : a Comparative Survey of the Conflict Rules Affecting Labour Legislation and Regulations.

Sikhs / by Christopher Shackle. – Rev. ed. – London : Minority Rights Group, 1986.
19p. – (Report).
Bibliography: p.18.
ISBN 0946690413

Silano, Julio →Register Notule Communium 14 of the Diocese of Barcelona (1345-1348) A Calendar with Selected Documents.

Silberberg, Harry
Law of Property / J Schoeman. – 2nd ed. – London : Butterworths, 1983.
ISBN 0409053120 Hbk £49.50
ISBN 0409053139 Pbk £35.40

Silent Revolution : Transformation of divorce law in the United States. – University of Chicago Press.
ISBN 0022639510 Hbk £15.90

Silke, Aubrey S
Estate duty : principles and planning / by Aubrey S. Silke and Michael L. Stein. – Kenwyn : Juta in association with Divaris Stein, 1984.
369 p.; 23 cm.
Includes indexes.
ISBN 0702115347
—Hambro Tax Guide / W. I. Sinclair. – London : Oyez Longman, 1982.
ISBN 0851206700 Hbk £8.95
—Silke on South African income tax : being an exposition of the law, practice and incidence of income tax in South Africa / Costa Divaris, Michael L. Stein. – 10th ed. – Cape Town : Juta, 1982.
xlvii,1696p.
Includes index.
ISBN 0702113360

Silke, Jonathan M. →Law of agency in South Africa.

Silke on South African income tax : being an exposition of the law, practice and incidence of income tax in South Africa / Costa Divaris, Michael L. Stein. – 10th ed. – Cape Town : Juta, 1982.
xlvii,1696p.
Includes index.
ISBN 0702113360

Silke, P. D. →Hambro Capital Taxes and Estate Planning Guide.

Silkin, S. C. →Marketing Legal services.

Silva, S.R. de
Some Concepts of Labour Law. – Colombo : Lake House Investments.
Hbk £2.00

Silverleaf, Michael →Passing off : law and practice.

Silverman, Frances S
Conveyancing Searches and Enquiries. – London : Butterworths, 1985.
ISBN 040625513X Pbk £26.95
—Professional Conduct for Solicitors. – London : Butterworths.
ISBN 0406504113 Pbk £8.95
—Searches and Enquiries : A Conveyancer's Guide. – London : Butterworths, 1985.
This book gives a step by step guide to the process of searches and enquiries made by conveyancers in the United Kingdom. The work includes an analysis of common searches and a reference guide to unusual searches.
ISBN 040625513X Pbk
—Standard conditions of sale. – 2nd ed. – London : Butterworths, 1987.
ISBN 0406255113 Pbk £25.95
—Standard Conditions of Sale : A Conveyancer's Guide. – London : Butterworths, 1986.
This work comparees the National Conditions of Sale and the Law Society's General Conditions of Sale and analyzes the ways in which they diverge. The discussion of conditions in the book follows that of events in a normal conveyancing transaction in the United Kingdom.
ISBN 0406255113 Pbk

Silverman, Robert A
Crime in Canadian society / James T Teevan. – 3rd. – Scarborough, Ontario : Butterworths (Canada).
440.
Opens with a discussion of the controversy surrounding the definition of crime, and then moves into a discussion and critique of the ways of measuring crime in Canada. Gives various explanations of crime from functional analysis to liberal criminology, labelling theory and critical theory. Concludes with a selection of contemporary Canadian criminological research.
ISBN 040986580X 1986

Silverstone Oil Company Limited Act, 1983, Bill Pr022 : An Act to Revive Silverstone Oil Company Limited. – Ontario : Ontario Government Publications Service, 1983.
2p.
Hbk £0.30

Silvertown, Alfred H.
Law of lien / Alfred H. Silvertown. – London : Butterworth, 1988.
190p; 25cm.
Includes index.
ISBN 040610395X Hbk £29.00

Sim, Ewe Eong
Introduction to tax appeals in Malaysia : notes on practice and procedure in appeals to the Special Commissioners of Income Tax / by Sim Ewe Eong : with a foreword by Tun Dr. Mohamed Suffian. – Kuala Lumpur : Malayan Law Journal, 1981.
xii,88p.
ISBN 9971700182

Sim, Heather →Highlights of federal initiatives in criminal justice, 1966- 1980.

Sim, Joe →British prisons.

Sim, R. S.
A-Level English Law / D M M Scott. – 6th ed. – London : Butterworths, 1984.
This work includes theoretical and empirical material designed to set legal principles in a sociological context for students requiring an introduction to the English legal system.
ISBN 0406657076 Hbk £14.00
ISBN 0406657084 Pbk £8.95

Simcock, Donald H. →New Zealand income tax law and practice.

Simeon Moquet Borde & Associates
Doing Business in France. – Simeon Moquet Borde & Associates. – Matthew Bender, 1983.
ISBN 0000999039 Hbk £105.00

Simeonsson →Family Assessment and Early Intervention.

Simey, Margaret
Government by Consent : The Principle and Practice of Accountability in Local Government. – London : Bedford Square Press, 1985.
ISBN 0719911400 Hbk £2.95

Simey, N.
Democracy Rediscovered : Study in Police Accountability. – Pluto Press.
ISBN 0745302629 Hbk £14.95

Similar fact evidence : probative value and prejudice / by Donald K. Piragoff. – Toronto : Carswell, 1981.
xxiii,309p.
Includes bibliographical references and index.
ISBN 0459337807

Simkin →Young Solicitors' Guide, The.

Simmie, J. M.
Power, property and corporatism : the political sociology of planning / James Simmie. – London : Macmillan Press, 1981.
ix,351p.
Bibliography: p.321-345.
ISBN 0333243455

Simmonds and Mercer
Business Associations. – Simmonds and Mercer. – Agincourt : Carswell, 1984.
806p.
Hbk £75.75

Simmonds, K.
Sweet and Maxwell's Employment Law Manual. – London : Sweet & Maxwell, 1987.
ISBN 0421352205 Hbk

Simmonds, K. R.
Community Secondary Legislation, 3 Vols. Vol. 3. – Edinburgh : W Green, 1985. – (Encyclopedia of European Community Law Ser.).
ISBN 0421207604 Llf £480.00
—Encyclopedia of European Community Law : Volume B : European Community Treaties. – Edinburgh : W Green.
Llf £290.50
—European Community Treaties, 3 Vols. Vol. 2. – Edinburgh : W Green, 1985. – (Encyclopedia of European Community Law Ser.).
ISBN 0421193603 Llf £170.00
—European Community Treaties. – Edinburgh : W Green, 1983. – (Encyclopedia of European Community Law Ser.: Vol. 2).
Llf £155.00
→ New directions in the law of the sea : new series.

Simmonds, N. E.
Central issues in jurisprudence : justice, law and rights / by N.E. Simmonds. – London : Sweet & Maxwell, 1986.
xi,155p; 22cm.
Includes bibliographies and index.
ISBN 0421351101 Hbk £18.00
ISBN 0421351209 Pbk £8.95
—Decline of juridical reason : doctrine and theory in the legal order / N.E. Simmonds. – Manchester : Manchester University Press, 1984.
137p; 23cm.
Includes index.
ISBN 0719010896 £19.50
→ Philosophy and the criminal law : Association for Legal and Social Philosophy Tenth Annual Conference at the University of Manchester, 8-10th April 1983.

Simmonds, Ralph L. → Canadian business organizations law.
—Introduction to business associations in Canada : cases, notes, and materials / by R.L. Simmonds and Peter P. Mercer. – Toronto, Canada : Carswell Legal Publications, 1984.
xxviii, 778 p.; 25 cm.
Spine title: Business associations in Canada.
ISBN 0459365304 Pbk

Simmons, C. G.
Labour Arbitration Cases (L.A.C.) 1973-81, 30 Vols. – Aurora : Canada Law Book Co. – (Second Ser.).
Hbk £1530.00
—Labour Arbitration Cases (L.A.C.) 1982-Present. – Aurora : Canada Law Book Co. – (Third Ser.).
Hbk £78.00
—Labour Arbitration Cases (Second Series) Consolidated Index, List of Awards Vols. 1-30. – Aurora : Canada Law Book Co, 1982.
400p.
Pbk £30.00

Simmons, Howard S.
Family Home and Income Tax. – Agincourt : Carswell, 1986.
245p.
This work is a guide to the tax consequences of home ownership in Canada for tax practitioners. The book treats the subject of capital gains exemptions, home improvements, mixed use properties, recreational dwellings, and other tax issues.
Hbk £40.50

Simmons, M.
Successful Mergers : Planning, Strategy and Execution. – Waterlow.
ISBN 0080369022 Pbk £12.95

Simmons, N.
Anatomy of Professional Practice. – London : Law Society.
ISBN 0948736003 Pbk £4.95

Simon, Frances → Unemployment and magistrates' courts.

Simon, John Allesbrook Simon → Simon's Taxes.
→ Simon's Weekly Tax Service.

Simon, John Allsebrook Simon → Simon's taxes : income tax, corporation tax, capital gains tax, D : Companies.

Simon, Paul
Employment Law : the New Basics. – North Ryde : C.C.H. Australia.
384p.
ISBN 0887964648 Pbk £19.95
—Hazardous Products : Canada's Right-to-Know Laws. – Don Mills : CCH Canadian Ltd.
310p.
ISBN 0887964524 Pbk £18.95

Simon's tax cases. – London : Butterworths, 1974.
Kept up to date by supplement, Simon's weekly tax service. Index in each vol. - Cumulative tables and index, 1973-1985. 1986.

Simon's tax intelligence. – London : Butterworths, 1983.

Simon's Taxes, 9 Vols. / J. F. Avery Jones. – 3rd ed. – Wellington : Butterworths.
Llf

Simon's Taxes / John Allesbrook Simon Simon. – London : Butterworths.
Service to Date.
Hbk £510.00

Simon's taxes : income tax, corporation tax, capital gains tax
A : General principles, procedure, schedules A, B and C / John Allsebrook Simon Simon. – rev. 3rd ed. n v, loose leaves in folder. – London : Butterworths, 1983.
26cm.
Updated periodically by supplements.
ISBN 0406072493
B : Schedule D - Capital allowances. – 1983.
26cm.
Updated periodically by supplements.
ISBN 0406072418
C : Capital gains trusts. – 1985.
looseleaf.
Previous ed.: 3rd ed. 1970. 'Originally published under the editorship of the Right Hon. Viscount Simon'.
ISBN 0406072426
D : Companies. – 1983.
26cm.
Updated periodically by supplements.
ISBN 0406072434
E : Individuals. – 1985.
looseleaf.
Previous ed.: 3rd ed. 1970. 'Originally published under the editorship of the Right Hon. Viscount Simon'.
ISBN 0406072442
F : Double tax relief, agreements. – 1983.
loose-leaf; 26cm.
Updated periodically by supplements.
G : Statutes-1. – 1983.
26cm.
ISBN 0406072469 Hbk
H : Statutes - 2, concessions, practice. – 1982.
26cm.
Updated periodically by supplements.
ISBN 0406072477
I : Tables of statutes and cases, master index. – 1985.
looseleaf.
Previous ed.: 3rd ed. 1976. 'Originally published under the editorship of the Right Hon. Viscount Simon'.
Tax Acts before 1988. – 1988.
looseleaf.
Contents: pages discarded from vols. G and H on filing issue 132. Binder title: Former legislation: Taxes Act 1970, Finance Acts etc, 1970-87.

Simon's Weekly Tax Service / John Allesbrook Simon Simon. – London : Butterworths, 1984.
Hbk
Cumulative Index, 1973-1982. –
ISBN 0406070768 Pbk £18.00

Simon's Weekly Tax Service : Simon's Tax Cases. – London : Butterworths.
Cases Only for 1973, 1974, 1975, 1976, 1977, 1978, 1979, 1980 and 1981. –
Hbk
Cumulative Index (1973-81). –
ISBN 0406069964 Hbk £16.50 each

Simon's Weekly Tax Service : Simon's Tax Intelligence. – London : Butterworths.
This weekly publication provides complete information on developments in the fields of income tax, capital gains tax, corporation tax, capital transfer tax, stamp duty, and value added tax in the United Kingdom.
Llf

Simons, William B → Party statutes of the Communist world.

Simple Book of Jurisprudence / Prayag Singh. – Delhi : SBD Enterprises.
Hbk £25.00

Simpson
Forensic Medicine / Knight. – 9th ed. – London : Edward Arnold, 1985.
ISBN 073144521 Pbk £17.50
→ International audit in public sector.

Simpson, A. W. B. → Biographical dictionary of the common law.
—History of the common law of contract. – Oxford : Oxford University Press, 1987.
ISBN 019825573X Pbk £19.50
—History of the land law / A.W.B. Simpson. – 2nd ed. – Oxford : Clarendon, 1986.
316p; 22cm.
Previous ed.: published as An introduction to the history of land law. Oxford : Oxford University Press, 1961. Bibliography: p292-295. - Includes index.
ISBN 0198255365 Pbk £12.50
ISBN 0198255373 Hbk £25.00
—Invitation to law / by A.W.B. Simpson. – Oxford : Blackwell, 1988.
227p.
Includes index.
ISBN 0631145389 Pbk
—Legal theory and legal history : essays on the common law / A.W.B. Simpson. – London : Hambledon, 1987.
xiii,432p; 24cm.
Includes index.
ISBN 0907628834 £24.00
—Pornography and politics : the Williams Committee in retrospect / A. W. B. Simpson. – London : Waterlow Publishers, 1983.
143p.
ISBN 0080391567

Simpson, Anne Frazer → Handbook of charities, 1987-1988.

Simpson, B.
Cannibalism and the common law. – University of Chicago Press, 1984.
ISBN 0226759423 Hbk £21.25

Simpson, Bob → Striking a balance? : employment law after the 1980 Act.

Simpson, G → Need for and the feasibility of an appeals process in regard to municipal grants-in-lieu of taxes : a report prepared for the Minister of Public Works Canada.

Simpson, Kieran
Toronto Legal Directory (Metropolitan List) and Tariff Guide. – Toronto : University of Toronto Press, 1985.
Hbk £17.00

Simpson, S.
Music : the Business and the Law / G. Stevens. – North Ryde : Law Book Co, 1986.
xii, 247p.
ISBN 045520621X Pbk £24.00

Simpson, S.D., et al
Discovery and Interrogatories. – Butterworths, 1984.
325p.
ISBN 0409492728 Hbk £33.50

Simpson, Shane
Visual artist and the law / by Shane Simpson. – Sydney : Law Book Co., 1982.
xiii,182p.
Bibliography: p.169-173. - Includes index.
ISBN 0455204527 Hbk £19

Sims, B. J. → Sergeant and Sims on stamp duties and capital duty and stamp duty reserve tax.
—Simon's Taxes, 9 Vols. / J. F. Avery Jones. – 3rd ed. – Wellington : Butterworths.
Llf

Sims, E. M. E. → Sergeant and Sims on stamp duties and capital duty and stamp duty reserve tax.

Sims, John → Building contract claims.
→ Building Sub-Contract Documentation.
→ Contract Documentation for Contractors.
→ Determination and Suspension of Construction Contracts.
→ Quantification of building claims.

Sin, Kam Fan
Building Project Finance in Hong Kong : Law and Practice. – Butterworths, 1987.
265p.
Describes the law and practice of building project finance in Hong Kong. Examines the 'financing', 'project', and 'security' aspects of a project loan in a comprehensive manner. Explains the typical transactions involved, the roles of various documents, and the problems which have to be dealt with.
ISBN 0409995363 Hbk £110.00

Sinclair, Allen
Introduction to Real Property Law. – 3rd ed. – Butterworths, 1987.
120p.
Covers the doctrine of the estate in land, concurrent ownership, a prologue to modern law, and the statutes of uses and modern law. Takes into account recent changes in this area, including family law, easements, and water rights.
ISBN 0409808849 Hbk £23.95

Sinclair, Ian
International Law Commission / by Sir Ian Sinclair. – Cambridge : Grotius, 1987.
viii,177p.
Examines the constitution and working methods of the International Law Commission, and reviews the activity of the Commission since 1949 in the codification process. Analyses the contribution it has made to the development of general international law.
ISBN 0949009105
—Measures of police effectiveness and efficiency / Ian Sinclair, Clive Miller. – London : Home Office, 1984.
v,38p.
Bibliography: p.38.
ISBN 0862521599
—Vienna convention on the law of treaties / Ian Sinclair. – 2nd ed. – Manchester : Manchester University Press, 1984.
x,270p; 25cm.
Previous ed.: 1973. Includes index.
ISBN 0719014808

Sinclair, J.
Handbook Conveyancing Practice in Scotland. – London : Butterworths, 1986.
ISBN 0406206007 Pbk £19.00

Sinclair, June D.
Introduction to the Matrimonial Property Act 1984 / June D. Sinclair. – Cape Town : Juta, 1984.
ix,102p.
ISBN 0702115096

Sinclair, Mary Jane T.
Updating statutes and regulations for all Canadian jurisdictions (as of Dec. 1984) / by Mary Jane T. Sinclair. – New ed. – Ottawa : Canadian Law Information Council, 1985.
44p.
Previous ed.: published as How to update a statute for all Canadian jurisdictions / edited by Gail S. Dykstra.
ISBN 0920358772

Sinclair, Neil
Warranties and indemnities on share sales / Neil Sinclair. – London : Oyez Longman, 1984.
xxiv,331p.
Includes index.
ISBN 0851208703

Sinclair, Ruth
Decision making in statutory reviews on children in care / Ruth Sinclair. – Aldershot : Gower, 1984.
vi,171p; 23cm.
Bibliography: p165-171.
ISBN 0566007576 £16.45

Sinclair, W.I.
Allied Dunbar Tax Guide 1988-89. – London : Longman Professional.
ISBN 0851214614 Hbk £13.50
—Hambro Capital Taxes and Estate Planning Guide / P. D. Silke. – London : Oyez Longman, 1982.
ISBN 085120662X Hbk £9.95
→ Hambro Tax Guide.

Sing, Veer
Industrial Employment Injuries : an Overview of the Legal Protection System. – New Delhi : Deep and Deep Publications, 1986.
388p.
Hbk £250.00

Singapore →Statutes of the Republic of Singapore.

Singapore Association of Women Lawyers
Legal Status of Singapore Women. – Singapore Association of Women Lawyers. – Singapore : Asiapac Books and Educational Aids.
ISBN 9971985128 Hbk £1.40

Singapore Law Series
Landlord and Tenant /. – Butterworths, 1988.
ca 200p.
Discusses leases, and the relationship between landlords and tenants, and contains chapters on leases of major landlords such as the Jurong Town Corporation and the Urban Renewal Authority, and rent control.
ISBN 0409995347 Pbk

Singapore Property Tax Cases [1959-1986]. – Singapore : Malayan Law Journal, 1987.
xxii,413.
Collection of cases that was determined by the Judicial Committee of the Privy Council, the Court of Appeal, the High Court, and the Valuation Review Board of Singapore.
ISBN 9971700573 Hbk

Singapore Real Property Guide. – 2nd ed. – Singapore : Quins, 1983.
Pbk £54.00

Singapore Taxation / Damian C.F. Hong. – Butterworths, 1985.
636p.
ISBN 0409995053 Pbk £90.00

Singbal
Criminal Court Practice : with Model Forms. – 2nd ed. – North Ryde : Law Book Co, 1987.
Hbk £250.00

Singer, H. W.
Developing Countries Western Interests and Actions. – Exeter : European Atlantic Movement, 1982.
Hbk £0.50

Singer, Peter →Ethical and Legal Issues in Guardianship Options for Intellectually Disadvantaged People.
—Expanding circle : ethics and sociobiology / Peter Singer. – Oxford : Clarendon Press, 1981.
xii,190p; 22cm.
Includes index.
ISBN 0198246463 £6.95
—Reproduction revolution / Wells. – Oxford : Oxford University Press, 1984.
ISBN 0192177362 Hbk £15.00
ISBN 0192860445 Pbk £3.95

Singh
Cattle Trespass Act : as Amended Up-To-Date with Up-To-Date Case Law. – 3rd ed. – Allahabad : Law Book Company, 1988.
146p.
Hbk £65.00
—E.C. Act with Central Control Orders. – Allahabad : Orient Law House, 1984.
Hbk £35.00
→ Law of Kidnapping and Sexual Offences.
—Nuclear Weapons and Contemporary International Law / Edward McWhinney. – 2nd ed. – Martinus Nijhoff.
ISBN 9024736374 Hbk £86.50
—Ship Owners (BSL) / Raoul Colinvaux. – Sweet & Maxwell, 1967.
ISBN 0420416609 Hbk £75.00

Singh, Amar
Law of Contract in India. – New Delhi : Deep and Deep Publications, 1985.
326p.
Hbk £175.00
—Studies in Commercial Law and Judicial Activism. – New Delhi : Deep and Deep Publications, 1988.
220p.
Hbk £150.00

Singh, Avtar
Company Law. – 7th ed. – Lucknow : Eastern Book Company, 1982.
493p.
Hbk £45.00
—Introduction to the Law of Contract. – 2nd ed. – Lucknow : Eastern Book Company, 1983.
419p.
Pbk £30.00
—Law of Contract. – 4th ed. – Lucknow : Eastern Book Company, 1985.
526p.
Hbk £65.00
—Law of Insolvency (In Nutshell). – repr. 1983. – Lucknow : Eastern Book Company.
82p.
Pbk £6.00
—Law of Monopolies, Restrictive and Unfair Trade Practices. – Lucknow : Eastern Book Company, 1984.
134p.
Pbk £20.00
—Law of Partnership : Principles, Practice, Taxation. – Lucknow : Eastern Book Company, 1981.
627p.
Hbk £60.00
→ Law Relating to Private Companies, Includes Supplement-1986.
→ Legal Remedies.
—Mercantile Law. – 4th ed. – Lucknow : Eastern Book Company, 1985.
1,172p.
Hbk £85.00
—Negotiable Instruments with Supplement. – 1980 repr. – Lucknow : Eastern Book Company, 1984.
329p.
Hbk £35.00
—Sale of Goods and Hire-Purchase. – 3rd ed. – Lucknow : Eastern Book Company, 1985.
189p.
Pbk £20.00

Singh, Awther
Company Law of Singapore and Malaysia. – Singapore : Quins.
Hbk
—Directors Handbook : Singapore and Malaysia. – Singapore : Quins, 1983.
Hbk £54.00
—Emergency Laws in Malaysia. – Singapore.
160p.
Pbk £27.00
—How to Pay Less Malaysian Income Tax. – Singapore, 1982.
Hbk £36.00
—How to Pay Less Singapore Income Tax. – Singapore : Quins, 1982.
Pbk £27.00
—Law of Evidence in Malaysia and Singapore. – Singapore : Quins, 1983.
Hbk £81.00
—Malaysian Income Tax. – 4th ed. – Singapore : Quins, 1982.
lxi, 800p.
£135.00 with free Supplements
—Motorist and the Law in Malaysia. – Singapore : Quins.
Hbk £54.00
—Motorist and the Law in Singapore. – Singapore : Quins.
Hbk £54.00
—Real Property Gains Tax in Malaysia. – 2nd ed. – Singapore : Quins, 1982.
£36.00
—Sale of Goods, Hire Purchase and Moneylending in Malaysia. – Singapore : Quins.
xliv, 391p.
Hbk £81.00
—Singhs Commentary on the Malaysian Criminal Procedure Code. – Singapore : Quins.
lxix, 338p.
Hbk £45.00
—Singhs Commentary on the Malaysian Estate Duty Ordinance. – Singapore : Quins, 1982.
Pbk £27.00
—Singhs Commentary on the Malaysian Income Tax Act. – Singapore : Quins, 1982.
Pbk £18.00
—Singh's Contract Law of Malaysia. – Singapore : Quins.
xl, 515p.
Hbk £81.00
—Singh's Law and Practice of Singapore Income Tax. – 2nd ed. – Singapore : Quins, 1982.
Hbk £153.00 2 vol. ed.)
—Singhs Malaysian Statutes, Vol. 1 : Taxation. – Singapore : Quins, 1982.
Hbk £234.00
—Tarling's Case and Directors Liabilities in Singapore and Malaysia. – Singapore : Quins, 1982.
Hbk £63.00

Singh, Chhatrapati
Law from anarchy to Utopia : an exposition of the logical, epistemological and ontological foundations of the idea of law, by an inquiry into the nature of legal propositions and the basis of legal authority / Chhatrapati Singh. – Delhi : Oxford University Press, 1986.
xxi,299p; 22cm.
Bibliography: p278-292. - Includes index.
ISBN 0195617045 £30.00

Singh, D.K. →Constitution of India.

Singh, Guru Prasanna
Principles of Statutory Interpretation. – 3rd ed. repr. 1984. – New Delhi : Bharat Law House.
lxxx, 664p.
Hbk £125.00

Singh, Harminder →Law of Simple Discharge (In Private and Public Sectors).

Singh, Janardan Prasad
Sir William Jones, His Mind and Art. – New Delhi : S. Chand and Company, 1982.
312p.
Hbk £80.00

Singh, K.K.
Central Criminal Minor Acts : With state Amendments / Rakesh Bagga. – 3rd ed. – Allahabad : Law Book Company, 1988.
1,500p.
Hbk £350.00
—Digest of Central Excise and Customs Cases. – Nagpur : Wadhura & Co, 1987.
1,425p.
Hbk £350.00
—Law of Central Sales Tax, 2 Vols. – Allahabad : Orient Law House, 1984.
Hbk £280.00

Singh, Mahendra Pal
German administrative law in common law perspective / Mahendra P. Singh. – Berlin : Springer-Verlag, 1985.
xxiv,194p.
Bibliography: p.188-191. - Includes index.
ISBN 0387156186

Singh, Nagendra
Enforcement of human rights in peace and war and the future of humanity / Nagendra Singh. – Dordrecht : Nijhoff, 1986.
ISBN 9024733022 Hbk
—International Maritime Law Conv (BSL) 4 vols. – London : Sweet & Maxwell, 1983.
ISBN 042066002 Hbk £310.00
—Maritime Safety and Environment Conventions. – London : Sweet & Maxwell, 1983.
– (British Shipping Laws).
Hbk £290.00

Singh, Prayag →Simple Book of Jurisprudence.

Singh, R.P.
Central Legislature in India (1909-1935). – Calcutta, 1984.
282p.
ISBN 8185109389 Hbk £90.00

Singh, S.D.
Judgements and How to Write Them. – 3rd ed. – Lucknow : Eastern Book Company, 1974.
216p.
Hbk £40.00
—Law of Central Sales Tax. – 4th ed. – Lucknow : Eastern Book Company, 1985.
859p.
Hbk £150.00
—Law of Partnership in India / J.P. Gupta. – 2nd ed. – Allahabad : Orient Law House, 1983.
Hbk £200.00
—Law of Sales Tax in Uttar Pradesh, 2 Vols. / G.C. Mathur. – 5th ed. – Lucknow : Eastern Book Company, 1986.
Hbk £175.00

Singh, S.S.
Administration of Natural Justice in India. – New Delhi : Uppal Publishing House, 1986.
358p.
ISBN 818502409X Hbk £250.00
→ Lokapukta (Ombudsman in India) : a Socio-Legal Study.

Singh, V.D.
Digest of Supreme Court Sales Tax Cases 1950-1987. – Allahabad : Modern Law Publications, 1987.
Hbk £140.00

Singhal
Indian Partnership Act : With a Special Reference to Taxation Laws. – 5th ed. – Allahabad : Law Book Company, 1986.
1,700p.
Hbk £320.00

Singhal, J.P.
Indian Contract Act, 3 Vols. / E.S. Subrahmanyam. – 3rd ed. – Allahabad : Law Book Company, 1989.
Hbk £550.00

Singhal, M.K.
Civil Court Practice. – 3rd ed. – Allahabad : Law Book Company, 1986.
1,100p.
Hbk £240.00

Singhs Commentary on the Malaysian Criminal Procedure Code. – Singapore : Quins.
lxix, 338p.
Hbk £45.00

Singhs Commentary on the Malaysian Estate Duty Ordinance. – Singapore : Quins, 1982.
Pbk £27.00

Singhs Commentary on the Malaysian Income Tax Act. – Singapore : Quins, 1982.
Pbk £18.00

Singh's Contract Law of Malaysia. – Singapore : Quins.
xl, 515p.
Hbk £81.00

Singh's Law and Practice of Singapore Income Tax. – 2nd ed. – Singapore : Quins, 1982.
Hbk £153.00 2 vol. ed.)

Singhs Malaysian Statutes, Vol. 1 : Taxation. – Singapore : Quins, 1982.
Hbk £234.00

Singhvi, Abhishek Manu
State of emergency and permissible measures of derogation / A. M. Singhvi. – Bombay : Lawasia-Bar Association of India, 1986.
45p.
Working paper of the Joint Regional Conference (Asia) of the International Bar Association, Law Asia and Bar Association of India (Bombay, Feb.22-23, 1986) on Topic 2 'International support for protection of human rights'. Includes references, p30-41.

Single act and Europe : a moment of truth / by Jacques Delors. – Luxembourg : Office for Official Publications of the European Communities, 1986.
37p.

Single European Act / and, Final Act. – Luxembourg : Office for Official Publications of the European Communities, 1986.
v, 76p.
Title on cover: Single European Act.
ISBN 9282403289

Single Payments : the Disappearing Safety Net 1988 / Tarpey. – London : Central Books.
ISBN 0946744076 Pbk £3.95

Singleton, Alan
Role of subscription agents / by Alan Singleton : with a supplementary report on U.K. libraries, trade with agents by Alan Cooper. – Leicester : Primary Communications Research Centre, University of Leicester, 1981.
68p; 21cm. – (Occasional papers).
ISBN 0906083176 Pbk

Sinha, B.P.
Reminiscences and Reflections of a Chief Justice. – Delhi : B.R. Publishing Corporation, 1985.
ix, 234p.
ISBN 8170182530 Hbk £150.00

Sinha, B.S.
Law of Torts. – 4th ed. 1976 repr. – Lucknow : Eastern Book Company, 1981.
528p.
Pbk £22.50

Sinnadurai, Dato' Visu →Law, Justice and the Judiciary : Transitional.
—Law of Contract in Malaysia and Singapore : Cases and Commentary. – 2nd ed. – Butterworths, 1987.
900p.
Chapters cover interpretation of contracts, conditional contracts, collateral contracts, economic duress, contracting out of a statute, the application of the doctrine of frustration to contracts for the sale of land, rescission under the Contract Act, equitable relief against forfeiture of deposits and part payments, and Foreign Investment Committee regulations.
ISBN 0409995290 Hbk £78.00
—Multilateral treaties between Asian countries. – London : Butterworths, 1986.
ISBN 0409995185 Hbk £24.00
—Sale and purchase of real property in Malaysia. – London : Butterworths, 1984.
ISBN 0406181187 Hbk £45.00

Sinnadurai, Visu
Survey of Malaysian Law
1983. – Singapore : Malayan Law Journal, 1985.
399.
Spiral bound £65
1984. – 1985.
360.
Surveys for each year since 1979.
Spiral bound £65

Sinnott, J.P.
World Patent Law and Practice. – Matthew Bender, 1974.
ISBN 0000999078 Hbk £270.00

Siong, Jap Kim →Taxation in the Asian-Pacific region : a country by country survey.

Sir Henry Maine : a study in Victorian jurisprudence. – Cambridge : Cambridge University Press.
Study of the ideas on jurisprudence of Sir Henry Maine, an important member of the Victorian intellectual establishment.
ISBN 0521353432

Sir John Davies and the conquest of Ireland. – Cambridge : Cambridge University Press.
Examines law reports of Sir John Davies as Solicitor-General and Attorney-General in Ireland in the seventeenth-century. Discusses the use of law in consolidating the conquest of Ireland. Examines the origin of precedent in Anglo-American law.
ISBN 0521253284

Sir John Did His Duty : Australian Constitutional Law. – Wamberal : Serendip Publications.
ISBN 094937900X Hbk £10.00

Sir Justice Udo Udoma / by D.S. Udo-Inyang. – Calabar, Nigeria : Wusen Press, 1985.
72p.
ISBN 9782281689

Sir William Jones, His Mind and Art. – New Delhi : S. Chand and Company, 1982.
312p.
Hbk £80.00

Sir William Scott, Lord Stowell. – Cambridge : Cambridge University Press.
Analyses Sir William Scott's work as a judge of the admiralty court during the Revolutionary and Napoleonic wars. Illustrates his contribution to the development of the international law of war, especially concerning neutral and belligerant rights at sea.
ISBN 0521340764

Sircar, V.K.
Commentaries on Uttar Pradesh Imposition of Ceiling on Land Holdings Act, 1960. – Lucknow : Eastern Book Company, 1977.
304p.
Hbk £35.00
—Uttar Pradesh Urban Buildings (Regulation of Letting, Rent and Eviction) Act, 1972. – 2nd ed. – Lucknow : Eastern Book Company, 1983.
833p.
Hbk £105.00

Sirkin, G.
Lexeconics : the Interaction of Law and Economics. – Dordrecht : Kluwer, 1981.
272p.
ISBN 0898380537 Hbk £75.00

Sisson, Keith
Management of collective bargaining : an international comparison / Keith Sisson. – Oxford : Basil Blackwell, 1987.
280p; 23cm.
Includes bibliography and index.
ISBN 0631134395 £25.00

Sit, Victor Fung-shuen →Commercial laws & business regulations of the People's Republic of China 1949-1983.

Situation of Industrial Property in the Countries of Africa. – Geneva : World Intellectual Property Organization, 1987.
715p.
Hbk £40.00

Situation of Industrial Property in the Countries of Asia and the Pacific. – Geneva : World Intellectual Property Organization, 1984.
420p.
Hbk £40.00

Situational crime prevention : from theory into practice / edited by Kevin Heal and Gloria Laycock. – London : H.M.S.O., 1986.
vii,159p; 25cm.
Research shows doubts as to the ability of traditional responses to control rising crime rates. Discusses the reduction of opportunity for crime as the most promising method of prevention. Examines the theory of crime prevention and its implementation.
ISBN 0113408269

Sivamohan, M. V. K →Law and society : lectures and writings of Justice P. Jaganmohan Reddy.

Sivaramayya, B.
Inequalities and the Law. – Lucknow : Eastern Book Company, 1984.
192p.
Hbk £60.00

Sixteenth Annual Workshop on Commercial and Consumer Law, October 17-18, 1986 : papers and other materials. – Toronto : Faculty of Law, University of Toronto, 1986.
vi,372p.
Includes bibliographical references.

Sixteenth report from the Committee of Public Accounts, session 1987-88 : monitoring and control of charities in England and Wales. – London : H.M.S.O., 1988.
ix,14p; 30cm. – (H.C.).
ISBN 0102116881

Sixth International Colloquy About the European Convention of Human Rights. – Council of Europe. – Dordrecht : Kluwer, 1987.
1,168p.
ISBN 9024735394 Hbk £550.00

Sixth report from the Home Affairs Committee, session 1981-82 : miscarriages of justice : together with proceedings of the Committee, the minutes of evidence and appendix. – London : H.M.S.O., 1982.
xix,69p. – (HC).
ISBN 010242182X

Sixth report from the Home Affairs Committee, session 1984-85 : Immigration and Nationality Department of the Home Office, together with the proceedings of the Committee, minutes of evidence and appendices. – London : H.M.S.O., 1985.
xxviii,119p. – (H.C.).
ISBN 0102277850

Sixth report to Parliament on subordinate legislation concerning County Court (Bailiff's Fees) Order 1986 ... / Legal and Constitutional Committee. – Melbourne : Government Printer, 1986.
v,11p.

Size of the Crime Problem in Australia. – 2nd ed. – Canberra : Australian Institute of Criminology.
free

Sizer, Richard →Computer generated output as admissible evidence in civil and criminal cases : a report.
→ Computer in court : a guide to computer evidence for lawyers and computing professionals.

Sizewell Syndrome : Nuclear Power, Nuclear Weapons and Public Policy. – London : Spokesman Books, 1984.
128p. – (Endpapers Ser. No. 7).
ISBN 0851244025 Hbk £3.95

Sjaastad, Larry A. →How Protection Taxes Exporters.

Skapinker →Sale of land : commentary and cases.

Skapinker, Diane →Sale of Land : Commentary and Cases.

Skarsgard, Anne
Layperson's Guide to Treaty Rights in Canada. – Saskatoon : University of Saskatchewan, Native Law Centre, 1985.
59p.
ISBN 0888801610 Hbk £15.00

Skeet, L. →Law and Management of Water Resources and Supply.

Skegg, P.D.G.
Law, Ethics and Medicine : Studies in Medical Law. – New Edition. – Oxford : Oxford University Press.
ISBN 00198256426 Pbk £11.95
—Law, ethics and medicine : studies in medical law / by P.D.G. Skegg. – Oxford : Clarendon, 1984.
xii,268p; 23cm.
Includes index.
ISBN 0198253656 £25.00

Skelhorn, Norman
Public prosecutor : the memoirs of Sir Norman Skelhorn, Director of Public Prosecutions, 1964-1977 / Sir Norman Skelhorn. – London : Harrap, 1981.
8,207p.
ISBN 0245537635

Skene, J.
Lawes and Acts of Parliament Made by King James the First and His Successours Kinges of Scotland : 1424-1597. – Repr. of 1597 ed. – Abingdon : Professional Books.
116p.
Hbk £350.00

Sketch of the lives of Lords Stowell and Eldon : comprising, with additional matter, some corrections of Mr.Twiss's work on the Chancellor / by William Edward Surtees. – London : Chapman and Hall, 1846.
vii,180p.

Skiing and the law. – Edinburgh : Green (W.) & Son, 1987.
Covers problems arising from liability for accidents likely to occur in connection with skiing, with reference to past cases incolving skiing and other sports from Scotland, England, France and North America, as well as to the provisions of the Consumer Protection Act.
ISBN 0414008332 Pbk

Skilling, H. Gordon
Charter 77 and human rights in Czechoslovakia / H. Gordon Skilling. – London : Allen & Unwin, 1981.
xv,363p; 24cm.
Bibliography: p345-351. - Includes index.
ISBN 0043210260

Skip Registries - Panama. – London : Lloyd's of London Press.
ISBN 1850441421 Hbk £25.00

Skyrme, Thomas
Changing Image of the Magistracy. – 2nd ed. – London : Macmillan, 1984.
272p.
ISBN 0333362799 Hbk £33.00
ISBN 0333362802 Pbk £7.95

Slabotzky, Albert
Grain contracts and arbitration for shipments from the United States and Canada / by Albert Slabotzky. – London : Lloyd's, 1984.
x,109p.
Bibliography: p.105-106. - Includes index.
ISBN 0907432883 Hbk £24.00

Slade, Elizabeth A.
Tolley's Employment Handbook. – 5th ed. – Croydon : Tolley.
456p.
Includes Employment Act 1988. Gives information on: ACAS, Disabled Employees, Equal Pay, Maternity Rights, Racial Discrimination, Trade Unions and Unfair Dismissal.
ISBN 0854593276 Hbk £17.95

Sladen, M.
Practical trust administration. – 2nd ed. – London : Europa Publications, 1984.
ISBN 0905118944 Hbk £17.50

Slater →Cash Flow and Credit Management.

Slater, A.H.
Australian Proprietary Company Articles : a Practical Guide with Precedents. – North Ryde : C.C.H. Australia, 1982.
320p.
Hbk £35.00

Slater, John C. N. →Cases and statutes on criminal law.

Slatter, Frans F.
Parliament and administrative agencies : a study paper prepared for the Law Reform Commission of Canada / by Frans F. Slatter. – Ottawa : Law Reform Commission of Canada, 1982.
6,154p; 25cm. – (Study paper).
ISBN 0662116259

Slatter, M.
Agricultural Holdings. – Oxford : Blackwell Scientific, 1987.
ISBN 0003833364 Hbk £20.00

Slattery, Brian
Ancestral Lands, Alien Laws : Judicial Perspectives on Aboriginal Title. – Saskatoon : University of Saskatchewan, Native Law Centre, 1983.
49p.
ISBN 0888801009 Hbk £9.00
—Canadian Native Law Cases
Vol. 2 1870-1890 /. – Saskatoon : University of Saskatchewan, Native Law Centre, 1981.
634p.
ISBN 0888801068 Hbk £65.00

Vol. 3 1891-1910. – 1985.
663p.
ISBN 0888801467 Hbk £65.00

Vol. 4 1911-1930. – 1986.
491p.
ISBN 0888801734 Hbk £65.00

Vol. 5 1931-1959. – 1987.
691p.
ISBN 0888801750 Hbk £70.00

Vol. 6 1960-1970. – 1988.
781p.
ISBN 0888801947 Hbk £70.00

Vol. 7 1971-1973. – 1988.
550p.
ISBN 0888802110 Hbk £70.00

Slave laws in the Americas. – University of Georgia, 1990.
224; 22.
ISBN 0820311790 Hbk £21.50

Slayton, Philip
Tariff Board : a study prepared for the Law Reform Commission of Canada / by Philip Slayton and John J. Quinn : assisted by James Cassels. – Ottawa : Minister of Supply and Services, 1981.
ix,154p; 25cm. – (Administrative law series).
ISBN 0662116224
—Trade Law Topics / Steven Cass. – Toronto : Butterworths.
ISBN 0409811890 Hbk £165.00

Slevin, Kevin S
Practical Aspects of Capital Gains Tax : Exemptions and Reliefs Explained. – Bicester : CCH.
ISBN 0863251935 Pbk £25.50
—Retirement relief - New CGT Rules. – London : CCH, 1986.
ISBN 0863250815 Pbk £7.50
—Retirement relief; the capital gains tax rules explained. – 2nd. – Bicester : CCH Editions Ltd, 1988.
Examines the changes introduced by the 1987 and 1988 Finance Acts. Includes two new chapters on two-tier relief and the Inland Revenue concession on date of disposal. Also covers how retirement relief works, the date of disposal, unincorporated businesses, partners, directors, trustees, full-time employees, furnished holiday lettings, husband and wife, interactions with tax, and a legislation finding list.
ISBN 0863251668 Hbk £15.50
—Roll-over relief for business assets : the Capital Gains Tax Rules explained / Kevin S. Slevin. – Bicester : CCH Editions, 1987.
v,66p; 23cm.
Includes index.
ISBN 0863251196

Slinn, Judy
History of Freshfields / Judy Slinn. – London : Freshfields, 1984.
208p.
Bibliography: p.181-187. - Includes index.

Slinn, Peter →Evolution of the modern Commonwealth : 1902-80.
—International Law of Development / Francis G Snyder. – London : Butterworths.
ISBN 0862052408 Pbk £19.50
→ International law of development : comparative perspectives.

Sloan, Kenneth
Law Relating to Traffic. – London : Police Review Publishing, 1982.
ISBN 0851649920 Pbk £3.50
—Police law primer. – 3rd ed. – London : Butterworths, 1987.
ISBN 0406846529 Pbk £8.95

Slomnicka, B. I.
Law of child care / B.I. Slomnicka. – Plymouth : Macdonald & Evans, 1982.
xlvi,415p.
Includes index.
ISBN 0712112529

Slot, P J →Toward a Community air transport policy: the legal dimension.

Slusser, Robert M. →Calendar of Soviet treaties, 1958-1973.

Slynn, Gordon
Judicial review of Community administrative acts / Sir Gordon Slynn. – Exeter : University of Exeter, 1985.
16p.
Includes bibliographical references.
→ Rights of working women in the European Community.

Smailes
Tolley's Tax Data 1988-89 / Dolton. – Finance Bill 1988 Edition. – Tolley Publishing.
ISBN 08545493459 Hbk £7.95

Small Business and the Law. – Department of Industry & Commerce. – Repr. of 1981 ed. – Canberra : Australian Government Publishing Service, 1983.
40p. – (Managing the Small Business Ser.).
ISBN 0642069085 Hbk £2.30

Small Business Banks and Small Business Administration Loan Subsidising the Weak or Bridging a Credit Gap. – London : Eurospan.
ISBN 0899302564 Hbk £32.95

Small business in Europe / Dewhurst. – London : Macmillan, 1986.
ISBN 0333384067 Pbk £12.95

Small Business Venture Capital Act. – Vancouver : Continuing Legal Education Society of British Columbia, 1986.
347p.
ISBN 086504290X Hbk £75.00

Small businesses / by Michael Chesterman. – 2nd ed. – London : Sweet & Maxwell, 1982.
xxi,288p; 19cm.
Previous ed.: 1977. Includes index.
ISBN 0421286008 Hbk £13.00
ISBN 0421286105 Pbk £7.95

Small Claims Court Guide for Alberta : How to Win Your Case. – 4th ed. – North Vancouver : International Self-Counsel Press, 1985.
122p.
ISBN 0889082286 Hbk £7.50

Small Claims Court Guide for British Columbia : How to Win Your Case!. – 18th ed. – North Vancouver : International Self-Counsel Press, 1986.
138p.
ISBN 0889081859 Hbk £7.95

Small Claims Court Guide for Ontario : How to Win Your Case!. – 6th ed. – North Vancouver : International Self-Counsel Press, 1986.
144p.
ISBN 0889083568 Hbk £7.50

Small Claims Court Materials : Can They Be Read? Can They Be Understood? / Marilyn Hiebert. – Ottawa : Canadian Law Information Council, 1985.
184p.
ISBN 0920358837 Pbk

Small Claims Court Practice and Procedure. – Vancouver : Continuing Legal Education Society of British Columbia, 1988.
434p.
ISBN 0865049718 Hbk £85.00

Small Claims Court Practice in the Ontario Provincial Court (Civil Division)-1987. – Agincourt : Carswell, 1987.
ca 300p.
Hbk £39.25

Small claims courts. – Oxford : Clarendon Press, 1989.
250; 21.5.
Compares and contrasts some of the principles which have been applied in informal methods of adjudicating small claims, and some of the solutins which have been adopted in eight countries. Analyses the dilemmas which alternative options pose for justice.
ISBN 0198256272 Hbk £25.00

Small claims in Northern Ireland : a 'step-by-step' guide / by D.S. Greer. – 3rd ed. – Belfast : SLS Publications, 1987.
63p. – (The law in action).

Small Claims in Ontario. – Community Legal Education Ontario. – Toronto : Community Legal Education Ontario, 1982.
70p.
ISBN 0889030588 Pbk £6.50

Small claims in the county court : how to sue and defend actions without a solicitor / by Michael Birks. – Rev. ed. – London : Lord Chancellor's Department, 1984.
73p.

Small Claims Litigation. – Butterworths, 1988.
160p.
Guide to the conduct of small claims court actions. Takes the reader step by step from the initial client interview and preliminary issues such as limitations, parties and forums, to drafting effective pleadings. Shows how to handle interlocutory proceedings and how to effectively negotiate settlement. Contains annotated Court Rules, and a set of sample forms.
ISBN 0409806528 Pbk £24.95

Small claims procedure in the Sheriff court : detailed proposals : consultation paper. – Scottish Courts Administration. – Edinburgh : Scottish Courts Administration, 1987.
94p in various pagings.
Includes example of forms. Issued on behalf of the Lord Advocate and the Sheriff Court Rules Council.

Small Estates (Distributions) Act, 1955 (Act 98) and Regulations. – Kuala Lumpur : International Law Books Services.
Hbk £10.00

Small is dangerous : micro states in a macro world: report of a Study Group of the David Davies Memorial Institute of International Studies / edited by Sheila Harden. – London : Frances Pinter, 1985.
ix,212p.

Small print : the language and layout of consumer contracts : Report to the National Consumer Council / Martin Cutts and Chrissie Maher : Plain English Campaign. – London : National Consumer Council, 1983.
39p.
ISBN 0905653661

Small Security Appeals. – Administrative Review Council. – Canberra : Australian Government Publishing Service, 1981.
144p.
ISBN 0642066663 Hbk £4.80

Small self-administered pension scheme. – Croydon : Tolley, 1988.
ISBN 085459311X Hbk £16.95

Small, Stephen →Police and people in London, vol.2 : A group of young black people : Stephen Small.

Small Works Contract Documentation : An Architectural Press Legal Guide. – 3rd ed. – London : Architectural Press, 1986.
176p : Illus.
ISBN 0851399762 Hbk £14.95

Smart, Carol
Ties that bind : law, marriage and the reproduction of patriarchal relations / Carol Smart. – London : Routledge & Kegan Paul, 1984.
xiv,273p; 22cm.
Bibliography: p259-268. - Includes index.
ISBN 0710098324 Pbk £6.95
→ Women in law.

Smart, P E
Cases in the Law of Banking 1983-1985. – 2nd ed. – London : Sweet & Maxwell, 1986.
ISBN 0421357606 Pbk £7.50
→ Chorley and Smart leading cases in the law of banking.
→ Legal Decisions Affecting Bankers, Vols. 1-11.

Smart, W. B., et al
Sexual Offences : Bill C-127. – Vancouver : British Columbia Continuing Legal Education Society, 1983.
155p.
ISBN 0865041032 Hbk £45.00

Smead, H.
Blood Justice : Lynching of Mack Charles Parker. – Oxford : Oxford University Press.
ISBN 00195054296 Pbk £5.95

Smellie, Robert
Commentary on Standard Conditions of Contract : NZSS 623:1964 / M.C. Barker. – Butterworths, 1983.
ISBN 0409600806 Pbk £52.80

Smeltzer, James S. →Guidebook to Alberta Business Corporations Act.

Smiley, G. W.
Implications of marital separation for young children / compiled by the Australian Institute of Family Studies from a report of a survey conducted in 1982-83 by G.W. Smiley, E.R. Chamberlain and L.I. Dalgleish. – Melbourne : Australian Institute of Family Studies, 1987.
ix,45p. – (Working paper).
Bibliography: p.33-45.

Smit
Law Of The European Economic Community / P E Herzog. – Matthew Bender, 1976.
ISBN 0000999047 Hbk £247.00

Smith
Child Care and the Courts / Lane. – London : Macmillan.
ISBN 0333420772 Pbk £6.95
→ Coming to Terms with Policing : Perspectives on Policy.
—Evaluating Police Work : An Action Research Project / Horton. – Policy Studies Institute.
ISBN 0853743533 Pbk £7.95
—Expert Evidence : Perspectives on Science and Law / Wynne. – Routledge.
ISBN 0415009413 Hbk £29.95
—Financial Accounting. – Maidenhead : McGraw-Hill, 1988.
ISBN 0070590028 Hbk £27.00
→ How to conduct arbitrations.
—Industrial law / Wood. – 3rd ed. – London : Butterworths, 1986.
ISBN 0406381453 Pbk £17.95
—Introduction to Canadian Law of Trusts. – London : Butterworths.
ISBN 0409868108 Hbk £22.00
→ Landlord and Tenant.
→ Law Relating to Trade Descriptions.
—Practical Social Work / Lane. – London : Macmillan.
ISBN 0333420764 Hbk £20.00

Smith : Trading Financial Options. – London : Butterworths, 1986.
ISBN 0406100470 Pbk £57.75

Smith, A.
Trading financial options. – London : Butterworths, 1986.
ISBN 0406100470 Hbk £27.50

Smith, A. J. →Criminal Law : The Protection of Property.

Smith, A. T. H.
Offences against public order : including the Public Order Act 1986 / by A.T.H. Smith. – London : Sweet and Maxwell, 1987.
xlvii,326p; 25cm.
Analysis of the Public Order Act 1986, explaining provisions and their practical applications. Also deals with features of existing law not affected by the act, such as obstructing the highway, obstructing a police officer in the execution of his duty, and the possession of offensive weapons.
ISBN 0421365803 Pbk £10.00

Smith and Keenan's company law / Denis Keenan, Kenneth Smith. – 7th ed. – London : Pitman, 1987.
xl,596p; 22cm.
Includes index.
ISBN 0273027921 Pbk £11.95

Smith and Keenan's Company law / Denis Keenan, Kenneth Smith. – 6th ed. – London : Pitman, 1986.
xl,596p; 22cm.
Previous ed.: published as Company law. 1983. Includes index.
ISBN 0273024876 Pbk £10.95

Smith and Keenan's mercantile law / Denis Keenan. – 7th ed. – London : Pitman, 1988.
688p; 22cm.
Previous ed.: 1985. Includes index.
ISBN 027302843X Pbk £12.95

Smith and Thomas : a casebook on contract / J. A. C. Thomas, J. C. Smith. – 8th ed. – London : Sweet & Maxwell, 1987.
600p; 24cm.
Previous ed.: published as A casebook on contract. 1982. Includes index.
ISBN 0421346108 Hbk £26.00
ISBN 0421346205 Pbk £18.50

Smith, Andrew L. H.
Smith : Trading Financial Options. – London : Butterworths, 1986.
ISBN 0406100470 Pbk £57.75

Smith, Arnold
Stitches in time : the Commonwealth in world politics / Arnold Smith with Clyde Sanger. – London : Deutsch, 1981.
xix,322p.

Smith, Brian D.
State responsibility and the marine environment : the rules of decision / Brian D. Smith. – Oxford : Clarendon, 1988.
xviii,281p; 24cm. – (Oxford monographs in international law).
Bibliography: p257-276. - Includes index.
ISBN 0198255810 £30.00

Smith, Catherine
Law of insolvency / by Catherine Smith. – 2nd ed. – Durban : Butterworths, 1982.
xiii,476p.
Previous ed.: 1973. Includes index.
ISBN 0409056022 Hbk R98
ISBN 0409056030 Pbk R71

Smith, Charles
Company procedures manual. – London : Longman Professional (UK).
Selection of over 300 precedent documents, covering administration, shares and shareholders, officers and loan capital, and includes minutes, resolutions, notices, letters, agreements. Also available on disk.
ISBN 0851212263 Llf £85.00

Smith, Colin M.
Law of betting, gaming and lotteries / by Colin M. Smith & Stephen P. Monkcom. – London : Butterworth, 1987.
600p.
Includes index.
ISBN 0406296596 £50.00

Smith, D. →Unions and Arbitration '81 - Papers and Discussion of the Armidale Industrial Law and Relations Seminar.

Smith, Daniel J. →Police and people in London, vol.3 : A survey of police officers : David J. Smith.

Smith, David
Board of visitor adjudications / David Smith, Claire Austin and John Ditchfield. – London : Home Office, 1981.
v,45p. – (Research Unit paper).
Bibliography: p40.
ISBN 0862520045
—Crime and penal policy / David Smith and A.J. Fowles. – York : Longman, 1986.
24p; 30cm.
Bibliography: p23-24.
ISBN 0582172551 Pbk
→ Reducing the prison population : an exploratory study in Hampshire.

Smith, David J. →Police and people in London, vol.1 : A survey of Londoners : David J. Smith.

Smith, Douglas W.
Trade Union Law in Australia : the Legal Status of Australian Trade Unions / Donald W. Rawson. – 2nd ed. – Butterworths, 1985.
224p.
ISBN 0409492736 Hbk £49.00

Smith, Edgar Dennis →Brief to counsel.

Smith, Garry J →Charter of Rights and administrative law, 1983-1984.

Smith, Graham F.
Public Employment Law : The Role of the Contract of Employment in Australia and Britain. – Sydney : Butterworths, 1987.
208p.
This book describes the statutory and institutional framework of public employment law in Australia and Britain. Also discussed are the distinctions between Crown servants and other public employees, discipline, dismissal, tenure of employment, and remedies.
Pbk £29.00

Smith, I. T.
Industrial law / I.T. Smith, Sir John C. Wood. – 3rd ed. – London : Butterworths, 1986.
516p; 25cm.
Previous ed.: 1983. Includes index.
ISBN 0406381445 Hbk £
ISBN 0406381453 Pbk

Smith, J.
Liability in Negligence. – London : Sweet & Maxwell, 1984.
ISBN 0459365908 Hbk £24.00

Smith, J. C.
Casebook on contract / by J.C. Smith and the late J.A.C. Thomas. – 7th ed. – London : Sweet & Maxwell, 1987.
xxxi,604p; 24cm.
Previous ed.: 1977. Includes index.
ISBN 0421283203 Hbk £
ISBN 0421283300 Pbk £12.95
—Codification of the criminal law : a public lecture / delivered by J.C. Smith on ... 17th March 1986. – London : Inns of Court School of Law, 1986.
16p.
—Contract . – Sweet & Maxwell.
ISBN 0421364203 Hbk £14.00
ISBN 0421364303 Pbk £8.95
—Criminal law / by J.C. Smith and Brian Hogan. – 6th ed. – London : Butterworths, 1988.
900p; 25cm.
Previous ed.: 1983. Includes index.
ISBN 0406658110 Hbk £35.00 :
ISBN 0406658129 Pbk £19.00
—Criminal law : cases and materials / J.C. Smith, Brian Hogan. – 3rd ed. – London : Butterworths, 1986.
700p; 25cm.
Previous ed.: 1980. Includes index.
ISBN 0406658242 Pbk £ :
ISBN 0406658250
—Justification and excuse in the criminal law. – London : Stevens & Sons, 1989.
– (Hamlyn lectures).
Examines the distinction between justification and excuse, asks whether circumstances unknown to the defendant may amount to a defence, looks at judicial interpretation of statutory 'let-out' clause, necessity and duress, and the future of justification and excuse, in case law, legislation, and codification.
ISBN 0420478108 Hbk £17.50
ISBN 0420478205 Pbk £8.95
—Justification and Excuse in the Criminal Law. – Stevens & Sons.
ISBN 00420478205 Pbk £11.00
ISBN 0420478108 Hbk £15.00
→ Law and its presuppositions : actions, agents and rules.
—Law of theft / J.C. Smith. – 5th ed. – London : Butterworths, 1984.
xxxii,257p; 26cm.
Previous ed.: 1979. Includes index.
ISBN 0406379084 Hbk £
ISBN 0406379092 Pbk £13.95
—Liability in negligence / by J.C. Smith. – Toronto : Carswell, 1984.
xxxiii, 273 p.; 24 cm.
Includes indexes.
ISBN 0459366009 Pbk
—Reform of the law of sexual offences / J.C. Smith : with comments by Antony Grey. – Leeds : University of Leeds, Centre for Social Work and Applied Social Studies, 1981.
ii,17p. – (Occasional paper).
→ Smith and Thomas : a casebook on contract.
—Smith and Thomas : a casebook on contract / J. A. C. Thomas, J. C. Smith. – 8th ed. – London : Sweet & Maxwell, 1987.
600p; 24cm.
Previous ed.: published as A casebook on contract. 1982. Includes index.
ISBN 0421346108 Hbk £26.00
ISBN 0421346205 Pbk £18.50
—Towards a rational criminal law : being the Presidential Address of Professor J. C. Smith, President of the Holdsworth Club of the faculty of Law in the University of Birmingham, 1982-83. – Birmingham : Holdsworth Club, 1983.
15p. – (Holdsworth Club Presidential Addresses, 1983).
ISBN 0704406624
—Western idea of law / by J. C. Smith and David N. Weisstub. – London : Butterworths, 1983.
xxii,685p.
Highlights the unique aspects of Western law by comparing it to other legal traditions, past and present. More than 170 great thinkers are excerpted, and a feminist perspective is incorporated, raising questions about women and power. Covers issues such as state sovereignty egalitarianism, and constitutional guarantees of human rights.
ISBN 0409868191

Smith, J. E. →Northern Ireland supplement to Smith and Hogan, Criminal law, fifth edition.

Smith, Julian
Rules to Keep the Rascals Out. – Vancouver : November House.
ISBN 0920156045 Hbk £1.95

Smith, K.J.M.
James Fitzjames Stephen : Portrait Victorian Rationalist. – Cambridge : Cambridge University Press.
ISBN 0521340292 Hbk £30.00

Smith, Keith →Charitable status : a practical handbook.

Smith, Kenneth
Cases and Materials on Criminal Law / Brian Hogan. – 3rd ed. – London : Butterworths.
ISBN 0406658242 Hbk £29.00
ISBN 0406658250 Pbk £19.95
—Cases and Materials On English Legal Systems / Bailey. – Sweet & Maxwell, 1987.
ISBN 0421359404 Hbk
ISBN 0421359501 Pbk
→ Charitable Status - A Practical Handbook.
—Company Law / Dennis Keenan. – 7th ed. – London : Pitman Publishing, 1987.
ISBN 0273027921 Pbk £12.95
—English Law / Keenan. – 8th ed. – London : Pitman Publishing, 1986.
ISBN 027302342X Pbk £11.95
ISBN 0406677611 Hbk £19.50
—Mercantile Law / Keenan. – 7th ed. – Pitman, 1988.
ISBN 027302843X Pbk £12.95
—Mercantile law / Kenneth Smith, Denis Keenan. – 5th ed. – London : Pitman, 1982.
xiii,753p; 22cm.
Previous ed.: 1977. Includes index. 3rd ed. and earlier entitled: Essentials of mercantile law.
ISBN 0273017691 Pbk
—Smith and Keenan's Company law / Denis Keenan, Kenneth Smith. – 6th ed. – London : Pitman, 1986.
xl,596p; 22cm.
Previous ed.: published as Company law. 1983. Includes index.
ISBN 0273024876 Pbk £10.95

—Smith and Keenan's company law / Denis Keenan, Kenneth Smith. – 7th ed. – London : Pitman, 1987.
xl,596p; 22cm.
Includes index.
ISBN 0273027921 Pbk £11.95

—Smith and Keenan's mercantile law / Denis Keenan. – 7th ed. – London : Pitman, 1988.
688p; 22cm.
Previous ed.: 1985. Includes index.
ISBN 027302843X Pbk £12.95

Smith, Kenneth M.
Canadian Private Security Manual / Robert J. Prouse. – Agincourt : Carswell, 1987.
352p.
This work for Canadian private security officers discusses the question of security for emergency situations, investigational procedures, and surveillance in depth.
Hbk £33.75

Smith, L Laggard
Blasphemy and the battle for faith. – London : Hodder & Stoughton, 1990.
208; 18.
ISBN 0340522798 Pbk £2.99

Smith, Lacey Baldwin
Treason in Tudor England : Politics and Paranoia. – London : Jonathan Cape.
352p.
ISBN 0224028057 Hbk £16.00

Smith, Larry
Australian Tax Office Practice. – Woolloomooloo : International Business Communications, 1986.
ISBN 0949072036 Llf £195.00

Smith, Lorna J. F.
Criminal justice comparisons : the case of Scotland and England and Wales / Lorna J.F. Smith. – London : Home Office, 1983.
v,57p.
Bibliography: p.50.
ISBN 0862521009

Smith, Lynn
Righting the Balance : Canada's New Equality Rights. – Agincourt : Carswell, 1986.
450p.
Hbk £39.50

Smith, M.
ABC guide to the Federal Court of Australia. – North Ryde : Law Book Co, 1986.
xvii, 230p.
ISBN 0455206864 Pbk £29.50

—Butterworths Student Companions Contracts /. – 2nd ed. – Butterworths, 1988.
144p.
ISBN 0409493252

—Legal Counselling in Canada-Japan Business Transactions - II. – Vancouver : British Columbia Continuing Legal Education Society, 1983.
425p.
ISBN 0865041016 Hbk £65.00

Smith, M. G.
Pastoral Discipline and the Church Courts : The Hexham Court, 1680-1730. – York : St. Anthony's Press, 1982.
– (Borthwick Papers Ser.).
Pbk £3.00

Smith, Malcolm D. →Legal process : commentary and materials.

Smith, Martin →Consuming secrets : how official secrecy affects everyday life in Britain.

Smith, Mel →Rape study : a study directed by Mel Smith and Warren Young and undertaken by the Department of Justice and the Institute of Criminology.

Smith, Nigel
Legal research techniques / by Nigel Smith. – Hebden Bridge : Legal Information Resources, 1987.
ii,40p.
ISBN 1870369017

—Legal thesaurus / compiled by Nigel Smith and Christine Miskin. – Hebden Bridge : Legal Information Resources, 1987.
204p.
ISBN 1870369009

Smith, P.
Criminal Law : Essays in Honour of J.C. Smith. – London : Butterworths, 1987.
ISBN 0406501106 Hbk £26.00

—Distribution on Intestacy. – London : Longman Professional, 1988.
ISBN 0851214010 Pbk £2.95

→ Non-means tested benefits: the legislation.

—Non-means-tested social security benefits / Rowland. – 9th ed. – London : CENT, 1986.
ISBN 0903963965 Pbk £4.00

—Worker-controlled businesses and the law. – Spokesman Books, 1988.
ISBN 0851244521 Hbk £25.00
ISBN 0851244629 Pbk £8.95

Smith, P. F.
Housing Act Nineteen-Eighty. – London : Butterworths, 1981.
This book gives an extensive narrative exposition of the Act followed by the text of the Act with extensive annotations. The work is a thorough guide to the provisions of the United Kingdom's Housing Act of 1980.
ISBN 0406657904 Hbk
→ Law of landlord and tenant.

—Modern English legal system / by P.F. Smith and S.H. Bailey. – London : Sweet & Maxwell, 1984.
xxxix,783p; 24cm.
Includes index.
ISBN 0421271809 Hbk £30.00
ISBN 0421271906 Pbk £16.00

Smith, P. W. →Barnsley's conveyancing law and practice.

Smith, Peter →Criminal law : essays in honour of J.C. Smith.

Smith, R.
Cost and Management Accounting 1 ACCA Study and Revision Pack 1.2. – Pitman.
ISBN 0273027964 Pbk £11.95

—Exclusive Economic Zone Claims : an Analysis and Primary Documents. – Dordrecht : Kluwer, 1986.
600p.
ISBN 9024732506 Hbk £350.00

—Matrimonial and Family Proceedings Act 1984. – London : Longman Professional.
ISBN 0851212867 Pbk £19.95

—Matrimonial Causes (Amend No 2) Rules 1985. – London : Longman Professional, 1986.
ISBN 0851212069 Pbk £6.50

Smith, R.M.
Contracts for Work in Industry (NSW) : Section 88F. – Butterworths, 1981.
ISBN 0409490474 Pbk £35.00

Smith, Richard M.
Matrimonial and Family Proceedings Act 1984 : a practical guide / Richard M. Smith. – London : Oyez, 1984.
xviii,125p.
Includes index.
ISBN 0851208789

Smith, Roger
Trial by medicine : insanity and responsibility in Victorian trials / by Roger Smith. – Edinburgh : Edinburgh University Press, 1981.
ix,238p.
ISBN 085224407X
→ 'We don't give clothing grants any more' : the 1980 supplementary benefit scheme.

Smith, Ronald T.
Accounting for Damages : a Framework for Litigation Support. – Don Mills : CCH Canadian Ltd, 1987.
240p.
ISBN 0887963986 Hbk £40.00

Smith, S.C.H.
Taxation 1988-89. – Pontefract : Lofthouse Publications.
ISBN 0900370874 Pbk £17.50

Smith, Stephen
Britain's shadow economy / Stephen Smith. – Oxford : Clarendon, 1986.
192p; 22cm.
Includes bibliography and index.
ISBN 0198285698 £16.95

Smith, Thomas M. →Statutes : Rules and Examples.

Smith's taxation 1985-86. – London : Longman Professional, 1985.
ISBN 0900370637 Pbk £12.75

Smuts, F. S →Second report : Commission of Inquiry into the Appearance of Advocates in the Supreme Court of South Africa.

Smyth, Ailbhe
Womens Rights in Ireland. – Dublin, 1983.
223p.
ISBN 0907085687 Pbk £4.95

Smyth Town Plot Land Act, 1983, Bill Pr033 : An Act Respecting Certain Land in the Town of Smyth, in the District of Nipissing. – Ontario : Ontario Government Publications Service, 1983.
3p.
Hbk £0.30

Smyth, Yvonne M. →Information technology : the challenge to copyright.

Smythe, B. →Judicial review : legal limits of official power.

Snaith, Ian
Law of co-operatives / Ian Snaith. – London : Waterlow, 1984.
xxviii,218p; 22cm.
Bibliography: p210-213. - Includes index.
ISBN 0080391591 Hbk £31.00

—Law of corporate insolvency. – London : Waterlow, 1990.
912; 23.
ISBN 0080392059 Hbk £70

Snell, Edmund Henry Turner
Snell's Principles of equity / P. V. Baker, P. St. J. Langan. – 28th ed. – London : Sweet & Maxwell, 1982.
clv,703p; 25cm.
Previous ed.: 1973. Includes index.
ISBN 0421250208 £22.00

Snell, James G.
Supreme Court of Canada : History of the Institution / Frederick Vaughan. – Toronto : University of Toronto Press, 1985.
ISBN 0802034179 Hbk £40.00
ISBN 0802034187 Pbk £17.50

Snell, Mandy
Equal pay and opportunities : a study of the implementation and effects of the Equal Pay and Sex Discrimination Acts in 26 organizations / by M.W. Snell, P. Glucklich and M. Povall. – London : Department of Employment, 1981.
7,110p. – (Research paper).
Bibliography: p108-110.

Snell's Principles of equity / P. V. Baker, P. St. J. Langan. – 28th ed. – London : Sweet & Maxwell, 1982.
clv,703p; 25cm.
Previous ed.: 1973. Includes index.
ISBN 0421250208 £22.00

Snider, D. Laureen
Legal services in rural areas : an evaluation : report / prepared for the Department of Justice, Ottawa, and the Faculty of Law, Queen's University by D. Laureen Snider. – Rev. ed. – Ottawa : Department of Justice, Evaluation and Statistics Section, 1981.
303p. – (An evaluation report).
Bibliography: p.257-266.

Snow, J. W.
Off-Road Vehicles Act, 1983, Bill 061 : An Act to Regulate Off-Road Vehicles. – Ontario : Ontario Government Publications Service, 1983.
11p.
Hbk £0.50

Snow, R. F.
Problems for the Business Client in the Marketing of Goods : Licensing and the Infringement of Rights. – London : Law Society, 1986.
17p.
Hbk £1.95

Snowden, P. N. →International institutions in trade and finance.

Snowden, Robert
Artificial family : a consideration of artificial insemination by donor / R. Snowden and G.D. Mitchell. – London : Allen & Unwin, 1981.
138p; 23cm.
Bibliography: p128-136. - Includes index.
ISBN 0041760018

Snow's Annotated Criminal Code, 1 Vol. – Bound Edition. – Agincourt : Carswell, 1988.
This looseleaf service contains the annotated text of the Criminal Code of Canada and its amendments. Extensive case law citations are provided in the work.
Llf £74.00

Snow-white image : the hidden reality of crime in Switzerland / Flemming Balvig. – Oslo : Norwegian University Press, 1988.
123p.
Bibliography: p.119-123.. Translation of: Hvid som sne.
ISBN 8200074722 £17.50

Snyder, F.E.
Third World Attitudes Toward International Law : an Introduction / S. Sathirathai. – Dordrecht : Kluwer, 1987.
852p.
ISBN 0898389143 Hbk £375.00

Snyder, Francis →Political economy of law : a third world reader.

Snyder, Francis G →International Law of Development.
→ International law of development : comparative perspectives.
→ Labour, law and crime : an historical perspective.

—Law of the Common Agricultural Policy / by Francis G. Snyder. – London : Sweet & Maxwell, 1985.
130p; 22cm.
Includes index.
ISBN 0421318805 Hbk £11.50 :
ISBN 0421318902 Pbk £6.50

Snyman, C.R.
Criminal Law. – London : Butterworths, 1983.
ISBN 0409056170 Hbk £46.20
ISBN 0409056189 Pbk £34.70

—Criminal law / by C.R. Snyman : translation by the author, assisted by Lesbury van Zyl. – Durban : Butterworths, 1984.
545; 25 cm.
Includes indexes. Bibliography: p. 486-492. Translation of: Strafreg.
ISBN 0409056189 Pbk R64.00

So, You Have to Go to Court : a Child's Guide to Testifying as a Witness in Child Abuse Cases / Anne Watson-Russell. – Butterworths, 1986.
48p.
ISBN 040980519X Pbk £7.95

So You Want a Fight! : Shareholder Rights and Remedies in Canada. – North Ryde : C.C.H. Australia, 1986.
195p.
ISBN 0887963668 Pbk £16.95

So, You've Been Busted! / Anne Watson-Russell. – Butterworths, 1988.
48p.
Guide to the Youth Court. Discusses what the reader needs to know about court, how to get a lawyer, what to talk about with a lawyer, seeing the youth worker, letters of reference, getting parents ready for court, seeing a psychologist, the trial, taking the oath, witnesses and cross-examination, and the verdict and sentencing.
ISBN 0409809853 Pbk £7.95

Soanes, P.C.
Value Added Tax Property Planning after the EEC Decision. – 2nd ed. – London : Longman Professional.
ISBN 0851214630 Hbk £95.00

Soar, Peter H M
Conveyancing After the Act. – London : Butterworths, 1986.
ISBN 0406504105 Pbk £9.75
→ Solicitor's practice, 1.

Soares, Patrick C → Death and Taxes.
—Land and Tax Planning. – 3rd ed. – London : Longman Professional.
– (Practical Tax Series).
ISBN 0851214541 Hbk £32.50
—Land and Tax Planning. – 2nd ed. – London : Longman Professional, 1984.
ISBN 0851208800 Pbk £22.00
—Land and Tax Planning. – London : Oyez Longman, 1982.
300p. – (Oyez Longman Practical Tax Ser.).
ISBN 0851206077 Hbk £15.00
—Non-Resident Trusts : The Tax Planning Opportunities. – London : Oyez Longman, 1984.
– (Oyez Longman Intelligence Report Ser.).
ISBN 0851208169 Hbk
—Tax Strategy for Conveyancing and Land Transactions. – London : Oyez Longman, 1984.
ISBN 0851208797 Hbk
—Taxation of Land Development / Sheila Parrington. – London : Butterworths.
Llf
—Trusts and Tax Planning. – 2nd ed. – London : Oyez Longman, 1982.
– (Oyez Longman Practical Tax Ser.).
Hbk £16.00
—Trusts and tax planning. – 3rd ed. – London : Longman Professional, 1987.
ISBN 0851208762 Pbk £35.88

Social and Economic Research Council → Industrial relations : challenges and prospects : a report on the Warwick conference of March 1986.

Social contract / Michael Lessnoff. – London : Macmillan, 1986.
x,178p; 23cm.
Bibliography: p169-173. - Includes index.
ISBN 0333367901 Hbk £18.00
ISBN 033336791X Pbk £6.95

Social control and the state : historical and comparative essays / edited by Stanley Cohen and Andrew Scull. – Oxford : Basil Blackwell, 1985.
vii,341p; 23cm.
Survey of the way society maintains conformity and responds to deviance. Discusses state, class and individual power, legal repression and civil rights and role of reform movements in producing social change.
ISBN 0631142614

Social democracy and the rule of law / Otto Kirchheimer and Franz Neumann : edited by Keith Tribe : translated by Leena Tanner and Keith Tribe. – London : Allen & Unwin, 1987.
224p; 22cm.
Includes bibliography and index. Translated from the German.
ISBN 0043013007 £25.00

Social Democratic Lawyers' Association → Controlling the state : towards fairer administration.
—Divided we stand : a report on the legal profession / Social Democratic Lawyers' Association : chairman William Goodhart. – London : The Association, 1986.
53p.

Social Democratic Party
Controlling the state : towards fairer administration / by an SDP working party on citizens' rights and the Social Democratic Lawyers' Association Working Party on Administrative Law : with a foreward by Robert MacLennan. – London : SDP Open Forum Committee, 1983.
26p.

Social history and law reform / by O.R. McGregor. – London : Stevens, 1981.
x,66p; 19cm.
Includes index.
ISBN 0420459200 Hbk £9.50
ISBN 0420459308 Pbk £4.25

Social justice and individual responsibility in the welfare state / edited by Jan M. Broekman, Kazimierz Opaek, Djangir A.A. Kerimov : preface by Carl Wellman Soziale Gerechtigkeit und individuelle Verantwortlichkeit im Wohlfahrtsstaat / herausgegeben von Jan M. Broekman, Kazimierz Opaek, Djangir A.A. Kerimov ; vorwort von Carl Wellman. – Stuttgart : F. Steiner Verlag Wiesbaden, 1985.
299 p.; 24 cm. – (Archives for philosophy of law and social philosophy).
English, French, and German. 'Eleventh World Congress of the IVR convened in Helsinki 15-20 August 1983'–P. 5. Includes bibliographical references and index.
ISBN 3515044590 Pbk DM35.00

Social policy harmonisation in the European Community / John Holloway. – Farnborough, Hants. : Gower, 1981.
vi,318p; 23cm.
Bibliography: p305-318.
ISBN 0566001969 £10.50

Social relations and human attributes / Paul Hirst and Penny Woolley. – London : Tavistock, 1982.
xi,297p; 24cm.
Bibliography: p274-286. - Includes index.
ISBN 0422772208 Hbk £12.00
ISBN 0422772305 Pbk £4.95

Social Sciences and Humanities Research Council of → Canadian law faculties : a report to the Consultative Group on Research and Education in Law based on the 1981 survey of Canadian law faculties and statistics of the Canadian deans of law.
→ Canadian law professors : a report to the Consultative Group on Research and Education in Law based on the 1981 survey of full-time law professors in Canada.
→ Canadian law professors : a staff report on the survey of full-time law professors in Canada.
→ Law and learning : report to the Social Science and Humanities Research Council of Canada.
—Law and learning : report to the Social Science and Humanities Research Council of Canada / by the Consultative Group on Research and Education in Law. – Ottawa : The Council, 1983.
ix, 186, 212, x p.; 23 cm.
English and French. Title on added t.p.: Le droit et le savoir. Includes bibliographies.
ISBN 0662524365 Pbk
→ Profile of published legal research : a report to the Consultative Group on Research and Education in Law based on a survey of Canadian legal publications.
→ Sources of support for legal research : a report to the Consultative Group on Research and Education in Law based on a survey of foundations, law reform commissions, departments of justice, and attorneys and solicitors general in Canada.

Social security - abolition of independent appeals under the social fund : special report / by the Council on Tribunals. – London : H.M.S.O., 1986.
6p; 25cm.
ISBN 0101972202

Social Security Act 1975 : reform of the industrial injuries scheme / presented to Parliament by the Secretary of State for Social Services .. – London : H.M.S.O., 1981.
iv,30p; 25cm.
At head of title: Department of Health and Social Security.
ISBN 0101840209 unbound £3.05

Social Security and State Benefits 1987-1988. – Tolley Publishing.
ISBN 0854592830 Pbk £17.95

Social security contributions / Neil D. Booth. – London : Butterworths, 1982.
xxviii,204p; 25cm.
Includes index.
ISBN 0406128995 Pbk £8.00

Social Security Law and Policy. – North Ryde : Law Book Co, 1986.
xxvi, 272p.
ISBN 0455206155 Pbk £29.50

Social security law in Britain and Ireland : a bibliography / Paul O'Higgins and Martin Partington with the assistance of Sally Hughes. – London : Mansell, 1986.
424p; 24cm.
Includes index.
ISBN 0720117941 £36.00

Social Security Legislation for Labour in India. – New Delhi : Deep and Deep Publications, 1986.
382p.
Hbk £250.00

Social security reporter. – Clayton, Vic. : Legal Service Bulletin Co-operative, 1981.
Indexes: Nos 1-22 in no 22 (Dec 1984); annually in Dec. issue except for 1983.
ISBN 08173524

Social security taxation : a guide to contributions and contributory conditions under the social security acts / by David W. Williams. – London : Sweet & Maxwell, 1982.
xxxiii,536p; 26cm.
Includes index.
ISBN 0421262303 £40.00

Social Service Tax Act, 1984. – Vancouver : British Columbia Continuing Legal Education Society, 1984.
ISBN 0865041474 Hbk £55.00

Social services law / by John Williams. – London : Fourmat, 1981.
xxii,338p; 22cm.
Includes index.
ISBN 185190039X Pbk £18.95

Social theory as science / Russell Keat and John Urry. – 2nd ed. – London : Routledge & K. Paul, 1982.
xi,301p.
Includes index. Bibliography: p278-295.
ISBN 0710094310

Social welfare law / David Pearl and Kevin Gray. – London : Croom Helm, 1981.
308p; 23cm.
Bibliography: p265. - Includes index.
ISBN 085664644X Hbk £14.95
ISBN 0709920040 Pbk £8.95

Social Welfare Law. – London : Longman Professional.
ISBN 0851204694 Llf £125.00

Social welfare law in Ireland : a guide to its sources / Gerry Whyte. – Dublin : Round Hall Press, 1987.
86p; 23cm.
Includes index.
ISBN 0947686258 Pbk £9.95

Social Work : Annotated Ontario Mental Health Statutes. – Agincourt : Carswell, 1988.
358p.
Hbk £46.25

Social work and child abuse / Ball. – London : Macmillan, 1987.
ISBN 033363973 Hbk £15.00
ISBN 0333363981 Pbk £5.95

Social work and criminal law in Scotland / by George Moore and Chris Wood. – Aberdeen : Aberdeen University Press, 1981.
xii,208p; 26cm.
Provides information and guidance about those aspects of the judicial and penal systems and measures relating to child offenders which affect social workers. Chapters cover prosecution, social worker at court, social enquiry reports, non-custodial measures, probation, community service and unpaid work, and custodial measures. Includes bibliography and index.
ISBN 0080257313 Hbk

Social work decisions in child care : recent research findings and their implications / appraisal by the Research on Child Care Working Party of Child Care Practitioners; report written by Jane Rowe. – London : H.M.S.O., 1985.
73p.
Includes summaries of the reports discussed. At head of title-page: Department of Health and Social Security. 7 sheets of charts in end pocket.
ISBN 0113210469

Social work, justice and control. – Oxford : Blackwell, 1985.
ISBN 0631137327 Pbk £8.50

Social Work (Scotland) Act / Rosemary Gray. – 2nd. – Edinburgh : Green (W.) & Son, 1984.
Full text of the Act as amended and in force, along with prospective amendments as at 25 May 1984. Also with an appendix tabulating legislation, as amended and prospectively amended to the same date, relating to elderly and handicapped persons, welfare rights, children and young persons, mentally ill people and adult offenders.
ISBN 0414007417 Pbk

Social work statutes. – 2nd ed. – London : Sweet & Maxwell, 1985.
ISBN 0421348305 Pbk £11.00

Social work with young offenders / Behan. – London : Butterworths, 1981.
ISBN 0406556903 Pbk £7.50

Social workers and solicitors in child care cases / by Linden Hilgendorf with the assistance of Deborah Holland, Barrie Irving, Diana Schlaefli. – London : H.M.S.O., 1981.
ix,150p.
ISBN 0113207697

Social workers, their clients and the law / Michael Zander. – 3rd ed. – London : Sweet & Maxwell, 1981.
xiv,180p; 22cm.
Previous ed.: 1977. Includes index.
ISBN 0421279303 Pbk £5.75

Socialism in the Courtroom. – Sydney : Pathfinder Press, 250p.
ISBN 0873486226 Hbk £20.00
ISBN 0873486234 Pbk £5.95

Socialism, The State, and Public Policy in France / Martin A. Schain. – London : Pinter Publishers Ltd, 1984.
220p.
ISBN 086187384X Hbk £21.00

Socialist lawyer. – London : Haldane Society of Socialist Lawyers, 1986.

Socialist Legality and Indian Law. – Calcutta : Sujan Publications.
104p.
Hbk £35.00

Socialist Society →What is to be done about law and order?.

Societies Act, 1966 (No. 13 of 1966) and Regulations, 1984 (P.U.(A) 402/84). – Kuala Lumpur : International Law Books Services.
Hbk £9.00

Societies Registration Act. – 7th ed. – Allahabad : Law Book Company, 1983.
460p.
Hbk £130.00

Society against crime : penal practise sic in modern Britain / edited by Howard Jones. – Harmondsworth : Penguin Books, 1981.
284p. – (Penguin education).
Bibliographies.
ISBN 0140804374

Society for Applied Philosophy →Journal of applied philosophy : journal of the Society for Applied Philosophy.

Society for Computers and Law
Applications of computer technology to law : a selected bibliography (1969-1981) for British lawyers / Society for Computers and Law. – Didcot : Society for Computers and Law, 1982.
60p.
ISBN 0906122112

—Communications : a guide to the electronic office for practising lawyers / compiled by the Communications Committee of the Society for Computers and Law. – 2nd fully rev ed. – Didcot : The Society, 1985.
iii,67 leaves.
ISBN 0906122198

→ Computer contracts : the deeper issues : conference organised by the Society for Computers and Law on Monday 19th November 1984 at the Royal Garden Hotel, London, W.8.

—Evidence of the Society for Computers and Law and Technology and Law Limited to The Farrand Conveyancing Committee. – Society for Computers and Law. – S.l. : The authors?, 1984.
10p; 30cm.

→ Tomorrow's lawyers : computers and legal training : a paper prepared by the Society's Legal Education Committee to discuss the teaching of computer applications to intending lawyers and to qualified practitioners.

—Warwick 1984 communications conference held at the University of Warwick in Coventry from Thursday 5 July to Sunday 8 July 1984. – Society for Computers and Law. – Didcot, Oxon. : Society for Computers and Law, 1984.
93p.
ISBN 0906122155

Society for Research into Higher Education → Excellence in diversity : towards a new strategy for higher education : the Leverhulme report.

Society of Arab Comparative and International Law →Arab law quarterly.

Society of Labour Lawyers →More law reform NOW : a collection of essays on law reform.

Society of Town Clerks' Education and Research Trust →Open government : freedom of information and local government : a study conducted for the Local Government Legal Society Trust and the Society of Town Clerks' Education and Research Trust.

Socio-economic and legal implications of Urban Land (Ceiling and Regulation) Act, 1976 / Gopal Bhargava. – New Delhi : Adhinav, 1983.
xiv,172p.
Bibliography: p.167-170. - Includes index. Includes the text of the Urban Land Ceiling Bill.

Socio-Economic Justice under Indian Constitution. – New Delhi : Deep and Deep Publications, 1984.
460p.
Hbk £200.00

Socio-Economic Re-evaluation of the Torts Law of Liability for Personal Injuries. – Lucknow : Eastern Book Company, 1962.
115p.
Pbk £5.00

Socio-Legal Problems and Developing Society. – New Delhi : Deep and Deep Publications, 1986.
331p.
Hbk £225.00

Sociolegal Status of Women in India. – Delhi : Mittal Publications, 1987.
208p.
Hbk £140.00

Socio-legal studies and social welfare / Martin Partington : a report for the Government and Law Committee of the Economic and Social Research Council. – London : Economic and Social Research Council, 1986.
78p.
Bibliography: p59-78.
ISBN 0862261872

Sociological approaches to law / edited by Adam Podgorecki and Christopher J. Whelan. – London : Croom Helm, 1981.
251p; 23cm.
Includes bibliographies and index.
ISBN 0709927010 £12.95

Sociological theory of law. – Routledge, 1985.
ISBN 0710097476 Hbk £32.50

Sociology of Criminal Law. – London : Butterworths.
ISBN 0409862207 Hbk £14.00

Sociology of law / Roman Tomasic. – London : Sage, 1985.
288p.
Includes bibliography and index.
ISBN 0803997167 Pbk £10.00

Sociology of law : an introduction / Roger Cotterrell. – London : Butterworths, 1984.
xiii,409p; 23cm.
Bibliography: p368-392. - Includes index.
ISBN 0406010684 Hbk £17.00
ISBN 0406010722 Pbk £16.95

Sociology of law and legal anthropology in the Dutch speaking countries / J. van Houtte, editor. – Dordrecht : M. Nijhoff Publishers, 1985.
Bibliography of 'The sociology of law in Dutch-speaking countries': p67-102. Bibliography of 'Current legal anthropology in the Netherlands': p149-162.
ISBN 9024731755

Sociology of the professions : lawyers, doctors and others / edited by Robert Dingwall and Philip Lewis. – London : Macmillan, 1983.
ix,314p; 23cm.
Bibliography: p286-306. - Includes index.
ISBN 0333309618 Hbk £15.00

Soek, Myint
Insurance Law of Malaysia. – rev ed. – Singapore : Quins, 1982.
Hbk £81.00

—Law of Banking and Negotiable Instruments in Singapore and Malaysia. – 2nd ed. – Singapore : Quins, 1983.
Hbk £99.00

Soell, Herman
Special Depreciation Allowances or Subsidies : Reflections on Governmental Assistance with Respect to Environmental Protection. – Berlin : Erich Schmidt.
68p. – (BZU Ser.: Vol. A33).
ISBN 3503011544 Pbk £24.00

Soetemans, Dirk →Law and practice relating to pollution control in Belgium and Luxembourg.

Softley, Paul
Fine enforcement : an evaluation of the practices of individual courts / Paul Softley and David Moxon. – London : Home Office, 1982.
iv,23p; 30cm.
Bibliography: p16.
ISBN 0862520711 Pbk

Sohn, Louis B →Contemporary issues in international law : essays in honor of Louis B. Sohn.

→ International organization and integration : annotated basic doucments of international organizations and arrangements.

Sohoni
Code of Criminal Procedure in 5 Vols. – 18th ed. – Allahabad : Law Book Company, 1984.
Hbk £700.00

Sola, R. de
Crime Dictionary. – Revised Edition. – London : Facts On File.
ISBN 0816018723 Hbk £18.50

Solanes, Miguel
Irrigation users' organizations in the legislation and administration of certain Latin American countries / by Miguel Solanes. – Rome : Food and Agriculture Organization of the United Nations, 1983.
vii,87p. – (Legislative study).
Includes bibliographical references.
ISBN 9251011702

Solar Energy and the Law. – North Ryde : Law Book Co, 1984.
xxxiii, 324p.
ISBN 0455203407 Pbk £54.50

Solarz, Artur →Drug criminality and drug abuse in Sweden, 1969-1981.

Sold! : With or Without an Estate Agent. – Tadworth : Elliot Right Way. – (Paperfronts Series).
ISBN 0716007894 Pbk £1.50

Solf, Waldemar A →New rules for victims of armed conflicts : commentary on the two 1977 protocols additional to the Geneva Conventions of 1949.

Solft, Waldemar A.
Index of International Humanitarian Law / J. Ashley Roach. – Geneva : Comite International de la Croix-Rouge, 1987.
283p.
Hbk £20.00

Solicitor and the automated office / Theodore Ruoff. – London : Sweet & Maxwell, 1984.
x,136p; 22cm.
Includes index.
ISBN 0421331100 £8.50

Solicitor and The Silicon Chip. – London : Oyez Longman, 1981.
ISBN 0851205690 Hbk £6.95

Solicitor General's study of conditional release : report of the Working Group, March 1981. – Ottawa : Minister of Supply and Services Canada, 1981.
vii,155,55,63,192,viip.
Includes bibliography. Pages numbered in opposite directions. Text in English and French.
ISBN 0662514521

Solicitors' accounts : student guide. – 2nd ed. – London : Financial Training, 1985.
ISBN 0906322944 Pbk £8.95

Solicitors Accounts Rules 1976, The Solicitors Trust Accounts Rules 1986, The Accountants Reports Rules 1986, The Solicitors Accounts (Deposit Interest) Rules 1986. – Law Society. – London : Law Society.
Hbk £5.00

Solicitors and barristers directory and diary Diary. – London : Waterlow, 1987.
ISBN 0080330940 Hbk £35.00
Directory. –
ISBN 0080330932 Hbk £27.00

Solicitors' and barristers' directory and diary : an almanac and directory incorporating the Law Society list of practising solicitors and the Senate of the Inns of Court and the Bar list of members. – London : Waterlow, 1984.
Merger of: The Bar list of the United Kingdom; and, The Solicitors' diary ... almanac and legal directory.
ISBN 0080391710

Solicitors and local authorities / by R.J.B. Morris. – Chichester : Rose, 1983.
ciii,349p; 23cm.
Includes index.
ISBN 0859923304

Solicitors and their business clients / Barlow. – 3rd ed. – London : Financial Training, 1986.
ISBN 1851850317 Pbk £16.50

Solicitors and VAT / Gizzi. – London : Butterworths, 1986.
ISBN 0406503605 Pbk £8.75

Solicitors Benevolent Association →Annual report of the Council of the Law Society : intended to be presented to the general meeting of the members on.

Solicitors Checklists / Stephen A. Karas. – Butterworths, 1988.
ca 232p.
ISBN 0409494690 Llf £29.00

Solicitors' Compendium 1985. – Edinburgh : W Green.
– (Reprint from Parliament House Book).
ISBN 0414007700 Hbk £4.00

Solicitors' Compendium Nineteen Eighty-Two : Extracted from the Parliament House Book. – Edinburgh : W Green, 1983.
ISBN 0414007077 Hbk £3.75

Solicitors' Considerations for Family Law Lawyers. – Vancouver : British Columbia Continuing Legal Education Society, 1983.
310p.
ISBN 0865040885 Hbk £60.00

Solicitor's guide to advertising & publicity / Stephen Townley. – 5 pamphlets. – London : Professional Direction and Sweet & Maxwell, 1985.
49p; in folder, 22x31cm.
Authors: Stephen Townley et al.
ISBN 0421342706 £39.50

Solicitor's Guide to Corporate Tax Planning. – Vancouver : British Columbia Continuing Legal Education Society, 1983.
112p.
ISBN 0865040974 Hbk £45.00

Solicitor's Guide to Estate Practice in Ontario. – Butterworths, 1986.
280p.
Practical guide covering retainer, application for Probate and Letters of Administration, asset administration, interpretation of wills finding beneficiaries, estate litigation, distribution of estate, preparation and passing off of accounts, and tax returns.
ISBN 0409810266 Hbk £50.00

Solicitor's Journal : 1855-1981, 125 Vols. – Abingdon : Professional Books.
Hbk £5950.00

Solicitors' Legal Opinions. – Vancouver : Continuing Legal Education Society of British Columbia, 1985.
244p.
ISBN 0865042403 Hbk £60.00

Solicitor's practice
1 / editor Peter H.M. Soar. – 1. – London : Butterworths, 1981.
loose-leaf; 26cm.
ISBN 0406373531 unbound

Solicitors' regional directory 1984
Greater London North. – London : Law Society, 1984.
viii,184p.
Supersedes: The legal aid solicitors list. Includes index.

Solicitors' trust accounts and the Solicitors' Fidelity Fund / New South Wales Law Reform Commission. – Sydney : The Commission, 1981.
xxix,241p; 25cm. – (Discussion paper no 6).

Solity
Teacher's Guide to Special Needs : A Positive Response to the 1981 Education Act / Raybould. – Open University Press.
ISBN 0335158439 Hbk £16.95
ISBN 0335158420 Pbk £5.95

Solly, Mark
Isle of Man : a low-tax area / by Mark Solly. – Croydon : Tolley, 1984.
ix,458p.
Includes index.
ISBN 0854591397
—Jersey : a low tax area / by Mark Solly. – Croydon : Tolley, 1982.
iv,323p; 24cm.
Includes index.
ISBN 0854590536 Hbk
ISBN 0854590544 Pbk £15.00

Solomon, David Harris
Australia's Government and Parliament. – 7th ed. – Melbourne : Nelson, 1987.
194p : Illus.
ISBN 0170071944 Hbk £16.95

Solomon Islands law reports. – Solomon Islands : s.n., 1982.
'Published by authority of the High Court of Solomon Islands'. Annual indexes.

Solomon Islands Law Reports for 1983, 1984, 1985. – Suva : University of the South Pacific, Institute of Pacific Studies.
296p.
Hbk £5.00

Solomon Jr., Peter H.
Criminal Justice Policy : From Research to Reform. – Butterworths, 1983.
152p.
Asks whether a particular problem is actually as serious as it is assumed to be, and whether it deserves a prominent place in the agenda of the policy makers. Concludes that neither ple-bargaining nor court delay is as threatening as commonly supposed, and that the processing of minor crimes in court imposes unjustifiably heavy costs.
ISBN 0409868426 Hbk £40.00

Solomon, Robert M.
Cases and Materials on the Law of Torts / Bruce P. Feldthusen. – 2nd ed. – Agincourt : Carswell, 1986.
Hbk £75.75

Solomos → Racism and equal opportunity policy in the 1980's.

Solovjev, A.
Greek Charters of Serbian Rulers / V. Mosin. – Repr. of 1936 ed. – Northampton : Variorum.
696p.
ISBN 090208965X Hbk £20.00

Some aspects of aid to the civil power in Australia / B.D. Beddie and S. Moss. – Canberra : Department of Government, University of New South Wales, 1982.
92p. – (Occasional monograph).
ISBN 0959325409

Some Aspects of Building Contracts. – Belfast : Queen's University of Belfast, 1982.
31p.
Pbk £2.95

Some Aspects of Capital Transfer Tax for Businesses and Farms. – Belfast : Queen's University of Belfast, 1986.
30p.
Pbk £2.95

Some aspects of inheritance tax for businesses and farms / David Moore. – Belfast : SLS Legal Publications, 1986.
40p.
Includes bibliographical references.

Some aspects of international law considered in relation to apartheid, racism and racial discrimination / by T.O. Elias. – Lagos : Nigerian Institute of Advanced Legal Studies, 1986.
27p. – (Occasional paper).
ISBN 9782353043

Some Aspects of the Law of Unjust Enrichment. – Colombo : Lake House Investments.
Hbk £4.70

Some cases heard in the Hooge Raad / reported by Willem Pauw : translated and edited by R. Feenstra, P. van Warmelo, D.T. Zeffertt. – Pretoria : Government Printer on behalf of the South African Law Commission, 1985.
viii,117p. – (Research series).
Includes index. Translation of: Observationes tumultuariae novae.
ISBN 0621097152

Some Concepts of Labour Law. – Colombo : Lake House Investments.
Hbk £2.00

Some Developments in the Law of Contract. – Armidale : University of New England, Publications Office.
49p.
ISBN 0858342146 Pbk £3.00

Some key issues for the world periphery : selected essays / by Miguel S. Wionczek. – Oxford : Pergamon, 1982.
xiv,432p; 24cm.
Includes bibliographies and index.
ISBN 0080257836 £37.50

Some legal issues arising out of the miners' strike 1984/5 / Dawn Oliver. – London : Faculty of Laws, University College London, 1985.
26p. – (Working papers).
Includes bibliographical references. Edited by Dawn Oliver. Caption title.

Some miscellaneous topics in the law of succession / Scottish Law Commission. – Edinburgh : The Commission, 1986.
155p. – (Consultative memorandum).

Some obsolete and discriminatory rules in the law of husband and wife / Scottish Law Commission. – Edinburgh : The Commission, 1982.
61p. – (Consultative memorandum).

Some of the selective institutions of higher learning in USA. – Hong Kong : Hang Seng Bank, 1981.
423 p.

Some recent developments in individual employment law and practice : the text of a lecture delivered to the Belfast Solicitors' Association on 11th March 1982 / by Richard Steele. – Belfast : SLS, 1982.
31p.
Includes bibliographical references.

Some tax implications of marriage breakdown / David Moore. – Belfast : SLS Legal Publications, 1987.
35p.
Includes bibliographical references.

Sonarikar, Sunanda S.
Implementation of Labour Enactments. – Bombay : Popular Prakashon.
Hbk £60.00

Soni, Ramanlal
Control of marine pollution in international law / Ramanlal Soni. – Cape Town : Juta, 1985.
301p.
Bibliography: p277-293.
ISBN 0702116602

Sonnenfeld, Renata
Resolutions of the United Nations Security Council. – Dordrecht : Nijhoff (Martinus), 1989.
179. – (Legal aspects of international organisation 8).
Presents a picture of the legal questions concerning Security Council resolutions and their place in the international legal order. Makes a comparison of Charter provisions with the Security Council's practice. The last chapter of the book examines the question of whether a Security Council resolution is binding.
ISBN 902473567X Hbk Gld120.00

Sonte, A.
Law of Psychiatry and Morality. – Cambridge : Cambridge University Press, 1986.
ISBN 0521339545 Pbk £12.95

Soonavala, R.K.
Treatise on the Law of Bails. – Bombay : Tripathi, 1968.
li, 898p.
bd £45.00

Soons, Alfred H. A
Marine scientific research and the law of the sea / Alfred H.A. Soons. – Deventer, Netherlands : Kluwer Law and Taxation Publishers, 1982.
xix, 383 p.; 24 cm.
At head of title: T.M.C. Asser Instituut, The Hague. Includes index. Bibliography: p. 370-377.
ISBN 9065440658

Sopinka, John
Law of Evidence in Civil Cases / W R Lederman. – London : Butterworths.
ISBN 0409868507 Hbk £68.00
—Trial of an Action. – Butterworths, 1981.
280p.
Examines the legal and practical aspects of a trial from the selection of the tribunal to the final judgement. Looks at rules of practice and procedure, and with tactics and techniques of a trial lawyer. Covers the mode of trial, devices to facilitate or supplant testimony, the role of counsel, the role of the trial judge, the charge to the jury, and the verdict.
ISBN 040986854X Hbk £55.00

Sorell, Tom
Moral theory and capital punishment / Tom Sorell. – Oxford : Basil Blackwell in association with the Open University, 1987.
240p; 23cm.
Includes index.
ISBN 0631153217 Hbk £25.00 :
ISBN 0631153225 Pbk £5.95

Sornarajah, M
Pursuit of nationalized property / M. Sornarajah. – Dordrecht : M. Nijhoff, 1985.
248p.
Bibliography.
ISBN 9024731305 Hbk £120.00
—South West Dam Dispute : The Legal and Political Issues. – Hobart : University of Tasmania, 1983.
151p. – (Sir Elliot Lewis Memorial Publication Ser.).
ISBN 0859012344 Pbk £10.00, 015

Sotinwa, G.
Nigerian Tax Handbook. – Tolley Publishing, 1987.
ISBN 0854592318 Pbk £11.50

Soulsby → Business Law.
→ Outlines of English Law.

Sourcebook of Singapore and Malaysian company law / Philip N. Pillai. – 2nd ed. – Singapore : Butterworths, 1986.
xlviii,1338p.
Brings together the principle legislative provisions, legislative history and background, all Singapore and Malaysia case law and selected case law from the UK, Australia, and other common law jurisdictions. The cases are set out with brief summaries of the points of law discussed or decided.
ISBN 0409995118

Sourcebook on planning law in Ireland / Katherine Shepherd. – Abingdon : Professional Books, 1984.
xxxviii,568p.
ISBN 0862050901 Hbk £31
Supplement. – 1987.
ISBN 086205219X Hbk £11

Sources and development of Muslim law. – Singapore : Malayan Law Journal, 1965.
142.
Studies the sources of Muslim law, and attempts to bring together the views of the 'Orientalists' and the Muslim authorities. Traces the development of Muslim law from the year 13 before Hijrah to the present day, and also looks to the future of Muslim law. Looks at the writing of Muslim jurists.
Hbk

Sources of English Legal and Constitutional History / R. Ian Jack. – Butterworths, 1984.
432p.
ISBN 0409493821 Hbk £49.00

Sources of English legal history : law, history and society in England and Wales 1750-1950 / A.H. Manchester. – London : Butterworths, 1984.
xiv,443p; 26cm.
Includes bibliographies and index.
ISBN 0406516596 Hbk £39

Sources of English legal history : private law to 1750 / (compiled by) J.H. Baker, S.F.C. Milsom. – London : Butterworths, 1986.
xl,698p; 22cm.
Includes index.
ISBN 0406016402 Hbk £35.00
ISBN 0406016410 Pbk £20.00

Sources of funding for research and publication / Helen Peden and Philip Hills. – Leicester : Primary Communications Research Centre, University of Leicester, 1983.
46p; 20x21cm.
Bibliography: p46. - Includes index.
ISBN 0906083249 Pbk

Sources of law, legal change, and ambiguity / Alan Watson. – Edinburgh : T. & T. Clark, 1985.
xviii,164p; 23cm.
Previously published: Philadelphia : University of Pennsylvania Press, 1984.
ISBN 0567093603

Sources of Nigerian Law, The. – Sweet & Maxwell, 1972.
ISBN 0421172703 Pbk £10.00

Sources of support for legal research : a report to the Consultative Group on Research and Education in Law based on a survey of foundations, law reform commissions, departments of justice, and attorneys and solicitors general in Canada / John S. McKennirey. – Ottawa : Consultative Group on Research and Education in Law, 1982.
iii,53p.

South Afican Law Commission
Anton Piller-type orders / South African Law Commission. – Pretoria : The Commission, 1986.
iii,23 leaves. – (Poject).

South Africa and the consociational option : a constitutional analysis / by L.J. Boulle. – Cape Town : Juta, 1984.
xii, 270 p.; 25 cm.
Includes indexes. Bibliography: p. 227-229.
ISBN 0702114340 Pbk

South Africa by Treaty 1806-1986 : a Chronological and subject index. – Braam Fontein : South African Insitute of International Affairs, 1987.
Hbk £40.00

South Africa in crisis / edited by Jesmond Blumenfeld. – London : Croom Helm for the Royal Institute of International Affairs, 1987.
x,207p; 23cm.
Includes index.
ISBN 0709942524 £19.95

South Africa in the American mind / Alan Pifer. – Braamfontein : South African Institute of International Affairs, 1981.
17p. – (Commemoration Day Lecture).
ISBN 0909239932

South Africa Institute of Race Relations
Detention Without Trial in South Africa 1976-1977. – South Africa Institute of Race Relations. – Johannesburg : South African Institute of Race Relations.
Hbk

South African Attorneys handbook / Randell and Bax. – 3rd ed. – Durban : Butterworths, 1983.
xxv,345p.
Bibliography: p.xx - Includes index. Addendum (Appendix 9) as loose insert.
ISBN 0409050113

South African company law through the cases : a collection of leading South African and English cases on company law, with explanatory notes and comments / H. R. Hahlo. – 4th ed. – Cape Town : Juta, 1984.
xli,673p.
ISBN 0702114316

South African Constitution : Euphoria and Rejection. – Johannesburg : Witwatersrand University Press, 1982.
vi, 20p.
ISBN 0854947434 Pbk £3.00

South African criminal law and procedure
Vol.1 : General principles of criminal law : by E.M. Burchell and P.M.A. Hunt / E. M. Burchell, P. M. A. Hunt, J. R. L. Milton, Jonathan M Burchell. – 2nd ed. – Cape Town : Juta, 1983.
lxii,512p.
In 6 vols. Includes bibliographical references and index.
ISBN 070211345X
Vol. 2 : Common-law crimes : by P.M.A. Hunt. – 1982.
xcv,870p.
Includes bibliographical references and index.
ISBN 0702112569

Vol.5 : Criminal procedure : by Alfred V. Lansdown : Evidence : Jean Campbell. – 1982.
cxxvi,966p; 26cm.
Previous ed: 1957 by Gardiner and Lansdown.
ISBN 0702112577

South African Encyclopedia of Forms and Precedents, 16 vols. – Durban : Butterworths. – (Eng. and Afrikaans).
Wo
Suppl. 1984. –
ISBN 0409006033 Pbk

South African journal on human rights. – Braamfontein : Ravan Press, 1985.

South African Law Commission
Committal to prison in respect of debt / South African Law Commission. – Pretoria : The Commission, 1986.
viii,37,9p. – (Report).
Includes the text of draft legislation.
ISBN 0621113468

—Domicile / South African Law Commission. – Pretoria : The Commission, 1987.
xiii,109p. – (Project).
Bibliography: pp.vi-x.. Includes the text of draft legislation.
ISBN 0797014365

→ Index to the opinions of Roman-Dutch lawyers and the decisions of the courts of the Netherlands which have been digested in the Algemeen Beredeneerd Register of Nassau La Leck (1741-1795).

—Investigating into the legal position of illegitimate children / South African Law Commission. – Pretoria : The Commission, 1984.
viii,167 leaves. – (Project).
Bibliography: p.161-167.

—Investigation into the advancement of the age of majority / South African Law Commission. – Pretoria : The Commission, 1985.
xviii,63p. – (Report).
Includes bibliographical references.
ISBN 0621102466

—Investigation into the advancement of the age of majority / South African Law Commission. – Pretoria : The Commission, 1984.
iv,36p. – (Project).
Bibliography: p.30-34.

—Investigation into the courts' powers of review of administrative acts / South African Law Commission. – Pretoria : The Commission, 1986.
v,110p. – (Project).

—Investigation into the legal consequences of suspensive conditions in contracts of sales / South African Law Commission. – Pretoria : The Commission, 1986.
vi,32p. – (Report).
Includes text of draft legislation.
ISBN 0621113506

—Investigation into the legal position of illegitimate children / South African Law Commission. – Pretoria : The Commission, 1985.
xx,157p. – (Report).
Includes bibliographical references.
ISBN 0621102059

—Investigation into the limits for the institution of actions against the state / South African Law Commission. – Pretoria : The Commission, 1985.
iv,50p. – (Report).
Includes bibliographical references. Includes draft of Bill.

—Investigation into the possibility of making provision for a divorced woman to share in the pension benefits of her former husband / South African Law Commission. – Pretoria : The Commission, 1984.
v,67leaves. – (Project).
Bibliography: p.66-67.

—Investigation into the possiblity of making provision for a divorced woman to share in the pension benefits of her former husband / South African Law Commission. – Pretoria : The Commission, 1986.
x,77p. – (Report).
Bibliography: pp.vi-x. Includes draft legislation.
ISBN 0621113573

—Law of succession : intestate succession. – South African Law Commission. – Pretoria : South African Law Commission, 1983.
vii,49p. – (Working paper).
Project 22. Bibliography: pv-vi.

—Law of trusts. – South African Law Commission. – Pretoria : South African Law Commission, 1983.
vi,63p. – (Working paper).
Project 9. Bibliography: pv-vi.

→ Life and works of Hugo Grotius (1583-1645) : address delivered to members of the South African Law Commission and other dignitaries on 26 July 1983 at the University of Pretoria to commemorate the 400th birthday of Hugo Grotius.

—Marriages and customary unions of black persons / South African Law Commission. – Pretoria : The Commission, 1985.
xix,222p. – (Project).
Bibliography: p.vii-xi.
ISBN 062110180X

—Offences committed under the influence of liquor or drugs / South African Law Commission. – Pretoria : The Commission, 1986.
vii,132p. – (Report).
Bibliography: p.123-132.
ISBN 0621102075

—Offences committed under the influence of liquor or drugs / South African Law Commission. – Pretoria : The Commission, 1984.
vi,118 leaves. – (Project).
Bibliography: p.113-118.

—Preferences on insolvency : working paper 1 / South African Law Commission. – Pretoria : Government Printer, 1982.
ix,119p.
On title page: Project 37.
ISBN 0621078387

—Protection of a purchaser of securities / South African Law Commission. – Pretoria : The Commission, 1987.
ii,47p. – (Project).

—Protection of a purchaser of securities / South African Law Commission. – Pretoria : The Commission, 1987.
xiv,116p. – (Project 62).
Bibliography: pp.ix-xi. Includes draft legislation.
ISBN 0797014608

→ Quaestiones juris privati.

—Removal of certain restrictions in respect of land / South African Law Commission. – Pretoria : The Commission, 1984.
iv,9p. – (Report).
ISBN 0621102008

—Report on the review of the law of admiralty / South African Law Commission. – S.l. : s.n., 1984.
47p. – (Report).
Photocopy.

—Review of preferent claims in insolvency / South African Law Commission. – Pretoria : The Commission, 1984.
viii,75p. – (Report).
Bibliography: p.vii-viii.

—Review of the law of evidence / South African Law Commission. – Pretoria : The Commission, 1986.
vii,88 leaves. – (Project).
Bibliography: p.81-88.

—Review of the law of evidence / South African Law Commission. – Pretoria : The Commission, 1986.
xi,60p. – (Report).
Bibliography: pp.vi-ix. Includes draft legislation.
ISBN 0621113484

—Review of the law of prize. – South African Law Commission. – Pretoria : The Commission, 1984.
iv,17p. – (Project).

—Review of the law of succession / South African Law Commission. – Pretoria : The Commission, 1986.
ix,34 leaves. – (Project).
Bibliogrpahy: p.iv-viii.

—Review of the law of succession : alteration and revocation of wills / South African Law Commission. – Pretoria : The Commission, 1987.
vii,86 leaves. – (Project).
Bibliography: leaves vi-viii.

—Review of the law of succession : disqualification from inheriting, substitution, succession rights of adopted children / South African Law Commission. – Pretoria : The Commission, 1987.
ix,99p. – (Project).
Photocopy of original. Includes bibliographical references.
ISBN 0797014020

—Review of the law of succession : formalitites of a will / South African Law Commission. – Pretoria : South African Law Commission, 1986.
xiii,139 leaves. – (Project).
Bibliography: p.viii-xiii.

—Review of the law of succession : intestate succession / South African Law Commission. – Pretoria : The Commission, 1985.
vii,37p. – (Report).
Bibliography: p.vi-vii.
ISBN 0621096113

—Review of the law of succession : the introduction of a legitimate portion or the granting of a right to maintenance to the surviving spouse / South African Law Commission. – Pretoria : The Commission, 1987.
x,46p. – (Report).
Bibliography: pp.v-ix. Includes draft legislation.
ISBN 0621113603

—Review of the law of trusts / South African Law Commission. – Pretoria : The Commission, 1987.
viii,135p. – (Report).
Bibliography: p. vii-viii. Includes text of bill.

—Risk as a ground for liability in delict / South African Law Commission. – Pretoria : The Commission, 1986.
x,41p. – (Report).
Includes bibliographical references.
ISBN 0621102024

→ Some cases heard in the Hooge Raad.

→ Treatise on the quasi-contract called promutuum and on the condictio indebiti.

→ Two lectures on law reform : delivered at the workshop on Marriage and Family Life by the Human Sciences Research Council on 26 September 1985.

—Women and sexual offences in South Africa / South African Law Commission. – Pretoria : The Commission, 1985.
xvi.,200p. – (Report).
Bibliography: p.vii-xvi.
ISBN 0621096091 Hbk

South African law conference 1981 : consumer protection / Suid-Afrikaanse Regskonferensie 1981 : Verbruikersbeskerming : papers delivered at the SA Law Conference, Durban, 13-16 April 1981. – Pretoria : Association of Law Societies of the Republic of South Africa, 1981.
63p.
Includes bibliographies. Includes six articles in English and two in Afrikaans.
ISBN 0620057319

South African law of evidence / D. T. Zeffertt. – 3rd ed. – Durban : Butterworths, 1981.
lxxii,504p.
Previous ed.: 1970. Includes index.
ISBN 0409033227 Pbk
ISBN 0409033235

South African law of husband and wife / H. R. Hahlo. – 5th ed. – Cape Town : Juta, 1985.
lxx,526p.
ISBN 0702115681

South African law of trusts / by Tony Honore. – Cape Town : Juta, 1985.
lxvi,551p.
Previous ed.: 1976. Includes bibliographical references and index.
ISBN 0702115320

South African Law Reports (1947 to Date) / J. L. Buchanan. – Durban : Butterworths.
Hbk

South African Maritime Law and Marine Insurance : Selected Topics. – Durban : Professional Publishers, 1983.
ISBN 0409023779 Pbk £55.00

South African mercantile and company law / by J.T.R. Gibson assisted by R. G. Comrie. – 5th ed. – Cape Town : Juta, 1983.
xl,668p.
Previous ed.: 1977. Includes index.
ISBN 070211359X

South African patent law and practice / by Timothy Donald Burrell. – 2nd ed. – Durban : Butterworths, 1986.
xxxvii,699p.
ISBN 0409013552

South African Police →Annual report of the Commissioner of South African Police.

South African Tax Journal / H. R. Levin. – Durban : Butterworths, 1985.
Hbk

South America, Central America and the Caribbean: survey and directory of the countries of the region. – London : Europa Publications, 1985-.

South Asian States and Sea Laws. – Bapu Nagar : Printwell, 1987.
218p.
ISBN 8170440467 Hbk £165.00

South Australian Reports : 1865-date. – Abingdon : Professional Books, 1984.
Hbk

South Korea : violations of human rights. – Amnesty International. – London : Amnesty International Publications, 1986.
109p,18p. of plates.
ISBN 086210100X

South Pacific Forum Fisheries Agency → Regional compendium of fisheries legislation (Western Pacific region).

South West Africa and the sacred trust 1919-1972 / T.D. Gill. – The Hague : T.M.C. Asser Instituut, 1984.
ix,107p.
Bibliography: p.106-107.
ISBN 9067040274

South West Dam Dispute : The Legal and Political Issues. – Hobart : University of Tasmania, 1983.
151p. – (Sir Elliot Lewis Memorial Publication Ser.).
ISBN 0859012344 Pbk £10.00, 015

Southam
AIDS and Employment Law / Howard. – London : Financial Training, 1988.
ISBN 1851850937 Pbk £14.95

Southern Africa and the Law of the Sea : Problems Common, Uncommon and Unique. – Rondebosch : University of Cape Town, 1986.
17p.
ISBN 0799210242 Pbk £0.30

Southern Africa in need of law reform : proceedings of the Southern African Law Reform Conference, Sun City, Bophuthatswana, 11-14 August 1980 / edited by A.J.G.M. Sanders. – Durban : Butterworths, 1981.
256p.
Includes bibliographical references.
ISBN 0409051845

Southern Vectis Omnibus Company Limited : refusal to allow access to Newport bus station, Isle of Wight / a report by the Director General of Fair Trading on an investigation under section 3 of the Competition Act 1980. – London : Office of Fair Trading, 1988.
34p.

Southgate, Peter
Contacts between police and public : findings from the British crime survey / by Peter Southgate and Paul Ekblom. – London : H.M.S.O., 1984.
v,37p; 25cm.
A Home Office Research and Planning Unit report.
ISBN 0113407718
→ Ethnic minorities, crime and policing : a survey of the experiences of West Indians and whites.
—Police probationer training in race relations / Peter Southgate. – London : Home Office, 1982.
iv,38p.
Bibliography: p.31.
ISBN 0862520630
—Police-public encounters / by Peter Southgate with the assistance of Paul Ekblom. – London : H.M.S.O., 1986.
vi,143p; 25cm.
Report from the Research and Planning Unit. Describes a study of everyday contact between the public and uniformed police in London, Birmingham and Bristol. Examines problems during such encounters.
ISBN 011340834X
→ Public disorder : a review of research and a study in one inner city area.
—Racism awareness training for the police : report of a pilot study for the Home Office / Peter Southgate. – London : Home Office, 1984.
v,17p.
Bibliography: p.17.
ISBN 0862521726

Southwick, L.H., et al
Liquor Laws of New Zealand. – 4th ed. – Butterworths, 1983.
ISBN 0409600776 Hbk £106.15

Southwood, Richard →Eleventh report : managing waste : the duty of care.
→ Ninth report : lead in the environment.
→ Tenth report : tackling pollution : experience and prospects.

Sovereign borrowers : guidelines on legal negotiations with commercial lenders / edited by Lars Kalderen, Qamar S. Siddiqi : in co-operation with Francis Chronnell and Patricia Watson. – Uppsala : Dag Hammarskjold Foundation, 1984.
264p.
ISBN 9185214124

Sovereign lending : managing legal risk / edited by Michael Gruson and Ralph Reisner. – London : Euromoney Publications, 1985.
xii,257p; 30cm.
Includes bibliographical references.
ISBN 0903121611

Sovereignty. – Cambridge : Cambridge University Press, 1986.
ISBN 052133988X Pbk £8.95

Sovereignty Dispute over the Falkland (Malvinas) Islands. – Oxford : Oxford University Press.
ISBN 0195041844 Hbk £32.50

Sovereignty of Parliament in India. – New Delhi : Deep and Deep Publications, 1985.
212p.
Hbk £150.00

Soviet civil law / by Olimpiad S. Ioffe. – Dordrecht : M. Nijhoff, 1988.
392p.
Includes index.
ISBN 9024736765 Hbk £205.00

Soviet law. – 2nd. – London : Butterworths, 1989. – (Legal systems of the world).
ISBN 040656261X Hbk £21.95

Soviet law and economy / Olimpiad S. Ioffe and Mark W. Janis, editors. – Dordrecht Holland : M. Nijhoff, 1986.
300p. – (Law in Eastern Europe).
Includes index.
ISBN 9024732654 Hbk £165.00

Soviet law and Soviet reality / Olimpiad S. Ioffe. – Dordrecht : M. Nijhoff, 1985.
240p. – (Law in Eastern Europe).
Includes bibliographies and index.
ISBN 9024731062 Hbk £135.00

Soviet law of property : the right to control property and the construction of communism / by George M. Armstrong, Jr. – The Hague : M. Nijhoff Publishers, 1983.
vii,167p.
Includes index. Bibliography: p155-163. Based on the author's thesis (Ph. D.–Princeton).
ISBN 9024728649 Hbk £80.00

Soviet military strategy in space / Nicholas L. Johnson. – London : Jane's, 1987.
287p.
ISBN 0710604491

Soviet system of Justice : figures and policy / by Ger P. van den Berg. – The Hague : M. Nijhoff Publishers, 1984.
Includes bibliographical references and index.
ISBN 9024730864

Soviet Union : The Internal Situation and its Implications for the West. – Enstone : Ditchley Foundation, 1982.
– (The Ditchley Conference Reports).
Hbk

Soviet Union in Artic waters : security implications for the northern flank of NATO / by Willy Ostreng : translated by Eric Hansen from the original Norwegian text. – Honolulu : Law of the Sea Institute, 1987.
ix,77p. – (Occasional paper).
Includes bibliographical references. Translation of: Soviet i nordlige farvann, published by Gylendal Norsk, Oslo, 1982.
ISBN 0911189157

Soviet Views on the Use of Force in International Law. – Hong Kong : Asian Research Service.
ca 200p.
Hbk £12.00

Sowden, Terry →Jersey law of trusts.

Sowler, Richard
Taxation of leasing transactions. – London : Butterworths, 1984.
ISBN 0406538026 Pbk £15.00

Sownik prawniczy polsko-angielski [Polish-English law dictionary] / opracowanie redakcyjne Danuta Rydlewska-Szewczykowa, Jolanta Zaczkiewiczowa. – Wrocaw : Zakad Narodowy im. Ossolinskich, 1986.
211 p.; 21 cm.
English and Polish. Title on added t.p.: Polish-English dictionary of legal terms. At head of title: Polska Akademia Nauk. Instytut Panstwa i Prawa.
ISBN 8304018977 z500.00

Soye, David P.
Guide to the Heavy Goods Vehicle Driving Test and Licenses. – 5th ed. – London : Kogan Page, 1986.
120p.
ISBN 1850911304 Pbk £5.95

Space activities and emerging international law / edited by Nicolas Mateesco Matte. – Montreal : Centre for Research of Air & Space Law, 1984.
xvii,627p.
Bibliography: p.591-619. - Includes index.
ISBN 0421345802 Hbk £58

Space activities and implications : where from and where to at the threshold of the 80's : proceedings of the symposium held on October 16-17, 1980 / Centre for Research of Air & Space Law : d'ou vient-on et ou va-t-on a l'aube des annees 80 : Centre de recherche en droit aerien et spatial. – Montreal : ICASL, McGill University, 1981.
xvi,367p; 24cm.
ISBN 0771700393

Space debris: legal and policy implications. – Dordrecht : Nijhoff (Martinus), 1989.
192. – (Utrecht studies in air and space law 6).
Describes the legally relevant aspects of the space debris issue, and analyses the legal and policy implications derived from these facts. Includes discussion of the source of space debris, the risk posed by debris to space activities, and locations of space debris.
ISBN 0792301668 Hbk £43

Space, earth and communication / Edward W. Ploman. – London : Pinter, 1984.
xi,237p; 22cm.
Bibliography: p225-229. - Includes index.
ISBN 0861873610 Hbk £26.00

Space Law Changes and Expectations at the Turn to Commercial Space Law Activities. – Dordrecht : Kluwer, 1987.
32p.
ISBN 9065442561 Pbk £29.50

Space weapons and US strategy. – Oxford : Croom Helm, 1985.
ISBN 0709923694 Hbk £25.00

Spain : the question of torture : documents exchanged by Amnesty International & the Government of Spain. – Amnesty International. – London : Amnesty International Publications, 1985.
60p.
Translated from the Spanish.
ISBN 0862100860

Spanish business law / Bernardo M. Cremades, general editor. – Deventer, The Netherlands : Kluwer Law and Taxation Publishers, 1985.
Includes index.
ISBN 9065442200 Hbk £315.00

Spare a Copper. – London : Police Review Publishing, 1982.
ISBN 0851640001 Pbk £1.95

Spatial analysis of legal systems : towards a geography of law? / Kim Economides, Mark Blacksell and Charles Watkins. – Exeter : University of Exeter, 1985.
49p. – (Working paper).
Includes bibliographical references.

Spearman, Richard →Sale of Goods Litigation.

Special damages for disability 1988 / by Philip Noble, Elizabeth Fanshawe, Bart Hellyer. – 2nd ed. – London : Sweet & Maxwell, 1988.
x,85p; 22cm.
Catalogues the expenses which a plaintiff in a personal injuries action can claim as part of his award. Each of the expenses, such as accommodation requirements and the cost of future care, are described in the context of the four disabilities of spinal injury, partial and total loss of sight, loss of a limb, and head injury. Each item is given an up-to-date value.
ISBN 0421393807 Pbk £7.50

Special Depreciation Allowances or Subsidies : Reflections on Governmental Assistance with Respect to Environmental Protection. – Berlin : Erich Schmidt.
68p. – (BZU Ser.: Vol. A33).
ISBN 3503011544 Pbk £24.00

Special Hindu Marriage Act, 1942 : Bare Act with Commentary. – Delhi : SBD Enterprises.
Hbk £5.00

Special Prosecutors Office : Report to the Attorney-General. – Canberra : Australian Government Publishing Service, 1983.
15p.
ISBN 0644012528 Hbk £1.70

Special report from the Select Committee on the Armed Forces Bill. – London : H.M.S.O., 1981.
xix,130p.
ISBN 0102253811 £7.00

Special requirements in probation or supervision orders : a local case study / W.F. Bullock, W.M.S. Tildesley. – Cambridge : Institute of Criminology, 1984.
iii,131p. – (Occasional paper).
Bibliography: p.129-131.

Specialized agencies and the United Nations : the system in crisis / Douglas Williams : with a foreword by Sir Anthony Parsons. – London : Hurst in association with the David Davies Memorial Institute of International Studies, London, 1987.
xvi,279p; 23cm.
Bibliography: p271-274. - Includes index.
ISBN 185065025X £17.50

Specific performance / William Goodhart. – London : Butterworths, 1986.
ISBN 0406258090 Hbk £40.00

Specific Performance of Contracts : Including Those of Public Companies. – 5th ed. Repr. of 1911 ed. – Abingdon : Professional Books.
131p.
Hbk £40.00

Specific Relief Act : Based on Tagore Law Lectures. – 8th ed. – Allahabad : Law Book Company, 1988.
1,100p.
Hbk £250.00

Specification 87. – London : Architectural Press, 1987.
1400p : Illus.
ISBN 0851396232 Pbk £65.00

Specimen letters for solicitors. – London : Longman Professional, 1987.
ISBN 0851208630 Pbk £15.95

Spectacle of suffering : executions and the evolution of repression - from a preindustrial metropolis to the European experience. – Cambridge : Cambridge University Press, 1984.
286.
Examines the decline of public, physical punishment in the penal system of Western Europe.
ISBN 0521261864 Hbk £30.00

Speedy, SquireL.
Economic Approach to Property Value. – Auckland : Legal Research Foundation, 1981.
35p.
Pbk £5.50

Speight, Anthony
AJ Legal Handbook / Gregory Stone. – 4th ed. – London : Architectural Press, 1985.
264p : Illus.
ISBN 0851397514 Pbk £19.95
—Law of defective premises / Anthony Speight, Gregory Stone : foreword by the Honourable Mr Justice Wood. – London : Pitman, 1982.
xxi,205p; 23cm.
Includes index.
ISBN 0273017705 Hbk £15.95

Speiser
Law Suit : A Study in Damages (U.S.A.) 1980. – London : Wildy & Sons.
Hbk £12.95

Spelman, H.
Spelmanni Reliquiae : The Posthumous Works of Sir Henry Spelman Relating to the Laws and Antiquity of England. – Repr. of 1698 ed. – Abingdon : Professional Books.
37p.
Hbk £225.00

Spelmanni Reliquiae : The Posthumous Works of Sir Henry Spelman Relating to the Laws and Antiquity of England. – Repr. of 1698 ed. – Abingdon : Professional Books.
37p.
Hbk £225.00

Spence, James M.
Foreign Investment Review Law in Canada / W.P. Rosenfeld. – Butterworths, 1984.
432p.
Provides practical information and a commentary for those who must deal with the Foreign Investment Review Act (FIRA). Shows the reader how to proceed with applications under the Act, describes the business and political context in which it operates, and clarifies the meaning of its essential concepts. Chapters deal with FIRA-related problems particular to the petroleum and banking industries.
ISBN 0409863009 Hbk £75.00
—Guide to the Investment Canada Act / Gabor S.G. Takach. – Butterworths, 1986.
176p.
ISBN 0409805203 Hbk £50.00

Spencer, J.R. →Cambridge-Tilburg Law Lectures, Vol. 3.
—Jackson's Machinery of Justice. – 8th ed. – Cambridge : Cambridge University Press.
ISBN 0521362571 Hbk £75.00
ISBN 0521317673 Pbk £25.00
→ What is International Law and How Do We Tell it When We See It?.

Spencer, John →Wilkinson's road traffic offences.

Spencer, P.
Property tax planning manual. – London : Butterworths, 1987.
ISBN 0406137390 Pbk £18.95

Spencer, Sarah
Called to account : the case for police accountability in England and Wales / Sarah Spencer. – London : National Council for Civil Liberties, 1985.
146p; 20cm.
Includes bibliography.
ISBN 0946088128 Pbk £3.95

Spending on law and order : the police service in England and Wales / M. A. S. Joyce. – London : National Institute of Economic and Social Research, 1985.
64p. – (Discussion paper).

Spenke, Gerrit te
Taxation in the Netherlands / by Gerrit te Spenke. – Deventer : Kluwer, 1985.
xvii,135p; 25cm.
Includes index.
ISBN 9065440836

Spent convictions / Law Reform Commission. – Canberra : Australian Government Publishing Service, 1987.
viii,126p. – (Report).
Bibliography: p.123-126.
ISBN 0644013702

Spero, Joan Edelman
Politics of international economic relations / Joan Edelman Spero. – 3rd. ed. – London : Allen & Unwin, 1985.
viii,447p.
Bibliography: p405-431.
ISBN 0043820441

Spetz, Alenda S. →Take Notice : An Introduction to Canadian Law.

Spetz, Steven N.
Take Notice : An Introduction to Canadian Law / Alenda S. Spetz. – 2nd ed. – Toronto : Copp Clark, 1984.
512p : Illus.
ISBN 0773043144 Hbk £24.94

Spheres of justice : a defence of pluralism and equality / Michael Walzer. – Oxford : Robertson, 1983.
xviii,345p; 24cm.
Introduction for students to abstract discussions of justice. Includes case studies.
ISBN 0855206837 £15.00

Spicer and Pegler
Accounts and Audits of Pension Schemes. – Spicer and Pegler. – London : Butterworths, 1987.
ISBN 040667910X Pbk £18.95
—Book Keeping and Accounts Workbook. – Spicer and Pegler. – London : Butterworths.
ISBN 0406678138 Pbk £9.50
—Book-Keeping and Accounts. – Spicer and Pegler. – 19th ed. – London : Butterworths, 1985.
ISBN 0406678103 Pbk £13.50
—Practical auditing. – Spicer and Pegler. – 17th ed. – London : Butterworths, 1985.
ISBN 0406678014 Pbk £13.50
→ Spicer and Pegler's the business of partnerships.

Spicer and Pegler's management buy-outs / Coyne. – Cambridge : Woodhead-Faulkner, 1987.
ISBN 0859413411 Hbk £30.00

Spicer and Pegler's the business of partnerships / by Peter J. Oliver and Nigel T. Davey. – London : Sweet & Maxwell, 1986.
xii,193p; 22cm.
Includes index.
ISBN 0421353309 Pbk £16.75

Spicer, Ernest E →Business Law for Accountants.
→ Company Law.
→ Executorship Law and Accounts.
→ Ranking, Spicer and Pegler's Mercantile Law.

Spicer, Robert
Conspiracy : law, class and society / Robert Spicer. – London : Lawrence and Wishart, 1981.
190p; 23cm.
Bibliography: p178-184. - Includes index.
ISBN 0853155488 £7.50
—Mahaffy and Dodson : Road Traffic. – 3rd ed. – London : Butterworths.
Hbk
→ Sweet & Maxwell's Statutes for the Law Society finals.

Spicer, W. Wylie
Canadian Maritime Law and the Offshore : a Primer. – Calgary : Canadian Institute of Resources Law.
65p.
Hbk £13.00
→ New directions in maritime law 1984.
→ New directions in maritime law.

Spicer's and Pegler's Executorship Law and Accounts. – 21st ed. – London : HFL, 1983.
Llf £55.00

Spicker, Paul
Allocation of council housing / Paul Spicker. – London : Shelter, 1983.
43p; 21cm.
ISBN 0901242683 Pbk £1.50

Spicker, S.F.
Law-Medicine Relations : a Philosophical Exploration : Proceedings of the 8th Trans-Disciplinary Symposium on Philosophy and Medicine Held at Farmington, Conn., 1978 / J.M. Healey. – Dordrecht : Kluwer, 1981.
319p.
ISBN 9027712174 Hbk £75.00

Spierenberg, Pieter
Spectacle of suffering : executions and the evolution of repression - from a preindustrial metropolis to the European experience. – Cambridge : Cambridge University Press, 1984.
286.
Examines the decline of public, physical punishment in the penal system of Western Europe.
ISBN 0521261864 Hbk £30.00

Spill →Pension Scheme Trustee.

Spiller : A History of the District and Supreme Courts of Natal 1846-1910. – Durban : Professional Publishers, 1986.
ISBN 0409057568 Pbk £55.00

Spiller : A Manual of Roman Law. – Durban : Professional Publishers, 1986.
ISBN 040905755X Pbk £39.00

Spiller, Peter
Cox and Crime. – Cambridge : Institute of Criminology, 1985.
Hbk £4.00
—Manual of Roman Law. – London : Butterworths, 1986.
ISBN 040905755X Pbk £14.00
—Spiller : A History of the District and Supreme Courts of Natal 1846-1910. – Durban : Professional Publishers, 1986.
ISBN 0409057568 Pbk £55.00
—Spiller : A Manual of Roman Law. – Durban : Professional Publishers, 1986.
ISBN 040905755X Pbk £39.00

Spills Bill : Duties, Rights and Compensation. – Butterworths, 1986.
144p.
Collection of essays which intends to clear up the initial confusion surrounding the Environmental Protection Act. Covers common law liability, an overview of the bill, compensation and insurance, defence considerations, and factual situations; how the Bill will be and should be applied.
ISBN 0409805769 Hbk £44.95

Spinelli, Altiero
Towards the European union : Florence, 13 June 1983 / by Altiero Spinelli. – Luxembourg : Office for Official Publications of the European Communities, 1983.
28p.

Spirit of Uppsala : proceedings of the Joint UNITAR-Uppsala University Seminar on International Law and Organization for a New World Order (JUS 81), Uppsala 9-18 June 1981 / edited by Atle Grahl-Madsen and Jiri Toman. – Berlin : W. de Gruyter, 1983.
English and French. Includes index and bibliography.
ISBN 3110088223

Spiro, Erwin
General principles of the conflict of laws : with the exclusion of the special principles relative to the law of persons, property, succession and obligations / Erwin Spiro. – Cape Town : Juta, 1982.
xxxiii,145p.
Bibliography: p.xi-xvi. - Includes index.
ISBN 0702112895
—Law of parent and child / by Erwin Spiro. – 4th ed. – Cape Town : Juta, 1985.
lxv, 661 p.; 26 cm.
Includes bibliographical references and indexes.
ISBN 0702115746
—Recent extra-marital child legislation annotated : being also a cumulative supplement to the fourth edition of Spiro's Law of parent and child / Erwin Spiro. – Cape Town : Juta, 1988.
ix,20p.
Includes index.
ISBN 0702120510

Spitz, Barry
International tax planning. – 2nd ed. – London : Butterworths, 1983.
ISBN 0406382379 Hbk £18.00
→ Tax havens encyclopaedia.

Splintered Market : Barriers to Interprovincial Trade in Canadian Agriculture / David R. Hughes. – Toronto : Lorimer & Co, 1981.
ISBN 0888625170 Hbk £16.95
ISBN 0888625162 Pbk £7.95

Splitting Up : Legal & Financial Guide Separation & Divorce. – London : Kogan Page.
ISBN 1850917663 Hbk £5.95

Spokesman University
ITT-CIA Subversion in Chile : A Case Study of U.S. Corporate Intrigue in the Third World. – Spokesman University. – London : Spokesman Books, 1983.
114p.
ISBN 0851240402 Pbk £2.50

Sponsorship. – London : Longman Professional (UK), 1987.
– (Longman Intelligence Report).
Looks at the increase in sponsorship expenditure and range of applications, providing guidance to enable companies to realise full marketing potential. Considers aspects of evaluation, setting-up and monitoring of the sponsorship deal.
ISBN 0851213324 Hbk £85.00

Sponsorship of sport, arts, and leisure : law, tax and business relationships / by Stephen Townley and Edward Grayson : with forewords by Lord Goodman, Dick Jeeps and Sir William Rees-Mogg. – London : Sweet & Maxwell, 1984. xliii,333p; 23cm.
Guide to the law and tax considerations involved in the business of sponsorship. The legal status of sponsorship rights and licences is interpreted with reference to statute and case law. Intellectual property law, competition law, copyright and the remedies for its infringement, trade-marks, and passing-off are examined.
ISBN 0421304103 £19.75

Sport and Recreation Law in Canada. – North Vancouver : International Self-Counsel Press. Hbk

Sport and the Law 1985 : Centre for Commercial Law and Applied Legal Research. – Monash University, Faculty of Law. – Clayton : Monash University Press. Hbk £20.00

Sport and the law / by Edward Grayson : with forewords by Lord Havers, Denis Howell. – London : Butterworths, 1988. xviii,376p; 22cm.
Includes index.
ISBN 0406253005 Pbk £16.95

Sport and the Law. – North Ryde : Law Book Co, 1987. 350p.
ISBN 0455207127 Pbk £27.50

Sport Physical Activity and the Law. – Ottawa : Canadian Association for Health, Physical Education and Recreation. Hbk £14.95

Sports and Entertainment Law. – Vancouver : Continuing Legal Education Society of British Columbia, 1986. 284p.
ISBN 0865042705 Hbk £65.00

Sports and the Law in Canada. – Toronto : Butterworths, 1983. 400p.
ISBN 0409812919 Pbk £40.00

Sports and the Law in Canada. – 2nd ed. – Butterworths, 1988. 416p.
Covers criminal prosecution for hockey violence, collective agreements and labour relations, agents and contract negotiations, government policies in support of sport, discrimination on the basis of sex and nationality, antitrust law aspects of professional league organisation, players' service contracts, public regulation of different sports, tort liability and compensation for sports injuries.
ISBN 0409811815 Pbk £30

Sports Law for Educational Institutions / Hay. – Quorum Press.
ISBN 0899303358 Hbk £31.95

Spousal agreements / Law Reform Commission of British Columbia. – Vancouver : The Commission, 1985. iii,74p. – (Working paper).
Includes bibliographical references.

Spousal Maintenance. – Vancouver : Continuing Legal Education Society of British Columbia, 1988. 164p.
ISBN 086504984X Hbk £70.00

Spousal Property Rights Under the Ontario Family Law Act. – Butterworths, 1987. 80p.
Contains commentary on present and prospective interpretation of the Act, insights into the prospective operation of Parts I, II, and IV of the Act, up-to-date reported and unreported judgements incorporated in the commentary, applicable provincial rules and forms, and an analysis of issues including business valuation, professional licences and pensions.
ISBN 0409809365 Hbk £55.00

Spratt
Law of Insolvency / P D McKenzie. – 2nd ed. – London : Butterworths, 1981.
ISBN 0409667900 Hbk £25.50

Spread of the ombudsman plan in western Europe / by Donald C. Rowat. – Edmonton : International Ombudsman Institute, 1983. 30p. – (Occasional paper).
'An excerpt from the chapter on developed countries in Professor Rowat's book, The Ombudsman Plan (Toronto, McClelland and Stewart, 1973), as revised for publication in Japanese by Waseaa University Press, Tokyo, in 1983'.

Springman, Mel
Debtor-Creditor Law : Practice and Doctrine / Eric Gertner. – Butterworths, 1985. 768p.
Addresses the practical issues which dominate debtor-creditor law in Canada. Covers execution against negotiable instruments, third party demands, fraudulent conveyances and unjust preferences, PPSA, repossession, corporate receivership, construction liens, the enforcement of foreign judgements, executions against shares in BC and enforcement against life insurance, pensions, and RRSP's.
ISBN 0409868833 Hbk £95.00

Sproule, Clarey B. →Canadian Sentencing Digest : Quantam Service, 2 Vols.

Spry, I.C.F.
Principles of Equitable Remedies. – 3rd ed. – North Ryde : Law Book Co, 1984. lix, 668p.
ISBN 0455203997 Hbk £73.00
—Principles of equitable remedies : specific performance, injunctions, rectification and equitable damages / by I.C.F. Spry. – 3rd ed. – London : Sweet & Maxwell, 1984. lix,668p; 25cm.
Sets out the principles by reference to which injunctions and orders for specific performance are granted and analyses equitable doctrines such as laches and part performance. Covers the changes in the law relating to Mareva injunctions and Anton Piller orders. Also includes a new chapter on rectification.
ISBN 0421332409 Canada £
ISBN 0459368001

Spry, John
Expediting Civil Litigation : A Study of Commonwealth Jurisdictions. – London : Commonwealth Secretariat, 1983.
ISBN 0850922313 Hbk £5.00
—Problems of jury trials in small jurisdictions / John Spry. – London : Commonwealth Secretariat, 1985. 19p.
Includes bibliographical references.

Spurling, D.
Discover Book-Keeping and Accounts. – Pitman.
ISBN 0273028707 Pbk £5.95

Spurway, M.
Aviation Insurance Abbreviations: Organs and instruments. – Witherby, 1983.
ISBN 0900886773 Pbk £4.50

Spycatcher Trial. – Richmond : Heinemann, 1988. 208p.
ISBN 0855612398 Hbk £29.95

Squatting / by A.M. Prichard. – London : Sweet & Maxwell, 1981. xvi,177p; 19cm.
Includes index.
ISBN 0421267402 Hbk £9.50
ISBN 042126750X Pbk £5.75

Squibb, G. D.
Precedence in England and Wales / G.D. Squibb. – Oxford : Clarendon Press, 1981. xviii,139p; 23cm.
Bibliography: p126-130. - Includes index.
ISBN 0198253893 £12.50

Squires, M. B.
Tax Planning for Groups of Companies. – London : Butterworths, 1985.
This book examines the various aspects of taxation of groups or consortia in the United Kingdom and considers commercial factors to determine the most appropriate group structure. Pro forma tax elections and sample agreements for the surrender of tax advantages between group companies are included.
ISBN 0406075808 Hbk

Sri Lanka : a mounting tragedy of errors: report of a mission to Sri Lanka in January 1984 on behalf of the International Commission of Jurists and its British Section, Justice / Paul Sieghart. – London : International Commission oof Jurists and Justice, 1984. 95p.
Bibliography: p93-94.
ISBN 0907247040

Sri Lanka's hybrid presidential parliamentary system & the separation of powers doctrine / H.M. Zafrullah. – Kuala Lumpur : University of Malaya Press, 1981. xxii,140p.
Bibliography: p. 133-137. - Includes index.

Srinivasagam, Elizabeth →Sesquicentennial choronological tables of the written laws of the republic of Singapore 1834-1984.

Srinivasan, N
Hindu Succession Act. – 2nd ed. – Allahabad : Law Publishers, 1982. Hbk £21.00
—Taxation Laws, Part 1 : General Principles. – Allahabad : Orient Law House.
ISBN 0861256336 Hbk £35.00

Srivastava
Judicial Panorama. – Allahabad : Law Book Company, 1981. Hbk £10.00

Srivastava, Dhirendra K. →Context of contract in Papua New Guinea.

Srivastava, I.N.
Woman and the Law. – New Delhi : Intellectual Book Corner, 1985. xii, 228p. Hbk £130.00

Srivastava, K.D.
Commentaries on Contract Labour Act, 1970 : Regulation and Abolition / G. Saran. – 3rd rev. ed. – Lucknow : Eastern Book Company, 1982. 520p. Hbk £70.00
—Commentaries on Employees' Provident Funds and Miscellaneous Provisions Act, 1952 : Together with Schemes and Notifications. – 5th ed. – Lucknow : Eastern Book Company, 1985. Hbk
—Commentaries on Employees' State Insurance Act, 1948. – 3rd ed. – Lucknow : Eastern Book Company, 1986. 928p. Hbk £150.00
—Commentaries on Industrial Disputes Act, 1947. – 6th ed. – Lucknow : Eastern Book Company, 1985. 1,590p. Hbk £250.00
—Commentaries on Industrial Employment Standing Orders Act, 1946 : Including Model Standing Orders, Recognition of Unions and Unfair Labour Practices. – 2nd ed. – Lucknow : Eastern Book Company, 1982. 844p. Hbk £95.00
—Commentaries on Payment of Gratuity Act, 1972. – 3rd ed. – Lucknow : Eastern Book Company, 1982. 593p. Hbk £90.00
—Commentaries on Payment of Wages Act, 1936. – 3rd ed. – Lucknow : Eastern Book Company, 1983. 814p. Hbk £110.00
—Commentaries on the Uttar Pradesh Industrial Disputes Act, 1947. – 4th ed. – Lucknow : Eastern Book Company. Hbk
—Commentaries on Workmen's Compensation Act, 1923 / by K.D. Srivastava and G. Saran. – 4th rev. ed. – Lucknow : Eastern Book Company, 1984. 692p. Hbk £100.00
—Contract Labour : Regulation and Abolition Act, 1970 / G. Saran. – 4th ed. – Lucknow : Eastern Book Company, 1987. 602p. Hbk £125.00
—Disciplinary Action Against Government Servants and its Remedies. – 5th ed. – Lucknow : Eastern Book Company, 1985. 1,239p. Hbk £225.00
—Factories Act, 1948. – 4th ed. – Lucknow : Eastern Book Company, 1984. Hbk
—Law Relating to Trade Unions in India. – 2nd ed. – Lucknow : Eastern Book Company, 1982. 831p. Hbk £110.00
—Payment of Bonus Act, 1965. – 5th ed. – Lucknow : Eastern Book Company, 1982. 588p. Hbk £80.00
—Uttar Pradesh Shop and Commercial Establishments Act, 1962. – 3rd ed. – Lucknow : Eastern Book Company, 1984. 410p. Hbk £50.00

Srivastava, Kumar Avadhesh →Commentaries on State Financial Corporations Act, 1951.

Srivastava, O.P.
Principles of Criminal Law : With Model Questions and Suggested Readings. – 1979 repr. – Lucknow : Eastern Book Company, 1985. 186p. Pbk £12.00
→ Principles of the Law of Crimes.

Srivastava, S.C.
Treatise on Social Security and Labour Law. – Lucknow : Eastern Book Company, 1985. Hbk £60.00

Srivastava, S.N. →Uttar Pradesh State Universities Act, 1973 : as Amended Up-to-Date with Exhaustive Comments and Allied Laws.

Srivastva, L.N.
International Law. – 3rd ed. – Delhi : SBD Enterprises. Hbk £35.00
—Simple Book of Jurisprudence / Prayag Singh. – Delhi : SBD Enterprises. Hbk £25.00

Staff associations / Certification Office for Trade Unions and Employers' Associations. – London : Certification Office for Trade Union and Employers' Associations, 1981. iii,52p.
Supplement to: Annual report of the Certification Officer 1979.

Staff management in library and information work / Noragh Jones, Peter Jordan. – Aldershot : Gower, 1982. vii,215p; 23cm. – (A Grafton book).
Bibliography: p205-212. - Includes index.
ISBN 0566034301

Staff resource implications of an independent prosecution system / Peter R. Jones. – London : Home Office, 1983. v,39p.
Bibliography: p.32.
ISBN 086252119X

Stafford, L. W. T.
Modern Commercial Knowledge. – 4th ed. Repr. of 1977 ed. – Plymouth : Macdonald & Evans, 1982.
320p. – (M and E Handbook Ser.).
ISBN 0712113991 Hbk £3.95

Stafford, Richard J
Private prosecutions. – London : Shaw & Sons, 1988.
ISBN 0712910904 Pbk £9.95

Stage 1 Business Law : CIMA Study Text. – Revised ed. – London : BPP.
ISBN 0862771420 Pbk £12.95

Stage 3 Business Taxation / Murphy. – 2nd ed. – Pitman.
ISBN 027303418 Pbk £12.95

Stage 3 Business Taxation : CIMA Study Text. – Revised ed. – London : BPP.
ISBN 0862771536 Pbk £14.95

Stage One Law. – Northwick Publishers, 1983.
ISBN 0907135102 Pbk £6.00

Staines, Anne
How to Make Money from Your Software : Legal and Business Aspects. – Oxford : ESC Publishing Ltd, 1985.
108p.
ISBN 0906214319 Pbk £9.50

Stair, James Dalrymple
Institutions of the law of Scotland : deduced from its originals, and collated with the civil, canon and feudal laws, and with the customs of neighbouring nations in iv books / by James, Viscount of Stair : edited by David M. Walker. – Edinburgh : University Presses of Edinburgh and Glasgow, 1981.
xvii,1186p,1leaf of plates; 24cm.
Originally published: Edinburgh : s.n., 1693. Includes index.
ISBN 0852243979 £40.00

—Institutions of the Law of Scotland : Deduced From its Originals and Collated With the Civil, Canon, and Feudal Laws and With the Customs of Neighbouring Nations. – Repr. of 1681 ed. – Abingdon : Professional Books.
108p.
Hbk £295.00

→ Laws of Scotland : Stair memorial encyclopaedia.

Stair Society →Court of the official in pre-Reformation Scotland : based on the surviving records of the officials of St. Andrews and Edinburgh.
→ Miscellany two.
→ Stair tercentenary studies.

Stair Society Publications, 28 Vols. – Abingdon : Professional Books, 1984.
Hbk

Stair tercentenary studies / by various scholars : edited by David M. Walker. – Edinburgh : The Stair Society, 1981.
viii,267. – (Publications).
Bibliography: p253-259.
ISBN 0902292080

Stalbecker, Barbro E.
Legal Deskbook : 1988. – Agincourt : Carswell.
530p.
This softcover text provides a summary of resources and factual information pertinent to legal and non-legal researchers. It includes directories of courts, judges, law associations, government bodies, sources of legal information, etc. Special features include a legal information directory for business law, criminal law, family law and social services, litigation and real estate.
£58.50

Stallworthy, et al
Takeovers, Acquisitions and Mergers. – London : Kogan Page.
ISBN 1850914591 Hbk

Stamp Duties / R. S. Nock. – 6th ed. – London : Sweet & Maxwell, 1986.
Hbk £47.00

Stamp Duties and Capital Duty Supplement-1986. – London : Butterworths.
ISBN 0406370419 Pbk £16.00

Stamp duties for conveyancers / J T Farrand. – 4th ed. – London : Longman Professional, 1986. – (Longman Practice Note. No.48).
ISBN 0851211739 Pbk £15.95

Stamp Duty Aspects of Trusts, Settlements and Gifts in Australia / F.P. Zipfinger. – Butterworths, 1984.
367p.
ISBN 0409494216 Hbk £56.00

Stamp Duty for Conveyancers / Roger Gregory. – 3rd ed. – London : Oyez Longman, 1983. – (Oyez Longman Practice Note Ser.: No. 48).
ISBN 0851206352 Hbk £7.95

Stamp Duty Guide. – London : Butterworths, 1986.
This practical work for practitioners in the United Kingdom presents a transaction-based analysis of stamp duties. The book explains the administrative procedures involved and discusses how to avoid or minimize the duty wherever possible.
ISBN 0406260303 Pbk

Stamp Law and Practice. – Allahabad : Universal Book Agency.
Hbk £225.00

Stamp Ordinance, 1949 (F.M. Ord. No. 59 of 1949). – Kuala Lumpur : International Law Books Services.
Hbk £10.00

Stanbrook, Clive →Dumping and subsidies : the law and procedures governing the imposition of anti-dumping and countervailing duties in the European Community.
→ International trade : law and practice.

Stanbrook, Ivor
British nationality : the new law / by Ivor Stanbrook. – London : Clement, 1982.
xxiii,213p; 23cm.
Includes text of the act.
ISBN 0907027024 £9.50

Stanbury, W.T.
Regulatory Reform in Canada / Fred Thompson. – Ottawa : Institute for Research on Public Policy, 1982.
vi, 139p.
ISBN 0920380719 Hbk £7.95

Standard Automobile Policy Annotated. – Toronto : Butterworths, 1986.
296p.
Hbk £45.00

Standard business contracts / A.J Hawkins. – London : Sweet & Maxwell, 1986.
Examines the law with particular reference to exclusion and limitation clauses, and related devices operating as indirect or implied exclusions. Includes clauses of indemnity, insurance, invoicing back, certification and inspection, warning notices, and instructions. Includes the Unfair Contract Terms Act 1977, the Supply of Goods and Services Act 1982, the Hague-Visby Rules, and the Warsaw Convention on Carriage by Air.
ISBN 0421307609 Hbk £72

Standard Catalog of World Paper Money. – Munich : Ernst Battenberg, 1983.
959p.
Hbk £85.00

Standard conditions of sale. – 2nd ed. – London : Butterworths, 1987.
ISBN 0406255113 Pbk £25.95

Standard Conditions of Sale : A Conveyancer's Guide. – London : Butterworths, 1986.
This work comparees the National Conditions of Sale and the Law Society's General Conditions of Sale and analyzes the ways in which they diverge. The discussion of conditions in the book follows that of events in a normal conveyancing transaction in the United Kingdom.
ISBN 0406255113 Pbk

Standard Conditions of Sale of Land. – 3rd ed. – London : Oyez Longman, 1982. – (Oyez Longman Practitioner Ser.).
ISBN 0851206468 Hbk £15.95

Standard Contract for Sale of Land in New South Wales with Supplement. – North Ryde : Law Book Co, 1985.
lxxiv, 948p.
ISBN 045520697X Hbk £115.50

Standard contracts for building. – London : Longman Professional, 1984.
ISBN 0711457522 Pbk £6.50

Standard for justice : a critical commentary on the proposed Bill of Rights for New Zealand / Jerome Elkind and Antony Shaw : with a foreword by P.T. Mahon. – Auckland : Oxford University Press, 1986.
xvi,238p.
Includes index.
ISBN 019558144X

Standard form of building contract : JCT 80 / John Parris. – 2nd ed. – London : Collins, 1985.
xii,256p; 24cm.
Previous ed.: London : Granada, 1982. Includes index.
ISBN 0003830276 £17.50

Standard form of building contract JCT 1980. – 2nd ed. – Oxford : Blackwell Scientific, 1985.
ISBN 0003830276 Hbk £19.95

Standard Holdings for Law Office Libraries in Nigeria. – Abingdon : Professional Books, 1986.
ISBN 0862050782 Hbk £14.00

Standard minimum rulesfor the implementation of non-custodial sanction and measures involving restriction of liberty / Edited by J J J Tulkens for the International Penal and Penitentiary Foundation. – Kluwer Law and Taxation, 1989.
84.
Collection of contributions regarding standard minimum rules, prepared for the meeting ofthe International Penal and Penitentiary Foundation. Covers operational aspects of control, supervision, and the recording and use of information about the offender, and individual obligations to persons subject to enforcment and organizational requirements.
ISBN 9065444173 Pbk £17.50/Dfl 55

Standard of 'civilization' in international society / Gerrit W. Gong. – Oxford : Clarendon, 1984.
xvi,267p; 23cm.
Bibliography: p251-261. - Includes index.
ISBN 0198219482 £19.50

Standard Trust Income Tax Guide 1988. – Durban : Professional Publishers.
Hbk £15.00

Standing Committee on the Black Coimmunities and the Legal Profession →Black communities and the legal profession.

Standing Conference of Local and Regional Authorities of Europe
Texts adopted / Standing Conference of Local and Regional Authorities of Europe : Conference Permanente des Pouvoirs Locaux et Regionaux de l'Europe. – Strasbourg : Council of Europe, 1984.
Continues: Texts adopted / Conference of Local and Regional Authorities of Europe. Parallel English and French texts.

Standing Conference of National and University Libraries →SCONUL statistical database part 2 : library operations.

Standing Conference on Library Materials on Africa →SCOLMA directory of libraries and special collections on Africa in the United Kingdom and Western Europe.

Standing, Guy
Unemployment and labour market flexibility : the United Kingdom / Guy Standing. – Geneva : International Labour Office, 1986.
xi, 147 p.; 24 cm.
Includes bibliographies.
ISBN 9221052915 Pbk £30.00

Standing in public interest litigation / Law Reform Commission. – Canberra : Australian Government Publishing Service, 1985.
xxx,273p. – (Report).
Bibliography: p.259-263 - Includes index.
ISBN 0644013109

Standing of a Common Law Spouse to Apply Under the Family Compensation Act. – Victoria : Government of British Columbia, 1983.
Hbk

Standing Order 5. – London : Home Office, 1981.
ISBN 0862520207 Pbk £1.00

Standing Orders of the House of Commons : Feb. 1986. – Ottawa : Canadian Government Publishing Centre, 1986.
182p.
ISBN 0660532751 Pbk £22.50

Stanesby, A.
Consumer Rights Handbook. – Pluto Press.
ISBN 0745301622 Pbk £5.95

Stanley Foundation →Peace and security : the United Nations and national interests : report of the nineteenth United Nations of the Next Decade Conference convened June 17-22 1984 in Cape Cod, Mass., USA.

Stanley, Oliver
Offshore tax planning / Vlarke. – London : Butterworths, 1986.
ISBN 0406502102 Hbk £32.00

—Taxation of farmers and landowners. – 3rd. – London : Butterworths, 1987.
ISBN 040638391X Hbk £20.00

Stanley, Stephen
Alternatives to prison : an examination of non-custodial sentencing of offenders / Stephen Stanley and Mary Baginsky. – London : Peter Owen, 1984.
183p; 23cm.
Bibliography: p171-175. - Includes index.
ISBN 0720605229 Hbk £12.50
ISBN 0720606268 Pbk £6.95

Stannard, John E.
Northern Ireland supplement to Smith and Hogan, Criminal law, fifth edition / by John E. Stannard. – Belfast : SLS Legal, 1984.
xxxiv,207p; 25cm.
Includes index.
Pbk

Stansfield, Ronald
Understanding Criminal Offenses / Barrie J. Saxton. – Agincourt : Carswell, 1987.
383p.
This textbook for students of Canadian criminal law discusses the main criminal offenses under the Canadian criminal justice system. Each offense is broken down to the component elements specific to that offense.
Hbk £40.50

Stanton, John
Labour Arbitration : Boon or Bane for Unions?. – Toronto : Butterworths.
70p.
ISBN 0409988618 Pbk £29.95

Stanton, K. M.
Breach of statutory duty in tort / by K.M. Stanton. – London : Sweet & Maxwell, 1986.
xvii,155p; 23cm.
Includes index.
ISBN 0421331402 Hbk £12.50
ISBN 042133150X Pbk £9.50
→ Professional Negligence.

Stanworth, M.
Reproductive technology. – Oxford : Blackwell, 1987.
ISBN 0745602096 Pbk £7.95

Stapleton, J.
Elements of Export Marketing. – Cambridge : Woodhead-Faulkner, 1984.
ISBN 0859412334 Pbk £7.95

Stapleton, Jane
Disease and the compensation debate / Jane Stapleton. – Oxford : Clarendon, 1986.
224p; 22cm.
Includes index.
ISBN 0198255527 £22.50

Stapleton, T.
Estate management practice. – 2nd ed. – London : Estates Gazette, 1986.
ISBN 0728200945 Pbk £14.50

Starck, Christian →Rights, institutions and impact of international law according to the German Basic Law : the contribution of the Federal Republic of Germany to the Second World Congress of the International Association of Constitutional law.

Stare decisis in Commonwealth appellate courts / David J. Murphy and Robert Rueter. – Toronto : Butterworths, 1981.
xv,117p.
Includes index.
ISBN 0409853739

Stares, P.
Space weapons and US strategy. – Oxford : Croom Helm, 1985.
ISBN 0709923694 Hbk £25.00

Stark, Hugh G.
Domestic Contracts / Kirstie MacLise. – Agincourt : Carswell, 1987.
ca 420p.
Llf £56.25
—Family Law and Practice for Legal Assistants. – Vancouver : British Columbia Continuing Legal Education Society, 1983.
208p.
ISBN 0865041040 Hbk £50.00

Starke, J G
Assignments of Choses in Action in Australia. – London : Butterworths, 1982.
ISBN 0409395900 Hbk £28.00
—Cheshire and Fifoot's Law of Contract : Fifth Australian Edition / N. C. Seddon. – Sydney : Butterworths, 1988.
880p.
This new edition has been revised to take into account the legislative and judicial developments in Australian contract law since 1981.
Hbk £85.00

—Introduction to International Law. – 9th ed. – London : Butterworths, 1984.
ISBN 0406659575 Hbk £25.00
ISBN 0406659583 Pbk £18.95

—Science of peace / by J.G. Starke. – 2nd ed. – Sydney : Law Books, 1986.
xvi,193p.
Previous ed. published by A.W. Sijthoff, 1968.
Bibliography: p.180-183. Includes index.
ISBN 0949553298

Starkie, D.
Privatising London's Airports / D. Thompson. – London : Institute for Fiscal Studies. – (Report Ser.).
Hbk £10.00

Starr, J. Barton
United States Constitution : Its Birth, Growth and Influence in Asia. – Hong Kong : Hong Kong University Press, 1988.
ISBN 9622092102 Pbk £19.00

Starting business operations in Germany : a practical guide with emphasis on sales agency agreements, limited liability companies, branch operations / by Harald Jung and Joachim Gres. – Deventer : Kluwer, 1984.
79p.
Bibliography: p.73-74. - Includes index.
ISBN 9065441794
ISBN 3787540229

Starting in business. – Cambridge : Woodhead-Faulkner, 1985.
ISBN 0959412954 Pbk £6.95

Starting in practice. – London : Sweet & Maxwell, 1984.
ISBN 0421320508 Pbk £6.95

State : authority and autonomy / Bill Jordan. – Oxford : Blackwell, 1985.
vi,352p.
Includes bibliography and index.
ISBN 0631142738 £19.50

State aids under the EEC treaty articles 92 to 94 / Despina Schina. – Oxford : ESC Publishing, 1987.
xviii, 221p.
Bibliography: p.179-185. - Includes index.
ISBN 0906214440

State and community aids for European industry : their control and grant / Philip Bentley. – 1 v. – London : European Business Publications, 1983.
looseleaf.
ISBN 0946262012

State and diplomatic immunity. – 3rd. – London : Lloyds of London Press, 1989.
approx 240.
Explains the law affecting the immunity from judicial action of foreign governments, their embassies, staff, and their property. Includes a new chapter on the International Tin Council Litigation, and a discussion of the effects of the Diplomatic and Consular Premises Act 1987.
ISBN 1850442541 Hbk

State and the unions : labour relations, law and the organized labour movement in America, 1880-1960. – Cambridge : Cambridge University Press, 1985.
364.
Examines the impact of the National Labour Relations Act on American trade unions.
ISBN 0521258405 Hbk £35.00
ISBN 0521314526 Pbk £12.50

State as defendant : governmental accountability and the redress of individual grievances / Leon Hurwitz. – London : Aldwych Press, 1981.
xv,211p.
Bibliography: p.197-203.
ISBN 0861720172

State Autonomy in Indian Federation. – New Delhi : Deep and Deep Publications, 1984.
318p.
Hbk £150.00

State Benefits 1986. – London : Labour Research Department.
ISBN 090050885X Hbk £0.90

State enterprise in Singapore : legal importation and development / Philip Nalliah Pillai. – Singapore : Singapore University Press, National University of Singapore, 1983.
xxiv, 223 p.; 23 cm.
Originally presented as the author's thesis (doctoral–Harvard). Includes bibliographical references and index.
ISBN 9971690764 Pbk

State immunity : an analytical and prognostic view / Gamal Moursi Badr. – The Hague : M. Nijhoff, 1984.
248p.
Includes bibliographical references and index.
ISBN 9024728800 Hbk £120.00

State immunity : some recent developments / by Christoph H. Schreuer. – Cambridge : Grotius, 1988.
xxiii,200p.
Examines the principle international and national aspects of suits against States and State-owned corporations in foreign courts.
ISBN 0949009148

State, law and the family. – London : Sweet & Maxwell, 1984.
ISBN 042279080X Pbk £9.95

State of emergency and permissible measures of derogation / A. M. Singhvi. – Bombay : Lawasia-Bar Association of India, 1986.
45p.
Working paper of the Joint Regional Conference (Asia) of the International Bar Association, Law Asia and Bar Association of India (Bombay, Feb.22-23, 1986) on Topic 2 'International support for protection of human rights'. Includes references, p30-41.

State of the environment in the European Community, 1986 / Commission of the European Communities, Directorate-General Environment, Consumer Protection and Nuclear Safety. – Luxembourg : Commission of the European Communities, 1987.
xvi,370p.
ISBN 928256973X

State punishment : political principles and community values / Nicola Lacey. – London : Routledge, 1988.
xiii, 222 p.; 23 cm.
Includes index. Bibliography: p. 202-218.
ISBN 0415001714

State responsibility
Pt.1 / by Ian Brownlie. – Oxford : Clarendon, 1983.
xvi,302p; 24cm.
Includes index.
ISBN 0198254520 £25.00

State responsibility and the direct broadcast satellite / Marika Natasha Taishoff. – London : Pinter, 1987.
xii,203p; 24cm.
Bibiography: p183-197. - Includes index. 'A publication of the Graduate Institute of International Studies'.
ISBN 0861877004 Hbk £25

State responsibility and the marine environment : the rules of decision / Brian D. Smith. – Oxford : Clarendon, 1988.
xviii,281p; 24cm. – (Oxford monographs in international law).
Bibliography: p257-276. - Includes index.
ISBN 0198255810 £30.00

State Responsibility for Technological Damage in International Law. – Berlin : Duncker and Humblot, 1987.
xxviii, 326p.
ISBN 3428062388 Hbk £136.00

State Supreme Courts in State and Nation / Porter. – Yale University Press.
ISBN 03000039123 Hbk £22.50

State, the law, and the family / critical perspectives : edited by Michael D.A. Freeman. – London : Tavistock, 1984.
318p; 22cm.
Includes bibliographies and index.
ISBN 042279080X Pbk

State Trials New Series 1820-1858. – 8 vols. – Professional Books.
ISBN 0862052815 Hbk £231.00

Statement of change in immigration rules : laid before Parliament on 21 October 1986 under section 3(2) of the Immigration Act 1971. – London : H.M.S.O., 1986.
1p. – (H.C. 1985-86).
ISBN 0102584869

Statement of change in immigration rules : laid before Parliament on 29 January 1987 under section 3(2) of the Immigration Act 1971. – London : H.M.S.O., 1987.
1 leaf. – (1986-87 HC).
ISBN 0102154872

Statement of change in immigration rules : presented to Parliament by the Secretary of State for the Home Department by Command of Her Majesty October 1986. – London : H.M.S.O., 1986.
1 leaf.
ISBN 0101991401

Statement of changes in immigration rules. – London : H.M.S.O., 1983.
iv,41p; 25cm. – (1982-83 H.C.).
Rules laid down by the Home Secretary.
ISBN 0102169837 unbound £3.80

Statement of changes in immigration rules / presented to Parliament by the Secrtary of State for the Home Department. – London : H.M.S.O., 1985.
2p.
ISBN 0101953909

Statement of changes in immigration rules : laid before Parliament on 14 December 1987 under section 3(2) of the Immigration Act 1971. – London : HMSO, 1987.
3p. – (1987-88 H.C.).
ISBN 0102208883

Statement of changes in immigration rules : laid before Parliament on 15 July 1985 under section 3(2) of the Immigration Act 1971. – London : H.M.S.O., 1985.
8p. – (H.C.).
ISBN 0102503850

Statement of changes in immigration rules : laid before Parliament on 26 March 1985 under section 3(2) of the Immigration Act 1971. – London : H.M.S.O., 1985.
3p. – (H.C.).
ISBN 0102293856

Statement of changes in immigration rules : Laid before Parliament on 6 December 1982 under section 3(2) of the Immigration Act 1971. – London : H.M.S.O., 1982.
ii,40p. – (1982-83 H.C. 66).
ISBN 0102066833

Statement of changes in immigration rules : laid before Parliament on 7 July 1988 under section 3(2) of the Immigration Act 1971. – London : HMSO, 1988.
5p.
ISBN 0102555885

Statement of preliminary views / Constitutional Commission. Australian Judicial System Advisory Committee. – Canberra : The Commission, 1986.
40p.

Statement on insider dealing / Council for the Securities Industry. – London : The Council, 1981.
7p. – (CSI).

Statement on the recommendations of the Security Commission. – London : H.M.S.O., 1982.
14p; 25cm.
ISBN 0101854005 unbound £1.90

Statements. – Panel on Take-Overs and Mergers. – London : The Panel, 1968.

Statements by an accused. – Vancouver : British Columbia Continuing Legal Education Society, 1981.
252p.
ISBN 0865040214 Hbk £45.00

Statements, Proofs and Confession. – 2nd ed. – Allahabad : Law Publishers, 1982.
Hbk £24.00

States and societies / edited by David Held ... et al. – Oxford : Robertson in association with the Open University, 1983.
x,629p; 23cm. – (An Open University set book).
Includes bibliographies and index.
ISBN 0855206586 Hbk £19.50
ISBN 0855206594 Pbk £5.95

States of emergency : British governments and strikebreaking since 1919 / Keith Jeffery and Peter Hennessy. – London : Routledge & K. Paul, 1983.
312p.
Includes index. Bibliography: p300-304.
ISBN 0710094647

States of emergency : their impact on human rights / a study prepared by the International Commission of Jurists. – Geneva : International Commission of Jurists, 1983.
iii,477p.
Includes bibliographical references.
ISBN 929037019X

Statesman and the fanatic : Thomas Wolsey and Thomas More / Jasper Ridley. – London : Constable, 1982.
338p,16p of plates; 24cm.
Bibliography: p294-299. - Includes index.
ISBN 009463470X £12.50

Statesman's Year Book 1986-87. – London : Macmillan.
ISBN 0333390458 Hbk £24.95

Statistical bulletin / Scottish Home and Health Department : prepared by the Government Statistical Service. – Edinburgh : The Department, 1983.
ISBN 02641178

Statistical Office of the European Communities
→Protection of privacy, automatic data processing and progress in statistical documentation.

Statistics for property people. – London : Estates Gazette, 1986.
ISBN 0728200929 Pbk £14.00

Status in the Common Law 1953. – London : Wildy & Sons.
Hbk £12.50

Status of children : revised report, 1985 / Institute of Law Research and Reform. – Edmonton : The Institute, 1985.
137p. – (Report).

Status of observers in the United Nations / R.G. Sybesma- Knol. – Brussels : Vrije Universiteit Brussel, Centrum voor de Studie van het Recht van de Verenigde Naties en de Gespecialiseerde Organisaties, 1981.
xi,484p.
Bibliography: p.456-484. - Includes index.
ISBN 9063210825

Status of refugees in international law / Foreword by Felix Schnyder. – Leyden : A. W. Sijthoff, 1966.
v.; 25 cm.
Bibliography: 1, p. 441-458. Contents: 1. Refugee character.

Status of Tibet : history, rights and prospects in international law / Michael C. van Walt van Praag : with a foreword by Franz Michael and an introduction by Rikhi Jaipal. – London : Wisdom, 1987.
400p; 23cm.
Includes bibliography and index.
ISBN 0861710703 Pbk

Statut juridique international des minorites : bibliographie selective / preparee par la Bibliotheque du Palais de la Paix, La Haye : selective biliography : prepared by the Library of the Peace Palace, the Hague. – The Hague : Center for Studies and Research of the Hague Academy of International Law, 1984.
29 leaves.

Statute law. – 3rd. – London : Longman Professional (UK), 1990.
Investigation of the processes involved in creating statute law, with analysis of the problems resulting. New edition revised to take account of new European Community law, the Law Commission's report on the codification of criminal law, and amendments to the Interpretation Act 1978.

Statute Law of Scotland : Abridged with Historical Notes. – Repr. of 1757 ed. – Abingdon : Professional Books.
57p.
Hbk £225.00

Statute Law Review. – London : Sweet & Maxwell.
Hbk £40.00
Bound Vol.. –
Hbk £16.75
Back Vols. avail.. –
Hbk £48.00

Statute law revision
12th report : Draft Statute Law (Repeals) Bill / the Law Commission and Scottish Law Commission. – London : H.M.S.O., 1985.
ii,107p.
ISBN 0101964803

Statute Law Revision Committee, Victoria
Progress report on the Constitution Act 1975 : the role of Upper Houses of Parliament (interim report) / Statute Law Revision Committee. – Melbourne : Government Printer, 1982.
iv,4p. – (D v no 1/1982).

Statute law revision, eleventh report : obsolete provisions in the Companies Act 1948 / the Law Commission. – London : H.M.S.O., 1984.
ii,14p; 25cm.
ISBN 0101923600

Statute of Frauds and related legislation / Institute of Law Research and Reform. – Edmonton : The Institute, 1985.
iv,88p. – (Report).

Statutes : Rules and Examples / Thomas M. Smith. – 2nd ed. – Butterworths, 1989.
ca 288p.
This book is designed to teach students how to read and understand statutes and how to apply them to specific sets of circumstances. It describes specific principles and illustrates them with extracts from appropriate cases.
ISBN 040949397X Pbk £39.00

Statutes and regulations of the People's Republic of China. – 3. – Hong Kong : University of East Asia Press, 1987.
looseleaf.
Cumulative index issued annually as a bound vol..

Statutes for the Law Society Finals. – London : Sweet & Maxwell, 1985.
ISBN 0421325208 Pbk £16.95

Statutes in Force, 90 Vols. – London : HMSO.
Pbk £3900.00
Back Vols. avail. Index to the Statutes. –
ISBN 0118402374 Hbk £133.00

Statutes in Force : Index. – London : Sweet & Maxwell.
ISBN 0421317809 Hbk

Statutes Law / Edgar. – 7th ed. – Sweet & Maxwell, 1971.
ISBN 0421145102 Hbk £68.00

Statutes of Alberta judicially considered. – R.S.A. 1980 ed. 1 v. – Calgary : Carswell, 1985.
looseleaf.
Previous ed.: 1977-1980.

Statutes of British Columbia Judicially Considered 1960-1978. – Agincourt : Carswell.
Hbk £54.25
1979-1980. –
Pbk £30.50
1980 to date. –
This text contains annotations of the decisions interpreting British Columbia statute law. Included are the Rules of Court, the Acts contained in the Revised Statutes of 1979 and the public statutes enacted since 1979 with cites to all amendments, repeals and new legislation.
Hbk £57.75

Statutes of Manitoba Judicially Considered. – Agincourt : Carswell.
This looseleaf volume includes statutory provisions referred to in a case. It covers the Rules of the Court, the Acts contained in the Revised Statutes of Manitoba 1970, and the public general statutes enacted during the session of 1971 and subsequent sessions.
Hbk £82.00

Statutes of Natal / compiled and edited by R. L. Hitchins : assisted and revised on behalf of the colonial government by G.W. Sweeney. – 3 v. – Pietermaritzburg : P. Davis, 1900.
Includes index. A compilation of the statutes of the colony for the period 1845 to 1899 with an appendix containing the Acts of 1900.

Statutes of Saskatchewan Judicially Considered. – Agincourt : Carswell.
Llf £69.25

Statutes of the Republic of Singapore / prepared and published by the Law Revision Commission under the authority of the Revised Edition of the Laws Act (Chapter 275). – Rev. ed. 1985. 12. – Singapore : Government Printer, 1986.
looseleaf.
Includes index.

Statutes of the Republic of South Africa / I. Isaacs. – Durban : Butterworths.
Hbk

Statutes on constitutional law. – Sofia : Sofia Press, .
172,1p.
At head of t.p.: National Assembly of the People's Republic of Bulgaria.

Statutes on Slavery : the Pamphlet Literature. – London : Garland.
ISBN 082406724X Hbk

Statutes revised, Northern Ireland. – 2nd ed. – Belfast : H.M.S.O., 1982.
Previous ed.: 1956. Contents: Public general statute law in force in Northern Ireland on 31 March 1981 except for Acts of the United Kingdom Parliament passed after 1920.
ISBN 0337233640 Llf

Statutory Changes in Hindu Law. – Allahabad : Law Publishers, 1982.
Hbk £12.00

Statutory instruments. – Belize. – Belmopan : Government Printery, 1973.
Supplement to the Government gazette. Continues: Statutory instruments of British Honduras.

Statutory instruments : Antigua and Barbuda. – Antigua and Barbuda : Government Printer, 1985-.
Extracted from the Government gazette.

Statutory instruments : Botswana. – Gaborone : Government Printer, 1966-.
Published as supplements to the Republic of Botswana government gazette.

Statutory instruments : Zambia. – Lusaka : Government Printer, 1964-.
Published as separate supplements to the Republic of Zambia government gazette.

Statutory instruments other than those of a local, personal or temporary character. – London : H.M.S.O., 1949.
Continues: Statutory rules and orders other than those of a local, personal, or temporary character.

Statutory interpretation. – 2nd ed. – London : Butterworths, 1987.
ISBN 0406570175 Hbk £11.95

Statutory interpretation : problems in communication. – Auckland : Oxford University Press (NZ), 1989.
256.
An introduction to statutory interpretation, dealing with common problems in the application of statutes to particular cases and with the common law method of statutory interpretation.
ISBN 019558189X Pbk £20.00

Statutory Interpretation in Australia. – 3rd ed. – Butterworths, 1988.
288p.
ISBN 0409495255 Hbk £49.00
ISBN 0409308102 Pbk £42.00

Statutory maternity allowance : a consultation paper / issued by the Department of Health and Social Security. – London : The Department, 1985.
11,12 leaves.
Includes press release.

Statutory powers of entry : seventeenth report of the Public and Administrative Law Reform Committee. – Wellington : the Committee?, 1983.
18,42vp.

Statutory restrictions on the use of custody for young offenders : a consultative paper. – Parliamentary All-Party Penal Affairs Group. – London : Parliamentary All-Party Penal Affairs Group, 1985.
8,3 leaves.

Statutory rules and orders : other than those of a local, personal, or temporary character : issued prior to 1890, and now in force. – 8 v. – London : H.M.S.O., 1896.
Prepared under the direction of the Statute Law Committee. Title page heading and spine title: The Statutory rules and orders revised.

Statutory rules and orders and statutory instruments revised to December 31, 1948. – 3rd ed. 25 v. – London : H.M.S.O., 1949.
Previous ed.: 1903. Prepared under the direction of the Statute Law Committee.

Statutory Rules Made Under the Road Traffic Ordinance 1958. – Kuala Lumpur : International Law Books Services.
Hbk £29.50

Statutory Sick Pay Guide. – London : Engineering Employers Federation.
Hbk £5.00

Statutory Sick Pay - Practical Guide. – 2nd ed. – London : Longman Professional, 1986.
ISBN 0851212336 Pbk £11.95

Statutory succession rights / Law Reform Commission of British Columbia. – Vancouver : The Commission, 1982.
vii,401p. – (Working paper).

Statutory Succession Rights. – Victoria : Government of British Columbia, 1983.
Hbk £15.00

Statutory variations. – Routledge, 1983.
ISBN 0710093489 Hbk £17.95

Staunford
Plees del Coron. – 1st ed. – Abingdon : Professional Books, 1986 Reprint.
ISBN 0862053285 Hbk £24.75

Staying OK / Amy Bjork Harris and Thomas A. Harris. – London : Pan, 1986.
xv,297p; 18cm.
Originally published: London : Cape, 1985. Includes index.
ISBN 033029136X Pbk £2.95

Stead, P.
Police of Britain. – London : Macmillan.
ISBN 0029307600 Hbk £19.95

Stearman, Kaye →Aboriginal Australians.
→ Western Europe's migrant workers.

Stedman, Graham →Computer contracts.
—Shareholders' agreements / Graham Stedman, Janet Jones. – London : Longman, 1986.
xvii,396p; 24cm. – (Longman commercial series).
Includes index.
ISBN 0851210252 £42.50

Steeck, Wolfgang →Rail Unions in Britain and West Germany : A Study of their Structure and Policies.

Steel, Freda
Issues in Tort Law / Sanda Rodgers-Magnet. – Agincourt : Carswell, 1983.
388p.
This book is a collection of papers on key issues in Canadian tort law by leading scholars in the field.
Hbk £43.75

Steele, J. T. →Introduction to insurance.

Steele, R.
Do-It-Yourself Conveyancing. – 3rd ed. – London : David & Charles, 1984.
ISBN 0715386697 Hbk £6.95

Steele, Richard
Some recent developments in individual employment law and practice : the text of a lecture delivered to the Belfast Solicitors' Association on 11th March 1982 / by Richard Steele. – Belfast : SLS, 1982.
31p.
Includes bibliographical references.

Steen, Michael
Tolley's Guide to Directors' Transactions / John Aldis. – Croydon : Tolley.
120p.
ISBN 0854591184 Hbk £5.95

Steenbergen, Jacques → Leading cases and materials on the external relations law of the European Community, with emphasis on the common commercial policy.

Stegar, Debra P. → Understanding the Canada-U.S. Free Trade Agreement.

Steiger, Heinhard
Competence of the European Parliament for Environmental Policy. – Berlin : Erich Schmidt.
101p. – (BZU Ser.: Vol. A63).
ISBN 3503015698 Pbk £22.50
→ Law and practice relating to pollution control in the Federal Republic of Germany.

Stein, Eric → Courts and free markets : perspectives from the United States and Europe, Vol.1.

Stein, Michael L → Estate duty : principles and planning.
→ Silke on South African income tax : being an exposition of the law, practice and incidence of income tax in South Africa.

Stein, N.D.
Accounting. – London : VanNostrand Reinhold, 1988.
ISBN 0278000096 Pbk £13.95
—Auditing . – Pitman.
– (ACCA Series).
ISBN 0273027972 Pbk £12.95

Stein, P. G. → Studies in Justinian's Institutes in memory of J.A.C. Thomas.

Stein, Peter
Legal institutions : the development of dispute settlement / Peter Stein. – London : Butterworths, 1984.
ix,236p; 23cm.
Includes index.
ISBN 0406400253 Hbk £16.00
ISBN 0406400261 Pbk £12.95

Stein, Peter G
Regulae Iuris: From Juristic Rules to Legal Maxims / J. Shand. – Edinburgh : Edinburgh University Press.
216p.
ISBN 0852241437 Hbk £8.50

Stein, R T J
Land Titles Reform / Andrew G Lang. – Auckland : Legal Research Foundation, 1983.
Hbk £12.50
→ Understanding land law.

Steinberg, David M.
Family law in the family courts. – 2nd ed. – Toronto : Carswell, 1981.
Previous ed.: 1973, edited by H.T.G. Andrews. Includes index.
ISBN 0459337300

Steiner, J
Practical approach to EEC Law. – London : Financial Training, 1988.
ISBN 1851850988 Pbk £14.95
—Textbook on EEC Law. – London : Blackstone Press.
ISBN 1854310003 Pbk £15.00

Steiss, Carl F. → Taxation of Partnerships in Canada.

Stelck, Sheila → Canadian Native Law Cases, Vol. 6 1960-1970.

Stenning → Take-Over Guide.

Stenning, Philip C.
Appearing for the Crown : a Legal and Historical Review of Criminal Prosecutorial Authority in Canada. – Cowansville : Brown Legal Publications.
450p.
Pbk £39.95
—Legal status of the police : a study paper prepared for the Law Reform Commission of Canada / by Philip C. Stenning. – Ottawa : Law Reform Commission of Canada, 1982.
169p; 25cm. – (Study paper).
ISBN 0662119967
—Postal Security and Mail Opening : a Review of the Law. – Toronto : University of Toronto, Centre of Criminology, 1981.
vi, 233p.
ISBN 0919584527 Pbk £8.00

Stepensons → Industrial Law.

Stephen, David
Central America's Indians / by David Stephen and Phillip Wearne : with a summary by Rodolfo Stavenhagen. – London : Minority Rights Group, 1984.
23p. – (Report).
→ Inequalities in Zimbabwe.

—San of the Kalahari / by David Stephen. – London : Minority Rights Group, 1982.
16p. – (Report).
Includes bibliographical references.

Stephen, J. F.
General View of the Criminal Law of England. – Repr. of 1863 ed. – Abingdon : Professional Books.
339p.
Hbk £45.00

Stephen, Leslie
English Utilitarians : by Leslie Stephen
Vol. 1-3. – 1. – s.l. : Micro-Offset Books, 1900.
Various pagings.
Complete in 3 vols.. Reproduction of 1950 reprint (New York: Peter Smith) of 1900 original published by Duckworth and Co., London. Includes bibliographical references and index. 3 vols. in one.

Stephen, Ninian
Constitutional Change in Canada : Lessons and Analogies From Across the Pacific. – North Ryde : Association for Canadian Studies in Australia and New Zealand, 1984.
Hbk £3.00

Stephens, M. L → International business and national jurisdiction.

Stephenson → Commercial and Consumer Law.
→ Law of Torts.

→ SWOT Law of Torts.

Stephenson, B.
Teachers' Superannuation Act, 1983, Bill 148 : An Act to Revise the Teachers' Superannuation Act. – Ontario : Ontario Government Publications Service, 1983.
49p.
Hbk £0.70

Stephenson, Douglas A.
Arbitration for contractors / Douglas A. Stephenson. – London : Northwood Books, 1982.
ix,150p.
Bibliography: p.145. - Includes index.
ISBN 0719829003

Stephenson, Graham
Consumer Credit. – London : Collins, 1987.
256p.
ISBN 0003833038 Hbk £20.00
—Criminal law and consumer protection / by Graham Stephenson. – Chichester : Rose, 1983.
xxxv,151p; 22cm.
Includes index.
ISBN 0859923096 corrected : Pbk £12.00

Stephenson, J.
Building Regulations 1976. – Northwood, 1978.
ISBN 0719836802 Hbk £13.50
—Building Regulations 1985 Explained. – Northwood, 1986.
ISBN 1850320195 Hbk £24.95

→ Civil Engineering Claims.

Stepick, Alex
Haitian refugees in the U.S. / by Alex Stepick : with the assistance of Dale Frederick Swartz. – Updated ed. – London : Minority Rights Group, 1986.
20p. – (Report).
Bibliography: p.18-19.
ISBN 0946690464

Step-Parent Adoptions. – North Vancouver : International Self-Counsel Press, 1987.
ISBN 0889086605 Hbk £12.95

Sterk, John
Alberta conveyancing law and practice / by John Sterk. – Toronto : Carswell, 1981.
xvi,279p.
ISBN 0459337106

Sterk's Alberta Conveyancing Law and Practice. – 2nd ed. – Agincourt : Carswell, 1987.
300p.
This practitioner's quick reference text provides materials on real estate transactions practice in Alberta, Canada. Forms, checklist, precedents, and other items needed to conduct the typical real estate transaction are included.
Hbk £46.25

Sterling commercial paper market. – Cambridge : Woodhead-Faulkner, 1988.
ISBN 0859414108 Hbk £40.00

Sterling, J. A. L.
Copyright law in Australia and the rights of performers, authors and composers in the Pacific region / by J.A.L. Sterling and Geoffrey E. Hart. – Sydney : Legal Books, 1981.
xli,278p; 23cm.
Bibliography: p.263-265. - Includes index.
ISBN 0959656871
—Copyright law in the United Kingdom and the rights of performers, authors and composers in Europe / by J.A.L. Sterling and M.C.L. Carpenter. – London : Legal Books, 1986.
cxi,749p; 26cm.
Kept up to date by supplements.
ISBN 0947926003
ISBN 0949553190
—Data Protection Act 1984 : a guide to the new legislation / J.A.L. Sterling. – 2nd ed. – Bicester : CCH, 1985.
v,330p; 23cm.
Previous ed.: 1984?. Bibliography: p313-314. - Includes index.
ISBN 0863250769 Pbk

Stern
New Developments in International Finance / Chew. – Oxford : Blackwell, 1988.
ISBN 063115115X Hbk £40.00
ISBN 0631152040 Pbk £15.00

Stern, Vivien
Bricks of shame : Britain's prisons / Vivien Stern. – Harmondsworth : Penguin, 1987.
309p; 20cm. – (Penguin special).
ISBN 0140523839

Stetsovskii, IU. I
Right of the accused to defence in the USSR / Yuri Stetsovsky : translated from the Russian by H. Campell Creighton. – Moscow : Progress Publishers, 1982.
283 p.; 21 cm.
Includes bibliographical references and index.

Steven, Mark → British workplace industrial relations 1980-1984 : the DE/PSI/ESRC/ACAS surveys.

Stevens
Work out accounting / Kriefman. – London : Macmillan, 1988.
ISBN 0333451244 Pbk £6.50

Stevens, Edward F.
Shipping practice : with consideration of the relevant law / C. S. J. Butterfield. – 11th ed. – London : Pitman, 1981.
xi,173p; 22cm.
Previous ed.: 1978. Includes index.
ISBN 0273016164 Pbk £9.95

Stevens, Elizabeth
Civil and criminal procedure in a nutshell / Elizabeth Stevens. – London : Sweet & Maxwell, 1981.
vii,86p; 18cm. – (New nutshells).
Includes index.
ISBN 0421280409 Pbk £1.75

Stevens, Francis
Law centre staff research project / Francis Stevens. – London : Law Centres Federation, 1983.
34p.
Summary of a report commissioned by the Law Centres Federation Evaluation Sub-Committee.

Stevens, G. → Music : the Business and the Law.

Stevens, I.
Constitutional and Administrative Law Supplement 1987. – Plymouth : Macdonald & Evans, 1982.
ISBN 0712103988 Pbk £6.50

Stevens, I. N.
Protection of liberty / I.N. Stevens & D.C.M. Yardley. – Oxford : Basil Blackwell, 1982.
x,188p; 24cm.
Examines the extent to which incursions are made on our civil liberties.
ISBN 0631129448 Hbk £15.00
ISBN 0631131760 Pbk £5.95

Stevens, Philip → Abstracts of race relations research.
—Ethnic minorities and complaints against the police / Philip Stevens and Carole Willis with the assistance of Clare Oxby. – London : Home Office, 1981.
v,40p. – (Research and Planning Unit paper).
Bibliography: p.33-34.
ISBN 0862520266

Stevens, R. D. S.
Bias and impartiality in magistrates' courts / R.D.S. Stevens. – Chichester : Rose, 1982.
xvii,105p; 22cm.
Includes index.
ISBN 0859922316 Pbk £6.80
—Frankfurter and Due Process. – London : Eurospan, 1988.
ISBN 0819156159 Hbk £26.25
ISBN 0819156167 Pbk £15.50

Stevenson, John R.
United States law of sovereign immunity relating to international financial transactions / John R. Stevenson, Jeffrey F. Browne and Lori Fisler Damrosch. – London : Euromoney Pubns, 1983.
158p.
Includes bibliographical references.
ISBN 090312145X

Stewart
Family at Law : In which the Hendersons find out what to do after an accident / Campbell. – London : Fourmat.
ISBN 1851900446 Pbk £5.95
→ Package holiday law and contracts.

Stewart, Bill
Skiing and the law. – Edinburgh : Green (W.) & Son, 1987.
Covers problems arising from liability for accidents likely to occur in connection with skiing, with reference to past cases incolving skiing and other sports from Scotland, England, France and North America, as well as to the provisions of the Consumer Protection Act.
ISBN 0414008332 Pbk

Stewart, D. G. →Report of the Royal Commission to inquire into certain matters related to drug trafficking.

Stewart, Donald E.
Divorce in Australia / by Donald E. Stewart and Margaret Harrison. – Melbourne, Vic. : Institute of Family Studies, 1982.
9 p.; 23 cm. – (Working paper).
Cover title. 'October 1982.'. Bibliography: p. 9.
ISBN 0642886504 Pbk

Stewart, Gillian
Children in custody / Gill Stewart, Norman Tutt. – Aldershot : Avebury, 1987.
viii,237p; 23cm.
Bibliography: p223-230. - Includes index.
ISBN 0566050757 £17.50

Stewart, Gordon
Administrative receivers and administrators / Gordon Stewart. – Bicester : CCH Editions, 1987.
xvii,359p; 23cm.
Traces receiverships and administrations from the events leading up to appointment through to termination and discharge of the office holder. Gives details of licensing requirements, and covers for both receivers and administrators, the appointment, nature and capacity, powers and duties. Also looks at payments and duties, termination, tax, and relevant forms.
ISBN 0863251404 Hbk
ISBN 0863250858 Pbk

Stewart, Jean Cantlie
History and practice of the law of mines and minerals / Jean Cantlie Stewart. – Banff : Rowan Books, 1987.
ISBN 0950993212

Stewart, M. A →Law, morality, and rights.
—Selection from the Proceedings of the Royal Institute of Philosophy Conference on the Philosophy of Law (September 1979). – Dordrecht : Kluwer, 1982.
184p.
Pbk £43.50

Stewart, Peter →Product liability : the new law under the Consumer Protection Act 1987.

Stewart, Stephen M.
International copyright and neighbouring rights / Stephen M. Stewart. – London : Butterworths, 1983.
xii,740p; 26cm.
This book covers the underlying general principles of both international and national copyright laws with particular reference to neighbouring rights including coverage of corporate ownership rights. This work is directed at the international law student and practitioner.
ISBN 0406662207 Hbk £73.50

Stewart, William
Introduction to the Scots law of delict. – Edinburgh : Green (W.) & Son, 1989.
An introduction to the most important principles and rules, with coverage of negligence, defamation, occupiers' liability, employers' liability and other forms of liability. Case summaries and statutory extracts provided along with references to other sources such as journal articles.
ISBN 0414008901 Pbk

Steytler, N. C. →Criminal justice in South Africa : selected aspects of discretion.

Stickler, Alan D.
Canada Business Corporations Act : an Accountant's View of the Highlights. – 3rd ed. – Butterworths, 1987.
136p.
Includes a revised study of the law introduced (in 1975) by the new Act. Covers detailed disclosure requirements for financial statements, information not contained in the body of the Act, but substantially prescribed by regulations.
ISBN 0409806560 Pbk £18.95

Stikeman, H. Heward, et al
Canada Tax Letter. – Toronto : DeBoo.
This series of studies, intended for the tax specialist, contains analyses and opinions of important legislation and jurisprudence. Approximately six issues per year are planned.
ISBN 0888201664 Hbk £140.00
—Canada Tax Service. – Toronto : DeBoo.
This multi-volume looseleaf service provides a seate taxation; business, property, and employment income; taxation of non-residents; and tax appeals cases.
ISBN 0888201656 Llf £725.00
—Doing Business in Canada, 3 Vols. / Elliott. – Agincourt : Carswell.
Service.
Llf £178.00

Stilling, P J
Company Accounting Requirements / Wild. – 2nd ed. – London : Longman Professional, 1985.
ISBN 0851211461 Pbk £19.95

Stitches in time : the Commonwealth in world politics / Arnold Smith with Clyde Sanger. – London : Deutsch, 1981.
xix,322p.

Stober, Michael I.
Entrapment in Canadian Criminal Law. – Agincourt : Carswell, 1985.
250p.
Hbk £35.75
—Entrapment in Canadian Criminal Law. – Agincourt : Carswell, 1985.
250p.
This book focuses on the problems inherent in the investigations of victimless crimes and sets out the theoretical bases for the defense of entrapment in criminal cases under Canadian law.
ISBN 045937060X Hbk £19.80

Stock Exchange
Admission of securities to listing. – Stock Exchange. – New loose-leaf ed. Nov. 1984. – London : Council of the Stock Exchange, 1984.
1 v. (loose-leaf).
Includes index.
ISBN 0900872195
—Stock Exchange regulations. – Stock Exchange. – London : Council of the Stock Exchange, 1985.
looseleaves in binder; 23cm.
Superseded by Regulations of the International Stock Exchange.

Stock exchange listing : the new requirements / Robert R. Pennington. – London : Butterworths, 1985.
ix,199p; 26cm.
Includes the text of The Stock Exchange (Listing) Regulations 1984.
ISBN 0406337004

Stock Exchange Press Dictionary of Financial Regulations. – Stock Exchange Press.
ISBN 0948209291 Hbk £29.95

Stock Exchange regulations. – Stock Exchange. – London : Council of the Stock Exchange, 1985.
looseleaves in binder; 23cm.
Superseded by Regulations of the International Stock Exchange.

Stock Markets and the Securities Industry : Law and Practice. – 3rd ed. – Butterworths, 1988.
340p.
ISBN 0409494674 Pbk £45.00

Stock purchase agreements / by Alain John Gaucher. – Toronto, Canada : Carswell, 1984.
xxvii, 286 p.; 24 cm.
Includes index. Bibliography: p. 275-280.
ISBN 045935910X

Stock Relief / David Williams. – London : Oyez Longman, 1981.
– (Oyez Longman Practical Tax Ser.).
ISBN 0851205852 Hbk £9.95

Stockbroking tomorrow. – London : Macmillan, 1985.
ISBN 0333219945 Hbk £27.50

Stockdale, Eric
Sentencing / Eric Stockdale and Keith Devlin. – London : Waterlow, 1987.
xxviii,297p; 24cm.
Bibliography: p285-291. - Includes index.
ISBN 0080392482 £30.00

Stockholm Chamber of Commerce →Arbitration in Sweden.

Stockholm International Peace Research Institute
Armaments or disarmament? : SIPRI brochure / Stockholm International Peace Research Institute. – Bergshamra : The Institute, 1983.
→ Falklands/Malvinas conflict : a spur to arms build-ups.

Stockholm University, Faculty of Law
Scandinavian Studies in Law, 30 Vols. / Folke Schmidt. – Stockholm : Almqvist & Wiksell.
Hbk £188.00 ea.

Stocking, B.
Expensive Health Technologies : Regulatory and Administrative Mechanisms in Europe. – Oxford : Oxford University Press.
ISBN 0192617141 Hbk £25.00

Stockmair, Wilfried →New German Patent Law (1981) in English and German.

Stockwood, David
Civil Litigation : A Practical Handbook / David Stockwood. – 2nd ed. – Agincourt : Carswell, 1986.
286p.
This book presents a guide to modern civil litigation in Canada for the practitioner. Each step in the preparation of a case is accompanied by checklist and sample forms.
Hbk £44.00
—Injunctions : A Practical Handbook. – Agincourt : Carswell, 1985.
725p.
This manual is a practitioners' guide to the preparation and presentation of injunction motions in Canadian courts. Sample forms and model motions are provided in the book.
ISBN 0459376500 Hbk £19.80

Stoddart, Charles N. →Casebook on Scottish criminal law.
→ Criminal procedure in Scotland : cases & materials.

—Law and Practice of Legal Aid in Scotland. – 2nd ed. – Edinburgh : W Green, 1985.
ISBN 0414007638 Llf £18.00

Stokes, Roy
Function of bibliography / Roy Stokes. – 2nd ed. – Aldershot : Gower, 1982.
xi,201p; 24cm. – (A Grafton book).
Previous ed.: London : Deutsch, 1969. Includes index.
ISBN 0566034409

Stolte, B.H.
Henrik Brenkman (1681-1736). Jurist and Classicist : a Chapter from the History of Roman Law as Part of the Classical Tradition. – Groningen : Egbert Forsten Publishing, 1981.
viii, 141p.
ISBN 9060880757 Hbk £38.50

Stone →Conflict of Law in the European Community.
—Forensic Medicine / Johnson. – London : Waterlow, 1987.
ISBN 0080392199 Hbk £30.00

→ Private international law in the European Community.

Stone, Evan →Coroners courts in England and Wales : a report.

Stone, Gregory →AJ Legal Handbook.
→ Law of defective premises.

Stone, I.F.
Trial of Socrates. – Aurora : Cape.
ISBN 0224025910 Hbk £12.95

Stone, Julius →Legal change : essays in honour of Julius Stone.
—Precedent and law : dynamics of common law growth / Julius Stone. – Sydney : Butterworths, 1985.
xx,289p.
Account of the sources from which categories of illusory reference in precedent law spring, of the refinements and elaborations of the operations and of the social and political problems which the operation creates. The author's concepts and arguments are applied to the realities of contemporary judicial process.
ISBN 040949304X A$59

Stone, Lawrence
Family, sex and marriage in England 1500-1800 / Lawrence Stone. – Abridged ed. – Harmondsworth : Penguin, 1982.
446p,16p of plates; 20cm. – (A Peregrine book).
Previous ed.: London : Weidenfeld & Nicolson, 1977. Includes index.
ISBN 0140551670 Pbk £3.50

Stone, Marcus
Cross examination in criminal trials / Marcus Stone. – London : Butterworths, 1988.
xix,224p.
Includes index.
ISBN 0406105057 Pbk £14.95
—Proof of fact in criminal trials. – Edinburgh : Green (W.) & Son, 1984.
Based on extensive court experience and psychological study, it is a systematic and comprehensive analysis of the fact-finding process in criminal trials examining lying and its detection, examination of witnesses, how real issues of fact emerge and the principles on which evidence is assessed and verdicts reached.
ISBN 0414007399 Pbk

Stone, N.
Probation Law : Social Work Law File Social Work Monographs. – Norwich : University of East Anglia.
ISBN 0946751528 Pbk £4.95

Stone, O.
Sweet and Maxwell's family law statutes. – 4th ed. – Sweet & Maxwell.
ISBN 0421382503 Pbk £16.95

Stone, Olive M.
Child's voice in the court of law : an account of the representation of minors in civil proceedings in Canada and some other (mostly common law) jurisdictions / Olive M. Stone. – Toronto : Butterworth & Co. (Canada), 1982.
x, 248p; 24cm.
Examination of the representation of minors in civil litigation, looking primarily at Canadian and English practices. Gives a historical discussion of women's legal position in the past and how the issue of guardianship was affected by it. Description of the relevant Canadian federal and provincial legislation in which each province is treated separately.
ISBN 0409870544 Hbk £30.00

Stone, P. A. →Conflict of laws in the European Community.

Stone, Peter →Law : a Guide to Select Law Sources in the Canberra College of Advanced Education Library.

Stone, Richard
Entry, search and seizure / Richard Stone. – London : Sweet & Maxwell, 1985.
lii,326p; 26cm.
Takes into account changes enacted by the Drug Trafficking Offences Act 1986, with a discussion of the application of the Police and Criminal Evidence Act 1985. Considers case law for Anton Piller orders, and Mareva injunctions. Defines the categories of persons and authorities who may lawfully exercise entry powers.
ISBN 0421298901 £35.00

Stonehenge : a report into the civil liberties implications of the events relating to the convoys of summer 1985 and 1986. – National Council for Civil Liberties. – London : National Council for Civil Liberties, 1986.
43p.
ISBN 0946088284

Stone's Justices' Manual / John Richman, A T Draycott. – 120th ed. 3 vols. – London : Butterworths, 1988.
ISBN 0406386803 Hbk £102.00

Stop the Deportations!. – Sydney : Pathfinder Press.
16p.
Hbk £0.50

Stop the SX00 Million Legal Tender Crime microform . – Berrima : Peace Plans.
microform

Stopford, John M.
Britain and the multinationals / John Stopford and Louis Turner. – Chichester : Wiley, 1985.
xiv,282p; 24cm. – (Wiley/IRM series on multinationals).
Includes index.
ISBN 0471908398 £12.75
—Multinationals : company performance and global trends / John M. Stopford and John H. Dunning...et al. – London : Macmillan, 1983.
ix,147p.
Bibliographies.
ISBN 0333340930

Storey, H.
Real Estate Agency in Victoria / A.H. Goldberg. – 2nd ed. – Butterworths, 1975.
386p.
ISBN 0409420700 Hbk £74.00

Storey, I. R.
Conveyancing. – 2nd ed. – London : Butterworths, 1987.
This text for students of conveyancing is an introduction to the theory and practice of conveyancing of land in the United Kingdom. A comprehensive work including materials on landlord and tenant, housing, and land law.
ISBN 0406010641 Pbk £15.95

Storm, Paul M. →Business law in Europe : legal, tax and labour aspects of business operations in the ten European Community countries and Switzerland.

Storme, M.
Effectiveness of Judicial Protection and the Constitutional Order. – Dordrecht : Kluwer.
228p.
ISBN 9065441522 Pbk £70.00

Stormorken, Bjrn
HURIDOCS standard formats for the recording and exchange of information on human rights / by Bjrn Stormorken : with the assistance of Annie McMorris. – Dordrecht : M. Nijhoff, 1985.
112p.
ISBN 9024731879 Hbk £80.00

Storrow, M. R. V., et al
International Commercial Crime Conference. – Vancouver : British Columbia Continuing Legal Education Society, 1981.
275p.
ISBN 0865040362 Hbk £25.00

Storry, J.
Consumer Credit Agreements Act. – Nettlebed Publications, 1985.
ISBN 0946628025 updat £45.00

Stott, V.
Hong Kong Company Law. – 2nd ed. – Pitman.
ISBN 0273030892 Pbk £8.95

Stott, Vanessa →Negotiable Instruments.

Stout, Ronald M.
Administrative law in Ireland / Ronald M. Stout. – Dublin : Institute of Public Administration, 1985.
514p.
Includes index.
ISBN 0906980402 £25.00

Stoy Hayward & Co.
Audit Guide. – Stoy Hayward & Co. – London : Butterworths, 1983.
ISBN 0406270600 Pbk £11.50
—Model financial statements. – Stoy Hayward & Co. – London : Butterworths, 1986.
ISBN 0406503907 Pbk £16.50

Stoy Hayward Business Tax Guides 1988-89 / Say. – London : Kogan Page.
ISBN 1850916440 Hbk £12.95

Strachan, B
Drinking Driver and the Law. – 3rd ed. – London : Shaw & Sons, 1983.
ISBN 0721905226 Pbk £16.00
—Matrimonial proceedings in magistrates courts / by Billy Strachan. – 2nd ed. – London : Sweet & Maxwell, 1987.
250p; 22cm.
Includes new material dealing with conciliation, and the effect of conduct on the amount of an order. Discusses grounds of an order for periodical payments, calculation and the amount of the order, orders for the custody of children, and for access to children, and the enforcement of orders.
ISBN 0421385006 Pbk £20.00

Strahan, Lynne →Half Open Door.

Straight from the Bench. – Oxford : Coronet Books.
ISBN 0340422718 Pbk £2.95

Strait of Dover / by Luc Cuyvers. – Dordrecht : Martinus Nijhoff, 1986.
xvi, 150p. – (International straits of the world).
ISBN 9024732522 Hbk £115.00

Stranks
Health and safety practice / M Dewis. – London : Pitman Publishing, 1986.
ISBN 0273025996 Pbk £22.50

Strasser, Daniel
Finances of Europe / by Daniel Strasser. – Revised and enlarged edition. – Luxembourg : Office for Official Publications of the European Communities, 1981.
xix,422p.
At head of title: Commission of the European Communities.
ISBN 9282520722

Strata Title Management Practice in New South Wales. – 4th ed. – North Ryde : C.C.H. Australia, 1985.
480p.
ISBN 0869036378 Hbk £35.00

Strata Title Units in New South Wales - A Guide to the Strata Titles Act. – 3rd ed. – Sydney : Butterworths, 1985.
200p.
ISBN 0409493147 Hbk

Strata Titles / R. Tzannes. – North Ryde : Law Book Co, 1978.
v, 353p.
ISBN 0455194994 Hbk £64.00
1980 Supplement. –
ISBN 045520246X £12.00

Strata Titles Act, 1985 (Act 318). – Kuala Lumpur : International Law Books Services.
Hbk £10.00

Strata Titles in Malaysia : Law and Practice. – Butterworths, 1987.
164p.
Deals with the current law and practice relating to the strata title system in Penninsular Malaysia, Sarawak, and Sabah. Covers the basic features of the Malaysian strata title system, and the rules governing the management corporation and its members, and third parties such as chargees, occupiers and insurers.
ISBN 040999538X Hbk £65.00

Strategic management in multinational companies / by Yves Doz. – Oxford : Pergamon, 1985.
250p; 25cm.
ISBN 0080318088 Hbk £19.25
ISBN 008031807X Pbk £10.75

Strategic planning for electronic banking. – London : Butterworths, 1987.
ISBN 040610087X Pbk £45.00

Strategic Planning of U.S. Commercial Banks in a Changing Legal Environment. – Idstein : Schultz-Kirchner, 1985.
ISBN 3925196013

Strathon, R. N.
Property Valuation Handbook. – Reading : College of Estate Management.
ISBN 090213289X Hbk £38.00

Stratmann, Gunther H. W. →Comparative survey of corporate investments, Vol. 1 : in the Far East and Middle East ... : edited by Gunther H. W. Stratmann : written by members of Committee G/Business Orgamisation of the Section on Business Law of the International Bar Association.

Stratospheric ozone : report ... – United Kingdom Stratospheric Ozone Review Group. – London : HMSO, 1987.
'The Stratospheric Ozone Review Group was set up jointly by the Department of the Environment and the Meteorological Office in November 1985'. - Annex A.

Stratton, Ian G.
Building Land and Estates. – 2nd ed. – London : Oyez Longman, 1983.
– (Oyez Longman Practice Note Ser.: No. 67).
ISBN 0851206964 Hbk £8.95

Straus, J. →Biotechnology and patent protection : an international review.

Strauss, S. A. →Punishment : an introduction to principles.
—You in the small claims court : a practical guide / S.A. Strauss. – Cape Town : Juta, 1985.
xv,126p.
Includes index.
ISBN 0702116637

Strayer, Barry L.
Canadian Constitution and the Courts : the Function and Scope of Judicial Review. – 3rd ed. – Butterworths, 1988.
400p.
New edition includes coverage of the major increase in the number of cases involving constitutional issues, the dominance of Charter questions in constitutional litigation, and the greatly heightened profile of the Supreme Court of Canada as innovating leader in the interpretation of the new constitutional provisions. Also notes early trends in judicial activism, or restraint, in Charter interpretation.
ISBN 0409806315 Hbk £80.00

Streamlining the cities : an analysis of the Government's case for reorganising local government in the six Metropolitan Counties : first report / Coopers & Lybrand Associates. – London? : Coopers & Lybrand Associates, 1983.
28p.

Streamlining the cities : government proposals for reorganising local government in Greater London and the metropolitan counties / presented to Parliament by the Secretary of State for the Environment ... – London : H.M.S.O., 1983.
31p.
ISBN 0101906307

Streeck, Wolfgang
Industrial relations in West Germany : a case study of the car industry / Wolfgang Streeck. – London : Heinemann, 1984.
178p; 23cm.
Bibliography: p170-172. - Includes index. At head of title: Policy Studies Institute.
ISBN 0435838393 £16.50

Street, Drainage and Building Act, 1974 (Act 133). – Kuala Lumpur : International Law Books Services.
Hbk £12.50

Street, H. A.
Ultra Vires : Being an Investigation of the Principles Which Limit the Powers and Liabilities of Corporations, Quasi-Corporate Bodies and Non-Sovereign Legislature. – Repr. of 1930 ed. – Abingdon : Professional Books.
344p.
Hbk £45.00

Street, Harry →Constitutional and administrative law.
—Freedom, the individual and the law / H. Street. – 5th ed. – Harmondsworth, Eng. : Penguin Books, 1982.
352p. – (Pelican Books).
ISBN 0140206469
—Law of Torts. – 8th ed. – London : Butterworths, 1988.
ISBN 0406662118 Hbk £34.00
ISBN 0406662126 Pbk £19.95

Streit, Manfred E. →Futures markets : modelling, managing and monitoring futures trading.

Strict and vicarious liability : a study in administrative criminal law / by L.H. Leigh. – London : Sweet & Maxwell, 1982.
xix,121p; 19cm.
Includes index.
ISBN 0421267607 Hbk £
ISBN 0421267704 Pbk £6.85

Strict settlement : a guide for historians / Barbara English and John Saville. – Hull : University of Hull Press, 1983.
144p. – (Occasional papers in economic and social history).
Bibliography: p.132-137. - Includes index.
ISBN 0859584399

Stridhana or Woman's Property in Indian Law : An Appraisal of its Concept and Contents. – Hoshiarpur : Vishveshvaranand Institute.
Hbk £2.65

Strijbosch, Fons →Anthropology of law in the Netherlands : essays on legal pluralism.

Strike. – Milan : Giuffre, 1987.
xvi, 554p.
Hbk L37,000.00

Strike law in Australia / by Edward I. Sykes. – 2nd ed. – Sydney : Law Book Co., 1982.
xxiii, 369 p.; 25 cm.
Includes bibliographical references and index.
ISBN 0455200890

Strike-free procedures : are they what they seem? / Roy Lewis. – Coventry : University of Warwick. School of Industrial and Business Studies. Industrial Relations Research Unit, 1988.
14 leaves.
Bibliography: p14.

Strikes and lockouts in Canada 1981 : labour data / Greves et lock-out au Canada 1981. – Ottawa : Canadian Government Publishing Centre, Supply and Services Canada, 1982.
83p.
Parallel English and French text.

Strikes in essential services / Gillian S. Morris. – London : Mansell, 1986.
x,221p; 24cm.
Bibliography: p209-215. - Includes index.
ISBN 0720117917 Hbk £25.00
ISBN 0720118697 Pbk £15.00

Striking a balance? : employment law after the 1980 Act / Roy Lewis and Bob Simpson. – Oxford : Martin Robertson, 1981.
ix,269p; 22cm.
Includes index.
ISBN 0855204427 Hbk £
ISBN 0855204435 Pbk £4.95

Striking a Bargain?. – London : Sweet & Maxwell, 1985.
– (Sweet and Maxwell's Law Files Ser.: No. 7).
ISBN 0421340401 Llf £29.50

Striking out strikes : changing employment relations in the British labour market / Charles G. Hanson and Graham Mather. – London : Institute of Economic Affairs, 1988.
94p; 22cm.
ISBN 0255362080

Strip searching : an inquiry into the strip searching of women remand prisoners at Armagh Prison between 1982 and 1985. – London : National Council for Civil Liberties, 1986.
36p; 20cm.
ISBN 0946088209 Pbk £1.95

Stripinis, Daniels
Probability Theory and Circumstantial Evidence. – Oslo : Norwegian University Press, 1983.
38p.
ISBN 8200067467 Hbk £23.00

Stromholm, Stig
Copyright and jurisprudence : selected papers / melanges : Stig Stromholm. – Stockholm : Norstedt, 1983.
291p.
Bibliography: p.271-291. 'Edited by the Faculty of Law, Uppsala University and P.A. Norstedt & Soners forlag, Stockholm' - Cover. Papers in English, French and German.
ISBN 9118276210
→ Introduction to Swedish law.

—Introduction to Swedish Law. – 2nd ed. – Stockholm : Almqvist & Wiksell.
ISBN 9118771521 Hbk

—Short history of legal thinking in the West / Stig Stromholm. – Stockholm, Sweden : Norstedts, 1985.
317 p.; 23 cm.
Includes index.
ISBN 9118571425

Stroud, C.
Close Pursuit : Week In The Life Of A New York Homicide Cop. – Viking.
ISBN 0140083979 Pbk £3.50
ISBN 0670808377 Hbk £10.95

Stroud, D. A.
Mens Rea : Imputability Under the Law of England. – Repr. of 1914 ed. – Abingdon : Professional Books.
345p.
Hbk £75.00

Stroud, Frederick
Strouds judicial dictionary of words and phrases / John S. James, Frederick Stroud. – 5th ed. 6 v. – London : Sweet & Maxwell, 1986.
Kept up to date by supplements.
ISBN 0421366303

Strouds judicial dictionary of words and phrases / John S. James, Frederick Stroud. – 5th ed. 6 v. – London : Sweet & Maxwell, 1986.
Kept up to date by supplements.
ISBN 0421366303

Structural Criminology. – Polity Press.
ISBN 0745605168 Hbk £29.50

Structure and Process of International Law : Essays in Legal Philosophy, Doctrine and Theory / Douglas M. Johnston. – Dordrecht : Kluwer, 1986.
1,234p.
ISBN 9024732735 Pbk £175.00

Structure of Public Limited Companies. – Kirchberg : Commission of the European Communities.
68p. – (Bulletin of the European Communities Ser.).
Hbk

Structure of the courts : a discussion paper / Law Commission. – Wellington, N.Z. : The Commission, 1987.
x,93p. – (Preliminary paper).
Bibliography: pp.50-54.

Structure of the profession
Part 1 / New South Wales Law Reform Commission. – Sydney : The Commission, 1981.
340p; 25cm. – (Discussion paper no 4 (1)).
Bibliography: p. 324-340.
Part 2 / New South Wales Law Reform Commission. – 1981.
p.344-644; 25cm. – (Discussion paper no 4 (2)).

Structure of tobacco taxes in the European Community / J.A. Kay, M.J. Keen. – London : Institute for Fiscal Studies, 1982.
44p; 22cm.
Bibliography: p44.
ISBN 0902992295 Pbk

Structured Settlements. – Agincourt : Carswell, 1984.
xx, 250p.
This book for the Canadian practitioner examines the procedure for arriving at a fair settlement figure, the negotiation process, and how to proceed with insurers and Revenue Canada. Actual correspondence relating to a structured award is included in the appendix.
Hbk £43.75

Structures of Injustice : a Report of a Consultation on Violations of Human Rights, held in Khartoum, Sudan from 16-22 February, 1975. – All Africa Conference of Churches. – Nairobi Westlands : All Africa Conference of Churches.
47p.
Hbk £15.00

Structuring foreign investment in US real estate / W D Knight, R L Doernberg. – Kluwer Law and Taxation, 1989.
780.
Explores the considerations of concern to foreign individuals and organisations making US real property investments. Covers US income, estate, and gift tax aspects of foreign investment. Also techniques that may be employed to reduce or eliminate US tax liability. Includes the Foreign Investment in Real Property Act 1980.
ISBN 9065449752 Llf £112/Dfl 350
Supplement. – 1989.
ISBN 90T275002X Llf £80.75/Dfl 250

Struggle for the Falkland Islands : a study in legal and diplomatic history / Julius Goebel : with a preface and an introduction by J.C.J. Metford. – New Haven : Yale University Press, 1982.
xxx,482p; 23cm.
Originally published: 1927. Includes index.
ISBN 0300029438 Hbk £12.00
ISBN 0300029446 Pbk £5.95

Struggle of Islam in modern Indonesia / B. J. Boland. – The Hague : Martinus Nijhoff, 1982.
viii,283p.
'Slightly revised reprint' of 1971 edition. Bibliography: p267-274.
ISBN 9024761816 Hbk

Stuart-Buttle, Elizabeth →Tax Aspects of the Administration of Estates.

Stuart, Donald
Canadian criminal law : a treatise / by Don Stuart. – Toronto : Carswell, 1982.
liii,602p.
Bibliography: p.x - Includes index.
ISBN 0459348000

—Learning Canadian criminal law / by Don Stuart and Ronald Joseph Delisle. – Toronto : Carswell, 1982.
xix,913p.
ISBN 0459348205

—Learning Canadian Criminal Procedure / Ronald Joseph Delisle. – Agincourt : Carswell, 1986.
798p.
This work for law students in Canada discusses the principles and policies underlying criminal procedure. Full coverage is given to the Canadian Charter of Rights and Freedoms and its impact on criminal procedure in the text.
Hbk £80.00

Stuart, J.
Answers to Dirleton's Doubts in the Laws of Scotland. – Repr. of 1715 ed. – Abingdon : Professional Books.
117p.
Hbk £220.00

Stubbs
Digests of Irish Reports and Irish Law Times Reports
Incl. 1867-93. – Abingdon : Professional Books.
Hbk

Stuchka, P.I.
Selected Writing on Soviet Law and Marxism. – Sharpe.
ISBN 0873324730 Hbk £51.50

Student Law Reporter 1983. – Dublin : Round Hall Press, 1982.
106p.
ISBN 0950872504 £6.95p

Students' Casebook on Mercantile Law. – Durban : Professional Publisher, 1975 repr. 1980.
ISBN 0409020303 Pbk £45.00

Student's glossary of Scottish legal terms / by Andrew Dewar Gibb. – 2nd ed. – Edinburgh : Green, 1982.
100p.
Previous ed.: published as 'Dictionary of words and phrases' by A.W. Dalrymple and Andrew Dewar Gibb, 1946.
ISBN 0414006968

Student's Property Statutes. – Repr. of 1927 ed. – Aalen Wuertt : Scientia.
xv, 244p.
Hbk £70.00

Studies and Essays on International Humanitarian Law and Red Cross Principles, in Honour of Jean Pictet. – Geneva : Comite International de la Croix-Rouge, 1984.
1,143p.
Hbk £100.00

Studies in 13th century justice and administration / C.A.F. Meekings. – London : Hambledon, 1981.
342p; 25cm. – (History series).
ISBN 0950688231

Studies In Banking Theory, Financial History, Vertical Contr. – London : Macmillan.
ISBN 0333457390 Hbk £33.00

Studies in Canadian company law / Etudes sur le droit canadien des compagnies : edited by Jacob S. Ziegel. – 2. – Toronto : Butterworths, 1967.
Includes bibliographical references and index. Vol. 2 signed by the editor. Vol. 2 has subtitle: Corporation and securities law in the seventies. English or French.

Studies in Canadian Tort Law. – London : Butterworths.
ISBN 0409843008 Hbk £60.00

Studies in Caribbean labour relations / Roop L. Chaudhary. – 2nd ed. – Barbados : Coles Printery, 1984.
xi,234p.
Includes index.

Studies in Civil Procedure. – London : Butterworths.
ISBN 0409832502 Hbk £40.00

Studies in Commercial Law and Judicial Activism. – New Delhi : Deep and Deep Publications, 1988.
220p.
Hbk £150.00

Studies in Comparative Law
Vol. 1: Security Over Corporeal Movables. – Dordrecht : Kluwer, 1974.
320p.
ISBN 9028600744 Hbk £92.00

Studies in constitutional law. – London : Butterworths, 1987.
ISBN 040626144X Hbk £16.50
ISBN 0406261458 Pbk £9.95

Studies in Contractual Claims under the ICE Conditions of Contract. – 3rd rev. ed. – King's Ride : Institute of Building, 1987.
34p.
ISBN 0906600170 Hbk £7.75

Studies in English legal history / T.F.T. Plucknett. – London : Hambledon, 1983.
352p in various pagings; 24cm.
Includes index. Includes text in Latin.
ISBN 0907628117 £24.00

Studies in Income Tax. – 2nd ed. – Cape Town : Legal and Financial Publishing Co.
Hbk £14.40

Studies in international labour migration / W.R. Bohning. – London : Macmillan, 1984.
350p.
Bibliography: p293-308. - Includes index.
ISBN 0333369718 £30.00

Studies in International Law. – Colombo : Lake House Investments.
Hbk £1.40

Studies in International Law. – New Delhi : Oxford University Press.
Hbk £60.00

Studies in Justinian's Institutes in memory of J.A.C. Thomas / edited by P.G. Stein and A.D.E Lewis. – London : Sweet & Maxwell, 1983.
xii,209p; 26cm.
Bibliography: p189-197. - Includes index. Includes quotations from the Latin, and 2 papers in German.
ISBN 0421303204 £25.00

Studies in labour law / edited by Kenneth P. Swan, Katherine E. Swinton. – Toronto : Butterworths, 1983.
xxiii,349p. – (Canadian legal studies series).
Includes index.
ISBN 040987129X

Studies in Labour Law / Katherine E Swinton. – London : Butterworths.
ISBN 0409487129X Hbk £64.00

Studies in Roman law in memory of A. Arthur Schiller / edited by Roger S. Bagnall and William V. Harris. – Leiden : Brill, 1986.
xviii,168p; 25cm.
Eleven papers in English; 1 each in German and Italian.
ISBN 9004075682

Studies in Swedish Post-War Industrial Investments. – Stockholm : Almqvist & Wiksell, 1982.
122p.
ISBN 9155413587 Hbk £62.00

Studies in the causation and prevention of traffic crime / Thor Norstrom. – Stockholm : Almqvist & Wiksell, 1981.
106p.
Bibliography: p.99-104.
ISBN 9122004211

Studies in World Public Order. – Myres S. McDougal and Associates. – Dordrecht : Kluwer, 1987.
1,080p.
ISBN 08938389003 Hbk £350.00

Studies on criminal responsibility and psychiatric treatment of mentally ill offenders : reports presented to the seventh Criminological Colloquium (1985). – Council of Europe. – Strasbourg : Council of Europe, 1986.
103p; 21cm. – (Legal affairs).
On cover: European Committee on Crime Problems.
ISBN 9287108994

Studies on the Dutch prison system / edited by M.J.M. Brand-Koolen. – Amstelveen Netherlands : Kugler Publications BV, 1987.
viii, 189 p.; 23 cm.
Includes bibliographies.
ISBN 9062990355 Pbk

Study and Practice of Military Law. – New Delhi : Deep and Deep Publications, 1988.
496p.
ISBN 8171000126 Hbk £250.00

Study Commission on the Family
Families in the future / final report of the Study Commission. – London : Study Commission on the Family, 1983.
56p; 21cm.
ISBN 0907051170 Pbk £3.25
—Values and the changing family / a final report from the Working Party on Values. – London : Study Commission on the Family, 1982.
52p; 21cm.
Bibliography: p48. Cover title.
ISBN 0907051138 Pbk £2.75

Study Group on Censorship
Protection of military information : report of the Study Group on Censorship ... : presented to Parliament by the Secretary of State for Defence ... December 1983. – Study Group on Censorship. – London : H.M.S.O., 1983.
vii,91p; 25cm.
Bibliography: p60-63. - Includes index.
ISBN 0101911203 Pbk £6.40

Study Group on the World Political Map → Maritime boundaries and ocean resources.

Study in Law of Evidence. – Lucknow : Eastern Book Company, 1982.
292p.
Pbk £15.00

Study of Industrial Law, Vol 1 : Law Relating to Industrial Disputes, Trade Unions, Wages and Workmen's Compensation / A.G. Kothari. – Bombay : Tripathi, 1987.
404p.
bd £90.00

Study of Parliament Group →Commons today. → New select committees : a study of the 1979 reforms.

Study of police management information systems / study team: Ted M. Zaharchuk (project director), Robert M. Atcheson ...et al. – Ottawa : Communication Division, Ministry of the Solicitor General of Canada, 1981.
vii,58p.
Bibliography: p.24-58. 'Prepared by Decision Dynamics Corporation under contract with the Research Division, Ministry of the Solicitor General of Canada' - verso t.p..
ISBN 0662116437

Study on common standards for query languages in computerised legal retrieval systems / prepared for the Council of Europe by Werner Robert Svoboda. – Strasbourg : Council of Europe, 1981.
52p.
'Based on a proposal put forward by Working Party No. II of the Committee of Experts on Legal Data Processing' - p.4. At head of cover title: Council of Europe, Legal Affairs.

Study on marine casualty investigations in Canada (for the Minister of Transport) / Bernard M. Desch$enes. – Ottawa : Minister of Supply and Services, 1984.
x,273p.
ISBN 0662134036

Study on the legislative framework, agreements and financial impositions affecting the mining industry in Pacific Commonwealth countries / by Macbul Rahim and Ruckia Hamisi. – 1. – London : Commonwealth Secretariat, 1981.
various pagings.
Cover title: The legislative framework, agreements and financial impositions affecting the mining industry in Pacific Commonwealth countries.

Study on the legislative framework, agreements and financial impositions affecting the mining industry in African Commonwealth countries / prepared for the Commonwealth Fund for Technical Co-operation by Macbul Rahim and Juliet Broad under the supervision of Roland Brown and Mike Faber. – 1. – London : Commonwealth Secretariat, 1981.
various pagings.
Cover title: The legislative framework, agreements and financial impositions affecting the mining industry in African Commonwealth countries.

Study Paper on the Office of the Sheriff. – Victoria : Government of British Columbia, 1983.
Hbk £10.00

Studying law / Phillip H. Kenny. – London : Butterworths, 1985.
viii,170p; 23cm.
Bibliography: p162-163. - Includes index.
ISBN 0406016089 Hbk £9.00
ISBN 0406016097 Pbk £4.95

Studying rural lawyers : research strategy and context / Kim Economides, Charles Watkins and Mark Blacksell. – Exeter : University of Exeter, 1985.
66,9p. – (Working paper).

Stumpf, Herbert →Know-how contract in Germany, Japan, and the United States.

Sturges →Decision Making in Magistrates' Courts.

Sturt, R. H. B.
Collision regulations : the application and enforcement of the Merchant Shipping (Distress Signals and Prevention of Collisions) Regulations 1983 / by R.H.B. Sturt : illustrations by Ann L. Sturt. – 2nd ed. – London : Lloyd's of London Press, 1984.
xlvi,177p, 5p of plates.
Previous ed.: 1977. Includes index.
ISBN 0907432670

Stuyck, Jules
Product differentiation in terms of packaging presentation, advertising, trade marks, etc. : an assessment of the legal situation regarding pharmaceuticals and certain other consumer goods / Jules Stuyck. – Antwerp : Kluwer, 1983.
xv,118p.
Bibliography: p.111-118.
ISBN 9065440844

Style, Christopher
Documentary evidence / Christopher Style, Charles Hollander : consulting editor: W.D. Park : with a foreword by Robert Alexander. – London : Oyez Longman, 1984.
xxi, 280p.
ISBN 085120970X

Style writs for a Sheriff Court Ordinary Cause. – Edinburgh : Green (W.) & Son, 1989.
Provides styles of written pleading in a range of writs for a variety of ordinary action commonly encountered in a Sheriff Court practice.
ISBN 0414008456 Hbk

Sub-contracts under JCT intermediate form. – Oxford : Blackwell Scientific, 1987.
240p.
ISBN 0003831752 Hbk £19.95

Subject compilations of state laws 1979-1983 : research guide and annotated bibliography / Cheryl Nyberg and Carol Boast. – Westport : Greenwood, 1984.
x,556p; 24cm.
Includes index.
ISBN 0313233357

Subject guide and chronological tables to the subordinate legislation of the Isle of Man / prepared on the directions of H.M. Attorney General for the Isle of Man. – Douglas : Isle of Man Government Printer, 1983-.
looseleaf.

Subject Guide to Native Law Cases and Annotated Text of the Indian Act of Canada / Zandra MacEachern. – Saskatoon : University of Saskatchewan, Native Law Centre, 1985.
267p.
ISBN 0888801599 Hbk £45.00

Subject guide to the Acts of Tynwald. – Rev. to 31 Oct. 1984. – Douglas : Isle of Man Government, 1984.
84p.

Subject Index to the Acts and Regulations of the Commonwealth of Australia, 1986 Edition. – North Ryde : Law Book Co, 1987.
Pbk £36.00

Subject index to the Acts of New South Wales / compiled by B.M. Wicks. – 1983 ed. – Sydney : Law Book Co., 1984.
141p.

Subject-to-Contract Procedures in House Purchase. – Reading : College of Estate Management, 1984.
28p.
ISBN 0902132989 Hbk £7.50

Submission by the Joint Working Party on Competition Law to the House of Lords Select Committee on the European Communities on procedures for administering EEC competition policy. – Joint Working Party on Competition Law. – London : Senate of the Inns of Court and the Bar, 1981.
10p; 30cm.
At head of title: The Senate of the Inns of Court and Bar, The Law Society.

Submission to the Home Office on Intermittent custody, Cmnd 9281 / from the National Association for the Care and Resettlement of Offenders. – London : NACRO, 1984.
14p.

Subordinate courts practice 1981 / by K.S. Dass and Abdul Hamid Bin Haji Mohamed : with a foreword by Tun Mohamed Suffian Bin Hashim : and an introduction by Raja Tan Sri Dr. Azlan Shah. – Johor : Asian Book, 1981.
lix,945p.
Includes index.

Subordinate Courts Rules 1980 (P.U.(A) 328/80). – Kuala Lumpur : International Law Books Services.
Hbk £25.00

Subrahmanyam, E.S. →Indian Contract Act, 3 Vols.

Subramaniam, Arjunan
Introduction to real property gains taxation in Malaysia. – Singapore : Malayan Law Journal, 1982.
121.
Outlines the provisions of the Real Property Gains Tax Act 1976, giving the background and general principles of the tax computation, and examine specific cases. Discusses the administration involved in the returns and assessments, recovery and collection, the offence, and penalties indicated. Appendix reproduces the Real Property Gains Tax Act 1976, and other Acts.
Hbk
—Introduction to real property gains taxation in Malaysia / by Arjunan Subramaniam. – Kuala Lumpur : Malayan Law Journal, 1982.
x,121p.
Bibliography: p.x. - Includes index.
—Petroleum income tax in Malaysia. –.Singapore : Malayan Law Journal, 1982.
xv,240.
Covers oil exploration and PETRONAS, taxation of petroleum companies, and administration and appeals. Appendices reproduce the Petroleum (Income Tax) Act 1967 and all subsequent Amendments up to 1977, the Petroleum Mining Act 1966, and a map showing the location of oil and gas fields in Malaysia.
Hbk

Subramaniam, N
Annotation of the Singapore Companies (Amendment) Act 1987 / Dorothy Chan. – Singapore : Butterworths (Asia), 1987.
212.
Summarizes the changes effected by the Amendment Act and reproduces those provisions in the Companies Act which are affected by the Companies (Amendment) Act 1987. Covers shares, debentures and charges, judicial management, audit, winding-up, and various types of companies.
ISBN 0409995509 Pbk

Subramanian, N.A.
Case Law on the Indian Constitution. – Allahabad : Orient Law House.
ISBN 0861250265 Pbk £45.00

Subramanya, T.R.
Rights and Statutes of the Individual in International Law. – New Delhi : Deep and Deep Publications, 1984.
200p.
Hbk £110.00

Subrogation in insurance law / by S.R. Derham. – North Ryde, N.S.W. : Law Book Co. Ltd., 1985.
xxxiii,164p.
Bibliography: p.xxix-xxxiii. - Includes index.
ISBN 0455205922

Subscription television. – H.M.S.O., 1987.
213p.
ISBN 0113408552 Pbk £9.50

Subsidiary Legislation 1977. – Seychelles Government. – Mahe.
Hbk £100.00

Subsidiary Legislation, 1978 : Laws of Barbados. – London : Sweet & Maxwell, 1983.
ISBN 0421317604 Llf £260.00

Subsidiary legislation to the Gazette of the United Republic of Tanzania. – Dar es Salaam : Government Printer, 1964-.

Subsistence vs. Commercial Use. – Ottawa : Canadian Arctic Resources Committee, 1982.
54p.
Pbk £6.00

Substantive and reflexive elements in modern law / by Gunther Teubner. – Florence : European University Institute, 1982.
94p.

Substantive law of the EEC / by Derrick Wyatt and Alan Dashwood. – 2nd ed. – London : Sweet & Maxwell, 1987.
450p; 25cm.
Previous ed.: 1980. Includes index.
ISBN 0421348704 Hbk £ :
ISBN 0421348801 Pbk

Successful investment strategy. – 2nd ed. – Cambridge : Woodhead-Faulkner, 1988.
ISBN 0859413837 Hbk £25.00

Successful Mergers : Planning, Strategy and Execution. – Waterlow.
ISBN 0080369022 Pbk £12.95

Succession : cases and materials / Cherry E. Wright. – London : Butterworths, 1986.
xxv,436p; 25cm.
Includes index.
ISBN 0406563101 Hbk £34.00
ISBN 040656311X Pbk £20.50

Succession in International Law. – Allahabad : Orient Law House.
ISBN 0861252756 Hbk £65.00

Succession in the Muslim Family. – Cambridge : Cambridge University Press, 1971.
ISBN 0521078520 Hbk £30.00

Succession (Scotland) Act 1964 / by Michael C. Meston. – 3rd ed. – Edinburgh : Green, 1982.
xv,136p; 24cm.
Includes text of the Act. Previous ed.: 1969. Includes index.
ISBN 0414007050 Pbk

Succinct View of the Rule of Shelley's Case. – Repr. of 1794 ed. – Abingdon : Professional Books.
486p.
Hbk £40.00

Sudarshan, R. →Judges and the judicial power : essays in honour of Justice V.R. Krishna Iyer.

Suddards, Roger W.
Bradford disaster appeal : the administration of an appeal fund / by Roger W. Suddards : with contributions by Leolin Price and Hubert Picarda. – London : Sweet & Maxwell, 1986.
169p.
ISBN 0421379901

—Historic buildings : the law and practice. – 2nd ed. – London : Sweet & Maxwell, 1988.
ISBN 0421381302 Hbk £40.00

—Lawyer's Peregrination. – 2nd ed. – London : Sweet & Maxwell, 1987.
ISBN 0421391804 Pbk £1.95

—Listed buildings : the law and practice of historic buildings, ancient monuments and conservation areas / by Roger W. Suddards. – 2nd ed. – London : Sweet & Maxwell, 1988.
xxxi,307p.
Sets out and discusses the statutory basis for the protection and preservation of our 'built heritage'. Deals with listed buildings, conservation area control and the law relating to ancient monuments. Describes the effect of fixing canopies to listed buildings, and problems arising from cladding, rendering and cleaning of such buildings.
ISBN 0421381302 £40.00

Sudden deaths and fatal accident inquiries. – Edinburgh : Green (W.) & Son, 1986.
Covers the duties of the procurator fiscal in investigating sudden and unexpected deaths. With a chapter on medical mattres, a summary of the duties of the coroner in England and guidance for the medical professions as to which deaths shuld be reported to the fiscal.
ISBN 0414007751 Pbk

Suetens, L. P.
Law and practice relating to pollution control in Belgium and Luxembourg / Dirk Soetemans. – 2nd ed. – London : Graham & Trotman for the Commission of the European Communities, 1982.
200p.
Previous ed: /by J.M. Didier and Associates for Environmental Resources Limited. 1976. Includes index.
ISBN 0860103102 £18.00

Sufrin, B. E →Effect on English domestic law of membership of the European Communities and of ratification of the European Convention on Human Rights.

Sugarman, David
Conceptual and policy basis of directors' fiduciary duties under English company law / by David Sugarman. – 2 v. – London : Middlesex Polytechnic Faculty of Business Studies and Management, 1982.
– (Working paper).
Includes bibliographies. Parts 1 and 2.
ISBN 0904804135 pt. 2

—Fundamental rights and the EEC / by David Sugarman. – London : Middlesex Polytechnic Faculty of Business Studies and Management, 1981.
34p. – (Working paper).
ISBN 0904804119

→ Law, economy and society, 1750-1914 : essays in the history of English law.

→ Legality, ideology and the state.

Sugden →Interpreting company reports and accounts.

Suggested Answers in Mercantile Law (Q.A.). – 2nd ed. – New Delhi : Sultan Chand and Sons, 1985.
v, 317p.
Pbk £18.00

Suggested Changes in Canada's 1982 Access to Information Act. – Ottawa : Ken Rubin, 1986.
ISBN 0920621139 Hbk £30.00

Suggested Changes to Canada's 1982 Privacy Act. – Ottawa : Ken Rubin, 1986.
ISBN 0920621198 £25.00

Suggestions for traffic offence penalties. – Magistrates' Association. – 8th ed. – London : The Association, 1983.
4p.

Suhrawardy, Abdullah Al-Ma'mun
First Step in Islamic Law in West Africa / Alexander David Russel. – Lagos : Islamic Publications Bureau, 1986.
ISBN 9782470120 Hbk £7.50

Suing government : citizen remedies for official wrongs / Peter H. Schuck. – New Haven : Yale University Press, 1983.
xxi,262p; 22cm.
Includes index.
ISBN 0300029578 Hbk

Suing Government for Abuse of Power. – Vancouver : Continuing Legal Education Society of British Columbia, 1987.
67p.
ISBN 0865043221 Hbk £60.00

Suing the police / Hugh Tomlinson. – London : Longman Professional (UK), 1989.
Identifies the clauses of the damages claim and explains the types of damages that can be included. Offers advice on every stage of the procedure from taking instructions and financing the case to the trial itself. Includes costs, fees, and precedents.
ISBN 0851215297 Pbk £14.95

Suitability of concentration measures for EEC competition policy / Walter Piesch, Ingo Schmidt. – Luxembourg : Office for Official Publications of the European Communities, 1983.
101 p.; 25 cm.
ISBN 9282531783 Pbk £5.50 (U.S.)

Sujan, M.A.
Law Relating to Government Contracts 1979. – Bombay : Tripathi.
500p.
bd £100.00

Sukthankar, S.B.
Law of Customs. – Bombay : Tripathi.
Hbk

Sullivan, Eric
Marine encyclopaedic dictionary. – 2nd. – London : Lloyds of London Press, 1988.
Updated from the first edition, it contains definitions of technical shipping expressions, Latin usage in law and business. Abbreviations included carry varying meanings according to usage in different countries.
ISBN 1850441278 Hbk £37.50

Sullivan, M.
Financing International Trade. – London : Butterworths, 1988.
ISBN 0880631503 Hbk

Summaries of the judgements delivered in ... / document prepared by the registry of the Court. – Strasbourg : Council of Europe, 1983.
Contains summary judgements not binding on the Court.

Summary : 1A : the Human Rights Committee. – Amnesty International. – 1. – London : Amnesty International, 1987.
various pagings.
'This is a summary of a paper with the same title'. - Cover. Includes the text of the International Covenant on Civil and Political Rights.

Summary : 1B : the Human Rights Committee : examination of individual complaints under the optional protocol / Amnesty International. – London : Amnesty International, 1987.
71p in various pagings.
'This is a summary of a paper by the same title' - Cover. Includes the text of the International Covenant on Civil and Political Rights.

Summary : 1C : general comments of the Human Rights Committee. – Amnesty International. – London : Amnesty International, 1987.
3,7,22,8p.
'This is a summary of a paper by the same title'. - Cover. Includes the text of the International Covenant on Civil and Political Rights.

Summary : 2 : the Organization of African Unity and human rights. – Amnesty International. – London : Amnesty International, 1987.
21,10,1p.
'This is a summary of a paper by the same title'. - Cover. Bibliography: pp.17-21. Includes the text of the African Charter on Human and Peoples' Rights.

Summary Judgment Procedure. – Butterworths, 1988.
113p.
ISBN 0409788538 Hbk £40.00
Supplement-1989.

Summary of decisions of the Canada Labour Relations Board and court updates ... / Resume des decisions du Conseil Canadien des Relations du Travail et mise a jour des dossiers a la cour ... – Ottawa : The Board, 1987.
Parallel text in English and French.

Summary of proceedings... / ACP-EEC Joint Assembly. – Luxembourg : Directorate-General for Information and Public Relations, 1985-.
This single new body replaces the two institutions set up under the first two Lome Conventions, i.e. the Consultative Assembly and the Joint Committee. Title varies.

Summary of Salmond's Jurisprudence. – 3rd ed. – Bombay : Tripathi, 1981.
204p.
Hbk £15.00

Summary of the Pleas of the Crown : A Brief But Full Account of Whatsoever Can Be Found Relating to That Subject. – Repr. of 1716 ed. – Abingdon : Professional Books.
362p.
Hbk £125.00

Summary of the powers of the juvenile court / by Clifford E.M. Chatterton. – Plymouth : Basset Publications, 1985.
viii,33p.
ISBN 0946873089

Summary Proceedings and Police Court Practice. – Butterworths, 1985.
Covers changes in procedure such as increases in jurisdiction of District Court Judges, the removal of a defendant's right to make an unsworn statement from the dock, the liberalization of procedures relating to the prosecution of young persons, the rights of an accused to remain present throughout the hearing, and the power of a Judge to clear a court.
ISBN 0409600474 Hbk £93.90

Summerfield, Peter →Effective dispute resolution for the international commercial lawyer.

Summers, Dennis
HGV Law Guide. – London : Butterworths, 1981.
This work is written for those who operate or are responsible for goods vehicles in the United Kingdom. The Construction and Use Regulations of 1978 and the Special Types Order of 1979 are analyzed in the book. Numerous diagrams illustrate the text.
ISBN 0408005696 Pbk £10.00

Summers, Robert S. →Form and substance in Anglo-American law : a comparative study of legal reasoning, legal theory, and legal institutions.

—Lon L. Fuller. – London : Edward Arnold, 1984.
192p.
ISBN 0713164093 Pbk £9.95

Summerskill, Michael Brynmor
Laytime / Michael Brynmor Summerskill. – 4th ed. – London : Sweet & Maxwell, 1988.
ISBN 042079708 Hbk

Summerson, Henry
Crown Pleas of the Devon Eyre of 1238. – Exeter : Devon & Cornwall Record Society, 1985.
ISBN 0901853283 Hbk £8.00

Summonses and Charges / R. Houghton. – 4th rev. ed. – London : Police Review Publishing, 1983.
ISBN 085164001X Pbk £4.25

Sumner, Colin →Crime, justice and the mass media : papers presented to the 14th Cropwood Round-Table Conference, December 1981.
→ Crime, justice and underdevelopment.

Sumner, L. W.
Moral foundation of rights / L.W. Sumner. – Oxford : Clarendon Press, 1987.
228p; 22cm.
Includes bibliography and index.
ISBN 0198247516 £22.50

Sumption, A.
Capital Gains Tax. – London : Butterworths, 1981.
Service to Date.
ISBN 0406538824 Llf £80.00

Sumption and Clarke's tax and tax planning / Giles Clarke, Philip Lawton. – 10th ed. – London : Oyez Longman, 1982.
xxvii,265p; 22cm.
Previous ed.: published as Sumption and Lawton's tax and tax planning / by Anthony Sumption and Philip Lawton, 1981. Includes index.
ISBN 0851206921 Pbk

Sumption, Anthony
Capital gains tax / by Anthony Sumption. – London : Butterworths, 1981.
ISBN 0406538824

—Capital Gains Tax / Giles Clarke. – London : Butterworths, 1981.
Llf

—Sumption and Clarke's tax and tax planning / Giles Clarke, Philip Lawton. – 10th ed. – London : Oyez Longman, 1982.
xxvii,265p; 22cm.
Previous ed.: published as Sumption and Lawton's tax and tax planning / by Anthony Sumption and Philip Lawton, 1981. Includes index.
ISBN 0851206921 Pbk

—Taxation of overseas income and gains / Anthony Sumption. – 4th ed. – London : Butterworths, 1982.
xix,207p.
Previous ed.: 1979.
ISBN 0406538735

Sunday Telegraph 101 ways of investing. – Telegraph Publications, 1988.
ISBN 0863672027 Pbk £2.95

Sunday Times case. – 1 videocassette. – London : Sweet & Maxwell, 1984.
– (Sweet & Maxwell's lawfilms).

Sundberg, Hagar
Novgorod Kabala Books of 1614-1616. – Stockholm : Almqvist & Wiksell, 1982.
x, 200p.
ISBN 9122005528 Hbk £84.00

Sundberg, Jacob W. F.
Human rights in Sweden : the annual reports 1982-1984 from the national correspondent for Sweden to the Documentation Center for Human Rights at the Directorate for Human Rights, Council of Europe / Jacob W.F. Sundberg. – Stockholm : Institutet for offentlig och internationell ratt, 1985.
ix,118p. – (Publications).
Includes bibliographical references and index.
ISBN 9103487806
—Implementing the European Convention on Human Rights in Sweden : the Boll discussion / by Jacob W. F. Sundberg. – Stockholm : s.n., 1983.
14,9 leaves.
Includes bibliographical references.

Sundberg, Ross A. → Griffith's Probate law and practice in Victoria.

Sundstrom, Zacharias → EEC law and Nordic commercial relations with the Communities.

Sunnucks, J H G
Williams, Mortimer and Sunnucks on executors, administration and probate. – 16th ed. – London : Sweet & Maxwell, 1982.
ISBN 0420455000 Hbk £120.00
→ Williams, Mortimer and Sunnucks on executors, administrators and probate.

Sunt
Legal Aspects of the ECU / Dierciex. – London : Butterworths, 1988.
ISBN 0406112002 Hbk

Supakar, S.
Law of Procedure and Justice in Ancient India. – New Delhi : Deep and Deep Publications, 1986.
320p.

Superannuation and Insurance and the Sex Discrimination Act 1984. – Kingston : Australian Government Publishing Service, 1986.
127p.
ISBN 0644054964 Hbk £7.95

Superannuation and Retirement Benefits in Australia / John V. Edstein. – Butterworths, 1988.
ca 550p.
ISBN 0409494461 Llf £245.00

Supergrasses : the use of accomplice evidence in Northern Ireland : a report / by Tony Gifford. – London : Cobden Trust, 1984.
38p.
ISBN 0900137215

Supervision in European Community law : observance by the member states of their treaty obligations : a treatise on international and supra-national supervision / H.A.H. Audretsch. – 2nd rev. ed. – Amsterdam : North-Holland, 1986.
xix,782p.
Previous ed.: 1978. Bibliography: p.591-613. - Includes index.
ISBN 0444700277

Supervision of securities markets in the member states of the European Economic Community
Part 1 : Belgium, Federal Republic of Germany, Denmark, Ireland, France. – Luxembourg : Office for Official Publications of the European Communities, 1981.
255p. – (Studies collection).
At head of title: 'Commission of the European Communities'.
ISBN 9282515222 Hbk
Part 2 : United Kingdom, Italy, Luxembourg, Netherlands / report on a comparative law study submitted by E. Wymeersch. – 1981.
219p.
At head of title: Commission of the European Communities.
ISBN 9282522903 Hbk

Supiot, Alain
Delegalisation and normalisation / by Alain Supiot. – Florence : European University Institute, 1986.
34,xiiip.

Supperstone, Michael → Brownlie's Law of public order and national security.
—Immigration : Law and Practice / John Cavanagh. – 2nd ed. – London : Longman Professional.
– (Longman Practitioner Series).
ISBN 0851213898 Pbk £19.95

Supplement relating to the annex to the Convention on Facilitation of International Maritime Traffic, 1965. – London : International Maritime Organization, 1982.
63p; 25cm.
ISBN 9280111493 Pbk

Supplement Relating to the International Convention for the Prevention of Pollution of the Sea by Oil : 1954 (As Amended in 1962 and 1969). – International Maritime Organization Staff. – London : International Maritime Organization, 1981.
Hbk £1.25

Supplement to Ondo State of Nigeria gazette. – Akure : Government Printer, 1976.
Edicts and legal notices.

Supplement to the Administration of Deceased Estates in South Africa, Trusts in South Africa, The Making of a Will Plus The Matrimonial Property Act Including Estate Duty Aspects. – Cape Town : Legal & Financial Publishing, 1985.
Hbk £11.50

Supplementary Benefit and Family Income Supplement the Legislation
2nd Supplement to 4th ed. – Sweet & Maxwell.
ISBN 0421402504 Pbk £4.95

Supplementary Benefits Appeal Tribunals : a guide to procedure / Department of Health and Social Security. – Rev. ed. – London : H.M.S.O., 1982.
vi,60p; 21cm.
Previous ed.: 1977.
ISBN 0117608440 Pbk £2.00

Supplementary Benefits Handbook : A Guide to Claimants' Rights. – 10th ed. – London : HMSO, 1984.
162p.
Explains who is entitled to benefits and how to claim them. Describes special rules applying to people in particular situations.
ISBN 0117612189 Pbk £2.50

Supplementary Lists of Ratifications, Accessions, Withdrawals, etc. – London : HMSO, 1983.
ISBN 0101910703 Hbk £3.15

Supplementary Service to European Taxation, 13 Vols. – Amsterdam : International Bureau of Fiscal Documentation, 1988.
Hbk £2000.00
1989 renewal. –
Hbk £860.00

Supply of Goods and Services Act 1982 : a practical guide / R.G. Lawson. – London : Oyez Longman, 1982.
xix,136p; 22cm.
Includes index.
ISBN 0851206727 Pbk £16.50

Supranationals / edited by S. Melvin Rines and Christine A. Bogdanowicz-Bindert. – London : Euromoney, 1986.
200p.
ISBN 0903121840

Supreme Court : Fundamental Rights and Directive Principles. – New Delhi : Deep and Deep Publications, 1984.
120p.
Hbk £60.00

Supreme Court Act 1981 / with annotations by Robin White. – London : Sweet & Maxwell, 1981.
ca.150p; 25cm.
ISBN 0421294108 Pbk £6.85

Supreme Court Cases 1987, Vol. 1. – Lucknow : Eastern Book Company, 1987.
Hbk £110.00

Supreme Court Chambers Orders, 3 Vols. – Vancouver : Continuing Legal Education Society of British Columbia, 1981.
700p.
ISBN 0865040281 Hbk £70.00
Supplement-1983. –
150p.
ISBN 0865041156 £40.00
Supplement-1986. –
184p.
ISBN 0865042748 £50.00

Supreme Court Civil Digest 1950-80, 5 Vols. – 2nd ed. – Allahabad : Law Book Company, 1950-80.
Hbk £500.00

Supreme Court Civil Procedure. – Butterworths, 1987.
442p.
ISBN 0409492183 Hbk £36
ISBN 0409492078 Pbk £29

Supreme Court Criminal Digest 1950-80, 2 Vols. – Allahabad : Law Book Company.
Hbk £180.00

Supreme Court Criminal Digest. – Allahabad : Orient Law House, 1973-1982.
Hbk £120.00

Supreme Court Decisions. – Manila : National Book Store.
Hbk
Vol. 1 January, 1982. – 1982.
586p.
ISBN 9710817078 Pbk £6.65
Vol. 2 February, 1982. – 1982.
388p.
ISBN 9710817086 Pbk £5.00
Vol. 3 March, 1982. – 1982.
752p.
ISBN 9710800418 Pbk £9.00
Vol. 4 April, 1982. – 1982.
342p.
ISBN 9710800426 Pbk £5.00
Vol. 5 May, 1982. – 1982.
352p.
ISBN 9710800434 Pbk £5.50
Vol. 6 June, 1982. – 1982.
582p.
ISBN 9710800442 Pbk £7.50
Vol. 7 July, 1982. – 1982.
858p.
ISBN 9710817094 Pbk £12.00
Vol. 8 August, 1982. – 1982.
510p.
ISBN 9710817108 Hbk £10.00
Vol. 9 September, 1982. – 1983.
972p.
ISBN 9710800515 Hbk £17.50
Vol. 10 October, 1982. – 1983.
432p.
ISBN 971080054X £9.50
Vol. 11 November, 1982. – 1983.
774p.
ISBN 971080085X Hbk £15.00
Vol. 12 December, 1982. – 1983.
528p.
ISBN 9710801090 Hbk £12.00
Vol. 13 January, 1983. – 1983.
788p.
ISBN 9710801104 Hbk £12.00
Vol. 14 February, 1983. – 1983.
479p.
ISBN 9710801767 Hbk £9.50
Vol. 15 March, 1983. – 1983.
440p.
ISBN 9710802275 Hbk £9.50
Vol. 16 April, 1983. – 1983.
558p.
ISBN 9710802879 Hbk £12.00
Vol. 17 May, 1983. – 1983.
720p.
ISBN 9710803557 Hbk £16.00
Vol. 18 June, 1983. – 1983.
640p.
ISBN 971080393X Hbk £14.00
Vol. 19 July, 1983. – 1984.
608p.
ISBN 971080412X Hbk £18.00
Vol. 20 August, 1983. – 1984.
472p.
ISBN 9710805177 Hbk £15.00

Supreme Court decisions on the Canadian Constitution. – Toronto : J. Lorimer, 1981.
xxi,141p.
ISBN 0888625383 Pbk

Supreme Court Fees and Fixed Costs. – 13th ed. – London : Fourmat.
ISBN 1851900551 Pbk £3.50

Supreme Court Guide to Words and Phrases. – Calcutta : Eastern Law House, 1986.
Hbk £48.00

Supreme Court Industrial, Services and Labour Law Digest, 1977-87 : Central and States. – Allahabad : Law Book Company.
500p.
Hbk £150.00

Supreme Court Labour and Services Digest, 1983-1986, 4 Vols. – Lucknow : Eastern Book Company, 1987.
Hbk £360.00

Supreme Court Labour Digest, 1950-82. 2 Vols. / V.K. Kharbanda. – 2nd ed. – Allahabad : Law Publishing House, 1984.
Hbk £200.00

Supreme Court Labour Judgments 1950-1983. 15 Vols. – Allahabad : Law Publishing House, 1984.
Hbk £160.00

Supreme Court Law Review
Vol. 1: 1980 / Eric Gertner. – Butterworths.
544p.
ISBN 0409832618 Hbk £75.00
Vol. 2: 1981. –
496p.
ISBN 0409832626 Hbk £75.00
Vol. 3: 1982. –
616p.
ISBN 0409832634 Hbk £75.00

Vol. 5: 1983. –
464p.
ISBN 0409832650 Hbk £95.00
Vol. 8: 1986. –
580p.
ISBN 0409804843 Hbk £110.00
Vol. 9: 1987. –
544p.
Analysis of the Supreme Court of Canada's key decision and a critical examination of the Court's performance in reaching them. This volume covers the Court's decisions for 1985 and 1986.
ISBN 0409806412 Hbk £128.00

Supreme Court of Canada : History of the Institution / Frederick Vaughan. – Toronto : University of Toronto Press, 1985.
ISBN 0802034179 Hbk £40.00
ISBN 0802034187 Pbk £17.50

Supreme Court of Canada as an Instrument of Political Change / Andree Lajoie. – Toronto : University of Toronto Press, 1986.
240p.
ISBN 0802072925 Hbk £16.95

Supreme Court of Canada Decisions (1980-Present). – Aurora : Canada Law Book Co.
– (Summary Services, National Ser.).
Llf £79.50

Supreme Court of Canada handbook on assessment of damages in personal injury cases / by W.H.R. Charles. – Ontario : Carswell Co., 1982.
129p.
'Reprint of an article in Volume 18 Part 1 of Canadian cases on the law of torts'.
ISBN 0459346709

Supreme Court of Canada Practice and Advocacy. – Vancouver : Continuing Legal Education Society of British Columbia, 1987.
297p.
ISBN 0865043310 Hbk £85.00

Supreme Court of Nigeria judgments. – Kaduana Nigeria : Liberty Publications, 1987-.

Supreme Court of Nigeria Law Reports
Vol. 1. – Lagos : Nigerian Law Publications, 1983.
ISBN 9782325010 Hbk £40.00
Vol. 2. –
ISBN 9782325011 Hbk £40.00

Supreme Court on Church and State. – Oxford : Oxford University Press.
ISBN 0195050282 Hbk £35.00

Supreme Court on Constitutional Aspects of Labour Laws. – Allahabad : Law Publishing House, 1987.
1,400p.
Hbk £350.00

Supreme Court on Direct Taxes 1950 to 1986. – Allahabad : Modern Law Publications, 1986.
Hbk £220.00

Supreme Court on Direct Taxes. – New Delhi : Bharat Law House, 1986.
Hbk £220.00

Supreme Court on Essential Commodities Act, 1955. – Lucknow : Eastern Book Company, 1984.
161p.
Hbk £40.00

Supreme Court on Law of Limitation 1950-79. – Lucknow : Eastern Book Company, 1981.
226p.
Hbk £25.00

Supreme Court on Preventive Detention, 1950 to Date. – Lucknow : Eastern Book Company, 1985.
478p.
Hbk £90.00

Supreme Court practice. – London : Sweet & Maxwell, 1966-.
Continues: The annual practice. Includes index. Kept up to date by supplements.

Supreme Court Practice and Procedure. – 4th ed. – Lucknow : Eastern Book Company, 1985.
550p.
Hbk £135.00

Supreme Court Practice and Procedure. – 4th ed. – London : Fourmat, 1987.
ISBN 1851900365 Pbk £12.95

Supreme Court Quinquennial Digest, 1981 to 1985. – Allahabad : Law Book Company.
1,000p.
Hbk £250.00

Supreme Court Referencer, 5 Vols. – Allahabad : Orient Law House.
Hbk £600.00

Supreme Court Rules, 1950 : as Intepreted by Supreme Court. – Allahabad : Law Publishers, 1982.
vi, 199p.
Hbk £7.50

Supreme Court Rules, 1966. – Lucknow : Eastern Book Company, 1984.
119p.
Hbk £20.00

Supreme Court Rules 1985. – Lagos : Federal Government Press, 1985.
98p.

Supreme court rules : guide to time limits, civil proceedings. – Melbourne : Law Institute of Victoria, 1983.
31p.
'Supplement to August 1983 Law Institute journal',

Supreme Court Rules : Supplements from January 1978 to March 1981. – London : HMSO.
Hbk

Supreme Court Rulings. – Manila : National Book Store.
Pbk
1: January 1984. – 1984.
147p.
ISBN 9710805223 £7.00
2: February 1984. – 1984.
152p.
ISBN 9710805460 Hbk £8.00
3: March 1984. – 1984.
175p.
ISBN 9710806564 Hbk £9.80
4: April 1984. – 1984.
153p.
ISBN 9710808869 £9.80
5: May 1984. – 1984.
177p.
ISBN 9710816861 £9.50
6: June 1984. – 1984.
158p.
ISBN 9710819291 £8.80
7: July 1984. – 1984.
211p.
ISBN 9710821687 £11.40
8: August 1984. – 1985.
167p.
ISBN 9710822241 £6.80

Supreme Court Sales Tax Judgements, 1974-1985. – Allahabad : Law Publishers, 1986.
1,100p.
Hbk £250.00

Supreme Court Services and Labour Digest 1950-1979. – Allahabad : Law Book Company, 1976-1979.
851p.
Hbk £250.00

Supreme Court Taxing Office : Practice Notes on Taxation of Costs. – London : HMSO.
40p.
ISBN 0113906269 Hbk

Supreme Court Yearly Digest
1980 /. – Lucknow : Eastern Book Company, 1981.
443p.
Hbk £45.00
1981. – 1982.
391p.
Hbk £55.00
1983. – 1984.
286p.
Hbk £65.00
1984. – 1985.
467p.
Hbk £85.00

Supreme courts and judicial law-making : constitutional tribunals and constitutional review / by Edward McWhinney. – Dordrecht : M. Nijhoff, 1985.
320p.
Includes index.
ISBN 9024732034 Hbk £165.00

Supreme Labor Court in Nazi Germany : a jurisprudential analysis / Marc Linder. – Frankfurt a. M. : Klostermann, 1987.
xix,290p.
Includes bibliographical references.
ISBN 3465017579

Suratgar, David → Default and rescheduling : corporate and sovereign borrowers.

Suretyship. – London : Longman Professional. – (LPPN70).
ISBN 0851206123 Pbk £17.95

Surrey, Stanley S → International aspects of tax expenditures : a comparative study.

Surrogate motherhood / New South Wales Law Reform Commission. – Sydney : Government Printer, 1988.
xviii,143p. – (D.P v 18).
Bibliography: pp.133-141.
ISBN 0730555399 Hbk

Surtees, William Edward
Sketch of the lives of Lords Stowell and Eldon : comprising, with additional matter, some corrections of Mr.Twiss's work on the Chancellor / by William Edward Surtees. – London : Chapman and Hall, 1846.
vii,180p.

Survey of adult living arrangements : a technical report / Institute of Law Research and Reform. – Edmonton : The Institute, 1984.
v,93,19p. – (Research paper).

Survey of commercial agency / edited by Hans Henrik Lidgard, Claude D. Rohwer, Dennis Campbell. – Deventer : Kluwer Law and Taxation, 1984.
xxv,718p; 25cm.
Conference papers. Bibliography: p394-395. - Includes index.
ISBN 9065441816 Hbk

Survey of company car schemes. – 7th ed. – Tolley Publishing, 1987.
ISBN 0854593144 Hbk £29.50

Survey of computer fraud and abuse. – Audit Commission for Local Authorities in England and Wales. – London : H.M.S.O., 1987.
88p.
Report finds lack of basic control mechanisms. Suggests that the opportunity for fraud is widespread and a large numnber remain undiscovered.
ISBN 0117010650

Survey of computing in European local and regional authorities / ... prepared under the guidelines of the Committee of Experts on Management in Local and Regional Government by G.Gaits. – Strasbourg : Council of Europe, 1981.
iii,61p.

Survey of defenders in debt actions in Scotland / Janet Gregory and Janet Monk. – London : H.M.S.O., 1981.
ix,109p. – (Research report for the Scottish Law Commission).
Includes index.
ISBN 0116907746

Survey of Documentary Sources for Property-Holding in London Before the Great Fire / V. A. Harding. – London : London Record Society, 1985.
ISBN 0900952229 Hbk £12.00

Survey of extradition and fugitive offenders legislation as between Commonwealth jurisdictions / prepared for the Commonwealth Secretariat by the Commonwealth Legal Advisory Service of the British Institute of International and Comparative Law. – Rev. – London : Commonwealth Secretariat, 1982.
iii,70p; 30cm.
Previous ed.: 1977.
ISBN 0850922356 Pbk £10.00

Survey of legal measures in the Commonwealth designed to assist the disabled / a survey prepared by the Commonwealth Secretariat for the International Year of Disabled Persons. – London : Commonwealth Secretariat, 1981.
60p.

Survey of Malaysian Law
1981. – Singapore : Malayan Law Journal, 1983.
xvi, 304p.
ISBN 9971700328 Spiral bound £46
1982. – 1984.
xvi, 306p.
ISBN 9971700360 Spiral bound £50
1983. – 1985.
399.
Spiral bound £65

Survey of the complaint-handling institutions in Hong Kong / by Rebecca Wong Kit Lin. – Edmonton : International Ombudsman Institute, 1983.
19 leaves. – (Occasional paper).

Survey of the Legal Profession in the Philippines : Focus on Region 4 / Merlin M. Magalona. – Quezon City : University of the Philippines, Law Center, 1982.
182p.
Pbk £20.00

Survey of the structure and finances of the legal profession in private practice 6th January 1986 / Law Society, Special Committee on Remuneration. – 3. – London : Law Society, 1986.
Contents: 1 Commentary - 2 Major tables - 3 Detailed tables.

Surveying for Delapidations : A Practical Guide to the Law and its Applications. – London : Estates Gazette.
ISBN 0728201046 Pbk £24.50

Surveying offshore Canada lands for mineral resource development / edited by Harold E. Jones. – 3rd ed. – Ottawa : Department of Energy, Mines and Resources, Surveys and Mapping Branch, 1982.
viii,158p.
Bibliography: p.149-154. - Includes index. 'Based on the findings of government/industry workshops convened between 1970 and 1982 to study the technical and legal aspects of surveying for mineral resource development on offshore Canada lands'.
ISBN 0660113430

Surveyor in Court. – London : Estates Gazette, 1985.
ISBN 0728200910 Pbk £25.00

Survivorship / Institute of Law Research and Reform, Edmonton, Alberta. – Edmonton : The Institute, 1986.
65p. – (Report).

Sushakumari, V.K.
Law of Income Tax. – 3rd ed. – Lucknow : Eastern Book Company, 1982.
350p.
Hbk £30.00

Susskind, Richard E.
Expert systems in law : a jurisprudential inquiry / Richard E. Susskind. – Oxford : Clarendon, 1987.
xvi,300p; 23cm.
Bibliography: p271-292. - Includes index.
ISBN 0198255829 £30.00

Sussmann, Frederick B →Law and the citizen : looking to the '80s : a Colloquium on Public Legal Education held on April 29 and 30, 1977.

Sustainable development : exploring the contradictions / Michael Redclift. – London : Methuen, 1987.
viii,200p; 22cm.
Includes index.
ISBN 0416902405 Hbk £20.00 :
ISBN 0416902502 Pbk £7.95

Suter, Erich
Contracts at work / Erich Suter. – London : Institute of Personnel Management, 1982.
x,276p; 22cm.
Includes index.
ISBN 0852922973 Pbk £13.95

Suter, J.
Insider dealing. – London : Butterworths, 1988.
ISBN 1862052573 Hbk

Suter, Keith
Aboriginal Australians / by Keith D. Suter, Kaye Stearman. – New ed. – London : Minority Rights Group, 1982.
20p. – (Report).
Previous ed. published 1978 as: Australia's policy towards Aborigines 1967-1977 / by H.C. Coombs. Bibliography: p.20.
—East Timor and West Irian / by Keith Suter. – Rev. ed. – London : Minority Rights Group, 1982.
24p. – (Reports).
Previous ed. published 1979, as: West Irian, East Timor and Indonesia. Bibliography: p.24.
→ Forgotten treaties : a practical plan for world disarmament.
—International Law of International Welfare : The Politics of Law-Making. – London : Pinter Publishers Ltd, 1984.
200p.
ISBN 0861872894 Hbk £21.00

Sutherland, Donald W. →Eyre of Northamptonshire : 3-4 Edward III, A.D. 1329-1330, Vol.1.

Sutherland, Edwin H.
White collar crime / Edwin H. Sutherland : with an introduction by Gilbert Geis and Colin Goff. – Uncut version. – New Haven : Yale University Press, 1983.
xxxiii,291p; 24cm.
Previous ed.: New York : Dryden, 1949. Includes index.
ISBN 0300029217 Hbk

Sutherland, J. A.
Offensive literature : decensorship in Britain, 1960-1982 / John Sutherland. – London : Junction Books, 1982.
207p; 22cm.
ISBN 0862450640

Sutton, D.G.
Domestic Assault of Women. – London : Allyn & Bacon, 1988.
ISBN 0205113230 Hbk £28.90

Sutton, K. C. T.
Sales and consumer law in Australia and New Zealand / by K.C.T. Sutton. – Being 3rd ed. of The law of sale of goods in Australia and New Zealand. – Sydney : Law Book Co., 1983.
lxx,658p.
Includes bibliographical references and index.
ISBN 0455204675

Sutton, W.
Trading in currency options. – Cambridge : Woodhead-Faulkner, 1987.
ISBN 0859413233 Hbk £45.00

Suviranta, A. J.
Labour law and industrial relations in Finland / by A.J. Suviranta. – Helsinki : Finnish Lawyers, 1987.
187p; 25cm.
Bibliography: p57-61. - Includes index.
ISBN 9065443444 Pbk
ISBN 9516403573 Finland

Suzman, Arthur
Suzman, Gordon and Hodes on the law of compulsory motor vehicle insurance in South Africa / Lionel H. Hodes. – 3rd ed. – Cape Town : Juta, 1982.
xxxvii,538p.
Previous ed.: 1970, entitled: Suzman and Gordon on the law of compulsory motor vehicle insurance in South Africa. Bibliography: p.ix. - Includes index.
ISBN 0702112585

Suzman, Gordon and Hodes on the law of compulsory motor vehicle insurance in South Africa / Lionel H. Hodes. – 3rd ed. – Cape Town : Juta, 1982.
xxxvii,538p.
Previous ed.: 1970, entitled: Suzman and Gordon on the law of compulsory motor vehicle insurance in South Africa. Bibliography: p.ix. - Includes index.
ISBN 0702112585

Sviridov, F. A. →Role of patent information in the transfer of technology : proceedings of the International Conference held at Varna, Bulgaria, May 27-30, 1980.

Svoboda, Werner Robert
Common standards for legal retrieval systems : proposals for a model retrieval language for legal users / Important features of a common command language within a network of legal information systems : studies prepared for the Council of Europe and the Commission of the European Communities by Werner Robert Svoboda. – Strasbourg : Council of Europe, 1983.
104p; 21cm.
At head of title: Legal Affairs.
ISBN 9287102732
—Study on common standards for query languages in computerised legal retrieval systems / prepared for the Council of Europe by Werner Robert Svoboda. – Strasbourg : Council of Europe, 1981.
52p.
'Based on a proposal put forward by Working Party No. II of the Committee of Experts on Legal Data Processing' - p.4. At head of cover title: Council of Europe, Legal Affairs.

Swaaningen, Rene van →Abolitionism : towards a non-repressive approach to crime : proceedings of the Second International Conference on Prison Abolition, Amsterdam, 1985.

Swaigan, John →Environmental rights in Canada.
—How to Fight for What's Right : the Citizen's Guide to Public Interest Law. – Toronto : James Lorimer & Co.
ISBN 0888624220 Pbk £12.95
ISBN 0888624239 Hbk £24.95
—Sentencing in environmental cases : a study paper / prepared for the Law Reform Commission of Canada by John Swaigan and Gail Bunt. – Ottawa : The Commission, 1985.
81p. – (Study paper).
ISBN 0662138295

Swain, D.
Managing Public Money. – University Press Of America, 1988.
ISBN 0819165050 Hbk £22.95
ISBN 0819165069 Pbk £11.50

Swaine, P. F. →Taxation Aspects of Banking Operations.

Swami, Narasimha
How to Become an Immigrant to Canada and the United States of America. – Lucknow : Eastern Book Company, 1985.
Hbk £50.00

Swamikamu
Commentaries on General Clauses Act. – 2nd ed. – Allahabad, 1983.
Hbk £30.00

Swan, John
Contracts : Cases, Notes and Materials / Barry J. Reiter. – 3rd ed. – Aurora : Canada Law Book Co, 1985.
734p. – (Case Books).
This new edition provides a complete review of contract law including: Remedies for Breach of Contract, The Kinds of Promises that the Law Will Enforce, The Formation of Contracts, The Statute of Frauds, Contractual Undertakings – Their Determination and Range, and Remedies for Breach; Control of Contract Power, and Illegality.
Hbk £79.50

Swan, Kenneth P. →Studies in labour law.

Swan, Peter L.
On Buying a Job : The Regulation of Taxicabs in Canberra. – Turramura : Centre for Independent Studies.
20p.
ISBN 0959648550 Hbk £2.00

Swanepoel, J.P.A., et al
Introduction to Mercantile Law / Swanepoel, Makins, Lapping and Reynecke. – Durban : Professional Publisher, 1984.
ISBN 0409057800 Pbk £39.00

Swann, Dennis
Economics of the Common Market / Dennis Swann. – 6th ed. – Harmondsworth : Penguin, 1988.
Previous ed.: 1984.
ISBN 0140227814

Swanson, Kathryn
Affirmative action and preferential admissions in higher education : an annotated bibliography / by Kathryn Swanson. – Metuchen : Scarecrow, 1981.
viii,336p; 23cm.
Includes index.
ISBN 0810814110 £12.25

Swanton, Bruce
Australia's External Territory Police Forces. – Canberra : Australian Institute of Criminology.
Hbk £1.00
—Chronological Account of Crime, Public Order and Police in Sydney 1788-1810. – Canberra : Australian Institute of Criminology.
free
—Criminal Justice Research Methodology. – Canberra : Australian Institute of Criminology.
free
—Nature and Scope of Police and Police Related Research. – Canberra : Australian Institute of Criminology.
Hbk £1.00
—Police Institutions and Issues : American and Australian Perspectives. – Canberra : Australian Institute of Criminology.
Hbk £5.00
—Police Source Book. – Canberra : Australian Institute of Criminology.
Hbk £8.00
—Protecting the Protectors. – Canberra : Australian Institute of Criminology.
Hbk £12.50

Swanton, I.
Traders Directory 1987. – London : Euromoney.
ISBN 0903121867 Pbk £65.00

Swap agreement documentation / Klein. – London : Euromoney, 1987.
ISBN 1870031717 Pbk £110.00

Swap Finance
Vol. 1. – London : Euromoney, 1987.
Service.
ISBN 0903121875 Pbk £75.00
Vol. 2. –
ISBN 0903121883 Pbk £75.00

Swart
Public Advocate Act, 1983, Bill 125 : An Act to Provide for a Public Advocate in Ontario. – Ontario : Ontario Government Publications Service, 1983.
3p.
Hbk £0.30

Swartz, Barbara
Family Planning Legislation : Euro Reports and Studies No. 85. – London : HMSO, 1984.
86p.
Report on a survey of family planning legislation in Greece, Italy, Morocco, Portugal, Spain, Tunisia and Turkey.
ISBN 928901251X Hbk £3.20

Swarup
Protection of Civil Rights Act. – 2nd ed. – Allahabad : Law Book Company, 1986.
Hbk £75.00

Swatton, R. →Marine Insurance Clauses.

Swedish code of judicial procedure : the translation is that of the wording of the code of judicial procedure as at January 1, 1985 / National Council for Crime Prevention Sweden. – Stockholm : The Council, 1985.
230 p.; 25 cm. – (Report).
ISBN 9138088452 Pbk

Swedish Companies Act 1975 : With Excerpts from the Accounting Act 1976. – Stockholm : Industriforbundet, 1986.
144p.
ISBN 9171761004 Hbk £180.00

Swedish intellectual property and market legislation : collection of statutory texts / edited by Ulf Bernitz. – Stockholm : Institute for Intellectual Property and Market Law, Stockholm University, 1984.
ii,181p. – (Publications).
ISBN 9138081717

Swedish Parliamentary Ombudsmen / Ulf Lundvik. – Stockholm : JO, 1982.
29p.
Bibliography: p.29.

Swedish penal code 1986. – Stockholm : National Council for Crime Prevention, 1986.
110p. – (Report 1986:2).
'The translation is that of the wording of the Penal Code as at April 1, 1986'.
ISBN 9138093049

Swedish Statutes, 3 Vols.
Vol. 3 / Anders Victorin. – Abingdon : Professional Books, 1984.
– (Law and the Weaker Party : An Anglo-Swedish Comparative Study Ser.).
ISBN 0862050456 Hbk £21.00

Sweeney, C. A. →Federal Court reports : the authorised reports of decisions of the Federal Court of Australia.

Sweeney, G. W. →Statutes of Natal.

Sweet & Maxwell Law
File 1, Land law (Co Habiting). – London : Sweet & Maxwell, 1984.
ISBN 0421321407 Pbk £29.50
File 2, Trusts : Fitzkenton Estate. – 1984.
ISBN 0421321504 Pbk £29.50
File 3, Torts from accidents to liability. – 1984.
ISBN 0421321601 Pbk £29.50

File 4, Land law (Neighbours). – 1985.
ISBN 0421340010 Pbk £29.50

File 5, Trusts : Trustees Fitzkenton Estate. – 1985.
ISBN 0421340207 Pbk £29.50

File 6, Torts liability of an industrialist. – 1985.
ISBN 0421340304 Pbk £29.50

File 7, striking a bargain. – 1985.
ISBN 0421340401 Pbk £29.50

Sweet & Maxwell's companies statutes for students / edited by Harry Rajak. – 2nd ed. – London : Sweet & Maxwell, 1987.
350p; 26cm.
Previous ed.: 1985. Includes index.
ISBN 0421383402 Pbk £16

Sweet & Maxwell's criminal law statutes / edited by Sweet & Maxwell's Legal Editorial Staff : advisory editor, I.H. Dennis. – London : Sweet & Maxwell, 1982.
ix,144p; 26cm.
Includes index.
ISBN 042130300X Hbk £
ISBN 0421303107 Pbk £4.85

Sweet and Maxwell's Employment Law Manual. – London : Sweet & Maxwell, 1987.
ISBN 0421352205 Hbk

Sweet & Maxwell's encyclopedia of health services and medical law. – London : Sweet & Maxwell, 1987.
loose-leaf.
Includes index.
ISBN 0421315008 £145.00

Sweet and Maxwell's family law statutes. – 4th ed. – Sweet & Maxwell.
ISBN 0421382503 Pbk £16.95

Sweet and Maxwell's labour relations statutes and materials / edited by Sweet & Maxwell's legal editorial staff : advisory editors B.A. Hepple, Paul O'Higgins, Lord Wedderburn of Charlton. – 2nd ed. – London : Sweet & Maxwell, 1983.
x,693p; 25cm.
Previous ed.: 1979. Includes index.
ISBN 0421320109 Pbk £15.00

Sweet & Maxwell's property statutes / Nigel Gravell. – 5th ed. – London : Sweet & Maxwell, 1988.
550p; 24cm.
Includes index.
ISBN 0421352701 Pbk £13.00

Sweet & Maxwell's social work statutes / edited by Richard M. Jones. – 2nd ed. – London : Sweet & Maxwell, 1985.
150p.
Previous ed.: 1980. Includes index.
ISBN 0421348305 Pbk £9.00

Sweet & Maxwell's Statutes for the Law Society finals / advisory editors, Alasdair Benzie, Christine Elgey, Alastair Murdie : edited by Sweet & Maxwell's legal editorial staff and Robert Spicer. – London : Sweet & Maxwell, 1985.
620p; 24cm.
Includes index.
ISBN 0421325208 Pbk £16.95

Sweet and Maxwell's Students' Law Reporter Spring 1986. – London : Sweet & Maxwell.
ISBN 0421360909 Hbk £6.50

Summer 1986. –
ISBN 042136100X Hbk £6.50

Autumn 1986. –
ISBN 0421361107 Hbk £6.50

Sweet & Maxwell's tax computations and tables 1984/85 / by Clifford S. Perkins : computations on double taxation relief contributed by Richard Briffett. – 2nd ed. – London : Sweet & Maxwell, 1984.
395p; 25cm.
ISBN 042133200X

Sweet & Maxwell's tax statutes 1984/85 / edited by Sweet & Maxwell's legal editorial staff : advisory editors Julian Farrand, Geoffrey Morse, David Williams. – 3rd ed. – London : Sweet & Maxwell, 1984.
vii,457p.
Previous ed.: 1983. Includes index.
ISBN 0421330902

Sweet, Justin → Selected problems of construction law : international approach.

Sweetman, John → Parliamentary Assembly : procedure and practice.

Swift, A. → Control Without Custody.

Swinarski, Christophe → Commentary on the additional protocols of 8 June 1977 to the Geneva Conventions of 12 August 1949.
→ Etudes et essais sur le droit international humanitaire et sur les principes de la Croix-Rouge en l'honneur de Jean Pictet : Studies and essays on international humanitarian law and Red Cross principles in honour of Jean Pictet.

Swinbank, Alan → Food and farm policies of the European Community.

Swinfen, David B.
Imperial appeal : the debate on the appeal to the Privy Council, 1833-1986 / David B. Swinfen. – Manchester : Manchester University Press, 1987.
viii,268p; 23cm.
Bibliography: p255-260. - Includes index.
ISBN 0719018951 £35.00

Swinson, Chris
Group Accounting. – London : Butterworths, 1988.
ISBN 0406500193 Pbk

Swinton, Katherine E.
Competing Constitutional Visions : the Meech Lake Accord / Carol J. Rogerson. – Agincourt : Carswell, 1988.
338p.
Hbk £50.50
→ Studies in Labour Law.

Swiss capital markets / by Henri B. Meier. – 2nd ed. – London : Euromoney, 1985.
xi,128p.
Bibliography: p.125-126 - Includes index.
ISBN 0903121816

Swiss company law / translation of the official text with an introduction, synoptic tables, annotations and appendices by Bruno Becchio, Allan D.M. Phillips, Urs Wehinger. – Chichester : Barry Rose, 1984.
184p.
Bibliography: p.12-13.
ISBN 3905203014

Swiss Federal Code of Obligations : as of January 1, 1984. – Dordrecht : Kluwer, 1987.
318p.
ISBN 9065443231 Hbk £155.00

Swiss review of international competition law. – Geneva : Werner & Sieber, 1984.
Continues: Revue suisse du droit international de la concurrence.
ISBN 02558246

Switzerland's private international law statute / Pierre A Karrer, Karl W Arnold. – Kluwer Law and Taxation, 1989.
304.
Examines the approximately two hundred articles of the statutes covering international conflicts of jurisdiction, private international law, and recognition and enforcement. Technical terms used by the statutes are rendered in the original, and explained. References to Swiss substantive law, and translations of texts relevant to international arbitration in Switzerland are included.
ISBN 9065442901 Hbk £48.50/Dfl 150

SWOT Family Law. – London : Blackstone Press.
ISBN 1854310313 Pbk £8.50

SWOT Law of Torts / Stephenson. – London : Blackstone Press.
ISBN 1854310291 Pbk £7.95

Sybesma-Knol, R. G.
Status of observers in the United Nations / R.G. Sybesma- Knol. – Brussels : Vrije Universiteit Brussel, Centrum voor de Studie van het Recht van de Verenigde Naties en de Gespecialiseerde Organisaties, 1981.
xi,484p.
Bibliography: p.456-484. - Includes index.
ISBN 9063210825

Sydenham, Angela
Land law lecture notes / Angela Sydenham. – London : Polytechnic of North London Students' Union, 1981.
224p; 21cm.
Bibliography: p221-222. Cover title.
ISBN 0906513014 Pbk £3.00

—Trusts in a nutshell / Angela Sydenham. – London : Sweet & Maxwell, 1987.
116p; 22cm.
Includes index.
ISBN 0421368500 Pbk £3.95

Sykes, Edward I
Australian private international law / by Edward I. Sykes and Michael C. Pryles. – 2nd ed. – North Ryde, N.S.W. : Law Book Co, 1987.
lxxxix, 772 p.; 25 cm.
Includes bibliographical references and indexes.
ISBN 0455207038 Pbk

—Cases and materials on administrative law / Richard R. S. Tracey. – 4th ed. – Sydney : Butterworths, 1982.
lii,547p.
Previous ed.: 1975, by Peter Brett and Peter W. Hogg. First ed.: cases and materials in constitutional and administrative law. Includes index.
ISBN 0409309192 Hbk £54
ISBN 0409309206 Pbk £42.5

—General Principles of Administrative Law / D.J. Lanham. – 3rd ed. – Butterworths, 1989.
ca 450p.
ISBN 0409495395 Pbk £55.00
ISBN 0409495387 Hbk £69.00

—International and interstate conflict of laws / Edward I. Sykes, Michael C. Pryles. – 2nd ed. – Sydney : Butterworths, 1981.
lv,966p.
Bibliography; p.943-950. - Includes index.
ISBN 0409455342 Pbk
ISBN 0409300438

—Law of securities : an account of the law pertaining to securities over real and personal property under the laws of the Australian States / Edward I.Sykes. – 4th edition. – Sydney : Law Book Company, 1986.
xcv,1043p.
ISBN 0455206287

—Strike law in Australia / by Edward I. Sykes. – 2nd ed. – Sydney : Law Book Co., 1982.
xxiii, 369 p.; 25 cm.
Includes bibliographical references and index.
ISBN 0455200890

Sykes, John → Exporting goods from the United Kingdom : export co-operatives and contract warehousing.

Sykes, Richard → Gore-Browne on companies.

Symes, P. D. → Real property and real people : principles of land law.

Symposium on Commercial Crime, 15-19 December 1982, Jesus College, Cambridge / organised by the Commonwealth Secretariat and the Centre for Commercial Law Studies : documentation edited by Susan Grace Lie. – S.l. : s.n., 1983.
ii,382p.
Includes bibliographical references.

Symposium on Industrial Property and Economic and Technological Development. – Geneva : World Intellectual Property Organization, 1988.
ca 150p.
Hbk £30.00

Symposium on statutory interpretaion, Canberra, 5 February 1983. – Canberra : Australian Government Publishing Service, 1983.
iii,136p.
At head of title: Attorney-General's Department.
ISBN 0644025859

Symposium on the Effective Protection of Industrial Property Rights. – Geneva : World Intellectual Property Organization, 1987.
299p.
£35.00

Symposium on the Protection of Biotechnological Inventions. – Geneva : World Intellectual Property Organization, 1987.
185p.
Hbk £30.00

Syndicated credits market / by I.D.Bond. – London : Economics Division, Bank of England, 1985.
67,28p. – (Bank of England discussion papers).
Bibliography: pi-iii.
ISBN 0903312735

Synopsis of the Work of the Court of Justice of the European Communities in 1984 and 1985 : and Record of Formal Sittings in 1984 and 1985. – Luxembourg : Office for Official Publications of the European Communities, 1987.
177p.
ISBN 9282901416 Pbk

Sypnowich, Christine
Concept of Socialist law. – Oxford : Clarendon Press.
21.5.
Intends to remedy the contempt for law prominent in Socialist writings. Argues that legal institutions would be necessary to adjudicate fairly conflict between private and public interest. Covers the rule of law, natural and legal rights, obligations, and the sources of law.
ISBN 0198252463 Hbk £25.00224

System for Settlement of Disputes under the United Nations Convention on the Law of the Sea : a Drafting History and a Commentary. – Dordrecht : Kluwer, 1987.
302p.
ISBN 9024733243 Hbk £165.00

System of Industrial Relations in New Zealand. – 2nd rev. ed. – Butterworths, 1988.
496p.
ISBN 0409788546 Pbk £70.00

System of law and courts governing New South Wales. – 2nd ed. – London : Butterworths, 1985.
ISBN 0409492531 Hbk £40.00

Systematic index of international water resources treaties, declarations, acts and cases by basin Vol. 2 / Repertoire systematique par bassin de traites, declarations, textes legislatifs et jurisprudence concernant les ressources en eau internationales. – Rome : Food and Agriculture Organization of the United Nations, 1984.
xxxiii,332p. – (Legislative study).
Explanatory text in English, French and Spanish.
ISBN 9250021895

Szakats, Alexander
Dismissal and Redundancy Procedures / Margaret A. Mulgan. – Butterworths, 1985.
Outline of the different procedures which may be taken by the dismissed employee after the termination of the employment contract. Unjustified and 'victimisation' dismissals are examined in detail with the appropriate remedial procedures. Analyses judicial decisions, and deals with the problems of redundancy dismissals and payment of compensation.
ISBN 040970136X pHbk £57.20
→ Industrial Law Bulletin.

—Introduction to the Law of Employment. – 3rd ed. – Butterworths, 1988.
435p.
ISBN 0409787922 Pbk
—Introduction to the law of employment / by Alexander Szakats. – 2nd ed., completely revised. – Wellington : Butterworths, 1981.
li,522p.
Previous ed.: 1975. Includes bibliographical references and index.
ISBN 0409601063
—Mazengarb's Industrial Law / Angus McLeod. – Butterworths.
Llf
Szakats, Brian
Industrial Law / Stepensons. – 7th ed. – Wellington : Butterworths.
ISBN 0409667706 Hbk
Szakats, Vranken Martin
Industrial Law Bulletin / Alexander Szakats. – Wellington : Butterworths.
ISBN 040978107X Pbk
Szasz, Ivan →CMEA uniform law for international sales.
—CMEA uniform law for international sales / by Ivan Szasz. – 2nd rev. ed. – Dordrecht : Nijhoff, 1985.
viii,291p; 25cm.
Previous ed.: published as : A uniform law on international sales of goods, 1976. Includes index. Translation of: A KGST altalanos szalltasi feltelek.
ISBN 9024727855 Hbk £125.00
Szaszy, I.
International Labour Law : a Comparative Survey of the Conflict Rules Affecting Labour Legislation and Regulations / A.W. Sijthoff. – Budapest : Akademiai Kiado, 1968.
465p.
Hbk £24.00
Szeftel, Morris →Dynamics of the one-party state in Zambia.
Sztucki, J.
Interim Measures in the Hague Court : an Attempt at a Scrutiny. – Dordrecht : Kluwer, 1983.
350p.
ISBN 9065440933 Hbk £104.00
Szwed, Elizabeth →Providing civil justice for children.
Szyszczak, Erika →Equality and sex discrimination law.
T.A.K.
Law at play. – T.A.K. – Edinburgh : W Green, 1984.
ISBN 0414007433 Hbk £2.50
T.M.C. Asser Institute →Basic documents on United Nations and related peace-keeping forces.
→ Essays on human rights in the Helsinki process.
→ Guide to EC court decisions.
→ Guide to EEC-legislation.
→ Hague-Zagreb Essays.
→ International law in the Netherlands.
→ Marine scientific research and the law of the sea.
→ Methodology of international law.
—Netherlands yearbook of international law. – T.M.C. Asser Institute. – Dordrecht : Nijhoff (Martinus), 1989.
600.
Articles on the practice of the Iran-United States Claims Tribunal. The documentation section surveys Dutch state practice for the parliamentary year 1987-1988; international agreements to which the Netherlands is a party, and Netherlands judicial decisions and municipal legislation involving questions of public international law, and Dutch literature in this field, and related matters.
ISBN 0792301048 Hbk £45
→ New York Arbitration Convention of 1958 : towards a uniform judicial interpretation.
→ Right to strike in Community law : the incorporation of fundamental rights in the legal order of the European Communities.
→ South West Africa and the sacred trust 1919-1972.
T. M. C. Asser Instituut →Prohibiting restrictions on trade within the EEC : the theory and application of Articles 30-36 of the EEC Treaty.
T. O. Elias : citations, honours and awards / edited by M.A. Ajomo. – Lagos : Nigerian Society of International Law, 1983.
viii,38p.
ISBN 9782283037
Tabatabai, Hossein Modarressi
Introduction to Shii law : a bibliographical study / Hossein Modarressi Tabatabai. – London : Ithaca Press, 1984.
258p; 24cm.
Bibliography: p218-237. - Includes index.
ISBN 0863720153 £18.00
Table of Alberta Legislation. – Edmonton : Queen's Printer, 1981.
151p.
Hbk
Table of Governmental Orders. – London : HMSO, 1983.
ISBN 0118402382 Hbk £65.00
Table of Proceedings in Juvenile Courts. – London : Shaw & Sons, 1984.
ISBN 0721901891 Hbk £0.80
Tables of persons acquiring citizenship of the United Kingdom and Colonies 1980 / Home Office. – London : H.M.S.O., 1981.
12p.
ISBN 0101832508
Tables to the statutes of Saskatchewan and Saskatchewan regulations. – Saskatchewan : Queen's Printer, 1980-.
26cm.
Tablot, J.
Lawyer's Pocketbook. – Durban : Professional Publishers, 1982.
ISBN 0409034533 Hbk
Tabory, Mala →International law at a time of perplexity, Essays in honour of Shabtai Rosenne.
→ Israel yearbook on human rights, Volume 18, 1988.
Tackling drug misuse : a summary of the governments strategy / Home Office. – 2nd ed. – London : Home Office, 1986.
39p.
Includes bibliographical references.
ISBN 086252234X
Tacon
Tort Liability in a Collective Bargaining Regime. – London : Butterworths.
ISBN 0409871540 Hbk £32.00
Tager, L.
Negotiable Instruments / T. J. Scott. – Durban : Professional Publisher, 1984.
ISBN 0409040215 Pbk £30.00
Taggart, Michael →Judicial review of administrative action in the 1980's : problems and prospects : papers presented at a Conference held by the Legal Research Foundation Inc. at the University of Auckland on 20 and 21 February 1986.
Taggart, W John
Computer law in Australia. – London : Legal Books, 1986.
ISBN 0949553271 Pbk £12.00
→ Computer law in Australia : a collection of essays.
Taishoff, Marika Natasha
State responsibility and the direct broadcast satellite / Marika Natasha Taishoff. – London : Pinter, 1987.
xii,203p; 24cm.
Bibliography: p183-197. - Includes index. 'A publication of the Graduate Institute of International Studies'.
ISBN 0861877004 Hbk £25
Takach, Gabor S.G. →Guide to the Investment Canada Act.
Takagi, Paul →Crime and Social Justice.
Take Notice : An Introduction to Canadian Law / Alenda S. Spetz. – 2nd ed. – Toronto : Copp Clark, 1984.
512p : Illus.
ISBN 0773043144 Hbk £24.94
Takeover bids. – London : Butterworths, 1988.

Company executives
ISBN 0406103690 Hbk
Take-Over Guide / Stenning. – London : Longman Professional.
ISBN 0851213634 Pbk £12.95
Takeovers, Acquisitions and Mergers. – London : Kogan Page.
ISBN 1850914591 Hbk
Takeovers, Trading Trusts and More, 1984. – Monash University, Faculty of Law. – Clayton : Monash University Press, 1984.
ISBN 0867463546 Hbk £28.00
Taking account of crime : key findings from the second British crime survey / Mike Hough and Pat Mayhew. – London : H.M.S.O., 1985.
vi,110p.
Reports on extent, risks and nature of selected crime, including incidents neither reported to nor recorded by police. Examines changing trends in crime between 1981 and 1983. Discusses differences between reported and unreported crime, the impact of crime on victims and public attitudes to crime.
ISBN 0113408102
Taking juvenile justice seriously / Ruth M. Adler. – Edinburgh : Scottish Academic Press, 1985.
viii,172p.
Bibliography: p157-167.
ISBN 0707304660
Taking of 28 : Women Challenge the Constitution. – Toronto.
124p.
ISBN 0889610835 Pbk £6.95
Taking statements. – 2nd ed. – Police Review, 1987.
ISBN 0851640338 Pbk £3.75
Taking Up a Franchise / Colin Barrow. – 3rd ed. – London : Kogan Page, 1986.
264p.
ISBN 1850910758 Hbk £12.95
Takwani, C.K.
Civil Procedure. – Lucknow : Eastern Book Company, 1983.
570p.
Hbk £40.00
Talbot, J.B.
Butterworths Consolidated Legislation Service. – London : Butterworths.
ISBN 0409014001 Llf £281.00
—Lawyer's Pocketbook. – Durban : Butterworths, 1985.
ISBN 0409034568 Hbk
Talk to My Lawyer : Great Stories of Southern Alberta's Bar and Bench. – Edmonton : Hurtig.
224p.
ISBN 0888303254 Hbk £24.95
Tallon, Denis →Contract law today: Anglo-French comparisons.
Tame, P.
Transport and the Farmer. – Shaw & Sons.
ISBN 0721911501 Hbk £9.95
Tamils of Sri Lanka / by Walter Schwarz. – 3rd rev ed. – London : Minority Rights Group, 1986.
15p. – (Report).
Previous edition: 1983.
ISBN 0946690375
Tamsitt, Gary →Hutley's Australian Wills Precedents.
Tan, Chwee Huat →Handbook of Singapore and Malaysian Corporate Finance.
Tan, Lee Meng
Law in Singapore on carriage of goods by sea / by Tan Lee Meng. – Singapore : Malayan Law Journal Pte., 1986.
lv,509p.
Deals with voyage charterparties, time charterparties, demise charterparties, bills of lading, the Carriage of Goods by Sea Act 1872, exclusion of liability, limitation of liability, and limitation of action, loading, proceeding on the voyage, discharge and delivery, laytime and demurrage, salvage and wreck, and remedies for breach of contract.
ISBN 9971700492
Tan, Lyn
Let's Look at Law / Jennifer Bollen. – Butterworths, 1985.
78p.
ISBN 0409492647 Pbk £9.50
Tandon, B.N.
Guide to Company Law. – New Delhi : S. Chand and Company.
Hbk £18.00
—Guide to Mercantile Law. – New Delhi : S. Chand and Company.
Hbk £24.00
—Principles of Mercantile Law. – New Delhi : S. Chand and Company, 1983.
Hbk £27.50
Tandon, Nidhi →Women in sub-Saharan Africa.
Tandon, Raj K.
Canada : Income Tax. – Delhi : Rangnath Publications.
Hbk £200.00
—Commonwealth Tax Laws. – Delhi : Rangnath Publications.
Hbk £500.00
Tandon, Yash
New position of East Africa's Asians : problems of a displaced minority / by Yash Tandon and Arnold Raphael. – 2nd rev. ed. – London : Minority Rights Group, 1984.
20p. – (Report).
Previous ed.: 1978. Bibliography: p.20.
ISBN 0946690200
Tang
Multinational Transfer Pricing. – London : Butterworths.
ISBN 0409871806 Hbk £23.00
Tang, See Chim →Contract Law.
→ Directors' Duties and Liabilities.
→ Your Rights as a Consumer.
Tanguay, Guy →Guide to purchasing law reports.
Tank, Ronald W.
Legal aspects of geology / Ronald W. Tank. – New York : Plenum, 1983.
xii,583p; 24cm.
Includes bibliographies and index.
ISBN 0306411598 Hbk
ISBN 0306412152 Pbk
Tanker voyage charter parties / by F. M. Ventris. – S.l. : Kluwer Law Publishers, 1986.
xvi,411p.
ISBN 0903393972
Tanna, Suresh →Executorship and Trust Law and Accounts.
→ Regulatory Framework of Accounting.
Tannett, A.
Land Law. – Stockholm : Anderson Keenan, 1982.
– (Law Unit).
ISBN 0906501288 Pbk £4.30
Tanzania law reports. – Dar es Salaam : s.n., 1987.
Cover cases decided in the Court of Appeal of Tanzania and the High Court of Tanzania.

Tanzil-ur-Rahman
Code of Muslim personal law / by Tanzil-ur-Rahman. – 2. – Karachi : Hamdard Academy, 1978.
Bibliography: vol.1, p.v-viii. - Includes index. Vol. 2 published: Karachi: Islamic Publishers.
ISBN 0195772857 v.2

Tape recording of police interviews with suspects : field trials : procedural guidance. – London : Home Office, 1983.
27p.
ISBN 0862521181

Tape-recording of police interviews with suspected persons in Scotland / report by the Working Group appointed by the Secretary of State for Scotland. – Edinburgh : Scottish Home & Health Department, 1985.
24p.
Title from cover. Accompanied by Appendices 1-2, Research report by Edward C.M. Wozniak (viii,189p) and Technical details (iv,13p).

Tape-recording of police interviews with suspects : an interim report / Carole F. Willis. – London : H.M.S.O., 1984.
v,39p.
Outlines background to field trials of tape recording police interviews. Reviews literature describing research methodologies used in trials. Discusses preliminary results of the research.
ISBN 0113407769

Taperell, G. Q.
Trade practices and consumer protection : a commentary on the Trade Practices Act 1974 / by G.Q. Taperell, R.B. Vermeesch, D.J. Harland. – 3rd ed. – Sydney : Butterworths, 1983.
liii,922p.
Previous ed.: 1978. Includes bibliographies and index. Legislation set against the economic and commercial background in which it operates.
ISBN 0409491217 Pbk

Tapp, Julian → Insurance: competition or regulation? : a comparative study of the insurance markets in the United Kingdom and the Federal Republic of Germany.

Tapp, Pauline
Domestic violence : the Domestic Protection Bill 1982 : paper presented at Auckland law Faculty Seminar Series 1982 at University of Auckland / by Pauline Tapp. – Auckland : Legal Research Foundation Inc., 1982.
14,14p.
Includes the text of the Bill.
ISBN 090858122X

—Women and the Law in New Zealand / Margaret A Wilson. – Birkenhead : Reed Methuen.
120p.
ISBN 0456029907 Pbk £8.95

Tapper, Colin
Computer law / Colin Tapper. – 3rd ed. – London : Longman, 1983.
xxvii,242p. – (Business data processing).
Includes index. Bibliography: p231-234.
ISBN 0582497175

→ Crime, proof and punishment : essays in memory of Sir Rupert Cross.

→ Cross on evidence.

—Experiment in the Use of Citation Vectors in the Area of Legal Data. – Oslo : Norwegian University Press, 1982.
112p.
ISBN 8200064794 Hbk £61.00

→ Outline of the law of evidence.

Tapping, A P de B
Guarantees For New Homes / R Rolfe. – 3rd ed. – London : Longman Professional, 1981.
ISBN 0851295437 Pbk £23.00

Tariff Board : a study prepared for the Law Reform Commission of Canada / by Philip Slayton and John J. Quinn : assisted by James Cassels. – Ottawa : Minister of Supply and Services, 1981.
ix,154p; 25cm. – (Administrative law series).
ISBN 0662116224

Tariff Classifications : 7th Amending Supplement. – Kirchberg : Commission of the European Communities, 1984.
116p.
Hbk

Tariff of Costs. – Vancouver : British Columbia Continuing Legal Education Society, 1985.
Audiocassettes £45.00

Tarling, Roger → Clearing up crime.

→ Juvenile sentencing : is there a tariff?.

→ Policing today.

→ Time taken to deal with juveniles under criminal proceedings.

Tarling's Case and Directors Liabilities in Singapore and Malaysia. – Singapore : Quins, 1982.
Hbk £63.00

Tarnopolsky, Walter Surma
Canadian Charter of Rights and Freedoms. – Agincourt : Carswell, 1982.
ISBN 045934920 Hbk £33.00

→ Canadian charter of rights and freedoms : commentary.

—Discrimination and the law in Canada / by Walter Surma Tarnopolsky. – Toronto : De Boo, 1982.
vii,595p.
Bibliography: p. 493-510. - Includes index.
ISBN 0888201052 Hbk

Tarpey → Single Payments : the Disappearing Safety Net 1988.

Tarr
State Supreme Courts in State and Nation / Porter. – Yale University Press.
ISBN 03000039123 Hbk £22.50

Tarr, Anthony A.
Australian Insurance Law. – North Ryde : Law Book Co, 1987.
xlv, 368p.
ISBN 0455207232 Pbk £49.50

—Insurance law in New Zealand / by A.A. Tarr. – Sydney : Law Book Co., 1985.
xxxv,257p.
Includes bibliographical references and index.
ISBN 0455205698

Taschereau, H. E.
Criminal Code : 1893. – Repr. of 1980 ed. – Agincourt : Carswell.
1200p. – (Carswell's Classic Reprints).
This book is a reproduction of the 1893 treatise on the first Criminal Code of Canada.
Hbk £109.25

Tasmanian reports. – Hobart : Law Book Co. for the Council of Law Reporting of Tasmania, 1897-.
Continues: The Tasmanian state reports.

Tate, Michael → IVF and the status of children.

Tate, Nick
Sponsorship. – London : Longman Professional (UK), 1987.
– (Longman Intelligence Report).
Looks at the increase in sponsorship expenditure and range of applications, providing guidance to enable companies to realise full marketing potential. Considers aspects of evaluation, setting-up and monitoring of the sponsorship deal.
ISBN 0851213324 Hbk £85.00

Tauroa, E. Te R.
Report of Advisory Committee on Youth and Law in our Multicultural Society / E. Te R. Tauroa. – Wellington : The Committee, 1983.
284p.

Tax and Financial Planning for Family Businesses / George J. Bell. – London : Butterworths, 1984.
This book addresses the tax problems faced by owners of small and medium sized family business in the United Kingdom. The work examines the benefits to be gained from allowances, reliefs, exemptions, and Revenue concessions.
ISBN 0406557306 Pbk £16.00

Tax and financial planning for Lloyd's members. – London : Longman Professional, 1988.
– (A Longman Intelligence Report).
ISBN 0851213421 Hbk £85.00

Tax and Financial Planning for Medical Practitioners. – 2nd ed. – London : Butterworths, 1987.
ISBN 0406190054 Pbk

Tax and Financial Planning for Professional Partnerships / Brian Gilligan. – 2nd ed. – London : Butterworths, 1986.
This work explains how the tax liability of United Kingdom professional partnerships can be minimized by effective tax planning. The effects of the Finance Act of 1985 on professional partnerships is discussed in detail.
ISBN 0406501807 Pbk

Tax and financial planning for sportsmen and entertainers / Richard Harvey. – London : Butterworths, 1987.
ISBN 040650220X Pbk £18.50

Tax and Financial Planning Through Pensions / Abramson. – London : Butterworths.
ISBN 0406503478 Pbk £26.50

Tax and Interest Tables / Nuttall. – London : Fourmat.
ISBN 1851900470 Hbk £6.95

Tax and the Australian film industry : being a commentary on division 10BA of the Income Assessment Act 1936 together with text of the legislation / by E.F. Mannix. – Sydney : Butterworths, 1981.
xii,92p.
Includes index.
ISBN 040936018X

Tax and the farmer / NFU. – London : Shaw & Sons, 1988.
ISBN 0721911609 Pbk

Tax appeals : system of General Commissioners of Income Tax for Northern Ireland : a consultative document. – London : Board of Inland Revenue, 1987.
6p.

Tax appeals handbook. – London : Butterworths, 1983.
ISBN 0406535221 Pbk £13.00

Tax aspects of acquisitions and mergers / edited by Philip Cooke, Jan M. van der Beek. – 2nd ed. – Deventer : Kluwer, 1983.
150p.
ISBN 9065441514

Tax Aspects of General Practice. – Vancouver : British Columbia Continuing Legal Education Society, 1985.
646p.
ISBN 0865042233 Hbk £75.00

Tax Aspects of Home Ownership. – London : Butterworths, 1983.
ISBN 0406254311 Pbk £20.00

Tax Aspects of Incorporation. – Toronto : Butterworths, 1983.
128p.
Pbk £19.95

Tax Aspects of Litigation. – Vancouver : British Columbia Continuing Legal Education Society, 1982.
138p.
ISBN 086504077X Hbk £40.00

Tax Aspects of the Administration of Estates / Elizabeth Stuart-Buttle. – London : Butterworths, 1984.
This work discusses the numerous tax considerations associated with the administration of an estate in the United Kingdom. The book details the appropriate procedures which are a pre-condition to a grant of probate.
ISBN 0406259003 Pbk

Tax avoidance 1981 : the new law : being a commentary on part IVA of the Income Tax Assessment Act 1936 together with the text of the legislation / by E.F. Mannix. – Sydney : Butterworths, 1981.
ix,41p.
Includes index.
ISBN 0409357782

Tax avoidance, tax evasion : a survey of the treatment of tax aviodance and tax evasion in the main industrialised countries of the world / compiled in 1982 for Committee N of the Section on Business Law of the International Bar Association by a team of international rapporteurs and updated and revised for this edition. – 2nd ed. – London : International Bar Association in co-operation with Sweet & Maxwell, 1987.
viii,160p.
Includes bibliographical references.
ISBN 0948711124 Pbk £15.00

Tax avoidance, tax evasion : a survey of the treatment of tax avoidance and tax evasion in the main industrialized countries of the world / compiled for Committee N of the Section on Business Law of the International Bar Association by a team of international rapporteurs. – London : International Bar Association in co-operation with Sweet & Maxwell, 1982.
viii,104p; 22cm.
ISBN 0950587672 Pbk £8.50

Tax Avoision. – London : Institute of Economic Affairs.
Pbk £2.50

Tax Benefits and Family Finance / T. Lyon. – London : Sweet & Maxwell, 1985.
ISBN 0421324600 Hbk

Tax Bumph 1987-88. – Tolley Publishing.
ISBN 0854583004 Pbk £19.95

Tax Case Leaflets April 1985-March 1986. – London : HMSO.
Hbk £37.50

Tax Cases : 1875-1982, 53 Vols. – Abingdon : Professional Books.
Hbk £1900.00
Individual vols.. –
Hbk £60.00
Index Vol. 1-52. –
Hbk £63.00

Tax Computations 1987-88. – Tolley Publishing.
ISBN 0854593012 Pbk £20.95

Tax consequences of receivership and liquidation / David Bertram. – London : Butterworths, 1982.
xxxii,423p; 22cm.
Includes index.
ISBN 0406220603 Pbk £20.00

Tax Data 1987-88. – Tolley Publishing.
ISBN 0854592962 Pbk £7.50

Tax efficient personal investments. – 2nd ed. – Croydon : Tolley, 1987.
ISBN 0854593152 Pbk £12.95

Tax evasion in Canada / William I. Innes. – Toronto : Carswell, 1987.
xxvi,326p.
Includes index.
ISBN 0459305719

Tax expenditures : a review of the issues and country practices / report by the Committee on Fiscal Affairs. – Paris : Organisation for Economic Co-operation and Development, 1984. 88p.
Examines how governments account for tax expenditures which favour particular types of taxpayers.
ISBN 9264125892 Hbk £30.00

Tax Facts 4 : The Canadian Consumer Tax Index and You, No. 4. – Vancouver : Fraser Institute.
ISBN 0889750726 Hbk £4.95

Tax for the Self-Employed. – 2nd ed. – London : Oyez Longman, 1983.
ISBN 085120712X Hbk £3.50

Tax for the self-employed. – London : Longman Professional, 1988.
– (Allied Dunbar Money Guide).
ISBN 08512113855 Hbk

Tax Guide 1987-1988. – London : Longman Professional.
ISBN 0851212921 Hbk £12.95

Tax Guide 1987-88. – Tolley Publishing.
ISBN 0854592938 Hbk £14.95

Tax havens and offshore finance : a study of transnational economic development / Richard Anthony Johns. – London : Frances Pinter, 1983.
xiv,259p.
Bibliography: p248-255.

Tax havens and the corporate sector : a consultative document. – London : Board ofInland Revenue, 1981.
3 leaves.

Tax Havens and Their Uses. – new ed. – London : Economist Intelligence Unit, 1981.
Illus, updated to March 1983. – – (QER Special: No. 105).
ISBN 0900351403 Hbk £60.00

Tax havens encyclopaedia / edited by Barry Spitz. – 1. – London : Butterworths, 1975-.
Tab indexed. Includes bibliographies.
ISBN 0406382263 Llf £95

Tax Havens Of The World / Diamond. – Matthew Bender, 1974.
ISBN 0000999084 Hbk £132.00

Tax Investigation Handbook. – London : Butterworths, 1981.
ISBN 0406254109 Pbk £25.00

Tax investigations. – Croydon : Tolley, 1988.
ISBN 0854593187 Hbk £14.95

Tax Law. – London : Sweet & Maxwell.
– (Irish Law Texts Ser.).
ISBN 0421299304 Hbk

Tax law in the melting pot / a study by the Revenue Law Committee of the Law Society of the 'Ramsay' doctrine after 'Furniss v. Dawson', with proposals. – London : Law Society, 1985.
iii,119p.
Bibliography: p.119.

Tax Laws. – New Delhi : Sultan Chand and Sons.
Hbk £65.00

Tax Locator 1988. – New York : Bowker, 1988.
ISBN 0835223493 Hbk £30.00

Tax minimisation techniques : a specially commissioned report / by R.W. Maas. – London : Oyez Longman, 1984.
xi,102leaves; 30cm. – (Oyez Longman intelligence reports).
Previous ed.: 1982.
ISBN 0851209300 spiral £45.00

Tax Offences, Black Money and the Law. – New Delhi : Deep and Deep Publications, 1987.
416p.
Hbk £250.00

Tax Office Addresses 1988. – Tolley Publishing.
ISBN 0854593284 Pbk £4.50

Tax on all the people : poll tax. – Oxford : Bookspeed, 1988.
ISBN 0946744068 Pbk £1.95

Tax on company reorganizations / Malcolm Gammie with Susan Ball. – 2nd ed. – London : Taxation Publishing, 1982.
xxvii,518p; 22cm.
Previous ed.: 1980. Includes index.
Pbk £18.00

Tax On Maintenance Payments 1985/86 / Joel Newman. – 8th ed. – London : Longman Professional.
ISBN 0851210759 Pbk £11.95

Tax on the Farm. – Shaw & Sons.
ISBN 0721911609 Pbk £9.95

Tax Planned Will Precedents, 2 Vols.
Vol. 1 /. – Agincourt : Carswell.
ISBN 0459314300 Hbk £75.75
Vol. 2. –
This looseleaf service is a guide to tax savings in estate planning in Canada. Annotated precedents, master will form, will instruction checklist, alternative clauses, relevant legislation, coverage of trust, and other relevant materials are included in the two volumes.
ISBN 0459326007 Hbk £50.50

Tax Planning 1988. – Tolley Publishing.
ISBN 0854593020 Pbk £35.00

Tax Planning for Businesses in Europe. – 2nd ed. – London : Butterworths, 1984.
ISBN 0406535515 Hbk

Tax Planning for Executive and Employee Compensation and Retirement. – Toronto : Canadian Tax Foundation, 1985.
– (Conference Reports).
Hbk £40.00

Tax Planning for Family Business. – London : Butterworths, 1984.
ISBN 0406556806 Pbk

Tax Planning for Groups of Companies. – London : Butterworths, 1985.
This book examines the various aspects of taxation of groups or consortia in the United Kingdom and considers commercial factors to determine the most appropriate group structure. Pro forma tax elections and sample agreements for the surrender of tax advantages between group companies are included.
ISBN 0406075808 Hbk

Tax planning for medical practitioners / Stephen Burwood. – 2nd ed. – London : Butterworths, 1987.
ISBN 04066190054 Pbk £18.50

Tax Planning for Multinational Companies. – Cambridge : Woodhead-Faulkner.
ISBN 0859415589 Hbk £40.00

Tax planning for new businesses. – 2nd ed. – Croydon : Tolley, 1987.
ISBN 0854592032 Pbk £9.95

Tax planning for the family. – 3rd ed. – London : Longman Professional, 1986.
ISBN 0851209203 Pbk £22.00

Tax planning on marriage breakdown. – 4th ed. – London : Longman Professional, 1986.
ISBN 0851210740 Pbk £26.50

Tax Planning Strategies for Companies in South East Asia. – London : Oyez Longman, 1984.
– (Oyez Longman Intelligence Report Ser.).
ISBN 0851208126 Hbk

Tax Planning Through Inheritance Trusts. – London : Oyez Longman, 1983.
– (Oyez Longman Intelligence Report Ser.).
ISBN 0851208193 Hbk £45.00

Tax planning through trusts / Robert Venables. – London : Butterworths, 1983.
xxxiv,371p; 24cm.
Includes index.
ISBN 0406406014

Tax Planning Uses of the Caribbean. – London : Oyez Longman, 1984.
– (Oyez Longman Intelligence Report Ser.).
ISBN 0851208533 Hbk

Tax Planning with Precedents / H. H. Monroe. – London : Sweet & Maxwell, 1987.
Hbk

Tax Policy : New Directions and Possibilities. – London : Eurospan.
ISBN 0944237096 Pbk £8.50

Tax policy options in the 1980s / edited by Wayne R. Thirsk, John Whalley. – Toronto : Canadian Tax Foundation, 1982.
vi,452p.
Includes bibliographical notes and index. Papers from Canadian Tax Foundation conference 'Tax policy options in the 1980s' held in Toronto, March 1981.
ISBN 0888080077

Tax policy towards the national heritage : proceedings of a seminar held in Venice, 1983, during the 37th Congress of the International Fiscal Association / organised by the International Fiscal Association. – Deventer, Netherlands : Kluwer Law and Taxation Publishers, 1984.
ISBN 9065441786

Tax practice manual. – Touche Ross. – 2nd ed. – London : Butterworths, 1985.
ISBN 0406402205 Pbk £18.50

Tax Practitioner 1989. – Butterworths, 1989.
712p.
ISBN 0409788775 Pbk £55.00

Tax practitioner's diary 1989-1990. – London : Butterworths, 1989.
Covers a 15-month period beginning in September. Contains addresses of all UK tax offices.

Tax Practitioner's Pocketbook. – Durban : Professional Publisher.
ISBN 0409064068 Hbk £45.00

Tax raiders. – London : Financial Training, 1985.
ISBN 0906322766 Hbk £10.95

Tax Rates and Tables 1988-89. – Bicester : CCH.
ISBN 0863251528 Pbk £2.75

Tax reform : options for the third term / edited by Bill Robinson : with contributions from Michael Devereux ... et al. – London : IFS, 1987.
65leaves; 30cm.
Bibliography: leaves 64-65.
ISBN 0902992643 Pbk

Tax Reform Around the World. – London : Eurostudy Publishing.
ISBN 1852710381 Pbk £50.00

Tax Reform in Disequilibrium Economics. – Cambridge : Cambridge University Press.
ISBN 0521355885 Hbk £19.50

Tax Reforms and Asset Markets. – Stockholm : Industriens Utredningsinstitut, 1985.
181p.
Hbk £154.00

Tax Reports : Live and Leading Cases 1875-1985 7 vols. – Professional Books.
ISBN 0862052831 Hbk £435.00

Tax Reports (New Zealand), 10 Vols. – Wellington : Butterworths, 1986.
Pbk
Back Vols. avail..

Tax Shelters in the United Kingdom. – Oxford : BSP Professional.
ISBN 0632034895 Pbk £99.50

Tax Strategies for Directors, Executives and Employees. – London : Oyez Longman, 1983.
ISBN 0851206735 Hbk £15.00

Tax Strategy. – 2nd ed. – Durban : Butterworths, 1983.
ISBN 0409013595 Pbk

Tax strategy for companies. – 4th ed. – London : Longman Professional, 1986.
xxviii,511p; 22cm.
Previous ed.: 1983. Includes index.
ISBN 0851209211 Pbk £30.00

Tax Strategy for Conveyancing and Land Transactions. – London : Oyez Longman, 1984.
ISBN 0851208797 Hbk

Tax strategy for directors, executives and employers. – 2nd ed. – London : Longman Professional, 1985.
– (Tax Strategy Series).
ISBN 0851210767 Pbk £30.00

Tax Tables 1988-89. – Tolley Publishing.
ISBN 0854593217 Pbk £5.75

Tax warranties and indemnities / John Clark. – London : Butterworths, 1983.
ISBN 0406395403 Hbk £18.00

Taxation 1988-89. – Pontefract : Lofthouse Publications.
ISBN 0900370874 Pbk £17.50

Taxation 2.3 / Murphy. – Pitman.
– (ACCA Series).
ISBN 0273028634 Pbk £12.95

Taxation / general editors Emile Woolf, Suresh Tanna, Karam Singh. – Plymouth : Macdonald & Evans, 1985.
792p. – (M & E professional studies).
Includes index.
ISBN 0712104879 Pbk £14.95

Taxation. – 7th ed. – London : Pitman Publishing, 1986.
ISBN 0712120378 Pbk £7.95

Taxation. – London : DP Publications.
ISBN 0905435915 Pbk £8.50

Taxation : ICSA Study Text. – Institute of Chartered Secretaries and Administrators. – Rev. ed. – London : BPP.
ISBN 086277215X Pbk £15.95

Taxation : Level 2.3. – London : BPP.
– (ACCA Practice and Revision Series).
ISBN 0862772699 Pbk £6.95

Taxation : the leading authority on the law, practice and administration of taxation. – London : Taxation Publishing Co., 1927.
ISBN 00400149

Taxation - A Handbook for Insurance and Estate Planners. – 1986 Edition. – Don Mills : Life Underwriters Association of Canada.
ISBN 0921219032 Hbk £22.50

Taxation and Estate Planning. – 3rd ed. – Agincourt : Carswell.
Hbk

Taxation and estate planning / by Maurice C. Cullity and Catherine A. Brown. – 2nd ed. – Toronto, Canada : Carswell Co., 1984.
xxvi, 764 p.; 24 cm.
At head of title: Cullity, Forbes, Brown. Includes bibliographical references and index.
ISBN 0459362305 Pbk

Taxation and Fiscal Federalism. – Pergamon.
ISBN 0080344011 Pbk £10.00

Taxation and human rights : proceedings of a seminar held in Brussels in 1987 during the 41st Congress of the International Fiscal Association / Marc Baltus, chairman of the seminar. – Deventer, Netherlands : Kluwer Law and Taxation, 1988.
vii,83p.
ISBN 9065443843

Taxation and trusts / by Geraint W. Thomas. – London : Sweet & Maxwell, 1981.
xxiv,205p; 19cm.
Includes index.
ISBN 0421277203 Hbk
ISBN 0421277300 Pbk £6.95

Taxation Aspects of Banking Operations / P. F. Swaine. – London : Butterworths, 1985.
This book describes the tax consequences of all significant banking operations and how the effect of various taxes on banks differs from other corporations. An in-depth look at the taxation of banks in the United Kingdom.
ISBN 0406010692 Hbk £35.00

Taxation aspects of currency fluctuations / Jill C. Pagan. – London : Butterworths, 1983.
xi,162p.
Describes the United Kingdom tax law and the attitude of the Inland Revenue on the subject of currency fluctuations. Foreign exchange management, accounting treatment, and taxation are analyzed in the book.
ISBN 0406406308 Hbk £22.00

Taxation (FA87) : ACCA Study Text 2.3. – London : BPP.
ISBN 0862772427 Pbk £14.95

Taxation for Executors and Trustees. – 6th ed. – London : Butterworths, 1984.
ISBN 0406623961 Hbk
ISBN 040662397X Pbk

Taxation in Canada / J. Harvey Perry. – 4th ed. – Toronto : Canadian Tax Foundation, 1984.
xii,248p.
Bibliography: p.234-240. - Includes index.

Taxation In Channel Islands and Isle Of Man 1987. – Tolley Publishing.
ISBN 0854592954 Pbk £11.95

Taxation in developed countries : an international symposium / organised by the French Ministry of Finance in association with the Committee on Fiscal Affairs of the OECD, Paris, 12th and 13th January 1987. – Paris : O.E.C.D., 1987.
99p.
ISBN 9264129294

Taxation in Europe : 1983. – Deloitte, Haskins and Sells. – London : Oyez Longman, 1983.
ISBN 0906052068 Hbk £10.95

Taxation in European socialist countries / J. van Hoorn and T. Nagy, managing editors : W.G. Kuiper, co-ordinating editor, T.G. Brierley, editor. – 2. – Amsterdam : International Bureau of Fiscal Documentation, 1984.
loose-leaf.
Updated by loose-leaf supplements.

Taxation In Republic Of Ireland 1987-88. – Tolley Publishing.
ISBN 0854592946 Pbk £12.95

Taxation in the Asian-Pacific region : a country by country survey / compiled by Jap Kim Siong and Ahmad Khan. – 2nd rev. ed. – Singapore : Asian-Pacific Tax and Investment Research Centre, 1985.
vi,218p.
Based on the 8-volume loose-leaf work 'Taxes and Investment in Asia and the Pacific' published by the International Bureau of Fiscal Documentation.

Taxation in the Netherlands / by Gerrit te Spenke. – Deventer : Kluwer, 1985.
xvii,135p; 25cm.
Includes index.
ISBN 9065440836

Taxation, Inflation and the Role of Government. – Turramura : Centre for Independent Studies.
56p.
ISBN 0949769002 Hbk £3.50

Taxation international. – Croydon, Surrey : Tolley, 1988.
Published as a supplement to Taxation.
ISBN 09547053

Taxation issues of the 1980s : papers presented at a conference organised by the Centre of Policy Studies, Monash University / John G. Head, editor. – Sydney : Australian Tax Research Foundation, 1983.
xii,438p.
Includes bibliographies and index.
ISBN 0949482005

Taxation Law and Practice : Revision Exercises. – Randwick : New South Wales University Press, 1983.
80p.
Pbk

Taxation Law in Australia / Cynthia Coleman. – Butterworths, 1989.
ca 960p.
ISBN 0409301388 Hbk £85.00
ISBN 0409494704 Pbk £75.00

Taxation Laws, Part 1 : General Principles. – Allahabad : Orient Law House.
ISBN 0861256336 Hbk £35.00

Taxation of accumulation and discretionary trusts. – Tolley Publishing, 1987.
ISBN 0854592709 Pbk £14.95

Taxation of capital gains / by Vern Krishna. – Toronto : Butterworths, 1983.
xxiii,251p.
Includes index.
ISBN 0409843776 Hbk £51.95

Taxation of clubs and voluntary associations. – Croydon : Tolley, 1988.
ISBN 0854593179 Hbk £11.95

Taxation of Companies : a Handbook. – Calcutta : Eastern Law House, 1969.
260p.
Hbk £15.00

Taxation of Companies and Company Reconstructions. – 4th ed. – Sweet & Maxwell.
ISBN 0421404302 Hbk £75.00

Taxation of Companies and Corporate Investors. – London : Butterworths, 1983.
ISBN 0409701424 Pbk £10.50

Taxation of Companies in Europe. – International Bureau of Fiscal Documentation. – Amsterdam : International Bureau of Fiscal Documentation, 1988.
– (Guides to European Taxation Ser.: Vol. 2).
Llf £1800.00
Supplements-1989 renewal. –
Llf £750.00

Taxation of controlled foreign corporations : an international comparison / Brian J. Arnold. – Toronto, Ont. : Canadian Tax Foundation, 1986.
xxiii, 816; 23 cm. – (Canadian tax paper).
Includes index. Bibliography: p. 797-811.
ISBN 0888080239 Pbk £75.00

Taxation of Co-operative Societies in South Africa. – Cape Town : Legal & Financial Publishing, 1983.
ISBN 0869940317 Hbk £13.50

Taxation of corporations and shareholders / Martin Norr. – Deventer, Netherlands : Kluwer Law and Taxation Publishers, 1982.
xii, 214 p.; 25 cm.
On page opposite t.p.: International Tax Program, Harvard Law School. Bibliography: p. 199-214.
ISBN 9065440151

Taxation of Corporations and Shareholders : Cases and Materials
Includes 1987-88 Supplements / D. Keith McNair. – Agincourt : Carswell, 1986.
616p.
This text contains both cases and materials pertaining to corporate tax. The bulk of the text is explanatory in nature. These explanations are supplemented with short cases extracts to further illustrate a point.
Hbk £75.75

Taxation of directors / Sargent. – London : CCH, 1986.
ISBN 0863251129 Pbk £5.00

Taxation of domestic shareholders on undistributed income of foreign corporate affiliates : objectives, techniques, and consequences : proceedings of a seminar held in New York in 1986 during the 40th Congress of the International Fiscal Association / edited by Brian J. Arnold. – Deventer, Netherlands : Kluwer Law and Taxation Publishers, 1987.
Includes bibliography.
ISBN 9065443347

Taxation of farmers and landowners. – 3rd. – London : Butterworths, 1987.
ISBN 040638391X Hbk £20.00

Taxation of foreign investment in the People's Republic of China / A J Easson, L Jinyan. – Kluwer Law and Taxation, 1989.
260.
Describes China's tax laws as they relate to foreign business and investment within the context of current economic reforms and the overall policy towards economic relations, including investment incentives and the impact of China's tax treaties. Reference is made to other Chinese legislation. Covers the situation at February 1988.
ISBN 9065443835 Hbk £56.25/Dfl 174

Taxation of fringe benefits / Sargent. – London : CCH, 1988.
ISBN 0863251455 Pbk £8.50

Taxation of Income and Tax Laws. – New Delhi : Deep and Deep Publications.
240p.
Hbk £120.00

Taxation of income of foreign affiliates / by David A. Ward. – Toronto : Carswell, 1983.
vi,237p.
Includes index. 'Being Chapter 20 of Ward's Tax Law and Planning by The Partners of Davies, Ward & Beck and Brian J. Arnold' - t.p.
ISBN 0459358707

Taxation of insolvent companies. – Croydon : Tolley, 1986.
ISBN 0854592326 Pbk £9.95

Taxation of Insurance Business / A R Levitt. – 2nd ed. – London : Butterworths.
ISBN 0406501017 Hbk £45.00

Taxation of international business. – London : Board of Inland Revenue, 1982.
125 leaves.
Revised draft proposals on international tax avoidance.

Taxation of international business : dual resident companies : consultative document. – London : Inland Revenue, 1984.
7p.

Taxation of international business : memorandum / by the Society's Standing Committee on Revenue Law. – London : Law Society, 1983.
21p.

Taxation of international business : the charge to tax on investment managers acting for non-residents : consultative paper. – London : Inland Revenue, 1984.
5p.

Taxation of international income. – London : Butterworths, 1988.
ISBN 0409788015 Pbk

Taxation of Investment in Shares and Securities. – London : Butterworths.
ISBN 0406504504 Pbk £30.00

Taxation of Land Development / Sheila Parrington. – London : Butterworths.
Llf

Taxation of land transactions. – 4th ed. – London : Butterworths, 1988.
ISBN 0406624100 Pbk

Taxation of Lawyers' Accounts. – Vancouver : Continuing Legal Education Society of British Columbia, 1986.
130p.
ISBN 086504256X Hbk £55.00

Taxation of leasing transactions. – London : Butterworths, 1984.
ISBN 0406538026 Pbk £15.00

Taxation of legal costs. – London : LEST, 1986.
ISBN 0907822657 Pbk £19.50

Taxation of Lloyd's Underwriters. – Croydon : Tolley, 1984.
ISBN 085459129X Pbk £17.50

Taxation of Lloyd's Underwriters / Peter H Wolstenholme. – 3rd ed. – London : Butterworths, 1985.
ISBN 0406511012 Pbk £18.95

Taxation of Lloyds Underwriters. – 2nd ed. – Croydon : Tolley.
300p.
ISBN 0854593063 Hbk £29.95

Taxation Of Management Expenses. – Tolley Publishing.
ISBN 0854592806 Hbk £9.95

Taxation of marriage and marriage breakdown. – Croydon : Tolley, 1988.
ISBN 0854593233 Hbk

Taxation of non-resident entertainers and sportsmen. – Croydon : Tolley, 1987.
ISBN 0854593128 Hbk £35.00

Taxation of North Sea Oil. – London : Institute for Fiscal Studies, 1981.
24p.
Hbk £5.00

Taxation of overseas income and gains / Anthony Sumption. – 4th ed. – London : Butterworths, 1982.
xix,207p.
Previous ed.: 1979.
ISBN 0406538735

Taxation of Partnerships in Canada / Carl F. Steiss. – Butterworths, 1983.
104p.
ISBN 0409859761 Hbk £29.95

Taxation of Party-Party Costs. – Vancouver : Continuing Legal Education Society of British Columbia, 1987.
107p.
ISBN 0865042926 Hbk £60.00

Taxation of Patent Royalties, Dividends, and Interest in Europe. – International Bureau of Fiscal Documentation. – Amsterdam : International Bureau of Fiscal Documentation, 1988.
– (Guides to European Taxation Ser.: Vol. 1).
Llf £690.00
Fl looseleaf 1989 suppl. renewal. –
£350.00

Taxation of private corporations and their shareholders / Howard J. Kellough, Peter E. McQuillan. – Toronto : Canadian Tax Foundation, 1983.
ix,825p.
ISBN 0888080174

Taxation of Private Investment Income. – International Bureau of Fiscal Documentation. – Amsterdam : International Bureau of Fiscal Documentation, 1988.
– (Guides to European Taxation Ser.: Vol. 3).
Llf £690.00
Supplements-1989 renewal. –
Llf £350.00

Taxation of property transactions / by John Prebble. – Wellington, N.Z. : Butterworths, 1986.
xxxii,237p.
Includes index.
ISBN 040978740X

Taxation of Renumeration Packages. – London : Longman Professional.
ISBN 085121374X Pbk £95.00

Taxation of Resource Industries. – Agincourt : Carswell, 1987.
392p.
This text discusses the relevant sections of the Income Tax Act. Also included are discussions on depletion, successor corporation rules and resource allowances. Special coverage includes sample calculations and tables listing the order of deductions for different types of enterprises.
Hbk £54.75

Taxation of the family / O.P. Wylie. – London : Butterworths, 1983.
xxv,229p; 22cm.
ISBN 0406580200

Taxation of the income arising from the international seabed : proceedings of a seminar held in Berlin in 1981 during the 35th Congress of the International Fiscal Association / organised by the International Fiscal Association. – Deventer : Kluwer, 1982.
159p. – (IFA congress seminar series).
ISBN 9065440593

Taxation of Transactions in Intellectual Property / W. G. S. Massey. – London : Sweet & Maxwell, 1982.
ISBN 042129390X Hbk

Taxation of woodlands in the UK. – Edinburgh : Green (W.) & Son, 1989.
Traces the history and development of the special tax system for woodlands including changes in the income tax provision since April 1988. Covers transitional provision for income tax to 5 April 1993 with relevant statutory provisions and case law on the definition of what constitutes the management of commercial woodlands relative to income tax questions.
ISBN 0414008952 Hbk

Taxation on divorce and separation / J. Gray. – Bicester : CCH Editions, 1987.
xi,103p; 23cm.
Includes index.
ISBN 0863251072 Pbk

Taxation Simplified : 1988 Finance Act / Fieldhouse. – Pontefract : Lofthouse Publications.
ISBN 0900370866 Pbk £2.95

Taxation Treatment of Interest. – London : Butterworths, 1984.
This book brings together all the legislation, case law, and extrastatutory concessions relevant to taxation of interest in the United Kingdom.
ISBN 0406258155 Pbk

Taxes Acts : the oil taxation enactments in force from 8 May up to and including the Finance (No. 2) Act 1987 : with other legislation and statutory regulations affecting the application of the tax and an index. – London : HMSO, 1988.
iv,436p.
On cover: 1987 ed.. At head of title: Inland Revenue. Spine title: The Oil Taxation Acts.
ISBN 0116413751

Taxes and Investment in Asia and the Pacific. – Amsterdam : International Bureau of Fiscal Documentation, 1988.
Llf £2100.00
Fl looseleaf 1989 suppl. renewal. – £1100.00

Taxes in France. – 4th ed. – London : Butterworths, 1986.
This work is a comprehensive look at French taxation law covering income tax, company tax, value added tax, and stamp and registration duties. The major reforms enacted by the Socialist government in France are included in the text.
ISBN 0406520860 Pbk

Taxes on capital income in Canada : analysis and policy / Robin W. Boadway, Neil Bruce, Jack M. Mintz. – Toronto : Canadian Tax Foundation, 1987.
xi,176p.
Includes index.
ISBN 088808028X Hbk

Taxes on immovable property : report by the Committee on Fiscal Affairs and the ad hoc Group on Urban Problems. – Organisation for Economic Co-operation and Development. – Paris : O.E.C.D., 1983.
201p.
ISBN 9264124756

Taxing Currency Fluctuations? / J. R. King. – London : Institute for Fiscal Studies.
– (Report Ser.).
Hbk £10.00

Taxing Pensions : The Taxation of Occupational Pension Schemes in the United Kingdom / E. M. Hammond. – London : Institute for Fiscal Studies.
– (Report Ser.).
Hbk £10.00

Taxing unfair international trade practices : a study of U.S. antidumping and countervailing duty laws / Greyson Bryan. – Lexington : Lexington Books, 1981.
xxii,370p; 24cm.
Includes index.
ISBN 0669037524 £20.00

Taxwise Taxation
Workbook No 1 1987-88. – Tolley Publishing.
ISBN 0854592784 Pbk £14.25

Taxwise Taxation Workbook No 2 1987-1988. – Tolley Publishing.
ISBN 0854592792 Pbk £11.25

Tay, Alice Ehr-Soon
Human Rights for Australia : Survey of Literature and Developments, and a Select and Annotated Bibliography of Recent Literatue in Australia and Abroad. – Kingston : Australian Government Publishing Service, 1986.
360p.
ISBN 0644034327 Hbk £6.00
→ Teaching human rights.

Tay, Catherine S K
Contract Law / See Chim Tang. – Singapore : Times Booker International.
140p.
ISBN 9971653761 Pbk £9.50
—Directors' Duties and Liabilities / See Chim Tang. – Singapore : Times Booker International.
160p.
ISBN 9971651688 Pbk £9.90
—Your Rights as a Consumer / See Chim Tang. – Singapore : Times Booker International.
160p.
ISBN 9971652102 Pbk £9.50

Taylor →Copyright, Design and Patents Act 1988.
—Crime, Capitalism and Community. – Toronto : Butterworths, 1983.
168p.
ISBN 0409871923 Pbk £15.95
—Principle and Practice of Medical Jurisprudence / Mant. – 13th ed. – Edinburgh : Churchill Livingstone, 1984.
ISBN 0443014817 Hbk £35.00

Taylor, Ann C. M. →International handbook of universities and other institutions of higher education.

Taylor, Betty W.
Automation in the law school, including law libraries / by Betty W. Taylor and Dan F. Henke. – London : Glanville, 1986.
iv,124p.
Includes bibliographical references and appendices.
ISBN 0878020829

Taylor, D.B.
Guide to Stamp Duties. – Bicester : CCH.
ISBN 0863251153 Pbk £19.50

Taylor, Ernest Miles →Partnership Law.

Taylor, Felicity
Careers in Local Government. – London : Kogan Page, 1981.
96p.
ISBN 0850384370 Hbk £6.95
ISBN 0850384389 Pbk £2.95

Taylor, Frank R.
Corporation Law for Canadian Business. – Butterworths, 1981.
448p.
ISBN 0409988340 Hbk £21.95

Taylor, Ian
Law and order : arguments for socialism / Ian Taylor. – London : Macmillan, 1981.
xxii,234p.
Bibliography: p224-234.

Taylor, J. A. →Bingham's motor claims cases.

Taylor, James →British Columbia Court Forms, 3 vols.
→ British Columbia Court Forms.

Taylor, James P. →British Columbia Court Forms, 3 Vols.
→ British Columbia Practice, 3 vols.

Taylor, John L. →Urban planning practice in developing countries.

Taylor, Laurie →Psychological survival : the experience of long-term imprisonment.

Taylor, M.
Into the 1990's : Voluntary Organisations and Public Sector. – Royal Institute of Public Administration.
ISBN 0900628464 Pbk £3.00

Taylor, M.P.G.
The Joint Operating Agreement : oil and gas law / M.P.G. Taylor, with T.P. Winsor and S.M. Tyne. – 1st ed. – London : Longman Professional (UK), 1989.
Examination of the Joint Operating Agreement, including a full specimen JOA, with key clauses considered in detail. Discusses the legal relationships created by the Agreement, and contains seperate chapters on withdrawal, and abandonment of fields.
ISBN 0851212395 Hbk £50

Taylor, Michael
Community, anarchy and liberty / Michael Taylor. – Cambridge : Cambridge University Press, 1982.
184p; 23cm.
Bibliography: p172-180. - Includes index.
ISBN 0521246210 Hbk £14.00
ISBN 0521270146 Pbk £4.95

Taylor, R.
Guide to the 1985 Companies Act. – London : Longman Professional, 1985.
ISBN 0851210279 Pbk £8.95
—Joint Operating Agreements 1988. – London : Longman Professional.
ISBN 08512112395 Hbk
—Law of Contract (SWOT). – 2nd ed. – London : Blackstone Press.
ISBN 1851850910 Pbk £7.50
—Questions on the Law and Practice of Company Accounting / B. O'Shea. – 4th ed. – Sydney : Butterworths, 1987.
206p.
ISBN 040949206X Pbk

Taylor, R B →Law and Practice of Company Accounting in Australia.

Taylor, Robert
Workers and the new depression / Robert Taylor. – London : Macmillan, 1982.
x,212p; 23cm.
Includes index.
ISBN 0333192958 Hbk
ISBN 0333334116 Pbk

Taylor, S. E. T.
Aviation Law for Pilots / S.E.T. Taylor. – 6th ed. – Oxford : BSP Professional.
ISBN 0632023597 Pbk £9.95
—Aviation Law for Pilots / H. A. Parmar. – 5th ed. – London : Collins, 1986.
172p.
ISBN 0003832732 Pbk £7.95

Teacher in international law : (teachings and teachers) / Manfred Lachs. – The Hague : Nijhoff, 1982.
236p; 25cm.
Bibliography: p211-225. - Includes index.
ISBN 9024725666

Teacher in international law : teachings and teaching / Manfred Lachs. – Rev. 2nd ed. – Dordrecht : M. Nijhoff, 1986.
Includes index. Bibliography.
ISBN 9024733138 Pbk

Teachers and the Law / J. Partington. – 6th ed. – London : Sweet & Maxwell, 1985.
ISBN 0416421709 Hbk £22.50
ISBN 0416395309 Pbk £12.95

Teacher's Guide to Special Needs : A Positive Response to the 1981 Education Act / Raybould. – Open University Press.
ISBN 0335158439 Hbk £16.95
ISBN 0335158420 Pbk £5.95

Teachers' Superannuation Act, 1983, Bill 148 : An Act to Revise the Teachers' Superannuation Act. – Ontario : Ontario Government Publications Service, 1983.
49p.
Hbk £0.70

Teaching about prejudice / by Michael Banton ... et al. : edited by Ben Whitaker. – London : Minority Rights Group, 1983.
24p. – (Report).
Bibliography: p.23-24.
ISBN 0946690006

Teaching and research in international law in Asia and the Pacific : report of a regional consultation meeting including nine country status surveys Seoul, Republic of Korea 10-13 October 1984. – Unesco. – Bangkok : Unesco Regional Office for Education in Asia and the Pacific, 1985.
264p.
Includes bibliographcial references.
ISBN 9231023950 Hbk £60.00

Teaching, enacting and sticking up for human rights : an evaluation report on the Human Rights Commission's 'Teaching for Human Rights: Activities for Schools'. / Colin Henry, David Hitchcock, Michelle Michie. – Canberra : Australian Government Publishing Service, 1985.
viii,83p. – (Occasional paper).
Includes bibliographical references.
ISBN 0644039639

Teaching human rights / edited by Alice Ehr-Soon Tay in collaboration with Graeme Connelly and Roger Wilkins. – Canberra : Australian Government Publishing Service, 1981.
vi,216p.
Bibliography: p.207-208. - Includes index. Papers presented at a seminar held in the University of Sydney Law School, 20-22 June 1980. At head of title: Australian National Commission for UNESCO.
ISBN 0642067627

Teaching Materials and Cases on Commercial Transactions. – 2nd ed. – Butterworths, 1983.
559p.
ISBN 0409493643 Hbk £51.00

Teaching of human rights : proceedings of the conference held by the Human Rights Commission and UNESCO in Adelaide, 25-27 August 1983. – Canberra : Australian Government Publishing Service, 1984.
167p. – (Occasional paper).
Bibliography: p.150-167.
ISBN 0644035714

Teaching, research and training in the field of 'computers and the law' : recommendation no. R (80)3 adopted by the Committee of Ministers of the Council of Europe on 30 April 1980 and explanatory memorandum. – Council of Europe. – Strasbourg : Council of Europe, 1981.
12p.
'Prepared by the Committee of Experts on Legal Data Processing' - verso t.p.. At head of cover title: Council of Europe, Legal Affairs.

Teale, B.
Law Librarian : Bulletin of the British and Irish Association of Law Librarians. – London : Sweet & Maxwell, 1986.
Hbk £13.50

Team Work : Sashatoon's Unified Family Court Project 1978-1981. – Regina : Prairie Justice Research, 1982.
ISBN 0773100385 Hbk £24.00

Tearle, Barbara →Index to legal essays : English language legal essays in festschriften, memorial volumes, conference papers and other collections, 1975-1979.

Technical report / Solicitor General Canada. Programs Branch. – Ottawa : Solicitor General Canada, 1983.

Technique in litigation / Eric Morris. – 3rd ed. – Cape Town : Juta, 1985.
xxxiii, 373 p.; 26 cm.
Includes bibliographical references and index.
ISBN 0702115525 Pbk

Technique of advocacy / by John H. Munkman. – London : Sweet & Maxwell, 1986.
xiv,173p.
Originally published: London: Stevens, 1951. Includes bibliographical references.
ISBN 0421361700

Technique of persuasion / David Napley : with a foreword by Melford Stevenson. – 3rd ed. – London : Sweet & Maxwell, 1983.
xvi,187p; 18cm.
Follows the same pattern as previous editions, but includes a new section on the strategy and tactics of advocacy. Also considers topics such as preparation for trial, the ethics of advocacy, and presentation in court.
ISBN 0421252804 Hbk £14.00
ISBN 0421252901 Pbk £5.85

Technological change, rationalisation and industrial relations / edited by Otto Jacobi ... et al. – London : Croom Helm, 1986.
283p; 23cm.
Includes bibliography and index.
ISBN 0709914482 £19.95

Technology Agreements. – Vancouver : British Columbia Continuing Legal Education Society, 1985.
260p.
ISBN 0865042314 Hbk £65.00

Technology transfer : a case study / Mingsam Santikam. – Singapore : Singapore University Press, 1981.
xiv,270p.
Bibliography: p257-264.

Technology transfer in the Peoples' Republic of China : law and practice / Richard J. Goossen. – Dordrecht : M. Nijhoff, 1987.
Bibliography.
ISBN 9024734428

Technology transfer within the E.E.C. : a summary of papers and discussion of a seminar held in the house of the Royal Society of Arts on Thursday 31 January 1985. – Foundation for Science and Technology. – London : London Science Centre, 1985.
23p.

Teckert, H.E.
You and the Law / M.J. McDonald. – Toronto : Maclean-Hunter.
ISBN 0888960875 Hbk £9.95
ISBN 0770516491 Pbk £6.95

Teco Mines and Oils Limited Act, 1983, Bill Pr052 : An Act to Revive Teco Mines and Oils Limited. – Ontario : Ontario Government Publications Service, 1983.
2p.
Hbk £0.30

Teevan, James T →Crime in Canadian society.

Teh, G. L.
Introduction to Property Law / B. M. Dwyer. – Sydney : Butterworths, 1988.
240p.
This volume, intended for student use, describes concepts of property, tenure and estates, registration, the Torrens system, gifts, leases, covenants, mortgages, and other topics.
ISBN 0409493082 Pbk £29.00
—Residential Tenancies Handbook - Victoria. – Butterworths, 1982.
224p.
ISBN 0409309168 Pbk £39.00

Teichova, Alice →Multinational enterprise in historical perspective.

Telecommunications : pressures and policies for change. – Organisation for Economic Co-operation and Development. – Paris : Organisation for Economic Co-operation and Development, 1983.
142p.
ISBN 9264124284

Telecommunications and the Law. – Freeman (WH).
ISBN 0716781557 Hbk £39.95

Telecommunications development : draft development control policy note / Department of the Environment. – London : Department of the Environment, 1986.
24p.

Telecommunications law and practice. – London : Sweet & Maxwell, 1988.
Examines satellite and cable television, the more technical aspects of licensing and the supply of apparatus and services. Discusses the Telecommunications Act 1984, system licensing, value added and data services licence, competition law, copyright, criminal and contractual liability, and contracting by telecommunications.
ISBN 0421377801 Hbk £29

Teleforum - 1983 : Part III : Legal Aspects of International Telecommunications. – Geneva : International Telecommunications Union.
Hbk £80000

Telephone Legal Information Services : Review and Current Issues. – Ottawa : Canadian Law Information Council, 1982.
37p.
ISBN 0920358993 Pbk £5.00

Telephone tapping and the recording of telecommunications in some Council of Europe member states / Council of Europe Directorate of Legal Affairs. – Strasbourg : Council of Europe, 1982.
12p; 30cm. – (Legislative dossier).
ISBN 9287100551

Television by satellite : legal aspects / edited by Stephen de B. Bate. – Oxford : ESC Publishing, 1987.
vi,146p.
Includes bibliographical references.
ISBN 0906214432

Television without frontiers : green paper on the establishment of the common market for broadcasting, especially by satellite and cable / communication from the Commission to the Council. – Luxembourg : Office for Official Publications of the European Communities, 1984.
xii,367p. – (Documents).
ISBN 9277010045

Telling, A. E.
Planning law and procedure / A.E. Telling. – 7th ed. – London : Butterworth, 1986.
xxxii,351p; 23cm.
Previous ed.: 1982. Includes index.
ISBN 0406665214 Hbk £22.00
ISBN 0406665222 Pbk £14.50

Temblett, R.
Fraud. – London : Sweet & Maxwell, 1988.
ISBN 0421365307 Hbk

Temby, Ian
Age Materials. – Canberra : Australian Government Publishing Service, 1984.
21p.
ISBN 0644035447 Pbk £2.60

Temkin, Jennifer
Rape and the legal process / by Jennifer Temkin. – London : Sweet & Maxwell, 1987.
220p; 23cm.
Includes index.
ISBN 0421338407 Hbk £16.00
ISBN 0421338504 Pbk £10.00

Tempest, Paul →International energy markets.
→ International energy options : an agenda for the 1980s : selected papers from leading contributors to the 1980 Annual Conference of the International Association of Energy Economists in Cambridge, UK.

Temple-Lang, John
Draft Treaty establishing the European Union and the member states : Ireland / by John Temple-Lang. – Florence : European University Institute, 1985.
38,5p.

Temple Lectures →Evidence & advocacy.

Templeman, F.
Templeman on marine insurance : its principles and practice / R. J. Lambeth. – 6th ed. – London : Pitman, 1986.
608p.
Previous ed.: 1981. Includes index. Previous control number ISBN 0-7121-0654-5.
ISBN 0273025376 Hbk £50.00

Templeman on marine insurance : its principles and practice / R. J. Lambeth. – 6th ed. – London : Pitman, 1986.
608p.
Previous ed.: 1981. Includes index. Previous control number ISBN 0-7121-0654-5.
ISBN 0273025376 Hbk £50.00

Templeman, Sydney William Templeman
Appellate mosaic : being the presidential address of the Rt. Hon. Lord Templeman, president of the Holdsworth Club of the Faculty of Law in the University of Birmingham 1938-84. – Birmingham : The Holdsworth Club of the University of Birmingham, 1984.
18p; 22cm. – (The Holdsworth Club).
ISBN 0704407132

Ten, C. L.
Crime, guilt, and punishment : a philosophical introduction / C.L. Ten. – Oxford : Clarendon, 1987.
176p; 22cm.
Includes bibliography and index.
ISBN 019875082X Hbk £19.50
ISBN 0198750811 Pbk £8.95

Tenancy Law and Practice Victoria / Chernov. – 2nd ed. – London : Butterworths.
ISBN 0409356115 Hbk £32.10

Tench, David
Towards a middle system of law / David Tench. – London : Consumers' Association, 1981.
73p.
ISBN 085202214X

Tendron, G.
Problems encountered by local and regional authorites as a result of their new tasks in respect of environmental protection / report prepared under the guidance of the Committee of Experts on Social and Economic Activities of the Steering Committee for Regional and Municpal Matters by G. Tendron. – Strasbourg : Council of Europe, 1986.
29p.
Bibliography: p.28-29.

Tennison, Patrick
Family Court : the Legal Jungle. – Ashburton : Patrick Tennison Enterprises.
Pbk £8.95

Tentative proposals for a compulsory mental health care act / Law Reform Commission of Saskatchewan. – Saskatoon : Law Reform Commission of Saskatchewan, 1981.
46,xlixp.

Tentative proposals for a Frustrated Contracts Act / Law Reform Commission of Saskatchewan. – Saskatoon : The Commission, 1987.
55p.
Includes text of proposed Act.

Tentative proposals for a human artificial insemination act / Law Reform Commission of Saskatchewan. – 1. – Saskatoon : Law Reform Commission of Saskatchewan, 1981.
various pagings.
Includes bibliographical references.

Tentative proposals for a Lieutenant Governor's Review Board in Saskatchewan / Law Reform Commission of Saskatchewan. – Saskatoon : The Commission, 1984.
28p.
Includes text of proposed Act.

Tentative proposals for an Enforcement of Maintenance Orders Act / Law Reform Commission of Saskatchewan. – Saskatoon : The Commission, 1982.
100,xiiip.

Tentative proposals for an equality of status of married persons act / Law Reform Commission of Saskatchewan. – Saskatoon : Law Reform Commission of Saskatchewan, 1981.
68p.
Includes bibliographical references.

Tentative proposals for changes in limitations legislation
Part 1 : The effect of limitations on title to real property / Law Reform Commission of Saskatchewan. – Saskatoon : Law Reform Commission of Saskatchewan, 1981.
27p.
Part 2 : The Limitation of Actions Act / Law Reform Commission of Saskatchewan. – 1986.
149p.

Tentative proposals for compensation of accused on acquittal / Law Reform Commission of Saskatchewan. – Saskatoon : The Commission, 1987.
38p.
Includes bibliographical references. Includes text of proposed Act.

Tentative proposals for reform of the Matrimonial Property Act / Law Reform Commission of Saskatchewan. – Saskatoon : The Commission, 1984.
167p.
Includes bibliographical references.

Tentative proposals relating to testamentary custody and guardianship of children / Law Reform Commission of Saskatchewan. – Saskatoon : The Commission, 1984.
58p.
Includes texts of proposed Acts.

Tenth report : tackling pollution : experience and prospects / Royal Commission on Environmental Pollution : Chairman: Sir Richard Southwood. – London : H.M.S.O., 1984.
ISBN 0101914903

Tenth report to Parliament on subordinate legislation concerning the issues of Premier's certificates / Legal and Constitutional Committee. – Melbourne : Government Printer, 1987.
v,12p.

Teo, Keang Sood
Land Law in Malaysia : Cases and Commentary / Lake Tee Khaw. – 1987. – Butterworths.
539p.
Covers the Malaysian Torrens system, rights and powers of the State authority, the nature and extent of private ownership, the registration of dealings, transfers, leases and tenancies, security transactions, restraints of dealings, planning law use under the national code, and powers of the court.
ISBN 0409995312 Hbk £130.00
—Strata Titles in Malaysia : Law and Practice. – Butterworths, 1987.
164p.
Deals with the current law and practice relating to the strata title system in Penninsular Malaysia, Sarawak, and Sabah. Covers the basic features of the Malaysian strata title system, and the rules governing the management corporation and its members, and third parties such as chargees, occupiers and insurers.
ISBN 040999538X Hbk £65.00

Ter Kah Leng
Law of charities - cases & materials : Singapore & Malaysia / Ter Kah Leng. – Singapore : Butterworths, 1985.
xxvii,353p; 23cm.
Covers trusts for the relief of property, trusts for the advancement of education, religion, and other purposes beneficial to the community, 'Sin Chew' (ancestor worship) and ceremonies in memory of souls, and trusts for graves, memorials, and burial grounds.
ISBN 0409995037 Hbk

Termination and Dismissal. – Vancouver : British Columbia Continuing Legal Education Society, 1985.
65p.
ISBN 0865042098 Hbk £50.00

Termination of Employment. – London : Longman Professional.
ISBN 0851214444 Pbk £10.95

Termination of Employment. – 2nd ed. – North Ryde : C.C.H. Australia, 1984.
192p.
ISBN 0869037390 Hbk £23.00

Termination of employment / Robert Upex. – 2nd ed. – London : Sweet & Maxwell, 1986.
xlii,148p; 26cm.
Examines entitlement to the various remedies, defines the status of employment and 'marginal employment', and looks at statutory rights with regard to redundancy and unfair dismissal. Contains examples of the calculation of compensation for redundancy and unfair dismissal, and looks at taxation of damages, and mitigation.
ISBN 0421347708 £16.50

Termination of treaties in international law : the doctrines of Rebus Sic Stantibus and Desuetude / Athanassios Vamvoukos. – Oxford : Clarendon, 1985.
xxiii,325p; 22cm.
Bibliography: p304-315. - Includes index.
ISBN 0198761791 £35.00

Terminology of business and company law / Bailey. – London : Kogan Page, 1987.
ISBN 0850914133 Pbk £8.95

Terrell on the law of patents / William Aldous. – 13th ed. – London : Sweet & Maxwell, 1984.
lxi,1157p; 26cm.
The text and rules of the 1977 Patents Act are reproduced, and their effect is examined. Provisions of the 1949 Act which are still in force are also discussed. Contains an appraisal of the European Patent Convention.
ISBN 0421249005

Terrell, Thomas
Terrell on the law of patents / William Aldous. – 13th ed. – London : Sweet & Maxwell, 1984.
lxi,1157p; 26cm.
The text and rules of the 1977 Patents Act are reproduced, and their effect is examined. Provisions of the 1949 Act which are still in force are also discussed. Contains an appraisal of the European Patent Convention.
ISBN 0421249005

Terrible Truth About Lawyers. – New Edition. – London : Fontana.
ISBN 0006372694 Pbk £3.95

Terrorism and the liberal state. – 2nd ed. – London : Macmillan, 1986.
ISBN 0333394917 Pbk £7.95

Test cases for the poor : legal techniques in the politics of social welfare / Tony Prosser. – London : Child Poverty Action Group, 1983.
v,102p.
ISBN 090396371X

Test Yourself on the 1987 Highway Code. – London : Shaw & Sons, 1987.
ISBN 0721906923 Pbk £1.75

Testamentary guardianship in the Australian Capital Territory / Human Rights Commission. – Canberra : Australian Government Publishing Service, 1983.
vii,10p. – (Report).
ISBN 0644024593

Testamentary intent and unexpected circumstances / Law Reform Commission of British Columbia. – Vancover : The Commission, 1987.
iv,77p. – (Working paper).
Includes bibliographical references.
ISBN 0771886047

Testing the Spirit of Canada's Access to Information Act, 2 Vols. – Ottawa : Ken Rubin, 1984.
Hbk £30.00

Tetley, William
Marine Cargo Claims. – 3rd ed. – Montreal : International Shipping Publications, 1988.
1,448p.
Hbk £125.00
—Maritime liens and claims / William Tetley with assistance from Brian G. McDonough. – London : Business Law Communications, 1985.
lxiv,686p.
Includes bibliographical references and index.
ISBN 0948406003

Tettenborn, A. M.
Introduction to the law of obligations / A.M. Tettenborn. – London : Butterworths, 1984.
xxv,238p; 23cm.
Includes index.
ISBN 0406260672 Hbk £19.50
ISBN 0406260680 Pbk £13.95

Teubner, Gunther
After legal instrumentalism? : strategic models of post- regulatory law / by Gunther Teubner. – Florence : European University Institute, 1984.
58p.
Bibliography: p.52-58. At head of title: European University Institute, Florence, Law Department.
→ Autopoietic law : a new approach to law and society.
→ Contract and organization : legal analysis in the light of economic and social theory.
—Corporate responsibility as a problem of company constitution / by Gunther Teubner. – Florence : European University Institute, 1983.
47p.
At head of title page: European University Institute, Florence, Law Department.
→ Dilemmas of law in the welfare state.
—Enterprise corporatism : new industrial policy and the essence of the legal person / by Gunther Teubner. – Florence : European University Institute, 1987.
47p.
→ Juridification of social spheres : a comparative analysis in the areas of labor, corporate, antitrust, and social welfare law.
—Substantive and reflexive elements in modern law / by Gunther Teubner. – Florence : European University Institute, 1982.
94p.
—Verrechtlichung : Begriffe, Merkmale, Grenzen, Auswege / by Gunther Teubner. – Florence : European University Institute, 1984.
104p.
At head of title: European University Institute, Florence, Law Department.

Tew, Brian
Evolution of the international monetary system, 1945-85 / Brian Tew. – 3rd ed. – London : Hutchinson, 1985.
256p; 22cm.
Previous ed.: 1982. Includes bibliography and index.
ISBN 0091615615 Pbk £7.95

Teweles
Futures Game / Jones. – 2nd ed. – Maidenhead : McGraw-Hill, 1986.
ISBN 0070637288 Hbk £39.95

Text, Commentary and Cases on Trusts / E.E. Gillese. – 3rd ed. – Agincourt : Carswell, 1987.
1,046p.
ISBN 0459397400 Pbk £22.00

Textbook for Legal Studies - Tasmania. – Butterworths, 1983.
322p.
ISBN 0409491209 Hbk £23.00

Textbook of Banking : Law Practice and Theory of Banking / S.V. Vasudevan. – 3rd ed. – New Delhi : S. Chand and Company, 1984.
xv, 834p.
Hbk £42.00

Textbook of commerce / J W Loveridge. – 3rd ed. – London : Butterworths, 1981.

Students
ISBN 0408709286 Pbk £6.95

Textbook of criminal law / by Glanville Williams. – 2nd ed. – London : Stevens, 1983.
xlvii,1007p; 24cm.
Previous ed.: 1978. Includes index.
ISBN 0420468501 Hbk £
ISBN 0420468609 Pbk £19

Textbook of English Legal History. – 2nd ed. – Lucknow : Eastern Book Company, 1983.
296p.
Pbk £12.00

Textbook of Industrial Law / K.C. Garg. – 5th ed. – New Delhi : Kalyani Publishers, 1986.
Hbk £25.00

Textbook of insurance broking. – 2nd ed. – Cambridge : Woodhead-Faulkner, 1987.
ISBN 0859413861 Hbk £25.00

Textbook on Contract. – London : Financial Training.
ISBN 1851850767 Hbk £14.95

Textbook on Criminology / Ryan. – London : Blackstone Press.
ISBN 1854310127 Hbk £9.95

Textbook on EEC Law. – London : Blackstone Press.
ISBN 1854310003 Pbk £15.00

Textbook on Muslim personal law / David Pearl. – 2nd ed. – London : Croom Helm, 1987.
284p; 23cm.
ISBN 0709940890 Pbk £14.95

Textbook on torts. – London : Financial Training, 1986.
ISBN 1851850260 Pbk £13.95

Texts adopted / Conference of Local and Regional Authorities of Europe : Conference Permanente des Pouvoirs Locaux et Regionaux de l'Europe. – Strasbourg : Council of Europe, 1976-.
Continues: Texts adopted / European Conference of Local Authorities. - Continued by : Texts adopted / Standing Conference of Local and Regional Authorities of Europe. Parallel English and French texts.

Texts adopted / Standing Conference of Local and Regional Authorities of Europe : Conference Permanente des Pouvoirs Locaux et Regionaux de l'Europe. – Strasbourg : Council of Europe, 1984.
Continues: Texts adopted / Conference of Local and Regional Authorities of Europe. Parallel English and French texts.

Texts adopted for transmission to national parliaments / Assembly of Western European Union. – Paris : The Assembly, 1955.
From 22nd session, entitled: Texts adopted and brief account of the session. Some parts in French.

Texts established by the Luxembourg Conference on the Community Patent, 1985. – Luxembourg : Office for Official Publications of the European Communities, 1986.
214p.
ISBN 9282403122

Thakur, K.
Outer Space and Military Supremacy : Jurisdiction in International Law. – New Delhi : Deep and Deep Publications, 1985.
180p.
Hbk £100.00

Thames Polytechnic →Fiduciary duties of directors : a review.

Thames Television Limited : a report by the Director General of Fair Trading on an investigation under section 3 of the Competition Act 1980 / Office of Fair Trading. – London : Office of Fair Trading, 1984.
87p; 30cm.

That noble science of politics : a study in nineteenth-century intellectual history / Stefan Collini, Donald Winch, John Burrow. – Cambridge : Cambridge University Press, 1983.
x,385p; 24cm.
Includes index.
ISBN 052125762X Hbk £25.00
ISBN 0521277701 Pbk £9.95

Theatre nurse and the law / Eileen Dixon. – London : Croom Helm, 1984.
141p; 22cm.
Includes index.
ISBN 0709908180 Pbk £8.95

Thee, Marek →Frontiers of Human Rights Education.

Theft Act 1978 / Janet M. Dine. – London : Financial Training, 1985.
xvii,223p.
Includes the text of the Theft Acts, 1968 and 1978.
ISBN 0906322804

Theft Acts 1968 and 1978 / by Edward Griew. – 4th ed. – London : Sweet & Maxwell, 1982.
xxix,240p; 25cm.
Previous ed.: 1978. Includes index. Includes the texts of The Theft Act 1968 and The Theft Act 1978.
ISBN 0421286407 Hbk £
ISBN 0421286504 Pbk £9.50

Theft Acts 1968 and 1978 / by Edward Griew. – 5th ed. – London : Sweet & Maxwell, 1986.
xxxiii,269p; 26cm.
For the first time, this edition covers the following major cases; Ghosh, on dishonesty; Morris, on appropriation; Bloxham, on handling; and Wilson, on alternative verdicts. Includes other decisions on theft, taking a conveyance, obtaining property by deception, and the 1978 Act.
ISBN 0421353007 Hbk £21.00
ISBN 0421353104 Pbk £13.95

Then and Now : 1799-1974. – Sweet & Maxwell, 1974.
ISBN 042104907 Hbk £19.50

Theobald, Henry Studdy
Law of wills
Supplement 1984 / J.B. Clark. – 4th ed. – Sweet & Maxwell.
ISBN 0420452508 Hbk £120.00
—Theobald on wills / J. B. Clark. – London : Stevens, 1982.
cxcviii,842p; 26cm.
Previous ed.: 1971. Bibliography: pcxcvii-cxcviii. - Includes index. Latest supplement held: 1st, 1983.
ISBN 0420452508 £78.00

Theobald on wills / J. B. Clark. – London : Stevens, 1982.
cxcviii,842p; 26cm.
Previous ed.: 1971. Bibliography: pcxcvii-cxcviii. - Includes index. Latest supplement held: 1st, 1983.
ISBN 0420452508 £78.00

Theoretical criminology / Bernard. – 3rd ed. – Oxford : Oxford University Press, 1986.
ISBN 0195036166 Hbk £17.50

Theories of evidence : Bentham and Wigmore / William Twining. – London : Weidenfeld & Nicolson, 1985.
x,265p.
Includes bibliographical references and index.
ISBN 0297786687 Hbk £17.95
ISBN 0297786695 Pbk £8.95

Theories of rights / edited by Jeremy Waldron. – Oxford : Oxford University Press, 1984.
209p; 21cm. – (Oxford reading in philosophy).
Bibliography: p202-205. - Includes index.
ISBN 0198750633 Pbk £4.95

Theories of trade unionism : a sociology of industrial relations / Michael Poole. – London : Routledge and Kegan Paul, 1981.
xi,265p; 23cm.
Bibliography: p221-242. - Includes index.
ISBN 0710006950 £12.50

Theory and History of Ocean Boundary Making. – Witney : Academic & University Publishing Group.
ISBN 0773506241 Hbk £37.95

Theory and History of Ocean Boundary-Making. – Montreal : McGill-Queen's University Press, 1988.
ISBN 0773506241 Hbk £39.95

Theory and practice of human rights. – Smith (Maurice Temple), 1985.
ISBN 0851172563 Hbk £12.95

Theory and practice of international law in Nigeria / by C. Nwachukwu Okeke. – Enugu, Nigeria : Fourth Dimension Publishers, 1986.
xx, 316p.
Bibliography: p.293-309. - Includes index.
ISBN 9781562420

Theory and Practice of Private International Law. – Repr. of 1892 ed. – Aalen Wuertt : Scientia.
xlvi, 1162p.
Hbk £265.00

Theory and practice of the European convention on human rights / P. van Dijk, G.J.H. van Hoof. – Deventer : Kluwer Law and Taxation, 1984.
xiii,512p; 25cm.
Bibliography: p489-493. - Includes index. Translated from Dutch.
ISBN 9065440798 Pbk

Theory and Practice of Valuation. – 2nd ed. – Calcutta : Eastern Law House, 1986.
Hbk £138.00

Theory of legal science : proceedings of the Conference on Legal Theory and Philosophy of Science, Lund, Sweden, December 11-14, 1983 / edited by Aleksander Peczenik, Lars Lindahl, and Bert van Roermund. – Dordrecht : Reidel, 1984.
xv, 666 p.; 23 cm.
Includes bibliographies and index.
ISBN 9027718342

Theory of Legislation / R. Hildreth. – Repr. of 1864 ed. – Abingdon : Professional Books.
Hbk £85.00

Theory of local argumentation : the theory of rational discourse as a theory of legal justification. – Oxford : OUP, 1989.
320.
An attempt to define 'rational legal argument' and to justify the demand for rationality in legal affairs.
ISBN 0198255039 Hbk £30.00

Thesaurus of provincial statutory terminology / compiled and edited by Mary K. McLean, with assistance from Lorna K. Rees-Potter. – 1st ed. – Ottawa : Canadian Law Information Council, 1986.
ix, 179 p.; 28 cm.
ISBN 0920358896 £40.00

Theunis, Jan Th. F. → Arrest of ships 2.
→ International carriage of goods by road (CMR).

Theunissen, Andrew
Guide to Successful Debt Collecting. – 1st ed. – Bristol : Jordan & Sons Ltd, 1982.
Pbk £4.00

Theutenberg, Bo Johnson
Evolution of the law of the sea : a study of resources and strategy with special regard to the polar regions / Bo Johnson Theutenberg. – Dublin : Tycooly International, 1984.
viii,261p; 25cm.
Bibliography: p97-111. Includes full text of United Nations Convention on the Law of the Sea. Spine title : The law of the sea.
ISBN 0863460410 Hbk
ISBN 0863460429 Pbk
—United Nations Convention on the Law of the Sea / Bo Johnson Theutenberg. – Dublin : Tycooly International, 1984.
viii,261p; 25cm.
Bibliography: p97-111. Includes full text of United Nations Convention on the Law of the Sea. Spine title : The law of the sea.
ISBN 0863460410 Hbk
ISBN 0863460429 Pbk

Third and Fourth Parts of the Institutes of the Lawes of England : Concerning High Treason and Other Pleas of the Crown and Criminal Causes. – Repr. of 1644 ed. – Abingdon : Professional Books.
360p.
Hbk £1900.00

Third generation world organization. – Dordrecht : Nijhoff (Martinus), 1989.
232.
Describes why the search for peace through international organisations has always failed. Proposes a theory of peace and its relationship with the mode of production. Shows that the present United Nations System, including the Bretton Woods organizations, is not equipped for the needs of the modern world.
ISBN 0792303822 Hbk £40

Third party protection of software and firmware : direct protection of zeros and ones / John J. Borking. – Amsterdam : North-Holland, 1985.
xx,521p; 24cm.
Bibliography: p491-510. - Includes index.
ISBN 0444876774 £48.78

Third report from the Defence Committee : the D notice system : House of Commons paper 773 session 1979-80 : observations presented by the Secretary of State for Defence. – London : H.M.S.O., 1981.
2p; 25cm.
Bound with: Third report from the Defence Committee.
ISBN 0101812906

Third report from the Home Affairs Committee, session 1980-81 : vagrancy offences : together with proceedings of the Committee, the minutes of evidence and appendices. – London : H.M.S.O., 1981.
xxiv,70p; 25cm. – (HC).
Bound with: The Government's reply.
ISBN 010227181X

Third report from the Home Affairs Committee, session 1986-87 : state and use of prisons. – 2 pt. – London : H.M.S.O., 1987.
30cm. – (H.C.).

Third report on the legal profession : advertising and specialisation / New South Wales Law Reform Commission. – Sydney : The Commission, 1982.
155p. – (L.R.C. 33).

Third report to Parliament on subordinate legislation concerning Adoption (Inter County Adoption Fees) Regulations 1986 ... / Legal and Constitutional Committee. – Melbourne : Government Printer, 1986.
v,8p.

Third report to Parliament on the operation of section 32 of the Interpretation of Legislation Act 1984 concerning Dental Technicians (Members Fees) (Amendment) Regulations 1986 (S.R. No. 180/1986) / Legal and Constitutional Committee. – Melbourne : Government Printer, 1987.
v,6p.

Third special report from the Social Services Committee, session 1985-86 : reform of social security : observations by the government on the first report from the Committee, session 1985-86. – London : H.M.S.O., 1986.
vii p. – (H.C. 1985-86).
ISBN 0102484864

Third special report from the Transport Committee, session 1985-86 : government response to the fourth report of the Committee, session 1985-86 : togerther with the proceedings of the Committee. – London : H.M.S.O., 1986.
xviii p. – (H.C. 1985-86).
ISBN 0102602867

Third United Nations Conference on the Law of the Sea
Vol. 15. – United Nations. – London : HMSO, 1984.
243p.
Official records of the conference and a list of documents issued during the tenth session.
ISBN 0119080710 Pbk £20.70

Third World Attitudes Toward International Law : an Introduction / S. Sathirathai. – Dordrecht : Kluwer, 1987.
852p.
ISBN 0898389143 Hbk £375.00

Third World city / David Drakakis-Smith. – London : Methuen, 1987.
vi,116p; 21cm. – (Methuen introductions to development).
Includes bibliography and index.
ISBN 041691960X Pbk £
ISBN 0416919707 correct

Thirlway, H.
Non-appearance before the International Court Justice. – Cambridge : Cambridge University Press, 1985.
ISBN 0521265940 Hbk £27.50

Thirsk, Wayne R. → Tax policy options in the 1980s.

Thirteenth report to Parliament on subordinate legislation concerning : Police Gaols Regulations 1988 (SR No. 292/1988) / Legal and Constitutional Committee. – Melbourne : Government Printer, 1988.
vii,24p.
Includes the texts of the Regulations.

Thirty years of Community law / Commission of the European Communities. – Luxembourg : Office for Official Publications of the European Communities, 1981.
xxiv,498p.
ISBN 9282526526 Pbk £8.50

Thirty-Second Legal Aid Annual Report of the Law Society and of the Lord Chancellor's Advisory Committee 1981-82. – London : HMSO, 1983.
ISBN 0102189838 Hbk £9.25

Thom → Company Secretarial Practice, 1984 Supplement.

Thomas → Mortgages and Securities.
—Motoring Law A-Z. – Ibadan : African Universities Press.
Hbk £2.95

Thomas, Brook
Cross-examination of law and literature. – Cambridge : Cambridge University Press, 1987.
312.
Studies the effect of the American legal system on the formation of American consciouess. Describes the relationship between law and literature in the nineteenth century.
ISBN 0521330815 Hbk £27.50

Thomas, C. D.
Company Law for Accountants. – London : Butterworths, 1985.
This text is a straightforward presentation of the company law of the United Kingdom for students of accounting.
ISBN 0406009600 Pbk £11.95

Thomas, Charles H.
Index to Reports of Tax Cases : 1875-1981, 52 Vols. – Abingdon : Professional Books, 1984.
ISBN 0862050707 Hbk £63.00
—Legal lexicon of taxation / Charles H. Thomas. – Abingdon, Oxon : Professional Books, 1987.
139p; 23cm.
ISBN 0862050367

Thomas, D.
Criminal Appeal Reports (Sentencing). – London : Sweet & Maxwell.
Hbk £52.00

Thomas, David A
Current sentencing practice / David Thomas. – 1. – London : Sweet & Maxwell, 1982.
25cm.
Includes index.
ISBN 0421257407 Llf £120

Thomas, Eric-Jean → Immigrant workers in Europe : their legal status : a comparative study.

Thomas, Franklin
Liberty of the citizen / Franklin Thomas, John Mortimer, Lord Hunt of Tanworth. – London : Granada, 1983.
93p.
ISBN 0246121157

Thomas, Geraint W.
Taxation and trusts / by Geraint W. Thomas. – London : Sweet & Maxwell, 1981.
xxiv,205p; 19cm.
Includes index.
ISBN 0421277203 Hbk
ISBN 0421277300 Pbk £6.95

Thomas, J. A. C. → Casebook on contract.
→ Smith and Thomas : a casebook on contract.
→ Studies in Justinian's Institutes in memory of J.A.C. Thomas.

Thomas, J.E.
House of Care : Prisons and Prisoners in England 1500-1800. – Nottingham : Department of Adult Education, University of Nottingham.
ISBN 1850410216 Hbk £18.50

Thomas, John M. → Enforcing Regulation.

Thomas McLintock
Expatriate Tax Manual. – London : Butterworths, 1985.
ISBN 0406259968 Pbk £15.00

Thomas, N.
Professional indemnity claims. – London : Architectural Press, 1984.
ISBN 0851397484 Hbk £14.50

Thomas, Ph. J
Introduction to Roman law / by Ph. J. Thomas. – Deventer Netherlands : Kluwer Law and Taxation Publishers, 1986.
xv, 168 p.; 25 cm.
Bibliography: p. 168.
ISBN 9065442456 Pbk

Thomas, Philip A. → How to use a law library.
→ Law in the balance : legal services in the 1980s.

Thomas, R. L. → Netherlands Securities Trading Act and Securities Trading Decree : with supplementary regulations and official commentary.

Thomas, Richard
Plain words for consumers : the language and layout of consumer contracts : the case for a plain language law / Liz Dunbar. – London : National Consumer Council, 1984.
78p.
'Written by Richard Thomas with considerable help from Liz Dunbar'.
ISBN 090565370X

Thomas, Robert Wilson → Industrial property citator.

Thomas, Roderick → Trade union law and the pursuit of prosperity - the next step : submission to the Secretary of State for Employment in response to the green paper on trade union immunities.

Thomas, Roger → Pinson on revenue law : comprising income tax; capital gains tax; development land tax; corporation tax; inheritance tax; value added tax; stamp duties; tax planning.

Thomas, S.
Family Finance. – Cambridge : Woodhead-Faulkner, 1987.
ISBN 0859414205 Pbk £4.95

Thomas, William → Bean and Lockwood's Rating valuation practice.

Thommen, T. Kochu
Bills of Lading in International Law and Practice. – Lucknow : Eastern Book Company, 1985.
Hbk £80.00

Thompson → UNCITRAL Arbitration Model in Canada.

Thompson, A.R.
Environmental Regulation in Canada : an Assessment of the Regulatory Process. – Vancouver : University of British Columbia, Westwater Research Center, 1981.
134p.
ISBN 0920146090 Pbk £6.95

Thompson, Andrew R. → Canadian Oil and Gas, 9 Vols.

Thompson, B. A.
Professional Driver's Guide : A Reference Handbook. – 8th rev. ed. – New Malden : Croner Publications, 1986.
ISBN 0900319453 Hbk £6.00

Thompson, D. → Privatising London's Airports.

Thompson, E. P.
Human Rights and Disarmament / Vaclav Racek. – London : Spokesman Books, 1983.
60p.
Pbk individual 4.00

Thompson, Fred → Regulatory Reform in Canada.

Thompson, Ian → Case through the courts : Ford v. Warwickshire.
→ Land law & landscape.

Thompson, M. P.
Co-ownership / M.P. Thompson. – London : Sweet & Maxwell, 1988.
xxv,151p.
Analyses forms of co-ownership of freehold and leasehold interests in real property, and such items of personal property as joint bank accounts. Explores the legal principles involved, and applies them to practical problems. Co-habitation, financial contribution, marriage, divorce, death and insolvency are also discussed.
ISBN 0421375000 £19.50

Thompson, Ruth
Aboriginal Title and Mining Legislation in the Northwest Territories. – Saskatoon : University of Saskatchewan, Native Law Centre, 1982.
32p.
ISBN 0888801149 Hbk £8.00
→ Rights of Indigenous Peoples in International Law : an Annotated Bibliography.
—Rights of Indigenous Peoples in International Law : Selected Essays on Self-Determination. – Saskatoon : University of Saskatchewan, Native Law Centre, 1987.
68p.
ISBN 0888801858 Hbk £15.00
—Rights of Indigenous Peoples in International Law : Workshop Report. – Saskatoon : University of Saskatchewan, Native Law Centre, 1986.
66p.
ISBN 0888801696 Hbk £15.00

Thomsett, M.C.
Complete Guide to Selling Your Home. – Merehurst.
ISBN 01556231237 Hbk £14.95

Thomson, George M. → Canadian children's law : cases, notes and materials.

Thomson, J
Law Reform (Miscellaneous Provisions) (Scotland) Act 1985. – Edinburgh : Green (W.) & Son, 1986.
Annotated text of the Act from Scottish Current Law Statutes.
ISBN 0414007883 Pbk

Thomson, J. M.
Family law in Scotland / J.M. Thomson. – London : Butterworths, 1987.
xxiv,232p; 22cm.
Includes index.
ISBN 0406261903 Pbk £20

Thoolen, Hans
Human rights missions : a study of the fact-finding practice of non-governmental organizations / Hans Thoolen and Berth Verstappen. – Dordrecht : M. Nijhoff, 1986.
ISBN 9024733642 Pbk
→ Indonesia and the rule of law: twenty years of 'New Order' government.

Thorn, Gaston
European union or decline : to be or not to be / by Gaston Thorn. – Luxembourg : Office for Official Publications of the European Communities, 1984.
23p; 23cm.
Seventh Jean Monnet lecture delivered at the European University Institute, Florence, 24 May 1984.
→ Working for Europe : January 1981 - January 1985.

Thornberry, Patrick
Minorities and human rights law / Patrick Thornberry. – London : Minority Rights Group, 1987.
19p. – (Report).
Bibliography: p19.
ISBN 0946690480

Thornhill, Andrew
Passing down the family business: solving the tax problems. – 4th. – London : Longman Professional (UK), 1988.
– (Longman Intelligence Report).
Information and advice on reducing the tax burden and maximising the prosperity of the business when transferring control to another member of the family. Outlines tax planning strategies, and how to use tax reliefs to their full advantage.
ISBN 0851212719 Hbk £95.00
—Passing Down the Family Farm / Robert Venables. – London : Oyez Longman, 1983.
– (Oyez Longman Intelligence Report Ser.).
ISBN 0851207367 Hbk £45.00

Thornhill, Andrew R → Inheritance tax planning.
—Potter and Monroe's Tax Planning with Precedents / K Prosser. – 11th ed. – Sweet & Maxwell.
ISBN 00421396008 Hbk
→ Revival of the Discretionary Trust : 1983.

Thornhill, R.J.
Intermediate Accounting Step by Step. – London : Edward Arnold.
ISBN 0713176660 Pbk £7.50

Thorniley, Daniel → Economics and sociology of rural communities : East-West perspectives.

Thornley, Judy
List of constitutional and Privy Council judgments affecting the Isle of Man from 1523 to 1986 and a complete year by year list of written Reasons for Judgment of Her Majesty's High Court of Justice of the Isle of Man and other Manx courts from 1884 to 1986 / compiled and with an introduction by Judy Thornley on the directions of H.M. Attorney General for the Isle of Man. – Douglas : Government Printer, 1987.
94p.
Cover title: A book of precedents.

Thornton
Goods Operator Licensing / Airey. – London : Kogan Page, 1988.
ISBN 1850914796 Hbk

Thornton, C. E. I.
Building society law : cases and materials / C.E.I. Thornton and J.P. McBrien. – 3rd ed. – London : Sweet & Maxwell, 1988.
xxi,202p; 22cm.
Previous ed.: 1975. Includes index.
ISBN 0421383704 Pbk £9.95

Thornton, David → Tougher regimes in detention centres : report of an evaluation by the Young Offender Psychology Unit.

Thornton, G. C.
Legislative drafting / G.C. Thornton. – 3rd ed. – London : Butterworth, 1987.
396p; 24cm.
Previous ed.: 1979. Includes index.
ISBN 0406399824 £38.00

Thornton, Peter
Public Order Act : Elizabeth II, 1986. Chapter 64 / Peter Thornton. – London : Financial Training Publications, 1987.
xxi, 226p.
Bibliography: p.219-220. Includes the text of the Public Order Act 1986.
ISBN 1851850406
—We protest : the public order debate / Peter Thornton. – London : National Council for Civil Liberties, 1985.
96p; 20cm.
ISBN 0946088217 Pbk £2.95

Thorpe → Commercial law in New Zealand.
→ Payment Systems and Productivity.

Thorpe, G. C.
Floating charges, crystallisation and after-acquired property / by G.C. Thorpe. – Auckland : Legal Research Foundation, 1981.
49p.
ISBN 0908581130

Thou shalt not be aware : society's betrayal of the child / by Alice Miller : translated from the German by Hildegard and Hunter Hannum. – London : Pluto, 1985.
viii, 331p.
Originally published: Frankfurt am Main: Surkamp Verlag, 1981. Bibliography: p.327-331. Translation of: Du sollst nicht merken.
ISBN 0745300499

Thought of John Austin : jurisprudence, colonial reform and the British constitution / Wilfrid E. Rumble. – London : Athlone, 1985.
278p.
Includes bibliography and index.
ISBN 0485112922 £20.00

Three Essays on the Theory of Legal Norms. – 1986. – Helsinki : Suomalainen Tiedeakatemia.
54p.
Hbk £46.00

Three international conventions on hijacking and offences on board aircraft : (i) Convention on Offences and Certain Other Acts Committed on Board Aircraft ... 1963. (ii) Convention for Suppression of Unlawful Seizure of Aircraft ... 1970. (iii) Convention for the Suppression of Unlawful Acts Against the Safety of Civil Aviation ... 1971 : explanation documentation prepared for Commonwealth jurisdictions by David Lloyd Jones in association with the Commonwealth Secretariat / David Lloyd Jones. – London : Commonwealth Secretariat, 1982.
vi,146p; 30cm.
ISBN 0850922151

Three law tracts. – Reprint. – Abingdon : Professional Books, 1986.
– (Classical English Law Texts Ser.).
ISBN 0862053129 Hbk £32.75

Three Lectures. – Lucknow : Eastern Book Company, 1983.
75p.
Hbk £35.00

Thurow, S.B.
Constitutionalism in America
Vol. 1. – London : Eurospan.
ISBN 0819167762 Hbk £25.95

Thurston, Gavin
Thurston's coronership : the law and practice on coroners / Paul Knapman, Michael J. Powers. – 3rd ed. – Chichester : Barry Rose, 1985.
xxiv,544p.
Includes index. Includes legislation.
ISBN 085992355X Hbk £85

Thurston's coronership : the law and practice on coroners / Paul Knapman, Michael J. Powers. – 3rd ed. – Chichester : Barry Rose, 1985.
xxiv,544p.
Includes index. Includes legislation.
ISBN 085992355X Hbk £85

TI Raleigh Industries Limited and Raleigh Limited : a report by the Director General of Fair Trading on an investigation under Section 3 of the Competition Act, 1980. – London : Office of Fair Trading, 1981.
40p.

Tibetans : two perspectives on Tibetan-Chinese relations / by Chris Mullin and Phuntsog Wangyal. – New ed. – London : Minority Rights Group, 1983.
27p. – (Report).
Previous ed.: 1981. Includes bibliographical references.
ISBN 0946690014

Tidd, W.
Forms of Practical Proceedings in the Courts of King's Bench. – 6th ed. Repr. of 1824 ed. – Abingdon : Professional Books.
357p.
Hbk £45.00
—Practice of the Court of King's Bench and Common Pleas in Personal Actions and Ejectments, 2 Vols. – 6th ed. Repr. of 1824 ed. – Abingdon : Professional Books.
279p.
Hbk £85.00

Tiernan, Ralph
Tort in a nutshell / by Ralph Tiernan. – London : Sweet & Maxwell, 1987.
120p; 22cm.
Includes index.
ISBN 0421368403 Pbk £3.95

Tierney, Brian
Religion, law, and the growth of constitutional thought 1150-1650 / Brian Tierney. – Cambridge : Cambridge University Press, 1982.
xi,114p; 23cm.
Bibliography: p109-114.
ISBN 0521234956 £12.50

Tierney, Francis
Effective Insurance : A Guide For Buyer and Seller / Paul Braithwaite. – Toronto : Butterworths, 1984.
352p.
Topics covered include insurers, agents, brokers, reinsurers, various types of coverage, policies, riders, endorsements (with appropriate illustrations) and specific advice on minimizing corporate insurance costs.
ISBN 0409872857 Hbk £39.95

Tierney, Martin
Irish Trade Marks Law and Practice : Introduction by Mr Justice Declan Costello. – Dublin : Gill and Macmillan, 1987.
ISBN 0717114406 Hbk £30.00

Ties that bind : law, marriage and the reproduction of patriarchal relations / Carol Smart. – London : Routledge & Kegan Paul, 1984.
xiv,273p; 22cm.
Bibliography: p259-268. - Includes index.
ISBN 0710098324 Pbk £6.95

Tikriti, Abdul-Karim
Tripartism and the International Labour Organisation : a study of the legal concept : its origins, function and evolution in the law of nations / Abdul-Karim Tikriti. – Stockholm : Distributed by Almqvist & Wiksell, 1982.
xxviii,417p. – (Studies in international law).
Thesis (Doctoral) - Uppsala University 1982. Bibliography: p.400-410. - Includes index. Published under the auspices of the Swedish Institute of International Law.
ISBN 9122005609

Tilbury, M.
Civil Remedies / M. Tilbury. – Sydney : Butterworths, 1988.
550p.
This work discusses the nature and interrelation of civil remedies. Included are materials on damages, restitution, statutory remedies, injuries to rights in tangible property, personal injuries, and other topics.
Hbk £69.00

Tildesley, W. M. S. →Special requirements in probation or supervision orders : a local case study.

Tiley
Longman Exam Guide : Business Law / Bailey. – London : Longman Professional, 1986.
ISBN 0582296781 Pbk £6.95

Tillmouth, Sydney
Criminal Law Advocacy / Nicholas Pengelley. – Cowandilla : Wakefield Press, 1986.
192p.
ISBN 0949268445 Pbk £17.50

Tillotson, John
Contract law in perspective / John Tillotson. – 2nd ed. – London : Butterworths, 1985.
ix,240p; 22cm.
Previous ed.: 1981. Includes bibliographies and index.
ISBN 0406666210 Pbk £9.95

Tilotson, John →Law Teacher : Journal of the Association of Law Teachers.

Timagenis, J.
Law and practice relating to pollution control in Greece / prepared by J. Timagenis, B Pavlopoulos for Environmental Resources Limited. – 2nd ed. – London : Graham & Trotman for the Commission of the European Communities, 1982.
200p.
Previous ed.: 1976. Bibliography: p139-140. - Includes index.
ISBN 0860103145 £18.00

Time barred actions / H G Rohreke. – London : Lloyd's of London Press, 1984.
ISBN 0907432425 Hbk £34.00

Time bars in maritime matters : a study / by Kaj Pineus. – London : Lloyd's of London Press, 1982.
168p.
ISBN 0907432425

Time charter withdrawals : an examination of shipowners' rights to withdraw vessels from the service of time charterers / W.E. Astle. – London : Fairplay, 1984.
xxiii,136p; 25cm.
ISBN 0905045637 Pbk

Time charters. – 2nd ed. – London : Lloyd's of London Press, 1982.
lxix,505p; 25cm.
Previous ed.: 1978. Includes index.
ISBN 0907432131

Time for a change? : deposits on exchange of contracts in residential conveyancing / a consultation paper from the Conveyancing Standing Committee of the Law Commission and the Law Society. – London : Conveyancing Standing Committee, 1988.
14p.

Time for change / report of the Committee. – London : General Council of the Bar, 1988.
221p.
At head of t.p.: The Committee on the Future of the Legal Profession (The Marre Committee). Chairman: Lady Marre.

Time in the performance of contracts : especially for the sale of land / K.E. Lindgren. – 2nd ed. – Sydney : Butterworths, 1982.
xxv,201p.
Previous ed.: 1976. Includes bibliographical references and index.
ISBN 0409303909 Hbk £49

Time Limits for Tax Claims, Elections and Reliefs. – London : Butterworths, 1984.
ISBN 0406535108 Pbk

Time, Rates of Wages and Hours of Work 1982. – London : HMSO, 1982.
276p.
ISBN 0113612281 Hbk £17.00

Time taken to deal with juveniles under criminal proceedings / Catherine Frankenburg and Roger Tarling. – London : Home Office, 1983.
v,21p.
Bibliography: p.14.
ISBN 0862521025

Times atlas of the oceans / edited by Alastair Couper. – London : Times Books, 1983.
272p; 37cm.
Bibliography: p256-257. - Includes index.
ISBN 0723002460 £30.00

The Times Guide to 1992 : A Complete Handbook to Europe Without Frontiers. – Times.
ISBN 0723003165 Pbk £5.95

Times Law Reports. – Abingdon : Professional Books, 1984.
Llf £160.00

Times law reports. – Abingdon, Oxon. : Professional Books, 1985.
Index published separately annually and kept up to date by interim issues.

Times Law Reports : 1884-1952, 71 Vols. – Abingdon : Professional Books.
Hbk

Time-Sharing. – London : Kogan Page.
ISBN 185091463X Pbk £6.95

Timing and income taxation : the principles of income measurement for tax purposes / B. J. Arnold. – Toronto : Canadian Tax Foundation, 1983.
xiv,388p.
Includes index.
ISBN 088808014X

Timothy →Guide to Land Registry Practice.

Tiner
Accounting For Treasury Products / Conneely. – Cambridge : Woodhead-Faulkner, 1987.
ISBN 0859413896 Hbk £45.00

Tingle →Law for Doctors and Nurses.
→ Your Legal Position in Teaching.

Tingle et al. →Medicine, Nursing, and the Law.

Tingley, K.
Income tax guide. – London : Daily Mail, 1988/89.
ISBN 0851444369 Pbk £1.95

Tinker, Anthea →Housing alternatives for the elderly.

Tinker, Hugh →Fiji.

Tiplady, D.
Introduction to the Law of International Trade. – Oxford : BSP Professional.
ISBN 0632023767 Pbk £14.95

Tiruchelvam, Neelan →Role of the judiciary in plural societies.

Tiruray Justice. – Metro Manila : Institute of Philippine Culture.
Hbk £19.00 (not for export)

Title
Supplement-1983. – London : Butterworths.
ISBN 0406421498 Pbk £17.50

Title Searching in Ontario. – 2nd ed. – Butterworths, 1982.
200p.
Explains the procedure required for a 40-year search of title with a copy of an abstract page and sketches relating to land descriptions, the procedure required under the Land Titles Act, the procedure required under the Condominium Act, under the Registry Act, the Certification of Titles Act, and the provisions allowed under section 29 of the Planning Act.
ISBN 0409834165 Hbk £29.95

Title to territory in Africa : international legal issues / Malcolm Shaw. – Oxford : Clarendon, 1985.
xii,428p; 22cm.
Includes bibliography and index.
ISBN 0198253796 £35.00

Titles and forms of address : a guide to correct use. – 18th ed. – London : Black (A. & C.), 1985.
224p.
Previous ed.: 1980. Includes index.
ISBN 0713626941 Pbk £5.95

Titman & Camp, individual employment law / Barry Titman, Peter Camp. – 2nd ed. – London : Sweet & Maxwell, 1986.
xxv,240p; 22cm.
Includes the contract of employment, termination; wrongful and unfair dismissal, remedies for unfair dismissal, redundancy, problems arising on the change of employer, overlapping claims, and procedure before industrial tribunals. Contains forms and codes of practice.
ISBN 0421353201 Pbk £9.95

Titman, B. M.
Consumer Credit : Points For the Practitioner. – London : Law Society, 1985.
19p. – (Nineteen Eighty-Five Crash Course Transcripts).
Hbk £2.05

Titman, Barry
Dismissal and taxation of employees / Barry Titman, Peter Camp. – London : Butterworths, 1982.
xxvi,233p.
ISBN 0406129010
—Titman & Camp, individual employment law / Barry Titman, Peter Camp. – 2nd ed. – London : Sweet & Maxwell, 1986.
xxv,240p; 22cm.
Includes the contract of employment, termination; wrongful and unfair dismissal, remedies for unfair dismissal, redundancy, problems arising on the change of employer, overlapping claims, and procedure before industrial tribunals. Contains forms and codes of practice.
ISBN 0421353201 Pbk £9.95

To ride the storm : the 1980 Bristol 'riot' and the state / Harris Joshua, Tina Wallace and Heather Booth. – London : Heinemann, 1983.
vii,221p.
Bibliography: p211-216.
ISBN 0435824813

To see the world. – Dordrecht : Nijhoff (Martinus), 1989.
600. – (Utrecht studies in air and space law).
Analyses the principles governing the use of artificial earth satellites for international direct television broadcasting, adopted by the United Nations General Assembly in 1982. Proposes revisions to the principles. Includes Appendixes containing United Nations documentation on the subject.
ISBN 9024737443 Hbk £87.50

To Settle the Oceans : the Law of the Sea in Practice. – Toronto : University of Toronto Press, 1986.
256p.
ISBN 0802057071 Hbk £30.00
ISBN 0802066356 Pbk £14.95

Tobi, Niki
Legal impact of the Constitution (Suspension and Modification) Decree, 1984 : on the constitution of the Federal Republic of Nigeria, 1979 / Niki Tobi. – Calabar, Nigeria : Centaur Press, 1985.
xi,110p.
Includes the text of the Constitution (Suspension and Modification) Decree 1984.

Tobin
Interviewing and Counselling : Skills for Legal Practitioners. – Toronto : Butterworths, 1987.
168p.
ISBN 0409873454 Hbk

Tobolewski, Aleksander
Monetary limitations of liability in air law : legal, economic and socio-political aspects / Aleksander Tobolewski. – Montreal : De Daro, 1986.
vii,277p.
Bibliography: p.261-277.
ISBN 0969270305

Toch, Henry
Cases in Income Tax Law. – 1st ed. – Plymouth : Macdonald & Evans, 1981.
276p. – (M and E Handbook Ser.).
ISBN 0712103783 Hbk £4.95
—How to pay less income tax. – London : Pitman Publishing, 1986.
ISBN 0712108254 Pbk £2.95
—Income Tax, 1983-84. – 13th ed. Repr. of 1981 ed. – Plymouth : Macdonald & Evans, 1984.
xi, 192p. – (M and E Handbook Ser.).
ISBN 0712109706 Hbk £3.95

Today and Yesterday. – Cape Town : Legal and Financial Publishing Co.
Hbk £9.50

Todd, I. A. →Introduction to law.
→ Organisation in its environment.

Todd, Paul
Cases and Materials on Bills of Lading. – Oxford : Blackwell Scientific, 1987.
ISBN 0003833844 Hbk £30.00
—Charter Parties. – Oxford : Blackwell Scientific, 1988.
ISBN 063202061X Hbk
—Contracts for the Carriage of Goods by Sea. – Oxford : BSP Professional.
ISBN 063202061X Hbk £20.00
—Equity and Trusts. – London : Financial Training, 1986.
– (SWOT).
ISBN 1851850457 Pbk £7.95
—Introduction to Law of Trusts. – London : Financial Training, 1986.
ISBN 185185021X Pbk £9.95
—Modern Bills of Lading. – Oxford : Blackwell Scientific, 1987.
ISBN 0003833224 Hbk £19.95

Todd, Stephen
Limitation periods in personal injury claims / by Stephen Todd. – London : Sweet & Maxwell, 1982.
xxii,131p; 23cm.
Includes index.
ISBN 0421285907 £13.00

Toepke, Utz
EEC competition law : business issues and legal principles in Common Market antitrust cases / Utz Toepke. – 1. – New York : Wiley, 1982.
27cm.
Bibliography: p907-909. - Includes index.
ISBN 0471093661 Llf

Toft, Susan → Domestic violence in Papua New Guinea.
→ Domestic violence in urban Papua New Guinea.
→ Marriage and domestic violence in rural Papua New Guinea.

Tokelau : subdelgated legislation 1877 - 1948. – Wellington : Tokelau Administration, 1986.
399p.

Tolley
Social Security and State Benefits 1987-1988. – Tolley Publishing.
ISBN 0854592830 Pbk £17.95

Tolley's Accounting Problems of the Companies Acts : Practical Guidance on Recent Legislation / Sells. – Croydon : Tolley, 1984.
136p.
ISBN 0854591478 Hbk £7.95

Tolley's Anti-Avoidance Provisions. – Croydon : Tolley, 1984.
344p.
ISBN 0854591516 Hbk £17.50

Tolley's capital gains tax 1981-82 / David Harrington and Glyn Saunders. – Croydon : Tolley, 1981.
viii,245p.
Includes index. Up to date to 1 August 1981.
ISBN 0854590315

Tolley's capital gains tax 1986-87 / Patrick Noakes and John Boulding. – 9th ed. – Croydon : Tolley Publishing, 1986.
viii,349p.
Includes index.
ISBN 0854592407

Tolley's capital gains tax 1987-88 / Patrick Noakes and John Boulding. – 10th ed. – Croydon : Tolley, 1987.
viii,356p.
ISBN 0854592903

Tolley's capital transfer tax 1981-82 / by Eric L. Harvey. – Croydon : Tolley, 1981.
vii,63p.
Includes index. Up to date to 1 August 1981.
ISBN 0854590366

Tolley's captial gains tax 1988-89 / Patrick Noakes and John Boulding. – Croydon : Tolley, 1988.
viii,376p.
Includes index.
ISBN 0854593489

Tolley's Charities Manual. – 2nd ed. – Tolley Publishing.
ISBN 085459325X Hbk £25.00

Tolley's Companies Act : 1980 / George Eccles. – Croydon : Tolley.
324p.
ISBN 0854590595 Hbk £11.95
ISBN 0510494153 Pbk £7.95

Tolley's Companies Act : 1981 / Jenny Cox. – Croydon : Tolley.
520p.
ISBN 0854590587 Hbk £11.95
ISBN 0854590390 Pbk £8.95

Tolley's company law / edited by A. L. Chapman and R. M. Ballard. – Croydon : Tolley, 1983.
lxxii,959p.
Includes index.
ISBN 0854590692

Tolley's company law / edited by Stephen Barc and Nicholas Bowen. – 2nd ed. 2. – Croydon : Tolley, 1988.
Previous ed.: 1983. Includes indexes.
ISBN 0854592687

Tolley's corporation tax 1981-82 / by Glyn Saunders and David Harrington. – Croydon : Tolley, 1981.
viii,292p.
Includes index. Up to date to 1 August 1981.
ISBN 0854590358

Tolley's corporation tax 1986-87 / by Glyn Saunders and John Boulding. – 22nd ed. – Croydon : Tolley, 1986.
ix,356p.
ISBN 0854592393

Tolley's corporation tax 1987-88 / by Glynn Saunders and John Boulding. – Croydon : Tolley Publishing, 1987.
ix,357p.
ISBN 085459289X

Tolley's corporation tax 1988-89 / by Glyn Saunders and John Boulding. – Croydon : Tolley, 1988.
x,345p.
Includes index.
ISBN 0854593470

Tolley's Double Taxation Relief / Sells. – Croydon : Tolley.
175p.
ISBN 0510493874 Hbk £8.95

Tolley's employees' rights in receiverships and liquidations / Guy T.E. Parsons, William F. Ratford. – 2nd ed. – Croyden : Tolley, 1984.
xiv,210p; 30cm.
Previous ed.: 1979. Bibliography: p201. - Includes index.
ISBN 0854591443 £25.00

Tolley's Employment Act 1982. – Croydon : Tolley.
256p.
ISBN 085459082X Hbk £7.95

Tolley's Employment Handbook. – 5th ed. – Croydon : Tolley.
456p.
Includes Employment Act 1988. Gives information on: ACAS, Disabled Employees, Equal Pay, Maternity Rights, Racial Discrimination, Trade Unions and Unfair Dismissal.
ISBN 0854593276 Hbk £17.95

Tolley's Estate Planning. – Linklater & Paines. – Tolley Publishing.
ISBN 0854592725 Hbk £17.95

Tolley's European insolvency guide / Anthony R. Houghton, Neil H. Cooper. – Croydon : Tolley Publishing Co., 1984.
xv,364p; 23cm. – (An Extel Group publication).
Includes index.
ISBN 0854590978 Pbk £19.95

Tolley's factoring : a guide to factoring practice and law / by F.R. Salinger. – Croydon : Tolley, 1984.
xvii,253p; 23cm.
Includes index.
ISBN 0854591648 Pbk £17.50

Tolley's Focus on the Purchase and Sale of a Private Company's Shares. – 2nd ed. – Croydon : Tolley.
152p.
ISBN 0854591850 Hbk £6.95

Tolley's focus on the purchase or redemption by a company of its own shares : a review of the tax and company law provisions / by Peter Wolstenholme, Robert Willott. – Croydon : Tolley, 1982.
x,93p.
Includes index.
ISBN 0854590935

Tolley's Guide to Directors' Transactions / John Aldis. – Croydon : Tolley.
120p.
ISBN 0854591184 Hbk £5.95

Tolley's Health and Safety at Work Handbook. – 2nd ed. – Tolley Publishing.
ISBN 0854593829 Hbk £39.95

Tolley's income tax 1986-87 / by Eric L. Harvey and Glyn Saunders with Patrick Noakes. – 71st ed. – Croydon : Tolley Publishing, 1986.
xi,596p.
Includes index.
ISBN 0854592385

Tolley's income tax 1988-89 / by Eric L. Harvey and Glyn Saunders : with David Smailes. – 73rd ed. – Croydon, Surrey : Tolley, 1988.
xii,623p.
Includes index.
ISBN 0854593462

Tolley's inheritance tax 1986-87 / by Robert Wareham. – Croydon : Tolley Publishing, 1986.
viii,223,iv,236p.
Includes indexes. Contents: Tolley's inheritance tax 1986-1987 - Tolley's capital transfer tax final edition.
ISBN 0854592415

Tolley's inheritance tax 1987-88 / by Robert Wareham and John Newth. – Croydon : Tolley Publishing, 1987.
viii,246p.
ISBN 0854592911

Tolley's inheritance tax 1988-89 / by Patrtick Noakes and John Newth. – Croydon : Tolley, 1988.
viii,245p.
Includes index.
ISBN 0854593497

Tolley's Law Data
1988-89. – Tolley Publishing.
ISBN 0854593616 Pbk £7.95

Tolley's National Insurance Contributions 1988-89. – Tolley Publishing.
ISBN 0854593594 Hbk £18.95

Tolley's Payroll Handbook. – 2nd ed. – Tolley Publishing.
ISBN 0854593632 Hbk £21.00

Tolley's Property Taxes. – 2nd ed. – Tolley Publishing.
ISBN 0854593268 Hbk £19.95

Tolley's Social security and state benefits 1983/84 / by Jim Matthewman and Nigel A.D. Lambert. – Croydon : Tolley, 1984.
xii,496p; 23cm.
Includes index.
ISBN 0854591354 Pbk £10.95

Tolley's social security and state benefits 1985 / by Jim Matthewman and Nigel A.D. Lambert. – Croydon : Tolley, 1985.
x,485p.
Includes index.
ISBN 0854591737

Tolley's Social Security and State Benefits 1988-89 / Robinson. – Tolley Publishing.
ISBN 0854593608 Hbk £19.95

Tolley's Stamp Duties. – 3rd ed. – Tolly Publishing.
ISBN 0854593683 Hbk £9.95

Tolley's tax bumph 1983-84 / edited by Robert Wareham. – Croydon : Tolley, 1983.
viii,536p.
Includes index.
ISBN 0854591389

Tolley's tax cases 1988 / by Victor Grout. – 8th ed. – Croydon : Tolley, 1988.
xxvi,516p.
Includes index.
ISBN 0854591508

Tolley's Tax Data 1988-89 / Dolton. – Finance Bill 1988 Edition. – Tolley Publishing.
ISBN 08545493459 Hbk £7.95

Tolley's Tax Guide 1988-89. – Tolley Publishing.
ISBN 0854593535 Hbk £19.95

Tolley's tax planning 1982-83 / edited by A. L. Chapman. – Truro : TLPC and Tolley Publishing, 1982.
xxxviii, 806p.
ISBN 0854590897

Tolleys tax planning 1985 / edited by Glyn Saunders ... et al. – Croydon : Tolley, 1985.
xiv,911p.
Includes index.
ISBN 0854591435

Tolley's tax planning 1986 / edited by Glyn Saunders ... et al. – Croydon : Tolley Publishing, 1985.
xiv,890p.
ISBN 0854592032

Tolley's tax planning 1987 / edited by Glyn Saunders ... et al. – Croydon : Tolley Publishing, 1986.
xv,863p.
Includes index.
ISBN 0854592466

Tolley's tax planning 1988 / edited by Glyn Saunders, Robert Wareham and Deborah Hicks. – 2 v. – Croydon : Tolley Publishing, 1987.
ISBN 0854593020

Tolley's Tax Planning
1989. – Tolley Publishing.
ISBN 085459356X Pbk £39.95

Tolleys tax planning supplement / edited by A.L. Chapman. – Croyden : Tolley, 1984.
xxii,170p.
Supplements: Tolleys tax planning. 1982/83 ed.. Includes index.
ISBN 0854591729

Tolley's taxation in Gibraltar 1981-82 / by James Levy and Simon Caplan : with an introduction by Sir Joshua Hassan. – 2nd ed. – Croydon : Tolley, 1982.
vii,152p.
Includes index.
ISBN 0854590447

Tolley's taxation in the Channel Islands and Isle of Man 1987 / John Boulding. – Croydon : Tolley, 1987.
vi,207p.
ISBN 0854592954

Tolley's taxation in the Channel Islands and Isle of Man. – Croydon : Tolley Pub. Co., 1981.
vi,163p.
ISBN 0854590269 £6.25

Tolley's taxation in the Republic of Ireland 1981-82 / by Glyn Saunders and Eric L. Harvey. – Croydon : Tolley, 1981.
x,193p.
Includes index.
ISBN 0854590439

Tolley's taxation in the Republic of Ireland 1987-88 / by John Newth and Glyn Saunders : from an original text by Eric L. Harvey. – Croydon : Tolley, 1987.
vii,293p.
Includes index.
ISBN 0854592946

Tolley's taxation of marriage and marriage breakdown / by David Brodie. – Croydon : Tolley, 1988.
xxiii,184p; 23cm.
Includes index.
ISBN 0854593233 Pbk £14.95

Tolley's trading within the European Community : a United Kingdom executive guide / Dennis Evans. – Croydon : Tolley, 1983.
xviii,212p; 30cm.
Bibliography: p206-208. - Includes index. Cover title: Trading within the European Community.
ISBN 085459132X Pbk

Tolley's value added tax 1986-87 / by Robert Wareham and Patrick Noakes. – Croydon : Tolley, 1986.
vii,488p.
Includes index.
ISBN 0854592423

Tolley's value added tax 1987-88 / by Robert Wareham and Patrick Noakes. – Croydon : Tolley, 1987.
vii,502p.
Includes index.
ISBN 085459292X

Tolley's value added tax 1988-89 / by Robert Wareham and Nicholas Bowen. – Croydon : Tolley, 1988.
vii,512p.
Includes index.
ISBN 0854593500

Tolley's Value Added Tax Cases : 1983. – 3rd ed. – Croydon : Tolley.
530p.
ISBN 0854592970 Hbk £29.95

Toman, Jiri →Laws of armed conflicts : a collection of conventions, resolutions and other documents.
→ Spirit of Uppsala : proceedings of the Joint UNITAR-Uppsala University Seminar on International Law and Organization for a New World Order (JUS 81), Uppsala 9-18 June 1981.

Tomasevski, Katarina →Children in adult prisons : an international picture.
—Right to Food : Guide through Applicable International Law. – Dordrecht : Kluwer, 1986.
388p.
ISBN 9024733650 Hbk £165.00

Tomasic, Roman
Sociology of law / Roman Tomasic. – London : Sage, 1985.
288p.
Includes bibliography and index.
ISBN 0803997167 Pbk £10.00

Tombs, Jacqueline →British crime survey Scotland.
→ Prosecution in the public interest.

Tomlin, T. E.
Law Dictionary : Explaining the Rise, Progress, and Present State of the British Law, 2 Vols. – 3rd ed. Repr. of 1820 ed. – Abingdon : Professional Books.
259p.
Hbk £90.00

Tomlins, Christopher L.
State and the unions : labour relations, law and the organized labour movement in America, 1880-1960. – Cambridge : Cambridge University Press, 1985.
364.
Examines the impact of the National Labour Relations Act on American trade unions.
ISBN 0521258405 Hbk £35.00
ISBN 0521314526 Pbk £12.50

Tomlinson, Hugh →Civil actions against the police.
→ Suing the police.

Tomlinson, Jim
Unequal struggle? : British socialism and the capitalist enterprise / Jim Tomlinson. – London : Methuen, 1982.
160p; 23cm.
Bibliography: p149-157. - Includes index.
ISBN 0416331505 Hbk £
ISBN 0416331602 Pbk

Tomlinson, M.W.
Whose Law and Order? Aspects of Crime, Social Control and Irish Society. – Belfast : Sociological Society of Ireland.
ISBN 0951341103 Hbk £10.95
ISBN 0951341111 Pbk £4.95

Tomlinson, Mary →Wilson: children and the law.

Tomorrow's lawyers : computers and legal training : a paper prepared by the Society's Legal Education Committee to discuss the teaching of computer applications to intending lawyers and to qualified practitioners / Society for Computers and Law. – Milton, Oxon : Society for Computers and Law, 1981.
7p; 22cm.
ISBN 0906122082 Pbk

Tomsett, Eric
Company Reorganisations : Tax and Tax Planning / Nicholas Noble. – London : Butterworths, 1986.
ISBN 0406501904 Hbk £35.00
—Tax Planning for Multinational Companies. – Cambridge : Woodhead-Faulkner.
ISBN 0859415589 Hbk £40.00

Tong, Robert
Sale of Goods and Consumer Law /. – North Ryde : Law Book Co, 1986.
x, 102p. – (Nutshells).
ISBN 0455206783

Tonnage Measurement : Treatment of Shelter-Deck and Other 'Open' Spaces French Edition /. – London : International Maritime Organization.
Hbk £1.00

Tonry, Michael →Reform and punishment : essays on criminal sentencing.

Toohe, Joycey G.
Guidebook to Victorian Real Estate Law and Practice. – North Ryde : C.C.H. Australia, 1986.
557p.
ISBN 0869035118 Hbk

Toole, Chris →Police, Race and Ethnicity : A Guide For Law Enforcement Officers.

Tope, T.K.
Hindu Family Law and Social Change. – Bombay : University of Bombay, Publications Department.
Hbk £21.00

Topple, B.S.
Consolidated Accounts. – 4th ed. – Witney : A.T.C. Publications.
ISBN 0747790019 Pbk £7.95
—Corporation Tax. – 5th ed. – Plymouth : Macdonald & Evans, 1981.
ISBN 0712104674 Pbk £4.95

Tornaritis, Criton G.
Institution of Ombudsman in the English legal system and especially that of Cyprus / by Criton G. Tornaritis. – Nicosia : s.n., 1983.
27 leaves.
—Legal aspects of the problem of refugees in Cyprus / by Criton G. Tornaritis. – Nicosia : s.n., 1975.
25 leaves.
—Legal links between Cyprus and the Balkans especially Macedonia during the Byzantine era / Criton G. Tornaritis. – Nicosia : s.n., 1982.
24 leaves.
—Modern trends concerning the reduction of prosecutions / by Criton G. Tornaritis. – Nicosia : s.l., 1984.
13 leaves.
—Note on the law of Cyprus relating to offshore operations, shipping operations and shipping companies, foreign investments in Cyprus and transit trade / by Criton G. Tornaritis. – Nicosia : s.n., 1984.
52 leaves.

Torno, Barry
Crown copyright in Canada : a legacy of confusion / Barry Torno. – 1 microfiche. – Ottawa : Minister of Supply and Services, 1981.
78 fr.; 10x15cm.
Bibliography: p.65-67.
ISBN 0662113942

Tornudd, Klaus
Finland and the international norms of human rights / K. Tornudd. – Dordrecht : M. Nijhoff, 1986.
Bibliography.
ISBN 9024732573

Toronto Legal Directory (Metropolitan List) and Tariff Guide. – Toronto : University of Toronto Press, 1985.
Hbk £17.00

Toronto Stock Exchange : a Procedural Guide for Companies and Their Professional Advisers. – Butterworths, 1986.
576p.
ISBN 0409805998 Hbk £95.00

Torrance, Thomas F.
Juridical law and physical law : towards a realist foundation for human law / by Thomas F. Torrance. – Edinburgh : Scottish Academic Press, 1982.
xii,70p.
ISBN 0707303141

Torrens register book / Law Reform Commision of Victoria. – Melbourne : The Commission, 1986.
iv,19p. – (Discussion paper).
Includes bibliographical references.

Torrens system in Australia / by Douglas J. Whalan. – Sydney : Law Book Co., 1982.
lxvii,410p.
Includes bibliographical references and index.
ISBN 0455203571 Pbk
ISBN 045520358X

Torrens Title in Australia, 2 Vols.
Vol. 2 /. – London : Butterworths, 1973.
ISBN 0409365122 Hbk £52.10

Torrman, Wolfgang
Investment Institutions. – 4th ed. – Plymouth : Macdonald & Evans, 1984.
180p.
ISBN 0712155074 Pbk £4.75

Tort / by C.D. Baker. – 4th ed. – London : Sweet & Maxwell, 1986.
xxxii,398p; 23cm.
Previous ed.: 1981. Includes index.
ISBN 0421349409 Hbk £15.00
ISBN 0421349506 Pbk £8.95

Tort : cases and materials / compiled by B.A. Hepple, M.H. Matthews. – 3rd ed. – London : Butterworths, 1985.
750p; 25cm.
Previous ed.: 1980. Includes index.
ISBN 0406594848 Hbk £25.00 :
ISBN 0406594902 Pbk £16.95

Tort in a nutshell / by Ralph Tiernan. – London : Sweet & Maxwell, 1987.
120p; 22cm.
Includes index.
ISBN 0421368403 Pbk £3.95

Tort Law / Daniel J. Baum. – Toronto : IPI Publishing, 1982.
84p. – (You and the Law Ser.).
ISBN 0458957003 Pbk £7.95

Tort law / B S Markesinis. – Oxford : Oxford University Press, 1984.
ISBN 0198761503 Hbk £22.50
ISBN 0198761511 Pbk £15.00

Tort Liability in a Collective Bargaining Regime. – London : Butterworths.
ISBN 0409871540 Hbk £32.00

Tortious Liability for Unintentional Harm Vol. 1 / B S Markesinis. – Cambridge : Cambridge University Press.
ISBN 0521272092 Pbk £17.50
Vol. 2. –
ISBN 0521272106 Pbk £17.50

Tortious liability for unintentional harm in the common law and the civil law / by F.H. Lawson, B.S. Markesinis. – 2. – Cambridge : Cambridge University Press, 1982.
Includes index.
ISBN 0521235863 v. 2

Torts /. – North Ryde : Law Book Co, 1984.
xii, 108p. – (Nutshells).
ISBN 0455203474

Torts : Cases and Commentary / D Hambly. – 2nd ed. – London : Butterworths.
ISBN 0409493506 Hbk £38.90
Supplement-1986. –
75p.
ISBN 0409491187 £4.00
Supplement-1986.

Torts In New Zealand : Cases and Materials / Allin. – Oxford : Oxford University Press.
ISBN 00195581814 Pbk £22.50

Torts in the 80s. – Don Mills : R. De Boo, 1983.
504p.
Includes bibliographical references and index.
ISBN 0888201508

Torture. – Oxford : Blackwell, 1985.
ISBN 0631137238 Pbk £5.95

Torture in the eighties. – Amnesty International. – Oxford : Robertson, 1984.
250p.
ISBN 0855207809 Hbk £15.00
ISBN 0855207817 Pbk £4.95

Total environment control : the economics of cross-media pollution transfers / by Julian Lowe, David Lewis and Martin Atkins. – Oxford : Pergamon, 1982.
viii,126p; 23cm.
Includes index.
ISBN 0080262767 Pbk £10.95

Totty, Peter
Corporate insolvency / Peter Totty and Michael Crystal. – London : McGraw-Hill, 1982.
xv,155p; 26cm.
Includes index.
ISBN 0070845824 £12.95
—Insolvency / Peter Totty and Michael Jordan. – London : Longman Professional (UK).
Covers areas such as the disqualification of directors, wrongful trading, voluntary arrangements, appointment of administrators, and antecedent transactions. Contains statutes, statutory instruments and guidance notes, forms and practice directions, tables of destination, derivations and special definitions. New chapters cover the Government Insolvency Service, the construction industry and insurance companies.
ISBN 0851211429 Llf £205
—Insolvency - Introduction to the 1985 Act / Jordan. – London : Longman Professional, 1986.
ISBN 0851212166 Pbk £7.95

Touch Ross
Entertainment Expenses and Substantiation : the New Tax Rules. – Touch Ross. – North Ryde : C.C.H. Australia, 1986.
94p.
ISBN 0869038656 Hbk

Touche Ross
Civil justice review : study of debt enforcement procedures. – Touche Ross. – London : Touche Ross, 1986.
iii,90 leaves.
A study carried out as part of the Lord Chancellor's review of civil justice.
—Corporate Insolvency Practice Manual. – Touche Ross. – London : Butterworths, 1988.
ISBN 0406503508 Pbk
—Manual of Financial Reporting and Accounting. – Touche Ross. – 2nd ed. – London : Butterworths, 1985.
ISBN 0406500509 Pbk £18.50
—Rights and duties of directors. – Touche Ross. – London : Butterworths, 1987.
ISBN 0406504709 Pbk £18.50
—Tax practice manual. – Touche Ross. – 2nd ed. – London : Butterworths, 1985.
ISBN 0406402205 Pbk £18.50

Touche Ross : Tax Practice Manual. – 3rd ed. – London : Butterworths.
ISBN 0406402221 Pbk £22.95

Touche Ross Tax Guide for the Family 1988-89 / Sandy. – London : Macmillan.
ISBN 033346835X Pbk £4.95

Touche Ross Tax Guide to Pay and Perks 1988-89 / Sandy. – London : Macmillan.
ISBN 0333468376 Pbk £4.95

Touche Ross VAT : a business by business guide. – London : Butterworths, 1988.
ISBN 0406501440 Pbk £23.95

Touch-Stone of Common Assurances : Treatise Opening the Learning of Common Assurances or Conveyances of the Kingdome. – 2nd ed. Repr. of 1648 ed. – Abingdon : Professional Books.
487p.
Hbk £250.00

Tougher regimes in detention centres : report of an evaluation by the Young Offender Psychology Unit / by David Thornton ... et al. – London : H.M.S.O., 1984.
v,277p; 25cm.
Reports findings of Young Offenders Psychology Unit investigating the effectiveness of tougher regimes designed to provide a 'short, sharp shock'. Doubt is cast on whether pilot regimes are sufficiently more rigorous. Finds that pilot regimes had the same effect on reconviction rates as ordinary detention centres.
ISBN 0113407963 Pbk £6.50

Toulson, N.
Pensions Revolution : An Employers Guide. – London : Kogan Page.
ISBN 1850917639 Hbk £12.95
ISBN 1850917647 Pbk £6.95

Tourism law / Jim Corke. – Huntingdon, Cams. : Elm, 1988.
xxvi,288p.
Includes bibliography and index.
ISBN 0946139954 tutor's pack £10.95
ISBN 0946139962 £39.00

Toward a Community air transport policy: the legal dimension / P J Slot, P D Dagtoglou. – Kluwer Law and Taxation, 1989.
400.
A selection of essays dealing with the (de)regulation of air transport in the European Community and its member states. Discusses the development of the concept of EC air space law in which all carriers established within the community will be free to compete. Gives views of a European law and the impact on a national level.
ISBN 9065444076 Hbk £41/Dfl 132

Toward a New Criminal Law for Canada. – Ottawa : Canadian Criminal Justice Association, 1982.
32p.
Hbk free

Toward equality : the response to the report of the Parliamentary Committee on Equality Rights. – Ottawa, Ont. : Communications and Public Affairs, Dept. of Justice Canada, 1986.
65, 69 p.; 28 cm.
English and French. Title on added t.p.: Cap sur l'egalite.
ISBN 0662543181 Pbk

Towards a 21st century company philosophy : oration delivered in the Assembly Hall at the University of Malta Graduation Ceremony, 26th April 1984 / by J.A. Micallef. – Valletta : Malta University Press, 1984.
9p.

Towards a cashless society? : a report to the Prime Minister / by the Australian Science and Technology Council (ASTEC) prepared by the Technological Change Committee. – Canberra : Australian Government Publishing Service, 1986.
xi,175p.
Includes bibliographies.
ISBN 0644049995

Towards a dynamic European economy : green paper on the development of the Common Market for telecommunications services and equipment / communication by the Commission. – Luxembourg : Commission of the European Communities, 987.
192p. – (Document).
ISBN 9277257415

Towards a just immigration policy / edited by Ann Dummett. – London : Cobden Trust, 1986.
240p; 20cm.
ISBN 0900137266 Pbk £6.95

Towards a middle system of law / David Tench. – London : Consumers' Association, 1981.
73p.
ISBN 085202214X

Towards a new Arbitration Act for Alberta / Institute of Law Research and Reform. – Edmonton, Alberta : Institute of Law Research and Reform, 1987.
xvi,199p.

Towards a New International Marine Order : conference of the Youth Movement for a New International Order (1980, Amsterdam). – Dordrecht : Kluwer, 1982.
224p.
ISBN 9024725976 Hbk £100.00

Towards a rational criminal law : being the Presidential Address of Professor J. C. Smith, President of the Holdsworth Club of the faculty of Law in the University of Birmingham, 1982-83. – Birmingham : Holdsworth Club, 1983.
15p. – (Holdsworth Club Presidential Addresses, 1983).
ISBN 0704406624

Towards a Sociology of Law in India. – New Delhi : Satvahan Publications, 1986.
Hbk £96.00

Towards a theory of contract / by A. G. Bischoff. – Reading : Bischoff (A. G.), 1984.
v,13p.
ISBN 0950971405

Towards a unified family court : court orders concerning children : overlapping jurisdictions / Jean Graham Hall, Douglas F. Martin. – s.l. : s.n., 1986.
88p.

Towards a unified Family Court : the collection of maintenance and the enforcement of court orders for maintenance / research by Jean Graham Hall and Douglas F. Martin. – s.l. : s. n., 1984.
ca.200 leaves.
Includes some French text.

Towards open government
1 : General report / Alan Danks. – Wellington : Government Printer, 1981.
54p.
Chairman: Sir Alan Danks.
2 : Supplementary report. – 1981.
138p.
Chairman: Sir Alan Danks.

Towards the European union : Florence, 13 June 1983 / by Altiero Spinelli. – Luxembourg : Office for Official Publications of the European Communities, 1983.
28p.

Towers, Brian
Worker-directors in private manufacturing industry in Great Britain / Brian Towers, Derek Cox, Elizabeth Chell. – London : Department of Employment, 1987.
34p. – (Research paper).
Bibliography: p33-34.

Town and country planning / report of a Committee of Inquiry appointed by the Nuffield Foundation. – London : Nuffield Foundation, 1986.
xiv,204p.
ISBN 0904956253

Town and Country Planning Act, 1976 (Act 172). – Kuala Lumpur : International Law Books Services.
Hbk £10.00

Town and country planning in Britain / J.B. Cullingworth. – 8th ed. – London : Allen & Unwin, 1982.
369p; 23cm.
Previous ed.: 1979. Bibliography: p349-360. - Includes index.
ISBN 0047110104 Hbk £
ISBN 0047110112 Pbk

Town and country planning in Britain / J.B. Cullingworth. – 9th ed. – London : Allen & Unwin, 1985.
430p; 22cm.
Previous ed.: 1982. Includes bibliography and index.
ISBN 0047110139 Pbk £8.95

Town and country planning law. – Plymouth : Macdonald & Evans, 1981.
ISBN 0712120319 Pbk £3.95

Town of Harrow Act, 1983, Bill Pr050 : An Act Respecting the Town of Harrow. – Ontario : Ontario Government Publications Service, 1983.
2p.
Hbk £0.30

Town planning in practice. – London : Butterworths, 1988.
ISBN 0406500754 Pbk

Townley, Stephen → Solicitor's guide to advertising & publicity.
—Sponsorship of sport, arts, and leisure : law, tax and business relationships / by Stephen Townley and Edward Grayson : with forewords by Lord Goodman, Dick Jeeps and Sir William Rees-Mogg. – London : Sweet & Maxwell, 1984.
xliii,333p; 23cm.
Guide to the law and tax considerations involved in the business of sponsorship. The legal status of sponsorship rights and licences is interpreted with reference to statute and case law. Intellectual property law, competition law, copyright and the remedies for its infringement, trade-marks, and passing-off are examined.
ISBN 0421304103 £19.75

Townsend, B.D.
Euro DM. – London : Butterworths.
ISBN 0406194009 Hbk £35.00
—Financing of Countertrade. – London : Butterworths, 1986.
ISBN 0406102007 Pbk £32.00

Townsend Gault, Ian
International Legal Context of Petroleum Operations in Canadian Arctic Waters. – Calgary : Canadian Institute of Resources Law.
76p.
Hbk £9.00
—Petroleum Operations on the Canadian Continental Margin : the Legal Issues in a Modern Perspective. – Calgary : Canadian Institute of Resources Law.
113p.
Hbk £10.00

Township of Mattice-Val Cote Act, 1983, Bill Pr039 : An Act to Continue the Corporation of the Union of Townships of Elber and Devitt Under the Name of The Corporation of the Township of Mattice-Val Cote. – Ontario : Ontario Government Publications Service, 1983.
1p.
Hbk £0.30

Townsley → Finance.

Tracey, Richard R. S. → Cases and materials on administrative law.

Trade and Merchandise Marks Act, 1958 / V.P. Sarathi. – 2nd rev. and enl. ed. – Lucknow : Eastern Book Company, 1982.
789p.
Hbk £140.00

Trade associations, fairness and competition / by Warren Pengilley. – Sydney : Law Book Company, 1981.
xxvii,247p.
Includes index. Includes text of Trade Practices Act 1974.
ISBN 0455200866

Trade Description Act 1970. – London : Wildy & Sons.
Hbk £2.25

Trade Descriptions Act 1972 : possible successor regime / Department of Trade and Industry. – London : The Department, 1987.
4,5 leaves.
Includes the text of the proposed Trade Descriptions (Places of Production) (Marking) Order 1988.

Trade financing / edited by Charles J. Gmur. – 2nd ed. – London : Euromoney, 1986.
xxi,234p.
ISBN 0903121999

Trade Law Topics / Steven Cass. – Toronto : Butterworths.
ISBN 0409811890 Hbk £165.00

Trade Mark Cases, 2 Vols. – Calcutta : Eastern Law House, 1985.
Hbk £775.00

Trade mark cases and passing off cases. – 2 vols. – Sweet & Maxwell, 1986.
ISBN 0421344601 Hbk £110.00

Trade Marks Act, 1976. – Kuala Lumpur : International Law Books Services.
Hbk £9.50

Trade marks and industrial designs / by Immanuel Goldsmith. – Toronto : Carswell, 1982.
ix,344p.
Reprinted from the Canadian Encyclopedic Digest 3rd ed.
ISBN 0459349805

Trade marks and names. – Oxford : ESC, 1985. – (Casebook).
ISBN 0906214351 Pbk £9.00

Trade Marks and Passing off. – 3rd ed. – Calcutta : Eastern Law House, 1981.
Hbk £300.00

Trade Marks Law in India with Up-to-date Act and Supreme Court Decision / S.C. Sarkar. – Calcutta : Sarkar & Sons.
xvi, 88p.
Hbk £7.00

Trade Policy Issues of Interest to the Third World. – London : Trade Policy Research Centre, 1981.
76p.
Hbk £2.00

Trade Policy Research Centre → Competition among international airlines.
→ Role of tariff quotas in commercial policy.

Trade practices and consumer protection : a commentary on the Trade Practices Act 1974 / by G.Q. Taperell, R.B. Vermeesch, D.J. Harland. – 3rd ed. – Sydney : Butterworths, 1983.
liii,922p.
Previous ed.: 1978. Includes bibliographies and index. Legislation set against the economic and commercial background in which it operates.
ISBN 0409491217 Pbk

Trade Practices Commission
Bulletin : trade practices developments / Trade Practices Commission. – Belconnen, A.C.T. : Australian Trade Practices Commission, 1981.

Trade Practices Law. Supplement. – North Ryde : Law Book Co, 1982.
ISBN 0455205337 £26.00

Trade Practices Legislation and Materials 1986. – Kingston : Australian Government Publishing Service.
Hbk £14.95

Trade Secrets. – Vancouver : Continuing Legal Education Society of British Columbia, 1986.
163p.
ISBN 0865042896 Hbk £65.00

Trade secrets / Institute of Law Research and Reform, Edmonton, Alberta and a Federal Provincial Working Party. – Edmonton : The Institute, 1986.
284p. – (Report).
Includes bibliographical references.

Trade Union Acts. – London : Sweet & Maxwell, 1985.
ISBN 0421338008 Pbk £16.50

Trade union democracy, members' rights and the law / Patrick Elias and Keith Ewing. – London : Mansell, 1987.
300p; 24cm.
Includes bibliography and index.
ISBN 0720107296 Hbk £30.00 :
ISBN 0720118719 Pbk £16.00

Trade union immunities. – London : H.M.S.O., 1981.
ISBN 0101812809

Trade union law / Richard Kidner. – 2nd ed. – London : Stevens, 1983.
xl,290p; 25cm.
Previous ed.: London : Sweet & Maxwell, 1979. Includes index.
ISBN 0420465502 £25.00

Trade Union Law. – Calcutta : Sarkar & Sons, 1970.
xxiv, 247p.
Hbk £17.50

Trade union law / Bryn Perrins. – London : Butterworths, 1985.
350p.
Includes index.
ISBN 0406258309 Hbk £26.50
ISBN 0406258317 Pbk £17.95

Trade union law and the pursuit of prosperity - the next step : submission to the Secretary of State for Employment in response to the green paper on trade union immunities / prepared by Roderick Thomas. – London : Director Publications, 1981.
66p; 30cm.
At head of title: Institute of Directors.
Pbk £4.95

Trade Union Law in Australia : the Legal Status of Australian Trade Unions / Donald W. Rawson. – 2nd ed. – Butterworths, 1985.
224p.
ISBN 0409492736 Hbk £49.00

Trade union powers and the anti-nuclear campaign. – London : Lawyers Versus the Bomb, 1982.
19p; 21cm. – (Pamphlet).
Pbk

Trade Union Representatives Handbook. – London : Industrial Society.
Hbk £1.95

Trade unionists and the law / Jennifer Horne. – London : Shaw, 1983.
xii,84p; 21cm.
ISBN 072190940X Pbk

Trade unions : selected readings / edited by W.E.J. McCarthy. – 2nd ed. – Harmondsworth : Penguin, 1985.
562p. – (Penguin books).
Previous ed.: 1972.
ISBN 0140226419

Trade Unions Act, 1969 (Act 262) and Regulations 1969 (P.U.(A) 390/1982). – Kuala Lumpur : International Law Books Services.
Hbk £12.50

Trade Unions and Change in the British Car Industry / Patricia Wallace. – London : Policy Studies Institute, 1984.
72p. – (PSI Research Papers).
Hbk £3.50

Trade unions and their members / presented to Parliament by the Secretary of State for Employment and the Paymaster General .. – London : H.M.S.O., 1987.
iii,33p; 30cm.
ISBN 0101009526

Trade unions, the Labour Party and the law : a study of the Trade Union Act 1913 / K. D. Ewing. – Edinburgh : Edinburgh University Press, 1982.
x,249p; 22cm.
ISBN 0852244533

Trademark Registration Treaty (TRT) Original Text of the Treaty and Regulations Adopted by the Vienna Conference (1973). – Geneva : World Intellectual Property Organization.
131p.
Hbk £15.00

Trademarks and Unfair Competition. – Vancouver : British Columbia Continuing Legal Education Society, 1982.
352p.
ISBN 0865040591 Hbk £55.00

Traders Directory 1987. – London : Euromoney.
ISBN 0903121867 Pbk £65.00

Trades Union Congress
Hands up for democracy. – Trades Union Congress. – London : Trades Union Congress, 1983.
40p.
ISBN 0900878983

Trading Canada's Natural Resources : (Essays from the Third Banff Conference on Natural Law) Canadian Institute of Resources Law. – Agincourt : Carswell, 1987.
374p.
This work contains a collection of essays outlining the issues associated with the resource sector trade in Canada. It provides a discussion of Canadian and international trade in natural resources. Other discussions include trade distortions brought about by government protectionism, the impact of domestic regulatory schemes, and the ways in which private sector players can best structure their own legal relations in order to adapt to the changing nature of resources trade.
Hbk £63.00

Trading financial options. – London : Butterworths, 1986.
ISBN 0406100470 Hbk £27.50

Trading in commodities. – 4th ed. – Cambridge : Woodhead-Faulkner, 1983.
ISBN 0859411788 Pbk £10.95
ISBN 0859411796 Hbk £19.95

Trading in currency options. – Cambridge : Woodhead-Faulkner, 1987.
ISBN 0859413233 Hbk £45.00

Trading in gold futures. – Cambridge : Woodhead-Faulkner, 1985.
ISBN 0859412687 Hbk £25.00

Trading in options. – 2nd ed. – Cambridge : Woodhead-Faulkner, 1982.
ISBN 0859412180 Hbk £16.95

Trading in soft commodity futures. – Cambridge : Woodhead-Faulkner, 1985.
ISBN 0859412393 Hbk £25.00

Trading law. – Chichester : Barry Rose, 1981-.
From 2 Trading law reports published as pullout insert in each issue.

Trading Law Cases. – London : Butterworths.
Service to Date.
Hbk £85.00

Trading law reports. – Chichester : Barry Rose, 1983.
Published as pullout insert in Trading law.

Trading with the Enemy Act. – London : Butterworths, 1988.
ISBN 0880631880 Hbk

Tradition and progress in modern legal cultures / edited by Stig Jrgensen, Juha Poyhonen, Csaba Varga : preface by Jose Llompart Tradition und Fortschritt in den modernen Rechtskulturen / herausgegeben von Stig Jrgensen, Juha Poyhonen, Csaba Varga ; vorwort von Jose Llompart. – Stuttgart : F. Steiner Verlag Wiesbaden, 1985.
263 p.; 24 cm. – (Archives for philosophy of law and social philosophy).
English, French, and German. Includes bibliographies and index. .
ISBN 3515044582 Pbk DM35.00

Traditional and Modern Legal Institutions in Asia and Africa. – Leiden : E.J. Brill, 1967.
ISBN 9004010505 Hbk £48.00

Traditions of Joashua Ben Hananiah, Part 1 : the Early Legal Traditions. – Leiden : E.J. Brill, 1981.
ISBN 9004063196 Hbk £110.00

Traffic accident case studies / New South Wales, Law Reform Commission. – Sydney : New South Wales. Law Reform Commission, 1984.
77p.

Traffic Offences. – London : Butterworths.
ISBN 0409495174 Hbk £35.00

Traffic offences : an examination of the principles of law governing offences committed by motorists on the roads in Australia / Douglas Brown. – Sydney : Butterworths, 1983.
lx,323p.
Includes index.
ISBN 040949190X

Traffic officer's companion. – 3rd ed. – Police Review, 1987.
ISBN 0851640273 Pbk £4.25

Traffic Officer's Companion. – London : Police Review Publishing, 1982.
ISBN 0851649955 Pbk £2.75

Training Course on Patent Information. – Geneva : World Intellectual Property Organization, 1987.
620p.
Hbk £50.00

Trakman, Leon E. →Professional competence and the law.

Tramp ship agency practice. – London : Lloyd's of London Press, 1987.
ISBN 1850441480 Hbk £23.50

Trankell, Arne →Reconstructing the past : the role of psychologists in criminal trials.

Transborder data flows : proceedings of an OECD conference held December 1983 / edited for the OECD by Hans-Peter Gassmann. – Amsterdam : North-Holland, 1985.
Bibliography: p.
ISBN 0444877002

Transboundary air pollution : international legal aspects of the co-operation of states / editors, K. Flinterman, B. Kwiatkowska, and J. Lammers. – Dordrecht : M. Nijhoff, 1987.
390p.
Includes bibliographies and index.
ISBN 9024732859 Hbk £199.00

Transcarceration : essays in the sociology of social control / edited by John Lowman, Robert J. Menzies, T.S. Palys. – Aldershot : Gower, 1987.
x,370p; 22cm.
Includes bibliography and index.
ISBN 0566051060 £19.50

Transfer of land : formalities for contracts for sale etc. of land / the Law Commission. – London : H.M.S.O., 1987.
37p. – (1987/88 HC2).
ISBN 0102002886

Transfer of land : formalities for contracts for sale etc of land. – London : H.M.S.O., 1985.
iv,79p. – (Working paper).
ISBN 0117301736

Transfer of land : formalities for deeds and escrows. – London : H.M.S.O., 1985.
iv,44p. – (Working paper).
ISBN 0117301744

Transfer of land : implied covenants for title / the Law Commission. – London : HMSO, 1988.
v,57,11p. – (Working paper).
Includes excerpts from relevant acts.
ISBN 0117301892

Transfer of land : liability for chancel repairs / The Law Commission. – London : H.M.S.O., 1983.
vi,62p; 21cm. – (Working paper).
ISBN 0117301663

Transfer of land : passing of risk from vendor to purchaser / the Law Commission. – London : HMSO, 1988.
v,87p. – (Working paper).
ISBN 0117301914

Transfer of land : the rule in Bain v. Fothergill / The Law Commission. – London : H.M.S.O., 1986.
iv,49p; 21cm. – (Working paper).
Includes bibliographical references.
ISBN 0117301795

Transfer of land : the rule in Bain v. Fothergill / the Law Commission. – London : H.M.S.O., 1987.
iv,28p.
ISBN 010101922X

Transfer of land : title on death / the Law Commission. – London : HMSO, 1987.
viii,106p. – (Working paper).
ISBN 0117301876

Transfer of land, the law of positive and restrictive covenants ... / the Law Commission. – London : H.M.S.O., 1984.
x,331p; 25cm. – (H.C.1983-84).
ISBN 0102201846

Transfer of marine technology to developing nations in international law / Boleslaw A. Boczek. – Honolulu : Law of the Sea Institute, University of Hawaii, 1982.
vi,79p. – (Occasional paper).
Includes bibliographical references.

Transfer of Property Act, 1882. – 7th ed. in prep. – Bombay : Tripathi.
1100p.
Hbk £50.00

Transfer of Property Act, 2 Vols. – 5th ed. – Allahabad : Law Book Company, 1988.
3,000p.
Hbk £600.00

Transfer of Technology for Development. – Paris : International Chamber of Commerce.
42p.
Hbk £10.00

Transfer of undertakings : the legal pitfalls : a specially commissioned report / by Patrick Elias and John Bowers. – London : Longman Professional, 1985.
54 leaves.
ISBN 0851208061

Transfer pricing and multinational enterprises : three taxation issues : reports of the OECD Committee on Fiscal Affairs, 1984. – Paris : O.E.C.D., 1984.
91p.
ISBN 9264126260

Transfrontier Movements of Hazardous Wastes : Legal and Institutional Aspects. – Paris : OECD, Organisation for Economic Co-operation and Development, 1985.
304p.
ISBN 9264126945 Hbk £28.00

Transfrontier Pollution and International Law : Pollution Transfrontiere et le Droit International / Academie de droit international de La Haye, Centre d'etude et de recherche de droit international et de relations internationales Transfrontier pollution ad international law / Hague Academy of International Law, Centre for Studies and Research in International Law and International Relations. – Dordrecht : Martinus Nijhoff, 1986.
133p.
English and French.
ISBN 9024733944 Pbk £50.00

Transkei law journal. – Umtata, Transkei : University of Transkei, 1986.
ISBN 02591286

Transnational corporations in world development. – United Nations. – London : Published in co-operation with the United Nations by Graham & Trotman, 1984.
256p.
ISBN 0860105083 £37.00

Transnational investment law and national development / by Samuel K.B. Asante. – Lagos : Published for the Faculty of Law, University of Lagos by the Lagos University Press, 1981.
111p.
ISBN 9782264148

Transnational law of international commercial transactions / edited by Norbert Horn and Clive M. Schmitthoff. – Antwerp : Kluwer-Devanter/The Netherlands, 1982.
Includes index and bibliography.
ISBN 9065440925 : est.

Transnational legal practice : a survey of selected countries / edited by Dennis Campbell. – Deventer, The Netherlands : Kluwer, 1981.
Includes index.
ISBN 9065440186 v. 2

Transplants and mongrels and the law : the Nigerian experiment : an inaugural lecture delivered at the University of Ife on 17th May, 1983 / by A.A.O. Okunniga. – Ile-Ife, Nigeria : University of Ife Press, 1984.
32p. – (Inaugural lecture series).
Includes bibliographical references.

Transport : International Transport Treaties / M.H. Claringbould. – Dordrecht : Kluwer.
Hbk £285.00

Transport Acts 1981 and 1982 : Penalty Points, Drinking and Driving, Fixed Penalties. – 2nd ed. – London : Fourmat, 1985.
115p.
ISBN 0906840929 Pbk £8.95

Transport and the environment / Department of Transport. – London : The Department, 1987.
32p.

Transport and the Farmer. – Shaw & Sons.
ISBN 0721911501 Hbk £9.95

Trapline Outlaw : Simon Peter Gunanoot. – Victoria : Sono Nis Press.
170p.
ISBN 0919462979 Hbk £12.95

Trasler, Gordon
British Journal of Criminology. – London : Sweet & Maxwell.
Hbk £26.50

Travellers' handbook - guide to law affecting gypsies. – TUAR, 1985.
ISBN 0948309008 Pbk £5.95

Travers →London Government Handbook.

Travis, B.
Auditing Development of Computer Systems. – London : Butterworths, 1987.
ISBN 0406500932 Pbk £26.50

Treanor, D.
Buying Your Home With Other People. – Shelter.
ISBN 090124799 Pbk £5.95

Treason in Tudor England : Politics and Paranoia. – London : Jonathan Cape.
352p.
ISBN 0224028057 Hbk £16.00

Treasure trove : law reform issues / The Law Commission. – London : The Commission, 1987.
7 leaves.

Treat me right : essays on medical law and ethics. – Oxford : Oxford University Press, 1988.
xvii,375p.
Brings together a wide selection of the author's work in the field of medical law and ethics. Many of the articles contained have already been published in journals, but some appear for the first time.
Lawyers, doctors, students of law, ethics and medicine
ISBN 0198255586 Pbk
ISBN 0198255594 Hbk £35

Treaties and alliances of the world / compiled and written by Henry W. Degenhardt. – 3rd ed. – Harlow : Longman, 1981.
ix,409p; 26cm. – (A Keesing's reference publication).
Previous ed.: 1974. Includes index.
ISBN 0582902509 £27.00

Treaties and Related International Documents / Sann. – 7th ed. – Matthew Bender, 1973.
ISBN 0000999053 Hbk £112.00

Treaties establishing the European Communities : treaties amending these treaties : Single European Act : resolutions, declarations
Vol. 1. – Luxembourg : Office for Official Publications of the European Communities, 1987.
1118p.
Also published in Spanish, Danish, German, Greek, English, French, Irish, Italian, Dutch and Portuguese. ' ... up to date as at 1 July 1987 ...'. - p.3.
ISBN 9277192259

Treaties Establishing the European Communities Amending Treaties : Other Basic Instruments. – abr. ed. – Kirchberg : Commission of the European Communities, 1983.
542p.
Hbk

Treatise of the Principle Grounds and Maximes of the Lawes of This Kingdome by W.N. A Dialogue and Treatise of the Laws of England and on Tenures, Estates, Heriditaments and Chattels / W. N. Bythewood. – 9th ed. Repr. of 1821 ed. – Abingdon : Professional Books.
243p.
ISBN 0862053269 Hbk £35.25

Treatise on Air-Aeronautical Law. – 3rd ed. – Agincourt : Carswell, 1981.
848p.
This work for students of air law in Canada is a comprehensive study of the subject from the first days of flight to the present.
Hbk £63.00

Treatise on air-aeronautical law / Nicolas Mateesco Matte. – Montreal : Institute and Centre of Air and Space Law, McGill University, 1981.
832p; 24cm.
ISBN 0771700407

Treatise on Criminal Law. – Lucknow : Eastern Book Company, 1984.
Hbk £80.00

Treatise on Judicial Evidence / J. Bentham. – Repr. of 1825 ed. – Abingdon : Professional Books.
Hbk £60.00

Treatise On Law Of Dower. – Professional Books.
ISBN 086205298X Hbk £49.75

Treatise on Social Security and Labour Law. – Lucknow : Eastern Book Company, 1985.
Hbk £60.00

Treatise on the Law of Bails. – Bombay : Tripathi, 1968.
li, 898p.
bd £45.00

Treatise on the quasi-contract called promutuum and on the condictio indebiti / by Robert-Joseph Pothier : translated by W.J. Hosten and C. van Soelen : and edited by W.J. Hosten. – Pretoria : Government Printer on behalf of the South African Law Commission, 1987.
v,40p. – (Research series).
ISBN 0621107220

Treatment and Rehabilitation : Report of the Advisory Council on the Misuse of Drugs. – London : HMSO, 1982.
ISBN 0113208219 Hbk £3.95

Treatment of disabled persons in social security and taxation law. – Canberra : Australian Government Publishing Service, 1986.
viii,149p. – (Occasional paper).
Bibliography: p134-149.
ISBN 0644048123

Treatment of prisoners under international law / Nigel S. Rodley. – Paris : Unesco, 1987.
xxii,374; 25cm.
Includes index.
ISBN 0198255519 Hbk £40.00
ISBN 0198255632 Pbk £15.00

Treaty, grant, usage or sufferance? : some legal aspects of the status of Hong Kong / by Anthony Dicks. – London : Contemporary China Institute, School of Oriental and African Studies, 1983.
p.427-455.
Offprint from: The China quarterly (September 1983).

Treaty Law in Canada. – Ottawa : University of Ottawa Press, 1975.
xvii, 432p.
ISBN 0776620134 Hbk £17.00

Treaty on Pleading and Parties to Actions with Precedents, 2 Vols. – Repr. of 1809 ed. – Abingdon : Professional Books.
64p.
Hbk £45.00

Treaty series. – London : H.M.S.O., 1893-.
Chronological and classified indexes.

Trebilcock, Michael J.
Canadian Market Place : a Consumer Rights Handbook / Patricia McNeill. – Toronto : Canadian Broadcasting Corporation Enterprises.
160p.
ISBN 0887941192 Pbk £5.95
—Common law of restraint of trade : a legal and economic analysis / by Michael J. Trebilcock. – Toronto : Carswell, 1986.
xxvi,419p.
ISBN 0459396404 Hbk £35.00
—Help : Marketplace Handbook of Consumer Rights in Canada. – Toronto : Canadian Broadcasting Corporation Enterprises.
84p.
Pbk £3.00
→ Lawyers and the consumer interest : regulating the market for legal services.

Tree of life : diversity, flexibility, and creativity in Jewish law / Louis Jacobs. – Oxford : Published for the Littman Library by Oxford University Press, 1984.
310p; 25cm.
Bibliography: p278-293. - Includes index.
ISBN 0197100392 £18.00

Treisman, S. H. →Practitioner's Guide to the Alienation of Land Act.
→ VanRensburg and Treisman : The Practitioner's Guide to the Alienation of Land Act.

Treitel, G. H.
Doctrine and discretion in the law of contract : an inaugural lecture delivered before the University of Oxford on 7 March 1980 / by G.H. Treitel. – Oxford : Clarenden, 1981.
31p; 22cm.
ISBN 0199515271 Pbk £1.95
—Law of contract / by G.H. Treitel. – 7th ed. – London : Stevens, 1987.
850p; 25cm.
Previous ed.: 1983. Includes index.
ISBN 0420474900 Hbk £30.00 :
ISBN 0420475001 Pbk £22.00
—Outline of the law of contract / G.H. Treitel. – 3rd ed. – London : Butterworths, 1984.
xxxiii,366p; 22cm.
Previous ed.: 1979. Includes index.
ISBN 0406668485 Pbk
—Remedies for breach of contract : a comparative account / G.H. Treitel. – Oxford : Clarendon Press, 1988.
xliii,422p.
Includes index. Discusses remedies for a breach of contract from a comparative perspective. Contrasts civil and common law solutions, and differences between English and American common law, and French and German civil law. The aim is to identify types of solutions and consider how far differences in theoretical approaches are reflected in practical results.
ISBN 0198255004 Hbk £45/$60

Treitel, Phyllis →Juvenile justice in the United Kingdom : comparisons and suggestions for change.

Treky, T.
Dictionary of Insurance Terms English-Arabic. – Witherby, 1985.
ISBN 090088696X Hbk £34.00

Tremaine, J.
Placita Coronae : Pleas of the Crown in Matters Criminal and Civil. – Repr. of 1723 ed. – Abingdon : Professional Books.
366p.
Hbk £210.00

Tremeear, William James
Criminal Code : 1988. – Agincourt : Carswell, 1987.
780p.
Pbk £62.25
—Criminal Code Annotations : 1964-1970. – Agincourt : Carswell, 1981.
388p.
Hbk £50.50
—Tremeear's 1971-1986 criminal annotations / by Leonard J. Ryan : 1985 and 1986 annotations by F. Dwight Richardson. – 2. – Toronto : Carswell, 1986.
Includes index. Kept up to date by annual supplement. Companion volumes to Tremeear's criminal code. Supplement to: Tremeear's annotated criminal code. 6th ed..
→ Tremeear's 1981 criminal code and miscellaneous statutes : as amended to January 1, 1981.
→ Tremeear's 1982 criminal code and miscellaneous statutes : as amended to January 1, 1982.
→ Tremeear's 1983 criminal code and miscellaneous statutes : as amended to January 1, 1983.
→ Tremeear's 1984 criminal code and miscellaneous statutes : as amended to January 1, 1984.
→ Tremeear's 1985-86 criminal code and miscellaneous statutes : as amended to January 1, 1986.
→ Tremeear's 1987 criminal code and miscellaneous statutes : as amended to January 1, 1987.

—Tremeear's criminal annotations 1964-1970 / being the permanent supplement to the sixth edition of Tremeear's annotated criminal code by Leonard J. Ryan. – Toronto : Carswell, 1981.
xxvi,361p.
Includes index.
ISBN 0459344803

Tremeear's 1971-1986 criminal annotations / by Leonard J. Ryan : 1985 and 1986 annotations by F. Dwight Richardson. – 2. – Toronto : Carswell, 1986.
Includes index. Kept up to date by annual supplement. Companion volumes to Tremeear's criminal code. Supplement to: Tremeear's annotated criminal code. 6th ed..

Tremeear's 1981 criminal code and miscellaneous statutes : as amended to January 1, 1981 / William James Tremeear. – Toronto : Carswell, 1981.
xiv,526p.
'The companion volume to Tremeear's Criminal annotations'. Includes index. Earler eds. held.
ISBN 0459335405

Tremeear's 1982 criminal code and miscellaneous statutes : as amended to January 1, 1982 / William James Tremeear. – Toronto : Carswell, 1982.
xiv,676p.
'The companion volume to Tremeear's Criminal annotations'. Includes index.
ISBN 0459347101

Tremeear's 1983 criminal code and miscellaneous statutes : as amended to January 1, 1983 / William James Tremeear. – Toronto : Carswell, 1983.
xvi,715p.
Previous ed.: 1982. Includes index. 'The companion volume to Tremeear's Criminal Annotations'.
ISBN 0459355503

Tremeear's 1984 criminal code and miscellaneous statutes : as amended to January 1, 1984 / William James Tremeear. – Toronto : Carswell, 1984.
xvi,712p.
'The companion volume to Tremeear's Criminal Annotations'. Previous ed.: 1983. Includes index.
ISBN 0459367609

Tremeear's 1985-86 criminal code and miscellaneous statutes : as amended to January 1, 1986 / William James Tremeear. – Toronto : Carswell, 1985.
xvi,732p.
Previous ed.: 1984. 'The companion volume to the Tremeear's criminal annotations'. Includes index.
ISBN 0459377108

Tremeear's 1987 criminal code and miscellaneous statutes : as amended to January 1, 1987 / William James Tremeear. – Toronto : Carswell, 1987.
xvi,731p.
Previous ed.: 1985-86. Includes index. 'The companion volume to the Tremeears criminal annotations'.
ISBN 0459399209

Tremeear's 1988 criminal code ... : as amended to Jan. 1, 1988. – Toronto : Carswell, 1988.
xviii,751p.
'The companion volume to the Tremeear's criminal annotations' - t.p.. Includes index.
ISBN 045931341X

Tremeear's criminal annotations 1964-1970 / being the permanent supplement to the sixth edition of Tremeear's annotated criminal code by Leonard J. Ryan. – Toronto : Carswell, 1981.
xxvi,361p.
Includes index.
ISBN 0459344803

Trends in child abuse, 1977-82 : the fourth report on the children placed on N.S.P.C.C. Special Unit registers / by Susan J. Creighton. – London : N.S.P.C.C., 1984.
57p.
Bibliography: p.35.
ISBN 0902498126

Trends in corporate governance and investor protection / by Louis Loss. – Lagos : Lagos University Press, 1981.
64p.
Includes bibliographies.
ISBN 9782264261

Trescott, Pamela →Outrage : the abuse of diplomatic immunity.

Trespass on residential premises : a consultation paper / Home Office. – London : Home Office, 1983.
26p.

Treumann, Walter
U.S. Business Law : A Bilingual Guide for the German Businessman and Investor U.S. - Amerikanisches Wirtschaftsrecht : E. Zweisprach. / Martin Peltzer. – Cologne : Otto Schmidt, 1986.
ISBN 3504400048 Hbk £120.00

Trevelyan, John →Rights of way : a guide to law and practice.
→ Rights of way guide to law and practice.

Treverton-Jones, G
Imprisonment: the legal status and rights of prisoners. – London : Sweet & Maxwell, 1989.
Describes the history and structure of the prison system, focusing on the various categories of prisons and prisoners within it. Analyses the body of case law, including issues such as disciplinary hearings, prisoners' correspondence, visits, and access to the courts. Summarises the law on remission and parole. Contains the European Prison Rules as an appendix.
ISBN 0421322306 Pbk £25.00
—Rights of Prisoners After Sentence. – Sweet & Maxwell.
ISBN 0421322306 Pbk £20.00

Triable-either-way cases : Crown Court or Magistrates' Court? / by David Riley and Julie Vennard. – London : H.M.S.O., 1988.
52 p.
Discusses whether the balance of either-way business could be redistributed in favour of the Magistrates' Court by encouraging them to accept jurisdiction more often in such cases.
ISBN 0113408900

Trial and error : the Maguires, the Guildford pub bombings and British justice / Robert Kee. – London : Hamish Hamilton, 1986.
284p; 22cm.
Includes index.
ISBN 0241119588 £10.95

Trial by fire and water : the medieval judicial ordeal / Robert Bartlett. – Oxford : Clarendon, 1986.
xiii,200p; 22cm.
Includes bibliography and index.
ISBN 0198219733 £19.50

Trial by jury : social and psychological dynamics / Ramesh Deosaran. – St. Augustine, Trinidad, West Indies : Institute of Social and Economic Research, University of the West Indies, 1985.
324 p.; 23 cm.
Includes indexes. Bibliography: p. 283-297.
ISBN 9766180008 Pbk

Trial By Jury (Hamlyn No. 8). – Sweet & Maxwell, 1966.
ISBN 0420434909 Pbk £6.50

Trial by medicine : insanity and responsibility in Victorian trials / by Roger Smith. – Edinburgh : Edinburgh University Press, 1981.
ix,238p.
ISBN 085224407X

Trial Jury in England, France, Germany 1700-1900. – Berlin : Duncker and Humblot, 1987.
305p.
ISBN 3428061780 Hbk £124.00

Trial of an Action. – Butterworths, 1981.
280p.
Examines the legal and practical aspects of a trial from the selection of the tribunal to the final judgement. Looks at rules of practice and procedure, and with tactics and techniques of a trial lawyer. Covers the mode of trial, devices to facilitate or supplant testimony, the role of counsel, the role of the trial judge, the charge to the jury, and the verdict.
ISBN 040986854X Hbk £55.00

Trial of Beyers Naude : Christian Witness and the Rule of Law. – Geneva : International Commission of Jurists, 1975.
188p.
Hbk £15.00

Trial of Paulin Croos. – Colombo : Gunasena and Co..
Hbk £10.00

Trial of Socrates. – Aurora : Cape.
ISBN 0224025910 Hbk £12.95

Trial of Sunny Ang. – Singapore : Times Booker International.
160p.
ISBN 9971651548 Pbk £6.50

Trial of the expert : a study of expert evidence and forensic experts / Ian R. Freckelton. – Melbourne : Oxford University Press, 1987.
xxxii,289p.
A textbook of the rules of expert evidence, and an analysis of the difficulties experienced when experts from non-legal disciplines are called as witnesses. Examines the impact of new scientific disciplines, and looks at how the forensic expert's duties to maintain confidentiality may conflict with the court's need for all the relevant evidence.
ISBN 0195545664 Hbk £30

Trial Practice. – Vancouver : Continuing Legal Education Society of British Columbia, 1987.
180p.
ISBN 0865043205 Hbk £65.00

Trials and punishments / R.A. Duff. – Cambridge : Cambridge University Press, 1986.
336p; 22cm. – (Cambridge studies in philosophy).
Includes bibliography and index.
ISBN 0521308186 £22.50

Trials of Strength. – Allahabad : Orient Law House.
ISBN 0861253574 Hbk £13.00

Tribal Law and Justice : a Report on the Santal. – New Delhi : Concept Publishing Company, 1984.
xxxvi, 741p.
Hbk £200.00

Tribal Law of the Pathans in Historical Perspective. – Islamabad : Quaid-i-Azam University.
Hbk

Tribe →Senate, the Courts and the Constitution : a Debate.

Tribunal practice and procedures. – London : Law Society, 1988.
ISBN 0948736011 Pbk £19.50

Tribunals on trial: a study of decision-making under the Mental Health Review Tribunals. Based on empirical enquiry into the operation of the Tribunal system, assesses the process of decision-making from the initial application by a patiTribunals on trial: a study of decision-making under the Mental Health Act 1983. – Oxford : Clarendon Press, 1989.
240; 21.5.
Insight into the decision-making processes of the Mental Health Review Tribunals. Based on empirical enquiry into the operation of the Tribunal system, assesses the process of decision-making from the initial application by a patient, through descriptions of tribunal hearings, to an examination of their deliberations. Examines individual cases in detail.
ISBN 0198252498 Hbk £25.00

Tribunals practice and procedure / general editor, John Bowers : with a foreword by Sir Jack Jacob : and an introduction by J.A.G. Griffith. – 1. – London : Legal Studies and Services, 1985.
looseleaf; 26cm.
Includes index.
ISBN 0907822592 £98.00

Tricker, R. I.
Corporate governance : practices, procedures and powers in British companies and their boards of directors / R.I. Tricker. – Aldershot : Gower, 1984.
vii,319p; 22cm.
Includes index.
ISBN 0566007495 £18.95
→ Governing the Institute : a study, commissioned by the Institute of Chartered Accountants in England and Wales, on the direction, control and regulation of the Institute.
—Independent Director, The. – Tolley Publishing, 1978.
ISBN 0510493785 Pbk £4.50

Trickey, Geoffrey
Presentation and settlement of contractors' claims / Geoffrey Trickey. – London : Spon, 1983.
xiv,358p; 24cm.
Includes index.
ISBN 0419114300

Triennial review report ... / Police Complaints Board. – 3. – London : HMSO, 1980-.

Triggs, Gillian D. →Antarctic Treaty regime : law, environment and resources.
—International law and Australian sovereignty in Antarctica / by Gillian D. Triggs. – Sydney : Legal Books, 1986.
xxix,403p.
Bibliography: p.379-391. - Includes index.
ISBN 0949553239

Trill, David →Rowland's Tax Guide, 1984-1985.

Trilling, Diana
Mrs. Harris : the death of the Scarsdale diet doctor / Diana Trilling. – London : Abacus, 1983.
341p.
Originally published: New York : Harcourt Brace Jovanovich, 1981. Previously published: London : Hamilton, 1982.
ISBN 0349133948

Trimble, W. David →Housing Law in Northern Ireland.
→ Northern Ireland housing law : the public and private rented sectors.

Trimm →Life Assurance : Its Tax Implications Etc.

Trindade, A.
Exhaustion of Local Remedies in International Law. – Cambridge : Cambridge University Press, 1983.
ISBN 0521229472 Hbk £42.50

Trindade, Antonio Augusto Cancado
Application of the rule of exhaustion of local remedies in international law : its rationale in the international protection of individual rights / A.A. Cancado Trindade. – Cambridge Cambridgeshire : Cambridge University Press, 1983.
xiii,443p.
Includes index. Bibliography: p422-440.
ISBN 0521229472

Trindade, Francis A →Constitution of Malaysia : further perspectives and developments : essays in honour of Tun Mohamed Suffian.
—Law of torts in Australia / F.A. Trindade, Peter Cane. – Melbourne : Oxford University Press, 1985.
lxv, 763 p.; 24 cm.
Includes indexes.
ISBN 0195544633 Pbk £39.00
ISBN 0195544641 Hbk £55.00

Trinidad and Tobago Bar Association →Lawyer : a quarterly journal of the Trinidad & Tobago Bar Association.

Trinidad and Tobago consolidated index of statutes and subsidiary legislation to 1st January 1983 / compiled at the Faculty of Law Library, University of the West Indies, Barbados. – Rev. ed. – Port-of-Spain : Government Printer, 1983.
ix,105p.
Previous ed.: 1st January 1979. One of a series in the West Indian Legislation Indexing Project (WILIP) compiled in cooperation with the British Development Division.

Trinidad and Tobago Laws
Vols. 1-17. – Sweet & Maxwell, 1981.
ISBN 0421287306 Hbk £245.00

Trinidad, Gabriel V.
Revised Penal Code. – Quezon City, 1983.
366p.
Pbk Univeristy of the Philippines, Law Center

Tripartism and the International Labour Organisation : a study of the legal concept : its origins, function and evolution in the law of nations / Abdul-Karim Tikriti. – Stockholm : Distributed by Almqvist & Wiksell, 1982.
xxviii,417p. – (Studies in international law).
Thesis (Doctoral) - Uppsala University 1982. Bibliography: p.400-410. - Includes index. Published under the auspices of the Swedish Institute of International Law.
ISBN 9122005609

Tripartite Declaration of Principles concerning Multinational Enterprises and Social Policy : history, contents, follow-up and relationship with relevant instruments of other organisations / Hans Gunter. – Geneva : Interntional Labour Office, 1981.
iii,29p.
ISBN 9221029093

Tristram, Thomas Hutchinson
Probate Practice / Cootes. – 27th ed. – London : Butterworths.
ISBN 0406403406 Hbk £135.00

Trivedi, H.D.
Indian Penal Code. – 2nd ed. – Lucknow : Eastern Book Company, 1981.
406p.
Hbk £30.00
→ Law Relating to Identification and Expert Opinion.
→ Prevention of Food Adulteration Act, Includes Supplement-1986.

Troister, Sidney H.
Law of Subdivision Control in Ontario : a Practical Guide to Section 49 of the Planning Act. – Agincourt : Carswell, 1988.
350p.
Hbk £48.75

Trollope and the law. – London : Macmillan, 1986.
ISBN 0333400135 Hbk £25.00

Tromans, Stephen
Commercial leases / Stephen Tromans. – London : Sweet & Maxwell, 1987.
250p; 23cm.
Examines the impact of recent case law, rating, and planning development. Covers licences, agreements for lease, rent reviews, 'clear leases', dilapidations, user and covenants, and the practicalities of leaseholding conveyancing in its own right.
ISBN 0421354607 £19.50

Troops in strikes : military intervention in industrial disputes / Steve Peak. – London : Cobden Trust, 1984.
177p.
Bibliography: p172-174.
ISBN 0900137223

Trotman, L.
Corporate Debt Securities : Priority Rules. – Auckland : Legal Research Foundation, 1986.
Hbk £10.00

Trouble with Legal Language. – Ottawa : Canadian Law Information Council, 1985.
33p.
ISBN 0920358845 Pbk

Troubled lives : John and Sarah Austin / Lotte and Joseph Hamburger. – Toronto : University of Toronto Press, 1985.
xiii,261p.
Includes index.

Troughton, H.
Japanese finance : Deregulation. – London : Euromoney, 1986.
ISBN 1870031253 Hbk £110.00

Troy, Patrick N.
Federal Power in Australia's Cities. – Neutral Bay : Hale & Iremonger.
ISBN 0908094043 Hbk £19.00, 015

Trubek, David → Integration through law : Europe and the American federal experience : a series, Vol.3 : Consumer law, common markets and federalism in Europe and the United States : by Thierry Bourgoignie and David Trubek : (with Louise Trubek and Denis Stingl).

Trudeau, Pierre Elliot
With a Bang, Not a Whimper. – Don Mills : Stoddart Publishing Co, 1988.
ISBN 0773752463 Hbk £12.95

True Crime Diary. – London : Futura.
ISBN 0708842143 Pbk £3.50

Truner, J.
Behind Closed Doors. – Thorsons, 1988.
ISBN 0722515677 Hbk £5.99

Trussler, Marguerite → Practice in Mortgage Actions in Alberta.

Trust Accounting. – Vancouver : Continuing Legal Education Society of British Columbia, 1987.
110p.
ISBN 0865043477 Hbk £70.00

Trust in Liechtenstein law. – Watford : Alvescot Press, 1983.
512p.
Translation of: Die Treuhanderschaft des liechtensteinischen Rechts.
ISBN 0950583413 £45.00

Trust law & practice : pension funds, commercial trusts and charities. – London : Cass, 1986-.

Trust Practice Manual. – Deloitte, Haskins and Sells. – London : Butterworths, 1985.
This book provides the basis for setting up standard procedures for the organization and operation of a trust department in a law office in the United Kingdom. Practical issues of management and procedures are addressed in the work.
ISBN 040650010X Pbk

Trust taxation manual. – London : Butterworths, 1986.
ISBN 0406503303 Pbk £18.50

Trustee Act, 1949 (Act 206) and Trustees (Incorporation) Act, 1962 (Act 258). – Kuala Lumpur : International Law Books Services.
Hbk £9.00

Trustee companies' internal trading relationships : report of the Property Law and Equity Reform Committee. – Wellington : Property Law and Equity Reform Committee, 1982.
6p.

Trustee savings banks bill : report on the consolidation of the Trustee Savings Banks Acts 1969 to 1978 / the Law Commission and the Scottish Law Commission. – London : H.M.S.O., 1981.
11p; 25cm.
ISBN 0101825706

Trustees of the Fitzkenton Estate. – London : Sweet & Maxwell, 1985.
– (Sweet and Maxwell's Law Files Ser.: No. 5).
ISBN 0421340207 Llf £29.50

Trusts. – Vancouver : Continuing Legal Education Society of British Columbia, 1985.
233p.
ISBN 0865042373 Hbk £60.00

Trusts. – Butterworths, 1989.
ca 98p.
ISBN 040949481X Pbk £10.95

Trusts /. – North Ryde : Law Book Co, 1985.
ix, 102p. – (Nutshells).
ISBN 0455206317

Trusts : Maximising the Tax Advantages. – London : Oyez Longman, 1983.
– (Oyez Longman Intelligence Report Ser.).
ISBN 0851207375 Hbk £45.00

Trusts and Tax Planning. – 2nd ed. – London : Oyez Longman, 1982.
– (Oyez Longman Practical Tax Ser.).
Hbk £16.00

Trusts and tax planning. – 3rd ed. – London : Longman Professional, 1987.
ISBN 0851208762 Pbk £35.88

Trusts and trust-like devices / edited by W.A. Wilson. – S.l. : United Kingdom National Committee of Comparative Law, 1981.
244p; 25cm.
'Based on revised papers and contributions originally submitted to a colloquium held by the United Kingdom National Committee for Comparative Law at the University of Exeter'. Includes bibliographical references.

Trusts for accountants. – London : Butterworths, 1987.
ISBN 0406500908 Pbk £10.95

Trusts in a nutshell / Angela Sydenham. – London : Sweet & Maxwell, 1987.
116p; 22cm.
Includes index.
ISBN 0421368500 Pbk £3.95

Trusts in South Africa with Up-to-Date Addendum. – Cape Town : Legal and Financial Publishing Co.
Hbk £33.50

Trusts Law : Texts and Materials / Chesterman. – Weidenfeld & Nicolson.
– (Law in Context Series).
ISBN 0297794027 Hbk £35.00
ISBN 0297794035 Pbk £22.95

Trusts of land / the Law Commission. – London : H.M.S.O., 1985.
iv,76p. – (Working paper).
ISBN 0117301752

Trusts of Land : overreaching / the Law Commission. – London : H.M.S.O., 1988.
iv,42,20p. – (Working paper).
ISBN 0117301884

Tsoukalis, Loukas → Political economy of international money : in search of a new order.

Tsutsui, W.M.
Banking Policy in Japan American Efforts at Reform During the Occupation. – Routledge.
ISBN 0145000033 Hbk £30.00

Tuck, Mary
Ethnic minorities, crime and policing : a survey of the experiences of West Indians and whites / by Mary Tuck and Peter Southgate. – London : H.M.S.O., 1981.
iv,50p.
Bibliography: p50. A Home Office Research and Planning Unit report.
ISBN 0113407653

Tucker → Remedies for victims of crime.

Tucker, R. A.
Select Cases of Newfoundland : 1817-1828. – Repr. of 1938 ed. – Agincourt : Carswell.
600p. – (Carswell's Classic Reprints).
This work is a reprint of a rare 1893 collection of early decisions of the courts of province of Newfoundland, Canada.
Hbk £71.50

Tuddenham, Richard → Family law and practice.

Tudor on charities / Spencer G. Maurice, David B. Parker. – 7th ed. – London : Sweet & Maxwell, 1984.
lxxiii,737p; 26cm.
Previous ed.: 1967. Includes index.
ISBN 0421249102 £75.00

Tudor, Owen Davies
Tudor on charities / Spencer G. Maurice, David B. Parker. – 7th ed. – London : Sweet & Maxwell, 1984.
lxxiii,737p; 26cm.
Previous ed.: 1967. Includes index.
ISBN 0421249102 £75.00

Tulkens, J J J → Standard minimum rulesfor the implementation of non-custodial sanction and measures involving restriction of liberty.

Tullett, T.
Clues to Murder. – Aurora : Cape, 1986.
ISBN 0370308522 Hbk £12.95

Tullock, G.
Logic of the Law. – London : Eurospan.
ISBN 0802600182 Pbk £12.75

Tullock, Gordon
Economics of Bureaucracy and Statutory Authorities / Warren Hogan. – Turramura : Centre for Independent Studies.
112p.
ISBN 094976910X Hbk £5.95

Tumim, Stephen
Great legal fiascos / Stephen Tumim. – London : Barker (Arthur), 1985.
126p.
ISBN 0213169274

Tun Tan : Portrait of a Statesman. – Singapore : Quins, 1981.
Hbk (special ed.) £45.00

Tunkel, Victor → Court of Appeal (Civil Division) judgments, 1951-1980.

Tunkin, Grigory I.
International Law and Municipal Law : Proceedings of the German-Soviet Colloquy on International Law at the Institut fur Internationales Recht an der Universitat Kiel 4 to 8 May 1987 / Rudiger Wolfrum. – Berlin : Duncker and Humblot, 1988.
210p.
ISBN 3428064267 Hbk £96.00

Tunnicliffe, H.
Wardship : A Guide for the Non-Lawyer. – PEPAR Publications.
ISBN 094868013X Pbk £1.95

Tunstall, Jeremy
Communications deregulation : the unleashing of America's communications industry / Jeremy Tunstall. – Oxford : Blackwell, 1986.
425p; 23cm.
Includes bibliography and index.
ISBN 0631148191 £17.50

Tur, Richard → Essays on Kelsen.

Turkey : testimony on torture. – Amnesty International. – London : Amnesty International Publications, 1985.
76p.
ISBN 0862100887

Turkey's banks and banking systems. – London : Euromoney, 1985.
ISBN 0903121859 Hbk £58.00

Turks and Caicos Islands consolidated index of statutes and subsidiary legislation to 1st January 1983 / compiled at the Faculty of Law Library, University of the West Indies, Barbados. – Rev. ed. – Barbados : s.n., 1983.
iv,46p.
Previous ed.: 1st January 1981. One of a series in the West Indian Legislation Indexing Project (WILIP) compiled in cooperation with the British Development Division.

Turks and Caicos Islands consolidated index of statutes and subsidiary legislation to 1st January 1981 / compiled at the Faculty of Law Library, University of the West Indies, Barbados. – Bridgetown, Barbados? : Faculty of Law Library, University of the West Indies?, 1981.
iv,43 leaves.
One of a series in the West Indian Legislation Indexing Project (WILIP) compiled in cooperation with the British Development Division.

Turlock, L. A., et al
Trademarks and Unfair Competition. – Vancouver : British Columbia Continuing Legal Education Society, 1982.
352p.
ISBN 0865040591 Hbk £55.00

Turnbull, David →Receiving juvenile justice : adolescents and state care and control.

Turnbull, Malcolm
Spycatcher Trial. – Richmond : Heinemann, 1988.
208p.
ISBN 0855612398 Hbk £29.95

Turnbull-Walker, A.
PACEA 1984 : Guide for Duty Solicitors. – London : Fourmat, 1986.
ISBN 1851900195 Pbk £4.95

Turner
Principles of marine insurance / Alexander. – 7th ed. – Stone & Cox, 1986.
ISBN 0854431128 Pbk £15.00

Turner, Adrian John
New fixed penalty system : and disqualification, endorsement and penalty points : including a detailed guide to part III of the Transport Act 1982 and associated provisions / by Adrain John Turner and Malcolm Marsh. – Chichester : Rose (Barry), 1986.
x,170p.
Includes index.

Turner, Barbara
Law for councillors / by Barbara Turner. – London : Sweet & Maxwell, 1986.
xii,146p; 21cm.
ISBN 0421353600 Pbk £5.00

Turner, C. F. →Precedents in matrimonial causes and ancillary matters.

Turner, C.W.O.
Contracts Building and Engineering their Planning and Administration. – London : Butterworths, 1983.
ISBN 0409701270 Pbk

Turner, Clive →Australian mercantile law.

Turner, Dennis F
Building Contract Disputes : Their Avoidance and Resolution. – London : Longman Scientific.
ISBN 0582037344 Hbk £25.00
—Building Contracts - Practical Guide. – 4th ed. – London : Longman Professional, 1983.
ISBN 0711456569 Hbk £19.95
—Building Sub-Contract Forms. – Oxford : Blackwell Scientific, 1985.
ISBN 0003830152 Hbk £22.50
—Design and Building Contract Practice. – London : Longman Professional, 1986.
ISBN 0582494842 Pbk £19.50
—Standard contracts for building. – London : Longman Professional, 1984.
ISBN 0711457522 Pbk £6.50

Turner, J. Neville →Family law casebook.

Turner, Kaye →Civil liberties cases in Zambia.

Turner, Louis →Britain and the multinationals.
—Oil companies in the international system / Louis Turner. – 3rd ed. – London : Allen & Unwin for the Royal Institute of International Affairs, 1983.
279p; 22cm.
Previous ed.: 1980. Bibliography: p253-268. - Includes index.
ISBN 0043820409 Pbk

Turner, Michael
Recent Developments in the Law Relating to Damages With Particular Reference to Professional Claims / Alexander Layton. – London : Law Society, 1981.
– (Oxford Weekend Courses).
Hbk £2.00

Turner, Ralph V.
English judiciary in the age of Glanvill and Bracton c.1176-1239. – Cambridge : Cambridge University Press, 1985.
335.
Study of the evolution of the professional judiciary in medieval England. Describes the growth of a professional civil service.
ISBN 052126510X Hbk £30.00

Turow, S.
One L : What They Really Teach You at Harvard Law School. – Sceptre.
ISBN 0340431008 Pbk £2.95

Turpin, Colin C.
British government and the constitution : text, cases and materials / Colin Turpin. – London : Weidenfeld (George) & Nicolson, 1985.
xxviii,476p; 25cm.
Includes index.
ISBN 0297786512 Hbk £25.00
ISBN 0297786520 Pbk £15.00
→ British nationality and the right of abode 1945-1983.
—British nationality and the right of abode 1945-1983 / by K.J. Gray : by C.C. Turpin. – Deventer : Kluwer, 1986.
vii,269p.
Includes bibliographical references.
ISBN 9065442510
→ Property, divorce and retirement pension rights.

Turriff, Gordon
Office of sheriff / by Gordon Turriff and Elizabeth Edinger. – Victoria : Queen's Printer, 1983.
246p.
'A study prepared for the Law Reform Commission of British Columbia with financial assistance from the Law Foundation of British Columbia' - title page.
ISBN 0771883927

Turriff, Gordon N, et al
Practice Before the Registrar in British Columbia. – Vancouver : British Columbia Continuing Legal Education Society, 1982.
199p.
ISBN 0865040427 Hbk £40.00

Tutorials in Contract. – 4th ed. – North Ryde : Law Book Co, 1986.
xxii, 377p.
ISBN 0455206430 Hbk £35.00
ISBN 0455206449 Pbk £25.00

Tutt, N.
Tax raiders. – London : Financial Training, 1985.
ISBN 0906322766 Hbk £10.95

Tutt, Norman →Children in custody.

Twelfth report to Parliament on subordinate legislation concerning Melbourne and Metropolitan Board of Works By-law no. 235 : Melbourne and Metropolitan Board of Works Employees' Superannuation Fund Regulations (SR No. 231/1987) / Legal and Constitutional Committee. – Melbourne : Government Printer, 1988.
v,7p.
Includes text of legislation.

Twelve Schedule. – Cape Town : Legal & Financial Publishing, 1983.
– (Merlen P.A.Y.E. Registers).
Hbk £2.95

Twentieth Report. – Criminal Injuries Compensation Board. – London : HMSO, 1984.
ISBN 0101939906 Hbk £4.50

Twenty years of statutory redundancy payments in Great Britain / Paul Lewis. – Nottingham : The Universities of Leeds and Nottingham in association with the Institute of Personnel Management, 1985.
50p; 21cm.
ISBN 0900572639

Twenty-eighth annual report of the Commonwealth Scholarship Commission in the United Kingdom : for the year ending 30 September 1987 to the Minister for Overseas Development. – Commonwealth Scholarship Commission in the United Kingdom. – London : The Commission, 1987.
110p.

Twenty-four Schedule. – Cape Town : Legal & Financial Publishing, 1983.
– (Merlen P.A.Y.E. Registers Ser.).
Hbk £4.04

Twenty-fourth report (latent damage) / Law Reform Committee. – London : H.M.S.O., 1984.
iv,34p; 25cm. – (Report).
ISBN 0101939000

Twice Condemned : Slaves & Criminal Laws : Virginia 1705-1865. – Louisiana : Louisiana State University Press.
ISBN 0807114014 Hbk £35.65

Twin Acts Simplified : Company and M.R.T.P. Law / P.C. Jain. – New Delhi : S. Chand and Company.
Hbk £25.00

Twining, William →Facts in law.
—How to do things with rules : a primer of interpretation / William Twining, David Miers. – 2nd ed. – London : Weidenfeld and Nicholson, 1982.
xx,387p; 23cm.
Previous ed. 1976.
ISBN 0297780832 Hbk £18.50
ISBN 0297780840 Pbk
—Jurists : Profiles in Legal Theory. – London : Edward Arnold.
—Karl Llewellyn and Realist Movement (LIC). – Weidenfeld & Nicolson, 1985.
ISBN 0297786679 Pbk £12.95
ISBN 0297994828 Hbk £20.00
→ Law publishing and legal information : small jurisdictions of the British Isles.
→ Legal literature in small jurisdictions : a report of a conference held at Osgoode Hall Law School, York University, Downsview, Ontario on 3-5 November 1978.
→ Legal theory : papers presented at the W.G. Hart Legal Workshop, 3rd-6th July 1984 at the Institute of Advanced Legal Studies, University of London.
→ Legal theory and common law.
—Theories of evidence : Bentham and Wigmore / William Twining. – London : Weidenfeld & Nicolson, 1985.
x,265p.
Includes bibliographical references and index.
ISBN 0297786687 Hbk £17.95
ISBN 0297786695 Pbk £8.95

Twiss, Travers →Black Book of the Admiralty : with an appendix.

Two cultures of policing : street cops and management cops / Elizabeth Reuss-Ianni. – New Brunswick, N.J. : Transaction Books, 1983.
145p; 24cm.
Bibliography: p137-142. - Includes index.
ISBN 0878554696

Two Irelands : the problem of the double minority / by Harold Jackson and Anne McHardy. – 3rd rev. ed. – London : Minority Rights Group, 1984.
16p. – (Report).
Bibliography: p.16.

Two Laws : Managing Disputes in a Contemporary Aboriginal Community. – Canberra City : Australian Institute of Aboriginal Studies, 1986.
176p.
ISBN 0855751746 Hbk £25.95

Two lectures on law reform : delivered at the workshop on Marriage and Family Life by the Human Sciences Research Council on 26 September 1985 / by J.T. Delport and C.R.M. Dlamini. – Pretoria : Government Printer on behalf of the South African Law Comission, 1987.
iv,38p. – (Research series).
Bibliography: pp.19-21.
ISBN 0621106704

Twohill, B.A.
Government Regulation of Industry : Proceedings of the Conference held at the University of Newcastle Feb 1981. – Newcastle : University of Newcastle, 1981.
x, 454p.
ISBN 0725904054 Hbk £15.00

Twumasi, Paul K
Criminal law in Ghana / P.K. Twumasi. – Tema : Ghana Pub. Corp., 1985.
xlviii, 634 p.; 24 cm.
Includes bibliographical references and index.
ISBN 9964102933

Tyas, J. G.
Law of Torts. – 4th ed. – Plymouth : Macdonald & Evans, 1982.
– (M and E Handbook Ser.).
ISBN 0712127046 Hbk £5.95

Tyler, E. L. G.
Cases and statutes on land law / by E.L.G. Tyler. – 2nd ed. – London : Sweet & Maxwell, 1986.
334p; 22cm.
Previous ed.: 1974. Includes index.
ISBN 0421343508 Pbk £13
→ Fisher & Lightwood's law of mortgage.
—Research paper on the variation of private trusts / by E.L.G. Tyler. – Hobart? : Government Printer?, 1985.
54p.
—Tyler's family provision / R. D. Oughton. – 2nd ed. – Abingdon : Professional Books, 1984.
xlvi,408p.
Includes index.
ISBN 0862050758 Hbk £30.75

Tyler's family provision / R. D. Oughton. – 2nd ed. – Abingdon : Professional Books, 1984.
xlvi,408p.
Includes index.
ISBN 0862050758 Hbk £30.75

Tyne, S.M. →The Joint Operating Agreement : oil and gas law.

Tyree, Alan L.
Australian Law of Cheques and Payment Orders. – Butterworths, 1988.
199p.
ISBN 0409495417 Pbk £35.00
—New Zealand Banking Law. – Butterworths.
400p.
Pbk £119.00

Tyrrell, Alan R.
Parliamentary challenge to the community law making process : the Exeter Lecture in European Community Law, delivered in the University on 4 March 1983 / by Alan R. Tyrrell. – Exeter : University of Exeter, 1983.
11p.

Tzannes, R. →Strata Titles.

U.K. onshore oil and gas law : a practical guide to the legal regime relating to United Kingdom onshore oil and gas operations / by J.R. Salter : preface by Terence Daintith and Geoffrey Willoughby. – London : Sweet & Maxwell, 1986.
xxvi,505p; 25cm.
A compendium of the relevant statute law and all the secondary legislation made pursuant to it. Includes forms and precedents for every stage of legal proceedings and a section on government memoranda, departmental guidance notes, and other policy documents.
ISBN 0421347805 £55.00

U.P. Industrial Disputes Act, 1947 : With Rules and Notifications. – 2nd ed. – Lucknow : Eastern Book Company, 1986.
Hbk £30.00

U.P. Muslim Wakfs Acts. – Lucknow : Eastern Book Company, 1984.
91p.
Hbk £20.00

U.P. Revenue Digest (1960-1963), 2 Vols. – Allahabad : Law Publishing House, 1984.
Hbk £160.00

U.S. Business Law : A Bilingual Guide for the German Businessman and Investor U.S. - Amerikanisches Wirtschaftsrecht : E. Zweisprach. / Martin Peltzer. – Cologne : Otto Schmidt, 1986.
ISBN 3504400048 Hbk £120.00

U.S. legal system : a practice handbook / edited by Dennis Campbell and Winifred Hepperle. – The Hague : Nijhoff, 1983.
x,319p; 25cm.
Includes bibliography.
ISBN 9024727820 Hbk £130.00

U.S.S.R. Contract Law. – Helsinki : Lakimiesliiton Kustannus, 1982.
219p.
Hbk £113.00

U.S. Shipping Act of 1984 / by John McConnell. – London : Lloyd's of London, 1985.
345p; 25cm.
ISBN 1850440360 £38.00

U.S. Trade Expansion Act of 1962 : How Will It Affect Canadian-U.S. Trade?. – Toronto : C.D. Howe Institute, 1963.
ISBN 0888060998 Hbk £5.00

Udo-Inyang, D. S.
Sir Justice Udo Udoma / by D.S. Udo-Inyang. – Calabar, Nigeria : Wusen Press, 1985.
72p.
ISBN 9782281689

Uexkull, J.-Detlev Frhr. von
German Patent Law, 1981 : With Annotations. – Cologne : Carl Heymanns Verlag, 1981.
xiii, 99p.
ISBN 3452190005 Pbk £39.00

Uff, John
Construction law : law and practice relating to the construction industry / by John Uff. – 4th ed. – London : Sweet & Maxwell, 1985.
xvii,350p; 22cm.
Deals with the principles of building and civil engineering contracts as well as the standard forms of contract issued by the JCT and the ICE. Enlarged section on the law and practice of arbitration, including an introduction to the ICE Arbitration Procedure 1983. Also covers the Building Act 1984, and the new Building Regulations.
ISBN 0421343605 Hbk £18
ISBN 0421343702 Pbk £16
→ Institute of Civil Engineers' arbitration practice.

Uganda : six years after Amin : torture, killings, disappearances / Amnesty International. – London : Amnesty International, 1985.
40p.

Uganda and Sudan - North and South. – London : Minority Rights Group, 1982.
27p. – (Report).
Bibliographies.
ISBN 0946690243

Ugeux, Georges
Floating rate notes / by Georges Ugeux : preface by Michael von Clemm. – 2nd ed. – London : Euromoney, 1985.
xix,171p.
Bibliography: p.171.
ISBN 0903121808

Uglow, Jennifer → Legal literature in small jurisdictions : a report of a conference held at Osgoode Hall Law School, York University, Downsview, Ontario on 3-5 November 1978.

Uglow, Steve
Policing liberal society / Steve Uglow. – Oxford : Oxford University Press, 1988.
viii, 165 p.; 23 cm. – (An OPUS book).
Examines the role of the police force in late twentieth-century Britain; how it has changed, and prospects for the future. Questions whether the police are crime-fighters, social workers, guardians of the law, or maintainers of public order. Suggests that the constitutional role of the police should be re-examined.
ISBN 0192192221 Hbk £19.50

Ujjannavar, S. S.
Cases and material on contract / by S.S. Ujjannavar. – Hubli India : G. S. Ujjannavar, 1983.
xiv,543p.

UK Companies Operating Overseas : Tax and Financial Strategies / M. J. Packman. – 2nd ed. – London : Oyez Longman, 1984.
– (Oyez Longman Intelligence Report Ser.).
ISBN 0851208770 Hbk £45.00

UK Companies Operating Overseas : Tax and Financial Strategies / M. J. Packman. – London : Oyez Longman, 1981.
– (Oyez Longman Intelligence Report Ser.).
ISBN 0851205321 Hbk £45.00

UK financial accounting standards. – Cambridge : Woodhead-Faulkner, 1983.
ISBN 0859412016 Hbk £25.00
ISBN 0859412024 Pbk £10.95

UK marine oil pollution legislation. – London : Lloyd's of London Press, 1987.
ISBN 185044028 Hbk £45.00
ISBN 185044109X Pbk £16.50

UK money markets / David G Ferrier. – London : Butterworths, 1988.
ISBN 0406100306 Hbk

UK oil taxation. – 2nd. – London : Longman Professional, 1988.
ISBN 0851214207 Pbk £50

UK Serials Group
Information chain : proceedings of the UK Serials Group conference, held at Christ Church College Canterbury, 29 March - 1 April 1982 / edited by John A. Urquhart. – London : UK Serials Group, 1983.

UK Tax Guide 1986-1987. – Butterworths. – London : Butterworths.
ISBN 0406504954 Pbk £12.00

UK Tax Offshore Oil and Gas / Rouse. – 2nd ed. – London : Butterworths.
Service to Date.
ISBN 0406220719 Hbk £100.00

UK-France road freighting-legal guide. – London : Kogan Page, 1988.
ISBN 185091320X Pbk £28.00

Ukrainians and Georgians / by Bohdan Nahaylo and C.J. Peters. – London : Minority Rights Group, 1981.
20p. – (Report).
Bibliography: p.20.

UK-US Tax Planning Under the Treaty. – London : Oyez Longman, 1981.
– (Oyez Longman Intelligence Report Ser.).
ISBN 0851205399 Hbk £35.00

Ullmann, W.
Law and Jurisdiction in the Middle Ages. – London : Variorum.
– (Variorum Collected Studies Series).
ISBN 086078231X Hbk £34.00

Ullstein, Augustus → Matrimonial and domestic injunctions : practice and precedents.

Ulpian / Tony Honore. – Oxford : Clarendon Press, 1982.
ix,303p; 24cm.
Bibliography: p285-294. - Includes index.
ISBN 0198253583

Ulrich Zasius : a jurist in the German Renaissance, 1461-1535 / Steven Rowan. – Frankfurt a. M. : Klostermann, 1987.
xiii,286p.
Includes bibliographies and index.
ISBN 3465017722

Ultimate penalties. – London : Eurospan, 1988.
ISBN 0814204368 Hbk £23.25

Ultra Vires : Being an Investigation of the Principles Which Limit the Powers and Liabilities of Corporations, Quasi-Corporate Bodies and Non-Sovereign Legislature. – Repr. of 1930 ed. – Abingdon : Professional Books.
344p.
Hbk £45.00

Uma, Shankar
Uttar Pradesh Regulation of Building Operations Act, 1958 : with Rules and Regulations and Urban Planning and Development Act, 1973. – 3rd ed. repr. – Lucknow : Eastern Book Company, 1986.
396p.
Hbk £110.00

Umbricht, Victor H.
Multilateral mediation : practical experiences and lessons. – Dordrecht : Nijhoff (Martinus), 1989.
384.
Analyses the successful mediation; the resolution of the dispute amongst members of the East African Community after its termination in 1977. By narrating his own involvement in a mediation exercise, the author intends to provide governments, practitioners and scholars of international law with a guide to the settlement process.
ISBN 9024737796 Hbk Gld175.00

Umoh, P. U.
Nigerian constitution today / by P.U. Umoh. – Uyo, Nigeria : Modern Business Press, 1985.
x,182p.
Includes bibliographical references and index.
—Precedent in Nigerian courts / by P.U. Umoh. – Enugu : Fourth Dimension Publishers, 1984.
xxviii,334p.
Bibliography: p.xxv-xxvi. Based on University of London Ph.D. thesis no. 526.
ISBN 9781561696

UN Convention on the Law of the Sea 1982 : a guide for national policy making legislation and administration
Book 1 : General introduction / prepared by E.D. Brown in association with the Commonwealth Secretariat. – London : The Secretariat, 1987.
viii,132p.

UN Draft Convention on the Law of the Sea : how it affects the United Kingdom's oil rights / E.D. Brown. – S.l. : s.n., 1981.
56p.
'Paper read at seminar on recent developments in U.K. petroleum law, London, June, 1981'. Includes bibliographical references.

UN international law and Rhodesian industrial crisis. – Oxford : Oxford University Press, 1985.
ISBN 019825394X Hbk £30.00

UN Under Attack / Schrijver. – Aldershot : Avebury.
ISBN 056605695X Hbk £18.50

UNCITRAL : the United Nations Commission on International Law. – Geneva : United Nations Publications.
ISBN 9211332842 Hbk £15.00

UNCITRAL Arbitration Model in Canada / Thompson. – Agincourt : Carswell, 1987.
262p.
This work outlines the process of adopting and implementing the UNCITRAL Model Law. Canadian legislation and the UNCITRAL Model Law and Rules are provided. Discussions include that of arbitration as a universally accepted method of resolving international commercial disputes and the adoption in British Columbia of the model law on international commercial arbitration.
Hbk £41.25

UNCITRAL Draft Convention on international bills of exchange and internnational promissory notes, and Draft Convention on international cheques / memorandum by the Joint Working Party of the Law Reform Committees of the Senate of the Inns of Court and the Bar and the Law Society. – London? : the Joint Working Party?, 1983.
7p.

UNCITRAL model law on international commercial arbitration : a consultative document / Departmental Advisory Committee on Arbitration Law and Scottish Advisory Committee on Arbitration Law. – London : Dept. of Trade and Industry, 1987.
67p.

UNCITRAL's project for a model law on international commercial arbitration / general editor, Pieter Sanders : with the cooperation of the T.M.C. Asser Institute for International Law. – Deventer, Netherlands : Kluwer Law and Taxation Publishers, 1984.
At head of title: International Council for Commercial Arbitration. Proceedings of the International Council for Commercial Arbitration interim meeting, May 9-12, 1984 in Lausanne, Switzerland.
ISBN 9065441832

Uncommon Law - 66 Misleading Cases. – Methuen, 1969.
ISBN 041338540X Pbk £5.95

Unconscionable Contracts and Economic Duress. – North Ryde : C.C.H. Australia, 1985.
260p.
ISBN 0869035495

Undemocratic Elements in the Indian Constitution. – New Delhi : Somaiya Publications, 1977.
380p.
Hbk £75.00

Under One Roof : A Guide for Flat Owners in Scotland. – London : HMSO, 1984.
95p : Illus.
ISBN 0114923809 Pbk £2.00

Undercover investigation. – London : Butterworths, 1983.
ISBN 0409950769 Hbk £25.00

Underdown → Cost Accounting.
→ Cost Accounting Lecturer's Guide.

Underhill, Arthur
Law relating to trusts and trustees / Underhill and Hayton. – 14th ed. – London : Butterworths, 1987.
cxxxv,858p; 26cm.
Previous ed.: published as Underhill's law relating to trusts and trustees. 1979. Includes index.
ISBN 040640593X Hbk £110.00
—Underhill's principles of the law of partnership / D. R. Jones, E. R. Hardy Ivamy. – 12th ed. – London : Butterworths, 1986.
250p; 22cm.
Previous ed.: published as Principles of the law of partnership. 1981. Includes index.
ISBN 0406669074 Hbk £23.00
ISBN 0406669082 Pbk £15.00

Underhill, M.
Underhill's Licensing Guide. – 11th ed. – London : Longman Professional. – (Longham Practitioner Series).
Guide to the law and procedure of liquor, gaming, betting and lottery licensing. Details each step in making or opposing a successful licensing application, with key precedents. Revised to take account of the changes introduced by the Licensing Act 1988.
ISBN 0851215378 Hbk £17.95

Underhill's Licensing Guide. – 11th ed. – London : Longman Professional. – (Longham Practitioner Series).
Guide to the law and procedure of liquor, gaming, betting and lottery licensing. Details each step in making or opposing a successful licensing application, with key precedents. Revised to take account of the changes introduced by the Licensing Act 1988.
ISBN 0851215378 Hbk £17.95

Underhill's principles of the law of partnership / D. R. Jones, E. R. Hardy Ivamy. – 12th ed. – London : Butterworths, 1986.
250p; 22cm.
Previous ed.: published as Principles of the law of partnership. 1981. Includes index.
ISBN 0406669074 Hbk £23.00
ISBN 0406669082 Pbk £15.00

Understanding Business Taxation. – London : Waterlow, 1984.
192p.
ISBN 0080391362 Pbk £7.95

Understanding child abuse. – 2nd ed. – London : Macmillan, 1987.
ISBN 0333428935 Pbk £7.95

Understanding Commercial and Industrial Licensing 1984. – Waterlow.
ISBN 0080391540 Pbk £8.50

Understanding Commercial Law / Lawrence. – Butterworths, 1988.
476p.
ISBN 0409787876 Pbk £65.00

Understanding company accounts. – 2nd ed. – Pitman, 1983.
ISBN 0273019449 Pbk £4.95

Understanding company accounts / Newman. – Telegraph Publications, 1988.
ISBN 0863671918 Pbk £6.95

Understanding company financial statements. – 2nd ed. – Pelican, 1982.
ISBN 0140091025 Pbk £4.95

Understanding Company Law / A. Herzberg. – 2nd ed. 1986. – North Ryde : Law Book Co.
xxxvi, 453p.
ISBN 0455206392 Hbk £42.00
ISBN 0455206406 Pbk £29.50

Understanding computer contracts. – London : Waterlow, 1983.
ISBN 0803091346 Pbk £7.95

Understanding contract law / John N. Adams and Roger Brownsword. – London : Fontana, 1987.
229p.
Bibliography: p213-216.
ISBN 0006860702

Understanding Contract Law / Yvonne Yamouni. – 2nd ed. – Butterworths, 1988.
312p.
ISBN 0409302538 Pbk £32.00

Understanding crime prevention / National Crime Prevention Institute. – Boston : Butterworths, 1986.
xiv,207p; 24cm.
Includes index.
ISBN 0409900753

Understanding crime rates : police and public roles in the production of official statistics / Keith Bottomley, Clive Coleman. – Farnborough : Gower, 1981.
ix,170p; 23cm.
Bibliography: p155-160. - Includes index.
ISBN 0566003090 £11.50

Understanding Criminal Law 1987 / Chodse. – London : Fontana.
ISBN 0006860745 Pbk £4.95

Understanding Criminal Offenses / Barrie J. Saxton. – Agincourt : Carswell, 1987.
383p.
This textbook for students of Canadian criminal law discusses the main criminal offenses under the Canadian criminal justice system. Each offense is broken down to the component elements specific to that offense.
Hbk £40.50

Understanding deviance : a guide to the sociology of crime and rule-breaking / David Downes and Paul Rock. – 2nd ed. – Oxford : Clarendon Press, 1988.
viii,369p.
Bibliography: pp.335-360. - Includes index.
ISBN 0198762143 Hbk £30.00
ISBN 0198762135 Pbk £10.95

Understanding dismissal law / Martin Edwards. – London : Waterlow, 1984.
xiv,188p; 21cm. – (Waterlow's business library).
Includes index.
ISBN 0080391745 Pbk £7.95

Understanding Equity and Trusts. – London : Fontana.
ISBN 0006860729 Pbk £4.95

Understanding factoring and trade credit / Charles W Ferrier. – London : Waterlow, 1986.
ISBN 0080392040 Pbk £13.50

Understanding Income Tax Law the Flowchart Way. – 3rd ed. – Butterworths, 1985.
436p.
ISBN 0409491748 Pbk £39.00
Supplement-1983. – 1983.
45p.
ISBN 0409491519 Pbk £5.00

Understanding juvenile justice / Allison Morris Henri Giller. – London : Croom Helm, 1987.
287p; 23cm.
ISBN 0709938322 Hbk £22.50
ISBN 070993890X Pbk £9.95

Understanding land law / R T J Stein. – North Ryde : Law Book Co, 1985.
ISBN 0455203032 Hbk £13.00
ISBN 0455203040 Pbk £8.50

Understanding Law : Introduction to Australia's Legal System 1978 / Garth Nettheim. – 3rd ed. – Butterworths, 1988.
ca 152p.
This introductory text for first year law students provides an overview of the Australian legal system. Emphasized are the ways in which laws are made and the function of courts and lawyers. A list of suggested further reading is also included.
ISBN 0409495190 Pbk £14.00

Understanding Locke : an introduction to philosophy through John Locke's Essay / John J. Jenkins. – Edinburgh : Edinburgh University Press, 1983.
xviii,256p; 21cm.
Bibliography: p241-252. - Includes index.
ISBN 0852244428 Hbk £15.00
ISBN 0852244495 Pbk

Understanding Occupational Health and Safety Law in Victoria. – North Ryde : C.C.H. Australia, 1986.
236p.
ISBN 0869038389

Understanding pension schemes. – 3rd ed. – London : Fourmat, 1987.
ISBN 185190025X Pbk £10.95

Understanding personal and business finance. – 2nd ed. – Cambridge : Woodhead-Faulkner, 1986.
ISBN 0859413624 Pbk £5.25

Understanding property law / Roberts. – London : Fontana, 1987.
ISBN 0006860737 Pbk £4.95

Understanding public law. – London : Fontana, 1987.
ISBN 0006861180 Pbk £4.95

Understanding recruitment law / David Newell. – London : Waterlow, 1984.
xi,189p; 21cm. – (Waterlow's business library).
Includes index.
ISBN 0080391559 Pbk £9.75

Understanding residential leases / by Charles Boston. – 2nd ed. – London : Sweet & Maxwell, 1986.
22p; 21cm.
ISBN 0421366109 Pbk £1.75

Understanding Social Policy. – 3rd ed. – Oxford : Blackwell.
ISBN 0631162259 Pbk £8.50

Understanding the Canada-U.S. Free Trade Agreement / Debra P. Stegar. – Ottawa : Institute for Research on Public Policy, 1988.
ISBN 0886450799 Hbk

Understanding the Constitution. – 11th ed. – Holt.
ISBN 0030229332 Pbk £7.95

Understanding the Occupational Health and Safety Act 1983. – 2nd ed. – North Ryde : C.C.H. Australia, 1985.
90p.
ISBN 086903605X £25.00

Understanding tort law / Powell. – London : Sweet & Maxwell, 1987.
Pbk £4.95

Underwood, Ashley
Professional negligence / by Ashley Underwood and Stephen Holt. – London : Fourmat, 1981.
xv,96p; 23cm.
ISBN 0906840368

Underwood, G.E.
Company Law. – North Ryde : Law Book Co, 1985.
xi, 116. – (Nutshells).
ISBN 0455205957

Underwriters bedside book. – London : Lloyd's of London Press, 1987.
ISBN 1850441332 Hbk £16.50

Undy, Roger
Ballots and trade union democracy / Roger Undy and Roderick Martin with the assistance of R. Blackwell and J. Hulton. – Oxford : Blackwell, 1984.
viii,240p; 24cm.
ISBN 0631135391 £19.50

Unemployment and labour market flexibility : the United Kingdom / Guy Standing. – Geneva : International Labour Office, 1986.
xi, 147 p.; 24 cm.
Includes bibliographies.
ISBN 9221052915 Pbk £30.00

Unemployment and magistrates' courts / Iain Crow and Frances Simon. – London : NACRO, 1987.
52p.
ISBN 0850690579

Unemployment and Your Rights. – Montreal : McGill Campus Legal Aid Clinic, 1983.
36p.
Hbk £1.00

Unemployment, Crime and Offenders. – Routledge.
ISBN 041501834X Hbk £27.50

Unemployment insurance / by Clare E. Choate. – Toronto : Carswell Co., 1982.
xii, 386 p.; 26 cm.
'Reprinted from the Canadian encyclopedic digest, third edition.'. Includes index.

Unemployment Insurance. – 2nd ed. – Agincourt : Carswell, 1985.
418p.
Hbk £34.75

Unemployment Insurance / Bob Ludlow. – Vancouver : Vancouver People's Law School.
Illus.
Hbk

Unemployment Insurance. – Vancouver : British Columbia Continuing Legal Education Society, 1983.
266p.
ISBN 0865041067 Hbk £55.00

UNEP Environmental Law In-Depth Review 1981 Vol. VII. – Berlin : Erich Schmidt, 1982.
ISBN 3503021213 Hbk £24.00

Unequal struggle? : British socialism and the capitalist enterprise / Jim Tomlinson. – London : Methuen, 1982.
160p; 23cm.
Bibliography: p149-157. - Includes index.
ISBN 0416331505 Hbk £
ISBN 0416331602 Pbk

Unequal treaty, 1898-1997 : China, Great Britain, and Hong Kong's new territories / Peter Wesley-Smith. – Hong Kong : Oxford University Press, 1983.
xix, 270 p., 8 p. of plates; 21 cm.
Includes index. Bibliography: p. 242-256.
ISBN 0195837274 Pbk

Unesco →ABC of copyright.
→ Concept of international organization.
—Copyright Bulletin. – UNESCO. – London : HMSO.
Hbk £6.60
→ Existing legislative protection of the cultural and natural heritage of the Pacific region.
→ Model handbook for interlending and copying.
→ National legal control of illicit traffic in cultural property.
→ Protection of movable cultural property : compendium of legislative texts.
→ Protection of the underwater heritage.
—Teaching and research in international law in Asia and the Pacific : report of a regional consultation meeting including nine country status surveys Seoul, Republic of Korea 10-13 October 1984. – Unesco. – Bangkok : Unesco Regional Office for Education in Asia and the Pacific, 1985.
264p.
Includes bibliographcial references.
ISBN 9231023950 Hbk £60.00

Unfair Contracts and Copyright. – Milsons Point : Australian Copyright Council.
Hbk £1.00

Unfair dismissal / Malcolm Mead. – London : Oyez, 1981.
xxxv,287p; 24cm.
Includes index.
Pbk £15.00

Unfair dismissal : a guide to relevant case law / by Michael Rubenstein and Yvonne Frost. – 4th edition. – London : Industrial Relations Service, 1986.
iv, 84p.

Unfair dismissal : a guide to relevant case law / by Michael Rubenstein and Yvonne Frost. – S.l. : s.n., 1983.
63p; 30cm.

Unfair dismissal handbook / Malcolm Mead. – 2nd ed. – London : Oyez Longman, 1983.
xxxvii,368p.
Previous ed.: published as 'Unfair dismissal', 1981.
Includes index.
ISBN 0851206913

Unfair dismissal handbook. – 3rd ed. – London : Longman Professional, 1988.
ISBN 0851212522 Pbk

Unfair Publication : Defamation and Privacy. – Kingston : Australian Government Publishing Service.
273p.
Hbk £24.95

Unfair Terms in Consumer Contracts Legal Treatment, Effective Implementation and Final Impact on the Consumer : Proceedings of the Second European Workshop on Consumer Law. – Brussels : Emile Bruylant, 1983.
iv, 268p.
ISBN 2870771991 Hbk £860.00

Unfitness. – Shelter. – 2nd ed. – London : Shelter, 1984.
ISBN 0862650038 Hbk £1.95

Unfolding Westward in Treaty and Law Land Documents US History-Appalachians to Pacific. – Folkestone : Bailey Bros., 1783-1934.
ISBN 089950308X Hbk £33.75

Unger, Aryeh L.
Constitutional development in the USSR : a guide to the soviet constitutions / Aryeh L. Unger. – London : Methuen, 1981.
viii,310p; 22cm.
Bibliography: p297-298. - Includes index. Includes English text of the RSFSR constitution of 1918, and the USSR constitutions of 1924, 1936 and 1977.
ISBN 0416716806 Pbk £13.50
ISBN 0416716903 £7.50

Unger, R.
Law In Modern Society. – London : Macmillan, 1976.
ISBN 0029328802 Pbk £13.95

Unger, Roberto Mangabeira
Critical legal studies movement / Roberto Mangabeira Unger. – Cambridge, Mass. : Harvard University Press, 1986.
128p; 24cm.
Bibliography: p121-122. - Includes index.
ISBN 0674177355 Hbk £15.25
ISBN 0674177363 Pbk

Ungovernable people : the English and their law in the seventeenth and eighteenth centuries / edited by John Brewer and John Styles. – London : Hutchinson, 1983.
400p,4p of plates; 22cm.
Includes index.
ISBN 0091382017 Pbk £6.95

Unichem Limited : allocation of shares by co-operative upon reconverting to a public limited company / a report by the Director General of Fair Trading on an investigation under section 3 of the Competition Act 1980. – London : Office of Fair Trading, 1988.
49p.

UNIDROIT : Draft Convention on Agency in the International Sale of Goods : memorandum / by a working party of the Council's Law Reform Committee. – London : Law Society, 1983.
2p.

Unification : and comparative law in theory and practice : et le droit compare dans la theorie et la pratique / contributions in honour of Jean Georges Sauveplanne. – Deventer : Kluwer Law & Taxation, 1984.
vi,307p; 25cm.
Text in English and French.
ISBN 9065441735

Uniform Building By-Laws, 1964 (G.N. 5178/85). – Kuala Lumpur : International Law Books Services.
Hbk £12.00

Uniform Evidence Act 1981 : a basis for uniform evidence legislation / Institute of Law Research and Reform. – Edmonton : The Institute, 1982.
ii,109p. – (Report).

Uniform Law Conference of →Report of the Federal/Provincial Task Force on Uniform Rules of Evidence.

Uniform Rules of Evidence : Report of the Federal-Provincial Task Force. – Carswell Legal Publications. – Agincourt : Carswell, 1982.
650p.
This report contains a complete statement of the current Canadian law of evidence, with proposals for reform.
Hbk £54.75

Uniform Sale of Goods Act / Institute of Law Research and reform. – Edmonton : The Institute, 1982.
iii,323p. – (Report).

Uniform sales law : the UN Convention on Contracts for the International Sale of Goods / Peter Schlectriem. – Wien : Manz, 1986.
120p.
Bibliography: pp.11-16. - Includes index. Translation of: Einheitliches UN-Kaufrecht. - Tubingen: Mohr, 1981.
ISBN 3214065580

Unincorporated associations : law and practice / by Jean Warburton. – London : Sweet & Maxwell, 1986.
100p; 22cm.
Guide to the law in respect of sports clubs, political parties, self-help groups, and community associations. Covers funding, the holding of property, rates and taxes, and the rights and liabilities of members. Contains several precedents for the formation of an association and the establishment of rules and objects.
ISBN 0421345403 Pbk £14.00

Union list of law periodicals held in libraries within the City of Liverpool / compiled by Susan Frost, Robert Caley. – Liverpool : Liverpool Polytechnic Library Service, 1985.
30p.

Union list of law reports and statutes held in libraries within the City of Liverpool / compiled by Susan Frost, Robert Caley. – Liverpool : Liverpool Polytechnic Library Service, 1985.
30p.

Union list of legal bibliographies and digests and other law-related material held in libraries within the City of Liverpool / compiled by Susan Frost, Robert Caley. – Liverpool : Liverpool Polytechnic Library Service, 1985.
15p.

Union List of Legal Serials in Selected Library of the Federal Republic of Germany Including Berlin (West), 2 Vols. – Munich : Saur, 1984.
x, 1,896p.
ISBN 3598105258 Hbk £600.00

Union of Arab Lawyers →Human rights in Islam : report of a seminar held in Kuwait, December 1980.

Union Security and the Charter : an Analysis of the Law. – Butterworths, 1987.
216p.
Analysis of the effects of sections 1 and 2(d) of the Charter, dealing with 'freedom of association', on union security. Makes reference to Canadian cases decided on this issue. Contains analysis based on the legal regimes in place in the United States, western Europe, Australia, and those reflected in international covenants.
ISBN 0409806536 Hbk £50.00

Unions and Arbitration '81 - Papers and Discussion of the Armidale Industrial Law and Relations Seminar / D. Smith. – Sydney : Butterworths, 1981.
152p.
ISBN 040930929X Pbk

Unions, change and crisis : French and Italian union strategy and the political economy, 1945-1980 / Peter Lange, George Ross, Maurizio Vannicelli. – London : Allen & Unwin, 1982.
viii,295p; 25cm.
Includes index.
ISBN 0043310885

Unit Trust Guide For Investors. – Cambridge : Woodhead-Faulkner.
ISBN 0859414019 Pbk £4.95

Unit trusts. – 3rd ed. – Cambridge : Woodhead-Faulkner, 1982.
ISBN 0859412083 Pbk £9.95
ISBN 0959412091 Hbk £17.95

United Kingdom Association for Legal and Social Philosophy
Equality and discrimination : essays in freedom and justice : papers presented at the United Kingdom Association for Legal and Social Philosophy eleventh annual conference at University College London, 6th-8th April 1984 / edited by Stephen Guest and Alan Milne. – Stuttgart : Steiner, 1985.
102p; 24cm.
Bound with Beihefte nos. 22 and 23..

United Kingdom Central Office of Information
Justice and the Law in Britain. – United Kingdom Central Office of Information. – London : Central Office of Information, 1982. – (References Services Ser.).
ISBN 0117010340 Hbk £3.15

United Kingdom Committee of Comparative Law
Colloquium on choice of law in contract and the E.E.C. Contractual Obligations Convention / Peter M North. – 2. – s.l. : s.n., 1981.
Held from 15-16th Sept. 1981. Includes bibliographical references. Chairman: Peter North.

United Kingdom Competition Law. – London : Sweet & Maxwell.
ISBN 0421314907 Hbk

United Kingdom National Committee on Comparative Law →Comparative product liability.
→ Effect of treaties in domestic law.
→ Human rights in criminal procedure : a comparative study.
→ Trusts and trust-like devices.

United Kingdom Offshore Legislation Guide. – Tonbridge : Ernest Benn.
300p.
ISBN 0854591524 Hbk £110.00

United Kingdom oil and gas law / edited by Terence Daintith and Geoffrey Willoughby. – 2nd ed. 1. – London : Sweet & Maxwell, 1984.
loose-leaf; 26cm.
Describes the historical development of the industry, and examines the different roles of the government and the oil companies. Looks at offshore licensing operations, and discusses the legal and commercial implications of financing such operations. Also outlines the various forms of UK taxation of the oil industry.
ISBN 0421307005 £130.00 (non-net)

United Kingdom Oil Taxation. – London : Longman Professional.
ISBN 0851214207 Hbk £50.00

United Kingdom Sources
Service only. – Edinburgh : W Green.
Llf £70.00

United Kingdom Stratospheric Ozone Review Group
Stratospheric ozone : report ... – United Kingdom Stratospheric Ozone Review Group. – London : HMSO, 1987.
'The Stratospheric Ozone Review Group was set up jointly by the Department of the Environment and the Meteorological Office in November 1985'. - Annex A.

United Nations →Action-oriented research on youth crime : an international perspective.
→ Coastal area management and development.
→ Global resources and international conflict : environmental factors in strategic policy and action.
—Human Rights : A Compilation of International Instruments. – United Nations. – London : HMSO, 1983.
ISBN 0119078589 Hbk £13.50
—International human rights instruments of the United Nations 1948-1982 / collected and arranged by the UNIFO editorial staff. – London : Mansell, 1984.
ix,175p; 29cm.
Originally published: Pleasantville, N.Y. : UNIFO Publishers, 1983. Includes index.
ISBN 0720116988 £25.00
—International Register of Potentially Toxic Chemicals, 2 Vols. – United Nations. – London : HMSO, 1984.
Provides information on the danger to humans and the environment of chemicals and details of individual nations' controlling legislation.
ISBN 0119079860 Hbk £58.50
—International Tax Agreements : Supplement No. 40. – United Nations. – London : HMSO, 1985.
ISBN 0119083663 Hbk £5.70
→ Natural resources forum.
—Quiet Revolution. – United Nations. – London : HMSO, 1984.
61p. – (The United Nations Convention on the Law of the Sea).
Describes the processes by which the negotiation of the Convention on the Law of the Sea took place.
ISBN 0119081733 Pbk £4.75
→ Report of the Working Group on Current Problems in the International Protection of Refugees and Displaced Persons in Asia, International Institute of Humanitarian Law, San Remo (Italy), 19-22 January 1981.
—Reports of International Arbitral Awards. – United Nations. – London : HMSO, 1982.
532p.
Reports on awards in three arbitration cases; the delimitation of the continental shelf between UK and France, the air service agreement between USA and France, and the taxation liability of EURATOM.
ISBN 0119074761 Hbk £24.75
→ Security Council adopts resolution demanding cessation of hostilities and withdrawal of Argentine forces from the Falkland Islands : Council also calls for diplomatic solution of the situation.
—Third United Nations Conference on the Law of the Sea
Vol. 15. – United Nations. – London : HMSO, 1984.
243p.
Official records of the conference and a list of documents issued during the tenth session.
ISBN 0119080710 Pbk £20.70
—Transnational corporations in world development. – United Nations. – London : Published in co-operation with the United Nations by Graham & Trotman, 1984.
256p.
ISBN 0860105083 £37.00
—United Nations Commission of International Trade Law Yearbook. – United Nations. – London : HMSO, 1984.
Includes reports on international trade contracts, international payments, commercial arbitration and conciliation and transport law.
ISBN 0119082985 Hbk £36.10
—United Nations Convention on the Law of the Sea / Bo Johnson Theutenberg. – Dublin : Tycooly International, 1984.
viii,261p; 25cm.
Bibliography: p97-111. Includes full text of United Nations Convention on the Law of the Sea. Spine title : The law of the sea.
ISBN 0863460410 Hbk
ISBN 0863460429 Pbk

—Weekly news summary / United Nations Information Centre for the United Kingdom and Ireland. – London : The Centre, 1982.
Continues: London weekly summary.

→ World environment 1972-1982 : a report.

United Nations and international law: the Rede Lecture / Brian Urquhart. – Cambridge : Cambridge University Press, 1985.
20p.
ISBN 0521338743 Pbk £2.95

United Nations and the control of international violence : a legal and political analysis / John F. Murphy. – Manchester : Manchester University Press, 1983.
xii,212p; 24cm.
Includes index.
ISBN 0719009421 £22.50
ISBN 0865980799

United Nations Commission of International Trade Law Yearbook. – United Nations. – London : HMSO, 1984.
Includes reports on international trade contracts, international payments, commercial arbitration and conciliation and transport law.
ISBN 0119082985 Hbk £36.10

United Nations Conference on Trade and Development
Further elaboration and implementation of a strategy for the technological transformation of developing countries : comparative tables of proposals made by regional groups at the first special session of the Committee on Transfer of Technology / prepared by the UNCTAD secretariat. – s.l. : United Nations Conference on Trade and Development, 1984.
43p. – (TD/B/C.6/108).
Item 3 of the provisional agenda for the fifth session of the Committee on Transfer of Technology, Geneva, 22 October 1984.
→ New, other activities and intiatives : (a) interregional linkages and co-operative arrangements : interregional linkages and co-operative arrangements among developing countries for their technological transformation.

—New, other activities and intiatives : (a) interregional linkages and co-operative arrangements : interregional linkages and co-operative arrangements among developing countries for their technological transformation / report by the UNCTAD secretariat. – s.l. : United Nations Conference on Trade and Developoment, 1984.
ii, 21p, 3 leaves. – (TD/B/C.6/118).
Item 6 (a) of the provisional agenda for the fifth session of the Committee on Transfer of Technology, Geneva, 22 October 1984.

United Nations Convention Against Torture International Studies in Human Rights / Danelius. – Martinus Nijhoff.
ISBN 9024736099 Hbk £44.95

United Nations Convention on the Law of the Sea, 1982 : a commentary / Myron H. Nordquist. – Dordrecht : Martinus Nijhoff, 1985.
512p.
At head of title: Center for Oceans Law and Policy, University of Virginia.
ISBN 9024731453 Hbk £265.00

United Nations Convention on the law of the sea. – Geneva : The Conference, 1982.
xxiv,194p.
Text dated 7 October 1982. - Supersedes: Convention on the law of the sea (April, 1982).

United Nations Convention on the Law of the Sea / Bo Johnson Theutenberg. – Dublin : Tycooly International, 1984.
viii,261p; 25cm.
Bibliography: p97-111. Includes full text of United Nations Convention on the Law of the Sea. Spine title : The law of the sea.
ISBN 0863460410 Hbk
ISBN 0863460429 Pbk

United Nations, divided world : the UN's roles in international relations / edited by Adam Roberts and Benedict Kingsbury. – Oxford : Clarendon Press, 1988.
xii, 287 p.; 23 cm.
Bibliography: p. 274-278. Includes index.
ISBN 0198275447

United Nations Environment Programme → Cultural norms, war and the environment.

United Nations, international law, and the Rhodesian independence crisis / Jericho Nkala. – Oxford : Clarendon Press, 1985.
xii,288p.
Bibliography: p.275-283. - Includes index.

United Nations Lawmaking : Cultural and Ideological Relativism and International Lawmaking for an Era of Transition. – Paris : UNESCO.
ISBN 9231021478 Hbk £156.00

United Nations Office for Ocean Affairs and the Law of the Sea
Annual review of ocean affairs. – United Nations Office for Ocean Affairs and the Law of the Sea. – 2 vol. – London : Lloyds of London Press, 1989.
These two volumes contain protocols, conventions, treaties, decisions, and other matters enacted by governmental organisations concerned with ocean affairs. Includes illicit drug-trafficking, fisheries management, and the marine environment. This first edition contains documentation covering the years 1985-1987.

United Nations Social Defence Research Institute
Juvenile social maladjustment and human rights in the context of urban development. – United Nations Social Defence Research Institute. – Rome : Fratelli Palombi, 1984.
504p. – (Publication).
'Funded by the United Nations Development Programme'. Parallel Spanish and French titles. English, Spanish and French text.
ISBN 8876218289
→ World directory of criminological institutes.

United Nations Treaties on Outer Space. – Geneva : United Nations Publications.
ISBN 9211002389 Hbk £2.00

United Nations versus South Africa : a legal assessment of United Nations and United Nations related activities in respect of South Africa / Jan C. Heunis. – 1st ed. – Johannesburg : Lex Patria, 1986.
593 p., 1 folded leaf of plates; 25 cm.
: Originally presented as the author's thesis (doctoral–Rand Afrikaans University, 1984). Includes index. Bibliography: p. 583-593.
ISBN 0628030363

The United States : A Short Political Guide. – 2nd ed. – London : Macmillan.
ISBN 0333461460 Hbk £25.00
ISBN 0333461452 Pbk £8.95

United States and Common Market antitrust policies. – Matthew Bender, 1987.
ISBN 0000999063 Hbk £50.00

United States and the control of world oil / Ed Shaffer. – London : Croom Helm, 1983.
246p; 23cm.
Bibliography: p232-236. - Includes index.
ISBN 070992366X £15.95

United States and the Law of the Sea Treaty / Peter Digester. – John Hopkins University, Foreign Policy Institute, 1990.
52; 23.
ISBN 0941700542 Pbk £12

United States and the World Court 1920-1935. – Pinter.
ISBN 0861879716 Hbk £25.00

United States Constitution : Its Birth, Growth and Influence in Asia. – Hong Kong : Hong Kong University Press, 1988.
ISBN 9622092102 Pbk £19.00

United States Copyright Act of 1976. – Milsons Point : Australian Copyright Council.
Hbk £1.00

United States law of sovereign immunity relating to international financial transactions / John R. Stevenson, Jeffrey F. Browne and Lori Fisler Damrosch. – London : Euromoney Pubns, 1983.
158p.
Includes bibliographical references.
ISBN 090312145X

United States of America - the death penalty / Amnesty International. – London : Amnesty International, 1987.
vi,245p; 22cm.
ISBN 086210114X Pbk

United States Ratification of the Human Rights Treaties : With or Without Reservations?. – London : Eurospan.
ISBN 0813908817 Hbk £12.95

United States treaties, executive agreements & guide to participation in international organizations. – Gaithersburg : Marketing Internationals Washington Group, 1985.
x,364p; 28cm.
Bibliography: p357-364.
ISBN 0406658609
ISBN 0912257024

Unity of law and morality : a refutation of legal postivisim / M.J. Detmold. – London : Routledge & Kegan Paul, 1984.
xix,271p; 23cm.
Bibliography: p265-268. - Includes index.
ISBN 0710200307 £15.00

Universitat Frankfurt am Main → Mining ventures in developing countries.

Universite Catholique de Louvain → European consumer law : prospects for integration of consumer law and policy within the European Community : proceedings of the seminar held in Louvain-la-Neuve on May 14 and 15, 1981.

Universiteit van Amsterdam → Leading cases and materials on the competition law of the E.E.C.
→ Leading cases and materials on the external relations law of the European Community, with emphasis on the common commercial policy.
→ Leading cases on the law of the European Communities.
→ Legal issues of European integration.
→ Materials on the law of the European Communities.
→ Protectionism and the European Community : import relief measures taken by the European Economic Community and the member states, and the legal remedies available to private parties.

University Association for Contemporary European Studies → European Community law and national law : the irreversible transfer?.

University College Hospital
Experience at a clinical research ethical review committee / Ethical Committee, University College Hospital. – London : British Medical Association, 1981.
7p.
Reprinted from: British medical journal, 14 No 1981, 283, 1312-1314.

University College London → Political aspects of the Westland affair.

University of Birmingham → Civil justice quarterly.

University of Bristol → Effect on English domestic law of membership of the European Communities and of ratification of the European Convention on Human Rights.

University of British Columbia → Proceedings of the Administrative Law Conference : held at the University of British Columbia Faculty of Law on 18-19 October 1979.

University of British Columbia Law Review : 1959-date. – Abingdon : Professional Books, 1984.
Hbk

University of Cambridge → Corporations in and under international law.
→ Crime, justice and the mass media : papers presented to the 14th Cropwood Round-Table Conference, December 1981.
→ Future of policing : papers presented to the 15th Cropwood Round-Table Conference, December 1982.
→ Future of sentencing.
→ Human rights in internal strife : their international protection.
→ International arbitration : three salient problems.
→ International Law Commission.
→ Recognition and the United Nationsby John Dugard.
→ State immunity : some recent developments.
→ Women and crime : papers presented to the 13th Cropwood Round Table Conference, December 1980.

University of Dundee → Journal of energy & natural resources law.

University of Durham → New politics of labour law.

University of Ghana law journal. – London : Sweet & Maxwell, 1964-.

University of Ibadan → Ibadan University law review : the journal of the Faculty of Law, University of Ibadan.

University of Ife law journal. – Ife, Nigeria : University of Ife Press, 1986.

University of Jos law journal. – Jos, Nigeria : Faculty of Law, University of Jos, 1984-.

University of Lagos → Journal of private & property law.
→ Lawyer : journal of the Law Society, University of Lagos, Lagos, Nigeria.

University of Leicester → Data protection : perspectives on information privacy : contributions made to a conference on 11 May 1983 at the University of Leicester.
→ Role of subscription agents.
→ Sources of funding for research and publication.

University of London → British and French statutory drafting : the proceedings of the Franco-British conference of 7 and 8 April 1986.
→ Groups of companies : the law and practice in Britain, France and Germany.
→ Intermediate examination in laws.
→ Labour law and the community : perspectives for the 1980's.
→ Legal research in the United Kingdom 1905-84 : a classified list of legal theses and dissertations successfully completed for postgraduate degrees awarded by universities and polytechnics in the United Kingdom from 1905-1984.
→ List of current legal research topics : being topics forming the subject of research by students for degrees in universities and polytechnics in the United Kingdom.

University of Missouri–Columbia → Abortion and the status of the fetus.

University of Natal → Legal aid and law clinics in South Africa : proceedings of a conference held at the Howard College School of Law, University of Natal, Durban, from 11-13 July 1983.

University of New South Wales → New Tax Penalties 1984.

University of Santa Clara → Abortion and protection of the human fetus : legal problems in a cross-cultural perspective.
University of Saskatchewan → Indian acts and amendments 1868-1975 : an indexed collection.
University of Sydney → Takeovers, Trading Trusts and More, 1984.
University of the West Indies → Antigua and Barbuda consolidated index of statutes and subsidiary legislation to !st January 1984.
→ Barbados consolidated index of statutes and subsidiary legislation to 1st January 1986.
→ British Virgin Islands consolidated index of statutes and subsidiary legislation to 1st January 1985.
→ Canadian law reports and statutes held by the Faculty of Law Library, University of the West Indies, Cave Hill, Barbados.
→ Commonwealth Caribbean legal essays.
→ Jamaica consolidated index of statutes and subsidiary legislation to 1st January 1983.
→ Saint Christopher and Nevis consolidated index of statutes and subsidiary legislation to 1st January 1984.
→ Saint Lucia consolidated index and subsidiary legislation to 1st January 1984.
→ Saint Vincent and the Grenadines consolidated index of statutes and subsidiary legislation to 1st January 1986.
University of Toronto → New dimensions in international trade law : a Canadian perspective.
University of Toronto Faculty of Law Review. – Agincourt : Carswell.
Hbk £17.50 ea.
University of Toronto Law Journal : 1935-date. – Abingdon : Professional Books, 1984.
Hbk
University of Virginia → United Nations Convention on the Law of the Sea, 1982 : a commentary.
University of Warwick → Future of labour law : two views.
→ Strike-free procedures : are they what they seem?.
University of Zimbabwe → Zimbabwe law review.
Unjust enrichment / George B. Klippert. – Toronto : Butterworths, 1983.
xlix,389p.
Explains how Canadian restitution law has developed its own independent and unique voice: increasingly relying less on English authority and more on American jurisprudence. Recognises that the Supreme Court of Canada, in the process of affirming the concept of restitution as a distinct head of civil liability, has also carved a way to an independent interpretation of unjust enrichment.
ISBN 0409842931
Unlawful gain and legitimate profit in Islamic law : riba, gharar and Islamic banking / Nabil A. Saleh. – Cambridge : Cambridge University Press, 1986.
xii,130p; 24cm. – (Cambridge studies in Islamic civilization).
Examines ban on taking interest and rejection of aleatory contracts in Islamic law. Considers consequent conflict with world banking system. Studies these rules in the four Sunni schools of law and the Ibadi.
ISBN 0521322987 £19.50
Unlawful sex : offences, victims and offenders in the criminal justice system of England and Wales / the report of a Howard League working party. – London : Waterlow, 1985.
xvi,264p. – (Waterlow's legal and social policy library).
Includes bibliography and index.
ISBN 0080392202 Pbk £9.95
Unlocking community resources : four experimental government small grants schemes / Hilary Jackson. – London : Home Office, 1986.
iv,61p; 30cm.
Bibliography: p61.
ISBN 0862522617 Pbk
Unmarried couples : legal aspects of cohabitation / by Winifred H. Holland : Tax aspects, D. Keith McNair. – Toronto : Carswell, 1982.
xxxii,249p.
Includes bibliographical references and index.
ISBN 0459348701
Unmarried Family. – Kortrijk-Heule : UGA Editions, 1982.
186p.
ISBN 9067681296 £605.00
Unmasking of medicine / Ian Kennedy. – London : Allen & Unwin, 1981.
xiii,189p; 23cm.
Bibliography: p169-182. - Includes index.
ISBN 0046100164
Unpublished Opinions of the Burger Court. – Oxford : Oxford University Press.
ISBN 00195053176 Hbk £26.00
Unquoted companies. – London : Macmillan, 1988.
ISBN 03334371995 Hbk £105.00
Unsafe Product, The / Derrick Owles. – London : Kogan Page.
ISBN 1850916888 Hbk £16.95
Unsolved : classic true murder cases. – Star Books, 1988.
ISBN 0352321741 Pbk £2.95
Unsworn statements in criminal trials / Law Reform Commissioner, Victoria. – Melbourne : The Commission, 1981.
43p. – (Report no 11).
Includes bibliographical references.
Unsworn statements in criminal trials / Law Reform Commission of Victoria. – Melbourne : The Commission, 1985.
x,43p. – (Report no 2).
Includes bibliographical references.
Unsworth, Clive
Politics of mental health legislation / Clive Unsworth. – Oxford : Clarendon, 1987.
384p; 22cm.
Includes bibliography and index.
ISBN 0198255128 £30.00
Untouchability in India : Implementation of the Law and Abolition. – New Delhi : Deep and Deep Publications, 1986.
368p.
Hbk £250.00
Untouchables of India / by Dilip Hiro. – New 1982 ed. – London : Minority Rights Group, 1982.
19p. – (Report).
Previous ed.: 1975. Bibliography: p.19.
Unwanted sexual attention and sexual harassment : results of a survey of Canadians. – S.l. : Canadian Human Rights Commission, Research and Special Studies Branch, 1983.
26, 28 p.; 28 cm.
English and French. Added t.p. in French: Attentions sexuelles non sollicitees et harcelement sexuel.
ISBN 0662523725 Pbk
Unwin, Margaret
Property, Planning and Compensation Reports. – London : Sweet & Maxwell.
Hbk £80.00
Uotila, Jaakko → Finnish legal system.
Uotop, S.
Principles of Australian administrative law. – 6th ed. – North Ryde : Law Book Co, 1985.
ISBN 0455205752 Hbk £40.00
Upadhayaya, J.J. Ram
Licensing Power in India : a Government Action for Social Welfare. – New Delhi : S. Chand and Company.
Hbk £100.00
Upadhya
Law of Easements. – Allahabad : Orient Law House, 1984.
Hbk £75.00
Upadhyay, Chandra Bhushan
Forest Law : Containing Commentaries on Indian Forest Act with State Amendments and Rules as Amended... – 6th ed. – Allahabad : Hind Publishing House, 1986.
Hbk £130.00
Upadhyay, Satindra K.
Law of Essential Services in India : a Critical Study of the Essential Services Maintenance Act 1981. – New Delhi : Deep and Deep Publications, 1983.
211p.
Hbk £70.00
Upadhyaya, B.N.
Commentaries on U.P. Government Servants' Conduct Rules, 1956. – 3rd ed. – Lucknow : Eastern Book Company, 1983.
163p.
Pbk £20.00
Updating of the Radio Regulations. – Geneva : International Telecommunications Union, 1984.
Hbk £33.00
Updating statutes and regulations for all Canadian jurisdictions (as of Dec. 1984) / by Mary Jane T. Sinclair. – New ed. – Ottawa : Canadian Law Information Council, 1985.
44p.
Previous ed.: published as How to update a statute for all Canadian jurisdictions / edited by Gail S. Dykstra.
ISBN 0920358772
Upex, Robert
Termination of employment / Robert Upex. – 2nd ed. – London : Sweet & Maxwell, 1986.
xlii,148p; 26cm.
Examines entitlement to the various remedies, defines the status of employment and 'marginal employment', and looks at statutory rights with regard to redundancy and unfair dismissal. Contains examples of the calculation of compensation for redundancy and unfair dismissal, and looks at taxation of damages, and mitigation.
ISBN 0421347708 £16.50
Uppsala Universitet → Copyright and jurisprudence : selected papers.
→ Spirit of Uppsala : proceedings of the Joint UNITAR-Uppsala University Seminar on International Law and Organization for a New World Order (JUS 81), Uppsala 9-18 June 1981.
Uprising! : the police, the people and the riots in Britain's cities / Martin Kettle and Lucy Hodges. – London : Pan Books, 1982.
271p; 18cm.
ISBN 0330268457
Upson, A.
Financial Management for Contractors. – Oxford : Blackwell Scientific, 1987.
ISBN 0003830616 Hbk £19.95
Uranium Advisory Council
Uranium Mining Laws in the Northern Territory. – Uranium Advisory Council. – Canberra : Australian Government Publishing Service, 1981.
177p.
ISBN 0642068607 Hbk £6.60
Uranium Mining Laws in the Northern Territory. – Uranium Advisory Council. – Canberra : Australian Government Publishing Service, 1981.
177p.
ISBN 0642068607 Hbk £6.60
Urata, Kenji
Freedom, peace and their guarantees, from the viewpoint of the Constitution of Japan / Kenji Urata. – s.l. : s.n., 1982.
p.22-45.
'Originally presented as a draft to the Waseda University Centennial International Symposium at Waseda University on August 22 and 23, 1982'. Reprinted from: Waseda bulletin of comparative law, 2 (1982).
Urban government finance : emerging trends / edited by Roy Bahl. – Beverly Hills : Sage, 1981.
287p; 22cm. – (Urban affairs annual reviews 20).
Includes bibliographies.
ISBN 0803915640 Hbk
ISBN 0803915659 Pbk
Urban land economics / Paul N. Balchin and Jeffrey L. Kieve. – 3rd ed. – London : Macmillan, 1985.
xvi,302p; 22cm. – (Macmillan building and surveying series).
Previous ed.: 1977. Bibliography: p282-283. - Includes index.
ISBN 0333397843 Pbk £7.95
Urban land policy : issues and opportunities / Harold B. Dunkerley, cordinating editor : with the assistance of Christine M.E. Whitehead. – New York : Oxford University Press for the World Bank, 1983.
viii,214p; 25cm.
Bibliography: p199-206. - Includes index.
ISBN 0195204034 £15.00
Urban Planning Law
Supplement 1986 /. – Sweet & Maxwell.
ISBN 0421369906 Pbk £10.00
Supplement. – 1986.
ISBN 0421395605 Hbk £18.95
Urban planning practice in developing countries / editors, John L. Taylor and David G. Williams. – Oxford : Pergamon, 1982.
x,357p; 24cm. – (Pergamon international library).
Includes bibliographies.
ISBN 0080222250 £19.50
Urban riots and public order : a select bibliography, 1975-1985 / compiled by: E. Edwards, R. Golland & S. Leach for the GLC Intelligence Unit. – Letchworth : Technical Communications, 1986.
iii,159p; 30cm.
ISBN 0946655103 Hbk
Urbanisation and planning in the 3rd World : spatial perceptions and public participation / Robert B. Potter. – London : Croom Helm, 1985.
284p; 23cm. – (Croom Helm series in geography and environment).
Bibliography: p254-275. - Includes index.
ISBN 0709920555 £19.95
Uribe-Rolden, Jorge
Legal problems arising from supranational institutions : the Andean Pact : a case study / by Jorge Uribe-Rolden. – London : The author, 1984.
55 leaves.
Includes bibliographical references.
Urquhart, Brian
United Nations and international law: the Rede Lecture / Brian Urquhart. – Cambridge : Cambridge University Press, 1985.
20p.
ISBN 0521338743 Pbk £2.95
Urquhart, John A. → Information chain : proceedings of the UK Serials Group conference, held at Christ Church College Canterbury, 29 March - 1 April 1982.
Urry, John → Social theory as science.
Ury, William → Getting to YES : negotiating agreement without giving in.
US business tax : law and practice after the Tax Reform Act / Derrick & Margot Owles. – London : Financial Times Business Information, 1987.
xviii,146p; 30cm.
Includes index.
ISBN 0902101994 spiral
US design patents. – Washington Group. – London : Butterworths, 1985.
ISBN 040665865 Hbk £100.00

Use and abuse of emergency legislation in Northern Ireland / Dermot P. J. Walsh. – London? : Cobden Trust, 1983.
138p.
ISBN 0900137207

Use and Usefulness of Trademarks in Developing Countries : Collection of Lectures Given at the Asian and Pacific Symposium (1982, Colombo, Sri Lanka). – Geneva : World Intellectual Property Organization.
205p.
Hbk £40.00

Use, effectiveness and impact of police stop and search powers / Carole F. Willis. – London : Home Office, 1983.
v,40p.
Bibliography: p.32-33.
ISBN 0862520983

Use of Computers in the Criminal Justice System. – Canberra : Australian Institute of Criminology.
Hbk £2.50

Use of management techniques in regional and local government : report / prepared under the guidance of the Committee of Experts on Management in Local and Regional Government of the Steering Committee for Regional and Municipal Matters by F. Boersma. – Strasbourg : Council of Europe, 1985.
38p.
Bibliography: p.33.

Use of paperbacks in public libraries in the United Kingdom : a review of research / edited by Marilyn Hart. – Loughborough : Centre for Library and Information Management, Department of Library and Information Studies, Loughborough University, 1983.
iii,103p. – (Report).
Includes bibliographical references.
ISBN 0904924483

Use of the law list to assess the distribution and characteristics of solicitors in England and Wales / Charles Watkins, Mark Blacksell and Kim Economides. – Exeter : University of Exeter, 1984.
24p. – (Working paper).
Bibliography: p.23-24.

Use of the Patent System by Industrial Enterprises in Developing Countries. – Geneva : World Intellectual Property Organization, 1981.
97p.
Hbk £25.00

Use of trademarks in Colombia. – Bogota, Colombia : Cavelier Abogados, 1985.
22 leaves.

Use of video technology at trials of alleged child abusers / Home Office. – London : Home Office, 1987.
14p.
ISBN 0862522749

Used Car Buyers Protection Act, 1983, Bill 131 : An Act to Protect the Purchasers of Used Motor Vehicles. – Ontario : Ontario Government Publications Service, 1983.
4p.
Hbk £0.30

User's guide to copyright / Michael F. Flint. – 2nd ed. – North Ryde : Butterworths (Australia), 1985.
xvii,289p; 22cm.
Explains the operation and scope of the law and provides answers to problems. Deals with the copyright problems of particular professions, making use of charts and tables. Includes new chapters dealing with cable and satellite television, video games, teletext and electronic publishing, and piracy and counterfeiting.
ISBN 0406200742 Pbk

Usher, Elizabeth
Careers in the law. – 2nd ed. – London : Kogan Page, 1986.
ISBN 1850911002 Pbk £3.25

Usher, J. A.
European Community law and national law : the irreversible transfer? / John Usher. – London : University Association for Contemporary European Studies, 1981.
96p; 23cm.
Bibliography: p85-91. - Includes index.
ISBN 0043410170 Pbk £6.95
ISBN 0043410189
—European court practice / by John A. Usher. – London : Sweet & Maxwell, 1983.
xli,357p; 26cm.
Discusses industrial and intellectual property rights, external relations with the UN, the OECD, and North America, Euratom, ECSC, the financing of Community activities including a discussion of the background to Britain's budget rebate. Bibliography annexed to each chapter.
ISBN 0421267801 £32.00

Usher, John A
Legal aspects of agriculture in the European Community / J.A. Usher. – Oxford : Clarendon Press, 1988.
xxxvi,170p.
Includes index. Examines legal issues arising from the Common Agricultural Policy, and sets out the principles underlying changing legislation. Includes agricultural legislation which is behind European Court case law on the relationship between Community law and national law.
ISBN 0198255659 Hbk £30

Ushewkunze, C. →Constitutional Options for Namibia : a Historical Perspective.

Using a law library. – 4th ed. – Agincourt : Carswell, 1985.
ISBN 0459376101 Hbk £17.60

Ussher, Patrick
Company law in Ireland / by Patrick Ussher. – London : Sweet & Maxwell, 1986.
xlvii,577p; 22cm.
Includes index.
ISBN 0421297506 Pbk £18.95
—Doing Business in Ireland. – Matthew Bender, 1987.
ISBN 0000999034 Hbk £50.00

USSR, Eastern Europe and the development of the law of the sea / compiled, translated and edited by William E. Butler. – New ed. 2 v. – London : Oceana, 1983.
looseleaf.
Previously published as: The Eastern European states and the development of the law of the sea / by Viktor Sebek. 1979. Bibliography: Vol. 2.
ISBN 0379208512

Usurpation and Tort Liability in Islamic and Iranian Law. – Royston.
ISBN 0946706514 Hbk £15.00

Utilising company tax losses and reliefs / by Nigel A. Eastaway and Edward P. Magrin. – 2nd ed. – London : Institute of Chartered Accountants in England and Wales, 1982.
xxxiv,321p; 21cm.
Previous ed.: 1979. Includes index.
ISBN 0852913133 Pbk

Utilitarianism / On liberty : John Stuart Mill : edited with an introduction by Mary Warnock. – 17th impression. – Glasgow : Fontana, 1985.
352p.
This selection originally published: 1962. Bibliography: p.343-4. - Includes index.

Utility and rights / R.G. Frey, editor. – Oxford : Blackwell, 1985.
ix,245p; 24cm.
Includes index.
ISBN 0631137130 £19.50

Utility Deposits Interest Act, 1983, Bill 126 : An Act to Require the Payment of Interest on Consumers' Utility Deposits. – Ontario : Ontario Government Publications Service, 1983.
1p.
Hbk £0.30

Utility of international economic sanctions / edited by David Leyton-Brown. – London : Croom Helm, 1987.
320p; 23cm.
Includes index.
ISBN 070991699X £25.00

Utilization of nuclear energy and international law / Vanda Lamm. – Budapest : Akademiai Kiado, 1984.
155p.
ISBN 963053892X

Utilization of outer space and international law / Gijsbertha C.M. Reijnen. – Amsterdam : Elsevier Scientific, 1981.
xvi,179p; 25cm.
Bibliography: p169-171. - Includes index.
ISBN 0444419659

Uttar Pradesh Agricultural Credit Act, 1973. – 4th ed. repr. – Lucknow : Eastern Book Company, 1985.
Hbk £30.00

Uttar Pradesh Excise Act, 1910 : Together with Rules and Notifications. – 3rd ed. – Lucknow : Eastern Book Company.
Hbk

Uttar Pradesh Land Revenue Act, 1901 / P.L. Malik. – 7th ed. – Lucknow : Eastern Book Company, 1983.
243p.
Hbk £25.00

Uttar Pradesh Local Acts in about 12 Volumes / Surendra Malik. – 5th rev. ed. – Lucknow : Eastern Book Company.
ca 800p per vol.
Hbk £90.00 ea.

Uttar Pradesh Police Regulations. – 3rd ed. – Lucknow : Eastern Book Company, 1985.
Hbk

Uttar Pradesh Regulation of Building Operations Act, 1958 : with Rules and Regulations and Urban Planning and Development Act, 1973. – 3rd ed. repr. – Lucknow : Eastern Book Company, 1986.
396p.
Hbk £110.00

Uttar Pradesh Sales Tax Act, 1948 : Together with Rules and Notifications as Amended up to U.P. Act No. 22 of 1984. – 6th ed. – Lucknow : Eastern Book Company, 1985.
220p.
Hbk £36.00

Uttar Pradesh Shop and Commercial Establishments Act, 1962. – 3rd ed. – Lucknow : Eastern Book Company, 1984.
410p.
Hbk £50.00

Uttar Pradesh State Universities Act, 1973 : as Amended Up-to-Date with Exhaustive Comments and Allied Laws / S.N. Srivastava. – Allahabad : Hind Publishing House, 1981.
ii, 146p.
Hbk £20.00

Uttar Pradesh Urban Buildings (Regulation of Letting, Rent and Eviction) Act, 1972. – 2nd ed. – Lucknow : Eastern Book Company, 1983.
833p.
Hbk £105.00

Vaartnou, Peter →Creditors' Remedies in Alberta.

Vaccination Certificate Requirements for International Travel and Health Advice to Travellers 1985. – World Health Organization. – London : HMSO, 1985.
81p.
ISBN 9241580100 Hbk £4.80

Vagg, Jon →Accountability and prisons : opening up a closed world.

Vagts, Detlev F.
Question of a Reference to International Obligations in the United Nations Code of Conduct on Transnational Corporations : a Different View. – Geneva : United Nations Publications.
ISBN 9211041864 Hbk £4.00

Vaines, P.
Bottom Line. – Plymouth : Macdonald & Evans, 1988.
ISBN 0356155382 Hbk £7.95

Vakil, B.C.
Please Your Worship : Lighter Side of a Magistrate's Court. – Bombay : Tripathi, 1965.
196p.
Hbk £10.00

Valencia, Mark J. →Shipping, energy, and environment : Southeast Asian perspectives for the eighties : proceedings of a Workshop held in Honolulu, Hawaii, 10-12 December 1980.

Valentine →Business of Banking.

Valentine, B. J. A. C.
County court procedure in Northern Ireland including a supplement for the Republic of Ireland / B. J. A. C. Valentine and T. F. Grass. – Belfast : SLS Publications, 1985.
lviii,350p.
Kept up to date by supplements.
ISBN 0853892342

Valentine, S.P.
International Dictionary of the Securities Industry. – 2nd ed. – London : Macmillan.
ISBN 0333449738 Hbk £45.00

Vali
Servitudes To International Law. – Sweet & Maxwell, 1958 Reprint.
ISBN 0421375302 Hbk £29.50

Validity of the reconviction prediction score / by Denis Ward. – London : HMSO, 1987.
vi,45p.
Describes the method used to calculate the score, based on data for men discharged in 1965. Compares this with data from 1977-79. Concludes that the RPS should continue in substantially its present form.
ISBN 011340882X

Valk
Conservatism in Modern Chinese Family Law. – Leiden : E.J. Brill, 1956.
ISBN 9004032630 Hbk £28.00

Vallebona, Antonio →Law of collective agreements in the countries of the European Community.

Valuation 85 : a Conceptual Outline / Fiona Abbott. – 1st ed. – North Ryde : C.C.H. Australia, 1984.
56p.
ISBN 0887962882 Pbk £5.00

Valuation : principles into practice. – 2nd ed. – London : Estates Gazette, 1984.
ISBN 0728201070 Pbk £22.00

Valuation and Conversion Tables. – London : Estates Gazette, 1978.
ISBN 0728200641 Hbk £10.00

Valuation and development appraisal. – London : Estates Gazette, 1982.
ISBN 0728201097 Pbk £16.50

Valuation and investment appraisal. – London : Estates Gazette, 1983.
ISBN 0728200686 Pbk £18.00

Valuation and rating in Scotland: proposals for reform / presented to Parliament by the Secretary of State for Scotland. – London : H.M.S.O., 1983.
10p.
ISBN 0101901801

Valuation and selection of convertible bonds. – Praeger, 1988.
ISBN 0275924661 Hbk £27.50

Valuation of property investments. – 3rd ed. – London : Estates Gazette, 1984.
ISBN 0728200732 Pbk £10.00

Valuation of the Nationalised Property in International Law. – London : Eurospan.
ISBN 081390465X Hbk £12.95

Value Added Tax
1987-88. – Tolley Publishing.
ISBN 085459292X Pbk £13.95
1988-89. –
ISBN 0854593500 Pbk £15.95

Value Added Tax. – London : Butterworths.
Service to Date.
ISBN 0406514593 Llf £160.00

Value Added Tax : A Practical Guide for Your Business. – Coopers & Lybrand Associates. – London : Kogan Page.
ISBN 1850917515 Hbk £12.95
ISBN 1850917493 Pbk £5.95

Value Added Tax Cases. – revised 3rd ed. – Belfast : Tolley Publishing.
ISBN 00854592970 Pbk £29.95

Value Added Tax Property Planning after the EEC Decision. – 2nd ed. – London : Longman Professional.
ISBN 0851214630 Hbk £95.00

Value Added Tax Tribunal Reports : 1973-82, 10 Vols. – Abingdon : Professional Books, 1984.
Hbk £280.00

Value Added Tax Tribunals Report 1984, 4 parts
Part 1. – London : HMSO.
ISBN 0112604986 Hbk £4.55
Part 2. –
ISBN 0112604994 Hbk £4.15
Part 3. –
ISBN 0112605028 Hbk £4.55
Part 4. –
ISBN 0112605095 Hbk £4.15

Value Added Taxation in Europe. – International Bureau of Fiscal Documentation. – Amsterdam : International Bureau of Fiscal Documentation, 1988.
– (Guides to European Taxation Ser.: Vol. 4).
Llf £950.00
Supplements-1989 renewal. –
Llf £400.00

Value for Money in Taxation Stamp Memorial Lecture. – London : University of London.
ISBN 00718708571 Pbk £1.00

Value-added tax : orthodoxy and new thinking / David G Raboy, Ernest S Christian Jr. – Dordrecht : Kluwer, 1989.
304.
Considers questions about the features and effects of tax proposals which are commonly called 'consumption taxes'. Presents issues from the perspective of the practical problems which would affect, or arise from, the imposition of such taxes.
ISBN 0792390024 Hbk £26.25

Valuer. – Durban : Professional Publishers, 1983.
ISBN 0409027103 Hbk £64.00

Values and the changing family / a final report from the Working Party on Values. – London : Study Commission on the Family, 1982.
52p; 21cm.
Bibliography: p48. Cover title.
ISBN 0907051138 Pbk £2.75

Values in conflict : life, liberty, and the rule of law / compiled by Burton M. Leiser. – London : Collier Macmillan, 1981.
xii,478p; 24cm.
ISBN 002369520X Pbk £7.50

Vamvoukos, Athanassios
Termination of treaties in international law : the doctrines of Rebus Sic Stantibus and Desuetude / Athanassios Vamvoukos. – Oxford : Clarendon, 1985.
xxiii,325p; 22cm.
Bibliography: p304-315. - Includes index.
ISBN 0198761791 £35.00

Van Agtmael, A.
Emerging Securities Markets. – London : Euromoney, 1984.
ISBN 090312162X Pbk £75.00

Van Bael
EEC Anti-Dumping and other Trade Protection laws / Bellis. – London : CCH, 1985.
ISBN 0863250602 Pbk £16.50

Van Den Berg, Albert Jan
New York Arbitration Convention of 1958 : towards a uniform judicial interpretation / door Albert Jan Van Den Berg. – The Hague : T.M.C. Asser Institute, 1981.
xv,480p.
Proefschrift: Erasmus Universiteit, Rotterdam. Bibliography: p440-450. With summary and conclusion in Dutch.
ISBN 9065440356
→ Yearbook Commercial Arbitration, 1989.

Van den Berghe, Guido
Political rights for European citizens / Guido van den Berghe. – Aldershot : Gower, 1982.
xii,245p; 23cm.
Bibliography: p218-235. - Includes index.
ISBN 0566005247

Van der Merwe, C.G.
Sectional titles, share blocks and time-sharing / by C.G. van der Merwe and D.W. Butler. – Durban : Butterworths, 1985.
xiii,573p.
Bibliography: p. xv-xxi. - Includes indexes.
ISBN 0409059293 Hbk R105
—VanDerMerwe : The Law of Things. – Durban : Professional Publisher, 1987.
ISBN 0409058374 Hbk £39.00

Van der Merwe, S. E.
Evidence / S.E. van der Merwe ... et al. – Cape Town : Juta, 1983.
xxxviii,450p.
Includes index.
ISBN 0702113778
—VanDerMerwe, Kemp and Barton : Plea Procedures in Summary Criminal Trials / VanDerMerwe, Kemp and Barton. – Durban : Professional Publisher, 1983.
ISBN 0409059285 Pbk £49.00

van der Walt, J. C.
Index to the South African Law Reports : 1828-1946, 2 vols. / F. R. Malan. – Durban : Butterworths.
ISBN 0409040770 Hbk

Van der Westhuizen, J.V.
VanDerWesthuizen and Viljoen : A Bill of Rights for South Africa / H.P. Viljoen. – Durban : Professional Publisher, 1988.
ISBN 0409061085 Pbk

Van Houtte, A.
Court of Justice of the European Communities. – Luxembourg : Office for Official Publications of the European Communities, 1985.
Hbk

Van Hulle, K.
Fourth Company Law Directive : Implementation by Member States / J.G. Demas. – Luxembourg : Office for Official Publications of the European Communities, 1987.
100p.
ISBN 9282571211 Pbk £400.00

Van Lier, Irene H.
Acid rain and international law / by Irene H. van Lier. – Halifax : Dalhousie University, 1981.
xxii,278p.
Originally presented as the author's thesis (LL.M.) - Dalhousie University 1980. Bibliography: p.257-266.
ISBN 9028622314 Hbk
ISBN 0770301851 Hbk

van Niekerk, J. P.
Decline, revival and future of the Roman-Dutch law of insurance in South Africa / by J.P. van Niekerk. – s.l. : Department of Mercantile Law, University of South Africa, 1986.
78p. – (Monograph series).
Includes bibliographical references.
ISBN 0869814001

Van Rensburg, A. D. J.
Practitioner's Guide to the Alienation of Land Act / S. H. Treisman. – 2nd ed. – Durban : Butterworths, 1984.
– (Eng. & Afrikaans).
ISBN 040906078X Hbk
ISBN 0409060798 Pbk
—VanRensburg and Treisman : The Practitioner's Guide to the Alienation of Land Act / S.H. Treisman. – 2nd ed. – Durban : Professional Publisher, 1984.
ISBN 0409060666 Hbk £69.00

Van Rooyen, J. C. W.
Censorship in South Africa : being a commentary on the application of the Publications Act / J.C.W. van Rooyen. – Cape Town : Juta, 1987.
xxiv,152p.
Includes bibliograpical references and index.
ISBN 0702119059

Van Walt van Praag, Michael C.
Status of Tibet : history, rights and prospects in international law / Michael C. van Walt van Praag : with a foreword by Franz Michael and an introduction by Rikhi Jaipal. – London : Wisdom, 1987.
400p; 23cm.
Includes bibliography and index.
ISBN 0861710703 Pbk

Van Warmelo, Paul → Our legal heritage.

van Zyl, D.H.
History and Principles of Roman Private Law. – Durban : Professional Publisher, 1983.
This book presents a systematic approach to the basic principles of Roman law and its history for students of the subject.
ISBN 0409060631 Pbk £72.00
—Negotiorum Gestio in South African Law. – Durban : Butterworths, 1985.
ISBN 0409060704 Pbk

Van Zyl Smit, Dirk → Constitutional change in South Africa : the next five years.

Vancouver People's Law School → Wills and Estates.

Vancouver Stock Exchange : 1988 Update: Timely Material Corporate Disclosure. – Vancouver : Continuing Legal Education Society of British Columbia, 1988.
91p.
ISBN 086504998X Hbk £70.00

Vancouver Stock Exchange Practice for Legal Assistants. – Vancouver : Continuing Legal Education Society of British Columbia, 1986.
429p.
ISBN 0865042764 Hbk £65.00

Vandamme
Emp. Consultation and Information in Multinational Corps. – Oxford : Croom Helm, 1986.
ISBN 0709926243 Hbk £19.95

Vandenberghe, G P V → Advanced topics of law and information technology.
→ Freedom of data flows and EEC law.

VanDerMerwe : The Law of Things. – Durban : Professional Publisher, 1987.
ISBN 0409058374 Hbk £39.00

VanDerMerwe, Kemp and Barton : Plea Procedures in Summary Criminal Trials / VanDerMerwe, Kemp and Barton. – Durban : Professional Publisher, 1983.
ISBN 0409059285 Pbk £49.00

VanDerWesthuizen and Viljoen : A Bill of Rights for South Africa / H.P. Viljoen. – Durban : Professional Publisher, 1988.
ISBN 0409061085 Pbk

Vandesanden, G.
Pleading Before the Court of Justice of the European Communities : The Law Society's European Group. – London : Law Society.
free

Vani S → Armed separatism in Southeast Asia.

Vann, R. → Law of Public Company Finance.

Vanonal Insurance Contributions 1987-1988. – Tolley Publishing.
ISBN 0854959275 Pbk £16.95

VanRensburg and Treisman : The Practitioner's Guide to the Alienation of Land Act / S.H. Treisman. – 2nd ed. – Durban : Professional Publisher, 1984.
ISBN 0409060666 Hbk £69.00

Varadachari, V.K.
Law of Hindi Religious and Charitable Endowments. – 3rd ed. – Lucknow : Eastern Book Company, 1985.
Hbk £200.00
—President in the Indian Constitution. – New Delhi : Deep and Deep Publications, 1985.
180p.
Hbk £100.00
—Public Trusts and Taxation. – Lucknow : Eastern Book Company, 1987.
418p.
Hbk £125.00

Varges, Gabe Shawn
New international economic order legal debate : background, status, and alternatives / Gabe Shawn Varges. – Frankfurt am Main : Peter Lang, 1983.
vi,138p.
Bibliography: p. 121-128.
ISBN 382047613X

Vargo, Csaba
Anthropological jurisprudence? : Leopold Pospisil and the comparative study of legal cultures / by Csaba Varga. – Budapest : Hungarian Academy of Sciences, Institute of Sociology, 1986.
34p. – (Underdevelopment and modernization).
Bibliography: p.30-34.

Variations in Construction Contracts. – London : Collins, 1986.
240p.
ISBN 0003831914 Hbk £17.95

Varshni, D.P. → Criminal Trial and Judgement, Includes Supplement-1985.
—How to Frame a Charge. – 1981 repr. – Lucknow : Eastern Book Company, 1985.
174p.
Hbk £30.00

Varshni, Hari Pal
Criminal Trial and Judgement / D.P. Varshni. – 3rd rev. ed. 1981 repr. – Lucknow : Eastern Book Company, 1985.
477p.
Hbk £70.00

Vasdev, Krishna
Law of evidence in the Sudan / by Krishna Vasdev. – London : Butterworths, 1981.
xlviii,486p; 22cm.
Includes index.
ISBN 0406406103 Pbk
—Law of Homicide in the Sudan. – London : Butterworths, 1978.
ISBN 040640609X Pbk £17.60

Vassilyev, D.
Bibliography of the Institute of State and Law Scholar's (sic) works (1978 - 1982). – Moscow : The Institute, 1983.
37p.
'Compiled by D. Vassilyev, translated by N. Gheraseva'. At head of title: Academy of Sciences of the USSR, Order of the Red Banner of Labour, Institute of State and Law.

Vasudevan, S.V. →Textbook of Banking : Law Practice and Theory of Banking.

VAT. – London : Butterworths, 1984.
ISBN 0406514747 Llf £210.00

VAT : Experience of Some European Countries. – Dordrecht : Kluwer, 1982.
ISBN 9065440240 Hbk £155.00

VAT and the City. – London : CCH, 1987.
ISBN 086325120X Pbk £19.50

VAT and the New Business. – London : CCH, 1987.
ISBN 0863251056 Pbk £12.50

VAT disputes and how to avoid them. – London : CCH, 1986.
ISBN 0863251005 Pbk £12.50

VAT enforcement and appeals manual. – London : Butterworths, 1986.
ISBN 0406504202 Pbk £17.95

VAT Guide and Casebook / Christopher A. L. Preston. – London : Oyez Longman, 1983.
ISBN 0851206611 Llf £50.00

VAT - Imports and exports. – London : CCH, 1987.
ISBN 0863251048 Pbk £15.00

VAT investigations. – Croydon : Tolley, 1988.
ISBN 0854593195 Hbk £13.95

VAT on construction and development work. – Oxford : Blackwell Scientific, 1984.
ISBN 0246122501 Hbk £17.95

VAT planning. – Croydon : Tolley, 1988.
ISBN 0854592989 Pbk £16.95

VAT Tribunal Reports 1973-1986
Vols. 1-14. – Professional Books.
ISBN 086205284X Hbk £290.00

Vaughan →Virginia Statute for Religious Freedom : Its Evolution and Consequences in American History Conf. Proc.

Vaughan, D.
Law of the European Communities, 2 Vols. – London : Butterworths, 1986.
ISBN 0406003009 Hbk £140.00

Vaughan, Frederick →Supreme Court of Canada : History of the Institution.

Vaughan, Paul
Exporting goods from the United Kingdom : export co-operatives and contract warehousing / by Paul Vaughan, with John Sykes and Derek Pool. – London : Thames Polytechnic, School of Business, 1986.
22 p.
ISBN 0948296046

Vaulkhard, Susan
Family and child law statutes. – 3rd. – London : Longman Professional (UK), 1990.
Updated with 1988 and 1989 legislative changes including the Children Act 1989, plus the Adoption Act 1976.
ISBN 0851215750 Pbk £24.50

Vaulont, Nikolaus
Customs union of the European Economic Community / by Nikolaus Vaulont : translated from the French. – Luxembourg : Office for Official Publications of the European Community, 1981.
87 p.; 25 cm.
Includes bibliographical references.
ISBN 9282519112 Pbk £5.00 (U.S.)

Vaver, David
Intellectual Property Journal. – Agincourt : Carswell, 1985.
Hbk £75.75

Vayda, Elaine J.
Law for social workers : a Canadian guide / by Elaine J. Vayda, Mary T. Satterfield. – Toronto, Canada : Carswell, 1984.
xxi, 292 p.; 24 cm.
This second edition text reviews the structure of the Canadian legal system. Discussions include the rights of persons living in common law relationships, criteria for awarding support, possible courses of legal action for situations of family violence, basic grounds and procedure for obtaining divorce, custody and access, child protection proceedings, adoption and children that break the law. Also included in the new edition is divorce, custody, support, family property, and young offenders. Includes bibliographies and index.
ISBN 0459366602 Pbk

Veatch, R.
Foundations of Justice. – Oxford : Oxford University Press, 1986.
ISBN 0195040767 Hbk £22.50

Veen, F. van
Law Relating to Transport of Dangerous Wastes, Netherlands / V. di Martino. – Luxembourg : Office for Official Publications of the European Communities, 1987.
132p.
ISBN 9282567575 Pbk £450.00

Veenhoven, Willem Adriaan →Case studies on human rights and fundamental freedoms : a world survey.

Vekas, L.
Landmarks in the Development of the Contractual System. – Budapest : Akademiai Kiado.
192p.
ISBN 9630536668 Hbk £19.00
→ Law of Conflicts and Foreign Trade.

Veljanovski, Cento G.
Cable television : agency franchising and economics / Cento Veljanovski. – London : Faculty of Laws, University College London, 1986.
25p; 30cm. – (Working papers).
—Choice by cable : the economics of a new era in television / C.G.Veljanovski and W.D.Bishop. – London : Institute of Economic Affairs, 1983.
120p; 22cm.
ISBN 0255361599
→ Economic approach to law.
—New law-and-economics : a research review / C.G. Veljanovski. – Oxford : Centre for Socio-Legal Studies, 1982.
xi,169p.
Bibliography: p.144-169.
ISBN 0862260531
→ Readings in economics of law and regulation.
—Selling the state : privatisation in Britain / Cento Veljanovski. – London : Weidenfeld and Nicolson, 1987.
xiv, 239p.
Bibliography: p.213-217.
ISBN 0297790803

Velupillai, Jeyaratnam
Damages-Loss of Expectation of Life : Survival and Deductibility. – Singapore : Malayan Law Journal, 1984.
xiii, 82p.
Explores the survival of the claim for loss of expectation of life and the methods employed by courts for its quantification. Intends to determine the justification, if any, for deducting the compensation awarded to the estate under the Fatal Accidents Act 1846-1908. Comparison of the law in England, Canada (Manitoba), Australia and Malaysia.
ISBN 9971700379 Hbk £25.00

Venables
Internal audit / Impey. – London : Butterworths, 1985.
ISBN 0406013802 Pbk £18.50

Venables, J. S.
Internal Audit / Ken Impey. – London : Butterworths, 1985.
For students and practitioners, this book uses extensive illustrations and diagrams to present the state of the art in modern internal auditing. Techniques of examination and analysis are discussed.
ISBN 0406013802 Pbk

Venables, Robert →Passing Down the Family Farm.
—Tax planning through trusts / Robert Venables. – London : Butterworths, 1983.
xxxiv,371p; 24cm.
Includes index.
ISBN 0406406014

Vendataramanaiah, V.
Essays on Constitutional Law : Alladi Krishnaswami Aiyer Memorial Volume. – New Delhi : Concept Publishing Company, 1986.
xvi, 285p.
Hbk £175.00

Vendor and Purchaser : Commentary and Materials. – North Ryde : Law book Co, 1985.
xxviii, 436p.
ISBN 0455206066 Hbk £57.50
ISBN 0455206074 Pbk £38.50

Venezuela Law Governing Restrictive Business Practices. – London : Eurospan.
ISBN 0935328351 Hbk £66.50

Venkaiah
Law of Prints and Impressions. – 2nd ed 1972 2nd repr. – Allahabad : Law Book Company, 1988.
400p.
With supplement.
Pbk £100.00

Venkanna →Motor Transport Workers Act : with States Rules.

Venkataraman, S. →Civil Procedure Code.
→ Criminal Procedure Code.

Vennard, Julie
Contested trials in magistrates' courts / by Julie Vennard. – London : H.M.S.O., 1982.
v,32p; 25cm.
Bibliography: p.26-27. 'A Home Office Research and Planning Unit report.'.
ISBN 0113407661
→ Triable-either-way cases : Crown Court or Magistrates' Court?.

Venne, Sharon Helen →Indian acts and amendments 1868-1975 : an indexed collection.

Veno, Arthur
Psychologist in Criminal Justice : An Australian Perspective. – Canberra : Australian Institute of Criminology.
free

Ventris, F. M.
Banker's documentary credits : issued in accordance with the Uniform customs and practice (1974 revision) of the International Chamber of Commerce / by F.M. Ventris. – 2nd ed. – London : Lloyd's of London Press, 1983.
xxi,350p.
Previous ed.: 1980. Includes index.
ISBN 0907432379
—Tanker voyage charter parties / by F. M. Ventris. – S.l. : Kluwer Law Publishers, 1986.
xvi,411p.
ISBN 0903393972

Venture capital today. – Cambridge : Woodhead-Faulkner, 1985.
ISBN 085941275X Hbk £30.00

Verchere, David R.
Progression of Judges : a History of the Supreme Court of British Columbia. – Vancouver : University of British Columbia Press, 1988.
197p.
ISBN 0774802936 Hbk £31.95

Verdict According to Conscience : Perspectives on the English Criminal Trial Jury 1200-1800. – University of Chicago Press.
ISBN 0226306097 Pbk £13.50

Verdict in Peking : the trial of the Gang of Four / David Bonavia. – London : Burnett, 1984.
225p; 24cm.
Includes index.
ISBN 0091562007 £9.95

Verdier, Jean-Maurice →International labour law reports, Volume 7.

Verdun-Jones, Simon B →Criminal justice in Canada: an introductory text.

Verge, P. →Comparative dismissal law.

Verheyden-Jeanmart et al., N.
Unmarried Family. – Kortrijk-Heule : UGA Editions, 1982.
186p.
ISBN 9067681296 £605.00

VerLoren van Themaat, Pieter
Changing structure of international economic law : a contribution of legal history, of comparative law and of general legal theory to the debate on a new international economic order / by Pieter VerLoren van Themaat. – The Hague : Martinus Nijhoff, 1981.
xxv,395p.
English edition of VerLoren van Themaat, P. : Rechtsgrondslagen van een nieuwe internationale economische orde.
ISBN 9024725402 Hbk £165.00
→ Introduction to the law of the European Communities: after the coming into force of the Single European Act.

Verma
Commentary on Limitation Act. – Allahabad : Orient Law House, 1984.
Hbk £50.00
—Law of Muslim Marriage, Dissolution and Maintenance. – 2nd ed. – Allahabad : Law Book Company, 1988.
600p.
Hbk £175.00

Verma, B.L.
Development of Indian Legal System. – New Delhi : Deep and Deep Publications, 1987.
428p.
Hbk £275.00

Verma, J.C.
Law of Ownership of Property and Investigation of Title. – New Delhi : Bharat Law House, 1985.
Hbk £100.00
—Lease Financing (Concept, Law and Procedure). – repr. 1986. – New Delhi : Bharat Law House, 1986.
Hbk £200.00

Verma, P.R.P.
Digest of All India Control of Rent and Eviction Cases, 1970-1976. – Lucknow : Eastern Book Company, 1977.
136p.
Pbk £10.00

Vermeesch, R.B.
Business Law of Australia / K.E. Lindgren. – 5th ed. – Butterworths, 1987.
1,100p.
ISBN 0409492086 Hbk £39.50
→ Trade practices and consumer protection : a commentary on the Trade Practices Act 1974.

Vermulst, Edwin A.
Antidumping law and practice in the United States and the European Communities : a comparative analysis / Edwin A. Vermulst. – Amsterdam : North-Holland, 1987.
xx, 750 p.; 24 cm.
Includes bibliographical references and index.
ISBN 0444702229 Hbk

Verrechtlichung : Begriffe, Merkmale, Grenzen, Auswege / by Gunther Teubner. – Florence : European University Institute, 1984.
104p.
At head of title: European University Institute, Florence, Law Department.

Verschuur, W. E. →Ordinances and regulations of the Province of the Orange Free State.

Verstappen, Berth →Human rights missions : a study of the fact-finding practice of non-governmental organizations.
—Human rights reports : an annotated bibliography of fact-finding missions / by Berth Verstappen. – London : Zell, 1987.
400p; 21cm.
Includes index.
ISBN 0905450353 Hbk £45.00

Verzijl, Jan Hendrik Willem
International law in historical perspective / By J. H. W. Verzijl. – Rockville : Sijthoff & Noordhoff, 1968-.
v.; 24 cm. – (Nova et vetera iuris gentium. Series A, Modern international law, no. 4, 6-9, 12-14).
Contents: 1. General subjects.– 2. International persons.– 3. State territory.– 4. Stateless domain.– 5. Nationality and other matters relating to individuals.– 6. Juridical facts as sources of international rights and obligations.– 7. State succession.– 8. Inter-state disputes and their settlements.–pt. 9a. The laws of war.–pt. 9b. The law of neutrality.
fl 62.50 (v. 1)

Veterans' Entitlements Act 1986. – North Ryde : C.C.H. Australia, 1986.
ISBN 0869035673 Hbk

Veterinary Jurisprudence. – 3rd ed. – New Delhi : Oxford University Press.
Hbk £50.00

Veterinary Law : Ethics, Etiquette and Convention. – North Hyde : Law Book Co, 1985.
xvi, 369p.
ISBN 0455205604 Hbk £32.50

Vicarious liability. – Witherby, 1986.
ISBN 094869100X Pbk £7.50

Vicarious liability of parents for actions of their children who are found to be delinquent / Elizabeth Beckett. – Ottawa : Ministry of the Solicitor General, 1985.
ii,79 leaves. – (User report).
Includes bibliographical references.

Vicarious liability under the Motor Vehicle Act. – Law Reform Commission of British Columbia. – Vancouver : The Commission, 1988.
ii,60p. – (Working paper).
ISBN 0771886241

Vicente, Mendoza, V
Bar Review Guide in Political Law. – 3rd ed. – Quezon City : University of the Philippines, Law Center, 1981.
190p.
Pbk £20.00

Vickery, B. C.
Information system dynamics : the impact of interactive information networks on the UK library and information system : final report for the period August 1979 - July 1982 : report to the British Library Research and Development Dept., on project SI/G/327 / Brian C. Vickery, Richard G. Heseltine, Carolyn S. Brown. – London : School of Library, Archive and Information Studies, University College London, 1982.
392p; 30cm.

Vickery, Michael
Kampuchea : politics, economics and society / Michael Vickery. – London : Pinter, 1986.
xviii,211p; 23cm.
Bibliography: p199-205. - Includes index.
ISBN 0861874226 Hbk £17.50
ISBN 0931477743 : Pbk £5.95

Vickery's law and accounts of executors administrators and trustees. – 21st. – London : Cassell plc.
Textbook for people taking examinations for the Institute of Chartered Accountants in England and Wales. Relates developments in the subject, including inheritance tax, since 1980.
ISBN 0304313890

Victim of rape : institutional reactions / Lynda Lytle Holmstrom, Ann Wolbert Burgess. – New ed. – New Brunswick : Transaction, 1983.
xl,293p; 23cm.
Previous ed.: New York : Chichester : Wiley, 1978.
ISBN 0878559329 Pbk

Victims and witnesses of crime in Canada / by Dick Weiler and Jean-Guy Desgagne of the Canadian Council on Social Development. – Ottawa : Ministry of Supply and Services, Canada, 1984.
98p,111p.
With French t.p.: Victimes et temoins d'infractions penales au Canada. French and English text.
ISBN 0662530136

Victims Before the Law : the Organizational Domination of Criminal Law. – Butterworths, 1983.
304p.
Hbk £55.00

Victims in the criminal justice system / Joanna Shapland, Jon Willmore, Peter Duff. – Aldershot : Gower, 1985.
vi,203p; 23cm.
Bibliography: p195-201. - Includes index.
ISBN 0566008947 Hbk £20.45
ISBN 0566008777 Pbk £8.95

Victims of crime : the dimensions of risk / by Michael R. Gottfredson. – London : H.M.S.O., 1984.
iv,54p; 25cm.
Results of a survey of groups most at risk from crime in England and Wales. Examines lifestyles related to high risks of crime. Provides information for planners of crime-prevention policy.
ISBN 0113407750

Victims of the law. – London : Allen & Unwin, 1982.
216p.
ISBN 0868613959 £17.95

Victoria Civil Procedure. – North Ryde : C.C.H. Australia, 1987.
1,200p.
ISBN 0869039326 Hbk

Victoria Law Foundation →Australian legal directory.

Victoria University of Wellington →Mergers and takeovers : legal and financial issues : written proceedings of a seminar, 29 August 1985.
→ Rape study : a study directed by Mel Smith and Warren Young and undertaken by the Department of Justice and the Institute of Criminology.

Victorian Bar. – Robert Hale, 1982.
ISBN 0709005334 Hbk £9.95

Victorian consumer credit legislation / with annotations by Jane R. Levine. – North Ryde, N.S.W. : CCH Australia, 1984.
xl,353p.
Includes index.
ISBN 086903779X

Victorian Conveyancing Costs Annotated. – 3rd ed. – Sydney : Butterworths, 1983.
80p.
ISBN 0409493112 Pbk

Victorian divorce. – Oxford : Croom Helm, 1985.
ISBN 0709937652 Hbk £17.95

Victorian Law of Real Estate. – Woolloomooloo : International Business Communications, 1986.
ISBN 094955328X Hbk £19.50

Victorian pleading precedents / by Tony Graham : with a foreword by Norman M. O'Bryan. – Sydney : Law Book Co., 1982.
xii,333p.
Includes index.
ISBN 0455203628

Victorian Real Property Legislation. – North Ryde : C.C.H. Australia, 1986.
288p.
ISBN 086903880X Hbk

Victorin, Anders →Law and the weaker party : an Anglo-Swedish comparative study, Vol. 3 : Swedish statutory material : edited by Alan C. Neal and Anders Victorin.
→ Perspective on labour law.
—Scandinavian Studies in Law, 30 Vols.
Vol. 31 (1987). – Stockholm : Almqvist & Wiksell, 1988.
238p.
ISBN 9185142417 Hbk £188.00
→ Swedish Statutes, 3 Vols., Vol. 3.

Video law : a specially commissioned report / by Stephen de B. Bate and Richard McD. Bridge. – London : Longman Professional, 1985.
x,119p.
Includes index.
ISBN 0851210287

Video Piracy and the Law. – New Delhi : Deep and Deep Publications, 1986.
160p.
Hbk £100.00

Vidya, Bhushan →World Constitutions.

Viega, Anita C.
Legal Secretary's Handbook. – Toronto : Butterworths, 1986.
288p.
Contains standard forms (not found in the Rules of Civil Procedure), prescribed Forms and proper usage, examinations for discovery and discovery of documents, pleadings, defences, counterclaims, crossclaims, third and subsequent party claims, amendments of pleadings, briefs, preparation of pleadings, discovery and trial briefs assembly of documents and sample Indexes.
ISBN 0409801720 Hbk £40.00

Vienna Agreement for the Protection of Type Faces and Their International Deposit : Original Text of the Agreement, Regulations and Protocol Adopted by the Vienna Conference. – Geneva : World Intellectual Property Organization.
63p.
Hbk £10.00

Vienna convention on the law of treaties / Ian Sinclair. – 2nd ed. – Manchester : Manchester University Press, 1984.
x,270p; 25cm.
Previous ed.: 1973. Includes index.
ISBN 0719014808

Vietnamese refugees : a study of their reception and resettlement in the United Kingdom. – London : Home Office, 1982.
iv,63p.
Bibliography: p.56.
ISBN 0862520789

View from the shadows : the Ministry of the Solicitor General of Canada and the making of the justice for victims of crime initiative / Paul Rock. – Oxford : Clarendon, 1986.
xix,396p; 22cm. – (Oxford socio-legal studies).
An empirical study of the evolution of the Canadian Solicitor General's Justice for Victims of Crime Initiative. Focuses on the complexity of policies for victims, and also the more general problems of the policy-making process in a federal government.
ISBN 0198255233 Hbk £35

Vigod, Toby →Pesticides in Canada : an examination of federal law and policy.

Vijaya Kumar, P.S.
Income Tax Law. – New Delhi : Kalyani Publishers.
Hbk £20.00

Viljoen, H.P. →VanDerWesthuizen and Viljoen : A Bill of Rights for South Africa.

Villiger, Mark E
Customary international law and treaties : a study of their interactions and interrelations, with special consideration of the 1969 Vienna Convention on the Law of Treaties / Mark E. Villiger. – Dordrecht : Nijhoff, 1985.
xxxiii, 432p. – (Developments in international law).
Originally presented as the author's Habilitationsschrift (University of Zurich). Includes index. Bibliography: p.409-420.
ISBN 9024729807 Hbk £225.00

Vimadalal
Introduction to Negotiable Instrument Act. – Bombay : Universal Book Corporation.
Hbk £6.00

Vincent →Charity Accounting.
→ In the child's best interest?.

Vincent, R
Foreign Policy and Human Rights. – Cambridge : Cambridge University Press, 1986.
ISBN 0521323967 Hbk £25.00
—Human rights and international relations. – Cambridge : Cambridge University Press, 1987.
ISBN 0521327989 Hbk £20.00
ISBN 0521339952 Pbk £7.95

Vincenzini, Enrico
International Regulation Of Salvage At Sea. – London : Lloyd's of London Press.
ISBN 1850441502 Hbk £32.00

Violence against women : report of an ad-hoc working group / Women's National Commission. – London : Cabinet Office, .
59, 28p.
Includes bibliographical references.

Violence and Law in the Modern Age. – Polity Press.
ISBN 0745604919 Hbk £19.50

Violence in the Family. – Canberra : Australian Institute of Criminology.
Hbk £3.00

Violence in the family : Recommendation no.R (85) 4 adopted by the Committee of Ministers of the Council of Europe on 26 March 1985 and Explanatory memorandum. – Council of Europe. – Strasbourg : Council of Europe, 1986.
15p; 21cm. – (Legal affairs).
' ... prepared by a select committee of experts under the authority of the European Committee on Crime Problems' - p.3.

Violence in the Family : Theory and Practice in Social Work. – London : HMSO, 1982.
71p.
ISBN 0114919917 Pbk £3.75

Virginia Law Reporters Before 1880. – London : Eurospan.
ISBN 0813907470 Hbk £9.95

Virginia Statute for Religious Freedom : Its Evolution and Consequences in American History Conf. Proc. / Vaughan. – Cambridge : Cambridge University Press.
ISBN 0521343291 Hbk £35.00

Virtue, commerce, and history : essays on political thought and history, chiefly in the eighteenth century / J.G.A. Pocock. – Cambridge : Cambridge University Press, 1985.
x,321p; 24cm.
Includes index.
ISBN 0521257018 Hbk £25.00
ISBN 0521276608 Pbk

Visano →Deviant Designations : Crime Law and Deviance in Canada.

Vision and the Game : the Canadian Constitution. – Calgary : Detselig Enterprises Ltd., 1987.
197p.
ISBN 0920490670 Pbk £14.95

Visions of social control : crime, punishment and classification / Stanley Cohen. – Cambridge : Polity, 1984.
300p.
ISBN 0745600204 Hbk £19.50
ISBN 0745600212 Pbk £7.95

Viski, Laszlo
Road traffic offenders and crime policy / by Laszlo Viski. – Budapest : Akademiai Kiado, 1982.
205p.
Bibliographies: p.175-201. - Includes index. Translation of: Kozlekedesi buntetojog. - Tr. by: J. Decsenyi.
ISBN 963052841X

Viskovic, G.G.F.
Commercial Securities in New Zealand : an introduction to the Law / S.C. Calderwood. – 2nd ed. – North Ryde : Law Book Co, 1986.
xxxi, 214p.
ISBN 0455207070 Pbk £27.00

Visser and Vorster : General Principles of Criminal Law through the Cases. – 2nd ed. – Durban : Professional Publisher, 1987.
ISBN 0409061190 Pbk £80.00

Visser, Coenraad →Contract and mercantile law : a source book, Vol. 1 : General principles of contract, agency and representation : edited by Ellison Kahn, Carole Lewis and Coenraad Visser.

Visser, D. P.
Daedalus in the Supreme Court : the common law today / D. P. Visser. – S.l. : University of Cape Town, 1985.
12 p. – (Inaugural lecture).
ISBN 0799209996

Visser, J
European trade unions in figures. – Kluwer Law and Taxation, 1989.
Presents a comparative set of data and sources on union membership in ten European countries - Austria, Denmark, France, West Germany, Italy, the Netherlands, Norway, Sweden, Switzerland and the UK. Gives emphasis to comparative definitions of union membership and union density, that is, the ratio of actual to potential memberships.
ISBN 9065444092 Pbk £24.50/Dfl 79

Visser, P. J.
General principles of criminal law through the cases / by P.J. Visser and J.P. Vorster. – Durban : Butterworths, 1982.
xxv,523p.
Bibliography: p. 487-501. - Includes index.
ISBN 0409061182
—Visser and Vorster : General Principles of Criminal Law through the Cases. – 2nd ed. – Durban : Professional Publisher, 1987.
ISBN 0409061190 Pbk £80.00

Visual artist and the law / by Shane Simpson. – Sydney : Law Book Co., 1982.
xiii,182p.
Bibliography: p.169-173. - Includes index.
ISBN 0455204527 Hbk £19

Visual Artists and Photographers : Copyright and Designs. – Milsons Point : Australian Copyright Council.
Hbk £6.50

Vitug, Jose C.
Pandect of Commercial Law and Jurisprudence. – Manila : National Book Store, 1984.
515p.
ISBN 9710805185 Hbk £34.00

Vitzthum, Wolfgang →Seerecht : Testausgabe Law of the sea.

Vivadaratnakara of Candesvara Thakkura : Law of Partition and Inheritance / Digambar Chattopadhyaya. – Delhi : Gian Publishing House, 1986.
ii, liii, 94, 61, xvp.
ISBN 8121200121 Hbk £140.00

Vizkelety, Beatrice
Proving Discrimination in Canada. – Agincourt : Carswell, 1987.
281p.
This book deals with the factual requirements of the three theories of proving discrimination in Canada and available defenses. Canadian law is analyzed in comparison to the American and British experience.
Hbk £38.00

Vlachonikolis, Ioannis G. →Impact of residual disability from illness and injury on the distribution of household income : a lognormal approach.

Vlarke →Offshore tax planning.

Vocabulary of Community Primary Law
1985 Provisional Edition / Bernard de Mello. – Luxembourg : Office for Official Publications of the European Communities, 1985.
427p.
ISBN 9282554392 Pbk £1,200.00
1985 Provisional Version. – 1985.
365p.
ISBN 9282556522 Pbk £1,200.00
1986 Provisional Version. – 1986.
370p.
ISBN 928256486X Pbk £1,200.00

Vocational Rehabilitation Services for Disabled Persons : Legislative Provisions. – Geneva : International Labour Office, 1982.
ii, 120p.
ISBN 9221030156 Hbk £17.50

Voices for freedom. – Amnesty International. – London : Amnesty International, 1986.
208p; 27cm.
Includes index.
ISBN 086210095X Pbk

Volcansek, Mary L.
Judicial Politics in Europa : an Impact Analysis. – Bern : Peter Lang, 1986.
xii, 325p.
ISBN 0820402893 Hbk £35.05

Vold
Theoretical criminology / Bernard. – 3rd ed. – Oxford : Oxford University Press, 1986.
ISBN 0195036166 Hbk £17.50

Volhard, R.
Real Property in Germany / D. Weber. – 2nd ed. – Plymouth : Macdonald & Evans, 1983.
200p.
ISBN 0712154760 Hbk £18.00

Volker, E. L. M
Leading cases and materials on the external relations law of the European Community, with emphasis on the common commercial policy / by E.L.M. Volker and J. Steenbergen. – Deventer, The Netherlands : Kluwer Law and Taxation Publishers, 1985.
At head of title: Europa Institute, University of Amsterdam.
ISBN 9065442219
→ Materials on the law of the European Communities.
—Protectionism and the European Community : Import Relief Measures Taken by the European Economic Community and the Member States, and the Legal Remedies Available to Private Parties. – 1983 2nd rev. update ed. – Dordrecht : Kluwer, 1987.
252p.
ISBN 9065443134 Pbk £94.00

Volpe, Peter L.
Sanctity of contract : wisdom or folly? : an inaugural lecture given in the University of Fort Hare on the 24th May 1984 / by Peter L. Volpe. – Alice, South Africa : Fort Hare University Press, 1984.
14p.
ISBN 094997465X

Voluntary but not amateur. – London : London Voluntary, 1988.
ISBN 0901171662 Pbk £6.00

Voluntary Corporate Liquidations. – Quorum Press.
ISBN 0899302750 Hbk £32.50

Voluntary liquidation and receivership : a practical guide / Ian S. Grier and Richard E. Floyd. – London : Oyez Longman, 1985.
xvii,187p.
Includes index.
ISBN 0851209548

Voluntary Organisations and the Media : An NCVO Practical Guide. – London : Bedford Square Press, 1984.
ISBN 0719911206 Hbk £3.50

von Bar, Carl Ludwig
Theory and Practice of Private International Law. – Repr. of 1892 ed. – Aalen Wuertt : Scientia.
xlvi, 1162p.
Hbk £265.00

Von Glahn, Gerhard
Law among nations : an introduction to public international law / Gerhard von Glahn. – 4th ed. – New York : Macmillan, 1981.
xv,810p; 25cm.
Previous ed.: 1976. Includes bibliographies and index.
ISBN 0024231606 £15.95

Von Hirsch, Andrew
Past or future crimes : deservedness and dangerousness in the sentencing of criminals / Andrew von Hirsch. – Manchester : Manchester University Press, 1986.
xii,220p; 24cm.
Originally published: New Brunswick, N.J. : Rutgers University Press, 1985. Bibliography: p201-212. - Includes index.
ISBN 0719017122 £21.00
ISBN 0813511151

Von Prondzynski, Ferdinand
Employment Law (ILT). – 2nd ed. – London : Sweet & Maxwell, 1988.
ISBN 0421380705 Pbk
—Freedom of association and industrial relations : a comparative study / Ferdinand von Prondzynski. – London : Mansell, 1987.
250p; 24cm.
Includes bibliography and index.
ISBN 0720117755 Pbk £30.00 :
ISBN 0720118700 £15.00

Vondracek, Theodor Jan
Commentary on the Czechoslovak civil code / by Th. J. Vondracek. – Dordrecht : Nijhoff, 1988.
504p.
Includes index.
ISBN 9024736692 Hbk £235.00

Vorster, H.V. →Practitioner's Guide to Legal Costs.

Vorster, J. P. →General principles of criminal law through the cases.

Vorster, Jacob Petrus
Implied terms in the law of contract in England and South Africa / submitted for the degree of PhD by Jacob Petrus Vorster. – S.l. : s.n., 1987.
xii,240p.
Thesis (PhD): St. John's College, Cambridge, 1987. Bibliography: pp.204-212. - Includes index.
ISBN 0620113057

Vorster, M.P. →Constitutions of Transkei, Bophuthatswana, Venda and Ciskei.

Vos, George de
Japan's minorities : Burakumin, Koreans, Ainu and Okinawans / by George A. De Vos and William O. Wetherall. – New ed. – London : Minority Rights Group, 1983.
18p. – (Report).
Previous ed.: 1974. Bibliography: p. 17-18.
ISBN 0946690022

Voskuil, C. C. A. →Credit and Guarantee Financing, Transfer of Technology.
→ Hague-Zagreb Essays, 4: On the Law of International Trade.

Vossius, Volker →Industrial property laws of the Federal Republic of Germany : patent, utility model, trademark, design : texts of the laws, orders, regulations, guidelines and index.

Vredeling, H →Vredeling proposal : information and consultation of employees in multinational enterprises.

Vredeling proposal : information and consultation of employees in multinational enterprises / R. Blanpain ... et al. : foreword by H. Vredeling. – Deventer : Kluwer, 1983.
219 p.; 25 cm.
Includes bibliographical references.
ISBN 9031202088

Vrije Universiteit Brussel →Status of observers in the United Nations.

Vulnerability : small states in the global society / report of a Commonwealth Consultative Group. – London : Commonwealth Secretariat, 1985.
xii,126p.
Chairman: P. T. Georges.
ISBN 0850922801

Vuuren, D. J. van →Constitutions of Transkei, Bophuthatswana, Venda and Ciskei.

W. Green and Son Publishing
Compendium of Legal Aid and Advice 1983 : Extracted from the Parliament House Book. – W. Green and Son Publishing. – Edinburgh : W Green, 1983.
ISBN 0414007220 Hbk £5.00

W. M. Still & Sons Limited, W. M. Still Service Limited : a report by the Director General of Fair Trading on an investigation under section 3 of the Competition Act 1980 / Office of Fair Trading. – London : Office of Fair Trading, 1982.
39p; 30cm.

Wacks, Raymond I →Civil liberties in Hong Kong.
—Future of the law in Hong Kong / edited by R.I. Wacks. – Hong Kong : Oxford University Press (Hong Kong), 1989.
320.
Examines the theoretical and procedural aspects of the common law of Hong Kong and evaluates its development up to and beyond 1997 when sovereignty returns to China.
ISBN 0195849183 Hbk £19.50
—Jurisprudence 1987. – London : Financial Training.
ISBN 1851850481 Pbk £7.95
—Personal information: privacy and the law. – Oxford : Clarendon Press, 1989.
320.
Argues that at the core of the privacy problem is a concern for the use and misuse of personal information. Identifies four main areas of privacy, and suggests that by finding the centre of the problem, it may more easily be solved.
ISBN 0198256116 Hbk £30

Wada, Hideo
Continental systems of judicial review (I) / Hideo Wada. – Tokyo : Institute of Social Sciences, Meiji University, 1981.
30p.
Reprint from: Bulletin of the Institute of Social Sciences Meiji University, Vol. 5, no. 1 (1981).
—Continental systems of judicial review (II) / Hideo Wada. – Tokyo : Institute of Social Sciences, Meiji University, 1981.
16p.
Reprint from: Bulletin of the Institute of Social Sciences Meiji University, Vol. 5, no. 2 (1981).

Waddams, Stephen M
Introduction to the Study of Law. – 3rd ed. – Agincourt : Carswell, 1987.
ISBN 0459302418 Hbk £11.50
—Law of contracts / S.M.Waddams. – 2nd edition. – Toronto : Canada Law Book Co.Inc, 1984.
cxli,614p.
ISBN 0888040237

—Law of damages / by S.M. Waddams. – Toronto : Canada Law Book Ltd., 1983.
cx,755p.
ISBN 0888040164

—Milner's Cases and Materials on Contracts. – 4th ed. – Aurora : Canada Law Book Co, 1985.
884p. – (Case Books).
This casebook examines the present common law of contracts with reference to the leading Canadian and English cases. Chapters include, among others: Remedies for Breach of Promise, The Kind of Promises Legally Enforced, Third Party Beneficiaries, Assignment and Agency, Third Parties and Mistakes in Dealings Between Others, and Written Documents.
ISBN 0920722172 Hbk £84.00

Waddington, P.A.J.
Arming an Unarmed Police : Policy and Practice in the Metropolitan Police. – Police Foundation.
ISBN 0947692096 Pbk £8.95

—Flashpoints; Studies in Public Disorder / Jones. – Routledge.
ISBN 0415012384 Hbk £25.00
ISBN 0415012392 Pbk £8.95

—Protest, Policing and the Law / P. Leopold. – London : Institute for the Study of Conflict, 1985.
– (Conflict Studies Ser.: No. 175).
Hbk £5.50

Wade → Introduction To The Study Of The Constitution.

—Sports Law for Educational Institutions / Hay. – Quorum Press.
ISBN 0899303358 Hbk £31.95

Wade, David
Disaster and resolution : two discussion papers dealing with distinct aspects of the aftermath of man-made disasters, the process of litigation, settlement and compensation and the factors affecting the provision of speedy relief and effective rehabiliation / David Wade, Carmel Goldwater : commissioned and published by Centre for Public Affairs Studies. – London : Centre for Public Affairs Studies, 1985.
viii,162p.

Wade, E. C. S.
Constitutional and administrative law / E.C.S. Wade and A.W. Bradley. – 10th ed. – London : Longman, 1985.
xlv,758p; 24cm.
Previous ed.: 1977. Bibliography: p741-748. - Includes index.
ISBN 058249124X Hbk £17.00
ISBN 0582491258 Pbk £14.95

Wade, H. W. R
Administrative law / by H.W.R. Wade. – 6th ed. – Oxford : Clarendon Press, 1988.
lxxi,1028p.
Includes bibliographical references and index.
ISBN 0198762194 Pbk £30.00
ISBN 0198762208 Hbk £60.00
→ Law of real property.

Wade, J. A. → Credit and Guarantee Financing, Transfer of Technology.
→ Hague-Zagreb Essays, 4: On the Law of International Trade.

Wade, J.H.
Property Division on Marriage Breakdown. – North Ryde : C.C.H. Australia, 1984.
660p.
ISBN 0869035797 Hbk £50.00

Wadegaonkar, Damodar
Orbit of space law / Damodar Wadegaonkar : foreword by Y.V. Chandrachud. – London : Stevens, 1984.
xii,172p.
Includes index.
ISBN 0420470107 Hbk £16.00

Wadhwa, D C
Companies Act With Exhaustive Referencer. – Nagpur : Wadhura & Co, 1988.
Hbk £150.00

—Re-promulgation of ordinances : a fraud on the constitution of India / D. C. Wadhwa. – Pune : Gokhale Institute of Politics and Economics, 1983.
xxxi,259p.
ISBN 0861314328 Hbk £95.00

Waelbroeck, Denis → Judicial protection in the European Communities.

Wage Discrimination : The Sex Discrimination Issue of the 1980's. – London : Pinter Publishers Ltd, 1984.
200p.
ISBN 0861872487 Hbk £15.00

Wage indexation and its aftermath / by the CCH industrial law editors. – North Ryde, N.S.W. : CCH Australia, 1981.
18p.
Forms part of the service to CCH Australian labour law reporter.
ISBN 0869033476

Wages and the law. – London : Shaw & Sons, 1988.
ISBN 0721911102 Pbk

Waging war : a philosophical introduction / Ian Clark. – Oxford : Clarendon Press, 1988.
154 p.; 23 cm.
Bibliography: p. 143-147. Includes index.
ISBN 0198273258

Waight, P.K.
Cases and Materials on Evidence / C.R. Williams. – 2nd ed. – North Ryde : Law Book Co, 1985.
iii, 860p.
ISBN 0455205671 Hbk £37.50
ISBN 045520568X Pbk £27.50

Wainberg, J.M.
Guidebook to Canada Business Corporations Act / M.I. Wainberg. – 2nd ed. – Don Mills : CCH Canadian Ltd, 1981.
104p.
ISBN 0887961533 Pbk £9.50

—Guidebook to Ontario Business Corporations Act / M.I. Wainberg. – 1st ed. – North Ryde : C.C.H. Australia, 1985.
122p.
ISBN 088796267X Pbk £12.00

—O'Brien's Encyclopedia of Forms : Division Two-Corporations
Vols. 4-6. – Aurora : Canada Law Book Co. – (Abridgments and Encyclopedias).
Hbk £150.00

Wainberg, M.I. → Guidebook to Canada Business Corporations Act.
→ Guidebook to Ontario Business Corporations Act.

Wainman, D.
Currency Fluctuation. – 2nd ed. – Cambridge : Woodhead-Faulkner, 1984.
ISBN 0859412652 Hbk £30.00

Waiting for a Move : Elderly People and Allocation Transfer Policies of Scottish Local Authorities. – London : Age Concern Scotland.
ISBN 0946505535 Pbk £1.50

Waiting for justice : an SCC survey of facilities in Scotland's Sheriff Courts : results and recommendations by Sheila Gilmore. – Glasgow : Scottish Consumer Council, 1981.
44,A1-A6p,11leaves; 30cm.
ISBN 0907067069 Pbk £1.50

Waiving the Rules : The Constitution Under Thatcherism / Tony Prosser. – Open University Press.
ISBN 0355155804 Hbk £25.00

Wakeford, A H
Manual of Employee Taxation. – London : Butterworths.
Service.
ISBN 0406413894 Llf £55.00

Waldron, Jeremy → Nonsense upon stilts : Bentham, Burke and Marx on the rights of man.

—Right to private property / Jeremy Waldron. – Oxford : Clarendon Press, 1988.
viii,470p.
Bibliography: pp.446-463. - Includes index..
ISBN 0198249594
→ Theories of rights.

Walentowicz, P.
Caught in the Act : Critical Guide to the 1988 Housing Act. – SHAC.
ISBN 0948857315 Pbk £3.00

Walicki, Andrzej
Legal philosophies of Russian liberalism / Andrzej Walicki. – Oxford : Clarendon, 1987.
480p; 22cm.
Includes index.
ISBN 0198249306 £45.00

Walker → Court Divided : The Fifth Circuit Court of Appeals And the Policies of Judicial Reform.
→ Industrial tribunal practice.
→ Political Violence and the Law in Ireland.

—Racial Discrimination / Redman. – Shaw & Sons, 1977.
ISBN 0721907709 Pbk £7.50

Walker, A G
Law of evidence in Scotland / N M L Walker. – Edinburgh : Clark (T. & T.) Ltd, 1986.
A practical handbook for practitioners and for situations in which questions of evidence arise. Where the law is undecided, the authors indicate the general principle which should be applied. There is a concluding chapter on international private law.
ISBN 0852791208 Pbk

Walker-Arnott, Edward I.
Recent and Prospective Changes in Company Law / Charles M. Allen-Jones. – London : Law Society, 1982.
– (Oxford Weekend Courses).
Hbk £2.00

Walker, Christopher J. → Armenians.

Walker, Clive
Prevention of terrorism in British Law. – Manchester : Manchester University Press, 1986-1988.
ISBN 0719022037 Pbk £9.95

Walker, D.M.
Law of Contract and related obligations in Scotland. – 2nd ed. – London : Butterworths, 1985.
ISBN 0406677875 Hbk £44.50

—Principles of Scottish Law. – 4th ed. – Oxford : Clarendon Press.
ISBN 0198762178 Hbk £40.00

Walker, David M. → Institutions of the law of Scotland : deduced from its originals, and collated with the civil, canon and feudal laws, and with the customs of neighbouring nations in iv books.

—Law of delict in Scotland / by David M. Walker. – 2nd ed., rev. – Edinburgh : Published under the auspices of the Scottish Universities Law Institute by W. Green, 1981.
cxli,1111p; 26cm.
Previous ed.: 1966. Includes index.
ISBN 0414006690

—Law of Prescription and Limitation of Actions in Scotland. – 3rd ed. – Edinburgh : W Green, 1981.
ISBN 0414006674 Hbk £12.50

—Legal history of Scotland
Vol.1 : The beginnings to A.D. 1286 / by David M. Walker. – Edinburgh : Green (W.) & Son, 1988.
xxi,435p; 24cm.
A systematic examination of the development of public, criminal and private law up to the death of Alexander III, with attention to the emerging lawmaking institutions, the deciding of cases and the procedure and principles of substantive law. Bibliography: p408-420. - Includes index.
ISBN 0414008162

—Principles of Scottish private law
Vol. 1: Introductory international private law, law of persons / by David M. Walker. – 4th ed. – Oxford : Clarendon, 1988.
584; 24cm.
Previous ed.: 1982. Includes index.
ISBN 0198762151 £40.00

Vol.2. Bk.4: Obligations / by David M. Walker. – 1988.
816; 24cm.
Previous ed.: 1982. Includes index. Volume 1 contains an outline of the sources, scope and literature of Scottish private law and discusses fundamental legal concepts and basic doctrines. Volume 2 gives a statement of the principles and rules of the private law of Scotland and specifically examines the law of obligations.
ISBN 019876216X Hbk £40.00

Vol.3 Bk.5: Law of property / by David M. Walker. – 1988.
cxi,595p.
Previous ed: 1983. Includes index.
ISBN 0198762178 £40.00

Vol.4 Bk.6 - Bk.10 / by David M. Walker. – 1983.
lxix,421p; 24cm.
Previous ed.: 1975. Includes index. Contents: bk.VI. Law of trusts - bk.VII. Law of succession - bk.VIII. Law of civil remedies - bk.IX. Law of diligence - bk.X. Law of insolvency.
ISBN 019876135X Hbk £25.00.

—Scottish jurists / by David M. Walker. – Edinburgh : W. Green, 1985.
xv,492p.
ISBN 0414007573

—Scottish legal system : an introduction to the study of Scots law / by David M. Walker. – 5th ed., rev. – Edinburgh : Green, 1981.
xlv,543p; 23cm.
Previous ed.: 1976. Includes bibliographies and index.
ISBN 0414006836
→ Stair tercentenary studies.

Walker, Geoffrey de Q.
Rule of Law : Foundation of Constitutional Democracy. – Carlton : Melbourne University Press, 1988.
504p.
ISBN 0522843476 Hbk £62.95

Walker, Gladys
Points of Order. – 4th ed. – London : Shaw & Sons, 1987.
ISBN 0721904025 Pbk £4.95

Walker, Graham → Property Companies : Accounting, Audit and Tax.

Walker, I. K
Occupational safety : an inquiry into the coordination of legislation on industrial safety, health, and welfare / by I.K. Walker. – Wellington, N.Z. : State Services Commission, 1981.
vi, 142 p.; 30 cm.
Bibliography: p. 140-142.
ISBN 0477015085 Pbk

Walker, John
Australian Prisoners, 1982 / David Biles. – Canberra : Australian Institute of Criminology.
Hbk £3.00

—Physical Planning and Crime in Canberra. – Canberra : Australian Institute of Criminology.
Hbk £1.50
→ Sentencing the Federal Drug Offender.

—Use of Computers in the Criminal Justice System. – Canberra : Australian Institute of Criminology. Hbk £2.50

Walker, Julienne →Law of guarentees.

Walker, M. G. →English legal system.

Walker, Monica A.
Crime
Vol.15 : Crime / by Monica A. Walker. – Oxford : Published for the Royal Statistical Society and the Social Science Research Council by Pergamon, 1981.
xii,406p; 26cm.
Bibliography: p281-284. - Includes index. Originally titled: Reviews of United Kingdom statistical sources.
ISBN 0080261043 £18.25

Walker, N M L →Law of evidence in Scotland.

Walker, Neil →Scottish community charge.

Walker, Nigel
Crime and criminology : a critical introduction / Nigel Walker. – Oxford : Oxford University Press, 1987.
xv,219p; 23cm.
Bibliography: p210-212. - Includes index.
ISBN 0192192124 Hbk £12.95
ISBN 0192891936 Pbk £4.95

—Crime and Punishment in Britain : An Analysis of the Penal System in Theory, Law, and Practice. – Amsterdam : University Press.
Hbk

—Sentencing : Theory, Law and Practice. – London : Butterworths, 1985.
Pbk

—Sentencing : theory, law and practice / Nigel Walker. – London : Butterworth, 1985.
xlix,510p; 26cm.
Bibliography: pxxxiii-xl - Includes index.
ISBN 0406252637 Hbk £33
ISBN 0406252815 Pbk £21.95

Walker, P.B. →Brief Case : Collection of Papers on Tasmanian Legal Memorabilia and Tasmanian Places.

Walker, Peter
Consumer law / Peter Walker. – 1st ed. – London : Longman Professional (UK), 1988. – (Longman Practice Notes).
Covers consumer safety, unsolicited goods, resale prices, sale of goods and services, and consumer credit. Contains precedents and checklists.
ISBN 0851214495 Hbk £9.95

—Consumer Protection Act 1987. – London : Longman Professional.
ISBN 0851213499 Hbk £13.95

Walker, Philip H. G.
Real Estate and Landlord and Tenant. – 2nd ed. – Agincourt : Carswell, 1986.
853p. – (Bar Admission Course Materials).
This work for the law student is a practical guide to the handling of most real estate transactions under Canadian law. The Planning Act of 1983 and the Land Registration Reform Act of 1984 are reviewed in the text.
ISBN 045939500 Hbk £39.60

Walker, R. J.
English legal system / Walker & Walker. – 6th ed. – London : Butterworths, 1985.
li,709p; 25cm.
ISBN 0406677603

Walker, Richard →Carter-Ruck on libel and slander.

Walker-Smith, Derek, et al
Walker-Smith on the Standard Forms of Building Contract. – Tonbridge : Ernest Benn.
450p.
ISBN 085314317X Hbk £75.00

Walker, Val →Marital violence : the community response.

Walker, W.B. Gordon
Mining Exploration Agreements. – Montreal : Canadian Institute of Mining and Metallurgy.
Hbk £40.00

Walker-Smith on the Standard Forms of Building Contract. – Tonbridge : Ernest Benn.
450p.
ISBN 085314317X Hbk £75.00

Walkland, S. A. →Commons today.

Walkley, J.
Police interrogation. – Police Review, 1987.
ISBN 0851640311 Pbk £5.95

Wall Chart of the English Reports Reprint Vols. 1-176. – Agincourt : Carswell.
Hbk £6.50

Wallace : the final verdict / Roger Wilkes. – London : Bodley Head, 1984.
269p,16p of plates; 22cm.
Bibliography: p261-263. - Includes index.
ISBN 037030571X £8.95

Wallace and McNeil's banking law. – 9th. – Edinburgh : Green (W.) & Son, 1986.
Analyses the banker/customer relationship dealing extensively with special customers. Coverage of bills of exchange and other financial instruments and description of some miscellaneous banking services. Ohter chapters cover securities over heritable and moveable property and personal guarantees. Includes the law of insolvency, sequestration, receivership and liquidation.
ISBN 0414007824 Pbk

Wallace, B. J., et al
Real Property Assessment. – Vancouver : British Columbia Continuing Legal Education Society, 1982.
200p.
ISBN 0865040729 Hbk £45.00

Wallace, Cynthia D
Legal control of the multinational enterprise : national regulatory techniques and the prospects for international controls / Cynthia D. Wallace. – The Hague : Martinus Nijhoff, 1983.
354p.
Originally presented as the author's thesis (Ph.D.)–Cambridge University. Includes index. Bibliography: p331-355.
ISBN 9024726689 Hbk £135.00

Wallace, D.
Building and Engineering Forms Supplements 1 & 2. – Sweet & Maxwell, 1969.
ISBN 0421124504 Hbk £52.00

—International Civil Engineering Contract. – Sweet & Maxwell, 1974.
ISBN 0421201606 Hbk £58.00

Wallace, E.W.
Financial Institutions Duties : Untangling the Web / J.L. Mansfield. – Butterworths, 1983.
191p.
ISBN 0409492310 Pbk £42.00

—Stamp Duty Aspects of Trusts, Settlements and Gifts in Australia / F.P. Zipfinger. – Butterworths, 1984.
367p.
ISBN 0409494216 Hbk £56.00

Wallace, Helen →Policy-making in the European Community.

Wallace, Herbert
Land Registry Practice in Northern Ireland. – Belfast : Queen's University of Belfast, 1984.
xxiii, 142p.
Hbk £11.95

—Occupiers' rights and constructive notice : the text of a lecture delivered to the Belfast Solicitors' Association on 2 December 1982 / by Hebert Wallace. – Belfast : SLS Legal Publications, 1982.
35p.
Includes bibliographical references.

Wallace, I. N. Duncan
Construction contracts : principles and policies in tort and contract / by I.N. Duncan Wallace. – London : Sweet & Maxwell, 1986.
xliii,696p; 26cm.
Contains articles on contractors' claims and owners' damages, certificates and their effect, guarantees and bonds in construction contracts, nominated sub-contractors, choice of contracting agreement, comparative law, the UK JCT standard forms, and the SIA Contract 1980.
ISBN 042134900X Hbk £74

Wallace, John →Part-time employment and sex discrimination legislation in Great Britain : a study of the demand for part-time labour and of sex discrimination in selected organizations and establishments.

Wallace, Patricia →Trade Unions and Change in the British Car Industry.

Wallace, Pauline
Company Law in Hong Kong. – Butterworths, 1986.
393p.
Deals with Hong Kong company law, in light of the changes introduced by the Companies (Amendments) Ordinance 1984. Gives an account of Company law in Hong Kong, from the incorporation of a company, to its liquidation. Discussion of the registration requirements which companies incorporated overseas must comply if they wish to operate in Hong Kong.
ISBN 0409995223 Pbk £40.00

Wallace, Rebecca M. M.
International law / by Rebecca M.M. Wallace. – London : Sweet and Maxwell, 1986.
275p; 18cm.
Includes index.
ISBN 0421335009 Hbk £15.00
ISBN 0421335106 Pbk £10.00

Wallace, Tina →To ride the storm : the 1980 Bristol 'riot' and the state.

Wallace, Wilfred J. →Canadian Law of Architecture and Engineering.

Waller, K. M.
Coronial law and practice in New South Wales / by K.M. Waller. – 2nd ed. – Sydney : Law Book Co., 1982.
xvi,215p.
Previous ed.: 1973. Includes bibliographical references and index. Includes the text of the Coroners Act, 1980, No. 27.
ISBN 0455203652 Hbk £39.50

Waller, Louis →Legal process : commentary and materials.
→ Well and truly tried : essays on evidence in honour of Sir Richard Eggleston.

Waller, P.L.
Brett, Waller and Williams Criminal Law Text and Cases / C.R. Williams. – Butterworths, 1989.
ca 960p.
ISBN 0409495336 Hbk £84.00
ISBN 0409495344 Pbk £66.00

Wallington
Blackstones Statutes on Public Law / R G Lee. – London : Blackstone Press.
ISBN 1854310208 Pbk £10.95

Wallington, P.
Civil Liberties 1984. – Oxford : Blackwell, 1984.
ISBN 0855207027 Pbk £7.50

Wallington, Peter →Butterworths employment law handbook.
→ Essays in memory of Professor F.H. Lawson.

Wallington, R. A. →Williams' law relating to wills.
→ Williams on wills.

Wallis, Peter S.
Transport Acts 1981 and 1982 : Penalty Points, Drinking and Driving, Fixed Penalties. – 2nd ed. – London : Fourmat, 1985.
115p.
ISBN 0906840929 Pbk £8.95
→ Wilkinson's road traffic offences.

Walls, H. J.
Drink, drugs and driving / by H.J. Walls and Alistair R. Brownlie. – 2nd ed. – London : Sweet & Maxwell, 1985.
xxix,281p; 22cm.
Previous ed.: 1970. Bibliography: p247-268. - Includes index.
ISBN 0421296003 Pbk £19.50

Walmsley, J.
Handbook of international joint ventures / John Walmsley. – London : Graham & Trotman, 1983.
viii,161p; 24cm.
Includes index.
ISBN 0860103692 £22.00

—Joint ventures in the Kingdom of Saudi Arabia / John Walmsley. – 2nd ed. – London : Graham & Trotman, 1985.
388p; 25cm.
Previous ed.: 1979. Bibliography: p381. - Includes index.
ISBN 0860106799 £43.00

—Macmillan Dictionary of International Finance. – 2nd ed. – London : Macmillan, 1986.
ISBN 0333398343 Pbk £8.95

Walmsley, Keith →Butterworths company law guide.
→ Handbook of company administration.

Walmsley, Roy
Personal violence / by Roy Walmsley. – London : H.M.S.O., 1986.
vi, 79p; 25cm.
A Home Office Research and Planning Unit report.
ISBN 0113408277

Walpole, Martin E. →Bringing people together : mediation and reparation projects in Great Britain.

Walsh, Clifford →Jowitt's dictionary of English law.

Walsh, Dermot →Dictionary of criminology.

Walsh, Dermot P. J.
Use and abuse of emergency legislation in Northern Ireland / Dermot P. J. Walsh. – London? : Cobden Trust, 1983.
138p.
ISBN 0900137207

Walsh, Edward M.
Planning and development law / by Edward M. Walsh. – 2nd ed. – Dublin : Incorporated Law Society of Ireland, 1984.
xxi,209p.
Previous ed.: 1979. Includes index.
ISBN 0902027247

Walsh, Elizabeth →Family Law Journal.

Walsh, P.
Copyright for the Canadian Visual Artist. – repr. 1981. – Ottawa : CARFAC.
Hbk £6.00

Walsh, R. J.
Report of the review of the Australian Institute of Aboriginal Studies / by R.J. Walsh. – Canberra : Australian Government Publishing Service, 1982.
89p.
ISBN 0644022698

Walt, J.C. van der
Index to the Southern African Law Reports 1828-1946, 4 Vols. / F.R. Malan. – Durban : Professional Publishers, 1981-1982.
Hbk

Walter, Otto L. →Handbook on the United States-German Tax Convention.

Walter, Philip
Claims to the possession of land : the law and practice / by Philip Walter and James Harris. – London : Fourmat, 1987.
xlvii,616p; 26cm.
ISBN 1851900004 Hbk £37.50

Walter, R. →On the Issue of the Continental Shelf : Two Legal Opinions.

Walter, Raymond
English Encyclopedia of Forms and Precedents / Robert B Roper. – 5th ed. – Wellington : Butterworths.
Hbk

Walters, G.
Criminal Proceedings Against Juveniles. – London : Longman Professional, 1984.
ISBN 0851208460 Pbk £21.00

Walters, R.
Inheritance tax. – London : Pitman Publishing, 1986.
ISBN 0712106928 Pbk £7.95

Waltman, Jerold L. →Political role of law courts in modern democracies.

Walton →Introduction To French Law.

Walton, Anthony →Law and Practice as to Receivers.

Walton, C.
Hobbes's Science of Natural Justice / P.J. Johnson. – Dordrecht : Kluwer, 1987.
326p.
ISBN 9024732263 Hbk £195.00

Walton, Raymond →Adkin's landlord and tenant.
→ Buckley on the Companies Acts.
→ Encyclopaedia of forms and precedents.

Walzer, Michael
Spheres of justice : a defence of pluralism and equality / Michael Walzer. – Oxford : Robertson, 1983.
xviii,345p; 24cm.
Introduction for students to abstract discussions of justice. Includes case studies.
ISBN 0855206837 £15.00

Wan
Studies in Labour Law / Katherine E Swinton. – London : Butterworths.
ISBN 0409487129X Hbk £64.00

Wanasundera, R. S. →Report of the Sri Lanka Law's Delays and Legal Culture Committee.

Wand, C.
Daily Mail Guide to Employment Law. – Southampton : Associated Magazines, 1988.
ISBN 0851444261 Pbk £5.95

Wang, Guiguo
China's investment laws : new directions / Guiguo Wang. – Singapore : Butterworths, 1988.
ix,272p.
Covers China's investment environment, foreign investment, new revisions promulgated by the central government, the relaxed rules of the SEZ, the corporate law of the SEZ, SEZ regulations on foreign banks, comparative analysis of the new laws, and the practical significance of the new law. An appendix gives practical guidance to investing in China. With an index.
ISBN 0409995606 Hbk £119

Wangyal, Phuntsog →Tibetans : two perspectives on Tibetan-Chinese relations.

Wani, A.A.
Exclusion of Judicial Review : Administrative Efficiency Confronts Legitimacy of Power. – Delhi : Metropolitan Book Co, 1987.
349p.
ISBN 8120002679 Hbk £200.00

Waque, Stephen F. →New Law of Expropriation.

War, aggression and self-defence / Yoram Dinstein. – Cambridge : Grotius, 1988.
xxx,292p.
Re-examines the topics of war, aggression and self-defence, as well as related issues such as collective security, and the use of force short of war. The first part deals with such questions as what war is, whilst the second looks at the contemporary prohibition of the use of force and its standing as jus cogens. The third section deals with the concept of self-defence.
ISBN 0949009156 £46.00

War and conscience in the nuclear age / Sydney D. Bailey. – Basingstoke : Macmillan, 1987.
xviii,210p; 23cm.
Bibliography: p200-202. - Includes index.
ISBN 0333436857 Hbk £25.00
ISBN 0333443845 Pbk £12.95

War crimes and laws of war / Donald A. Wells. – Lanham : University Press of America, 1984.
x,137p; 24cm.
Bibliography: p123-132. - Includes index.
ISBN 081913841X Hbk
ISBN 0819138428 Pbk £8.25

War Crimes in Vietnam / Vladimir Dedijer. – London : Spokesman Books.
40p.
Pbk individual 4.00

War in international society : a study in international sociology / Evan Luard. – London : Tauris, 1986.
468p.
Includes bibliographical references and index.
ISBN 1850430128 £24.50

War, law and labour : the Munitions Acts, state regulation and the unions, 1915-1921 / Gerry R. Rubin. – Oxford : Clarendon Press, 1987.
288p; 22cm.
Includes index.
ISBN 0198255381 Hbk £27.50

War risks : the Tower Hotel, London, 24th June 1982. – London : Lloyd's of London Press, 1982.
49leaves; 31cm.
Conference papers.
ISBN 090743245X

Warburton, Jean
Unincorporated associations : law and practice / by Jean Warburton. – London : Sweet & Maxwell, 1986.
100p; 22cm.
Guide to the law in respect of sports clubs, political parties, self-help groups, and community associations. Covers funding, the holding of property, rates and taxes, and the rights and liabilities of members. Contains several precedents for the formation of an association and the establishment of rules and objects.
ISBN 0421345403 Pbk £14.00

Ward
Guide to Housing Benefit 1988-1989 / Zebedee. – 2nd ed. – London : London Housing Aid.
ISBN 0948857196 Pbk £5.95

Ward, A. J.
Planning Law in Practice. – London : Butterworths, 1985.
ISBN 0406260508 Hbk £22.50

Ward, C.
Guide to Company Flotation. – London : Fitzwilliam, 1988.
ISBN 1870555058 Hbk £40.00

Ward, D. A., et al
Ward's Tax Law and Planning, 8 Vols. – Agincourt : Carswell, 1988.
Llf £332.00

Ward, D.A.S.
Mercantile Law in New Zealand / H.R.C. Wild. – 8th ed. – Auckland : Whitcoulls, 1983.
347p.
ISBN 0723307059 Hbk £14.95

Ward, David A.
Taxation of income of foreign affiliates / by David A. Ward. – Toronto : Carswell, 1983.
vi,237p.
Includes index. 'Being Chapter 20 of Ward's Tax Law and Planning by The Partners of Davies, Ward & Beck and Brian J. Arnold' - t.p.
ISBN 0459358707

Ward, Denis
Validity of the reconviction prediction score / by Denis Ward. – London : HMSO, 1987.
vi,45p.
Describes the method used to calculate the score, based on data for men discharged in 1965. Compares this with data from 1977-79. Concludes that the RPS should continue in substantially its present form.
ISBN 011340882X

Ward, R, et al
Encyclopedia of road traffic law and practice / R Hosking, M Brealey. – 4 looseleaf volumes. – London : Sweet & Maxwell, 1989.
Contains annotated versions of the relevant statutes and statutory instruments, a revised EEC section and a section on general procedure in Britain. Includes tables of Statutes, SLs and cases, and an index. Three updating issues per year and 'stop press' bulletins.
ISBN 0421007605 Llf £210.00

Ward, Sue →Women won't benefit : the impact of the Social Security Bill on women's rights.

Warda, Jacek P. →Canadian R & D incentives : their adequacy and impact.

Warden →Law and Ethics in the Medical Office incl. Bioethical Issues.

Wardlaw, Grant
Political terrorism : theory, tactics, and counter-measures / Grant Wardlaw. – Cambridge : Cambridge University Press, 1982.
xiii,218p; 24cm.
Bibliography: p204-212. - Includes index.
ISBN 0521250323 Hbk £
ISBN 0521271479 Pbk
—Role of Psychologists in the Criminal Justice System. – Canberra : Australian Institute of Criminology.
Hbk £4.00

Wardley guide to world money and securities markets / by Lynette J. Kemp. – London : Euromoney Publications, 1984.
xvii,472p.
ISBN 0903121662

Wards of court / N. V. Lowe and R. A. H. White. – 2nd ed. – London : Barry Rose, part of Kluwer Law Publishers, 1986.
xxviii,388p; 23cm.

Wards of court : Law Commission working paper no. 101 / JUSTICE. – London : JUSTICE, 1987.
3 leaves.

Ward's Tax Law and Planning, 6 Vols. / Beck. – Agincourt : Carswell, 1983.
This multi-volume looseleaf service is a comprehensive treatise on Canadian tax law. Analysis of the statutory language of the Canadian Income Tax Act is the main focus of the work.
Llf £332.00

Ward's Tax Law and Planning, 8 Vols. – Agincourt : Carswell, 1988.
Llf £332.00

Wardship : A Guide for the Non-Lawyer. – PEPAR Publications.
ISBN 094868013X Pbk £1.95

Wardship : the law and practice. – London : Fourmat, 1986.
ISBN 090684097X Pbk £12.95

Wardship Proceedings. – 2nd ed. – London : Oyez Longman, 1982.
– (Oyez Longman Practice Note Ser.: No. 21).
ISBN 0851206360 Hbk £7.95

Wareham, Robert
Tolley's inheritance tax 1986-87 / by Robert Wareham. – Croydon : Tolley Publishing, 1986.
viii,223,iv,236p.
Includes indexes. Contents: Tolley's inheritance tax 1986-1987 - Tolley's capital transfer tax final edition.
ISBN 0854592415
—Tolley's inheritance tax 1987-88 / by Robert Wareham and John Newth. – Croydon : Tolley Publishing, 1987.
viii,246p.
ISBN 0854592911
→ Tolley's tax bumph 1983-84.
—Tolley's value added tax 1986-87 / by Robert Wareham and Patrick Noakes. – Croydon : Tolley, 1986.
vii,488p.
Includes index.
ISBN 0854592423
—Tolley's value added tax 1987-88 / by Robert Wareham and Patrick Noakes. – Croydon : Tolley, 1987.
vii,502p.
Includes index.
ISBN 085459292X
—Tolley's value added tax 1988-89 / by Robert Wareham and Nicholas Bowen. – Croydon : Tolley, 1988.
vii,512p.
Includes index.
ISBN 0854593500

Warendorf, H. C. S →Netherlands Securities Trading Act and Securities Trading Decree : with supplementary regulations and official commentary.

Waring, Anne
Charterparties : a comparative study of South African, English and American law / Anne Waring. – Cape Town : Juta, 1983.
lx,417p.
Based on a thesis submitted for PhD, University of the Witwatersrand, Johannesburg. Bibliography: p.xix-xxvi. - Includes index.
ISBN 0702113441

Warner, C. A.
Research paper on fines / by C.A. Warner. – Hobart? : Government Printer?, 1984.
vi,115,6p. – (Research paper).
Includes bibliographical references.

Warner, Kate
Child witnesses in sexual assault / Kate Warner. – Hobart : Law Reform Commission of Tasmania, 1987.
123p. – (Discussion paper).
Includes bibliographical references.

Warnock, Mary →Question of life : the Warnock report on human fertilisation and embryology.
→ Report of the Committee of Inquiry into Human Fertilisation and Embryology.
→ Utilitarianism.

Warranties and indemnities on share sales / Neil Sinclair. – London : Oyez Longman, 1984.
xxiv,331p.
Includes index.
ISBN 0851208703

Warren
Computer Auditing. – London : Butterworths, 1984.
ISBN 0406252629 Pbk
—Warren's forms of agreement / Markuson. – Matthew Bender, 1987.
ISBN 0000999062 Hbk £223.50

Warren's forms of agreement / Markuson. – Matthew Bender, 1987.
ISBN 0000999062 Hbk £223.50

Warsaw Convention Annotated : A Legal Handbook. – Martinus Nijhoff.
ISBN 9024736196 Hbk £82.00

Warton →Prisons and Prisoners.

Warwick 1984 communications conference held at the University of Warwick in Coventry from Thursday 5 July to Sunday 8 July 1984. – Society for Computers and Law. – Didcot, Oxon. : Society for Computers and Law, 1984.
93p.
ISBN 0906122155

Washington Group
US design patents. – Washington Group. – London : Butterworths, 1985.
ISBN 040665865 Hbk £100.00

Wasik, Martin →Sentencing reform : guidance or guidelines?.

Wason, Frances →Living Together : A Guide to the Law on Marriage and Cohabitation in Scotland.

Wass, Douglas
Government and the governed : BBC Reith Lectures 1983 / Douglas Wass. – London : Routledge and Kegan Paul, 1984.
viii,120p.
ISBN 0710203128

Wassenbergh, H. A. →International air transport in the eighties : including the proceedings of the first Netherlands Colloquium on International Air Transport, 'The Changing Scene', Wassenaar, August 25-29, 1980.
—Regulatory reform in international air transport : address by H.A. Wassenbergh on the occasion of the introduction of the International Institute of Air and Space Law of the State University at Leyden 17 March 1986. – Deventer : Kluwer Law and Taxation Publishers, 1986.
10p; 25cm.
ISBN 9065442618 Pbk

Wasson, David K.
Community based preventive policing : a review 1984-90 / David K. Wasson, John D. Crawford & Company Ltd. – Ottawa : Ministry of the Solicitor General, 1984.
iii,198p. – (User report).
Bibliography: p.197-198.

Watchman
Regulating Scotland / Jeremy Rowan-Robinson. – T & T Clark.
ISBN 00567291502 Pbk £14.95

Watchman, Paul
Homelessness and the law / by Paul Q. Watchman and Peter Robson. – Glasgow : The Planning Exchange, 1983.
xvi,182p; 21cm.
Bibliography: p148-158. - Includes index.
ISBN 0905011201 Pbk £6.95

Watchman, Paul Q.
Developments in homelessness and the law 1983-1985 / by Paul Q. Watchman and Peter Robson. – Glasgow : Planning Exchange, 1986.
ii, 118p.
Supplements the authors' Homelessness and the law (1983). Bilbiography: p.98-103 - Includes index.
ISBN 090501121X
→ Justice, Lord Denning and the constitution.

Water and sewerage law : consultation paper / Department of the Environment, Welsh Office. – London : Department of the Environment, 1986.
44p.

Water and the environment : the implementation of Part II of the Control of Pollution Act 1974 : joint circular / from the Department of the Environment and Welsh Office. – London : H.M.S.O., 1984.
– (Circular).
ISBN 0117517437

Water environment : the next steps : the Government's proposals for environmental protection under a privatised water industry / Department of the Environment, Welsh Office. – London? : The Department, 1986.
44p.

Watêr law. – 2nd ed. – London : Longman Professional, 1985.
ISBN 0851209556 Pbk £19.95

Water law : principles and practice / Richard Macrory. – London : Longman Professional, 1985.
xiii,167p; 22cm.
ISBN 0851209556

Water law in selected European Countries : (Cyprus, Finland, the Netherlands, Union of Soviet Socialist Republics, Yugoslavia). – Food and Agriculture Organization. – Rome : Food and Agriculture Organization of the United Nations, 1983.
ISBN 9251014906

Water Laws in Moslem Countries, Vol. 2. – Rome : FAO, Food and Agricultural Organization of the United Nations, 1978.
314p.
ISBN 9251005362 Hbk £19.50

Water management and environmental protection in Asia and the Pacific / edited by Ichiro Kato ... et al. – Tokyo : University of Tokyo Press, 1983.
x, 202 p.; 24 cm.
Includes bibliographies and index.
ISBN 0860083357 Y5000

Water pollution law / by William Howarth. – London : Shaw, 1988.
xxxvii,608p.
Bibliography: p.580-594. - Includes index.
ISBN 0721911005 £19.95

Water (Prevention and Control of Pollution) Act, 1974. – 1982 repr. – Lucknow : Eastern Book Company, 1984.
147p.
Hbk £30.00

Water Resources Legislation and Administration in Selected Caribbean Countries. – Geneva : United Nations Publications.
ISBN 9211231051 Hbk £16.50

Waterhouse
Memoirs of Edwin Waterhouse / Jones. – London : Batsford.
ISBN 0713455799 Hbk £15.00

Waterhouse, Price
Standard Trust Income Tax Guide 1988. – Durban : Professional Publishers.
Hbk £15.00

Waters around the British Isles : their conflicting uses : report of a study group of the David Davies Memorial Institute of International Studies / R.B. Clark. – Oxford : Clarendon, 1987.
xvi,386p; 24cm.
Includes index.
ISBN 0198284926 £32.50

Waters, D.
Law of Trusts in Canada. – Agincourt : Carswell, 1984.
ISBN 045936200 Hbk £41.80

Waters, D. W. M.
Common law trust in the modern world / D.W.M. Waters. – Deventer : Kluwer, 1984.
24p; 25cm.
ISBN 9065442111

Waters, Malcolm →Building Societies Act 1986.

Watkins, Charles →Legal services in rural Britain : access, accessibility and need.
→ Spatial analysis of legal systems : towards a geography of law?.
→ Studying rural lawyers : research strategy and context.
—Use of the law list to assess the distribution and characteristics of solicitors in England and Wales / Charles Watkins, Mark Blacksell and Kim Economides. – Exeter : University of Exeter, 1984.
24p. – (Working paper).
Bibliography: p.23-24.

Watkins, D.
Drinking and Driving - The Decided Cases. – Police Review, 1987.
ISBN 0851640281 Pbk £5.25

Watkins, T →Marketing Financial Services.

Watkins, Tasker →Report.

Watson
Institute for Christian Studies Act, 1983, Bill Pr021 : An Act Respecting the Institute for Christian Studies. – Ontario : Ontario Government Publications Service, 1983.
12p.
Hbk £0.50

Watson, A.
Failures of the Legal Imagination. – Witney : Academic & University Publishing Group.
ISBN 081228089X Hbk £23.70

Watson, Adam
Diplomacy : the dialogue between states / Adam Watson. – London : Eyre Methuen, 1982.
239p; 24cm.
Bibliography: p227-228. - Includes index.
ISBN 0413481905 £10.50

Watson, Alan
Evolution of law / Alan Watson. – Oxford : Blackwell, 1985.
xi,155p; 23cm.
Discusses theory that legal tradition is the most important factor in legal development.
ISBN 0631142983 £17.50
—Sources of law, legal change, and ambiguity / Alan Watson. – Edinburgh : T. & T. Clark, 1985.
xviii,164p; 23cm.
Previously published: Philadelphia : University of Pennsylvania Press, 1984.
ISBN 0567093603

Watson, Catherine →Aid : rhetoric and reality.
—New Zealand Company Law Casebook. – Butterworths, 1984.
Collation of cases that deal with the law relating to companies, in particular the provisions of the Companies Act 1955. Takes into account the Companies Amendment Act 1983 (No 2). Includes leading cases.
ISBN 0409701777 Pbk £41.25

Watson, Garry D. →Advocates' Quarterly (A.Q.).
—Canadian Civil Procedure : Cases and Materials. – 3rd ed. – Toronto : Edmond-Montgomery, 1988.
925p.
ISBN 0920722245 Hbk £94.00
—Ontario Supreme and District Court Practice 1989 / Michael McGowan. – Agincourt : Carswell, 1988.
1,192p.
Hbk £40.50

Watson, J.
Nothing but the Truth. – 2nd ed. – London : Estates Gazette, 1975.
ISBN 0728200155 Hbk £3.50

Watson, Ray
Criminal law in New South Wales
Vol. 1 : by Ray Watson and Howard Purnell / Howard Purnell. – 2nd ed. – Sydney : Law Book Co., 1981-.
Loose-leaf.
Includes index. Contents: Indictable offences.
Vol. 2 : by Ray Watson and Reg Bartley. – 1978.
Loose-leaf.
Supersedes: Hamilton and Addison's Criminal law and procedure. Includes index. Contents: Summary offences.

Watson-Russell, Anne →So, You Have to Go to Court : a Child's Guide to Testifying as a Witness in Child Abuse Cases.
→ So, You've Been Busted!.

Watt, David →Constitution of Northern Ireland : problems and prospects.
—Criminal Procedure / Marc Rosenberg. – 2nd ed. – Agincourt : Carswell, 1986.
403p. – (Bar Admission Course Materials Ser.).
This book for law students provides an overview of basic Canadian criminal procedure from police investigation and searches, through arrest, preliminary inquiry, interim release, trial, sentencing, and appeal. Proceedings under the Young Offenders Act is covered in the work.
Hbk £63.00
—New Offences Against the Person : the Provisions of Bill C-127. – Butterworths, 1984.
288p.
Contains analysis of all relevant decisions, tables of included offences, assaults, abduction offences, evidentiary and procedural rules, hypothetical examples, sample verdict sheets simplifying the jury's task, sexual assaults and defences and exemptions.
ISBN 0409875759 Hbk £65.00

Watt, James Muir
Agricultural Holdings. – 13th. 1 volume, supplement. – London : Sweet & Maxwell, 1987.
xxiv,200p.
States the law contained in the Agricultural Holdings Act 1986. Includes the nature and inception of the tenancy of an agricultural holding, termination by notice to quit and otherwise, and the procedure of agricultural land tribunals. Chapter on arbitration revised. Includes annotations, text of statutory instruments, and forms.
ISBN 0421318007 Hbk £95.00

Watters, Douglas →Professional competence and the law.

Watterson, Ray →Media law in Australia.

Watts Pocket Guide to Building Cases 1989. – Watts & Partners.
ISBN 01870776011 Hbk £2.50

Waverman, Leonard →Canadian financial institutions : changing the regulatory environment.

Way
Death and Taxes / Patrick C Soares. – London : Longman Professional, 1986.
ISBN 0851209309 Pbk £19.95

Way, P.
Business Expansion Scheme and Assured Tenancies : New Rules. – London : Longman Professional.
ISBN 0851214932 Pbk £12.50
—Exploiting the Business Expansion Scheme. – London : Longman Professional, 1987.
ISBN 0851212484 Pbk £17.50

'We don't give clothing grants any more' : the 1980 supplementary benefit scheme / Janet Allbeson and Roger Smith. – London : Child Poverty Action Group, 1984.
113p.
Includes bibliographical references.
ISBN 0903963736

We protest : the public order debate / Peter Thornton. – London : National Council for Civil Liberties, 1985.
96p; 20cm.
ISBN 0946088217 Pbk £2.95

Weale →British Banking 1960-85.

Wealth Tax Act with Rules. – 2nd ed. – Allahabad : Law Publishers, 1982.
Hbk £10.50

Wealth Taxation in India. – Allahabad : Vohra, 1987.
195p.
ISBN 8185072094 Hbk £150.00

Weapons Law. – Waterlow.
– (Waterlow's Practitioners Library).
ISBN 0080331041 Pbk £9.95

Weapons That May Cause Unnecessary Suffering or Have Indiscriminate Effects. – Geneva : Comite International de la Croix-Rouge, 1973.
72p.
Hbk £6.00

Wearing
Bankruptcy Procedure / Freize. – 9th ed. – London : Longman Professional, 1987.
ISBN 08512313073 Pbk £13.95
→ Cases In Company Financial Reporting.

Wearne, Phillip →Central America's Indians.

Weatherill, J.F.W.
Practical guide to labour arbitration procedure. – Aurora : Canada Law Book, 1987.
Hbk £16.50

Webb →Immigration Emergency Procedures.

Webb, A. M. F.
Scheme for the transfer of convicted offenders within the Commonwealth : explanatory documentation prepared for Commonwealth jurisidictions / by A.M.F. Webb. – London : Commonwealth Secretariat, 1987.
iii,92p.

Webb, Anne →Principles of the Law of Partnership.

Webb, P.
Church in the Sandalwood Islands 1960-1980. – Townsville : James Cook University Publications.
Hbk £3.00

Webb, P. R. H.
Conflict of laws and contract / by P.R.H. Webb. – Auckland : Legal Research Foundation, 1985.
63p.
Includes bibliographical references.
ISBN 090858136X

—Family law 1981 / by P.R.H. Webb and J.G. Adams. – New Zealand : Legal Research Foundation Inc., 1981.
128p; 21cm. – (Seminar Papers Ser.).
Includes bibliographical references. At head of title: Legal Research Foundation Inc. Seminar.
ISBN 0908581122

—Family law 1984 style / by P.R.H. Webb and J.G. Adams. – Auckland : Legal Research Foundation, 1984.
182p.
Includes bibliographical references. At head of title: Legal Research Foundation Inc. Seminar.
ISBN 0908581327

—Family law 1986 style / by Professor P.R.H. Webb and J.G. Adams. – 4th ed. – Auckland : Legal Research Foundation, 1986.
i,207p.
Previous edition: 1984. Includes bibliographical references.
ISBN 0908581416

—Further aspects of maintenance law : some post Family law 1981 chapters / by P.R.H. Webb. – Auckland : Legal Research Foundation, 1981.
44p.
ISBN 0908581157

—Principles of the Law of Partnership / Anne Webb. – 4th ed. – Butterworths, 1987.
ISBN 0409787892 Pbk

Webb, Patricia M.
History of custodial and related penalties in New Zealand / Patricia M. Webb. – Wellington : Government Printer, 1982.
197p.
ISBN 0477011969

Webb, Sylvia P.
Creating an information service / Sylvia P. Webb : illustrated by Patricia Calderhead. – London : Aslib, 1983.
v,101p; 24cm.
ISBN 0851421865

Webber, G
Residential possession proceedings / R Davidson. – 3rd. – London : Longman Professional (UK), 1990.
– (Practitioner series).
Contains legal and procedural instructions as to how to effect or prevent the recovery of possession of residential premises. Explains the relevant law, procedure to adopt, evidence required, and orders the court may make. Over 100 specimen forms.

Weber, D. →Real Property in Germany.

Webster and Page : South African Law of Trade Marks / N.S. Page. – 3rd ed. – Durban : Professional Publisher, 1983.
ISBN 0409019127 Hbk £139.00

Webster, Bruce
Acts of David II 1329-71. – Edinburgh : Edinburgh University Press.
550p. – (Regesta Regum Scottorum Ser.: Vol. 6).
ISBN 0852243952 Hbk £35.00

Webster, Charles A. R.
Environmental health law / by Charles A.R. Webster. – London : Sweet & Maxwell, 1981.
xxiii,177p; 22cm.
Includes index.
ISBN 0421266201 Hbk £11.50
ISBN 0421266309 Pbk £1.50

Webster, Christopher D.
Clinical assessment before trial : legal issues and mental disorder / Christopher D. Webster, Robert J. Menzies, Margaret A. Jackson : with the collaboration of Brian T. Butler...et al. – Toronto : Butterworths, 1982.
xxvii,319p.
Discusses fitness to stand trial, psychiatric recommendations for treatment, evaluation of mental status and the clinical prediction of dangerous behaviour. Chapter deals with the effect of psychiatric opinion on judicial decision-making.
ISBN 0409875775
→ Mental disorder and criminal responsibility.

Webster, Daniel
Papers of Daniel Webster
Vol.1 : The New Hampshire practice : Alfred S. Konefsky and Andrew J. King / Alfred S. Konefsky, Andrew J. King. – Hanover, N.H. : Published for Dartmouth College by the University Press of New England, 1982.
xxxix,571p; 25cm.
Includes index.
ISBN 0874512328

Webster, G.C.
Webster and Page : South African Law of Trade Marks / N.S. Page. – 3rd ed. – Durban : Professional Publisher, 1983.
ISBN 0409019127 Hbk £139.00

Webster, Waveney →Canadian law reports and statutes held by the Faculty of Law Library, University of the West Indies, Cave Hill, Barbados.

Wechsler, Mary H.
Marriage and Family Law in Washington : the Rights of Husbands, Wives, Children and Cohabiting Couples. – 3rd ed. – North Vancouver : International Self-Counsel Press, 1988.
ISBN 0889087377 Hbk

Wedd, G.
Bigger Bang. – Waterlow, 1987.
ISBN 0080331009 Pbk £5.50

Wedderburn of Charlton, Kenneth William → International labour law reports, Volume 7.

Wedderburn of Charlton, Kenneth William Wedderburn
New politics of labour law / Lord Wedderburn of Charlton. – Durham : The University of Durham, Industrial Relations Group, 1983. – (Occasional paper).

—Worker and the law / Lord Wedderburn. – 3rd ed. – London : Sweet & Maxwell, 1986.
xiv,1026p.
Traces the developing relationship between the worker and the law, by analysis of the employment relationship, job security and dismissal, industrial conflict and the law, and trade unions and their members. Seeks to show the patterns which run through labour law.
ISBN 0421370602

Wedderburn, T. M. →British tax encyclopaedia.

Wedgwood, A. J. →Guide to the Financial Services Act 1986.

Wee, Carolyn →Index to Singapore/Malaysia legal periodicals 1932-1984.

Weekly Criminal Bulletin (W.C.B.) 1987-Present / Chris N. Buhr. – Aurora : Canada Law Book Co.
Llf Parts and Bound Vol. 123.00
Back Vols. 31.00 ea..
Binder. – £20.00
Parts Only. – Llf £108.00

Weekly Digest of Civil Procedure. – Agincourt : Carswell, 1987.
Hbk £189.00

Weekly Digest of Family Law. – Agincourt : Carswell, 1986.
Hbk £248.00

Weekly news summary / United Nations Information Centre for the United Kingdom and Ireland. – London : The Centre, 1982.
Continues: London weekly summary.

Weems, P.R.
Enforcement of Money Judgments Abroad. – Matthew Bender, 1988.
ISBN 0000999070 Hbk £53.00

Weeramantry, C. G.
Invitation to the law / by C.G. Weeramantry. – Sydney : Butterworths, 1982.
xiv,369p.
Includes bibliographies and index.
ISBN 0409309346 Pbk

—Islamic jurisprudence : an international perspective / C.G. Weeramantry : foreword by M. Hidayatullah : message from His Eminence the Grand Sheikh of Al-Azhar University, Cairo. – Basingstoke : Macmillan, 1988.
xix,207p; 23cm.
Bibliography: p189-200. - Includes index.
ISBN 0333446682 £29.50

Weerasooria, W.A.
Banking Law and Practice in Australia / F.W. Coops. – 2nd ed. – Butterworths, 1988.
552p.
ISBN 0409494577 Pbk £45.00
ISBN 0409494569 Hbk £65.00

Wegenast, F. W.
Law of Canadian Companies : 1931. – Repr. of 1980 ed. – Agincourt : Carswell.
1226p.
This book is a reprint of the 1931 text on the Companies Act of Canada and the case law applicable to companies incorporated under the Act.
Hbk £92.50

Wegg-Prosser, Charles
Police and the law / Charles Wegg-Prosser. – 3rd ed. – London : Longman Professional, 1986.
xiv,287p; 20cm. – (It's your law series).
Previous ed.: London : Oyez, 1979. Bibliography: p273-279. - Includes index.
ISBN 0851207588 Pbk £6.95

Wehinger, Urs →Swiss company law.

Weidenbaum, Murray L
Value-added tax : orthodoxy and new thinking / David G Raboy, Ernest S Christian Jr. – Dordrecht : Kluwer, 1989.
304.
Considers questions about the features and effects of tax proposals which are commonly called 'consumption taxes'. Presents issues from the perspective of the practical problems which would affect, or arise from, the imposition of such taxes.
ISBN 0792390024 Hbk £26.25

Weil, Prosper
Law of maritime delimitation - reflections. – Cambridge : Grotius, 1989.
343.
Assesses the scope and meaning of the solutions already reached to the problem of maritime delimitation and submits them to critical analysis. Also intends to identify the directions in which the evolution of the law is heading and to advance some suggestions as to desirable developments.
ISBN 0949009407 Hbk £55.00

Weiler, Dick
Victims and witnesses of crime in Canada / by Dick Weiler and Jean-Guy Desgagne of the Canadian Council on Social Development. – Ottawa : Ministry of Supply and Services, Canada, 1984.
98p,111p.
With French t.p.: Victimes et temoins d'infractions penales au Canada. French and English text.
ISBN 0662530136

Weiler, Joseph
Creation of the European Union and its relation to the EEC treaties / by Joseph Weiler and James Modrall. – Florence : European University Institute, 1985.
44p.
→ Integration through law : Europe and the American federal experience : a series, Vol. 1 : Methods, tools and institutions : edited by Mauro Cappelletti, Monica Seccombe, Joseph Weiler.

Weiler, Joseph H. H. →Ever closer union : a critical analysis of the draft treaty establishing the European Union.

—International Crimes of State : a Critical Analysis of the ILC's Draft Article 19 on State Responsibility. – Berlin : De Gruyter, 1989.
xii, 368p.
ISBN 3110116197 Hbk £152.00

Weiler, Joseph M.
Labour Law Digest, 6 Vols. – Agincourt : Carswell, 1985.
This multi-volume set digests over fifteen thousand reported Canadian labor law cases under federal and provincial law. A cumulative supplement is supplied every six months to keep the work up-to-date.
Hbk £332.00

—Litigating the Values of a Nation : The Canadian Charter of Rights and Freedoms / Robin M. Elliot. – Agincourt : Carswell, 1986.
448p.
This work is a collection of essays by leading Canadian Charter and American constitutional authorities on legal history, political science, legal philosophy, legal theory, and practical advice to litigators.
Hbk £65.75

Weiler, Richard →Services to victims and witnesses of crime in Canada.

Weinberg →Criminal Fraud 1987.

Weinberg, C.
South African Encyclopedia of Forms and Precedents, 16 vols. – Durban : Butterworths. – (Eng. and Afrikaans).
Wo

Weinberg, M.S. →Property Offences.

Weinberger, Ota →Institutional theory of law : new approaches to legal positivism.

Weinrib, Arnold S.
Land Compensation Reports Current Series (1971-Present). – Aurora : Canada Law Book Co.
– (Law Reports).
Hbk £80.00

—Land Compensation Reports (L.C.R.) 1971-Present. – Aurora : Canada Law Book Co.
Hbk £80.00

Weir, J. A.
Negligence for 'A' Level. – 2nd ed. – London : Sweet & Maxwell, 1983.
ISBN 0421321709 Pbk £5.95

—Negligence for A' Level. – 2nd ed. – London : Sweet & Maxwell, 1981.
ISBN 0421289805 Pbk £8.25

Weir, John P.
Annotated Insurance Act of Ontario, 2 Vols. – Agincourt : Carswell, 1986.
This two volume looseleaf work contains the Insurance Act of Ontario, with amendments, extensive case annotations, schedules, and regulations. Each section of the Act is cross-referenced to equivalent sections in the law of all Canadian common law provinces.
Llf £138.75
—Structured Settlements. – Agincourt : Carswell, 1984.
xx, 250p.
This book for the Canadian practitioner examines the procedure for arriving at a fair settlement figure, the negotiation process, and how to proceed with insurers and Revenue Canada. Actual correspondence relating to a structured award is included in the appendix.
Hbk £43.75

Weir, Tony
Casebook on Tort, A. – 6th ed. – Sweet & Maxwell.
ISBN 0421363908 Hbk £30.00
ISBN 0421364009 Pbk £21.00
→ Introduction to comparative law.

Weis, Rene J. A.
Criminal justice : the story of Edith Thompson / by Rene Weis. – London : Hamish Hamilton, 1988.
xviii,327p,8p of plates; 24cm.
Includes index.
ISBN 0241122635 £14.95

Weisbrot, David →Criminal law and practice of Papua New Guinea.
→ Law and social change in Papua New Guinea.

Weiss, G. A. →European insolvency practitioners' handbook : the AEPPC compendium of insolvency law and practice.

Weiss, Manfred
Labour law and industrial relations in the Federal Republic of Germany / Manfred Weiss. – Deventer : Kluwer, 1987.
190p; 25cm.
Bibliography: p37. - Includes index.
ISBN 9065443002 Pbk

Weiss, Peter
Prevent the Crime of Silence : The Report of the Vietnam War Crimes Tribunal / Peter Limqueco. – London : Spokesman Books, 1983.
384p.
ISBN 0713901802 Hbk £10.00

Weisstub, David N →Western idea of law.

Weisweiller, R.
Arbitrage. – Cambridge : Woodhead-Faulkner, 1986.
ISBN 0859413535 Hbk £55.00
—Foreign Exchange Manual Supplement. – Cambridge : Woodhead-Faulkner, 1988.
ISBN 0859414396 Hbk £150.00
—Introduction to Foreign Exchange. – 2nd ed. – Cambridge : Woodhead-Faulkner, 1984.
ISBN 0859412865 Pbk £9.95
—Managing a foreign exchange department. – Cambridge : Woodhead-Faulkner, 1985.
ISBN 0859412768 Hbk £45.00

Welbourn, R. B. →Dictionary of medical ethics.

Welch, Jane →Regulation of banks in the member states of the EEC.

Welfare and justice / Maria Los. – Sheffield : Centre for Criminological and Socio-Legal Studies, 1982.
136p.
Bibliography: p.130-136.

Welfare benefits / by Ruth Lister. – London : Sweet and Maxwell, 1981.
xxvi,284p; 22cm.
Bibliography: p251. - Includes index.
ISBN 0421249609 Pbk £8.00

Welfare law and order : a critical introduction to law for social workers / Pete Alcock and Phil Harris. – London : Macmillan, 1982.
xvi,219p. – (Critical texts in social work and the welfare state).
Includes index. Bibliography: p207-213.
ISBN 0333294904

Welfare Rights and GAIN / Marjorie Martin. – 3rd ed. – Vancouver : Vancouver People's Law School.
Illus.. – – (Public Legal Education Series).
ISBN 0888470223 Hbk £0.60

Welfare State and Supreme Court in India. – New Delhi : Deep and Deep Publications, 1986.
140p.
Hbk £175.00

Well and truly tried : essays on evidence in honour of Sir Richard Eggleston / edited by Enid Campbell and Louis Waller, assisted by Gretchen Kewley. – Sydney : Law Book Company, 1983.
xxxvi,307p.
Bibliography: p8-9.
ISBN 0455204470 Hbk £30

Well-being : its meaning, measurement, and moral importance / James Griffin. – Oxford : Clarendon Press, 1988.
xii,412p.
Bibliography: pp.391- 402. - Includes index.
ISBN 0198249039

Welling, Bruce →Canadian Company Law : Cases, Notes and Materials.
—Corporate Law in Canada : the Governing Principles. – Butterworths, 1984.
784p.
Shows where old law may be safely discarded and demonstrates how current governing principles may be balanced in potential conflict situations. Also looks at the distinction between company statutes in each province, the role of the Charter of Rights in the regulation of corporate activity, corporate crime and tort capital structure, and the legal duties of corporate managers.
ISBN 0409857645 Hbk £100.00

Wellings →Law Landlord and Tenant, Service 1988.

Wellings, V.G. →Encyclopedia of rating and local taxation : law and practice.

Wellington District Law Society
Administrative Tribunals Handbook. – Wellington District Law Society. – Butterworths, 1989.
76p.
ISBN 0409702277 Pbk £27.00

Wellman, F.
Art of Cross Examination The. – 4th ed. – London : Macmillan, 1936.
ISBN 0020749600 Pbk £5.95

Wells →Reproduction revolution.

Wells, Celia →Elliott and Wood's casebook on criminal law.

Wells, Donald A.
War crimes and laws of war / Donald A. Wells. – Lanham : University Press of America, 1984.
x,137p; 24cm.
Bibliography: p123-132. - Includes index.
ISBN 081913841X Hbk
ISBN 0819138428 Pbk £8.25

Wells, Gary L.
Eyewitness identification : a system handbook / Gary L. Wells. – Toronto : Carswell, 1988.
xiv,142p. – (The Carswell law enforcement series).
Bibliography: pp.105-115. - Includes index.
ISBN 0459311611

Wells, O.
National Association of Probation Officers Directory 1988. – Wells (Owen).
ISBN 0904553183 Pbk £5.85

Wells, Sidney J. →International economics.
—Shape of Britain's Tariff. – London : Institute of Economic Affairs.
Pbk £0.50

Wells, W.A.N.
Evidence and Advocacy. – Butterworths, 1988.
327p.
ISBN 040949349X Hbk £59.00

Welsh →McNae's Essential Law for Journalists.

Welsh Development Agency Act 1974. – London : HMSO, 1983.
ISBN 0118027255 Hbk £1.25

Welsh language in the courts / by J.A. Andrews and L.G. Henshaw. – Aberystwyth : University College of Wales, 1984.
ix,116p.
Includes index. With Welsh version of the oaths.

The Welsh Laws. – Cardiff : University of Wales Press.
ISBN 070831032X Pbk £3.50

Welsh National Board for Nursing
Nurses, Midwives and Health Visitors Act 1979. – Welsh National Board for Nursing. – London : HMSO, 1983.
Hbk £2.20

Welsh Office →Water and the environment : the implementation of Part II of the Control of Pollution Act 1974 : joint circular.
→ Water environment : the next steps : the Government's proposals for environmental protection under a privatised water industry.

Welsh Office Local Government Finance Wales : The Welsh Rate Support Grant Supplementary No. 3 Report 1981-82. – London : HMSO, 1983.
Hbk £3.15

Welsh Office Local Government Finance Wales : The Welsh Rate Support Grant Supplementary Report 1983-84. – London : HMSO, 1983.
Hbk £3.60

Welsh Veto : The Wales Act 1978 and the Referendum / J. Barry Jones. – Cardiff : University of Wales, 1983.
238p.
ISBN 0708308317 Hbk £11.95

Welt, Leo G. B.
Countertrade / by Leo G.B. Welt. – London : Euromoney, 1985.
xv,185p.
Added cover title: Special Euromoney report.
ISBN 090312176X

Wendt, Frantz
Cooperation in the Nordic countries : achievements and obstacles / by Frantz Wendt. – Stockholm : Almqvist & Wiksell for the Nordic Council, 1981.
408p.
Bibliography: p.395-400. - Includes index. Translation by Geoffrey Dodd.
ISBN 9122004653

Wener, Geoffrey
Legitimate grievance : a report on the role of the ombudsman in the prison system / Geoffrey Wener. – London : Prison Reform Trust, 1983.
23p.
Bibliography: p20.
ISBN 0946209030

Wentworth, T.
Office and Duty of Executors : Treatise of Wills and Executors Directed to Testators in the Choice of Their Executors and Contrivance of Their Wills. – Repr. of 1774 ed. – Abingdon : Professional Books.
494p.
Hbk £40.00

Werner, R.
Legal and Economic Regulation in Marketing. – Quorum Press.
ISBN 0899302874 Hbk £34.95

Wesley-Smith, Peter
Basic Law and Hong Kong's Future / Albert H.Y. Chen. – Butterworths, 1988.
ca 400p.
Covers the present constitution of Hong Kong, the political values of the Hong Kong Chinese, the Hong Kong model of 'one country, two systems', the relationship between central government and the SAR, the protection of civil liberties, economic, cultural and social aspects, and foreign, external and defence affairs.
ISBN 0409995673 Pbk £145.00
ISBN 040999569X Hbk £230.00
—Introduction to the Hong Kong legal system / Peter Wesley-Smith. – Hong Kong : Oxford University Press, 1987.
ix, 118 p.; 22 cm.
An overview of the Hong Kong legal system; the constitution, imported law and law made in Hong Kong, literary sources, structure of the courts, operation of judge-made laws, the process of legislative law-making, and the institutions of the law.
ISBN 0195840577 Pbk £10.00
—Unequal treaty, 1898-1997 : China, Great Britain, and Hong Kong's new territories / Peter Wesley-Smith. – Hong Kong : Oxford University Press, 1983.
xix, 270 p., 8 p. of plates; 21 cm.
Includes index. Bibliography: p. 242-256.
ISBN 0195837274 Pbk

West African Court Of Appeal Reports Vol. 1-15. – Sweet & Maxwell, 1930-60.
ISBN 0421123508 Hbk £275.00

West African Court of Appeal Reports : 1930-1960
Vol. 1-15. – London : Sweet & Maxwell, 1960.
ISBN 0421123508 Hbk £260.00

West Bengal Laws, 5 Vols. – Calcutta : Hindustan Law Book Co., 1987.
Hbk £125.00

West Bengal Laws
Vol. 5 : Annotated Cooperative Societies Act to Establishments and Luxuries Tax Acts. – Calcutta : Hindustan Law Book Co., 1987.
467p.
Hbk £125.00

West Bengal Premises Tenancy Act 1956. – Calcutta : B. Chand and Sons.
Hbk £8.00

West, Christopher →Concise land registration practice.
→ Land registration forms.

West, D. J.
Delinquency : its roots, careers and prospects / D.J. West. – London : Heinemann Educational, 1982.
186p; 23cm. – (The Heinemann library of criminology and penal reform).
Bibliography: p172-181. - Includes index.
ISBN 0435829327 Hbk £13.50
ISBN 0435829335 Pbk
—Sexual crimes and confrontations : a study of victims and offenders / D.J. West. – Aldershot : Gower, 1987.
x,319p; 22cm.
Bibliography: p285-306. - Includes index.
ISBN 0566053802 £18.50

West Indian cases on the law of contract / Roop L. Chaudhary and Andrew Burgess. – 2nd ed. – Barbados : Coles Printery, 1984.
xvii,316p.

West Indian Law Reports : 1959-date. – Abingdon : Professional Books, 1984.
Hbk

West Indian Reports, 32 Vols. – London : Butterworths.
Hbk

West Indian Reports, 34 Vols. – London : Butterworths.
Hbk £1,645.00

West Nigerian Law Reports. – London : Sweet & Maxwell, Rp 1982 (1955-66).
ISBN 0421291605 Hbk £170.00

West, W.
Drugs Law. – Chichester : Barry Rose, 1982.
ISBN 0859922286 Pbk £12.00

West, W.A.
Law of Dilapidations. – 9th ed. – London : Estates Gazette, 1988.
ISBN 0728200449 Pbk £11.00
ISBN 0728201151 Hbk £18.50

West, W.Gordon
Young offenders and the state: Canadian perspective on delinquency. – Scarborough, Ontario : Butterworths (Canada), 1984.
288.
Argues that the institutions that the Canadian state has created to del with young offenders - schools, courts, reformatories, group homes and jails, are not politically neutral. Analyses methodological problems in dealing with official statistics and social experiments, and draws upon Canadian, American and British sources.
ISBN 0409875830 Pbk

West, W. T. →County court : practice and procedure, general.
—Drugs law / W.T. West. – Chichester : Rose, 1982.
xiii,93p; 22cm.
Includes index.
ISBN 0859922286 Pbk £12.00

Westby-Nunn
Company Secretarial Handbook. – 9th ed. – London : Longman Professional, 1986.
ISBN 0851210686 Pbk £20.95

Westerman, G.S.
Judicial Bay : Its Designation and Delimitation In Int Law. – Oxford : Oxford University Press.
ISBN 019503998X Pbk £29.50

Western Australian Industrial Relations Law. – Nedlands : University of Western Australia Press, 1987.
ca viii, 264p.
ISBN 0855642572 Pbk

Western Australian introduction to law. – 2nd ed. – London : Butterworths, 1986.
ISBN 0409490571 Pbk £18.00

Western Charter Digest : 1983. – Agincourt : Carswell, 1983.
190p.
ISBN 0459364103 Pbk £29.50

Western Charter Digest : 1984. – Agincourt : Carswell, 1985.
188p.
Pbk £29.50

Western European Union
Texts adopted for transmission to national parliaments / Assembly of Western European Union. – Paris : The Assembly, 1955.
From 22nd session, entitled: Texts adopted and brief account of the session. Some parts in French.

Western Europe's migrant workers / by Jonathan Power in collaboration with Anna Hardman. – 2nd rev. ed. – London : Minority Rights Group, 1984.
35p. – (Report).
Bibliography: p.34.
ISBN 0946690197

Western idea of law / by J. C. Smith and David N. Weisstub. – London : Butterworths, 1983.
xxii,685p.
Highlights the unique aspects of Western law by comparing it to other legal traditions, past and present. More than 170 great thinkers are excerpted, and a feminist perspective is incorporated, raising questions about women and power. Covers issues such as state sovereignty egalitarianism, and constitutional guarantees of human rights.
ISBN 0409868191

Western Labour Arbitration Cases
Vol. 1. – Vancouver : British Columbia Continuing Legal Education Society, 1981.
Hbk £65.00
Vol. I (1979). –
Llf £60.00
Vol. I (1980). –
Llf £65.00
Vol. 2. –
Hbk £65.00
Vol. II (1979). –
Llf £60.00
Vol. II (1980). –
Llf £65.00
Vol. 3. –
Hbk £65.00

Western Nigeria law reports. – 3. – London : Reprinted for the Institute of Advanced Legal Studies, Lagos, Nigeria by Sweet & Maxwell, 1955.
Originally published as: Law reports of cases decided in the Federal Supreme Court (on appeal from the High Court of the Western Region) and the High Court of the Western Region / edited by the Committee for Law Reporting, Western Region, Nigeria. - Ibadan : Government Printer, 1956-1967?. Original title varies.
ISBN 0421291605

Western Region of Nigeria
Annual volume of the laws of the Western Region of Nigeria ... : containing the laws of the Western Region of Nigeria and subsidiary legislation made thereunder. – Western Region of Nigeria. – 15 v. – Ibadan : Government Printer, 1954-.
Previously published as separate supplements in the Western Regional Gazette, vol. 1 (1952)-9(1960) and the Western Nigeria Gazette, vol.10(1961)-15(1966).

Western Saharans / by Tony Hodges. – London : Minority Rights Group, 1984.
20p. – (Report).
Bibliography: p.19-20.
ISBN 0946690219

Western systems of juvenile justice / edited by Malcolm W. Klein. – Beverly Hills : Sage, 1984.
240p; 23cm.
Includes bibliographies and index.
ISBN 080392125X £22.00

Western Weekly Reports : 1911-1950, 108 Vols. – Carswell Legal Publications. – Agincourt : Carswell, 1983.
Hbk £2721.75
Index to Vols. 1-75. –
Hbk £35.50

Western Weekly Reports : 1951-1970, 75 Vols. – Carswell Legal Publications. – Agincourt : Carswell, 1983.
– (New Ser. 1951-1970).
Hbk £1890.00
Consolidated Index Vols. 1-75. –
Hbk £35.50

Western Weekly Reports : 1971-1980, 60 Vols. – Carswell Legal Publications. – Agincourt : Carswell, 1983.
Hbk £1512.00
Vol. 1. – 1987.
Hbk £78.25

Western Weekly Reports : 1981-1985, 31 Vols. – Agincourt : Carswell, 1981-82.
Hbk £882.00
Individual Vols.. –
Hbk £33.75

Westin, David →International civil litigation in United States courts: commentary and materials.

Westing, Arthur H →Cultural norms, war and the environment.
→ Global resources and international conflict : environmental factors in strategic policy and action.

Weston →International Claims : Contemporary European Practice.
→ International Claims : Settlement by Lump Sum Agreement.
→ International trade finance.
—Managing Foreign Exchange Risk Exposure. – London : Law Book Co.
ISBN 0455206252 Pbk

Wetherall, William O. →Japan's minorities : Burakumin, Koreans, Ainu and Okinawans.

Wetherill, G. Barrie
Elementary statistical methods / G. Barrie Wetherill. – 3rd ed. – London : Chapman and Hall, 1982.
356p; 24cm. – (Science paperbacks).
Previous ed.: 1972. Bibliography: p348-351. - Includes index.
ISBN 0412240009 Pbk £7.95

Wexler, David B.
Mental health law : major issues / David B. Wexler. – New York : Plenum, 1981.
x,270p; 24cm.
Includes index.
ISBN 0306405385

Whalan, Douglas J.
Torrens system in Australia / by Douglas J. Whalan. – Sydney : Law Book Co., 1982.
lxvii,410p.
Includes bibliographical references and index.
ISBN 0455203571 Pbk
ISBN 045520358X

Whale →Emergency Applications to Magistrates.

Whale on copyright / Jeremy Phillips, R. F. Whale. – 3rd ed. – Oxford : ESC Publishing, 1983.
xv,291p; 23cm.
ISBN 0906214181 Hbk £16.50
ISBN 0906214173 Pbk £9.95

Whale, R. F.
Whale on copyright / Jeremy Phillips, R. F. Whale. – 3rd ed. – Oxford : ESC Publishing, 1983.
xv,291p; 23cm.
ISBN 0906214181 Hbk £16.50
ISBN 0906214173 Pbk £9.95

Whalley, John →Tax policy options in the 1980s.

What Every Attorney Should Know About Income Tax. – Cape Town : Legal & Financial Publishing, 1983.
– (Merlen Ser. of Income Tax Publications).
Hbk £12.64

What Every Company Secretary Should Know About Income Tax. – Cape Town : Legal & Financial Publishing, 1983.
– (Merlen Ser. of Income Tax Publications).
Hbk £12.64

What Every Dental Surgeon Should Know About Income Tax. – Cape Town : Legal & Financial Publishing, 1983.
– (Merlen Ser. of Income Tax Publications).
ISBN 0869940341 Hbk £12.64

What Every Engineer Should Know about Patents. – London : European Book Service.
ISBN 0824780108 Hbk £47.50

What Every Executor-Trustee Should Know About Income Tax. – Cape Town : Legal & Financial Publishing, 1983.
– (Merlen Ser. of Income Tax Publications).
ISBN 0869940201 Hbk £12.64

What Every Farmer Should Know About Income Tax. – Cape Town : Legal & Financial Publishing, 1983.
– (Merlen Ser. of Income Tax Publications).
Hbk £12.64

What Every Hotelier Should Know About Income Tax. – Cape Town : Legal & Financial Publishing, 1983.
– (Merlen Ser. of Income Tax Publications).
ISBN 0869940074 Hbk £12.64

What Every Insurance Company or Broker Should Know About Income Tax. – Cape Town : Legal & Financial Publishing, 1983.
– (Merlen Series of Income Tax Publications).
ISBN 0869940228 Hbk £12.64

What Every Medical Practitioner Should Know About Income Tax. – Cape Town : Legal & Financial Publishing, 1983.
– (Merlen Ser. of Income Tax Publications).
Hbk £12.64

What Every Merchant-Trader Should Know About Income Tax. – Cape Town : Legal & Financial Publishing, 1983.
– (Merlen Ser. of Income Tax Publications).
ISBN 0869940112 Hbk £12.64

What Every Ophthalmic Surgeon Should Know About Income Tax. – Cape Town : Legal & Financial Publishing, 1983.
– (Merlen Ser. of Income Tax Publications).
ISBN 086994021X Hbk £12.64

What Every Pharmacist Should Know About Income Tax. – Cape Town : Legal & Financial Publishing, 1983.
– (Merlen Ser. of Income Tax Publications).
ISBN 086994035X Hbk £12.64

What Every Professional Person Should Know About Income Tax. – Cape Town : Legal & Financial Publishing, 1983.
– (Merlen Ser. of Income Tax Publications).
ISBN 0869940082 Hbk £12.64

What Every Property Owner Should Know About Income Tax. – Cape Town : Legal & Financial Publishing, 1983.
– (Merlen Ser. of Income Tax Publications).
Hbk £10.82

What Every Real Estate Agent Should Know About Income Tax. – Cape Town : Legal & Financial Publishing, 1983.
– (Merlen Ser. of Income Tax Publications).
ISBN 0869940066 Hbk £12.64

What Every Salaried Person Should Know About Income Tax. – Cape Town : Legal & Financial Publishing, 1983.
– (Merlen Ser. of Income Tax Publications).
ISBN 0869940104 Hbk £12.64

What Every Taxpayer Should Know About Income Tax. – 9th ed. – Cape Town : Legal & Financial Publishing, 1983.
– (Merlen Ser. of Income Tax Publications).
Hbk £12.64

What goes on in insurance?. – Cambridge : Woodhead-Faulkner, 1982.
ISBN 0859411613 Pbk £3.95

What goes on in the City?. – 4th ed. – Cambridge : Woodhead-Faulkner, 1986.
ISBN 0859413217 Hbk £7.95
ISBN 0859413225 Pbk £4.25

What Is A Pension. – Tolley Publishing.
ISBN 0854593349 Pbk £1.50

What is International Law and How Do We Tell it When We See It? / J.R. Spencer. – Dordrecht : Kluwer.
66p.
Hbk £26.00

What is to be done about law and order? / John Lea and Jock Young. – Harmondsworth : Penguin Books in association with the Socialist Society, 1984.
284p.
Includes index. Bibliography: p275-284.
ISBN 0140065938

What Next in the Law. – Wellington : Butterworths, 1982.
This work deals with proposals for reform in various areas of the law of the United Kingdom, including: trial by jury, legal aid, personal injuries, libel, privacy, and confidence.
ISBN 0406176019 Hbk
ISBN 0406176027 Pbk

What should be done about corruption and bribery? / Law Reform Commission of Papua New Guinea. – Waigani : The Commission, 1982.
24p. – (LRC working paper).
Prepared for the Commission by Ross DeVere.

What should we do about old restrictive covenants? : a consultation paper / Conveyancing Standing Committee. – London : The Committee, 1986.
12p.

What's in a name / Denis Owen : illustrated by Andrew Martin. – London : BBC, 1985.
143p; 20cm.
Bibliography: p137-138. - Includes index.
ISBN 0563203358 Pbk £3.95

Wheare, K.C.
Modern Constitutions. – 2nd ed. 1966 repr. 1984. – New Delhi : Oxford University Press.
Pbk £25.00

Wheatcroft, G. S. A. →British tax encyclopaedia.
→ Encyclopedia of value added tax.

Wheatley, J
Road traffic law in Scotland. – London : Butterworths, 1989.
Concentrates of those areas of law which arise most frquently in practice. Covers reckless and careless driving, road side breath tests, defences to drink driving cases, construction and use regulations, public service vehicles and carriage of goods by road. Includes relevant EEC legislation and schedules with penalties and the DVLC codes.
ISBN 0406112258 Pbk

Wheatley, John Wheatley
One man's judgement : an autobiography / Lord Wheatley. – London : Butterworths, 1987.
ix,230p,8p of plates; 24cm.
Includes index.
ISBN 0406100195 Hbk £17.50

Wheble →Modern Merchant Banking.

Whelan, C
Small claims courts. – Oxford : Clarendon Press, 1989.
250; 21.5.
Compares and contrasts some of the principles which have been applied in informal methods of adjudicating small claims, and some of the solutins which have been adopted in eight countries. Analyses the dilemmas which alternative options pose for justice.
ISBN 0198256272 Hbk £25.00

Whelan, Christopher J. →Military intervention in democratic societies.
→ Sociological approaches to law.

When Freedoms Collide : the Case for Our Civil Liberties. – Toronto : Lester & Orpen Dennys, 1988.
384p.
ISBN 0886191890 Hbk £27.95

When salem came to the Boro. – Pan Books, 1988.
ISBN 0330305034 Pbk £3.99

Whence They Came : Deportation from Canada 1900-35. – Witney : Academic & University Publishing Group.
ISBN 0776601636 Pbk £19.95

Where is William Beausire? : disappearance in Chile. – Amnesty International. – London : Amnesty International, 1981.
57p.

Where's the justice ? : a manifesto of law reform / Tony Gifford. – Harmondsworth : Penguin, 1986.
126p. – (A Penguin special).
ISBN 0140523588

Which firm of solicitors?. – 2nd ed. – London : Legalease, 1988.
ISBN 1870854101 Hbk £6.90

Whillans
Whillans's Tax Tables / Sheila Parrington. – London : Butterworths, 1988-89.
ISBN 0406543232 Pbk £2.70

Whillans's Tax Tables / Sheila Parrington. – London : Butterworths, 1988-89.
ISBN 0406543232 Pbk £2.70

Whincup, Michael
Right to dismiss. – Oxford : Blackwell Scientific, 1987.
ISBN 0632018933 Hbk £17.95

Whipple, R.T.M.
Commercial Rent Reviews : Law and Valuation Practice. – North Ryde : Law Book Co, 1986.
xxvii, 205p.
ISBN 0455206414 Pbk £27.50

Whippman →Short guide to Landlord and Tenant Act 1987.

Whish, Richard
Competition law / Richard Whish. – London : Butterworths, 1985.
350p; 22cm.
Includes index.
ISBN 0406012784 Hbk £33.00
ISBN 0406012792 Pbk £21.95
→ Contract.
→ Conveyancing Solutions No. 2 : The Contract.

Whitaker, B.
Police In Society. – London : Sinclair Browne.
ISBN 0863000185 Pbk £4.95

Whitaker, Ben
Bharis in Bangladesh. – 4th rev. ed. – London : Minority Rights Group, 1982.
31p. – (Report).
Previous ed.: 1977.
→ Teaching about prejudice.

Whitaker, R.
Agenda For Implementing New Law Product Liability. – Deddington : Pandora Press, 1987.
ISBN 1870317858 £84.00
—Defects in Components and Ingredients. – Product Liability Briefing, 1988.
ISBN 1870317602 Pbk £4.95
—Defects in Natural Commodities and Raw Materials. – Product Liability Briefing, 1988.
ISBN 1870317556 Pbk £4.95
—Defects In Standards Of Product Marketing and Presentation. – Product Liability Briefing.
ISBN 1870317459 Pbk £6.50
—Defects through Storage and Transport. – Product Liability Briefing, 1988.
ISBN 187031770X Pbk £4.95
—Design Defects. – Product Liability Briefing, 1988.
ISBN 1870317505 Pbk £6.50
—Development of UK Product Safety Law. – Product Liability Briefing, 1988.
ISBN 1870317807 Hbk £24.00
—Personal and Corporate Liabilities. – Product Liability Briefing.
ISBN 1870317351 Pbk £6.50
—Producers, importers and own-branders. – Product Liability Briefing, 1988.
ISBN 1870317254 Pbk £6.50
—Protecting consumers and the public at large. – Product Liability Briefing, 1988.
ISBN 1870317157 Pbk £6.50
—Protection of people at work. – Product Liability Briefing, 1988.
ISBN 1870317203 Pbk £6.50
—Retailers, dealers, wholesalers and distributors. – Product Liability Briefing, 1988.
ISBN 1870317300 Pbk £6.50

Whitaker, R. A. →Quaestiones juris privati.

White
Canadian Franchise Guide / Zaid. – Toronto : DeBoo.
Designed for franchisees, franchisors, and their professional advisors, this all-Canadian service discusses legal and tax considerations, current and future trends, marketing and financial planning strategies, and contains a selection of forms and agreements. Monthly updates are also provided.
ISBN 0888201397 Llf £275.00
→ Managing Institutional Change : Role of Staffing Commissions in the Public Sector.

White, A. →Abolishing the Diplock courts : the case for restoring jury trial to scheduled offences in Northern Ireland.

White, Alan R.
Grounds of liability : an introduction to the philosophy of law / Alan R. White. – Oxford : Clarendon, 1985.
x,128p; 23cm.
Bibliography: p122-126. - Includes index.
ISBN 0198761910 Hbk £15.00
ISBN 019876197X Pbk £6.95
—Rights / by Alan R. White. – Oxford : Clarendon, 1984.
viii,186p; 23cm.
Bibliography: p177-184. - Includes index.
ISBN 0198247168 £12.50

White Books, 2 Vols. – London : Sweet & Maxwell, 1984.
ISBN 0421302801 Hbk £150.00

White, Carr and Lowe: a guide to the Children Act 1989 / A Carr, N V Lowe, Brenda M Hoggett. – London : Butterworths, 1990.
255; 248.
This Act is reproduced in full, with annotations. A commentary explains the new law and hows how it will affect, in practical terms, the actions of all who deal with child cases.
ISBN 0406502099 Pbk £12.95

White collar crime / Edwin H. Sutherland : with an introduction by Gilbert Geis and Colin Goff. – Uncut version. – New Haven : Yale University Press, 1983.
xxxiii,291p; 24cm.
Previous ed.: New York : Dryden, 1949. Includes index.
ISBN 0300029217 Hbk

White, D.
Practice and procedure in Sheriff Court. – London : Fourmat, 1988.
ISBN 1851900373 Pbk £12.95

White, Dorcas →Commonwealth Caribbean legal essays.

White, G.E.
American Judicial Tradition : Profiles of Leading American Jud. – Oxford : Oxford University Press.
ISBN 019505685X Pbk £9.95

White, Gilbert F. →World environment 1972-1982 : a report.

White, Gillian M. →International economic law and developing states : some aspects.

White, Jerry S
Government Assistance for Canadian Business. – Toronto : DeBoo.
This reference work, intended for business owners and financial advisors seeking financial assistance from the Federal and Provincial governments, sets out the eligibility requirements for all Canadian jurisdictions. Subscribers receive a complimentary newsletter and six updates annually.
ISBN 0888201451 Llf £245.00
—Law office practice management guide. – Scarborough, Ontario : Butterworths (Canada), 1988.
350.
Guide to the operation and management of a law office practice. Provides information on starting the practice, human resource planning, interviewing process selection and salary determination, avoiding wrongful dismissal, financing the practice, law firm recruitment, performance appraisal techniques, training and development, and marketing of professional services.
ISBN 0409805610 Hbk

White, L.J.
Private antitrust legislation. – London : MIT Press, 1988.
ISBN 026223131X Hbk £35.95

White law : racism in the police courts and prisons / Paul Gordon. – London : Pluto Press, 1983.
159p; 20cm.
ISBN 0861047060 Pbk £3.95

White, Longman Professional
Family Company : Law and Taxation. – London : P..
ISBN 00851208258 Pbk £35.00

White, Margaret
Law for Migrant Welfare Workers. – North Sydney : Allen & Unwin, 1983.
112p.
ISBN 0868610380 Hbk £19.95
ISBN 0868610461 Pbk £12.95
—Law for Youth Workers. – North Sydney : Allen & Unwin, 1983.
124p.
ISBN 0868610305 Pbk £12.95

White, Michael
Shorter working time through national industry agreements / by Michael White. – London : Department of Employment, 1982.
– (Research paper).

White, Peter
Law and Tax for the Family Company. – London : Oyez Longman, 1982.
– (Law and Tax Ser.).
ISBN 085120614X Hbk £15.00
—Post-death Rearrangements of Wills and Intestacies. – 3rd ed. – London : Longman Professional.
– (Longham Practical Tax Series).
ISBN 0851214223 Hbk £9.95
—Professional partnerships: law and taxation. – 2nd. – London : Longman Professional (UK), 1990.
Considers partnerships from the time of creation through changes in the partnerships by admission, retirement and merger, to the ultimate dissolution. Covers the Insolvency Act 1986, and changes brought about by the Finance Act 1989. New chapter on mergers and demergers.
ISBN 0851215734 Pbk £35.00
—Tax planning for the family. – 3rd ed. – London : Longman Professional, 1986.
ISBN 0851209203 Pbk £22.00
—Tax planning on marriage breakdown. – 4th ed. – London : Longman Professional, 1986.
ISBN 0851210740 Pbk £26.50
—Trusts : Maximising the Tax Advantages. – London : Oyez Longman, 1983.
– (Oyez Longman Intelligence Report Ser.).
ISBN 0851207375 Hbk £45.00

White, R →Non-means tested benefits: the legislation.
—White, Carr and Lowe: a guide to the Children Act 1989 / A Carr, N V Lowe, Brenda M Hoggett. – London : Butterworths, 1990.
255; 248.
This Act is reproduced in full, with annotations. A commentary explains the new law and hows how it will affect, in practical terms, the actions of all who deal with child cases.
ISBN 0406502099 Pbk £12.95

White, R. A. H. →Wards of court.

White, R.L.
Law and Regulation of International Space Communication : The Artech Telecommunication Library. – London : Artech House.
ISBN 0890062749 Hbk

White, Robin
Administration of justice / Robin C.A. White. – Oxford : Blackwell, 1985.
400p.
Introduction to the English legal system of justice. Critique of how the system works in reality.
ISBN 0631143068 Hbk £27.50 :
ISBN 0631143076 Pbk £12.50
→ Changing law.
→ Supreme Court Act 1981.

White, Robin C. A →Guide to the civil jurisdiction and judgments convention.

White, Stephen →Party statutes of the Communist world.

Whitehall and Westminster : Government informs Parliament : the changing scene / Dermot Englefield. – Harlow : Longman, 1985.
x,218p; 24cm.
Includes index.
ISBN 058290272X Pbk £15.00

Whitehead
People and employment / Baruch. – London : Butterworths, 1981.
ISBN 0408106921 Pbk £8.50

Whitehead, Geoffrey →Elements of Cargo Insurance.
—Elements of export law / Geoffrey Whitehead. – Cambridge : Woodhead-Faulkner, 1983.
xiv,255p; 22cm.
Bibliography: p246. - Includes index.
ISBN 0859412288 Hbk
—Elements of International Trade and Payments. – Cambridge : Woodhead-Faulkner, 1983.
ISBN 0859412261 Pbk £6.25
→ Law of the carriage of goods by land, sea and air.
—Test Yourself on the 1987 Highway Code. – London : Shaw & Sons, 1987.
ISBN 0721906923 Pbk £1.75

Whitehead, Tony
Mental illness and the law / Tony Whitehead. – Oxford : Basil Blackwell, 1982.
viii,181p; 23cm.
Includes index.
ISBN 0631127216 Hbk £
ISBN 0631126155 Pbk

Whitehill, Arthur M. →Doing business in Korea.

Whitehorn, Norman
Court of Protection Handbook. – 7th ed. – London : Longman Professional, 1986.
– (LPPN 39).
ISBN 0851209920 Pbk £13.95
→ Court of Protection practice.
—Court of Protection Procedure. – London : Oyez Longman, 1983.
– (Oyez Longman Practice Note Ser.: No. 39).
Hbk £7.95

Whitehouse, C. J.
Reconstructions, Hive-Downs and Management Buyouts. – London : Law Society, 1984.
28p.
Hbk £1.95

Whitehouse, Chris
Revenue law : principles and practice / Chris Whitehouse, Elizabeth Stuart-Buttle. – 6th ed. – London : Butterworths, 1988.
xxxi,690p.
Previous ed.: 1987.
ISBN 0406502692 Pbk £23.50
—Tax Aspects of the Administration of Estates / Elizabeth Stuart-Buttle. – London : Butterworths, 1984.
This work discusses the numerous tax considerations associated with the administration of an estate in the United Kingdom. The book details the appropriate procedures which are a pre-condition to a grant of probate.
ISBN 0406259003 Pbk

Whiteman, Arthur
Nigeria : its petroleum geology, resources and potential / by Arthur Whiteman. – 2 v. – London : Graham & Trotman, 1982.
394p,5leaves of plates(folded).
In 2 vols. Bibliography: p.376-381.
ISBN 0860102645

Whiteman on Capital Gains Tax / Malcolm Gammie. – 4th ed. – Sweet & Maxwell.
ISBN 0421372605 Hbk £130.00

Whiteman, Peter G
Whiteman on Capital Gains Tax / Malcolm Gammie. – 4th ed. – Sweet & Maxwell.
ISBN 0421372605 Hbk £130.00

Whithear, Deborah →Family : Australian family studies database, Vol. 2 1985.
→ FAMILY thesaurus : Australian family studies indexing terms.

Whiting, D.
Elements of Banking. – 3rd ed. – Plymouth : Macdonald & Evans, 1985.
ISBN 071210657X Pbk £4.95
—Finance of Foreign Trade. – 6th ed. – Plymouth : Macdonald & Evans, 1986.
ISBN 0712106618 Pbk £4.95
—Finance of International Trade. – 5th ed. – London : Pitman Publishing, 1987.
ISBN 0273027344 Pbk £8.95
—Mastering Banking. – London : Macmillan, 1985.
ISBN 0333369122 Pbk £3.25

Whitley, James Stuart
Jurisdiction in Criminal Law. – Agincourt : Carswell, 1985.
275p.
This work for the practitioner examines all aspects of the exercise of jurisdiction by Canadian criminal courts and discusses the remedies available in cases of error. The book provides a theoretical approach to analyzing the validity of the exercise of jurisdiction.
Hbk £43.75

Whitmore, Harry
Loval Government and Environmental Planning Law in New South Wales. – North Ryde : Law Book Co, 1981.
xvi, 174p.
ISBN 045520361X Pbk £28.50
→ Public torts and contracts.

Whitmore, John →Discrimination equal pay.

Whittaker
Aborigines Today : Land and Justice / Burger. – Third World Publications, 1988.
ISBN 0900918225 Pbk £4.95

Whittaker, Andrew M.
Encyclopaedia of Investor Protection. – London : Butterworths, 1987.
Hbk
→ Financial Services Act 1986 : a guide to the new law.

Whitteron, C.
Survey of company car schemes. – 7th ed. – Tolley Publishing, 1987.
ISBN 0854593144 Hbk £29.50

Whittington-Egan
Jack the Ripper : A Casebook 1976. – London : Wildy & Sons.
Hbk £6.50

Who controls training? : the rise of the Manpower Services Commission / Caroline St John-Brooks. – London : Fabian Society, 1985.
20p; 22cm.
ISBN 0716305062 unbound £1.50

Who Guards the Guardians? Judicial Control of Administration. – University of Georgia Press.
ISBN 082030963X Hbk £17.50

Who is who in the judiciary / Rosaline Odeh. – Lagos : Department of Information, 1983.
105p.
Editor, Rosaline Odeh.

Who needs the wages councils?. – Low Pay Unit. – London : Low Pay Unit, 1983.
56p. – (Low pay unit publication).
Bibliography: p54.

Who prosecutes? : the future of the prosecuting service / Association of County Councils. – London : The Association, 1983.
5p.

Who uses social inquiry reports? : a study of the use of social inquiry reports outside the courts and their influence upon decisions / Roger Shaw. – Cambridge : Institute of Criminology, 1981.
53p. – (Institute of Criminology occasional papers).
Includes bibliographical references.

Who was who : a cumulated index 1897-1980. – London : Black, 1981.
ISBN 071362177X

Who's watching you? / Crispin Aubrey. – Harmondsworth : Penguin, 1981.
204p,8p of plates; 18cm. – (Pelican books).
Bibliography: p197-199. - Includes index.
ISBN 0140222839 Pbk £1.50

Who's Who in Canadian Law 1985-86. – 4th ed. – Toronto : Trans-Canada Press, 1986.
Hbk £43.00

Who's Who in International Banking 1988-89. – London : Cedar Tree House.
ISBN 1852710233 Pbk £95.00

Whose interest? : solicitors and their clients' accounts : a discussion paper. – London : National Consumer Council, 1984.
74p.
ISBN 0905653556

Whose justice? Which rationality? / Alasdair MacIntyre. – London : Duckworth, 1988.
422p; 24cm.
Includes index.
ISBN 071562198X Hbk £35.00 :
ISBN 0715621998 Pbk £12.95

Whose Law and Order? Aspects of Crime, Social Control and Irish Society. – Belfast : Sociological Society of Ireland.
ISBN 0951341103 Hbk £10.95
ISBN 0951341111 Pbk £4.95

Why do we sell butter to Russia? : and other common questions from the Common Market / by Nicholas Bethell. – London : European Democratic Group, 1987.
9 p.

Why the history of canon law is not written / Selden Society lecture delivered in the Old Hall of Lincoln's Inn, July 3rd 1984 by Charles Donahue. – London : Selden Society, 1986.
31p. – (Selden Society lecture).
Includes bibliographical references.

Whybrow, J. C. →Custody law in practice in the divorce and domestic courts.

Whyte, Gerry →Irish trade union law.
—Social welfare law in Ireland : a guide to its sources / Gerry Whyte. – Dublin : Round Hall Press, 1987.
86p; 23cm.
Includes index.
ISBN 0947686258 Pbk £9.95

Whyte, John D →Canada Notwithstanding : The Making of a Constitution 1976-1982.
—Canadian Constitutional Law / W R Lederman. – 3rd ed. – Toronto : Butterworths, 1987.
ISBN 0409876046 Hbk
ISBN 0409876054 Pbk

Whyte, W. S.
Building Regulations : Explained and Illustrated / Vincent Powell Smith. – 7th ed. – London : Collins, 1986.
310p : Illus.
ISBN 0003832813 Hbk £18.50
ISBN 0003832260 Pbk £10.95

Wibaut, S.
Tax Reform in Disequilibrium Economics. – Cambridge : Cambridge University Press.
ISBN 0521355885 Hbk £19.50

Wickerson, John
Motorist and the Law. – 2nd ed. – London : Oyez Longman, 1982.
– (It's Your Law Ser.).
ISBN 0851204775 Hbk £3.95
ISBN 0851204783 Pbk

Wicks, B.M.
Subject Index to the Acts and Regulations of the Commonwealth of Australia, 1986 Edition. – North Ryde : Law Book Co, 1987.
Pbk £36.00
—Subject index to the Acts of New South Wales / compiled by B.M. Wicks. – 1983 ed. – Sydney : Law Book Co., 1984.
141p.

Wiechers, M.
Administrative Law. – Durban : Professional Publisher, 1984.
ISBN 0409067040 Hbk £79.00
ISBN 0409067059 Pbk £69.00
→ Constitutions of Transkei, Bophuthatswana, Venda and Ciskei.

Wiehahn, N. E. →Complete Wiehahn report.

Wigan, T. K. →Prideaux's Forms and precedents in conveyancing.

Wigmore, John Henry →Law and justice in Tokugawa Japan : materials for the history of Japanese law and justice under the Tokugawa Shogunate 1603-1867, Part IV-C : Contract : commercial customary law.

Wihak, Christine
Review and Analysis of Canadian PLEI Research. – Ottawa : Canadian Law Information Council, 1983.
104p.
ISBN 0920358527 Pbk £7.50

Wihtol, R.
Asian Development Bank and Rural Development. – London : Macmillan.
ISBN 0333464362 Hbk £33.00

Wiktor, Christian L
Canadian bibliography of international law / Christian L. Wiktor. – Toronto : University of Toronto Press, 1984.
xxiii, 767 p.; 25 cm.
Includes indexes.
ISBN 0802056156
—Index to Commonwealth Legal Periodicals : 1978-1981, 1 Bound Vol. – Agincourt : Carswell, 1982.
Hbk £63.00
—Marine Affairs Bibliography : a Comprehensive Index to Marine Law and Policy Literature / Leslie A. Foster. – Dordrecht : Kluwer, 1987.
702p.
ISBN 902473570X Hbk £375.00

Wilcocks, Julie
Countries and islands of the world : a guide to nomenclature / Julie Wilcocks. – London : Bingley, 1981.
133p; 23cm.
ISBN 085157338X

Wilcox, J. B.
Model of the building society sector / J. B. Wilcox. – London : Bank of England, 1985.
29p. – (Discussion papers).
Bibliography: p29.
ISBN 090331276X

Wild →Company Accounting Requirements.
→ Practice of Banking 2.

Wild, H.R.C. →Mercantile Law in New Zealand.

Wildavsky, A.
Searching for Safety. – Oxford : Clio Distribution.
ISBN 0887387144 Hbk £11.25

Wildsmith, Bruce H.
Aboriginal Peoples and Section 25 of the Canadian Charter of Rights and Freedoms. – Saskatoon : University of Saskatchewan, Native Law Centre, 1988.
52p.
ISBN 0888801939 Hbk £15.00
—Agriculture : The Legal Framework. – Aurora : Canada Law Book Co, 1982.
300p. – (Text Books-Civil).
Hbk £45.00

—Aquaculture : the Legal Framework. – Aurora : Canada Law Book, 1982.
Hbk £25.00

—Aquaculture : the legal framework / Bruce H.Wildsmith. – Toronto : Emond-Montgomery, 1982.
xii,313p.
Bibliography: p.295-305. - Includes index.
ISBN 0920722083 Hbk £45.00

→ Canadian Charter of Rights : law practice revolutionized.

Wilford, Michael
Time charters. – 2nd ed. – London : Lloyd's of London Press, 1982.
lxix,505p; 25cm.
Previous ed.: 1978. Includes index.
ISBN 0907432131

Wilkes, John →Fractured Federation?.

Wilkes, Roger
Wallace : the final verdict / Roger Wilkes. – London : Bodley Head, 1984.
269p,16p of plates; 22cm.
Bibliography: p261-263. - Includes index.
ISBN 037030571X £8.95

Wilkie →Criminal Evidence and Procedure, No. 2.
→ Criminal Law P.P.H. 1.

→ General Police Duties.

Wilkie, Meredith
Aboriginal Landrights in New South Wales. – Chippendale : Alternative Publishing Cooperative, 1985.
ISBN 090918884X Hbk £22.50
ISBN 0909188858 Pbk £12.95

Wilkins →Outline of the law of evidence.

Wilkins, Leslie T →Bail : Issues and Prospects.
—Consumerist criminology / Leslie T. Wilkins. – London : Heinemann, 1984.
viii,184p; 23cm.
Includes index.
ISBN 0435825283 Pbk £16.00
ISBN 0389204102

→ Human Rights Guarantees in the Administration of Criminal Justice.

Wilkins, Nancy →Outline of the law of evidence.

Wilkins, Roger →Teaching human rights.

Wilkinson, A. B. →Introduction to the law of Scotland.
—Scottish law of evidence / A.B. Wilkinson. – London : Butterworths, 1986.
200p; 22cm.
Includes index.
ISBN 0406261105 Pbk £25.00

Wilkinson, C.F.
American Indians, Time and the Law Native Societies in a Modern Constitutional Democracy. – Yale University Press.
ISBN 0300041365 Pbk £9.95

Wilkinson, G. S.
Wilkinson's road traffic offences / Eleventh edition by Patrick Halnan, John Spencer. – 11th ed. – London : Oyez Longman, 1982.
cx,1318p.
ISBN 0851206689
—Wilkinson's road traffic offences / Patrick Halnan. – 13th ed. 2 vols. – London : Longman, 1987.
24cm.
Takes into account recent changes in the law including: Pelican Crossing Regulations and Directions 1987; Motor Vehicle Driving Licences Regulations 1987 and 'Cracknell v Willis'. Previous ed.: 1984. Includes index.
ISBN 0851212891 v.2 £168.00
ISBN 0851213294

Wilkinson, Guy →Food and farm policies of the European Community.

Wilkinson, H. W.
Conveyancer and Property Lawyer. – London : Sweet & Maxwell.
Hbk £36.00
—Pipes, mains, cables and sewers. – 5th. – London : Longman Professional (UK), 1989.
– (Practitioner series).
Guide to the basic principles of the law governing the laying of conduits by private agreement and statutory authority for electricity, telecommunicatins, water, gas, oil and effluent. Takes account of the privatisation of British Telecom, British Gas and British Petroleum, the building of the Channel Tunnel, and the abolition of the Metropolitan Councils. Includes about 60 new cases.
Hbk £17.95
—Standard Conditions of Sale of Land. – 3rd ed. – London : Oyez Longman, 1982.
– (Oyez Longman Practitioner Ser.).
ISBN 0851206468 Hbk £15.95

Wilkinson, K. H. P. →Commercial litigation : pre-emptive remedies.

Wilkinson, P.
Terrorism and the liberal state. – 2nd ed. – London : Macmillan, 1986.
ISBN 0333394917 Pbk £7.95

Wilkinson, Paul →British perspectives on terrorism.

Wilkinson, Philip
Case for the conversational analysis of courtroom interaction : some interactional dimensions of legal procedures / by Philip Wilkinson. – Oxford : Centre for Socio-Legal Studies, 1981.
24p. – (Working paper).
Includes bibliographical references.

Wilkinson, Tony P. →Juvenile court : a guide to law and practice.

Wilkinson's road traffic offences / Peter S Wallis, Patrick Halnan. – 14th. 2 vols. – London : Longman Professional (UK), 1989.
New edition revised to take account of the Road Traffic Act 1988; the Road Traffic Offenders Act 1988; the Road Traffic (Consequential Provisions) Act 1988; the Criminal Justice Act 1988.
ISBN 085121159X Hbk £195.00

Wilkinson's road traffic offences / Patrick Halnan. – 13th ed. 2 vols. – London : Longman, 1987.
24cm.
Takes into account recent changes in the law including: Pelican Crossing Regulations and Directions 1987; Motor Vehicle Driving Licences Regulations 1987 and 'Cracknell v Willis'. Previous ed.: 1984. Includes index.
ISBN 0851212891 v.2 £168.00
ISBN 0851213294

Wilkinson's road traffic offences / Eleventh edition by Patrick Halnan, John Spencer. – 11th ed. – London : Oyez Longman, 1982.
cx,1318p.
ISBN 0851206689

Will Draftsman's Handbook. – 5th ed. – London : Longman Professional.
ISBN 0851212743 Hbk £20.75

Will Draftsman's Handbook. – 3rd ed. – London : Oyez Longman, 1983.
ISBN 0851208037 Hbk £13.50

Will Making and the Administration of Estates : a Short Guide. – Butterworths, 1984.
223p.
This book aims at assisting the practitioner in the drafting of a will which accurately effects and carries out the wishes of the testator and then the efficient administration of the estate after death.
ISBN 0409492329 Hbk £36.00

Will precedents and inheritance tax / D.T. Davies. – 3rd ed. – London : Butterworth, 1988.
xxiii,283p.
Previous ed.: published as Will precedents and capital transfer tax. 1983. Includes index.
ISBN 0406175128 £25.00

Will-Draftsman's Handbook. – 4th ed. – Butterworths, 1987.
ISBN 0409652415 Hbk

Wille and Millin's Mercantile law of South Africa / by Philip Millin and George Wille. – 18th ed. – Johannesburg : Hortors Stationery, 1984.
civ, 952 p.; 26 cm.
Includes indexes. Bibliography: p. ciii-ci.
ISBN 0620073470 R58.00

Wille, George
Wille and Millin's Mercantile law of South Africa / by Philip Millin and George Wille. – 18th ed. – Johannesburg : Hortors Stationery, 1984.
civ, 952 p.; 26 cm.
Includes indexes. Bibliography: p. ciii-ci.
ISBN 0620073470 R58.00
—Wille's law of mortgage and pledge in South Africa / T. J. Scott, Susan Scott. – 3rd ed. – Cape Town : Juta, 1987.
lvi,283p.
Previous ed. published in 1961 as: The law of mortgage and pledge in South Africa. Bibliography: pp.xxi-xxii. - Includes index. .
ISBN 0702118966

Willemin, G., et al
International Committee of the Red Cross. – Dordrecht : Kluwer, 1984.
300p.
ISBN 9024730643 Hbk £120.00

Wille's law of mortgage and pledge in South Africa / T. J. Scott, Susan Scott. – 3rd ed. – Cape Town : Juta, 1987.
lvi,283p.
Previous ed. published in 1961 as: The law of mortgage and pledge in South Africa. Bibliography: pp.xxi-xxii. - Includes index. .
ISBN 0702118966

William Nelson Cromwell Foundation →Law practice of Alexander Hamilton : documents and commentary.

William Sheppard: Cromwell's law reformer. – Cambridge : Cambridge University Press.
Appraisal of William Sheppard's legal works including writings on conveyancing, tithe collection and guides for local law enforcement. Examines the importance of Sheppard's books to his contemporaries and to legal literature in general.
ISBN 0521264839

Williams
City of North York Act, 1983, Bill Pr051 : An Act Respecting the City of North York. – Ontario : Ontario Government Publications Service, 1983.
6p.
Hbk £0.30
—Criminological Theory / Mcshane. – Prentice-Hall.
ISBN 0131936409 Pbk £10.35

→ Duties and Responsibilities of Pension Plan Trustees.

—Hungarian Canadian Cultural Centre (Hungarian House) Act, 1983, Bill Pr054 : An Act Respecting the Hungarian Canadian Cultural Centre (Hungarian House). – Ontario : Ontario Government Publications Service, 1983.
4p.
Hbk £0.30

—Industrial tribunal practice / Walker. – 2nd ed. – Stewart (Henry), 1985.
ISBN 0946700184 Pbk £24.00

→ Intellectual Property : the New Law.

—Juris and Practice Eng Courts / Bruce. – Professional Books.
ISBN 0862053080 Hbk £53.75

—Lloyd's Bank Tax Guide 1988-89 / Willman. – Penguin.
ISBN 0140113169 Pbk £4.95

—Textbook on Criminology / Ryan. – London : Blackstone Press.
ISBN 1854310127 Hbk £9.95

Williams, A.
Planning law casebook. – London : Laureate-Thomson Press, 1984.
ISBN 0907392091 Pbk £19.50
—Town and country planning law. – Plymouth : Macdonald & Evans, 1981.
ISBN 0712120319 Pbk £3.95

Williams, A. Graham
Principles of corporation tax in the Republic of Ireland / by A. Graham Williams. – 1. – Dublin : Incorporated Law Society of Ireland, 1981.
loose-leaf; 27cm.
Includes index.
ISBN 0902027166

Williams, A. M.
Town and Country Planning Law. – 1st ed. – Plymouth : Macdonald & Evans, 1981.
128p. – (M and E Handbook Ser.).
ISBN 0712120319 Hbk £3.95

Williams, A. N. →Anti-dumping and anti-subsidy law : the European Communities.

Williams' and Rhodes' Canadian Law of Landlord and Tenant, 2 Vols. – 5th ed. – Agincourt : Carswell, 1983.
1400p.
This two volume looseleaf text is a comprehensive guide to commercial and residential tenancies in every province of Canada. Topics covered include: rent control, the creation of the landlord and tenant relationship, recovery of rent, and related issues.
Llf £143.00

Williams and Rhodes on the Canadian Law of Landlord and Tenant. – 6th ed. – Agincourt : Carswell, 1988.
432p.
Llf £75.75

Williams, Anne
Planning law casebook. – London : Laureate-Thomson, 1984.
288p.
ISBN 0907392091 Pbk £17.50

Williams, Anthony →Hong Kong Banking Ordinance.

Williams, Brian K.
Australian Takeovers Practice and Precedents Manual. – North Ryde : C.C.H. Australia, 1983.
200p.
ISBN 0869036807 Hbk £63.00

Williams, C.R.
Brett and Waller's Criminal Law : Text and Cases. – 5th ed. – Butterworths, 1984.
784p.
This introductory work, containing cases, statutory materials, and commentary, is intended to be equally useful in the common law states of New South Wales, South Australia, and Victoria. Variations in the law from one state to another are discussed.
ISBN 0409492116 Hbk £74.00
→ Brett, Waller and Williams Criminal Law Text and Cases.
→ Cases and Materials on Evidence.
—Property Offences / M.S. Weinberg. – 2nd ed. – North Ryde : Law Book Co, 1986.
xl, 445p.
ISBN 0455206325 Hbk £65.00
ISBN 0455206333 Pbk £45.00

Williams Committee →Pornography and politics : the Williams Committee in retrospect.

Williams, D.
Casebook on repairs. – London : Estates Gazette, 1987.
ISBN 0728201038 Pbk £16.00
—Criminal Injuries Compensation. – 2nd ed. – London : Waterlow, 1986.
ISBN 008039244X Pbk £9.95
—Hit and run and uninsured drivers. – 5th ed. – Chichester : Barry Rose, 1987.
ISBN 0870080653 Pbk
—Landlord and Tenant Casebook. – London : Estates Gazette, 1985.
ISBN 0728200880 Pbk £12.00
—Tax Benefits and Family Finance / T. Lyon. – London : Sweet & Maxwell, 1985.
ISBN 0421324600 Hbk

Williams, D.F.
Share Schemes for Directors and Employees. – 2nd ed. – London : Butterworths.
ISBN 0406503346 Pbk £40.00

Williams, D.W.
Customs Duties. – London : Deloitte Haskins & Sells.
ISBN 0863491332 Pbk £20.00
—Handbook of business tenancies / D.W. Williams : assisted by C.M. Brand : consultant on valuation and practice C.C. Hubbard. – 1. – London : Sweet & Maxwell, 1985.
looseleaf.
Includes index.
ISBN 0421327901 £75.00
→ Howell James' Notes on the Need for Planning Permission.
→ Planning law for conveyancers.

Williams, David
Investigations by Adminstrative Agencies. – North Ryde : Law Book Co, 1987.
ca 1,250p.
ISBN 0455205868 Hbk £125.00
→ Stock Relief.
→ Sweet & Maxwell's tax statutes 1984/85.
—Tax for the self-employed. – London : Longman Professional, 1988.
– (Allied Dunbar Money Guide).
ISBN 08512113855 Hbk

Williams, David G. →Urban planning practice in developing countries.

Williams, David R.
Trapline Outlaw : Simon Peter Gunanoot. – Victoria : Sono Nis Press.
170p.
ISBN 0919462979 Hbk £12.95

Williams, David Ricardo
Duff : a Life in the Law. – Vancouver : University of British Columbia Press, 1984.
344p.
ISBN 0774802030 Hbk £34.95

Williams, David W. →Introduction to revenue law.
—Social security taxation : a guide to contributions and contributory conditions under the social security acts / by David W. Williams. – London : Sweet & Maxwell, 1982.
xxxiii,536p; 26cm.
Includes index.
ISBN 0421262303 £40.00

Williams, Delyth W. →Handbook of leasehold reform.

Williams, Donald B.
Tax On Maintenance Payments 1985/86 / Joel Newman. – 8th ed. – London : Longman Professional.
ISBN 0851210759 Pbk £11.95

Williams, Douglas
Specialized agencies and the United Nations : the system in crisis / Douglas Williams : with a foreword by Sir Anthony Parsons. – London : Hurst in association with the David Davies Memorial Institute of International Studies, London, 1987.
xvi,279p; 23cm.
Bibliography: p271-274. - Includes index.
ISBN 185065025X £17.50

Williams, E. V.
Williams, Mortimer and Sunnucks on executors, administrators and probate / by J.H.G. Sunnucks, J.G. Ross Martyn, K.M. Garnett. – London : Stevens & Sons, 1982.
clxxxviii,1157p; 26cm.
Concerned with probate practice and the work of executors and administrators, discussions of changes in the law of family provision, capital transfer tax and social security. Includes appendices which set out the relevant statutes, rules of court and statutory instruments.
ISBN 0420455000 £75.00

Williams, Emlyn
ABC guide to the practice of the county court / by Emlyn Williams. – 3rd ed. – London : Sweet & Maxwell, 1987.
200p; 22cm.
Includes amendments embodied in the County Courts Act 1984, and within other acts such as the Administration of Justice Act 1985, the Companies Act 1985 and the Insolvency Act 1986. Updated to cover amended Costs rules, the privatisation of registration of judgements, and the change of procedure in appeals to the Court of Appeal.
ISBN 0421346906 £14.50
—ABC guide to the practice of the magistrates' courts / by Emlyn Williams. – London : Sweet & Maxwell, 1986.
viii,187p; 22cm.
ISBN 0421344903 Pbk £14.50
—ABC Guide to the Practice of the Supreme Court, 1988-1989. – 45th ed. – Sweet & Maxwell.
ISBN 0421405902 Pbk £16.50

Williams, F. R.
Law Reports of Nigeria, 3 Vols. / F. A. Ajayi. – London : Butterworths.
Hbk

Williams, Geraint →John Stuart Mill's On liberty.

Williams, Glanville
Criminal Law : The Protection of Property / A. J. Smith. – London : Sweet & Maxwell, 1986.
ISBN 0420470409 Hbk
—Foundations of the law of tort / Glanville Williams, B.A. Hepple. – 2nd ed. – London : Butterworths, 1984.
xxiv,230p; 23cm.
This text for students in the United Kingdom provides an examination of the underlying principles of tort law and liability in the modern context. The function of tort law and its history, the concepts of damage and fault, the effects of insurance and social security, and possibilities for reform are covered.
ISBN 0406683867 Hbk £14.00
ISBN 0406683875 Pbk £10.95
—Learning the law / by Glanville Williams. – 11th ed. – London : Stevens, 1982.
viii,241p; 19cm.
Previous ed.: 1978. Includes index. .
ISBN 0420462902 Hbk £
ISBN 0420463003 Pbk £4.50
—Proof Of Guilt, The (Hamlyn 3). – 3rd ed. – Belfast : Sweet & Maxwell, 1963.
ISBN 0420383204 Pbk £9.25
—Textbook of criminal law / by Glanville Williams. – 2nd ed. – London : Stevens, 1983.
xlvii,1007p; 24cm.
Previous ed.: 1978. Includes index.
ISBN 0420468501 Hbk £
ISBN 0420468609 Pbk £19

Williams, Jeremy S
Law of libel and slander in Canada / Jeremy S. Williams. – 2nd ed. – Toronto : Butterworths, 1988.
xxxi, 145 p.; 24 cm.
Analysis of the law of defamation as it applies in each common law province of Canada, covering both jurisdictions which retain libel and slander as distinct torts, and jurisdictions which have adopted the Uniform Defamation Act. Covers the publication requirements, credit reporting and other commercial representations, limitation periods, damages and injunctions.
ISBN 0409876410 Hbk £57
—Limitation of Actions. – 2nd ed. – Toronto : Butterworths.
344p.
Hbk £55.00

Williams, John
Hooligans abroad : the behaviour and control of English fans in Continental Europe / John Williams, Eric Dunning and Patrick Murphy. – London : Routledge & Kegan Paul, 1984.
xiv,230p,12p of plates; 22cm.
Includes index.
ISBN 0710201435 Pbk £8.95
—Law of mental health. – London : Fourmat, 1990.
244; 22.
ISBN 1851900837 Pbk uk19.95
—Social services law / by John Williams. – London : Fourmat, 1981.
xxii,338p; 22cm.
Includes index.
ISBN 185190039X Pbk £18.95

Williams, John F.
Manager's Guide to Patents, Trade Marks and Copyright. – London : Kogan Page, 1986.
150p.
ISBN 1850912033 Hbk £13.95
ISBN 1850912041 Pbk £6.95

Williams, Karen →Competition law : antitrust policy in the U.K. and the EEC.

Williams, Kevin
Aftermath of tribunal reinstatement and re-engagement / by Kevin Williams and David Lewis. – London : Department of Employment, 1981.
46p. – (Research paper).
Bibliography: p.45-46.

Williams, L. N.
Road Traffic Reports : 1986 / N. P. Metcalf. – London : Mason Publications Ltd, 1987.
416p. – (Road Traffic Reports Ser.).
ISBN 0859373398 Hbk £20.00

Williams' law relating to wills / C. H. Sherrin, R. F. D. Barlow, R. A. Wallington. – 6th ed. 2 vols. – London : Butterworths, 1987.
25cm.
This work is presented in two volumes containing narrative and precedents on wills in the United Kingdom. The book has been updated in the light of the Administration of Justice Act of 1982 and changes to the capital transfer tax.
ISBN 0406421978 £166
ISBN 0406421994

Williams, Marler M.
Law of Real Property : Quebec. – Repr. of 1932 ed. – Agincourt : Carswell, 1986.
686p.
This work originally published in 1932, is a detailed English language reference guide to the law of 'unmovable property' under the Quebec Civil Code. The book offers a basic understanding of the Quebec law of real property.
Hbk £59.00

Williams, Mortimer and Sunnucks on executors, administration and probate. – 16th ed. – London : Sweet & Maxwell, 1982.
ISBN 0420455000 Hbk £120.00

Williams, Mortimer and Sunnucks on executors, administrators and probate / by J.H.G. Sunnucks, J.G. Ross Martyn, K.M. Garnett. – London : Stevens & Sons, 1982.
clxxxviii,1157p; 26cm.
Concerned with probate practice and the work of executors and administrators, discussions of changes in the law of family provision, capital transfer tax and social security. Includes appendices which set out the relevant statutes, rules of court and statutory instruments.
ISBN 0420455000 £75.00

Williams, N.
Two Laws : Managing Disputes in a Contemporary Aboriginal Community. – Canberra City : Australian Institute of Aboriginal Studies, 1986.
176p.
ISBN 0855751746 Hbk £25.95

Williams, Neil J.
Civil Procedure, Victoria. – Butterworths.
Llf
—New Victorian Supreme Court Rules. – Butterworths, 1986.
184p.
ISBN 0409491551 Pbk £18.00
—Supreme Court Civil Procedure. – Butterworths, 1987.
442p.
ISBN 0409492183 Hbk £36
ISBN 0409492078 Pbk £29

Williams on Title
Nineteen Eighty-Three supplement only /. – London : Butterworths.
This text is a comprehensive treatment of the law of title in the United Kingdom. The work provides a thorough discussion of the subject from contract to completion. Extensive quotations from case law and analysis of principles of law are given throughout the text.
ISBN 0406421498 Pbk £33.50

Williams on wills / R F D Barlow, R A Wallington. – 6th ed. 2 vols. – London : Butterworths, 1987.
ISBN 0406421978 Hbk £175.00

Williams, Philip M. →Diary of Hugh Gaitskell, 1945-1956.

Williams, R.
Agricultural Valuations. – London : Estates Gazette, 1985.
ISBN 0728200872 Pbk £11.00

Williams, R.G.
Comprehensive Aspects of Taxation. – London : Cassell, 1988.
ISBN 0304314250 Pbk £17.95

Williams, Richard- →Limitation of liability for maritime claims.

Williams, Roland Lomax Vaughan →Muir Hunter on personal insolvency.

Williams, S.
Unit Trust Guide For Investors. – Cambridge : Woodhead-Faulkner.
ISBN 0859414019 Pbk £4.95

Williams, Sharon Anne
Canadian criminal law, international and transnational aspects / Sharon A. Williams, J.-G. Castel. – Toronto : Butterworths, 1981.
xxx, 513 p.; 24 cm.
Includes bibliographical references and indexes. Part one is devoted to jurisdiction and the criminal law under international law and Canadian law. Part two deals with Canadian law applicable to specific offences of an international and transnational nature. Part three covers international cooperation in the field of criminal law and criminal procedure.
ISBN 0409876348 £80.00
—Introduction to International Law / Armand L.C. de Mestral. – 2nd ed. – Butterworths, 1987.
472p.
Contains new material on the treaty-implementation power in Canada, recognition of foreign states and governments, sovereign immunity, the international protection of human rights, the international protection of the environment, the law of the sea, fisheries, international crimes, and extraterritoriality.
ISBN 0409875597 Pbk £70.00

Williams, Tony
Fighting Privatisation : The Victory in Gloucester. – London : Spokesman Books, 1984. – (IWC Pamphlet: No. 87).
ISBN 0901740861 Pbk £0.90

Williams, William J.
Williams' law relating to wills / C. H. Sherrin, R. F. D. Barlow, R. A. Wallington. – 6th ed. 2 vols. – London : Butterworths, 1987.
25cm.
This work is presented in two volumes containing narrative and precedents on wills in the United Kingdom. The book has been updated in the light of the Administration of Justice Act of 1982 and changes to the capital transfer tax.
ISBN 0406421978 £166
ISBN 0406421994

Williamson, O.
Antitrust Economics. – Oxford : Blackwell Scientific, 1987.
ISBN 0631153632 Hbk £32.50

Williman, Daniel
Legal Terminology : an Historical Guide to the Technical Language of Law. – Peterborough : Broadview Press Ltd., 1986.
192p.
ISBN 0921149026 Hbk £18.95

Willis
The Dealing Room : Getting Value for Money. – Online.
ISBN 0863531490 Pbk £75.00
—Law of Trespass / Birts. – London : Butterworths, 1987.
ISBN 040614816 Pbk £15.95

Willis, Alan → Law and Procedure.

Willis, Carole F. → Ethnic minorities and complaints against the police.
—Tape-recording of police interviews with suspects : an interim report / Carole F. Willis. – London : H.M.S.O., 1984.
v,39p.
Outlines background to field trials of tape recording police interviews. Reviews literature describing research methodologies used in trials. Discusses preliminary results of the research.
ISBN 0113407769
—Use, effectiveness and impact of police stop and search powers / Carole F. Willis. – London : Home Office, 1983.
v,40p.
Bibliography: p.32-33.
ISBN 0862520983

Willis, John → Australian and New Zealand Journal of Criminology.
→ Criminal justice in Australia.

Willis, Nigel
Banking in South African law / by Nigel Willis. – Cape Town : Juta, 1981.
xxxiii,388p.
Includes bibliographical notes and index.
ISBN 0702112593

Willis, Peter
Dissertation handbook : a guide to research and writing / by Peter Willis. – London : RIBA, 1983.
55p; 30cm.
ISBN 0900630868

Willis, Virginia
Britons in Brussels : Officials in the European Commission and Council Secretariat. – London : Policy Studies Institute, 1983.
ISBN 0853742170 Pbk £3.00

Willisch, Jan
State Responsibility for Technological Damage in International Law. – Berlin : Duncker and Humblot, 1987.
xxviii, 326p.
ISBN 3428062388 Hbk £136.00

Williston and Rolls : Court Forms, 2 Vols.
Vol. 1: 1987. – 2nd ed. – Butterworths.
ISBN 0409801836 Llf £150.00

Williston, R.B.
Conduct of an Action / R.J. Rolls. – Butterworths, 1982.
216p.
Examination of the legal and practical aspects of non-jury trials. Covers preparation, the brief, the course of the trial, nonsuit, examination in chief, cross-examination, re-examination, argument, and the rights and duties of judge and counsel at trial.
ISBN 0409877107 Hbk £50.00

Willman → Lloyd's Bank Tax Guide 1988-89.

Willmore, Jon → Victims in the criminal justice system.

Willmott, P.
Problems of public housing. – Policy Studies Institute, 1988.
ISBN 0853743509 Pbk £6.95

Willms, A. M. → Public administration in Canada : selected readings.

Willott, Robert → Tolley's focus on the purchase or redemption by a company of its own shares : a review of the tax and company law provisions.

Willoughby, Geoffrey → United Kingdom oil and gas law.

Willoughby, H M → Legal secretary's handbook.

Willoughby, P.G.
Hong Kong revenue law. – Matthew Bender, 1981.
ISBN 0000999046 Hbk £140.00

Wills / Edited by Clive Brand. – London : Longman Professional, 1988. – (Longman Practice Notes Series).
ISBN 085121410X Pbk

Wills : substantial compliance / the Law Reform Commission of Western Australia. – Perth : Law Reform Commission of Western Australia, 1984.
37p. – (Discussion paper).

Wills administration and taxation: a practical guide / Lesley King, Anthony King. – 3rd. – London : Sweet & Maxwell, 1988.
Covers substantive law, tax considerations, will drafting. The chapter dealing with inheritance tax has been updated to include the new rules introduced in the Finance Act 1986. Also covers the new provisions of the Insolvency Act 1986. The text is illustrated with worked examples.
ISBN 0421382708 Pbk £17.50

Wills and Estates. – 3rd ed. rev. ed. – Vancouver : Vancouver People's Law School.
39p : Illus.. – – (Public Legal Education Series).
ISBN 0888470304 Hbk £0.60

Wills and intestacy in Australia and New Zealand : being a revised and consolidated version of Hardingham, Neave and Ford's The Law of Wills and Hardingham's The Law of Intestate Succession in Australia and New Zealand / by I.J. Hardingham, M.A. Neave, H.A.J. Ford. – Sydney : Law Book Co., 1983.
xliv,518p.
Includes bibliographical references and index.
ISBN 0455204152

Wills Drafting 1983. – Vancouver : Continuing Legal Education Society of British Columbia, 1983.
204p.
ISBN 0865041288 Hbk £60.00

Wills for Alberta : How to Make Your Own Will. – 6th ed. – North Vancouver : International Self-Counsel Press, 1985.
108p.
ISBN 0889082294 Hbk £6.50

Wills for British Columbia : How to Make Your Own Will. – 13th ed. – North Vancouver : International Self-Counsel Press, 1988.
ISBN 0889084327 Hbk

Wills for Ontario : How to Make Your Own Will. – 8th ed. – North Vancouver : International Self-Counsel Press, 1986.
112p.
ISBN 0889083584 Hbk £5.95

Wills Longman Practice Notes Series. – London : Longman Professional.
ISBN 095121410X Pbk £10.95

Wills Practice. – Vancouver : Continuing Legal Education Society of British Columbia, 1986.
176p.
ISBN 0865042969 Hbk £65.00

Wills Precedents (Victoria) / N.B. Dowdle. – North Ryde : Law Book Co, 1986.
xvii, 144p.
ISBN 0455203067 Hbk £35.00

Wills Probate and Administration Service, New South Wales / L.G. Handler. – Butterworths, 1985.
ISBN 0409491314 Hbk

Wills, Probate and the Administration of the Estates of Deceased Persons in Victoria. – 2nd ed. – Butterworths, 1988.
272p.
ISBN 0409494747 Hbk £54.00
ISBN 0409338613 Pbk £35.00

Wills/Probate Procedure for Manitoba and Saskatchewan / Jane Gordon. – 3rd ed. – North Vancouver : International Self-Counsel Press, 1985.
81p.
ISBN 088908503X Hbk £5.95

Willy, A.A.P → High Court Forms.

Wilmot, T.
Inside the over-the-counter market. – Cambridge : Woodhead-Faulkner, 1985.
ISBN 08593413095 Hbk £25.00

Wilner, G.M.
International Law and Economic Development and Cooperation. – Dordrecht : Kluwer.
ISBN 9065441921

Wilson → Diefenbaker for the Defence.
→ House of Lords Appeals : 1821-1873, 28 Vols., 1825-1835, 7 Vols.
—Managerial Accounting : Method and Meaning / Chua. – London : VanNostrand Reinhold.
ISBN 00278000215 Pbk £14.95
—Managing Bank Assets and Liabilities. – London : Euromoney.
ISBN 1870031768 Hbk £75.00
—What Is A Pension. – Tolley Publishing.
ISBN 0854593349 Pbk £1.50
—Your new pensions choice / Davies. – 2nd ed. – Croydon : Tolley, 1988.
ISBN 0854593330 Hbk £2.95

Wilson, A. G.
Taxation of Transactions in Intellectual Property / W. G. S. Massey. – London : Sweet & Maxwell, 1982.
ISBN 042129390X Hbk

Wilson, Aubrey
Practice development for professional firms / Aubrey Wilson. – London : McGraw-Hill, 1984.
xvi,232p; 26cm.
Bibliography: p221-223. - Includes index.
ISBN 0070847614 £15.95

Wilson, Beth
National survey of law libraries in Australia / by Beth Wilson : supervised by E.J. Glasson ; prepared for the Australian Law Librarians' Group. – Sydney : Australian Law Librarian's Group, 1984.
xv, 479 p.; 31 cm.
Includes bibliographical references.
ISBN 0959135901 £39.95

Wilson, C.
Mammoth Book of True Crime. – Robinson Publishers.
ISBN 0948164700 Pbk £4.95

Wilson, Des
Secrets file : the case for freedom of information in Britain today / Des Wilson. – London : Heinemann Educational Books, 1984.
viii,(2),166p.
Bibliography: p59.
ISBN 0435839403

Wilson, Duncan → Modern public records : selection and access : report of a committee appointed by the Lord Chancellor.

Wilson, Frances
New Zealand Law Reports. – Butterworths.
Hbk £187.50

Wilson, G.
Beat Officer's Companion. – 2nd ed. – Police Review, 1986.
ISBN 0851640249 Pbk £4.25
—Traffic officer's companion. – 3rd ed. – Police Review, 1987.
ISBN 0851640273 Pbk £4.25

Wilson, Garrett
Diefenbaker for the Defence / Wilson. – Toronto : James Lorimer & Co, 1988.
250p.
ISBN 1550281046 Hbk £24.95

Wilson, Gordon
Beat Officer's Companion. – London : Police Review Publishing, 1983.
ISBN 0851640036 Pbk £3.25
—Traffic Officer's Companion. – London : Police Review Publishing, 1982.
ISBN 0851649955 Pbk £2.75

Wilson, Harriet
4 what it's worth / Harriet Wilson. – London : Thames, 1988.
192p; 20cm.
Includes index.
ISBN 0356148629 Pbk £5.95

Wilson, Heather A.
International law and the use of force by national liberation movements / Heather A. Wilson. – Oxford : Clarendon, 1988.
208p; 24cm.
Includes bibliography and index.
ISBN 0198255705 Hbk £25.00

Wilson, J.F.
Carriage of Goods by Sea. – Pitman.
ISBN 0273029878 Pbk £15.95
—Second Survey of Legal Education in the United Kingdom : Supplement No. 2 / S. B. Marsh. – London : Institute of Advanced Legal Studies, 1981.
ISBN 090119025X Hbk £2.00

Wilson, J.N.
Contractors' Liens and Charges. – 2nd ed. – London : Butterworths, 1981.
ISBN 0409676004 Hbk £15.80

Wilson, J.R. → Ontario Estate Practice.

Wilson, James
Canada's Indians / by James Wilson. – Rev. ed. – London : Minority Rights Group, 1982.
20p. – (Report).
Previous ed.: 1977. Bibliography: p.20.
—Original Americans : U.S. Indians / by James Wilson. – New ed. – London : Minority Rights Group, 1986.
24p. – (Report).
Previous edition: 1980. Bibliography: p.24.
ISBN 0946690391

Wilson, Jeffery →Ontario Family Law Reports.
—Wilson: children and the law / Mary Tomlinson. – A completely rev. and re-written 2nd ed. – Toronto : Butterworths, 1986.
liii,505p.
Includes bibliographies and index.
ISBN 040987762X

Wilson, Larry C.
Juvenile courts in Canada / by Larry C. Wilson. – Toronto, Canada : Carswell, 1982.
xx, 272 p.; 24 cm.
Includes index. 'Table of cases': p. vii-xx.
ISBN 0459352709

Wilson, Margaret A. →Sexual violence : a case for law reform : papers presented at seminar, University of Auckland, 27 August 1982.
→ Women and the Law in New Zealand.

Wilson, P.A.
Petroleum Taxation Law. – Glenside : Australian Mineral Foundation, 1985.
Hbk £40.00

Wilson, Paul →Australian Criminal Justice System : The Mid 1980's.

Wilson, R., et al
Primary Sector Taxation. – Butterworths, 1987.
Pbk

Wilson, R B
Criminal law / Brian Harrie KevinB.H.K. Donovan. – North Ryde : Law Book Co, 1984.
xiv, 98p. – (Nutshells).
ISBN 0455203458 Hbk

Wilson, Thelma →Panel services for offenders : comparative studies of England and Poland 1984/85.

Wilson, W. A. →Introduction to the law of Scotland.
—Introductory essays on Scots law / by W.A. Wilson. – 2nd ed. – Edinburgh : Green, 1984.
ix,156p; 21cm.
Previous ed.: 1978. Includes index.
ISBN 0414007298 Pbk
—Law of Scotland relating to debt / W.A. Wilson. – Edinburgh : Green (W.) & Son, 1982.
lxxvii,380p; 22cm.
Deals with ways in which debts arise out of common transactions such as sale and hire purchase, debt recovery and defences such as payment and compensation. Full treatment of relevant sections of the Consumer Credit Act 1974, with discussion of securities, diligence, insolvency and documents on debt. Includes index.
ISBN 0414006828 Pbk
→ Trusts and trust-like devices.

Wilson: children and the law / Mary Tomlinson. – A completely rev. and re-written 2nd ed. – Toronto : Butterworths, 1986.
liii,505p.
Includes bibliographies and index.
ISBN 040987762X

Wilton, A. M. →Law of supplementary benefits.

Wiltshire, J. A. →Regulation of insurance in the United Kingdom and Ireland.

Wily, E. H. J. →High Court Forms.

Wily, Heather J
District Court Practice / J. S. Crutchley. – 8th ed. – Wellington : Butterworths, 1981.
ISBN 0409600466 Hbk

Winch, Donald →That noble science of politics : a study in nineteenth-century intellectual history.

Winchester, Stuart
Residential burglary : the limits of prevention / by Stuart Winchester and Hilary Jackson. – London : H.M.S.O., 1982.
v,42p; 25cm.
Bibliography: p40-42. 'A Home Office Research and Planning Unit report'.
ISBN 0113407696

Winding up and receivership under the Companies Act 1981 / by James O'Donovan. – Sydney : Law Book Co., 1982.
xix,48p.
ISBN 0455204438

Winding up of companies in Northern Ireland : a practitioner's guide / by John M. Hunter. – Belfast : SLS Legal Publications, 1984.
xxxvi,142p.
Bibliography: p.135. - Includes index.
ISBN 0853892482

Winding up of insolvent companies in England and France / Christopher Livadas. – Deventer, Netherlands : Kluwer Law and Taxation Publishers, 1983.
xxxvi, 384 p.; 25 cm.
: Originally presented as the author's thesis (Ph.D.–City of London Polytechnic, 1981). Bibliography: p. 383-384.
ISBN 9065440879

Winding Up Trusts. – North Ryde : C.C.H. Australia, 1984.
225p.
ISBN 0869034677 Hbk £50.00

Winding-up and bankruptcy procedures. – Shaws Linton Publications, 1988.
ISBN 0906653142 Hbk £12.95

Windlesham, David James George Hennessy
Responses to crime / Lord Windlesham. – Oxford : Clarendon, 1987.
xviii,357p; 24cm.
Includes index.
ISBN 0198255837 £17.95

Windmuller, J. P. →Collective bargaining in industrialised market economies : a reappraisal.

Windsor, Roderick S.W.
Annotated Insurance Act of Ontario / Harry B. Radomski. – Butterworths, 1987.
704p.
Contains summary and analysis of the law under each section of the Act, traces the legislative history of each section to the present, defines problem wording and terms, directing the reader to all possible interpretations, and covers several thousand relevant cases from all Canadian jurisdictions.
ISBN 0409811440 Hbk £120.00

Windsor yearbook of access to justice / Recueil annuel de Windsor d'acces a la justice. – Windsor, Ontario : University of Windsor, 1981.

Wine, Humphrey
Buying and selling private companies and businesses / Humphrey Wine. – 3rd ed. – London : Butterworths, 1986.
260p; 23cm.
Previous ed.: 1983. Includes index.
ISBN 0406424187 Pbk £22.50

Winfield and Jolowicz on tort / John Anthony Jolowicz, W. V. H. Rogers. – 12th ed. – London : Sweet & Maxwell, 1984.
lxiii,767p; 26cm.
Previous ed.: 1979. Includes index.
ISBN 0421325801 Hbk £28.00
ISBN 0421325909 Pbk £17.50

Winfield, Percy Harry
Winfield and Jolowicz on tort / John Anthony Jolowicz, W. V. H. Rogers. – 12th ed. – London : Sweet & Maxwell, 1984.
lxiii,767p; 26cm.
Previous ed.: 1979. Includes index.
ISBN 0421325801 Hbk £28.00
ISBN 0421325909 Pbk £17.50

Wingate, E.
Exact Abridgment of All Statutes : Magna Carta, 1641-1666. – 3rd ed. – Abingdon : Professional Books.
566p.
Hbk £45.00

Winiata, Whatarangi →Mergers and takeovers : legal and financial issues : written proceedings of a seminar, 29 August 1985.

Winsor, T.P. →The Joint Operating Agreement : oil and gas law.

Winston, W.
Petroleum Law 1985. – London : Applied Science.
ISBN 0853343314 Hbk £25.00

Winters, L. Alan
International economics / Sidney J. Wells. – 3rd ed. – London : Allen & Unwin, 1985.
xxiii,369p; 25cm.
Previous ed.: by Sidney J. Wells. 1973. Bibliography: p343-362. - Includes index.
ISBN 0043303498 Hbk £20.00
ISBN 0043303501 Pbk £9.95

Winterton, George
Monarchy to republic : Australian republican government / George Winterton. – Melbourne : Oxford University Press, 1986.
xi, 211 p.; 23 cm.
Includes index. Bibliography: p. 192-194.
ISBN 019554563X
—Parliament, the executive, and the governor-general : a constitutional analysis / George Winterton. – Carlton, Vic. : Melbourne University Press, 1983.
viii, 376 p.; 23 cm.
Includes index. Bibliography: p. 329-346.
ISBN 0522842429

Winyard, Steve →Case for a national minimum wage.

Wionczek, Miguel S.
Some key issues for the world periphery : selected essays / by Miguel S. Wionczek. – Oxford : Pergamon, 1982.
xiv,432p; 24cm.
Includes bibliographies and index.
ISBN 0080257836 £37.50

WIPO Glossary of Terms of the Law of Copyright and Neighboring Rights
Terms and Definitions in English, in Alphabetical Order with Equivalencies in French and Arabic. – Geneva : World Intellectual Property Organization, 1981.
281p.
Hbk £40.00 ea.
Terms and Definitions in English, in Alphabetical Order, with Equivalencies in French and Japanese. – 1986.
283p.
Hbk
Terms and Definitions in English, in Alphabetical Order, with Equivalencies in French and Portuguese. – 1983.
281p.
Hbk

WIPO International Forum on the Collective Administration of Copyrights and Neighboring Rights. – Geneva : World Intellectual Property Organization, 1986.
122p.
Hbk £15.00

WIPO Worldwide Forum on the Piracy of Broadcasts and of the Printed Word. – Geneva : World Intellectual Property Organization, 1983.
ca 240p.
Hbk £25.00

WIPO Worldwide Forum on the Piracy of Sound and Audiovisual Recordings, Geneva (1981). – Geneva : World Intellectual Property Organization.
240p.
Hbk £25.00

Wiretaps and Conspiracy. – Vancouver : British Columbia Continuing Legal Education Society, 1981.
127p.
ISBN 0865040370 Hbk £40.00

Wirsing, Robert G.
Baluchis and Pathans / by Robert G. Wirsing. – Rev & updated ed. – London : Minority Rights Group, 1987.
23p. – (Report).
Previous ed.: 1981. Bibliography: p.20.
ISBN 0946690510

Wirtschaftsverkehr
Arbitration in U.S.-German Business Relations : Schiedsgerichtsbarkeit im deutsch-amerikanischen / Karl-Heinz Bockstiegel. – Cologne : Carl Heymanns Verlag, 1985.
vi, 287p.
ISBN 3452202577 Pbk £230.00

Wisdom, A. S.
Aspects of water law / by A.S. Wisdom. – Chichester : Rose (Barry), 1981.
xxi,102p; 21cm.
Includes index.
ISBN 0859921549 Pbk £12.50
—Law and Management of Water Resources and Supply / L. Skeet. – London : Shaw & Sons, 1981.
ISBN 0721909108 Pbk £16.00

Wishart, Linda →Consumer affairs : a select bibliography.

With a Bang, Not a Whimper. – Don Mills : Stoddart Publishing Co, 1988.
ISBN 0773752463 Hbk £12.95

Witherby
Reference book of marine insurance clauses. – 58th ed. – London : Witherby & Co, 1986.
ISBN 0948691182 Pbk £18.00

Witherby dictionary of insurance. – 2nd ed. – London : Witherby & Co, 1987.
ISBN 0948691212 Hbk £14.50

Withers, J.
Marketing Your Service. – North Vancouver : International Self-Counsel Press, 1987.
ISBN 0889086540 Hbk £12.95

Without the law : administrative justice and legal pluralism in nineteenth-century England / H. W. Arthurs. – Toronto : University of Toronto Press, 1985.
xvi,312p; 24cm.
ISBN 0802056547

Witness of war crimes in Lebanon / testimony given to the Nordic Commission, Oslo, October 1982. – London : EAFORD, 1983.
xviii,146p; 22cm.
ISBN 0863720056 Pbk £4.50

Witnesses in the criminal courts : a report / by Justice : chairman of committee Peter Crawford. – London : Justice, 1986.
25p.
ISBN 0907247067

Witt, J.
101 Plus Uses Of A Police Helmet. – Police Review, 1985.
ISBN 0851640192 Pbk £1.95
—Plodding . – Police Review, 1986.
ISBN 0851640257 Pbk £1.95

Wives and Property : Reform of the Married Women's Property Law in Nineteenth-Century England. – Toronto : University of Toronto Press, 1982.
ISBN 0802055737 Hbk £35.00
ISBN 0802064760 Pbk £12.50

Wives and property : reform of the married women's property law in nineteenth-century England / Lee Holcombe. – Oxford : Martin Robertson, 1983.
viii,311p; 24cm.
Bibliography: p275-292. - Includes index.
ISBN 0855206071 £15.00

Woellner, R.H. →Powers of Investigation in Revenue, Companies and Trade Practices Law.

Woffinden, Bob
Miscarriages of justice / Bob Woffinden. – London : Hodder & Stoughton, 1987.
xiii,376p; 24cm.
Bibliography: p367. - Includes index.
ISBN 0340374209 £14.95

Wolchover, David
Exclusion of improperly obtained evidence : with special reference to the Police and Criminal Evidence Act / by David Wolchover. – Chichester : Barry Rose, 1986.
v,260p.
Includes bibliographical references and index.
ISBN 0859923800

Wolcott, Ilene
Workers with family responsibilities : implications for employers / Ilene Wolcott. – Melbourne : Australian Institute of Family Studies, 1987.
vii,62p. – (Discussion paper).
Includes bibliographical references.
ISBN 0642110212

Wolfe
Rules of Civil Procedure : A Guide for Legal Secretaries and Law Clerks. – Toronto : Butterworths, 1985.
196p.
Summarizes and explains the various sections of the Courts of Justice Act and the new Rules. Contains special chapters on divorce, family law, and mortgage action proceedings.
ISBN 0409810304 Pbk £24.95

Wolff, A →Legal aspects of business transactions and investment in the Far East.

Wolfrum, Rudiger →International Law and Municipal Law : Proceedings of the German-Soviet Colloquy on International Law at the Institut fur Internationales Recht an der Universitat Kiel 4 to 8 May 1987.

Wolstenholme, Peter H →Taxation of Lloyd's Underwriters.
—Tolley's focus on the purchase or redemption by a company of its own shares : a review of the tax and company law provisions / by Peter Wolstenholme, Robert Willott. – Croydon : Tolley, 1982.
x,93p.
Includes index.
ISBN 0854590935

Woman and the Law. – New Delhi : Intellectual Book Corner, 1985.
xii, 228p.
Hbk £130.00

Woman in Shari'ah (Islamic law) / Abdur Rahman I. Doi. – s.l. : s.n., 1983.
286p.
Bibliography: pp.267-281. - Includes index.

Woman's role in economic development / Ester Boserup. – Aldershot : Gower, 1986.
283p.
Originally published: George Allen & Unwin, 1970. Bibliography: pp.263-275. - Includes index. Published in association with the London School of Economics and Political Science.
ISBN 0566051397

Women against violence against women / edited by dusty rhodes and Sandra McNeill. – London : Onlywomen Press, 1985.
280p.
ISBN 0906500168

Women and children first : the legal obligation to make provision on death for family and dependants / lecture delivered to the Belfast Solicitors' Association by Norma Dawson. – Belfast : SLS Legal Publications, 1984.
45p.
Bibliography: p.46.

Women and crime / Frances Heidensohn. – Basingstoke : Macmillan, 1985.
xii,216p; 23cm.
Bibliography: p201-213. - Includes index.
ISBN 0333362160 Hbk £20.00
ISBN 0333362179 Pbk £6.95

Women and crime : papers presented to the 13th Cropwood Round Table Conference, December 1980 / edited by Allison Morris with the assistance of Loraine Gelsthorpe. – Cambridge : University of Cambridge Institute of Criminology, 1981.
iii,141p.
Includes bibliographical references.

Women and harassment at work. – Pluto Press, 1983.
ISBN 086104729X Pbk £3.95

Women and Insurance. – Pandora Press.
ISBN 004440378X Pbk £3.50

Women and legal affairs / a paper jointly prepared by Mariam Denton, Amie Bensouda, Fola Mendy Allen. – Banjul, the Gambia? : s.n., 1985.
10p.
At head of cover title: The Gambia National Women's Council and Bureau. Cover title: End of Women's Decade Conference on Women in Development, 24th-26th April 1985.

Women and men in Britain : a research profile / Equal Opportunities Commission. – London : HMSO, 1988.
79p.
Bibliography: pp.74-76. - Includes index.
ISBN 0117013897

Women and men in Britain : a statistical profile. – London : H.M.S.O., 1986.
45p.
ISBN 0117012955

Women and sexual offences in South Africa / South African Law Commission. – Pretoria : The Commission, 1985.
xvi.,200p. – (Report).
Bibliography: p.vii-xvi.
ISBN 0621096091 Hbk

Women and the constitution in Canada / edited by Audrey Doerr and Micheline Carrier. – Ottawa : Canadian Advisory Council on the Status of Women, 1981.
x,223p.
Includes bibliographical notes. Contains papers prepared for Canadian Advisory Council on the Status of Women conference scheduled for September 1980.
ISBN 0660108720

Women and the law / edited by Sue McLaughlin. – London : Faculty of Laws, University College London, 1987.
75p. – (Working papers).
Includes bibliographical references.

Women and the law / Susan Atkins and Brenda Hoggett. – Oxford : Basil Blackwell, 1984.
234p; 24cm.
Includes index.
ISBN 0855201819 Hbk £17.50
ISBN 0855201800 Pbk

Women and the law / Norma Monica Forde. – Cave Hill, Barbados : Institute of Social and Economic Research, University of the West Indies, 1981.
x,125p.
Includes bibliographies.

Women and the Law in New Zealand / Margaret A Wilson. – Birkenhead : Reed Methuen.
120p.
ISBN 0456029907 Pbk £8.95

Women and the New Law. – Patiala : Punjab University, Publication Bureau.
Hbk £50.00

Women and Work : Inequality in the Labour Market / Erin Phillips. – Toronto : Lorimer & Co, 1983.
– (Canadian Issues Ser.).
ISBN 0888626088 Hbk £15.95
ISBN 088862607X Pbk £6.95

Women as Participants In the Criminal Justice System. – Canberra : Australian Institute of Criminology.
free

Women as Victims of Crimes. – Canberra : Australian Institute of Criminology.
free

Women, crime and criminal justice / Allison Morris. – Oxford : Basil Blackwell, 1987.
256p; 23cm.
Considers all aspects of women and crime including women as defendants and prisoners, as victims and as criminal justice professionals.
ISBN 0631154442 Hbk £25.00 :
ISBN 0631154450 Pbk £7.95

Women employment and European law. – Oxford : Eclipse, 1988.
ISBN 1870771001 Hbk £25.00

Women in Asia / edited by Rounaq Jahan. – Rev. ed. – London : Minority Rights Group, 1982.
24p. – (Report).
Previous ed.: 1980. Includes bibliographical notes.

Women in Canadian Law. – Markham : Fitzhenry and Whiteside.
96p.
ISBN 0889023778 Pbk £4.95

Women in law / Carol Smart. – Routledge, 1985.
ISBN 0710202598 Pbk £7.50
ISBN 0710206070 Hbk £19.95

Women in sub-Saharan Africa / Edda Ivan-Smith, Nidhi Tandon and Jane Connors. – London : Minority Rights Group, 1988.
18p. – (Report).
Includes bibliographical references.
ISBN 094669057X

Women in the penal system / by Baroness Seear and Elaine Player : report prepared for the Howard League for Penal Reform. – London : Howard League for Penal Reform, 1986.
20p.

Women on trial : a study of the female suspect, defendant and offender in the criminal law and criminal justice system / Susan S.M. Edwards. – Manchester : Manchester University Press, 1984.
1v.
Bibliography: p227-236. - Includes index.
ISBN 0719009952 £14.50

Women, power and political systems / edited by Margherita Rendel with the assistance of Georgina Ashworth. – London : Croom Helm, 1981.
262p; 23cm.
Includes bibliographies and index.
ISBN 0709922043 £12.95

Women Prisoners In Victoria : A Review of the Nature and Size of Facilities Needed. – Canberra : Australian Institute of Criminology.
Hbk £4.50

Women, the Law and the Economy / Mahoney. – Toronto : Butterworths, 1985.
414p.
ISBN 0409988650 Pbk £31.95

Women won't benefit : the impact of the Social Security Bill on women's rights / Hilary Land and Sue Ward. – London : National Council for Civil Liberties. Rights for Women Unit, 1986.
48p.
ISBN 0946088268

Women-in-law : explorations in law, family and sexuality / edited by Julia Brophy and Carol Smart. – London : Routledge & Kegan Paul, 1985.
x,219p.
ISBN 0710202598

Women's Economic Equality Act, 1983, Bill 108 : An Act to Provide for Affirmative Action and Equal Pay for Work of Equal Value. – Ontario : Ontario Government Publications Service, 1983.
11p.
Hbk £0.50

Women's imprisonment : a study in social control / Pat Carlen. – London : Routledge & K. Paul, 1983.
viii,248p.
Includes index. Bibliography: p240-245.
ISBN 0710094418

Women's Law : an introduction to feminist jurisprudence / Tove Stang Dahl : translated by Ronald L. Craig. – Oslo : Norwegian University Press, 1987.
195p; 23cm.
A theoretical introduction, and a discussion of three areas within women's law; the legal situation affecting housewives, paid workers, and women as recipients of social security benefits.
ISBN 8200184900 £20.00

Women's National Commission
Homelessness among women : report of an Ad Hoc Working Group, Women's National Commission / Norma Nelson. – London : Cabinet Office, 1983.
56p; 30cm.
Report prepared under the chairmanship of Norma Nelson.
—Report on secondary education / by an ad-hoc working group of the Women's National Commission. – London : Women's National Commission, 1983.

Women's rights : a practical guide / Anna Coote and Tess Gill : drawings by Posy Simmonds. – 3rd ed. – Harmondsworth : Penguin, 1981.
555p; 20cm.
Previous ed.: 1977. Includes index.
ISBN 0140465324 Pbk £3.95

Women's rights at work : campaigns and policy in Britain and the United States / Elizabeth M. Meehan. – Basingstoke : Macmillan, 1985.
xvii,253p; 22cm.
Bibliography: p227-241. - Includes index.
ISBN 0333361253 Hbk £
ISBN 0333361261 Pbk £5.95

Womens Rights in Ireland. – Dublin, 1983.
223p.
ISBN 0907085687 Pbk £4.95

Wong, G.M.
Essentials of Amateur Sports Law. – London : Eurospan.
ISBN 0865691312 Hbk £30.95

Wong, Rebecca Kit Lin
Survey of the complaint-handling institutions in Hong Kong / by Rebecca Wong Kit Lin. – Edmonton : International Ombudsman Institute, 1983.
19 leaves. – (Occasional paper).

Wong, Steven G.
Wills for British Columbia : How to Make Your Own Will. – 13th ed. – North Vancouver : International Self-Counsel Press, 1988.
ISBN 0889084327 Hbk

Wontner
Guide to Land Registry Practice / Timothy. – 16th ed. – London : Longman Professional, 1985.
ISBN 0851212840 Pbk £19.95

Wood
CIMA Stage 2 Financial Accounting / Anderson. – Pitman.
ISBN 0273028626 Pbk £11.95
—Finance / Townsley. – London : Pitman Publishing, 1986.
ISBN 0273025872 Pbk £6.95
→ Industrial law.
—JCT Agreement For Minor Building Works. – Spon (E & FN).
ISBN 0728200767 Pbk £15.00

Wood, Chris →Social work and criminal law in Scotland.

Wood, Christopher →Planning and pollution : an examination of the role of land use planning in the protection of environmental quality.

Wood, D.
Basic Construction and Surveying Law. – Oxford : Blackwell Scientific, 1984.
ISBN 0246119632 Pbk £10.95
—Casebook on Profesional Negligence. – Oxford : Blackwell Scientific, 1988.
ISBN 0003834182 Hbk £30.00

Wood, F.
Business Accounting
Vol 1. – 4th ed. – Pitman, 1984.
ISBN 0582412427 Pbk £7.50
—Chartered Association of Certified Accountants Accounting. – Pitman.
ISBN 0273027956 Pbk £11.95

Wood, H.
Collection of Decrees by the Court of Exchequer (1650-1798) in Tithe Causes, 4 Vols. – Repr. of 1799 ed. – Abingdon : Professional Books.
197p.
Hbk £30.00

Wood, J., et al
Psychiatric Issues in Criminal Law. – Vancouver : British Columbia Continuing Legal Education Society, 1982.
ISBN 0865040826 Hbk £45.00

Wood, John →Encyclopedia of Northern Ireland labour law and practice.

Wood, John C. →Elliott and Wood's casebook on criminal law.
→ Industrial law.

Wood, M. C. →Legal status of Berlin.

Wood, P.
International Banking Set-Off. – London : Sweet & Maxwell.
ISBN 0421324503 Pbk
—Law of Set-Off. – London : Sweet & Maxwell, 1988.
ISBN 0421324503 Pbk

Wood, P. R. →Encyclopaedia of banking law.

Wood, R. D.
Builder's Claims Under the JCT Form of Contract. – King's Ride : Institute of Building, 1983.
46p.
Hbk £4.00
—Building and Civil Engineering Claims. – 3rd ed. – London : Estates Gazette, 1985.
ISBN 0728200775 Hbk £26.00
—Contractor's Claims Under the GC-Works-1 : Edition 2 Form of Contract. – King's Ride : Institute of Building, 1986.
68p.
ISBN 0906600855 Hbk £7.75

Wood, Roderick J. →Handbook on the Saskatchewan Personal Property Security Act.

Woodcock, C.
Guardian Guide to running a Small Business. – London : Kogan Page, 1986.
ISBN 1850910952 Pbk £6.95

Woodfall
Law Landlord and Tenant
Service 1988 / Wellings. – 28th ed. – Sweet & Maxwell, 1978.
ISBN 0421228202 Hbk £255.00

Woodhead
Financial Services Act: Index / Faulkner. – Cambridge : Woodhead-Faulkner, 1986.
ISBN 0859413888 Hbk £16.50

Woodhead, D.K. →Regulation of Building Standards Queensland.

Woodhouselee →Decisions of the Court of Session : Abridged in Form of a Dictionary.

Woodley, John M →Hughes and Woodley on patents.

Woodley, M. G. →Introduction to law.

Woodman, Gordon R. →Ollennu's principles of customary land law in Ghana.
→ People's law and state law : the Bellagio papers.

Woodman, R.A. →Cases and Materials on Succession.
—Law of Real Property in New South Wales. – North Ryde : Law Book Co.
xli, 372p.
ISBN 0455202397 Hbk £38.00

Woodroffe, G. F. →Consumer law and practice.
—Consumer Law in the EEC. – London : Sweet & Maxwell, 1984.
ISBN 0421326409 Pbk £10.00
—Goods and services - the new law / by Geoffrey F. Woodroffe. – London : Sweet & Maxwell, 1982.
xviii,164p; 22cm.
Includes index.
ISBN 0421302003 Pbk £9.85
→ Service please : services and the law : a consumer view.

Woods →BAC Business Law.

Woods, Gerald
Highlights of federal initiatives in criminal justice, 1966- 1980 / prepared by Gerald Woods and Heather Sim. – Ottawa : Research Division, Ministry of the Solicitor General of Canada, 1981.
vii,78p.
Bibliography: p.71-78.
ISBN 0662118294

Woods, James A.
Cases and materials on civil procedure / by James A. Woods. – Toronto : Carswell, 1987.
xviii,838p.
ISBN 0459306618

Woods, Judith M. →Business Law.

Woods, Patrick J.
Guidebook to Civil Claims in New South Wales. – North Ryde : C.C.H. Australia, 1986.
470p.
ISBN 0869039865 Hbk £38.00

Woodward, Allan
Forensic Psychologists. – Canberra : Australian Institute of Criminology.
free

Wooldridge, Frank
Administration procedure / Frank Wooldridge. – Bristol : Jordans, 1987.
xxii,113p; 21cm.
Includes index.
ISBN 0853081247 Pbk £8.50
→ Company law in the European Communities.
—Groups of companies : the law and practice in Britain, France and Germany / by Frank Wooldridge. – London : Institute of Advanced Legal Studies, 1981.
xxvi,159p; 21cm.
Includes bibliographical references.
ISBN 0901190268

Woolf, Emile →Advanced taxation.
—Executorship and Trust Law and Accounts / Suresh Tanna. – Plymouth : Macdonald & Evans, 1985.
360p. – (M and E Professional Studies Ser.).
ISBN 0712104585 Hbk £13.95
—Executorship/Trust Law and Accounts. – 2nd ed. – London : Pitman Publishing, 1986.
ISBN 0712107517 Pbk £14.95
→ Law.
—Legal Liabilities of Practising Accountants. – London : Butterworths, 1984.
The unprecedented increase in professional liability for accountants and the new legal standards for auditing, accounting and taxation practice are discussed. Oriented to the private practitioner, this book gives practical approaches to minimizing the risk of professional liability.
ISBN 0406259607 Pbk £28.00
—Regulatory Framework of Accounting / Suresh Tanna. – Plymouth : Macdonald & Evans, 1985.
320p. – (M and E Professional Studies Ser.).
Hbk £13.95
→ Taxation.

Woolley, Penny →Social relations and human attributes.

Woolman, S
Introduction to the Scots law of contract. – Edinburgh : Green (W.) & Son, 1987.
An introduction to the basic principles at student level.
ISBN 0414008197 Pbk

Woon, Walter C M →Annotation of the Singapore Companies Act.
—Commercial law of Singapore : an introduction / Walter C.M. Woon. – Cambridge : Woodhead-Faulkner, 1986.
256p; 23cm.
Includes bibliography and index.
ISBN 0859412814 £45.00

Wootton, Barbara
Crime and the criminal law : reflections of a magistrate and social scientist / by Barbara Wootton. – 2nd ed. – London : Stevens, 1981.
xii,119p; 19cm.
Previous ed.: 1963.
ISBN 0420461701 Hbk £
ISBN 0420461809 Pbk £5.00

Worcester, John Leslie
Land Transfer Conveyancing Kit. – Nunawading : Harrison-Ede Book Publishing.
Hbk £20.00

Words and Phrases, 4 Vols.
Individual vols. – Toronto : DeBoo.
Hbk £40.00

Words and Phrases Legally Defined. – 3rd ed. – Butterworths, 1988-89.
Supplement-1988. –
ISBN 0409888486
Vol. 1. –
450p.
ISBN 0409888443 Hbk £75.00
Vol. 2. –
ISBN 0409888451
Vol. 3. –
ISBN 040988846X
Vol. 4. –
The definitions comprise direct quotations from statutes, judicial statements and Halsbury's Laws of England. Also includes materials from Canadian sources. Approximately 700 Canadian entries, with 385 recently decided cases. Also contains extracts from American sources in commercial law areas.
ISBN 0409888478

Wordsall, A.
Consumer Law for the Motor Trade. – 2nd ed. – London : Butterworths, 1987.
ISBN 0406425914 Pbk £13.95

Work and organisation of the legal profession / presented to Parliament by the Lord High Chancellor by Command of Her Majesty, January 1989. – London : HMSO, 1989.
iv,72p.
ISBN 0101057024

Work of the Commissioner for Local Administration in Scotland, 1975-1983 / by Ken Bratton. – Edmonton, Alta. : International Ombudsman Institute, 1984.
78p. – (Occasional paper).

Work out accounting / Kriefman. – London : Macmillan, 1988.
ISBN 0333451244 Pbk £6.50

Workable government? : Constitution after 200 years. – Norton (WH), 1988.
ISBN 0393024806 Hbk £14.95
ISBN 0393304310 Pbk £7.50

Workbook in accounting / Caldicott. – 3rd ed. – London : Butterworths, 1981.
ISBN 0408106808 Pbk £10.50

Workbook on Estates and Future Interests. – Agincourt : Carswell, 1987.
130p.
Discussions include a review of the common law in its present form as it relates to property law, a survey of the rules set in textual format, and a quick review of the subject matter from the advanced reader. This text has been written from use with a first year property text.
Pbk £12.50

Workbook On Financial Accounting. – 1st ed. – Tolley Publishing.
ISBN 0854592652 Hbk £10.95

Workbook On Statistics. – Tolley Publishing.
ISBN 0854592342 Hbk £9.95

Worker and the law / Lord Wedderburn. – 3rd ed. – London : Sweet & Maxwell, 1986.
xiv,1026p.
Traces the developing relationship between the worker and the law, by analysis of the employment relationship, job security and dismissal, industrial conflict and the law, and trade unions and their members. Seeks to show the patterns which run through labour law.
ISBN 0421370602

Worker-controlled businesses and the law. – Spokesman Books, 1988.
ISBN 0851244521 Hbk £25.00
ISBN 0851244629 Pbk £8.95

Worker-directors in private manufacturing industry in Great Britain / Brian Towers, Derek Cox, Elizabeth Chell. – London : Department of Employment, 1987.
34p. – (Research paper).
Bibliography: p33-34.

Workers and the new depression / Robert Taylor. – London : Macmillan, 1982.
x,212p; 23cm.
Includes index.
ISBN 0333192958 Hbk
ISBN 0333334116 Pbk

Workers' Children Ordinance 1972 / Javed Altaf. – Lahore : Pakistan Law Times.
Hbk

Workers' Compensation. – Vancouver : Continuing Legal Education Society of British Columbia, 1988.
474p.
ISBN 0865049939 Hbk £85.00

Workers' Compensation in Canada. – Butterworths, 1983.
208p.
Hbk £43.95

Workers' compensation in Canada / by Terence G. Ison. – Toronto : Butterworths, 1983.
xxvii,179p.
Includes index.
ISBN 040984005X

Workers' Compensation in Ontario. – Butterworths, 1987.
256p.
Guide to matters falling within the jurisdiction of the Ontario Workers' Compensation Board. Deals with practice and procedure of the Board as they currently exist, and makes reference to various published documents of the WCB on issues of policy and procedure. Section examines the availability of civil actions.
ISBN 0409804908 Hbk £80.00

Workers' Compensation Law and Practice in New South Wales. – North Ryde : C.C.H. Australia, 1983.
309p.
ISBN 0869033484 Hbk

Workers' compensation legislation in Australia 1980 / Department of Social Security. – Canberra : Australian Government Publishing Service, 1981.
ix,100p.
Previously published as: 'Conspectus of workers' compensation legislation in Australia as at 1 January 19–'.

Workers Compensation, New South Wales. – Butterworths, 1987.
ISBN 0409492868 Hbk £210.00

Workers' Compensation Practice and Procedure. – Vancouver : British Columbia Continuing Legal Education Society, 1982.
265p.
ISBN 086504063X Hbk £50.00

Workers' Compensation Practice Guide / Newhouse. – London : Butterworths.
ISBN 0409804908 Hbk £64.00

Workers' management in Yugoslavia : recent developments and trends / edited by Najdan Pasic, Stanislav Grozdanic, Milorad Radevic. – Geneva : International Labour Office, 1982.
viii, 198 p.; 24 cm.
ISBN 9221030342 hard £25.00

Workers' participation in the European Community : the fifth directive / R. Blanpain, J. L. Janssen van Raay, A. Mouty. – Deventer : Kluwer, 1984.
ix,294p.
ISBN 9065441875

Workers' Rights Versus the Secret Police. – Sydney : Pathfinder Press.
46p.
Hbk £1.00

Workers Welfare Fund Ordinance. – Karachi : Bureau of Labour Publications, 1986.
Pbk £2.00

Workers with family responsibilities : implications for employers / Ilene Wolcott. – Melbourne : Australian Institute of Family Studies, 1987.
vii,62p. – (Discussion paper).
Includes bibliographical references.
ISBN 0642110212

Workforce reductions in undertakings : policies and measures for the protection of redundant workers in seven industrialised market economy countries / edited by Edward Yemin. – Geneva : International Labour Office, 1982.
x, 214 p.; 24 cm.
Includes bibliographical references.
ISBN 9221029107 hard

Working Abroad : You and Tax / Greaves. – London : Deloitte Haskins & Sells.
ISBN 0863491278 Pbk £5.95

Working for Europe : January 1981 - January 1985 / The European Commission. – Luxembourg : Office for Official Publications of the European Communities, 1984.
79p; 25cm.
Preface by Gaston E. Thorn.
ISBN 928254740X

Working Group on Current Problems in the International Protection of Refugees and Displaced Persons in Asia
Report of the Working Group on Current Problems in the International Protection of Refugees and Displaced Persons in Asia, International Institute of Humanitarian Law, San Remo (Italy), 19-22 January 1981. – Working Group on Current Problems in the International Protection of Refugees and Displaced Persons in Asia. – Geneva : under the auspices of the Office of the United Nations High Commissioner for Refugees, 1981.
17p.

Working Guide to the Administration of Private Companies. – Durban : Butterworths, 1981.
ISBN 0409029254 Pbk

Working in Accountancy. – 2nd ed. – London : Careers and Occupational Information Centre.
ISBN 0861104897 Pbk £1.95

Working Manual of Criminal Law, 1 Vol. – Agincourt : Carswell.
This work for Canadian practitioners in the field of criminal law covers defences, evidence, offenses, procedure, and sentencing. The book is designed to facilitate the preparation of a case for trial as prosecutor or defense counsel.
Pbk £71.50

Working order : workplace industrial relations over two decades / Eric Batstone. – Oxford : Basil Blackwell, 1984.
viii,363p; 24cm.
Bibliography: p344-357. - Includes index.
ISBN 0631137513 £19.50

Working paper : the judicial review of administrative decisions / Law Reform Commission of Western Australia. – Perth : Law Reform Commission of Western Australia, 1981.
178p. – (Project).
Includes bibliographical references.

Working paper and survey : privacy and statutory powers of intrusion / Law Reform Commission of Western Australia. – Perth : Law Reform Commission of Western Australia, 1981.
25,ii,112p. – (Project v no 26 part 2).

Working paper of the Law Reform Commission on a bill in respect of an act to replace the Oaths Act 1867-1981. – Brisbane : Queensland. Law Reform Commission?, 1988.
iii,162p. – (Q.L.R.C.W.P.).

Working paper on a bill to alter the civil jurisdiction of the District Court of Queensland / Queensland Law Reform Commission. – Brisbane? : the Commission?, 1984.
41,6p. – (Q.L.R.C.W.P.).

Working paper on a bill to amend the Property Law Act 1974-1985 / Queensland Law Reform Commission. – Brisbane : The Commission, 1986.
53p. – (Q.L.R.C.W.P.).
Includes the text of the proposed bill.

Working paper on a bill to amend the real property acts with respect to those provisions relating to writs of execution, bills of encumbrance and bills of mortgage, and caveats. – Brisbane : The Commission, 1982.
28p. – (Q.L.R.C.W.P.).

Working paper on a bill to consolidate, amend and reform the Supreme Court acts and ancillary acts regulating civil proceedings in the Supreme Court / Queensland Law Reform Commission. – Brisbane : The Commission, 1982.
142p. – (Q.L.R.C.W.P.).

Working paper on a bill to prevent the avoidance of civil liability in cases of death or personal injury caused by negligence / Queensland Law Reform Commission. – Brisbane? : the Commission?, 1984.
8 leaves. – (Q.L.R.C.W.P.).
Includes text of proposed Act.

Working paper on contribution in civil cases / Contracts and Commercial Law Reform Committee. – Wellington : Contracts and Commercial Law Reform Committee, 1983.
ii,49 leaves.
Bibliography: 1.37. Includes extracts from the Law Reform Act 1936 and the Contributory Negligence Act 1947 and the text of the Civil Liability (Contribution) Act 1978 (U.K.).

Working paper on legislation to review the role of juries in criminal trials / Queensland Law Reform Commission. – Brisbane : The Commission, 1984.
viii,146p. – (Q.L.R.C.W.P 28).

Working paper on limitation of actions / Newfoundland Law Reform Commission. – St. John's : The Commission, 1985.
xi,481p.
Includes bibliographical references. With a supplement.

Working paper on Local Courts Act 1904-1982, and rules / the Law Reform Commission of Western Australia. – Perth : Law Reform Commission of Western Australia, 1983.
307p. – (Project).
Bibliography: p.276-279.

Working paper on offences relating to prostitution and allied offences. – London : H.M.S.O., 1982.
vi,57p.
ISBN 011340784X

Working paper on powers of attorney / Newfoundland Law Reform Commission. – St. John's : The Commission, 1987.
iv,64p.
Includes bibliographical references.

Working paper on the law relating to contracts and the disposition of property by minors / by D.R.C. Chalmers. – Hobart? : Government Printer?, 1985.
49,iip.
Cover title.

Working paper on the Mechanics' Liens Act : certain substantive issues / Newfoundland Law Reform Commission. – St.John's : The Commission, 1987.
vi,294p.
Includes bibliographical references. Includes text of the Acts.

Working Party on Company Political Donations
Company donations to political parties : a suggested code of practice / Edmund Dell. – London : Constitutional Reform Centre, 1985.
34p.
'The report of the Working Party on Company Political Donations established jointly by the Constitutional Reform Centre and the Hansard Society for Parliamentary Government'. - Back Cover. Chairman: Edmund Dell.
ISBN 0948419008

Working Party on Prosecution Arrangments
Organisation of an independent prosecution service : a discussion paper / Working Party on Prosecution Arrangements. – London : Home Office, 1982.
11 leaves.

Working with FIDIC : A Practical Approach to its Use in the Middle East. – King's Ride : Institute of Building, 1983.
25p.
ISBN 0906600154 Hbk £6.30

Workmen's Compensation Act, 1923 : Commentary and Case-Law. – Delhi : Metropolitan Book Co, 1987.
296p.
ISBN 8120002601 Hbk £150.00

Workmen's Compensation Act, 1952 (Act 273) and Regulations 1953 (P.U.(A) 329/1983). – Kuala Lumpur : International Law Books Services.
Hbk £10.00

Workmen's Compensation Act. – 3rd ed. – Allahabad : Law Book Company, 1986.
1,050p.
Hbk £220.00

Workmen's compensation in twentieth century Britain : law, history and social policy / P.W.J. Bartrip. – Aldershot : Gower, 1987.
262p; 22cm.
Includes index.
ISBN 056605485X £17.50

Workplace communications / Advisory Conciliation and Arbitration Service. – rev. – London : ACAS, 1983.
– (Advisory booklet).
ISBN 0906073057 Hbk

Workplace industrial relations and technical change / W.W. Daniel. – London : F. Pinter in association with Policy Studies Institute, 1987.
312 p.; 23 cm.
Includes bibliographical references and index.
ISBN 0861879171

Workplace industrial relations in Britain : the DE/PSI/SSRC survey / W.W. Daniel and Neil Millward. – London : Heinemann Educational, 1983.
xiii,338p; 23cm.
Includes index.
ISBN 0435831909

Workplace pollution / Law Reform Commission of Canada. – Ottawa : The Commission, 1986.
94,106p. – (Working paper).
Includes bibliographical references. Added t.p. in French: La pollution en milieu de travail. Pages numbered in opposite directions. Text in English and French.
ISBN 0662545702

Workshop on information technologies and personal privacy in Canada / Science Council of Canada. – Ottawa : The Council, 1985.
62p.
Includes bibliographical references.
ISBN 0662140354

World accounting / Orsini. – Matthew Bender, 1986.
ISBN 0000999081 Hbk £100.00

World Arbitration Reporter, 7 Vols. – London : Butterworths.
Service.
ISBN 0409999911 Hbk £270.00

World Bank →Cities in the developing world : policies for their equitable and efficient growth.
→ Urban land policy : issues and opportunities.

World coal mining law : a comparative survey / edited by Ronald V. Cowles. – 2. – London : International Bar Association, 1984.
At foot of t.p.: Section on Energy and National Resources Law, International Bar Association.

World Commission on Environment and Development →Environmental protection and sustainable development : legal principles and recommendations.
—Our common future / World Commission on Environment and Development. – Oxford : Oxford University Press, 1987.
320p; 21cm.
ISBN 019282080X Pbk £5.95

World conservation strategy →Introduction to the World conservation strategy.

World Constitution. – New Delhi : Varma Brothers.
Hbk £18.00

World Constitutions / Bhushan Vidya. – New Delhi : Sterling Publishers, 1986.
752p.
ISBN 8120705459 Hbk £300.00
ISBN 8120704614 £45.00

World directory of criminological institutes / compiled and edited by Carla Masotti Santoro. – 4th ed. – Rome : UNSDRI, 1986.
xxvi,582p. – (Publication).
ISBN 9290780029

World Directory of Sources of Patent Information. – Geneva : World Intellectual Property Organization, 1985.
ca 300p.
Hbk £55.00

World environment 1972-1982 : a report / by the United Nations Environment Programme : edited by Martin W. Holdgate, Mohammed Kassas, Gilbert F. White with the assistance of David Spurgeon : study co-ordinator Essam El-Hinnawi. – Dublin : Published for the United Nations Environment Programme by Tycooly International, 1982.
xxxii,637p; 25cm.
Includes bibliographies and index.
ISBN 0907567134 Hbk
ISBN 0907567142 Pbk

World finance and adjustment : an agenda for reform / Graham Bird. – London : Macmillan, 1985.
288p.
Includes bibliography and index.
ISBN 0333314778 Hbk £25.00 :
ISBN 0333388771 Pbk £8.95

World Health Organization
International Digest of Health Legislation. – World Health Organization. – London : HMSO.
Hbk £48.00
—International Health Regulations (1969). – World Health Organization. – 3rd ed. – London : HMSO, 1983.
ISBN 9241580070 Hbk £4.40
→ Law and treatment of drug- and alcohol-dependent persons : a comparative study of existing legislation.
→ Legislative action to combat the world smoking epidemic.
→ Regulation of pharmaceuticals in developing countries : legal issues and approaches.
—Vaccination Certificate Requirements for International Travel and Health Advice to Travellers 1985. – World Health Organization. – London : HMSO, 1985.
81p.
ISBN 9241580100 Hbk £4.80

World Intellectual Property Organization
Committee of Experts on Biotechnological Inventions and Industrial Property : third session, Geneva, June 29 to July 3, 1987 : report prepared by the International Bureau. – World Intellectual Property Organization. – Geneva : World Intellectual Property Organization, 1987.
32,11p. – (BioT/CE/III/3).
'Convened ... as part of the 1986/87 program of the International (Paris) Union for the Protection of Industrial Property ...'. - Introduction.
—Committee of Experts on Biotechnological Inventions and Industrial Property : third session, Geneva, June 29 to July 3, 1987 : industrial property protection of biotechnological inventions / revised report prepared by the International Bureau. – Geneva : World Intellectual Property Organization, 1987.
73p. – (BioT/CE/III/2).
At head of cover: International Union for the Protection of Industrial Property (Paris Union).
—Committee of Experts on Biotechological Inventions and Industrial property : first session, Geneva, November 5 to 9, 1984 / report adopted by the Committee of Experts. – Geneva : World Intellectual Property Organizatioan, 1984.
23,7p. – (BioT/CE/I/3).
'Convened ... as part of the 1984/85 program of the International (Paris) Union for the Protection of Industrial Property ... '. - Introduction.
—Counterfeiting and national laws : counterfeiting and the Paris Convention / memorandum of the Director General. – Geneva : World Intellectual Property Organization, 1986.
46,4p. – (PAC/CE/I/2).
Prepared for an intergovernmental group of experts called Committee of Experts on the Protection Against Counterfeiting and scheduled to meet at W.I.P.O. Headquarters Geneva from May 5 to 7 1986'.
—Draft Treaty : Memorandum of the Director General. – World Intellectual Property Organization. – Geneva : World Intellectual Property Organization, 1985.
29p. – (IPIC/CE/I/2).
The Committee met in Geneva from November 26 to 29, 1985. 'Draft treaty on the protection of intellectual property in respect of integrated circuits'.
—Draft treaty with explanatory notes / memorandum of the Director General. – Geneva : World Intellectual Property Organization, 1986.
45,3p. – (IPIC/CE/II/2).
'Submitted by the Director General of W.I.P.O. for what will be the second session of the W.I.P.O. Committee of Experts on Intellectual Property in Respect of Integrated Circuits ... to take place from June 23 to 27, 1986, at Geneva' - Background. Draft treaty entitled: Draft Treaty on the Protection of Intellectual Property in Respect of Semiconductor Integrated Circuits.
→ Industrial property laws and treaties.
—International Patent Classification : Valid by the 1st January 1985, 9 Vols. – World Intellectual Property Organization. – 4th ed. – Cologne : Carl Heymanns Verlag, 1984.
ISBN 3452185990 Pbk DM618.00
—Official Catchword Index to the Fourth Edition (1984) of the International Patent Classification. – World Intellectual Property Organization. – Cologne : Carl Heymanns Verlag.
335p.
ISBN 3452200299 Pbk £125.00
→ Regional Forum on the Judiciary and the Intellectual Property system.
—Report / adopted by the Committee of Experts. – Geneva : World Intellectual Property Organization, 1986.
10p. – (BIOT/CE/II/3).
'Convened ... as part of the 1986/87 program of the International (Paris) Union for the Protection of Industrial Property' - Introduction.
—Report : adopted by the Committee of Experts. – World Intellectual Property Organization. – Geneva : World Intellectual Property Organization, 1985.
22,10p. – (IPIC/CE/I/7).
The Committee met in Geneva from November 26 to 29, 1985. Draft treaty entitled: Draft Treaty on the Protection of Intellectual Property in Respect of Integrated Circuits.
→ Role of patent information in the transfer of technology : proceedings of the International Conference held at Varna, Bulgaria, May 27-30, 1980.

World Intelletual Property Organisation
Copyright and neighboring rights laws and treaties / compiled and published by the World Intellectual Property Organization Geneva. – Geneva : World Intellectual Property Organization, 1987.
Llf

World oceans : a selected bibliography of social and natural sciences / Des oceans du monde: une selection bibliographique des sciences sociales et naturelles : compiled by Paul Te-Hsien Huang. – Halifax : Huang, 1985.
xii,754p.
ISBN 0969218109

World of international tax planning / Milton Grundy. – Cambridge : Cambridge University Press, 1984.
x,143p; 23cm.
Includes index.
ISBN 052125955X £19.50

World of science and the rule of law : a study of the observance and violations of the human rights of scientists in the participating states of the Helsinki Accord / by John Ziman, Paul Sieghart, John Humphrey. – Oxford : Oxford University Press, 1986.
viii,343p; 23cm.
Includes index.
ISBN 0198255160 £19.50

World Patent Law and Practice. – Matthew Bender, 1974.
ISBN 0000999078 Hbk £270.00

World trademark law and practice. – 2nd ed. – Matthew Bender, 1985.
ISBN 0000999080 Hbk £141.00

World's Fair Limited and Marcus Publishing PLC : refusal to publish advertisements which contain certain price information : a report by the Director General of Fair Trading on two investigations under section 3 of the Competition Act 1980 / Office of Fair Trading. – London : Office of Fair Trading, 1987.
30p.

Worldwide Space Law Bibliography. – Montreal : De Daro Publishing.
Hbk £120.00
Yearly Update 1988. –
ISBN 0969270313 Hbk £20.00
Vol. 1: 1900-1976. –
ISBN 0969270321 Hbk £65.00
Vol. 2: 1976-1986. –
ISBN 096927033X Hbk £75.00

Wormell →Introduction to working in the Lloyds Market.

Worsfold, D.
Scottish Mutual guide to the Financial Services Act. – Rosters Ltd, 1988.
ISBN 0948032162 Hbk £12.95

Wounded soldiers of industry : industrial compensation policy 1833-1897 / P.W.J. Bartrip and S.B. Burman. – Oxford : Clarendon, 1983.
xi,253p; 23cm. – (Oxford socio-legal studies).
Includes index.
ISBN 0198275099 £15.00

Wozniak, Edward →Origins and consequences of default : an examination of the impact of diligence (summary).

Wreh, Tuan
Evidence law of Liberia : statutes, cases and materials
Vol.1 / by Tuan Wreh. – 2nd ed. – Monrovia, Liberia : Wreh Agency, 1981.
vii,357p.

Wrenbury, Henry Burton Buckley
Buckley on the Companies Acts / by the late Lord Wrenbury. – 14th ed. – London : Butterworths, 1981.
Previous ed.: 1957. Includes index. Post-consolidation materials are set out in a loose-leaf volume.
ISBN 0406141045 v.2
ISBN 0406141053

Wright
Business of Banking / Valentine. – 2nd ed. – Northcote House.
ISBN 0746305354 Pbk £7.95
—Marketing Financial Services / T Watkins. – London : Butterworths, 1986.
ISBN 0402502706 Hbk £18.95
—Mediation and Criminal Justice : Victims, Offenders and Community / Galaway. – Sage Publications.
ISBN 0803980639 Hbk £27.50
ISBN 0803980647 Pbk £11.95

Wright, Cecil A.
Canadian Tort Law / Allen M. Linden. – 8th ed. – Butterworths, 1985.
1,072p.
Contains two new chapters on liability for negligent statements, and tort liability of public officials and bodies. The chapter on occupier's liability has been expanded, and the text also includes excerpts from law journals, treaties, and government documents, and review questions.
ISBN 0409845612 Pbk £75.00

Wright, Cherry E.
Succession : cases and materials / Cherry E. Wright. – London : Butterworths, 1986.
xxv,436p; 25cm.
Includes index.
ISBN 0406563101 Hbk £34.00
ISBN 040656311X Pbk £20.50

Wright, Christopher J.
Housing improvement and repair / Christopher J. Wright. – London : Sweet & Maxwell, 1986.
xiv,130p; 26cm.
Bibliography: p125. - Includes index.
ISBN 0421358203 £16.50

Wright, Desmond
Rights and duties of directors / Desmond Wright. – London : Butterworths, 1987.
140p; 22cm.
Includes index.
ISBN 0406504709 £33.50

Wright, F. B. →Introduction to commercial law.

Wright, Frank B. →Law of health and safety at work : the new approach.

Wright, M.
Introduction to the Law of Tenures. – Repr. of 1730 ed. – Abingdon : Professional Books.
460p.
Hbk £95.00
—Labour law / M. Wright and C.J. Carr. – 4th ed. – Plymouth : MacDonald and Evans, 1984.
xx,211p. – (The M & E handbook series).
Bibliography: p.195. - Includes index.
ISBN 0712101918

Wright, Martin
Making good : prisons, punishment and beyond / Martin Wright : foreword by Barbara Wootton. – London : Burnett, 1982.
316p; 23cm.
Bibliography: p271-292. - Includes index.
ISBN 0091472202 Hbk £
ISBN 0091472210 Pbk £5.95

Wrights, E.J.
Doing Business In Australia. – Matthew Bender, 1988.
ISBN 0000999043 Hbk £50.00

Wrightsman →American Jury on Trial : Psychological Perspectives.

Wrigley, Chris →History of British industrial relations 1875-1914.

Writ Jurisdiction Under the Constitution. – Bombay : Tripathi, 1984.
Hbk £90.00

Write Your Own Will. – Ibadan : African Universities Press.
Hbk £2.95

Writers and the Law / M. McDonald. – North Ryde : Law Book Co, 1986.
xix, 262p.
ISBN 0455207119 Pbk £29.50

Writers on organizations / D. S. Pugh, D. J. Hickson and C. R. Hinings. – 3rd ed. – Harmondsworth : Penguin, 1983.
234p; 20cm. – (Penguin education).
Previous ed.: 1971. Includes bibliographies and indexes.
ISBN 0140802665 Pbk £2.50

Writing a living will : using a durable power of attorney. – Praeger, 1988.
ISBN 0275928012 Hbk £24.95
ISBN 0275929396 Pbk £10.75

Written evidence given to the Royal Commission on Criminal Procedure, EV1-EV412. – London : The Commission, 1978.
16v.
Report of the Royal Commission published as Cmnd. 8092 in Parliamentary Papers, session 1980/81. IALS copy not bound. - Includes index. Gaps occur in numerical sequence of evidence numbers.

Wroblewski, Jerzy
Meaning and Truth in Juridical Decision. – Tampere : A-Tiete Oy.
ISBN 9419464271 Pbk £130.00

Wrongful Dismissal
Ann. supplement. – Toronto : DeBoo.

Wrongful Dismissal. – Toronto : DeBoo, 1984.
This treatise presents the Canadian law of wrongful dismissal. Awards for mental distress, constructive dismissal, punitive damages, just cause for dismissal, special status of Crown employees, and other related issues are discussed in depth in the work.
ISBN 0888201613 Hbk £85.00

Wrongful Dismissal : 1986. – Vancouver : Continuing Legal Education Society of British Columbia, 1986.
150p.
ISBN 0865042667 Hbk £55.00

Wrongful Dismissal : 1988 Update. – Vancouver : Continuing Legal Education Society of British Columbia, 1988.
238p.
ISBN 0865049882 Hbk £70.00

Wrongful Dismissal : Practical Perspectives. – Vancouver : Continuing Legal Education Society of British Columbia, 1987.
174p.
ISBN 0865043299 Hbk £65.00

Wu, Min Aun
Introduction to the Malaysian legal system / Wu Min Aun. – Rev. 3rd ed. – Kuala Lumpur : Heinemann Educational (Asia), 1982.
xii,196p.
Previous ed.: 1978. Bibliography: p.189-196.

Wu, Yuan-Li
Human rights in the People's Republic of China. – Westview Press, 1988.
ISBN 0813374391 Hbk £29.95

Wuhler, Norbert → Dispute settlement in public international law : texts and materials.

Wurtzburg
Building Society Law / Mills. – 15th ed. – Sweet & Maxwell, 1988.
ISBN 0420473009 Hbk

Wyatt, Derrick → Basic Community laws.
—Substantive law of the EEC / by Derrick Wyatt and Alan Dashwood. – 2nd ed. – London : Sweet & Maxwell, 1987.
450p; 25cm.
Previous ed.: 1980. Includes index.
ISBN 0421348704 Hbk £ :
ISBN 0421348801 Pbk

→ Yearbook of European law, Vol 8: 1988.

Wyatt, Joan → Yearbook of European law, Vol 8: 1988.

Wyatt, Michael
Company acquisition of own shares / Michael Wyatt. – London : Longman, 1986.
180p; 22cm.
New ed.: Previous ed.: 1983. Includes index.
ISBN 0851212506 Pbk £19.95
→ Inland Revenue Clearances.

Wydrzynski, Christopher J.
Canadian immigration law and procedure / Christopher J. Wydrzynski. – Aurora, Ont. : Canada Law Book, 1983.
xli,511p.
Includes index.
ISBN 0888040156

Wyk, A.H. von
Power to Dispose of the Assets of the Universal Matrimonial Community of Property. – Pijnacker : Dutch Efficiency Bureau.
ISBN 9062310060 Hbk £43.60

Wylie, I.M.
Law and Practice of the District Courts of Queensland. – 2nd ed. – Butterworths, 1983.
608p.
ISBN 040949240X Hbk £102.00

Wylie, J C W
Casebook on Equity and Trusts in Ireland. – Abingdon : Professional Books, 1985.
700p.
ISBN 0862051126 Hbk £44.00
ISBN 0862051142 Pbk £34.00
—Casebook on Irish land law / by J.C.W. Wylie. – Abingdon, Oxon. : Professional Books, 1984.
xxxxii,723p.
Includes index.
ISBN 0862050642
—Irish conveyancing law. – London : Butterworths, 1982.
ISBN 0903486458 Hbk £41.00
—Irish land law / by J.C.W. Wylie : consultant editor for the Republic of Ireland, The Hon. Mr. Justice Kenny. – 2nd ed. – Abingdon, Oxon. : Professional Books, 1986.
cxxi,1004p.
Previous ed.: 1975. Includes index.
ISBN 0862052173
—Irish Landlord and Tenant Law / John Farrell. – Abingdon : Professional Books, 1984.
ISBN 0862050626 Hbk £63.00
ISBN 0862050677 Pbk

Wylie, J. Kerr
Roman Constitutional History. – Rotterdam : A.A. Balkema, 1948.
195p.
Hbk £50.00

Wylie, O. P.
Taxation of the family / O.P. Wylie. – London : Butterworths, 1983.
xxv,229p; 22cm.
ISBN 0406580200

Wymeersch, E.
Supervision of securities markets in the member states of the European Economic Community Part 1 : Belgium, Federal Republic of Germany, Denmark, Ireland, France. – Luxembourg : Office for Official Publications of the European Communities, 1981.
255p. – (Studies collection).
At head of title: 'Commission of the European Communities'.
ISBN 9282515222 Hbk
Part 2 : United Kingdom, Italy, Luxembourg, Netherlands / report on a comparative law study submitted by E. Wymeersch. – 1981.
219p.
At head of title: Commission of the European Communities.
ISBN 9282522903 Hbk

Wynia, Gary W.
Politics of Latin American development / Gary W. Wynia. – 2nd ed. – Cambridge : Cambridge University Press, 1984.
xv,318p,2p of plates; 24cm.
Previous ed.: 1978. Includes bibliographies and index.
ISBN 0521261201 Hbk £25.00
ISBN 0521278422 Pbk

Wynne → Expert Evidence : Perspectives on Science and Law.

Wynne, Brian
Rationality and ritual : the Windscale inquiry and nuclear decisions in Britain / Brian Wynne. – Faringdon : British Society for the History of Science, 1982.
x,222p. – (Monographs).
Bibliography: p178.
ISBN 0906450020

Xuereb, Peter G
Rights of shareholders. – 1st. – Oxford : Blackwell Scientific, 1990.
275. – (Blackwell Law Library).
Discusses the exercise of power and control over companies and explains the principles and structure of shareholders rights. Reference is made to European Community proposals for the harmonisation of company law. Considers in some detail self-regulatory codes such as the Stock Exchange 'Yellow Book' and the City Code on Take-Overs and Mergers.
Practitioners, Financial advisers
ISBN 0632012489 Hbk £35

Xydis, Dorothy Peaslee → Constitutions of nations, Vol. 2 : Asia, Australia and Oceania.

Yadav, B.L. → Law of Private Defence.

Yakubu
Land law in Nigeria / M. G. Yakubu. – London : Macmillan, 1985.
xxvi,270p. – (Macmillan international college edition).
Bibliography: p.260-261. - Includes index.
ISBN 0333350901

Yakubu, M.G.
Land Use Act. – Zaria : Ahmadu Bello University Press.
Hbk £10.00

Yale AIDS Law Project → AIDS and the law : a guide for the public.

Yamouni, Yvonne → Understanding Contract Law.

Yankee One and George. – Police Review, 1984.
ISBN 0851640133 Pbk £2.50

Yaqin, Anwarul
Protection of Women under the Law : an Annotated Bibliography / Badar Anwar. – New Delhi : Deep and Deep Publications, 1982.
200p.
Hbk £75.00

Yardley, D. C. M.
Introduction to British constitutional law / D.C.M. Yardley. – 6th ed. – London : Butterworths, 1984.
xviii, 180p; 23cm.
Previous ed.: 1978. Includes index.
ISBN 0406690073 Hbk £12.00
ISBN 0406690081 Pbk £10.50
→ Introduction to English law.
—Principles of administrative law / D.C.M. Yardley. – 2nd ed. – London : Butterworths, 1986.
275p; 22cm.
A collection of essays, with particular emphasis on issues of control of power and the maintenance of a fair balance between competing interests of the individual and governmental entities in the United Kingdom, make up this book. Privatization of corporations, rent assessment, and the changing role of the Ombudsman are addressed.
ISBN 040668992X Hbk £14.50
ISBN 0406689938 Pbk £8.95
→ Protection of liberty.

Yates, David
Exclusion clauses in contracts / by David Yates. – 2nd ed. – London : Sweet & Maxwell, 1982.
xxvi,338p; 18cm.
Previous ed.: 1978. Includes index.
ISBN 0421286806 Hbk £9.75
ISBN 0421286903 Pbk £4.85
—Landlord and tenant law / by David Yates and A.J. Hawkins. – 2nd ed. – London : Sweet & Maxwell, 1986.
cviii,839p; 26cm.
Includes legislation enacted between 1980 and 1985. Covers the common law framework of landlord and tenant, the Rent Acts, protected tenants, council tenants, housing associations, the Housing Act 1985, the Landlord and Tenant Act 1985, the Housing Associations Act 1985, and the Housing (Consequential Provisions) Act 1985. The law applying to business tenants, and agricultural tenants is also discussed.
ISBN 0421354208 Hbk £36.50
ISBN 0421354305 Pbk £26.50
—Standard business contracts / A.J Hawkins. – London : Sweet & Maxwell, 1986.
Examines the law with particular reference to exclusion and limitation clauses, and related devices operating as indirect or implied exclusions. Includes clauses of indemnity, insurance, invoicing back, certification and inspection, warning notices, and instructions. Includes the Unfair Contract Terms Act 1977, the Supply of Goods and Services Act 1982, the Hague-Visby Rules, and the Warsaw Convention on Carriage by Air.
ISBN 0421307609 Hbk £72

Year Book of law, computers and technology. – London : Butterworths, 1990.
25.
ISBN 0406187037 Hbk £24.95

Year book of the Commonwealth 1983. – 15th ed. – London : H.M.S.O., 1983.
vii,535p.
Includes index.
ISBN 0115802320

Year Books, 11 Vols. – Abingdon : Professional Books.
Hbk £390.00
Individual vols.. –
Hbk £35.00
Unbound. –
£210.00

Year End and Accounting Period Tax Planning / G. J. Bell. – 2nd ed. – London : Oyez Longman, 1984.
– (Oyez Longman Practical Tax Ser.).
ISBN 0851208398 Hbk £10.50

Yearbook 1982-83. – International Court of Justice. – London : HMSO, 1984.
ISBN 0119080028 Hbk £9.00

Yearbook 1982, 2 Vols.
Vol. 2, Part 1. – International Law Commission. – London : HMSO.
ISBN 0119080702 Hbk £18.05
Vol. 2, Part 2. –
Hbk

Yearbook Commercial Arbitration
1981 /. – Dordrecht : Kluwer, 1981.
352p.
ISBN 9065440038 Hbk Gld62.00
1982. – 1982.
465p.
ISBN 9065440461 Hbk Gld75.00
1983. –
482p.
ISBN 9065441182 Pbk Gld82.50
1984. –
ISBN 9065441719 Hbk Gld95.00
1985. – 1985.
640p.
ISBN 9065442138 Pbk Gld110.00
1986. – 1986.
716p.
ISBN 9065442472 Pbk Gld150.00
1987. – 1987.
ISBN 9065443045 Pbk Gld180.00 (Including key index for all volumes 1-12)
ISBN 9065443037 Pbk Gld50.00 (key index only)
1989. – 1989.
872.
In co-operation with the T M C Asser Institute for International and European law. Covers the national reports and updates, court decisions and updates, commercial and maritime arbitral awards and rules, Iran-US claims tribunal, and court decisions in the New York Convention, the European Convention, and the Washington (ICSID) Convention.
ISBN 9065444084 Pbk Gld59/Dfl 185

Yearbook Commercial Arbitration, Volumes 1-12 (including Key). – Dordrecht : Kluwer.
ISBN 9065441352 Pbk Gld840.00

Yearbook European Communities and other European Organisations 1988. – London : Cedar Tree House.
ISBN 2802900781 Hbk £38.50

Yearbook Maritime Law. – Dordrecht : Kluwer, 1987.
528p.
ISBN 9065442545 Hbk Gld275.00

Yearbook Nineteen Eighty and Case Citator 1977-80 and Statute Citator 1972-80. – London : Sweet & Maxwell.
ISBN 0421284102 Hbk £14.00

Yearbook of European Law. – Oxford : Oxford University Press.
Vol. 1. – 1981.
ISBN 0198253842 Hbk £50.00
Vol. 2. – 1982.
ISBN 0198254903 Hbk £50.00
Vol. 3. – 1983.
ISBN 0198255047 Hbk £50.00
Vol. 4. – 1984.
ISBN 0198255217 Hbk £50.00
Vol. 5. – 1985.
ISBN 0198255462 Hbk £50.00
Vol. 6. – 1986.
ISBN 0198256051 Hbk £45.00
Vol. 7. – 1988.
490.
As well as practical and theoretical articles, contains Annual Surveys of the Council of Europe, the European Convention on Human Rights, and the European Parliament. There is a book review section andlist of Commission Decision Competitors. Fully indexed with a table of cases.
ISBN 0198256256 Hbk £55
Vol 8: 1988. – 1989.
500; 23.5.
Contains articles on prominent aspects of EEC law, including one by O. Due. Covers the European monetary system, the Lugano Convention on Civil Jurisdiction and Judgements, the application of EEC compeition rules to trade associations, and the Strasbourg option for regulating transfrontier television. Contains book reviews and tables of cases.
ISBN 0198252633 Hbk £60.00

Yearbook of the European Convention on Human Rights
Vol. 23 (1980) /. – Dordrecht : Kluwer, 1982.
766p.
ISBN 9024727170 Hbk Gld320.00
Vol. 24 (1981). – 1983.
602p.
ISBN 9024727227 Hbk Gld255.00
Vol. 25 (1982). – 1986.
896p.
ISBN 902473262X Hbk Gld395.00
Vol. 26 (1983). – 1987.
860p.
ISBN 9024732638 Hbk Gld425.00

Yearbook of the European Institute for Social Security / 1980-1981 /. – Dordrecht : Kluwer, 1982.
ISBN 9031201685 Hbk Gld123.00
Part 1: Social Security Reforms in Europe 2. – 1982.
285p.
ISBN 9031201669 Hbk Gld72.00
Part 2: Social Security and the Economic Crisis. – 1982.
146p.
ISBN 9031201677 Hbk Gld60.00

Yearbook of the European Institute for Social Security / 1982-1983 /. – Dordrecht : Kluwer.
Part 2: Sociological Research and Social Security. – 1984.
ISBN 9065442006 Pbk £53.20

Yearbook of the International Commission, 1985, Vol. 2, Part 2 : Report of the Commission to the General Assembly on the Work of its 37th Session. – Geneva : United Nations Publications.
ISBN 9211332818 Hbk £9.50

Yearbook of the International Law Commission, 1985, Vol. 2, Part 1 : Documents of the 37th Session. – Geneva : United Nations Publications.
ISBN 9211332796 Hbk £25.00

Yearbooks : Maynard Edition 11 vols. – Professional Books.
ISBN 0862053858 Hbk £263.50

Yearly All India Civil Digest, 1986 : Excluding Labour and Taxation. – Allahabad : Law Book Company.
750p.
Hbk £225.00

Yearly All India Civil Digest. – Allahabad : Law Book Company, 1987.
Hbk £225.00

Yearly All-India Criminal Digest, 1986. – Allahabad : Law Book Company, 1987.
400p.
Hbk £140.00

Yearly Digest of Supreme Court Criminal Cases 1980 /. – Lucknow : Eastern Book Company, 1981.
250p.
Pbk £15.00

Yearly Supreme Court Digest, 1987
Vol. 22. – Allahabad : Law Book Company, 1988.
550p.
Hbk £150.00

Yearly Supreme Court Digest. – Allahabad : Law Book Company, 1986.
Hbk £50.00

Yeldham, R F
Probate Manual / Angela Plumb. – 23rd ed. – Waterlow.
ISBN 0080331092 Hbk £29.95

Yell, Nicholas
County court : practice and procedure, general / by Nicholas Yell and W.T. West. – Chichester : Barry Rose, 1982.
184p; 22cm.
ISBN 0859923347 corrected £27.50

Yelland →Consumer Credit Legislation.

Yelland, John
Conduct of Meetings. – 22nd ed. – Bristol : Jordan & Sons Ltd, 1982.
ISBN 0907313019 Pbk £6.00

Yelle, A.
Income Tax References. – Toronto : DeBoo.
This service contains primary and secondary tax references from English and French language sources. Included are articles, treatises, case summaries, Income Tax Regulations, and government bulletins going back to 1972. Six updates per year are planned, in addition to annual consolidations.
ISBN 0888201214 Llf £175.00

Yellow Tax Handbook 1986-1987. – Butterworths. – London : Butterworths.
ISBN 0406510032 Pbk £19.00

Yelpaala, K., et al
From the Waidring Conferences, 4 Vols. Licensing Agreements: Patents, Know-How, Trade Secrets and Software /. – Dordrecht : Kluwer.
444p.
ISBN 9065443142
Drafting and Enforcing Contracts in Civil and Common Law Jurisdictions. – 1987.
292p.
ISBN 9065442790 Pbk £85.00

Yemin, Edward →Workforce reductions in undertakings : policies and measures for the protection of redundant workers in seven industrialised market economy countries.

Yeo, Meng Heong Stanley →Breaches of Trust in Singapore and Malaysia.

Yerokun, Olusegun
Hire purchase law and cases / by Olusegun Yerokun. – Jos : Salama Press, 1983.
ix,125p.

Yilma, Makonnen
International law and the new states of Africa : a study of the international legal problems of state succession in the newly independent states of Eastern Africa / by Yilma Makonnen : with a foreword by T.O. Elias. – Addis Ababa : Ethiopian National Agency for UNESCO, 1983.
xxvi, 575 p.; 23 cm.
'Published with the assistance of UNESCO under the Regional Participation Programme for Africa.'. Includes index. Bibliography: p. 541-564.
ISBN 0961193409 Pbk

Yin, John
Soviet Views on the Use of Force in International Law. – Hong Kong : Asian Research Service.
ca 200p.
Hbk £12.00

Yoder, Christian G.
Canadian Regulation of Offshore Installations. – Calgary : Canadian Institute of Resources Law.
116p.
ISBN 0919269184 Hbk £17.00
—Liability for Drilling- and Production-Source Oil Pollution in the Canadian Offshore. – Calgary : Canadian Institute of Resources Law.
84p.
ISBN 0919269206 Hbk £17.00

Yogis, John →Comparison of automated and manual legal research : a computer study.
—Legal writing and research manual / John A. Yogis and Innis M. Christie. – 3rd ed. – Toronto : Butterworths, 1988.
xx, 199 p.; 23 cm.
Intends to help develop an understanding of, and some facility in, the techniques of legal research and writing. The distinction between primary and secondary materials is explained, Canadian and English sources are emphasised, but an outline of principle American materials is also provided.
ISBN 0409811548

Yoingco, A.O. →Philippine Agrarian Reform and The New Taxation.

Yorston, Keith
Australian mercantile law / Yorston & Fortescue. – 16th ed. – Sydney : Law Book Co., 1981.
xxxi,784p.
Previous ed.: 1978. Includes index.
ISBN 0455203636

You and the law. – Enugu : ABC Books, 1982.
vi,57p.

You and the Law / M.J. McDonald. – Toronto : Maclean-Hunter.
ISBN 0888960875 Hbk £9.95
ISBN 0770516491 Pbk £6.95

You and the law : layman's guide to rights and liabilities / by Funke Fagbohun. – Lagos : MIJ Professional Publishers, 1986.
xxii,211p.
ISBN 9782486035

You and your home. – London : Shaw & Sons, 1984.
ISBN 0721909906 Pbk £4.50

You in the small claims court : a practical guide / S.A. Strauss. – Cape Town : Juta, 1985.
xv,126p.
Includes index.
ISBN 0702116637

Young
Accounting For Pensions / Buchanan. – Cambridge : Woodhead-Faulkner, 1981.
ISBN 0859411249 Hbk £25.00

Young, Agnes Freda
Chairmanship in Magistrates' Courts / Keith Clarke. – Chichester : Barry Rose, 1981.
93p.
ISBN 0859921875 Hbk £4.00

Young, Andrew J.
Law and policy in the space stations' era. – Dordrecht : Nijhoff (Martinus), 1989.
352. – (Utrecht studies in air and space law 2).
Addresses the policy implications for all current participants in the Space Stations Era. Deals with a constitutional perspective of the treaty-making process in the space field, the optimum framework for management of the US/International Space Station based on a review of the most significant cooperative agreements, and a presentation of commercial issues involved.
ISBN 9024737222 Hbk £52

Young, David
Allied Hambro Expatriate Tax and Investment Guide. – London : Oyez Longman, 1984.
ISBN 0851208355 Hbk £9.95
—Passing off. – London : Longman Professional, 1988.
ISBN 0851213928 Pbk

Young, Eric →Planning by agreement in Scotland.
—Scottish planning law and procedure / by Eric Young and Jeremy Rowan-Robinson : with a contribution by C.M.G. Himsworth. – Glasgow : William Hodge, 1985.
xliv,564p.
Supersedes Eric Youngs The law of planning in Scotland. Includes index. Provides a guide through the legislative and regulatory system of Scottish planning law and procedure and sets the subject matter in the context of administrative law. Considerable attention is given to control of development.
ISBN 0852791224

Young, Jennifer
Small Claims Court Guide for Ontario : How to Win Your Case!. – 6th ed. – North Vancouver : International Self-Counsel Press, 1986.
144p.
ISBN 0889083568 Hbk £7.50

Young, Jock →Confronting crime.
→ Islington crime survey : crime, victimization and policing in inner-city London.
→ Losing the fight against crime.
→ Manufacture of news : social problems, deviance and the mass media.
→ What is to be done about law and order?.

Young, John →Report to the Attorney-General concerning the administration of civil justice in Victoria, Volume 2 : Appendices.

Young, M. J. →National Crimes Commission?.

Young, Martin
Rough justice / Martin Young & Peter Hill. – London : British Broadcasting Corporation, 1983.
176p,4p of plates; 20cm. – (Ariel books).
ISBN 0563201290 Pbk £1.95

Young, Maurice →Matrimonial Suits and Property Proceedings : A Practitioner's Index of Practice and Procedure.

Young, N. F. →Court surveys and studies 1978-1984, concerning the civil caseloads of the Supreme Court, the County Court and the Magistrates' Courts of Victoria.

Young Offenders Act, 1982 : highlights. – Ottawa : Minister of Supply and Services Canada, 1982.
25,27p.
Added t.p. in French. Text in English and French.
ISBN 0662522206

Zegveld, Walter →Industrial Innovation and Public Policy : Preparing for the 1980's and the 1990's.

Zeidman
Short guide to Landlord and Tenant Act 1987 / Whippman. – Temple Lectures, 1987.
ISBN 1870800052 Pbk £8.00

Zellick, Graham
Criminal justice revolution : the third Sir Gwilym Morris memorial lecture delivered on 24th October 1986 / by Graham Zellick. – Cardiff? : University of Wales Institute of Science and Technology, 1986.
24p.
Includes bibliographical references.
→ Law Commission and law reform.
—Law, religion and the Jewish community / by Graham Zellick. – London : Jews' College, 1987.
Delivered at Jews' College on April 2 1986. Revised February 1987.
—Public Law / A. Bradley. – London : Sweet & Maxwell.
Hbk £36.00

Zemans, F. H.
Perspective on Legal Aid. – London : Pinter Publishers Ltd.
Hbk

Zenoff, David B
Corporate Finance in Multinational Companies. – London : Euromoney, 1986.
ISBN 1870031350 Pbk £75.00
→ International banking : management and strategies.

Zheng, Henry R.
China's civil and commercial law / Henry R. Zheng. – Singapore : Butterworths, 1988.
lii,490p; 26cm.
Presents an overview of chinese laws and legislative structure, a review of the major principles of the Civil Code, and an examination of the different facets of Chinese business law. Covers principles of civil law, contract law, banking law, insurance law, and foreign investment law.
ISBN 040999555X Hbk £142.50
—Legal Structure of International Textile Trade. – Westport Publications.
ISBN 089930334X Hbk £36.95

Ziegel, Jacob S., et al
Canadian Business Law Journal (C.B.L.J.) 1976-Present. – Aurora : Canada Law Book Co.
Hbk £82.00
→ Canadian financial institutions : changing the regulatory environment.
—Commercial and Consumer Transactions. – 2nd ed. – Toronto : Edmond-Montgomery, 1987.
ca 1,400p.
ISBN 0920722202 Hbk £96.00
—Commercial and consumer transactions : cases, text and materials / by Jacob S. Ziegel, Benjamin Geva. – Toronto : Emond-Montgomery, 1981.
xlv,1230p.
Bibliography: p.xliii-xli - Includes index.
ISBN 0920722040
→ New dimensions in international trade law : a Canadian perspective.
→ Papers and comments delivered at the ninth annual Workshop on Commercial and Consumer Law, Toronto, November 2-3, 1979.
→ Papers and comments delivered at the tenth annual Workshop on Commercial and Consumer Law, Toronto, October 17-18, 1980.
→ Studies in Canadian company law.

Ziegler, Charles E.
Environmental policy in the USSR / Charles E. Ziegler. – London : Pinter, 1987.
195p; 24cm.
Includes index.
ISBN 0861879015 £18.50

Ziembinski, Zygmunt
Polish Contributions to the Theory and Philosophy of Law. – Amsterdam : Editions Rodopi, 1987.
212p.
ISBN 9062037992 Hbk £170.00

Ziller →Making European Policies Work, Vol. 1.

Ziman, John
World of science and the rule of law : a study of the observance and violations of the human rights of scientists in the participating states of the Helsinki Accord / by John Ziman, Paul Sieghart, John Humphrey. – Oxford : Oxford University Press, 1986.
viii,343p; 23cm.
Includes index.
ISBN 0198255160 £19.50

Ziman, L. D.
Butterworth's Company Law Service / S. J. Barton. – London : Butterworths.
Llf

Zimbabwe law journal. – Salisbury, Zimbabwe : Department of Law, University of Zimbabwe, 1979-.
Continues: Rhodesian law journal. Includes indexes.

Zimbabwe law review. – Harare : Department of Law, University of Zimbabwe, 1985-.

Zimbabwean women in colonial and customary law / by Joan May. – Gweru : Mambu Press, 1983.
vii,128p.
Bibliography: p.123-128. Cover title: Zimbabwean women in customary and colonial law.
ISBN 0869222406

Zimmerman, Bruno →Commentary on the additional protocols of 8 June 1977 to the Geneva Conventions of 12 August 1949.

Zimmerman, Reinhard
Legal History : Does it Still Deserve Its Place in the Curriculum?. – Rondebosch : University of Cape Town, 1981.
10p.
ISBN 0799204153 Pbk £0.30

Zimrin, H. →Medicolegal Library, Vol. 1 Child Abuse.

Zimring, Franklin E.
Capital punishment and the American agenda / Franklin E. Zimring, Gordon Hawkins. – Cambridge : Cambridge University Press, 1987.
xviii,192p; 24cm.
Includes index.
ISBN 0521330335 £20.00
→ Reform and punishment : essays on criminal sentencing.

Zines, Leslie
High Court and the Constitution / Leslie Zines. – Sydney : Butterworths, 1981.
xvii, 358 p.; 25 cm.
Includes bibliographical references and index.
ISBN 0409300195
—High Court and the Constitution. – 2nd ed. – Butterworths, 1987.
423p.
ISBN 0409491780 Hbk £69.00
ISBN 0409491799 Pbk £49.00
→ Royal prerogative.

Zinkhofer, Fred
Small Claims Court Guide for Alberta : How to Win Your Case. – 4th ed. – North Vancouver : International Self-Counsel Press, 1985.
122p.
ISBN 0889082286 Hbk £7.50

Zipfinger, F.P. →Stamp Duty Aspects of Trusts, Settlements and Gifts in Australia.

Zloch-Christy, I.
Debt Problems of Eastern Europe. – Cambridge : Cambridge University Press, 1988.
ISBN 0521335426 Hbk £25.00

Zube, John
Stop the SX00 Million Legal Tender Crime microform. – Berrima : Peace Plans.
microform

Zuckerman, A A S
Principles of criminal evidence. – Oxford : Clarendon Press, 1878.
352; 21.5. – (Clarendon Law Series).
Examines the role played by the lay judgements of jurors. Discusses judicial practices which have evolved to satisfy the desire to discover the truth, the need to protect the innocent from conviction, and the need to maintain standards in the criminal process. A central feature of the law of criminal evidence is the attempt to balance these three principles.
Students and teachers of criminal law, evidence and legal philosophy
ISBN 0198761031 Hbk £30
ISBN 0198762348 Pbk £11.95

Zuckerman, Ruth Jane →Laws and policies affecting adolescent health.

Zuijdwijk, Ton J. M.
Petitioning the United Nations : a study in human rights / Ton J.M. Zuijdwijk. – Aldershot : Gower, 1982.
xv,397p; 23cm.
Bibliography: p383-389. - Includes index.
ISBN 0566004631 £
ISBN 0312603819

Zuker, Marvin A.
Ontario Provincial Court Civil Division Practice : 1987. – Agincourt : Carswell, 1987.
309p.
This work sets out the complete text of the rules of the civil Division courts, previously known as the 'Small Claims Court'. The book includes commentary and annotations to the rules of practice, along with relevant forms and fee schedules.
Hbk £41.75
—Small Claims Court Practice in the Ontario Provincial Court (Civil Division)-1987. – Agincourt : Carswell, 1987.
ca 300p.
Hbk £39.25

Zulu Law / Shooter. – Pietermaritzburg : Shuter & Shooter, 1984.
Hbk

Zvekic, Ugljesa →Action-oriented research on youth crime : an international perspective.

Zweigert, Konrad
Introduction to comparative law / Konrad Zweigert and Hein Kotz : translated from the German by Tony Weir. – 2nd rev ed. 2. – Oxford : Clarendon Press, 1987.
Previous edition: 1977. Includes indexes. Contents: 1 The framework. - 2 The institutions of private law. German title: Einfuhrung in die Rechtsvergleichung auf dem Gebiete des Privatsrechts.
→ Origins of the conflict of laws.

Zwicker, M. W. →Financial Management for Law Firms.